PLANT FINDER
2005-2006

DEVISED BY CHRIS PHILIP
AND REALISED BY TONY LORD

CONSULTANT EDITOR
TONY LORD

RHS EDITORS
JAMES ARMITAGE   JANET CUBEY   MIKE GRANT
NEIL LANCASTER   CHRISTOPHER WHITEHOUSE

COMPILER
JUDITH MERRICK

A Dorling Kindersley Book

LONDON, NEW YORK, MUNICH, MELBOURNE, DELHI

Published by
Dorling Kindersley Ltd
80 Strand, London WC2R 0RL
A Penguin company

British Library Cataloguing Publication Data.
A Catalogue record for this book is available from the British Library.

ISBN 1 4053 0736 6

Compiled by
The Royal Horticultural Society
80 Vincent Square,
London SW1P 2PE
Registered charity no: 222879

www.rhs.org.uk

Royal
Horticultural
Society

Illustrations by Sarah Young
Maps by Alan Cooper

Produced for Dorling Kindersley Ltd by
COOLING BROWN
Printed and bound in England by Clays Ltd, St Ives Plc

The Compiler and the Editors of the *RHS Plant Finder* have taken every care, in the time available,
to check all the information supplied to them by the nurseries concerned. Nevertheless, in a work of this
kind, containing as it does hundreds of thousands of separate computer encodings, errors and omissions
will, inevitably, occur. Neither the RHS, the Publisher nor the Editors can accept responsibility for
any consequences that may arise from such errors.

If you find mistakes we hope that you will let us know so that the matter can be corrected in the next edition.

See our complete catalogue at
www.dk.com

CONTENTS

INTRODUCTION

The *RHS Plant Finder* exists to put enthusiastic gardeners in touch with suppliers of plants. The book is divided into two related sections – PLANTS and NURSERIES. PLANTS includes an A–Z Plant Directory of some 73,000 plant names, against which are listed a series of nursery codes. These codes point the reader to the full nursery details contained in the NURSERIES section towards the back of the book.

The *RHS Plant Finder* is comprehensively updated every year and provides the plant lover with the richest source of suppliers known to us, whether you are looking for plants locally, shopping from your armchair or touring the country in search of the rare and unusual.

NEW IN THIS EDITION

The essay in this year's edition is by Alan Leslie, formerly the RHS Principal Registrar, on *The Cultivated Plant Code*. In it, he explains how the new International Code of Nomenclature for Cultivated Plants is being followed in this edition of the **RHS Plant Finder**.

This edition contains few major changes to plant names. However, there have been a number of corrections to entries in *Agapanthus*, *Crocosmia*, and *Vaccinium* following recent authoritative books. Now that *Lobelia fulgens* and *L. splendens* are considered to be synonyms of *L. cardinalis*, *L.* x *gerardii* becomes a synonym of *L.* x *speciosa*, resulting in some changes to the names of the cultivars. John Richards' *Primula* (2nd edition, 2002) has been followed for the classification of the genus by Section, with corrections to Section names required by the International Code of Botanical Nomenclature, Article 21.2.

One significant change has been the decision to adopt the "sinking" of *Smilacina* into *Maianthemum*, as in *Flora of China* and *Flora of North America*. The only significant morphological difference between them is that *Smilacina* has floral parts in threes, whereas *Maianthemum* has floral parts in twos. This is generally considered not to be a sufficient distinction to put them in separate genera and their closeness is further supported by DNA analysis.

AVAILABLE FROM THE COMPILER

APPLICATION FOR ENTRY

Nurseries appearing in the *RHS Plant Finder* for the first time this year are printed in bold type in the *Nursery Index by Name* starting on p.907.

If you wish your nursery to be considered for inclusion in the next edition of the *RHS Plant Finder* (2006-2007), please write for details to the Compiler at the address below.

PLANTS LAST LISTED IN EARLIER EDITIONS

Plants cease to be listed for a variety of reasons. For more information turn to *How to Use the Plant Directory* on p.18.

A listing of the 24,000 or so plants listed in earlier editions, but for which we currently have no known supplier, is available from the Compiler. Please send a self-addressed A4 envelope stamped with £1.10 stamps.

LISTS OF NURSERIES FOR PLANTS WITH MORE THAN 30 SUPPLIERS

To prevent the book from becoming too big, we do not print the nursery codes where more than 30 nurseries offer the same plant. The plant is then listed as having "More than 30 suppliers". This is detailed more fully in *How to Use the Plant Directory* on p.18.

If any readers have difficulty in finding such a plant, we will be pleased to send a full list of all the nurseries that we have on file as stockists. All such enquiries must include the full name of the plant being sought, as shown in the *RHS Plant Finder*, together with an A5 size SAE. For more than one plant, please send an A4 1st class SAE.

The above may all be obtained from:
The Compiler, *RHS Plant Finder*, RHS Garden Wisley, Woking, Surrey GU23 6QB
Email: plantfinder@rhs.org.uk

THE RHS PLANT FINDER ONLINE

The *RHS Plant Finder* is available on the Internet. Visit the Royal Horticultural Society's website **www.rhs.org.uk** and search the *RHS Plant Finder* database online.

> ## TO AVOID DISAPPOINTMENT,
> WE SUGGEST THAT YOU ALWAYS
> **check with the nursery before visiting or ordering and always use the current edition of the book.**

ACKNOWLEDGMENTS

Judith Merrick, assisted by Alison Cundy, with the help of June Skinner and Patty Boardman, compiled this year's edition, whilst Richard Sanford managed the editing of plant names on the database. Rupert Wilson and Graham Hawkes administered the Horticultural Database from which the book is produced.

We would like to acknowledge the help of Simon Maughan, RHS Publications, London, John David, RHS Head of Botany, Kerry Walter of BG-BASE (UK) Ltd., Max Phillips of Strange Software Ltd. and Alan Cooper, who produces the nursery maps. We are also grateful to Alan Leslie for contributing an informative essay on the ICNCP to this edition.

The team of RHS botanists has once again seen staff changes. Mike Grant left in late 2004 to become Deputy Editor of *The Plantsman*. We are greatly indebted to him for his scholarly, but never dry, contributions to the *RHS Plant Finder* over the years. In his place, Neil Lancaster has joined James Armitage and Christopher Whitehouse at Wisley.

Once again this year we are indebted to our colleagues on the RHS Advisory Panel on Nomenclature and Taxonomy, along with the RHS International Registrars and the RHS Keeper of the Herbarium, Diana Miller, all of whom have provided much valuable guidance and information. Scores of nurseries have sent helpful information about asterisked plants which has proved immensely useful in verifying some of the most obscure names, as well as suggesting corrections to existing entries. Some of these suggested corrections remain to be checked and entered in our next edition and we are grateful for your patience while information is checked and processed, though those that contravene the Codes of Nomenclature may have to be rejected for reasons covered in the section on nomenclature. We are grateful, too, to our regular correspondents.

Actaea	J. Compton ('94)
Camellia	T.J. Savige, International Registrar, NSW, Australia ('96)
Cistus	R. Page ('97, '99 & '02)
Clematis	V. Matthews, International Registrar, RHS ('00–'05)
Conifers	P. Trehane, former International Registrar, RHS Wisley ('94 & '99)
Cotoneaster	Jeanette Fryer, NCCPG Collection Holder ('99)
Dahlia	R. Hedge, RHS Wisley ('96–'00 & '02)
Delphinium	Dr A.C. Leslie, International Registrar, RHS Wisley ('97–'00 & '02)
Dianthus	Dr A.C. Leslie, International Registrar, RHS Wisley ('91–'00 & '02)
Geranium	D.X. Victor, International Registrar ('03)
Hebe	Mrs J. Hewitt ('94–'99)
Hypericum	Dr N.K.B. Robson ('94–'97)
Ilex	Ms S. Andrews ('92–'98)
Iris	Mrs J. Hewitt ('95–'99, '02 & '05)
Jovibarba & Sempervivum	P.J. Mitchell, International Registrar, Sempervivum Society ('98)
Lavandula	Ms S. Andrews ('02, '03 & '05)
Lilium	Dr A.C. Leslie, International Registrar, RHS Wisley ('91–'00 & '02)
Liriope	Dr P.R. Fantz ('99)
Meconopsis	Dr E. Stevens ('02, '03 & '05)
Narcissus	Mrs S. Kington, International Registrar, RHS ('91–'00 & '02)
Ophiopogon	Dr P.R. Fantz ('99)
Rhododendron	Dr A.C. Leslie, International Registrar, RHS Wisley ('91–'00 & '02)
Sorbus	Dr H. McAllister ('01)
Thymus	Mrs M. Easter ('03–'05)

To all these, as well as to the many readers and nurseries who have also made comments and suggestions, we are once again extremely grateful.

Tony Lord, Consultant Editor, and Janet Cubey, RHS Principal Botanist, February 2005

CONSERVATION AND THE ENVIRONMENT

As the *RHS Plant Finder* demonstrates, gardens in Britain have been greatly enriched by the diversity of plants introduced to cultivation from abroad. Whilst the vast majority of those introduced have enhanced our gardens, a few have proved to be highly invasive and to threaten native habitats. Once such plants are established it is very difficult, costly and potentially damaging to native eco-systems to eradicate or control the invasive "alien" species. Gardeners can help by choosing not to buy or distribute non-native invasive plants and by taking steps to prevent them escaping into the wild and by disposing of them in a responsible way.

The top seven invasive non-native species are no longer listed in the *RHS Plant Finder*. Any cultivars or varieties of them that are listed are believed to be less invasive than the species themselves. These seven plants are:

Azolla filiculoides - fairy fern
Crassula helmsii - New Zealand pygmy weed
Fallopia japonica - Japanese knotweed
Heracleum mantegazzianum - giant hogweed
Hydrocotyle ranunculoides - floating pennywort
Impatiens glandulifera - Himalayan balsam
Myriophyllum aquaticum - parrot's feather

Bringing plants back from abroad

Travelling can be a great source of inspiration for gardeners and often provides an introduction to new and interesting plants. Anyone thinking of bringing plants back into Britain from overseas must realise, however, that this is a complex matter. Various regulations are in force which apply to amateur gardeners as well as to commercial nurseries. The penalties for breaking these can be serious.

Some of the most important regulatory bodies are listed below.

Plant Health regulations are in place to control the spread of pests and diseases. Plants are divided into the categories of prohibited, controlled and unrestricted, but there are also limits that vary according to the part of the world you are travelling from. For full details contact the Plant Health division of DEFRA,

or visit www.defra.gov.uk/planth/ph.htm

The Convention on International Trade in Endangered Species (CITES) affects the transport of animal and plant material across international boundaries. Its aim is to prevent exploitative trade and thereby to prevent harm and the ultimate extinction of wild populations. Export and import licences are required for any plants listed on the CITES Appendices. A broad range of plants is covered in these Appendices, including *Cactaceae* and *Orchidaceae* and, although species are mentioned in the convention title, the restrictions cover all cultivars and hybrids too. Details of the plants listed in the Appendices can be found on the CITES website, www.ukcites.gov.uk/intro/cites_species.htm, or in the leaflets detailed below.

The Convention on Biological Diversity (CBD or the "Rio Convention") recognises the property rights of individual countries in relation to their own biodiversity. It exists to enable access to that biodiversity, but equally to ensure the sharing of any benefit derived from it. Export permits are required for plant material taken from the country of origin, with prior informed consent being gained for any uses that the material will be used for in the future. Further information on the Convention can be found on the CBD website, www.biodiv.org.

If you would like to read more about these subjects, *Conservation and Environment Guidelines* leaflets are available on request from the RHS. Please write to the Compiler at the address given on page 4 enclosing an A4 SAE, or find them online at www.rhs.org.uk/publications. Leaflets are also available on a wider range of subjects, with topics including:

Peat and the gardener
Potentially harmful garden plants
The use of limestone in horticulture
Trees and timber products
Wild and endangered plants in cultivation
Wildlife in gardens

EXTENDED GLOSSARY

This glossary combines some of the helpful introductory sections from older editions in an alphabetical listing. A fuller, more discursive account of plant names, *Guide to Plant Names,* and a detailed guide to the typography of plant names, *Recommended Style for Printing Plant Names*, are both available as RHS Advisory Leaflets. To request a copy of either please send an A4 SAE to The Compiler at the contact address given on page 4.

ADVISORY PANEL ON NOMENCLATURE AND TAXONOMY

This Panel advises the RHS on individual problems of nomenclature regarding plants in cultivation and, in particular, use of names in the *RHS Horticultural Database*, reflected in the annual publication of the *RHS Plant Finder*.

The aim is always to make the plant names in the *RHS Plant Finder* as consistent, reliable and stable as possible and acceptable to gardeners and botanists alike, not only in the British Isles but around the world. Recent proposals to change or correct names are examined with the aim of creating a balance between the stability of well-known names and botanical and taxonomic correctness. In some cases the Panel feels that the conflicting views on the names of some groups of plants will not easily be resolved. The Panel's policy is then to wait and review the situation once a more obvious consensus is reached, rather than rush to rename plants only to have to change them again when opinions have shifted.

The Panel is chaired by Dr Alan Leslie (RHS) and includes Dr Crinan Alexander (RBGE), Susyn Andrews, Chris Brickell, Dr James Compton (University of Reading), Dr Janet Cubey (RHS), Mike Grant (RHS), Dr Christopher Grey-Wilson, Dr Stephen Jury (University of Reading), Sabina Knees, Dr Tony Lord, Julian Shaw (RHS) and Adrian Whiteley.

AUTHORITIES

In order that plant names can be used with precision throughout the scientific world, the name of the person who coined the name of a plant species (its author, or authority) is added to the plant name. Usually this information is irrelevant to gardeners, except in cases where the same name has been given to two different plants. Although only one usage is correct, both may be encountered in books, so indicating the author is the only way to be certain about which plant is being referred to. This can happen equally with cultivars. Authors' names, where it is appropriate to cite them, appear in a smaller typeface after the species or cultivar name to which they refer and are abbreviated following Brummitt and Powell's *Authors of Plant Names*.

☿ AWARD OF GARDEN MERIT

The Award of Garden Merit (AGM) is intended to be of practical value to the ordinary gardener and is therefore awarded only after a period of assessment by the Society's Standing and Joint Committees. An AGM plant:

- must be available
- must be of outstanding excellence for garden decoration or use
- must be of good constitution
- must not require highly specialist growing conditions or care
- must not be particularly susceptible to any pest or disease
- must not be subject to an unreasonable degree of reversion

The AGM symbol is cited in conjunction with the **hardiness** rating. The RHS publication *AGM Plants 2004* gives the full list of AGM plants. Copies can be ordered from RHS Enterprises on (01483) 211320. Information about AGM plants is also available on the RHS website at www.rhs.org.uk.

BOTANICAL NAMES

The aim of the botanical naming system is to provide each different plant with a single, unique, universal name. The basic unit of plant classification is the species. Species that share a number of significant characteristics are grouped together to form a genus (plural **genera**). The name of a species is made up of two elements; the name of the genus followed by the specific epithet, for example, *Narcissus romieuxii*.

Variation within a species can be recognised by division into subspecies (usually abbreviated to subsp.), varietas (or variety abbreviated to var.) and forma (or form abbreviated to f.). Whilst it is unusual for a plant to have all of these, it is possible,

as in this example, *Narcissus romieuxii* subsp. *albidus* var. *zaianicus* f. *lutescens.*

The botanical elements are always given in italics, with only the genus taking an initial capital letter. The rank indications are never in italics. In instances where the rank is not known it is necessary to form an invalid construction by quoting a second epithet without a rank. This is an unsatisfactory situation, but requires considerable research to resolve.

CLASSIFICATION OF GENERA

Genera that include a large number of species or with many cultivars are often subdivided into informal horticultural classifications or more formal Cultivar Groups, each based on a particular characteristic or combination of characteristics. Colour of flower or fruit and shape of flower are common examples and, with fruit, whether a cultivar is grown for culinary or dessert purposes. How such groups are named differs from genus to genus.

To help users of the *RHS Plant Finder* find the plants they want, the classifications used within cultivated genera are listed using codes and plants are marked with the appropriate code in brackets after its name in the Plant Directory. To find the explanation of each code, simply look it up under the genus concerned in the **Classification of Genera** starting on p.28. The codes relating to edible fruits are also listed here, but these apply across several genera.

COLLECTORS' REFERENCES

Abbreviations (usually with numbers) following a plant name refer to the collector(s) of the plant. These abbreviations are expanded, with a collector's name or expedition title, in the section **Collectors' References** starting on p.20.

A collector's reference may indicate a new, as yet unnamed range of variation within a species. The inclusion of collectors' references in the *RHS Plant Finder* supports the book's role in sourcing unusual plants.

The Convention on Biological Diversity calls for conservation of biodiversity, its sustainable use and the fair and equitable sharing of any derived benefits. Since its adoption in 1993, collectors are required to have prior informed consent from the country of origin for the acquisition and commercialisation of collected material.

COMMON NAMES

In a work such as this, it is necessary to refer to plants by their botanical names for the sake of universal comprehension and clarity. However, at the same time we recognise that with fruit and vegetables most people are more familiar with their common names than their botanical ones. Cross-references are therefore given from common to botanical names for fruit, vegetables and the commoner culinary herbs throughout the Plant Directory.

CULTIVAR

Literally meaning cultivated variety, cultivar names are given to denote variation within species and that generated by hybridisation, in cultivation. To make them easily distinguishable from botanical names, they are not printed in italics and are enclosed in single quotation marks. Cultivar names coined since 1959 should follow the rules of the International Code of Nomenclature for Cultivated Plants (**ICNCP**).

CULTIVAR GROUP

This is a collective name for a group of cultivars within a genus with similar characteristics. The word Group is always included and, where cited with a cultivar name, it is enclosed in brackets, for example, *Actaea simplex* (Atropurpurea Group) 'Brunette', where 'Brunette' is a distinct cultivar in a group of purple-leaved cultivars.

Another example of a cultivar group is *Rhododendron polycladum* Scintillans Group. In this case *Rhododendron scintillans* was a species that is now botanically 'sunk' within *R. polycladum*, but it is still recognised horticulturally as a Group.

Cultivar Group names are also used for swarms of hybrids with the same parentage, for example, *Rhododendron* Polar Bear Group. These were formerly treated as **grex** names, a term now used only for orchids. A single clone from the Group may be given the same cultivar name, for example, *Rhododendron* 'Polar Bear'.

DESCRIPTIVE TERMS

Terms that appear after the main part of the plant name are shown in a smaller font to distinguish them. These descriptive elements give extra information about the plant and may include the **collector's reference**, **authority**, or what colour it is. For example, *Fritillaria thessala* SBEL 443, *Penstemon* 'Sour Grapes' M. Fish, *Lobelia tupa* dark orange.

FAMILIES

Genera are grouped into larger groups of related plants called families. Most family names, with the exception of eight familiar names, end with the same group of letters, *-aceae*. While it is still acceptable to use these eight exceptions, the modern trend adopted in the *RHS Plant Finder* is to use

alternative names with *–aceae* endings. The families concerned are *Compositae* (*Asteraceae*), *Cruciferae* (*Brassicaceae*), *Gramineae* (*Poaceae*), *Guttiferae* (*Clusiaceae*), *Labiatae* (*Lamiaceae*), *Leguminosae* (split here into *Caesalpiniaceae*, *Mimosaceae* and *Papilionaceae*), *Palmae* (*Arecaceae*) and *Umbelliferae* (*Apiceae*). Also the traditionally large family *Liliaceae* is split into a number of smaller, more natural, families that as yet may be unfamiliar to readers.

GENERA

Genera used in the *RHS Plant Finder* are almost always those given in Brummitt's *Vascular Plant Families and Genera*. For spellings and genders of generic names, Greuter's *Names in Current Use for Extant Plant Genera* has also been consulted. See **Botanical Names**.

GREX

Within orchids, hybrids of the same parentage, regardless of how alike they are, are given a grex name. Individuals can be selected, given cultivar names and propagated vegetatively. For example, *Pleione* Versailles g. 'Bucklebury', where Versailles is the grex name and 'Bucklebury' is a selected **cultivar**.

HARDINESS

Hardiness ratings are shown for **Award of Garden Merit** plants. The categories used are as follows:
H1 = plants requiring heated glass in the British Isles
H2 = plants requiring unheated glass in the British Isles
H3 = plants hardy outside in some regions of the British Isles or in particular situations, or which, while usually grown outside in summer, need frost-free protection in winter (eg. dahlias)
H4 = plants hardy throughout the British Isles
H1-2, H2-3, H3-4 = plants intermediate between the two ratings given
H1+3 = requiring heated glass; may be grown outside in summer

HYBRIDS

Some species, when grown together, in the wild or in cultivation, are found to interbreed and form hybrids. In some instances a hybrid name is coined, for example hybrids between *Primula hirsuta* and *P. minima* are given the name *Primula × forsteri*, the multiplication sign indicating hybrid origin. Hybrid formulae that quote the parentage of the hybrid are used where a unique name has not been coined, for example *Rhododendron calophytum × R. praevernum*.

Hybrids between different genera are also possible, for example × *Mahoberberis* is the name given to hybrids between *Mahonia* and *Berberis*.

There are also a few special-case hybrids called graft hybrids, where the tissues of two plants are physically rather than genetically mixed. These are indicated by an addition rather than a multiplication sign, so *Laburnum + Cytisus* becomes +*Laburnocytisus*.

ICNCP

The ICNCP is the International Code of Nomenclature for Cultivated Plants. First published in 1959, the most recent edition was published in 2004.

Cultivar names that do not conform to this Code, and for which there is no valid alternative, are flagged I (for invalid). The cultivar names flagged I in the last edition of the *RHS Plant Finder* have been reviewed to ensure only those still considered invalid by the 2004 Code are flagged.

See **The Cultivated Plant Code** (page 12) for more details.

NOTES ON NOMENCLATURE AND IDENTIFICATION

The **Notes on Nomenclature and Identification**, starting on p.23, give further information for names that are complex or may be confusing. See also **Advisory Panel on Nomenclature and Taxonomy**.

PLANT BREEDERS' RIGHTS

Plants covered by an active grant of Plant Breeders' Rights (PBR) are indicated throughout the Plant Directory. Grants indicated are those awarded by both UK and EU Plant Variety Rights offices. Because grants can both come into force and lapse at any time, this book can only represent the situation at one point in time, but it is hoped that this will act as a useful guide to growers and gardeners. UK grants represent the position as of the end of December 2004 and EU grants as of the end of December 2004.

To obtain PBR protection, a new plant must be registered and pass tests for distinctness, uniformity and stability under an approved name. This approved name, under the rules of the **ICNCP**, established by a legal process, has to be regarded as the cultivar name. Increasingly however, these approved names are a code or "nonsense" name and are therefore often unpronounceable and meaningless, so the plants are given other names designed to attract sales when they are released. These secondary names are often referred to as selling names but are officially termed **trade designations**.

For further information on UK PBR contact:

**Mr R Greenaway
Plant Variety Rights Office,
White House Lane,
Huntingdon Road,
Cambridge CB3 0LF
Tel: (01223) 342396
Fax: (01223) 342386.
Website: www.defra.gov.uk/planth/pvs/
default.htm**

For details of plants covered by EU Community Rights contact the Community Plant Variety Office (CPVO):

**Office Communautaire des Variétés Végétales,
PO Box 62141, 3 Boulevard Maréchal Foch,
F-49021 Angers, Cedex 02, France
Tel: 00 33 (02) 41 25 64 00
Fax: 00 33 (02) 41 25 64 10
Website: www.cpvo.eu.int**

The *RHS Plant Finder* takes no responsibility for ensuring that nurseries selling plants with PBR are licensed to do so.

REVERSE SYNONYMS

It is likely that users of this book will come across names in certain genera that they did not expect to find. This may be because species have been transferred from another genus (or genera). In the list of **Reverse Synonyms** on p.33, the name on the left-hand side is that of an accepted genus to which species have been transferred from the genus on the right. Sometimes all species will have been transferred, but in many cases only a few will be affected. Consulting **Reverse Synonyms** enables users to find the genera from which species have been transferred. Where the right-hand genus is found in the Plant Directory, the movement of species becomes clear through the cross-references in the nursery code column.

SELLING NAMES

See **Trade Designations**

SERIES

With seed-raised plants, series have become increasingly popular. A series contains a number of similar cultivars, but differs from a **Cultivar Group** in that it is a marketing device, with cultivars added to create a range of flower colours in plants of similar habit. Individual colour elements within a species may be represented by slightly different

cultivars over the years. Series names are styled similarly to **Cultivar Groups**.

SPECIES

See under **Botanical Names**

SUBSPECIES

See under **Botanical Names**

SYNONYMS

Although the ideal is for each species or cultivar to have only one name, anyone dealing with plants soon comes across a situation where one plant has received two or more names, or two plants have received the same name. In each case, only one name and application, for reasons of precision and stability, can be regarded as correct. Additional names are known as synonyms. Further information on synonyms and why plants change names is available in *Guide to Plant Names*. See the introduction to this glossary for details of how to request a copy.

See also **Reverse Synonyms**.

TRADE DESIGNATIONS

A **trade designation** is the name used to market a plant when the cultivar name is considered unsuitable for selling purposes. It is styled in a different typeface and without single quotation marks.

In the case of **Plant Breeders' Rights** it is a legal requirement for the cultivar name to appear with the trade designation on a label at the point of sale. Most plants are sold under only one trade designation, but some, especially roses, are sold under a number of names, particularly when cultivars are introduced from other countries. Usually, the correct cultivar name is the only way to ensure that the same plant is not bought unwittingly under two or more different trade designations. The *RHS Plant Finder* follows the recommendations of the **ICNCP** when dealing with trade designations and PBR. These are always to quote the cultivar name and trade designation together and to style the trade designation in a different typeface, without single quotation marks.

TRANSLATIONS

When a cultivar name is translated from the language of first publication, the translation is regarded as a **trade designation** and styled accordingly. We endeavour to recognise the original cultivar name in every case and to give an English translation where it is in general use.

VARIEGATED PLANTS

Following a suggestion from the Variegated Plant Group of the Hardy Plant Society, a (v) is cited after those plants which are "variegated". The dividing line between variegation and less distinct colour marking is necessarily arbitrary and plants with light veins, pale, silver or dark zones, or leaves flushed in paler colours, are not shown as being variegated unless there is an absolutely sharp distinction between paler and darker zones.

For further details of the Variegated Plant Group, please write to:

**Jerry Webb, Esq.,
17 Heron Way, Minster Heights,
Ilminster TA19 0BX**

VARIETY

See under **Botanical Names** and **Cultivar**

'The question of nomenclature is always a vexed one. The only thing certain is, that it is impossible to please everyone.'

W.J. BEAN – PREFACE TO FIRST EDITION OF *Trees & Shrubs Hardy in the British Isles*

THE CULTIVATED PLANT CODE

International Code of Nomenclature for Cultivated Plants (Published in 2004 by the International Society for Horticultural Science as *Acta Horticulturae* No 647)

The seventh edition of the ICNCP, or *Cultivated Plant Code*, was published early in 2004. This new Code is the culmination of international discussion and debate which reached peaks of activity during the Third International Symposium on the Taxonomy of Cultivated Plants held in Edinburgh in 1998 and at the following Fourth Symposium held within the 2002 International Horticultural Congress in Toronto. The object remains the same as it did when the first edition appeared in 1953: to put the naming of the past into order and to provide for that of the future.

The Code is the responsibility of a Commission of the International Union of Biological Sciences and in 1995 the Commission was responsible for a major revision, re-ordering and re-structuring of the rules which has essentially stood up well to practical use. This new edition therefore maintains the overall style of the 1995 Code but contains a few note-worthy changes and additions. As far as possible the language of the Code has been simplified to remove technical or jargon words and the number of illustrative examples has been increased.

The Code now deals with the names of plants in just two categories: the cultivar and the Group (the latter term replacing the more cumbersome "cultivar-group" and reflecting the fact that Groups may contain individual plants as well as named cultivars). Extensive examples of what may constitute a cultivar or a Group are provided.

For the first time the Code also includes full provision for the formation and use of grex names, the particular sort of Group used only by orchidists and defined solely by parentage.

One structural innovation in the layout of the Code concerns the removal of the provisions relating to registration of names and International Cultivar Registration Authorities (formerly International Registration Authorities), as well as those concerning nomenclatural standards (formerly Standards), to separate Divisions within the Code. As registration and the citation of nomenclatural standards are not requirements for new names it was considered they would sit more easily outside the formal rules. A new Division has also been included, summarised from the *Botanical Code*, dealing with how hybrid generic names should be formed. This is an area of especial importance to orchid breeders where intergeneric crosses are very common.

Following representations from some of the major user groups of the Code a new section gives explicit guidance on how the status of cultivar and Group names should be indicated. Cultivar status should only be indicated by enclosing the epithet in single quotes and not by using the abbreviation "cv." i.e. 'Longworth Double', not cv. Longworth Double or cv. 'Longworth Double'. Formal Group status is indicated by the use of the word Group (note the capital letter), or its equivalent in other languages, used as the first or final word in the epithet depending on linguistic custom e.g. *Hydrangea macrophylla* Groupe Hortensis (in French), *Begonia* Elatior Group (in English).

In this new revision the Commission has tried to take as liberal approach as possible, only seeking to maintain restrictions when a real chance of significant confusion would arise if certain words or practices were to be employed. This is most evident in Article 19, dealing with the formation of cultivar epithets. This is the longest Article in the Code and probably that most frequently consulted. The provisions have been grouped for easier comprehension into five sections and some of the more notable changes incorporated include the following:

- allowing the use of Latin words which are in current use in a language other than Latin e.g. as terms, common phrases, personal names or place names
- removal of the 10 syllable limit on epithet length, the only restrictions now being a maximum length of 30 characters
- allowing epithets to be novel inventions (i.e. made up words)
- making it unacceptable to form an epithet from a single letter or solely of Arabic or Roman numerals
- removal of the word "cross" from the list of words banned in cultivar epithets
- explicit indication that numerals may form part of a cultivar epithet
- explicit banning of the use of fractions and most symbols in epithets

Moreover rules on the use of the latin or common names of a genus or species as part of cultivar epithet have been considerably relaxed. It is still not possible to use the name of the genus to which a cultivar belongs as part of its cultivar epithet, but so long as confusion is unlikely the use of other names is allowed. Thus if a rhododendron breeder wants to name a series of his new seedlings after his daughters Lily, Veronica, Erica, Victoria and Daphne he can now do so.

This section ends with a series of further Recommendations (i.e. not Rules) which, whilst not mandatory for the purposes of the Code, give guidance on names which might prove unacceptable to others such as statutory authorities considering names under National Listing or Plant Breeders' Rights legislation.

Further consideration has also been given to the often contentious issue of correct spelling, in the full knowledge that this area can generate more heated debate than all the rest put together (the taxon/culton debate aside perhaps). New departures in this Code include:-

- provision to *add* accents and other diacritical marks if it is thought that demands of linguistic custom are better served by doing so, even if they were not used in the original publication
- in transcribed Japanese epithets if a long vowel is to be indicated with an accent that must be the macron (e.g. ō) not the circumflex or any other device
- the ligatures "æ" and "œ" indicating the letters are pronounced together should be transcribed as separate letters –ae- and –oe-
- the ampersand ("&") is to be transcribed as "and" – or its equivalent in other languages depending on the language used when establishment of the name took place
- the symbol #, when meaning 'number' in English is be to be written as "No" or spelt out in full: again provision being made for different words in other languages.

In general this edition of the Code aims to provide standardisation in dealing with spelling in order that compilers of listings, especially in electronic databases may have consistency in their works.

Of particular significance to future nomenclatural stability are the clarified and augmented provisions for the continued recognition of names contrary to the Code but which are in widespread/long established use. Gradually botanists have been extending provision in the *Botanical Code* for well-known, widely used generic and species names that fall foul of some nomenclatural rule and the ICNCP has similarly been developing provisions in this respect. If the Codes are not to be seriously undermined such action has to be taken sparingly and only with good reason. In the 1995 Code a combination of sanctioning (by an ICRA) linked to conservation (by the Commission) was outlined, but the detail of its operation was not clear and the conservation element rarely invoked. In the 2004 Code ICRAs have been given wider authority to designate a name as acceptable (sanctioning as a term disappears) and the Commission only becomes actively involved if no ICRA exists or an objection is raised to an ICRA decision. All decisions, either of an ICRA or the Commission, are only effective following their publication.

Trademarks are beyond the jurisdiction of this Code and it is made clear that should an established cultivar name be successfully challenged as being in conflict with a prior trademark right, then a new name has to be found for the plant concerned.

Similarly the formation of trade designations is not regarded as a matter governed by the Code. Indeed these devices, used to market a plant in place of the accepted name, are not considered to be names in the sense of the Code. The Code merely indicates that trade designations should not be enclosed within single quotes and recommends they should be typographically distinguished from cultivar epithets.

There is much more besides the rules within the slim volume that forms the new Code, including a full glossary, lists of the current ICRAs and statutory registration authorities, as well as a listing of special denomination classes and institutions maintaining nomenclatural standards.

This Code is part of a continuing process of evolution and improvement. A Code that changes too much or too frequently will soon lose effect and standing, but at the same time the rules need to change to respond to changing practice and opinion. If you have views that you feel are not reflected in the Code please make them known to the Commission.

Dr A C Leslie
IUBS Code Commission
RHS Garden, Wisley, Woking
Surrey GU23 6QB, UK

December 2004

SYMBOLS AND ABBREVIATIONS

SYMBOLS APPEARING TO THE LEFT OF THE NAME

*   Name not validated. Not listed in the appropriate International Registration Authority checklist nor in works cited in the Bibliography. For fuller discussion see p.7
I   Invalid name. See *International Code of Botanical Nomenclature 2000* and *International Code of Nomenclature for Cultivated Plants 2004.* For fuller discussion see p.7
N   Refer to Notes on Nomenclature and Identification on p.23
§   Plant listed elsewhere in the Plant Directory under a synonym
×   Hybrid genus
+   Graft hybrid genus

SYMBOLS APPEARING TO THE RIGHT OF THE NAME

✿   National Council for the Conservation of Plants and Gardens (NCCPG) National Plant Collection® exists for all or part of this genus. Provisional Collections appear in brackets. Full details of the NCCPG Plant Collections are found in the *National Plant Collections® Directory 2005* available from: www.nccpg.com or NCCPG, RHS Garden, Wisley, Woking, Surrey GU23 6QP
♡H4   The Royal Horticultural Society's Award of Garden Merit, see p.7

(d)   double-flowered
(F)   Fruit
(f)   female
(m)   male
(v)   variegated plant, see p.11
PBR   Plant Breeders Rights see p.9
new   New plant entry in this edition

For abbreviations relating to individual genera see **Classification of Genera** p.28
For **Collectors' References** see p.20
For symbols used in the **Nurseries** section see p.784

SYMBOLS AND ABBREVIATIONS USED AS PART OF THE NAME

×   hybrid species
aff.   affinis (allied to)
agg.   aggregate, a single name used to cover a group of very similar plants, regarded by some as separate species
ambig.   ambiguous, a name used by two authors for different plants and where it is unclear which is being offered
cl.   clone
cv(s)   cultivar(s)
f.   forma (botanical form)
g.   grex
sp.   species
subsp.   subspecies
subvar.   subvarietas (botanical subvariety)
var.   varietas (botanical variety)

IT IS NOT WITHIN THE REMIT
OF THIS BOOK TO CHECK
that nurseries are applying the right names
to the right plants or to ensure nurseries
selling plants with Plant Breeders' Rights
are licensed to do so.

Please, never use an old edition

RHS Plant Trials Bulletins

RHS Plant Trials Bulletins are full colour A4 booklets that provide information for both the professional and keen amateur gardener on specific plant groups.

Each year the results of some of the RHS Plant Trials are published as bulletins; these list, illustrate and describe the plants that have been given the Award of Garden Merit ♥ during the trial. Background botanical and cultivation information is also included as are useful selection tables, comparing the different entries in the trial.

Currently the following eight bulletins are available:

Canna
Delphinium
Hardy Lavender
Miscanthus
Perennial Yellow Daisies
Salad Potatoes
Shrubby Potentilla
Spiraea

If you would like a copy of any of these, please contact: The Trials Office, RHS Garden Wisley, Woking, Surrey GU23 6QB. Please enclose an A4 SAE and a cheque for £2.50 per copy (a donation towards costs) made out to the Royal Horticultural Society.

To view the RHS Plant Trials Bulletins online, please visit **www.rhs.org.uk/plants/trials_bulletins.asp**

PLANTS

WHATEVER PLANT YOU ARE LOOKING FOR,
MAYBE AN OLD FAVOURITE OR A MORE UNUSUAL
CULTIVAR, SEARCH HERE FOR A LIST OF THE
SUPPLIERS THAT ARE CLOSEST TO YOU.

How to Use the Plant Directory

Nursery Codes

Look up the plant you require in the alphabetical Plant Directory. Against each plant you will find one or more four-letter codes, for example LLin, each code represents one nursery offering that plant. The first letter of each code indicates the main area of the country in which the nursery is situated. For this geographical key, refer to the **Nursery Codes and Symbols** on p.784.

Turn to the **Nursery Details by Code** starting on p.788 where, in alphabetical order of codes, you will find details of each nursery which offers the plant in question. If you wish to visit any nursery, you may find its location on one of the maps (following p.917). Please note, however, that not all nurseries, especially mail order only nurseries, choose to be shown on the maps. For a fuller explanation of how to use the nursery listings please turn to p.785. **Always check that the nursery you select has the plant in stock before you set out.**

Plants with more than 30 Suppliers

In some cases, against the plant name you will see the term 'more than 30 suppliers' instead of a nursery code. If we were to include every plant listed by all nurseries, the *RHS Plant Finder* would become unmanageably bulky. We therefore ask nurseries to restrict their entries to those plants that are not already well represented. As a result, if more than 30 nurseries offer any plant the Directory gives no nursery codes and the plant is listed instead as having 'more than 30 suppliers'. You should have little difficulty in locating these in local nurseries or garden centres. However, if you are unable to find such plants, we will be pleased to send a full list of all the nurseries that we have on file as stockists. To obtain a list, please see the Introduction on p.4.

Finding Fruit, Vegetables and Herbs

You will need to search for these by their botanical names. Common names are cross-referenced to their botanical names in the Plant Directory.

If you have Difficulty Finding your Plant

If you cannot immediately find the plant you seek, look through the various species of the genus. You may be using an incomplete name. The problem is most likely to arise in very large genera such as *Phlox* where there are a number of possible species, each with a large number of cultivars. A search through the whole genus may well bring success. Please note that, for space reasons, the following are not listed in the Plant Directory: annuals, orchids, except hardy terrestrial orchids; cacti, except hardy cacti.

Cross-references

It may be that the plant name you seek is a synonym. Our intention is to list nursery codes only against the correct botanical name. Where you find a synonym you will be cross-referred to the correct name. Occasionally you may find that the correct botanical name to which you have been referred is not listed. This is because it was last listed in an earlier edition as explained below.

Plants Last Listed in Earlier Editions

It may be that the plant you are seeking has no known suppliers and is thus not listed.

The loss of a plant name from the Directory may arise for a number of reasons – the supplier may have gone out of business, or may not have responded to our latest questionnaire and has therefore been removed from the book. Such plants may well be still available but we have no current knowledge of their whereabouts. Alternatively, some plants may have been misnamed by nurseries in previous editions, but are now appearing under their correct name.

To obtain a listing of plants last listed in earlier editions please see the Introduction on p.4.

Please, never use an old edition

USING THE PLANT DIRECTORY

The main purpose of the Plant Directory is to help the reader correctly identify the plant they seek and find its stockist. Each nursery has a unique identification code which appears to the right of the plant name. Turn to Nursery Details by Code (p.788) for the address, opening times and other details of the nursery. The first letter of each nursery code denotes its geographical region.

Turn to the map on p.784 to find your region code and then identify the nurseries in your area.

Another purpose of the Directory is to provide more information about the plant through the symbols and other information. For example, if it has an alternative name, is new to this edition or has received the RHS Award of Garden Merit.

Euonymus (Celastraceae)

B&L 12543	EPla EWes
B&SWJ 4457	WPGP
CC 4522	CPLG
alatus ♥H4	More than 30 suppliers
– B&SWJ 8794	WCru
– var. *apterus*	EPfP
– Chicago Fire	see *E. alatus* 'Timber Creek'
– 'Ciliodentatus'	see *E. alatus* 'Compactus'
– 'Compactus' ♥H4	More than 30 suppliers
§ – 'Fire Ball'	EPfP
– Little Moses = 'Odom'	MBlu
* – 'Macrophyllus'	EPfP
– 'Rudy Haag'	CPMA EPfP
– 'Select'	see *E. alatus* 'Fire Ball'
– 'Silver Cloud' **new**	EPfP
§ – 'Timber Creek'	CPMA EPfP MBlu MBri NLar
americanus	EPfP GIBF MBlu NLar
– 'Evergreen' **new**	EPfP
– narrow-leaved	EPfP NLar
atropurpureus	EPfP
'Benkomoki' **new**	MGos
bungeanus	CMCN EPfP EPla NLar
– 'Dart's Pride'	CPMA EPfP NLar
– 'Fireflame'	EPfP NLar
* – var. *mongolicus*	EPfP
– 'Pendulus'	EPfP MBlu SIFN
– var. *semipersistens*	CPMA EPla
carnosus	EPfP NLar
'Copper Wire'	EMil SPoG
cornutus var.	CPMA EPfP LPan MBlu NBhm NLar
quinquecornutus	SIFN SPoG WPGP WPat
'Den Haag'	EPfP MBri
echinatus	EPfP EPla
– BL&M 306	SLon
europaeus	More than 30 suppliers
– f. *albus*	CPMA CTho EPfP LTwo NLar
– 'Atropurpureus'	CMCN CTho EPfP MBlu MBri NLar
	SIFN
– 'Atrorubens'	CPMA
– 'Aucubifolius' (v)	EPfP
* – 'Aureus'	CNat
– 'Brilliant' **new**	EPfP
* – f. *bulgaricus*	EPfP
– 'Chrysophyllus'	EPfP MBlu NLar
– 'Howard'	EPfP
– var. *intermedius*	ENot EPfP MAsh MBlu NLar
– 'Miss Pinkie'	CEnd CMCN
– 'Pumilis' **new**	EPfP
– 'Red Cascade' ♥H4	More than 30 suppliers
– 'Scarlet Wonder'	CPMA EPfP MBri NLar
– 'Thornhayes'	CTho EPfP
I – 'Variegatus' **new**	EPfP
farreri	see *E. nanus*
fimbriatus	EPfP
fortunei Blondy =	More than 30 suppliers
'Interbolwi'PBR (v)	

ABBREVIATIONS
To save space a dash indicates that the previous heading is repeated. If written out in full the name would be Euonymus alatus 'Fire Ball'.

NEW
Plant new to this edition.

DESCRIPTIVE TERM
See p.8.

SYMBOLS TO THE LEFT
OF THE NAME
Provides information about the name of the plant. See p.15 for the key.

SYMBOLS TO THE
RIGHT OF THE NAME
Tells you more about the plant itself, e.g. (v) indicates that the plant is variegated, (F) = fruit. See p.15 for the key.

SELLING NAMES
See p.10.

♥H4
This plant has received the RHS Award of Garden Merit. See p.7.

CROSS-REFERENCES
Directs you to the correct name of the plant and the nursery codes. See p.18.

NURSERY CODE
A unique code identifying each nursery. Turn to p.788 for details of the nurseries.

MORE THAN 30 SUPPLIERS
Indicates that more than 30 Plant Finder nurseries supply the plant, and it may be available locally. See p.18.

PBR
Plant Breeders' Rights. See p.9.

SUPPLEMENTARY KEYS TO THE DIRECTORY

COLLECTORS' REFERENCES

Abbreviations following a plant name, refer to the collector(s) of the plant. These abbreviations are expanded below, with a collector's name or expedition title. For a fuller explanation, see p.8.

A&JW	A. & J. Watson
A&L	Ala, A.; Lancaster, Roy
AB&S	Archibald, James; Blanchard, John W; Salmon, M.
AC	Clark, Alan J.
AC&H	Apold, J.; Cox, Peter; Hutchison, Peter
AC&W	Albury; Cheese, M.; Watson, J.M.
ACE	AGS Expedition to China (1994)
ACL	Leslie, Alan C.
AGS/ES	AGS Expedition to Sikkim (1983)
AGSJ	AGS Expedition to Japan (1988)
Airth	Airth, Murray
Akagi	Akagi Botanical Garden
AL&JS	Sharman, Joseph L.; Leslie, Alan C.
ARG	Argent, G.C.G.
B L.	Beer, Len
B&L	Brickell, Christopher D.; Leslie, Alan C.
B&M & BM	Brickell, Christopher D.; Mathew, Brian
B&S	Bird P. & Salmon M.
B&SWJ	Wynn-Jones, Bleddyn; Wynn-Jones, Susan
B&V	Burras, K. & Vosa, C.G.
BB	Bartholomew, B.
BC	Chudziak, W.
BC&W	Beckett; Cheese, M.; Watson, J.M.
Beavis	Beavis, Derek S.
Berry	Berry, P.
Berry & Brako	Berry, P. & Brako, Lois
BL&M	University of Bangor Expedition to NE Nepal
BM	Mathew, Brian F.
BM&W	Binns, David L.; Mason, M.; Wright, A.
BOA	Boardman, P.
Breedlove	Breedlove, D.
BR	Rushbrooke, Ben
BS	Smith, Basil
BSBE	Bowles Scholarship Botanical Expedition (1963)

BSSS	Crûg Expedition, Jordan (1991)
Bu	Bubert, S.
Burtt	Burtt, Brian L.
C	Cole, Desmond T.
C&C	Cox, P.A. & Cox, K.N.E.
C&Cu	Cox, K.N.E. & Cubey, J.
C&H	Cox, Peter; Hutchison, Peter
C&K	Chamberlain & Knott
C&R	Christian & Roderick
C&S	Clark, Alan; Sinclair, Ian W.J.
C&V	K.N.E. Cox & S. Vergera
C&W	Cheese, M.; Watson, J.M.
CC	Chadwell, Christopher
CC&H	Chamberlain, David F.; Cox, Peter; Hutchison, P.
CC&McK	Chadwell, Christopher; McKelvie, A.
CC&MR	Chadwell, Christopher; Ramsay
CCH&H	Chamberlain, D.F.; Cox, P.; Hutchison, P.; Hootman, S.
CCH&H	Chamberlain, Cox, Hootman & Hutchison
CD&R	Compton, J.; D'Arcy, J.; Rix, E.M.
CDB	Brickell, Christopher D.
CDC	Coode, Mark J.E.; Dockrill, Alexander
CDC&C	Compton, D'Arcy, Christopher & Coke
CDPR	Compton, D'Arcy, Pope & Rix
CE&H	Christian, P.J.; Elliott; Hoog
CEE	Chengdu Edinburgh Expedition China 1991
CGW	Grey-Wilson, Christopher
CH&M	Cox, P.; Hutchison, P.; Maxwell-MacDonald, D.
CHP&W	Kashmir Botanical Expedition
CL	Lovell, Chris
CLD	Chungtien, Lijiang & Dali Exped. China (1990)
CM&W	Cheese M., Mitchel J. & Watson, J.
CN&W	Clark; Neilson; Wilson
CNDS	Nelson, C. & Sayers D.
Cooper	Cooper, R.E.
Cox	Cox, Peter A.
CPC	Cobblewood Plant Collection
CPN	Compton, James

CSE	Cyclamen Society Expedition (1990)
CT	Teune, Carla
Dahl	Dahl, Sally
DBG	Denver Botanic Garden, Colorado
DC	Cheshire, David
DF	Fox, D.
DJH	Hinkley, Dan
DJHC	Hinkley China
DM	Millais, David
Doleshy	Doleshy, F.L.
DS&T	Drake, Sharman J.; Thompson
DWD	Rose, D.
DZ	Zummell, D.
ECN	Nelson, E. Charles
EDHCH	Hammond, Eric D.
EGM	Millais, T.
EKB	Balls, Edward K.
EM	East Malling Research Station
EMAK	Edinburgh Makalu Expedition (1991)
EMR	Rix, E.Martyn
EN	Needham, Edward F.
ENF	Fuller, E. Nigel
ETE	Edinburgh Taiwan Expedition (1993)
ETOT	Kirkham, T.S.; Flanagan, Mark
F	Forrest, G.
F&W	Watson, J.; Flores, A.
Farrer	Farrer, Reginald
FK	Kinmonth, Fergus W.
FMB	Bailey, F.M.
G	Gardner, Martin F.
G&K	Gardner, Martin F.; Knees, Sabina G.
G&P	Gardner, Martin F.; Page, Christopher N.
GDJ	Dumont, Gerard
GG	Gusman, G.
GS	Sherriff, George
Green	Green, D.
Guitt	Guittoneau, G.G.
Guiz	Guizhou Expedition (1985)
GWJ	Goddard, Sally; Wynne-Jones, Bleddyn & Susan
G-W&P	Grey-Wilson, Christopher; Phillips
H	Huggins, Paul
H&B	Hilliard, Olive M.; Burtt, Brian L.
H&D	Howick, C.; Darby
H&M	Howick, Charles; McNamara, William A.
H&W	Hedge, Ian C.; Wendelbo, Per W.
Harry Smith	Smith, K.A.Harry
Hartside	Hartside Nursery
HCM	Heronswood Expedition to Chile (1998)
HH&K	Hannay, S&S & Kingsbury, N
HLMS	Springate, L.S.
HM&S	Halliwell, B., Mason, D. & Smallcombe
HOA	Hoog, Anton
Hummel	Hummel, D.
HW&E	Wendelbo, Per; Hedge, I.; Ekberg, L.
HWEL	Hirst, J.Michael; Webster, D.
HWJ	Crûg Heronswood Joint Expedition
HWJCM	Crûg Heronswood Expedition
HWJK	Crûg Heronswood Expedition, East Nepal (2002)
HZ	Zetterlund, Henrik
ICE	Instituto de Investigaciónes Ecológicas Chiloé & RBGE
IDS	International Dendrological Society
ISI	Int. Succulent Introductions
J&JA	Archibald, James; Archibald, Jennifer
J. Jurasek	Jurasek, J.
JCA	Archibald, James
JE	Jack Elliott
JJ	Jackson, J.
JJ&JH	Halda, J.; Halda, J.
JJH	Halda, Joseph J.
JLS	Sharman, J.L.
JM-MK	Mahr, J.; Kammerlander, M.
JMT	Mann Taylor, J.
JN	Nielson, Jens
JR	Russell, J.
JRM	Marr, John
JW	Watson, J.M.
K	Kirkpatrick, George
K&LG	Gillanders, Kenneth; Gillanders, L.
K&Mc	Kirkpatrick, George; McBeath, Ronald J.D.
K&P	Josef Kopec, Milan Prasil
K&T	Kurashige, Y.; Tsukie, S.
KC	Cox, Kenneth
KEKE	Kew/Edinburgh Kanchenjunga Expedition (1989)
KGB	Kunming/Gothenburg Botanical Expedition (1993)
KM	Marsh, K.
KR	Rushforth, K.D.
KRW	Wooster, K.R. (distributed after his death by Kath Dryden)
KW	Kingdon-Ward, F.
L	Lancaster, Roy C.
L&S	Ludlow, Francis; Sherriff, George
LA	Long Ashton Research Station clonal selection scheme
LB	Bird P., Salmon, M.
LEG	Lesotho Edinburgh/Gothenburg Expedition (1997)
Lismore	Lismore Nursery, Breeder's Number
LM&S	Leslie, Mattern & Sharman
LP	Palmer, W.J.L.
LS&E	Ludlow, Frank; Sherriff, George; Elliott, E. E.
LS&H	Ludlow, Frank; Sherriff, George; Hicks, J. H.
LS&T	Ludlow, Frank; Sherriff, George; Taylor, George
M&PS	Mike & Polly Stone
M&T	Mathew; Tomlinson
Mac&W	McPhail & Watson

McB	McBeath, R.J.D.
McLaren	McLaren, H.D.
MDM	Myers, Michael D.
MESE	Alpine Garden Society Expedition, Greece 1999
MF	Foster, Maurice
MH	Heasman, Matthew T.
MK	Kammerlander, Michael
MP	Pavelka, Mojmir
MPF	Frankis, M.P.
MS	Salmon, M.
MS&CL	Salmon, M.; Lovell, C.
MSF	Fillan, M.S.
NJM	Macer, N.J.
NNS	Ratko, Ron
NS	Turland, Nick
NVFDE	Northern Vietnam First Darwin Expedition
Og	Ogisu, Mikinori
P&C	Paterson, David S.; Clarke, Sidney
P&W	Polastri; Watson, J. M.
PB	Bird, Peter
PC&H	Pattison, G.; Catt, P.; Hickson, M.
PD	Davis, Peter H.
PF	Furse, Paul
PJC	Christian, Paul J.
PJC&AH	P.J. Christian & A. Hogg
PNMK	Nicholls, P.; Kammerlander, M.
Polunin	Polunin, Oleg
Pras	Prasil, M.
PS&W	Polunin, Oleg; Sykes, William; Williams, John
PW	Wharton, Peter
R	Rock, J.F.C.
RB	Brown, R.
RBS	Brown, Ray, Sakharin Island
RCB/Arg	Brown, Robert, Argentina, (2002)
RCB/Eq	Brown, Robert, Ecuador, (1988)
RCB/TQ	Brown, Robert, Turkey (2001)
RH	Hancock, R.
RMRP	Rocky Mountain Rare Plants, Denver, Colorado
RS	Suckow, Reinhart
RSC	Richard Somer Cocks
RV	Richard Valder

RWJ	Crûg Farm-Rickards Ferns Expedition to Taiwan (2003)
S&B	Blanchard, J.W.; Salmon, M.
S&F	Salmon, M. & Fillan, M.
S&L	Sinclair, Ian W.J.; Long, David G.
S&SH	Sheilah and Spencer Hannay
Sandham	Sandham, John
SB&L	Salmon, Bird and Lovell
SBEC	Sino-British Expedition to Cangshan
SBEL	Sino-British Lijiang Expedition
SBQE	Sino-British Expedition to Quinghai
Sch	Schilling, Anthony D.
SD	Sashal Dayal
SDR	Rankin, Stella; Rankin, David
SEH	Hootman, Steve
SEP	Swedish Expedition to Pakistan
SF	Forde, P.
SG	Salmon, M. & Guy, P.
SH	Hannay, Spencer
Sich	Simmons, Erskine, Howick & Mcnamara
SLIZE	Swedish-Lithuanian-Iranian Zagros Expedition to Iran (May 1988)
SOJA	Kew / Quarryhill Expedition to Southern Japan
SS&W	Stainton, J.D.Adam; Sykes, William; Williams, John
SSNY	Sino-Scottish Expedition to NW Yunnan (1992)
T	Taylor, Nigel P.
T&K	Taylor, Nigel P.; Knees, Sabina
TH	Hudson, T.
TS&BC	Smythe, T and Cherry, B
TSS	Spring Smyth, T.L.M.
TW	Tony Weston
USDAPI	US Department of Agriculture Plant Index Number
USDAPQ	US Dept. of Agriculture Plant Quarantine Number
USNA	United States National Arboretum
VHH	Vernon H. Heywood
W	Wilson, Ernest H.
WM	McLewin, William
Woods	Woods, Patrick J.B.
Wr	Wraight, David & Anke
Yu	Yu, Tse-tsun

NOTES ON NOMENCLATURE AND IDENTIFICATION

These notes refer to plants in the Plant Directory that are marked with a 'N' to the left of the name. 'Bean Supplement' refers to W.J. Bean *Trees & Shrubs Hardy in the British Isles* (Supplement to the 8th edition) edited by D L Clarke 1988.

Acer davidii 'Ernest Wilson' and *A. davidii* 'George Forrest'
These cultivars should be grafted in order to retain the characteristics of the original clones. However, many plants offered under these names are seed-raised.

Acer palmatum 'Sango-kaku'/ 'Senkaki'
Two or more clones are offered under these names. *A. palmatum* 'Eddisbury' is similar with brighter coral stems.

Achillea ptarmica The Pearl Group/ *A. ptarmica* (The Pearl Group) 'Boule de Neige' / *A. ptarmica* (The Pearl Group) 'The Pearl'
In the recent trial of achilleas at Wisley, only one of the several stocks submitted as 'The Pearl' matched the original appearance of this plant according to Graham Stuart Thomas, this being from Wisley's own stock. At rather less than 60cm (2ft), this needed little support, being the shortest of the plants bearing this name, with slightly grey, not glossy dark green, leaves and a non-invasive habit. This has been designated as the type for this cultivar and only this clone should bear the cultivar name 'The Pearl'. The Pearl Group covers all other double-flowered clones of this species, including seed-raised plants which are markedly inferior, sometimes scarcely double, often invasive and usually needing careful staking. It has been claimed that 'The Pearl' was a re-naming of Lemoine's 'Boule de Neige' but not all authorities agree: all plants submitted to the Wisley trial as 'Boule de Neige' were different from each other, not the same clone as Wisley's 'The Pearl' and referrable to The Pearl Group.

Anemone magellanica
According to *The European Garden Flora*, this is a variant of the very variable *A. multifida*.

Anemone nemorosa 'Alba Plena'
This name is used for several double white forms including *A. nemorosa* 'Flore Pleno' and *A. nemorosa* 'Vestal'.

Artemisia granatensis hort.
Possibly a variant of *A. absinthium*.

Artemisia ludoviciana var. *latiloba* / *A. ludoviciana* 'Valerie Finnis'
Leaves of the former are glabrous at maturity, those of the latter are not.

Artemisia stelleriana 'Boughton Silver'
This was thought to be the first validly published name for this plant, 'Silver Brocade' having been published earlier but invalidly in an undated publication. However, an earlier valid publication for the cultivar name 'Mori' has subsequently been found for the same plant. A proposal to conserve 'Boughton Silver' has been tabled because of its more widespread use.

Aster amellus Violet Queen
It is probable that more than one cultivar is sold under this name.

Aster dumosus
Many of the asters listed under *A. novi-belgii* contain varying amounts of *A. dumosus* blood in their parentage. It is not possible to allocate these to one species or the other and they are therefore listed under *A. novi-belgii*.

Aster × *frikartii* 'Mönch'
The true plant is very rare in British gardens. Most plants are another form of *A.* × *frikartii*, usually 'Wunder von Stäfa'.

Aster novi-belgii
See note under *A. dumosus*. *A. laevis* is also involved in the parentage of most cultivars.

Azara paraguayensis
This is an unpublished name for what seems to be a hybrid between *A. serrata* and *A. lanceolata*.

Berberis buxifolia 'Nana'/ 'Pygmaea'
See explanation in Bean Supplement.

Berberis stenophylla 'Lemon Queen'
This sport from 'Pink Pearl' was first named in 1982. The same mutation occurred again and was named 'Cream Showers'. The older name has priority.

Betula utilis var. *jacquemontii*
Plants are often the clones *B. utilis* var. *jacquemontii* 'Inverleith' or *B. utilis* var. *jacquemontii* 'Doorenbos'

Brachyscome
Originally published as *Brachyscome* by Cassini who later revised his spelling to *Brachycome*. The original spelling has been internationally adopted.

Calamagrostis × *acutiflora* 'Karl Foerster'
C. × *acutiflora* 'Stricta' differs in being 15cm taller, 10-15 days earlier flowering with a less fluffy inflorescence.

Caltha polypetala
This name is often applied to a large-flowered variant of *C. palustris*. The true species has more (7-10) petals.

Camassia leichtlinii 'Alba'
The true cultivar has blueish-white, not cream flowers.

Camassia leichtlinii 'Plena'
  This has starry, transparent green-white flowers; creamy-white 'Semiplena' is sometimes offered under this name.

Camellia japonica 'Campbellii'
  This name is used for five cultivars including 'Margherita Coleoni' but applies correctly to Guichard's 1894 cultivar, single to semi-double full rose pink.

Campanula lactiflora 'Alba'
  This refers to the pure white flowered clone, not to blueish- or greyish-white flowered plants, nor to seed-raised plants.

Carex morrowii 'Variegata'
  C. oshimensis 'Evergold' is sometimes sold under this name.

Carya illinoinensis
  The correct spelling of this name is discussed in *Baileya*, **10**(1) (1962).

Cassinia retorta
  Now included within *C. leptophylla*. A valid infra-specific epithet has yet to be published.

Ceanothus 'Italian Skies'
  Many plants under this name are not true to name.

Chamaecyparis lawsoniana 'Columnaris Glauca'
  Plants under this name might be *C. lawsoniana* 'Columnaris' or a new invalidly named cultivar.

Chamaecyparis pisifera 'Squarrosa Argentea'
  There are two plants of this name, one (valid) with variegated foliage, the other (invalid) with silvery foliage.

Chrysanthemum 'Anastasia Variegated'
  Despite its name, this seems to be derived from 'Mei-kyo', not 'Anastasia'.

Clematis chrysocoma
  The true *C. chrysocoma* is a non-climbing erect plant with dense yellow down on the young growth, still uncommon in cultivation.

Clematis montana
  This name should be used for the typical white-flowered variety only. Pink-flowered variants are referable to *C. montana* var. *rubens*.

Clematis 'Victoria'
  There is also a Latvian cultivar of this name with petals with a central white bar.

Colchicum 'Autumn Queen'
  Entries here might refer to the slightly different *C.* 'Prinses Astrid'.

Cornus 'Norman Hadden'
  See note in Bean Supplement, p.184.

Cotoneaster dammeri
  Plants sold under this name are usually *C. dammeri* 'Major'.

Cotoneaster frigidus 'Cornubia'
  According to Hylmø this cultivar, like all other variants of this species, is fully deciduous. Several evergreen cotoneasters are also grown under this name, most are clones of *C.* × *watereri* or *C. salicifolius*.

Crataegus coccinea
  C. intricata, *C. pedicellata* and *C. biltmoreana* are occasionally supplied under this name.

Crocus cartwrightianus 'Albus'
  The plant offered is the true cultivar and not *C. hadriaticus*.

Dianthus fringed pink
  D. 'Old Fringed Pink' and *D.* 'Old Fringed White' are also sometimes sold under this name.

Dianthus 'Musgrave's Pink' (p)
  This is the registered name of this white-flowered cultivar.

Elymus magellanicus
  Although this is a valid name, Roger Grounds has suggested that many plants might belong to a different, perhaps unnamed species.

Epilobium glabellum hort.
  Plants under this name are not *E. glabellum* but are close to *E. wilsonii* Petrie or perhaps a hybrid of it.

Erodium glandulosum
  Plants under this name are often hybrids.

Erodium guttatum
  Doubtfully in commerce; plants under this name are usually *E. heteradenum*, *E. cheilanthifolium* or hybrids.

Erysimum cheiri 'Baden-Powell'
  Plant of uncertain origin differing from *E. cheiri* 'Harpur Crewe' only in its shorter stature.

Fagus sylvatica **Cuprea Group/Atropurpurea Group**
  It is desirable to provide a name, Cuprea Group, for less richly coloured forms, used in historic landscapes before the purple clones appeared.

Fagus sylvatica 'Pendula'
  This name refers to the Knap Hill clone, the most common weeping form in English gardens. Other clones occur, particularly in Cornwall and Ireland.

Fuchsia loxensis
  For a comparison of the true species with the hybrids 'Speciosa' and 'Loxensis' commonly grown under this name, see Boullemier's Check List (2nd ed.) p.268.

Gentiana cachemirica
  Most plants sold are not true to type.

Geum 'Borisii'
  This name refers to cultivars of *G. coccineum* Sibthorp & Smith, especially *G.* 'Werner Arends' and not to *G.* × *borisii* Kelleper.

Halimium alyssoides and *H. halimifolium*
  Plants under these names are sometimes *H.* × *pauanum* or *H.* × *santae*.

Hebe 'C.P. Raffill'
  See note in Bean Supplement, p.265.

Hebe 'Carl Teschner'
  See note in Bean Supplement, p.264.

Hebe glaucophylla
A green reversion of the hybrid *H.* 'Glaucophylla Variegata' is often sold under this name.

Hedera helix 'Caenwoodiana' / 'Pedata'
Some authorities consider these to be distinct cultivars while others think them different morphological forms of the same unstable clone.

Hedera helix 'Oro di Bogliasco'
Priority between this name and 'Jubiläum Goldherz' and 'Goldheart' has yet to be finally resolved.

Helleborus × *hybridus* / *H. orientalis* hort.
The name *H.* × *hybridus* for acaulescent hellebore hybrids does not seem to follow the *International Code of Botanical Nomenclature* Article H.3.2 requiring one of the parent species to be designated and does not seem to have been typified, contrary to Article 7 of the Code. However, the illustration accompanying the original description in Vilmorin's *Blumengärtnerei* 3(1): 27 (1894) shows that one parent of the cross must have been *H. guttatus*, now treated as part of *H. orientalis*. Taking this illustration as the type for this hybrid species makes it possible to retain *H.* × *hybridus* formally as a hybrid binomial (rather than *H. hybridus* as in a previous edition), as the Code's requirement to distinguish one parent is now met.

Hemerocallis fulva 'Kwanso', 'Kwanso Variegata', 'Flore Pleno' and 'Green Kwanso'
For a discussion of these plants see *The Plantsman*, 7(2).

Heuchera micrantha var. *diversifolia* 'Palace Purple'
This cultivar name refers only to plants with deep purple-red foliage. Seed-raised plants of inferior colouring should not be offered under this name.

Hosta montana
This name refers only to plants long grown in Europe, which differ from *H. elata*.

Hydrangea macrophylla Teller Series
This is used both as a descriptive common name for Lacecap hydrangeas (German *teller* = plate, referring to the more or less flat inflorescence) and for the series of hybrids raised by Wädenswill in Switzerland bearing German names of birds. It is not generally possible to link a hydrangea described by the series name plus a colour description (e.g. Teller Blau, Teller Rosa, Teller Rot) to a single cultivar.

Hypericum fragile
The true *H. fragile* is probably not available from British nurseries.

Hypericum 'Gemo'
Either a selection of *H. prolificum* or *H. prolificum* × *H. densiflorum*.

Ilex × *altaclerensis*
The argument for this spelling is given by Susyn Andrews, *The Plantsman*, 5(2) and is not superceded by the more recent comments in the Supplement to Bean's Trees and Shrubs.

Iris
Apart from those noted below, cultivar names marked 'N' are not registered. The majority of those marked 'I' have been previously used for a different cultivar.

Iris histrioides 'Major'
Two clones are offered under this name, the true one pale blue with darker spotting on the falls, the incorrect one violet-blue with almost horizontal falls.

Juniperus × *media*
This name is illegitimate if applied to hybrids of *J. chinensis* × *J. sabina*, having been previously used for a different hybrid (P.A. Schmidt, *IDS Yearbook 1993*, 47-48). Because of its importance to gardeners, a proposal to conserve its present use was tabled but subsequently rejected.

Lavandula angustifolia 'Lavender Lady' / *L.* 'Cambridge Lady'
Might be synonyms of *L. angustifolia* 'Lady'.

Lavandula × *intermedia* 'Arabian Night'
Plants under this name might be *L.* × *intermedia* 'Impress Purple' or *L.* × *intermedia* 'Sussex'.

Lavandula spica
This name is classed as a name to be rejected (*nomen rejiciendum*) by the *International Code of Botanical Nomenclature*.

Lavatera olbia and *L. thuringiaca*
Although *L. olbia* is usually shrubby and *L. thuringiaca* usually herbaceous, both species are very variable. Cultivars formally ascribed to one species or the other have been shown to be hybrids and are referable to the recently-named hybrid species *L.* × *clementii*.

Lobelia 'Russian Princess'
This name, originally for a pink-flowered, green-leaved cultivar, is now generally applied to a purple-flowered, dark-leaved cultivar that seems to lack a valid name.

Lonicera periclymenum 'Serotina'
See note in Bean Supplement, p.315.

Lonicera sempervirens f. *sulphurea*
Plants in the British Isles usually a yellow-flowered form of *L. periclymenum*.

Malus domestica 'Dummellor's Seedling'
The phonetic spelling 'Dumelow's Seedling' contravenes the ICBN ruling on orthography, i.e. that, except for intentional latinizations, commemorative names should be based on the original spelling of the person's name (Article 60.11). The spelling adopted here is that used on the gravestone of the raiser in Leicestershire.

Meconopsis **Fertile Blue Group**
This Cultivar-group comprises seed-raised and intrinsically perennial tall blue poppies of as yet indeterminate origin (i.e. fertile forms other than the species *M. betonicifolia, M. grandis* and *M. simplicifolia*). The only cultivar so far established is *M.* 'Lingholm' (syns 'Blue Ice' and 'Correnie'). The bulk of seed-raised plants in cultivation and offered for sale are very likely to be *M.* 'Lingholm', although sometimes poorly selected. Many of these plants are currently being distributed erroneously as *M. × sheldonii* and as *M. grandis*.

Meconopsis **George Sherriff Group**
This Cultivar-group comprises a number of sterile (almost invariably) clones of large blue poppies previously (and erroneously) known collectively as *M. grandis* GS600.

Meconopsis grandis ambig.
See note under *M.* Fertile Blue Group. The true species has been recently reintroduced into cultivation in the British Isles but is still rarely offered.

Meconopsis **Infertile Blue Group**
This cultivar-group comprises long-established sterile (almost invariably) clones of large blue poppies other than George Sherriff Group and often given the epithet × *sheldonii*.

Meconopsis × sheldonii ambig.
See notes for *M.* Fertile Blue Group and *M.* Infertile Blue Group.

Melissa officinalis 'Variegata'
The true cultivar of this name had leaves striped with white.

Nemesia caerulea 'Joan Wilder'
The lavender blue clone 'Joan Wilder', described and illustrated in *The Hardy Plant*, 14(1), 11-14, does not come true from seed; it may only be propagated from cuttings.

Osmanthus heterophyllus 'Gulftide'
Probably correctly *O. × fortunei* 'Gulftide'.

Papaver orientale agg.
Plants listed as *P. orientale* agg. (i.e. aggregate) or as one of its cultivars may be *P. orientale* L., *P. pseudo-orientale* or *P. bracteatum* or hybrids between them.

Pelargonium 'Lass o' Gowrie'
The American plant of this name has pointed, not rounded leaf lobes.

Pelargonium quercifolium
Plants under this name are mainly hybrids. The true species has pointed, not rounded leaf lobes.

Penstemon 'Taoensis'
This name for a small-flowered cultivar or hybrid of *P. isophyllus* originally appeared as 'Taoense' but must be corrected to agree in gender with *Penstemon* (masculine). Presumably an invalid name (published in Latin form since 1958), it is not synonymous with *P. crandallii* subsp. *glabrescens* var. *taosensis*.

Pernettya
Botanists now consider that *Pernettya* (fruit a berry) is not separable from *Gaultheria* (fruit a capsule) because in some species the fruit is intermediate between a berry and a capsule. For a fuller explanation see D. Middleton, *The Plantsman*, 12(3).

Picea pungens 'Glauca Pendula'
This name is used for several different glaucous cultivars.

Pinus ayacahuite
P. ayacahuite var. *veitchii* (syn. *P. veitchii*) is occasionally sold under this name.

Pinus nigra 'Cebennensis Nana'
A doubtful name, possibly a synonym for *P. nigra* 'Nana'.

Prunus laurocerasus 'Castlewellan'
We are grateful to Dr Charles Nelson for informing us that the name 'Marbled White' is not valid because although it has priority of publication it does not have the approval of the originator who asked for it to be called 'Castlewellan'.

Prunus serrulata var. *pubescens*
See note in Bean Supplement, p.398.

Prunus × subhirtella 'Rosea'
Might be *P. pendula* var. *ascendens* 'Rosea', *P. pendula* 'Pendula Rosea', or *P. × subhirtella* 'Autumnalis Rosea'.

Rheum × cultorum
The name *R. × cultorum* was published without adequate description and must be abandoned in favour of the validly published *R. × hybridum*.

Rhododendron (azaleas)
All names marked 'N', except for the following, refer to more than one cultivar.

Rhododendron 'Hinomayo'
This name is based on a faulty transliteration (should be 'Hinamoyo') but the spelling 'Hinomayo' is retained in the interests of stability.

Rhus typhina
Linnaeus published both *R. typhina* and *R. hirta* as names for the same species. Though *R. hirta* has priority, it has been proposed that the name *R. typhina* should be conserved.

Rosa gentiliana
Plants under this name are usually the cultivar 'Polyantha Grandiflora' but might otherwise be *R. multiflora* 'Wilsonii', *R. multiflora* var. *cathayensis, R. henryi* or another hybrid.

Rosa 'Gros Choux de Hollande' hort. (Bb)
It is doubtful if this name is correctly applied.

Rosa 'Jacques Cartier' hort.
For a discussion on the correct identity of this rose see *Heritage Rose Foundation News*, Oct. 1989 & Jan. 1990.

Rosa 'Professeur Emile Perrot'
For a discussion on the correct identity of this rose see *Heritage Roses*, Nov. 1991.

Rosa Sweetheart
This is not the same as the Sweetheart Rose, a common name for *R.* 'Cécile Brünner'.

Rosa wichurana
This is the correct spelling according to the ICBN 1994 Article 60.11 (which enforces Recommendation 60C.1c) and not *wichuraiana* for this rose commemorating Max Wichura.

Rubus fruticosus L. agg.
Though some cultivated blackberries do belong to *Rubus fruticosus* L. *sensu stricto,* others are more correctly ascribed to other species of *Rubus* section *Glandulosus* (including *R. armeniacus, R. laciniatus* or *R. ulmifolius)* or are hybrids of species within this section. Because it is almost impossible to ascribe every cultivar to a single species or hybrid, they are listed under *R. fruticosus* L. agg. (i.e. aggregate) for convenience.

Salvia microphylla var. *neurepia*
The type of this variety is referable to the typical variety, *S. microphylla* var. *microphylla.*

Salvia officinalis 'Aurea'
S. officinalis var. *aurea* is a rare variant of the common sage with leaves entirely of gold. It is represented in cultivation by the cultivar 'Kew Gold'. The plant usually offered as *S. officinalis* 'Aurea' is the gold variegated sage *S. officinalis* 'Icterina'.

Sambucus nigra 'Aurea'
Plants under this name are usually not *S. nigra.*

Sedum nevii
The true species is not in cultivation. Plants under this name are usually either *S. glaucophyllum* or occasionally *S. beyrichianum.*

Skimmia japonica 'Foremanii'
The true cultivar, which belongs to *S. japonica* Rogersii Group, is believed to be lost to cultivation. Plants offered under this name are usually *S. japonica* 'Veitchii'.

Sorbus
Except for the following, *Sorbus* species marked N refer to names proposed by Dr Hugh McAllister for apomictic microspecies but not yet published.

Sorbus multijuga Sch 1132
Though this is an accepted name, this collection was obtained from outside the usual range of this species.

Spiraea japonica 'Shirobana'
Shirobana-shimotsuke is the common name for *S. japonica* var. *albiflora.* Shirobana means white-flowered and does not apply to the two-coloured form.

Staphylea holocarpa var. *rosea*
This botanical variety has woolly leaves. The cultivar 'Rosea', with which it is often confused, does not.

Stewartia ovata var. *grandiflora.*
Most, possibly all, plants available from British nurseries under this name are not true to name but are derived from the improved Nymans form.

Thymus Coccineus Group
Thymes under this have dark crimson (RHS 78A) flowers whereas those of 'Alan Bloom' are purplish-pink (RHS 78C).

Thymus serpyllum cultivars
Most cultivars are probably correctly cultivars of *T. polytrichus* or hybrids though they will remain listed under *T. serpyllum* pending further research.

Thymus 'Silver Posie'
The cultivar name 'Silver Posie' is applied to several different plants, not all of them *T. vulgaris.*

Tricyrtis Hototogisu
This is the common name applied generally to all Japanese *Tricyrtis* and specifically to *T. hirta.*

Tricyrtis macropoda
This name has been used for at least five different species.

Uncinia rubra
This name is also misapplied to *U. egmontiana* and *U. uncinata.*

Verbena
Entries marked (G) are considered by some botanists to belong to a separate genus, *Glandularia.*

Verbena 'Kemerton'
Origin unknown, not from Kemerton.

Viburnum opulus 'Fructu Luteo'
See note below.

Viburnum opulus 'Xanthocarpum'
Some entries under this name might be the less compact *V. opulus* 'Fructu Luteo'.

Viburnum plicatum
Entries may include the 'snowball' form, *V. plicatum* f. *plicatum* (syn. *V. plicatum* 'Sterile'), as well as the 'lacecap' form, *V. plicatum* f. *tomentosum.*

Viola labradorica
See Note in *The Garden,* 110(2): 96.

Wisteria floribunda 'Violacea Plena' and *W.f.* 'Yae-kokuryū'
We are grateful to Yoko Otsuki, who has established through Engei Kyokai (the Horticultural Society of Japan) that there are two different double selections of *Wisteria floribunda.* 'Violacea Plena' has double lavender/lilac flowers, while 'Yae-kokuryū' has more ragged and tightly double flowers with purple/indigo centres. Each is distinctive but it is probable that both are confused in the British nursery trade. 'Yae-fuji' might be an earlier name for 'Violacea Plena' or a Group name covering a range of doubles but, as *fuji* is the Japanese common name for the species, would not be a valid name under ICNCP.

CLASSIFICATION OF GENERA

Genera including a large number of species, or with many cultivars, are often subdivided into informal horticultural classifications, or formal cultivar groups in the case of *Clematis* and *Tulipa*. The breeding of new cultivars is sometimes limited to hybrids between closely-related species, thus for *Saxifraga* and *Primula*, the cultivars are allocated to the sections given in the infrageneric treatments cited. Please turn to p.8 for a fuller explanation.

ACTINIDIA

(s-p)	Self-pollinating

BEGONIA

(C)	Cane-like
(R)	Rex Cultorum
(S)	Semperflorens Cultorum
(T)	× *tuberhybrida* (Tuberous)

CHRYSANTHEMUM

(By the National Chrysanthemum Society)

(1)	Indoor Large (Exhibition)
(2)	Indoor Medium (Exhibition)
(3a)	Indoor Incurved: Large-flowered
(3b)	Indoor Incurved: Medium-flowered
(3c)	Indoor Incurved: Small-flowered
(4a)	Indoor Reflexed: Large-flowered
(4b)	Indoor Reflexed: Medium-flowered
(4c)	Indoor Reflexed: Small-flowered
(5a)	Indoor Intermediate: Large-flowered
(5b)	Indoor Intermediate: Medium-flowered
(5c)	Indoor Intermediate: Small-flowered
(6a)	Indoor Anemone: Large-flowered
(6b)	Indoor Anemone: Medium-flowered
(6c)	Indoor Anemone: Small-flowered
(7a)	Indoor Single: Large-flowered
(7b)	Indoor Single: Medium-flowered
(7c)	Indoor Single: Small-flowered
(8a)	Indoor True Pompon
(8b)	Indoor Semi-pompon
(9a)	Indoor Spray: Anemone
(9b)	Indoor Spray: Pompon
(9c)	Indoor Spray: Reflexed
(9d)	Indoor Spray: Single
(9e)	Indoor Spray: Intermediate
(9f)	Indoor Spray: Spider, Quill, Spoon or Any Other Type
(10a)	Indoor, Spider
(10b)	Indoor, Quill
(10c)	Indoor, Spoon
(11)	Any Other Indoor Type
(12a)	Indoor, Charm
(12b)	Indoor, Cascade
(13a)	October-flowering Incurved: Large-flowered
(13b)	October-flowering Incurved: Medium-flowered
(13c)	October-flowering Incurved: Small-flowered
(14a)	October-flowering Reflexed: Large-flowered
(14b)	October-flowering Reflexed: Medium-flowered
(14c)	October-flowering Reflexed: Small-flowered
(15a)	October-flowering Intermediate: Large-flowered
(15b)	October-flowering Intermediate: Medium-flowered
(15c)	October-flowered Intermediate: Small-flowered
(16)	October-flowering Large
(17a)	October-flowering Single: Large-flowered
(17b)	October-flowering Single: Medium-flowered
(17c)	October-flowering Single: Small-flowered
(18a)	October-flowering Pompon: True Pompon
(18b)	October-flowering Pompon: Semi-pompon
(19a)	October-flowering Spray: Anemone
(19b)	October-flowering Spray: Pompon
(19c)	October-flowering Spray: Reflexed
(19d)	October-flowering Spray: Single
(19e)	October-flowering Spray: Intermediate
(19f)	October-flowering Spray: Spider, Quill, Spoon or Any Other Type
(20)	Any Other October-flowering Type
(22a)	Charm: Anemone
(22b)	Charm: Pompon
(22c)	Charm: Reflexed
(22d)	Charm: Single
(22e)	Charm: Intermediate
(22f)	Charm: Spider, Quill, Spoon or Any Other Type
(23a)	Early-flowering Outdoor Incurved: Large-flowered
(23b)	Early-flowering Outdoor Incurved: Medium-flowered
(23c)	Early-flowering Outdoor Incurved: Small-flowered
(24a)	Early-flowering Outdoor Reflexed: Large-flowered

(24b)	Early-flowering Outdoor Reflexed: Medium-flowered
(24c)	Early-flowering Outdoor Reflexed: Small-flowered
(25a)	Early-flowering Outdoor Intermediate: Large-flowered
(25b)	Early-flowering Outdoor Intermediate: Medium-flowered
(25c)	Early-flowering Outdoor Intermediate: Small-flowered
(26a)	Early-flowering Outdoor Anemone: Large-flowered
(26b)	Early-flowering Outdoor Anemone: Medium-flowered
(27a)	Early-flowering Outdoor Single: Large-flowered
(27b)	Early-flowering Outdoor Single: Medium-flowered
(28a)	Early-flowering Outdoor Pompon: True Pompon
(28b)	Early-flowering Outdoor Pompon: Semi-pompon
(29a)	Early-flowering Outdoor Spray: Anemone
(29b)	Early-flowering Outdoor Spray: Pompon
(29c)	Early-flowering Outdoor Spray: Reflexed
(29d)	Early-flowering Outdoor Spray: Single
(29e)	Early-flowering Outdoor Spray: Intermediate
(29f)	Early-flowering Outdoor Spray: Spider, Quill, Spoon or Any Other Type
(29K)	Early-flowering Outdoor Spray: Korean
(29Rub)	Early-flowering Outdoor Spray: Rubellum
(30)	Any Other Early-flowering Outdoor Type

CLEMATIS

(Cultivar Groups as per Matthews, V. (2002) *The International Clematis Register & Checklist 2002*, Royal Horticultural Society, London.)

(A)	Atragene Group
(Ar)	Armandii Group
(C)	Cirrhosa Group
(EL)	Early Large-flowered Group
(F)	Flammula Group
(Fo)	Forsteri Group
(H)	Heracleifolia Group
(I)	Integrifolia Group
(LL)	Late Large-flowered Group
(M)	Montana Group
(T)	Texensis Group
(Ta)	Tangutica Group
(V)	Viorna Group
(Vb)	Vitalba Group
(Vt)	Viticella Group

DAHLIA

(By the National Dahlia Society with corresponding numerical classification according to the Royal Horticultural Society's International Register)

(Sin)	1 Single
(Anem)	2 Anemone-flowered
(Col)	3 Collerette
(WL)	4 Waterlily (unassigned)
(LWL)	4B Waterlily, Large
(MWL)	4C Waterlily, Medium
(SWL)	4D Waterlily, Small
(MinWL)	4E Waterlily, Miniature
(D)	5 Decorative (unassigned)
(GD)	5A Decorative, Giant
(LD)	5B Decorative, Large
(MD)	5C Decorative, Medium
(SD)	5D Decorative, Small
(MinD)	5E Decorative, Miniature
(SBa)	6A Small Ball
(MinBa)	6B Miniature Ball
(Pom)	7 Pompon
(C)	8 Cactus (unassigned)
(GC)	8A Cactus, Giant
(LC)	8B Cactus, Large
(MC)	8C Cactus, Medium
(SC)	8D Cactus, Small
(MinC)	8E Cactus, Miniature
(S-c)	9 Semi-cactus (unassigned)
(GS-c)	9A Semi-cactus, Giant
(LS-c)	9B Semi-cactus, Large
(MS-c)	9C Semi-cactus, Medium
(SS-c)	9D Semi-cactus, Small
(MinS-c)	9E Semi-cactus, Miniature
(Misc)	10 Miscellaneous
(O)	Orchid-flowering (in combination)
(B)	Botanical (in combination)
(DwB)	Dwarf Bedding (in combination)
(Fim)	Fimbriated (in combination)
(Lil)	Lilliput (in combination)

DIANTHUS

(By the Royal Horticultural Society)

(p)	Pink
(p,a)	Annual Pink
(pf)	Perpetual-flowering Carnation
(b)	Border Carnation
(M)	Malmaison Carnation

FRUIT

(B)	Black (*Vitis*), Blackcurrant (*Ribes*)
(Ball)	Ballerina (*Malus*)
(C)	Culinary (*Malus, Prunus, Pyrus, Ribes*)
(Cider)	Cider (*Malus*)
(D)	Dessert (*Malus, Prunus, Pyrus, Ribes*)
(F)	Fruit
(G)	Glasshouse (*Vitis*)
(O)	Outdoor (*Vitis*)
(P)	Pinkcurrant (*Ribes*)
(Perry)	Perry (*Pyrus*)
(R)	Red (*Vitis*), Redcurrant (*Ribes*)
(S)	Seedless (*Citrus, Vitis*)
(W)	White (*Vitis*), Whitecurrant (*Ribes*)

GLADIOLUS

(B)	Butterfly
(E)	Exotic
(G)	Giant
(L)	Large
(M)	Medium
(Min)	Miniature
(N)	Nanus
(P)	Primulinus
(S)	Small
(Tub)	Tubergenii

HYDRANGEA MACROPHYLLA

(H)	Hortensia
(L)	Lacecap

IRIS

(By the American Iris Society)

(AB)	Arilbred
(BB)	Border Bearded
(Cal-Sib)	Series *Californicae* × Series *Sibiricae*
(CH)	Californian Hybrid
(DB)	Dwarf Bearded (not assigned)
(Dut)	Dutch
(IB)	Intermediate Bearded
(La)	Louisiana Hybrid
(MDB)	Miniature Dwarf Bearded
(MTB)	Miniature Tall Bearded
(SDB)	Standard Dwarf Bearded
(Sino-Sib)	Series *Sibiricae*, chromosome number 2n=40
(Spuria)	Spuria
(TB)	Tall Bearded

LILIUM

(Classification according to *The International Lily Register* (ed. 3, 1982) with amendments from Supp. 10 (1992), Royal Horticultural Society)

(I)	Early-flowering Asiatic Hybrids derived from *L. amabile*, *L. bulbiferum*, *L. cernuum, L. concolor*, *L. davidii, L.* × *hollandicum*, *L. lancifolium, L. leichtlinii*, *L.* × *maculatum* and *L. pumilum*
(Ia)	Upright flowers, borne singly or in an umbel
(Ib)	Outward-facing flowers
(Ic)	Pendant flowers
(II)	Hybrids of Martagon type, one parent having been a form of *L. hansonii* or *L. martagon*
(III)	Hybrids from *L. candidum*, *L. chalcedonicum* and other related European species (excluding *L. martagon*)
(IV)	Hybrids of American species
(V)	Hybrids derived from *L. formosanum* and *L. longiflorum*
(VI)	Hybrid Trumpet Lilies and Aurelian hybrids from Asiatic species, including *L. henryi* but excluding those from *L. auratum, L. japonicum, L. rubellum* and *L. speciosum.*
(VIa)	Plants with trumpet-shaped flowers
(VIb)	Plants with bowl-shaped flowers
(VIc)	Plants with flat flowers (or only the tips recurved)
(VId)	Plants with recurved flowers
(VII)	Hybrids of Far Eastern species as *L auratum, L. japonicum, L. rubellum* and *L. speciosum* (Oriental Hybrids)
(VIIa)	Plants with trumpet-shaped flowers
(VIIb)	Plants with bowl-shaped flowers
(VIIc)	Plants with flat flowers
(VIId)	Plants with recurved flowers
(VIII)	All hybrids not in another division
(IX)	All species and their varieties and forms

MALUS *SEE* FRUIT

NARCISSUS

(By the Royal Horticultural Society, revised 1998)

(1)	Trumpet
(2)	Large-cupped
(3)	Small-cupped
(4)	Double
(5)	Triandrus
(6)	Cyclamineus
(7)	Jonquilla and Apodanthus
(8)	Tazetta
(9)	Poeticus
(10)	Bulbocodium
(11a)	Split-corona: Collar

(11b)	Split-corona: Papillon
(12)	Miscellaneous
(13)	Species

NYMPHAEA

(H)	Hardy
(D)	Day-blooming
(N)	Night-blooming
(T)	Tropical

PAEONIA

(S)	Shrubby

PELARGONIUM

(A)	Angel
(C)	Coloured Foliage (in combination)
(Ca)	Cactus (in combination)
(d)	Double (in combination)
(Dec)	Decorative
(Dw)	Dwarf
(DwI)	Dwarf Ivy-leaved
(Fr)	Frutetorum
(I)	Ivy-leaved
(Min)	Miniature
(MinI)	Miniature Ivy-leaved
(R)	Regal
(Sc)	Scented-leaved
(St)	Stellar (in combination)
(T)	Tulip (in combination)
(U)	Unique
(Z)	Zonal

PRIMULA

(Classification by Section as per Richards. J. (2002) *Primula* (2nd edition). Batsford, London)

(Ag)	*Auganthus*
(Al)	*Aleuritia*
(Am)	*Amethystinae*
(Ar)	*Armerina*
(Au)	*Auricula*
(A)	Alpine Auricula
(B)	Border Auricula
(S)	Show Auricula
(St)	Stripped Auricula
(Bu)	*Bullatae*
(Ca)	*Capitatae*
(Cf)	*Cordifoliae*
(Ch)	*Chartaceae*
(Co)	*Cortusoides*
(Cr)	*Carolinella*
(Cu)	*Cuneifoliae*
(Cy)	*Crystallophlomis*
(Da)	*Davidii*
(De)	*Denticulatae*

(Dr)	*Dryadifoliae*
(F)	*Fedtschenkoanae*
(G)	*Glabrae*
(Ma)	*Malvaceae*
(Mi)	*Minutissimae*
(Mo)	*Monocarpicae*
(Mu)	*Muscarioides*
(Ob)	*Obconicolisteri*
(Or)	*Oreophlomis*
(Pa)	*Parryi*
(Pe)	*Petiolares*
(Pf)	*Proliferae*
(Pi)	*Pinnatae*
(Pr)	*Primula*
(Poly)	Polyanthus
(Prim)	Primrose
(Pu)	*Pulchellae*
(Py)	*Pycnoloba*
(R)	*Reinii*
(Si)	*Sikkimenses*
(So)	*Soldanelloides*
(Sp)	*Sphondylia*
(Sr)	*Sredinskya*
(Su)	*Suffrutescentes*
(Y)	*Yunnannenses*

PRUNUS *SEE* FRUIT

PYRUS *SEE* FRUIT

RHODODENDRON

(A)	Azalea (deciduous, species or unclassified hybrid)
(Ad)	Azaleodendron
(EA)	Evergreen azalea
(G)	Ghent azalea (deciduous)
(K)	Knap Hill or Exbury azalea (deciduous)
(M)	Mollis azalea (deciduous)
(O)	Occidentalis azalea (deciduous)
(R)	Rustica azalea (deciduous)
(V)	Vireya rhododendron
(Vs)	Viscosa azalea (deciduous)

RIBES *SEE* FRUIT

ROSA

(A)	Alba
(Bb)	Bourbon
(Bs)	Boursault
(Ce)	Centifolia
(Ch)	China
(Cl)	Climbing (in combination)

(D)	Damask
(DPo)	Damask Portland
(F)	Floribunda or Cluster-flowered
(G)	Gallica
(Ga)	Garnette
(GC)	Ground Cover
(HM)	Hybrid Musk
(HP)	Hybrid Perpetual
(HT)	Hybrid Tea or Large-flowered
(Min)	Miniature
(Mo)	Moss (in combination)
(N)	Noisette
(Patio)	Patio, Miniature Floribunda or Dwarf Cluster-flowered
(Poly)	Polyantha
(PiH)	Pimpinellifolia hybrid (Hybrid Scots Briar)
(Ra)	Rambler
(RH)	Rubiginosa hybrid (Hybrid Sweet Briar)
(Ru)	Rugosa
(S)	Shrub
(T)	Tea

SAXIFRAGA

(Classification by Section from Gornall, R.J. (1987). *Botanical Journal of the Linnean Society,* **95**(4): 273-292)

(1)	*Ciliatae*
(2)	*Cymbalaria*
(3)	*Merkianae*
(4)	*Micranthes*
(5)	*Irregulares*
(6)	*Heterisia*
(7)	*Porphyrion*
(8)	*Ligulatae*
(9)	*Xanthizoon*
(10)	*Trachyphyllum*
(11)	*Gymnopera*
(12)	*Cotylea*
(13)	*Odontophyllae*
(14)	*Mesogyne*
(15)	*Saxifraga*

TULIPA

(Classification by Cultivar Group from *Classified List and International Register of Tulip Names* by Koninklijke Algemeene Vereening voor Bloembollenculture 1996)

(1)	Single Early Group
(2)	Double Early Group
(3)	Triumph Group
(4)	Darwinhybrid Group
(5)	Single Late Group (including Darwin Group and Cottage Group)
(6)	Lily-flowered Group
(7)	Fringed Group
(8)	Viridiflora Group
(9)	Rembrandt Group
(10)	Parrot Group
(11)	Double Late Group
(12)	Kaufmanniana Group
(13)	Fosteriana Group
(14)	Greigii Group
(15)	Miscellaneous

VERBENA

(G)	Species and hybrids considered by some botanists to belong to the separate genus *Glandularia*.

VIOLA

(C)	Cornuta Hybrid
(dVt)	Double Violet
(ExVa)	Exhibition Viola
(FP)	Fancy Pansy
(PVt)	Parma Violet
(SP)	Show Pansy
(T)	Tricolor
(Va)	Viola
(Vt)	Violet
(Vtta)	Violetta

VITIS *SEE* FRUIT

REVERSE SYNONYMS

The following list of reverse synonyms is intended to help users find from which genus an unfamiliar plant name has been cross-referred. For a fuller explanation see p.10.

Abelmoschus – Hibiscus
Abutilon – Corynabutilon
Acacia – Racosperma
Acca – Feijoa
× Achicodonia – Eucodonia
Achillea – Anthemis
Achillea – Tanacetum
Acinos – Calamintha
Acinos – Clinopodium
Acinos – Micromeria
Acmella – Spilanthes
Actaea – Cimicifuga
Actaea – Souliea
Aethionema – Eunomia
Agapetes – Pentapterygium
Agarista – Leucothoe
Agastache – Cedronella
Agathosma – Barosma
Agave – Manfreda
Agrostis – Eragrostis
Aichryson – Aeonium
Ajania – Chrysanthemum
Ajania – Dendranthema
Ajania – Eupatorium
Albizia – Acacia
Alcea – Althaea
Allardia – Waldheimia
Allocasuarina – Casuarina
Aloysia – Lippia
Althaea – Malva
Alyogyne – Anisodontea
Alyogyne – Hibiscus
Alyssum – Ptilotrichum
× Amarygia – Amaryllis
Amaryllis – Brunsvigia
Amomyrtus – Myrtus
Amsonia – Rhazya
Anacamptis – Orchis
Anaphalis – Gnaphalium
Anchusa – Lycopsis
Androsace – Douglasia
Androstoma – Cyathodes
Anemanthele – Oryzopsis
Anemanthele – Stipa
Anemone – Eriocapitella
Anisodontea – Malvastrum
Anisodus – Scopolia

Anomatheca – Freesia
Anomatheca – Lapeirousia
Anredera – Boussingaultia
Antirrhinum – Asarina
Aphanes – Alchemilla
Apium – Apium × Petroselinum
Arctanthemum – Chrysanthemum
Arctostaphylos – Arbutus
Arctotis – Venidium
Arctotis – × Venidioarctotis
Arenga – Didymosperma
Argyranthemum – Anthemis
Argyranthemum – Chrysanthemum
Armoracia – Cochlearia
Arnoglossum – Cacalia
Arundinaria – Pseudosasa
Asarina – Antirrhinum
Asarum – Hexastylis
Asparagus – Myrsiphyllum
Asparagus – Smilax
Asperula – Galium
Asphodeline – Asphodelus
Asplenium – Camptosorus
Asplenium – Ceterach
Asplenium – Phyllitis
Asplenium – Scolopendrium
Aster – Crinitaria
Aster – Doellingeria
Aster – Erigeron
Aster – Microglossa
Aster – Symphyotrichum
Astilboides – Rodgersia
Asyneuma – Campanula
Athanasia – Hymenolepis
Atropanthe – Scopolia
Aurinia – Alyssum
Austrocedrus – Libocedrus
Austromyrtus – Myrtus
Azorella – Bolax
Azorina – Campanula

Bambusa – Arundinaria
Bashania – Arundinaria
Bassia – Kochia
Beaucarnea – Nolina
Bellevalia – Muscari
Bellis – Erigeron
Bignonia – Campsis
Blechnum – Lomaria
Blepharocalyx – Temu
Bolax – Azorella
Bolboschoenus – Scirpus
Bonia – Indocalamus
Borago – Anchusa

Bothriochloa – Andropogon
Bouteloua – Chondrosum
Boykinia – Telesonix
Brachyglottis – Senecio
Brimeura – Hyacinthus
Brodiaea – Triteleia
Brugmansia – Datura
Brunnera – Anchusa
Buglossoides – Lithospermum
Bulbine – Bulbinopsis

Cacalia – Adenostyles
Calamagrostis – Stipa
Calamintha – Clinopodium
Calamintha – Thymus
Calibrachoa – Petunia
Callisia – Phyodina
Callisia – Tradescantia
Calocedrus – Libocedrus
Calomeria – Humea
Caloscordum – Nothoscordum
Calylophus – Oenothera
Calytrix – Lhotzkya
Camellia – Thea
Campanula – Campanula
    × Symphyandra
Campanula – Symphyandra
Cardamine – Dentaria
Carpobrotus – Lampranthus
Cassiope – Harrimanella
Cedronella – Agastache
Centaurium – Erythraea
Centella – Hydrocotyle
Centranthus – Kentranthus
Centranthus – Valeriana
Cephalaria – Scabiosa
Ceratostigma – Plumbago
Chaenomeles – Cydonia
Chaenorhinum – Linaria
Chamaecytisus – Cytisus
Chamaedaphne – Cassandra
Chamaemelum – Anthemis
Chamerion – Chamaenerion
Chamerion – Epilobium
Chasmanthium – Uniola
Cheilanthes – Notholaena
Chiastophyllum – Cotyledon
Chimonobambusa –
    Arundinaria
Chimonobambusa – Qiongzhuea
Chionohebe - Parahebe
Chionohebe – Pygmea
× Chionoscilla – Scilla
Chlorophytum – Diuranthera

Chrysanthemum – Dendranthema
Chrysopsis – Heterotheca
Cicerbita – Lactuca
Cissus – Ampelopsis
Cissus – Parthenocissus
× Citrofortunella – Citrus
Clarkia – Eucharidium
Clarkia – Godetia
Clavinodum – Arundinaria
Claytonia – Calandrinia
Claytonia – Montia
Clematis – Atragene
Clematis – Clematopsis
Cleyera – Eurya
Clinopodium – Calamintha
Clytostoma – Bignonia
Clytostoma – Pandorea
Cnicus – Carduus
Codonopsis – Campanumoea
Consolida – Delphinium
Cordyline – Dracaena
Cornus – Chamaepericlymenum
Cornus – Dendrobenthamia
Coronilla – Securigera
Cortaderia – Gynerium
Corydalis - Capnoides
Corydalis – Fumaria
Corydalis – Pseudofumaria
Cosmos – Bidens
Cotinus – Rhus
Cotula – Leptinella
Crassula – Rochea
Crassula – Sedum
Crassula – Tillaea
Cremanthodium – Ligularia
Crinodendron – Tricuspidaria
Crocosmia – Antholyza
Crocosmia – Curtonus
Crocosmia – Montbretia
Cruciata – Galium
Ctenanthe – Calathea
Ctenanthe – Stromanthe
× Cupressocyparis – Chamaecyparis
× Cupressocyparis – × Cuprocyparis
Cupressus – Chamaecyparis
Cyclosorus – Pneumatopteris
Cymbalaria – Linaria
Cymophyllus – Carex
Cyperus – Mariscus
Cypripedium – Criogenes
Cyrtanthus – Anoiganthus
Cyrtanthus – Vallota
Cyrtomium – Phanerophlebia
Cyrtomium – Polystichum
Cytisus – Argyrocytisus
Cytisus – Genista
Cytisus – Lembotropis
Cytisus – Spartocytisus

Daboecia – Menziesia
Dacrycarpus – Podocarpus
Dactylorhiza – Orchis
Dalea – Petalostemon
Danae – Ruscus
Darmera – Peltiphyllum
Datura – Brugmansia
Davallia – Humata
Delairea – Senecio
Delosperma – Lampranthus
Delosperma – Mesembryanthemum
Desmodium – Lespedeza
Deuterocohnia – Abromeitiella
Dicentra – Corydalis
Dichelostemma – Brodiaea
Dicliptera – Barleria
Dicliptera – Justicia
Diervilla – Weigela
Dietes – Moraea
Diplazium – Athyrium
Dipogon – Dolichos
Disporopsis – Polygonatum
Dracaena – Pleomele
Dracunculus – Arum
Dregea – Wattakaka
Drepanostachyum – Bambusa
Drepanostachyum –
    Chimonobambusa
Drepanostachyum – Gelidocalamus
Drepanostachyum –
    Thamnocalamus
Drimys – Tasmannia
Duchesnea – Fragaria
Dypsis – Chrysalidocarpus
Dypsis – Neodypsis

Echeveria – Cotyledon
Echinacea – Rudbeckia
Echinospartum – Genista
Edraianthus – Wahlenbergia
Egeria – Elodea
Elatostema – Pellionia
Eleutherococcus – Acanthopanax
Elliottia – Botryostege
Elliottia – Cladothamnus
Elymus – Agropyron
Elymus – Leymus
Ensete – Musa
Epipremnum – Philodendron
Epipremnum – Scindapsus
Episcia – Alsobia
Eranthis – Aconitum
Eremophila – Myoporum
Erepsia - Semnanthe
Erigeron – Haplopappus
Erysimum – Cheiranthus
Eucalyptus – Corymbia
Eupatorium – Ageratina

Eupatorium – Ayapana
Eupatorium – Bartlettina
Euphorbia – Poinsettia
Euryops – Senecio
Eustachys – Chloris
Eustoma – Lisianthus

Fallopia – Bilderdykia
Fallopia – Polygonum
Fallopia – Reynoutria
Farfugium – Ligularia
Fargesia – Arundinaria
Fargesia – Borinda
Fargesia – Semiarundinaria
Fargesia – Sinarundinaria
Fargesia – Thamnocalamus
Fatsia – Aralia
Felicia – Agathaea
Felicia – Aster
Fibigia – Farsetia
Filipendula – Spiraea
Foeniculum – Ferula
Fortunella – Citrus

Galium – Asperula
Gaultheria – Chiogenes
Gaultheria – Pernettya
Gaultheria – × Gaulnettya
Gelasine – Sisyrinchium
Genista – Chamaespartium
Genista – Cytisus
Genista – Echinospartum
Genista – Teline
Gethyum – Ancrumia
Geum – Sieversia
Gladiolus – Acidanthera
Gladiolus – Anomalesia
Gladiolus – Homoglossum
Gladiolus – Petamenes
Glebionis – Chrysanthemum
Glebionis – Xanthophthalmum
Glechoma – Nepeta
Gloxinia – Seemannia
Gomphocarpus – Asclepias
Gomphocarpus – Asclepias
Goniolimon – Limonium
Graptopetalum – Sedum
Graptopetalum – Tacitus
Greenovia – Sempervivum
Gymnadenia – Nigritella
Gymnospermium – Leontice

Habranthus – Zephyranthes
Hacquetia – Dondia
× Halimiocistus – Cistus
× Halimiocistus – Halimium
Halimione – Atriplex
Halimium – Cistus

Halimium – Helianthemum
Halimium – × Halimiocistus
Halocarpus – Dacrydium
Hanabusaya – Symphyandra
Hedychium – Brachychilum
Helianthella – Helianthus
Helianthemum – Cistus
Helianthus – Coreopsis
Helianthus – Heliopsis
Helichrysum – Gnaphalium
Helicodiceros – Dracunculus
Helictotrichon – Avena
Helictotrichon – Avenula
Hepatica – Anemone
Herbertia – Alophia
Hermodactylus – Iris
Heterocentron – Schizocentron
Heteromeles – Photinia
Heterotheca – Chrysopsis
× Heucherella – Heuchera
× Heucherella – Tiarella
Hibbertia – Candollea
Hieracium – Andryala
Himalayacalamus – Arundinaria
Himalayacalamus –
    Chimonobambusa
Himalayacalamus –
    Drepanostachyum
Himalayacalamus –
    Drepanostachyum
Himalayacalamus –
    Thamnocalamus
Hippocrepis – Coronilla
Hippolytia – Achillea
Hippolytia – Tanacetum
Hoheria – Plagianthus
Homalocladium – Muehlenbeckia
Howea – Kentia
Hyacinthoides – Endymion
Hyacinthoides – Scilla
Hylomecon – Chelidonium
Hymenocallis – Elisena
Hymenocallis – Ismene
Hymenoxys – Dugaldia
Hymenoxys – Helenium
Hyophorbe – Mascarena
Hypoxis – Rhodohypoxis

Incarvillea – Amphicome
Indocalamus – Sasa
Iochroma – Acnistus
Iochroma – Cestrum
Iochroma – Dunalia
Ipheion – Tristagma
Ipheion – Triteleia
Ipomoea – Calonyction
Ipomoea – Mina
Ipomoea – Pharbitis

Ipomopsis – Gilia
Ischyrolepis – Restio
Isolepis – Scirpus
Isotoma – Laurentia
Isotoma – Solenopsis

Jamesbrittenia – Sutera
Jeffersonia – Plagiorhegma
Jovibarba – Sempervivum
Juncus – Scirpus
Jurinea – Jurinella
Justicia – Beloperone
Justicia - Duvernoia
Justicia – Jacobinia
Justicia – Libonia

Kalanchoe – Bryophyllum
Kalanchoe – Kitchingia
Kalimeris – Aster
Kalimeris – Asteromoea
Kalimeris – Boltonia
Kalopanax – Acanthopax
Kalopanax – Eleutherococcus
Keckiella - Penstemon
Keckiella - Penstemon
Kitagawia – Peucedanum
Knautia – Scabiosa
Kniphofia – Tritoma
Kohleria – Isoloma
Krascheninnikovia – Ceratoides
Kunzea – Leptospermum

Lablab – Dolichos
Lagarosiphon – Elodea
Lagarostrobos – Dacrydium
Lamium – Galeobdolon
Lamium – Lamiastrum
Lampranthus – Mesembryanthemum
Lavatera – Malva
Ledebouria – Scilla
× Ledodendron – Rhododendron
Ledum – Rhododendron
Leontodon – Microseris
Lepechinia – Sphacele
Lepidothamnus – Dacrydium
Leptecophylla – Cyathodes
Leptinella – Cotula
Leptodactylon – Gilia
Leucanthemella – Chrysanthemum
Leucanthemella – Leucanthemum
Leucanthemopsis –
    Chrysanthemum
Leucanthemum – Chrysanthemum
Leucocoryne – Beauverdia
Leucophyta – Calocephalus
Leucopogon – Cyathodes
Leucopogon – Styphelia
× Leucoraoulia – Raoulia

× Leucoraoulia – Raoulia
× Leucogenes
Leymus – Elymus
Ligularia – Senecio
Ligustrum – Parasyringa
Lilium – Nomocharis
Limonium – Statice
Linanthus – Linanthastrum
Lindelofia – Adelocaryum
Lindera – Parabenzoin
Lindernia – Ilysanthes
Liriope – Ophiopogon
Lithodora – Lithospermum
Lobelia – Monopsis
Lophomyrtus – Myrtus
Lophospermum – Asarina
Lophospermum – Maurandya
Lotus – Dorycnium
Lotus – Tetragonolobus
Ludwigia – Jussiaea
Luma – Myrtus
× Lycene – Lychnis
Lychnis – Agrostemma
Lychnis – Silene
Lychnis – Viscaria
Lycianthes – Solanum
Lytocaryum – Cocos
Lytocaryum – Microcoelum

Macfadyena – Bignonia
Macfadyena – Doxantha
Machaeranthera – Xylorhiza
Machaerina – Baumea
Mackaya – Asystasia
Macleaya – Bocconia
Maclura - Cudrania
Macropiper – Piper
Magnolia – Parakmeria
Mahonia – Berberis
Maianthemum – Smilacina
Mandevilla – Dipladenia
Mandragora – Atropa
Marrubium – Ballota
Matricaria – Tripleurospermum
Maurandella – Asarina
Maurandya – Asarina
Melanoselinum – Thapsia
Melicytus – Hymenanthera
Melinis – Rhynchelytrum
Mentha – Preslia
Merremia – Ipomoea
Mimulus – Diplacus
Minuartia – Arenaria
Moltkia – Lithodora
Moltkia – Lithospermum
Morina – Acanthocalyx
Morina – Acanthocalyx
Mukdenia – Aceriphyllum

Muscari – Hyacinthus
Muscari – Leopoldia
Muscari – Muscarimia
Muscari – Pseudomuscari
Myrteola – Myrtus

Naiocrene – Claytonia
Naiocrene – Montia
Nectaroscordum – Allium
Nemananthus – Hypocyrta
Nemesia – Diascia × Linaria
Neolitsea – Litsea
Neopaxia – Claytonia
Neopaxia – Montia
Neoregelia – Nidularium
Nepeta – Dracocephalum
× Niduregelia – Guzmania
Nipponanthemum –
 Chrysanthemum
Nipponanthemum –
 Leucanthemum
Nolina – Beaucarnea
Nymphoides – Villarsia

Ochagavia – Fascicularia
Oemleria – Osmaronia
Oenothera – Chamissonia
Olsynium – Sisyrinchium
Onixotis – Dipidax
Onoclea – Matteuccia
Ophiopogon – Convallaria
Orchis – Anacamptis
Orchis – Dactylorhiza
Oreopteris – Thelypteris
Orostachys – Sedum
Oscularia – Lampranthus
Osmanthus – Phillyrea
Osmanthus – × Osmarea
Othonna – Hertia
Othonna – Othonnopsis
Ozothamnus – Helichrysum

Pachyphragma – Cardamine
Pachyphragma – Thlaspi
Pachystegia - Olearia
Packera – Senecio
Paederota – Veronica
Pallenis – Asteriscus
Papaver – Meconopsis
Parahebe – Derwentia
Parahebe – Hebe
Parahebe – Veronica
Paraserianthes – Albizia
Paris – Daiswa
Parthenocissus – Ampelopsis
Parthenocissus – Vitis
Passiflora – Tetrapathaea
Paxistima – Pachystema

Pecteilis – Habenaria
Pelargonium – Geranium
Peltoboykinia – Boykinia
Penstemon – Chelone
Penstemon – Nothochelone
Penstemon – Pennellianthus
Pentaglottis – Anchusa
Pericallis – Senecio
Persea – Machilus
Persicaria – Aconogonon
Persicaria – Bistorta
Persicaria – Polygonum
Persicaria – Tovara
Petrocoptis – Lychnis
Petrophytum – Spiraea
Petrorhagia – Tunica
Petroselinum – Carum
Phegopteris – Thelypteris
Phoenicaulis – Parrya
Photinia – Stransvaesia
Photinia – × Stravinia
Phuopsis – Crucianella
Phyla – Lippia
Phymatosorus – Microsorum
Phymosia – Sphaeralcea
Physoplexis – Phyteuma
Physostegia – Dracocephalum
Pieris – Arcterica
Pilosella – Hieracium
Platycladus – Thuja
Plecostachys – Helichrysum
Plectranthus – Coleus
Plectranthus – Solenostemon
Pleioblastus – Arundinaria
Pleioblastus – Sasa
Podophyllum – Dysosma
Podranea – Tecoma
Polygonum – Persicaria
Polypodium – Phlebodium
Polyscias – Nothopanax
Poncirus – Aegle
Potentilla – Comarum
Pratia – Lobelia
Prenanthes – Nabalus
Pritzelago – Hutchinsia
Prumnopitys – Podocarpus
Prunus – Amygdalus
Pseudocydonia – Chaenomeles
Pseudogynoxys – Senecio
Pseudopanax – Metapanax
Pseudopanax – Neopanax
Pseudosasa – Arundinaria
Pseudotsuga – Tsuga
Pseudowintera – Drimys
Pterocephalus – Scabiosa
Pteryxia - Cymopterus
Ptilostemon – Cirsium
Pulicaria – Inula

Pulsatilla – Anemone
Purshia – Cowania
Puschkinia – Scilla
Pyrrocoma – Aster
Pyrrocoma – Haplopappus

Reineckea – Liriope
Retama – Genista
Retama – Lygos
Rhamnus – Frangula
Rhapis – Chamaerops
Rhodanthe – Helipterum
Rhodanthemum – Argyranthemum
Rhodanthemum –
 Chrysanthemopsis
Rhodanthemum – Chrysanthemum
Rhodanthemum – Leucanthemopsis
Rhodanthemum – Leucanthemum
Rhodanthemum – Pyrethropsis
Rhodiola – Clementsia
Rhodiola – Rosularia
Rhodiola – Sedum
Rhododendron – Azalea
Rhododendron – Azaleodendron
Rhododendron – Rhodora
Rhododendron – Therorhodion
Rhododendron – Tsusiophyllum
Rhodophiala – Hippeastrum
× Rhodoxis – Hypoxis ×
 Rhodohypoxis
× Rhodoxis – Rhodohypoxis
Rhus – Toxicodendron
Rhyncospora – Dichromena
Rosularia – Cotyledon
Rosularia – Sempervivella
Rothmannia – Gardenia
Ruellia – Dipteracanthus

Saccharum – Erianthus
Sagina – Minuartia
Sanguisorba – Dendriopoterium
Sanguisorba – Poterium
Sasa – Arundinaria
Sasaella – Arundinaria
Sasaella – Pleioblastus
Sasaella – Sasa
Sauromatum – Arum
Scadoxus – Haemanthus
Schefflera – Brassaia
Schefflera – Dizygotheca
Schefflera – Heptapleurum
Schizachyrium – Andropogon
Schizostachyum – Arundinaria
Schizostachyum – Thamnocalamus
Schizostylis – Hesperantha
Schoenoplectus – Scirpus
Scilla – Oncostema
Scirpoides – Scirpus

Sedum – Hylotelephium
Sedum – Sedastrum
Semiaquilegia – Aquilegia
Semiaquilegia – Paraquilegia
Semiarundinaria – Arundinaria
Semiarundinaria – Oligostachyum
Senecio – Cineraria
Senecio – Kleinia
Senecio – Ligularia
Senna – Cassia
Seriphidium – Artemisia
Shortia – Schizocodon
Sibbaldiopsis – Potentilla
Silene – Lychnis
Silene – Melandrium
Silene – Saponaria
Sinacalia – Ligularia
Sinacalia – Senecio
Sinningia – Gesneria
Sinningia – Rechsteineria
Sinobambusa – Pleioblastus
Sinobambusa – Pseudosasa
Siphocranion – Chamaesphacos
Sisymbrium – Hesperis
Sisyrinchium – Phaiophleps
Smallanthus – Polymnia
Solanum – Lycianthes
Soleirolia – Helxine
Solenostemon – Coleus
× Solidaster – Aster
× Solidaster – Solidago
Sorbaria – Spiraea
Sparaxis – Synnotia
Sphaeralcea – Iliamna
Sphaeromeria – Tanacetum
Spirodela – Lemna
Stachys – Betonica
Stemmacantha – Centaurea
Stemmacantha – Leuzea
Stenomesson – Urceolina
Stewartia – Stuartia
Stipa – Achnatherum
Stipa – Agrostis

Stipa – Calamagrostis
Stipa – Lasiagrostis
Stipa – Nassella
Strobilanthes – Parachampionella
Strobilanthes – Pteracanthus
Succisa – Scabiosa
Sutera – Bacopa
Syagrus – Arecastrum
Syagrus – Cocos
Syncarpha - Helipterum
Syzygium – Caryophyllus

Talbotia – Vellozia
Tanacetum – Achillea
Tanacetum – Balsamita
Tanacetum – Chrysanthemum
Tanacetum – Matricaria
Tanacetum – Pyrethrum
Tanacetum – Spathipappus
Tecoma – Tecomaria
Telekia – Buphthalmum
Tetradium – Euodia
Tetraneuris - Actinella
Tetraneuris – Actinella
Tetraneuris – Hymenoxys
Tetrapanax – Fatsia
Thamnocalamus – Arundinaria
Thlaspi – Hutchinsia
Thlaspi – Noccaea
Thlaspi – Vania
Thuja – Thujopsis
Thymus – Origanum
Tiarella – × Heucherella
Tonestus – Haplopappus
Toona – Cedrela
Trachelium – Diosphaera
Trachycarpus – Chamaerops
Tradescantia – Rhoeo
Tradescantia – Setcreasea
Tradescantia – Zebrina
Trichopetalum – Anthericum
Tripetaleia – Elliottia
Tripogandra – Tradescantia

Tristaniopsis – Tristania
Triteleia – Brodiaea
Tritonia – Crocosmia
Tritonia – Montbretia
Trochiscanthes – Angelica
Tropaeolum – Nasturtium hort.
Tulipa – Amana
Tupistra – Campylandra
Tutcheria – Pyrenaria
Tweedia – Oxypetalum

Ugni – Myrtus
Utricularia – Polypompholyx
Uvularia – Oakesiella

Vaccaria – Melandrium
Vaccinium – Oxycoccus
Verbascum – Celsia
Verbascum – × Celsioverbascum
Verbena – Glandularia
Verbena – Lippia
Veronicastrum – Veronica
Vigna – Phaseolus
Viola – Erpetion
Vitaliana – Androsace
Vitaliana – Douglasia

Wedelia – Zexmenia
Weigela – Diervilla
Weigela – Macrodiervilla

Xanthorhiza – Zanthorhiza
Xerochrysum – Bracteantha
Xerochrysum – Helichrysum

Yushania – Arundinaria
Yushania – Sinarundinaria
Yushania – Thamnocalamus

Zantedeschia – Calla
Zauschneria – Epilobium
Zephyranthes – × Cooperanthes
Zephyranthes – Cooperia

THE PLANT DIRECTORY

A

Abelia ✿ (*Caprifoliaceae*)

biflora	NLar WWes
chinensis misapplied	see *A.* x *grandiflora*
§ chinensis R. Br.	CBcs ECre EPfP MAsh SDnm SEND SMer SPer SPla SPoG WFar WHCG WLeb WPat WSHC WTel
§ dielsii	CPLG CTrw
'Edward Goucher'	CBcs CDoC CPle EBee ECrN EGra ELan EPfP LPan LRHS MBri MGos MRav NBea NBir NHol SEND SPer SPlb SRGP SWvt WDin WFar WPat WSHC
engleriana	CPle EBee EPfP EPla MAsh NLar WFar
floribunda ♀H3	CBcs CMac CPLG CPle CSBt CSam CTrw CWib ECre ELan EPfP EWTr LRHS MAsh SBrw SDnm SHBN SMur SPer SPoG SSpi WAbe WFar WPat
§ x grandiflora ♀H4	More than 30 suppliers
- 'Aurea'	see *A.* x *grandiflora* 'Gold Spot'
- 'Compacta'	LRHS WFar
- Confetti = 'Conti'PBR (v)	CBcs CBrm CDoC COtt CSBt CSPN CWSG EBee EHoe ELan EPfP LAst LPan LRHS MCCP MGos MLan NEgg SBod SLim SLon SMur SPer SPoG SSta SWvt WDin WFar WGob WWeb
- dwarf	CDoC
§ - 'Francis Mason' (v)	More than 30 suppliers
§ - 'Gold Spot'	CBcs CDoC CWSG EPfP MWat SSto WBrE WGob WWeb
- 'Gold Strike'	see *A.* x *grandiflora* 'Gold Spot'
- 'Goldsport'	see *A.* x *grandiflora* 'Gold Spot'
- 'Hopleys'PBR (v)	CBcs CDoC CSBt EBee LHop LRHS MAsh SBra SPoG WFar WGob WLeb
- 'Panache' (v)	MGos MRav
- 'Prostrate White'	MAsh NLar
- 'Sherwoodii'	WFar WPat
- 'Sunrise'PBR (v)	CDoC CSBt EHoe ELan ENot EPfP LRHS NCGa NLar SBod SBra SHBN SLim SLon SMur SPla SPoG
- 'Tanya' **new**	WSPU
- 'Variegata'	see *A.* x *grandiflora* 'Francis Mason'
mosanensis	NLar
rupestris misapplied	see *A.* x *grandiflora*
rupestris Lindl.	see *A.* chinensis R. Br.
schumannii ♀H4	CAbP CBcs CHar CMHG CPLG CSBt CSam CTri EBee ELan EPfP LHop LRHS LSRN MAsh MBri MRav MSwo SLim SLon SPer SPoG SWvt WCFE WFar WHCG WPat WSHC WTel
- 'Saxon Gold'PBR	LAst NEgg SPoG SSto
spathulata	WFar
triflora	CAbP CPLG CPle CWib ECre EPfP LAst LHop LRHS MMuc NLar SLon WFar WPat

zanderi	see *A. dielsii*

Abeliophyllum (*Oleaceae*)

distichum	More than 30 suppliers
- Roseum Group	CBcs CDoC CPLG CPMA EBee ELan EPfP EWTr GBuc LAst LHop LRHS MAsh MGos MRav NSti SBrw SHBN SLon SPer SPoG WFar WPGP WWes

Abelmoschus (*Malvaceae*)

§ manihot	EWin

Abies ✿ (*Pinaceae*)

alba	CDul GTSp LCon MBar NWea WMou
- 'Compacta'	CKen
- 'King's Dwarf'	CKen
- 'Microphylla'	CKen
- 'Munsterland'	CKen NLar
- 'Pendula'	ECho
- 'Schwarzwald'	NLar
amabilis	GTSp LCon
- 'Spreading Star'	LCon
x arnoldiana	MBar NLar
- 'Cyrille'	MBlu
balsamea	CDul GTSp LCon NWea WMou
- Hudsonia Group ♀H4	CDoC CKen CMac ECho EHul IMGH LCon LLin LRHS MBar NDlv NHol NMen SLim SPoG WDin WEve
- 'Jamie'	CKen NLar
- 'Le Feber'	CKen
- 'Nana'	CKen CRob ECho EHul EOrn LBee LCon LRHS MAsh NLar WDin WFar
- var. phanerolepis 'Bear Swamp'	CKen
- 'Piccolo'	CDoC CKen ECho EHul IMGH NLar SLim SPoG WFar WGor
- 'Prostrata'	ECho EHul LLin LRHS NLar WEve
- 'Renswoude'	CKen
- 'Tyler Blue'	CKen
- 'Verkade's Prostrate'	CKen
borisii-regis	GTSp LCon
* - 'Pendula'	CKen
brachyphylla dwarf	see *A. homolepis* 'Prostrata'
cephalonica	CDul GTSp LCon
- 'Greg's Broom'	CKen ECho
§ - 'Meyer's Dwarf'	CDoC EBrs ECho EHul LCon LLin LRHS MBar NLar SCoo SLim SPoG WEve
- 'Nana'	see *A. cephalonica* 'Meyer's Dwarf'
chensiensis	LCon
concolor ♀H4	CBcs CDul CTho EHul EWTr GTSp GWCH LCon LPan LRHS MBar NWea SEND WDin
- 'Archer's Dwarf'	CKen ECho LCon MGos NLar SLim
I - 'Argentea'	ECho LCon NLar
- 'Aurea' **new**	MGos
- 'Birthday Broom'	CKen
- 'Blue Sapphire' **new**	NLar
- 'Blue Spreader'	CKen MGos

§ - 'Compacta' 🏆H4	CDoC CKen EBrs ECho EOrn LCon LLin LRHS MAsh MBar MGos NEgg NLar SCoo SLim SPoG WEve WFar
- 'Fagerhult'	CKen
- 'Gable's Weeping'	CKen
- 'Glauca'	see *A. concolor* Violacea Group
- 'Glauca Compacta'	see *A. concolor* 'Compacta'
§ - 'Hillier's Dwarf'	CKen
- 'Husky Pup'	CKen
- Lowiana Group	LCon
- - 'Creamy'	CKen
- 'Masonic Broom'	CKen MGos NLar
- 'Mike Stearn'	CKen
- 'Mora'	CKen
- 'Ostrov nad Ohri'	CKen
- 'Piggelmee'	CKen ECho LLin NLar SLim
- 'Scooter' **new**	CKen
- 'Sherwood's Blue'	ECho
* - 'Swift's Silver'	LBee LCon LRHS WBVN WEve
§ - Violacea Group	CDoC CKen ECho LCon LLin MAsh MBar MBri MGos SLim WEve WFar
- 'Wattez Prostrate'	ECho NLar SLim WFar
- 'Wattezii'	CKen ECho LCon LLin
- 'Wintergold'	CKen EBrs ECho MGos NLar WEve
delavayi	CMCN GTSp LCon MGos
- var. *delavayi*	see *A. fabri*
Fabri Group	
- 'Major Neishe'	ECho
I - 'Nana'	CKen
- 'Nana Headfort'	see *A. fargesii* 'Headfort'
§ *fabri*	GTSp
§ *fargesii*	GTSp LCon
§ - 'Headfort'	LCon MBar NLar
firma	GTSp
forrestii	CKen
- var. *ferreana* SF 95168	ISea
- - SF 95226	ISea
fraseri	CTri GIBF MBar NWea SEND WMou WWes
- 'Blue Bonnet'	CKen
- 'Raul's Dwarf'	CKen ECho
grandis	CBcs CDul GIBF LCon LRav MBar NWea SHBN WDin WMou
- 'Compacta'	CKen
- 'Van Dedem's Dwarf'	CKen NLar
holophylla	CMCN LCon
homolepis	CDul CMCN LCon NLar NWea
§ - 'Prostrata'	CKen
koreana	More than 30 suppliers
- 'Alpin Star'	CKen
- 'Aurea'	see *A. koreana* 'Flava'
- 'Blaue Zwo'	CKen ECho MAsh NLar
- 'Blauer Eskimo'	CKen LCon MBlu NLar SLim
- 'Blauer Pfiff'	CKen ECho LPan NLar
- 'Blinsham Gold'	CKen
- blue	EHoe
- 'Blue Emperor'	CKen NLar
- 'Blue Magic'	CKen NLar
- 'Blue 'n' Silver'	ECho LLin NLar WEve
- 'Bonsai Blue' **new**	NLar
- 'Cis'	CDHC CKen ECho NLar SCoo SLim
- 'Compact Dwarf'	ECho EPot LLin MBar MGos NLar WEve
- 'Crystal Globe'	CKen ECho LCon NLar
- 'Doni Tajuso' **new**	CKen
§ - 'Flava'	CKen ECho IMGH LLin MBar MGos NLar SCoo WEve
- 'Frosty'	NLar SLim
- 'Gait'	CKen ECho NLar
- 'Golden Dream'	CKen ECho
- 'Golden Glow'	NLar WFar
- 'Green Carpet'	CKen NLar SLim
- 'Grübele' **new**	CKen
- 'Inverleith'	CKen
- 'Knospenkoningin' **new**	NLar
- 'Kohout'	CKen ECho
- 'Lippetal'	CKen ECho
- 'Luminetta'	CKen ECho LRHS MBri MGos NLar SLim SPoG
- 'Nadelkissen'	CKen ECho
- 'Nisbet'	ECho GBin IMGH LLin NLar SLim WEve WGor
- 'Oberon'	CKen CRob ECho EHul LCon MAsh NLar SLim
- 'Piccolo'	CKen ECho NLar
- 'Pinocchio'	CKen ECho NLar
- 'Prostrata'	see *A. koreana* 'Prostrate Beauty'
§ - 'Prostrate Beauty'	ECho EOrn LLin SPoG WEve WFar WGor
- 'Schneestern' **new**	NLar
- 'Silberkugel'	CKen ECho SLim
- 'Silberlocke' 🏆H4	CDoC CKen CRob EBrs ECho LBee LCon LLin LPan LRHS MAsh MBar MBlu MBri MGos NBea NEgg SCoo SLim SPer SPoG WEve WFar WOrn
- 'Silbermavers'	CKen
- 'Silberperl'	CKen ECho LCon NLar
- 'Silberschmelze'	ECho LLin
- 'Silver Show'	CKen NLar
- 'Taiga'	NLar
- 'Threave'	CKen
- 'Tundra'	NLar
- 'Winter Goldtip'	ECho LLin WEve
lasiocarpa	CDul LCon NWea
I - var. *arizonica*	NWea
'Argentea'	
- - 'Compacta' 🏆H4	CDoC CKen CMac EBrs ECho EHul ELan LBee LCon LLin LRHS MAsh MBar MBri MGos NHol SCoo SLim SPoG WBrE WEve WFar WGor
- - 'Kenwith Blue'	CKen ECho LLin MGos NLar WFar
- 'Day Creek'	CKen
- 'Duflon'	CKen
- 'Green Globe'	CKen ECho LLin MBar NLar WEve
* - 'King's Blue'	CKen
- 'Logan Pass'	CKen NLar
- 'Mikolas' **new**	NLar
- 'Mulligan's Dwarf'	CKen ECho
- 'Prickly Pete'	CKen
- 'Roger Watson'	WEve
- 'Toenisvorst'	CKen
magnifica	LCon
I - 'Nana'	CKen NEgg NLar
- witches' broom	CKen
nephrolepis	GTSp
nobilis	see *A. procera*
nordmanniana 🏆H4	CDul CTri EHul EPfP EWTr GIBF LBuc LCon LPan LRHS MBar MGos NWea SEND WDin WEve WMou
- 'Arne's Dwarf'	CKen
- 'Barabits' Compact'	ECho LLin MBar MGos NLar
- 'Barabits' Gold'	ECho LLin
- 'Barabits' Spreader'	CKen ECho LLin
- subsp. *equi-trojani*	GTSp LCon NWea
- - 'Archer'	CKen
- 'Golden Spreader' 🏆H4	CDoC CKen EBrs ECho EOrn LBee LCon LLin LRHS MAsh MBar MBri MGos NLar SCoo SLim SPoG WEve WFar WWes
- 'Hasselt' **new**	CKen
- 'Jakobsen'	CKen
- 'Pendula'	LPan
- 'Silberspitze'	CKen
numidica	LPan
- 'Glauca'	CKen LCon
- 'Lawrenceville'	ECho
I - 'Pendula'	LCon
pindrow	ECho LCon

	pinsapo	GTSp LCon LRHS MBar SEND
	- 'Aurea'	CKen CRob EBrs ECho LCon LLin MGos NLar SLim WEve WFar
I	- 'Aurea Nana'	CKen
	- 'Fastigiata'	MPkF
	- 'Glauca' ♀H4	CDoC CKen CTho ECho EHul ELan LCon LLin LPan MBar MBlu NLar SLim SPoG WDin WEve WMou
	- 'Hamondii'	CKen
I	- 'Horstmann'	CKen ECho LCon LLin NLar WEve
	- 'Kelleriis'	ECho LCon
	- 'Pendula'	ECho LCon MGos MPkF NLar WEve
	- 'Quicksilver'	CKen
§	*procera* ♀H4	CBcs CDoC CDul EHul GIBF LCon MBar NWea WBVN WDin WEve WMou
	- 'Bizarro' **new**	NLar
	- 'Blaue Hexe'	CKen ECho NLar SLim SPoG WFar
	- Glauca Group	CDoC CMac CTho ECho LCon LLin LPan LRHS MAsh MBar MBlu MBri MGos WEve WFar WGer WOrn
	- - 'Glauca Prostrata'	CRob ECho LBee LCon LPan LRHS MBar MGos SCoo WEve WFar
	- 'Noble's Dwarf' **new**	ECho
	- 'Obrighofen' **new**	NLar
	- 'Sherwoodii'	CKen ECho
	recurvata	LCon
	Rosemoor hybrid	CKen
	squamata	GTSp
	veitchii	CBcs CDul LCon NWea
	- 'Hedergott'	CKen ECho LCon MGos NLar SLim
	- 'Heine'	CKen NLar
I	- 'Pendula'	CKen
	- 'Rumburg'	CKen

Abromeitiella (*Bromeliaceae*)

brevifolia ♀H1	EPem WCot

Abrotanella (*Asteraceae*)

sp.	ECho

Abutilon ✿ (*Malvaceae*)

	'Amiti'	MOak
	'Amsterdam'	ERea
	'Apricot Belle'	MOak
	'Ashford Red'	CBcs SOWG WKif
*	'Benary's Giant'	EAro
	'Boule de Neige'	CHal ERea MOak SOWG
	'Canary Bird' misapplied	see *A.* 'Golden Fleece'
	'Canary Bird' ♀H2	CBcs CCCN CHEx CHal ERea MLan MOak SHBN SYvo WWlt
	'Cannington Carol' (v) ♀H2	ERea EWin MOak SRGP
	'Cannington Peter' (v) ♀H2	CCCN CHal MOak
	'Cannington Sally' (v)	EWin MLan SRGP
	'Cannington Sonia' (v)	ERea
	'Cloth of Gold'	SOWG
	'Cynthia Pike' (v)	LRHS SPoG
§	'Feuerglocke'	MOak
	Firebell	see *A.* 'Feuerglocke'
	'Frances Elizabeth'	MOak
§	'Golden Fleece'	ERea MOak
	'Hinton Seedling'	CCCN CRHN MOak
	x *hybridum* apricot	CHEx
	- red	CHEx
	indicum	CPLG
	'J. Morris'	LRHS MAsh SPoG SSta
	'Kentish Belle' ♀H2-3	CBcs CCCN CDoC CHEx CMHG CMac CRHN CTbh EBee ECot ELan EPfP LSRN MOak NPal SBra SHBN SPer WFar

I	'Kentish Belle Variegatum' (v)	ELan SBrw
	'Linda Vista Peach' ♀H2	MOak
	'Louis Marignac'	MOak
	'Marion' ♀H2	CHrt CRHN LRHS MOak SOWG SPoG WCot
	megapotamicum ♀H3	CBcs CBrm CCCN CHEx CMHG CPLG CRHN CSBt CTrC EBee ELan EPfP EPla ERea GQui LRHS MAsh MGos MLan MOak MRav SOWG SPer SPoG SRms WFar WSHC XPep
	- 'Compactum'	ENot
	- 'Variegatum' (v)	CBcs CBrm CCCN CPLG CSBt ELan EPfP GQui LRHS MAsh MGos MOak SBod SBrw SOWG SPer SPoG SWvt WFar
	- 'Wakehurst'	see *A.* 'Wakehurst'
	- 'Wisley Red'	CRHN SBrw
	x *milleri* ♀H2	CMac CPLG CRHN EDsa ERea MLan WCot
	- 'Variegatum' (v)	CHEx CMac CPLG EWin LRHS MOak SEND SPoG
	'Moonchimes'	MOak
	'Nabob' ♀H2	CCCN CDoC CHal CRHN ERea LRHS MLan MOak MTis SLdr SOWG SPoG
	'Orange Glow' (v) ♀H2	MOak
	'Orange Vein'	CHal EShb
	'Patrick Synge'	CCCN CMHG CPle ERea EShb LPhx MOak SOWG
	'Peaches and Cream'	LRHS
§	*pictum*	ERea
	- 'Thompsonii' (v)	CHEx CHal ERea EShb MJnS MOak WDyG
	'Pink Lady'	ERea GQui
	'Red Bells'	EPla GQui MOak
	'Rotterdam'	MOak
§	'Savitzii' (v) ♀H2	CHal MOak SOWG SRms
	sellowianum var. *marmoratum*	ERea
	'Simcox White' **new**	CCCN
	'Snowfall'	MOak
	'Souvenir de Bonn' (v) ♀H2	CHal ERea EShb MLan MOak MTis SAga WCot
	x *suntense*	CDul CMHG CPLG CSBt EPfP ERea LHyd LRHS LSou MJnS MWgw NPer SOWG WTel
	- 'Jermyns' ♀H3	EPfP LRHS MBri MFOX SLon SPoG WFar
	- 'Violetta'	CBcs CEnd CHEx MSte SPer
	- white-flowered	CBcs
	theophrasti	MSal
	variegated, salmon (v)	LAst
	vitifolium	ECot EPfP IDee MGos MHer NBid NEgg SPer WHil WKif
	- var. *album*	CDul CHEx CMHG CPLG CRHN EAro EMan EPfP IDee LHyd LSou MLan MWgw SEND SSpi WBor WCru WFar WSHC
	- 'Buckland'	CHll
	- 'Simcox White'	WEas
	- 'Tennant's White' ♀H3	CAbP CCCN ELan EPfP ERea LRHS MBri NBur WCru
	- 'Veronica Tennant' ♀H3	ERea MSte SAga WKif
	'Wakehurst'	WCot
	'Westfield Bronze' **new**	CRHN

Acacia ✿ (*Mimosaceae*)

acinacea	SPlb
adunca	SPlb
alpina	WCel
armata	see *A. paradoxa*
baileyana ♀H2	CBcs CSBt CTbh CTrG ECot ELan EMil EPfP ERea EShb GQui LRHS MGol MPRe SBig SBrw SCoo SEND

	SPer SPlb SPoG SWvt WCMO WFar WMul WPat
- var. *aurea*	SPlb WCMO
- 'Purpurea' ♀H2	CAbb CBcs CBos CCCN CDoC CDul CEnd CKno CTbh CWib EBee EMil EPfP GQui LHop MGos MLan MPRe SBig SBrw SPlb SPoG SWvt WCMO WFar WMul WPGP WPat
boormanii	ISea WCel
cultriformis	CPle CTrC SEND
cyanophylla	see *A. saligna*
dealbata ♀H2	More than 30 suppliers
- 'Gaulois Astier'	MPRe
- subsp. *subalpina*	WCel WMul WPGP
Exeter hybrid	CSBt
filicifolia	WCel
fimbriata **new**	CRHN
floribunda 'Lisette'	EPfP
frigescens	WCel
julibrissin	see *Albizia julibrissin*
juniperina	see *A. ulicifolia*
karroo	CArn CPLG WMul XPep
kybeanensis	WCel WPGP
longifolia	CAbb CBcs CHen EAmu EBee EPfP IDee SEND SPer SRms WGer
- subsp. *sophorae*	GGar
macradenia	SPlb
mearnsii	WCel WMul
melanoxylon	CDul CHen CTrC GGar IDee ISea WCel WHer
motteana	ECot
mucronata	CTrC EShb
myrtifolia	EWll
obliquinervia	WCel
§ *paradoxa* ♀H2	IDee WPat
pataczekii	CWSG EBee EPfP ERea LRHS
pendula	IDee
podalyriifolia	CDoC SPlb WPGP
pravissima ♀H2-3	More than 30 suppliers
retinodes ♀H2	CAbb CBcs CCCN CDoC CPLG CPle CRHN EBee EPfP ERea GQui LRav MLan SEND WCFE WMul
riceana	CCCN CPLG CTrG GQui IDee LRav
rubida	LRav MGos MPRe SPoG WCel WMul
§ *saligna*	CBcs CHen CSec EBee EShb SBLw
sentis	see *A. victoriae*
spectabilis	SPlb
suaveolens	SPlb
§ *ulicifolia*	CPLG CSBt CTrG
verticillata	CBcs CCCN CHll CTrG EBee GGar
- riverine	CTrC WCMO
§ *victoriae*	ERea

Acaena (Rosaceae)

adscendens misapplied	see *A. magellanica* subsp. *magellanica, A. saccaticupula* 'Blue Haze'
adscendens M. Fish	see *A. affinis*
adscendens Vahl	see *A. magellanica* subsp. *laevigata*
- 'Glauca'	CMdw EMan NBir NFor SBla
§ *affinis*	COIW ECha SDix
anserinifolia misapplied	see *A. novae-zelandiae*
§ *anserinifolia* (Forst. & Forst. f.) Druce	ECha GGar NHol
buchananii	CSpe CTri EBee ECho EDAr EGoo EPot GAbr GGar IHMH MBar MLLN NBro NFor SRms WFar WGHP WPer
caerulea hort.	see *A. caesiiglauca*
§ *caesiiglauca*	CBcs CTri EBee GAbr GGar MLHP NBid NFor NJOw SBla SGar WEas WGHP WPer

caespitosa	GKev
fissistipula	EHoe NJOw WHer WMoo
glaucophylla	see *A. magellanica* subsp. *magellanica*
inermis	EBee MLLN SPlb WGHP
- 'Purpurea'	CBcs CBrm EChP ECha EShb GAbr GGar MSph NJOw NLar SIng SPlb WHoo WMoo WWFP
macrocephala	EBee
§ *magellanica* subsp. *laevigata*	GGar
§ - subsp. *magellanica*	EBee LEdu
microphylla ♀H4	CSam CTri EBee ECho GAbr GGar IHMH LBee LRHS MBar NJOw NMen SHFr SIng SPlb SRms WFar WGHP
- Copper Carpet	see *A. microphylla* 'Kupferteppich'
- 'Glauca'	see *A. caesiiglauca*
§ - 'Kupferteppich'	CBrm CEnt EBee ECho EHoe EMan GAbr GGar IHMH MBri MRav MWgw NBir NVic SBch WGHP WMoo WPat WPer
- 'Pulchella'	EMan LRHS
myriophylla	EBee ECho EDAr
§ *novae-zelandiae*	CTri EBee GGar SDix WMoo WPer
ovalifolia	EBee ECho
'Pewter'	see *A. saccaticupula* 'Blue Haze'
pinnatifida	NBro
platycantha F&W 9293	WCot
poeppigiana **new**	EBee
profundeincisa	see *A. anserinifolia* (Forst. & Forst. f.) Druce
'Purple Carpet'	see *A. microphylla* 'Kupferteppich'
'Purple Haze'	CSpe
saccaticupula	MWgw NLar
§ - 'Blue Haze'	CMea EAEE EBee ECha ECho EDAr GGar LRHS MBar MLLN NVic SIng SPer SPlb SRms WFar WHoo WMoo
sanguisorbae	see *A. anserinifolia* (Forst. & Forst. f.) Druce
viridior	see *A. anserinifolia* (Forst. & Forst. f.) Druce

Acalypha (Euphorbiaceae)

hispaniolae ♀H1	CKob ERea MOak
hispida ♀H1	LRHS MBri
pendula	see *A. reptans*
§ *reptans*	CHal SPet
wilkesiana var. *obovata* **new**	CKob

Acanthocalyx see *Morina*

Acantholimon (Plumbaginaceae)

sp.	EMan
androsaceum	see *A. ulicinum*
glumaceum	MWat NLAp WPat
§ *ulicinum*	ECho EPot WAbe

Acanthopanax see *Eleutherococcus*

ricinifolius	see *Kalopanax septemlobus*

Acanthus ✿ (Acanthaceae)

balcanicus misapplied	see *A. hungaricus*
caroli-alexandri	EMon IPot WHil
dioscoridis	EMon MAvo SMHy WSel
- var. *perringii*	CDes EBee LHop MAvo NChi SBla WCot WFar WHil WPGP WSHC
hirsutus	CFis EMar EMon NBre SPav WCot WHil
- JCA 109.700	SBla
- f. *roseus*	SBla WFar
- subsp. *syriacus*	EHrv GCal NBre NLar NPro WCot WHil WLin WViv
- - JCA 106.500	LPhx
§ *hungaricus*	More than 30 suppliers

- AL&JS 90097YU	EMon WPrP
- MESE 561	EPPr
longifolius	see *A. hungaricus*
mollis	More than 30 suppliers
- 'Feilding Gold'	see *A. mollis* 'Hollard's Gold'
- free-flowering	GCal WHil
§ - 'Hollard's Gold'	More than 30 suppliers
- 'Jefalba'	see *A. mollis* (Latifolius Group) 'Rue Ledan'
- Latifolius Group	EBee ECrN EMan EPfP LRHS MRav MSte SRms WHil WHoo WTin
§ - - 'Rue Ledan'	CBct EBee EMon IPot LPhx MSte SUsu WCot WFar WHil WSel
- 'Sjaak' **new**	EBee
- 'Summerdance'	LHop WHil
sennii	LPhx
spinosus ♀H4	More than 30 suppliers
- Ferguson's form	WCot
- 'Lady Moore' (v)	EMon IBlr IFro IPot MCCP NLar SBch WCot WHil
- 'Royal Haughty'	MSte WHil
- Spinosissimus Group	CBct CMHG ECha EHrv ELan EMan EMon GCal LEdu LPhx MCCP MRav NChi SBla SMad SWat WCot WFar WHil WMnd WTin
'Summer Beauty'	EWTr MBri MSte NBre NLar NPro WCMO WCot WFar WGer WHil

Acca (Myrtaceae)

sp.	SBLw SWvt
sellowiana (F)	More than 30 suppliers
- 'Coolidge' (F)	LEdu
- 'Mammoth' (F)	CBcs
- 'Triumph' (F)	CBcs
- 'Variegata' (F/v)	ELan LAst

Acer ✿ (Aceraceae)

HWJK 2040 from Nepal	WCru
acuminatum	CMCN WNor
argutum	CMCN IMGH WCwm WNor
barbinerve	CMCN EPfP WNor
buergerianum	CBcs CDul CMCN CMen CPMA ECrN IArd LRHS MBlu MBri MMuc MPkF SBLw SBir SEND STre WCwm WGer WNor
- 'Goshiki-kaede' (v)	CPMA WWes
- 'Integrifolium'	see *A. buergerianum* 'Subintegrum'
- 'Mino-yatsubusa'	MPkF
- 'Miyasama-yatsubusa'	MPkF
- 'Naruto'	CMCN MPkF
- subsp. *ningpoense*	WWes
§ - 'Subintegrum'	CMCN
* - 'Variegatum' (v)	CMCN
calcaratum	CDul CMCN
campbellii B&SWJ 7685	WCru
* - var. *fansipanense* B&SWJ 8270	WCru
- - HWJ 569	WCru
§ - subsp. *flabellatum* B&SWJ 8057	WCru
- - var. *yunnanense*	CBcs CDoC ECrN GTSp IMGH NPen WCwm WHCr
- subsp. *sinense*	see *A. sinense*
- subsp. *wilsonii*	see *A. wilsonii*
campestre ♀H4	More than 30 suppliers
- 'Carnival' (v)	CBcs CDul CEnd CMCN CPMA CWib EBee ECrN EMil LRHS MAsh MBlu MBri NHol NLar SMad SPer SPoG SPur SWvt WCot WPGP
- 'Commodore'	LPan
- 'Elsrijk'	CCVT CLnd EBee SBLw
- 'Evenly Red'	MBlu
- 'Pendulum'	CEnd
- 'Postelense'	CEnd CMCN CPMA MBlu MGos MPkF

- 'Pulverulentum' (v)	CDoC CEnd CMCN CPMA SMad SSta
- 'Queen Elizabeth'	CCVT MGos
- 'Red Shine'	MGos
- 'Royal Ruby'	CWSG GTSp MGos SSta WFar
* - 'Ruby Glow'	CDoC CEnd
- 'Schwerinii'	CDul
I - 'Silver Celebration' (v)	CPMA
- 'William Caldwell'	CEnd CTho
capillipes ♀H4	CBcs CCVT CDul CMCN CTho CWib ECrN EMui ENot LRHS MBar MDun MGos NBea SBLw SBir SBrw SPer WDin WFar WHCr WNor WOrn WPGP WPat
- 'Candy Stripe'	NLar SLim SSpi SSta
- 'Golden Increase'	MBri
- 'Honey Dew'	NLar
- var. *morifolium*	see *A. morifolium*
cappadocicum	CDul CMCN CSam ECrN GTSp MDun MLan NWea SBLw WDin WNor WWes
- 'Aureum' ♀H4	More than 30 suppliers
- subsp. *divergens*	MPkF
- var. *mono*	see *A. pictum*
- 'Rubrum' ♀H4	CBcs CLnd CMCN EBee ECrN EPfP LAst LBuc LPan LRHS MBlu MBri MGos MRav SBLw SHBN SLim SPer WDin WFar WHer WOrn
- subsp. *sinicum*	CEnd CMCN EPfP GBin WFar WPGP
- - GWJ 9360	WCru
§ - - var. *tricaudatum*	CPLG WPGP
carpinifolium	CBcs CBrd CMCN ECrN EWTr IArd MPkF NLar WCwm WNor
- 'Esveld Select'	WWes
catalpifolium	see *A. longipes* subsp. *catalpifolium*
§ *caudatifolium*	CMCN SBir WCwm WPGP
- B&SWJ 3531	WCru
- B&SWJ 6734	WCru
§ *caudatum*	MDun
- GWJ 9279	WCru
- subsp. *ukurunduense*	CMCN MPkF WNor
cinnamomifolium	see *A. coriaceifolium*
circinatum	CBcs CDoC CDul CLnd CMCN CPMA CSam ECrN EPfP EShb EWTr LRHS MBlu MBri MLan NBea NFor NLar SHBN SSta WDin WFar WNor
- B&SWJ 9565	WCru
- 'Little Gem'	CPMA
- 'Little Joe' **new**	CPMA
- 'Monroe'	WWes
- 'Pacific Fire'	CPMA
- 'Sunglow'	WWes
circinatum x *palmatum*	SIFN
cissifolium	CBcs CDoC CLnd CMCN CTho EPfP IArd LRHS WNor
x *conspicuum* 'Candy Stripe'	CLnd CPMA SIFN
- 'Elephant's Ear'	CPMA EPfP NLar
I - 'Phoenix'	CEnd CMCN CPMA CTho EPfP MBlu NLar SIFN SSpi WDin WPat
- 'Silver Ghost'	MGos
§ - 'Silver Vein'	CDoC CDul CEnd CMCN CPMA EBee ECrN EPfP LRHS MGos MWea NLar SIFN SPur SSta
§ *cordatum*	WWes
§ *coriaceifolium*	WNor
crataegifolium	CMCN WNor
- 'Meuri-keade-no-fuiri' (v)	MPkF
- 'Meuri-no-ōfu' (v)	MPkF
- 'Veitchii' (v)	CDoC CMCN CPMA EPfP MBlu MPkF NLar SIFN SSpi
creticum L.	see *A. sempervirens*
dasycarpum	see *A. saccharinum*

davidii	More than 30 suppliers
- B&SWJ 8183	WCru
- 'Canton'	MPkF
N - 'Ernest Wilson'	CBcs CMCN MBlu NEgg NLar
N - 'George Forrest' ♀H4	CBcs CCVT CDoC CDul CMCN
	CTho EBee ECrN ELan EPfP LPan
	LRHS MAsh MBlu MBri MDun
	NBea NEgg NWea SBLw SBod
	SBrw SEND SHBN SLim SPer SPoG
	WDin WFar WOrn
- 'Hagelunie'	MPkF
- 'Karmen'	CLnd CPMA MBri MPkF SBir SIFN
	WPGP
- 'Madeline Spitta'	CMCN CPMA MBlu MPkF SIFN
- 'Purple Bark'	SBir
- 'Rosalie'	EPfP MBlu MBri SBir
- 'Serpentine' ♀H4	CBcs CDoC CMCN CPMA CTho
	EPfP MBlu MBri NEgg NLar SBir
	SIFN SSpi SSta WFar WOrn WPGP
- 'Silver Vein'	see *A.* x *conspicuum* 'Silver Vein'
diabolicum	CMCN GIBF
- f. *purpurascens*	GIBF
distylum	WCwm
divergens	CMCN
elegantulum	CDoC CMCN WCwm WNor WPGP
erianthum	CLnd CPne CTho WHCr WNor
fabri	CBcs CMCN WNor
flabellatum	see *A. campbellii* subsp.
	flabellatum
§ ***forrestii***	CMCN CTho EPfP IArd NBea NHol
	WCwm WNor
- 'Alice'	CBcs CDul CEnd CLnd CMCN
	CPMA SIFN SSta
- 'Sirene'	CPMA
- 'Sparkling'	CPMA MBri
x ***freemanii***	CMCN
- 'Armstrong'	SBLw WFar WWes
- Autumn Blaze =	CBcs CCVT CDoC CDul CMCN
'Jeffersred'	EPfP LRHS MBlu MGos SBLw SMad
	SPoG WDin WFar WOrn WPat
- Autumn Fantasy =	MBlu SIFN
'DTR 102'	
- Celebration = 'Celzam'	MGos WFar
§ - 'Elegant'	SBLw
- 'Morgan'	CEnd CPMA SBir SIFN
fulvescens	see *A. longipes*
ginnala	see *A. tataricum* subsp. *ginnala*
glabrum	WNor
globosum	see *A. platanoides* 'Globosum'
grandidentatum	see *A. saccharum* subsp.
	grandidentatum
griseum ♀H4	More than 30 suppliers
grosseri	CDul CMCN CTri IArd
- var. *hersii* ♀H4	More than 30 suppliers
- 'Leiden'	EPfP MBlu
heldreichii	CMCN EPfP
henryi	CBcs CDul CLnd CMCN CTho
	EPfP MBri NLar WBVN WCwm
	WNor
hookeri	CMCN
hyrcanum	CMCN
japonicum	CMCN LRHS MBar NHol SSta
	WHCr WNor
- B&SWJ 5950	WCru
§ - 'Aconitifolium' ♀H4	More than 30 suppliers
- 'Attaryi'	CMCN MPkF NLar
- 'Aureum'	see *A. shirasawanum* 'Aureum'
- 'Ezo-no-momiji'	see *A. shirasawanum* 'Ezo-no-momiji'
- 'Fairy Lights'	WWes
- 'Filicifolium'	see *A. japonicum* 'Aconitifolium'
- 'Green Cascade'	CBdw CEnd CMCN CPMA ECho
	MPkF NLar SIFN SPoG WPGP WPat
	WWes
* - 'King Copse'	LPan
- 'Laciniatum'	see *A. japonicum* 'Aconitifolium'

- f. *microphyllum*	see *A. shirasawanum*
	'Microphyllum'
§ - 'Mikasa-yama'	LRHS
- 'Ogurayama'	see *A. shirasawanum* 'Ogurayama'
- 'Ō-isami'	CMCN EPfP LRHS MPkF SIFN
- 'Ō-taki'	ECho
- 'Vitifolium' ♀H4	CDoC CEnd CMCN CPMA CSBt
	ECho ELan EPfP LPan LRHS MBlu
	MBri MGos MPkF NBea NEgg NLar
	NPal SBrw SCoo SIFN SPer SPoG
	SSpi SSta WDin WPGP WPat
kawakamii	see *A. caudatifolium*
laevigatum	CMCN
laxiflorum	CBcs ISea
- HWJK 2240	WCru
leucoderme	see *A. saccharum* subsp.
	leucoderme
lobelii Bunge	see *A. turkestanicum*
lobelii Tenore	CLnd CTho WPGP
§ ***longipes***	CMCN
- subsp. *catalpifolium*	CMCN
macrophyllum	CMCN CTho EPfP IDee ISea LHyd
	NLar
mandschuricum	CBcs EPfP IArd MPkF WCwm
	WDin WNor
§ ***maximowiczianum***	CBcs CMCN CSam CTho ELan
	GIBF WFar WNor
maximowiczii	CMCN ECrN WHCr WNor
§ ***metcalfii***	WNor
micranthum	CDoC CEnd CMCN EPfP IMGH
	MBlu MPkF SHGN SIFN SSpi
	WCwm WNor WPGP
miyabei	MPkF
mono	see *A. pictum*
monspessulanum	CBcs CDul CMCN IArd SEND
	XPep
§ ***morifolium***	CCVT MPkF
morrisonense	see *A. caudatifolium*
negundo	CDul CLnd CMCN CTho CWib
	ECrN NWea SBLw WNor
- IDS 2000	WHCr
- 'Argenteovariegatum'	see *A. negundo* 'Variegatum'
- 'Auratum'	CMCN MBar SBLw WDin WPat
- 'Aureomarginatum' (v)	ECrN LAst LBuc WOrn
- 'Aureovariegatum' (v)	CBcs MBar
- subsp. *californicum*	WNor
§ - 'Elegans' (v)	CDul CEnd CLnd CMCN COtt
	ECrN EPfP LRHS NHol SHBN SPer
	WFar WWes
- 'Elegantissimum'	see *A. negundo* 'Elegans'
- 'Flamingo' (v)	More than 30 suppliers
- 'Kelly's Gold'	CBcs CLnd CTho CWSG ECho
	EGra LRHS MAsh MBri MGos NPro
	SCoo SCrf SLim SPoG WDin WFar
	WOrn WWes
- 'Sensation'	WWes
§ - 'Variegatum' (v)	CBcs CLnd ECrN ENot LAst LRHS
	SBLw SPer WDin WFar
- var. *violaceum*	CBcs CEnd CMCN
- 'Winter Lightning' **new**	LPan
nikoense	see *A. maximowiczianum*
oblongum	CDul CMCN
- HWJK 2422	WCru
oliverianum	EBee EPfP WNor WPGP
- subsp. *formosanum*	WCru
B&SWJ 6773	
- - B&SWJ 6797	WCru
opalus	CMCN WCwm
orientale	see *A. sempervirens*
Pacific Sunset =	LRHS
'Warrenred'	
palmatum	More than 30 suppliers
- 'Abigail Rose'	CBdw
§ - 'Aka Shigitatsusawa'	CBcs CMCN CMac CMen CPMA
	ECho LMil LRHS MGos MPkF NLar
	SIFN SMur SPer SVil WFar WPat

	– 'Akane'	CBdw CMen ECho MPkF
	– 'Akebono'	CBdw CPMA
	– 'Akegarasu'	CMen ECho LRHS NLar
	– 'Alpine Sunrise' **new**	CBdw
	– 'Alpine Surprise'	CPMA
	– 'Amagi-shigure' **new**	CBdw CPMA
	– 'Ao-kanzashi' (v)	CBdw MPkF NLar
	– 'Aoba-jo'	CMen CPMA ECho MPkF NLar
	– 'Aoshime-no-uchi'	see *A. palmatum* 'Shinobugaoka'
	– 'Aoyagi'	CEnd CMCN CMen CPMA ECho EPfP LAst LMil LRHS MAsh MBri MGos NHol SIFN WFoF WPat WWes
§	– 'Arakawa'	CEnd CMCN CMen ECho EZes SIFN WWes
	– 'Arakawa-ukon' **new**	CPMA
	– 'Aratama'	CBdw CPMA MGos SCoo WPat WWes
	– 'Ariake-nomura'	CMen MPkF WWes
	– 'Asahi-zuru' (v)	CBcs CBdw CDoC CMCN CMen CPMA EBee ECho LPan LRHS MAsh MBri MGos MPkF NHol NLar SPer SVil WDin WFar WFoF WPat WWes
	– 'Ashurst Wood'	SIFN
	– 'Atrolineare'	CMen ECho MPkF NBea NLar WPat
	– 'Atropurpureum'	CBcs CBrm CCVT CDul CMen CSBt CTho CTri CWCL CWib EBee ECrN EMui GKev ISea LAst LSRN MDun MGos MSwo NEgg SBrw SLon STre SWvt WHCr WWes
	– f. *atropurpureum*	CBcs CDoC CEnd CWSG EBee ECho EPfP EWTr LBuc LHyd LRHS MBar MGos NBea NBee NBlu NHol NWea SHBN SPer SReu WCFE WDin WFar WHar WPat WTel
	– 'Atropurpureum Novum'	MPkF
	– 'Atsugama' **new**	CBdw
	– 'Attraction'	CMCN CMen
	– 'Aureum'	CBdw CMCN CMen CWib ECho EPfP LRHS MAsh MBlu MGos MPkF NLar SIFN SSpi WFar WWes
	– Autumn Glory Group	CEnd CPMA ECho WWes
	– 'Autumn Red'	ECho LPan LRHS
*	– 'Autumn Showers'	CEnd CPMA
	– 'Azuma-murasaki'	CMen CPMA ECho MPkF NLar
	– 'Barrie Bergman'	CBdw CPMA
	– 'Beni-chidori'	CMen ECho
	– 'Beni-gasa'	CPMA
	– 'Beni-hime'	CPMA NLar
	– 'Beni-hoshi'	CBdw WPat
	– 'Beni-kagami'	CEnd CMCN CPMA EPfP LRHS MBlu NBea NLar WWes
	– 'Beni-kawa'	CBdw CMen CPMA ECho LMil MPkF SIFN SPur SSpi WPat WWes
	– 'Beni-komachi'	CBcs CEnd CMCN CMac CMen CPMA ECho EPfP LMil LRHS MAsh MBri MGos MPkF NLar SIFN SVil WPat WWes
	– 'Beni-komachi Sport'	CPMA
	– 'Beni-maiko'	CBdw CEnd CMCN CMen CPMA CWib ECho EPfP LBuc LRHS MBri MPkF MWea NLar SCoo SIFN WDin WPGP WPat WWes
	– 'Beni-otake'	CBcs CBdw CLnd CMCN CMen CPMA ECho EPfP LMil LRHS MBri MGos MPkF NLar SBod SIFN SMur SPer SVil WPat WWes
	– 'Beni-schichihenge' (v)	CBcs CBdw CEnd CMCN CMen CPMA ECho EPfP LPan LRHS MAsh MBri MGos MPkF NHol SCoo SIFN SMur SPoG SVil WPGP WPat
	– 'Beni-shi-en'	CBdw CPMA
	– 'Beni-shigitatsu-sawa'	see *A. palmatum* 'Aka Shigitatsusawa'
	– 'Beni-tsukasa' (v)	CBdw CEnd CMen CPMA ECho LMil LPan LRHS MPkF SIFN SSpi SSta WPGP WWes
	– 'Beni-ubi-gohon'	CPMA MPkF NLar
	– 'Beni-yatsubusa'	WWes
	– 'Beni-zuru'	CBdw
I	– 'Berry Broom'	CBdw
	– 'Bloodgood' ♀H4	More than 30 suppliers
*	– 'Bonfire'	CPMA LRHS
	– 'Bonnie Bergman'	CPMA
	– 'Boskoop Glory'	CMen ECho WWes
	– 'Brandt's Dwarf'	CBdw WPat
	– 'Burgundy Lace' ♀H4	CBcs CDoC CEnd CMCN CPMA CWib EBee ECho EMil LPan LRHS LSRN MAsh MBlu MBri MGos MPkF NHol SBrw SCoo SIFN SPer SPoG WDin WFar WPGP WPat
	– 'Butterfly' (v)	More than 30 suppliers
	– 'Calico'	CBdw CPMA
	– 'Carlis Corner'	CPMA
I	– 'Carlis Corner Broom'	CBdw
	– 'Carminium'	see *A. palmatum* 'Corallinum'
	– 'Chikuma-no'	MPkF
	– 'Chirimen-nishiki' (v)	CMCN MPkF
	– 'Chishio'	see *A. palmatum* 'Shishio'
	– 'Chishio Improved'	see *A. palmatum* 'Shishio Improved'
	– 'Chishio-hime'	CBdw
	– 'Chitoseyama' ♀H4	CEnd CMCN CMen CPMA CWib EBee ECho EPfP LRHS MBar MBri MGos MLan MPkF NEgg NLar SBrw SCoo SIFN SLim SMur SSpi SSta WFar
	– 'Chiyo-hime' **new**	CBdw
	– 'Collingwood Ingram'	WWes
	– 'Coonara Pygmy'	CBdw CMCN CMen CPMA ECho LRHS MGos MPkF SMur WFar WPat WWes
	– 'Coral Pink'	CBdw CPMA ECho MPkF WWes
§	– 'Corallinum'	CEnd CMCN CMen CPMA ECho MPkF NLar WDin WPat
	– var. *coreanum*	CMCN LMil SIFN WNor
	– – B&SWJ 4474	WCru
	– – B&SWJ 8606	WCru
	– – 'Korean Gem'	CPMA ECho
	– 'Crimson Carol' **new**	CBdw
	– 'Crippsii'	CBcs CDoC CMen ECho EMil LRHS MBri MGos MPkF SCoo WFar WPat WWes
	– 'Demi-sec'	CBdw CMen WWes
	– 'Deshōjō'	CBdw CMCN CMen ECho LPan MBar MBlu MGos MLan MPkF NHol SHBN
	– 'Deshōjō-nishiki'	CBdw
	– 'Diana'	CMen MPkF NLar WWes
	– 'Diane Verkade'	CPMA
	– var. *dissectum* ♀H4	More than 30 suppliers
	– – 'Ao-shidare' (v)	CBdw CPMA
	– – 'Ariadne' (v)	CBdw CPMA CWib MBri MGos MPkF NLar SIFN WPat WWes
	– – 'Autumn Fire'	CBdw CPMA
	– – 'Baby Lace'	CBdw CPMA NLar
	– – 'Balcombe Green'	SIFN
	– – 'Baldsmith'	CBdw CPMA MGos WPat
	– – 'Beni-fushigi'	CBdw MPkF NLar WPat WWes
	– – 'Beni-kumo-no-su' **new**	CBdw
	– – 'Beni-shidare Tricolor' (v)	CBdw CMen NLar
	– – 'Beni-shidare Variegated' (v)	CMCN CPMA ECho
	– – 'Beni-tsukasa-shidare'	CBdw
	– – 'Berrima Bridge'	CBdw CPMA
	– – 'Bewley's Red'	CBdw CPMA

- - 'Brocade'	CBdw CMCN MPkF WPat WWes
- - 'Bronzewing' **new**	CPMA
- - 'Chantilly Lace'	CBdw CPMA ECho
- - 'Chelwood'	SIFN
- - 'Crimson Prince'	CBcs ECho SVil
- - 'Crimson Queen' ♀H4	More than 30 suppliers
- - 'Dissectum	CBcs CPMA CTri CWCL ELan EPfP
Atropurpureum Group	LHyd LRHS MAsh MGan MGos
	NBea NHol NWea SHBN SLim
	SReu SSpi SSta WDin WFar WHCr
	WOrn WPat
- - 'Dissectum Flavescens'	CBdw CEnd CMac CPMA ECho
	MBlu
§ - - 'Dissectum Nigrum'	CPMA CWCL CWSG ECho LRHS
	MAsh MPkF NBea NBee NHol SSpi
	WPat
- - 'Dissectum	CDoC CLnd ECho LRHS MPkF
Palmatifidum'	SCoo SPer SVil WFar WPat WWes
- - 'Dissectum Rubrifolium'	ECho WWes
§ - - 'Dissectum Variegatum'	CBcs CPMA EPfP LRHS MPkF
(v)	
- - Dissectum Viride	CBcs CMCN CMen CPMA CSBt
Group	CWSG ECho ELan EMui EPfP LMil
	LPan LRHS MAsh MDun MGan
	MGos MSwo NBea NBlu NEgg
	SBod SBrw SLim SPer SPla SSta
	WFar WOrn
- - 'Doctor Baker'	CBdw
- - 'Ellen'	CBdw CPMA WPat WWes
- - 'Emerald Lace'	CPMA MBlu WWes
- - 'Felice'	CBdw CPMA MPkF WPat
- - 'Filigree' (v)	CBdw CMCN CMen CPMA ECho
	EPfP LMil LRHS MAsh MGos MPkF
	NLar SIFN SSpi WDin WPat WWes
- - 'Garnet' ♀H4	More than 30 suppliers
- - 'Goshiki-shidare' (v)	CEnd CMen CPMA ECho MPkF
	WWes
- - 'Green Globe'	CBdw LPan LRHS NLar WWes
- - 'Green Hornet' **new**	CPMA
- - 'Green Lace'	LPan MPkF
- - 'Green Mist'	CBdw CPMA WPat WWes
- - 'Hanzel' **new**	WPat
- - 'Inaba-shidare' ♀H4	More than 30 suppliers
I - - 'Kawaii' **new**	CPMA
- - 'Kiri-nishiki'	CMen CPMA ECho MPkF NLar
- - 'Lemon Chiffon'	CBdw
* - - 'Lionheart'	CBdw CDoC CPMA ECho EMil
	LPan LRHS MBri MGos MPkF SBod
	SCoo SPer WFar WPat
- - 'Mioun' **new**	CBdw
- - 'Nomura-nishiki' (v)	WWes
- - 'Octopus'	CBdw CPMA
- - 'Orangeola'	CBdw CEnd CMen CPMA ECho
	MAsh MGos MPkF NHol NLar
	SCoo SIFN WPat WWes
- - 'Ornatum'	CDoC CMCN CMen COtt CWib
	ECho EPfP IMGH LMil LPan MBar
	MDun MGos MPkF NBea NBlu
	NEgg SBrw SCoo WDin WFar
	WGer WHCr WHar
- - 'Otto's Dissectum' **new**	CBdw CPMA
- - 'Pendulum Julian'	CMCN MPkF NLar SIFN
- - 'Pink Ballerina' (v)	CPMA
- - 'Pink Filigree'	CBdw LPan WWes
- - 'Raraflora'	CBdw LPan WPat WWes
- - 'Red Autumn Lace'	CBcs CDoC CMen CPMA ECho
- - 'Red Dragon'	ECrN LPan LRHS MPkF NLar SBod
	WPat
- - 'Red Feather'	CBdw CPMA
- - 'Red Filigree Lace'	CBdw CEnd CMCN CMen CPMA
	ECho EPfP LRHS MAsh MBlu SIFN
	WPat
- - 'Red Select'	ECho MPkF
- - 'Rilas Red'	CBdw
- - 'Seiryû' ♀H4	More than 30 suppliers

§ - - 'Shôjô-shidare'	CBdw CEnd CPMA ECho LRHS
	NLar WWes
- - 'Sumi-shidare' **new**	CBdw
- - 'Sunset'	CBdw CMCN CPMA EMui MDun
	MPkF WPat
- - 'Tamukeyama'	CBcs CLnd CMCN CMen CPMA
	ECho LMil LPan LRHS MDun MGos
	MPkF NLar SBod SCoo SMur SVil
	WBVN WFar WPat
- - 'Toyama-nishiki' (v)	CMCN CMen ECho NLar SIFN
	WPat
- - 'Waterfall'	CMCN CMen CPMA ECho
- - 'Watnong'	CBdw CPMA
- - 'Zaaling'	CPMA ECho
- 'Doctor Tilt' **new**	WPat
- 'Dormansland'	LMil SIFN
- 'Dragon's Fire'	CBdw EMui MDun
- 'Eddisbury'	CEnd CMen CPMA MDun MPkF
	NBea NLar SSta WOrn WPat
	WWes
- 'Edna Bergman'	CPMA
- 'Effegi'	see *A. palmatum* 'Fireglow'
- 'Eimini'	WPat WWes
- 'Elegans'	CMen ECho EPfP MPkF NLar SIFN
	WDin
- Emperor 1 = 'Wolff'	WPat
new	
- 'Englishtown'	CBdw WPat WWes
- 'Enkan'	CBdw CPMA MBri MPkF NLar
	WPat WWes
- 'Eono-momiji' **new**	CMen
- 'Ever Red'	see *A. palmatum* var. *dissectum*
	'Dissectum Nigrum'
- 'Fall's Fire'	CBdw CPMA
- 'Fascination'	CBdw CPMA
- 'Filigree Rouge'	CBdw WWes
- 'Fior d'Arancio'	CPMA NBea NLar WPat
§ - 'Fireglow'	CBcs CDoC CEnd CLnd CMCN
	CMen CPMA CSBt CWib ECho
	EMil LPan LRHS MBlu MBri MGos
	MPkF NBea NEgg NLar SBod SCoo
	SIFN SPoG WFar WPGP WPat
	WWes
- 'First Ghost' **new**	CPMA
- 'Fjellheim'	CBdw CPMA
- 'Frederici Guglielmi'	see *A. palmatum* var. *dissectum*
	'Dissectum Variegatum'
- 'Fûhjin' **new**	CBdw
- 'Garyû'	WWes
- 'Gassho'	CBdw
- 'Geisha'	CBdw CPMA MGos WPat
- 'Gekkô-nishiki'	CBdw WWes
- 'Germaine's Gyration'	CBdw CPMA WWes
- 'Gibbsii' **new**	CMen
- 'Glowing Embers'	WPat
- 'Golden Pond'	CBdw CPMA WWes
- 'Goshiki-kotohime' (v)	CMCN CPMA MPkF NLar WPat
- 'Goten-nomura' **new**	CBdw
- 'Green Star' **new**	CBdw
- 'Green Trompenburg'	CMCN CMen ECho MGos MPkF
	NLar SIFN
- 'Groundcover'	CBdw WWes
§ - 'Hagoromo'	CDoC CMen ECho MPkF WFar
- 'Hanami-nishiki'	CMen ECho MPkF WPat
- 'Harusame' (v)	CBdw MPkF
- 'Hatsukoi' (v) **new**	CBdw
- 'Hazeroino' (v)	MPkF
- 'Heartbeat'	CBdw CPMA WWes
- 'Helena'	see *A. shirasawanum* 'Helena'
- var. **heptalobum**	CMCN WWes
§ - 'Heptalobum Elegans'	CMCN LRHS MBlu SHBN SSpi
- 'Heptalobum Elegans	see *A. palmatum* 'Hessei'
Purpureum'	
- 'Herbstfeuer'	CMen CPMA
§ - 'Hessei'	CEnd CMCN ECho LRHS MBlu
	NBea NLar WWes

- 'Higasayama' (v)	CBcs CBdw CEnd CMCN CMen CPMA ECho LRHS MAsh MGos MPkF NHol NLar SCoo SIFN WPGP WPat WWes
- 'Hime-shojo'	CBdw
- 'Hino-tori-nishiki'	CMen
- 'Hi-no-tsukasa'	CBdw
- 'Hiryu'	WWes
- 'Hôgyoku'	CMCN CPMA MPkF
- 'Hondoshi'	CBdw
- 'Honô' (v) **new**	CBdw
- 'Hoshi-kuzu'	CBdw
- 'Hupp's Dwarf'	WWes
- 'Ibo-nishiki'	CMen MPkF SIFN
- 'Ichigyôji'	CEnd CMCN CMen CPMA ECho LMil LRHS SIFN WPGP WPat
- 'Improved Shishio'	see *A. palmatum* 'Shishio Improved'
- 'Inazuma'	CBcs CDoC CMCN CMen CPMA ECho EPfP LRHS MPkF NLar SCoo WFar WWes
- 'Irish Lace'	CBdw CPMA
- 'Issai-nishiki'	ECho MPkF
* - 'Issai-nishiki-kawazu'	MPkF
- 'Itami-nishiki'	CBdw WWes
- 'Jane'	MPkF WWes
- 'Japanese Sunrise'	CPMA WWes
- 'Jerre Schwartz'	WPat
- 'Jirô-shidare'	CBdw CPMA EPfP LRHS MPkF NLar SIFN
- 'Junihitoe'	see *A. shirasawanum* 'Jûnihitoe'
- 'Kaba'	WWes
- 'Kagero' (v)	MBri MPkF WFar
§ - 'Kagiri-nishiki' (v)	CDul CMCN CMen CPMA CWSG ECho LRHS MPkF NEgg NHol SIFN SPur WFar WNor
- 'Kamagata'	CBcs CBdw CEnd CMCN CMen CPMA ECho EPfP EZes LMil LRHS MAsh MBri MGos MPkF NLar SBod SIFN SMur SPer SVil WPGP WPat WWes
- 'Kandy Kitchen'	CBdw CPMA MGos NLar WWes
- 'Karaori-nishiki' (v)	CMen ECho MBlu MPkF NLar
- 'Karasugawa' (v)	CBdw CMen CPMA ECho MGos MPkF NLar
- 'Kasagiyama'	CBdw CEnd CMCN CMen CPMA ECho LMil LRHS MPkF NBea NLar SIFN WPGP
- 'Kasen-nishiki'	CBdw CMen ECho MPkF
- 'Kashima'	CEnd CMCN CMen CPMA ECho MBNS MPkF NLar WFar WPat
- 'Kashima-yatsubusa'	CBdw
- 'Katja'	CMen WPat WWes
- 'Katsura' ♀H4	More than 30 suppliers
- 'Kenko-nishiki'	WWes
- 'Ki-hachijô'	CMCN CMen CPMA ECho EPfP MBri NLar WPat WWes
- 'Kingsville Variegated' (v)	CBdw WWes
- 'Kinran'	CMCN CMen ECho LRHS MPkF WWes
- 'Kinshi'	CBdw CEnd CMCN CMen CPMA ECho EPfP LRHS MPkF NBea NLar SIFN SSta WPat
- 'Kiyohime'	CBdw CDoC CMCN CMen ECho MBlu MPkF NBea WFar WPat
- 'Koba-shôjô'	CBdw
- 'Ko-chidori'	CBdw WWes
- 'Kogane-nishiki'	CMen ECho WWes
- 'Kogane-sakae' **new**	CPMA
- 'Koko'	WWes
- 'Kokobunji-nishiki' (v)	CBdw CMen CPMA ECho WPat
- 'Komache-hime'	CBdw CMen CPMA ECho WPat
* - 'Komaru'	NLar
- 'Komon-nishiki' (v)	CBdw CMen CPMA ECho WWes
- 'Koriba'	CBdw CPMA MPkF NLar
§ - 'Koshimino'	CPMA
- 'Kotohime'	CBdw CMCN CMen CPMA MBri MPkF NLar SCoo SIFN WWes
- 'Koto-ito-komachi'	CBdw CMen CPMA ECho MPkF NLar WPat
- 'Koto-maru'	MPkF WPat
- 'Koto-no-ito'	CBdw CMCN MBri MGos MPkF NLar WPat
- 'Koya-san'	CBdw CMen MPkF
- 'Koyô-ao-shidare'	CBdw
- 'Krazy Krinkle' **new**	CPMA
- 'Kurabu-yama'	CMCN CMen MPkF
- 'Kurenai' **new**	CBdw
- 'Kurui-jishi'	CBdw MGos MPkF NLar SIFN WPat
- 'Kyra'	CMen MPkF WWes
- 'Lemon Lime Lace'	CBdw CPMA WWes
- 'Linearilobum'	CDoC ECho EPfP LHyd LMil LRHS MBlu MGos MPkF NBea NHol NLar SCam SCoo WFar WNor WPat
- 'Linearilobum Atropurpureum'	LRHS NBea WNor
- 'Lin-ling'	LMil SIFN
- 'Little Princess'	see *A. palmatum* 'Mapi-no-machihime'
- 'Lozita'	WPat WWes
- 'Lutescens'	ECho MPkF
- 'Lydia'	MPkF
- 'Maiko'	CMen ECho MPkF
- 'Mai-mori' (v)	CMen WWes
- 'Mama'	CMen ECho
- 'Manyô-no-sato' (v) **new**	CBdw
§ - 'Mapi-no-machihime'	CBdw CEnd CMCN CMen CPMA ECho ELan LMil LRHS MAsh MBri MGos MPkF NHol SIFN SMur WPGP WPat
- 'Marakumo'	MPkF
- 'Mardi Gras' **new**	CPMA
- 'Margaret'	WWes
- 'Margaret Bee'	WWes
- 'Marjan'	NLar
- 'Masamurasaki'	WPat
- 'Masukagami' (v)	CEnd CPMA MPkF NLar
- 'Matsuga-e' (v)	CMen ECho MPkF
- 'Matsukaze'	CMCN CMen CPMA ECho SIFN WWes
- 'Meihô-nishiki'	CBdw CPMA
- 'Melanie'	CPMA SIFN
- 'Meoto'	WWes
- 'Midori-no-teiboku' **new**	CBdw
- 'Mikasayama'	see *A. japonicum* 'Mikasa-yama'
- 'Mikawa-yatsubusa'	CBdw CMCN CMen CPMA ECho LRHS MGos MPkF NBhm NLar SVil WPat WWes
- 'Milton Park'	CBdw
- 'Mimaye'	CPMA
- 'Mini Mondo'	WPat WWes
- 'Mirte'	CPMA MPkF SIFN WFar WPat WWes
- 'Mischa' **new**	CBdw
- 'Misty Moon'	CBdw WWes
- 'Mitsuba-yama' **new**	CBdw
- 'Mizuho-beni'	CMen CPMA ECho WPat
- 'Mizu-kuguri'	CMCN MPkF NLar WPat
- 'Momenshide'	CBdw
- 'Momoiro-koya-san'	CBdw CPMA MPkF NLar WWes
- 'Mon Papa'	CPMA WWes
- 'Monzukushi'	CMCN CPMA MPkF
- 'Moonfire'	CMCN CPMA EPfP LRHS MAsh NLar SIFN WPat WWes
- 'Mr Sun' **new**	CPMA
* - 'Muncaster'	LMil SIFN
- 'Murasaki-hime'	MPkF
- 'Murasaki-kiyohime'	CBdw CEnd CMCN CMen CPMA ECho MPkF NLar WPat
- 'Murasaki-shikibu'	CBdw
- 'Mure-hibari'	CMCN CPMA MPkF SIFN

- 'Murogawa'	CMen CPMA ECho
- 'Nanase-gawa'	MPkF
- 'Nathan'	WWes
- 'Nicholsonii'	CMCN CMen ECho EPfP LMil LPan
	MPkF NLar SIFN WFar WPat WWes
- 'Nigrum' ♀H4	CMCN ECho LPan WPat
- 'Nishiki-gasane' (v)	MPkF
§ - 'Nishiki-gawa'	CBdw CEnd CMCN CMen CPMA
	ECho MPkF WPGP WWes
- 'Nishiki-momiji'	CMen
- 'Nomura'	CMen CPMA
- 'Nomurishidare'	see *A. palmatum* var. *dissectum*
misapplied	'Shôjô-shidare'
- 'Nomurishidare' Wada	MAsh SSpi
- 'Nuresagi'	CBdw CEnd CPMA
- 'Ōgi-nagashi' (v)	CBdw
- 'Ōgon-sarasa'	CPMA
- 'Ojishi'	CMen
- 'Ō-kagami'	CBcs CDoC CEnd CMen CPMA
	ECho LMil LRHS MPkF NLar SCoo
	SHBN SIFN WPGP WPat
- 'Okina'	CBdw WWes
- 'Okukuji-nishiki'	CBdw CPMA
- 'Okushimo'	CBdw CEnd CMCN CMen CPMA
	ECho LRHS MBri MPkF NHol NLar
	WPGP WPat
- 'Olga'	WWes
- 'Omato'	CMen CPMA MPkF SIFN WFar
- 'Omurayama'	CBcs CDoC CEnd CMCN CMen
	CPMA ECho EPfP EZes LRHS
	MGos MPkF NBhm NLar SBod
	SCoo SMur SPer SSta SVil WFar
	WPat WWes
- 'Orange Dream'	CBcs CBdw CDul CEnd CMCN
	CMen CPMA CWib ECho LBuc
	LMil LPan LRHS LSRN MAsh MBar
	MBlu MBri MGos MPkF NLar SBrw
	SCoo SIFN SPer SPoG WOrn WPGP
	WPat WWes
- 'Oregon Sunset'	CBdw CMen MPkF WPat WWes
- 'Oridono-nishiki' (v)	CBcs CEnd CMCN CMen CPMA
	ECho ELan EPfP EZes LMil LPan
	LRHS MAsh MBar MBlu MGos
	MPkF NBea NBee NEgg SCoo SIFN
	SPer SSta WFar WOrn
- 'Ōsakazuki' ♀H4	More than 30 suppliers
- 'Ōshio-beni'	CPMA ECho NLar WWes
- 'Ōshū-shidare'	CBdw CMen CPMA ECho EPfP
	WFar
- 'Oto-hime'	CMen CPMA ECho MPkF
- 'Otome-zakura'	CMCN CMen CPMA ECho MPkF
	WPat
- 'Peaches and Cream' (v)	CBcs CBdw CPMA ECho MPkF
	NLar SPer WPat WWes
- 'Peve Multicolor'	CBdw CPMA MGos MPkF NLar
- 'Phoenix'	CBdw MPkF
- 'Pine Bark Maple'	see *A. palmatum* 'Nishiki-gawa'
- 'Pixie'	CBdw CMCN CMen CPMA MPkF
	NLar WPat
- var. *pubescens* B&SWJ	WCru
6886	
- 'Pung-kil'	CBdw CMen MPkF
- 'Purple Ghost' **new**	CBdw
- 'Purpureum'	WWes
- 'Red Baron'	CPMA
- 'Red Cloud' **new**	CBdw
- 'Red Flash'	LPan WPat WWes
- 'Red Jonas'	WPat WWes
- 'Red Pygmy' ♀H4	More than 30 suppliers
- 'Red Shadow'	SIFN
- 'Red Spider'	CPMA
- 'Red Wood'	CDoC CPMA ECho MBri MPkF SVil
	WPat
- 'Reticulatum'	see *A. palmatum* 'Shigitatsu-sawa'
- 'Ribesifolium'	see *A. palmatum* 'Shishigashira'
- 'Rising Sun' **new**	CPMA

- 'Rokugatsu-en-nishiki'	CBdw WPat
new	
- 'Roseomarginatum'	see *A. palmatum* 'Kagiri-nishiki'
- 'Roseum Ornatum'	CBdw
- 'Rough Bark Maple'	see *A. palmatum* 'Arakawa'
- 'Royle'	CBdw CPMA WWes
- 'Rubrum'	CMen ECho
I - 'Rubrum Kaiser'	CPMA ECho
- 'Ruby Star' **new**	CPMA
- 'Ryuzu'	CPMA MPkF WPat
- 'Sagara-nishiki' (v)	CBdw CEnd CMen CPMA ECho
	WWes
- 'Saint Jean'	CBdw
- 'Samidare'	CPMA EPfP MPkF NLar
- 'Sandra'	CMen MPkF WWes
N - 'Sango-kaku' ♀H4	More than 30 suppliers
- 'Saoshika'	CMCN CMen CPMA ECho MPkF
- 'Sa-otome'	ECho MPkF
- 'Satsuki-beni'	CMen ECho WWes
- 'Sawa-chidori'	CBdw
- 'Sazanami'	CEnd CMen CPMA ECho MPkF
	NBea NLar WNor WPGP WPat
- 'Scolopendriifolium'	CDoC LMil MPkF WFar WPat
- 'Seigai'	CBdw CPMA MPkF
- 'Seigen'	CBdw CEnd CMCN CMen CPMA
	ECho MPkF WPGP
I - 'Seigen Aureum'	CPMA
- 'Seiun-kaku'	CBdw CMen MBri WPat
	WWes
- 'Sekimori'	CBdw CMCN CPMA SIFN
- 'Sekka-yatsubusa'	CMCN CMen ECho
- 'Senkaki'	see *A. palmatum* 'Sango-kaku'
- 'Septemlobum Elegans'	see *A. palmatum* 'Heptalobum Elegans'
- 'Septemlobum	see *A. palmatum* 'Hessei'
Purpureum'	
- 'Sessilifolium' dwarf	see *A. palmatum* 'Hagoromo'
- 'Sessilifolium' tall	see *A. palmatum* 'Koshimino'
- 'Shaina'	CBcs CDoC CDul CEnd CMen
	CPMA CWib ECho LPan LRHS
	MBri MGos MPkF NBhm NLar SVil
	WFar WPat WWes
- 'Sharp's Pygmy'	CBdw CMen CPMA ECho MPkF
	NLar WPat WWes
- 'Sherwood Flame'	CMCN CMen CPMA CWib ECho
	LRHS MBlu MGos NLar SCoo WFar
	WPat WWes
- 'Shichigosan'	CMen
- 'Shidava Gold'	CBdw CPMA SIFN WPat
- 'Shigarami'	CPMA MPkF
- 'Shigi-no-hoshi'	CBdw
§ - 'Shigitatsu-sawa' (v)	CBcs CBdw CEnd CMCN CMen
	CPMA ECho EMil LPan LRHS
	MGos MPkF NBea NLar SIFN SPoG
- 'Shigure-bato'	CMCN CPMA MPkF
- 'Shigurezome'	CMCN MPkF WWes
- 'Shikageori-nishiki'	CMen CPMA ECho LRHS MPkF
- 'Shime-no-uchi'	CMCN CPMA LMil NLar SIFN
- 'Shindeshôjô'	More than 30 suppliers
§ - 'Shinobugaoka'	CMCN CMen CPMA ECho MPkF
- 'Shinonome'	CPMA MPkF
- 'Shiro-fu-nishiki' **new**	CBdw
§ - 'Shishigashira'	CDoC CMCN CMen COtt CPMA
	ECho EPfP LMil LRHS MBar MBlu
	MBri MDun MGos MPkF NBea
	NLar SCoo SIFN SPoG WDin WFar
	WPat
- 'Shishigashira-no-	CBdw CMen
yatsubusa'	
§ - 'Shishio'	CBcs CMCN CMen ECho LAst
	LHyd LRHS MPkF SBig SSpi SVil
	WPat
§ - 'Shishio Improved'	CBdw CEnd CMCN CPMA CTho
	CWSG ECho EPfP MBlu MGos
	MPkF NBhm NLar SIFN SPur SWvt
- 'Shôjô'	CMCN CPMA WFar WWes

	- 'Shōjō-no-mai'	CBdw
	- 'Shōjō-nomura'	CAbP CEnd CMen CPMA LRHS MGos MPkF NBea NLar WPGP WPat
	- 'Sister Ghost' **new**	CBdw CPMA
	- 'Skeeter's Broom'	CBdw CDoC CMen ECho EZes LPan LRHS MBri MPkF SBod SCoo SIFN SVil WPat
*	- 'Sode-nishiki'	CBdw CPMA MPkF NLar
	- 'Spreading Star'	WWes
	- 'Spring Delight' **new**	CBdw
	- 'Stella Rossa'	CBdw CEnd CMCN CPMA LPan LRHS MBlu MPkF NBea NLar WPat WWes
	- 'Suminagashi'	CDoC CMCN CMen ECho LRHS MBri MDun MGos MPkF NLar SBod SIFN SMur SVil WPat
I	- 'Summer Gold' **new**	LPan
	- 'Suruga-nishiki' (v) **new**	CBdw
	- 'Susan'	MPkF WWes
	- 'Taiyō-nishiki'	CBdw CPMA
	- 'Takao'	CMen WWes
	- 'Takinogawa'	LRHS
	- 'Tamahime'	CMCN CMen CPMA ECho SIFN
	- 'Tana'	CBdw CMCN CPMA EPfP MPkF SIFN WFar WPat WWes
	- 'Tarō-yama'	CBdw CPMA WPat
	- 'Tatsuta'	CMen ECho MPkF
	- 'Taylor' **new**	NLar
	- 'Tennyo-no-hoshi'	CMen ECho MPkF NLar
	- 'Tiger Rose' **new**	CBdw CPMA
	- 'Tiny Tim'	CBdw CPMA
	- 'Tōhoku Shichi-henge' **new**	CBdw
	- 'Trompenburg' ♀H4	More than 30 suppliers
	- 'Tsuchigumo'	CMCN CMen CPMA ECho MPkF
	- 'Tsukubane'	WPat
	- 'Tsukushigata'	CMCN
	- 'Tsuma-beni'	CBdw CMCN CMen CPMA EPfP LRHS MPkF
	- 'Tsuma-gaki'	CBdw CMCN CMen CPMA ECho EPfP MBri MGos MPkF NLar WPat WWes
	- 'Tsuri-nishiki'	CBdw CMen CPMA ECho NLar WWes
	- 'Ueno-homare'	CBdw MPkF SPoG WPat
	- 'Ueno-yama'	CBdw CPMA MGos
	- 'Ukigumo' (v)	CBcs CBdw CEnd CLnd CMCN CMen CPMA CSBt CWSG CWib ECho ELan EMil LMil LRHS MBlu MBri MGos MPkF NHol SBod SBrw SCoo SIFN SMur SPer SPoG SSta WDin WPat
	- 'Ukon'	CBdw CMCN CMen CPMA ECho EMil MBri MPkF SVil
	- 'Umegae'	CPMA
	- 'Usu-midori'	CPMA
	- 'Utsu-semi'	CPMA MPkF SIFN
	- 'Van der Akker' **new**	CPMA
	- 'Vanderhoss Red'	ECho WWes
	- 'Vens Red'	WPat
	- 'Versicolor' (v)	CBdw CEnd CMCN CMen CPMA
	- 'Vic Broom'	CBdw
	- 'Vic Pink'	CBdw CPMA WPat
	- 'Villa Taranto'	CBdw CDoC CEnd CMCN CMen CPMA ECho EPfP LMil LRHS MAsh MBlu MBri MPkF NBea NHol NLar SBrw SCoo SIFN SSpi SSta SVil WPGP WPat WWes
	- 'Volubile'	CMCN CMen ECho EPfP SMur
	- 'Wabito'	CMCN CMen CPMA ECho MPkF
	- 'Waka-midori'	CMen ECho
	- 'Waka-momiji' (v)	CBdw CPMA
	- 'Wakehurst Pink' (v)	CMCN CMen MPkF NLar WPat WWes

	- 'Wendy'	CMen CPMA MPkF NLar WPat WWes
	- 'Wetumpka Red' **new**	CPMA
	- 'Whitney Red' **new**	CMen
	- 'Wilson's Pink Dwarf'	CBdw CEnd CMen CPMA CWib ECho EPfP MBri MGos MPkF NLar WGer WPat
	- 'Winter Flame'	CBdw CPMA NLar WPat
	- 'Wolff's Broom'	CBdw WPat
	- 'Wou-nishiki'	CBdw CMCN CMen CWib ECho
	- 'Yana-gawa'	CMen ECho
	- 'Yasemin'	CBdw CMen CPMA MPkF NLar SIFN
	- 'Yatsubusa'	WWes
	- 'Yezo-nishiki'	CBdw CMCN CMen LRHS MPkF WFar
	- 'Yūba e'	WFar WPat
	- 'Yūgure'	MPkF NLar WFar
	papilio	see *A. caudatum*
	paxii	CMCN WWes
	pectinatum subsp. *forrestii*	see *A. forrestii*
	pensylvanicum ♀H4	More than 30 suppliers
	- 'Erythrocladum'	CEnd CMCN CPMA EPfP LRHS MAsh MBri MGos NBea NHol NLar SLim SPur SSpi SSta
	pentaphyllum	CMCN LRHS SBir SIFN SSpi
§	*pictum*	CMCN CTho IArd WNor WWes
	- subsp. *okamotoanum*	CMCN
	- - B&SWJ 8516	WCru
	- 'Shufu-nishiki'	CMCN
	- 'Usugomo' **new**	WPat
	platanoides ♀H4	CBcs CCVT CDoC CDul CLnd CMCN CTri CWib ECrN EPfP LBuc MGos MSwo NBee NWea SBLw SPer WDin WFar WHar WMou WNor WWes
	- 'Charles Joly'	WWes
	- 'Cleveland'	CBcs
	- 'Columnare'	CDul CLnd CMCN CWib ECrN SBLw WOrn
	- 'Crimson King' ♀H4	More than 30 suppliers
	- 'Crimson Sentry'	CDoC CDul CEnd CLnd CMCN COtt CWib EBee ECrN ENot EPfP IArd LAst LBuc LPan MAsh MBlu MBri MGos MLan MRav NBee SLim SPoG WDin WFar WHar
	- 'Cucullatum'	CMCN CTho
	- 'Deborah'	CBcs CLnd CTho LPan SBLw WOrn WWes
	- 'Dissectum'	CTho
	- 'Drummondii' (v)	More than 30 suppliers
	- 'Emerald Queen'	CLnd CWib ECrN SBLw SHBN WDin
	- 'Faassen's Black'	CPMA SBLw
§	- 'Globosum'	CLnd CMCN ECrN LBuc LPan SBLw SWvt
	- 'Goldsworth Purple'	CDul CLnd
	- 'Laciniatum'	CEnd CMCN ECrN
	- 'Lorbergii'	see *A. platanoides* 'Palmatifidum'
	- 'Marit' **new**	WPat
	- 'Meyering'	WWes
§	- 'Palmatifidum'	CLnd
	- Princeton Gold = 'Prigo'PBR	CDoC ECrN ELan ENot LPan LRHS MGos SCoo SPoG
	- 'Reitenbachii'	CDul WWes
	- 'Royal Red'	CBcs CDul CWib ECrN ENot LPan MRav NLar WWes
	- 'Schwedleri' ♀H4	CDul CMCN ECrN EPfP MGos NWea SBLw SPer WDin
	- 'Tharandt'	CMCN
	- 'Walderseei'	CLnd
	pseudoplatanus	CBcs CCVT CDul CLnd CMCN CSBt CTri ECrN LBuc LPan MBar MGos NBee NWea SBLw SPer WDin WFar WHar WMou

§ - 'Atropurpureum' — CDoC CLnd CTho NBee NWea SBLw WDin WGer
- 'Brilliantissimum' ♀H4 — More than 30 suppliers
- 'Corstorphinense' — CMCN
- 'Erectum' — WFar
- 'Prinz Handjéry' — CBcs CDul CEnd CLnd CMCN CTri CWib LPan LRHS MAsh MBar MGos NHol NWea SBLw SIFN SPer SPoG SSpi
- f. *purpureum* — LAst SEND
- 'Spaethii' misapplied — see *A. pseudoplatanus* 'Atropurpureum'
- 'Sunshine' **new** — ENot
§ - f. *variegatum* (v) — NEgg
- - 'Esk Sunset' (v) — CBcs ECho LRHS MBri MGos MPkF MLar
- - 'Leopoldii' misapplied — see *A. pseudoplatanus* f. *variegatum*
- - 'Leopoldii' ambig. (v) — CBcs CDul CLnd CMCN CTho ECrN EGra ELan LAst LPan MAsh NBee SBLw SEND SHBN SLim SPer SWvt WDin WFar WOrn WWes
- - 'Leopoldii' Vervaene (v) — SCrf
- - 'Nizetii' (v) — CMCN LRHS SBLw
- - 'Simon-Louis Frères' (v) — CCVT CDul CEnd CLnd CMCN CWSG CWib EBee ECrN EGra EMui LPan LRHS MAsh MBar MBri MDun MGos NBea SCrf SIFN SPer SWvt WFar WFoF WHar WOrn
- 'Worley' — CBcs CDul CLnd CMCN CSBt CTho CTri EBee ECrN LRHS MBar MRav NBee NWea SBLw SCrf SEND SHBN SLim SPer WDin WHar WOrn
pseudosieboldianum — CMCN IDee MBlu WNor
- B&SWJ 8746 — WCru
- var. *microsieboldianum* B&SWJ 8766 — WCru
pubipalmatum — WNor
pycnanthum — CMCN
robustum — CMCN WNor WWes
rubescens — CPMA WPGP
- B&SWJ 6735 — WCru
- variegated seedlings (v) — CPMA
rubrum — More than 30 suppliers
- 'Bowhall' — CMCN SBir
- 'Brandywine' **new** — MBri
- 'Candy Ice' (v) — CPMA
- 'Columnare' — CMCN EPfP
- 'Fairview Flame' — SPer
- 'October Glory' ♀H4 — CBcs CDoC CDul CEnd CLnd CMCN CPMA CSam CTho CTri EBee ELan EPfP LPan LRHS LSRN MBlu MBri MDun NWea SBir SCoo SIFN SMad SPer SPoG SSpi SSta WFar WPGP
- Red Sunset = 'Franksred' — CDoC CDul CEnd CMCN CPMA CTho EPfP LPan LRHS MBlu SBir SCoo SIFN SMad SSta WPGP
- 'Scanlon' — CBcs CDoC CDul CEnd CMCN CPMA CTho EBee ECho EPfP LAst LPan MBlu SBLw WOrn
- 'Schlesingeri' — CEnd CLnd CMCN CMac CPMA EPfP NLar
- 'Somerset' **new** — CPMA MBri
- 'Sun Valley' **new** — CPMA
- 'Tilford' — SBir SIFN SSta WWes
§ *rufinerve* ♀H4 — CBcs CCVT CDoC CDul CLnd CMCN CTho CTri ECrN EPfP EPla EWTr LRHS MAsh MBri MWat NBea NWea SBLw SPer WBVN WDin WGer WNor WOrn WPGP WWes
- 'Albolimbatum' — see *A. rufinerve* 'Hatsuyuki'
- 'Albomarginatum' — see *A. rufinerve* 'Hatsuyuki'
- 'Erythrocladum' — CPMA

§ - 'Hatsuyuki' (v) — CDoC CDul CEnd CMCN CPMA SIFN WPGP WPat
- 'Winter Gold' — CPMA CTho LRHS SIFN SPur SSpi
§ *saccharinum* — CBcs CCVT CDoC CDul CLnd CMCN CTri CWib EBee ECrN ELan EPfP MGos MLan NWea SBLw SHBN SPer WDin WFar WNor
- 'Born's Gracious' — CPMA
- 'Fastigiatum' — see *A. saccharinum* f. *pyramidale*
- f. *laciniatum* — CMCN EBee LAst LRHS MBlu MGos MMuc SPer WDin
- 'Laciniatum Wieri' — CDul CLnd CMCN CTho ECrN LAst LPan SBLw WDin
- f. *lutescens* — CDul CMCN CTho MBlu SBLw
§ - f. *pyramidale* — CDoC CLnd CMCN EBee ECrN SBLw SPer WDin
saccharum — CAgr CBcs CDoC CDul CLnd CMCN CTho ECrN EPfP IDee MBlu MLan NWea SBLw SPer WNor
- 'Adirondak' **new** — CPMA
- 'Arrowhead' **new** — CPMA
- subsp. *barbatum* — see *A. saccharum* subsp. *floridanum*
- 'Brocade' — CPMA MPkF SBir WWes
- 'Caddo' **new** — CPMA
- 'Fiddlers Creek' **new** — CPMA
§ - subsp. *floridanum* — CMCN
§ - subsp. *grandidentatum* — CMCN
- 'Green Mountain' **new** — CPMA LPan
- 'Legacy' **new** — LPan
§ - subsp. *leucoderme* — CMCN
- 'Louisa Lad' — WWes
- 'Majesty' **new** — CPMA
- subsp. *nigrum* — CMCN
- - 'Greencolumn' **new** — CPMA
- - 'Monumentale' — CMCN
- subsp. *skutchii* — CMCN
- 'Sugar Cone' **new** — CPMA
seiboldianum 'Osiris' — WWes
§ *sempervirens* — CMCN LEdu WPGP
'Sensu' **new** — CPMA
serrulatum B&SWJ 6760 — WCru
§ *shirasawanum* — CMCN WNor
- 'Aureum' ♀H4 — More than 30 suppliers
- 'Autumn Moon' — CBdw CPMA MBri MGos NLar WWes
§ - 'Ezo-no-momiji' — CMCN CMen CPMA NLar
- 'Gloria' — WWes
- 'Helena' — NLar
- 'Johin' **new** — CPMA
- 'Jordan' **new** — LPan
§ - 'Jūnihitoe' — WNor
- 'Lovett' **new** — CPMA
§ - 'Microphyllum' — CMCN ECho WNor
§ - 'Ogurayama' — CBdw CMen CPMA ECho
- 'Palmatifolium' — CBdw CMCN CPMA SIFN
- 'Susanne' **new** — CPMA
- var. *tenuifolium* — WNor WWes
sieboldianum — CMCN CMen CTho CTri ECho ECrN EPfP GTSp MDun SSpi WHCr WNor WPat
- 'Miyama-nishiki' **new** — CBdw
- 'Sode-no-uchi' — CMCN CMen SIFN
sikkimense subsp. *metcalfii* — see *A. metcalfii*
§ 'Silver Cardinal' (v) — CDoC CEnd CMCN CPMA EPfP MBlu MBri MGos NBhm NLar SMad SPoG
'Silver Vein' — see *A.* x *conspicuum* 'Silver Vein'
§ *sinense* — CMCN IArd WCwm WNor
spicatum — CMCN EPfP NLar WNor
§ *stachyophyllum* — GIBF GQui GTSp WWes
§ *sterculiaceum* — CMCN EBee WPGP
takesimense — MBri WCru
- B&SWJ 8500 — WCru

taronense	CMCN
tataricum	CMCN
§ - subsp. *ginnala*	CAgr CBcs CDul CLnd CMCN CTho CTri CWSG ECrN EPfP LRav MGos NBea NPal NWea SBLw SHBN SLim WCwm WDin WNor WPat
- - 'Flame'	CPMA CWSG EBee ECrN ELan EPfP MGos NLar SHBN SPoG
tegmentosum	CMCN CPMA EPfP LPan MBlu NLar WNor
- B&SWJ 8421	WCru
- subsp. *glaucorufinerve*	see *A. rufinerve*
tenuifolium	CMCN
tetramerum	see *A. stachyophyllum*
trautvetteri	CMCN EPfP WNor
triflorum ♀H4	CBcs CMCN CPMA CTho EPfP IArd IMGH LPan LRHS MBri NBea NLar SSpi WDin WFar WWes
truncatum	CMCN MPkF WNor
- 'Akikaze-nishiki' (v)	CPMA MPkF
tschonoskii	GQui WNor
- subsp. *koreanum*	CTho MPkF NLar WNor
§ *turkestanicum*	CMCN EBee WFar
velutinum	CMCN
- var. *vanvolxemii*	WPGP
villosum	see *A. sterculiaceum*
'White Tigress'	CTho MBlu WPGP WWes
§ *wilsonii*	CDul CMCN CSam GIBF WNor
x *zoeschense*	CMCN
- 'Annae'	CPMA MAsh SBLw

Aceriphyllum see *Mukdenia*

x *Achicodonia* (Gesneriaceae)

'Dark Velvet'	WDib

Achillea ❀ (Asteraceae)

ageratifolia ♀H4	EBla ECho ECtt LBee MTho NBre NJOw SRms WFar
- subsp. *serbica*	NBre SpoG
§ *ageratum*	CArn CHby CSev CWan ELau GBar GPoy MHer MNHC MSal NPri NTHB SIde SRms WGHP WGwG WHer WJek WPer WWye
- 'W.B. Childs'	CSli ECha EGle ELan GBuc MArl MAvo MNrw NDov SHar WCMO WCot WEas
'Alabaster'	CDes CSli EBee GBuc LPhx NBHF NBre NDov
Anthea = 'Anblo'PBR	CKno CSam CWCL EBee EBrs EGle EMan EMar EWsh GMaP GSki LRHS MLIN NChi NCob NLar SPer SRGP SRkn SRms WAul WFar XPep
§ 'Apfelblüte'	CPrp CSBt CSli CWCL EBee EChP ECtt EGle ELan GSki LRHS LSRN MRav MTis MWgw NCGa NDov NGdn NHol SPer WCAu WCot WFar WMnd WPer WTel WViv
Appleblossom	see *A.* 'Apfelblüte'
'Apricot Beauty'	CPrp CSli EBee EChP ECtt EMar GBBs GMaP GQue LBBr LSRN MBNS MBri NHol NPro SHop SPoG SSvw
argentea misapplied	see *A. clavennae*, *A. umbellata*
argentea Lamarck	see *Tanacetum argenteum*
aurea	see *A. chrysocoma*
'Bahama'	EBee EPPr GBBs GBin LRHS MAvo NBre NBro WSan WWeb
'Belle Epoque' ♀H4	CDes CSli EBee NBHF
'Bloodstone'	CSli EBee ECtt EShb EWes EWsh GBar GMac MRav NBHF WOut
brachyphylla	EPot
'Breckland Bouquet' **new**	EWes
'Breckland Ruby'	EPPr EWes
'Brilliant'	LRHS WWeb

'Caroline'	LRHS WWeb
cartilaginea	CSli EPPr NBHF NBre SPav WFar WMoo
- 'Silver Spray'	EBee GQue NBre NLar SDnm SPav WPtf
'Christine's Pink' ♀H4	CAby CKno CSli EBee EPPr EShb MAvo NBHF SUsu
§ *chrysocoma*	ECho ETow WMoo WTel XPep
- 'Grandiflora'	CHad CHar ECha ELan EMar NGdn
§ *clavennae*	CBrm ECho ECtt MLLN NRya SAga SBla SRms WAbe WCot WFar
clypeolata Sibth. & Sm.	CAby CSam EBee EPPr EShb LHop NBre NLar SMad SMar SPlb SRms WOut WPer
coarctata	NBir WPer XPep
'Coronation Gold' ♀H4	CDoC CPrp CSam CWCL EBee EBla EBrs ECtt ELan ENot EPfP ERou GMac GSki LRHS MBri MNFA MRav MWat SAga WCAu WCot WEas WFar WGHP WMnd XPep
'Credo' ♀H4	More than 30 suppliers
crithmifolia	XPep
decolorans	see *A. ageratum*
erba-rotta **new**	WPer
- subsp. *moschata*	ECho NBre NBro
§ 'Fanal'	More than 30 suppliers
'Faust'	CDes CElw CHar CKno CMil CSli CWoW EBee EBla MSph NBHF SMrm STes SUsu WPGP WPrP
'Feuerland'	More than 30 suppliers
filipendulina	NLRH NSti SWal WHrl
- 'Cloth of Gold' ♀H4	More than 30 suppliers
- 'Gold Plate' ♀H4	More than 30 suppliers
- 'Parker's Variety' ♀H4	EBee GQue LRHS MLan NBre WFar
Flowers of Sulphur	see *A.* 'Schwefelblüte'
'Forncett Beauty'	CSli NBHF WHil
'Forncett Bride'	CSli NBHF NBre NDov
'Forncett Candy'	CSli NBHF NDov
'Forncett Citrus'	CAby CSli EBee NBHF NBre WPGP
'Forncett Fletton'	CFir CSli CWCL EBee EGle EMan EMar EPPr EPfP EShb GBri IPot LHop MAvo MBnl MNFA MNrw NBHF NCob NGdn NHol SAga STes WCAu WTMC WViv WWlt
'Forncett Ivory'	CSli MSte NBHF NBre
fraasii	MDKP
glaberrima hybrid	EMan WCMO WCot
'Gloria Jean'	EBee SHar
'Gold and Grey'	CSli
'Golden Fleece' **new**	NScw
'Goldstar'	EBee NDov WFar
grandifolia misapplied	see *Tanacetum macrophyllum* (Waldst. & Kit.) Sch.Bip.
§ *grandifolia* Friv.	CElw COIW CSam EBee EChP EGle GBuc LEdu NBro SMad SPer SSvw WAul WBor WFar WHer WHil WMnd WMoo WOld WWye
'Great Expectations'	see *A.* 'Hoffnung'
'Grey and Gold'	SMrm
'Hannelore Pahl'	EBee NBre
'Hartington White'	GBuc MWgw SEND
'Heidi' ♀H4	CCVN CSli CWoW GBri
'Hella Glashoff' ♀H4	CDes CMea CSli EBee EBrs ECho EGle EGoo GBin LPhx MWea NCGa NDov WCMO WCot WHoo WWeb
§ 'Hoffnung'	CPrp CSli CWCL EBee EBla ECtt EGle EMan ERou GSki LRHS MBri MRav NPro SPer WCAu WMnd WPer
holosericea	EBee
'Huteri'	CLyd CPBP EBee EBla ECho ECtt EDAr EGoo EPfP EPot LBee MAvo MHer MRav NFor NJOw SBla SPoG WEas WFar WHil

Name	Suppliers
'Inca Gold'	CSli EAEE EBee EBla ECha ECtt EGle EHrv EMan EMar EPPr EShb GBuc GQue LRHS MRav NBro NCGa NCob NGdn NHol NPro SAga SBla SPav WTMC
'Jacqueline'	EBee EWll
'Joey'	MAvo NRnb WHil
'Judity'	LRHS WWeb
x *kellereri*	NLar XPep
'King Alfred' **new**	GKev LAst
x *kolbiana*	EMan LSou NHol NJOw NMen SRms WLin
§ - 'Weston'	ETow NBre
§ 'Lachsschönheit' ♀H4	More than 30 suppliers
x *lewisii*	NMen
- 'King Edward' ♀H4	CSam ECha ECho EPfP GBin GMaP LRHS NBir NJOw SAga SBch SBla SIng SPoG WFar
ligustica	WCot
'Lucky Break' ♀H4	EBla ECha SDix SMHy SUsu
macrophylla	EBee NBre
'Marie Ann'	CWCL EBee ECtt ERou GBri LPhx MAvo MBnl MLLN NBPC NBhm NLar NPro NSti SSvw WHil
'Marmalade'	CMdw CSli EBee LSou NDov WCMO WMnd WPGP
'Martina' ♀H4	More than 30 suppliers
'McVities'	CBos CDes CSli CWCL EBee EChP ECtt EPPr GMaP LEdu MBnl MFOX MLLN NCGa NPro SDnm SPav STes WCAu WCMO WCra WHal WHil WMnd WTin WWhi WWlt
millefolium	CArn COld CWan ELau EUnu GBar GPoy GWCH MBow MHer MNHC NLan NMir NSco SPlb WHbs WHer WJek WSFF WSel WWye XPep
- 'Bright Cerise'	WFar
- 'Carla Hussey'	WFar
- 'Cassis'	EAro EMag LDai MSph MTis NBre NEgg SDnm SPav SPur SWal WFar
§ - 'Cerise Queen'	More than 30 suppliers
- 'Christel'	CCVN CDes CSli EBee EWes GBin MSph SUsu
- 'Christine'	GBin NBre
- 'Colorado'	CSam CWCL EAro GAbr NBre NChi NHol NRnb SPav WFar WHrl
- 'Cottage White' **new**	NBre
- dark red	CSli
- 'Debutante'	WHil
- 'Fire King'	CElw CHal
- 'Harlekin'	EBee
- 'Kelwayi' ♀H4	CSli
- Kirschkönigin	see *A. millefolium* 'Cerise Queen'
- 'Lansdorferglut' ♀H4	CAby CKno CSli EBrs EPPr LRHS MBri MRav NDov NPro SUsu
- 'Lavender Beauty'	see *A. millefolium* 'Lilac Beauty'
- 'Lemon Curd'	LDai
§ - 'Lilac Beauty'	CElw CHar CMHG COIW CSli CWCL EBrs EChP ECha EHrv EPPr ERou EWTr GMaP GSki IPot LRHS MAvo MRav NBir NGHP NHol NPri NSti SPav WFar WHoo WPer WSan XPep
* - 'Lilac Queen'	CSli MArl SWat
- 'Lollypop'	LDai
- 'Oertels Rose'	WFar
- 'Paprika'	More than 30 suppliers
* - 'Pastel Shades'	IFoB WMoo
- 'Raspberry Ripple'	GBin
- 'Red Beauty'	CMHG CSli CWCL ERou LRHS LSou NBro SBch SRms SWat XPep
- 'Red Velvet'	More than 30 suppliers
- 'Rosie'	GBar
- 'Rougham Beauty'	CSli
- 'Rougham Cream'	CSli
- 'Rougham White'	CSli
- 'Ruby Port'	WFar
- 'Salmon Pink'	WFar
- 'Salmon Queen'	NHol WCra
- 'Sammetriese'	CAby CSli EBrs EGle GBuc LPhx LRHS MNrw MSte NBre NCGa SMad WCAu WCot WFar WGHP WHoo WTin
- 'Schneetaler'	GBin
- 'Serenade'	EBee EBla WFar
- 'Summer Berries' **new**	NBHF
- 'Summertime'	LAst SBod SPav
- 'Tickled Pink'	WPer
- 'White Queen'	EBee EGle EMar LBMP WPer
- 'Yellowstone'	EWes LAst LDai
'Mondpagode' ♀H4	CHar CPrp CSli EAEE EBee EChP EGle EMan EMar EPPr LPhx LRHS MAvo MBNS NCGa NGdn NPro SMHy SUsu WPtf
* 'Moonbeam'	EBla
'Moonshine' ♀H3	More than 30 suppliers
'Moonwalker'	CAbP EAro EBee LRHS MLLN MNHC MWrn NBre NLRH SIde SPav WFar WPer
nobilis	XPep
- subsp. *neilreichii*	CSli CSpe EBee EBla EChP EGoo EHrv EPPr GBri LRHS MAvo MLLN MNFA NSti SPer WCMO WCot WHal WPrP WTin
'Nostalgia'	EBee
odorata	XPep
'Old Brocade'	CHea CSli EBee EShb LPhx NBre NDov WPGP WPtf
'Peardrop'	NBre
'Peter Davis'	see *Hippolytia herderi*
pindicola subsp. *integrifolia*	EWes
Pink Island form	see *A.* pink-flowered, from Santa Cruz Island
pink-flowered, from Santa Cruz Island	CKno
'Pink Lady'	EBee EBla GBBs SPoG
'Pink Temptation'	MAvo WHil
'Prospero'	CMea WCot WCra
ptarmica	CArn CBre ELau EMFW GBar MHer MSal NMir NPri SECG SIde SPer WWye
* - 'Ballerina'	MWrn NBre NDov NLar
- Innocence	see *A. ptarmica* 'Unschuld'
- 'Major'	GMaP NBre
- 'Nana Compacta'	CSli CSpe EBee EBla EChP ECha EGle EMan ENor EPPr IGor LHop LRHS MLLN NBir SPlb SPoG SUsu WCFE WCMO WCot WHil
- 'Perry's White'	CBcs CBre EBee ECha EGle LBmB LRHS MNFA MNrw NGHP NGdn NHol SRGP WCMO WCot WWhi
- 'Stephanie Cohen'	see *A. sibirica* 'Stephanie Cohen'
N - The Pearl Group seed-raised (d)	ECha EGra ELan GMaP LHop NJOw NVic SPlb SPoG SWat WFar WMoo WPer WTin
N - - 'Boule de Neige' (clonal) (d)	CHal EBee EPfP GSki MBri NBre NCob NPer NSti SPer SPet SPla WFar
N - - 'The Pearl' (clonal) (d) ♀H4	CDes CSBt EBee EBrs EPfP ERou IFoB IHMH MLHP MRav MSte MWat MWgw NBPC NBid NBir NBro NEgg NGHP SRms SWal WBor WBrk WCAu WCot WEas WFar WHer WHil WSFF
§ - 'Unschuld'	NBir
'Rose Madder'	More than 30 suppliers
'Rougham Bright Star'	CSli
'Rougham Salmon'	CSli
'Sally'	EGoo NBre
'Sandstone'	see *A.* 'Wesersandstein'
§ 'Schwefelblüte'	MRav NBir SBch SBla

'Schwellenburg' — CDes CHar CSli NBre WPGP
sibirica — CBgR SRGP
- var. *camschatica* — CSec CSli EAEE EBee ECtt EMan EPfP EWTr GBar GMac GSki LRHS MEHN MGol MNFA MRav MTis NBPC NEgg NJOw NSti SPer SRGP SSvw WFar WMoo WViv
'Love Parade'

§ - 'Stephanie Cohen' — CPrp EBee ECtt EGle EMan ERou MLLN MSph NBhm SPoG WCMO WCot WFar WTMC
'Stephanie' — EBee EPPr EWes NBre
'Summer Glory' — NCob
Summer Pastels Group — CBrm CHrt EGra EMil EShb LRHS NBir NBlu NHol NOrc NRnb SECG SPav SPet SPoG SRms SWal SWat WFar WHil WMnd WRha WWeb
'Summerwine' ♀H4 — More than 30 suppliers
'Sunbeam' — LRHS WWeb
I 'Taygetea' — CSam CSli EBee EBla EChP ELan EMan EPPr EPfP EShb EWTr GMaP MNFA MSte MTis MWgw SDix SPer WCAu WCMO WCot WFar WKif WPer WSHC
'Terracotta' — More than 30 suppliers
'The Beacon' — see *A.* 'Fanal'
tomentosa ♀H4 — CTri ECha ECho ECtt EPfP
§ - 'Aurea' — EBla ECho ELau IHMH NBre NBro NJOw SRms WPer
- 'Maynard's Gold' — see *A. tomentosa* 'Aurea'
§ *umbellata* — EBee GBri GMac WCot XPep
- 'Weston' — see *A.* x *kolbiana* 'Weston'
'Walther Funcke' — More than 30 suppliers
§ 'Wesersandstein' — More than 30 suppliers
'Wilczekii' — NBre NChi SRms
'Will Scarlet' **new** — EMon
'Yellowstone' — EBee SMer WWeb

x *Achimenantha* (Gesneriaceae)
'Inferno' ♀H1 — WDib

Achimenes (Gesneriaceae)
'Ambroise Verschaffelt' ♀H1 — WDib
'Crummock Water' — WDib
erecta — WDib
'Hilda Michelssen' ♀H1 — WDib
'Little Beauty' — SWal WDib
'Orange Delight' — WDib
'Purple King' — SWal
'Stan's Delight' (d) ♀H1 — WDib
'Tarantella' — WDib

Achlys (Berberidaceae)
californica — IBlr
japonica — WCru
triphylla — GGar IBlr WCru

Achnatherum see *Stipa*

Achyranthes (Amaranthaceae)
bidentata — CArn MSal

Acidanthera see *Gladiolus*

Acinos (Lamiaceae)
§ *alpinus* — CArn CBrm CPBP EAro EDAr EMan LTwo MWgw NJOw NLar NOrc SBch SBla SHGN SPet WJek
§ *arvensis* — MHer MSal
§ *corsicus* — NLAp NWCA WHoo WPat

Aciphylla (Apiaceae)
aurea — GCal GCrs LTwo MCCP NLar NWCA SPlb

crenulata — WCot
dieffenbachii — EBee
glaucescens — ECou GCrs SMad
hectorii — EMan WCot
horrida — GCal
kirkii — EMan WCot
monroi — ITim
montana — WLin
pinnatifida — GCrs GGar
squarrosa — CTrC GCal SBig
subflabellata — EBee GCal

Acmella (Asteraceae)
§ *oleracea* — CArn EOHP MSal
- 'Brede Mafane' — EUnu
- 'Peek-a-boo' — SCoo

Acmena (Myrtaceae)
smithii — EShb SDEP

Acnistus (Solanaceae)
australis — see *Iochroma australe*

Acoelorraphe (Acanthaceae)
wrightii **new** — EAmu

Acoelorrhaphe (Arecaceae)
sp. — LPal WMul

Aconitum (Ranunculaceae)
ACE 1449 — GBuc
B&SWJ 2954 from Nepal — WCru
CC 4458 — CPLG
CNDS 036 from Burma — WCru
GWJ 9393 from Northern India — WCru
- GWJ 9417 — WCru
alboviolaceum — GCal
- var. *albiflorum* B&SWJ 4105 — WCru
anglicum — see *A. napellus* subsp. *napellus* Anglicum Group
anthora — GCal NBHF
arcuatum B&SWJ 774 — WCru
austroyunnanense BWJ 7902 — WCru
autumnale misapplied — see *A. carmichaelii* Wilsonii Group
autumnale Rchb. — see *A. fischeri* Rchb.
autumnale ambig. — NBir
bartlettii — NBre
- B&SWJ 337 — EBee GBin WCru
* 'Blue Opal' — EBee EWes
'Blue Sceptre' — EBee EMan GBin LDai MBNS MBri NBPC NLar NMoo WAul WSel
'Bressingham Spire' ♀H4 — More than 30 suppliers
x *cammarum* 'Bicolor' ♀H4 — More than 30 suppliers
- 'Grandiflorum Album' — CAby ERou LPhx MSte
§ *carmichaelii* — CArn CMea EBee EMan GSki IFro LLWP LRHS MBri MRav MWgw NBro NFor NOrc SPet SRms WCot WFar WHoo WMoo WPnP WSel WTin
- 'Arendsii' ♀H4 — More than 30 suppliers
- 'Blue Bishop' **new** — LSou
- 'Pink Sensation' — EBee EGle EMan ERou LTwo MBNS NBPC NBre NGHP NSti SHop SMrm SUsu WCAu WHil
- 'Royal Flush' — CFir CMil EBee GCai LAst MBNS MBri MLLN EBee GCal NEgg NGdn NLar SPoG SUsu WCMO WCot WKif WWeb WWhi
- var. *truppelianum* HWJ 732 — WCru

§ - Wilsonii Group — CAby EBee EMar GGar LPhx LRHS MLLN MRav MSte MWat NDov SBch SBla WFar WPGP WPer WSel WWye

§ - - 'Barker's Variety' — CFir CKno CPou EBee EChP EGle EMan EPfP GBuc GMac NCGa NHol NLar NSti WCMO WCot WViv

- - 'Kelmscott' ♀H4 — EBee EGle EMon EWes GMac MRav MSte SAga SDix SMHy WFar WRHF

- - 'Spätlese' — CAbP EBee EChP EGle EMan EMar EMon GAbr GCal GSki LHop MEHN MLLN MNFA MSte NBHF NBPC NBir NDov NEgg NGdn SAga SMHy SPer SUsu WCMO WCot WCra WWhi WWlt

- - 'The Grim Reaper' — EMon

chasmanthum **new** — WCot

cilicicum — see *Eranthis hyemalis* Cilicica Group

crassiflorum BWJ 7644 — WCru

'Eleonara' — CFir EBee EChP EGle EMan EMar EPPr EPfP ERou EWes GBuc LHop LRHS MAvo MBri MLLN NBPC NGHP NLar NMoo NSti SPer SSvw WFar WMoo

elwesii — EBee GGar NBre

episcopale — CPIN EWes WCru WFar

aff. *episcopale* — WSHC

- CLD 1426 — GBuc WFar

'Faun' — EBee

ferox — EBee EWes GBin MLLN

- HWJK 2217 — WCru

fischeri misapplied — see *A. carmichaelii*

§ *fischeri* Rchb. — CSpe GIBF NMoo

fukutomei var. *formosanum* — LEdu

- - B&SWJ 3057 — WCru

gammiei GWJ 9418 **new** — WCru

§ *hemsleyanum* — CPIN CRHN EBee EPfP GAbr ITer MDun MHar NBid NCGa NChi NGHP SGar SMad WBVN WBrE WCMO WCot WCru WFar WHoo WWhi

- dark blue — CMea

hyemale — see *Eranthis hyemalis*

'Ivorine' — More than 30 suppliers

aff. *jaluense* B&SWJ 8741 — WCru

japonicum — WFar

- subsp. *subcuneatum* B&SWJ 6228 — WCru

'Kleiner Ritter' **new** — EBee

kusnezoffii — GIBF

lamarckii — see *A. lycoctonum* subsp. *neapolitanum*

lasianthum — EBee

longecassidatum B&SWJ 4105 — WCru

- B&SWJ 8486 — WCru

lycoctonum — GCrs MGol SRms WBVN WCAu

- 'Dark Eyes' — CFir EBee EGle LSou MSph WCMO WCot WWlt

§ - subsp. *lycoctonum* — MSal MWgw SRms

- subsp. *moldavicum* — EBee

§ - subsp. *neapolitanum* — CBod EBee EChP ECtt EGle ELan EMan EMar EPfP GCal GMaP GSki MLLN MRav NGHP NGdn NLar SBla SWat WBor WFar

§ - subsp. *vulparia* — CArn CPrp EBee EMar GCal GKev GMac GPoy MNFA MSal NDov SPoG WAul WCMO WCot WEas WPer WSel WWhi WWye

napellus — More than 30 suppliers

- 'Albiflorus' — see *A. napellus* subsp. *vulgare* 'Albidum'

- 'Bergfürst' — CAby EBee EBrs EGle LPhx MBri NBre NDov SMHy

- 'Blue Valley' — EBee EChP EGle EMan EPfP EWes GBin NMyG NPro WFar

- 'Carneum' — see *A. napellus* subsp. *vulgare* 'Carneum'

- 'Gletschereis' — EBee GBin NBre

§ - subsp. *napellus* Anglicum Group — CRow CSev CWan EBee EChP GBuc MGol MSal MSte NEgg NHol NLar NSti SMac WCMO WCot WWhi

- 'Rubellum' — CFwr EBee EChP EGle ELan EMan EMar ENot EPfP ERou LAst NBPC NBid NBir NBro NOrc NPri SSvw WBor WHoo WMnd WMoo WPnP

- 'Schneewittchen' — EBee SSvw

- 'Sphere's Variety' — NOrc

§ - subsp. *vulgare* 'Albidum' — More than 30 suppliers

§ - - 'Carneum' — EGle EMan MLLN NChi WHer WKif WLin WSel WWye

napiforme — EBee WPGP WPnP

- B&SWJ 943 — SMeo WCru

neapolitanum — see *A. lycoctonum* subsp. *neapolitanum*

'Newry Blue' — CBos CMea CSam EMon ERou GBuc MFOX MRav NBir NBHF NEgg NHol SRms WCra WFar WPer

orientale misapplied — see *A. lycoctonum* subsp. *vulparia*

orientale ambig. — NPro

paniculatum — MBri WFar

- 'Roseum' — MBNS MTis WFar

'Pink Sensation' PBR — CFir CFwr EPfP IPot NLar

proliferum B&SWJ 4107 — WCru

pseudolaeve — LPhx

- B&SWJ 8444 — WCru

- B&SWJ 8663 — WCru

pyrenaicum — see *A. lycoctonum* subsp. *neapolitanum*

I *ranunculifolius* — see *A. lycoctonum* subsp. *neapolitanum*

sczukinii — EMon

seoulense B&SWJ 694 — WCru

- B&SWJ 864 — WCru

septentrionale — see *A. lycoctonum* subsp. *lycoctonum*

'Spark's Variety' ♀H4 — More than 30 suppliers

spicatum — NBre

'Stainless Steel' — More than 30 suppliers

'Tissington Pearl' — MTis

uchiyamai — NLar

- B&SWJ 1005 — WCru

- B&SWJ 1216 — WCru

- B&SWJ 4446 — WCru

variegatum (v) — EBee NGdn

violaceum — EBee

volubile misapplied — see *A. hemsleyanum*

volubile Pall. — NTHB

vulparia — see *A. lycoctonum* subsp. *vulparia*

'Wu To Di' — EBee GKev

yamazakii — WCru

Aconogonon see *Persicaria*

Acorus ✿ (Acoraceae)

calamus — CAgr CArn CBen CDWL CRow CWat EBee EHon ELau EMFW GPoy LNCo LPBA MCCP MGol MSal NBlu NPer SPer SWat WHer WMAq WWpP

- 'Argenteostriatus' (v) — CBcs CBen CRow CWat EBee EChP ECha ECtt EHon EMFW EPfP LNCo LPBA NBlu NOrc SWat WMAq WWpP

* *christophii* — EBee EPPr EWes WMoo

gramineus — ELau LPBA MLan MNHC NPer SWat WHer WMoo WTin WWpP

- 'Golden Delight'	CKno
- 'Golden Edge' (v)	EBee WMoo
- 'Hakuro-nishiki' (v)	More than 30 suppliers
- 'Licorice'	CBgR EBee EPPr EWin IFro LBuc MBNS MSal NHol WCHb WCot WLeb WMoo WPnP WWpP
- 'Masamune' (v)	EBee EPla GCal WBrk WMoo WTin
- 'Minimus Aureus'	CBgR CBre CWCL
- 'Oborozuki' misapplied	see *A. gramineus* 'Ogon'
- 'Oborozuki' (v)	CKno CPne CStu EBee EPla WPrP
§ - 'Ogon' (v)	More than 30 suppliers
- var. ***pusillus***	EBee EPla NBro
- 'Variegatus' (v)	More than 30 suppliers
- 'Yodo-no-yuki' (v)	EBee EPla WDyG
'Intermedius'	NPer

Acradenia (*Rutaceae*)

frankliniae	CBcs CCCN CMHG CPLG CPle CPne CTrC CTrG EWTr GGar IArd IDee LRHS SBrw SEND SSpi WFar WSHC

Acridocarpus (*Malpighiaceae*)

natalitius	CSec

Actaea (*Ranunculaceae*)

alba misapplied	see *A. pachypoda*, *A. rubra* f. *neglecta*
arizonica	CLAP EBee EBrs GCal SBri WCru
asiatica	CDes CLAP EBee WPGP
- B&SWJ 616	WCru
- BWJ 8174 from China **new**	WCru
biternata	CLAP MSte
- B&SWJ 5591	WCru
§ ***cimicifuga***	CDes CLAP EBee GCal GPoy
- B&SWJ 2966	WCru
§ ***cordifolia***	EMan GMaP LBMP MLLN MSal WCru WPnP
- 'Blickfang'	CLAP GBin
dahurica	EBee GBin GCal MGol MSal NLar SBla SWat
- B&SWJ 8426	WCru
- B&SWJ 8573	WCru
- B&SWJ 8653	GEdr
elata	WCru
erythrocarpa	see *A. rubra*
europaea	EBee LPhx WCru
frigida B&SWJ 2657	WCru
heracleifolia	GSki
- B&SWJ 8843	WCru
japonica	CLAP CMea CRow EBee EChP GCal LEdu LRHS NCGa WCot WFar
- B&SWJ 5828	WCru
I - var. ***acerina*** **new**	EBee NBre
- compact	GBin
- - B&SWJ 8758A	WCru
mairei	WCru
- BWJ 7939	WCru
matsumurae 'Elstead Variety' ♀H4	CRow GCal MRav NBre NDov SUsu
- 'Frau Herms'	CLAP
- 'White Pearl'	More than 30 suppliers
§ ***pachypoda*** ♀H4	COld CPom EBee ECha ELan GBBs GBuc GPoy IGor ITer MSal MSte NBid NCGa NLar NMen NSti WBVN WCru WMoo
- f. ***rubrocarpa***	EBee ELan
§ ***podocarpa***	CAby EBee GCal MSal SPlb SRms
racemosa ♀H4	CArn COld CRow CSam EBee EChP ELan EPfP ERou GBBs GCal GPoy LEdu LRHS MLLN MSal NBid NGdn SPer WCAu WCot WFar WMnd
§ ***rubra*** ♀H4	CBro CMHG EBee EChP ECha ELan GBuc GCal GGar GKev LRHS MSte NHol SMad SPoG WCru WEas WFar WMoo WPGP
- ***alba***	see *A. pachypoda*, *A. rubra* f. *neglecta*
§ - f. ***neglecta***	CDes EChP GBuc GEdr NLar SMad SPoG WCru
simplex	CSam GSki LRHS MWgw NDov NPri SWat
- B&SWJ 6355	WCru
- Atropurpurea Group	More than 30 suppliers
- - 'Bernard Mitchell'	CFir
- - 'Black Negligee' **new**	NBhm
- - 'Brunette' ♀H4	More than 30 suppliers
- - 'Hillside Black Beauty'	More than 30 suppliers
- - 'James Compton'	More than 30 suppliers
- 'Mountain Wave'	CLAP EBee WFar
- 'Pink Spike'	CBct CLAP EBee ERou IPot MBNS MSte NLar NMoo SMrm SPoG WCAu WCMO WFar WHil WMoo WPnP
§ - 'Prichard's Giant'	CLAP ECha GBuc LBMP LPhx LRHS MBri MRav MSte NEgg NHol WFar
- ***ramosa***	see *A. simplex* 'Prichard's Giant'
- 'Scimitar'	LPhx SMeo
- 'Silver Axe'	GCal NBre
§ ***spicata***	COld EBee GBuc GPoy ITer MFOX MSal MSte NLar WCot WCru
- from England **new**	WCru
- var. ***acuminata*** B&SWJ 6257	WCru
- var. ***rubra***	see *A. rubra*
taiwanensis	CLAP
- B&SWJ 343	CLAP
- B&SWJ 3413	EBee WCru
yesoensis	CFir GCal
yunnanensis ACE 1880	GBuc

Actinella see *Tetraneuris*

Actinidia (*Actinidiaceae*)

BWJ 8161 from China	WCru
arguta (m)	EMui SHBN
- (f/F)	CAgr EMui GIBF WPGP
- B&SWJ 569	WCru
- 'Issai' (s-p/F)	CBcs CPlN EPfP ERea LBuc LEdu MGos
- 'Kiwai Vert' (f/F)	CAgr
- LL #1 (m)	CAgr
- LL#2 (f/F)	CAgr
- LL#3 (m)	CAgr
- 'Weiki'	MGos
callosa var. ***ephippioidea*** B&SWJ 1790	WCru
- var. ***formosana*** B&SWJ 3806	WCru
chinensis misapplied	see *A. deliciosa*
coriacea	CPlN
§ ***deliciosa***	CPLG ERom MGos SLon WBVN WSHC
- (f/F)	MRav SHBN
- 'Atlas' (m)	ECrN MPRe NLar
* - 'Boskoop'	MWat
- 'Bruno' (f/F)	SLim
- 'Hayward' (f/F)	CBcs CDoC CHEx COtt EBee ECrN ELan EMil EMui EPfP ERea LRHS MPRe NLar NPal SDea SHBN SPer SWvt WCru
- 'Jenny' (s-p/F)	CPlN ECrN EMui LAst LBuc LRHS MBri MCoo MGos MLan SDea SKee SLim SPoG
- 'Solo' (F)	CDoC MPRe
- 'Tomuri' (m)	CBcs CDoC CHEx COtt EBee ELan EMil EMui EPfP ERea LRHS NLar NPal SHBN SLim SPer SWvt WCru
eriantha **new**	CPlN

hypoleuca B&SWJ 5942	WCru
kolomikta ♀H4	More than 30 suppliers
- (m)	CAgr MBlu NScw
- B&SWJ 4243	WCru
- 'Tomoko' (F)	WCru
- 'Yazuaki' (m)	WCru
latifolia	CPlN
- B&SWJ 3563	WCru
petelotii HWJ 628	WCru
pilosula	CBcs CPLG CPlN CSPN EBee GCal
	ISea LEdu LHop MGos NLar SCoo
	SLon WCru WPGP WPat WSHC
polygama (F)	CPlN GCal WCru
- B&SWJ 5444	WCru
- B&SWJ 8525 from Korea	WCru
- B&SWJ 8923 from Japan **new**	WCru
purpurea (f/F)	CAgr
rubricaulis B&SWJ 3111	WCru
rufa B&SWJ 3525	WCru
aff. *strigosa* HWJK 2367	WCru
tetramera B&SWJ 3564	WCru

Actinotus (*Apiaceae*)

helianthi	EMan

Adansonia (*Bombacaceae*)

gregorii	SPlb

Adelocaryum see *Lindelofia*

Adenia (*Passifloraceae*)

glauca	LToo
spinosa	LToo

Adenium (*Apocynaceae*)

obesum ♀H1	CRoM LToo MOak
- subsp. *boehmianum*	LToo

Adenocalymma (*Bignoniaceae*)

comosum ✿	CPlN

Adenocarpus (*Papilionaceae*)

decorticans	CArn SPlb

Adenophora (*Campanulaceae*)

BWJ 7696 from China	WCru
'Afterglow'	see *Campanula rapunculoides* 'Afterglow'
'Amethyst'	CBos
* *asiatica*	WFar
aurita	CBcs CFir CMdw CMea EChP
	MLLN NCGa NChi WCot WPrP
axilliflora	NSfd
bulleyana	CDMG CHar EBee EGle ELan
	EMan EWTr GBuc GIBF LRHS
	MWgw NBid NChi NRnb NSfd
	SDnm SMac SPav SPet SPlb WCMO
	WCot WFar WPer
* *campanulata*	WPer
coelestis	EBee EMan GIBF LPhx NBre NRnb
	NSfd
- ACE 2455	GBuc
- B&SWJ 7998	WCru
confusa	CPLG EMan GAbr LDai LHop
	LRHS MDKP MWea NBre NLRH
	NSfd SAga SPav WFar WHer WSHC
* *cymerae*	LDai NRnb NSfd WCMO
divaricata	EMan WFoF
forrestii	NBre NEgg WFar
grandiflora B&SWJ 8555	WCru
himalayana	GBri MNrw WPer
khasiana	CFir GIBF GMac LDai LTwo MDKP
	NLar NRnb NSfd WPrP WPtf
koreana	EBee NBre NSfd SPav
kurilensis	GIBF

latifolia misapplied	see *A. pereskiifolia*
latifolia Fischer	CWan GBri NBir WFar
liliifolia	CWoW EBee ECtt ELan EMan GCal
	GMac LRHS MNFA MWgw NCGa
	NPer NRnb NSfd NSti SPav WFar
	WGwG WTin
morrisonensis **new**	WCru
RWJ 10008	
§ *nikoensis*	CSec GIBF NBid NRnb NSfd WPat
§ - var. *stenophylla*	NBre WCMO WCot
nipponica	see *A. nikoensis* var. *stenophylla*
§ *pereskiifolia*	CWan EBee EWes GMac NBre
	NEgg NSfd SEND SHar SPlb
	WCMO WCot WFar WPer
- B&SWJ 8738	WCru
polyantha	CHar EBee EChP EHrv GAbr GBuc
	LRHS MNrw MWea NLar NSfd
	SBod SRms WFar
polymorpha	see *A. nikoensis*
potaninii	CFir EBee EChP EHrv ELan EMan
	GBuc MNrw NCGa NEgg NRnb
	NSfd NSti SBla SGar SPav SPoG
	WCHb WFar WHal WPtf
- pale-flowered **new**	EHrv
remotiflora B&SWJ 8562	WCru
stricta	LRHS
- subsp. *sessilifolia*	GBuc NBre NEgg SPla
sublata	NRnb NSfd WFar
takedae	NRnb
- var. *howozana*	EBee GIBF LHop MLHP NRnb
	WPrP
taquetii	EBee NEgg
- B&SWJ 1303	WCru
tashiroi	CMHG CNic CPrp ECtt EPfP GBri
	GBuc MNrw NLar NPro NRnb
	NSfd WCHb
triphylla	EBee GCal GIBF NBir SPav
	WFar
- Brown 0204	CStu
- var. *hakusanensis*	EBee NBre
- var. *japonica*	LDai NRnb
- - B&SWJ 8835	WCru
uehatae B&SWJ 126	WCru

Adenostyles see *Cacalia*

alpina	see *Cacalia hastata*

Adiantum ✿ (*Adiantaceae*)

aethiopicum	WHer
§ *aleuticum* ♀H4	CBcs CLAP EFer ELan EMon MAvo
	NBid NBro NHol WAbe WCMO
	WFib WPGP WTMC WWye
- 'Imbricatum'	CBcs CLAP EChP ECha LRHS NHol
	NLar NMyG SBla SPla SRms
	WCMO WFar WFib
§ - 'Japonicum'	CBos CDes CLAP CMil CWil EFtx
	ELan MAvo NBir NHol SBla SRms
	WCMO WCot WCru WFar WFib
	WHal WPGP
- 'Laciniatum'	SRms
* - f. *minimum*	CLAP SRms
- 'Miss Sharples'	CBgR CLAP CPrp ELan MAsh
	MWgw NEgg NHol NLar SPur
	SRms WCMO WCru WFar
§ - 'Subpumilum' ♀H4	CLAP MRav WAbe WCMO
capillus-veneris	CHEx MMHG MWat SChr WCot
	WFib
- 'Mairisii'	see *A.* x *mairisii*
cuneatum	see *A. raddianum*
hispidulum	CCCN CDes SRms WAbe
- 'Bronze Venus' **new**	CCCN MWgw
§ x *mairisii* ♀H3	EFtx
pedatum misapplied	see *A. aleuticum*
pedatum L. ♀H4	CBcs CHEx CLAP EBrs ECha EFer
	ELan EPfP GEdr GMaP LPBA LRHS
	MAsh MAvo MBri MMoz NHol

	NMoo SDix SPer SRot SSpi SWat WCot WFar WPGP WTMC
- var. *aleuticum*	see *A. aleuticum*
- Asiatic form	see *A. aleuticum* 'Japonicum'
- 'Japonicum'	see *A. aleuticum* 'Japonicum'
- 'Roseum'	see *A. aleuticum* 'Japonicum'
- var. *subpumilum*	see *A. aleuticum* 'Subpumilum'
peruvianum	EFtx
pubescens	MBri
§ *raddianum* ♀H2	CHal EFtx ERea
- 'Fluffy Ruffles'	EFtx
- 'Fragrans'	see *A. raddianum* 'Fragrantissimum'
§ - 'Fragrantissimum'	MBri
- 'Fritz Lüthi' ♀H2	CHal MBri
- 'Micropinnulum'	EFtx
- 'Monocolor'	MBri
venustum ♀H4	CBos CFwr CHEx CLAP EFer EFtx EGle EHyt EMon EPot EWTr GCal MAsh NVic SDix SHFr SRms SSpi SWat WAbe WCot WEas WFar WFib WHal WIvy WPGP

Adina (Rubiaceae)

rubella	IArd NLar

Adlumia (Papaveraceae)

fungosa	CPom CSpe LRHS

Adonis (Ranunculaceae)

amurensis misapplied	see *A.* 'Fukujukai', *multiflora*
- 'Pleniflora'	see *A. multiflora* 'Sandanzaki'
amurensis ambig.	CMea ECho EPot GIBF LTwo NLAp SCnR WCot WLin
brevistyla	EHyt ETow GBuc NSla
'Fukujukai'	ECha GEdr MBri WFar WWst
§ *multiflora* 'Sandanzaki' (d)	EPot EWes NLar SBod WCot WFar
sibirica	WCot
vernalis	GEdr GPoy NLar NSla SBla WBVN

Adoxa (Adoxaceae)

moschatellina	CRWN NMen WHer WPnP WShi WWye

Adromischus (Crassulaceae)

cooperi	EPem WCot WEas
cristatus	EPem
subdistichus	EPem

Aechmea (Bromeliaceae)

'Ann Vincent' **new**	EOas
apocalyptica **new**	EOas
caudata	EOas
'Covata'	EOas
cylindrata	EOas
distichantha	EOas
- var. *schlumbergeri*	CFir
fasciata ♀H1	LRHS MBri XBlo
gamosepala	EOas
- var. *nivea* **new**	EOas
kerteszrae **new**	EOas
ramosa	XBlo
recurvata	EOas
- var. *benrathii*	EOas
- var. *ortgiesii*	EOas
victoriana	XBlo

Aegle (Rutaceae)

sepiaria	see *Poncirus trifoliata*

Aegopodium (Apiaceae)

podagraria 'Bengt'	EMon
- 'Dangerous' (v)	CNat WCHb
- gold-margined (v)	EMon
- 'Variegatum' (v)	More than 30 suppliers

Aeonium (Crassulaceae)

arboreum ♀H1	CAbb CHEx EPem EShb MWya NPal WRos
- 'Atropurpureum' ♀H1	CHEx CSpe CTbh EAmu EPem EPfP ERea EShb MBri MLan MOak NPer SEND SMad SWal WCMO WCot
- green-leaved	SEND
I - 'Magnificum'	EBee EPfP EShb EWin EWll SAPC SArc
- 'Variegatum' (v)	EShb EWll NPer
balsamiferum	CAbb CHEx CTbh CTrC EBee EPfP EWin EWll SAPC SArc SChr WCot
'Black Cap' **new**	CCCN
'Blush'	EBee EWin
'Blushing Beauty' **new**	LRHS
canariense	CAbb CBrP CCCN CHEx EBee WCMO
- var. *palmense*	EBee EWin
§ - var. *subplanum*	CTrC
castello-paivae	EBee EShb EWin SChr
cuneatum	CTbh MLan SChr SEND SPet
decorum	SEND
* - 'Variegatum' (v)	CBow WCot
'Dinner Plate'	CHEx
'Dinner Plate' x *haworthii*	CHEx
x *domesticum*	see *Aichryson* x *domesticum*
goochiae	CBow EBee EWin
haworthii ♀H1	CAbb CArn CBrP CHEx CHal CTbh MLan SEND
- 'Variegatum' (v)	EShb EWin SChr
lindleyi	SChr
- var. *viscatum*	EBee EWin
* *multiflora*	EWin
* - 'Variegata' (v)	EWin
nobile	CBrP
percarneum	EShb
simsii	CHal CTbh EBee EWin SChr
- variegated (v)	EPem EShb
subplanum	see *A. canariense* var. *subplanum*
tabuliforme ♀H1	CAbb CCCN CSpe CTbh EPem EShb
- 'Cristatum'	EPem
urbicum	CHEx
'Zwartkop' ♀H1	More than 30 suppliers

Aeschynanthus (Gesneriaceae)

'Big Apple'	CHal EShb LRHS WDib
Black Pagoda Group	LRHS WDib
'Fire Wheel'	LRHS WDib
hildebrandii	WDib
'Holiday Bells'	WDib
'Hot Flash'	CSpe LRHS WDib
'Little Tiger'	LRHS
longicalyx	LRHS WDib
§ *longicaulis* ♀H1	LRHS WDib
marmoratus	see *A. longicaulis*
'Mona'	MBri
radicans ♀H1	EBak LRHS MBri WDib
'Scooby Doo'	WDib
speciosus ♀H1	CHal LRHS WDib

Aesculus ❀ (Hippocastanaceae)

arguta	see *A. glabra* var. *arguta*
x *arnoldiana*	CDul CMCN SBir
- 'Autumn Splendor'	EPfP
§ x *bushii*	CMCN CTho MGos NLar
californica	CBcs CDul CMCN CTho CTrw EPfP ERod IArd SSpi WPGP
- 'Blue Haze'	SSpi
x *carnea*	CDul CTri ELan MBar SBLw
- 'Aureomarginata' (v)	CTho ERod LTwo MAsh SMad WPat
- 'Briotii' ♀H4	CBcs CCVT CDoC CDul CEnd CLnd CSBt CTho CTri CWib EBee

	ECrN ELan EPfP EWTr LBuc LPan MAsh MBlu MBri MGan MGos NBee NWea SHBN SLim SPer WDin WFar WOrn
– 'Marginata' (v)	MBlu
– 'Plantierensis'	CDul ECrN MBlu SBLw
* – 'Variegata' (v)	CBcs CDul CMCN MGos WDin
chinensis	CMCN NLar
'Dallimorei' (graft-chimaera)	CTho SMad
§ *flava* ♀H4	CMCN CTho EBee ECrN EPfP LPan NWea SBLw SHBN SLim SSpi WFar WPGP
– f. *vestita*	CDoC CDul LPan MBlu
georgiana	see *A. sylvatica*
glabra	CDul CMCN CTho EGFP
§ – var. *arguta*	CMCN WDin
– 'Autumn Blaze' **new**	EPfP
– 'October Red'	EPfP MBlu WPGP
glaucescens	see *A. x neglecta*
hippocastanum ♀H4	More than 30 suppliers
§ – 'Baumannii' (d) ♀H4	CDoC CDul CLnd EBee ECrN EPfP ERod LPan MGos MSwo NWea SBLw SHBN SPer WDin WFar
– 'Digitata'	CDul CMCN SBLw
– 'Flore Pleno'	see *A. hippocastanum* 'Baumannii'
– 'Hampton Court Gold'	CBcs CDoC CDul CMCN NBhm
– 'Honiton Gold'	CTho
– 'Laciniata'	CBcs CDul CMCN ERod IArd MBlu NLar SMad
– 'Monstrosa'	MBri SMad
– 'Pyramidalis'	CDul SBLw SMad
– 'Wisselink'	CDul CLnd CMCN ECrN MBlu
indica	CDul CHEx CLnd CMCN CTho EBee ECrN ELan EPfP GGGa IArd IDee SHBN SMHT SSpi WDin WPGP
– 'Sydney Pearce' ♀H4	CDoC CDul CEnd CMCN ERod MBlu MBri MGos NLar SMad WDin WPGP
x *marylandica*	CDul
memmingeri	SBir
x *mississippiensis*	see *A. x bushii*
x *mutabilis* 'Harbisonii'	GTSp NLar WWes
– 'Induta'	CLnd CMCN EPfP GTSp IArd MBlu MBri NLar NSti SCoo SDix SMad SSpi WFar WWes
§ – 'Penduliflora'	CBcs CDul CEnd CTho EPfP MBlu SMad
§ x *neglecta*	CLnd CMCN
– 'Autumn Fire'	MBlu
– 'Erythroblastos' ♀H4	CBcs CDoC CEnd CLnd CMCN CTho ECrN EPfP ERod IDee MAsh MBlu SBir SCoo SHBN SLim SMad SSpi SSta WDin WPat
parviflora ♀H4	CBcs CDul CLnd CMCN CTri EBee ECrN ELan EPfP EWTr IDee LPan LRHS MBar MBlu MBri MGos MLan NBea NEgg SLPl SLim SMad SPer SSpi WDin WFar WOrn WPGP
§ *pavia* ♀H4	CBcs CDul CLnd CMCN CTho EPfP SSpi WDin
– 'Atrosanguinea'	CDul CEnd CLnd CMCN EBee EPfP ERod IArd IDee IMGH MBlu NPal SMad
– var. *discolor*	SBLw WDin
– – 'Koehnei'	CDul CMCN MBlu NLar SCoo
– 'Penduliflora'	see *A. x mutabilis* 'Penduliflora'
– 'Purple Spring'	MBlu
– 'Rosea Nana'	CMCN WPat
splendens	see *A. pavia*
§ *sylvatica*	CMCN CTho
turbinata	CBcs CDul CLnd CMCN GIBF SSpi
– var. *pubescens*	WPGP
wilsonii	CTho WPGP
x *woerlitzensis*	WCwm

Aethionema (Brassicaceae)

armenum	CSec
coridifolium	WPer
§ *grandiflorum* ♀H4	CElw GEdr NBro SBla SRms WPer
– Pulchellum Group ♀H4	CSpe
iberideum	ETow MDKP SRms
* *kotschyi* hort.	ECho NMen SBla WAbe
membranaceum **new**	CPBP
oppositifolium	CLyd MWat WAbe WHoo
pulchellum	see *A. grandiflorum*
schistosum	LTwo WAbe
spicatum	WFar
'Warley Rose' ♀H4	CLyd EAEE ECho ELan EPot LHop NLAp NMen SIng SRms WPat
'Warley Ruber'	CLyd CPBP NBir NMen SBla WAbe WFar

Afgekia (Papilionaceae)

sericea **new**	CPIN

Afrocarpus (Podocarpaceae)

falcatus	ECou GGar

Agalinis (Scrophulariaceae)

linariodes	EMan

Agapanthus ❀ (Alliaceae)

'Aberdeen'	CPne XDoo XPde
'Adonis'	IBal IBlr
'African Moon'	CPne
§ *africanus* ♀H1	CAbb CElw CTbh CWib ECho EHrv EPfP GSki IBlr LEdu LPan LRHS MNHC MOak NBlu SAPC SArc SBod SPav SPer SWat WBor WBrE WFar WPer XPep
* – 'Albus' ♀H1	CBcs CDes CDoC CHad CTbh ECho EMan EPfP GSki IBlr IFoB IHMM LRHS NBlu SBod SEND SMeo SPav SPer WGwG WPer XPep
'Albatross'	CPne ECha
'Albus' ambig.	CAvo CPLG GMaP LPan MGos MHer MWat SAga
I 'Albus Nanus'	ECho LPan
'Amsterdam'	XDoo XPde
'Angela'	CPne
'Anthea'	CPne
'Aphrodite'	IBlr
'Apple Court'	XPde
'Aquamarine'	CAvo
'Arctic Star'	CPLG CPne GSki
Ardernei hybrid	CBos CDes CPne CPrp EBee ECha EWes GCal GMac GQue IBal IBlr LSou MBNS MBnl MSte NEgg SAga SRos SUsu WCMO WCot WGwG WPGP XDoo
§ 'Argenteus Vittatus' (v) ♀H1	CDes CPrp ELan EPfP MBNS NOrc WSPU
'Atlas'	IBlr
'Baby Blue'	see *A.* 'Blue Baby'
'Back in Black' **new**	EBee EPfP IBal MBNS NChi SHBN SPoG WCMO
'Ballyrogan'	IBlr
'Bangor Blue'	IBal IBlr
'Basutoland'	EBrs LRHS
'Beatrice'	CPne
'Beeches Dwarf'	EBee ELan
'Ben Hope'	GBuc IBal IBlr SDnm SPav WCot XDoo
'Beth Chatto'	see *A. campanulatus* 'Albovittatus'
'Bethlehem Star'	CBgR CPne GSki SRos
'Bianco' **new**	XPde
'Bicton Bell'	IBal IBlr
'Big Blue'	CKno CPrp EBee
'Black Pantha'	More than 30 suppliers

§	'Blue Baby'	CAbb CCCN CLyd CPen CPrp CRez ELan IBal IBlr LRHS SMrm SMur WFar WThu XDoo XPde
	'Blue Bird'	CPne
	'Blue Boy' **new**	XPde
	'Blue Brush'	CPne CSBt CTbh EBee EMil SCoo SEND SPoG
	'Blue Cascade'	IBal IBlr
	'Blue Companion'	CPne CPrp IBal IBlr
	'Blue Diamond' ambig.	EHrv SRos
	'Blue Dot'	EBee
	'Blue Formality'	IBal IBlr
	'Blue Giant'	CBcs CBro CCVN CPen CPrp EBee ELan ERea IBlr LRHS MNFA MSte NEgg NGby SAga SWat WCMO WDav WFar WPGP
	'Blue Globe'	CMMP EChP ERou GMaP IBal STes WCAu WHil WTMC
	'Blue Gown'	CSam
	'Blue Haze'	SRos XPde
	'Blue Heaven'PBR	CPne EWTr EWll
	'Blue Imp'	CBro CPne EBee GBuc GSki IBlr LRHS NHol XDoo
	'Blue Méoni'	XPde
	'Blue Mercury'	IBlr
	'Blue Moon'	CBro CHad CPen CPne EBee IBal IBlr LRHS WCot
	'Blue Nile'	CPne
	'Blue Prince' **new**	CBro CPen EBee
	'Blue Ribbon' **new**	XPde
	'Blue Skies' ambig.	CBcs GSki NCGa SWat
I	'Blue Skies' Dunlop	IBlr
	'Blue Skies' from New Zealand	WTMC
	'Blue Triumphator'	EBee EPfP EWTr EWll GKev GMaP IBlr LBow LRHS NGby NScw SBod SMeo SMrm XDoo
	'Blue Velvet'	CPne XPde
	'Bluety' **new**	MOak
	'Bressingham Blue'	CBro CPne CPrp CTri EBrs ECho GCal IBal IBlr IFoB LRHS MRav MSte NVic SWat WGer XDoo
	'Bressingham Bounty'	EBrs
	'Bressingham White'	CPne EBee ECtt EHrv EMan LEdu LRHS MBri MRav NCGa SWat XDoo
	'Bristol'	XPde
	'Buckingham Palace'	CBro CDes CKno CPrp EBee ECho GAbr IBal IBlr NBre WPGP XDoo
	'Cally Blue'	GAbr GCal
	'Cambridge'	CPne
§	*campanulatus*	CPLG CPrp CWCL EBee ECho ELan EPfP GGar GKev GSki IBal IBlr IGor ISea LRHS MRav NCob SWat SYvo WAbe WCot WFar WPGP XPep
	- var. *albidus*	More than 30 suppliers
§	- 'Albovittatus'	CSam ECho IBal
	- bright blue	CWCL GCal
	- 'Buckland'	IBlr
	- 'Cobalt Blue'	ECha
	- 'Isis'	CAvo CBro CFir CSam CTri CWCL EBee EBla ECha EGra GBuc GSki IBal IBlr LRHS NCGa SRos
	- 'Oxford Blue'	CPrp EBee EBrs GBri GBuc IBal IBlr LRHS SRos WPGP XPde
	- subsp. *patens* ♀H3	CPrp CSec EBee EBla EBrs EMan EPfP GBri GBuc IBal SWat WHil WPGP
	- - deep blue	CFir CPrp EBrs IBlr LRHS
	- 'Profusion'	CBro CWCL EBee EBrs ECha IBal IBlr LRHS SRos WFar XPde
	- variegated (v)	EBla ECha NPer
	- 'Wedgwood Blue'	CPrp EBes IBal IBlr SRos XDoo
	- 'Wendy'	CPne EBrs IBal IBlr XPde
	'White Hope'	IBal IBlr SRos
	'Carefree' **new**	IBal
	'Castle of Mey'	CBro CPne GAbr GBuc IBal IBlr MTho SPav SRos WPGP XDoo XPde
	'Catharina'	CPne XDoo
§	*caulescens* ♀H1	EBee EBrs GBuc IBal IBlr IGor LRHS WBrE WCMO WCot WPGP
I	- 'Albus'	GCal
	- subsp. *angustifolius*	CBrm IBlr WCot XPep
	- subsp. *caulescens*	IBlr SWat
	'Cedric Morris'	IBal IBlr SRos XDoo XPde
	'Chandra'	IBlr
	'Cherry Holley'	CPne SRos
	'Clarence House'	CBro IBal
	coddii	CPLG EBee IBlr LRHS WCot XPde
	'Columba'	CPne XDoo
	comptonii	see *A.praecox* subsp. *minimus*
	'Crystal Drop'	CPne SWat
	Danube	see *A.* 'Donau'
	'Dark Star'	EBee WFar
	'Dartmoor' **new**	CPne
	'Dawn Star'	XDoo XPde
	'Debbie'	XDoo
	'Delft'	IBal IBlr
	'Density'	IBlr
	'Devon Dawn'	CPne
	'Dnjepr'	GSki
	'Dokter Brouwer'	CPen CPne EBee GSki MDKP WGwG XDoo
§	'Donau'	CBro CDoC CPen CPne EBee GKev NBir SMrm SWat WFar XDoo XPde
	'Dorothy Kate'	CPne
	'Duivenbrugge White' **new**	XPde
	dyeri	see *A.intermedius* subsp. *intermedius*
	'Ed Carman' (v)	WCMO WCot
	'Elisabeth'	CPne
	'Ethel's Joy'	CPen
	'Eve'	EBee IBlr
	'Evening Star'	CPne ECha GSki LRHS
	'Exmoor'	CPne
	'Findlay's Blue'	CLCN GBuc WPGP
	'Gayle's Lilac'	More than 30 suppliers
	'Gem'	CPne
	'Glacier Stream'	CBro CCVN CPen EBee GSki
	'Glen Avon'	CAbb CBro CFir CPne CPrp EBee EMil IBal NBPC NLar SCoo XPde
	'Golden Rule' (v)	CBow CDes CFir EBee EHoe GBuc IBal IBlr MAvo WPGP
	'Harvest Blue'	CPne
	Headbourne hybrid dwarf **new**	EBrs
§	Headbourne hybrids	More than 30 suppliers
	'Heavenly Blue'	CPne
	'Helen'	IBal IBlr
	'Holbeach'	CPne XDoo
	'Holbrook'	CSam
	'Hydon Mist'	XDoo XPde
	'Ice Blue Star'	CPne SRos
	'Ice Lolly'	CBro CPen EBee
	inapertus	CBro CMon CPLG GSki IGor MHer SMHy SMad SWat WCot WLin WPGP WWye XPep
	- dwarf	IBlr
	- subsp. *hollandii*	CAvo CPne GCal IBlr MSte SBla SWat WCot WHil
	- - 'Zealot'	IBlr
	- subsp. *inapertus*	EChP ERea IBlr SWat WCot
I	- - 'Albus'	IBlr
	- - 'Cyan'	IBlr
	- 'Indigo Cascade'	SWat
	- subsp. *intermedius*	EChP GCal IBlr SWat WCot
	- 'Midnight Cascade' **new**	SWat
	- subsp. *parviflorus*	IBlr

- subsp. **pendulus**	CAby CFir EBee EBrs ETow IBlr WPGP
- - 'Graskop'	IBlr
- - 'Violet Dusk'	IBlr
- 'Purple Cloud'	see *A.* 'Purple Cloud'
'Innocence'	IBlr
I 'Intermedius' van Tubergen	CPne EBee XDoo
§ **intermedius** subsp. **intermedius** **new**	CBro IBal IBlr
'Jack Elliott' **new**	SMHy
'Jack's Blue'	More than 30 suppliers
'Jersey Giant'	LEdu
'Jodie'	CPne XPde
'Johanna'	CPne
'Jolanda'	CPne
'K. Wiley'	SUsu
'Kalmthout Blue'	NBre
'Kew White'	SDix
'Kingston Blue'	CAbb CAby CBos CMea CPne CPrp EBee EBla ECha EHrv ENot IBal IBlr LRHS LSou MLLN SRGP SUsu WFar WPrP WSHC
'Kirsty'	CPne
'Kobold'	CPne EGle NBre SBod WFar
'Lady Edith'	IBlr
§ 'Lady Grey'	CPne IBlr
'Lady Moore'	EGle IBlr IGor SMHy XPde
'Latent Blue'	IBal IBlr
'Leicester'	EBee
'Lilac Bells'	CPne
'Lilac Time'	CPne IBlr
'Lilliput'	More than 30 suppliers
'Loch Hope' ♀H3	CAbb CBro CCtw CDoC CPne CPrp EBee EBrs EGle EMan GAbr GGar GSki IBal IGor LAst MFOX MLLN NBPC NCob SPav SRos SVil WCMO WCot WHoo WPnn WWhi XDoo
'Luly'	CPne IBal XPde
'Lydenburg'	IBal IBlr
'Mabel Grey'	see *A.* 'Lady Grey'
'Magnifico'	IBlr
'Majorie' **new**	CPne
'Marcus'	CPne
'Mariètte'	CPen CPne EBee XDoo
'Marjorie'	CLCN CWCL XPde
'Martine'	CPne
'Meibont' (v)	WCMO WCot
'Mercury'	CPne
'Midnight'	CHad SAga WSHC
'Midnight Blue' ambig.	CBos CDoC ECha ELan EPfP GBuc GSki IBal IGor MSte SPav WFar
'Midnight Blue' P.Wood	EBrs GCal IBlr
'Midnight Star'	More than 30 suppliers
'Miniature Blue'	SWat
'Montreal' **new**	XDoo XPde
* 'Mooreanus' misapplied	EBee EPfP GCal IBlr WPGP
'Morning Star'	CPne GSki SRos
'Mount Stewart'	IBal IBlr
'New Blue'	CPen CPne EBee ENot EWTr IBal NOrc SRos XPde
'New Love' **new**	EBee
'Nikki'	CPne
'Norman Hadden'	IBlr
nutans	see *A. caulescens*
'Nyx'	IBlr
'Oslo'	CPne XDoo
'Oxbridge'	IBlr
Palmer's hybrids	see *A.* Headbourne hybrids
'Parys' **new**	XDoo
'Patent Blue'	IBal IBlr
'Penelope Palmer'	IBal IBlr
'Penny Slade'	SRos
'Peter Pan' ambig.	More than 30 suppliers
'Phantom'	CPne IBlr
'Pinchbeck'	CPne XDoo XPde
'Pinocchio'	CPen ECho GSki MLan NHol
'Plas Merdyn Blue'	IBal IBlr
'Plas Merdyn White'	CFir IBal IBlr
'Podge Mill'	CWCL EGle IBlr XPde
'Polar Ice'	CFir CPen CPne EBee ERea GSki IBlr NHol WFar WHil XDoo
'Porcelain'	IBal IBlr
praecox	CPrp EBee EBrs EShb GAbr IBlr WViv
- 'Dwarf White'	see *A.* white dwarf hybrids
- 'Flore Pleno' (d)	CDes CPne EBee ECha EHrv ELan EMon IBal IBlr MBNS NBPC NGdn NLar SPoG WCMO WCot WFar WPGP WPrP XPde
- 'Floribundus'	SWat
- 'Maximus Albus'	CPou EBrs IBal IBlr WBrE
§ - subsp. **minimus**	CAvo CBrm CElw CMon CPne CPou GSki IBlr LBow SWat WCot WHil
- - 'Adelaide'	EBee SWat
- - blue	SWat
- - white	SWat
- 'Neptune'	IBlr
§ - subsp. **orientalis**	CCCN CSut CTbh EBee EHrv ERea GGar GSki IBlr NPal SWat WPic XPep
- - var. **albiflorus**	CBro CPne CPou CSut GSki IBal LBow
- - 'Weaver'	CPne WHil
- subsp. **praecox**	IBlr IGor
- - azure	SWat
- - 'Variegatus'	see *A.* 'Argenteus Vittatus'
- 'Saturn'	IBlr
- Slieve Donard form	IBlr
- 'Storms River'	SWat XPep
- 'Titan'	IBlr
- 'Uranus'	IBlr
- 'Venus'	IBlr
- 'Vittatus' (v)	ERea WCMO WCot WFar
'Premier'	CPrp EBee EBrs IBal IBlr SRos WPGP
'Proteus'	EBee
§ 'Purple Cloud'	More than 30 suppliers
'Purple Star'	EBee
'Queen Elizabeth The Queen Mother'	CPne IBal
'Raveningham Hall' **new**	XPde
'Rhone'	CPne IBlr
rich blue	XDoo
'Rosemary'	XPde
'Rosewarne'	CAbb CCCN CPne CPrp CTbh EBee IBlr NLar
'Rotterdam'	CPne
'Royal Blue'	CBro CHar CWCL GBuc GMaP MSte NHol
'Royal Purple' **new**	XPde
'Sandringham'	CDes CPne IBlr WPGP XDoo
'Sapphire'	CPLG IBal IBlr XPde
'Sea Coral'	CBcs CCCN CDoC CFir CPne IBal
'Sea Foam'	CBcs CPen CPne IBal MBNS MSte NLar
'Sea Mist'	CBcs CCCN CPne EBee EMil IBal
'Sea Spray'	CBcs CCCN CKno CPne EBee EMil ENot IBal XDoo
'Septemberhemel'	XDoo XPde
'Sevilla' **new**	XDoo
'Silver Baby'	CAbb CBcs CPen CPne MSte SRos
'Silver Mist'	CPne EBee IBlr XPde
Silver Moon = 'Notfred' (v)	EBee ELan EMan ENot EPfP LBuc MGos SPoG
'Silver Sceptre'	IBlr
silver variegated (v)	SMrm
'Sky'	CAbb CPne EBee IBal IBlr MSte
'Sky Rocket'	CPne IBlr
'Sky Star'	IBal
'Slieve Donard'	IBlr WFar

'Sneeuwwitje' **new** — XDoo XPde
'Snow Cloud' — CAbb CBro CPne CSBt EBee IBal NLar
'Snow Pixie' — CAbb CBro CPne CSBt CSpe EBee LSRN
'Snow Princess' — IBal
'Snowball' — CAby CBcs CDoC COIW CPne CPrp EBee ECho EMil GAbr IBal LSou MSte NBPC SVil WWhi XDoo
'Snowdrops' — More than 30 suppliers
'Spokes' — IBlr
'Starburst' — IBlr
'Stephanie' **new** — XPde
'Stéphanie Charm' — XDoo
'Storm Cloud' (d) — CBro CFir
'Streamline' — More than 30 suppliers
'Summer Clouds' — EBee EPfP IBal LRHS MBNS MWgw
'Summer Skies' — EPfP IBal LRHS SRos
'Summer Snow' **new** — CPne
'Sunfield' — CPen CPne EBee GBuc GSki LRHS NPer WDav WGer WHil XDoo
'Super Star' — XDoo
'Supreme' — IBal IBlr
'Suzan' **new** — XPde
'Sylvine' — XDoo
'Tall Boy' — IBlr
'Tarka' — CPne
'Taw Valley' — CPne
'Thumbelina' **new** — CAbb CBro CPne CSpe EBee
'Timaru' — More than 30 suppliers
'Tinkerbell' (v) — More than 30 suppliers
'Tiny Tim' — EBee GSki
'Torbay' — CPrp EAEE EBee ECtt EWll GSki IBlr NBre NCGa NHol SBla SRos XDoo
Tresco hybrid — CHEx
'Twilight' — IBlr
umbellatus L'Hérit. — see *A. africanus*
umbellatus Redouté — see *A. praecox* subsp. *orientalis*
'Underway' — CMon EWes GCal IBlr XPde
'Virginia' — XDoo
§ white dwarf hybrids — CBro CPen EBee ECha EMan EPfP LRHS MBri NBre WFar WHil XDoo
white-flowered — CHEx CTbh GGar NCob WCFE
'White Heaven'PBR — CPne EWTr
'White Ice' — CBcs CPne XDoo
'White Star' — XPde
'White Starlet' — XDoo
'White Superior' — CMMP CPne CSpe EChP ERou GMaP LAst NCGa SPet STes WCAu WMnd WTMC WWye
'White Triumphator' — WCot
'White Umbrella' — WPrP
'Whitney'PBR — IBlr MOak
'Windlebrooke' — EBee ECha XDoo
'Windsor Castle' — IBal IBlr XDoo XPde
'Windsor Grey' — CDes CPrp EBee IBal IBlr WPGP XDoo
'Winsome' — IBlr
'Wolga' — CPne
'Wolkberg' Kirstenbosch — IBlr
'Yves Klein' — IBlr
'Zachary' — CPne
'Zella Thomas' — EBee LHyd XDoo

Agapetes (Ericaceae)

'Ludgvan Cross' ♀H1-2 — CCCN SAga SBrw
serpens ♀H1 — CCCN CHEx CKob CPlN CWib EShb SAga SLon
- 'Nepal Cream' — SLon
- 'Scarlet Elf' — SBrw
smithiana var. *major* — GGGa

Agarista (Ericaceae)

§ *populifolia* — WFar

Agastache (Lamiaceae)

RCB/Arg X-1 — WCot
anethiodora — see *A. foeniculum*
anisata — see *A. foeniculum*
'Apricot Sunrise' — MNHC MSph
aurantiaca — CSec EAro GCal LHop LPhx NLar WLin
- 'Apricot Sprite' — CEnt CWCL EAro EBee EWin EWll LDai SDnm SPav SPoG SUsu WCHb WCot WFar WGwG WHil WWeb
'Black Adder' — EBee GQue LHop NDov SPoG
'Blue Fortune' ♀H3-4 — CBcs EBee ECha ECtt EMan ENot EPfP GBri IBal LBmB LPhx LRHS MLLN NCGa NDov NMoo SMer SMrm SPer WFar WHlf WWeb
breviflora — SWal
§ *cana* — EAro EBee ECtt EMan LDai LPhx MLLN MSph WCot WFar WLin
- 'Cinnabar Rose' — NBir WFar
- 'Purple Pygmy' — ECtt EShb MSph
'Firebird' — CFwr CWCL EBee EChP ECtt EHrv ELan GBri IBal LHop LRHS LSRN MNrw NBir NCGa NDov SAga SBla SGar SMrm SPla SRkn SUsu SWat SWvt WCAu WCot WFar
foeniculum misapplied — see *A. rugosa*
§ *foeniculum* (Pursh) Kuntze — CArn CBod CWan EBee EBrs ECha ELan ELau EOHP GMaP GPoy LPhx LRHS MHer MNHC MRav NDov NFor NGHP SBla SPav SRms SWal WCAu WFar WGHP WPer WWye XPep
- 'Alabaster' — CBcs EAro EGoo ELau EShb IHMH LPhx LRHS NDov SBch WCHb WGHP
- 'Alba' — MLLN NBre NGHP SHDw SPav WFar WHil
* 'Fragrant Delight' — SRms
'Globetrotter' — CSam LHop LPhx NDov SAga SUsu
'Glowing Embers' — ECtt ELan EPfP LRHS
'Hazy Days' — EAro EBee EPfP LPhx LSou WHil
'Heather Queen' — SRkn
§ *mexicana* — EAro EUnu LDai LSou MSal MWea SDnm SMHy SMrm SPav WGwG WJek
- 'Carille Carmine' — EMan
- 'Champagne' — MWea WCHb
- 'Marchants Pink' **new** — SMHy
- 'Mauve Beauty' — EBee LSou
- 'Red Fortune'PBR — CPrp EBee LHop MAsh NCGa
- 'Rosea' — see *A. cana*
* 'Toronjil Morado' — EBee LHop
nepetoides — CArn CSec EAro EMan EPPr MSal NLar NSti SDnm SPav SSvw WCHb WWye
occidentalis — EMan
'Painted Lady' — CSpe EAro EBee ECtt EWin LPhx MNrw SAga SBch SMrm SUsu WCot WHil
pallidiflora var. *pallidiflora* — EBee
- var. *neomexicana* 'Lavender Haze' — EBee EMag
palmeri — EAro EMan LHop
'Phoenix' **new** — SMHy
'Pink Panther' — EBee ECtt EMan LHop
'Pink Pearl' — WWeb
'Pink Pop' — EAro EBee ECGP LPhx NLar SPoG WHil
pringlei — EAro EBee EChP NBre NLar SWat WMoo
'Purple Candle' — EBee EWes SPla
'Purple Haze' — LPhx
§ *rugosa* — CAgr CArn CBod CFir CPne CSec ELau EOHP EUnu GPoy LPhx

	LRHS MLLN MNHC MSal SDnm
	SMeo SPav SUsu SWal SWat WGHP
	WJek WMoo WPer WSel XPep
- B&SWJ 4187 from Korea	WCru
- f. *albiflora*	NBre SDnm SPer WCAu WGwG
	WLin
- - 'Honey Bee White'	EMag
- - 'Liquorice White'	CPrp EBee LRHS MWgw NBre
	NLar SPav SWat WGHP WWhi
- 'Golden Jubilee'	CFwr CWCL EAro EBee ECha
	EGoo EMan EWin GAbr ITer LDai
	LHop LPhx LSou MCCP MHar
	NDov NLar NSti SPoG WHil WMoo
- 'Honey Bee Blue'	EWll GAbr LRHS
- 'Liquorice Blue'	CKno EAro EChP ECrN LPhx LRHS
	MLan MWgw NBid NEgg NGdn
	NLar SDnm SGar SPav SPoG SWat
	WFar WGHP WMoo WPer WWhi
- pink-flowered	CEnt SUsu
rupestris	CMdw CSec CSpe EAro EBee
	EChP EMan EShb LHop LPhx NLar
	SPur WKif
- 'Apache Sunset'	CBow LEdu MWgw NTHB SDnm
	SGar SPav SPlb WHal WPtf
scrophulariifolia	WCHb
'Serpentine'	EBee LPhx
'Spicy' **new**	ECha
'Tangerine Dreams' ♀H3	EBee ECtt EMan EWin LPhx SBla
'Tutti-frutti'	EBee ECtt EHrv EMan LDai LHop
	SDnm SPav
urticifolia	CArn CSpe GIBF LRHS MSal
- 'Alba'	CSec CSpe EAro EBee NBre NLar
	WGHP WPer
- 'Liquorice'	EBee
wrightii	NBre

Agathaea see *Felicia*

Agathis (Araucariaceae)
australis	CDoC LCon

Agathosma (Rutaceae)
ovata	CCCN
- 'Igoda'	EShb

Agave ✿ (Agavaceae)
albicans	MAga
albomarginata **new**	MAga
amaniensis **new**	MAga
americana ♀H1	More than 30 suppliers
- subsp. *americana* var. *expansa* **new**	MAga
- - var. *oaxacensis* **new**	MAga
- 'Marginata' (v) ♀H3-4	CBrP CHal CHll IBlr MAga MPRe
	SDnm WMul
- 'Mediopicta' misapplied	see *A. americana* 'Mediopicta Alba'
- 'Mediopicta' (v) ♀H1	CHEx SAPC SArc SBig STop
	WCMO WEas WMul
§ - 'Mediopicta Alba' (v) ♀H1	CBrP CHen EAmu SChr WCMO WMul
- subsp. *protoamericana* **new**	MAga
- 'Striata' (v)	EShb
- 'Variegata' (v) ♀H1	More than 30 suppliers
angustiarum **new**	MAga
angustifolia	MAga
asperrima **new**	EPem MPRe
§ - subsp. *maderensis* **new**	MAga
§ - subsp. *potosiensis* **new**	MAga
§ - subsp. *zarcensis* **new**	MAga
attenuata	CAbb CBrP CHEx CTrC EAmu
	EWll LRHS MAga SAPC SArc SBig
	WMul
boldinghiana **new**	MAga
bracteosa	CCCN EPem MAga MPRe SChr

cantala **new**	MAga
capensis **new**	MAga
§ *celsii*	CBrP CHEx CTbh CTrC EBee
	EPem MAga SAPC SArc SChr
cerulata subsp. *nelsonii*	MAga
chiapensis **new**	MAga
chrysantha	CCCN CTrC MAga SChr WCMO
	WLeb
chrysoglossa **new**	MAga
colorata	CCCN
- dwarf **new**	MAga
cupreata	MAga
decipiens **new**	MAga
- dwarf **new**	MAga
delamateri **new**	MAga
deserti	CBrP WCot
- subsp. *simplex* variegated (v) **new**	MAga
difformis **new**	MAga
durangensis **new**	MAga
ensifera **new**	MAga
felgeri **new**	MAga
ferdinandi-regis	see *A. scabra* x *A. victoriae-reginae*
ferox	CBrP CTrC CWil EWll MPRe SBig
	WCMO WMul
filifera ♀H1	CBcs CCCN CHEx EPem MAga
	SChr WMul
- subsp. *microceps* ISI 1184 **new**	MAga
flexispina **new**	MAga
fourcroydes	MAga MPRe
franzosinii	MAga
funkiana **new**	MAga
geminiflora	CHen EPem EShb MAga WCot
ghiesbreghtii	CBrP MAga MPRe
gigantea	see *Furcraea foetida*
gigantensis **new**	MAga
x *glomeruliflora* **new**	MAga
goldmaniana	MAga
x *gracilipes* **new**	MAga
guadalajarana dwarf **new**	MAga
- 'Trelease'	MPRe
guiengola **new**	MAga
havardiana	CTrC MAga
- dwarf **new**	MAga
hiemiflora **new**	MAga
horrida	MAga SChr
inaequidens **new**	MAga
karwinskii **new**	MAga
kerchovei	EPem MAga WCot
§ *lechuguilla*	MAga SChr
lophantha	CHen MAga WCot
- var. *caerulescens*	see *A. lechuguilla*
lophantha x *lechuguilla* **new**	MAga
lurida Aiton	MAga MPRe
macroacantha	MAga
missionum from The Virgin Islands **new**	MAga
§ *mitis*	see *A. celsii*
mitriformis	WMul
multifilifera **new**	MAga
neglecta **new**	MAga
neomexicana	CCCN MAga WCMO
nizandensis	CHEx MAga
obscura	CHen
ocahui **new**	MAga
- var. *longifolia* **new**	MAga
ornithobroma **new**	MAga
oroensis **new**	MAga
palmeri	CCCN CTrC EPem IDee MAga
	SChr
panamana	see *A. vivipara* var. *vivipara*
parrasana **new**	MAga

– dwarf **new**	MAga
parryi	CDoC CHen CTrC EAmu EDsa
	EWll GKev IDee LEdu MAga SChr
	WCMO WCot WLeb WMul
	WPGP
– var. **couesii**	see *A. parryi* var. *parryi*
§ – var. **parryi**	CBrP CFir EPem MAga MPRe
parvidentata new	MAga
parviflora ♀H1	MAga SChr
– subsp. **flexiflora new**	MAga
– – dwarf **new**	MAga
x **peacockii new**	MAga
pelona new	MAga
aff. **pelona**	EBee
polianthiflora new	MAga
polyacantha new	MAga
– var. **xalapensis**	MAga MPRe
potatorum ♀H1	SChr
– var. **potatorum new**	MAga
– var. **verschaffeltii**	EPem MPRe
– – dwarf **new**	MAga
promantorii new	MAga
pygmaea	see *A. seemanniana*
rhodacantha new	MAga
salmiana	EAmu MAga SBig WMul
– subsp. **crassispina new**	MAga
– subsp. **salmiana**	MAga SAPC SArc SChr
var. **ferox**	
– – variegated (v) **new**	MAga
scabra	CCCN EBee EPem MAga WCMO
– subsp. **maderensis**	see *A. asperrima* subsp. *maderensis*
– subsp. **zarcensis**	see *A. asperrima* subsp. *zarcensis*
§ **scabra** x **victoriae-reginae**	SChr
scaposa new	MAga
schidigera	CBrP CFir GCal MAga WCot
schottii	MAga WCot
– var. **treleasei new**	MAga
§ **sebastiana**	MAga
§ **seemanniana new**	MAga
shawii	MAga
shrevei subsp.	MAga
matapensis new	
sisalana	MAga WMul
I – f. **armata new**	MAga
sobria	MAga
– subsp. **sobria new**	MAga
striata	CTrC EPem IDee XPep
* – **rubra new**	EPem
stricta ♀H1	CCCN CHen EPem MAga MPRe
	WMul
– dwarf	CBrP MAga
stringens new	MAga
subsimplex new	MAga
tecta new	MAga
tequilana blue-leaved **new**	MAga
– green-leaved **new**	MAga
thomasae new	MAga
titanota new	MAga
toumeyana	EPem MAga SChr
– var. **bella new**	CHen MAga
triangularis	MAga
utahensis ♀H1	MAga SEND
– var. **discreta**	MAga
– dwarf **new**	MAga
– var. **eborispina**	MAga
– subsp. **kaibabensis**	EPem
– var. **nevadensis**	MAga
victoriae-reginae ♀H1	CBrP CCCN CTrC EPem EShb EWll
	MAga SWal WCMO WCot
– dwarf **new**	MAga
– variegated (v) **new**	SChr
vilmoriniana new	EPem MAga
vivipara new	MAga
– var. **letonae new**	MAga

– 'Marginata' **new**	MAga
– var. **nivea new**	MAga
– var. **sargentii new**	MAga
§ – var. **vivipara new**	MAga
vizcainoensis new	MAga
warelliana new	MAga
weberi new	MAga
wercklei new	MAga
x **winteriana new**	MAga
xylonacantha	EPem MAga SChr
yuccifolia new	MAga
zebra new	MAga

Ageratina see *Eupatorium*

Ageratum (Asteraceae)

corymbosum	CHll CSpe

Aglaonema (Araceae)

§ **crispum**	MBri
– 'Marie'	MBri
roebelinii	see *A. crispum*
'Silver Queen' ♀H1	MBri

Agonis (Myrtaceae)

flexuosa	CTrC
juniperina	LRav

Agrimonia (Rosaceae)

eupatoria	CArn COld CRWN EBee ELau
	GPoy MHer MNHC NMir NPri
	SECG SIde SWat WBri WGHP
	WHbs WHer WWye
* – var. **alba**	NBre NLar
– 'Topas'	ELau
grandiflora	EBee NBre
gryposepala	EBee
odorata misapplied	see *A. procera*
odorata (L.) Mill.	see *A. repens*
pilosa	CArn EBee MSal
§ **procera**	NEgg
§ **repens**	CSec GBar MSal WCHb WMoo

Agropyron (Poaceae)

glaucum	see *Elymus hispidus*
magellanicum	see *Elymus magellanicus*
pubiflorum	see *Elymus magellanicus*
scabrum	see *Elymus scabrus*

Agrostemma (Caryophyllaceae)

coronaria	see *Lychnis coronaria*
githago	CEnt GWCH MBow MWgw
	SBch

Agrostis (Poaceae)

calamagrostis	see *Stipa calamagrostis*
§ **canina** 'Silver Needles' (v)	CBre EBee EChP EGra EHoe EHul
	EMan EWes MMoz NBir NHol
	WFar WRos
'Lago Lago'	EBee
nebulosa	CKno EGoo

Aichryson (Crassulaceae)

§ x **domesticum**	CHal EBee EWin SEND
– 'Variegatum' (v) ♀H1	CHal EBak EWin WCot
tortuosum new	CFee

Ailanthus (Simaroubaceae)

§ **altissima**	CBcs CCVT CDul CHEx CLnd
	CPLG CTho EBee ECrN EMil EPfP
	EWTr LPan MBlu NBlu NEgg SAPC
	SArc SBLw SDnm SPer SPlb SWvt
	WBVN WDin WNor
– var. **tanakae**	WCru
B&SWJ 6777	
glandulosa	see *A. altissima*

Ainsliaea (Asteraceae)

acerifolia B&SWJ 4795   WCru
fragrans var. **integrifolia** WPtf

Aiphanes (Arecaceae)

aculeata   LPal

Ajania (Asteraceae)

§ **pacifica**   CHal EBee ELan EMan MOak SMer
       SPoG WHer XPep
pallasiana   GIBF
tibetica JJH 9308103   NWCA

Ajuga (Lamiaceae)

ciliata var. **villosior**   CFir GBin GCal WOut
genevensis   EPPr EShb EWTr WHil WOut
       WWeb
- 'Tottenham'   EBee
incisa new   CMil
- 'Bikun' (v)   MGos SPoG
- 'Blue Enigma' **new**   CLAP CWCL EBee LBBr SMac
       WOVN
'Little Court Pink'   LRHS
metallica hort.   see *A. pyramidalis*
'Monmotaro San'   EMan
'Pink Spires'   NCot
§ **pyramidalis**   CFee ECho WHer
- 'Metallica Crispa'   CBct COfd CRez CStu EBee
       ECho EMan EPPr EWes LAst MBNS
       NLar NRya SBch SMer SPoG SSvw
       SWvt WCMO WFar WWeb
       WWpP
reptans   CAgr CNic CRWN EBee ECtt ELau
       EMFW EWTr GKev GPoy LPBA
       MHer MNHC MSal NMir NSco
       SECG SGar WFar WWpP
- f. **albiflora** 'Alba'   CArn CNic CWan ECtt EMan
       EPfP GCal GGar IHMH MNrw
       MRav NBro NSti SRms WCAu
       WCHb WFar WHil WMoo
       WWye
- - 'Schneekerze'   EBee
- - 'Silver Shadow'   MAvo WTin
- 'Arctic Fox' (v)   More than 30 suppliers
- 'Argenta'   see *A. reptans* 'Variegata'
§ - 'Atropurpurea'   More than 30 suppliers
- 'Black Scallop' **new**   CBct CHVG EPPr EWin SVil
- 'Braunherz'   More than 30 suppliers
- 'Brean Down'   CNat
- 'Burgundy Glow' (v)   More than 30 suppliers
§ - 'Catlin's Giant' ♀H4   More than 30 suppliers
- 'Chocolate Chip'   see *A. reptans* 'Valfredda'
- 'Delight' (v)   ECho ECot WEas
- 'Ebony'   EBee LSRN SMac WBrE
- 'Ermine' (v)   EChP MNrw MTPN NLar SAga
- 'Flisteridge'   CNat
- 'Golden Beauty' **new**   EBee EWin
- 'Grey Lady'   GBuc NLar
- 'Harlequin' (v)   SWvt WBrE
- 'John Pierpoint'   SHar WCot
- 'Jumbo'   see *A. reptans* 'Jungle Beauty'
§ - 'Jungle Beauty'   CSev EAEE EBee EMan EPfP IHMH
       LSou MRav NCob SPoG WCAu
       WHen
- 'Little Pink Court'   EBee
- 'Macrophylla'   see *A. reptans* 'Catlin's Giant'
§ - 'Multicolor' (v)   CArn CBcs CHEx COfd COlW
       EBee ECho ELan GGar GKev
       IHMH LHop LPBA MBar MRav
       NFor SBod SPer SPlb SPoG SRms
       SWal SWvt WBrE WFar WMoo
       WTel
- 'Palisander'   EAEE EBee GSki LRHS MBNS
       NCob NLar
I - 'Pat's Selection' (v)   EMan LSou

- 'Pink Elf'   CBre CMHG CRow ECho EMan
       MRav NBro SBch SMac SWat WFar
       WHoo WWpP
- 'Pink Splendour'   CBre NBre NChi
- 'Pink Surprise'   CNic CRow EAEE ECha ECtt EHoe
       EPfP GBar GBuc LAst LRHS MHer
       MLHP NRya SSvw WEas WFar
       WGwG WMoo WTMC
- 'Purple Brocade'   EHoe
- 'Purple Torch'   EBee WEas WOut WTMC WWpP
- 'Purpurea'   see *A. reptans* 'Atropurpurea'
- 'Rainbow'   see *A. reptans* 'Multicolor'
- 'Rosea'   WHil WMoo
- 'Rowden Amethyst'   CRow
- 'Rowden Appleblossom'   CRow
- 'Rowden Blue Mist'   CRow
- 'Rowden Royal Purple'   CRow
- 'Silver Queen'   EBee ENor SMac
- 'Tricolor'   see *A. reptans* 'Multicolor'
§ - 'Valfredda'   EBee ECho ECtt EMan EShb EWin
       EWll GBin LAst LSou NCob NEgg
       NLar NPro SHar SPoG WCMO
       WCot WGwG WHil WOut WWeb
- 'Vanilla Chip' (v)   EBee EMan
§ - 'Variegata' (v)   CBcs CBct COfd ECho ECtt EDAr
       EHoe EPfP EShb LBMP LHop MHer
       MNHC NBid SBod SPer SPet SPoG
       SRms SWat WEas WFar WLin
       WMoo WWpP

Akebia (Lardizabalaceae)

longeracemosa   CBcs CPIN LEdu MBri NLar WCot
- B&SWJ 3606   WCru
x **pentaphylla**   CPIN EBee ELan EMil EPfP GQui
       LEdu LRHS SBra WSHC
- B&SWJ 2829   WCru
quinata   More than 30 suppliers
- B&SWJ 4425   WCru
- 'Alba'   CBcs CPIN CSPN WPat
- 'Amethyst' **new**   MWea
- 'Amethyst Glow'   LRHS MBri SPoG
- cream-flowered   EPfP ERea LRHS MWea SBra SPer
       SPoG SSta SWvt WCMO WCru
- variegated (v)   CBcs WCru WPat
- 'White Chocolate'   WCru
trifoliata   CBcs CHEx CPIN EBee EPfP LBuc
       LRHS MDun SLim
- B&SWJ 2829   WCru
- B&SWJ 5063   WCru
- 'Amethyst' **new**   SBra

Alangium (Alangiaceae)

chinense   CBcs EPla WBVN
platanifolium   CAbP CMCN CPLG IArd IDee
       MBlu NLar WPGP
- var. **macrophyllum**   CBcs
- var. **platanifolium**   NLar

Albizia (Mimosaceae)

chinensis   CSec
distachya   see *Paraserianthes lophantha*
§ **julibrissin**   CArn CSec CTrC EWin IDee LAst
       LPan LRHS MGol SBLw SECG SHFr
       SPlb WDin WMul
- 'Ernest Wilson' **new**   SMad
- Ombrella = 'Boubri'PBR   LPan LRHS SBLw
- f. **rosea** ♀H2-3   More than 30 suppliers
lophantha   see *Paraserianthes lophantha*

Albuca (Hyacinthaceae)

altissima   CStu EBee WCot
* **batliana new**   ECho
batteniana   CFir EBee ECho ERea LBow
canadensis   CStu WHil
caudata   CMon
clanwilliamigloria   WPrP

'Dirk Wallace' **new**	CPLG
flaccida **new**	LBow
from Lesotho	GCal WAbe
humilis	CDes CMon CNic CPLG CStu EBee ECho ETow NMen WAbe WCot WPrP
maxima	WCMO WCot
nelsonii	CAvo CMon EBee EREa LRHS WCMO WPGP
* *pumila*	NWCA
setosa	CMon
shawii	CAvo CBro CDes CFFs CPrp CStu EAEE EBee ECho EMan EMar EMil ERos LBow NCGa NSla NWCA SAga SBch SBla SPet WAbe WHil WPGP WPrP
spiralis	CDes
trichophylla	MDKP WCMO WCot
unifolia	WCot
wakefieldii	CMon

Alcea (Malvaceae)

'Antwerp'	SWal
'Apple Blossom' (d) **new**	NBHF
'Arabian Nights'	NBHF SPav
'Blackcurrant Whirl'	NBHF SPav
ficifolia	EChP EDsa GMac LSou MCCP MTis SDnm SPav WMoo
'Happy Lights'	CWib
kurdica **new**	EBee
pallida	SMar
'Peaches and Cream'	NRnb
'Peaches 'n' Dreams'	CWib CWoW EBee MBri NRnb
§ *rosea*	CHrt CSim EUnu GWCH LAst WFar XPep
- 'Black Beauty'	NBur
- Chater's Double Group (d)	CWib ECtt ENot EPfP MBri MLan MWat NFor SRms
- - chamois (d)	EShb WViv
- - chestnut brown (d)	WViv
- - pink (d)	ECtt NPri SPer WViv
- - red (d)	ECtt EShb NPri SMar WViv
- - salmon pink (d)	EPfP EShb WViv
- - violet (d)	EShb SMar SPer
- - white (d)	EPfP EShb NPri SMar SPer WViv
- - yellow (d)	ECtt EPfP NPri SPer WViv
- 'Crème de Cassis'	CWoW MSph MWat NRnb SPav
- double apricot (d)	NBHF NBur
- double pink (d)	MHer
- double red (d)	MHer
- double rose (d)	EBee SPer
- double scarlet (d)	SMar SPer SPla
- double white (d)	MHer
- double yellow (d)	EBee MHer
- 'Jet Black'	LAst
- 'Lemon Light'	LHop NBur
- 'Nigra'	CArn CHad CHby CSpe EBee EChP EGoo EHrv EPfP EShb LAst LHop LRHS MBNS MHer MSte MWat MWgw NFor NGdn NPri SGar SMad SPer WCAu WCMO WFar WHlf XPep
- single	MWat MWgw
- single pink	LHop LRHS
- Summer Carnival Group	CWib LAst SRms WGor
- 'Victoria Ann' (v)	LSou
- yellow	IHMH MMHG
§ *rugosa*	CHad CMea CSam CSim EMan EMar GKev LRHS MSte MWgw SPav WPGP
'The Watchman'	SECG

Alcea x *Althaea* (Malvaceae)

'Parkallee' (d)	EBee EChP ECtt EMan EMon GBin GBri LBmB LDai LPhx MAvo MCCP NBPC SUsu WCMO WCot
'Parkfrieden' (d)	EMan LPhx WCot
'Parkrondell' (d)	ECha EMan EMon GBri LBmB NCot WCot

Alchemilla ✿ (Rosaceae)

§ *abyssinica*	CNic EBee ECho WHen WHrl WOut
alpina misapplied	see *A. conjuncta*, *A. plicatula*
alpina L.	CFee CMea EBla ECho ECrN EPfP LEdu LRHS MRav NChi NFor NGHP NMir SBch SIng SPet SRms SWat WFar WKif WMoo WPer WWhi
aroanica	EBee EBla
arvensis	see *Aphanes arvensis*
§ *conjuncta*	More than 30 suppliers
elisabethae	EBla ECGP EMon WCHb
ellenbeckii	CFee CMCo EBee EBla ECho EDAr EWsh GAbr GBar GGar LAst MHar MTho MWgw NChi SWat WCHb WFar WHen WPGP WPat
epipsila	CFwr EBee EShb EWes LBBr LPhx MSte NLar WPer
erythropoda ♀H4	More than 30 suppliers
faeroensis	CMCo EBee WPer WPtf
- var. *pumila*	CLyd EBla EHyt NMen
filicaulis 'Minima'	CNat
§ *fulgens*	EWTr LEdu WHen
glaucescens	CNat EBla EMon
hoppeana misapplied	see *A. plicatula*
hoppeana (Reichenb.) Dalla Torre	GCal
iniquiformis	EBee WPGP
lapeyrousei	EBee EBla EMon EPPr
mollis ♀H4	More than 30 suppliers
I - 'Auslese'	EBee WWpP
* - 'Robusta'	EBee EPla NBur SEND SPlb SWat WFar WMoo WPnP WWpP
* - 'Senior'	IHMH
- 'Thriller'	EBee EWin IBal NBur WWeb
monticola	WPer
'Mr Poland's Variety'	see *A. venosa*
pentaphylla	EBee EBla
§ *plicatula*	WPer
psilomischa	EMon
pumila	NBre
robusta	SWvt
saxatilis	IFoB WPer
speciosa	EBee
splendens misapplied	see *A. fulgens*
straminea	MRav NBre
§ *venosa*	SPer
aff. *venosa*	EPla
vetteri	EBee EBla WHrl
vulgaris misapplied	see *A. xanthochlora*
§ *xanthochlora*	CArn EBee GBar GPoy MSal NBre NLar NSco SRms WFar WHer WPer

Aldrovanda (Droseraceae)

vesiculosa	EFEx

alecost see *Tanacetum balsamita*

Alectryon (Sapindaceae)

excelsus	CBcs

Alisma (Alismataceae)

plantago-aquatica	CBen CRow EHon EMFW LNCo LPBA NPer NSco SWat WFar WMAq WPnP WWpP
- var. *parviflorum*	CBen LPBA SPlb SWat WMAq WWpP

Alkanna (Boraginaceae)

orientalis	EDsa
tinctoria	MSal
- HH&K 345	CMdw

Allamanda (Apocynaceae)

§ **blanchetii**	SOWG
cathartica	ERea LRHS MBri MJnS
- 'Birthe'	MBri
- 'Cherry Red'	MJnS
- 'Grandiflora'	CPlN
- 'Halley's Comet'	SOWG
- 'Hendersonii' ♀H1	LRHS
'Cherries Jubilee' **new**	SOWG
'Jamaican Sunset'	MJnS SOWG
neriifolia	see *A. schottii*
§ **schottii** ♀H1	LRHS SOWG
violacea	see *A. blanchetii*

Alliaria (Brassicaceae)

petiolata	CAgr CArn GPoy NLan WHbs WHer

Allium ❁ (Alliaceae)

aciphyllum	WCot
§ **acuminatum**	CPom EBee ECho GBin GSki NBir NMen
I - 'Album'	ECho
aflatunense misapplied	see *A. hollandicum*
aflatunense B. Fedtsch.	EBee EBrs EMon LHop MNHC
'Akbulak'	ECho MSte
albopilosum	see *A. cristophii*
altissimum 'Goliath'	CGrW EBee LRHS WCot
amabile	see *A. mairei* var. *amabile*
ampeloprasum	CAgr ECha ECho WHer WShi
- var. **babingtonii**	CAgr CArn CAvo CNat GPoy ILis LEdu MLLN WHer WShi
amphibolum	EBee EHrv
§ **angulosum**	CAgr CAvo CMea EBee ECho MSph SMrm WCot WGHP
angustitepalum	see *A. jesdianum* subsp. *angustitepalum*
atropurpureum	CAby CBgR EBee EBrs EChP ECha EHrv ELan EMon EPfP LEdu LPhx LRHS MLLN MMHG NBPC SGar SMeo SPur WGwG
azureum	see *A. caeruleum*
balansae	SOkd
barszczewskii	EBee
'Beau Regard' ♀H4	CWCL EBee ERou NDvn
beesianum misapplied	see *A. cyaneum*
beesianum W.W. Smith	CLyd CPom EHyt EPot GCrs GEdr NBir NRya SBla SMeo
- CD&R 95 from Sichuan, China **new**	SMHy
blandum	see *A. carolinianum*
bolanderi new	GCrs
brevicaule	LRHS
bucharicum	ERos
bulgaricum	see *Nectaroscordum siculum* subsp. *bulgaricum*
§ - **caeruleum** ♀H4	More than 30 suppliers
- *azureum*	see *A. caeruleum*
callimischon	CBro
- subsp. **haemostictum**	CBgR ECho EHyt NMen SBla
campanulatum	GCrs
canadense	CArn EBee SHar
§ **carinatum**	ECho WSan
§ - subsp. **pulchellum** ♀H4	More than 30 suppliers
- - f. **album** ♀H4	CAvo CBgR CBro CPom CSWP EBee EBrs EChP ECha ECho EGle EMon EPot ERos ERou LLWP LPhx LRHS MBow MNrw NChi NDov NMen SBch WBor WCot WHil
- - 'Tubergen'	EBee EBrs ECho
§ **carolinianum**	GCrs MGol WCot
cassium subsp. **hirtellum new**	LRHS
cepa Aggregatum Group	GPoy ILis
- 'Kew White'	WCot
- 'Perutile'	CArn GBar GPoy ILis LEdu MHer
- Proliferum Group	CArn CBod CHby CPrp CSev CWan GBar GPoy ILis LEdu MHer MNHC NGHP SIde WCHb WGwG WHer WJek WSel
- var. **viviparum**	ECho
cernuum	More than 30 suppliers
§ - 'Hidcote' ♀H4	EMon MSte WBVN WGHP WKif
- 'Major'	see *A. cernuum* 'Hidcote'
- var. **obtusum**	WCot
- pink-flowered	EBrs GBBs GSki SIng
cirrhosum	see *A. carinatum* subsp. *pulchellum*
commutatum	WCMO
cowanii	see *A. neapolitanum* Cowanii Group
crenulatum	EHyt GCrs
§ **cristophii** ♀H4	More than 30 suppliers
§ **cyaneum** ♀H4	CGra CLyd CPBP CPom CSec EBrs ECho EHyt ERos GBBs GCrs GEdr LBee LRHS NChi NJOw NMen NRya SBla SUsu WCot WRHF
cyathophorum	ECho GBBs GCrs
§ - var. **farreri**	CArn CBgR CBre CBro CNic CSec EBee ECho EPot ERos GCrs GEdr GSki LBee LEdu LLWP MLHP MRav MSte NMen NRya SBch WCMO WCot WPrP
darwasicum	ECho
delicatulum	EBee
dichlamydeum	ERos
dregeanum	LBow
§ **drummondii**	CPom ECho ERos
'Early Emperor' **new**	CWCL
elatum	see *A. macleanii*
ericetorum	ERos WCot
eusperma	ECho WCot
falcifolium	EBee EChP ECho EPot NMen
farreri	see *A. cyathophorum* var. *farreri*
fasciculatum	ECho
fetisowii	EBee
fimbriatum	ECho
'Firmament'	CAvo CBro CFFs EBee EChP ECha ECho EMon IPot LPhx LRHS MSte
fistulosum	CArn CBod CHby CWan EBee ELau GBar GPoy GSki ILis LEdu MHer MNHC NFor NGHP NHol NPri SIde SWal WCHb WGwG WPer WWye
- red	CBod CPrp NGHP
- 'Red Welsh'	CAgr ILis SWal WJek
flavum ♀H4	CAby CArn CAvo CBgR CBro CFFs CPom EBrs ECha ECho EGle GSki IFoB MRav SBch SHBN SPer WBVN WGor WGwG WRHF
§ - 'Blue Leaf'	EBee ECho ERos MLLN NBir
- subsp. **flavum**	EBee ECho ERou LEdu LPhx MBow MMHG MNrw NJOw
- - var. **minus**	EBee ECho EHyt MTho NJOw NWCA
- 'Glaucum'	see *A. flavum* 'Blue Leaf'
- var. **nanum**	CNic ECho GCrs GEdr NJOw
- subsp. **tauricum**	EBee ECho LPhx NJOw
forrestii	CSec EBee GBin GCrs MDKP
geyeri	EBee ECho EHyt WCot
giganteum ♀H4	More than 30 suppliers
'Gladiator' ♀H4	CFir CWCL EBee EChP ECtt EMar EMon ERou LPhx LRHS MLLN MRav MSte NOrc SPer SPet WDav
glaucum	see *A. senescens* subsp. *montanum* var. *glaucum*
'Globemaster' ♀H4	CAvo CBro CFFs CFir CMea CPom CWCL EBee EBrs EHrv ELan EPfP ERou LEdu LPhx LRHS MBri

	MMHG MSte NFor SMeo SPer WCMO WCot WCra WFar WHal
globosum	ECho
'Globus'	EBee ERou LRHS
goodingii	CNic CPom EBee ECho EHyt GCrs
'Guna' **new**	LRHS
guttatum subsp. *dalmaticum*	EBee
- subsp. *sardoum*	ECho
haematochiton	WCot
'Hair'	see *A. vineale* 'Hair'
* *hirtifolium* var. *album*	EBee ECho
'His Excellency'	CFir EBee EBrs ECho ERou LRHS MSte
§ *hollandicum* ♀H4	More than 30 suppliers
- 'Purple Sensation' ♀H4	More than 30 suppliers
hookeri ACE 2430	EPot WCot
- var. *muliense*	GEdr
humile	WCot
hyalinum pink	EBee WCot WPrP
§ *insubricum* ♀H4	ECho ERos GCrs GEdr LEdu NBir NMen NRya SIng WAbe WDav
jajlae	see *A. rotundum* subsp. *jajlae*
jesdianum	CBro ECho EMon WCMO
- subsp. *angustitepalum*	EBee
- 'Michael Hoog'	see *A. rosenbachianum* 'Michael Hoog'
- 'Purple King'	CMdw EBee ECho ERou MNrw MSte
- white-flowered	EBee ECho ERou
kansuense	see *A. sikkimense*
karataviense ♀H3	More than 30 suppliers
- 'Ivory Queen'	CBro CMea EBee EBrs EChP ECha ECho ECtt EMar EMon EPfP GKev LRHS MNFA MSph MSte MWat NBPC NJOw NMRc SPer SPlb WAul WDav WFar WGwG WWhi
- 'Kara Tau'	LRHS
karelinii	EHyt
ledebourianum	ECho
lenkoranicum	EBee ECho
libani	WPer
§ *lineare*	CPom IHMH
'Lucy Ball'	EBee EBrs ECtt EMon EPot ERou LPhx LRHS MLLN MSte NBir NLar SPet
§ *macleanii*	CArn EBee ECho LRHS WDav
macranthum	EBee EBrs ECho GBBs GEdr MSte WCot
mairei	CLyd EAEE EBee ECho ERos GBBs LHop LLWP LRHS MBar NMen NRya WGwG WTin
§ - var. *amabile*	CLyd EBee ERos GCrs GEdr NChi NJOw NLAp NRya NSla WCot
'Mars'	CFir ERou LEdu LRHS MLLN NLar
maximowiczii	CBgR ECho
meteoricum	LRHS
moly	CArn CBro CWCL EBee EBrs ECho EPfP GSki IFoB MBow MBri MRav NGHP NJOw NRya SRms WBor WCHb WCot WHil WTin
- 'Jeannine' ♀H4	CBro CMea EBee ECho EPot GAbr LPhx MLLN
'Mont Blanc'	CMea EBee ELan ERou IPot
'Mount Everest'	CArn CAvo CBro CFfs CFir EBee EBrs EChP EMon EPot ERou EShb LPhx LRHS MLLN MSte MWgw NCGa WDav WShi
multibulbosum	see *A. nigrum*
murrayanum misapplied	see *A. unifolium*
murrayanum Reg.	see *A. acuminatum*
narcissiflorum misapplied	see *A. insubricum*
§ *narcissiflorum* Villars	ECho GCrs WCot WDav
neapolitanum	CAgr CArn EBee ECho EPot LRHS MBri NWCA SPer SRms WGwG
§ - Cowanii Group	CBro EBee ECho EHrv EWTr LRHS NLRH WCMO WCot
- 'Grandiflorum'	CSam EBee ECho LPhx LRHS MLLN WBrE
nevskianum	EBee ECho LRHS
§ *nigrum*	CArn CAvo CBro CFfs CHby CSec EBee EBrs ECho EHrv EMon EPot EShb LRHS MLLN MRav MWgw NBir NJOw WCot
noeanum	CSec
nutans	CBod EBee ECho EHol EUnu EWin IHMH LEdu NGHP SHDw WHal WJek
nuttallii	see *A. drummondii*
§ *obliquum*	CArn CMil CSec EBee ECha ECho EGle GSki LRHS MSte SUsu WCot WTin
odorum L.	see *A. ramosum* L.
oleraceum	WHer
§ *oreophilum*	CArn CAvo CBro CFfs CSam CWCL EBee ECha ECho ECtt EHrv EHyt EPfP GSki LRHS MLLN NJOw NRya SPer SRms WBor WCot WHoo WLin WTin
- 'Zwanenburg' ♀H4	CBro EBee ECho EPot NMen WCot
ostrowskianum	see *A. oreophilum*
ovalifolium var. *leuconeurum* **new**	WCot
pallens	CBre CHea NBir
§ *paniculatum*	CSec EChP EHyt
paradoxum	EBee LEdu LRHS NBir
- var. *normale*	CBgR CBro CDes CMea ECho EHyt EMan EMon EPot NJOw NMen WCMO WCot WDav
pedemontanum	see *A. narcissiflorum* Villars
peninsulare	EHyt
platycaule	WCot
plurifoliatum	ECho
polyphyllum	see *A. carolinianum*
pulchellum	see *A. carinatum* subsp. *pulchellum*
'Purple Giant'	NDvn WCMO
'Purple Pride' **new**	LPhx
pyrenaicum misapplied	see *A. angulosum*
pyrenaicum Costa & Vayreda	ELan
ramosum Jacquin	see *A. obliquum*
§ *ramosum* L.	EBee ECho NBre NCob NGHP WPer
'Rien Poortvliet'	CArn LRHS
rosenbachianum misapplied	see *A. stipitatum*
§ *rosenbachianum* Regel	CArn CBro CSec EBee EMon EPot ERou MLLN WDav
- 'Akbulak'	EBee ECho LRHS
- 'Album'	EBee ECha ECho EPot ERou MLLN WCot WDav
§ - 'Michael Hoog'	EBee ECho ERou LRHS WCot
- 'Purple King'	ECho LRHS SPur
- 'Shing'	EBee LRHS
roseum	CAgr CArn CMea CPBP EBee ECho ECtt ERos LLWP LRav MDKP NCGa
§ - var. *bulbiferum*	WCot
- 'Grandiflorum'	see *A. roseum* var. *bulbiferum*
§ *rotundum* subsp. *jajlae*	EBee ECho LLWP LRHS
'Round and Purple' **new**	EBee
rubellum	ERos
sarawschanicum	EBee ECho
- 'Chinoro'	ECho LRHS
sativum	CArn MHer MNHC SIde WSel WWye
- 'Arno' ♀H4	CPrp
- 'Cristo' ♀H4 **new**	CPrp
- 'Elephant'	CArn NGHP
- golden	GPoy

- 'Iberian Wight' **new** NGHP
- 'Mediterranean Wight' **new** NGHP
- var. **ophioscorodon** EBee ECho GPoy ILis MWgw
- - 'Early White' ♀H4 **new** NGHP
- - 'Purple Wight' **new** NGHP
- 'Printanor' CBod
- 'Solent White' ♀H4 NGHP
- 'Sprint' **new** CPrp
- 'Thermidrôme' CBod
saxatile EBee ECho ERos
schmitzii EMon
schoenoprasum More than 30 suppliers
- 'Black Isle Blush' CPbn GPoy MHer SMHy
- 'Corsican White' EMon
- fine-leaved ELau IHMH WGwG
- 'Forescate' CBgR CBod CPrp EAEE EBee ECha
EWes GBar GCal GSki LAst LHop
LRHS MLLN MRav SBch SIde SPet
SPla SSvw WCHb WHil
- 'Forncett Forescate' CBgR
- 'Grolau' EUnu
- medium-leaved ELau
- 'Netherbyres Dwarf' **new** CArn
- 'Pink Perfection' GPoy MHer SMHy
- 'Polyphant' CBre WCHb WRha
- 'Shepherds' Crooks' WThu
- var. **sibiricum** CAgr GBar GGar SDix WSel WShi
- 'Silver Chimes' CDes CMea CMil CWan EBee
MRav SBch SHDw WGHP
- thick-leaved NPri
- 'Wallington White' GBar
- white-flowered CArn CBgR CPbn CPrp CSWP
ECha ECrN GMaP IHMH LEdu
MHer MSte NBir NCGa NHol SIde
SSvw WCHb WEas WGHP WHer
WWye
schubertii More than 30 suppliers
scorodoprasum CAgr SIde WCHb WJek
- subsp. **jajlae** see *A. rotundum* subsp. *jajlae*
- subsp. **scorodoprasum** LEdu
senescens CAgr CArn CBro CTri EBee ECGP
ECho ERos EWsh IHMH MRav
NChi NJOw SBch SBla SIng SRms
SSvw WTin
- var. **calcareum** CPLG EBee IHMH
- giant **new** EMon
§ - subsp. **montanum** CBro CSpe ECha ECho EGoo EHol
EPot LEdu NBre NMen SDix SIng
SMHy WAbe WCot WGHP WMoo
§ - - var. **glaucum** CArn CBgR CLyd CMea CPBP
CPrp CSpe EAEE EBee EBrs ECha
EMar EPla ETow GEdr LEdu MNFA
SIng SMeo SPet WCot WPer WRos
WTin WWye
- subsp. **senescens** EBee EMon LEdu MLLN SUsu
WCMO WPrP
sibthorpianum see *A. paniculatum*
siculum see *Nectaroscordum siculum*
sieheanum EBee
§ **sikkimense** CBro CPom CWCL EAEE EBee
EBrs ECho ERos LRHS MDKP
NCGa NSla NWCA SBla SPet SPla
SSvw WCMO WCot WPer WPrP
sphaerocephalon More than 30 suppliers
splendens EBee ERos
stellatum CAgr EBee LRHS WGwG
stellerianum WPer
- var. **kurilense** CLyd CNic
§ **stipitatum** EChP EMon LPhx LRHS WCot
- 'Album' CArn CBro EBee EMon EPot LRHS
- 'Glory of Pamir' EBee LRHS
§ - 'Violet Beauty' CWCL EBee LPhx SMeo WCot
stracheyi WCot
strictum Schrad. see *A. lineare*
subhirsutum CLyd EBee

subvillosum ERos WCot
'Summer Beauty' see *A. senescens* subsp.
montanum
'Sweet Discovery' EBee
tanguticum EBrs LRHS NJOw
textile ERos
§ **thunbergii** ♀H4 EBee ECho GCrs NBir NDlv
- 'Nanum' CPom EPot
- 'Ozawa' EBee EHyt NMen SBla SIng WCot
tibeticum see *A. sikkimense*
* **tournefortii** EBee ECho
triquetrum CAgr CAvo CStu EBee ECho ELan
ELau EPfP EPot GGar IBlr ILis
LPhx MBow NBir NSti STes SYvo
WCot WCru WGHP WHer WLin
WMoo WShi
tuberosum More than 30 suppliers
- B&SWJ 8881 WCru
- purple/mauve CHby ELau GWCH WMoo
tubiflorum ECho
§ **unifolium** ♀H4 More than 30 suppliers
ursinum CArn CAvo CBgR CHby CWan
GPoy MBow MNHC MWat NGHP
NMir NTHB WAul WCHb WFar
WHen WJek WShi WWye
'Valerie Finnis' ECho SBla
victorialis GCal
vineale CArn EBee NMir WHer
§ - 'Hair' CBgR EBrs EChP ECho EMan EMar
EPfP ITer LRHS MBri MWgw
NJOw WHil WTMC
violaceum see *A. carinatum*
'Violet Beauty' see *A. stipitatum* 'Violet Beauty'
virgunculae EBee EHyt SBla SCnR
wallichii CLyd CPou ECho EMon MBNS
MGol NBir WCot WTin
- ACE 2458 WCot
- CC&McK 1025 WCot
- dark-flowered **new** WDav
- plum-flowered GEdr
- purple-flowered **new** GEdr
'White Giant' EBee ERou LPhx MSte SMeo
'World Cup' LRHS
zaprjagajevii LEdu
zebdanense EBee ECho ERos LRHS NJOw

Allocasuarina (Casuarinaceae)

monilifera ECou
nana EShb IDee
zephyrea CTrC

almond see *Prunus dulcis*

Alnus ✿ (Betulaceae)

cordata ♀H4 CBcs CCVT CDoC CDul CLnd
CMCN CSBt CTho CTri EBee ECrN
ELan EPfP EWTr LBuc MGos MRav
NBee NEgg NWea SBLw SHBN
SPer SPlb SSta WDin WFar WMou
WOrn
cremastogyne NLar
crispa see *A. viridis* subsp. *crispa*
fauriei from Niigata, CSto
Japan **new**
firma CDul CMCN IArd IDee
- var. **sieboldiana** see *A. sieboldiana*
formosana GIBF
fruticosa see *A. viridis* subsp. *fruticosa*
glutinosa CBcs CCVT CDoC CDul CLnd
CRWN CSBt CTri EBee ECrN EPfP
EWTr LBuc MGos NBee NBlu
NWea SBLw SHBN SHFr WDin
WMou WOrn
- from Corsica **new** CSto
- 'Aurea' CDul CEnd CLnd CTho CWib
EBee ECrN MBlu MDun SBLw SPer

- var. **barbata**	CSto GIBF
- 'Imperialis' ♀H4	CDoC CDul CEnd CPMA CTho
	EBee ECrN ELan EPfP EWTr IMGH
	LPan LRHS MBlu MBri MDun NBee
	NPal SBLw SPer SPoG WDin WOrn
- 'Laciniata'	CDoC CDul CTho ECrN MBlu
	MDun NBlu SBLw WFar
hirsuta	CMCN CSto
- var. **sibirica**	GIBF
x **hybrida**	GIBF
incana	CDoC CDul CLnd CMCN CWib
	ECrN LBuc MBar MGos MMuc
	NWea SBLw SHBN SPer WDin
	WMou
- 'Aurea'	CBcs CDul CEnd CLnd CTho ECrN
	ELan EPfP EPla IArd LPan LRHS
	MBar MBlu MBri MGos NPal SBLw
	SHBN SPer SPoG WDin WOrn WPat
- 'Laciniata'	CDul CTho LPan MGos SBLw
	WDin WFar
- 'Pendula'	CDul CLnd CTho SBLw
japonica	CLnd CSto NLar
- var. **arguta**	GIBF
lanata	CMCN WHCr
maximowiczii	CSto NLar
nepalensis	WCwm
nitida	CMCN CSto IArd IDee NLar
oregana	see *A. rubra*
orientalis	GIBF
rhombifolia	CMCN
§ **rubra**	CAgr CCVT CDoC CDul CLnd
	CMCN CPLG CTho ECrN ELan
	NLar NWea SBLw WDin WMou
- 'Pinnatifida'	see *A. rubra* f. *pinnatisecta*
§ - f. **pinnatisecta**	CLnd CMCN CTho
§ **rugosa**	CMCN
serrulata	see *A. rugosa*
§ **sieboldiana**	CSto
sinuata	see *A. viridis* subsp. *sinuata*
x **spaethii**	CDoC CTho SBLw SEND
subcordata	CLnd CSto
viridis	CAgr CMCN CSto ECrN NWea
	SBLw
§ - subsp. **crispa**	GIBF
- - var. **mollis**	CMCN
§ - subsp. **fruticosa**	GIBF
§ - subsp. **sinuata**	CAgr CMCN NWea

Alocasia ✿ (Araceae)

x **amazonica** ♀H1	ERea LRHS MBri XBlo
- 'Emerald Green' **new**	XBlo
'Calidora'	MJnS
cucullata	CFir WMul
gageana	CKob EAmu WMul
macrorrhiza	CHen CKob EAmu EZes MJnS
	MOak SBig WMul
- 'Lutea'	EZes SBig WMul
- 'Variegata' (v) ♀H1	EZes MJnS SBig WMul
odora	EAmu EZes MJnS MOak WMul
'Portodora'	EAmu MJnS MOak WMul
rubra new	XBlo
wentii	EAmu MOak

Aloe (Aloaceae)

aculeata	EShb WCot
arborescens	CAbb CHEx CTrC EShb EWll SChr
	WMul
- yellow-flowered	CTrC
aristata ♀H1	CAbb CHEx CHal EPem MBri
	SAPC SArc SChr SEND SPet SWvt
	WGwG WHer
barbadensis	see *A. vera*
barberae	WMul
bellatula	LToo
branddraaiensis	WCot
brevifolia ♀H1	CRoM EShb SAPC SArc

broomii	CCCN EPem EPfP SChr
camperi 'Maculata'	SChr
ciliaris	EMan ERea EShb SChr WCot
comptonii new	EShb
cooperi	CAbb CCCN
dawei	EPem EShb
dichotoma	CAbb EShb
distans	SEND
dumetorum	EPem
ecklonis	CCCN CTrC SChr SPlb
excelsa	SChr
ferox	CAbb CBrP CCCN CTrC EShb
	EUnu MSal SBig SChr SEND SWal
	WMul
globuligemma	WCot
greatheadii	CTrC SChr
- var. **davyana**	CCtw
humilis	CTrC EPem EShb SChr
imalotensis	LToo
immaculata	WCot
juvenna	EPem
littoralis	EPem
maculata	CHEx CHen CTrC
marlothii	CAbb CCCN EPem EShb WMul
microstigma new	CCCN SChr
mitriformis	EPfP NPri SChr SEND
mutabilis	CHEx CTrC SChr
parallelifolia	LToo
plicatilis	CAbb CCCN CTrC EShb
pratensis	CCCN CFir CPLG SChr SPlb
prinslooi	EPem
ramosissima	EShb
reitzii	CTrC IDee SPlb
speciosa new	EShb
x **spinosissima**	SChr
striata	CCCN EPem EShb SChr XPep
striatula	CAbb CBrP CHEx CHen CTbh
	CTrC EAmu EBee EShb IBlr LPJP
	SAPC SArc SBig SChr WGer WMul
	WPGP XPep
- var. **caesia**	IBlr
succotrina	CAbb
thraskii	CAbb WMul
variegata (v) ♀H1	EShb SWal SWvt WEas
§ **vera** ♀H1	CArn CCCN CDoC CHby COld
	CSpe CTbh ELau EOHP EPem
	ERea EShb GPoy IFro ILis MNHC
	MPRe MSal NPer NPri NScw SBch
	SIde SWal WCot WHer

Alonsoa (Scrophulariaceae)

'Bright Spark'	CSpe EMan
meridionalis	NJOw WWeb
- 'Shell Pink'	WWeb
'Pink Beauty'	CSpe NBur
unilabiata	CSpe
warscewiczii	CEnt CHll ELan NBlu SHFr
- pale-flowered	see *A. warscewiczii* 'Peachy-keen'
§ - 'Peachy-keen'	CSpe

Alopecurus (Poaceae)

alpinus	see *A. borealis*
§ **borealis**	EHoe EMan LRHS MMoz NBur
	WWye
- subsp. **glaucus**	CBrm CPen EBee EHoe GBin GCal
	NSti SPer SPoG
geniculatus	CRWN
lanatus	NBea
pratensis	NOrc
- 'Aureovariegatus' (v)	CWan EBee EHoe ENot EPPr EPla
	GCal GMaP GSki IHMH MBar MBnl
	MBri MMoz MSte MWgw NBid
	NFor NHol SLim SPer WFar WMoo
- 'Aureus'	EChP ECha EGra GBin LRHS MRav
	MWhi NBro NGdn SPlb WFar
- 'No Overtaking' (v)	EPPr WWpP

Alophia (Iridaceae)
drummondii	ERos
lahue	see *Herbertia lahue*

Aloysia (Verbenaceae)
chamaedrifolia	CPle XPep
citriodora	see *A. triphylla*
§ *triphylla* ♀H2	More than 30 suppliers

Alpinia (Zingiberaceae)
B&SWJ 3775 **new**	CKob WPGP
formosana	LEdu MOak
galanga	WMul
japonica	CKob LEdu MSal
– B&SWJ 8889	WCru
malaccensis	CKob
– B&SWJ 7196	WCru
nutans misapplied	see *A. zerumbet*
officinarum	CArn
purpurata	MJnS
– pink	MJnS
speciosa	see *A. zerumbet*
§ *vittata* (v)	EZes MOak SBig
§ *zerumbet*	MJnS MOak WMul
– 'Variegata' (v)	CKob EAmu MJnS MOak WMul XBlo

Alsobia see *Episcia*

Alstroemeria ✿ (Alstroemeriaceae)
'Aimi'	CDoC COtt LRHS MBri NBre SBai SWal SWvt WFar WViv
'Angelina'	CDoC LRHS SBai SPer SVil SWvt
angustifolia	GCrs
'Apollo' ♀H4	CDoC COtt LRHS MBNS MBri NBre SBai SPer SWvt WViv
aurantiaca	see *A. aurea*
§ *aurea*	CTri EPfP EWin GGar MDun MRav MWrn NLar SRms WMoo WSHC
– 'Apricot'	GCal
– 'Cally Fire'	GCal WCMO
– 'Dover Orange'	CBod EChP EPfP IGor LRHS MWgw NEgg SCoo SPoG
– 'Lutea'	EChP EWll LRHS NBre SPlb WCMO
– 'Orange King'	CBod CDoC EBee ELan EPfP EWll LRHS NLar WCMO WTin
'Blushing Bride'	CBcs CDoC EMar MBNS MBri SBai SPer SVil SWvt WViv WWlt
'Bonanza' **new**	CDoC SBai SPer
brasiliensis	EBee EShb GCal NChi WCMO WSHC
Butterfly hybrids	SWal
'Charm'	LRHS WFar
'Coronet' ♀H4	COtt LRHS MBNS WCra WViv
'Dandy Candy'	CBrm NLar WCMO
'Desire'	EBee
diluta subsp. *chrysantha* F&W 8700	WCot
Doctor Salter's hybrids	ECGP LTwo MWgw SRms SWal
'Elvira' **new**	CDoC EMar SBai SPer
'Eternal Love'	COtt
'Evening Song'	CDoC EMar LRHS MBNS MBri SBai SPer SVil SWal SWvt WViv
aff. *exserens*	WCot
'Firefly'	LRHS
'Flaming Star'	CBcs CDoC EMar LIck MBri SBai SVil WCMO WCot WViv
'Fortune'	LRHS
'Frances' (v)	CAvo CFFs
'Friendship' ♀H4	CBcs CDoC EMar NBre SBai SWal SWvt WCMO WViv
garaventae	NLar
gayana	WCot

'Gloria' **new**	WViv
'Glory of the Andes' (v)	EMan EMar NLar
'Golden Delight'	CDoC COtt LIck LRHS MBri SBai SPer SPla SVil WViv
'Golden Queen'	WFar
§ H.R.H. Princess Alice = 'Staverpi'PBR ♀H2	WFar
haemantha	MDKP
'Hawera'	WCMO
Hawera Seedlings	EBee
hookeri	ECho GCal SCnR
– subsp. *cummingiana*	LTwo WCMO WCot
huemulina	MDKP
'Inca Blaze'	WViv
'Inca Dream'	WViv
Inca Exotica = 'Koexotica' **new**	MGos WViv
Inca Glow = 'Koglow' **new**	MGos WViv
'Inca Ice' = 'Koice'	MGos WViv
'Inca Moonlight'	WViv
Inca Obsession = 'Koobsion' **new**	WViv
Inca Serin = 'Koserin' **new**	WViv
Inca Tropic = 'Kotrop'	MGos WViv
Isabella = 'Stalis' **new**	WCra
kingii	see *A. versicolor*
ligtu hybrids	CAvo CBcs CFFs CSBt EBrs EChP ECha ELan EPfP IFoB LAst LHop LRHS MDun MNrw MWgw NPer NVic SBla SPoG SRms SWal SWvt WBVN WBrE WFar WHoo WTin
– var. *ligtu*	LPhx WCot
'Lilac Wonder'	EBee NBhm
'Little Eleanor'	COtt EBee LRHS SWal WFar WViv
'Little Miss Charlotte'	COtt LRHS WFar WViv
'Little Miss Christina'	CBcs MBNS SBai SVil SWvt WCra WViv
'Little Miss Gloria'	MBNS SVil SWvt
'Little Miss Isabel'	CDoC SBai WViv
'Little Miss Lucy'	COtt
'Little Miss Matilda'	COtt WViv
'Little Miss Olivia'	WViv
'Little Miss Rosalind'	MBNS SBai SVil SWal SWvt WViv
'Little Miss Rosanna'	COtt LRHS SVil SWal WViv
'Little Miss Sophie'	MBNS SBai SVil SWvt WViv
'Little Miss Tara'	MBNS SVil SWvt WViv
'Little Miss Veronica'	MBNS SBai SVil WViv
'Lucinda'	CBcs CDoC LRHS MBri SBai SPer SVil SWvt WViv
magnifica	MDKP WCot
– subsp. *magnifica*	WCot
'Marina'	LRHS MBNS
'Marissa'	LRHS
'Mars'	LRHS SWal
Meyer hybrids	MTho
'Moulin Rouge'	MBNS SBai SVil WViv
'Natalie' **new**	WViv
'Orange Gem' ♀H4	COtt LRHS MBNS WFar
'Orange Glory' ♀H4	CDoC COtt IArd LRHS MBNS MBri SPla SWvt WCot WFar WViv WWlt
'Oriana'	SBai SVil SWvt
pallida	CPBP
– JCA 2.028.500	WCot
patagonica	EHyt
pelegrina	EBee ECho LTwo MTho
– 'Alba'	ELan
– var. *humilis*	WCMO
– 'Rosea'	ELan
'Perfect Blue' **new**	WViv
'Perfect Love'	COtt EBee
peruviana **new**	EBee
philippii	WCot
'Phoenix' (v)	CDoC CFir EBee EMar LRHS SBai SPla SVil SWvt WCot WViv
'Pink Perfection'	LRHS NLar

'Polka'	CDoC EBee EMar LRHS MBNS SVil SWal WViv
presliana	WCMO
– RB 94103	WCot
– subsp. *australis*	CPou
– subsp. *presliana*	WCot
Princess Aiko	CDoC EBee LIck SPla
= 'Zapriko' PBR	
Princess Alice PBR	see *A.* H.R.H. Princess Alice = 'Staverpi'
Princess Angela	CDoC COtt LIck MBNS SCoo
= 'Staprilan' PBR	
'Princess Anouska' **new**	CDoC
Princess Beatrix	WFar
= 'Stadoran'	
'Princess Camilla' **new**	CDoC
Princess Daniela	SCoo SPoG
= 'Stapridani' PBR	
Princess Ella	CDoC NLar
= 'Staprirange' PBR	
'Princess Isabella' **new**	CDoC
Princess Ivana	EBee NLar SPoG
= 'Staprivane'	
Princess Juliana	SPla SPoG
= 'Staterpa'	
Princess Julieta	EBee LIck
= 'Zaprijul' PBR	
Princess Leyla	CBcs MBNS
= 'Stapriley' PBR	
Princess Marilene	COtt EBee MBNS
= 'Staprilene' PBR	
Princess Monica	COtt EBee MBNS SPla
= 'Staprimon' PBR	
Princess Morana	COtt
= 'Staprirana'	
Princess Oxana	NLar SCoo
= 'Staprioxa' PBR	
Princess Paola	COtt MBNS SCoo SPla
= 'Stapripal' PBR	
Princess Sarah	MBNS
= 'Stalicamp'	
Princess Sissi	COtt SPoG
= 'Staprisis' PBR	
Princess Sophia	SPoG
= 'Stajello' PBR	
Princess Stephanie	NBre NLar SPla
= 'Stapirag'	
Princess Susana	EBee NLar SCoo
= 'Staprisusa' PBR	
Princess Victoria PBR	see *A.* 'Victoria'
Princess Zavina	CFir COtt MBNS NLar
= 'Staprivina' PBR	
§ *psittacina*	CAvo CBos CBro CHar CSam CSev CStu EBee EBla ECho EHrv ELan EPfP EWoo GCal IFoB LAst LHop MDun MHer MSte NChi SWal WCMO WCot WFar WPGP WSHC WTin
– 'Mona Lisa'	EShb EWll LTwo NLar WCMO WCot WViv
§ – 'Royal Star' (v)	CBro CHea EBee EBla EHol ELan EMan EMon EPPr EPfP LRHS NLar SPoG SUsu WCMO WCot WFar WHil WHoo WPrP WSHC
– variegated	see *A. psittacina* 'Royal Star'
pulchella Sims	see *A. psittacina*
pulchra	LTwo MDKP WCot
'Purple Rain'	EMar MBri SBai SVil SWvt WViv
pygmaea	EHyt MTho
'Red Beauty' (v)	CDoC LRHS MBNS MBri NBir NBre SBai SPer SPlb SVil SWvt WCMO WCot WViv
'Red Elf'	LRHS MBNS MBri NBre SVil SWvt WCra WFar WViv
'Regina' PBR	see *A.* 'Victoria'
revoluta	WCot

'Rosy Wonder' **new**	NMoo
'Selina'	EBee GBin LRHS MBNS NBre SVil SWal WFar WViv
'Serenade' **new**	EMar SBai
'Short Purple'	CDes
'Solent Candy'	WFar
'Solent Crest'	WFar
'Solent Dawn'	WFar
'Solent Pride'	WFar
'Solent Wings'	WFar
'Sovereign'	MDKP
'Spitfire' (v)	CDoC EBee MBri SBai SVil SWvt
'Spring Delight' (v)	EMan WCot
'Sunrise' **new**	WWlt
'Sunstar'	LRHS
'Sweet Laura' PBR	LTwo MMHG NLar NOrc
'Tapestry'	SWal
'Tessa'	CDoC EBee LIck LRHS MBNS SBai WCMO WCot WViv
'Verona'	LRHS
§ *versicolor* BC&W 4624	GBin
§ 'Victoria' PBR	WFar
werdermannii var. *flavicans* F&W 956289	MDKP
– var. *werdermannii* F&W 9585	MDKP
'White Apollo'	SPla WCMO WCot
'Yellow Friendship' ♀H4	COtt LRHS MBNS NLar SPer SPlb SWvt WCMO WCra WFar WViv
'Yellow Queen'	WFar

Althaea (*Malvaceae*)

armeniaca	EMon GMac MGol NLar WCot
cannabina	CFir CSpe EChP ELan EMon GBri GCal GQui MGol WBor WHal WHoo WOld WSHC WWhi XPep
officinalis	CAgr CArn CPrp CSev CWan ELan EMon GBar GMac GPoy ILis MHer MNHC MSal SECG SIde WGwG WPer WWye XPep
– *alba*	EBee EChP LSou NLar WHer
§ – 'Romney Marsh'	EBee EWll GCal MRav NCot SMad WFar WKif WSHC
rosea	see *Alcea rosea*
rugosostellulata	see *Alcea rugosa*

Altingia (*Hamamelidaceae*)

gracilipes	CMCN WPGP

x *Alworthia* (*Aloaceae*)

'Black Gem' **new**	CBct EShb EWll SPoG

Alyogyne (*Malvaceae*)

hakeifolia	CSpe ECou
– 'Elle Maree'	ECou ERea LRHS SOWG
– 'Melissa Anne'	ECou LRHS SOWG
§ *huegelii*	CSec ECou EMan MOak WDyG
– 'Santa Cruz'	CCCN CHll CMdw CPLG CSec CSpe ERea SOWG WPGP WRos

Alyssoides (*Brassicaceae*)

utriculata	WPer

Alyssum (*Brassicaceae*)

argenteum misapplied	see *A. murale*
corymbosum	see *Aurinia corymbosa*
idaeum	LRHS
montanum	CArn ECha ECho NBir NBlu SPlb SRms WMoo
§ – 'Berggold'	CBcs CHrt ECho EPfP LRHS LRav
– Mountain Gold	see *A. montanum* 'Berggold'
§ *murale*	IHMH NLar
ovirense	CSec
oxycarpum	SBla WAbe
repens subsp. *repens*	GIBF
saxatile	see *Aurinia saxatilis*

scardicum	LTwo
serpyllifolium	NWCA
spinosum	WFar WLin XPep
§ - 'Roseum' ♀H4	CTri ECha ELan GAbr LBee LRHS
	MLHP NLAp NMen NWCA SBla
	WAbe WCot WPer
- 'Strawberries and Cream'	WAbe WFar
stribrnyi	CNic
tortuosum	EDAr LSou WMoo
wulfenianum	CNic GAbr LTwo NEgg NLar

Amana see *Tulipa*

Amaranthus (Amaranthaceae)
hypochondriacus	CSpe
'Pygmy Torch' ♀H3	

x *Amarcrinum* (Amaryllidaceae)
memoria-corsii	CMon CPrp ECho
- 'Howardii'	CFir EBee ECho EMan LRHS
	WCMO WCot

x *Amarine* (Amaryllidaceae)
'Fletcheri'	CMon
tubergenii	CAvo
- 'Zwanenburg'	CAby EBee EMan WCot

x *Amarygia* (Amaryllidaceae)
parkeri	CMon
§ - 'Alba'	CAvo CBro CMon EBee ECho
	EMan MSte WCMO WCot

Amaryllis ✿ (Amaryllidaceae)
§ **belladonna** ♀H2-3	CAby CBcs CBgR CBro CHEx
	CPne CStu ECho EMan EMon EPfP
	LEdu LRHS MBri MSte NCGa SChr
	SDnm SPav SPer WCMO WCot
	WGer
- 'Bloemfontein'	CAvo
- 'Cape Town' **new**	EMon
- 'Hathor' **new**	EBee
- 'Johannesburg'	CAvo EMon LRHS WCMO WCot
- 'Kimberley'	CAvo CPne EMon
- 'Major'	CAvo
- 'Parkeri Alba'	see x *Amarygia parkeri* 'Alba'
- 'Purpurea'	EBee EBrs EMon WCot
- white-flowered	ECho WCot
- 'Windhoek'	CAvo

Ambrosinia (Araceae)
basii MS&CL 315	CMon
from Tunisia **new**	

Amelanchier ✿ (Rosaceae)
alnifolia	CTho EBee EPla GIBF
- 'Obelisk'PBR	CABP CDul EBee LBuc LTwo MAsh
	MBri MGos NLar SPoG SSta
- pink-fruited	NLar
§ - var. **pumila**	CTho GSki LHop MSte NHol SSta
	WDin WNor WTin
- 'Smokey'	CDul EMil NLar
* **alpina**	EHyt
arborea	CBcs CPle CTho WNor
bartramiana	CTho SSta
- 'Eskimo'	NLar
canadensis K. Koch	see *A. lamarckii*
canadensis Sieb. & Zucc.	see *A. arborea*
canadensis (L.) Medik.	More than 30 suppliers
x **grandiflora** 'Autumn Brilliance'	CDul CEnd LRHS MAsh NLar
- 'Ballerina' ♀H4	More than 30 suppliers
- 'Princess Diana'	NLar
- 'Robin Hill'	CBcs CWSG EBee LAst LBuc LPan
	LRHS MAsh MBlu MGos NEgg
	NLar SBLw SHBN SLim SMad
	WFar

- 'Rubescens'	CDul CEnd EBee LPan LRHS
	MAsh
'Honeywood'	NLar
humilis	CBcs NLar
'La Paloma'	CWSG MAsh MBri NLar SPoG
laevis	CBcs CDul CTri EPfP LPan LRHS
	MGos NLar SPer STre WGor
- 'Cumulus'	MAsh NLar
- 'Prince Charles'	NLar
- 'R.J. Hilton'	MBri MGos MLan
- 'Snow Cloud'	CDoC MAsh
- 'Snowflakes'	CDoC CEnd CWSG EBee LRHS
	MAsh MDun MGos SLim SPoG
	SPur
lamarckii ♀H4	More than 30 suppliers
ovalis	XPep
pumila	see *A. alnifolia* var. *pumila*
rotundifolia 'Edelweiss'	CEnd CPMA LPan MBlu MGos
	NEgg NLar
- 'Helvetia'	CEnd EBee WEas
spicata	ECrN GIBF

Amicia (Papilionaceae)
zygomeris	CHEx CHll CMdw CPLG CPle
	CPom CSpe EMan EWes GBuc
	GCal SMrm SUsu WCot WSHC
	WWye

Ammi (Apiaceae)
majus	CArn EMan LBMP MSal
	SDix
visnaga	CArn CHrt CSpe MSal
	WHal

Ammobium (Asteraceae)
calyceroides	EMan

Ammocharis (Amaryllidaceae)
coranica	WCMO WCot

Ammophila (Poaceae)
arenaria	CBig CRWN GQui NBre SMar

Amomum (Zingiberaceae)
dealbatum	CKob MOak
subulatum	CKob MOak WMul

Amomyrtus (Myrtaceae)
§ **luma**	CDoC CDul CTbh CTrG CTri
	CTrw ELan GQui IDee SArc WFar
	WPic

Amorpha (Papilionaceae)
canescens	CBcs EMan MWea NSti SBrw
	WBVN WSHC
fruticosa	CAgr CBcs CPle EWTr LEdu LRav
	MBlu MGol NLar SBrw SPlb
	WSHC
herbacea	NLar
ouachitensis	NLar
paniculata	NLar

Amorphophallus ✿ (Araceae)
albus	CKob LEdu
bulbifer	CKob EAmu EBee LRHS MOak
	SBig WCMO WMul WPGP
dunnii	CKob
henryi new	CKob
kiusianus	EShb
konjac	CHEx CKob CMon CStu EBee
	LEdu WCMO WCot WPGP
nepalensis	CKob
paeoniifolius	CKob MJnS MOak SBig WMul
rivieri	CFwr EBee GCal WCMO WMul
stipitatus	WCot
tonkinensis new	CKob

Ampelocalamus (Poaceae)
scandens   EPla WPGP

Ampelocissus (Vitaceae)
sikkimensis HWJK 2066   WCru

Ampelodesmos (Poaceae)
mauritanica   CBig CFwr CHrt ColW CPen
                     CSam ECha EHoe EPPr EShb LEdu
                     LRav NOGN SEND SMHy SMad
                     SPlb XPep

Ampelopsis (Vitaceae)
aconitifolia   CPlN EBee MGos NLar NVic SBra
                         WSPU
- 'Chinese Lace'   LRHS SBra WPGP
arborea   CPlN
§ **brevipedunculata**   CBcs CPlN CRHN ECrN ELan
                         LHop MTis SCoo SGar SLim SPer
                         SPoG WDin WFar
- 'Citrulloides' B&SWJ 1173 WCru
§ - var. **maximowiczii**   More than 30 suppliers
  'Elegans'
chaffanjonii   CPlN
delavayana new   MWea
glandulosa var.   see *A. brevipedunculata*
  brevipedunculata
- - 'Tricolor'   see *A. brevipedunculata* var.
                         maximowiczii 'Elegans'
- var. **hancei** B&SWJ 3855 WCru
henryana   see *Parthenocissus henryana*
japonica   GIBF
megalophylla   CBcs CHEx CPlN EBee ELan EPfP
                         EShb LRHS MBlu NCGa SPer SPoG
                         WBVN WCot WCru WFar WNor
                         WOVN
sempervirens   see *Cissus striata*
  hort. ex Veitch
sinica   CPlN
tricuspidata 'Veitchii' see *Parthenocissus tricuspidata*
                         'Veitchii'

Amphicome see *Incarvillea*

Amsonia (Apocynaceae)
ciliata   CFee CFir ELan LPhx MGol WFar
                         WPer
hubrichtii   CAby CMdw CPom CSim EBrs
                         ECha EGle EPPr GCal GMac
                         LHop MGol NDov NLar SMHy
                         SMad
illustris   CPom EBee EBrs GMac LRHS
                         MGol MSte NDov SHar WPer
                         WTin
jonesii   EBee
§ **orientalis**   More than 30 suppliers
palmeri new   EBee
tabernaemontana   More than 30 suppliers
* - **galacticifolia**   EBee
- var. **salicifolia**   CAby EBee EChP EGle GSki LPhx
                         LRHS MSte NDov WCAu WRos
                         WTin

Amygdalus see *Prunus*

Anacampseros (Portulacaceae)
alstonii   LToo
dinteri   LToo

Anacamptis (Orchidaceae)
  sp. **new**   NLAp
* **alba new**   NLAp
* **grandiflora new**   NLAp
§ **laxiflora**   CHdy
pyramidalis   EFEx WHer

Anacardium (Anacardiaceae)
occidentale (F)   SDEP

Anacyclus (Asteraceae)
pyrethrum   GPoy
- var. **depressus**   CTri ECho ECtt EDAr ELan EPfP
                         GMaP IHMH LRHS MSte NFor
                         NTHB NVic NWCA SBla SIng SPet
                         SPlb WCFE WFar WHoo WPer
- - 'Garden Gnome'   CTri ECho EWin MNHC NJOw
                         NPri NTHB SRms WFar
- - 'Silberkissen'   CBrm EDAr

Anagallis (Primulaceae)
arvensis   MHer MSal WHbs
linifolia   see *A. monellii* subsp. *linifolia*
§ **monellii** ♀H4   CNic SBla
- subsp. **linifolia**   EHyt
- - 'Blue Light'   CSpe
- 'Skylover'   LAst LSou MLan SPet
- 'Sunrise'   CPBP EHyt LAst SBla SUsu
tenella 'Studland'   CWCL EPot GAbr NJOw NMen
                         NWCA SBla SIng SPoG WAbe
                         WHoo

Anagyris (Papilionaceae)
foetida   XPep

Ananas (Bromeliaceae)
comosus (F)   CCCN LRHS
- var. **variegatus** (v) CKob MBri SMur

Anaphalis (Asteraceae)
  CC 3725   WCot
alpicola   EPot NMen
margaritacea   CBcs CSBt EBee ECha ECrN ECtt
                         EWTr GBin GMaP IHMH ITer
                         MLLN NBid SMer SRms WFar
                         WMoo
§ - var. **cinnamomea** EMon WEas
§ - 'Neuschnee'   CTri CWan EBee LBBr MWgw
                         NBPC NBre NGdn NMir NPri SPla
                         WFar WPer
- New Snow   see *A. margaritacea* 'Neuschnee'
§ - var. **yedoensis** ♀H4 CTri EAEE EBee ECot EGle MLHP
                         NBre NEgg SDix SGar SPer SPoG
                         WBrE WCAu WTin
§ **nepalensis** var.   EBee ELan EMon GIBF MWat NBre
  monocephala   NSti WCAu
nubigena   see *A. nepalensis* var.
                         monocephala
sinica 'Moon's Silver' EBee
transnokoensis   EBee EWes
triplinervis ♀H4   More than 30 suppliers
- CC 1620   WCot
§ - 'Sommerschnee' ♀H4 EAEE EBee EChP ECha ECot ECtt
                         EGle EPfP ERou LRHS MNFA MRav
                         NEgg NFor SPer WMnd WMow
                         WPer
- Summer Snow   see *A. triplinervis* 'Sommerschnee'

Anarrhinum (Scrophulariaceae)
bellidifolium   SPet SUsu

Anchusa (Boraginaceae)
angustissima   see *A. leptophylla* subsp. *incana*
§ **azurea**   CPom EUnu IHMH MGol NRnb
                         WPer XPep
- 'Dropmore'   CTri EBee ELan EPfP LAst LRHS
                         MGol MNHC NEgg NOrc SPav
                         SRms SSth WPer WRHF
- 'Feltham Pride'   CBrm CMdw CSBt CSim GMaP
                         GMac MSte NRnb NScw NVic
                         SMar SPav SRms SWvt WFar WHil
                         WHoo WPGP WPer WWeb

- 'Little John' — COtt ECot ERou SRms WTel
- 'Loddon Royalist' ♀H4 — More than 30 suppliers
- 'Opal' — EBee EChP ECot EPfP LRHS MWat NCGa NEgg SBch SPla SPoG WCAu
- 'Royal Blue' — LRHS
caespitosa misapplied — see *A. leptophylla* subsp. *incana*
capensis — CSec EBee WHil
- 'Blue Angel' — LRHS MNHC NJOw SWvt WFar WWeb
cespitosa Lam. — ECho EHyt ELan EWes SBla SIng WAbe
italica — see *A. azurea*
laxiflora — see *Borago pygmaea*
§ *leptophylla* subsp. *incana* — CEnt LRHS MSte NEgg SBch
- - F&W 9550 — MDKP
- 'Sapphire Blue' **new** — NBHF
'Loddon Gold' **new** — EBrs
myosotidiflora — see *Brunnera macrophylla*
officinalis — CArn EUnu LRHS MSal SPav
sempervirens — see *Pentaglottis sempervirens*

Ancylostemon (Gesneriaceae)
convexus B&SWJ 6624 — WCru
saxatilis **new** — NLAp

Andrachne (Euphorbiaceae)
colchica — WCot

Androcymbium (Colchicaceae)
europaeum MS 510 from Spain — CMon
gramineum SB&L 26 from Morocco — CMon
rechingeri SB&L 313 from Crete — CMon

Andromeda (Ericaceae)
glaucophylla — CBrm MBar SBrw
polifolia — CMHG ECho GCrs GKev NJOw SBrw WDin WFar
- 'Alba' — EBee ECho ELan GBin LRHS MAsh MBar NHol NLAp NRya SBod SBrw SPer SPlb SPoG SWvt WFar
- 'Blue Ice' — CWib ELan EPfP LRHS MAsh MBri NHar NLAp NMen SPer SPoG SSpi WAbe WFar WPat
- 'Compacta' ♀H4 — CDoC CWib EBee ECho EHoe GCrs LRHS MBar MBri NHol NMen SPer SPoG SRms SWvt WBVN WGwG WSHC
- 'Compacta Alba' ♀H4 — ECho
- 'Grandiflora' — ECho ELan GBin GGar ITim LRHS MAsh SBod
- 'Hayachine' — NLAp
- 'Kirigamine' — LRHS MAsh NHol
- 'Macrophylla' ♀H4 — ECho GBin GCrs ITim MAsh NDlv NHol WAbe WPat
- 'Minima' — WThu
- 'Nana' — CSBt ELan EPfP LRHS MAsh NMen
- 'Nikko' — CWib ITim NHol SBrw WFar WPat
- 'Shibutsu' — NMen

Andropogon (Poaceae)
gerardii — CBig CBrm CKno CPen CRWN EBee EHoe EHul EMan EPPr EPla LRav MWhi SMad WDyG WGHP
ischaemum — see *Bothriochloa ischaemum*
saccharoides — EBee LRav
scoparius — see *Schizachyrium scoparium*
virginicus — CBig

Androsace (Primulaceae)
CD&R 2477 from China — WCru
akbaitalensis — EHyt
albana — EHyt WAbe

alpina — CGra WAbe
armeniaca var. *macrantha* — EHyt
baltistanica — EHyt WAbe
barbulata — CNic CStu
bulleyana — CStu EHyt NLAp WAbe WLin
caduca **new** — EHyt
carnea — CPBP ECho
- *alba* — LRHS NWCA WLin
- subsp. *brigantiaca* — CPBP GCrs GKev ITim NJOw NLAp NSla NWCA WAbe WHoo
- subsp. *laggeri* ♀H4 — ECho EPot GCrs LTwo NLAp NSla NWCA WAbe
- - 'Andorra' — NLAp
carnea x *pyrenaica* — ECho EHyt EPot NMen WAbe
chamaejasme — ECho
ciliata — GCrs NSla WAbe
cylindrica — CGra CPBP EPot GCrs ITim LRHS NLAp NMen NSla SIng WAbe WFar
cylindrica x *hirtella* — ECho EHyt ITim LRHS WAbe
cylindrica x *hirtella*, ENF strain — WAbe
dasyphylla — EHyt
delavayi — WAbe
foliosa — GCrs
geraniifolia — CDes CPLG EBee ECha LHop MFOX SRms WCru WLin
globifera — EPot WAbe
gracilis PB 99/20 **new** — EPot
hausmannii — WAbe
hedraeantha — CLyd ITim NLAp NRya NSla WAbe
x *heeri* — EHyt
helvetica — EHyt GIBF NLAp
himalaica — CNic CPBP EHyt EPot GEdr NMen SBla
hirtella — CPBP ITim NLAp NMen WAbe
* *idahoensis* — CGra EPot WAbe
imbricata **new** — EHyt
incana — EHyt WAbe
jacquemontii — see *A. villosa* var. *jacquemontii*
kosopoljanskii — EHyt
lactea — GCrs NLAp WAbe
laevigata — CGra NLAp NMen SBla WAbe
- from Columbia River Gorge, USA — WAbe
- var. *ciliolata* — NLAp WLin
- 'Gothenburg' — EHyt WAbe
lanuginosa ♀H4 — CLyd CMea ECho EHyt EPot GKev MWat NMen NWCA SBla SIng SRms WAbe WPat
lehmanniana **new** — EHyt
lehmannii — GKev
limprichtii — see *A. sarmentosa* var. *watkinsii*
x *marpensis* — EPot WAbe
mathildae — EHyt ITim NLAp NWCA WAbe
microphylla — see *A. mucronifolia* G. Watt
'Millstream' — CPBP
minor **new** — EPot
§ *mollis* — CPBP EPot SIng
§ *montana* — WAbe
mucronifolia misapplied — see *A. sempervivoides*
§ *mucronifolia* G. Watt — EHyt EPot NJOw
- Schacht's form — EHyt
mucronifolia x *sempervivoides* — EHyt EPot NJOw
muscoidea — EHyt EPot WAbe
- SEP 132 — EHyt
- 'Breviscapa' — EPot
- f. *longiscapa* — WAbe
- Schacht's form — EHyt GCrs SBla WAbe
§ *nivalis* — WAbe WLin
x *pedemontana* — ITim
primuloides — see *A. studiosorum*
pubescens — CGra ITim LRHS LTwo NMen WAbe

pyrenaica   CGra ECho EHyt ITim LRHS NLAp
                            NMen NSla SIng WAbe
rigida   NLAp WAbe
- KGB 168   EPot
- SDR 2855   GKev
robusta   GCrs
- TJR 419-99   EHyt
- subsp. *purpurea*   WAbe
rotundifolia   GEdr WCru
sarmentosa misapplied   see *A. studiosorum*
sarmentosa Wall.   EHyt ELan GKev MWat SRms
                            WHoo WTel
- CC 407   LRHS
- from Namche, Nepal   EHyt WAbe
- 'Sherriffii'   CFee EHyt EPot GEdr SIng SRms WHoo
§ - var. *watkinsii*   EPot NMen
- var. *yunnanensis*   see *A. studiosorum*
  misapplied
- var. *yunnanensis* Knuth see *A. mollis*
selago   WAbe
§ *sempervivoides* ♀H4   CLyd CMea EAEE ECha ECho EDAr
                            EHyt ELan EPot GKev GMaP LHop
                            LRHS NDlv NHol NLAp NMen
                            NWCA SBla SPlb SRms WHoo
                            WLin WPat
- CC 4622   ITim
- 'Greystone'   EPot NMen
- 'Susan Joan' (v)   CPBP EHyt EPot GEdr GKev SBla
                            WAbe
septentrionalis 'Stardust' CBrm ECho
sericea   EHyt WAbe
spinulifera   GKev
- SDR 2950   GKev
strigillosa   WAbe
§ *studiosorum* ♀H4   ECho EPot GAbr GEdr GKev
- 'Chumbyi'   EHol ETow GEdr LTwo NHol
                            NLAp NWCA SBla SIng SRms WPat
- 'Doksa'   CPBP EHyt EPot GCrs NLAp WAbe
                            WPat
- 'Salmon's Variety'   CMea CTri ECho NRya WAbe
tapete   WAbe
- ACE 1725   EPot
vandellii   CPBP EHyt ITim NLAp NSla WAbe
villosa   NLAp
- var. *arachnoidea*   CPBP EHyt
- var. *congesta*   EHyt
§ - var. *jacquemontii*   CPBP EHyt ETow GCrs NHar
                            NWCA SBla WLin
- - lilac   CPBP EPot WAbe
- - pink   EPot GKev NLAp WAbe
- subsp. *taurica*   EHyt
vitaliana   see *Vitaliana primuliflora*
watkinsii   see *A. sarmentosa* var. *watkinsii*
yargongensis   WAbe
zambalensis   EHyt WAbe

Andryala (*Asteraceae*)
agardhii   EPot NJOw WLin WPat
lanata   see *Hieracium lanatum*

Anemanthele (*Poaceae*)
§ *lessoniana*   More than 30 suppliers
- 'Autumn Tints'   EHoe EPPr
- 'Gold Hue'   EHoe

Anemarrhena (*Anthericaceae*)
asphodeloides   CArn MSal WCot

Anemone ✿ (*Ranunculaceae*)
B&SWJ 1452   WCru
B&SWJ 6716 from Taiwan   WCru
aconitifolia Michx.   see *A. narcissiflora*
aconitifolia ambig.   CSpe
altaica   GAbr MSal NEgg NLar NWCA
                            SRms WBVN
amurensis   EBla

apennina ♀H4   CAvo CLAP ECha GEdr IBlr WCru
                            WTin
- var. *albiflora*   CAvo CDes CFwr CLAP EBee ECha
                            EPot ERos GEdr GMac IBlr LRHS
                            MSte NDov SMeo WCot WPnP
- 'Ballyrogan Park'   IBlr
- double   EBee EBla ECha IBlr NDov SBla
                            WCru
- 'Petrovac'   CLAP EBee EPot IBlr LRHS WCot
baicalensis   EShb EWll WLin
baldensis   CSec ECho GCrs GKev LBee LRHS
                            NBre NBur NMen NOak NWCA
                            SRms
barbulata   CAby CLAP EChP EKen EMan
                            EWes GBuc LPhx NLar WBVN
                            WSHC
blanda ♀H4   GBBs LHop MBri MTis NBlu NChi
                            SEND SWal WFar WShi
- blue shades   CSam EBrs ECGP ECho EPfP EWTr
                            GEdr GKev GMaP IGor LPhx LRHS
                            SMeo SPer WBrE WLin
- 'Blue Star'   ECho
- blue-flowered   CAvo CBro CFFs CMea CTbh CTri
                            ELan ENot EPot GAbr LRHS MBri
                            MNFA MWgw NBPC SMrm SPoG
                            SRms WCra WFar
- 'Charmer'   CRez ECho EPot LHop NMen
- 'Ingramii'   WCot WCMO
- 'Pink Charmer'   ECho
- 'Pink Star'   CBro ECho EPot GAbr IPot LRHS
                            MWgw NBir WLin
- 'Radar' ♀H4   CAvo CBro CFFs CMea EBrs ECho
                            EPot MNrw NBir
- var. *rosea* ♀H4   CNic ECho ELan EPfP MLLN SPer
                            SPoG WFar
- 'Violet Star'   CMdw CMea CRez ECho EPot
                            LPhx LRHS MSph SMeo WGHP
- 'White Splendour' ♀H4   CAvo CBro CElw CFFs CMea CTri
                            EBrs ECho ELan EMar EPfP EPot
                            GAbr GEdr GKev IPot LHop LPhx
                            MNFA NBPC NBir NChi NMen
                            SMeo SPer SPoG SRms WCot WFar
                            WLin
canadensis   CHar CNic CPMA EBee EPPr EWsh
                            GAbr GBBs GBuc GKev MNrw
                            MSte NBur NCGa NEgg WBVN
                            WCot
caroliniana   EBee ECho GAbr GBuc GCrs LRHS
                            NEgg NWCA WCru
chapaensis HWJ 631   WCru
coronaria   LEdu
- 'Bicolor'   GKev
- De Caen Group   EPfP LHop SPoG SWal WCra WFar
§ - - 'Die Braut'   EPfP GKev SPer WFar
- - 'His Excellency'   see *A. coronaria* (De Caen Group)
                            'Hollandia'
§ - - 'Hollandia'   EBrs GKev SMeo SPer
- - 'Mister Fokker'   EBrs SMeo SPer WCra WFar
- - The Bride   see *A. coronaria* (De Caen Group)
                            'Die Braut'
- - 'The Governor'   WFar WRHF
- Jerusalem hybrids   WFar
- Saint Bridgid Group (d)   EPfP GKev MBri SPet SWal WFar
                            WGwG
- - 'Lord Lieutenant' (d)   NBir NBur SMeo WFar WRHF
- - 'Mount Everest' (d)   NBir SMeo
- - 'The Admiral' (d)   EBrs GKev NBir SMeo WFar
- 'Sylphide' (Mona Lisa   NBir SMeo WCra WFar
  Series)
crinita   GBuc WBVN WRHF
cylindrica   CMHG CSam CSec EBee EChP
                            MDKP MNrw NBre NLar
decapetala   GCal NChi NRnb WBVN WGwG
                            WLin
demissa   CSec EMan GBuc GKev NBid NRya
                            WCot

- BWJ 7785	WCru
- SDR 3307	EBee GKev
dichotoma	SSvw
drummondii	EChP GSki NBur NChi WBVN WWeb
elongata B&SWJ 2975	WCru
eranthoides	CLAP EBee ECho
fasciculata	see *A. narcissiflora*
flaccida	CBro CDes CLAP CMea EAEE EBee EHrv GBuc GMac LPhx LRHS MSte SBch SBla WCot WCru WFar WHal WSHC WWhi
x *fulgens*	ECha SAga
- 'Annulata Grandiflora'	ECGP
- 'Multipetala'	CMil SBla WCot
- Saint Bavo Group	ECGP
globosa	see *A. multifida* Poir.
'Green Apples' **new**	EKen
'Guernica'	ECho GBuc NRnb SRot WBVN
'Hatakeyama Double' (d)	CDes CMdw GCal
'Hatakeyama Single'	CDes CMdw
hepatica	see *Hepatica nobilis*
§ *hortensis*	LPhx NBre SBla
- subsp. *heldreichii*	CDes SBla
§ *hupehensis*	CBos CPLG EWll GBBs GCrs GMaP IGor LRHS NJOw NOrc NPen WFar
- BWJ 8190	WCru
- f. *alba*	CDes CMil EBee EBla WPGP WWeb
§ - 'Bowles' Pink' ♀H4	CElw CMil EBee EPPr IGor MWat SPet WBrk WCru WPGP WTin WWhi
- 'Crispa'	see *A.* x *hybrida* 'Lady Gilmour' Wolley-Dod
- 'Eugenie'	CMil EAEE EBee EChP GBuc GSki LRHS MBNS NBir SRGP
- 'Hadspen Abundance' ♀H4	More than 30 suppliers
- 'Hadspen Red'	WFar
§ - var. *japonica*	CBos CBrm CPou GCal NCob NFor
- - B&SWJ 4886	WCru
- - 'Bodnant Burgundy'	CDes CPrp EBee EChP ECtt EGle LRHS MCCP WCAu WPGP
§ - - 'Bressingham Glow'	CMHG CPLG EAEE EBee ECtt EGle ELan EPfP EPot ERou GSki LHop LRHS MBri MNrw MRav MWgw NBir NOrc NVic SHBN SPer SPet SWat WAbb WBrk WCAu WFar WMnd
§ - - 'Pamina' ♀H4	More than 30 suppliers
- - Prince Henry	see *A. hupehensis* var. *japonica* 'Prinz Heinrich'
§ - - 'Prinz Heinrich' ♀H4	More than 30 suppliers
§ - - 'Rotkäppchen'	CPar EAEE EBee EBla EMan EWTr GBin LRHS MRav NBur NGby NPro SMrm WWeb
- 'Ouvertüre'	CDes EBee WPGP
- 'Praecox'	CMea EAEE EBee EBla EHrv EPfP GBBs GBri GBuc GSki LRHS MAvo MBNS MNFA MWgw NBir NCGa NGdn NPri NSti SPoG SWvt WAbb WCru WHal WHil WHoo WMnd WWeb
- 'September Charm'	see *A.* x *hybrida* 'September Charm'
- 'Splendens'	CMHG EBee ENot GBBs GBuc LAst LHop LRHS NEgg SPoG SPur SWvt WAbb WFar WHal
- 'Superba'	EBee WKif
§ x *hybrida*	MWat MWrn NChi NCob SGar WCru WFar WMoo
- 'Alba' misapplied (UK)	see *A.* x *hybrida* 'Honorine Jobert'
- 'Albert Schweitzer'	see *Anemone* x *hybrida* 'Elegans'
- 'Andrea Atkinson'	CPrp CWib EAEE EBee EChP EPfP GBBs GBuc GSki LAst LRHS MBri
	MLLN MNFA MWat NBid NCGa NGdn NRnb SMrm SPla SRGP WBrk WCMO WCot WFar WHil WHoo WMnd WMoo
- 'Bowles' Pink'	see *A. hupehensis* 'Bowles' Pink'
- 'Bressingham Glow'	see *A. hupehensis* var. *japonica* 'Bressingham Glow'
- 'Coupe d'Argent'	NBre
§ - 'Elegans' ♀H4	CWCL EBee MRav NBPC NBir SWat WCru WHil WHoo
§ - 'Géante des Blanches'	CBos CHar GMac IGor LRHS MBri SHop SMrm WFar WHoo
§ - 'Honorine Jobert' ♀H4	More than 30 suppliers
§ - 'Königin Charlotte' ♀H4	More than 30 suppliers
- 'Kriemhilde'	EBee GBin
- 'Lady Gilmour' misapplied	see *A.* x *hybrida* 'Margarete'
§ - 'Lady Gilmour' Wolley-Dod	CBgR CSpe EBee EChP ECtt EGle EHol EHrv EPfP GMac LRHS MBri MCCP MRav NBPC NBir NCGa NChi NGdn SAga SPoG SRGP WCru WFar
- 'Loreley'	CMea CPrp EBee EChP GBuc MBNS MSte MWat NCGa SPet WHil
- 'Luise Uhink'	CPou EBee IGor LRHS NBir WEas
- 'Margarete'	CFwr COIW CPLG EBee EPPr LAst LRHS MWat SMrm STes WCot WCru WFar
- 'Max Vogel'	see *A.* x *hybrida* 'Elegans'
- 'Monterosa'	see *A.* x *hybrida* 'Margarete'
§ - 'Montrose'	CPar CPou EBee EChP EHrv EWes GCal LRHS NBir NEgg SRms SWat WBor WCra WFar
- 'Pamina'	see *A. hupehensis* var. *japonica* 'Pamina'
- Prince Henry	see *A. hupehensis* var. *japonica* 'Prinz Heinrich'
- 'Prinz Heinrich'	see *A. hupehensis* var. *japonica* 'Prinz Heinrich'
- 'Profusion'	CTri LBuc LRHS MLan NBlu SHBN WHal
- Queen Charlotte	see *A.* x *hybrida* 'Königin Charlotte'
- 'Richard Ahrens'	EAEE EBee EChP ECtt EGle ERou GBuc GMaP LHop LRHS MLHP MNFA NDov NOrc SAga SMeo SPla SRGP SWat WCAu WCru WFar WMnd WWeb
§ - 'Robustissima'	More than 30 suppliers
- 'Rosenschale'	CFwr EBee EGle GCal LRHS MBri NCGa WCru WFar
- 'Rotkäppchen'	see *A. hupehensis* var. *japonica* 'Rotkäppchen'
§ - 'September Charm' ♀H4	More than 30 suppliers
- 'Serenade'	CPar EBee ECtt EGle EPfP ERou GBBs LRHS MBri MLLN NBir NCGa NEgg NRnb SHBN SPoG SRkn SSvw WCAu WCMO WCot WFar WHil WHlf WMoo WHoo
- 'Terry's Pink'	see *A.* x *hybrida* 'Whirlwind'
§ - 'Tourbillon'	More than 30 suppliers
§ - 'Whirlwind'	More than 30 suppliers
- 'White Queen'	see *A.* x *hybrida* 'Géante des Blanches'
- Wirbelwind	see *A.* x *hybrida* 'Whirlwind'
japonica	see *A.* x *hybrida*, *A. hupehensis*
keiskeana	GEdr WCru
§ x *lesseri*	CBro CFir CSpe EBee EChP ECha ECho ECtt EDAr EHrv ELan GBBs GKev LPhx MHer NChi NEgg NJOw SBla SGar SRms WBVN WCru WFar WHoo
leveillei	More than 30 suppliers
§ x *lipsiensis*	More than 30 suppliers
- 'Pallida' ♀H4	CBos CHad EBee EBla ECho ERos GBuc GCrs GEdr GKev IGor LLWP

	MAvo MNFA SBla WCMO WCot WHil
lyallii	EBee GBuc WBrE
N *magellanica* hort. ex Wehrh.	see *A. multifida* Poir.
mexicana B&SWJ 8414	WCru
multifida misapplied, red-flowered	see *A.* x *lesseri*
§ *multifida* Poir.	More than 30 suppliers
- RCB/Arg RA-F-5	WCot
- 'Major'	CFir CHar CLyd CMea CSpe EHol EPfP LPhx LRHS MBow NCob NPro NWCA SBla WBVN WFar
- pink-flowered	GBuc WSan
* - 'Rubra'	CBgR CBrm CPrp EBee EHrv EPfP EWll GAbr GBuc GGar LRHS MBNS MNFA MNrw NBir NDlv NEgg NWCA SPet SPoG WCMO WLin WWeb
§ *narcissiflora*	EBee ECGP GBuc IGor NBir NBre NChi WLin
- var. *citrina*	CWan SBla
nemorosa ♀H4	More than 30 suppliers
N - 'Alba Plena' (d)	CBro CHea CSWP CSam EBee EBla ECha ECho ERos ETow GBuc GEdr GGar GMac LRHS MTho NMen SIng SUsu WAbb WCMO WCot WCru WEas WFar WPnP
- 'Allenii' ♀H4	CBro CHea CLAP EBee ECha ECho EHyt ERos GBuc GEdr GMaP ITim MAvo MNFA MRav NMen NRya SMac WCMO WCot WCru WHil WPGP WPnP
- 'Amy Doncaster'	CLAP
- 'Atrocaerulea'	CLAP EBee GBuc IBlr NLar WCru WHil
- 'Bill Baker's Pink'	CDes CLAP
- 'Blue Beauty'	CLAP CPom EBee EGle ERos ETow GBuc GMaP IBlr MAvo NMen SBch WCru WHil
- 'Blue Bonnet'	CElw CPom CStu EBee ECho GBuc IGor ITim MAvo MNrw WCot
- 'Blue Eyes' (d)	CAby CDes CElw CLAP EBee ECha EGle ETow GBuc GCrs GEdr GMaP IBlr IGor MAvo MSte NBir NMen SBla WCot WCru WPGP
- 'Blue Queen'	CStu GAbr GBuc
- 'Bowles' Purple'	CBos CPom CStu EBee ECho EPot ETow GBBs GBuc GMaP GMac IBlr MAvo MNrw NDov NLAp NMyG NRya WCot WCru WFar WIvy WPGP WTin
- 'Bracteata'	CAvo ECho EHrv ERos GEdr NDov NMen
- 'Bracteata Pleniflora' (d)	CBow CLAP CStu EBee EBla ECha ECho EGle GBuc GMaP IBlr IGor LHop MAvo MNFA MNrw NBir NMen WCot WCru WFar WHal
- 'Buckland'	CDes CFwr CLAP EHrv EPfP IBlr WCru
- 'Cedric's Pink'	CLAP EBee EPPr ERos GBBs IBlr IGor LTwo MNrw WCru
- 'Celestial'	EBee ECho GBuc
- 'Danica'	EBee
- 'Dee Day'	CAby CLAP EBee EHrv GBuc MAvo MNrw WCru
- 'Flore Pleno' (d)	CAby EBee EBla ECho EHyt GBBs NBir NDov NMen WCMO WHil WPGP
- 'Frost and Fire' **new**	SSvw
- 'Gerda Ramusen'	ECho EHyt
- 'Green Fingers'	CDes CLAP ECho EHrv EPPr GBuc GEdr GMaP IGor LPhx MAvo MNrw NDov NGby SCnR WCot WCru WIvy

- 'Hannah Gubbay'	CLAP GBuc IBlr IGor MAvo MNrw MSte
- 'Hilda'	EBee ECho EGle ERos ETow GBuc GEdr IPot MAvo MNFA MNrw NDlv NDov NLAp NMen NRya NSla WCru WHil
- 'Jack Brownless'	CLAP WCot
- 'Kentish Pink'	GBBs GBuc GCrs GMaP
- 'Knightshayes Vestal' (d)	CLAP EBee MRav WCMO WCot WCru WIvy
- 'Lady Doneraile'	CDes CLAP EBee ECha ETow GBuc NBir NLar WCru WFar
- 'Leeds' Variety'	CLAP EGle GCrs GMac IGor ITim LPhx MAvo MNrw MTho NDov NMen NSla SBla WCMO WCot WHil
- 'Lismore Blue'	EBee EPot
§ - 'Lismore Pink'	EHrv GBuc GEdr
- 'Lychette'	CAby CAvo EBee ECha ECho EGle EHrv GBuc IBlr ITim LPhx MAvo NDov NSla SHar WCot WCru WHil WLin
- 'Martin'	CStu
- 'Mart's Blue' **new**	GBuc
- 'Monstrosa'	CDes EBee ECho EPot GBuc MAvo SSvw WCot
- 'New Pink'	CLAP CPom IBlr
- 'Parlez Vous'	EBee EGle EHrv EPPr GEdr MAvo MNrw NDov NMen SMHy WCru
- 'Pentre Pink'	CBos IBlr MNrw MTho WBVN WCMO WCru WHal WIvy
- 'Picos Pink'	EHrv GBuc MAvo SCnR
- 'Pink Carpet'	GBuc GEdr
- pink-flowered	CLAP LPhx WCru
- red-flowered **new**	CStu
- 'Robinsoniana' ♀H4	More than 30 suppliers
- 'Rosea'	CLAP CStu ECho GEdr GMac MNFA WCru WHil
- 'Royal Blue'	CAvo CDes CLAP CMil CNic CStu ECha ECho EHrv EPPr EPot ETow GAbr GBuc GCrs GEdr GMac MAvo MNFA NDov NLAp NMen SBla WCot WCru WFar WHil WPnP WTin
- 'Tinney's Blush'	CLAP
- 'Tomas'	CDes EBee GBin GEdr MAvo WCMO
- 'Vestal' (d) ♀H4	More than 30 suppliers
- 'Virescens' ♀H4	CAby CAvo CLAP CStu EBee EChP ECha ECho EGle EHrv EPPr ERos GAbr GCrs GEdr GMaP MAvo NDov NHar NSla NWCA SMHy SUsu WCMO WHal WIvy WPGP
- 'Viridiflora'	CFwr CLAP ECho EPfP GAbr GBuc LHop MNrw MRav MTho NBir NSti WCMO WCot WCru WFar WHil WSHC
- 'Westwell Pink'	CBos CDes CLAP EBee LTwo MAvo MSte WCMO WCot WPGP
- 'Wilks' Giant'	CLAP EBee MAvo WCot WCru
- 'Wilks' White'	CBos CLAP EBee EGle GEdr LBuc NSla WCru
- 'Wyatt's Pink'	CLAP CPom GBuc MAvo NCGa NSla WCru WPnP WTin
- 'Yerda Ramusem'	EBee ECho
nemorosa x *ranunculoides*	see *A.* x *lipsiensis*
obtusiloba	CAby CLAP GBuc GCrs MTho SBla SRms WAbe
- CLD 1549	GEdr
- J&JA 4.044.010	NWCA
- *alba*	GMac SBla
- var. *polysepala*	GEdr
I - 'Sulphurea'	CDes GEdr NMen
- yellow-flowered	GBuc SBla

palmata	CFwr CLAP LDai MDKP NBre SMad WCru WRos
parviflora	CHea GBuc
patens	see *Pulsatilla patens*
pavonina	CDes CSpe ECha ERos MAsh MBri MSSP MTho NBir SBla SPoG SRot
- 'Chapeau de Cardinal'	SBla
- 'Grecian Sunset'	CDes MAsh WPGP
polyanthes	LRHS
- HWJK 2337	WCru
prattii	CLAP GEdr
pseudoaltaica	GEdr WCru WWst
- pale blue-flowered	CLAP
pulsatilla	see *Pulsatilla vulgaris*
quinquefolia	CLAP WAbe WCot
ranunculoides ♀H4	More than 30 suppliers
- 'Frank Waley'	WCot
* - laciniata	CLAP GBuc MSte NMen WCot
- 'Pleniflora' (d)	CAvo CDes CFwr CHea CLAP EBee EBla ECha ECho EHrv GBBs GCrs GMaP MRav NLar NMen SBla WCMO WCot WFar WIvy
- subsp. wockeana	CDes EBee ECho
riparia	see *A. virginiana* var. *alba*
rivularis	More than 30 suppliers
- B&SWJ 7611	WCru
- CC 4587	GKev MGol WCot
- CC 4588	MGol WCot
- CLD 573	CDes WLin
- GWJ 1259	WCru
rupicola	EBee GMac NBir SRot
x seemannii	see *A.* x *lipsiensis*
smithiana	WCot
stellata	see *A. hortensis*
subpinnata	WCot
sulphurea	see *Pulsatilla alpina* subsp. *apiifolia*
sylvestris	More than 30 suppliers
§ - 'Elise Fellmann' (d)	CLAP GBuc IGor WCot
- 'Flore Pleno' (d)	CDes CLAP WCot
- 'Macrantha'	CDes CLAP CPrp EBee EChP EMan EPfP GAbr GMac LAst NBPC WBrE WPGP
'Taiwan's Tiny Treasure'	WCru
tetrasepala	CLAP WCot WPGP
§ tomentosa	EBee ECha EMan GGar GSki IGor LRHS MWhi NBre SDix SRms SWat WBVN WFar WWeb
§ - 'Albadura'	CFwr EBee GSki NBre
- 'Robustissima'	see *A.* x *hybrida* 'Robustissima'
trifolia	CAby CDes EBee ECha EHyt EMan EPPr ERos GBuc GMac NBid NDov SCnR SRms SUsu WCot WPGP WPat
- pink-flowered	CLAP EBee MSte WFar
- 'Semiplena' (d)	CAby CDes EBee WCot
trullifolia	EBee EMar EPPr EPfP ETow GAbr GBin GCrs GEdr GGar GMac LRHS MMHG MRav MTis NBPC SBla WRos
- alba	GBBs GMac
- var. coelestina	CDes GBBs GBuc NBir
vernalis	see *Pulsatilla vernalis*
virginiana	CSpe EBee EPPr EWll GAbr LDai MDKP MFOX MSte NBid NBur NRnb WBVN WFar WHil
§ - var. alba	EBee EKen MTis NLar NSti WBVN WPrP WPtf
vitifolia misapplied	see *A. tomentosa*
vitifolia DC.	GKev
- B&SWJ 2320	WCru
- B&SWJ 8202 from Vietnam	WCru
- GWJ 9434	WCru
- HWJ 682	WCru
- HWJK 2044	WCru

Anemonella (Ranunculaceae)

thalictroides	More than 30 suppliers
- 'Alba Plena' (d)	ECho GBuc
- 'Amelia'	GEdr SOkd WAbe
- 'Betty Blake' (d)	GCrs GEdr
- 'Cameo'	CLAP EFEx SCnR WCru WWst
- 'Charlotte'	NHar
- 'Double Green' (d)	CLAP EFEx
- 'Flore Pleno' (d)	GCrs
- 'Full Double White' (d)	CWCL EFEx GEdr
- 'Green Hurricane' (d)	EFEx GEdr
- 'Jade Feather'	CGra
- f. rosea	CElw CLAP CPom CWCL EPot GBuc SMHy WAbe WCru WPrP
- - double pink (d)	SBla
- - 'Oscar Schoaf' (d)	CLAP GBuc WAbe
- - semi-double pink (d)	CLAP NLar
- - semi-double white (d)	CLAP EHrv ETow GBuc NMen SBla SOkd WCot
- 'Tairin' new	GEdr WWst
- 'White Bells'	NHar

Anemonopsis (Ranunculaceae)

| macrophylla | CDes CElw CLAP EHyt EMan EPPr ETow GBuc GCal GMac IGor LPhx MNrw MSte MTho NLar SBla SOkd WAbe WCMO WCru WSHC |

Anemopaegma (Bignoniaceae)

| chamberlaynii | CPIN CTrG |

Anemopsis (Saururaceae)

| californica | CDes EBee EMan EWes IFoB NLar WCru WPGP |

Anethum (Apiaceae)

graveolens	CArn CHrt GPoy LRHS MBow MHer MNHC MWat SECG SIde WPer WSel
- 'Dukat'	CSev ELau NGHP
- fern-leaved	EOHP

angelica see *Angelica archangelica*

Angelica (Apiaceae)

acutiloba	CSpe EBee EMan EWll GIBF MHer MLLN NLar NSti WCot WFar
archangelica	More than 30 suppliers
- subsp. archangelica new	GIBF
- 'Corinne Tremaine' (v)	CWan EBee EMan EMar NGHP NSti NTHB WCHb WCMO WCot
atropurpurea	CArn EBee EChP ECtt EMan EMar EShb EWll GKev GWWP ITer MHer MNrw NBur NCGa NDov NGHP NGdn NLar NSti SWat WCAu WCHb WCot WFar WJek WMnd WSel
'Coconut Ice' new	ITer
dahurica	CArn EBee EUnu MSal
- B&SWJ 8603	WCru
decurrens new	EBee
decursiva	MSal NDov
- B&SWJ 5746	WCru
'Ebony' new	EDAr MDKP
florentii	EBee WPGP
gigas	More than 30 suppliers
- B&SWJ 4170	WCru
hispanica	see *A. pachycarpa*
japonica B&SWJ 8816a	WLin
lineariloba	WLin
montana	see *A. sylvestris*
§ pachycarpa	More than 30 suppliers
paniculata	see *Trochiscanthes nodiflora*
polymorpha	EBee

pubescens	CSec LPhx MSte NDov
- B&SWJ 5593	WCru
- var. **matsumurae**	WCru
B&SWJ 6387	
sachalinensis	EBee GIBF
saxatilis	EBee GIBF
sinensis	GPoy WCHb
'Summer Delight'	CSpe EBee EKen ITer MDKP MWat
	NBre SPav SPoG
§ **sylvestris**	CAgr CArn CHrt CRWN GBar
	NGHP NSco NTHB WCHb WSel
	WWpP
* - 'Purpurea'	CKno CMil CSpe EBee EWes GCal
	SBla SDnm WCMO WGwG WPGP
- 'Vicar's Mead'	CFwr EBee IPot LPhx LSRN MDKP
	MLLN NBPC NBid NCGa NChi
	NDov NGHP NLar NSti SPoG
	WCHb WCot WHil WSHC WSel
taiwaniana	CArn CRez CSec CWan EBee ELan
	ITer NGHP NLar SGar SWat WCot
ursina	CHen EDAr GIBF MDKP
- RBS 0205	WBVN
venenosa new	EBee

Angelonia (Scrophulariaceae)

(Angelface Series)	SVil
Angelface Blue	
= 'Anzwei' **new**	
- Angelface Blue	LAst SVil
Bicolour = 'Anstern'	
- Angelface White	SVil
= 'Anwhit'PBR **new**	
'Stella Gem'	LRHS

Anigozanthos (Haemodoraceae)

'Big Red' **new**	SOWG
(Bush Gems Series)	SOWG
'Bush Eclipse' **new**	
- 'Bush Haze' **new**	SOWG
flavidus	CHEx CTbh CTrC ECre EOHP
	MBri MNHC SOWG SPlb
- 'Illusion'	CCCN
- 'Opal'	CCCN MNHC SPoG
- 'Pearl'	CCCN SPoG
- 'Splendour'	CCCN MNHC SPoG
- yellow	WBrE
manglesii ♀H1	CHEx SPlb WDyG
- 'Bush Dawn'(Bush§	SOWG
Gems Series)	
'Regal Claw' **new**	SOWG
'Royal Cheer' **new**	SOWG

anise see *Pimpinella anisum*

Anisodontea (Malvaceae)

§ **capensis**	CBcs CCCN EBee EChP ELan
	EMan ERea LAst MAsh MBNS NBir
	SAga SBod SLim SMrm SOWG
	SRkn SRms SWvt WDyG XPep
- 'Tara's Pink'	EPfP EWes IFoB LPhx MBNS SAga
	SMrm SPoG
'Elegant Lady'	GFai
huegelii	see *Alyogyne huegelii*
x **hypomadara** misapplied	see *A. capensis*
§ x **hypomadara**	ECtt SRms
(Sprague) D.M. Bates	
julii	SPlb
malvastroides	XPep
scabrosa	XPep

Anisodus (Solanaceae)

carnioliciodes BWJ 7501	WCru
§ **luridus**	GCal ITer MGol MSal

Anisotome (Apiaceae)

pilifera	EMan

Annona (Annonaceae)

cherimola (F)	CTrG MPRe XBlo

Anoiganthus see *Cyrtanthus*

Anomalesia see *Gladiolus*

Anomatheca (Iridaceae)

cruenta	see *A. laxa*
grandiflora	CHll ECho ERos
§ **laxa** ♀H2-3	More than 30 suppliers
- var. **alba** ♀H2-3	CPLG CPom CRHN CSpe CStu
	ECho EDif EHrv ELan ERos EShb
	IBal ITim MTho MWea NMen SBch
	WAbe WBrk WCFE
- **albomaculata**	LRHS
- blue	CRHN ERos WAbe
- 'Joan Evans'	CElw CPom CRHN CStu ECho
	ECtt ELan ERos LTwo NDlv NMen
	NWCA SRms WAbe WBrk WHrl
- red spot	CPLG ECho LHop SGar
- **viridiflora**	ECho
viridis	CPLG CPou EBee ECho ERos
	LBow LRHS WBrk WPGP

Anopterus (Escalloniaceae)

glandulosus	IBlr WCru WSHC

Anredera (Basellaceae)

§ **cordifolia**	CFwr CPIN CRHN ECho EShb
	LEdu LRHS

Antennaria (Asteraceae)

aprica	see *A. parvifolia*
dioica	CArn CBrm CEnt CTri GAbr GPoy
	MHer NBlu NJOw SPlb SRms WFar
	WWye
- 'Alba'	EDAr EHoe WFar
- 'Alex Duguid'	GCrs GMaP LBee LRHS NLAp SBla
- 'Aprica'	see *A. parvifolia*
§ - var. **hyperborea**	ECGP
- 'Minima'	ECho EPot NBro NJOw NMen SIng
	WAbe
- 'Nyewoods Variety'	EPot NLAp
- red	ECho
- var. **rosea**	see *A. rosea*
* - 'Rubra'	CTri ECha ECho EDAr GBin MHer
	NMen NPri NWCA SBla WDyG
	WHen
- **tomentosa**	see *A. dioica* var. *hyperborea*
'Joy'	SBla
macrophylla hort.	see *A. microphylla*
§ **microphylla**	CBrm ECho EHoe MBar NHol
	SRms WEas WPat WPer
neglecta	ECho
§ **parvifolia**	CNic CTri ECho MBar NLar SRms
	WPer
- var. **rosea**	see *A. microphylla*
plantaginifolia	EBee
'Red Wonder'	CMea NLar
§ **rosea** ♀H4	ECho NLAp NMen NVic SPlb SRms
	WFar

Anthemis ✿ (Asteraceae)

from Turkey	EWes LLWP
arvensis	MBow
§ 'Beauty of Grallagh'	ECtt ERou GBuc GCal GMac IGor
	MDKP MRav NCGa NGdn SDix
	WCMO
'Cally Cream'	GCal WCra
'Cally White'	GCal
carpatica	EBrs NBro
- 'Karpatenschnee'	CRez NBre
§ **cretica** subsp. **cretica**	CLyd
frutescens	see *Argyranthemum frutescens*

'Grallagh Gold' misapplied (orange-yellow)	see *A.* 'Beauty of Grallagh'
§ 'Grallagh Gold'	EBla ECha ECtt EMon EWes LDai LPhx LRHS MBri MRav MWat NFla NPer WFar WTel
§ *marschalliana*	CPBP EAEE ECha EDAr EPot IHMH LBee MSte SMrm
montana	see *A. cretica* subsp. *cretica*
nobilis	see *Chamaemelum nobile*
punctata subsp. *cupaniana* ♀H3-4	More than 30 suppliers
- - 'Nana'	EMon NPer SHar
rudolphiana	see *A. marschalliana*
sancti-johannis	CBgR CBrm CPrp CWib EAEE EBee EBla ERou EShb IGor LDai MBri MNHC MRav MSal NDov NPer SDix SPer SPet SPoG SRms WFar WMoo WPer
'Sauce Béarnaise'	WMnd
Susanna Mitchell = 'Blomit'	CHar CHea EBee EBla EChP ECtt EMan EPfP ERou EShb EWll GMaP GMac LRHS MLHP MNrw MSph NBir NCob NDov SBla SMrm WCAu WCra WMnd WSHC WTin WWeb WWhi XPep
'Tetworth'	CBgR EBee EBla EChP ECha ECtt EHrv ELan EMan EMon EWin GBuc MSte NCGa SMad WCMO WCot WFar WPer
tinctoria	CArn CHby EAro EBee ELau EMon EPoy LRHS 7MBow MHer MNHC NFor NPer SPet SWvt WJek WWye
- from Judaea	EMon
- 'Alba'	NBre WHen WPer
* - 'Compacta'	EWes NBre NCob WOut
- dwarf	EBee EBla EWin SBla SBri SUsu WFar
- 'E.C. Buxton'	More than 30 suppliers
- 'Eva'	EMon LRHS MBNS NBre NCob NDov NLar WEas WWhi
I - 'Golden Rays'	EBee EWin MDKP NPro SDix
- 'Kelwayi'	CEnt CPrp CSBt CTri EBee ECtt EPfP ERou EShb GMaP LRHS MBNS NBPC NBro NCob NPer SMer SPla SPoG SRms WFar WGHP WHen WMoo WPer
- 'Lemon Maid'	CFir EPPr NBre NCob SMrm
- 'Pride of Grallagh'	see *A.* 'Beauty of Grallagh'
- 'Sauce Hollandaise'	More than 30 suppliers
- 'Wargrave Variety'	More than 30 suppliers
triumfettii	NPer
tuberculata	EMan NChi SBla
'White Water'	WAbe

Anthericum (*Anthericaceae*)

algeriense	see *A. liliago*
baeticum	EBee ERos
* *fistulosum*	GSki
§ *liliago*	CAby CBro CSec EBee ECho ELan ERos EWTr GCal GKev GMaP GMac GSki LHop MAvo MLLN MRav MSte MWgw NCGa SBla SPer SSvw WPer
- 'Major' ♀H4	CAvo CDes EBee ECha ECho EHrv GBuc IBlr IGor LPhx MLHP NBre WPGP
ramosum	More than 30 suppliers
- *plumosum*	see *Trichopetalum plumosum*
saundersiae	CPLG CPne SHom
undulatum	ERos

Antholyza (*Iridaceae*)

coccinea	see *Crocosmia paniculata*
x *crocosmioides*	see *Crocosmia* x *crocosmioides*
paniculata	see *Crocosmia paniculata*

Anthoxanthum (*Poaceae*)

odoratum	CArn CBig CRWN GBar GIBF GPoy NBre WWye

Anthriscus (*Apiaceae*)

cerefolium	CArn CSev EOHP GPoy ILis MBow MDun MHer MNHC SECG WJek WSel
sylvestris	CAgr CArn CHrt MBow NSco WShi
- 'Broadleas Blush'	CNat
- 'Hullavington' (v)	CNat
- 'Kabir'	CNat
- 'Moonlit Night'	EHoe
- 'Ravenswing'	More than 30 suppliers

Anthurium (*Araceae*)

amazonicum	MBri
andraeanum ♀H1	MBri
- 'Glowing Pink'	XBlo
- 'Red Heart'	XBlo
'Aztec'	XBlo
crenatum	XBlo
'Crimson'	XBlo
'Magenta'	XBlo
'Porcelaine White'	XBlo
scherzerianum ♀H1	MBri

Anthyllis (*Papilionaceae*)

barba-jovis	CSpe XPep
hermanniae	XPep
- 'Compacta'	see *A. hermanniae* 'Minor'
§ - 'Minor'	EPot NLar NMen WLin
montana	SBla
- subsp. *atropurpurea*	LRHS
- 'Rubra' ♀H4	EChP ECho EPot LTwo NMen
vulneraria	CFee ECho EWin NMir NRya NSco SECG WSFF
- subsp. *atlantis* **new**	GKev
- var. *coccinea*	CHar CSpe EBee GAbr GGar GKev MCCP MLLN MSte MTho NLar NSla NWCA SGar SPet WAbe WBVN WFar WHil
- dark red-flowered **new**	MAvo

Antigonon (*Polygonaceae*)

leptopus	CPIN MJnS SOWG

Antirrhinum (*Scrophulariaceae*)

asarina	see *Asarina procumbens*
barrelieri	CSpe
braun-blanquetii	CHal EBee EMan ERou EShb EWin GAbr MLLN STes WCot WHil WPtf
'Candy Stripe'	EMan LSou
Chandelier Primrose Vein = 'Yaprim'	LSou
Chandelier Rose Pink = 'Yarob'	LSou
glutinosum	see *A. hispanicum* subsp. *hispanicum*
graniticum	EBee
§ *hispanicum*	NBir
- 'Avalanche'	CHal ECtt EMan EWin LAst MLan SPet
§ - subsp. *hispanicum*	CSam CSpe SRot WSPU XPep
§ - - 'Roseum'	CMea CPom CSpe EMan SAga SPet
latifolium	XPep
(Luminaire Series)	NPri
Luminaire Harvest Red = 'Balumrest' **new**	
- Luminaire Yellow = 'Balumyell'PBR **new**	NPri
majus	XPep
- 'Black Prince'	CHad CSpe EMan EShb LHop LSou SAga
- 'Candy Snap'PBR (v)	LAst

- 'Powys Pride' (v)	EWll
- 'Taff's White' (v)	LRHS
molle	CPom CSpe ECtt EHyt GKev MSte
	NBir NPer NWCA SRot SUsu
- pink	CSWP MSte
'Night and Day'	CSpe EShb SAga
I 'Pendula Lampion Appleblossom'	LAst LSou
I 'Pendula Lampion Purple'	LAst LSou
I 'Pendula Lampion Salmon/Orange'	LAst LSou
pulverulentum	EHyt LHop MArl SAga
sempervirens	EBee EMan EWin NGdn SAga
	WAbe WHil
siculum	EBee EDsa WMoo

añu see *Tropaeolum tuberosum*

Aphanes (Rosaceae)
§ *arvensis*	MSal WWye

Aphelandra (Acanthaceae)
squarrosa	CHal LRHS MBri
I - 'Citrina'	XBlo

Aphyllanthes (Aphyllanthaceae)
monspeliensis	CFee EBee ECho SBla

Apios (Papilionaceae)
§ *americana*	CAgr CMdw CPlN CPom CWan
	EBee EChP ECho EMan EMon
	GBin ITer LEdu NBir NSti WBVN
	WCMO WCot WCru WSHC
tuberosa	see *A. americana*

Apium (Apiaceae)
graveolens	CArn CBgR CBod CWan ELau
	EOHP GPoy MHer MNHC MSal
	SIde WBri WJek
- (Secalinum Group) 'Par-cel'	MHer NGHP
- - 'Zwolsche Krul'	MBow

Apium x *Petroselinum* (Apiaceae)
hybrid	see *A. graveolens* Secalinum Group

Apocynum (Apocynaceae)
cannabinum	CArn COld GPoy MGol MSal
	WWye

Aponogeton (Aponogetonaceae)
distachyos	CDWL CRow CWat EHon ELan
	EMFW EPfP LNCo LPBA NPer
	SCoo SWat WFar WMAq WPnP
	WWpP

apple see *Malus domestica*

Aptenia (Aizoaceae)
cordifolia ♀H1-2	CSec CSev LRav NPer SChr SDnm
	SEND SPet XPep
- 'Variegata' (v)	EWin LAst MRav

Aquilegia ❀ (Ranunculaceae)
akitensis misapplied	see *A. flabellata, A. flabellata* var. *pumila*
'Alaska' (State Series)	CThr
* *alba variegata* (v)	ECho WEas
alpina	CMea CPrp EBee ECho ECtt EDAr
	EPfP MHer MLan MRav NFor
	NJOw SPer SPet SRms WFar WHen
	WMoo WPer
- 'Alba'	CMMP MWgw NOak
amaliae	see *A. ottonis* subsp. *amaliae*
amurensis	CLAP

'Anja' (v)	WCot
'Apple Blossom'	EBee LSou WCMO
aragonensis	see *A. pyrenaica*
§ *atrata*	CLAP CPou ECho EDAr EShb
	MDKP NEgg NJOw SBch SMHy
	WBVN WHil WPer
atrovinosa	EBee
aurea misapplied	see *A. vulgaris* golden-leaved
barnebyi	EHyt NEgg
bernardii	NJOw NOak
bertolonii ♀H4	ECho EHyt GCrs GKev LBee LHop
	LRHS NDlv NLAp NMen NOak
	NRya SBla SRms WAbe WHoo
Biedermeier Group	ECho IHMH LRHS MBNS MDKP
	NBre NOrc NRnb SPoG WFar
	WPer
'Black Majic'	EMag
'Blue Berry'	WLin WPat
'Blue Jay' (Songbird Series)	ENot NPri SPer SSvw SWvt
'Blue Star' (Star Series)	CSam CSim EBee ECtt ELan EPfP
	LRHS SUsu WPer
'Bluebird' (Songbird Series) ♀H2	CThr GBBs NPer
buergeriana	MDKP NChi NEgg WPer
- 'Calimero'	CPLG MDKP MSte NGby NLar
	WHil
- var. *oxysepala*	see *A. oxysepala*
'Bunting' (Songbird Series) ♀H2	EWll NLar SSvw WFar
'Burnished Rose'	EKen NRnb WHil
'Cally Spice'	GCal
canadensis ♀H4	CLAP CMHG CPom CSim CSpe
	EBee EBrs EDAr ELan GKev GQue
	MHer MNFA MSte NBid NBir NBro
	NEgg NOak NWCA SGar SRms
	SUsu SWal WPer
- 'Corbett'	CLAP GBuc MDKP WHil
- 'Little Lanterns'	CBgR CEnt CLAP CSam EBrs EPPr
	GKev ITim LBMP MDKP MSte
	NLar SMar WFar WHil WWeb
- 'Nana'	EPot GBuc GKev MDKP MWea
	NLAp WPat
'Cardinal' (Songbird Series)	ENot EWll MBri NLar NPri SPer
	SSvw WFar
cazorlensis	see *A. pyrenaica* subsp. *cazorlensis*
'Chaffinch' (Songbird Series)	CThr
§ *chaplinei*	NBir NEgg SBch WEas
chrysantha	CBgR CHea CHrt CSam CWan
	EBee EWTr GCal GKev MLLN
	MNFA NBre NOak SMar SRms
	WAbe WBrE WEas WLin WPer
- var. *chaplinei*	see *A. chaplinei*
I - 'Flore Pleno' (d)	EMag MDKP NEgg
- 'Yellow Queen'	CHea CPLG CPrp CSpe EBee EGoo
	EPfP EShb GGar GMaP LHop
	MAvo MDKP NBre NLar NMoo
	NRnb SPla SPur SSvw SWal WHil
	WSan WWFP
* *clematidea* 'Gentian Blue' **new**	ITim
clematiflora	see *A. vulgaris* var. *stellata*
coerulea ♀H4	EBee GKev MDKP SRms WLin
- var. *coerulea* **new**	GKev
- 'Himmelblau'	EGoo NBre
- var. *ochroleuca*	EBee
'Colorado' (State Series)	CThr EWll
'Crimson Star'	CHea EBee ENot EPfP MDKP SPur
	WMoo
'Debutante'	MDKP MWea WGwG WHoo
desertorum	CPom MDKP WAbe
dinarica **new**	WLin
discolor	EPot LBee LHop LRHS LTwo NEgg
	NLAp NMen NRnb WPat
'Double Chocolate'	GAbr LRHS
'Double Rubies' (d)	CHea NRnb SHar

'Dove' (Songbird Series) ♀H2 — CThr EWll ITer MBri MHer NLar NPri SHar SPer SWat WCra WFar

I 'Dragonfly' — CBcs CWib EPfP GAbr MAvo MNHC NBlu NBre NMir SPet SPoG SPur WFar

ecalcarata — see *Semiaquilegia ecalcarata*

einseleana — EBee NEgg

elegantula — EBee GCrs GKev NEgg

'Firewheel' — see *A. vulgaris* var. *stellata* 'Firewheel'

§ *flabellata* ♀H4 — CTri EPot GGar NEgg NLap WPat WPer

§ - f. *alba* — CTri ECho ELan NEgg NWCA SBla WEas

* - - 'White Angel' — NLar WPer

- - 'White Jewel' (Jewel Series) — GKev SPla

- 'Blue Angel' — CBcs EWll WPer

- Cameo Series — CBrm EWll NJOw WFar WGor WHil

- - 'Cameo Blue and White' — CWib ECho MWat WFar

- - 'Cameo Blue' — ECho

- - 'Cameo Blush' — WFar

- - 'Cameo Pink and White' — ECho MHer WFar

- - 'Cameo Rose' — NBir

- 'Georgia' (State Series) **new** — CThr

- Jewel Series — CSpe CWCL ECho NLar SPet WHil WPer

- - 'Amethyst' **new** — CThr

- - 'Blue Jewel' — ECho SPla

- - 'Diamond' **new** — CThr

- - 'Pink Jewel' — SPla

- - 'Pink Topaz' **new** — CThr

- 'Ministar' — ECho EPfP EPyc LRHS MBNS MHer NBlu NCGa NVic SRot WBrE WFar WHil WPer

- 'Nana Alba' — see *A. flabellata* var. *pumila* f. *alba*

§ - var. *pumila* ♀H4 — CSam EAEE ECha ECho EHyt EPfP GAbr GKev LHop MAvo MDKP MNFA NEgg NLap SBla SIng WFar WHil WPat WPer

§ - - f. *alba* ♀H4 — ECha ECho EWTr GEdr GKev LBee LHop LRHS MBNS MFOX MSte SIng SRms WHil

- - 'Flore Pleno' — ECho

- - f. *kurilensis* — MSte

* - - 'Snowflakes' — EHyt

- 'Sapphire' **new** — CThr

- 'Vermont' (State Series) **new** — CThr

flavescens — WPer

'Florida' (State Series) ♀H2 — CThr

formosa — EBee ECho GGar LBMP MDKP NChi NEgg NPri WGwG WPer

- var. *truncata* — GBuc MLLN

§ *fragrans* — CDMG CHar CHrt CLAP COIW EBee EBrs GBBs GBin GEdr LBMP MTho MWat NEgg NOak NRnb SBla SOkd STes WGwG WHil WHoo WRha WWhi WWlt

- white-flowered — ELan GEdr

glandulosa — GEdr NDlv NEgg NLar WEas

glauca — see *A. fragrans*

'Golden Guiness' — EMag WCra WPnP

'Goldfinch' (Songbird Series) — CThr ENot EWll NBir NPri SPer

grahamii **new** — SBla

grata — MDKP NRnb

Harbutt's hybrids — ERou

§ 'Hensol Harebell' ♀H4 — CPou CSWP EBee GBuc MBow MWgw SHar SRms WHoo WPtf

'Ice Blue' — WCMO WCot

'Irish Elegance' — EGoo WRha

japonica — see *A. flabellata* var. *pumila*

'Jenny' — MDKP NPri

jonesii — CGra CPBP LBee NLAp WAbe

jonesii x *saximontana* — GKev ITim

'Kansas' (State Series) — CThr

karelinii — GKev NEgg

'Koralle' — CSam MDKP NBre NRnb WFar WHil

'Kristall' — EBee ERou EShb MDKP NBre NOak NRnb SSvw STes WHil

laramiensis — CGra CPBP NEgg WAbe

'Lavender and White' (Songbird Series) — see *A.* 'Nuthatch'

'Little Plum' — WHil

longissima ♀H4 — CHar CMea CSam GBri GBuc MDKP MHer MLLN MWea NEgg NRnb SHar WEas WGwG WHoo

'Louisiana' (State Series) ♀H2 — CThr

'Magpie' — see *A. vulgaris* 'William Guiness'

'Maxi' — MDKP NBre WHil

McKana Group — EAEE ELan ENot EPfP GMaP LAst LBMP LHop LRHS MNHC MWgw NEgg NFor NGdn NOak NRnb NVic SPer SPlb SPoG SRms WBVN WMnd WWlt

'Milk and Honey' — CBre CEnt EMag GBBs NRnb SSth STes WCMO WHil

'Montana' (State Series) — CThr

moorcroftiana — EBee NEgg

- CC 1371 — WCra

Mrs Scott-Elliot hybrids — COIW CSBt GAbr LHop LIck MLan NEgg SGar SPer SPet WFar

Music Series ♀H4 — NOak SRms

nigricans — see *A. atrata*

§ 'Nuthatch' (Songbird Series) — CThr NEgg WCra

olympica — EBee EWes NEgg WPer

'Oranges and Lemons' **new** — EDAr LSou

Origami Series — GAbr WFar

ottonis — LHop

§ - subsp. *amaliae* — EPot GEdr NEgg WAbe

§ *oxysepala* — CPLG GCal NEgg NLAp WCru

- B&SWJ 4775 — WCru

'Perfumed Garden' — CEnt

'Purple Emperor'PBR — LRHS

§ *pyrenaica* — EHyt GKev WLin

§ - subsp. *cazorlensis* — NEgg

'Raspberry Ice' — ITim

'Red Hobbit' — CBrm CSpe EBee ENot GAbr IBal ITim LRHS MAvo MDKP NBre NJOw NWCA WBrE WFar WHil WHoo

'Red Star' (Star Series) — CSim EAEE EBee ECho ECtt EPfP ERou SHar WHil WPer

'Redwing' (Songbird Series) — CThr

'Robin' (Songbird Series) — CThr EWll NPri SWat WFar

rockii — CLAP CSam GCal GKev LHop MDKP MSte NEgg NLAp WHil

- B&SWJ 7965 — WCru

- KGB 176 — EHyt

'Roman Bronze' — see *Aquilegia* x *Semiaquilegia* 'Roman Bronze'

'Rose Queen' — CSam MDKP NBre SSvw WHil WHoo

saximontana — CGra GEdr GKev ITim NLar NWCA WPer

§ 'Schneekönigin' — EBee WHen WPer

scopulorum — CGra EHyt EPot GKev NEgg SBla WAbe WLin

shockleyi — GBuc WCMO

sibirica — CPLG WPer

'Silver Queen' — CPrp ELan MDKP MLan

'Simone's White' — EBee

skinneri — CDMG CEnt CHrt CPLG CSec EBee EChP EShb GBBs ITer LHop MBNS MWat NCGa NEgg NRnb

	SPoG STes SWal WCMO WCra WCru WMnd WMoo WRha WRos
- 'Tequila Sunrise' **new**	SPoG
'Skylark' (Songbird Series)	CThr
Snow Queen	see *A.* 'Schneekönigin'
Songbird Series	CSpe MLLN NEgg NPri SWat WFar
'Spring Magic Blue and White' (Spring Magic Series)	NNor
stellata	see *A. vulgaris* var. *stellata*
'Stoulton Blue'	CHea EBee WSPU
'Sunburst Ruby'	EDAr ITer LHop MBri MDKP NEgg NOak NPro SPoG SSth WCMO WMoo
'Sweet Lemon Drops'	LSou NRnb SPoG STes WHil
'Sweet Rainbows' (d)	GBBs LSou
triternata	EBee GCal NEgg NWCA
'Virginia' (State Series)	CThr
viridiflora	CHar CLAP CPom CSec CTri ECrN GBuc MHer NRnb SBla SGar SIng SMHy SSth WCru WEas WFar WGwG WHil WMnd WPGP WPer WPrP WWhi
vulgaris	CArn CHrt CMHG CRWN EPfP GKev GPoy LLWP NBro NSco SGar SPlb WBri WCAu WMoo WPer WShi WTin WWye
- 'Adelaide Addison'	ECGP ECha GBuc GMac MFOX NEgg WEas WFar
- var. *alba*	CMea EBee LLWP MNFA WCAu WWhi
- 'Altrosa'	NBre
* - 'Anemoniflora'	EPyc
- 'Aureovariegata'	see *A. vulgaris* Vervaeneana Group
- *clematiflora*	see *A. vulgaris* var. *stellata*
- var. *flore-pleno*	EChP LLWP WHen WPer
- - black-flowered (d)	EBrs WCot
- 'Blue Bonnet' (d)	ERou WHil
- - blue-flowered (d)	WCot
- - Dorothy Series (d)	GBuc LHop LRHS
- - 'Double Pleat' blue/white (d)	CBgR WHil WPer
- - 'Double Pleat' pink/white (d)	NGdn WHil WPer
* - - 'Frilly Dilly Rose' (d)	STes
* - - 'Frilly Dilly Sky Blue' (d)	STes
- - 'Frilly Dilly White' (d) **new**	STes
- - 'Jane Hollow' (d)	CPou
- - pale blue-flowered (d)	LLWP NRnb
- - 'Pink Bonnet' (d)	WFar WMnd
- - pink-flowered (d)	GGar
- - 'Powder Blue' (d)	CHea
- - purple-flowered (d)	LLWP
- - red-flowered (d)	GGar
- - 'Strawberry Ice Cream' (d)	GBri LBMP NBro NBur WBrE
- - 'Tower Light Blue' (d) (Tower Series)	EGoo SAga
- - 'Tower White' (d)	EGoo
* - - 'White Bonnet' (d)	NFla SRos
- - white-flowered (d)	LLWP LPhx
- 'Foggy Bottom Blues' **new**	EBrs
§ - golden-leaved	ECho
- Grandmother's Garden Group	EWll
- 'Heidi'	EBee NBre WPer
- 'Magda'	WBrE
- 'Magpie'	see *A. vulgaris* 'William Guiness'
- 'Mellow Yellow'	ECtt EMag GBuc GKev MBNS MDKP NRnb WHil WMoo WPer WRos
- Munstead White	see *A. vulgaris* 'Nivea'
§ - 'Nivea' ♀H4	CNic CPou ECha LAst NChi WHoo

- 'Pink Spurless'	see *A. vulgaris* var. *stellata* pink-flowered
- 'Pom Pom Crimson' (Pom Pom Series)	NBro NBur WCot
§ - var. *stellata*	ELan EPot EWsh GBuc GKev ITim MBNS MWgw NBro NEgg WBVN WCMO WMoo WPer WWeb
- - Barlow Series (d)	NJOw WFar
- - - 'Black Barlow' (d)	More than 30 suppliers
- - - 'Blue Barlow' (d)	CBgR CThr EBee ECtt EMar EShb GMaP IBal LBmB NBre SPer WMnd WPer WSan WWeb
- - - 'Christa Barlow' (d)	EBee EBrs EChP IBal LBMP LRHS MDKP NBre WWeb
- - - 'Nora Barlow' (d) ♀H4	More than 30 suppliers
- - - 'Rose Barlow' (d)	CBgR CThr EBrs WHen WMnd WWeb
- - - 'White Barlow' (d)	CPLG
- - 'Crimson Shower'	WBrE
§ - - 'Firewheel'	EBee EMag LBMP MDKP WMoo
- - 'Greenapples' (d)	EBee EWll MDKP NRnb SMHy WCot WWhi
§ - - pink-flowered	LLWP NSti
- - purple-flowered	LLWP
- - red-flowered	ELan LLWP
- - 'Royal Purple' (d)	EDAr LSou MBNS NBro NCGa SPoG WBVN
- - 'Ruby Port' (d)	CAby COIW EAEE EBee EPyc EShb GCal GGar IBal LBmB LPhx MNrw MRav MTis NChi NPri SPer SPla SPoG SSvw STes WFar WMnd WPrP
- - 'Ruby Port' crimped (d)	NDov WPnP
- - 'Sunlight White' (d)	SWat WMnd WPer
§ - - white-flowered	CSpe LHop NBro WFar
- - variegated foliage	see *A. vulgaris* Vervaeneana Group
§ - Vervaeneana Group (v)	More than 30 suppliers
- - 'Graeme Iddon' (v)	GBuc
- - 'Woodside'	see *A. vulgaris* Vervaeneana Group
- - 'Woodside Blue' (v)	COIW ECtt EGoo MFOX NRnb
- - 'Woodside Pink' (v)	MGos MWgw
- - 'Woodside Red' (v)	NRnb
- - 'Woodside White' (v)	EBee MFOX NBir NRnb WOut
- 'Westfaeld'	NOak
- 'White Spurless'	see *A. vulgaris* var. *stellata* white-flowered
§ - 'William Guiness'	More than 30 suppliers
- 'William Guiness Doubles' (d)	WMnd WMoo
'White Star' (Star Series)	CSim EBee EPfP ERou LAst NFla WHil WPer
Winky Series	MAvo NJOw
- 'Winky Blue-White'	LAst NBre NLar NPri WFar WHil WWeb
- formula mixed	SMar
- 'Winky Pink' **new**	NLar
- 'Winky Purple-White'	NBre WFar WWeb
- 'Winky Red-White'	IBal LAst MBNS NBre NPri SWvt WFar WWeb
- 'Winky Rose-Rose' **new**	MBNS NBre
yabeana	CDMG EBee GGar GKev SPoG WHil WLin

Aquilegia × *Semiaquilegia* (Ranunculaceae)

hybrid, blue	WCru
§ 'Roman Bronze'	CEnt EBee EDAr GBBs GKev ITer LSou NEgg NOak WCMO WHoo WWhi

Arabis (Brassicaceae)

aculeolata **new**	GKev
- NNS 01-28	EPPr
albida	see *A. alpina* subsp. *caucasica*
alpina	NEgg SPlb
§ - subsp. *caucasica*	ECho NBlu WFar
- - 'Corfe Castle'	ECho ECtt

- - 'Douler Angevine' (v) — LSou NPri SPoG
§ - - 'Flore Pleno' (d) ♀H4 — CTri CWCL ECha ECho ECtt ELan GAbr GMaP MTho SRms WBrk WEas WFar
- - 'Pink Pearl' — ECho NBlu
- - 'Pinkie' — ECho
- - 'Revolution' **new** — WCot
- - 'Rosea' — NBir NBlu NJOw NPri SRms WFar WMoo
§ - - 'Schneehaube' ♀H4 — CTri CWib ECho ECtt EPfP EShb GMaP MBar NBlu NJOw NMir SPoG SRms WMoo WPer
- - 'Snow White' — ECho
- - Snowcap — see *A. alpina* subsp. *caucasica* 'Schneehaube'
- - 'Snowdrop' — MRav NPri WFar
- - 'Variegata' (v) — ECho ECtt EHoe ELan EPot GMaP LBee LHop MBri MHer NEgg NFor SPoG SRms WEas WFar
androsacea — CStu SRms
x *arendsii* 'Compinkie' — ECtt SPlb SRms
- 'Rosabella' (v) — LRHS MBNS
blepharophylla — CSec EPfP SIng SPet SPoG
§ - 'Frühlingszauber' ♀H4 — CWib IHMH MNHC NBir NBlu NPri SPoG SRms WBVN WFar
- Spring Charm — see *A. blepharophylla* 'Frühlingszauber'
bryoides — LRHS NMen
carduchorum — NMen
caucasica — see *A. alpina* subsp. *caucasica*
§ *collina* subsp. *rosea* — IHMH
cypria — LSou
double white (d) — CFee
'Doulier Anguine' — EPot
ferdinandi-coburgi — ECho WEas
- 'Aureovariegata' (v) — CMea CTri ECho ECtt EDAr EHoe IHMH SPet SWvt
- 'Old Gold' — ECho ECtt EDAr EPfP EPot LAst LBee MBar MHer NEgg NHol NJOw NVic SBla SPoG SRms SSvw SWvt WCFE WFar WHoo WRHF
- 'Variegata' — see *A. procurrens* 'Variegata'
glabra — WPer
x *kellereri* — NMen
lucida 'Variegata' (v) — NPro
§ *procurrens* 'Variegata' (v) ♀H4 — CTri ECha ECho ECtt ELan EPfP EPot EWes GKev LBee MBar MHer MWgw NFor SBla SHFr SHGN SPlb SRms WTel
rosea — see *A. collina* subsp. *rosea*
§ *scabra* — CNat
§ *soyeri* subsp. *coriacea* — NDlv
stelleri var. *japonica* — CNic
stricta — see *A. scabra*
'Tu Tu' — NLar

Arachniodes (Dryopteridaceae)
simplicior — CCCN MAsh WCot

Araiostegia (Davalliaceae)
hymenophylloides **new** — WCot

Aralia ✿ (Araliaceae)
EDHCH 9720 from China — WCru
armata B&SWJ 3137 — WCru
- RWJ 10060 — WCru
bipinnata B&SWJ 6719 — WCru
cachemirica — CDes CHad CPLG EBee EWes GCal NBid NLar SDix WHal WPGP
- CC 4578 — MGol
californica — COld EBee EPPr GCal GPoy LEdu MSal MSte NLar WCru
chapaensis HWJ 723 — WCru
chinensis misapplied — see *A. elata*
chinensis L. — CAgr MSal WBVN

- BWJ 8102 — WCru
continentalis — EBee EPPr GCal LEdu NLar
- B&SWJ 4152 — WCru
- B&SWJ 8524 — WCru
cordata — EBee EWes GAbr GCal LEdu MSal NEgg NLar
- B&SWJ 5511 — WCru
decaisneana B&SWJ 3588 — WCru
§ *elata* ♀H4 — More than 30 suppliers
- B&SWJ 5480 — WCru
- 'Albomarginata' — see *A. elata* 'Variegata'
- 'Aureovariegata' (v) — CBcs CDoC ELan EPfP MBlu NLar NMoo NPal SBrw WCot WDin WGer WOrn WPat
- 'Golden Umbrella' (v) — CPen NLar WDin
- 'Silver Umbrella' — CPen EPfP MGos NLar
§ - 'Variegata' (v) ♀H4 — CBcs CDoC CDul ELan EPfP MBlu MGos NMoo NPal SBrw SHBN SPoG WCot WDin WGer WPat
foliolosa B&SWJ 8360 — WCru
nudicaulis — GPoy
racemosa — EBee GCal GPoy LEdu MLLN MNrw MSal MSte MWgw NBre NLar SRms WFar
- B&SWJ 9570 — WCru
schmidtii **new** — GIBF
sieboldii — see *Fatsia japonica*
spinosa — GIBF MBlu NLar WHer
stipulata **new** — GIBF NLar

Araucaria (Araucariaceae)
angustifolia — ECho LCon
§ *araucana* — More than 30 suppliers
bidwillii — LCon
§ *columnaris* — LCon
cunninghamii — ECho LCon
excelsa misapplied — see *A. heterophylla*
§ *heterophylla* ♀H1 — CCCN CDoC CTbh EShb GTSp LCon LRHS MBri SAPC SArc SDEP WNor
imbricata — see *A. araucana*

Araujia (Asclepiadaceae)
sericifera — CHEx CMac CPLG CPIN CRHN CSpe CTrG EBee EMil ERea EShb GQui ITer SDnm SGar SPav WBor WSHC XPep

Arbutus ✿ (Ericaceae)
andrachne — CTri EPfP SBrw XPep
x *andrachnoides* ♀H4 — CAbP CBcs CDul CPMA ELan EPfP LRHS MAsh MWya SAPC SArc SBra SDnm SPer SReu SSpi SSta WHCG WPGP WPat XPep
glandulosa — see *Arctostaphylos glandulosa*
'Marina' — CAbP CDoC CDul CEnd CPMA CSam EBee ELan EPfP LHop LRHS MAsh MBlu MWya SBrw SEND SMad SPer SPoG SReu SSpi SSta SWvt WFar WPGP WPat
menziesii ♀H3 — CBcs CDoC CEnd CMCN CTho EBee ECrN EPfP LRHS MAsh MGos MLan NLar NPen SLon SMad SPoG SPur SSpi WDin WFar WOrn WPGP
unedo ♀H4 — More than 30 suppliers
- 'Atlantic' — EBee IArd LPan LRHS MGos SBrw SPoG SWvt WGer WPat
- 'Compacta' — CBcs CDoC EBee LPan LRHS MAsh MBri MGos SBrw SWvt WDin XPep
- 'Elfin King' — ELan EPfP LRHS MAsh SBrw SDnm SPoG SSta SWvt
- 'Quercifolia' — CPMA EPfP NLar SBrw SDnm SReu SSta WPat
- f. *rubra* ♀H4 — More than 30 suppliers

Archontophoenix (Arecaceae)

alexandrae	CRoM EAmu LPal WMul
cunninghamiana ♀H1	CBrP CRoM CTrC EAmu EShb LPal WMul

Arctanthemum (Asteraceae)

§ *arcticum*	CKno EBee ECha NBre
- 'Roseum'	CFwr GBin
- 'Schwefelglanz'	NCGa

Arcterica see *Pieris*

Arctium (Asteraceae)

lappa	CArn GBar GPoy MHer MNHC MSal NMir SIde
minus	MSal NSco

Arctostaphylos (Ericaceae)

§ *glandulosa*	SAPC SArc
x *media* 'Wood's Red'	MBar WFar
myrtifolia	MBar
stanfordiana C&H 105	GGGa
uva-ursi	CArn CTri EBee GPoy GTSp MBar NBlu NLar NMen SHBN SLon SPer SPlb SSta WDin
- 'Massachusetts'	GQui LRHS MAsh SMur SReu
- 'Snowcap'	MAsh NHol
- 'Vancouver Jade'	CDoC LRHS LSRN MAsh MBar MBri NHol SBrw SCoo SPer SPoG SReu SSta SWvt WWeb

Arctotheca (Asteraceae)

calendula	XPep

Arctotis (Asteraceae)

adpressa new	CPBP
fastuosa var. *alba* 'Zulu Prince'	MOak
Hannah = 'Archnah' new	CSpe LSou SPoG SRkn SVil
Hayley = 'Archley' new	LSou SRkn SVil
x *hybrida* 'Apricot'	CHEx EShb EWin LAst LSou SAga SMrm
- 'China Rose'	SAga SMrm
- cream-flowered	CHEx SAga
- 'Flame' ♀H1+3	CAby CWCL EShb EWin LAst LIck MBNS MLan MOak SCoo SMrm WEas WHlf
- 'Lydie' new	CWCL
* - 'Mahogany' ♀H1+3	CAby CBrm CHrt EShb LSou MBNS SUsu WHlf
- 'Red Devil'	CHEx CHVG CWCL EWin LAst LIck MBNS SAga SCoo SMrm SPoG SVil
- 'Wine'	CBrm CCCN CHEx CWCL EWin LAst LSou MBNS MLan SCoo SMrm SRkn
'Prostrate Raspberry'	CSpe

Ardisia (Myrsinaceae)

crenata	LRHS MBri SMur
japonica B&SWJ 3809	WCru
- var. *angusta*	SOkd WCot
- 'Miyo-nishiki' (v)	WCot
maclurei B&SWJ 3772	LRHS

Areca (Arecaceae)

catechu	MBri
concinna	LPal
vestiaria	LPal

Arecastrum see *Syagrus*

Arenaria (Caryophyllaceae)

balearica	CWCL ECho LBee LRHS SIng SPlb SRms WDyG
bertolonii	LRHS
festucoides	ITim NLAp
grandiflora	NJOw
ledebouriana	GEdr MWat NLar WAbe
magellanica	see *Colobanthus quitensis*
montana ♀H4	More than 30 suppliers
pinifolia	see *Minuartia circassica*
polytrichoides new	GIBF
procera subsp. *glabra*	NJOw
purpurascens	CBrm CPBP ECho EDAr EHyt NMen SBla SRms SRot
- 'Elliott's Variety'	NHol WPat
tetraquetra	NLAp NMen
§ - subsp. *amabilis*	EPot LRHS MBar NJOw NMen NSla NWCA
tmolea	NMen
tschuktschorum	GIBF
verna	see *Minuartia verna*

Arenga (Arecaceae)

engleri	EAmu LPal WMul

Argemone (Papaveraceae)

grandiflora	ELan SBch SPav
mexicana	ELan SPav
pleiacantha	LRav SPav

Argyranthemum ✿ (Asteraceae)

'Anastasia'	LIck MAJR
'Apricot Surprise'	see A. 'Peach Cheeks'
'Beth'	MAJR
'Blanche' (Courtyard Series)	IHMH MAJR
Blazer Primrose = 'Supanova' (Daisy Crazy Series)	MAJR
§ 'Blizzard' (d)	MAJR
Blushing Rose = 'Supaellie' (Daisy Crazy Series)	MAJR
'Bofinger'	MAJR
Boston yellow daisy	see A. *callichrysum*
'Bridesmaid'	MAJR
Bright Carmine = 'Supalight' PBR (Daisy Crazy Series)	MAJR
broussonetii	MAJR
Butterfly = 'Ulysses' ♀H1+3	EWin LIck MAJR WGor
§ *callichrysum*	MAJR
- 'Penny'	MAJR
'Camilla Ponticelli'	LIck MAJR
canariense hort.	see A. *frutescens* subsp. *canariae*
'Champagne'	MAJR
'Cheek's Peach'	see A. 'Peach Cheeks'
Cherry Love (Daisy Crazy Series)	LIck MAJR
'Christy Bell'	MAJR
* *compactum*	MAJR
'Comtesse de Chambord'	MAJR SPet
'Cornish Gold' ♀H1+3	CBcs CCCN LIck LSou MAJR
coronopifolium	MAJR XPep
Daisy Crazy Series	LIck
'Donington Hero' ♀H1+3	LIck MAJR MHom
double white (d)	EWin LIck MAJR
'Edelweiss' (d)	MAJR MHom WHen
'Flamingo'	see *Rhodanthemum gayanum*
§ *foeniculaceum* misapplied	CTri ELan WHen WKif
§ *foeniculaceum* (Willd.) Webb & Sch.Bip.	CHal MAJR
- pink-flowered	see A. 'Petite Pink'
- 'Royal Haze' ♀H1+3	CHll MAJR NPer
'Frosty'	MAJR MBNS
§ *frutescens*	CHEx LIck LRHS MAJR
- Blazer Rose = 'Supaglow' PBR (Daisy Crazy Series)	MAJR

§ - subsp. *canariae* ♀H1+3 ECtt LIck MAJR
- 'Ella'PBR MAJR
- 'Gretel'PBR MAJR
- Gypsy Rose = 'M9/18D' LSou
- 'Henriette'PBR MAJR
- subsp. *succulentum* MAJR
- - 'Margaret Lynch' MAJR
'Fuji Sundance' LIck MAJR
'George' MAJR
'Gill's Pink' CPne ECtt LIck MAJR MHom
WPnn
'Golden Treasure' LIck MAJR
§ *gracile* CHll
- 'Chelsea Girl' ♀H1+3 CHEx COlW ECtt LIck MAJR
MHom MLan MSte WKif WPnn
'Guernsey Pink' LIck MAJR
'Harvest Snow' LAst MBNS
'Icknield Jubilee' LIck MAJR
'Icknield Pink' MAJR
'Icknield Pink 2000' LIck
'Icknield Surprise' LIck MAJR
'Icknield Sylvia' MAJR
'Icknield Yellow' LIck MAJR
§ 'Jamaica Primrose' ♀H1+3 CHEx CPne CSpe ECtt LIck MAJR
MHar SDix WHen WPnn
'Jamaica Snowstorm' see *A.* 'Snow Storm'
'Julie Anna' (d) MBNS
'Julieanne' LAst LIck MAJR
'Lemon Chiffon' MAJR
'Lemon Delight' CHal LAst MAJR
'Lemon Meringue' (d) MAJR
'Lemon Soufflé' MAJR
lemsii LIck MAJR
§ 'Levada Cream' ♀H1+3 LIck MAJR MHom
'Libby Brett' MAJR
'Lilliput' MAJR
(Madeira Series) Madeira SPoG
Camara =
'Ohmadcama' **new**
- Madeira Madelana SVil
= 'Ohmadmade' **new**
- Madeira Monte SPoG SVil
= 'Ohar01241' **new**
- Madeira Porto Santo SVil
= 'Ohar0132' **new**
- Madeira Santa SPoG SVil
Catarina = 'Ohmadsaca'
new
- Madeira Santana SPoG SVil
= 'Ohmadsant' **new**
- Madeira Sao Martinho SVil
= 'Ohmadsaom' **new**
§ *maderense* ♀H1+3 CHal CHll LRHS MAJR MSte SUsu
- pale-flowered MAJR
'Maja Bofinger' EWin
'Mary Cheek' (d) ♀H1+3 EWin LIck MAJR SPet SRGP WHoo
'Mary Wootton' (d) ECtt LIck MAJR MHom
mawii see *Rhodanthemum gayanum*
'Mike's Pink' MAJR
'Millennium Star' LIck MAJR
'Mini-snowflake' see *A.* 'Blizzard'
§ 'Mrs F. Sander' (d) MAJR
'Nevada Cream' see *A.* 'Levada Cream'
ochroleucum see *A. maderense*
'Patches Pink' (d) MAJR
§ 'Peach Cheeks' (d) ECtt MAJR SPet
§ 'Petite Pink' ♀H1+3 ECtt EWin LAst MAJR MHom
WHen
Ping-Pong = 'Innping' (d) CBcs LIck
'Pink Australian' (d) LIck MAJR MHom
'Pink Break' MAJR
'Pink Dahlia' MAJR
'Pink Delight' see *A.* 'Petite Pink'
'Pink Pixie' MAJR
Pink Wonder = 'Supalily' MAJR
(Daisy Crazy Series)

pinnatifidium subsp. MAJR
succulentum
'Powder Puff' (d) ECtt LIck MAJR
'Primrose Petite' MAJR
(Courtyard Series)
prostrate double pink (d) MAJR
'Qinta White' (d) ♀H1+3 LIck MAJR
'Rising Sun' LIck MAJR
'Rosa Dwarf' MAJR
'Royal Haze' see *A. foeniculaceum* 'Royal Haze'
'Saimi' MAJR
'Silver Leaf' MAJR
'Silver Queen' see *A. foeniculaceum* misapplied
§ 'Snow Storm' ♀H1+3 LAst LIck MAJR MHom WPnn
'Snowball' MAJR
'Snowflake' misapplied see *A.* 'Mrs F. Sander'
'Snowflake' (d) WHen
'Starlight' MAJR
'Sugar and Ice'PBR MAJR
'Sugar Baby'PBR MAJR
'Sugar Lace' MAJR
Sultan's Lemon MAJR
(Daisy Crazy Series)
Sultan's Pride = 'Cosupri' MAJR
(Daisy Crazy Series) **new**
'Summer Angel' (d) MAJR
'Summer Eyes' MAJR
'Summer Melody'PBR (d) CBrm CSpe LIck MAJR SMrm
'Summer Pink'PBR CCCN LAst LIck LSou MAJR WGor
'Summer Stars Pink' MAJR
(Daisy Crazy Series) (d)
'Summertime' MAJR
'Sweety' MAJR WPnn
'Tenerife' MSte
'Tony Holmes' MAJR
'Tweeny' CSpe MAJR
'Tweety' MAJR
'Vancouver' (d) ♀H1+3 CHll CWCL ECtt EShb EWin LAst
MAJR MHom SEND SPet WHen
'Vara' EWin
* 'Vera' MAJR
'Wellwood Park' MAJR
'Weymouth Pink' MAJR
'Weymouth Surprise' LIck MAJR
White Blush = 'Supamorni' MAJR
(Daisy Crazy Series)
White Crystal = 'Supagem' MAJR
(Daisy Crazy Series)
'White Spider' ELan MAJR MHom
'White Star' (d) MAJR
'Whiteknights' ♀H1+3 MAJR
'Yellow Australian' (d) LIck MAJR

Argyreia (Convolvulaceae)

mollis CPIN
nervosa MGol

Argyrocytisus see *Cytisus*

Arisaema (Araceae)

ACE 2408 GBuc
B&L 12160 MGol
B&L 12161 MGol
C&H 7026 NMen
CC 3203 CPLG
CC 4462 MGol
CC 4593 MGol
CC 4595 MGol
CC 4686 MGol
CC 4688 MGol
Chen Yi 14 WCot
Chen Yi 38 WCot
Chen Yi 41 WCot
amurense CFir CLAP CStu EBee ECho GBuc
GCal GIBF ITer MLLN WCMO
WCot WFar

- B&SWJ 947	WCru
§ - subsp. *robustum*	CStu ECho LRHS NMen WCot WWst
- - B&SWJ 1186	WCru
- subsp. *serratum*	WCru
B&SWJ 711	
* *angustatum* var.	NLAp
amurense	
- var. *peninsulae*	GIBF
- - B&SWJ 841	WCru
* - - f. *variegatum* (v)	WCru
B&SWJ 4321	
- var. *serratum*	see *A. serratum*
asperatum	MLul
austroyunnanense	WCMO
bathycoleum	WCMO
biauriculatum	see *A. wattii*
black-spathed **new**	NLAp
brachyspathum	see *A. heterophyllum*
brevipes	CFwr NLAp
candidissimum ♀H4	More than 30 suppliers
- green	WCMO WCot
- white	WCMO WCot
- yellow **new**	WCMO
ciliatum	CBro CDes CPom CStu EBla GBuc GEdr ITer MLLN MLul MNrw NLar SRot WCot WIvy WSHC
- var. *liubaense*	CFwr CKob CLAP EPfP ITer MGol WCMO WPGP WWst
- - CT 369	SCnR WCot
* *coenobialis* **new**	WCot
concinnum	CFir CKob CStu EMar EPot MDun MGol MOak NLar WCMO WViv
- GG 94152	WCot
- 'Sikkim'	MGol
consanguineum	CAby CBro CDes CFwr CHEx CKob CLAP CMea CPLG CPom CRow EBee EPfP GBuc GCrs GGar GKev ITer ITim MGol MTho SGar WCMO WCot WHil WPGP
- B&SWJ 071	WCru
- CC 3635	WCot
- GG 92112	WCot
- PJ 277	WCot
* - bicolour	WCMO
- 'J. Balis'	WCot
- subsp. *kelung-insulare*	WCru
B&SWJ 256	
- marble-leaved	MGol WCMO WCot
- 'Qinling'	MGol WCot
- silver-centred-leaved	ITer WCMO
costatum	CHEx CKob CLAP CPom EBee ECho EPot GBuc GEdr ITer LRHS MDun MLul MOak NMen WCMO WCot WMul WPGP
- CC 2924	WCot
- CC 3237	ITer
dahaiense	MLul
dilatatum	ITer MLul WCot
dracontium	CLAP ECho ITer MDun MLul NLar NMen
du-bois-reymondiae	WCMO
elephas	ITer MLul
engleri	CKob MLul
- GG 98173	WCot
erubescens	CStu EPot ERos MLul NLar WCot
- white-lined-leaved **new**	WCot
exappendiculatum	CDes WPGP
fargesii	CLAP ECho EPot ITer MLul WCot WWst
- purple-leaved **new**	WCot
flavum	CBro CDes CKob CLAP CMea CStu EBee EHyt EPfP EPot GBuc GCal ITer ITim LRHS MLul MTho NJOw NMen NSla WBVN WCMO WCot WPGP

- CC 1782	WCot
- CC 3946	MGol
- subsp. *abbreviatum*	MGol WCot
- - GG 84193	WWst
* - *minus*	NWCA
- tall	CLAP ECho
- subsp. *tibeticum*	EBee
formosanum B&SWJ 280	WCru
- B&SWJ 390	CPou WCot
- var. *bicolorifolium*	WCru
B&SWJ 3528	
- f. *stenophyllum*	WCru
B&SWJ 1477	
§ *franchetianum*	GEdr ITer MGol MLul WCot
fraternum	WCot WWst
- CC 465	WCot
galeatum	EBee ECho EPot MDun MGol MOak WCMO WCot WMul WViv
§ *griffithii*	EBee ECho EPot GGar LRHS MDun MLul NMyG WCMO WCru WMul WViv
- var. *pradhanii*	WCMO
hatizyoense	MLul
helleborifolium	see *A. tortuosum*
§ *heterophyllum*	WCru
B&SWJ 2028	
- 'Baguo'	WCot
hunanense white-lined-leaved **new**	WCot
ilanense B&SWJ 3030	WCru
inkiangense	NLAp
intermedium	ECho EMar MNrw NMen
- CC 3102	WCot
- GG 96283	WCot
- var. *biflagellatum*	ITer
- - HWJCM 161	WCru
- - PB 022	WCot
iyoanum	WCru
jacquemontii	CBro CLAP EBla ECho EHyt GBuc GCrs GEdr GGar LRHS NLar NMen WCMO WCot
- B&SWJ 2719	WCru
- CC 4598	MGol
- GG 88172	WCot
- GG 94120	WCot
aff. *jacquemontii*	WCMO
- MECCN 29	NMen
- MECCN 76	NMen
japonicum Komarov	see *A. serratum*
jinshajiangense	MLul
kiushianum	EFEx SOkd WCMO WCot
leschenaultii	EBee WWst
lichiangense	GEdr WCot
lingyunense	CFir
§ *lobatum*	MLul WCMO
maximowiczii	GEdr WCru
meleagris	MLul
multisectum	CFir WCot
negishii	GEdr WCru
§ *nepenthoides*	CBro CKob ECho EMar EPot GEdr MDun MGol MLul MNrw NMyG WCot WMul WViv
- B&SWJ 2614b	WCru
ochraceum	see *A. nepenthoides*
omeiense	NLar
onoticum	see *A. lobatum*
penicillatum	WCMO
polyphyllum B&SWJ 3904	WCru
prazeri	WCMO
propinquum	CLAP ECho EHyt EPot MDun MGol NMen WCot WCru WViv
purpureogaleatum	see *A. franchetianum*
red-spathed from China **new**	CFwr
rhizomatum	MLul NLAp
rhombiforme	WCot

ringens misapplied — see *A. amurense* subsp. *robustum*
ringens (Thunberg) Schott — CDes EFEx EPot MLul WWst
- f. *praecox* B&SWJ 1515 — WCru
- f. *sieboldii* B&SWJ 551 — WCru
robustum — see *A. amurense* subsp. *robustum*
saxatile — MLul
sazensoo — GEdr WCru WWst
§ *serratum* — CDes EBee ECho MGol MNrw WPGP
- B&SWJ 5894 — WCru
'Siang' **new** — MLul
§ *sikokianum* — CBro CDes CKob EBee ECho EFEx EPot LBmB LRHS MGol MLul SOkd WCMO WCru WViv
- var. *serratum* — CFir MLul
- variegated (v) — WCru
speciosum — CHEx CKob CPLG EBee ECho ELan EPot GBuc GEdr GGar GSki MDun MGol MOak MMen WCMO WFar WMul WPnP WViv
- B&SWJ 2403 — WCru
- CC 3100 — WCot
* - *magnificum* — EBee
- var. *mirabile* B&SWJ 2712 — WCru
taiwanense — CFwr CLAP GEdr WCMO WCot
- B&SWJ 269 — WCru
- B&SWJ 356 — CPou
- var. *brevipedunculatum* B&SWJ 1859 — WCru
- f. *cinereum* B&SWJ 19121 — WCru
- silver-leaved — WCMO WCot
tashiroi — GEdr WCru WWst
ternatipartitum — WDav
- B&SWJ 5790 — WCru
thunbergii — CPom EFEx LBmB WCMO WCot WViv
- subsp. *autumnale* B&SWJ 1425 — WCru
- subsp. *urashima* — CLAP EBee EFEx GEdr WWst
§ *tortuosum* — CArn CBro CKob CLAP EBee ECho EHyt EMar EPot ERos GBin GCrs GEdr GGar ITer MDun MLul MNrw MOak MTho NLar NWCA WAbe WCMO WCot WPGP WPnP
- CC 1452 — CPou
- GG 85320 — ITer
- var. *helleborifolium* CC 3641 — WCot
- high altitude — GBuc NMen
- - B&SWJ 2386 — WCru
- low altitude — WSan
- - B&SWJ 2298 — WCru
tosaense — GEdr WWst
- B&SWJ 5761 — WCru
- GG 91224 — WCru
triphyllum — CLAP CPom ECho EPot GEdr GGar GSki ITer LBmB LEdu LRHS MLul MSal MTho NWCA SMad WFar WPGP WPnP WSan
- subsp. *stewardsonii* — ITer NMen
- subsp. *triphyllum* var. *atrorubens* — CLAP
unzenense B&SWJ 6226 — WCru
§ *utile* — EBee ECho MLul WCMO
- CC 3101 — WCot
- HWJCM 161 — WCru
verrucosum — see *A. griffithii*
- var. *utile* — see *A. utile*
§ *wattii* — MLul NLAp
yamatense — WCru
- subsp. *sugimotoi* B&SWJ 5092 — WCru
yunnanense — CLAP MGol NLAp WCot

Arisarum (Araceae)
proboscideum — More than 30 suppliers
- MS 958 — EMar
vulgare — ECho
- JRM 1396 from Crete — CMon
* - f. *maculatum* — ECho
- subsp. *simorrhinum* — CStu EBla WCot
- -MS 296 from Spain **new** — CMon
- subsp. *vulgare* — EBee WCot

Aristea (Iridaceae)
capitata — CPne
confusa — SWat
ecklonii — CAby CBod CHEx CPLG CPou CTbh EChP EDif EMan EShb GGar GSki IGor SChr SMar SWat WCot WDyG WOut WPic
ensifolia — CMdw WPrP WSHC
grandis — CFir SMar WCot
§ *major* — CAbb CCtw CHll CPen CPne CTrC EMan GSki
- pink-flowered — CAbb CDes EBee WPGP
montana — CTrC
spiralis — SWat
thyrsiflora — see *A. major*

Aristolochia ✿ (Aristolochiaceae)
baetica — CArn CPLG CPlN WCru WPGP
brasiliensis **new** — CPlN
californica — LEdu
clematitis — CArn EChP ECho GPoy LEdu MSal WCru WWye
contorta — EBee
delavayi — CHEx CPlN
durior — see *A. macrophylla*
elegans — see *A. littoralis*
fimbriata — CStu
gigantea — CPlN SMur
gorgona — CPlN
grandiflora — CPlN
griffithii — CPlN
- B&SWJ 2118 — WCru
heterophylla — see *A. kaempferi* f. *heterophylla*
kaempferi — CPlN
- B&SWJ 293 — WCru
§ - f. *heterophylla* B&SWJ 3109 — WCru
§ *littoralis* ♀H1 — CPlN LRHS SOWG
§ *macrophylla* — CBcs CHEx CPlN EBee EShb IDee MRav NPal SBig SHBN SLim WCru WDin
manshuriensis — CPlN WDin
- B&SWJ 962 — WCru
onoei — CPlN
- B&SWJ 4960 — WCru
paucinervis — CMon WCru
ringens Vahl. — CPlN
rotunda — CMon
sempervirens — CPlN CStu MBri WDin WSHC
sipho — see *A. macrophylla*
tomentosa — IDee WCru
trilobata — CPlN
zollingeriana B&SWJ 7030 — WCru

Aristotelia (Elaeocarpaceae)
§ *chilensis* — LEdu
- 'Variegata' (v) — CCCN CWib EBee GQui SEND SLim SPlb
fruticosa — CPne
- (f) — ECou
- (m) — ECou
- black-fruited (f) — ECou
- white-fruited (f) — ECou
macqui — see *A. chilensis*

peduncularis	CPLG
serrata	ECou
- (f)	ECou
- (m)	ECou

Armeria (*Plumbaginaceae*)

§ *alliacea*	CSpe ECha EPPr MWgw
- f. *leucantha*	SRms WMoo
Bees' hybrids	SRms WMoo
'Bees' Ruby'	WPer
'Bloodgood' **new**	ECho
'Brutus' **new**	CDes
caespitosa	see *A. juniperifolia*
euscadiensis	CSpe
§ *girardii*	EPot NJOw
Joystick Series	ECho NVic
- 'Joystick Lilac Shades'	CBrm EShb LBMP NLar
- 'Joystick Red'	CBrm EShb MSph SBri
- 'Joystick White'	EGoo EShb NLar
§ *juniperifolia* ♀H4	CLyd CMea ECho ECtt EDAr ELan
	EPfP GMaP LBee LRHS MWgw
	NJOw NMen NVic NWCA SIng
	SPoG SRms
- 'Alba'	ECho EDAr ELan EPfP EPot GBin
	GKev NMen NPri NRya SPoG
	SRms WAbe WFar WLin WThu
- 'Beechwood'	LRHS
- 'Bevan's Variety' ♀H4	ECha ECho ECtt ELan EPfP EPot
	GGar GMaP LRHS MWat NHol
	NJOw NLAp NMen NPri NRya SBla
	SPoG SRms SRot WAbe WFar WLin
	WPat
- 'Brookside'	EPot
- dark-flowered	EWes SBla WAbe
- rose-flowered	ITim
- spiny, dwarf	EPot NLAp
juniperifolia x	EAEE
maritima	
§ *maritima*	CArn ECho EPfP GAbr LAst LRHS
	MBar MBow MNHC NFor NJOw
	SECG SPet SWal WFar WGwG
	WMoo XPep
- 'Alba'	More than 30 suppliers
- 'Bloodstone'	CTri ECho ECot ELan MWat
	SPoG
- 'Corsica'	CMea CTri EPot MBNS NBir NRya
	SMer WFar XPep
- Düsseldorf Pride	see *A. maritima* 'Düsseldorfer
	Stolz'
§ - 'Düsseldorfer Stolz'	CElw EAEE ECha ECho ECtt EDAr
	ELan EPfP GGar ITim LHop LRHS
	MLHP NEgg NHol NJOw NLAp
	NMen NPri SPoG WCra WPat
- 'Glory of Holland'	EPot
- 'Laucheana'	SHGN WHoo WMoo
* - 'Pink Lusitanica'	ECho
I - 'Rubrifolia'	CBgR CFir CFwr CHVG CMea CMil
	CRez CSpe EBee ECGP ECho EHoe
	EMan EPPr EShb EWin GEdr GKev
	MAvo MSph NEgg NJOw NLAp
	NLar NRya SBla SPoG WAbe WFar
	WPat
- 'Ruby Glow'	CTri LBuc
- 'Splendens'	CBcs CHrt COlW ECho EMil ENot
	EPfP GMaP GWCH LAst MBow
	MHer MWgw NBlu NMir NNor
	NRya NVic SBch SPoG WFar
	WMoo WPer WPtf
- 'Vindictive' ♀H4	CMea CTri EPfP
morisii	SBch
'Nifty Thrifty' (v)	CBod CMea EBee ECho EHoe ENot
	EShb EWes EWin LRHS MHer
	NLAp SCoo SIde SPet SPoG SRot
	WPat WWFP
'Ornament'	ECtt LRav NJOw SHGN SPoG
	WHen

plantaginea	see *A. alliacea*
pseudarmeria	CHrt ELan MLan NBlu
- 'Drumstick Red'	ECho WPer
- 'Drumstick White'	WPer
- hybrids	CTri ELan NMir
pungens	EBee
setacea	see *A. girardii*
vulgaris	see *A. maritima*
welwitschii	IFoB SRms
'Westacre Beauty'	EWes

Armoracia (*Brassicaceae*)

§ *rusticana*	CArn CBod COld CPrp CSev ELau
	EUnu GPoy IHMH ILis MBri MHer
	MNHC MSal NPer NPri NTHB SIde
	WGwG WHer WJek WSel WWye
- 'Variegata' (v)	CPrp EBee ELau EMan EMar EMon
	GBar ITer LHop LRHS MAvo NSti
	SMad SPla WCHb WMoo WPnP
	WSel

Arnebia (*Boraginaceae*)

echioides	see *A. pulchra*
longiflora	see *A. pulchra*
§ *pulchra*	SBla

Arnica (*Asteraceae*)

angustifolia subsp.	SRms
alpina	
- subsp. *iljinii*	EBee NBir
chamissonis Schmidt	see *A. sachalinensis*
chamissonis Less.	CHby CHrt CWan GBar MNrw
	MSal NBre NLar WHil WJek WPer
	WWye
longifolia	NBre NEgg
montana	CArn CSam EUnu GBar GPoy
	MHer MLan MNHC SRms SWat
	WLin WPer WWye
- yellow-flowered	MLan
parryi **new**	GIBF
§ *sachalinensis*	GIBF NBre
- AER 0206	MGol
unalaschkensis **new**	EBee

Arnoglossum (*Asteraceae*)

§ *plantagineum*	EBee

Aronia (*Rosaceae*)

arbutifolia	CBcs CDul CTri EPfP EPla GIBF
	MBlu MGan NBlu SHBN SLdr SLon
	SPer WDin WOrn
- 'Erecta'	EBee ECrN ELan EPfP GBin LHop
	MBNS MBlu MBri MWea NLar
	SBrw SLPl SMac SPoG SRms SSpi
	WBor WFar
melanocarpa	CAgr CBgR CDul CMCN CMHG
	CWib EGra ELan EPfP EWTr GIBF
	LEdu LRHS MAsh MBar MBlu
	MRav SPer SSpi WDin WFar WHCG
- 'Autumn Magic'	CBcs CDoC CPMA EBee EPfP LAst
	LRHS MAsh MBlu NLar NMyG
	SBrw SCoo SPer
- var. *grandifolia*	CPMA
- 'Hugin'	CPMA
x *prunifolia*	CAgr CDoC CDul CMHG EBee
	LEdu SPer WHCG
- 'Aron' (F)	CPMA
- 'Brilliant'	CDoC CTri EBee LAst LRHS SCoo
	SPer SPur
- 'Nero' (F)	CAgr
- 'Serina' (F)	CPMA
- 'Viking' (F)	CAgr EBee ECrN EPfP LBuc MBlu
	MRav NScw SPoG WDin

Aronia x *Sorbus* (*Rosaceae*)

'Burka'	WPat

Arrhenatherum (Poaceae)

elatius var. *bulbosum* — NNor WFar
- - 'Variegatum' (v) — CHrt CSpe EBee EChP EHoe ELan ENot GBin GMaP LEdu LRHS MMoz MWgw MWhi NBid NGdn NHol NOrc SHFr SWal WFar WMoo WPer

Artemisia ✿ (Asteraceae)

RBS 0207 — EPPr
from Taiwan — WHer
§ *abrotanum* ♀[H4] — More than 30 suppliers
absinthium — CAgr CArn CPbn CSev CWan EEls ELau GPoy MBar MBow MHer MLLN MNHC NSti NTHB SAdn SECG SIde SPer SWat WPer WWye XPep
* - 'Argentea' — XPep
- - 'Corinne Tremaine' (v) — WHer
- - 'Lambrook Giant' — EEls
- - 'Lambrook Mist' ♀[H3-4] — CSev EAEE EBee EChP EEls ELan EPfP GBri GMaP GMac LRHS MRav NBre NCiC NHol SBch SSvw SWat WCAu WMnd
- - 'Lambrook Silver' ♀[H4] — More than 30 suppliers
- - 'Silver Ghost' — EEls
* - 'Variegata' (v) — CBcs
afra — CArn EBee EEls EMan EWin GBar IFro XPep
§ *alba* — CSev EEls EMan EMon EOHP GBar GPoy ILis MHer MSal NBur NSti SIde SMad WMow WPer WRha XPep
§ - 'Canescens' ♀[H4] — More than 30 suppliers
annua — EEls MSal SIde WJek WWye
anomala — EEls
arborescens ♀[H3] — CArn CMHG CTri ECrN EEls EWin SDix SPer WDin WHer XPep
- - 'Brass Band' — see *A.* 'Powis Castle'
- - 'Faith Raven' — CArn CPrp EBee EEls ERou GBin GBuc NLar WFar
- - 'Little Mice' — EBee NBre NLar WGwG
- - 'Porquerolles' — EEls XPep
arctica — EEls
argyi — EEls
§ *armeniaca* — ECho EEls XPep
assoana — see *A. caucasica*
atrata — EEls
barrelieri — EEls
brachyloba — MLLN WCHb
californica — EEls IFro XPep
- 'Canyon Gray' **new** — EEls
campestris subsp. *borealis* — EEls WRha WSel
- - var. *borealis* — GIBF
- subsp. *campestris* — EEls XPep
- subsp. *glutinosa* — XPep
- subsp. *maritima* — EEls XPep
- - from Wales — EEls
camphorata — see *A. alba*
cana — see *Seriphidium canum*
canariensis — see *A. thuscula*
canescens misapplied — see *A. alba* 'Canescens'
canescens Willd. — see *A. armeniaca*
capillaris — EBee EEls MSal XPep
§ *caucasica* ♀[H3-4] — ECho EEls EWes LPhx MBrN MHer NLRH SBla SRms SRot WCHb WEas WJek WPer XPep
- *caucasica* — EEls WFar
chamaemelifolia — CArn EEls IGor MHer NBre WWye XPep
cretacea — see *Seriphidium nutans*
discolor Dougl. ex Besser — see *A. michauxiana*
douglasiana — EEls
- 'Valerie Finnis' — see *A. ludoviciana* 'Valerie Finnis'

dracunculus — ECha ELan GAbr MBar MNHC MRav NBlu NVic SBch SPlb WBrk WFar WPer
- French — CAgr CArn CHby CHrt COfd CSev EEls ELau EUnu GBar GPoy GWCH MBow MHer MWat NGHP NPri SIde WEas WGwG WSel WWye XPep
- Russian — CArn CWan EEls EUnu GBar XPep
ferganensis — see *Seriphidium ferganense*
filifolia — EEls XPep
fragrans Willd. — see *Seriphidium fragrans*
frigida ♀[H3-4] — EEls WHCG XPep
genipi — EEls MSal
glacialis — ECha EEls NLar XPep
gmelinii — EBee EEls GBar
gnaphalodes — see *A. ludoviciana*
gorgonum — EEls
N *granatensis* misapplied — MSte
herba-alba — EEls XPep
'Huntington' — EEls WFar
kawakamii B&SWJ 088 — EEls WCru
kitadakensis — EEls
- 'Guizhou' — see *A. lactiflora* Guizhou Group
laciniata — EEls
lactiflora ♀[H4] — CPrp EBee ECha ECtt EEls ELan ERou GBar GMaP MRav NFor NGdn NOrc SDix SPer SRms WFar WMoo WTin WWpP
- dark — see *A. lactiflora* Guizhou Group
- 'Elfenbein' — EBee GCal LHop
§ - Guizhou Group — More than 30 suppliers
- 'Jim Russell' — CBow CDes CElw EBee EWes LPhx NBre NDov
- *purpurea* — see *A. lactiflora* Guizhou Group
- 'Variegata' — see *A. vulgaris* 'Variegata'
- 'Weisses Wunder' — EBee
lagocephala — EEls EMan LSou
lanata Willd. — see *A. caucasica*
laxa — see *A. umbelliformis*
longifolia — XPep
§ *ludoviciana* — CSec EBee EEls ELan ERou GBar IFoB MBrN MEHN MGol MRav MWat NBid NOak NOrc NPer SBch SGar SRms WBVN
N - var. *latifolia* — see *A. ludoviciana* subsp. *ludoviciana* var. *latiloba*
- subsp. *ludoviciana* var. *incompta* — ECha EEls EGle EMan MRav
§ - - var. *latiloba* — EEls EHoe GBar GBuc GMac LHop LRHS MRav NBro NOak NSti SBch SWvt WCot WEas WHoo WPer
- subsp. *mexicana* var. *albula* — EEls WFar
- 'Silver Queen' ♀[H4] — More than 30 suppliers
N - 'Valerie Finnis' ♀[H4] — More than 30 suppliers
manshurica — EMan LSou
maritima — see *Seriphidium maritimum*
§ *michauxiana* — EBee EEls NBur NSti WHer
molinieri — EEls XPep
mutellina — see *A. umbelliformis*
niitakayamensis — EEls EOHP GBar XPep
nitida — EEls
nutans — see *Seriphidium nutans*
palmeri hort. — see *A. ludoviciana*
pamirica — EEls
aff. *parviflora* — EBee
- CLD 1531 — EEls
pedemontana — see *A. caucasica*
pontica — CArn EBee ECha ECrN EEls EHoe ELan EShb GBar GMaP GPoy LRHS MBNS MHer MNFA MRav MWgw NBro NJOw NSti SDix SMer SPer SSvw WFar WHoo WPer WWye XPep

§   'Powis Castle' ♀H3   More than 30 suppliers
    princeps   CArn EEls MSal SIde
    procera Willd.   see *A. abrotanum*
    purshiana   see *A. ludoviciana*
    pycnocephala   EEls SMad
       'David's Choice'
    ramosa   EEls
    'Rosenschleier'   CAby CBre EBee EMon EPPr
                               LPhx NBre NCGa WFar WPGP
                               WTin
    rutifolia   EEls
    sachalinensis   WOut
    schmidtiana ♀H4   ECha ECot EEls EMan MWat NLAp
                               NOrc SRms
    - 'Nana' ♀H4   More than 30 suppliers
    selengensis   EEls
    splendens misapplied   see *A. alba* 'Canescens'
    splendens Willd.   EEls ELan LPhx NSti WEas
    stelleriana   ECha EDAr EEls EShb EWTr IFoB
                               MFOX MHer MWgw NBro NFor
                               NLar NSti SPer SPet SRms WCAu
                               WEas XPep
    - RBS 0207   EEls
N   - 'Boughton Silver'   CHrt EBee EChP EEls EGle EGoo
                               EHoe ELan EPfP GBBs GBri GMaP
                               GMac LDai LRHS MAsh MRav MTis
                               SPer SRms SWvt WFar WWye
                               XPep
N   - 'Mori'   see *A. stelleriana* 'Boughton Silver'
    - 'Nana'   EEls EMan NLRH SWvt
    - 'Prostrata'   see *A. stelleriana* 'Boughton Silver'
    - 'Silver Brocade'   see *A. stelleriana* 'Boughton Silver'
    suksdorfii new   EBee
    taurica   EEls
§   *thuscula*   EEls
    tilesii   EBee
    tridentata   see *Seriphidium tridentatum*
§   *umbelliformis*   EEls
    vallesiaca   see *Seriphidium vallesiacum*
    verlotiorum   EEls GBar
    vulgaris L.   CAgr CArn CPrp EEls ELau
                               GBar GPoy GWCH IHMH MGol
                               MHer MNHC WHbs WHer WJek
                               WWye
    - 'Cragg-Barber Eye' (v)   EBee EChP EEls EWin GSki NBid
                               NPro SAga WCHb WHer WRha
    - 'Crispa'   LSou
    - 'Obelisk'   EEls
    - Oriental Limelight   More than 30 suppliers
      = 'Janlim' (v)
    - 'Peddar's Gold' (v)   EBee EChP EWin
§   - 'Variegata' (v)   CEnt EEls GBar MHer NBir NPro
                               NSti SMad WCHb WFar WHer
                               WMoo WPer WRha
    x *wurzellii*   EEls

Arthrocnemum (Chenopodiaceae)
    glaucum   XPep

Arthropodium (Anthericaceae)
    candidum   CStu EBee ECha ECho ECou GEdr
                               ITim MBrN NWCA SHBN SRot
                               WFar WPer WPtf
    - *maculatum*   GEdr LEdu SPlb
    - *purpureum*   CBcs CPLG CSec EBee EChP EMan
                               GBri GCal GGar GKev LRHS MLan
                               NJOw NLAp WCot WFar WPGP
                               WPat
    cirratum   CHEx CPne ECou GGar IDee LEdu
                               MLan WSHC
    - 'Matapouri Bay'   CAbP CBcs CHEx EBee EMil ERea
                               WPGP
    milleflorum   GGar WCot

Arthrostylidium (Poaceae)
    naibuense   WPGP

artichoke, globe see *Cynara cardunculus* Scolymus Group

artichoke, Jerusalem see *Helianthus tuberosus*

Artocarpus (Moraceae)
    heterophyllus new   XBlo

Arum (Araceae)
    alpinum   NJOw NLar
    'Chameleon'   CDes CLAP EMan EMar EMon
                               MNrw MTho NBir SMad SPer
                               WCMO WCot WCru WFar WHal
                               WHil WTin WViv
§   *concinnatum*   CStu EMon EPot SChr SHar WCot
                               WPrP
    - JCA   CStu
    - black-spotted   EBee EMar
    - 'Mount Ida' new   EHyt
    cornutum   see *Sauromatum venosum*
    creticum   CArn CBro CFir CSpe EBee EChP
                               ECha EHyt EMan EMar ETow GBuc
                               GSki ITer MNrw MRav MTho SCnR
                               SDix SRot WBor WCMO WCot
    - MS 696   MNrw
    - FCC form   GKev SBla WCMO WCot WPGP
    - 'Marmaris White'   SCnR WCot
    - white   MNrw MTho
    - yellow   NBir WFar WIvy
    creticum x *italicum*   MDKP WCot WFar
    cyrenaicum   CDes CStu EBee ECho EHyt LEdu
                               MNrw MTho SSpi WCMO WCot
                               WPGP
    - from Crete   WCot
    - - MS 696   CMon
§   *dioscoridis*   CDes CMon CStu ECho EWes
                               MTho NLar WCMO WCot
    - JCA 195.197   WCot
    - MS&CL 524   ITer
    - var. *cyprium*   EBee ECho
§   - var. *dioscoridis*   EBee ERos WCot
    - - JCA 195200   WPrP
    - from Turkey   CMon
    - var. *liepoldtii*   see *A. dioscoridis* var. *dioscoridis*
    - var. *smithii*   see *A. dioscoridis* var. *dioscoridis*
    dracunculus   see *Dracunculus vulgaris*
    elongatum   WCot
    idaeum   WCMO
    italicum   CArn CLAP ECho EWTr GAbr
                               MTho MWat NJOw NLar SBod
                               SEND SWat WAbe WCot WFar
                               WPnP WSHC WShi
    - subsp. *albispathum*   CDes CStu EBee ECho EMon WCot
                               WFar WPGP
    - black-spotted   EHyt WFar
    - 'Green Marble'   SBla WFar
    - subsp. *italicum*   EBee EBrs ECho EPla EShb IHMH
                               NJOw NWCA
    - - 'Bill Baker'   EMon WFar
    - - 'Cyclops' EAF 7701   CLAP MNrw WCot
§   - - 'Marmoratum' ♀H4   More than 30 suppliers
    - - 'Sparkler'   WCMO WCot
    - - 'Spotted Jack'   MNrw NBre WCMO WCot WCru
    - - 'Tiny'   CFir EMon GCal SCnR WCMO
§   - - 'White Winter'   CElw EBee ECGP EMon GBuc
                               WCot WSPU
    - 'Nancy Lindsay'   EMar EMon
    - subsp. *neglectum*   SChr WFar
    - - 'Miss Janay Hall' (v) EBee WCMO WCot
    - 'Pictum'   see *A. italicum* subsp. *italicum*
                               'Marmoratum'
    italicum x *orientale* WCMO
       subsp. *lucanum* new
    jacquemontii   ECho
    korolkowii   WCot

maculatum	CArn CRWN EPot GPoy MBow MHer MRav MSal NLar NMyG WHer WShi WWye
- 'Painted Lady' (v)	WCot
- 'Pleddel'	MRav WCot
- Tar Spot Group	CNat
nickelii	see *A. concinnatum*
§ *nigrum*	ECho EWes WCot WGwG
orientale	EHyt EPot ETow WCot
- subsp. *amoenum*	MNrw
- subsp. *orientale*	GIBF
palaestinum	CMon
petteri misapplied	see *A. nigrum*
pictum	CDes CLAP EBee ECho ERos GEdr SBla WCot WWst
- PB 425 from Majorca	CMon
- 'Taff's Form'	see *A. italicum* subsp. *italicum* 'White Winter'
purpureospathum	CDes EHyt WCot WPGP
- from Crete PB 49	CMon
- - PB 51	CMon
rupicola var. *virescens*	SBig WCMO WCot
sintenisii	EBee WCot
'Streaked Spectre'	EMon

Aruncus ✿ (*Rosaceae*)

AGSJ 214	NHol
aethusifolius ♀H4	More than 30 suppliers
- 'Little Gem'	ECho WCru
asiaticus	EBee EBla
dioicus	More than 30 suppliers
§ - (m) ♀H4	CDoC CRow ECha ELan EPla GSki MBNS MRav MWgw NBro NFor NHol NSti SGar SMad SPer SRms SWat WFar WMoo WPer
- var. *acuminatus*	EBee
- Child of Two Worlds	see *A. dioicus* 'Zweiweltenkind'
- 'Glasnevin'	CRow CSev EBrs ECtt MRav NHol WFar
- var. *kamtschaticus*	EBee EChP EKen EWes GIBF MCCP MGos NBre NGdn NHol NLar WBVN
- - AER 0208	MGol
- - AGSJ 238	NHol
- - B&SWJ 8624	WCru
- - RBS 0208	MHar NVic
- 'Kneiffii'	More than 30 suppliers
§ - 'Zweiweltenkind'	CFwr CRez EBee EBla EHrv GCal GSki NBre NLar SMad WCot WWpP
'Horatio'	EBee EBla EMon IPot LPhx SMeo WCot
'Johannifest'	CDes EBee EBla EMon
'Noble Spirit'	EBee EBla EPPr LBuc MWrn NLar SCoo SWal WWeb WWpP
'Perlehuhn' **new**	EMon
plumosus	see *A. dioicus*
sinensis	EBla EShb NBre WFar
sylvestris	see *A. dioicus*
'Woldemar Meier'	EBla EMon

Arundinaria ✿ (*Poaceae*)

amabilis	see *Pseudosasa amabilis* (McClure) Keng f.
anceps	see *Yushania anceps*
auricoma	see *Pleioblastus viridistriatus*
chino	see *Pleioblastus chino*
disticha	see *Pleioblastus pygmaeus* 'Distichus'
falconeri	see *Himalayacalamus falconeri*
fargesii	see *Bashania fargesii*
fastuosa	see *Semiarundinaria fastuosa*
fortunei	see *Pleioblastus variegatus*
funghomii	see *Schizostachyum funghomii*
§ *gigantea*	MWht WJun
- subsp. *tecta*	CBcs MGos

hindsii	see *Pleioblastus hindsii*
hookeriana misapplied	see *Himalayacalamus falconeri* 'Damarapa'
hookeriana Munro	see *Himalayacalamus hookerianus*
humilis	see *Pleioblastus humilis*
japonica	see *Pseudosasa japonica*
jaunsarensis	see *Yushania anceps*
maling	see *Yushania maling*
marmorea	see *Chimonobambusa marmorea*
murielae	see *Fargesia murielae*
nitida	see *Fargesia nitida*
oedogonata	see *Clavinodum oedogonatum*
palmata	see *Sasa palmata*
pumila	see *Pleioblastus argenteostriatus* f. *pumilus*
pygmaea	see *Pleioblastus pygmaeus*
quadrangularis	see *Chimonobambusa quadrangularis*
simonii	see *Pleioblastus simonii*
spathiflora	see *Thamnocalamus spathiflorus*
tessellata	see *Thamnocalamus tessellatus*
vagans	see *Sasaella ramosa*
variegata	see *Pleioblastus variegatus*
veitchii	see *Sasa veitchii*
viridistriata	see *Pleioblastus viridistriatus*
'Wang Tsai'	see *Bambusa multiplex* 'Floribunda'

Arundo (*Poaceae*)

donax	More than 30 suppliers
I - 'Aureovariegata' **new**	MDKP
- 'Golden Chain'	EBee EPPr EWes
- 'Macrophylla'	CBig CKno CRow EPPr LEdu LPJP WPGP
- 'Variegata'	see *A. donax* var. *versicolor*
§ - var. *versicolor* (v)	More than 30 suppliers
- yellow-variegated (v)	CKno EShb SEND SPoG
formosana	CKno EBee EPPr
pliniana	CRow EPPr EPla WPGP

Asarina (*Scrophulariaceae*)

antirrhiniflora	see *Maurandella antirrhiniflora*
I *barclayana*	see *Maurandya barclayana*
erubescens	see *Lophospermum erubescens*
hispanica	see *Antirrhinum hispanicum*
lophantha	see *Lophospermum scandens*
lophospermum	see *Lophospermum scandens*
§ *procumbens*	CDMG CEnt CSec CStu CTri EBee ECho EPfP GAbr GBBs GKev MNFA MTho NRya SGar SHFr SIng SRms WFar WGwG WPer
'Victoria Falls'	see *Maurandya* 'Victoria Falls'

Asarum ✿ (*Aristolochiaceae*)

Chen Yi 5 **new**	WCot
albomaculatum B&SWJ 1726	WCru
arifolium	CDes CLAP EHrv GBBs NLar
asaroides	CKob WWst
campaniflorum	CLAP MLul WCru
canadense	CArn CBct EBee EChP ECho EMar EPot ERos GBBs GPoy GSki LRHS MSal NLar WCru
caudatum	CAvo CDes CLAP CRow CStu EBee ECha ECho EHyt EPPr GBuc ITer LEdu NBro NLar NSti NWCA SRms WCot WCru WFar WPGP
- white	CDes CLAP EHrv
caudigerum B&SWJ 1517	WCru
caulescens	CLAP ECho EPPr LEdu WCru
- B&SWJ 5886	WCru
costatum	CLAP
delavayi	CKob WCot WCru
epignum	LEdu
- B&SWJ 3443	WCru

- 'Silver Web'   CLAP LEdu WCru
europaeum   More than 30 suppliers
fauriei   WCru
forbesii   ECho NLar WCot
hartwegii   CDes CLAP EBee EHyt EMar ERos
                                        GBuc GGar GMac LEdu NLar
                                        WCot WCru WPGP
- NNS 00-74   EPPr
- NNS 00-78   WCot
hirsutisepalum   CLAP
hypogynum B&SWJ 3628   WCru
infrapurpureum   WCot
- B&SWJ 1994   WCru
kumageanum   WCot
lemmonii   EMan LEdu WCru
leptophyllum B&SWJ 1983   WCru
longirhizomatosum   WCMO WCru
macranthum   WCot
- B&SWJ 1691   WCru
maculatum   WCru
  B&SWJ 1114
magnificum   CFwr CKob CLAP MLul WCMO
                                        WCru
maximum   CFwr CKob CLAP ECho MLul
                                        NMen WCMO WCot WCru
                                        WMul
megacalyx   WCot
minamitanianum   CLAP WCru
naniflorum 'Eco Decor'   CLAP EBee EHrv GCai GMac GSki
                                        LAst MBNS NLar NMyG WCMO
                                        WCot
nipponicum   WCot
pulchellum   EHrv WCot WCru
rigescens   EHrv
shuttleworthii   CLAP NLar
sieboldii   CLAP WCru
splendens   More than 30 suppliers
taipingshanianum   WCot WCru
  B&SWJ 1688
taitonense new   WWst
takaoi   CKob

Asclepias (Asclepiadaceae)

asperula subsp.   CArn
  capricornu new
'Cinderella'   CSev LBuc SGar
curassavica   CHrt CSev EShb NBre SBig SHFr
                                        SPav WRos
incarnata   CAgr CPom CSec CSev EBee EBrs
                                        ELan ERou IFoB MRav MTis NBre
                                        SPav SPer WPer WTMC
- 'Alba'   CBos EChP ELan EMon MMuc
- 'Ice Ballet'   CPrp EBee EBrs ERou EShb IFoB
                                        LBuc LHop LRHS MCCP NBPC
                                        NBre NEgg NTHB SAga SBig SPoG
                                        SWat WMnd
* - 'Iceberg'   EBee
- 'Soulmate'   EBee EChP EPfP EWll LRav MLLN
                                        MMHG NBPC NBre NJOw NTHB
                                        SPoG WWpP
- 'White Superior'   EBee
ovalifolia   EBee
physocarpa   see *Gomphocarpus*
                                        physocarpus
purpurascens   CArn EChP EMon NEgg
speciosa   CAgr EBee NBre NLar WAul
sullivantii   EMan NBre SPav
syriaca   CAgr CArn CPom EBee MSal NBre
                                        SPav
tuberosa   CAgr CArn CBcs CWib EAEE EBee
                                        EMan EShb GPoy LHop MHer
                                        MNrw MSal NBir NEgg SECG SMad
                                        SPet SPoG WGHP WMnd
- Gay Butterflies Group   NBre NEgg NGdn NLar SMar
                                        SMrm WMnd
verticillata   NBre

Asimina (Annonaceae)

triloba (F)   CBcs IArd MBlu MBri MGol MJnS
                                        NLar SBrw SPlb WNor
- 'Davis' (F)   CAgr

Askidiosperma (Restionaceae)

chartaceum   CTrC
esterhuyseniae   WNor

Asparagus (Asparagaceae)

asparagoides ♀H1   ERea EShb SEND
§ - 'Myrtifolius'   CHal SYvo
  cochinchinensis   EBee
    B&SWJ 3425
  crassicladus   EShb
  densiflorus 'Mazeppa'   EShb
- 'Myersii' ♀H1   CHal ERea EShb SEND SRms
- Sprengeri Group ♀H1   CHal LRHS MBri
- - 'Variegatus'   EShb
denudatus new   EShb
falcatus   EShb SEND
filicinus var. *giraldii*   WCot
officinalis   MNHC SEND WFar WOut
- 'Backlim' ♀H4   EMui
- 'Butler'   SDea
- 'Cito' (m)   SDea
- 'Connover's Colossal'   CWan
  ♀H4
- 'Dariana'   SDea
- 'Franklim'   CTri WFar
- 'Gijnlim' ♀H4   EMil EMui NBlu SDea
- 'Jersey Giant' (m) new   EMui
- 'Purple Jumbo'   EBee
plumosus   see *A. setaceus*
pseudoscaber   EDsa EMan EShb MAvo SMad
  'Spitzenschleier'
racemosus new   EShb
retrofractus   EShb WPGP
scandens   EShb
schoberioides B&SWJ 871   WCru
§ *setaceus* ♀H1   CHal EShb LRHS MBri
- 'Pyramidalis' ♀H1   MBri
suaveolens   EShb
tenuifolius new   EMon
verticillatus   SRms
virgatus   EShb WPGP

Asperula (Rubiaceae)

§ *arcadiensis* ♀H3   CLyd ECho EHyt EPot SBla WAbe
  aristata subsp. *scabra*   CSpe EBee ECha ELan EMan EMon
- subsp. *thessala*   see *A. sintenisii*
  boissieri   ECho
  cyanchica   MSal NLar
  daphneola   CNic ECho EHyt EWes SBla WAbe
  gussonei   CLyd CMea CStu ECho GCrs
                                        LRHS MWat NLAp NMen NWCA
                                        SBla WAbe WLin WPat
  hirta   CNic
§ *lilaciflora*   ECho
- var. *caespitosa*   see *A. lilaciflora* subsp. *lilaciflora*
- subsp. *lilaciflora*   CLyd CPBP ECho NMen
  nitida   ECho
- subsp. *puberula*   see *A. sintenisii*
  odorata   see *Galium odoratum*
  orientalis   CSec WPGP
  scutellaris   EBee
§ *sintenisii* ♀H2-3   CLyd CMea ECho EPot LRHS
                                        NMen NWCA SBla WAbe WHoo
                                        WThu
  suberosa misapplied   see *A. arcadiensis*
  suberosa Sibth. & Sm.   ECho
  taurina subsp.   CPLG NLar NSti WCHb
    caucasica
  tinctoria   CArn EOHP GBar GPoy MHer MSal
                                        SRms WCHb

Asphodeline (Asphodelaceae)

RCB/TQ C-2 **new**	WCot
§ *brevicaulis*	GIBF
damascena **new**	EBee
liburnica	CAvo CBro EBee EChP ECha ELan EMan EMar ERos ERou GAbr GSki MAvo NEgg SEND WCAu WCot WFar WPer
§ *lutea*	More than 30 suppliers
§ - 'Gelbkerze'	GBBs NBre SPoG WBVN
- Yellow Candle	see *A. lutea* 'Gelbkerze'
taurica	CFis ECho NBre WPer

Asphodelus (Asphodelaceae)

acaulis	ECho EHyt WAbe WCot
§ *aestivus*	CDes EBee EMan GAbr GIBF GSki NBur SSvw SWat WCot WPer
albus	CArn CSpe EBee EBrs ECha EPyc GBuc GIBF GSki IBlr IFoB NBid SHop SPlb SRms WAul WPer
brevicaulis	see *Asphodeline brevicaulis*
cerasiferus	see *A. ramosus*
fistulosus	GIBF MMHG NBir SBch WPrP XPep
lusitanicus	see *A. ramosus*
luteus	see *Asphodeline lutea*
microcarpus	see *A. aestivus*
- Cally Spear **new**	GCal
§ *ramosus*	CBrm CMdw CPar EBee EChP ECho EMan GIBF GSki MGol MNrw MTho NEgg SMrm WBVN WCot WPer XPep

Aspidistra (Convallariaceae)

from China	WCot
attenuata	CKob
- B&SWJ 377	WCru
caespitosa 'Jade Ribbons'	IBlr WCMO WCot
'China Moon' (v)	WCMO
'China Star'	EBee IBlr WCMO WCot
'China Sun'	WCMO WCot
daibuensis	CKob IBlr
- B&SWJ 312b	WCru
elatior ♀H1	CBct CHEx CHal CKob EBak EBee EShb IBlr LRHS MBri NPal SAPC SArc SEND SMad SYvo WCMO WCot
- 'Akebono' (v)	WCMO WCot
- 'Asahi' (v)	IBlr WCMO WCot
- 'Hoshi-zora' (v)	IBlr WCMO WCot
- 'Milky Way' (v)	CAby CBct CBow EBee EShb EWin IBlr MTho SEND WCMO WCot
- 'Okame' (v)	WCMO WCot
- 'Variegata' (v) ♀H1	CBct CHEx CHal CKob EREa EShb IBlr IFoB IFro MTho NBir SYvo WCot
leshanensis (v)	IBlr
linearifolia 'Leopard'	IBlr WCot
lurida	CKob EDsa EREa IBlr
- 'Amanogawa' (v)	IBlr
- 'Fuji-no-mine' (v)	IBlr
- 'Irish Mist' (v)	IBlr
saxicola 'Uan Fat Lady'	WCru
typica	IBlr

Asplenium ✿ (Aspleniaceae)

adiantum-nigrum	LRHS SRms
bulbiferum ♀H1-2	CBgR CPLG CTrC EFtx EREa SMur WFib
bulbiferum x *oblongifolium*	EAmu
§ *ceterach*	CLAP EBee NMyG SRms WAbe WHer
csikii var. *trogyense* **new**	WAbe
dareoides	SRot WAbe WCot

x *ebenoides*	WAbe
fontanum	WAbe
'Maori Princess'	CTrC
nidus ♀H1	LRHS MBri
oblongifolium	CTrC
platyneuron	CDes
ruta-muraria	EFer NHol SRms
§ *scolopendrium* ♀H4	More than 30 suppliers
- 'Angustatum'	CBgR CFwr CLAP CMil CWCL EBee ECha EPfP ERod GBin GEdr LRHS MAsh MAvo MCCP MGos MMoz MWgw NHol NLar NVic SMac SRms WFar WMoo WPnP WPtf
- 'Capitatum'	MDun
* - 'Circinatum'	WPGP
- 'Conglomeratum'	SRms
- Crispum Group	CBgR CLAP CSBt CWCL EFer ELan NHol SRms SRot WAbe WFib WPGP WPtf
- - 'Golden Queen'	CLAP
- 'Crispum Bolton's Nobile' ♀H4	WFib WPGP
- Crispum Cristatum Group	CLAP EChP
- Crispum Fimbriatum Group	CLAP GQui
- Cristatum Group	CBgR CElw CLAP EHrv ELan EMar EPfP LRHS MBnl MBri MGos MMoz MRav MWgw NBid NDlv NHol NMoo SNut SPla SRms SWat WFib
- 'Cristatum'	CFwr CWCL EBee MAsh SHGC SMac SPoG SRot SSto WBVN
- Fimbriatum Group	CLAP
- 'Furcatum'	CFwr CLAP CPrp GEdr MAsh NEgg
- 'Kaye's Lacerated' ♀H4	CLAP EFer ELan NHol
- Laceratum Group	CLAP SRms
- Marginatum Group	EFer SWat WPGP
- - 'Irregulare'	NHol SRms
- 'Muricatum'	CFwr CLAP ELan GBin NBid SRms WFib WTin
- 'Ramocristatum'	CLAP
- Ramomarginatum Group	CLAP ELan NBid SRms WAbe WFar
- 'Sagittatocristatum'	SRms WPGP
- - 'Apple Court' **new**	CBgR
- 'Sagittato-projectum Sclater'	WFib
* - 'Sagittatum'	SRms
- 'Stagshorn'	SRms
- Undulatum Group	CBgR CLAP EAAE EBee ECha EFtx EPfP MAsh NBid NBir NEgg NMyG NSti NVic SPla SRms SWat WIvy WPnP
- Undulatum Cristatum Group	CLAP NDlv
septentrionale	SRms
trichomanes ♀H4	More than 30 suppliers
- Cristatum Group	SRms
- Grandiceps Group	EFer
- Incisum Group	CLAP CWCL NOrc SMad
- 'Ramocristatum'	WAbe
viride	SRms WFar

Astartea (Myrtaceae)

fascicularis	CPLG

Astelia (Asteliaceae)

alpina	IBlr
banksii	CBcs CDoC CPen ECou GGar IBal LRHS WAbe WCot WDyG WGer WMul
§ *chathamica* ♀H3	More than 30 suppliers
- 'Silver Spear'	see *A. chathamica*
cunninghamii	see *A. solandri*

fragrans	ECou EDsa GGar IBlr LEdu WCMO WCot WDyG WMul WPic
graminea	GCal IBlr
grandis	CTrC IBlr LEdu WMul
'Luzulliea Johnsen'	LPBA
nervosa	CAbb ECou IBlr LEdu SAPC SArc WMul WPat WPic
- 'Bronze Giant'	IBlr
- 'Westland'	CAbb CBcs CBod CDoC CKno CPen CTrC EBee EMan EMil GCal IBlr LEdu LRHS MBri MGos SPoG WCMO WCot WLeb WMul
nivicola	IBlr
- 'Red Gem'	CBos GCal IBlr LEdu
petriei	IBlr
§ *solandri*	CHEx IBlr
trinervia	IBlr

Aster ✿ (Asteraceae)

acris	see *A. sedifolius*
acuminatus **new**	EShb
§ *albescens*	CPle GKev WLin
alpigenus var. *alpigenus*	CPBP
- var. *haydenii*	NBid
alpinus ♀H4	CTri ECho EPfP IHMH MNrw MWgw NEgg NJOw SBla SEND SMar SPet SRms WBrk WFar WPer
- var. *albus*	EBee EMil EPfP IHMH NBre NBro SRGP WPer WWeb
- Dark Beauty	see *A. alpinus* 'Dunkle Schöne'
- var. *dolomiticus*	EBee
§ - 'Dunkle Schöne'	CHrt ECho GAbr LDai MHar NBre NVic SBch SMar SRGP SRms WFar WPer WWeb
- 'Goliath'	ECho NBre NBro SMar SPlb WFar WWeb
- 'Happy End'	CMMP ECho EMil IHMH LDai NBre NBro NLar SRGP SRms WFar WWeb
- 'Märchenland' (d)	CPBP NBre
- 'Pinkie'	CBrm EBee GAbr GKev NBre NHol NLar SBch SMad SMar WLin WWeb
- 'Trimix'	ECho NBir SRms WFar
- violet-flowered	WPer
- 'White Beauty'	SRms
* - 'Wolfii'	SRms
amelloides	see *Felicia amelloides*
amellus	LSou NFor SPer WMoo
- 'Blue King'	EBee EWsh MLLN SWvt WCAu
- 'Breslau'	EBee
- 'Brilliant'	EAEE EBee EBla EChP ECtt EGle EMan LAst LSou MBNS MLLN MNFA MRav MWat NDov NEgg SPer SRGP WIvy WOld
- 'Butzemann'	EBee GMac
- 'Doktor Otto Petschek'	WFar WViv
- 'Framfieldii' ♀H4	WFar WOld
- 'Gründer'	WHil
- 'Jacqueline Genebrier' ♀H4	CHar CMil EGle WCot WIvy WSHC
- 'Joseph Lakin'	WFar
- 'King George' ♀H4	More than 30 suppliers
- 'Kobold'	WFar
- 'Lac de Genève'	MRav NLar WCot WFar WOld
- 'Lady Hindlip'	WFar
- 'Louise' **new**	MBrN
- 'Mira'	GBin
- 'Moerheim Gem'	WIvy
- 'Nocturne'	ERou WCot WIvy WOld
- 'Pink Pearl'	EBee WFar
- Pink Zenith	see *A. amellus* 'Rosa Erfüllung'
§ - 'Rosa Erfüllung'	CDoC CHrt CPrp EAEE EBee EBla ECtt ELan EPfP ERou EShb GBuc GMaP LHop MNFA MRav NDov

	NEgg NFor SPet SPla SRGP SWvt WCMO WCot WMnd WOld WPer
- 'Rotfeuer'	NGby
- 'Rudolph Goethe'	EBee EMil EPyc ERou LAst LRHS MBnl MLLN MRav NRnb NVic SHBN SMer SRGP WCAu WFar WLin WMoo WOld WWye
- 'September Glow'	EGle
- 'Silbersee'	NDov
- 'Sonia'	EBee ECha EGle MRav NGby NLar WFar
- 'Sonora'	ECGP EGle ERou LHop MSte NBre NDov SAga SRGP WKif WOld
- 'Sternkugel'	WOld
- 'Ultramarine'	WFar
- 'Vanity'	GBuc WOld
§ - 'Veilchenkönigin' ♀H4	More than 30 suppliers
N - Violet Queen	see *A. amellus* 'Veilchenkönigin'
- 'Weltfriede'	WOld
'Anja's Choice'	EBee EMon EPPr EWsh MAvo NBre WCot WOld
asper	see *A. bakerianus*
asperulus	EBrs EPPr LPhx MBri MFOX NDov SBla SMeo SUsu
'Bahamas'	MBri SGar
§ *bakerianus*	WFar WPer
'Barbados'	MBri
capensis 'Variegatus'	see *Felicia amelloides* variegated
§ *carolinianus*	WOld
'Cassandra'	MBri
'Cassy'	MBri
'Chelsea'	MBri
chilensis	EBee
'Cirina Dark'PBR	MBri
'Claudia' **new**	SRGP
'Climax' misapplied	see *A. laevis* 'Calliope', *A. laevis* 'Arcturus'
'Climax' Vicary Gibbs	WOld
'Climax' ambig.	CElw GBuc GCal LPhx MRav NRnb NSti SAga SMrm
coelestis	see *Felicia amelloides*
coloradoensis	CGra CPBP NSla SBla
'Connecticut Snow Flurry'	see *A. ericoides* f. *prostratus* 'Snow Flurry'
'Coombe Fishacre' ♀H4	CHrt COIW CPrp EBee EChP EPPr ERou GBuc GCal MAvo MOne MRav MSte NBre SAga SPla SPoG SSvw SUsu WCot WFar WMnd WOld WTin
cordifolius	WFar
- 'Aldebaran'	LPhx
- 'Chieftain' ♀H4	IGor LPhx MNFA MNrw WIvy WOld
- 'Elegans'	IGor MBri MNFA MSte NSti WCot WIvy WMnd WMoo WOld
- 'Ideal'	EBee GMac NLar WOld WPer
- 'Silver Queen'	WOld
- 'Silver Spray'	CPrp EBee ERou GMaP GMac MLLN MNFA MWat NBre SRGP WOld WPer
- 'Sweet Lavender' ♀H4	ERou GMac WOld
corymbosus	see *A. divaricatus*
'Cotswold Gem'	WCMO WCot
§ 'Dark Pink Star'	WOld
'Deep Pink Star'	see *A.* 'Dark Pink Star'
delavayi	EBee SUsu WCot
diffusus	see *A. lateriflorus*
diplostephioides	CMdw EBrs EChP EDAr EMan EPPr EShb GCal LPhx LSou NBre NDov NLar SMar SPlb SSvw WAul WPtf
§ *divaricatus*	More than 30 suppliers
§ - 'Eastern Star'	CBos NCGa WBVN WCMO WCot WOld
- Raiche form	see *A. divaricatus* 'Eastern Star'
drummondii	EBee

N	*dumosus*	CPLG WFar WPer
	- 'Biteliness' **new**	NBre
	- Sapphire =	NPri
	'Kiestrbl' **new**	
§	*elliottii*	WOld
	ericoides	EShb NBre NOrc WFar XPep
	- 'Blue Star' ♀H4	CPrp CSam CWCL EBrs GBuc IGor
		LRHS MBnl MFOX MLLN MSte
		NBPC NBid NLar NSti SHGN SPoG
		WBor WCAu WCot WMnd WOld
	- 'Brimstone' ♀H4	EPPr IGor MRav NBre WOld
	- 'Cinderella'	COlW CPrp GBuc GMac MNFA
		NSti WOld
	- 'Cirylle'	LBmB MLLN NBre
	- 'Constance'	WOld
	- 'Enchantress'	ERou
	- 'Erlkönig'	EAEE EBee EChP EGra EMan EPPr
		LAst LRHS MNFA MRav MSte
		MWgw NCGa SPla SWat WMnd
		WOld WPer
	- 'Esther'	CHea CMea ECha EGle ELan ERou
		MSte NLar SDix WOld
	- 'Golden Spray' ♀H4	GMaP NLar NSti WFar WMnd
		WOld WOut
	- 'Herbstmyrte'	MLLN NGby
	- 'Hon. Edith Gibbs'	WOld
	- 'Hon. Vicary Gibbs'	see A. 'Hon. Vicary Gibbs'
	- 'Maidenhood'	WOld
	- 'Monte Cassino'	see A. *pilosus* var. *pringlei* 'Monte
		Cassino'
	- 'Pink Cloud' ♀H4	More than 30 suppliers
	- f. *prostratus*	EBee EMon EPot SGar SHGN WFar
§	- - 'Snow Flurry' ♀H4	CAby CBgR CMea CSam EBee
		ECha ECtt EGle IGor LPhx MAvo
		MLLN MNFA MNrw SDix SPla
		SRGP SUsu WBor WCAu WCot
		WEas WMnd WOld WOut
	- 'Rosy Veil'	CHea GMac IGor MHom MNFA
		NBir NGdn WOld
	- 'Ruth McConnell'	NSti
	- 'Schneegitter'	MLLN MSte WCot WFar
	- 'Schneetanne'	NBre NRnb
	- 'Sulphurea'	MWat
	- 'Vimmer's Delight'	WCot
	- 'White Heather'	CAby CPrp IGor MNFA NLar WIvy
		WMnd WOld WPer WRHF
	- 'Yvette Richardson'	MHom MSte SMHy WOld
	falcatus var.	EBee WCot
	commutatus	
	'Fanny's Fall'	see A. *oblongifolius* 'Fanny's'
	farreri	GKev
§	*flaccidus*	EBrs WCot
	foliaceus	WHil
	- from Montana	EPPr
	x *frikartii*	CPrp EBee EGle EHol ELan EPfP
		ERou EShb LAst MRav NFla SAga
		SHBN SRms SWvt WEas WMnd
		WOld WSHC
	- 'Eiger'	WOld
	- 'Flora's Delight'	MRav WOld
	- 'Jungfrau'	CFis COlW EBee ERou EShb GMaP
		MRav MSte NLar WOld WSHC
		WWhi
N	- 'Mönch' ♀H4	More than 30 suppliers
	- Wonder of Stafa	see A. x *frikartii* 'Wunder von
		Stäfa'
§	- 'Wunder von Stäfa' ♀H4	CEnd CKno EBee ECtt ELan EMan
		EPfP GBuc GMaP LHop LRHS
		MAvo MBNS MNFA MRav NBlu
		NLar WCMO WCot WMnd WOld
		WPGP WTel
	glaucodes **new**	EBee
	hayatae B&SWJ 8790	WCru
	'Herfstweelde'	CMil EBee EMon GBuc LRHS
		MAvo MSte NCGa SMad WFar
		WOld
	x *herveyi*	EBla EBrs EMan EMon LPhx LRHS
		MSph WOld
	himalaicus	EShb SRms
*	'Hittlemaar'	WCot
§	'Hon. Vicary Gibbs'	EBee GMac MNFA MSte WOld
	(*ericoides* hybrid)	WOut
	hybridus luteus	see x *Solidaster luteus*
§	'Kylie' ♀H4	CAby EMon EPPr ERou GBuc IGor
		LPhx MHom MSte NCGa SRGP
		WBor WCot WFar WOld WTin
	laevis	EBee MSte NBre NLar SMar WTin
	- 'Arcturus'	CFir CSam EBrs MHar MLLN NBre
		NCGa NRnb NSti SSvw WCot WFar
	- 'Blauhügel'	CMdw GCal
§	- 'Calliope'	CElw CHad CMea CSam CWan
		EBee ECtt GCal GMac LPhx MAvo
		MBri MWat NOak NSti SAga SBla
		SBri SMrm WBor WBrk WEas WFar
		WGHP WHoo WIvy WKif WMoo
		WOld
	- var. *geyeri*	MAvo MNrw
	- 'Nightshade'	WOld
	lanceolatus Kuntze	see *Pyrrocoma lanceolata*
	lanceolatus Willd.	WCot
	- 'Edwin Beckett'	CBre EMan GMac MHom MNFA
		WOld
§	*lateriflorus*	CPLG EBee EWin WOld WPer
	- 'Bleke Bet'	WCot WOld
	- 'Buck's Fizz'	CHrt EBee ELan NLar WOld
	- 'Chloe' **new**	NCGa
	- 'Datschi'	WFar
	- 'Delight'	MLLN
	- var. *horizontalis*	More than 30 suppliers
	♀H4	
	- 'Jan'	WOld
	- 'Lady in Black'	More than 30 suppliers
	- 'Lovely'	EBee LRHS MLLN NBre NCGa
		NNor NRnb
	- 'Prince'	More than 30 suppliers
	laterifolius 'Snow Flurry'	see A. *ericoides* f. *prostratus* 'Snow
		Flurry'
§	*linosyris*	EBee GBin NBre NLar NSti WHer
		WOld
	- 'Goldilocks'	see A. *linosyris*
§	'Little Carlow' (*cordifolius*	More than 30 suppliers
	hybrid) ♀H4	
§	'Little Dorrit' (*cordifolius*	EWsh MLLN NBro WHil WOld
	hybrid)	
	macrophyllus	CPou EBee EBrs ELan EMon LRHS
		NLar WOld
	- 'Albus'	EBee EMon EPPr WFar WIvy
		WOld
	- 'Twilight'	CBos CHVG CSam EAEE EBee
		EChP ECha ECtt EGle EPfP EPla
		GCal LLWP MLLN MNFA MSte
		NDov NSti SDix SRGP WCAu
		WCMO WCot WHil WIvy WMnd
		WOld
	'Midget'	NRnb
	mongolicus	see *Kalimeris mongolica*
	natalensis	see *Felicia rosulata*
	novae-angliae	ELau NBre WOld
	- 'Alex Deamon' **new**	WOld
	- 'Andenken an Alma	More than 30 suppliers
	Pötschke'	
	- 'Andenken an Paul	EBee EMon ERou NGby WBrk
	Gerber'	WOld
	- 'Annabelle de Chazal'	WOld
	- Autumn Snow	see A. *novae-angliae*
		'Herbstschnee'
	- 'Barr's Blue'	EBee ECtt EMon ERou EWsh LRHS
		MAvo MBNS MSte MWat NFla NLar
		NSti SRms WBrk WCAu WFar
		WMoo WOld
	- 'Barr's Pink'	CBcs CBre EChP ECtt EMon ERou
		MBnl MHer MHom MLHP MRav

		MWat NFla NLar SEND SHop WBrk WCAu WFar WHrl WOld WPer WSFF
*	- 'Barr's Purple'	ECtt WOld
	- 'Barr's Violet'	EGle EPPr MAvo MHom NFor SHop SRms WBrk WCot WHal WHoo WHrl WMoo WOld WPer WTin
	- 'Bishop Colenso'	NBre
	- 'Christopher Harbutt'	EGle ERou NPro SRGP WOld
	- 'Colwall Galaxy'	WOld
	- 'Colwall Orbit'	WOld
	- 'Crimson Beauty'	EMon EPPr MAvo MHom MNFA MWat WBrk WOld
	- 'Eric Palmer' **new**	ERou
	- 'Evensong'	WOld
	- 'Harrington's Pink' ♀H4	More than 30 suppliers
	- 'Helen Picton'	WOld
§	- 'Herbstschnee'	CPrp EBee EChP ECtt EHrv EMon EPfP ERou GMac LEdu MNFA MRav MSte MWat NFor NSti SPet SPoG SRGP WBor WBrk WFar WHil WMnd WMoo WOld WPer WTin WWye
	- 'James Ritchie'	WHoo WOld
	- 'John Davies'	WOld
	- 'Lachsglut'	WCot
	- 'Lou Williams'	WOld
I	- 'Lucida'	WBrk WHal WOld
	- 'Lye End Beauty'	CPou ECtt EGle EMon EPyc ERou LLWP LRHS MAvo MHom MNFA MRav MSte MWat NFor WCot WHoo WMoo WOld WTin
	- 'Marina Wolkonsky'	EBee WCMO WCot WOld
	- 'Millennium Star'	WOld
	- 'Miss K.E. Mash'	ERou SRGP WBrk WOld
	- 'Mrs S.T. Wright'	ECtt EGle EMon ERou MBrN MHom MNFA MSte SRGP WFar WOld
	- 'Mrs S.W. Stern'	WOld
	- 'Pink Parfait'	EBee EBrs GMac NBre NGdn WCot WOld
	- 'Pink Victor'	CTri EPPr NLar SEND WCra
	- 'Primrose Upward'	EWsh WCot WOld
	- 'Purple Cloud'	EMon ERou GMac LHop MHer MHom MNFA MWat MWgw NBre NGdn WBrk WFoF WHal WOld
I	- 'Purple Dome'	More than 30 suppliers
	- 'Quinton Menzies'	WOld
	- 'Red Cloud'	NBre WOld
	- 'Rosa Sieger' ♀H4	CBre CPrp EBee EGle EMon ERou GMac LPhx MAvo MHom NGdn SUsu WBor WBrk WHil WOld WViv
	- 'Rose Williams'	WOld
	- 'Roter Stern'	ECtt ERou
	- 'Rubinschatz'	MHom NBre WOld
	- 'Rudelsburg'	EMon ERou
	- 'Sayer's Croft'	EGle EMon ERou MHom MWat NBre WBrk WCot WHil WHoo WOld WTin
	- September Ruby	see *A. novae-angliae* 'September-angliae'
§	- 'Septemberrubin'	CAby CMea EBee ECtt EMon ERou EWsh LFoB LHop LPhx MNFA MRav MSte NEgg NSti SMer SRGP SUsu WFar WMoo WOld WPnP WPrP
	- 'Treasure'	CBre EMon NBre WFar WMoo WOld
	- 'Violetta'	CMea EBrs ECtt EGle EMon LPhx LSou MAvo MHom MNFA MSte WBrk WFar WHil WOld WTin WWye
	- 'W. Bowman'	WOld
	- 'Wow'	NBre SMrm WHil
N	*novi-belgii*	GWCH NSco WHer
	- 'Ada Ballard'	EBee EBrs ERou LRHS NBre NGdn NRnb SPer SPet SPoG SRGP WOld WWye
	- 'Albanian'	WOld
	- 'Alderman Vokes'	WOld
	- 'Alex Norman'	WOld
	- 'Algar's Pride'	CHrt ECtt ERou NBre NRnb SSvw WOld
	- 'Alice Haslam'	ECtt EPPr ERou GBri IHMH MCCP MWgw NOrc NPri NRnb SPoG SPur SRGP WOld WPer
	- 'Angela Peel' **new**	EBrs
	- 'Anita Ballard'	WOld
	- 'Anita Webb'	GBri NBir NBre NOak NRnb WOld
	- 'Anneke'	EBee SRGP WWeb
	- 'Apollo'	EBrs NBre NLar NPri
	- 'Apple Blossom'	WOld
	- 'Audrey'	ECho ECtt EPPr ERou GMaP LRHS MBnl MLLN MWgw NCGa NOrc SPla SRGP STes WOld WTel
	- 'Autumn Beauty'	WOld
	- 'Autumn Days'	WOld
	- 'Autumn Glory'	ERou WOld
	- 'Autumn Rose'	CHea WOld
	- 'Baby Climax'	WOld
	- 'Beauty of Colwall'	WOld
	- 'Beechwood Challenger'	MOne NBre NRnb WOld
	- 'Beechwood Charm'	WOld
	- 'Beechwood Rival'	EBee MOne MSte NBre NRnb
	- 'Beechwood Supreme'	ERou NBre NRnb WOld
	- 'Benary's Composition'	SECG SWal
	- 'Bewunderung'	NBre NRnb WOld
	- 'Blandie'	CHea CTri EBee MSte SHop SRGP WCAu WOld
	- 'Blauglut'	WOld
	- 'Blue Baby'	WPer WWye
	- 'Blue Bouquet'	SRms WOld
	- 'Blue Boy'	WBrk WOld
	- 'Blue Danube'	CBgR WOld
	- 'Blue Eyes'	CElw SAga WOld WWye
	- 'Blue Gown'	CMdw GCal NBre NRnb WOld WOut
	- 'Blue Lagoon'	CBgR ELan MBnl MBri NOrc NRnb SPoG SRGP WBor WHil WOld
	- 'Blue Patrol'	ERou NBre NRnb WOld
	- 'Blue Radiance'	WOld
	- 'Blue Whirl'	WOld
	- 'Bonanza'	WOld WTel
	- 'Boningale Blue'	WOld
	- 'Boningale White'	ERou WOld
	- 'Bridesmaid'	WOld
	- 'Bridgette' **new**	NBPC
	- 'Bright Eyes'	ERou SRGP
	- 'Brightest and Best'	WOld
	- 'Cameo'	WOld
	- 'Cantab'	WOld
	- 'Carlingcott'	ERou MOne WOld
	- 'Carnival'	CMMP EBee ECtt MMHG NBre NEgg NOrc SPer SRGP WOld
	- 'Cecily'	WOld
	- 'Charles Wilson'	WOld
	- 'Chatterbox'	CBgR COlW CPrp EBee EDAr LRHS MRav MWat NLar SRms WOld WRHF WWye
	- 'Chelwood'	WOld
	- 'Chequers'	CBrm CMMP ECot MSte SRGP WOld
	- 'Christina'	see *A. novi-belgii* 'Kristina'
	- 'Christine Soanes'	NBre NRnb WOld
	- 'Cliff Lewis'	ERou MOne NBre NRnb WOld
	- 'Climax Albus'	see *A.* 'White Climax'
	- 'Cloudy Blue'	NRnb WOld
	- 'Colonel F.R. Durham'	NBre NRnb
	- 'Coombe Delight'	NRnb
	- 'Coombe Gladys'	ERou NBre NRnb WOld
	- 'Coombe Joy'	ERou NRnb WOld

- 'Coombe Margaret'	ERou WOld WOut
- 'Coombe Pink'	ERou NBre NRnb
- 'Coombe Queen'	WOld
- 'Coombe Radiance'	MSte WOld
- 'Coombe Ronald'	MWat WOld
- 'Coombe Rosemary'	EBrs ECtt ERou LRHS NLar WBor WOld WTel
- 'Coombe Violet'	MRav MWat WOld
- 'Countess of Dudley'	WOld WPer
- 'Court Herald'	WOld
- 'Crimson Brocade'	CAby ENot LPhx MRav NLar SPoG SRGP WOld
- 'Dandy'	EBee ECot ELan MOne NBir NGdn SPoG SRGP WOld
- 'Daniela'	WBrk WOld
- 'Daphne Anne'	WOld
- 'Dauerblau'	WOld
- 'Davey's True Blue'	CTri MSte WOld
- 'David Murray'	WOld
- 'Dazzler'	WOld
- 'Destiny'	WOld
- 'Diana'	CNic MOne WOld WViv
- 'Diana Watts'	ERou NBre NRnb WOld
- 'Dietgard'	NRnb WOld
- 'Dolly'	NBir WOld
- 'Dusky Maid'	WBor WOld
- 'Elizabeth'	CElw WOld
- 'Elizabeth Bright'	WOld
- 'Elizabeth Hutton'	ERou WOld
- 'Elsie Dale'	WOld
- 'Elta'	WOld
- 'Erica'	CElw ERou MWat NBre NRnb WOld
- 'Ernest Ballard'	WOld
- 'Eva'	WOld
- 'Eventide'	CBcs CElw ENot LPhx NOak SPer WMoo WOld WRHF
- 'Fair Lady'	MWat WOld
- 'Faith'	WOld
- 'Farncombe Lilac'	EBrs
- 'Farrington'	WOld
- 'Fellowship'	CAby CDes CFir EBee ERou IHMH LPhx MAvo MBri MSte MWat SAga SHar SPer SRGP SRms WBrk WCot WOld WTel
- 'Fontaine'	WOld
- 'Freda Ballard'	CBgR ECtt EPPr EWll GMaP MBnl MWat NGdn SRGP WBor WCAu WOld
- 'Freya'	WOld WSHC
- 'Fuldatal'	WOld WOut
- 'Gayborder Blue'	WOld
- 'Gayborder Royal'	CFir MOne WOld
- 'Glory of Colwall'	WOld
- 'Goliath'	WOld
- 'Grey Lady'	WOld
- 'Guardsman'	WOld
- 'Gulliver'	WOld
- 'Gurney Slade'	ERou NBre NRnb WOld
- 'Harrison's Blue'	ERou LPhx NBre NRnb SAga WBrk WOld WPer
- 'Heinz Richard'	CMMP COlW EBee ECha LBMP MSte NBir NBre NEgg NGdn SBch SBla SPet SRGP WOld
- 'Helen'	WOld
- 'Helen Ballard'	CHea NBre NRnb WBrk WOld
- 'Herbstgruss vom Bresserhof'	EWTr NBre NRnb
- 'Herbstpurzel'	MOne
- 'Hilda Ballard'	NBre NRnb WOld
- 'Ilse Brensell'	MOne MSte WOld
- 'Irene'	WOld
- 'Isabel Allen'	WOld
- 'Janet Watts'	ERou WOld
- 'Jean'	MWat WOld
- 'Jean Gyte'	WOld

- 'Jenny'	More than 30 suppliers
- 'Jollity'	WOld
- 'Julia'	WOld
- 'Karminkuppel'	NBre NRnb WOld
- 'Kilmersdon'	GMaP
- 'King of the Belgians'	WOld
- 'King's College'	WOld
§ - 'Kristina'	COlW ECha ERou LRHS MBri MOne MRav SPet SPoG WCot WOld WTel
- 'Lady Evelyn Drummond'	WOld
- 'Lady Frances'	WOld
- 'Lady in Blue'	More than 30 suppliers
- 'Lady Paget'	WOld
- 'Lassie'	CElw CHea LLWP MWat SBri WCot WOld
- 'Lavender Dream'	WOld
- 'Lawrence Chiswell'	WOld
- 'Lilac Time'	WOld
- 'Lisa Dawn'	WOld
- 'Little Boy Blue'	ERou NBre NRnb SHBN WOld
- 'Little Man in Blue'	WOld
- 'Little Pink Beauty'	COlW CPrp EBee EBrs ECtt ELan ERou LHop LRHS MBNS MRav NBid NEgg NMir NVic SPer SRGP STes WOld WTel WViv
- 'Little Pink Lady'	EBrs WOld
- 'Little Pink Pyramid'	NRnb SRms
- 'Little Red Boy'	WOld
- 'Little Treasure'	WOld
- 'Lucy'	WOld
- 'Madge Cato'	WOld
- 'Mammoth'	MOne NBre NRnb WOld
- 'Margaret Rose'	NOrc WOld
- 'Margery Bennett'	GBri WOld
- 'Marie Ballard'	CBcs CHea CSBt EBee EBrs EChP EPfP ERou GMaP MBri MWat NGdn NOrc NPer SHBN SMer SPer SPoG SRGP SRms STes SWat WBrk WCAu WEas WOld WPer WTMC WTel
- 'Marie's Pretty Please'	WOld
- 'Marjorie'	NRnb SPoG WOld
- 'Marjorie Tilbury' **new**	ERou
- 'Marjory Ballard'	WOld
* - 'Mark Ballard'	MOne NBre NRnb
- 'Martonie'	WOld WPer
- 'Mary Ann Neil'	WOld
- 'Mary Deane'	MSte WOld WPer
- 'Mauve Magic'	WOld
- 'Melbourne Belle'	NBre NRnb WOld
- 'Melbourne Magnet'	CHea MOne WOld
- 'Michael Watts'	WOld
- 'Mistress Quickly'	CRez ERou GBri WOld
- 'Mount Everest'	ERou LPhx WOld WPer
- 'Mrs Leo Hunter'	NRnb WOld
- 'Neron' **new**	MBri
- 'Nesthäkchen'	ECho
- 'Nobilis'	WOld
- 'Norman's Jubilee'	EBee ERou NBir NBre NRnb WOld
- 'Nursteed Charm'	WOld
- 'Oktoberschneekuppel'	ERou LRHS NRnb
- 'Orlando'	NBre NRnb WOld
- 'Pamela'	ERou WOld
- 'Patricia Ballard'	CBcs CElw CPrp CSBt MBri MWat NPer SPer SPoG SRGP WCAu WFar WOld WPer WTel
- 'Peace'	ERou WOld
- 'Percy Thrower'	NRnb WOld
- 'Peter Chiswell'	WOld
- 'Peter Harrison'	GMaP GMac NBir WOld WPer
- 'Peter Pan'	CStu LSou WOld
- 'Picture'	NBre NRnb WOld
- 'Pink Gown'	WOld
- 'Pink Lace'	ERou MBNS MLLN WOld WPer
- 'Pink Pyramid'	NRnb WOld

	- 'Plenty'	MBri NBre NRnb WOld
	- 'Porzellan'	CElw CMMP COIW EBee ECtt EMar MAvo NCGa NEgg SRGP WCot
	- 'Pride of Colwall'	ERou MOne NBre NRnb WBrk
	- 'Priory Blush'	CHea LPhx WOld
	- 'Professor Anton Kippenberg'	EBee EPfP ERou GMaP IHMH LLWP LRHS MBow MBri MHer MRav NBre NRnb SPer SRGP WMoo WOld WTel
	- 'Prosperity'	NBre NRnb WOld
*	- 'Prunella'	NBre NRnb WOld
	- 'Purple Dome'	ECha LPhx MCCP NEgg NMoo SHar WOld WOut
	- 'Queen Mary'	ERou WOld
	- 'Queen of Colwall'	WOld
	- 'Ralph Picton'	WOld
	- 'Raspberry Ripple'	ECot ERou WOld
	- 'Red Robin'	MWat
	- 'Red Sunset'	SRms WOld
	- 'Rembrandt'	ECtt EWll SRGP
	- 'Remembrance'	NRnb WBrk WOld WWye
	- 'Reverend Vincent Dale'	WOld
	- 'Richness'	MFOX NBre NRnb SAga WOld
	- 'Robin Adair'	WOld
	- 'Roland Smith'	WOld
	- 'Rose Bonnet'	CSBt EBee ENot MWat SHBN SPlb
	- 'Rose Bouquet'	WOld
	- 'Rosebud'	WOld
	- 'Rosemarie Sallmann'	MOne NRnb
	- 'Rosenwichtel'	EMar MBri MWgw NCGa NLar NRnb WBrk WHil WOld
	- 'Royal Ruby'	EBee EBrs ECtt WOld
	- 'Royal Velvet'	NBre NRnb WOld
	- 'Royal Violet' **new**	NPri
	- 'Rozika'	WOld
	- 'Rufus'	WOld
	- 'Sailor Boy'	EBee ERou NRnb WOld
	- 'Saint Egwyn'	WOld
	- 'Sam Banham'	WOld
	- 'Sandford White Swan'	ERou GBuc MHom WBrk WEas WPer
	- 'Sapphire' **new**	SVil
	- 'Sarah Ballard'	ERou IHMH MBnl MBri SRGP WOld
§	- 'Schneekissen'	CPrp CStu ECho ECtt EGoo EPfP EPyc GMaP MHer MWgw NEgg NPri SPer SPoG SRGP STes SWvt WOld WRHF
	- 'Schöne von Dietlikon'	CKno WOld
	- 'Schoolgirl'	NBre NRnb WOld
	- 'Sheena'	MBri SRGP WOld
	- 'Silberblaukissen'	GBin
§	- 'Silberteppich'	GMac
	- Silver Carpet	see *A. novi-belgii* 'Silberteppich'
	- Snow Cushion	see *A. novi-belgii* 'Schneekissen'
	- 'Snowdrift'	WOld
	- 'Snowsprite'	CBcs CSBt ELan EPfP MWat NLar NOrc NPro SRGP SWat WBrk WOld
	- 'Sonata'	ERou GMaP NBre NOak NRnb WOld
	- 'Sophia'	NBre NOak NRnb WBrk WOld
	- 'Starlight'	EBee ECho ENot ERou LSou MBNS NMoo WBor WFar WHil WMoo WOld WRHF
	- 'Steinebrück'	WOld
	- 'Sterling Silver'	WOld
	- 'Sunset'	WOld
	- 'Susan'	ERou WOld
	- 'Sweet Briar'	CElw WOld
	- 'Tapestry'	WOld
	- 'Terry's Pride'	WOld
	- 'The Archbishop'	WOld
	- 'The Bishop'	WOld
	- 'The Cardinal'	ERou WOld

	- 'The Choristers'	WOld
	- 'The Dean'	ERou WOld
§	- 'The Rector'	WOld
	- 'The Sexton'	ERou WOld
	- 'Thundercloud'	MOne NBre NRnb WBrk WOld
	- 'Timsbury'	NBre NRnb WBrk WOld
	- 'Tony'	WOld
	- 'Tovarich'	WOld
	- 'Trudi Ann'	NBir WOld
	- 'Twinkle'	NEgg WOld
	- 'Victor'	MOne WOld
	- 'Vignem'	NSti
	- 'Violet Lady'	WOld
	- 'Waterperry'	MWat
	- 'Weisses Wunder'	WOld WOut
	- 'White Ladies'	CAby CBcs ERou GMaP LLWP MWat NOrc SPer SPoG SRGP
	- 'White Swan'	CPou ECtt EPPr LPhx NRnb WOld
	- 'White Wings'	WOld
	- 'Winston S. Churchill'	CMMP COIW CTri EBee ELan EPfP ERou GMaP LRHS MBnl MWat NOrc SHBN SPer SPlb SPoG SRGP WOld WPnP WTel
	oblongifolius	SUsu WOld
§	- 'Fanny's'	CPrp EBee EBla ECtt MNFA SPet SPoG SRGP WCAu WCot WFar WOld
	'Ochtendgloren' (*pringlei* hybrid) ♀H4	CPrp EGle EPPr GBuc GMac MAvo MNrw MSte NCGa SMrm WCAu WCot WFar WOld WWye
	Octoberlight	see *A.* 'Oktoberlicht'
§	'Oktoberlicht'	EMon WOld
	oolentangiensis	CAby EBee EPPr
	'Orchidee'	EBee ECtt EWes
	pappei	see *Felicia amoena*
	'Pearl Star'	WOld
	petiolatus	see *Felicia petiolata*
§	'Photograph' ♀H4	EWes MAvo MNFA MSte SMrm WFar WIvy WMnd WMoo WOld
§	*pilosus* var. *demotus* ♀H4	EBee EChP ECha EMon EWes MLLN MRav MSte WFar WOld WTin
§	- var. *pringlei* 'Monte Cassino' ♀H4	CBgR CHea CPrp CSBt EBee EBla EChP EPfP ERou GBBs IHMH LHop LPhx LRHS MBNS MLLN MRav MWat NCGa SMer SPav SPer SRGP SUsu WCAu WFar WMnd WOld WViv
	- - 'October Glory'	WFar
	- - 'Phoebe'	WOld
	- - 'Pink Cushion'	CMHG WCot
	'Pink Cassino'	WCAu
	'Pink Star'	CAby CMea EBrs GMac LPhx MNFA MRav MWat MWgw NSti SBch WBrk WFar WHoo WOld WTin
	'Pixie Dark Eye' (*ericoides* hybrid) **new**	WCot
	'Pixie Red Eye' (*ericoides* hybrid) **new**	WCot
	'Plowden's Pink'	WOld
	'Poollicht'	EBee
	'Prairie Lavender'	WOld
	'Prairie Pink'	WOld
	'Prairie Violet'	WOld
	'Primrose Path'	WCot
§	*ptarmicoides*	CSam EBee EBla EMon LPhx MLLN NBre WOld WPer
	puniceus	NBre
	- var. *elliottii*	see *A. elliottii*
	purdomii	see *A. flaccidus*
	pyrenaeus 'Lutetia'	CHea CSam EAEE EBee EChP ECha EMan EPPr GAbr GBuc GCal MNFA MSte MWgw NCGa NLar SBla SRGP WCAu WCMO WCot WFar WOld

	radula	EChP EMan EMon GCal MAvo MNrw NBre NLar NSti SUsu WOld WSHC
	'Ringdove' (*ericoides* hybrid) ♀H4	CPrp EAAE EBee EBla ECGP EPfP ERou GMac LRHS MHom MNFA MNrw MWgw NFla NSti NVic SRGP STes WCAu WCMO WCot WHil WIvy WOld
	'Rosa Star'	WOld
	rotundifolius 'Variegatus'	see *Felicia amelloides* variegated
	x *salignus*	WOld
	– Scottish form	WOld
	'Samoa'	MBri
*	*sativus atrocaeruleus*	EBrs
§	*scaber*	EBee WCot WPGP
	scandens	see *A. carolinianus*
	schreberi	CHea EBee EPPr MHar MHom MLLN NBre NCGa WCMO WCot WOld WWFD
§	*sedifolius*	EBee ELan EMan MDKP MSte MWat NBid NDov SBla SDix SPla WEas WFar WHil WMnd WOld WPer
	– 'Nanus'	CSam ERou MLLN MSte NBir NLar NSti SPer WCot WFar WHil WMnd WOld WOut WTin
	– 'Snow Flurries'	see *A. ericoides* f. *prostratus* 'Snow Flurry'
§	*sibiricus*	NBre NLar WOld
	'Snow Flurry'	see *A. ericoides* f. *prostratus* 'Snow Flurry'
	'Snow Star'	WOld
	souliei	EBee EBrs
	– B&SWJ 7655	WCru
	spathulifolius	NBir
	spectabilis	WOld
	subcaeruleus	see *A. tongolensis*
	'Sungal'PBR **new**	ERou
	'Sunhelene'	WCot WViv
	'Sunmarie' **new**	ERou
	Sunplum = 'Danasplum'PBR	ERou WViv
	'Sunqueen'	WCot WViv
	'Sunrio' **new**	ERou
	'Sunsky'	WViv
	'Sunspring' **new**	ERou
	tataricus	WOld WWye
	– 'Jindai'	WCot WFar
	thomsonii	WFar
	– 'Nanus'	CMdw GMaP LPhx MSte NBid NDov SAga WCot WFar WOld WSHC
	tibeticus	see *A. flaccidus*
	'Tonga'	MBri
§	*tongolensis*	EPfP SRms WFar WWFP
	– 'Berggarten'	CHar MBri NMoo SPoG WFar WWeb
	– 'Dunkleviolette'	GBuc NBro SRms
	– 'Lavender Star'	GBuc
	– 'Napsbury'	CDes EBee ERou MBri WPGP WRHF
	– 'Wartburgstern'	CPrp CSam EAAE EBee EChP EPfP LRHS NGdn WCFE WFar WMnd WPer
	tradescantii misapplied	see *A. pilosus* var. *demotus*
	tradescantii L.	EBee EGra ELan EMan MBNS MBnl MRav MWgw NBre NHol NSti SMad WBrk WCot WOld WTin
§	*trinervius* subsp. *ageratoides*	CPou WFar WOld
	– – 'Asran'	EBee EMon EWes LSou SHGN SSvw WFar WOld
	– var. *harae*	WOld
	– 'Morea'	SSvw
	tripolium	MBow WHer
	'Triumph'	WCot
	turbinellus Lindl.	EPPr SMar
	turbinellus misapplied ♀H4	EChP EMan EMon GBuc LPhx LRHS MBNS MBri MNFA MSte SDix SMHy SMar WCot WFar WHoo WOld WPtf WTin
	– hybrid	CMea WWeb
	umbellatus	CBre EMon EPPr GBin MNFA MWea NBre NCGa NLar NSti SRms WCot WOld WPrP WTin
	vimineus Lam.	see *A. lateriflorus*
	– 'Ptarmicoides'	see *A. ptarmicoides*
§	'White Climax'	CMea LPhx MSte WBrk WCot WOld
	yunnanensis	WSHC
	'Yvonne'	CBre

Asteranthera (Gesneriaceae)

ovata	CDes CPlN EBee GGGa GGar LSou NCGa WAbe WCru WPGP WPrP WSHC

Asteriscus (Asteraceae)

	'Gold Coin'	see *Pallenis maritima*
	maritimus	see *Pallenis maritima*
§	*spinosus*	CSec

Asteromoea (Asteraceae)

mongolica	see *Kalimeris mongolica*
pinnatifida	see *Kalimeris pinnatifida*

Asteropyrum (Ranunculaceae)

cavaleriei	CDes GEdr WCru

Asterotrichion (Malvaceae)

discolor	ECou

Astilbe ✿ (Saxifragaceae)

	'America'	CMHG ECtt GBri
	'Amethyst' (x *arendsii*)	CBcs CMHG EBrs EMFW GSki LRHS MRav NBir NBlu NBre SBod SMac SPer SRGP WCAu WFar WHoo WMoo WPnP WWpP
	'Anita Pfeifer' (x *arendsii*)	CMHG EBrs LPBA LRHS WFar WPnP WWpP
	'Aphrodite' (*simplicifolia* hybrid)	CMCo CWCL EChP LAst MDKP MLHP NBre NEgg NHol NPro SMac WBrE WGor
	x *arendsii*	CBrm ECho IFoB NBre NJOw SPet WGwG WMoo WPer
	astilboides	CMHG NHol SWvt
	'Atrorosea' (*simplicifolia* hybrid)	NCot SRms
	'Avalanche'	CSBt GAbr GBin MBNS NHol
	Bella Group (x *arendsii*)	NBre WMnd WRHF
	'Bergkristall' (x *arendsii*)	CMHG
	'Betsy Cuperus' (*thunbergii* hybrid)	CMHG CMil EBee MRav MSte NBre NPro SRGP WCAu WWpP
	biternata	EBee EMon
	'Bonn' (*japonica* hybrid)	CBcs CWCL CWat EBrs LPBA NBlu SCoo SRms
§	'Brautschleier' (x *arendsii*) ♀H4	CBgR CMHG CMMP CMac CPrp CTri CWCL EBrs EChP ECtt ENot EPfP LAst MOne NGdn NPri SRGP WPnP WPtf
	'Bremen' (*japonica* hybrid)	CMHG CMMP GBin LPBA NHol
	'Bressingham Beauty' (x *arendsii*)	CMHG CPrp CSam EBrs ECtt EHon ELan EMFW ENot EPfP ERou GMaP LPBA LRHS MRav MWrn NEgg NGdn NHol NPro SMer SPer SPoG SWvt WFar WMoo WWpP
	Bridal Veil (x *arendsii*)	see *A.* 'Brautschleier'
§	'Bronce Elegans' (*simplicifolia* hybrid) ♀H4	CBcs CMHG EChP ECha EPfP GBin GBuc GMaP GSki LAst LRHS MBNS MDun MRav NHol NOrc

NPro SMac SMer SPer WCAu WFar WMoo WWye

'Bronze Sprite'
(*simplicifolia* hybrid)   ECho WFar
'Bronzlaub' (x *arendsii*)   CRez
* **bumalda** 'Bronze Pygmy'   EBee EWTr MWgw NHol STes
'Bumalda' (x *arendsii*)   CFir CFwr CMCo CRez CWCL ENot EPPr GMaP GSki LRHS NDlv NMyG NOrc NPro SPlb WFar WMoo
'Carnea' (*simplicifolia* hybrid)   CMHG
'Catherine Deneuve'   see *A.* 'Federsee'
'Cattleya Dunkel' (x *arendsii*)   CMHG WFar
'Cattleya' (x *arendsii*)   CMHG CSam EBrs ECha GBri MBnl NBPC NLar NMoo WFar WMoo
'Ceres' (x *arendsii*)   CMHG NHol
'Cherry Ripe'   see *A.* 'Feuer'
chinensis   CMHG CWat ECho EShb GSki IBlr LRHS MBow NBre WSHC WWeb
- B&SWJ 8178   WCru
- from Russia   GCal
- 'Brokat' **new**   GBin
- 'Christian'   GBin
- var. *davidii*   CMHG GSki
- - B&SWJ 8583   WCru
- - B&SWJ 8645   WCru
- 'Finale'   CHar ECho EMFW NCGa NHol NPro SPer WFar WLin
- 'Frankentroll'   CMHG
- 'Intermezzo'   GMaP
§ - var. *pumila* ♀H4   More than 30 suppliers
- - 'Serenade'   EMil GSki LRHS MBri NGdn WFar
- 'Purple Glory'   CMHG
- 'Purpurkerze'   EChP EWTr GBin GMaP LDai MBNS MBri MNrw NBPC NBid NBro WBor
- 'Spätsommer'   CMHG
- var. *taquetii*   EBee EBrs EChP NBre NSti SRms
- - Purple Lance   see *A. chinensis* var. *taquetii* 'Purpurlanze'
§ - - 'Purpurlanze'   CKno CMHG CWCL EBrs ECha ECtt EGra EMFW EMan EPPr LLWP LPhx MRav MWat MWgw NBir NDov NGdn NHol NPro SPoG WCAu WFar WMoo WWpP
§ - - 'Superba' ♀H4   CMHG CMMP CPLG CRow CTri CWCL ECha EPfP GGar IHMH MCCP MLHP MLLN MSte NBro NHol SDix SPer SPoG SRms STes WEas WFar WMoo WPGP WWye
- 'Troll' **new**   GBin
- 'Veronica Klose'   CMHG NLar NPro WCAu
- 'Vision in Pink'PBR   CWCL ERou NBhm
- 'Vision in Red'PBR   CWCL CWat ERou GBin MBNS MBnl MBri NBhm NFor NLar NMyG NPro
- 'Visions'   CMHG CWCL EBrs EChP ECho ENot GBin GQue LRHS MBNS MBnl MBri MSte NBre NGdn NMyG NPro STes WFar
Cologne   see *A.* 'Köln'
'Crimson Feather'   see *A.* 'Gloria Purpurea'
x *crispa*   ECho IBlr WFar
- 'Gnom'   EMFW
- 'Lilliput'   CBcs CRez GBin GBri GEdr LRHS NDlv NLar NPro NRya
§ - 'Perkeo' ♀H4   More than 30 suppliers
- 'Peter Pan'   see *A.* x *crispa* 'Perkeo'
- 'Snow Queen'   LRHS NBir NMen NPro WFar
'Darwin's Dream'   MBnl NLar NPri WFar
'Darwin's Favourite' (x *arendsii*)   CWCL
'Deutschland' (*japonica* hybrid)   More than 30 suppliers

§ 'Diamant' (x *arendsii*)   CMHG ERou EShb LRHS MAvo MWrn NGdn NHol WFar
Diamond (x *arendsii*)   see *A.* 'Diamant'
'Drayton Glory' (x *arendsii*)   see *A.* x *rosea* 'Peach Blossom'
'Dunkellachs' (*simplicifolia* hybrid)   CMMP EBrs NHol NPro WFar
'Dutch Treat' (*japonica* hybrid) (v)   CMea
'Düsseldorf' (*japonica* hybrid)   CMHG CSam CWCL EBrs NHol
'Eden's Odysseus'   EBee EChP GBin MOne WWpP
'Elegans' (*simplicifolia* hybrid)   CMHG WFar
Elizabeth Bloom = 'Eliblo'PBR (x *arendsii*)   EBee EBrs GSki LRHS MRav NHol SVil WFar
'Elizabeth' (*japonica* hybrid)   CMHG EBee WCra
§ 'Ellie van Veen' (x *arendsii*)   CMHG CMMP CWCL EChP GBin MBri NBhm NHol
'Ellie' (x *arendsii*)   see *A.* 'Ellie van Veen'
'Else Schluck' (x *arendsii*)   ECha
'Erica' (x *arendsii*)   CMHG CTri EWll LRHS MAvo MBri MRav NPro WFar WMoo
'Etna' (*japonica* hybrid)   CBcs CMHG CRez CSam EBee EGra ERou GBri GSki MWrn NHol NLar NPro SRms WPnP
'Europa' (*japonica* hybrid)   CMHG CSBt EBrs ECtt EMFW GBin LHop LPBA MRav NEgg NOak SPla SPoG WFar WMoo
'Fanal' (x *arendsii*) ♀H4   More than 30 suppliers
'Fata Morgana' (x *arendsii* hybrid)   CMHG
§ 'Federsee' (x *arendsii*)   CBcs CMHG EBrs ECha ELan EMil EPyc LRHS NBre NBro NGdn NPro SPer WFar
§ 'Feuer' (x *arendsii*)   CMCo CMHG CMMP CPrp ELan EPPr EPfP LRHS MAvo MWgw NBid NHol NOrc NPro NVic SPer WMoo
Fire   see *A.* 'Feuer'
'Flamingo'PBR (x *arendsii*)   MBNS MBnl
'Gertrud Brix' (x *arendsii*)   CBcs NBir NGdn NPro SBod SPla
§ *glaberrima*   NBid NHol NMen
§ - var. *saxatilis* ♀H4   CLyd CRow EBee EPfP GBin GGar IFro IMGH LSou MBow NSla SPla WAbe WHal WThu
- *saxosa*   see *A. glaberrima* var. *saxatilis*
- - *minor*   see *A. glaberrima* var. *saxatilis*
'Gladstone' (x *arendsii*)   see *A.* 'W.E. Gladstone'
§ 'Gloria Purpurea' (x *arendsii*)   CMHG LRHS MDun NHol NMoo NMyG SRGP WMoo WWpP
'Gloria' (x *arendsii*)   CMHG CTri EBrs LPBA LRHS MRav WFar
Glow (x *arendsii*)   see *A.* 'Glut'
§ 'Glut' (x *arendsii*)   CFwr CMHG CWCL EBrs ECtt EGra EPPr GBin LRHS MAvo NHol NMyG SRms WFar
'Granat' (x *arendsii*)   CMHG CMMP CMac EMFW EWTr NBPC NBir NBre NHol NPro WMoo
* Grande Group (x *arendsii*)   NBre
grandis   CMHG WHer
'Grete Püngel' (x *arendsii*)   CFwr ECha GBri MLLN WFar
'Harmony' (x *arendsii*)   CMHG
'Hennie Graafland' (*simplicifolia* hybrid)   CBcs CMHG CWCL EBrs EChP EMil GAbr GBin MBNS NCGa NLar NPro WLin
'Holden Clough' (*japonica* hybrid)   NHol
Hyacinth (x *arendsii*)   see *A.* 'Hyazinth'
§ 'Hyazinth' (x *arendsii*)   CMHG CPLG CPrp EBrs EGra EMFW ERou GMaP GSki LRHS LSou MLan NFor NGdn NHol NPro SPoG WFar
'Inshriach Pink' (*simplicifolia* hybrid)   CBcs CCVN CMHG CPrp EBrs EHoe ELan EMFW GBin GCrs

LRHS MBri NBir NHol NOak SAga SBch SHGN WCot WCra WFar WHal WLin

'Irrlicht' (x *arendsii*) — CBcs CMHG CSBt EHon ELan EPfP EPla EShb GGar LHop LPBA LRHS NFor NHol SMac SWat WAul WPnP WWpP

japonica — CPLG
* - 'Pumila' — WBrE WCra
- var. *terrestris* — see *A. glaberrima*
'Jo Ophorst' (*davidii* hybrid) — CMHG EPPr GSki LPBA LRHS MRav NGdn NHol NLar NPro SPer SRGP WWpP
'Jump and Jive'PBR **new** — NCGa
'Koblenz' (*japonica* hybrid) — CMHG CWCL MDKP NMyG
§ . 'Köln' (*japonica* hybrid) — CMHG CWat GBin LPBA NMyG WFar WWpP
koreana — GGar WCot
- B&SWJ 8611 — WCru
- B&SWJ 8680 — WCru
'Koster' — LPBA
'Kriemhilde' — CMHG
'Kvele' (x *arendsii*) — CMHG WFar WMoo
§ 'Lachskönigin' (x *arendsii*) — CMHG
'Lady Digby' — LPBA
'Lilli Goos' (x *arendsii*) — CMHG
'Lollipop' — MBNS MBnl MBri NBhm NPro WBor
longicarpa B&SWJ 6711 — WCru
macroflora **new** — GCal
'Maggie Daley' — CMMP EBee LAst MBri NBro NPro SRGP WMoo WWeb
'Mainz' (*japonica* hybrid) — CMHG ELan EMil LPBA MBow WWpP
'Mars' (x *arendsii*) — CMHG
microphylla — CMHG CPLG NHol
- pink — CMHG NHol
'Moerheimii' (*thunbergii* hybrid) — CMHG
'Moerheim's Glory' (x *arendsii*) — CMMP GBin LAst NBre NGdn WWpP
'Mont Blanc' (x *arendsii*) — CMHG
'Montgomery' (*japonica* hybrid) — CMHG EBrs EChP ERou GAbr GBin LRHS LSRN MBNS MBri MRav NBPC NBro NFor NHol SBch SRGP WBVN WFar
'Obergärtner Jürgens' (x *arendsii*) — CMMP EChP GBin WWpP
Ostrich Plume — see *A.* 'Straussenfeder'
'Paul Gaärder' (x *arendsii*) — CMHG
'Peaches and Cream' — EBee LRHS MMHG MRav NBro NLar WPnP
'Peter Barrow' (*glaberrima* hybrid) — GBin SRms
'Pink Lightening'PBR (*simplicifolia* hybrid) — CWCL EBee EShb MAvo MBNS MBnl MTis NBPC NBhm NLar SMrm WBor
Pink Pearl (x *arendsii*) — see *A.* 'Rosa Perle'
'Poschka' — CFir NPro
I 'Poschka Alba' — CFir NMyG NPro
'Professor van der Wielen' (*thunbergii* hybrid) — CMHG CMil CWCL EBee EBrs EGle ETow GCal GGar LAst MSte SDix SPer SRms WCAu WFar
pumila — see *A. chinensis* var. *pumila*
* 'Queen' — ECho LPBA
§ 'Queen of Holland' (*japonica* hybrid) — MDun
'Radius' — CBgR CMMP EBee NGdn
* 'Red Admiral' — NFor
Red Light (x *arendsii*) — see *A.* 'Rotlicht'
'Red Sentinel' (*japonica* hybrid) — CBcs CMMP CWCL CWat EBrs EChP EMFW EMil ERou GBin GMaP LAst MOne MTis NBro NCGa NHol NOrc NPro SMrm SPoG WBor WFar WSan WWeb

'Rheinland' (*japonica* hybrid) ♀H4 — CMHG CMMP CWCL EPfP IHMH LPBA LRHS NPri SPoG STes WCAu WEas WFar WHoo WPnP WWpP
'Rhythm and Blues'PBR — GBin WWeb
rivularis — CMHG GBin WCot
- CC 4547 — WCot
- var. *myriantha* — NBre
- - BWJ 8076a — WCru
§ 'Rosa Perle' (x *arendsii*) — CMHG CSam NHol
§ x *rosea* 'Peach Blossom' — CBcs CMHG CMMP EBrs EChP GBuc LPBA NBir NEgg NGdn NHol NPro NSti SPoG WFar WHoo WMoo WWeb WWpP
- 'Queen Alexandra' — WFar
'Rosea' (*simplicifolia* hybrid) — NHol WFar
Rosemary Bloom = 'Rosblo' — EBee NHol
§ 'Rotlicht' (x *arendsii*) — CMHG EBrs ECot LRHS NHol NLar NMyG NPro WFar WGor
Salmon Queen (x *arendsii*) — see *A.* 'Lachskönigin'
'Salmonea' (*simplicifolia* hybrid) — CMHG
'Saxosa' — see *A. glaberrima* var. *saxatilis*
Showstar Group (x *arendsii*) — LRHS NBre NPen
simplicifolia ♀H4 — CRow WFar
- 'Alba' — CMHG GBin NEgg NHol NPro
- Bronze Elegance — see *A.* 'Bronce Elegans'
- 'Darwin's Snow Sprite' — CMac CRez ECho GBin MBnl MBri MSte NHol NLar NPri WFar
- 'Jacqueline' — EBee ECho NHol NLar WFar
* - 'Nana Alba' — NPro
- 'Praecox' — NEgg
- 'Praecox Alba' — CMCo CWan EBee EChP ENot NEgg NHol SMac WHoo
'Snowdrift' (x *arendsii*) — CBrm CMHG CWat EBrs EPla GMaP GSki LRHS MAvo MBNS MDKP NBir NCGa NFor NOak NOrc NPro SPer SWat WFar
'Solferino' (x *arendsii*) — CMHG
'Spartan' (x *arendsii*) — see *A.* 'Rotlicht'
'Spinell' (x *arendsii*) — CWCL MDun NOrc WFar WPnP WWpP
'Sprite' (*simplicifolia* hybrid) ♀H4 — More than 30 suppliers
§ 'Straussenfeder' (*thunbergii* hybrid) ♀H4 — CMHG CTri CWCL EBrs EChP EPfP EPla ETow GCal GMaP LAst LHop LRHS NBid NBir NBro NHol NOrc SMac SPer SPla SPoG WAul WCAu WMoo WPnP WPtf
'Sugar Plum' (*simplicifolia* hybrid) — EBee LAst NGdn
'Superba' — see *A. chinensis* var. *taquetii* 'Superba'
thunbergii — CPLG EBrs
- var. *hachijoensis* — EBee
- var. *terrestris* B&SWJ 6125 — WCru
'Touch of Pink'PBR (*simplicifolia* hybrid) — ERou
'Venus' (x *arendsii*) — CBrm CHar CSam EBrs ECha ECtt EGra EMFW EWTr GGar GMaP LPBA MSte NHol NOrc NVic SPer SRGP SWat WFar WMoo
'Vesuvius' (*japonica* hybrid) — CBcs EBrs MDKP NBlu NBro NEgg NSti WSan
§ 'W.E. Gladstone' (*japonica* hybrid) — CWat GSki MSte NBlu NHol NPro WGor WWpP
'Walküre' (x *arendsii*) — CMHG
'Walter Bitner' — EPPr GBin MBNS NHol SRGP SVil
§ 'Washington' (*japonica* hybrid) — CBcs EBee IHMH LAst MDKP NGdn
§ 'Weisse Gloria' (x *arendsii*) — CMHG EBrs ECha EPPr ERou LPBA MBow MLan NBPC NBro NEgg

	NHol NMyG NOrc NSti SBod SPoG SRGP WBor WMoo WTin
White Gloria (x *arendsii*)	see *Astilbe* 'Weisse Gloria'
'White Queen' (x *arendsii*)	NHol
'White Wings'^{PBR} (*simplicifolia* hybrid)	NLar
'William Reeves' (x *arendsii*)	CMHG NHol
'Willie Buchanan' (*simplicifolia* hybrid)	CBcs CMHG CPrp ECtt EHoe ENot GAbr GKev GMaP GSki LRHS MBar MWat NEgg NFor NHol NMen SIng SPer SPla SRms WAbe WFar WMoo
'Zuster Theresa' (x *arendsii*)	CMHG EBee EBrs LRHS MBNS NBPC NBro SMrm SRGP WFar

Astilboides (Saxifragaceae)
§ **tabularis**   More than 30 suppliers

Astragalus (Papilionaceae)
canadensis	EMan LPhx
glycyphyllos	CAgr CArn EBee
lusitanicus	LRav
membranaceus	CArn ELau MSal
- var. **mongholicus**	MSal
newberryi var. **castoreus new**	CGra

Astrantia ✿ (Apiaceae)
bavarica	CCge EBee EMan EMar GCal MDKP WFar WGwG WOut
'Bloody Mary'	CBgR IBal MBNS MWea NGdn NLar NRnb NSti
§ 'Buckland'	More than 30 suppliers
carniolica	EMon EPyc GSki NEgg WTel
- **major**	see *A. major*
- var. **rubra**	see *A. major* 'Rubra'
§ - 'Rubra'	CBcs MWrn NBre SMHy WCra WSHC
- 'Variegata'	see *A. major* 'Sunningdale Variegata'
'Dark Shiny Eyes' **new**	CKno EBee IBal NCGa NLar
'Hadspen Blood'	More than 30 suppliers
Harptree hybrid **new**	CHar
'Helen'	WCra
helleborifolia misapplied	see *A. maxima*
'Magnum Blush' **new**	NBhm
§ **major**	More than 30 suppliers
- 'Abbey Road'	EBee ECGP ENot IPot MWrn NLar SPoG WAul
* - **alba**	CBcs CMHG CPrp CWCL EBee EBla ECha EGle EHrv EMon GMac GSki MBnl MNFA MRav MTis MWgw MWrn NBir NGdn NPer WMnd WWeb
- 'Ann Cann'	CBct
- 'Berendien Stam'	CCge EBee EMon MAvo
- subsp. **biebersteinii**	CCge EBee EBla EMon NBir NBre
- 'Bo-Ann'	CWCL EBee EMan ERou IBal LBuc MAvo MBNS MBnl MBri NCob NLar NSti SHBN WAul
- 'Celtic Star'	CBcs CFir CKno EBee EBla EChP ELan ERou GBuc GSki LHop MAvo MBnl MSph NCob NEgg NGdn NMyG NOak SPla SPoG WCAu WCot WGwG WTMC WWhi
- 'Claret'	More than 30 suppliers
- 'Côte d'Azur' **new**	CBct MDKP
- 'Cyril James'	CBct
- dwarf	WFar
- 'Elmblut'	MAvo
- 'Gill Richardson'	CKno EBee EBla ECGP EMar EPPr EShb IPot LRHS MAvo MBnl MWgw NBre NCob NDov NFla NGdn NOrc SPoG
- 'Greenfingers'	EBee EWes

- 'Gwaun Valley'	WFar
- 'Hillview Red'	CCge CElw
- subsp. **involucrata**	EBla EHrv GSki LRHS SWat WFar
- - 'Barrister'	CBct CSam EMon GBuc WFar WOut WPGP
- - 'Canneman'	CBct EBee EBla EMon EWes LPhx MAvo MBnl NSti SMrm WCAu WCot WFar
- - 'Margery Fish'	see *A. major* subsp. *involucrata* 'Shaggy'
- - 'Moira Reid'	CBct CLAP CMil EAEE EBee EBla ECGP EMan GBri GCal IPot LRHS LSRN MAvo MBNS MNFA NBro NCob NDov SHar SRGP SUsu WWhi
- - 'Orlando'	EBee EMon
§ - - 'Shaggy' ♀^{H4}	More than 30 suppliers
- 'Jade Lady'	WFar
- 'Lars'	More than 30 suppliers
- 'Little Snowstar'	EHrv IBal MWgw NSti
- 'Maureen'	NOak
- 'Montelolor'	WFar
- 'Paper Moon'	WFar
- 'Primadonna'	CBct CCge CHea CKno EBee EBla EHrv EMan ERou EWsh GSki MBNS MNFA MTis MWrn NHol NLar SPlb WFar WMnd WPer WViv WCra
- 'Prockter'	WCra
- 'Roma'^{PBR}	CBct CCge CHad CKno CLAP COtt EBee EBla EHrv EMan EMon ERou GSki LHop LPhx MAvo MBri MWrn NBhm NCGa NCob NDov NOak SMHy SPoG SUsu WCAu WCra WFar WViv
- 'Rosa Lee'	CWCL EBee EMan IBal MBnl MWrn NCob NLar WAul WHil
- var. **rosea**	More than 30 suppliers
- - George's form	CBct CKno CSam EBee EBla EMan EMar EPPr GCal IPot LAst MAvo MWrn NCob NFla
- 'Rosensinfonie'	CPLG EBee EBla GMaP GSki MNFA MWrn NBro NOak NPro WFar WMnd WViv
§ - 'Rubra'	More than 30 suppliers
- 'Ruby Cloud'	CBct CCge CHea EBee EBla EHrv EMan GSki IBal MNrw MRav MWrn NBro NRnb NSti WFar WFoF WLin
- 'Ruby Wedding'	More than 30 suppliers
- 'Silver Glow' **new**	CKno EBee LBmB NSti
- 'Starburst'	EBee WFar
- 'Sue Barnes' (v)	EMon GCal
§ - 'Sunningdale Variegated' (v) ♀^{H4}	More than 30 suppliers
- 'Titoki Point'	EBee WCot
- 'Variegata'	see *A. major* 'Sunningdale Variegated'
§ **maxima** ♀^{H4}	More than 30 suppliers
- 'Mark Fenwick'	NBir
* - **rosea**	CWCL EBla ECtt LBmB MDKP MTis NBir NEgg NGdn STes WSan CPrp WCru
minor	CPrp WCru
'Moulin Rouge' **new**	CKno CLAP CPou GBri IPot LSou MBNS MBnl MSph NBPC NCGa NCob NGdn WCot WCra
'Rainbow'	NLar
rubra	see *A. major* 'Rubra'
'Snow Star'^{PBR}	CWCL CWib EBee EHrv IPot MAvo MBnl MBri MWrn
'Warren Hills'	EBla MWrn

Asyneuma (Campanulaceae)
canescens	CDMG CSec EBee ELan EMan LSou MBNS NBre NSfd SGar WCot
limonifolium	CPom
§ **prenanthoides**	ELan NSfd

pulvinatum	CPBP EHyt SIng WAbe

Asystasia (*Acanthaceae*)

bella	see *Mackaya bella*
§ *gangetica*	CSev EShb
violacea	see *A. gangetica*

Athamanta (*Apiaceae*)

turbith subsp. **haynaldii**	EBee
vestina	CBos WEas

Athanasia (*Asteraceae*)

dentata <u>new</u>	GGar
§ *parviflora*	SPlb

Atherosperma (*Monimiaceae*)

moschatum	CBcs CHll WSHC

Athrotaxis (*Cupressaceae*)

cupressoides	CDoC CDul CKen LCon MBar WThu
laxifolia	CDoC CKen EMil LCon MBar WThu
selaginoides	CDoC CDul CTrG

Athyrium ✿ (*Woodsiaceae*)

'Branford Beauty'	CCCN CDes CLAP
'Branford Rambler'	CLAP CRez
filix-femina ♀H4	More than 30 suppliers
- var. **angustum** 'Lady in Red'	CDes CElw CLAP CRez EBee
- 'Clarissimum'	CBos WIvy
* - **congestum cristatum**	CLAP WFib
- 'Corymbiferum'	GQui SRms
- 'Crispum Grandiceps Kaye'	SRms
- Cristatum Group	CLAP EFer EFtx ELan EMon MMoz NHol SBla SWat WAbe
§ - Cruciatum Group	CBgR CBos CFwr CLAP EBee ELan EMon EPfP MMoz NHol NOGN SPer SRms WCot WCru WFib WMoo WPtf WWye
- 'Fieldii'	CLAP NBid NHol SRms
- 'Frizelliae' ♀H4	More than 30 suppliers
- 'Frizelliae Capitatum'	CLAP WFib WPGP
- 'Frizelliae Cristatum'	EFtx SRms
- 'Grandiceps'	CLAP SRms
- 'Minutissimum'	CBgR CLAP EBee ECha ELan EMon LPBA MMoz SBla WPGP
* - 'Nudicaule'	SRms
- Percristatum'	EMon
- Plumosum Group	CLAP GBri GQui WAbe WFib
* - - 'Plumosum Aureum' <u>new</u>	NBhm
- - 'Plumosum Axminster'	CLAP EFer
- - 'Plumosum Cristatum'	CLAP
- - 'Plumosum Divaricatum'	SRms
- Red Stem	see *A. filix-femina* 'Rotstiel'
§ - 'Rotstiel'	CFwr CLAP MMoz NLar WFar WMoo WPnP
* - **superbum** 'Druery'	CLAP
- 'Vernoniae' ♀H4	CLAP EBee ELan EMon EWsh LPBA MAsh
- 'Vernoniae Cristatum'	CLAP NHol WFib
- 'Victoriae'	CCCN CFwr CPrp CWCL EKen GEdr LPBA MAsh MWgw NBid
- Victoriae Group	see *A. filix-femina* Cruciatum Group
'Ghost'	CBos CDes CLAP CRez WCMO
goeringianum 'Pictum'	see *A. niponicum* var. *pictum*
niponicum	SLdr WHal
- f. **metallicum**	see *A. niponicum* var. *pictum*
§ - var. **pictum** ♀H3	More than 30 suppliers
- - 'Apple Court'	CCCN CRez
- - 'Burgundy Lace'	EFtx ERou WPtf

* - - 'Cristatoflabellatum'	CBos CLAP EBrs ELan EMon
- - 'Pewter Lace'	EFtx
- - 'Red Beauty'	CFwr CLAP CRez EBee EFtx GBin MAvo WCMO WCot
- - 'Silver Falls'	CBcs CCVN CElw CLAP EFtx ERou LAst LRHS MBNS MBnl NCob NCot NMyG WCMO WCot
- - 'Soul Mate'	EFtx
- - 'Ursula's Red'	More than 30 suppliers
- - 'Wildwood Twist'	CLAP EFtx
otophorum ♀H4	CRez EMon NBid NHol NVic SRms WIvy WPGP
- var. **okanum**	More than 30 suppliers
vidalii	CFwr CLAP CRez EBee NBid WFib

Atractylodes (*Asteraceae*)

japonica	EFEx
macrocephala	CArn EFEx

Atragene see *Clematis*

Atriplex (*Chenopodiaceae*)

canescens	NLar WDin XPep
cinerea	GGar
halimus	CArn CBcs ECha EHoe EPPr LRHS MBla MBri MRav NLar SLon SPer SWat WCot WDin WHer WKif WSHC WTel WTin XPep
hortensis var. **rubra**	CArn CEnt CHad CHrt CSpe EGra ELan EOHP LSou MHer MNHC NDov NGHP SIde WCHb WCot WEas WJek WWye
nummularia	XPep
portulacoides	see *Halimione portulacoides*

Atropa (*Solanaceae*)

bella-donna	CArn GBar GPoy MGol MSal WTin WWye
- var. **lutea**	MSal
mandragora	see *Mandragora officinarum*

Atropanthe (*Solanaceae*)

§ *sinensis*	MSal

Aubrieta ✿ (*Brassicaceae*)

albomarginata	see *A.* 'Argenteovariegata'
'Alix Brett'	CMea CPBP ECho LRHS SPoG
'April Joy' (d)	ECho ECot
§ 'Argenteovariegata' (v) ♀H4	ECho ELan SBla WAbe WHoo
'Astolat' (v)	ECho ECtt NSla SBla SRms WEas
§ 'Aureovariegata' (v) ♀H4	CMea CNic ECho ECtt ELan IHMH LRHS MHer NJOw NPer NWCA SBla WAbe WFar
'Belisha Beacon'	ECho MBri
Bengal hybrids	CNic STre WGor
Blaue Schönheit	see *A.* 'Blue Beauty'
'Blaumeise'	IHMH
§ 'Blue Beauty'	WRHF
* 'Blue Mist'	ECho
§ 'Bob Saunders' (d)	CMea CNic ECho ECtt LTwo
'Bonfire'	ECho
'Bressingham Pink' (d) ♀H4	ECho ECtt ELan EPfP LRHS SPoG
'Bressingham Red'	ECho LRHS SPoG
'Campbellii'	ECho
'Carnival'	NEgg
Cascade Series	NEgg
- 'Blue Cascade'	ECtt EPfP NBlu NNor SPlb SPoG WGor
- 'Lilac Cascade'	SPoG
- 'Purple Cascade'	CTri CWib ECtt EPfP LRHS NBlu SPlb SPoG SRms WGor
- 'Red Cascade' ♀H4	CTri CWib ECtt EPfP MWgw NBlu NNor SPlb SPoG
'Crimson Queen' <u>new</u>	ECho

'Dantra'	ECho
deltoidea	SHGN
- 'Nana Variegata' (v)	CMea ECtt EPot NJOw WGor
- 'Tauricola'	ECho
- Variegata Group (v)	ECtt LRHS NMen NSla WFar WRHF
'Doctor Mules' ♀H4	CSpe ECho LRHS SRms
'Doctor Mules Variegata' (v)	ECho ECtt EPfP LAst MHer NEgg NPri SIng SPoG SWvt WFar
'Downers'	GBin
'Elsa Lancaster'	EHyt EPot NMen NSla
'Fire King'	NLar
§ 'Frühlingszauber'	SRms WGor
glabrescens	WAbe
'Gloriosa'	ECho
'Godstone'	ECho
'Golden Carpet'	ECho SIng
'Golden King'	see A. 'Aureovariegata'
gracilis	WAbe
* 'Graeca'	NPri
'Greencourt Purple' ♀H4	ECho ELan MHer MWat
'Gurgedyke'	ECho SRms
'Hamburger Stadtpark'	ECho EDAr
'Hemswell Purity'PBR	see A. 'Snow Maiden'
'Hendersonii'	SRms
'J.S. Baker'	SRms
'Joy' (d)	ECho ECtt LTwo NSla
'Kitte'	ECho LAst SPoG
'Leichtlinii'	ECho NJOw NLar
'Lemon and Lime'	ECho LRHS
'Little Gem'	ECho
macedonica	EPot
'Magician'	ECho
'Mars'	ECho
'Maurice Prichard'	ECho ECtt LRHS
'Mrs Lloyd Edwards'	ECho
'Mrs Rodewald' ♀H4	ECho SRms
'Novalis Blue'	SRms
'Oakington Lavender'	ECho
parviflora	CStu
'Pike's Variegated' (v)	ECho
pinardii	EHyt NSla
'Purple Charm'	SRms
'Red Carpet'	ECho ELan EPot LRHS MHer SPoG SRms
'Red Carpet Variegated' (v)	CMea ECho
'Rose Queen'	CMea CPBP LRHS SAga SMrm
Royal Series ♀H4	COlW
- 'Royal Blue'	GAbr GKev LRHS NEgg NJOw WFar WMoo
- 'Royal Lavender'	WFar
- 'Royal Lilac'	WFar
- 'Royal Red'	GAbr GKev MBow NJOw NPri SRms WFar WGor WMoo
- 'Royal Rose'	WFar
- 'Royal Violet'	LRHS MBow NJOw NPri WFar WPer
'Schofield's Double'	see A. 'Bob Saunders'
'Silberrand'	ECha ECtt NSla
§ 'Snow Maiden'PBR	ECho ECtt LRHS SPoG
'Somerfield Silver'	MBar
'Somerford Lime' (v)	ECtt MBar
Spring Charm	see A. 'Frühlingszauber'
'Swan Red' (v)	EPot LAst NSla SPoG WAbe WFar
thessala	CPBP
'Toby Saunders'	ECho
'Triumphante'	ECho ECtt LRHS LTwo
'Wanda'	ECho ELan
'Whitewell Gem'	ECho MWgw NJOw SRms WMoo

Aucuba ✿ (*Aucubaceae*)

japonica (f)	SMer WDin
- (m)	ENot SReu
- 'Crassifolia' (m)	EPla SAPC SArc
- 'Crotonifolia' (f/v) ♀H4	More than 30 suppliers
- 'Crotonifolia' (m/v)	MAsh NBlu SRms
- 'Dentata'	CHEx

- 'Golden King' (m/v) ♀H4	CDoC CMac CSBt CTrw CWib EBee ELan EPfP LRHS MAsh MGos MTis MWat NLar SLim SPla SPoG WFar WWeb
- 'Golden Spangles' (f/v)	CBcs CDoC CHEx ECot SWvt
- 'Goldstrike' (v)	EBee EHoe
- 'Hillieri' (f)	EPla
- Lance Leaf' (m)	EPla SLon
- f. *longifolia* ♀H4	CMac SAPC SArc SDix WCru
- - 'Salicifolia' (f)	CHEx EBee EPla LAst MRav NLar SLon SPla WCru WDin WFar WPGP
- 'Maculata' hort.	see A. *japonica* 'Variegata'
- 'Marmorata'	EPla LRHS
- 'Nana Rotundifolia' (f)	EPla
- Pepper Pot = 'Shilpot'	SSta
- 'Pepperpot' (m/v)	CHEx EPfP MAsh SPoG
- 'Picturata' (m/v)	CBow CDul CHEx CMac CSBt EBee ELan LRHS MAsh MGan MGos MRav NEgg NHol SHBN SLim SPer SPoG WCFE WFar
- 'Rozannie' (f/m) ♀H4	More than 30 suppliers
- 'Speckles'	GSki
- 'Sulphurea Marginata' (f/v)	CBcs CBow CMac EBee EMil EPla NPro SPoG
§ - 'Variegata' (f/v)	More than 30 suppliers
- Windsor form (f)	EPla LRHS MBri
omeiensis BWJ 8048 new	WCru

Aurinia (*Brassicaceae*)

§ *corymbosa*	LTwo
§ *saxatilis* ♀H4	ECho EPfP LAst MBar MWat SPlb STre WFar WTel
- 'Argentea' new	ECho
- 'Citrina' ♀H4	ECha ECho ECtt MWat SRms
- 'Compacta'	CTri ECho ECtt ENot
- 'Dudley Nevill'	ECho EHol LRHS MWat SBla SIng
- 'Dudley Nevill Variegated' (v)	CRez ECha ECho ECtt EWes MHar MHer NBir NGby SBla SIng WFar
- 'Flore Pleno' (d)	ECho EHol
- Gold Ball	see A. *saxatilis* 'Goldkugel'
- 'Gold Dust'	ECho ECtt SRms
- 'Golden Queen'	ECtt MHer
§ - 'Goldkugel'	ECho IHMH LRHS SPoG SRms
- 'Silver Queen'	WEas
- 'Variegata' (v)	EWin NPri SPoG
sinuata 'Pebbles'	LRav

Austrocedrus (*Cupressaceae*)

§ *chilensis*	CKen CPne CTho LRHS

Austromyrtus (*Myrtaceae*)

§ *dulcis*	ECou
tenuifolia new	CPLG

Avena (*Poaceae*)

candida	see *Helictotrichon sempervirens*
sativa 'French Black'	CSpe

Avenula see *Helictotrichon*

Averrhoa (*Oxalidaceae*)

carambola (F)	SDEP

Ayapana see *Eupatorium*

Azadirachta (*Meliaceae*)

indica	SDEP

Azalea see *Rhododendron*

Azara ✿ (*Flacourtiaceae*)

RCB/Arg C-15 new	WCot
alpina	CPLG ISea
dentata	CBcs CHll CMac ERea IDee LAst SBrw WDin WFar WSHC
- 'Variegata'	see A. *integrifolia* 'Variegata'

*	*integerrima*	GQui
	integrifolia	CCCN SBrw
	- 'Uarie' **new**	CCCN
§	- 'Variegata' (v)	ERea SBrw SDnm SMur SPoG
	lanceolata	CBcs CDul CMCN CPLG CTri ECrN IDee ISea LEdu NSti SBrw SLon WGer WPic
	microphylla ♀H3	CBcs CDul CLnd CMCN CMHG CPLG CPSs CSBt CTri ECrN EPfP EPla ISea LAst NSti SArc SBra SBrw SDnm SPer SSpi WFar WPGP WSHC WTel
	- 'Gold Edge' (v)	LBuc WFar
	- 'Variegata' (v)	CBcs CDoC CMac CPLG CPMA CWib EHoe EMil EPfP GQui IMGH ISea LAst MLan NHol NSti SBrw SDnm SLon SPoG SSpi SSta STre WCot WCru WFar WGer WPat WSHC
N	*paraguayensis*	GGar SDnm
	petiolaris	EPfP SBrw WGer WPic
	- G&P 5026	WPGP
	serrata ♀H3	CBcs CBrm CDul CEnd CMCN CPLG CSBt CWib ECrN EPfP EPla ERea GGar IDee ISea NCGa SAga SBrw SDix SPer SPoG SRms SSta WBor WCru WDin WFar WGer WHar WTel
	uruguayensis	CCCN CPLG SBrw

Azorella (Apiaceae)

	filamentosa	ECou
	glebaria misapplied	see *A. trifurcata*
	glebaria A. Gray	see *Bolax gummifer*
	gummifer	see *Bolax gummifer*
	lycopodioides	GEdr
*	*speciosa* **new**	EPot
§	*trifurcata*	CPar CSpe CTri ECho ECtt GAbr GEdr IHMH NLAp NWCA SBla SPlb WAbe WPer
	- 'Nana'	ECho GGar MWat NJOw WPat

Azorina (Campanulaceae)

§	*vidalii*	CSpe ERea EShb MGol SAPC SArc SGar WCot
	- 'Rosea'	CKob

B

Babiana (Iridaceae)

ambigua	CMon CStu
angustifolia	CPLG
'Blue Gem'	ECho
disticha	see *B. plicata*
dregei	WCot
ecklonii	CMon WCot
framesii	CStu
- var. *kamiesbergensis* **new**	CPLG
hybrids	LBow
nana	CGrW CMon CStu WCot
odorata	CPLG WCot
§ *plicata*	SYvo WCot
pulchra	CMon
purpurea **new**	LBow
pygmaea	CMon WCot
ringens	CPLG
rubrocyanea	WCMO WCot
sambucina	CStu
sinuata	CMon WCot
stricta ♀H1-2	CPLG CStu ECho LBow SBch WCot WRos
- var. *erectifolia*	WPrP

- 'Purple Star'	CPLG ECho
- 'Tubergen's Blue'	ECho LBow
truncata	CMon CStu WCot
vanzyliae	CStu WCot
villosa	WCot
'Zwanenburg's Glory'	ECho

Baccharis (Asteraceae)

genistelloides	SMad WCot
halimifolia	CBcs GQui LRav SEND SLon
- 'Twin Peaks'	XPep
patagonica	CTrC GGar SAPC SArc SPoG WPat
salicifolia	SBig WCMO WCot
'Sea Foam'	EChP EKen EMan LSou SBrw SHGN SMad

Bacopa (Scrophulariaceae)

caroliniana	EOHP
monnieri	EOHP EUnu
'Snowflake'	see *Sutera cordata* 'Snowflake'

Baeckea (Myrtaceae)

densifolia	ECou
gunniana	CPLG
virgata	CBcs CTrC ECou SPlb

Baillonia (Verbenaceae)

juncea	WSHC

Balbisia (Geraniaceae)

peduncularis	WCot WFoF

Baldellia (Alismataceae)

ranunculoides	CRow EMFW WMAq WWpP
- f. *repens*	EMan

Ballota ✿ (Lamiaceae)

	acetabulosa ♀H3-4	EBee ECha EGoo EMan EWes EWin MWgw SBch SDix WCot WKif XPep
	'All Hallow's Green'	CFee EAEE EBee EGoo EMan EWin GBuc LHop LRHS NSti SBla SLon XPep
	hirsuta	XPep
	hispanica **new**	IFro
	nigra	CArn EBee GPoy GWCH MHer MSal NMir SECG WMoo WWye XPep
§	- 'Archer's Variegated' (v)	CBow EChP ECrN ECtt EMan EWes LDai
	- 'Variegata'	see *B. nigra* 'Archer's Variegated'
	- 'Zanzibar' (v)	EMon
	pseudodictamnus ♀H3-4	More than 30 suppliers
	- from Crete	ECha
	- 'Candia'	MSph SBla
	rupestris 'Frogswell Carolyn' (v) **new**	IFro

Balsamita see *Tanacetum*

Balsamorhiza (Asteraceae)

sagittata	ECho

Bambusa ✿ (Poaceae)

	bambos **new**	MJnS
	glaucescens	see *B. multiplex*
	gracilis	see *Drepanostachyum falcatum*
	gracillima	COtt
§	*multiplex*	EFul XBlo
	- 'Alphonso-Karrii'	LEdu LPal SBig WPGP
	- 'Elegans'	see *B. muliplex* 'Floribunda'
	- 'Fernleaf'	see *B. muliplex* 'Floribunda'
§	- 'Floribunda'	CHEx COtt EFul EShb
	- 'Nana' **new**	XBlo
	- 'Tiny Fern' **new**	WPGP
	- 'Wang Tsai'	see *B. muliplex* 'Floribunda'

pubescens	see *Dendrocalamus strictus*
textilis	WJun
ventricosa	SBig XBlo
vulgaris	XBlo

banana see *Musa*

Banisteriopsis (*Malpighiaceae*)
caapi	CPIN MGol

Banksia (*Proteaceae*)
aemula new	SOWG
burdettii	SOWG
canei	SPlb WSAf
coccinea	SOWG
conferta var. *conferta* new	CPLG
ericifolia var. *ericifolia*	CBcs CTrC SOWG
grandis	CCCN CCtw SOWG
integrifolia	CBcs CCCN CCtw ECou
marginata	CTrC ECou SOWG SPlb
- mauve-flowered	SOWG
media	CTrC SPlb WSAf
oblongifolia	CBcs CTrC SPlb
occidentalis	CCtw SOWG
paludosa	CTrC SPlb
praemorsa	WSAf
robur	CAbb CTrC SPlb
serrata	CCtw SOWG SPlb
speciosa	CCtw SPlb
spinulosa	CTrC
- var. *collina*	CCtw CTrC
- pink	SOWG
- var. *spinulosa*	CBcs
violacea	SPlb

Baptisia (*Papilionaceae*)
§ *alba*	CPom EMan NLar
§ - var. *macrophylla*	CMdw CPle EWes LRHS NBir NDov NLar SMar WCMO WCot
australis ♀H4	More than 30 suppliers
- 'Caspian Blue'	CWCL EDAr LBBr LHop MLan MMHG MWrn NBPC SAga SPla WHil WSHC
- 'Exaltata'	ELan GBuc LHop LRHS
- var. *minor*	EDAr NLar
§ *bracteata* var. *leucophaea*	EBee LSou
lactea	see *B. alba* var. *macrophylla*
leucantha	see *B. alba* var. *macrophylla*
leucophaea	see *B. bracteata* var. *leucophaea*
pendula	see *B. alba*
tinctoria	CArn

Barbarea (*Brassicaceae*)
praecox	see *B. verna*
§ *verna*	CArn GPoy MHer NGHP
vulgaris 'Variegata' (v)	CArn CHal EBee ELan EMan IHMH LDai MDun NBid NBro NCob SPav WCHb WCot WMoo
- 'Variegated Winter Cream' (v)	GAbr LSou

Barleria (*Acanthaceae*)
micans new	CCCN
suberecta	see *Dicliptera suberecta*

Barnadesia (*Asteraceae*)
caryophylla RCB/Eq T-5	WCot

Barosma see *Agathosma*

Bartlettina see *Eupatorium*

Bartsia (*Scrophulariaceae*)
alpina	EMan

Basella (*Basellaceae*)
rubra	EShb EUnu

Bashania (*Poaceae*)
faberi Og 94053	EPla
§ *fargesii*	CDoC ENBC EPla ERod MRav MWht SEND WJun
I *qingchengshanensis*	EBee EPla WJun WPGP

basil see *Ocimum basilicum*

Bassia (*Chenopodiaceae*)
scoparia	MSal

Bauera (*Cunoniaceae*)
rubioides var. *alba*	ECou
- 'Candy Stripe'	SOWG
- pink-flowered	ECou SOWG
- 'Ruby Glow'	SOWG
sessiliflora	SOWG

Bauhinia (*Caesalpiniaceae*)
aureifolia new	CPIN
bidentata new	CPIN
corymbosa	CPIN SOWG
galpinii	CPLG EShb SOWG SPlb
monandra	SOWG WMul
natalensis	EShb SPlb
sirindhorniae new	CPIN
tomentosa	EShb
vahlii	CSec
yunnanensis	CPIN EShb SOWG

Baumea see *Machaerina*

bay see *Laurus nobilis*

Beaucarnea (*Dracaenaceae*)
recurvata ♀H1	CTrC LPal LToo MBri NScw WFar

Beaufortia (*Myrtaceae*)
sparsa	CTrC SOWG
squarrosa	SPlb

Beaumontia (*Apocynaceae*)
grandiflora	CPIN SOWG
multiflora	CPIN
murtonii new	CPIN

Beauverdia see *Leucocoryne*

Beccariophoenix (*Arecaceae*)
madagascariensis	LPal

Beckmannia (*Poaceae*)
eruciformis	WRos
syzigachne new	CPLG

Beesia (*Ranunculaceae*)
calthifolia	CLAP EBee WCru WPGP WPrP
- DJHC 98447	CDes
deltophylla new	WCot

Begonia ✿ (*Begoniaceae*)
B&SWJ 6606 from Thailand new	WCru
B&SWJ 6881 from Taiwan new	WCru
Chen Yi 5 new	WCot
DJHC 580	WCot
from China	NShi
- - BWJ 7840	WCru
from Ruwenzori, Uganda	NShi
from Siam new	NShi
from Sikkim, India	WCMO WCot

– – B&SWJ 2692	EMan
from Vietnam	ERhR NShi
'Abel Carrière'	CHal ERhR NShi WDib
acerifolia	see *B. vitifolia* Schott
acetosa	ERhR NShi
acida	ERhR NShi
aconitifolia	ERhR EShb NShi
acutifolia	ERhR NShi
'Aladdin'	ERhR NShi
'Alamo III'	ERhR NShi
albopicta (C)	CHal EBak ERhR NShi SAdn
– 'Rosea'	CHal NShi WDib
alice-clarkiae	ERhR
'Alleryi' (C)	ERhR NShi
alnifolia	ERhR
'Alto Scharff' ♀H1	ERhR NShi
'Alzasco' (C)	ERhR NShi
'Amigo Pink' (C)	ERhR
'Amigo Variegated' (v)	ERhR
amphioxus **new**	NShi
ampla	ERhR
angularis	see *B. stipulacea*
'Anita Roseanna' (C)	ERhR NShi
'Ann Anderson' (C)	ERhR NShi
'Anna Christine' (C)	ERhR NShi
§ *annulata*	ERhR NShi
'Aquarius'	ERhR NShi
'Arabian Sunset' (C)	ERhR NShi
'Argentea' (R)	EBak MBri NShi
x *argenteoguttata* (C)	CHal ERhR EShb NShi
'Aries'	ERhR NShi
'Art Monday' (C)	NShi
'Arthur Mallet'	ERhR NShi
'Aruba'	ERhR NShi
'Autumn Glow' (T)	ERhR NShi
'Avalanche' (T)	ERhR NShi
'Axel Lange' (R)	NShi
'Aya' (C)	NShi WDib
'Baby Down' **new**	NShi
'Baby Perfection'	NShi WDib
'Bahamas'	ERhR NShi
'Bantam Delight'	ERhR NShi
'Barbados' **new**	NShi
'Barbara Ann' (C)	ERhR
'Barbara Hamilton' (C)	ERhR
'Barbara Parker'	ERhR
'Barclay Griffiths'	ERhR NShi
'Beatrice Haddrell'	CHal ERhR NShi WDib
'Bedford Velvet' **new**	NShi
* *benichoma*	WDib
'Beningo' **new**	NShi
'Benitochiba' (R)	ERhR NShi WCot
'Bess'	ERhR NShi
'Bessie Buxton'	ERhR NShi
'Bethlehem Star'	ERhR NShi WDib
§ 'Bettina Rothschild' (R)	CHal ERhR NShi WDib
'Beverly Jean'	ERhR NShi
'Big Mac'	ERhR NShi
'Bill's Beauty'	ERhR NShi
'Bishop's Irish Eyes' (C)	NShi
'Black Jack' (C)	ERhR NShi
'Black Knight' (R)	CHal NShi
'Black Raspberry'	ERhR NShi
'Black Velvet'	NShi
'Blanc de Neige'	ERhR NShi
'Blue Vein'	ERhR NShi
'Blue Wave'	NShi
'Bokit'	ERhR NShi WDib
'Bokit' x *imperialis*	NShi WDib
boliviensis	GCal NShi WCot WCru
'Bonaire'	CHal
'Boomer' (C)	ERhR NShi
bowerae	CHal ERhR LRHS NShi
§ – var. *nigramarga*	ERhR NShi
'Boy Friend'	ERhR NShi
bracteosa	ERhR
bradei	ERhR
brevirimosa	ERhR
'Brown Lace'	NShi
'Brown Twist'	NShi WDib
'Bunchii'	ERhR NShi
'Burgundy Velvet'	ERhR NShi WDib
'Burle Marx' ♀H1	CHal ERhR EShb NShi SDix WDib
'Bush Baby'	CHal
'Butter Cup'	NShi
'Calico Kew'	ERhR
'Calla King' **new**	NShi
'Calla Queen' (S)	ERhR
'Can-can' (R)	see *B.* 'Herzog von Sagan'
'Can-can' (T)	NShi
'Candy Floss'	NShi WCru
'Captain Nemo'	ERhR NShi
cardiocarpa	ERhR
'Carol Mac'	ERhR NShi
'Carolina Moon' (R)	ERhR NShi
carolineifolia	CHal NShi WDib
carrieae	ERhR NShi
x *carrierei*	see *B.* Semperflorens Cultorum Group
'Cathedral'	ERhR NShi WDib
'Champagne' **new**	SPer
'Chantilly Lace'	CHal ERhR NShi
chapaensis	NShi
– HWJ 642	WCru
'Charles Chevalier'	ERhR NShi
'Charles Jaros'	ERhR NShi
'Charm' (S)	CHal ERhR NShi WDib
x *cheimantha* 'Gloire de Lorraine'	NShi
'Cheops' **new**	NShi
'Cherry Feast'	CHal
'Cherry Jubilee' (C)	NShi
'Cherry Sundae'	ERhR
'Chesson'	ERhR NShi
'China Curl'	ERhR NShi
'China Doll'	NShi
chloroneura	NShi WDib
'Chocolate Box'	ERhR
'Chocolate Chip'	ERhR NShi
'Christine'	NShi
'Christmas Candy'	ERhR WDib
'Christy White'	NShi
'Chumash'	ERhR NShi
'Cistine'	ERhR NShi
'Clara' (R)	MBri NShi
'Cleopatra' ♀H1	CHal ERhR MRav NShi WDib
'Clifton'	ERhR NShi
coccinea (C)	ERhR NShi WDib
'Coconut Ice'	EShb LAst SVil
compta	see *B. stipulacea*
'Comte de Lesseps' (C)	NShi WDib
'Comtesse Louise Erdody' (R) **new**	NShi
conchifolia var. *rubrimacula*	ERhR NShi
'Concord'	ERhR NShi
'Connee Boswell'	ERhR NShi WDib
convolvulacea	ERhR NShi
cooperi	ERhR NShi
'Cora Anne'	ERhR
'Cora Miller' (R)	ERhR NShi
x *corallina*	EBak
§ – 'Lucerna' (C)	CHal EBak ERhR LRav NShi
– 'Lucerna Amazon' (C)	CHal ERhR NShi
'Corbeille de Feu'	CHal ERhR NShi
'Cosie' (C)	NShi
'Cowardly Lion' (R)	ERhR NShi
'Cracklin' Rosie' (C)	ERhR NShi
crassicaulis	ERhR NShi
'Crestabruchii'	ERhR NShi
'Crystal Brook'	ERhR NShi
cubensis	ERhR NShi

cucullata	CHal ERhR NShi	
'Curly Fireflush' (R)	ERhR NShi	
'Curly Locks' (S)	CHal	
'Dales' Delight' (C)	ERhR NShi	
'Dancin' Fred'	ERhR NShi	
'Dancing Girl'	ERhR NShi	
'Dannebo'	MBri	
'D'Artagnan'	ERhR NShi	
'David Blais' (R)	NShi WDib	
'Dawnal Meyer' (C)	ERhR NShi WDib	
I 'de Elegans'	ERhR NShi WDib	
'Decker's Select'	ERhR NShi	
'Deco Diamond Dust' **new**	NShi	
decora	ERhR NShi	
deliciosa	ERhR NShi	
'Delray Silver'	NShi	
'Dewdrop' (R)	ERhR NShi WDib	
'Di Condue' **new**	NShi	
diadema	ERhR NShi	
'Di-anna' (C)	ERhR NShi	
dichotoma	ERhR NShi	
dichroa (C)	ERhR NShi	
'Dielytra'	ERhR NShi	
'Di-erna'	ERhR NShi	
dietrichiana Irmsch.	ERhR	
'Digswelliana'	ERhR	
dipetala	ERhR	
discolor	see *B. grandis* subsp. *evansiana*	
domingensis	ERhR	
'Don Miller'	ERhR NShi WDib	
'Doublet Pink'	ERhR	
'Doublet Red'	ERhR	
'Doublet White'	ERhR	
'Douglas Nisbet' (C)	ERhR	
Dragon Wing Red	NShi	
= 'Bepared'[PBR] ♀[H1+3]		
dregei (T) ♀[H1]	ERhR NShi	
- 'Bonsai'	NShi STre	
- 'Glasgow'	ERhR NShi	
- var. *macbethii*	NShi	
'Druryi'	ERhR NShi	
'Dwarf Houghtonii'	ERhR NShi	
'Earl of Pearl'	ERhR NShi	
'Easter Bonnet' **new**	NShi	
* 'Ebony' (C)	CHal ERhR NShi	
echinosepala	ERhR NShi	
echinosepala x	NShi	
sanguinea		
I 'Edinburgh Brevirimosa'	ERhR NShi	
edmundoi	ERhR	
egregia	ERhR	
'Elaine'	ERhR NShi	
'Elaine Ayres' (C)	ERhR NShi	
§ 'Elaine Wilkerson'	ERhR NShi	
'Elaine's Baby'	see *B.* 'Elaine Wilkerson'	
'Elda'	ERhR NShi	
'Elda Haring' (R)	ERhR NShi	
'Elizabeth Hayden'	ERhR	
'Elsie M. Frey'	ERhR NShi	
emeiensis **new**	NShi	
'Emerald Giant' (R)	ERhR NShi WDib	
'Emerald Isle'	NShi	
'Emerald Princess'	NShi	
'Emma Watson'	CHal ERhR NShi	
'Enchantment'	ERhR	
'Enech'	ERhR NShi	
'English Knight'	ERhR NShi	
'English Lace'	ERhR NShi	
epipsila	ERhR NShi	
x *erythrophylla*	EShb NShi	
- 'Bunchii'	ERhR NShi	
§ - 'Helix'	CHal ERhR NShi	
'Escargot'	GGar WDib	
'Essie Hunt'	ERhR	
'Esther Albertine' (C) ♀[H1]	CHal ERhR NShi	
'Evening Star'	ERhR NShi	

'Exotica'	ERhR	
'Fairy'	ERhR NShi	
feastii 'Helix'	see *B.* x *erythrophylla* 'Helix'	
fernando-costae	ERhR NShi	
§ 'Feuerkönigin' (S)	ERhR	
'Fever' **new**	NShi	
'Filigree'	ERhR NShi	
'Fire Flush'	see *B.* 'Bettina Rothschild'	
'Fireworks' (R)	ERhR NShi WDib	
'Five and Dime'	ERhR NShi	
'Flamboyant' (T)	ERhR MBri NShi	
Flaming Queen	see *B.* 'Feuerkönigin'	
'Flamingo'	ERhR NShi	
'Flamingo Queen'	ERhR NShi	
'Flo'Belle Moseley' (C)	CHal ERhR NShi WDib	
'Florence Carrell'	ERhR NShi	
'Florence Rita' (C)	ERhR NShi	
'Flying High'	ERhR	
foliosa	CHal ERhR NShi WDib	
- var. *amplifolia*	CHal ERhR NShi	
formosana	NShi	
- B&SWJ 7041	WCru	
'Frances Lyons'	ERhR NShi	
'Frau Hoffman' (R) **new**	NShi	
'Freckles' (R)	ERhR NShi	
'Fred Bedson'	ERhR NShi	
'Fred Martin' (R)	NShi	
friburgensis	ERhR	
'Friendship'	ERhR NShi	
'Frosty' (T)	NShi WDib	
'Frosty Fairyland'	ERhR	
'Frosty Knight'	ERhR NShi	
'Fuchsifoliosa'	ERhR	
fuchsioides ♀[H1]	CDoC EBak ERhR EShb EWin LIck MArl MOak NShi SDix SYvo WDib	
- pink-flowered	GGar LAst NShi	
- red-flowered	MOak WFar	
- 'Rosea'	CDoC CHal LRHS	
fusca	ERhR NShi	
'Fuscomaculata'	ERhR NShi	
'Gaystar'	NShi	
gehrtii	ERhR NShi	
geranioides	ERhR	
glabra	ERhR	
glandulosa	ERhR	
glaucophylla	see *B. radicans* Vell.	
'Glen Daniels'	NShi	
'Gloire de Lorraine'	NShi	
'Gloire de Sceaux'	ERhR NShi	
goegoensis	ERhR NShi	
'Good 'n' Plenty'	ERhR NShi	
gracilis var. *martiana*	NShi	
'Granada'	ERhR NShi	
grandis	NShi	
§ - subsp. *evansiana* ♀[H3-4]	CHEx CHal CKob CSam CStu ELan EMan EMar EMon ERhR EShb GCal LEdu MLLN MOak MSte MTho NCiC NMRc NShi SBch SDix SMad WBrk WCMO WCot WCru WFar	
- - var. *alba* hort.	CAby CHal CMdw EBee EDsa EMon ERhR EShb GCal MOak MSte MTho SSpi WCot WPGP	
- - 'Claret Jug'	EBee EMan EMon WCMO WCot WPGP	
- - hybrid	ERos	
- - 'Pink Parasol'	WCru	
- - 'Simsii'	NShi WFar	
- 'Maria'	EBee WCot	
- 'Sapporo'	EBee EMar EPPr GCal MSte SMrm WCru	
* 'Great Beverly'	ERhR NShi	
'Green Gold' (R)	NShi WDib	
'Green Lace'	ERhR NShi	
'Grey Feather'	ERhR NShi	
griffithii	see *B. annulata*	
'Gustav Lind' (S)	CHal ERhR EShb NShi	

'Guy Savard' (C)	NShi WDib
haageana	see *B. scharffii*
handelii	ERhR NShi
* 'Happy Heart'	ERhR NShi
'Harbison Canyon'	NShi
* 'Harry's Beard'	ERhR NShi
'Hastor'	ERhR NShi
hatacoa	ERhR NShi
- silver	CHal CSpe ERhR NShi
- spotted	ERhR NShi
'Hazel's Front Porch' (C)	ERhR NShi
'Helen Lewis'	ERhR NShi
'Helen Teupel' (R)	ERhR NShi WDib
'Helene Jaros'	ERhR NShi
'Her Majesty' (R)	ERhR
heracleifolia var.	ERhR NShi
longipila	
- var. *nigricans*	CHal NShi
- 'Wisley'	NShi
§ 'Herzog von Sagan' (R)	ERhR NShi
x *hiemalis* 'Elatior'	LRHS
hispida var. *cucullifera*	ERhR NShi
'Holmes Chapel'	ERhR NShi
homonyma (T)	ERhR
'Honeysuckle' (C)	ERhR NShi
'Hot Tamale'	ERhR
'Hottentot'	NShi
hydrocotylifolia	ERhR NShi
hypolipara	ERhR NShi
(Illumination Series)	SCoo
'Illumination Apricot'	
- 'Illumination Rose'	SCoo
- 'Illumination Salmon	SCoo
Pink' ♀H2-3	
- 'Illumination White'	SCoo
* *illustris* new	CSpe
imperialis	ERhR NShi
incarnata (C)	ERhR NShi
- 'Metallica'	see *B. metallica*
'Ingramii'	ERhR NShi
'Interlaken' (C)	ERhR NShi
'Irene' (C) new	NShi
'Irene Nuss' (C) ♀H1	ERhR NShi
'Ironstone' (R)	NShi
'Ivy Ever'	ERhR NShi
'Jade'	NShi
'Jelly Roll Morton'	ERhR
'Joe Hayden'	CHal ERhR NShi
'John Tonkin' (C)	ERhR NShi
johnstonii	ERhR NShi
'Joy Porter' (C)	NShi
'Jubilee Mine'	ERhR
juliana	ERhR NShi
'Jumbo Jeans'	ERhR NShi
'Jumbo Jet' (C)	ERhR NShi
'Kagaribi' (C)	ERhR NShi
kellermanii (C)	ERhR NShi
'Ken Lau Ren' (C)	NShi
keniensis	GCal
'Kentwood' (C)	ERhR NShi
kenworthyae	ERhR NShi
kingiana	NShi WDib
'Kit Jeans'	ERhR NShi
'Kit Jeans Mounger'	ERhR NShi
'Knutsford'	NShi
'Kyoto'	NShi
'La Paloma' (C)	NShi WDib
'Lacewing'	ERhR NShi
'Lady Carol'	CHal
'Lady Clare'	ERhR NShi
* 'Lady France'	ERhR MBri
'Lady Snow'	CHal
'Lana' (C)	ERhR NShi
'Langeana'	NShi
'Laurie's Love' (C)	ERhR
'Lawrence H. Fewkes'	ERhR
leathermaniae (C)	ERhR NShi
'Legia'	ERhR
'Lenore Olivier' (C)	ERhR NShi
'Leopard'	ERhR MBri NShi
'Lexington'	ERhR
'Libor' (C)	ERhR
'Lillian' (R)	NShi
'Lime Swirl'	ERhR NShi
limmingheana	see *B. radicans* Vell.
'Linda Dawn' (C)	ERhR NShi
'Linda Harley'	ERhR
'Linda Myatt'	ERhR
lindeniana	ERhR NShi
listada ♀H1	CHal ERhR MBri NShi WDib
'Lithuania'	ERhR
'Little Brother	ERhR GGar NShi SDix WDib
Montgomery' ♀H1	
'Little Darling'	ERhR NShi
'Little Iodine'	NShi
'Little Miss Mummey' (C)	NShi
new	
'Lois Burks' (C)	CHal ERhR NShi WDib
'Loma Alta'	ERhR
longimaculata new	NShi
longipetilata new	NShi
'Looking Glass' (C)	ERhR NShi WDib
'Lospe-tu'	ERhR NShi
'Lubbergei' (C)	ERhR NShi
'Lucerna'	see *B.* x *corallina* 'Lucerna'
'Lulu Bower' (C)	ERhR NShi
luxurians	CHll CKob ERhR NShi WCMO WCot
- 'Ziesenhenne'	ERhR NShi
lyman-smithii	ERhR NShi
'Mabel Corwin'	ERhR NShi
'Mac MacIntyre'	NShi
macdougallii var.	CHal NShi WDib
purpurea	
macduffieana	NShi
'Mac's Gold'	ERhR NShi
maculata ♀H1	ERhR NShi
- 'Wightii' (C)	CHal CSpe ERhR NShi WDib
'Mad Hatter'	ERhR NShi
'Madame Butterfly' (C)	ERhR NShi
'Magic Carpet'	ERhR NShi
'Magic Lace'	ERhR NShi
'Manacris'	ERhR NShi
'Mandarin Orange' (C)	NShi
manicata	ERhR NShi WDib
mannii new	NShi
'Maphil'	MBri NShi
'Margaritae'	ERhR NShi
* 'Marginata Crispa White'	SPer
new	
'Marmaduke' ♀H1	CHal NShi WDib
'Marmorata' (T)	LRHS
'Martha Floro' (C)	ERhR
'Martin Johnson' (R)	ERhR NShi WDib
'Martin's Mystery'	ERhR NShi
masoniana ♀H1	CHal ERea ERhR MOak NShi WDib
- light-leaved	NShi
'Maurice Amey'	ERhR NShi
'Maverick'	ERhR NShi
mazae	ERhR NShi
'Medora' (C)	ERhR NShi
'Melissa' (T)	NShi
'Merry Christmas' (R) ♀H1	ERhR NShi WDib
metachroa	ERhR
§ *metallica* ♀H1	CHal ERhR EShb NShi
'Michaele'	ERhR
'Midnight Sun'	ERhR NShi
'Midnight Twister'	ERhR NShi
'Mikado' (R)	ERhR NShi
minor	ERhR
'Mirage' ♀H1	ERhR NShi
'Miss Priss' (C)	NShi

mollicaulis	ERhR
'Moon Maid'	ERhR
'Mr Kartuz' (T) **new**	NShi
'Mrs Hashimoto' (C)	ERhR NShi
'Mrs Hatcher'	ERhR NShi
'Mrs Schinkle' (C)	NShi
multinervia	ERhR
'Munchkin' ♀H1	CHal ERhR NShi WDib
* 'Mystic'	ERhR NShi
'Mystique'	ERhR NShi
'Nancy Cummings'	ERhR
natalensis (T)	ERhR NShi
'Nelly Bly'	ERhR
nelumbiifolia	ERhR NShi
nigramarga	see *B. bowerae* var. *nigramarga*
nigritarum	ERhR
* *nitida alba*	ERhR
'Nokomis' (C)	ERhR NShi
'Norah Bedson'	ERhR NShi
'Northern Lights' (S)	ERhR NShi
obliqua	ERhR
obscura	ERhR
'Obsession'	ERhR
odorata	ERhR
'Odorata Alba'	ERhR NShi
odorata var. *rosea*	NShi
olbia	ERhR
'Old Gold' (T)	ERhR
'Oliver Twist'	ERhR
'Orange Dainty'	ERhR
'Orange Pinafore (C)'	ERhR
'Orange Rubra' (C) ♀H1	CHal ERhR NShi
'Orococo'	NShi
'Orpha C. Fox' (C)	ERhR NShi
'Orrell' (C)	ERhR NShi
'Othello'	ERhR NShi
'Otto Forster'	ERhR NShi
oxyphylla	ERhR
'Pachea' (R)	NShi
paleata	ERhR NShi
palmata	CAby CDes EBee EBla EMan EShb GCal LSou NShi WPGP
- B&SWJ 2692 from Sikkim	WCru
- from China	EBla NShi
- var. *palmata*	CKob NShi
- - B&SWJ 7175	WCru
'Palomar Prince'	ERhR NShi
'Panasoffkee'	ERhR NShi
'Pantaloon'	NShi
'Panther'	ERhR
'Papillon' (T)	ERhR NShi
paranaensis	ERhR NShi
* 'Parilis'	ERhR NShi
partita	ERhR EShb NShi
parva **new**	NShi
'Passing Storm'	ERhR NShi
'Patricia Ogdon'	ERhR NShi
'Paul Harley'	ERhR NShi
'Paul Henry'	NShi
'Paul-bee'	ERhR NShi
paulensis	ERhR NShi
'Peace' (R)	NShi
'Peach Parfait' (C)	ERhR NShi
pearcei	ERhR NShi
'Pearl Ripple'	ERhR NShi
'Pearls' (C)	ERhR NShi
'Peggy Stevens' (C)	ERhR
* *peldja* **new**	NShi
peltata	ERhR NShi
* 'Penelope Jane'	ERhR
* *perfectifolia* **new**	NShi
'Persian Brocade'	ERhR NShi
'Petite Marie' (C)	ERhR
'Phil Corwin' (R)	NShi
'Piccolo'	ERhR NShi
'Pickobeth' (C)	ERhR NShi
'Picotee' (T)	CSut
'Pinafore' (C) ♀H1	ERhR NShi
'Pink Basket'	NShi
'Pink Champagne' (R)	NShi WDib
'Pink Frosted'	NShi
'Pink Jade' (C)	NShi
'Pink Lady' (R)	NShi WCru
'Pink Nacre'	CHal ERhR NShi
'Pink Parade' (C)	ERhR NShi
'Pink Parfan'	NShi
'Pink Shasta' (C)	NShi
'Pink Slate' (C)	NShi
'Pink Spot Lucerne' (C)	ERhR NShi SYvo
'Pink Taffeta'	ERhR NShi
plagioneura	ERhR
platanifolia var. *acuminatissima*	ERhR
'Plum Rose'	ERhR NShi
plumieri	ERhR
polyantha	ERhR NShi
polygonoides	ERhR
popenoei	ERhR
'Posy Wahl' (C)	NShi
'Potpourri'	ERhR
'Président Carnot' (C)	ERhR NShi SYvo
'Pretty Rose'	ERhR
'Preussen'	ERhR NShi
'Princess of Hanover' (R)	ERhR NShi WDib
'Princessa Rio de Plata'	ERhR NShi
prismatocarpa	ERhR NShi
procumbens	see *B. radicans* Vell.
pustulata 'Argentea'	ERhR NShi
putii	NShi
- B&SWJ 7245	WCru
'Queen Mother' (R)	ERhR NShi
'Queen Olympus'	ERhR GGar NShi WDib
'Quinebaug'	NShi
§ *radicans* Vell. ♀H1	CHal ERhR LRHS MBri NShi
'Raquel Wood'	ERhR NShi
'Raspberry Swirl' (R) ♀H1	CHal ERhR NShi WDib
ravenii	CDes CKob EBee GCal NShi WCot
- B&SWJ 1954	LSou WCru
'Raymond George Nelson' ♀H1	CHal ERhR NShi
'Razzmatazz' (R)	NShi WDib
'Red Berry' (R)	ERhR NShi
'Red Planet'	ERhR NShi WDib
'Red Reign'	ERhR NShi
'Red Robin' (R)	NShi WDib
'Red Spider'	ERhR NShi
'Red Undies' (C)	NShi WCru
'Red Wing' (R)	NShi
'Regal Minuet' (R)	NShi WDib
'Regalia'	ERhR
'Reine des Neiges' (R)	NShi
rex	LRHS MBri MRav NShi
- 'Orient'	ERhR NShi
'Richard Robinson'	ERhR
'Richmondensis'	ERhR EShb NShi
'Ricinifolia'	ERhR NShi
'Ricky Minter' ♀H1	ERea ERhR NShi
'Rip van Winkle'	ERhR NShi
'Robert Blais' (R)	NShi
'Robin' (R)	ERhR NShi
'Robin's Red' (C)	ERhR NShi
'Rocheart' **new**	WDib
'Roi de Roses' (R)	ERhR NShi
roxburghii	ERhR NShi
'Royal Lustre'	ERhR NShi
'Rubacon'	ERhR NShi
rubro-setulosa	ERhR
'Sabre Dance' (R)	ERhR NShi
'Sachsen'	ERhR NShi
'Saint Albans Grey'	NShi
salicifolia (C)	ERhR
'Sal's Comet' **new**	WDib

	'Sal's Moondust' **new**	WDib
	sanguinea	ERhR NShi
*	*sansouci* **new**	NShi
	scapigera **new**	NShi
	'Scarlett O'Hara' (T)	ERhR
	scharffiana	ERhR
§	*scharffii*	CHal EBak ERhR NShi SDix
	'Scherzo'	CHal ERhR NShi WDib
	'Scottish Cup' **new**	NShi
	'Scottish Star'	NShi
	'Sea Captain'	NShi
	'Sea Serpent'	NShi
	'Secpuoc'	ERhR
	semperflorens hort.	see *B.* Semperflorens Cultorum Group
§	Semperflorens Cultorum Group	MBri NShi
	'Serlis'	ERhR NShi
	serratipetala	CHal EBak ERhR MBri NShi WDib
	'Shamus'	ERhR NShi
*	*sheperdii*	NShi WDib
	'Shiloh' (R)	ERhR NShi
*	'Shinihart'	ERhR NShi
	'Shoppy'	NShi
	'Sierra Bright Eyes' **new**	NShi
	'Sierra Mist' (C)	ERhR NShi
	'Silbreen'	NShi
	silletensis subsp. mengyangensis	GCal
	'Silver Cloud' (R)	ERhR NShi WDib
*	'Silver Dawn'	ERhR NShi
	'Silver Dollar'	NShi
	'Silver Dots'	NShi
	'Silver Giant' (R)	ERhR NShi
	'Silver Jewell'	NShi WDib
	'Silver King' (R)	NShi
	'Silver Lace'	NShi WDib
	'Silver Mist' (C)	ERhR NShi
	'Silver Points'	ERhR NShi
	'Silver Queen' (R) ♀H1	NShi
	'Silver Sweet' (R)	ERhR NShi
	'Silver Wings'	ERhR NShi
	'Sinbad' (C)	ERhR NShi
	sinensis	EMan NShi WCot
	– BWJ 8011	WCru
	aff. *sinensis* BWJ 8133	WCru
	'Sir Charles'	ERhR
	'Sir John Falstaff'	ERhR NShi
	'Sisquoc' (T) **new**	NShi
	Skeezar Group	ERhR
	– 'Brown Lake'	ERhR NShi
	'Snow Queen' **new**	NShi
	'Snow Storm' **new**	NShi
*	'Snowcap' (C) ♀H1	ERhR EShb NShi WDib
	socotrana	ERhR
	solananthera ♀H1	CHal ERhR EShb GGar NShi WDib
	soli-mutata	NShi
	sonderiana	ERea GCal
	'Sophie Cecile' (C) ♀H1	CHal ERhR NShi
	'Sophie's Jenny'	NShi
	'Sophie's White Spot' **new**	NShi
	'Speckled Roundabout'	NShi
	'Speculata' (R)	ERhR NShi
	'Spellbound'	ERhR NShi WDib
	'Spindrift'	ERhR NShi
	'Spotches'	ERhR NShi
	'Squiggles' **new**	NShi
	'Stained Glass' (R)	NShi WDib
	'Starburst' **new**	SPer
	'Stichael Maeae'	ERhR
	stigmosa **new**	NShi
§	*stipulacea*	CHal ERhR NShi
	subvillosa (S)	ERhR
	– var. *leptotricha* **new**	NShi
	'Sugar Plum'	ERhR NShi
	'Sun God'	NShi
	'Sunbright Pink' **new**	NShi
	'Sunbright Red' **new**	NShi
	Superba Group (C)	NShi
	'Superba Azella' (C)	NShi
	sutherlandii ♀H1	CHal EBak EOHP ERhR ERos GGar ITer LRHS MOak NBir NBlu NPer NShi SAdn SBch SDix SYvo WCot WCru WDib WEas WFar WHer
	– 'Papaya'	CSpe
	'Swan Song'	ERhR
	'Sweet Magic'	CHal ERhR NShi
	'Swirly Top' (C)	ERhR NShi
	'Sylvan Triumph' (C)	ERhR NShi
	taiwaniana	NShi
	'Tapestry' (R)	ERhR NShi
	'Tar Baby' (T)	ERhR NShi
*	*taya*	WDib
	'Tea Rose'	ERhR NShi
	'Tequesta'	NShi
	teuscheri (C)	ERhR NShi
	'Texas Pink' (C) **new**	NShi
	'Texastar'	ERhR NShi WDib
	'The Wiz'	ERhR NShi
	thelmae	ERhR NShi
	'Think Pink'	NShi
	'Thrush' (R)	NShi
	'Thumotec'	ERhR
	'Thunderclap'	CHal ERhR NShi
	'Thurstonii' ♀H1	ERhR EShb NShi
	'Tiger Paws' ♀H1	CHal ERhR MBri NShi
	'Tingley Mallet' (C)	ERhR NShi
	'Tiny Bright' (R)	ERhR NShi
	'Tiny Gem'	ERhR NShi
	'Tom Ment' (C)	ERhR NShi
	'Tom Ment II' (C)	ERhR
	tomentosa **new**	NShi
	'Tomoshiba'	ERhR
	'Tondelayo' (R)	ERhR NShi
	'Tornado' (R)	NShi
	'Tribute'	ERhR NShi
	'Trinidad'	ERhR NShi
	tripartita (T)	ERhR NShi WDib
	'Trout' (C)	NShi
	'Twilight'	ERhR NShi
	'Two Face'	ERhR NShi WDib
	ulmifolia	ERhR NShi
	undulata (C)	CHal ERhR NShi
	'Universe'	ERhR NShi
	'Valentine' **new**	NShi
	'Venetian Red' (R)	NShi
	venosa	CHal ERhR NShi
	'Venus'	CHal ERhR NShi
	'Vera Wyatt'	NShi
	x *verschaffeltii*	ERhR NShi
	versicolor	ERhR
	'Vesuvius' (R)	NShi WDib
	'Viaudii'	ERhR NShi
	'Viau-Scharff'	ERhR
§	*vitifolia* Schott	ERhR NShi
	'Wally's World'	NShi
I	'Wanda' (T) **new**	NShi
	'Weltoniensis'	ERhR NShi
	'Weltoniensis Alba' (T)	ERhR
	'Westland Beauty' **new**	NShi
	'White Cascade'	ERhR
	'White Magic' **new**	NShi
	'Wild Swan'	NShi WCru
	williamsii	NShi
	'Witch Craft' (R)	ERhR NShi
	'Withlacoochee'	ERhR NShi WDib
	wollnyi	ERhR
	'Wood Nymph' (R)	ERhR NShi
	'Zuensis'	ERhR

Belamcanda (Iridaceae)

chinensis	CArn CBro CMea CSec EBee EChP EGra ELau EMan ERos EShb GKev GPoy LRHS MHer MLLN MSal SDnm SIng SPav SPlb SRms SSto SYvo WBrE WCru WGwG WPer WWye
- 'Freckle Face'	CAbb EBee EKen GBri IBal LBmB NBPC SPoG
- 'Hello Yellow'	GBuc

Bellevalia (Hyacinthaceae)

brevipedicellata	ECho
ciliata	ERos
dubia	EBee WCot
fominii	WWst
forniculata	ERos WCMO
gracilis	WCot
hackelii	ERos
hyacinthoides	CStu WCot
kurdistanica	ERos
longipes	WCot
longistyla	WCot
maura	ECho
§ **paradoxa**	CMea CPom EChP ECho EHrv ERos ITim LTwo MAvo MSph NJOw WCot
- white-flowered	ERos
pycnantha misapplied	see *B. paradoxa*
romana	CFwr CNic CStu EBee ECho ERos GBin LPhx MTho WCot WHil
sarmatica	ERos WCot
spicata	WCot
tabriziana	ERos
webbiana	ERos

Bellis (Asteraceae)

§ **caerulescens**	NBir NBro SIng WOut
perennis	CArn NMir NSco
- 'Alba Plena' (d)	ECho
- 'Blue Moon'	WCHb
- 'Dresden China'	ECho EWes GAbr MTho WOut
- Hen and Chickens	see *B. perennis* 'Prolifera'
- 'Miss Mason'	GAbr WOut
- 'Parkinson's Great White'	GAbr
§ - 'Prolifera' (d)	WHer
- 'Red Alert' **new**	WOut
- 'Red Buttons'	NBlu
- 'Robert'	GAbr
- 'Rosella' **new**	WRHF
- 'Rusher Rose'	EPfP
- 'Single Blue'	see *B. caerulescens*
- 'Tasso Strawberries and Cream'	WRHF
rotundifolia 'Caerulescens'	see *B. caerulescens*
sylvestris	CArn

Bellium (Asteraceae)

* **crassifolium canescens**	WPer
minutum	MTho

Beloperone see *Justicia*

Bensoniella (Saxifragaceae)

oregona	EMon

Berberidopsis (Flacourtiaceae)

beckleri	CPIN WPGP
corallina	More than 30 suppliers

Berberis ✿ (Berberidaceae)

CC 4041	CPLG
CC 4730	CPLG
CC 4732	CPLG MGol

SDR 3256	GKev
aetnensis	GIBF
aggregata	NBir SRms WDin
amurensis var. **latifolia** B&SWJ 4353	WCru
aquifolium	see *Mahonia aquifolium*
- 'Fascicularis'	see *Mahonia* x *wagneri* 'Pinnacle'
aristata Parker	see *B. glaucocarpa*
N **aristata** ambig.	CAgr CArn CMCN
asiatica	CAgr CPLG GPoy
bealei	see *Mahonia japonica* Bealei Group
'Blenheim'	WFar
'Boughton Red'	MBri
brevipedunculata Bean	see *B. prattii*
x **bristolensis**	EPla SLon SPla SRms
buxifolia	LEdu MRav WCFE
- 'Nana' hort.	see *B. buxifolia* 'Pygmaea'
N - 'Pygmaea'	CAbP CBcs CDul CSBt EBee LAst MBNS MBar MGos MRav NEgg NHol SPer WDin WFar
calliantha	WFar
candidula C.K. Schneid.	EBee ECrN EPfP MBar MGan MRav MSwo NHol SLon SPer WDin
- 'Jytte'	see *B.* 'Jytte'
x **carminea** 'Barbarossa'	WDin
- 'Buccaneer'	EPfP
- 'Pirate King'	CSBt EBee MRav SWvt WPat
chingii new	CPle
chrysosphaera	WFar
coxii	GBin GGar
darwinii ♀H4	More than 30 suppliers
I - 'Compacta'	SPoG
darwinii x **valdiviana new**	CDul
dictyophylla ♀H4	CPMA EPfP MGos NLar SLon SPer SPoG SSpi WDin WPat WSHC
dulcis 'Nana'	see *B. buxifolia* 'Pygmaea'
franchetiana var. **macrobotrys**	GIBF
x **frikartii** 'Amstelveen' ♀H4	CDoC CSBt CSam EBee ELan EPfP LAst MBNS MRav NHol NLar WDin WFar
- 'Telstar'	ECrN LAst LBuc MGos MRav NPro
gagnepainii misapplied	see *B. gagnepainii* var. *lanceifolia*
gagnepainii C.K. Schneid.	CMac LRav MGan MRav NHol SLPl WTel
§ - var. **lanceifolia**	CBcs CTri EBee ECrN EPla MBar MDun MGos MWhi NEgg NHol NWea SLim WDin WFar
- - 'Fernspray'	EPfP EPla MRav SBod SRms
- 'Purpurea'	see *B.* x *interposita* 'Wallich's Purple'
'Georgei' ♀H4	CMHG CWib EPfP GQui LRHS SMur SPoG SSpi
§ **glaucocarpa**	EPfP EPla NHol
'Goldilocks'	CAbP CDul CPMA CPSs EPfP LAst MBlu SPoG WGer
x **hybridogagnepainii** 'Chenaultii'	CBcs ELan SPer
hypokerina	CMac
insignis	WFar
- subsp. **insignis** var. **insignis**	WFar
- - B&SWJ 2432	WCru
§ x **interposita** 'Wallich's Purple'	CCVT ECrN EPfP MBar MDun MRav MSwo NHol SPer WDin
julianae ♀H4	More than 30 suppliers
- 'Mary Poppins'	EBee
§ 'Jytte'	EBee MWhi WDin
kawakamii	SLPl
koreana	CMCN EPfP GIBF NLar
lempergiana	CMCN
lepidifolia	GBin
linearifolia	CMac
- 'Jewel'	SBrw

- 'Orange King'	CBcs CDoC CMac EBee ELan EPfP LRHS MAsh MGan MGos NHol SCoo SHBN SPer SPoG WDin WFar WHar WPat
'Little Favourite'	see *B. thunbergii* f. *atropurpurea* 'Atropurpurea Nana'
x *lologensis*	MGos NHol WDin
- 'Apricot Queen' ♀H4	CBcs CMac EBee EPfP LRHS MAsh MGos MRav NBea NBlu NLar SCoo SHBN SPer SPoG WDin
- 'Mystery Fire'	CDoC COtt LRHS MAsh MBlu MBri MDun MGos NBlu NEgg NLar SBrw SCoo SPoG SWvt WDin WFar WHar
- 'Stapehill'	ELan EPfP LRHS MAsh MBri NHol SPoG
macrosepala var. *macrosepala* B&SWJ 2124	WCru
x *media* Park Jewel	see *B.* x *media* 'Parkjuweel'
§ - 'Parkjuweel'	CBcs EBee IArd MRav NLar SCoo WDin WFar
- 'Red Jewel' ♀H4	CDoC CMac CSBt EBee EPfP LRHS MGos MWat NHol NScw SCoo SPer SPoG WCFE WDin WFar WMoo
mitifolia	NLar
montana	WPat
morrisonicola	GIBF
aff. *nepalensis*	GIBF
x *ottawensis*	MWhi
- 'Auricoma'	MRav
- f. *purpurea*	CWib EBee MGos SBod WDin WFar WHar
§ - - 'Superba' ♀H4	More than 30 suppliers
§ - 'Silver Miles' (v)	EHoe MRav NHol SPoG WFar WPat
§ *panlanensis*	MBar MRav SLon
poiretii	CPLG NBhm NLar WHrl
polyantha misapplied	see *B. prattii*
§ *prattii*	GIBF
pruinosa	CDul
'Red Tears'	CPMA CSam LRHS MBlu MBri MGos MLan MRav NLar SPer WHCG WMoo
replicata	CPle
x *rubrostilla* 'Wisley'	EPfP LRHS
sanguinea misapplied	see *B. panlanensis*
sargentiana	NFor SLPl
sherriffii	WCwm
sieboldii	LTwo WPat
souliecana **new**	MGan
x *stenophylla* Lindl. ♀H4	CBcs CDoC CSBt CTri EBee ECrN ENot EPfP GGar ISea LBuc LRHS MBar MBri MLan MRav NEgg NHol NWea SMer SPer SPoG WCFE WDin WFar WHar WMoo WTel
- 'Claret Cascade'	EBee LRHS MBri MGos NHol NLar SPer SPoG WFar
- 'Corallina Compacta' ♀H4	CFee CLyd ECho ELan EPfP EPot LHop LRHS MAsh NHol NRya SPer SPoG SRms WAbe WPat
- 'Cornish Cream'	see *B.* x *stenophylla* 'Lemon Queen'
- 'Crawley Gem'	CMHG GBin MBar MGos NHol NLar WFar
- Cream Showers	see *B.* x *stenophylla* 'Lemon Queen'
- 'Etna'	ELan LRHS MAsh SPoG
- 'Irwinii'	CMac CTri LAst MBar MGos MSwo NHol SLon SPer WFar WMoo WTel
N - 'Lemon Queen'	WTel
- 'Nana'	SRms WAbe
- 'Pink Pearl' (v)	CMHG MGos
temolaica ♀H4	CPMA CPLG LRHS MDun MGos NEgg NLar NPen NSti SDnm SPer SPoG SSpi SSta WDin WPGP WPat
thunbergii ♀H4	CBcs CDoC CDul CSBt ENot GBin LBuc MRav NEgg NWea SCoo SMer SPer SPlb SPoG WDin WFar
- f. *atropurpurea*	CBcs CCVT CDul CSBt CTri EBee ENot EPfP EWTr ISea LAst LBuc MAsh MBar MGan MGos MNHC MSwo NBlu NEgg NFor NWea SCoo SMer SPer SPoG WBVN WDin WFar WMoo
- - 'Admiration' **new**	EPfP MAsh MBri SPer SPoG
§ - - 'Atropurpurea Nana' ♀H4	More than 30 suppliers
- - 'Bagatelle' ♀H4	CDoC COtt EBee ELan EMil ENot EPfP EPot IArd LAst LHop LRHS LSRN MAsh MBar MBri MGos MLHP MRav NEgg SLim SPer SPoG SWvt WAbe WCFE WDin WFar WPat WWeb
- - 'Carmen'	MGos
- - 'Dart's Purple'	LRHS WFar
- - 'Dart's Red Lady'	CPLG CPMA CSBt CWib EBee ECrN ELan ENot EPfP LRHS MAsh MBri MRav NPro SCoo SLim SPoG SWvt WDin WFar WPat
- - 'Golden Ring' ♀H4	More than 30 suppliers
- - 'Harlequin' (v)	CBcs CDoC CSBt EBee EHoe ELan EMil EPfP LRHS LSRN MAsh MBri MGos MRav NEgg SLim SPer SPla SPoG WBVN WDin WFar WHar WPat WWeb
- - 'Helmond Pillar'	CDul CSBt CWib EBee EHoe ELan EMil ENot EPfP LAst LRHS MAsh MBar MBlu MBri MGos MRav NBlu NEgg SLim SMad SPer SPoG SWvt WCFE WDin WFar WPat
- - 'Red Chief' ♀H4	CBcs CMHG EBee ECrN EGra ELan EPfP LRHS MAsh MGos MRav NEgg SLim SLon SPer SPla SPoG SWvt WDin WFar WHCG WHar WMoo WPat WTel WWeb
- - 'Red King'	MRav WDin
- - 'Red Pillar'	CDoC EBee EHoe ELan LAst LRHS MAsh MBar MGos MWat NHol SHBN SPla SPoG WDin WFar WPat
- - 'Red Rocket'	EMil MBri MCCP NLar
- - 'Rose Glow' (v) ♀H4	More than 30 suppliers
- 'Atropurpurea Superba'	see *B.* x *ottawensis* f. *purpurea* 'Superba'
- 'Aurea'	More than 30 suppliers
- Bonanza Gold = 'Bogozam'PBR	CAbP CDoC EBee ELan EPfP LRHS MAsh MRav NLar SLim SMur SPer SPoG WDin WFar WPat
- 'Carpetbagger'	LBuc WHar
- 'Coronita'	MBri
- 'Crimson Pygmy'	see *B. thunbergii* f. *atropurpurea* 'Atropurpurea Nana'
- 'Erecta'	CMac EPfP MBar MGos MRav SPer WCFE WDin
- 'Golden Torch'	CSBt EBee LSRN MBri SPoG SWvt WWeb
- 'Green Carpet'	EBee LHop LRHS MBar NLar SPoG WFar
- 'Green Mantle'	see *B. thunbergii* 'Kelleriis'
- 'Green Marble'	see *B. thunbergii* 'Kelleriis'
- 'Green Ornament'	NHol
§ - 'J.N. Variegated' **new**	SPer
§ - 'Kelleriis' (v)	CDoC EGra EPfP LHop MBar MGos NHol NLar NPro SLon SPoG WDin WFar WRHF
- 'Kobold'	EBee EPfP LHop LRHS MAsh MBar MGos NHol NLar SLim SPer SPla SPoG WFar
- 'Pink Queen' (v)	CDul EBee ENot EPfP MAsh SPur WDin WFar WHar WPat
- 'Pow-wow'	CBcs EBee MGos NLar SPoG WDin

- 'Silver Beauty' (v)	CBcs CMHG EBee ELan MGos WDin
- 'Silver Carpet'	NLar
- 'Silver Mile'	see *B.* x *ottawensis* 'Silver Miles'
- 'Somerset'	CMac
- 'Starburst' **new**	CBcs EPfP MAsh MBri SPoG
- Stardust	see *B. thunbergii* 'J.N. Variegated'
* - 'Tricolor' (v)	CMac EHoe MRav NHol WFar WPat
tischleri var. *abbreviata*	GIBF
tsangpoensis	SLPl
valdiviana	CPMA EBee EPfP SMad SSpi WPGP
verruculosa ♀H4	CBcs CTri EBee EPfP LAst LHop MBar MGan MGos MRav NHol NWea SCoo SGar SPer SRms WCFE WDin WFar
- 'Hard's Rob'	NLar
virescens B&SWJ 2646D	WCru
vulgaris	CArn CNat GPoy
- 'Wiltshire Wonder' (v)	CNat
wilsoniae	CAgr CBcs CDul CTri EBee EPfP EPla LHop MBar NEgg NHol NWea SCoo SHBN SPer WCFE WDin WFar
- ACE 2462	EHyt
- L 650	WPGP
- blue	LRHS WFar WGer
- 'Graciella'	NPro
- var. *guhtzunica*	EPla EWes

Berchemia (Rhamnaceae)

polyphylla	CPlN
racemosa	CPlN NLar SBra WSHC
scandens	CPlN

bergamot see *Citrus bergamia*

Bergenia ✿ (Saxifragaceae)

'Abendglocken'	EBee ECGP ECha ECtt EGle EPfP LRHS MBri MNFA MWat NGdn NHol NSti SPla SWat WCot WEas WFar
§ 'Abendglut'	More than 30 suppliers
'Admiral'	CBct ECha MLHP
* *agavifolia*	CBct
'Apple Court White'	CBct
'Autumn Magic'	CBct COIW GAbr LAst LSou MSte NPri SPoG WHlf
'Baby Doll'	More than 30 suppliers
§ 'Ballawley' clonal ♀H4	CFir ECha GCal IBlr IGor MLHP MRav NEgg SWat WCAu WCot WFar
'Ballawley Guardsman'	CBct EBee EHrv ERou
§ Ballawley hybrids	EBee SDix SPer SWat
'Ballawley' seed-raised	see *B.* Ballawley hybrids
beesiana	see *B. purpurascens*
'Beethoven'	CBct CDes CLAP EBee ECha EGle EPla IGor MRav NBir NBre SUsu SWat WCot WPGP WSHC
Bell Tower	see *B.* 'Glockenturm'
'Bizet'	CBct
'Borodin'	CBct
'Brahms'	CBct GBuc
'Bressingham Beauty' **new**	EBrs
'Bressingham Bountiful'	CBct SPer WCot
'Bressingham Ruby'PBR	CBcs CBct CLAP COIW CRez EBee EBrs ECha ECtt EPPr LRHS MRav NBir NCGa NEgg NHol SHBN SWat WCAu WCot WPGP
'Bressingham Salmon'	CBct CHar EBee EBrs ELan ENot EPfP ERou GMaP GSki LRHS MBri MRav NLar SHBN WCot WMnd
'Bressingham White' ♀H4	More than 30 suppliers
ciliata	CDes CFee CHEx CLAP EBee EChP EShb GCal IFro LEdu MLHP MRav MSte NBir NHol NLar SDix SUsu
	WCot WEas WKif WLin WPGP WSHC
- f. *ciliata*	CBct WCot
- f. *ligulata*	see *B. pacumbis*
- 'Patricia Furness'	CLAP GCrs NBir
- 'Wilton'	CLAP WCot
ciliata x *crassifolia*	see *B.* x *schmidtii*
'Claire Maxine'	GCal
cordifolia	More than 30 suppliers
- 'Flore Pleno'	CBct
- 'Jelle' **new**	GBin
- 'Purpurea' ♀H4	CBcs CDoC COfd CSBt EAEE EBee ECha ELan EMFW ENot EPfP GSki IHMH LBuc LRHS MLHP MNFA MRav NBir SHBN SPer SPla SRms SWat WCAu WFar WPnP
- 'Rosa Schwester'	EBee
- 'Rosa Zeiten'	GBin
- 'Tubby Andrews' (v)	CBct CBow EBla EGle EMon IFro MBrN MBri MCCP MLLN NEgg NLar NPro WCMO
- 'Winterglut'	EBee EBrs GMaP IBal IFoB ITim NBre SWvt WBor WHil WPnP
crassifolia	EBee NBre SRms
- DF 90028	EMon
- 'Autumn Red'	CBct ECha
- 'Orbicularis'	see *B.* x *schmidtii*
* *cyanea*	CLAP WCot
'David'	EMon EWes
delavayi	see *B. purpurascens* var. *delavayi*
'Delbees'	see *Bergenia* 'Ballawley' clonal
'Doppelgänger'	EBee SUsu
'Eden's Dark Margin'	CBct CBgR EBee ERou LAst LHop NGdn
'Eden's Magic Carpet'	CFir
'Eden's Magic Giant'	CBct EBee EChP ERou EWTr GBin MAvo
emeiensis	CDes CLAP WCMO WCot
- hybrid	CBct MWat
'Eric Smith'	CBct EBee ECha EPla GCal IGor MBri WCMO WCot
'Eroica'	CBct EBrs EChP ECha ELan EMon GBin MBri MRav NBre NRnb NSti SHar SWat WCAu WCMO WMnd
'Evening Glow'	see *B.* 'Abendglut'
'Frau Holle'	MBri
§ 'Glockenturm'	CBct GCal NEgg
'Hellen Dillon'	see *B. purpurascens* 'Irish Crimson'
'Herbstblute'	EMon
'Jo Watanabe'	CBct MRav
'Lambrook'	see *B.* 'Margery Fish'
§ 'Margery Fish'	CBct EBee SPer
milesii	see *B. stracheyi*
§ 'Morgenröte' ♀H4	CBcs CBct CPrp EBee EBrs ECha EMil EPfP GMaP IHMH LAst LRHS MBNS MGos MRav NHol NSti SHBN SPer SRms SSvw SWat SWvt WCMO WCot
'Morning Light'	LAst NPro NSti
Morning Red	see *B.* 'Morgenröte'
'Mrs Crawford'	CBct ECha
'Oeschberg'	CBct GCal WCAu
'Opal'	CBct
'Overture'	CBct EBee EHrv GAbr GEdr LAst LDai MBri MNFA MWat MWgw NCGa NCob NEgg NGby NGdn SUsu WCAu WCMO WCot WFar WWFP
§ *pacumbis*	CBct CHEx CLAP EBee GBin GEdr LEdu NBid NBir NBre NSti SDix WCot
- B&SWJ 2693	WCru
- CC 1793	SBch
- CC 3616	ITim MSph WCot
'Perfect'	CBct WMnd

'Pink Dragonfly'	EBee GBin LHop NBhm NEgg
	SMac SPoG
'Profusion'	SPer WCAu
'Pugsley's Pink'	CBct SHBN
'Purple Queen' **new**	EBrs
§ **purpurascens** ♀H4	CMac EBee EBrs GBuc GCrs GMaP
	GSki IFoB IGor SDix SPer SPoG
	WCot
- ACE 2175	WCot
§ - var. **delavayi** ♀H4	MBri NBre SRms WPnP
- - CLD 1366	WPer
- 'Irish Crimson'	CBct SBla WCot
aff. **purpurascens**	SMad
- ACE 2175	WCot
'Purpurglocken'	GCal
'Red Beauty'	MBow MGos NEgg NPen SPoG
'Reitheim'	CBct EBee
'Rosi Klose'	More than 30 suppliers
'Rotblum'	CBct CBrm EBee ECGP ECtt EPfP
	GMaP GSki GWCH MAvo MDun
	NBir NCob NGdn NOrc NRnb
	NVic WFar WPer WWeb
§ x **schmidtii** ♀H4	CBct CMac EBee ENot IGor NBir
	NBre SDix WCot
'Schneekissen'	CBct EBee ECGP EGle LAst MNFA
	MRav SWat WCAu
§ 'Schneekönigin'	CBct ECha MRav
§ 'Silberlicht' ♀H4	More than 30 suppliers
Silverlight	see *B.* 'Silberlicht'
'Simply Sweet'	WCot
Snow Queen	see *B.* 'Schneekönigin'
§ **stracheyi**	CBct CPLG ECha EGle EGoo EMon
	IGor MLHP MRav NBid NLar SDix
	WCMO WCot WEas
- Alba Group	CBct CDes ECha EPfP GCal MSte
	WPGP WSHC
'Sunningdale'	CBcs CBct EBee ECha ELan EMFW
	EPfP EWTr GMaP GSki LRHS
	MLLN MRav NBir SPer SWat SWvt
	WCAu WMnd
tianquanensis new	EBee
Winter Fairy Tales	see *B.* 'Wintermärchen'
§ 'Wintermärchen'	CBct CRez EBee ECha ELan EPfP
	GSki LRHS MGos MRav MSte
	NCGa NOrc NPro NSti SPoG SWat
	WCot WMnd

Bergeranthus (Aizoaceae)

sp.	WThu
glenensis	EDAr
multiceps	SChr

Berkheya (Asteraceae)

macrocephala	WCot
multijuga	WCot
purpurea	CBcs CBct CCVN CElw CPLG
	EBee EMan GBri GGar GKev IGor
	LSou MAvo MBNS MDKP MWea
	SBch SPlb SPoG STes SUsu SWal
	WBor WCMO WCot WGwG WRos
	WSHC WWlt WWye
- 'Silver Spike' **new**	LBmB MBri WHlf
- 'Zulu Warrior' **new**	EKen

Berlandiera (Asteraceae)

lyrata	CBrm EMan GCal NJOw
- 'Chocolate Drop' **new**	EBrs

Berneuxia (Diapensiaceae)

thibetica	IBlr

Berula (Apiaceae)

erecta	EHon EMFW NPer WWpP

Berzelia (Bruniaceae)

galpinii	SPlb

lanuginosa	CPLG CSec CTrC GGar IDee

Beschorneria (Agavaceae)

septentrionalis	CAbP CFir CSpe CTrC EAmu EBee
	GAbr MBNS WCMO WCot WPGP
septentrionalis x **yuccoides new**	WPGP
tubiflora	CHEx EBee LEdu
wrightii	WPGP
yuccoides ♀H3	CAbb CBcs CHEx CPne CTrC
	EAmu EBee EShb IBlr IDee ISea
	LEdu MSte SAPC SArc SChr SDnm
	SLim SLon SMur WKif WMul WPGP
	XPep
- 'Quicksilver'	CBcs CBod CCCN CDoC CEnd
	CKno CTbh CTrC EBee EMan
	MDun MSte NVic SDnm SPoG SSpi
	WCMO WCot WGer WPGP

Bessera (Alliaceae)

elegans	CFir EBee EBrs ECho EPot LRHS
	WCMO WCot

Beta (Chenopodiaceae)

trigyna	WCot
vulgaris	EWin WHer
- 'Bull's Blood'	CArn CSpe EMan EWin MSte WCot
	WJek
- subsp. **cicla** var. **flavescens** 'Bright Lights' ♀H3	CArn
- - - 'Rhubarb Chard' ♀H3	WJek
- subsp. **maritima**	CAgr

Betonica see *Stachys*

Betula ✿ (Betulaceae)

Sich 543	GIBF
alba L.	see *B. pendula*, *B. pubescens*
albosinensis misapplied	see *B. utilis*
albosinensis Burkill ♀H4	CCVT CDul CMCN CTho CTri
	EBee EPfP GIBF LRHS MDun NLar
	NWea SBLw SPer WCwm WDin
	WFar WNor WOrn
- W 4106	CSto
- 'Bowling Green'	CPMA CTho WPGP
- 'China Ruby'	CDul CLnd CPMA MBri SIFN
- 'Chinese Garden'	CPMA CTho MBlu
- clone F	see *B. albosinensis* 'Ness'
- 'K. Ashburner'	CPMA CTho
- 'Kansu'	CLnd CPMA SBir SIFN
§ - 'Ness'	CPMA CTho
- 'Sable' **new**	SPer
- var. **septentrionalis** ♀H4	More than 30 suppliers
- - 'Purdom'	CPMA SIFN
§ **alleghaniensis**	CDul CMCN EBee EPfP IDee NLar
	NWea SPoG WDin
alnoides	GIBF WNor
apoiensis	GIBF WNor
- 'Mount Apoi'	CPMA SIFN
austrosinensis	WNor
borealis	see *B. pumila*
§ x **caerulea**	CDul CPMA CTho NLar
caerulea-grandis	see *B.* x *caerulea*
chichibuensis	GIBF SBir WHer
chinensis	CMCN GIBF WNor
'Conyngham'	CTho MBlu SBir
costata misapplied	see *B. ermanii* 'Grayswood Hill'
costata Trautv.	CLnd CTho EBee ELan EPfP GTSp
	MSwo SBLw WDin WOrn
* - 'Fincham Cream'	ERea SIFN WHCr
I x **cruithnei**	GIBF
dahurica Pall.	CMCN IArd WNor
- B&SWJ 4247	WHCr
- 'Maurice Foster'	CPMA CTho

- 'Stone Farm'	CPMA
divaricata	GIBF
ermanii	CBcs CCVT CDoC CDul CLnd
	CMCN CMHG CSBt CSam CTho
	CTri EBee ECrN ELan EPfP GQui
	LPan LRHS MAsh MBlu MGos
	MRav NBea NEgg NWea SBLw
	WDin WFar WMoo WNor
- from Hokkaido, Japan	CSto
- from Kamchatka	GIBF
- 'Blush'	EWTr MAsh SHBN WHCr
- var. *ermanii* MSF 865	WPGP
§ - 'Grayswood Hill' ♀H4	CDul CEnd CMHG CPMA CTho
	EBee GQui LRHS MBri MGos
	NWea SCoo SHBN SIFN SLim SMad
	SPer SPoG SSpi WHCr WOrn
- 'Hakkoda Orange'	CPMA CTho MBlu MBri SCoo
* - 'Pendula'	CPMA SCoo SIFN
- 'Polar Bear'	CPMA CWSG LRHS MBri SIFN
	SMad WHCr
* - *ussuriensis*	GIBF
'Fetisowii'	CEnd CLnd CMCN CTho IMGH
	LRHS MBlu MBri SCoo SIFN SLim
	SSpi SSta
fruticosa	see B. humilis
glandulifera	see B. pumila
globispica	EWTr GIBF SBir WCwm WNor
gmelinii	see B. ovalifolia
grossa	CMCN GIBF IDee
'Hergest'	EBee EPfP LRHS MAsh MBri MGos
	SCoo SLim SPoG WHCr WPGP
§ *humilis*	CMCN GIBF GQui WDin
- B&SWJ 8801	WCru
insignis	GIBF
'Inverleith'	see B. utilis var. jacquemontii
	'Inverleith'
jacquemontii	see B. utilis var. jacquemontii
kamtschatica	see B. humilis
§ *kenaica*	CTho
lenta	CLnd CMCN CSto CTho EPfP IArd
	NLar NWea WDin
luminifera	CMCN CPMA IDee NLar SIFN
lutea	see B. alleghaniensis
mandshurica	GIBF GQui WHCr
§ - var. *japonica*	CLnd EWes GBin GIBF NEgg NLar
	NPal WNor
- - 'Whitespire'	CWSG
- - 'Whitespire Senior'	CDul
maximowicziana	CBcs CDoC CLnd CMCN CTho
	CWib EPfP EWTr GIBF IArd LHop
	MDun NEgg WDin WNor
§ *medwedewii*	CDul CLnd CMCN EBee ECrN
	EPfP EPla EWTr GEdr GIBF GQui
	IArd NEgg NWea SBir SCoo
- from Winkworth	CTho
- 'Gold Bark'	CDoC MBlu
megrelica	see B. medwedewii
x *minor*	GIBF
nana	CDul EBee GIBF MBar NHol NSla
	SRms SSta STre WDin
- 'Glengarry'	EPot GBin NLar
§ *neoalaskana*	WNor
nigra	CBcs CCVT CDoC CDul CEnd
	CLnd CMCN CSBt CTho CTri
	ECrN LPan MAsh NEgg SBLw SBir
	SHBN SSta WDin WGer WMou
	WNor WOrn
- 'Heritage' ♀H4	CDoC CDul CEnd CLnd CMCN
	CPMA CTho EBee ECrN LPan
	LRHS MBlu MRav SBir SCoo SIFN
	SLim SSta WDin WFar WMoo WOrn
- 'Little King'	CPMA
- Wakehurst form	EPfP LRHS SPer SPoG
§ *ovalifolia*	GIBF IArd
papyrifera	More than 30 suppliers
- var. *commutata*	EWTr WDin
- subsp. *humilis*	see B. neoalaskana
- var. *kenaica*	see B. kenaica
- 'Saint George'	CPMA CTho
- 'Vancouver'	CPMA CTho
§ *pendula* ♀H4	More than 30 suppliers
- var. *aurea*	GIBF
- 'Bangor'	CLnd CPMA SIFN
* - 'Boeugh's Variety'	CEnd GBin
- f. *crispa*	see B. pendula 'Laciniata'
- 'Dalecarlica' misapplied	see B. pendula 'Laciniata'
- 'Dalecarlica' ambig.	CBcs CCVT CSBt ECrN ENot GTSp
	MDun MRav SCrf SLim WFar
- 'Dark Prince' new	CPMA
- 'Fastigiata'	CDoC CDul CLnd CSBt CTho EBee
	ECrN ELan LPan MGos NWea
	SBLw SCoo SLim SPer WDin WFar
	WMoo WOrn
- var. *fontqueri*	GIBF
* - 'Golden Beauty'	CDoC CTri LPan LRHS MAsh
	MGos NLar SCoo SLim SPer SPoG
	WDin WHCr WOrn
§ - 'Laciniata' ♀H4	CDoC CDul CLnd CMCN CTho
	CTri CWSG CWib EBee ECrN ELan
	EPfP LAst LPan MAsh MGos MRav
	MSwo NBea NBee NLar NWea
	SBLw SPer SSta WDin WMou
	WWes
- 'Long Trunk'	CDul EBee LPan
- 'Purpurea'	CBrm CCVT CDul CLnd CMCN
	CSBt CWib EBee ECrN ELan EPfP
	EWTr LAst LPan LRHS LSRN MDun
	MGos MSwo NBea NBlu NEgg
	SBLw SCoo SIFN SPer WDin WFar
	WOrn
- 'Silver Cascade'	MGos
- 'Silver Grace'	ENot MGos
- 'Tristis' ♀H4	More than 30 suppliers
- 'Youngii'	More than 30 suppliers
platyphylla Sukaczev	CMCN NWea
- var. *japonica*	see B. mandshurica var. japonica
- var. *kamtschatica*	see B. mandshurica var. japonica
- subsp. *platyphylla*	CMCN GIBF
populifolia	CSto
potaninii	GIBF
§ *pubescens*	CCVT CDul CLnd CSto CTri ECrN
	EMil NBee NWea SBLw SLPl WDin
	WFar WMou
- subsp. *carpatica*	see B. pubescens var. glabrata
- - var. *murithii*	see B. pubescens var. glabrata
§ - var. *glabrata*	GIBF
§ *pumila*	GGar GIBF WCwm
raddeana	GIBF WNor
I *refugia*	GIBF
resinifera Britton	see B. neoalaskana
'Royal Frost'	CPMA
schmidtii	CMCN EWTr GIBF IArd WCwm
szechuanica	CLnd GQui WDin WPGP
- 'Liuba White'	CPMA CTho
tianschanica	GIBF MDun WNor
'Trost's Dwarf'	WDin
§ *utilis*	CDul CMCN CMHG CSBt CSto
	EBee ECrN EMil ISea MAsh MBar
	MRav NBee NWea SSta WDin WFar
	WNor WPGP
- BL&M 100	CTho
- F 19505	CTho
- McB 1257	CTho
- RSC 1 from Langtang, Nepal new	CSto
- Sch 2168	MBri
- from Eastern Nepal new	CSto
- 'Fascination'	CCVT CDul CPMA EMil LPan LRHS
	MBri MGos NWea SBir SCoo SIFN
	SLim SMad SSpi WHCr
* - 'Fastigiata'	CLnd CPMA SIFN
- 'Forrest's Blush'	CDul EBee MBri SBir SIFN WGer

N - var. *jacquemontii*   More than 30 suppliers
 - - SF 00004   ISea
 - - 'Doorenbos' ♀H4   CLnd CMCN CPMA CTho EBee
       LPan MBlu MGos NEgg SIFN SPoG
       SSta WDin WOrn
 - - 'Grayswood Ghost'   CDul CEnd CLnd CMCN CMHG
   ♀H4   CPMA CTho ECrN ENot EPfP LPan
       LRHS MDun SBir SHBN SIFN SMad
       SSpi
§ - - 'Inverleith'   CDul CEnd CPMA EBee MBri
       MDun MWya SBir SCoo SIFN SLim
       WFar WOrn WPGP
 - - 'Jermyns' ♀H4   CDul CEnd CLnd CMCN CPMA
       CTho ECot EPfP LPan LRHS MBlu
       MBri SCoo SIFN SMad SPoG SSpi
       WHCr WOrn
 - - 'Silver Shadow' ♀H4   CLnd CMCN CPMA CTho EPfP
       LRHS MAsh MBlu NWea SCoo
       SHBN SIFN SLim SPer SPoG SSpi
       SSta WOrn
 - - 'Snowqueen'   CCVT CDul CEnd CLnd CMCN
       COtt CPMA CSBt CWSG EMui
       EPfP LPan LRHS LSRN MAsh MBri
       MDun MGos NWea SCoo SIFN
       SLim SPoG WBVN WHCr WOrn
 - - 'Trinity College'   CLnd CMCN CPMA EBee MBri SBir
       SIFN SSpi
 - 'Knightshayes'   CTho
 - 'Moonbeam'   CLnd CMCN CPMA MBri SCoo
       SIFN SSpi WGer WHCr
 - var. *occidentalis*   CPMA CTho
     'Kyelang'
 - var. *prattii*   CEnd CTho MDun
 - 'Ramdana River'   CTho MBlu
 - 'Thyangboche   MDun
     Monastery'
 - 'Wakehurst Place   CDul CPMA CWSG LRHS MAsh
     Chocolate'   MBri SCoo SIFN SMad SSpi WHCr
 cf. *utilis* GWJ 9259   WCru
 - HWJK 2345   WCru
 verrucosa   see *B. pendula*

Biarum (Araceae)

 SBLBL 597 **new**   WCot
 arundanum PB 154   CMon
   from Portugal
 carratracense   WCot
 - SF 233 from Spain   CMon
 davisii   CStu ECho EHyt GCrs WCot
 - subsp. *marmarisense*   CMon
 dispar   WCot
 ditschianum PB 289   CMon
   from Turkey
 ochridense   WCot
 tenuifolium   ECho ERos WCot
 - AB&S 4356   GCrs
 - subsp. *abbreviatum*   CMon
   from Greece
 - PB 357 from Minorca   CMon
 - subsp. *idomenaeum*   CMon
   from Crete
 - subsp. *zelebori*   CMon WCot
   LB 300 **new**
 - - MS&CL 223   CMon

Bidens (Asteraceae)

 atrosanguinea   see *Cosmos atrosanguineus*
§ *aurea*   EBee EBla ECtt EMon EPPr EWes
       GCal LAst LIck LRHS MDKP MNrw
       MOak NCGa NPer SBla SGar SPet
       STes WBor WFar WOld WWye
 - B&SWJ 9049 from   WCru
   Guatemala
 - 'All Gold' **new**   EBee
 - cream-flowered   MNrw MSte
 - 'Golden Drop' **new**   EWes

 - 'Hannay's Lemon Drop'   CFwr CHea CKno CMea CPen
       CSev EBee EBla ECtt GBri LHop
       MBnl MDKP MNrw MSph MSte
       NCGa SPoG STes SUsu WHrl
       WMoo WPGP
 - 'Rising Sun' **new**   EBee EWes
 - 'Super Nova' **new**   EWes
 ferulifolia ♀H1+3   ECtt NPer
 - Solaire = 'Bidtis 1' **new**   WGor
 - Solaire Yellow =   NBlu
   'Bidcomtis' **new**
 'Golden Star' **new**   LAst
 heterophylla Ortega   see *B. aurea*
 heterophylla misapplied.   CHad CKno ECtt EGra MRav SCoo
       SPoG WFar WHal WHrl WMoo
       WPrP WWlt
 humilis   see *B. triplinervia* var. *macrantha*
 integrifolia   EChP SMad
 Peter's Gold Carpet   SPoG
   = 'Goldteppich'
 Peter's Gold Rush   LSou NPri
   = 'Topteppich'
 pilosa   EBee
§ *triplinervia* var.   EBee LHop
   macrantha

Bignonia (Bignoniaceae)

 capreolata   CPlN WCot WSHC XPep
§ - 'Atrosanguinea'   CPlN LRHS MAsh
 - 'Dragon Lady'   WCot
 lindleyana   see *Clytostoma calystegioides*
 tweedieana   see *Macfadyena unguis-cati*
 unguis-cati   see *Macfadyena unguis-cati*

Bilderdykia see *Fallopia*

Billardiera (Pittosporaceae)

 cymosa   SOWG
 longiflora ♀H3   More than 30 suppliers
 - 'Cherry Berry'   CBcs EBee ECou ELan ERea IArd
       IDee LRHS MAsh MCCP SBra SBrw
       SLim SMur SPer SPoG SWvt WSHC
 - red-berried   GGar
 - white-berried   CBcs CHen EBee ELan EWes GGar
       IDee ITer LRHS SBrw SLim SPoG
 scandens   ECou

Billbergia (Bromeliaceae)

 amoena **new**   EOas
 distachya **new**   EOas
 nutans   CHEx CHal EBak EOHP EOas EShb
       IBlr IDee LEdu MBri NPal SChr
       SRms WGwG WMul XPep
 - var. *schimperiana*   EShb
* - 'Variegata' (v)   CSpe EShb NPal SChr WCMO
       WCot WGwG
 pyramidalis ♀H1   XBlo
I - 'Variegata' (v)   IBlr
 'Santa Barbara' (v)   EOas
 x *windii* ♀H1   CHEx CHal EBak EOas SDEP
       SRms
 zebrina   EOas

Bismarckia (Arecaceae)

 nobilis   EAmu LPal SBig

Bistorta see *Persicaria*

blackberry see *Rubus fruticosus*

blackcurrant see *Ribes nigrum*

Blechnum (Blechnaceae)

 alpinum   see *B. penna-marina* subsp.
       alpinum
 capense   CTrC

chilense ♀H3 — CAby CBcs CDes CHEx CLAP CWil EBee ECha EPfP GGar IBlr NVic SAPC SArc SDix WAbe WCMO WCru WMoo WMul WPGP WPnP

discolor — CBcs CLAP CTrC IDee LPal

- 'Silver Lady' — WMul

fluviatile — CBcs CLAP CTrC IDee WMul

gibbum — EAmu EFtx LRHS MBri WMul

magellanicum misapplied — see *B. chilense*

minus — EFtx

novae-zelandiae — CBcs CTrC WMul

nudum — EAmu EFtx EPfP NMoo

penna-marina ♀H4 — CBgR CCCN CElw CLAP CPLG CWil EFer EMon EPot EShb GAbr GGar GMaP LEdu MBri NRya NVic NWCA SDix SRms SRot WEas WMoo WWye

§ - subsp. **alpinum** — CLAP ECha GGar WAbe WMoo WOut

- 'Cristatum' — CLAP GAbr GGar SRms

spicant ♀H4 — More than 30 suppliers

tabulare misapplied — see *B. chilense*

N **tabulare** (Thunb.) Kuhn ♀H1 — CBcs EFtx WPGP

vulcanicum — CLAP

wattsii — EAmu

Blepharocalyx (Myrtaceae)

cruckshanksii — CPLG LRHS

- 'Heaven Scent' — EBee LAst LRHS MCCP NLar WBor

Blephilia (Lamiaceae)

'Cherokee' — EBee

ciliata — EBee MSal

Bletilla ✿ (Orchidaceae)

Coritani g. — WCMO

hyacinthina — see *B. striata*

ochracea — LEdu NLAp WCot

Penway Dragon g. — NLAp

Penway Paris g. — EMan

Penway Sunset g. — WCMO WCot

§ **striata** — CBct CDes CFwr CHdy CPom EBee EBrs ECho ERea ERos GSki IBlr IHMH LEdu MSal NCGa NHol NLAp NMen SBla SChr SMeo SPer WCMO WFar WPGP WViv

- **alba** — see *B. striata* var. *japonica* f. *gebina*

- 'Albostriata' — CBct CDes EBee EBla ECho ELan EMan IBlr NCGa WCot

- var. **japonica** — EPot

§ - - f. **gebina** — CDes CMea EBee ECho EPot GSki IBlr IHMH LEdu LRHS SBla SChr WCMO WCot WFar WPGP WViv

- - - variegated (v) — EPot LEdu NMen WCMO WCot

- variegated (v) **new** — CBow

- yellow-flowered **new** — EBee

Yokohama g. — EBla

Blighia (Sapindaceae)

sapida new — SDEP

Bloomeria (Alliaceae)

crocea — ECho

- var. **aurea** — ECho ERos LRHS

- var. **montana** — ECho

blueberry see *Vaccinium corymbosum*

Blumenbachia (Loasaceae)

insignia — EUnu

Bocconia (Papaveraceae)

cordata — see *Macleaya cordata* (Willd.) R. Br.

microcarpa — see *Macleaya microcarpa*

Boehmeria (Urticaceae)

nivea — MSal

sylvatica — NLar

Boenninghausenia (Rutaceae)

albiflora — CSpe GKev

- B&SWJ 1479 — WCru

- pink-flowered B&SWJ 3112 — WCru

japonica B&SWJ 4876 — WCru

Boesenbergia (Zingiberaceae)

longiflora — CKob

Bolandra (Saxifragaceae)

aff. **californica new** — EBee

Bolax (Apiaceae)

glebaria — see *B. gummifer*

§ **gummifer** — ECho EPot SBla WAbe

Bolboschoenus (Cyperaceae)

caldwellii — EPPr

§ **maritimus** — CRWN LPBA WFar

Boltonia (Asteraceae)

asteroides — CFee CSam ECtt EHrv EMon GSki LEdu NGdn NSti SPer SWat WBVN WCAu WDyG WRHF

- var. **latisquama** — EBee EPPr GMaP LSou MBrN MRav MSte MWat SSvw WBor WFar WHal WWFP

- - 'Nana' — CBre EGoo MLLN MRav MWgw NBre WPer

- - 'Snowbank' . — EBee EBla EBrs ELan EWTr EWsh

- 'Pink Beauty' — CBre EBla EMon LPhx

- var. **recognita** — EBee EMon LRHS

decurrens — EBee NBre

incisa — see *Kalimeris incisa*

* **richardsonii new** — EBee

Bomarea (Alstroemeriaceae)

acutifolia B&SWJ 9094 — WCru

boliviensis RCB/Arg P-18 — WCot

caldasii ♀H1 — CBcs CDes CFir CHEx CPIN CRHN EBee ERea LSou SBla SOWG WBGC WBor WCMO WPGP WSHC

edulis — ERea

hirtella — CHEx CPIN CRHN EBee EShb WCMO WCot WPGP WSPU

- B&SWJ 9017 — WCru

kalbreyeri — WCMO WCot

multiflora — CFir CPIN EShb WCMO

ovata — ERea

patacocensis — CPle

salsilla — CPIN CRHN GCal SBla WCMO WCot WPGP WSHC

Bongardia (Berberidaceae)

chrysogonum — CAvo EBee EHyt EPot GCrs LRHS WCot

Bonia (Poaceae)

§ **solida** — CBig CHEx EPla ERod LPal MMoz MWht NPal SEND WJun WMul

Boophone (Amaryllidaceae)

disticha — LToo

borage see *Borago officinalis*

Borago (Boraginaceae)

alba — EOHP MNHC WCHb

laxiflora — see *B. pygmaea*

officinalis	CArn CBod CSev CWan EChP ELau EPfP GPoy LRHS MBow MHer MNHC MWat NGHP NPri NVic SBch WCot WGwG WHer WSel WWye
- 'Alba'	CBre CSev EChP ELau ILis MBow MHer NGHP SBch SDnm SIde WCHb WGwG WHer WJek WPer WRha
- 'Bill Archer' (v)	CNat
§ *pygmaea*	CArn CCge CPLG CSev EChP ELan EMar EOHP GBar LHop MHar MHer MTho NGHP NLar NMRc NSti STes SWat WCHb WGwG WMoo

Borinda (Poaceae)

albocerea	EPla ERod MWht WJun
boliana **new**	SBig
edulis	WJun
frigida	EPla WJun
papyrifera	MWht WJun
scabrida	MWht WJun WPGP

Boronia (Rutaceae)

citriodora	SOWG
denticulata	ECou
heterophylla	CBcs CCCN CPLG CSWP ECou IDee SBrw SOWG
- white-flowered	ECou
megastigma	ECou
- 'Brown Meg'	CBcs
mollis	SOWG
pinnata	ECou SOWG
serrulata	ECou

Boschniakia (Scrophulariaceae)

himalaica **new**	GIBF

Bossiaea (Papilionaceae)

aquifolium	LToo

Bothriochloa (Poaceae)

§ *bladhii*	EPPr
caucasica	see *B. bladhii*
§ *ischaemum*	CBig EHoe EMan EPPr LRav WGHP

Botryostege see *Elliottia*

Bougainvillea (Nyctaginaceae)

'Ailsa Lambe'	see *B.* (Spectoperuviana Group) 'Mary Palmer'
'Alexandra'	MBri
'Apple Blossom'	see *B.* 'Elizabeth Doxey'
'Audrey Grey'	see *B.* 'Elizabeth Doxey'
'Aussie Gold'	see *B.* 'Carson's Gold'
'Begum Sikander'	ERea
'Bridal Bouquet'	see *B.* 'Cherry Blossom'
'Brilliance'	ERea LRHS
'Brilliant' misapplied	see *B.* x *buttiana* 'Raspberry Ice'
x *buttiana* 'Ametyst'	MBri
- 'Asia'	ERea
- 'Audrey Grey'	see *B.* 'Elizabeth Doxey'
- 'Barbara Karst'	ERea LPan SOWG
- 'Coconut Ice'	SOWG
- 'Daphne Mason'	ERea
§ - 'Enid Lancaster'	LRHS
- 'Golden Glow'	see *B.* x *buttiana* 'Enid Lancaster'
§ - 'Lady Mary Baring'	ERea SOWG
§ - 'Louise Wathen'	MJnS
§ - 'Mahara' (d)	ERea SOWG
- 'Mahara Double Red'	see *B.* x *buttiana* 'Mahara'
- 'Mahara Off-white'	see *B.* 'Cherry Blossom'
- 'Mahara Pink'	see *B.* 'Los Banos Beauty'
§ - 'Mardi Gras' (v)	ERea

§ - 'Miss Manila'	ERea SOWG
§ - 'Mrs Butt' ♀H1	ERea
§ - 'Poultonii'	ERea
§ - 'Poulton's Special' ♀H1	ERea
§ - 'Rainbow Gold'	ERea
§ - 'Raspberry Ice' (v)	ERea EShb MJnS SOWG
- 'Ratana Red' (v)	ERea
§ - 'Roseville's Delight' (d)	LRHS SOWG
§ - Texas Dawn = 'Monas'	ERea
- 'Tiggy'	ERea
'California Gold'	see *B.* x *buttiana* 'Enid Lancaster'
§ Camarillo Fiesta = 'Monle' (*spectabilis* hybrid)	ERea SOWG
§ 'Carson's Gold' (d)	ERea
§ 'Cherry Blossom'	ERea
§ 'Chiang Mai Beauty'	ERea
§ 'Closeburn'	ERea SOWG
'Crimson Lake' misapplied	see *B.* x *buttiana* 'Mrs Butt'
'Dauphine'	see *B.* 'Los Banos Beauty'
'David Lemmer'	ERea
'Donya'	ERea
'Double Yellow'	see *B.* 'Carson's Gold'
'Durban'	see *B. glabra* 'Jane Snook'
§ 'Elizabeth Angus'	ERea
§ 'Elizabeth Doxey'	ERea SOWG
'Elizabeth' (*spectabilis* hybrid)	ERea
'Enchantment'	see *B.* (Spectoperuviana Group) 'Mary Palmer's Enchantment'
'Flamingo Pink'	see *B.* 'Chiang Mai Beauty'
'Floribunda'	ERea
'Gillian Greensmith'	ERea
glabra ♀H1	CMen ERea MBri XPep
- 'Harrissii' (v)	ERea LRHS
- 'Jane Snook'	ERea
- 'Magnifica'	SOWG
- 'Magnifica Traillii'	ERea
- 'P J Weeping Beauty'	ERea
- 'Peggy Redman' (v)	ERea
- 'Pride of Singapore'	ERea
- 'Sanderiana'	ERea LPan WMul
'Gloucester Royal'	SOWG
'Glowing Flame' (v)	ERea
'Golden Doubloon'	see *B.* x *buttiana* 'Roseville's Delight'
'Golden Glow'	see *B.* x *buttiana* 'Enid Lancaster'
'Golden Tango'	ERea
'Harrissii'	see *B. glabra* 'Harrissii'
'Hawaiian Scarlet'	see *B.* 'San Diego Red'
'Jamaica Orange'	ERea
'James Walker'	ERea
'Jane Snook'	see *B. glabra* 'Jane Snook'
'Kauai Royal'	see *B.* 'Elizabeth Angus'
'Klong Fire'	see *B.* x *buttiana* 'Mahara'
'Lady Mary Baring'	see *B.* x *buttiana* 'Lady Mary Baring'
'Lavender Girl'	ERea
'Limberlost Beauty'	see *B.* 'Cherry Blossom'
'Little Caroline'	SOWG
'Lord Willingdon' misapplied	see *B.* 'Torch Glow'.
§ 'Los Banos Beauty' (d)	ERea
'Magnifica'	see *B. glabra* 'Magnifica'
'Mahara Double Red'	see *B.* x *buttiana* 'Mahara'
'Mahara Off-white'	see *B.* 'Cherry Blossom'
'Mahara Orange'	see *B.* x *buttiana* 'Roseville's Delight'
'Mahara Pink'	see *B.* 'Los Banos Beauty'
'Mahara White'	see *B.* 'Cherry Blossom'
'Manila Magic Red'	see *B.* x *buttiana* 'Mahara'
'Mardi Gras'	see *B.* x *buttiana* 'Mardi Gras'
'Mariel Fitzpatrick'	ERea
'Mary Palmer's Enchantment'	see *B.* (Spectoperuviana Group) 'Mary Palmer's Enchantment'
'Mini-Thai'	see *B.* 'Torch Glow'
'Mrs Butt'	see *B.* x *buttiana* 'Mrs Butt'

Natalii Group	ERea
* 'Orange Flame'	SOWG
'Orange Glow'	see *B.* Camarillo Fiesta = 'Monle'
'Orange King'	see *B.* x *buttiana* 'Louise Wathen'
'Orange Stripe' (v)	ERea
'Pagoda Pink'	see *B.* 'Los Banos Beauty'
'Penelope'	see *B.* (Spectoperuviana Group) 'Mary Palmer's Enchantment'
'Pink Champagne'	see *B.* 'Los Banos Beauty'
'Pixie'	see *B.* 'Torch Glow'
'Poultonii'	see *B.* x *buttiana* 'Poultonii'
'Poultonii Special'	see *B.* x *buttiana* 'Poulton's Special'
'Pride of Singapore'	see *B. glabra* 'Pride of Singapore'
'Princess Mahara'	see *B.* x *buttiana* 'Mahara'
'Purple Robe'	ERea
'Rainbow Gold'	see *B.* x *buttiana* 'Rainbow Gold'
'Raspberry Ice' (v)	see *B.* x *buttiana* 'Raspberry Ice'
'Red Diamond'	ERea
'Red Fantasy' (v)	ERea
'Reggae Gold' (v)	MJnS
'Robyn's Glory'	see *B.* x *buttiana* Texas Dawn = 'Monas'
'Rubyana'	ERea SOWG
§ 'San Diego Red'	ERea SOWG
'Sanderiana'	see *B. glabra* 'Sanderiana'
Scarlett O'Hara	see *B.* 'San Diego Red'
'Smartipants'	see *B.* 'Torch Glow'
'Snow Cap'	see *B.* (Spectoperuviana Group) 'Mary Palmer'
spectabilis 'Speciosa Floribunda'	ERea
§ Spectoperuviana Group (v)	ERea
§ - 'Mary Palmer'	LRHS
§ - 'Mary Palmer's Enchantment'	ERea
§ - 'Mrs H.C. Buck' Surprise	ERea see *B.* (Spectoperuviana Group) 'Mary Palmer'
'Tango'	see *B.* x *buttiana* 'Miss Manila'
'Temple Fire'	see *B.* 'Closeburn'
'Thai Gold'	see *B.* x *buttiana* 'Roseville's Delight'
§ 'Torch Glow'	EAmu
'Tropical Rainbow'	see *B.* x *buttiana* 'Raspberry Ice'
'Variegata'	see *B. glabra* 'Harrissii'
'Vera Blakeman'	ERea MJnS SOWG
'Wac Campbell' (d)	SOWG
* 'White Cascade'	ERea

Boussingaultia (Basellaceae)
baselloides Hook.	see *Anredera cordifolia*

Bouteloua (Poaceae)
curtipendula	CBig CRWN EBee EChP EMan EPPr LEdu LRav NBre
§ *gracilis*	CBig CBrm CHrt EBee EChP EPPr EWsh MBNS NJOw SUsu SWal WPGP WPer XPep

Bouvardia (Rubiaceae)
x *domestica*	EShb
longiflora	ERea EShb LRHS SOWG
§ *ternifolia* new	WCot

Bowenia (Boweniaceae)
serrulata	CBrP

Bowiea (Hyacinthaceae)
volubilis	CHal EBee EShb WCot

Bowkeria (Scrophulariaceae)
citrina	CPle
cymosa	CSec SPlb
verticillata	CPLG

Boykinia (Saxifragaceae)
aconitifolia	CAbP CSec EBee EBla GBuc GGar MLLN MRav NLar NRya SMad WCru WMoo WPtf WSHC
elata	see *B. occidentalis*
heucheriformis	see *B. jamesii*
§ *jamesii*	CGra GEdr GKev NJOw
major	CPLG EBee WBor WCru
§ *occidentalis*	EBee GGar WCru WMoo WPtf
rotundifolia	EBee GBuc NBir WCru WMoo WPnP
- JLS 86269LACA	EMon
tellimoides	see *Peltoboykinia tellimoides*

boysenberry see *Rubus* 'Boysenberry'

Brachychilum see *Hedychium*

Brachychiton (Sterculiaceae)
acerifolius	CHEx EShb
bidwillii	EShb
discolor	EShb
§ *rupestris*	EShb

Brachyelytrum (Poaceae)
japonicum	EBrs GIBF LRav NLar

Brachyglottis ✿ (Asteraceae)
bidwillii 'Basil Fox'	WAbe
§ *buchananii*	CPle WSHC
- 'Silver Shadow'	GGar MWgw
§ *compacta*	ECou EPfP LRHS MAsh SPer SPoG WEas
compacta x *monroi*	ECou LRHS
'County Park'	ECou
'Drysdale'	ELan EPfP GGar LRHS MAsh MBri MRav NPri SLon SPoG SWvt
§ (Dunedin Group) 'Moira Reid' (v)	EBee EGoo
§ - 'Sunshine' ♀H4	More than 30 suppliers
'Frosty'	ECou
greyi misapplied	see *B.* (Dunedin Group) 'Sunshine'
§ *greyi* (Hook. f.) B. Nord.	CTrG EBee EPfP MBar MWhi
greyi x *repanda*	CDoC CHEx EShb EWin GGar SAPC SArc SPoG
§ *huntii*	CHEx GGar
laxifolia misapplied	see *B.* (Dunedin Group) 'Sunshine'
'Leith's Gold'	CTrC
§ *monroi* ♀H4	CBcs CSBt CWib EBee ECou EGoo EHoe EHol ELan EPfP GGar LAst MAsh MBar MLLN MRav NHol SLon SPoG WDin WEas XPep
- 'Clarence'	ECou
repanda	CBcs CHEx CTrG
- 'Purpurea'	CHEx EShb
§ *rotundifolia*	CBcs CCCN CDoC EPfP GGar GTSp NLar WEas
'Silver Waves'	ECou
§ *spedenii*	GGar
I 'Sunshine Improved'	SWvt WSPU
'Sunshine Variegated'	see *B.* (Dunedin Group) 'Moira Reid'
'Walberton's Silver Dormouse'	SPoG

Brachypodium (Poaceae)
pinnatum	EHoe
retusum	XPep
sylvaticum	CBig EBee EHul NBre NNor

Brachyscome (Asteraceae)
'Blue Mist'	SPet
formosa	ECou
'Lemon Drops'	SPet
'Lemon Mist'	LAst

Mauve Mystique =   SVil
  'Picamamy' **new**
'Metallic Blue'   LIck
'Mini Mauve Delight'   SVil
'Mini Yellow'   NPri
multifida   MBri NPri
'Pink Mist'   LAst SPet
rigidula   ECou GKev
'Strawberry Mousse'   LAst SPet
'Tinkerbell'   LSou NPri SPoG

Brachysema (Papilionaceae)
  celsianum   SOWG

Brachystachyum (Poaceae)
  densiflorum   ENBC EPla NLar

Bracteantha see *Xerochrysum*

Brahea (Arecaceae)
  armata   CAbb CBrP CRoM EAmu EPfP
     EShb EZes LPal MGos MPRe NPal
     SAPC SAin SArc SChr SPer WMul
  edulis   CBrP CRoM EAmu LPal MPRe
     WMul

Brassaia see *Schefflera*

Brassica (Brassicaceae)
  japonica   see *B. juncea* var. *crispifolia*
§ *juncea* var. *crispifolia*   CArn MNHC
  nigra **new**   CArn
  oleracea   WHer
* *rapa* var. *japonica*   CArn WJek
* - var. *purpurea*   WJek

x *Brigandra* (Gesneriaceae)
  calliantha   SOkd

Briggsia (Gesneriaceae)
  aurantiaca   SOkd

Brillantaisia (Acanthaceae)
  subulugurica   GFai

Brimeura (Hyacinthaceae)
§ *amethystina* ♀H4   CAvo CFFs CPom ECho EHyt ERos
     GBin GCrs GIBF GKev LPhx LRHS
     MBow SMeo WCot
  - 'Alba'   CAvo CFFs ECho EPfP ERos GKev
     LPhx LRHS MBow
§ *fastigiata*   ERos

Briza (Poaceae)
  maxima   CBgR CHrt CKno EChP EGoo
     EHoe EPla EPyc LEdu LHop MFOX
     MWgw NGdn SBch WGwG WHal
     WHer WRos WWFP WWye
  media   More than 30 suppliers
  - 'Limouzi'   CElw CFir CFwr CKno EBee EBrs
     EGle ECho EHrv EMan EMon EPPr
     GCal LRHS MAvo MBri MSph NSti
     SDys SMad SPoG WPrP
  minor   WRos
  subaristata   CSec EBee MAvo NLar
  triloba   EChP EHoe EMan EPPr EWes
     EWsh GBin MMHG NOGN WGwG
     WMoo WPrP WRos

Brodiaea (Alliaceae)
§ *californica*   CNic EBee ECho ERos NMen
     WCot
  - NNS 00-108   WCot
  capitata   see *Dichelostemma capitatum*
  coronaria   GIBF WCot
  'Corrina'   see *Triteleia* 'Corrina'

elegans   CMon ERos GIBF WCot
ida-maia   see *Dichelostemma ida-maia*
jolonensis   ERos
laxa   see *Triteleia laxa*
§ *minor*   WCot
pallida   WCot
peduncularis   see *Triteleia peduncularis*
purdyi   see *B. minor*
stellaris   CMon EHyt GIBF
terrestris   CMon
- subsp. *kernensis*   WCot
  NNS 98-88

Bromus (Poaceae)
  inermis 'Skinner's   CHrt EBee EGra EHoe EHul EMan
    Gold' (v)   EMar EMil EPPr EWes LBBr NLar
     NSti SPer SPoG WCot
  ramosus   EHoe

Broussonetia (Moraceae)
  kazinoki   CBcs EBee IArd IDee NLar WDin
  papyrifera   CAbP CBcs CDoC CMCN CPLG
     ELan IDee MBri SMad SPer
     WDin
  - 'Laciniata'   MBri NLar

Bruckenthalia see *Erica*

Brugmansia ✿ (Solanaceae)
  'Apricot Goldilocks'   WVaB
  'Apricot Queen' **new**   MJnS
§ *arborea*   CArn CHEx EHol MGol SRms
     WaB
§ - 'Knightii' (d) ♀H1   CHEx CHal EBak EHol ELan EPfP
     ERea LRHS MJnS MOak SOWG
     WMul WVaB
  aurea   CCCN CHEx LRHS SAdn WVaB
  'Baby Orange' **new**   WVaB
  'Butterfly'   WVaB
  'Canary Bird'   MJnS
  x *candida*   CCCN CHEx EBak ERea WCot
     WMul WVaB
  - 'Blush'   ERea
  - 'Culebra'   WVaB
§ - 'Grand Marnier' ♀H1   CHEx CHll ECot ELan EPfP ERea
     MJnS SOWG WVaB
  - 'Maya'   MJnS WVaB
  - 'Ocre'   WVaB
  - 'Plena'   see *B. arborea* 'Knightii'
  - 'Primrose'   ERea
  - 'Tiara' (d)   WVaB
§ - 'Variegata' (v)   CCCN CHen CKob ERea MJnS
     MOak WCot WVaB
  'Charming' **new**   WVaB
§ *chlorantha*   MJnS
I 'Citronella'   WVaB
  x *cubensis* 'Charles   MJnS WVaB
    Grimaldi'
  'Dark Rosetta'   MJnS
  'Desirée' (d)   MJnS
  'Frosty Pink' **new**   WVaB
  'Full Rosea Magic' (d)   MJnS WVaB
  'Gilbert Reiss' **new**   WVaB
  'Golden Cornet'   MJnS
  'Golden Lady' (d)   WVaB
  'Golden Pausanne' **new**   WVaB
  'Goldrichter'   WVaB
  'Herrenhäuser Gärten'   MJnS WVaB
  'Herzenbrucke'   MJnS
  hybrids   WMul
  'Igea Pink'   WVaB
§ x *insignis*   CHll
  - 90-95   WVaB
  - 'Glockenfontäne'   WVaB
  - 'Pink' **new**   CTrG
  - 'Pink Delight'   WVaB

§ - pink-flowered   CHEx EPfP EShb
'Jacob'   WVaB
'Jean Pasko'   WVaB
'Kurfurst Ernst August' **new**   WVaB
'Logee's Orange'   WVaB
'Loreley'   WVaB
'Madeira' **new**   WVaB
'Marrakesch'   WVaB
meteloides   see *Datura inoxia*
'Mia'   WVaB
'Milk and Honey' **new**   WVaB
'Mobishu'   EShb
'Mon Amour' **new**   MJnS
'Morning Sun'   MJnS
'Pink Lady' **new**   MJnS
pink-flowered   WFar
'Pride of Hanover'   WVaB
'Rosabelle'   WVaB
'Rosalie' **new**   WVaB
rosei   see *B. sanguinea* subsp. *sanguinea* var. *flava*
'Rosenrot'   WVaB
'Rosie' **new**   WVaB
'Roter Vulkan'   WVaB
'Rothkirch'   WVaB
§ *sanguinea*   CCCN CHEx CHll EBak EShb MGol MOak MSal SOWG WMul
- 'Feuerwerk'   WVaB
- red-flowered   CHEx
- 'Rosea'   see *B.* x *insignis* pink-flowered
- 'Sangre'   WVaB
§ - subsp. *sanguinea*   CHEx WMul WVaB
   var. *flava*
- 'White Flame'   WVaB
'Shredded White Fantasy'   WVaB
   (d) **new**
§ *suaveolens* ♀H1   CHEx CHll CHrt ELan ERea MGol SPlb WMul WVaB
- pink-flowered   EShb WVaB
- *rosea*   see *B.* x *insignis* pink-flowered
- 'Variegata' (v)   CKob EShb WMul
- yellow-flowered   EShb
suaveolens x *versicolor*   see *B.* x *insignis*
'Sunrise'   MJnS
'Variegata Sunset'   see *B.* x *candida* 'Variegata'
versicolor misapplied   see *B. arborea*
§ *versicolor* Lagerh.   CCCN ERea SOWG WVaB
- 'Ecuador Pink'   EPfP ERea MJnS WVaB
- 'Lachs'   WVaB
'White Marble'   WVaB
* 'Yellow Trumpet'   EPfP
yellow-flowered   WFar

Brunfelsia (Solanaceae)

americana   SDEP SOWG
calycina   see *B. pauciflora*
* *gigantea* **new**   SDEP
grandiflora **new**   SDEP
jamaicensis   CSpe SOWG
lactea **new**   SDEP
nitida   ERea SDEP
pauciflora ♀H1   ELan LRHS MBri SDEP
- 'Floribunda'   SOWG
- 'Macrantha'   SOWG

Brunia (Bruniaceae)

albiflora   SPlb

Brunnera (Boraginaceae)

§ *macrophylla* ♀H4   More than 30 suppliers
- 'Alba'   see *B. macrophylla* 'Betty Bowring'
§ - 'Betty Bowring'   More than 30 suppliers
- 'Blaukuppel'   EMar EMon LRHS
- 'Dawson's White' (v)   More than 30 suppliers
- 'Gordano Gold' (v)   CBow EBee EHoe WCot WHal

- 'Hadspen Cream' (v)   More than 30 suppliers
   ♀H4
- 'Jack Frost'^PBR   More than 30 suppliers
- 'Langford Hewitt' (v)   MNrw WPrP
- 'Langtrees'   More than 30 suppliers
- 'Looking Glass' **new**   CElw CFir EBee IBal IPot NCGa NCob NLar NSti SPer SPoG SUsu WCot
* - 'Marley's White'   CLAP EBee LBuc
- 'Silver Wings' **new**   EBee
- 'Variegata'   see *B. macrophylla* 'Dawson's White'
sibirica   CDes CLAP EMon EWes

x *Brunscrinum* (Amaryllidaceae)

'Dorothy Hannibel'   CMon

Brunsvigia (Amaryllidaceae)

bosmaniae   CMon LToo
radulosa   WCot
rosea 'Minor'   see *Amaryllis belladonna*

Bryonia (Cucurbitaceae)

dioica   GPoy MSal

Bryophyllum see *Kalanchoe*

Buchloe (Poaceae)

dactyloides   CBig CRWN NBre

Buddleja ✿ (Buddlejaceae)

HCM 98.017 from Chile   WPGP
agathosma   CPle SLon WEas WKif WLav WPGP WSHC XPep
albiflora   SLon WLav
alternifolia ♀H4   More than 30 suppliers
- 'Argentea'   CBcs CDoC CPMA CPle EBee ELan EPfP MAsh MBNS MRav NLar NSti SHBN SMad SPer SPla SPoG SSpi WCot WHCG WLav WPat WSHC XPep
asiatica ♀H2   CPLG CPlN ERea EShb SBrw SLon WLav
- B&SWJ 7214   WCru
auriculata   CBcs CBgR CMCN CPLG CPSs CWib EHol EPfP ERea EShb GQui LAst MRav NSti SAga SDix SLon SOWG SPoG WCru WHCG WLav WPGP XPep
australis   SLon
* 'Blue Trerice'   CPLG
* 'Butterfly Ball'   SLon
caryopteridifolia   EHol SLon
colvilei   CDoC CPle CTrw EPfP IDee LAst MRav SBrw SDnm WBor
- B&SWJ 2121   WCru
- GWJ 9399   WCru
- 'Kewensis'   CPLG CRHN CSam EWes LAst NEgg NLar NSti SLon WCru WCwm WLav WPGP WSHC
cordata   SLon
coriacea   SLon
§ *crispa*   CBcs CPSs CPle ECha ELan EPfP EShb LRHS MRav NSti SAga SBrw SDnm SHBN SLon SOWG SPer SRkn SSpi WCMO WEas WFar WHCG WKif WPGP WSHC XPep
- var. *farreri*   CPle MSte SOWG
crotonoides   SLon
   amplexicaulis
curviflora f. *venenifera*   SLon
- - B&SWJ 6036   WCru
davidii   CArn GWCH NWea SGar SHFr STre WDin
- B&SWJ 8083   WCru
- from Beijing, China   CDul SLon WSFF

- Adonis Blue = 'Adokeep'	ENot WWeb
- 'African Queen'	SLon SRGP
- var. **alba**	CNic CWib SHBN
- 'Black Knight' ♀H4	More than 30 suppliers
- 'Blue Horizon'	CSam SEND SLon SRGP WCot WLav WMoo WRHF
- 'Border Beauty'	SLon
- Camberwell Beauty = 'Camkeep'	ENot
- 'Castle School'	CSam
§ - 'Charming'	CDul WMoo WSHC WWlt
- 'Croyde'	CSam
- 'Dartmoor' ♀H4	More than 30 suppliers
- 'Dart's Ornamental White'	MRav
- 'Dart's Papillon Blue'	SLPl
- 'Dubonnet'	SLon WLav
- 'Ecolonia'	MAsh
- 'Empire Blue' ♀H4	CBcs CDoC CDul CSBt EBee ECrN ECtt ENot EPfP LAst LRHS MAsh MBri MGan MGos MNHC MRav MWat NPer NWea SPer SPlb SRGP WDin WFar WTel WWeb WWlt
- 'Fascinating'	CTri MGan MRav WLav
- 'Flaming Violet'	SLon WLav
- 'Florence' **new**	SBra
- 'Glasnevin Hybrid'	NSti SAga SDix WLav
- 'Gonglepod'	SLon
- 'Harlequin' (v)	More than 30 suppliers
- 'Ile de France'	CBcs CWib MGos NWea SBod SLon SRms WLav
- Masquerade = 'Notbud'PBR (v)	ENot MBri MGos MRav SLon WGor
§ - 'Nanho Blue' ♀H4	More than 30 suppliers
- 'Nanho Petite Indigo'	see B. davidii 'Nanho Blue'
- 'Nanho Petite Plum'	see B. davidii 'Nanho Purple'
- 'Nanho Petite Purple'	see B. davidii 'Nanho Purple'
§ - 'Nanho Purple' ♀H4	CDoC CMHG CTri CWib EBee ELan EPfP LRHS LSRN MAsh MBar MRav NBlu SLim SLon SPer SPla SPlb SPoG SRGP WHar
- Nanho White = 'Monite'	ELan EPfP MAsh MBar SPer SRms WFar WWeb
- var. **nanhoensis**	CDul CHrt EBee SEND SIde SPer WHCG WLav
- - blue-flowered	SLon SPer
- Operette = 'Courtabud'	NBlu
- 'Orchid Beauty'	WLav
- 'Orpheus'	WLav
- 'Peace'	CDoC CPLG EBee EPfP MBri MRav NPer SPoG WLav
- Peacock = 'Peakeep'	ENot
- 'Pink Beauty'	LAst SHBN SRGP WHCG
- 'Pink Charming'	see B. davidii 'Charming'
- 'Pink Pearl'	SEND SLon WLav
- 'Pink Spreader'	MAsh SLon
- 'Pixie Blue'	LAst MAsh NBlu NLar SRGP WWeb
- 'Pixie Red'	MAsh NLar NPri WWeb
- 'Pixie White'	MAsh MBNS NBlu NLar SRGP WLav
- Purple Emperor = 'Pyrkeep'	ENot
- 'Purple Friend'	WLav
- 'Royal Purple'	SLim
- 'Royal Red' ♀H4	More than 30 suppliers
- 'Santana' (v)	CDul EWes LHop LRHS MAsh MWea NBlu SAga SBrw SPoG WCMO WCot WMoo WPat
- 'Summer Beauty'	CWib MGos MRav SLon WLav
- 'Variegata' (v)	LRHS SMrm WLav
- var. **veitchiana new**	CPLG
- 'White Ball'	EPfP LRHS MBNS NEgg NLar SLon WCMO
- 'White Bouquet'	CCVT CSBt EBee EPfP EWTr LAst MAsh MHer MNHC MSwo NWea
	SEND SMer SPer SRGP SReu SWal WLav WTel
- 'White Butterfly'	SLon
- 'White Cloud'	CBgR ECrN GQui MGos SRms WGwG
- 'White Harlequin' (v)	CRow WCFE WEas
- 'White Profusion' ♀H4	CBcs CDul CSam EBee ECtt ELan EPfP LRHS MBar MGan MGos MLHP MRav NBlu NFor NWea SHBN SLim SPla SWvt WBVN WCFE WDin WEas WFar WHCG WHar WMoo
- 'White Wings'	SLon WLav
§ **delavayi**	WCru
fallowiana misapplied	see B. 'West Hill'
fallowiana Balf. f.	ELan EWTr LRHS NFor WLav
- ACE 2481	LRHS
- BWJ 7803	WCru
- var. **alba** ♀H3	CDoC EBee ECrN ELan EPfP LRHS MRav NLar NSti SBrw SLon SPer SPoG WAbe WEas WFar WPGP WSHC WWeb XPep
forrestii	CHEx CRHN WCru
globosa ♀H4	More than 30 suppliers
- RCB/Arg C-11	WCot
- 'Cally Orange'	GCal
- 'Lemon Ball'	NPer WLav
- variegated (v) **new**	CBow
glomerata	EBee EShb XPep
heliophila	see B. delavayi
indica	SLon
japonica	IFro
- B&SWJ 8912	WCru
'Leela Kapila' **new**	MGos
x **lewisiana** 'Margaret Pike'	SLon SOWG
limitanea	SLon
lindleyana	More than 30 suppliers
'Lochinch' ♀H3-4	More than 30 suppliers
loricata	CFis CPle CWib ERea EShb GQui IDee MSte SGar SLon SOWG SPlb SSpi WCot WEas WLav WPGP XPep
macrostachya	WPGP
- HWJ 602	WCru
§ **madagascariensis** ♀H1	CRHN EDsa EShb SGar SOWG WCot XPep
marrubiifolia	XPep
megalocephala	WCru
B&SWJ 9106	
§ 'Morning Mist' **new**	SLon SPoG
myriantha	GQui XPep
* - f. **fragrans**	WCot
nappii	SLon
nicodemia	see B. madagascariensis
nivea	CMCN CPLG SOWG WLav XPep
- B&SWJ 2679	WCru
- pink-flowered	SLon
- var. **yunnanensis**	MSte WCFE
- - B&SWJ 8146	WCru
officinalis ♀H2	CPLG CRHN EHol ERea XPep
paniculata	SLon
parvifolia MPF 148	WLav
§ x **pikei** 'Hever'	CHal GQui SPer
'Pink Delight' ♀H4	More than 30 suppliers
'Pink Perfection'	WFar
saligna	CPle SLon XPep
'Salmon Spheres'	CPle
salviifolia	CBcs CPLG CRHN CSWP CSam CTrG EBee ELan EShb GGar GQui IDee IFro LAst NSti SBrw SDnm SWal WAbe WGwG WHer WLav XPep
- white-flowered	CRHN
'Silver Anniversary'	see B. 'Morning Mist'
stenostachya	CPLG

sterniana	see *B. crispa*
'Thai Beauty'	CPlN
tibetica	see *B. crispa*
tubiflora	CPLG SLon SOWG WLav
venenifera B&SWJ 895	WCru
§ 'West Hill'	SLon WLav
x ***weyeriana***	CBgR CDul CHad CRHN CSam
	EBee ECtt EPfP GQui IFoB MGos
	MNrw MSwo MTis NBir SGar SPlb
	SWvt WBVN WBor WBrE WDin
	WFar WHCG WLav WMoo WTel
- 'Golden Glow' (v)	CSBt CTri ECrN EPfP LSRN NFor
	SLon WLav
- 'Lady de Ramsey'	SEND WPer
- 'Moonlight'	CPLG IFro MSph SLon WCot WLav
	WSel
- 'Sungold' ♀H4	More than 30 suppliers
'Winter Sun'	SLon

Buglossoides (Boraginaceae)

§ ***purpurocaerulea***	CCge CHll CMHG CPom CSpe
	EBee ECha ELan EMan EMar
	LHop MLHP MSal MSte MWhi
	NBid NFla WAul WCot WFar WSHC
	WWye

Bukiniczia (Plumbaginaceae)

cabulica	CSpe WCot WLin

Bulbine (Asphodelaceae)

annua misapplied	see *B. semibarbata*
caulescens	see *B. frutescens*
§ ***frutescens***	CHll LToo WBrk WJek WPrP
	XPep
- 'Hallmark'	XPep
latifolia	EShb
§ ***semibarbata***	CPom

Bulbinella (Asphodelaceae)

angustifolia	ECho GCrs WCot
cauda-felis	WCot
eburnifolia	WCot
elata	WCot
floribunda	CWCL IBlr
gibbsii var. ***balanifera***	ECho GCrs
hookeri	CPom EBee EBrs GCrs GEdr GGar
	ITim NChi NDlv NLAp SRms SYvo
	WHal
nutans	CDes ECho
setosa var. ***latifolia*** new	CPne

Bulbinopsis see *Bulbine*

Bulbocodium (Colchicaceae)

vernum	CStu EBee EBrs ECho EHyt EPot
	ERos MBri MWgw NJOw
- white-flowered	ECho

bullace see *Prunus insititia*

Bunias (Brassicaceae)

orientalis	CAgr EUnu MSal

Bunium (Apiaceae)

bulbocastanum	CAgr LEdu

Buphthalmum (Asteraceae)

§ ***salicifolium***	CHrt CPLG CSam CSev EBee ELan
	EPfP EPyc LAst MBri MNFA MRav
	NBid NBlu NBro NGdn NOrc
	SHGN SMer SRms SWat WCAu
	WCot WFar WPer
- 'Alpengold'	ECha EShb GMaP NBre NLar
- 'Dora'	EGra EMan WCot
- 'Sunwheel'	EWll LRHS NBre NPri SRms
speciosum	see *Telekia speciosa*

Bupleurum (Apiaceae)

angulosum	EBee NChi SMrm WFar
- copper	see *B. longifolium*
benoistii	CPom
candollii GWJ 9405	WCru
falcatum	CArn CMea EBee EChP ECha
	EMan EPPr MLLN MSal NDov NLar
	SBri SPur WCot WFar WTin
fruticosum	CBcs CBos CPLG CPle ECtt EHol
	EPfP LHop LRHS SBla SBrw SDix
	SDnm SPoG SSpi SSta WCot WCru
	WDin WEas WPGP WSHC XPep
* ***griffithii***	MSal
- 'Decor'	CSpe
§ ***longifolium***	CElw CFee CMea CSpe EBee EChP
	ECha EGle EWes GBBs GBin GBuc
	MDKP MFOX MNrw NCGa NChi
	NLar SBri SMrm WCot WHal WHoo
	WWhi
- short bronze	WCru
- subsp. ***aureum***	LPhx MAvo NChi NGby
- bronze-leaved new	LSou
longiradiatum	WCru
B&SWJ 729	
ranunculoides	EPPr NLar
rotundifolium	MSal
- 'Copper'	NDov
spinosum	NLar SMad
stellatum	WBVN
tenue	CArn
- B&SWJ 2973	WCru
- var. ***humile*** B&SWJ 6470	WCru

Bursaria (Pittosporaceae)

spinosa	CCCN ECou EShb SBrw

Butia (Arecaceae)

bonnetii	WMul
capitata	CAbb CBcs CBrP CHEx CPHo
	CRoM CTrC EAmu EZes LPJP LPal
	LPan MGos NPal SAPC SAin SArc
	SBLw SChr WMul
- var. ***odorata*** new	EZes
eriospatha	EAmu EZes
yatay	CRoM EAmu LPal SBig WMul

Butomus (Butomaceae)

umbellatus ♀H4	CBen CDWL CRWN CRow CWat
	EBee ECha ECtt EHon EMFW EPfP
	GIBF LNCo LPBA MCCP MRav
	NPer NSco SWat WFar WMAq
	WMoo WPnP WTin WWpP
- 'Rosenrot'	CRow
- 'Schneeweisschen'	CRow NLar

butternut see *Juglans cinerea*

Buxus ✿ (Buxaceae)

aurea 'Marginata'	see *B. sempervirens* 'Marginata'
balearica ♀H4	EPla SLan SLon WPGP WSHC
	WSPU XPep
bodinieri	EPla SLan
'Glencoe' new	SLan
'Green Gem'	NGHP NHol SLan WSel
'Green Mound' new	SLan
'Green Mountain'	SLan
'Green Velvet'	EPfP NHol SLan STop
harlandii hort.	EPla SLan SRiv
- 'Richard'	SLan STre
japonica 'Nana'	see *B. microphylla*
macowanii	SLan
§ ***microphylla***	CSWP MHer NHol NWea SIng
	SLan STre WBVN
- 'Asiatic Winter'	see *B. sinica* var. *insularis* 'Winter Gem'

	Name	Suppliers
§	- 'Compacta'	NLAp SLan SRiv WCot WPat
	- 'Curly Locks'	EPla MHer SLan
	- 'Faulkner'	EBee ELan EPfP LBuc LHop LPan LRHS MBNS MBlu MGos NHol SLan SPoG SRiv STop WDin
	- 'Golden Triumph' PBR	SLan SPoG
	- 'Grace Hendrick Phillips'	SLan
	- 'Green Jade'	SLan
	- 'Green Pillow'	NHol SLan SRiv
	- 'Helen Whiting'	SLan
	- 'Henry Hohman' **new**	SLan
	- 'Herrenhausen' **new**	LPan SLan
	- var. *insularis*	see B. sinica var. insularis
	- var. *japonica* 'Gold Dust'	SLan
	- - 'Jim Stauffer' **new**	SLan
	- - 'Morris Dwarf'	SLan
	- - 'Morris Midget'	IArd NHol SLan
	- - 'National'	MHer SLan WPGP
	- - 'Sunnyside' **new**	SLan
	- - 'Trompenburg' **new**	SLan
	- - 'Winter Gem' **new**	SLan
	- f. *yakushima*	SLan
	- 'John Baldwin'	SLan SRiv STop
	- 'Kagushima' **new**	SLan
	- var. *koreana*	see B. sinica var. insularis
	- 'Quiet End' **new**	SLan
	- var. *riparia*	see B. riparia
	- var. *sinica*	see B. sinica
	- 'Winter Gem'	see B. sinica var. insularis 'Winter Gem'
	'Newport Blue'	see B. sempervirens 'Newport Blue'
§	*riparia*	EPla SLan
	rugulosa **new**	SLan
	sempervirens ♀H4	More than 30 suppliers
	- 'Agram'	SLan
	- 'Anderson' **new**	SLan
§	- 'Angustifolia'	EPla MGos MHer NHol SLan SMad
	- 'Arborescens'	LPan
	- 'Argentea'	see B. sempervirens 'Argenteovariegata'
§	- 'Argenteovariegata' (v)	EPfP IFoB MRav NGHP NHol SLan WFar WSHC
	- 'Aurea'	see B. sempervirens 'Aureovariegata'
	- 'Aurea Maculata'	see B. sempervirens 'Aureovariegata'
	- 'Aurea Marginata'	see B. sempervirens 'Marginata'
	- 'Aurea Pendula' (v)	CPMA EPla SLan SLon WDin WWye
§	- 'Aureovariegata' (v)	CBcs CSBt ECrN EPfP GBar ISea MAsh MBar MBow MGan MGos MHer MNHC MRav NHol NSti SLan SMer SPer SRiv WDin WFar WMoo WTel WWye
	- 'Belleville'	SLan
	- 'Bentley Blue'	NHol
	- 'Blauer Heinz'	ELan EMil LPan LRHS MHer SLan SRiv STop WSel
	- 'Blue Belle' **new**	SLan
§	- 'Blue Cone'	CHar NHol
	- 'Blue Spire'	see B. sempervirens 'Blue Cone'
	- 'Bowles' Blue'	SLan
	- 'Claverton' **new**	SLan
	- clipped ball	CWib EPfP LEar LPan MGos NBlu NGHP NLar SLan SLim SRiv WFar
	- clipped cone **new**	LPan
	- clipped pyramid	CWib EPfP LEar LPan MGos NBlu NGHP NLar SLan SLim SRiv
	- clipped spiral	LPan NBlu SLan SLim SRiv
	- 'Crossley' **new**	SLan
	- 'Dee Runk'	SLan
	- 'Egremont' **new**	SLan
	- 'Elegans' **new**	SMer
§	- 'Elegantissima' (v) ♀H4	More than 30 suppliers
	- 'Emir' **new**	SLan
	- 'Fiesta' **new**	SLan
	- 'Glauca' **new**	SLan
	- 'Gold Tip'	see B. sempervirens 'Notata'
	- 'Golden Frimley' (v)	LHop
§	- 'Graham Blandy'	MHer NHol SLan SRiv STop
	- 'Green Balloon'	LBuc SLan
	- 'Greenpeace'	see B. sempervirens 'Graham Blandy'
	- 'Handsworthiensis'	EBee ECrN LEar LPan SEND SLan SPer STop
	- 'Handsworthiensis' blue	SLan
	- 'Handsworthii'	CTri NWea SRms
	- 'Hermann von Schrenk' **new**	SLan
	- 'Holland' **new**	SLan
	- subsp. *hyrcana*	SLan
	- 'Ickworth Giant'	SLan STop
	- 'Inglis' **new**	SLan
	- 'Ingrid' **new**	SLan
	- 'Inverewe'	SLan
	- 'Ipek'	SLan
	- 'Japonica Aurea'	see B. sempervirens 'Latifolia Maculata'
	- 'Kensington Gardens'	SLan
	- 'Kingsville'	see B. microphylla 'Compacta'
	- 'Kingsville Dwarf'	see B. microphylla 'Compacta'
	- 'Krakow' **new**	NLar
	- 'Lace'	NHol NSti SLan
§	- 'Langley Beauty'	SLan
	- 'Langley Pendula'	see B. sempervirens 'Langley Beauty'
	- 'Latifolia Macrophylla'	SLan SLon SPoG WSel
§	- 'Latifolia Maculata' (v) ♀H4	CAbP CDoC CWib EBee EPfP EPla LEar LRHS MNHC NEgg NGHP NHol NPer SEND SLan SPoG SRiv STop STre WJek
*	- 'Latifolia Pendula'	NHol SLan
	- 'Longifolia'	see B. sempervirens 'Angustifolia'
§	- 'Marginata' (v)	CBrm ECtt EPla GBar IFoB LHop MHer MRav MWgw NHol SHBN SHFr SLan SLon SPer WBrE WHar WSel
	- 'Mary Gamble' **new**	SLan
	- 'Memorial'	MHer NHol SLan SRiv STop
	- 'Molesworth'	SLan
	- 'Myosotidifolia'	CMHG EPla NPro SLan SRiv WPGP
	- 'Myrtifolia'	EPla MHer NHol SLan SLon
	- 'Natchez' **new**	SLan
§	- 'Newport Blue'	SLan
§	- 'Notata' (v)	CSWP IFoB MAsh SPlb WDin
	- 'Obelisk' **new**	SLan
	- 'Parasol'	MHer SLan
	- 'Pendula'	CMHG EPla SLan SLon
	- 'Prostrata'	NHol NWea SLan
*	- 'Pygmaea'	SBla
	- 'Pyramidalis'	EBee SLan WFar
	- 'Rosmarinifolia'	MRav SLan
	- 'Rotundifolia'	CLnd EBee ELan MGos MHer SIde SLan STop WDin
	- 'Roy Lancaster' **new**	SLan
	- 'Saint Genevieve' **new**	SLan
	- 'Salicifolia Elata'	SLan
	- 'Silver Beauty' (v)	MGos
	- 'Silver Variegated'	see B. sempervirens 'Elegantissima'
	- 'Suffruticosa' ♀H4	More than 30 suppliers
I	- 'Suffruticosa Blue'	NHol
	- 'Suffruticosa Variegata' (v)	ECrN EOHP NEgg NWea SRms SWvt
	- 'Twisty' **new**	SLan
	- 'Vadar Valley'	SLan SLon
	- 'Vardar Valley'	NHol NPro SLan SRiv STop
*	- 'Variegata' (v)	ELan ENot LRHS SLon
	- 'Waterfall'	SLan
	- 'Welleri' **new**	SLan
	- 'Wisley Blue' **new**	SLan

§ *sinica* — SLan
§ - var. *insularis* — SLan
- - 'Chegu' **new** — SLan
- - 'Filigree' — EPla NHol SLan WSel
- - 'Justin Brouwers' — MHer SLan SRiv STop
- - 'Pincushion' — SLan
- - 'Tall Boy' **new** — SLan
- - 'Tide Hill' — SLan SRiv STop WFar WSel
- - 'Winter Beauty' — SLan
§ - - 'Winter Gem' — MHer MRav NHol NLar SLPl SLan
- - 'Wintergreen' **new** — SLan
- - var. *intermedia* **new** — SLan
wallichiana — EBee EPla SLan WPGP

C

Cacalia (*Asteraceae*)
atriplicifolia — EBee LRHS
corymbosa HWJK 2214 — WCru
delphinifolia — EBee GEdr
- B&SWJ 5789 — WCru
§ *hastata* — EBee NBre
muehlenbergii — EBee MSal
plantaginea — see *Arnoglossum plantagineum*
robusta — GIBF
suaveolens — EBee

Caesalpinia (*Caesalpiniaceae*)
gilliesii — EBee MJnS SOWG SPlb XPep
- RCB/Arg N-1 — WCot
pulcherrima — SOWG SPlb

Caladium (*Araceae*)
§ *bicolor* (v) — MBri
- 'Postman Joyner' — MOak
'Blaze' — MOak
'Candidum' (v) — MOak
'Carolyn Whorton' (v) — MOak
'Fannie Munson' (v) — MOak
'Festivia' (v) — MOak
'Flash Rouge' — MOak
'Galaxy' — MOak
'Gingerland' (v) — MOak
x *hortulanum* — see *C. bicolor*
'June Bride' (v) — MOak
'Kathleen' — MOak
§ *lindenii* (v) — MJnS
'Lord Derby' (v) — MOak
'Miss Muffet' — MOak
'Mrs F.M. Joyner' (v) — MOak
'Red Frill' (v) — MOak
* 'Scarlet Pimpernell' — MOak
'Symphonie Rose' — MOak
'White Christmas' (v) — MOak
'White Queen' (v) — MOak

Calamagrostis (*Poaceae*)
x *acutiflora* — LEdu
N - 'Karl Foerster' — More than 30 suppliers
- 'Overdam' (v) — More than 30 suppliers
- 'Stricta' — EPPr EWsh LPhx
argentea — see *Stipa calamagrostis*
§ *arundinacea* — CElw COIW CPLG CSpe EBee ECha ECou EGra EHoe EPGN EPla GCal LEdu MBNS MBow MNrw NBid NHol NVic SDix SGar SPlb SUsu WFar WMoo WPGP WPer WPrP WWye
§ *brachytricha* — More than 30 suppliers
emodensis — CBig CBod CBrm CFwr CKno CMil CPen CSam CWCL EBee EPPr EPla MMoz NDov NOak SYvo WGHP WLeb WPGP

§ *epigejos* — CBig CNat EPPr EWsh NBre NDov NHol NNor NOGN WDyG WRos
splendens misapplied — see *Stipa calamagrostis*
varia — EHoe EPPr NDov WHrl

calamondin see x *Citrofortunella microcarpa*

Calamintha (*Lamiaceae*)
alpina — see *Acinos alpinus*
§ *ascendens* — CArn CSec EAro EBee LPhx MLLN SGar WMoo WPtf
clinopodium — see *Clinopodium vulgare*
cretica — CLyd WPer
§ *grandiflora* — CAgr CArn CSam CSev EBee ECha ELan GGar GPoy LEdu MHer MRav MWgw NCGa NPer SBla SMad SPer SPet SPlb SSvw WBVN WCAu WCru WFar WMoo WTin WWeb WWhi WWye
- 'Elfin Purple' — EPfP LBMP LRav SPoG
- 'Variegata' (v) — CBgR CBrm CPLG EAro EBee ELan EMan EMil ERou EShb GGar GKev LAst LSou NPri SMar SPoG WCHb WFar
§ *menthifolia* — NBre NLar
- HH&K 163 — GBri
§ *nepeta* — More than 30 suppliers
- subsp. *glandulosa* — CEnt CSec EAro EBee NEgg WGHP WLin WMoo
- - ACL 1050/90 — LRHS WHoo
- - 'White Cloud' — CHea CSec CSpe EHrv ELan ERou GBar GBuc LLWP MBri MRav MSte NBir WCAu WMoo WOut WWye XPep
- 'Gottfried Kuehn' — MRav WCAu
§ - subsp. *nepeta* — CBgR ELan EMon EPfP ERou GBar IHMH LHop MHer MLHP MRav NSti SPer SUsu WCHb WEas WFar WTin
- - 'Blue Cloud' — CBgR CHea CSam CSec EAro EBee EChP ECha EHrv ILis LPhx MBri NBir NDov SBla SWat WCAu WCHb WCot WFar WGHP WMoo XPep
- 'Weisse Riese' — LPhx
nepetoides — see *C. nepeta* subsp. *nepeta*
officinalis misapplied — see *C. ascendens*
sylvatica — see *C. menthifolia*
I - 'Menthe' — EBee
vulgaris — see *Clinopodium vulgare*

Calandrinia (*Portulacaceae*)
depressa — CSec
discolor — LRHS
grandiflora — CSec MLLN
* *ranunculina* — CGra CPBP EHyt GKev
sericea — CPBP GKev
sibirica — see *Claytonia sibirica*
umbellata — NJOw WPer
- 'Ruby Tuesday' — NPri

Calanthe (*Orchidaceae*)
alismifolia — EFEx
arisanenesis — EFEx
aristulifera — EFEx
bicolor — see *C. striata*
caudatilabella — EFEx
delavayi **new** — GIBF
discolor — CLAP EFEx GEdr NLAp WCMO WWst
- subsp. *amamiana* — EFEx
- var. *flava* — see *C. striata*
- subsp. *tokunoshimensis* — EFEx
graciflora — EFEx
Kozu g. — CLAP LEdu
mannii — EFEx

nipponica	EFEx GEdr WWst
reflexa	EBee EFEx GEdr
sieboldii	see *C. striata*
§ *striata*	CLAP EFEx GEdr NLAp WCMO WCot WWst
tricarinata	EFEx GEdr WCMO

Calathea (Marantaceae)

argyrophylla 'Exotica'	XBlo
crocata ♀H1	LRHS MBri
'Greystar'	MBri
louisae 'Maui Queen'	MBri XBlo
§ *majestica* ♀H1	LRHS XBlo
makoyana ♀H1	MBri XBlo
metallica	MBri
oppenheimiana	see *Ctenanthe oppenheimiana*
ornata	see *C. majestica*
picturata 'Argentea' ♀H1	MBri XBlo
roseopicta ♀H1	LRHS MBri XBlo
rufibarba new	XBlo
* *stromata*	XBlo
veitchiana	MBri
warscewiczii	MBri
'Wavestar'	MBri
zebrina ♀H1	MBri XBlo
'Zoizia'	XBlo

Calceolaria (Scrophulariaceae)

acutifolia	see *C. polyrhiza* Cav.
alba	CPLG EBee EMan LSou NLar
arachnoidea	CSec
x *banksii*	EBee
bicolor	WCot
§ *biflora*	CSec ECho EHol EHyt EPfP GGar LEdu MHer NLAp NWCA WAbe
- 'Goldcap'	CBrm ECho
- 'Goldcrest Amber'	ECho SPlb WPer
'Briga Elite'	EBee EWin LSou
'Camden Hero'	MOak
chelidonioides	GGar MTho WLin
corymbosa	GKev
falklandica	ECho NLAp SPav SRms WHer WPer
fothergillii	GKev
'Goldcrest'	ECho EPfP GKev SRms
'Hall's Spotted'	NWCA
§ *integrifolia* ♀H3	CFis CHal CPLG CSpe EBee ELan SEND SGar SIng SPer SRms WAbe WWlt
- var. *angustifolia*	MOak
- bronze	SPer WAbe
'John Innes'	ECho LRHS WCot WRha WWeb
'Kentish Hero'	CHal MAJR MOak NPer
mexicana	CPLG CSec SHFr
petiolaris	CSec
plantaginea	see *C. biflora*
§ *polyrhiza* Cav.	ECho EHyt NRya
rugosa	see *C. integrifolia*
Sunset Series	EPfP IHMH NBlu
tenella	ECtt NMen NWCA WAbe
uniflora	CGra GKev
- var. *darwinii*	ECho EHyt NLAp SIng
'Walter Shrimpton'	ECho EDAr EPot EWes SIng WAbe

Caldcluvia (Cunoniaceae)

paniculata	ISea

Calea (Asteraceae)

zacatechichi	MGol

Calendula (Asteraceae)

meuselii	CFee
officinalis	CArn ELau GPoy GWCH MBow MHer MNHC MSal SIde SPav WGwG WJek WSel WWye

- Fiesta Gitana Group ♀H4	CPrp WJek
'Wintersun' new	LRav

Calibanus (Dracaenaceae)

hookeri new	EShb

Calibrachoa (Solanaceae)

(Callie Series) Callie Orange = 'Cal Oran' new	SVil
- Callie Purple = 'Cal Pur' PBR new	NBlu
- Callie Rose = 'Cal Rose' PBR new	NBlu
- Callie Rose Star = 'Cal Rose' PBR new	SVil
- Callie Scarlet Red = 'Cal Scared' PBR new	NBlu
- Callie Sunrise = 'Cal Sunre' PBR new	NBlu SVil
- Callie White = 'Cal White' PBR new	NBlu
- Callie Yellow = 'Cal Yel' PBR new	SVil
(Carillon Series) 'Carillon Burgundy'	WGor
- Carillon Lilac Pink = 'K7-1133' new	WGor
(Million Bells Series) Million Bells Apricot = 'Sunbel-ap' new	WGor
- Million Bells Cherry = 'Sunbelchipi' PBR	LAst LSou
- Million Bells Lemon = 'Sunbelkic'	LAst LSou WGor
- Million Bells Red = 'Sunbelre'	LAst NBlu NPri WGor
- Million Bells Terracotta = 'Sunbelkist'	LAst
- Million Bells Trailing Blue = 'Sunbelkubu' PBR	NBlu WGor
- Million Bells Trailing Fuchsia = 'Sunbelrkup' ♀H3	LAst NBlu WGor
- Million Bells Trailing Lavender Vein = 'Sunbelbura'	LAst WGor
- Million Bells Trailing Pink = 'Sunbelkupi' PBR ♀H3	LAst
- Million Bells Trailing Soft Pink = 'Sunbelkuopi' PBR new	WGor
- Million Bells Trailing White = 'Sunbelkuho' PBR	LAst
- Million Bells White = 'Sunbelho'	LSou
- Million Bells/Trailing Pink Morn = 'Sunbelkupapi' new	WGor
(Superbells Series) Superbells Candy White = 'USCALI48'	LAst LSou NPri SPoG
- Superbells Imperial Purple = 'USCALI100'	LAst LSou SPoG SVil
- Superbells Indigo = 'USCALI51'	LAst LSou
- Superbells Magenta = 'USCALI17'	LAst LSou NPri SVil
- Superbells Pink = 'USCALI11' ♀H3	LAst LSou SVil
- Superbells Red = 'USCALI28'	LAst LSou SPoG SVil
- Superbells Royal Blue = 'USCALI14'	LAst LSou SVil

- Superbells Strawberry   LAst SVil
  Pink = 'USCALI47'

Calicotome (Papilionaceae)
spinosa   XPep

Calla (Araceae)
aethiopica   see *Zantedeschia aethiopica*
palustris   CBen CRow CWat EHon EMFW
    EPfP LNCo LPBA MCCP NPer SPlb
    SWat WFar WMAq WPnP WWpP

Calliandra (Mimosaceae)
emarginata 'Minima'   LRHS SOWG
haematocephala   SOWG
tweediei   SOWG

Callianthemum (Ranunculaceae)
anemonoides   GCrs SBla WAbe
coriandrifolium   NMen
kernerianum   GCrs NMen

Callicarpa (Verbenaceae)
americana   NLar
- var. *lactea*   CMCN
bodinieri   NBir WFar
- var. *giraldii*   CEnt EBee GBin GIBF MGan MRav
    SMac WDin WWeb
- - 'Profusion' ♀H4   More than 30 suppliers
cathayana   CBcs CMCN MBri NLar
dichotoma   CPLG CPle CTrG ELan EPfP GIBF
    LRHS NLar WFar
- f. *albifructa*   GIBF
- 'Issai'   NLar
aff. *formosana*   WCru
    B&SWJ 7127
japonica   CBcs CPle NLar WWes
- B&SWJ 8587   WCru
- f. *albibacca*   NLar
- 'Koshima-no-homate'   MBri NLar
- 'Leucocarpa'   CBcs CMac CPLG EBee ELan EPfP
    LRHS MRav NLar SPer WFar
- var. *luxurians*   NLar
- - B&SWJ 8521   WCru
kwangtungensis   CBcs CMCN MBri NLar
mollis   NLar
I 'Selectie van der Broek'   NLar
    new
shikokiana   NLar
x *shirasawana*   NLar

Callirhoe (Malvaceae)
involucrata   CPBP EBee EMan GBri MGol NBur
    NWCA WHrl

Callisia (Commelinaceae)
elegans ♀H1   CHal
§ *navicularis*   CHal
repens   CHal MBri

Callistemon ✿ (Myrtaceae)
acuminatus   XPep
'Awanga Dam'   ECou
brachyandrus   NHol
'Burgundy'   SOWG
* 'Burning Bush'   MAsh SOWG
'Candy Pink' **new**   SOWG
chisholmii   SOWG
citrinus   CHll CSBt EBee ECot ECou ERom
    EShb GGar GSki ITim LAst SOWG
    SPlb WBrE WDin WHar
- 'Albus'   see *C. citrinus* 'White Anzac'
- 'Angela'   SOWG
- 'Canberra'   SOWG
- 'Firebrand'   CDoC LRHS SMur SOWG
- 'Horse Paddock'   SOWG

- 'Splendens' ♀H3   More than 30 suppliers
§ - 'White Anzac'   ELan EPfP LRHS SBra SBrw SOWG
    SPoG
comboynensis   SOWG
'Coochy Coochy Station'   SOWG
'Dawson River Weeper'   SOWG
flavescens   SOWG
flavovirens   SOWG
formosus   SOWG
glaucus   see *C. speciosus*
'Hannah's Child'   SOWG
'Happy Valley'   SOWG
'Harkness'   SOWG
'Injune'   SOWG
'Kings Park Special'   SOWG
laevis hort.   see *C. rugulosus*
linearis ♀H3   CBcs CMac CSBt CTrC CTri ECou
    ECrN ELan EPfP EPla LRHS LRav
    LSRN MDun MHer MWgw SCoo
    SLim SLon SOWG SPlb SRms SSpi
    SWvt WMul WNor WSHC
macropunctatus   SOWG SPlb
'Mauve Mist'   CDoC CHEx LRHS MAsh SBrw
    SOWG
pachyphyllus   ECou SOWG
- var. *viridis*   SOWG
pallidus   CBcs CHEx CMHG CMac CPLG
    CWib ECou ELan EPfP GGar IDee
    ITim LRHS MAsh MRav SBrw SMur
    SOWG SPer SPlb SPoG SSta
- 'Candle Glow' **new**   SOWG
- 'Father Christmas' **new**   SOWG
paludosus   see *C. sieberi* DC.
pearsonii   SOWG
- prostrate   SOWG
'Perth Pink'   CBcs CCCN CDoC ELan SBra SBrw
    SOWG SPoG
'Phil May' **new**   SOWG
phoeniceus   ECou IFro SOWG
- 'Pink Ice'   SOWG
pinifolius   SOWG SPlb
- green-flowered   SOWG
- red-flowered   SOWG
- 'Sockeye'   SOWG
'Pink Champagne'   SOWG
§ *pityoides*   CPLG ECou SOWG XPep
- from Brown's Swamp,   ECou
  Australia
polandii   SOWG
- dwarf   SOWG
'Purple Splendour'   SOWG
recurvus   SOWG
'Red Clusters'   CDoC CTrC CTrG ELan EREa IArd
    LAst LRHS MAsh MDun NLar SBod
    SBrw SMer SMur SOWG SSto SWvt
'Reeve's Pink'   SOWG
rigidus   More than 30 suppliers
§ *rugulosus*   CBcs EGra NCob SBrw SOWG
    XPep
'Running River' **new**   SOWG
salignus ♀H3   CBcs CCCN CDoC CHEx CPLG
    CSBt CTrC CTri ECrN EPfP GSki
    ISea LRHS MHer SBrw SEND SHFr
    SLim SOWG SPer SYvo WBVN
    WDin XPep
sieberi misapplied   see *C. pityoides*
§ *sieberi* DC.   CBcs CDoC CMHG CTrC ECou
    ELan EPfP EShb GGar GSki NBir
    NLar NPal SBod SBra SOWG SPlb
    SPoG WFar
- purple-flowered **new**   SOWG
§ *speciosus*   CDul CTrC EDsa LRHS MDun NLar
    SMur SOWG SPlb SPoG WAbe
subulatus   CDoC ECou EDsa MCCP NLar
    SAPC SArc SBrw SOWG SPlb SSto
    WMoo

- 'Crimson Tail'	CWCL MDun NEgg NLar
I - 'Packers Selection' **new**	SOWG
'Taree Pink' **new**	SOWG
teretifolius	SOWG
viminalis	CBcs CCCN CHEx SGar SOWG SPlb
- 'Captain Cook'	ECou ERea LAst LRHS MJnS NLar SBrw SOWG
- 'Endeavor' **new**	CCCN
- 'Hannah Ray'	IArd SOWG
- 'Little John'	CBcs CWSG ECou NLar SBrw SOWG XPep
- 'Malawi Giant'	SOWG
'Violaceus'	EDsa LRav XPep
viridiflorus	CTrC ECou EDsa GGar GQui MCCP MHer SBrw SOWG SWal WCru
- 'County Park Dwarf'	ECou
- 'Sunshine'	ECou
'White Anzac'	see *C. citrinus* 'White Anzac'

Callitriche (*Callitrichaceae*)

autumnalis	see *C. hermaphroditica*
§ *hermaphroditica*	EPfP WMAq
§ *palustris*	EHon EMFW
stagnalis	NSco
verna	see *C. palustris*

Callitris (*Cupressaceae*)

rhomboidea	CTrC GGar

Calluna ✿ (*Ericaceae*)

vulgaris	GWCH MBow
- 'Aberdeen'	EHea
- 'Adrie'	EHea
- 'Ahrensdorf' **new**	EHea
- 'Alba Argentea'	EHea
- 'Alba Aurea'	EHea MBar
- 'Alba Carlton'	EHea
- 'Alba Dumosa'	EHea
- 'Alba Elata'	CNCN EHea MBar
- 'Alba Elegans'	EHea
- 'Alba Elongata'	see *C. vulgaris* 'Mair's Variety'
- 'Alba Erecta'	EHea
- 'Alba Jae'	EHea MBar
- 'Alba Minor'	EHea
- 'Alba Multiflora'	EHea
- 'Alba Pilosa'	EHea
§ - 'Alba Plena' (d)	CSBt EHea LRHS MBar
- 'Alba Praecox'	EHea
- 'Alba Pumila'	EHea MBar
§ - 'Alba Rigida'	EHea LRHS MBar SRms
- 'Alec Martin' (d)	EHea
- 'Alex Warwick'	EHea
- 'Alexandra'PBR ♀H4	EHea LRHS NHol SPoG SRms
- 'Alice Knight'	EHea
- 'Alicia'PBR ♀H4	CBcs EHea LRHS SPoG
- 'Alieke'	EHea
- 'Alina' **new**	EHea
- 'Alison Yates'	EHea MBar
- 'Allegretto'	EHea
- 'Allegro' ♀H4	EHea EPfP MBar NHol SRms
- 'Alportii'	EHea MBar
- 'Alportii Praecox'	CNCN EHea MBar
- 'Alys Sutcliffe'	EHea
- 'Amanda Wain'	EHea
- 'Amethyst'PBR	CBcs EHea MBar NHol SPoG
- 'Amilto'	CNCN EHea NHol SRms
- 'Andrew Proudley'	EHea MBar
- 'Anette'PBR ♀H4	EHea LRHS MBar NHol
- 'Angela Wain'	EHea
- 'Anna'	EHea
- 'Annabel' (d)	EHea
- 'Anne Dobbin'	EHea
- 'Annegret'	see *C. vulgaris* 'Marlies'
- 'Anneke'	EHea
- 'Annemarie' (d) ♀H4	CNCN CSBt EHea EPfP LRHS MBar NHol SCoo SPer SPlb SRms
- 'Anne's Zwerg'	EHea SRms
- 'Anthony Davis' ♀H4	CNCN EHea MBar NHol
- 'Anthony Wain'	EHea
- 'Anton'	EHea
- 'Antrujo Gold'	EHea
- 'Aphrodite'PBR	EHea
- 'Apollo'	EHea
- 'Applecross' (d)	CNCN EHea
- 'Arabella'PBR	EHea LRHS NHol SRms
- 'Argentea'	EHea MBar
- 'Ariadne'	EHea
- 'Arina'	CNCN EHea LRHS MBri
- 'Arran Gold'	CNCN EHea MBar
- 'Ashgarth Amber'	EHea
- 'Ashgarth Amethyst'	EHea
- 'Ashgarth Shell Pink'	EHea
- 'Asterix'	EHea
- 'Atalanta'	EHea
- 'Atholl Gold'	EHea
- 'August Beauty'	CNCN EHea
- 'Aurea'	EHea LRHS
- 'Aurora' **new**	EHea
- 'Autumn Glow'	EHea
- 'Babette' **new**	EHea
- 'Baby Ben'	EHea
- 'Baby Wicklow'	EHea
- 'Barbara' **new**	EHea
- 'Barbara Fleur'	EHea
- 'Barja'	EHea
- 'Barnett Anley'	CNCN EHea
- 'Battle of Arnhem'	CNCN EHea MBar
- 'Bayport'	EHea
- 'Beechwood Crimson'	CNCN EHea
- 'Bella Rosa' **new**	EHea
- 'Ben Nevis'	EHea
- 'Bennachie Bronze'	EHea
- 'Bennachie Prostrate'	EHea
- 'Beoley Crimson'	CNCN EHea MBar
- 'Beoley Crimson Variegated' (v)	EHea
- 'Beoley Gold' ♀H4	CBrm CNCN CSBt CTri EHea EPfP LRHS MBar MBri MGos NHol SPer SRms
- 'Beoley Silver'	CNCN EHea MBar
- 'Bernadette'	EHea
- 'Betty Baum'	EHea
- 'Bispingen'	EHea
- 'Blazeaway'	CNCN CTri EHea EPfP LRHS MBar MBri NHol SRms
- 'Blueness'	EHea
- 'Bognie'	CNCN EHea
- 'Bonfire Brilliance'	CNCN CSBt EHea MBar NHol
- 'Bonita'PBR	EHea
- 'Bonne's Darkness'	EHea
- 'Bonsaï'	EHea
- 'Boreray'	CNCN EHea
- 'Boskoop'	CBrm CNCN EHea LRHS MBar NHol
- 'Bradford'	EHea
- 'Braemar'	CNCN EHea
- 'Braeriach'	EHea
- 'Branchy Anne'	EHea
- 'Bray Head'	CNCN EHea MBar
- 'Breivik' **new**	EHea
- 'Brita Elisabeth' (d)	EHea
- 'Bronze Beauty'	EHea
- 'Bud Lyle'	EHea
- 'Bunsall'	CNCN EHea
- 'Buxton Snowdrift'	EHea
- 'C.W. Nix'	CSBt EHea MBar
- 'Caerketton White'	EHea
- 'Caleb Threlkeld'	EHea NHol
- 'Calf of Man'	EHea
- 'Californian Midge'	EHea MBar NHol

- 'Carl Röders' (d)   EHea
- 'Carmen'   EHea
- 'Carngold'   EHea
- 'Carole Chapman'   EHea MBar
- 'Carolyn'   EHea
- 'Cassa'   EHea
- 'Catherine'   EHea
- 'Catherine Anne'   EHea LRHS
- 'Celtic Gold'   EHea
- 'Charles Chapman'   EHea
§ - 'Chernobyl' (d)   EHea NHol
- 'Chindit'   EHea
- 'Christina'   EHea
- 'Cilcennin Common'   EHea
- 'Clare Carpet'   EHea
- 'Coby'   EHea
- 'Coccinea'   EHea MBar
- 'Colette'   EHea
- 'Con Brio'   CBcs CNCN EHea LRHS SRms
- 'Copper Glow'   EHea
- 'Coral Island'   EHea MBar
- 'Corbett's Red'   EHea
- 'Corrie's White'   EHea
- 'Cottswood Gold'   EHea NHol SRms
- 'County Wicklow' (d)   CBcs CNCN CTri EHea EPfP LRHS
  ♀H4   MBar MBri NBlu NHol SRms
- 'Craig Rossie'   EHea
- 'Crail Orange'   EHea
- 'Cramond' (d)   CNCN EHea MBar
- 'Cream Steving'   EHea
- 'Crimson Glory'   EHea LRHS MBar NBlu NDlv
- 'Crimson Sunset'   CNCN EHea
- 'Crinkly Tuft'   EHea
- 'Crowborough Beacon'   EHea
- 'Cuprea'   CNCN EHea EPfP LRHS MBar MBri
                                  NHol SPer
- 'Dainty Bess'   EHea MBar MSwo NHol
- 'Dark Beauty'PBR (d) ♀H4   CNCN EHea EPfP LRHS MBar NDlv
                                  NHol
- 'Dark Star' (d) ♀H4   CBcs CBrm CNCN EHea EPfP
                                  LRHS MBar MGos NHol SCoo
                                  SRms
- 'Darkness' ♀H4   CBcs CNCN CSBt CTri EHea EPfP
                                  LRHS MBar MBri NHol SCoo SRms
- 'Darleyensis'   EHea MBar
- 'Dart's Amethyst'   EHea
- 'Dart's Beauty'   EHea
- 'Dart's Brilliant'   EHea
- 'Dart's Flamboyant'   EHea
- 'Dart's Gold'   EHea MBar
- 'Dart's Hedgehog'   EHea
- 'Dart's Parakeet'   EHea
- 'Dart's Parrot'   EHea
- 'Dart's Silver Rocket'   EHea
- 'Dart's Squirrel'   EHea
- 'Dart's Surprise'   EHea
- 'David Eason'   CNCN EHea
- 'David Hagenaars'   EHea
- 'David Hutton'   MBar
- 'David Platt' (d)   EHea
- 'Denkewitz'   EHea
- 'Denny Pratt'   EHea
- 'Desiree'   EHea
- 'Devon' (d)   EHea
- 'Diana'   EHea
- 'Dickson's Blazes'   EHea
- 'Dirry'   CNCN EHea
- 'Doctor Murray's White'   see *C. vulgaris* 'Mullardoch'
- 'Doris Rushworth'   EHea
- 'Drum-ra'   EHea MBar SRms
- 'Dunnet Lime'   EHea SPlb
- 'Dunnydeer'   EHea
- 'Dunwood'   EHea MBar
§ - 'Durford Wood'   EHea
- 'Dwingeloo Delight'   EHea
- 'E.F. Brown'   EHea

- 'E. Hoare'   EHea MBar
- 'Easter-bonfire'   CNCN EHea NHol
- 'Eckart Miessner'   EHea
- 'Edith Godbolt'   EHea
- 'Elaine'   EHea
- 'Elegant Pearl'   EHea MBar
- 'Elegantissima'   CBcs EHea
- 'Elegantissima Walter   see *C. vulgaris* 'Walter Ingwersen'
  Ingwersen'
- 'Elkstone White'   CNCN EHea MBar
- 'Ellen'   EHea
- 'Ellie Barbour'   EHea
- 'Elly'   EHea
- 'Else Frye' (d)   EHea
- 'Elsie Purnell' (d) ♀H4   CNCN CSBt EHea EPfP LRHS MBar
                                  MGos NHol SPlb SRms
- 'Emerald Jock'   EHea
- 'Emma Louise Tuke'   EHea
- 'Eric Easton'   EHea
- 'Eskdale Gold'   EHea
- 'Eurosa'PBR   EHea
- 'Fairy'   EHea
- 'Falling Star'   EHea
- 'Feuerwerk'   EHea
§ - 'Finale'   EHea MBar
- 'Findling'   EHea
- 'Fire King'   EHea MBar
- 'Fire Star'   EHea
- 'Firebreak'   EHea MBar NHol
- 'Firefly' ♀H4   CNCN CSBt EHea EPfP LRHS MBar
                                  MBri SPer SRms
- 'Flamingo'   CBcs CNCN CSBt EHea LRHS
                                  MBar MSwo NHol SRms
- 'Flatling'   EHea NHol
- 'Flore Pleno' (d)   EHea MBar
- 'Florrie Spicer'   EHea
- 'Fokko' (d)   EHea
- 'Fort Bragg'   EHea
- 'Fortyniner Gold'   EHea
- 'Foxhollow Wanderer'   CNCN EHea MBar
- 'Foxii'   EHea
- 'Foxii Floribunda'   EHea MBar
- 'Foxii Lett's Form'   see *C. vulgaris* 'Velvet Dome',
                                  'Mousehole'
- 'Foxii Nana'   CNCN EHea MBar NDlv NHol
                                  SRms
- 'Foya'   EHea
- 'Fred J. Chapple'   CNCN EHea LRHS MBar MBri
                                  NBlu
- 'Fréjus'   EHea
- 'French Grey'   CNCN EHea
- 'Fritz Kircher'PBR   EHea NHol
- 'Gaia'   EHea
- 'Gerda'   EHea
- 'Ginkel's Glorie'   EHea
- 'Glasa'   EHea
- 'Glen Mashie'   EHea
- 'Glencoe' (d)   EHea MBar MBri
- 'Glendoick Silver'   EHea
- 'Glenfiddich'   CSBt EHea MBar NHol
- 'Glenlivet'   EHea MBar
- 'Glenmorangie'   EHea MBar
- 'Gloucester Boy'   EHea
- 'Gnome' **new**   EHea
- 'Gold Charm'   EHea
- 'Gold Finch'   EHea
- 'Gold Flame'   EHea LRHS MBar
- Gold Hamilton   see *C. vulgaris* 'Chernobyl'
- 'Gold Haze' ♀H4   CBcs CNCN CTri EHea LRHS MBar
                                  MBri NHol SCoo SPer
- 'Gold Knight'   EHea EPfP LRHS MBar
- 'Gold Kup'   EHea MBar
- 'Gold Mist'   EHea LRHS NDlv
- 'Gold Spronk'   EHea
- 'Gold Star' (d) **new**   EHea
- 'Goldcarmen'   EHea

- 'Golden Blazeaway'	EHea
- 'Golden Carpet'	CNCN CSBt EHea LRHS MBar MBri
	MGos NDlv NHol SPer SRms
- 'Golden Dew'	EHea
- 'Golden Dream' (d)	EHea
- 'Golden Feather'	CNCN CSBt EHea LRHS MBar
- 'Golden Fleece'	CNCN EHea SRms
- 'Golden Max'	EHea
- 'Golden Rivulet'	EHea LRHS MBar MSwo
- 'Golden Turret'	CNCN EHea LRHS
- 'Golden Wonder' (d)	EHea
- 'Goldsworth Crimson'	CSBt EHea
- 'Goldsworth Crimson	CNCN EHea MBar
Variegated' (v)	
- 'Goscote Wine'	EHea
- 'Grasmeriensis'	EHea MBar
- 'Great Comp'	MBar
- 'Green Cardinal'	EHea
- 'Grey Carpet'	CNCN EHea LRHS MBar SRms
- 'Grijsje'	EHea
- 'Grizabella'	EHea
- 'Grizzly'	EHea
- 'Grönsinka'	EHea
- 'Grouse'	EHea
- 'Guinea Gold'	CNCN EHea LRHS MBar MBri
- 'Gunilla Uggla'	EHea
§ - 'H.E. Beale' (d)	CNCN CSBt CTri EHea EPfP LRHS
	MBar MBri MGos NHol
- 'Hamlet Green'	CNCN EHea MBar
- 'Hammondii'	CNCN EHea
- 'Hammondii Aureifolia'	CNCN EHea LRHS MBar MBri SPlb
- 'Hammondii Rubrifolia'	EHea LRHS MBar MBri
- 'Hannover **new**'	EHea
- 'Harlekin'	EHea
- 'Harry Gibbon' (d)	EHea
- 'Harten's Findling'	EHea
- 'Hatje's Herbstfeuer' (d)	EHea
- 'Hayesensis'	EHea
- 'Heidberg'	EHea
- 'Heidepracht'	EHea
- 'Heidesinfonie'	EHea
- 'Heideteppich'	EHea
- 'Heidezwerg'	EHea
- 'Heike' (d)	EHea
- 'Herbert Mitchell'	EHea
- 'Hester'	EHea
- 'Hetty'	EHea
- 'Hibernica'	EHea MBar
- 'Hiemalis'	EHea MBar
- 'Hiemalis Southcote'	see *C. vulgaris* 'Durford Wood'
- 'Highland Cream'	CNCN
- Highland Cream	see *C. vulgaris* 'Punch's Dessert'
- 'Highland Rose'	CNCN EHea LRHS SPlb
- 'Highland Spring'	EHea
- 'Hilda Turberfield'	EHea
- 'Hillbrook Limelight'	EHea
- 'Hillbrook Orange'	EHea MBar
- 'Hillbrook Sparkler'	EHea
- 'Hinton White'	EHea
- 'Hirsuta Albiflora'	EHea
- 'Hirsuta Typica'	CNCN EHea
- 'Hollandia'	EHea
- 'Holstein'	EHea
- 'Hookstone'	EHea MBar
- 'Hoyerhagen'	EHea
§ - 'Hugh Nicholson'	CNCN EHea
- 'Humpty Dumpty'	EHea MBar NHol
- 'Hypnoides'	EHea
- 'Ide's Double' (d)	EHea
- 'Inchcolm'	EHea
- 'Inchkeith'	EHea
- 'Ineke'	CNCN EHea MBar
- 'Inge'	EHea
- 'Ingrid Bouter' (d)	EHea
- 'Inshriach Bronze'	CNCN EHea MBar
- 'Iris van Leyen'	CNCN EHea MBar
- 'Islay Mist'	EHea
- 'Isle of Hirta'	CNCN EHea MBar NHol
- 'Isobel Frye'	EHea MBar
- 'Isobel Hughes' (d)	EHea MBar
- 'J.H. Hamilton' (d) ♀H4	CBrm CNCN CTri EHea LRHS
	MBar MBri NBlu NHol SRms
- 'Jan'	EHea
- 'Jan Dekker'	CNCN EHea LRHS MBar NHol
- 'Janice Chapman'	EHea MBar
- 'Japanese White'	EHea
- 'Jenny'	EHea
- 'Jill'	EHea
- 'Jimmy Dyce' (d)	EHea
- 'Joan Sparkes' (d)	CNCN EHea LRHS MBar
- 'Jochen'	EHea
- 'Johan Slegers'	EHea
- John Denver	see *C. vulgaris* 'Marleen Select'
- 'John F. Letts'	EHea LRHS MBar SRms
- 'Johnson's Variety'	CBcs CNCN EHea MBar
- 'Jos' Lemon'	EHea
- 'Jos' Whitie'	EHea
- 'Josefine'	EHea
- 'Joseph's Coat'	EHea
- 'Joy Vanstone' ♀H4	CNCN CSBt EHea EPfP LRHS MBar
	MBri MGos NHol SRms
- 'Julia'	EHea
- 'Julie Ann Platt'	EHea
- 'Juno'	EHea
- 'Kaiser'	EHea
- 'Karin Blum'	EHea
- 'Kermit'	EHea
- 'Kerstin' ♀H4	CBcs EHea LRHS MBar MSwo
	NHol SPlb SRms
- 'Kinlochruel' (d) ♀H4	CNCN CSBt CTri EHea EPfP LRHS
	MBar MBri MGos NHol SPlb SRms
- 'Kir Royal'	EHea
- 'Kirby White'	CNCN EHea LRHS MBar MBri
	NDlv NHol SPlb
- 'Kirsty Anderson'	EHea LRHS
- 'Kit Hill'	EHea MBar
- 'Kontrast'	EHea
- 'Kuphaldtii'	EHea MBar
- 'Kuppendorf'	EHea
- 'Kynance'	CNCN EHea MBar
- 'Lady Maithe'	EHea
- 'Lambstails'	EHea MBar
- 'L'Ancresse'	EHea
- 'Larissa'PBR	EHea
- 'Lemon Gem'	EHea
- 'Lemon Queen'	EHea
- 'Leslie Slinger'	EHea LRHS MBar NHol
- 'Lewis Lilac'	EHea
- 'Liebestraum'	EHea
- 'Lilac Elegance'	EHea
- 'Lime Glade'	CNCN EHea
- 'Lime Gold'	EHea
- 'Little John'	EHea
- 'Llanbedrog Pride' (d)	EHea MBar
- 'Loch Turret'	EHea MBar
- 'Loch-na-Seil'	EHea MBar
- 'Long White'	CNCN EHea MBar
- 'Loni'	EHea
- 'Lyle's Late White'	CNCN EHea
- 'Lyle's Surprise'	EHea MBar
- 'Lyndon Proudley'	EHea
- 'Lüneberg Heath'	EHea
- 'Macdonald of Glencoe'	EHea
§ - 'Mair's Variety' ♀H4	CBrm EHea MBar
- 'Mallard'	EHea
- 'Manitoba'	EHea
- 'Manuel **new**'	EHea
- 'Marianne'	EHea
- 'Marie'	EHea
- 'Marion Blum'	EHea MBar
- 'Marleen'	CNCN EHea MBar NHol
§ - 'Marleen Select'	EHea

§ - 'Marlies' EHea NHol
- 'Martha Hermann' EHea
- 'Martine Langenberg' EHea
- 'Masquerade' EHea MBar
- 'Matita' EHea
- 'Mauvelyn' EHea
- 'Mazurka' EHea
- 'Melanie' EHea LRHS MBar MSwo NHol
- 'Mick Jamieson' (d) EHea
- 'Mies' EHea
- 'Minima' EHea MBar
- 'Minima Smith's Variety' EHea MBar
- 'Miniöxabäck' EHea
- 'Minty' EHea
- 'Mirelle' CNCN EHea
- 'Miss Muffet' EHea NHol
- 'Molecule' EHea MBar
- 'Monika' (d) EHea
- 'Monja' EHea
- 'Moon Glow' EHea
- 'Mountain Snow' EHea
§ - 'Mousehole' CNCN EHea LRHS MBar NHol
- 'Mousehole Compact' see *C. vulgaris* 'Mousehole'
- 'Mrs Alf' EHea
- 'Mrs E. Wilson' (d) EHea
- 'Mrs Pat' CNCN EHea LRHS MBar NHol
- 'Mrs Pinxteren' EHea
- 'Mrs Ronald Gray' CNCN EHea MBar
- 'Mullach Mor' EHea
§ - 'Mullardoch' EHea MBar
- 'Mullion' ♀H4 EHea MBar
- 'Multicolor' CNCN EHea LRHS MBar NDlv NHol SRms
- 'Murielle Dobson' EHea MBar
§ - 'My Dream' (d) ♀H4 CNCN CSBt EHea EPfP LRHS MBar NHol SCoo
- 'Nana' EHea
- 'Nana Compacta' CNCN EHea MBar
- 'Natasja' EHea
- 'Naturpark' EHea MBar
- 'Nele' (d) **new** EHea
- 'Nico' EHea
- 'Nofretete' **new** EHea
- Nordlicht see *C. vulgaris* 'Skone'
- 'October White' CNCN EHea
- 'Odette' EHea
- 'Oiseval' EHea
- 'Old Rose' EHea
- 'Olive Turner' EHea
- 'Olympic Gold' EHea
- 'Orange and Gold' EHea LRHS
- 'Orange Carpet' EHea
- 'Orange Max' EHea
- 'Orange Queen' CNCN CSBt EHea LRHS MBar
- 'Öxabäck' EHea MBar
- 'Oxshott Common' CNCN EHea GQui MBar
- 'Pallida' EHea
- 'Parsons' Gold' EHea
- 'Parsons' Grey Selected' EHea
- 'Pastell' (d) EHea
- 'Pat's Gold' EHea
- 'Peace' EHea
- 'Pearl Drop' EHea MBar
- 'Peggy' EHea
- 'Penhale' EHea
- 'Penny Bun' EHea
- 'Pennyacre Gold' EHea
- 'Pennyacre Lemon' EHea
- 'Pepper and Salt' see *C. vulgaris* 'Hugh Nicholson'
- 'Perestrojka' EHea NHol
- 'Peter Sparkes' (d) ♀H4 CNCN CSBt EHea EPfP LRHS MBar MBri MGos NHol SRms
- 'Petra' EHea
- 'Pewter Plate' EHea MBar
- 'Pink Alicia' PBR **new** EHea
- 'Pink Beale' see *C. vulgaris* 'H.E. Beale'

- 'Pink Dream' (d) EHea
- 'Pink Gown' EHea
- 'Pink Spreader' EHea
- 'Pink Tips' EHea
- 'Plantarium' EHea
- 'Platt's Surprise' (d) EHea
- 'Polly' EHea
- 'Poolster' EHea
- 'Porth Wen White' EHea
- 'Prizewinner' EHea
* - 'Procumbens' **new** EHea
- 'Prostrata Flagelliformis' EHea
- 'Prostrate Orange' CNCN EHea MBar
§ - 'Punch's Dessert' EHea
- 'Purple Passion' EPfP
- 'Pygmaea' EHea MBar
- 'Pyramidalis' EHea
- 'Pyrenaica' EHea MBar
- 'Quail' EHea
- 'R.A. McEwan' EHea
- 'Radnor' (d) ♀H4 CBcs CNCN CSBt EHea LRHS MBar
- 'Radnor Gold' (d) EHea MBar
- 'Raket' EHea
- 'Ralph Purnell' CNCN EHea MBar
- 'Ralph Purnell Select' EHea
- 'Ralph's Pearl' EHea
- 'Ralph's Red' EHea
- 'Randall's Crimson' EHea
- 'Rannoch' EHea
- 'Rebecca's Red' EHea SRms
- 'Red Carpet' CNCN EHea LRHS MBar
- 'Red Favorit' (d) CBcs EHea LRHS SRms
- 'Red Fred' EHea NHol
- 'Red Haze' CNCN EHea EPfP LRHS MBar NHol
- 'Red Max' EHea
- 'Red Pimpernel' CNCN EHea EPfP MBar NHol
- 'Red Rug' EHea
- 'Red Star' (d) CNCN EHea LRHS MBar NHol
- 'Red Wings' EHea
- 'Redbud' EHea
- 'Redgauntlet' EHea
- 'Reini' EHea NHol
- 'Rica' EHea
- 'Richard Cooper' EHea MBar
- 'Rieanne' EHea
- 'Rigida Prostrata' see *C. vulgaris* 'Alba Rigida'
- 'Rivington' EHea
- 'Robber Knight' EHea
- 'Robert Chapman' ♀H4 CBrm CNCN CSBt CTri EHea LRHS MBar MBri NHol SRms
- 'Rock Spray' EHea
- 'Röding' EHea
- 'Rokoko' EHea
- 'Roland Haagen' ♀H4 EHea MBar
- 'Roma' EHea LRHS MBar
- 'Romina' CNCN EHea MSwo NHol
- 'Ronas Hill' CNCN EHea
- 'Roodkapje' EHea
- 'Rosalind' ambig. CNCN CSBt EPfP LRHS MBar NHol
- 'Rosalind, Crastock Heath' EHea
- 'Rosalind, Underwood's' EHea LRHS
- 'Ross Hutton' EHea
- 'Roswitha' EHea
§ - 'Roter Oktober' EHea
- 'Rotfuchs' EHea
- 'Ruby Slinger' CNCN EHea LRHS MBar
- 'Rusty Triumph' EHea
- 'Ruth Sparkes' (d) CNCN EHea LRHS MBar NHol
- 'Sabrina' (d) EHea
- 'Saima' EHea
- 'Saint Nick' EHea MBar

– 'Salland'	EHea
– 'Sally Anne Proudley'	CNCN EHea MBar
– 'Salmon Leap'	EHea MBar NHol
– 'Sam Hewitt'	EHea
– 'Sampford Sunset'	CSam EHea
– 'Sandhammaren'	EHea
– 'Sandwood Bay'	EHea
– 'Sandy'PBR	CBcs EHea SPoG
– 'Sarah Platt' (d)	EHea
– 'Saskia'	EHea
– 'Schneewolke'PBR **new**	EHea
– 'Scholje's Jimmy'	EHea
– 'Scholje's Rubin' (d)	EHea
– 'Scholje's Super Star' (d)	EHea
– 'Schurig's Sensation' (d)	CNCN EHea LRHS MBar
– 'Schurig's Wonder' (d)	EHea
– 'Scotch Mist'	EHea
– 'Sedloňov'	EHea
– 'Sellingsloh'	EHea
– 'September Pink'	EHea
– 'Serlei'	EHea LRHS MBar
– 'Serlei Aurea' ♀H4	CNCN CSBt EHea EPfP LRHS MBar NHol
– 'Serlei Grandiflora'	EHea MBar
– 'Serlei Purpurea'	EHea
– 'Serlei Rubra'	EHea
– 'Sesam'	EHea
– 'Sesse'	EHea
– 'Shirley'	EHea MBar
– 'Silberspargel'	EHea
– 'Silver Cloud'	CNCN EHea MBar
– 'Silver Fox'	EHea
– 'Silver King'	CNCN EHea LRHS MBar
– 'Silver Knight'	CNCN CSBt EHea EPfP LRHS MBar MBri MGos NHol SPlb
– 'Silver Pearl'	EHea
– 'Silver Queen' ♀H4	CNCN EHea LRHS MBar MBri NHol SPer SRms
– 'Silver Rose' ♀H4	CNCN EHea LRHS MBar
– 'Silver Sandra'	EHea
– 'Silver Spire'	CNCN EHea MBar
– 'Silver Stream'	EHea LRHS MBar
– 'Silver White'	EHea
– 'Silvie'	EHea
– 'Simone'	EHea
– 'Sir Anthony Hopkins'	EHea
– 'Sir John Charrington' ♀H4	CBcs CNCN CSBt EHea EPfP LRHS MBar MBri MGos NHol
– 'Sirsson'	EHea MBar
– 'Sister Anne' ♀H4	CNCN CSBt EHea EPfP LRHS MBri NHol SPer SRms
– 'Skipper'	EHea MBar
§ – 'Skone' (v)	EHea
– 'Snowball'	see *C. vulgaris* 'My Dream'
– 'Snowflake'	EHea
– 'Soay'	EHea MBar
– 'Sonja' (d)	EHea
– 'Sonning' (d)	EHea
– 'Sonny Boy'	EHea
– 'Sophia' (d)	EHea
– 'Sparkling Stars'	EHea
– 'Sphinx' **new**	EHea
– 'Spicata'	EHea
– 'Spicata Aurea'	CNCN EHea MBar
– 'Spicata Nana'	EHea
– 'Spider'	EHea
– 'Spitfire'	CNCN EHea LRHS MBar NHol
– 'Spook'	EHea
– 'Spring Cream' ♀H4	CBcs CNCN EHea LRHS MBar MBri NHol SPoG
– 'Spring Glow'	CNCN EHea LRHS MBar MBri
– 'Spring Torch'	CBcs CNCN CSBt EHea LRHS MBar MBri NHol SCoo SPoG
– 'Springbank'	EHea MBar
– 'Stag's Horn'	EHea
I – 'Startler'	EHea

– 'Stefanie'	EHea NHol SRms
– 'Stranger'	EHea
– 'Strawberry Delight' (d)	EHea EPfP NHol
– 'Summer Elegance'	EHea
– 'Summer Orange'	CNCN EHea LRHS MBar NHol
– 'Summer White' (d)	EHea
– 'Sunningdale'	see *C. vulgaris* 'Finale'
– 'Sunrise'	CNCN CSBt EHea EPfP LRHS MBar MGos NHol
– 'Sunset' ♀H4	CNCN CSBt EHea LRHS MBar NHol SRms
– 'Sunset Glow'	EHea
– 'Talisker'	EHea
– 'Tenella'	EHea
– 'Tenuis'	EHea MBar
– 'Terrick's Orange'	EHea
– 'The Pygmy'	EHea
– 'Theresa' **new**	EHea
– 'Tib' (d) ♀H4	CSBt EHea LRHS MBar MBri NBlu NDlv SRms
– 'Tijdens Copper'	EHea
– 'Tino'	EHea
– 'Tom Thumb'	EHea MBar
– 'Torogay'	EHea
– 'Torulosa'	EHea
– 'Tremans'	EHea
– 'Tricolorifolia'	CNCN EHea EPfP LRHS NHol
– 'Underwoodii'	EHea MBar
– 'Unity'	EHea
– 'Valorian'	EHea
– 'Van Beek'	EHea
§ – 'Velvet Dome'	EHea LRHS MBar
– 'Velvet Fascination' ♀H4	CBcs CNCN EHea EPfP LRHS MBar MGos NHol
– 'Violet Bamford'	EHea
– 'Visser's Fancy'	EHea
§ – 'Walter Ingwersen'	EHea
– 'Waquoit Brightness'	EHea
– 'Waquoit Gwen' **new**	EHea
– 'Westerlee Gold'	EHea
– 'Westerlee Green'	EHea
– 'Westphalia'	EHea
– 'White Bouquet'	see *C. vulgaris* 'Alba Plena'
– 'White Carpet'	EHea MBar
– 'White Coral' (d)	EHea EPfP MGos
– 'White Gold'	EHea
– 'White Gown'	EHea
– 'White Lawn' ♀H4	CNCN EHea LRHS MBar MSwo NDlv NHol SRms
– 'White Mite'	EHea MBar
– 'White Pearl' (d)	EHea
– 'White Princess'	see *C. vulgaris* 'White Queen'
§ – 'White Queen'	EHea MBar
– 'White Star' (d)	EHea LRHS
– 'Whiteness'	CNCN EHea MBar
– 'Wickwar Flame' ♀H4	CBcs CNCN CSBt EHea EPfP LRHS MBar MBri MGos NHol SPlb SRms
– 'Wilma'	EHea
– 'Wingates Gem'	EHea
– 'Wingates Gold'	EHea
– 'Winter Chocolate'	CNCN CSBt EHea EPfP LRHS MBar MBri MSwo NDlv NHol
– 'Winter Fire'	EHea
– 'Winter Red'	EHea
– 'Wollmer's Weisse' (d)	EHea
– 'Wood Close'	EHea
– 'Yellow Basket'	EHea
– 'Yellow Beauty'PBR **new**	EHea
– 'Yellow Dome'	CNCN
– 'Yellow Globe'	EHea
– 'Yellow One'	EHea
– 'Yvette's Gold'	EHea
– 'Yvette's Silver'	EHea
– 'Yvonne Clare'	EHea

Calocedrus (*Cupressaceae*)

§	***decurrens*** ♀[H4]	CBcs CDoC CDul CLnd CMac CTho CTri EHul EPfP LCon LPan LRHS MBar MBlu MBri MGos MMuc NWea SBLw SLim SPer SPoG WEve WMou
	- 'Aureovariegata' (v)	CBcs CKen CWib EBrs EHul LCon LPan LRHS MAsh MBar MBlu MBri NLar SBLw SCoo SLim SPoG WEve WFar
	- 'Berrima Gold'	CDoC CKen EBrs EPfP LCon LRHS MGos NLar SLim SPoG WEve
§	- 'Depressa'	CKen
	- 'Intricata'	CKen NLar SLim
	- 'Maupin Glow' (v)	NLar SLim
	- 'Nana'	see *C. decurrens* 'Depressa'
	- 'Pillar'	CKen MAsh NLar
	formosana	WPic
	macrolepis	EMon

Calocephalus (*Asteraceae*)

brownii	see *Leucophyta brownii*

Calochortus (*Liliaceae*)

albus	ECho
- var. ***rubellus***	ECho
argillosus	CPBP
barbatus	EPot
'Cupido'[PBR] **new**	ECho
luteus Douglas ex Lindl.	CPBP EPot
- 'Golden Orb'[PBR]	EChP ECho LRHS
splendens 'Violet Queen'	EBrs ECho
superbus	EChP ECho EPot LRHS
uniflorus	EPot WCot
venustus	EChP ECho EPot LRHS
vestae	WCot

Calomeria (*Asteraceae*)

§ ***amaranthoides***	WJek

Calonyction see *Ipomoea*

Calopsis (*Restionaceae*)

levynsiae **new**	CBig
paniculata	CBig CCCN CPne CTrC EBee IArd IDee WMul WPGP

Caloscordum (*Alliaceae*)

§ ***neriniflorum***	EBur WAbe WCot

Calothamnus (*Myrtaceae*)

blepharospermus	SOWG
gilesii	SOWG
homolophyllus	SOWG
quadrifidus	EShb SOWG
- yellow-flowered	SOWG
rupestris	SOWG
sanguineus	SOWG
validus	SOWG SPlb

Caltha ✿ (*Ranunculaceae*)

'Auenwald'	CLAP CRow
'Honeydew'	CDes CLAP CRow EBee GBuc WPGP
introloba	SWat
laeta	see *C. palustris* var. *palustris*
leptosepala	CLAP CRow EBee NWCA
natans	CRow
palustris ♀[H4]	More than 30 suppliers
- var. ***alba***	More than 30 suppliers
- var. ***barthei***	CFir GEdr GKev
- 'Flore Pleno' (d) ♀[H4]	More than 30 suppliers
- var. ***himalensis***	MGol WCot
- 'Marilyn'	CLAP GBuc
- 'Multiplex' (d)	CFwr COtt GBuc GGar SPoG

§	- var. ***palustris***	CBen CBre CRow ECha EHon ELan EMFW EMon EWTr GGar LPBA SWat WCra WFar WPnP WWpP
	- - 'Plena' (d)	COIW CRow CWat ENot EPfP LNCo LRHS SMac WFar WWpP
	- subsp. ***polypetala***	CDWL LNCo NPer SMad SWat WMAq WPnP
	- var. ***radicans***	CRow GCrs
	- - 'Flore Pleno' (d)	CRow
	- 'Semiplena' (d)	EMon
	- 'Stagnalis'	CRow WWpP
	- Trotter's form	GBuc
	- 'Tyermannii'	CRow
	- 'Yellow Giant'	CDWL
N	***polypetala*** misapplied	see *C. palustris* var. *palustris*
N	***polypetala*** Hochst. ex Lorent	CLAP CWat EBee EWll GBuc LNCo WBor
	- from Turkey **new**	GBuc
	sagittata	CLAP CRow
	scaposa	EBee
	'Susan'	CRow

Calycanthus (*Calycanthaceae*)

	fertilis	see *C. floridus* var. *glaucus*
	- 'Purpureus'	see *C. floridus* var. *glaucus* 'Purpureus'
	floridus	CAgr CArn CBcs CMCN CPMA CPle CTho CWib EBee ELan EPfP EWTr IDee LAst LEdu LRHS MBNS MBlu MBri MDun SBrw SDnm SMur SPer SPlb SPoG WDin
§	- var. ***glaucus***	CPLG EPfP LBuc MGos NBlu NLar WSHC
§	- - 'Purpureus'	CBcs CPMA MBlu NLar
	- var. ***laevigatus***	see *C. floridus* var. *glaucus*
	- var. ***oblongifolius***	NLar
	occidentalis	CAgr CArn CBcs CDul CMCN CPle CWib ECrN EPfP GIBF IDee MBlu SBrw SGar SMur SSpi
	- NNS 02-93	WCot

Calycanthus x *Sinocalycanthus* see x *Sinocalycanthus*

C. floridus x *S. chinensis*	see x *Sinocalycanthus raulstonii*

Calystegia (*Convolvulaceae*)

	affinis	CPIN
§	***hederacea*** 'Flore Pleno' (d)	CPIN EBee EChP ELan EMon MCCP NCGa NLar NSti SMad SSvw WCMO WCot WFar
	japonica 'Flore Pleno'	see *C. hederacea* 'Flore Pleno'
	silvatica 'Incarnata'	EBee EMon EWes
	soldanella	XPep
	- NNS 99-85	EBee WCot

Calytrix (*Myrtaceae*)

tetragona	SPlb
- compact, pink	SOWG

Cape gooseberry see *Physalis peruviana*

Comarum see *Potentilla*

Camassia ✿ (*Hyacinthaceae*)

	biflora	EBee
	cusickii	More than 30 suppliers
	- white-flowered **new**	IFoB
	- 'Zwanenburg'	EBee GKev LRHS MSte WDav
	esculenta Lindl.	see *C. quamash*
	fraseri	see *C. scilloides*
	howellii	EBee
	leichtlinii misapplied	see *C. leichtlinii* subsp. *suksdorfii*
	leichtlinii (Baker) S.Watson	ECho ISea SSto
N	- 'Alba' hort.	see *C. leichtlinii* subsp. *leichtlinii*

*	- 'Alba Plena'	NBPC NBir
	- 'Blauwe Donau'	see *C. leichtlinii* subsp. *suksdorfii* 'Blauwe Donau'
	- Blue Danube	see *C. leichtlinii* subsp. *suksdorfii* 'Blauwe Donau'
§	- subsp. **leichtlinii** ♀H4	More than 30 suppliers
	- 'Magdalen'	CAvo CFFs
N	- 'Plena' (d)	ECha MSte
	- 'Semiplena' (d)	CAvo CBro CFFs CFwr CMea CMil EBee EChP EMan EMon EPot LPhx LRHS MDun MSte NMen WAul WCot WDav WHoo
§	- subsp. **suksdorfii**	CAvo EBee ECho GBBs GBuc LRHS MSph MWat NBPC WAul
§	- - 'Blauwe Donau'	EBee EMar GKev LEdu MSte WDav
	- - Caerulea Group	More than 30 suppliers
	- - 'Electra'	ECha SUsu
§	**quamash**	More than 30 suppliers
	- 'Blue Melody' (v)	CBow CBro CMea EBee EBrs EMan EMon EPPr EPot GBuc GKev GMac GSki LPhx LRHS MCCP MDun MWgw NMRc NMen WCra
	- 'Orion'	CBro CMea EBee EMon GBuc GMac LPhx WAul WCot
§	**scilloides**	EBee WRos

Camellia ✿ (Theaceae)

'Adorable' (*pitardii* hybrid) **new**	CDoC
'Alpen Glo' **new**	CDoC
'Ariel's Song' (*fraterna* x *tsaii*) **new**	CDoC
'Auburn White'	see *C. japonica* 'Mrs Bertha A. Harms'
'Baby Bear' **new**	CDoC
'Baby Jane' **new**	CDoC
'Bacciochi'	NLar
'Barbara Clark' (*saluenensis* x *reticulata*)	CTrG MAsh MGos SCog
'Bertha Harms Blush'	see *C. japonica* 'Mrs Bertha A. Harms'
'Bett's Supreme' **new**	CDoC
'Black Lace' (*reticulata* x *williamsii*) ♀H4	CCtw CTbh CTrh CTri EKen EPfP GLld MAsh MBri NPri SBrw SCam SCog SPoG WCot WGob WMoo
'Blissful Dawn' **new**	CTrh
'Blondy' (*pitardii* x *fraterna*) **new**	CDoC
'Bonnie Marie' (hybrid)	CBcs MGos SCam SCog
'Brian' (*saluenensis* x *reticulata*) **new**	CDoC
'Canterbury' **new**	CDoC
'Charles Cobb'	see *C. japonica* 'Mrs Charles Cobb'
* 'Chatsworth Belle'	CTrh SCam
'China Lady' (*reticulata* x *granthamiana*)	MBri
'Cinnamon Cindy' (hybrid)	CDoC SCam SCog
'Contessa Lavinia Maggi'	see *C. japonica* 'Lavinia Maggi'
* 'Cornish Clay'	ISea
'Cornish Snow' (*cuspidata* x *saluenensis*) ♀H4	CDoC CSBt CSam EPfP ISea MGos SBrw SCam SCog SHBN SPur SSpi SSta WFar
'Cornish Spring' (*japonica* x *cuspidata*) ♀H4	CCCN CCtw CDoC CSBt CTbh CTrh ENot EPfP LHyd NVic SBrw SCog WCot
'Corsica'	SHBN
'Cotton Tail' **new**	CDoC
cuspidata	LHyd
'Czar'	see *C. japonica* 'The Czar'
'Dainty Dale' (hybrid)	SCam SSta
'Delia Williams'	see *C.* x *williamsii* 'Citation'
'Diana's Charm'	CDoC LSRN
'Doctor Clifford Parks' (*reticulata* x *japonica*) ♀H2	GLld LHyd SCam SCog
'Donckelaeri'	see *C. japonica* 'Masayoshi'

'El Dorado' (*pitardii* x *japonica*)	CTrG
'Elizabeth Bolitho'	SBrw
'Emerald Jade' **new**	CDoC
'Extravaganza' (*japonica* hybrid)	CBcs CTrh IArd MBri SCog
'Fairy Blush' **new**	CDoC
'Faustina Lechi'	see *C. japonica* 'Faustina'
'Felice Harris' (*sasanqua* x *reticulata*)	MBri SCam SCog
'Fire 'n' Ice'	SCam SCog
forrestii **new**	CPLG
'Fox's Fancy' **new**	CDoC
'Fragrant Pink' (*rusticana* x *lutchuensis*)	CTrh
'Francie L' (*saluenensis* x *reticulata*) ♀H3-4	CDoC CDul CTrh EPfP LHyd SBrw SCam SCog SSta
'Freedom Bell' (hybrid) ♀H4	CCtw CMHG CTbh CTrG CTrh ENot GGGa ISea LHyd MAsh SCam SCog
'Gay Baby' (hybrid)	CDoC MGos
'Geenty's Green' **new**	CDoC
'Golden Anniversary'	see *C. japonica* 'Dahlohnega'
grijsii	CTrh LHyd
§ **hiemalis** 'Bonanza'	CTrh SCam
- 'Chansonette'	CDoC SCam SCog
§ - 'Dazzler'	CBcs CSBt LHyd SBrw SCam SCog
- 'Kanjirō'	CDoC CTrh LHyd SCam SCog
- 'Showa Supreme'	SCam
- 'Shōwa-no-sakae'	SCog
§ - 'Sparkling Burgundy' ♀H3	CBcs CBrm CDoC ENot EPfP GLld LHyd MGos SCam SCog
'High Fragrance' **new**	CDoC
'Hooker'	CDoC
'Howard Asper' (*reticulata* x *japonica*)	SCam
'Ice Follies'	SCam SCog
'Imbricata Rubra'	see *C. japonica* 'Imbricata'
'Innovation' (x *williamsii* x *reticulata*)	NBlu SCam
'Inspiration' (*reticulata* x *saluenensis*) ♀H4	CBcs CDoC CMHG CMac CSBt CTrG CTrh CWSG EBee ENot EPfP GGGa LHyd MBri MGos NBlu SBod SCam SCog SHBN SPoG SSpi
japonica 'Aaron's Ruby'	CBcs COtt SBrw SCam SCog
- 'Ace of Hearts'	MBri
- 'Ada Pieper'	CTrh
- 'Adelina Patti' ♀H4	CBcs CCtw CMHG CSBt CTrh ENot LHyd SCog
- 'Adolphe Audusson' ♀H4	More than 30 suppliers
§ - 'Akashigata' ♀H4	CBcs CDoC CTrG CTrw ENot EPfP MAsh SBrw SCam SCog SPoG SSta WCot
§ - 'Akebono'	CBcs CTrw
- 'Alba Plena' ♀H4	CTbh CTrh CWSG EGra LHyd MGos SBod SCog WFar
- 'Alba Simplex'	CDoC CMac ELan EPfP SBod SBrw SCam SCog SHBN SMer SPer SSpi SSta WGob
- 'Alexander Hunter' ♀H4	LHyd SBod SCam SCog
- 'Alexis Smith'	CBcs
§ - 'Althaeiflora'	CBcs CDoC MGos SCam SCog
- 'Ama-no-gawa'	LHyd
- 'Amazing Graces' **new**	CDoC
- 'Anemoniflora'	CDoC CTrG ELan SBrw SCam WFar
- 'Angel'	CBcs SCam SCog
- 'Angello' **new**	EKen
- 'Annie Wylam' ♀H4	CTrh LHyd SCog
- 'Apollo' ambig. **new**	CBcs
I - 'Apollo' Pauls	CSam CTrG CTrh EPfP MGos MSwo NBlu SCam SCog SHBN SBrw
- 'Apollo 14' **new**	SBrw
§ - 'Apple Blossom' ♀H4	CBcs CMac ELan
- 'Arajishi' misapplied	see *C. rusticana* 'Beni-arajishi'
* - 'Augustine Supreme'	CMac

- 'Australis' ♀H4 — CTrh SCam
- 'Ave Maria' ♀H4 — CDoC CTrh MAsh
- 'Baby Pearl' **new** — SCam
- 'Baby Sis' — SBrw SCam
- 'Ballet Dancer' ♀H4 — MGos SCam SCog
- 'Bambino' **new** — CDoC
- 'Barbara Woodroof' — CBcs
- 'Baron Gomer' — see *C. japonica* 'Comte de Gomer'
- 'Baronne Leguay' — SCam
- 'Beau Harp' — SCam
- 'Bella Romana' — SCam
- 'Benidaikagura' — SCam
- 'Benten' (v) — CTrG CTrw
- 'Berenice Boddy' ♀H4 — CBcs CTrh SCam
- 'Berenice Perfection' — CMHG LHyd WFar
- 'Betty Foy Sanders' — CTrh
- 'Betty Sheffield' — COtt CTrG MGos SCog SHBN WFar
- 'Betty Sheffield Pink' — CTrG SCam
- 'Betty Sheffield Supreme' — CBcs
- 'Bienville' — SCog
- 'Billie McCaskill' — SCam
- 'Black Tie' — CTbh LHyd MGos SBrw SCog
- 'Blackburnia' — see *C. japonica* 'Althaeiflora'
- 'Blaze of Glory' — CTrh NLar SCog
§ - 'Blood of China' — CBcs CCtw CSBt CWSG LRHS NLar SCam SCog WCwm WFar WMoo
- 'Bob Hope' ♀H4 — CBcs CDoC CTrh GLld MGos NBlu
- 'Bob's Tinsie' ♀H4 — CDoC CMHG CSBt CTrw ENot EPfP ISea
§ - 'Bokuhan' ♀H4 — CCtw CDoC EPfP SCog
- 'Bright Buoy' — CDoC
- 'Brushfield's Yellow' ♀H4 — CBcs CDoC CMHG COtt CSBt CTbh ELan EPfP GLld IArd IMGH ISea LHyd MAsh MBri MDun MGos NBlu SBrw SCam SCog SSta WFar WGob
§ - 'C.M. Hovey' ♀H4 — CMHG CMac CTrh EPfP MAsh SCam SHBN
- 'C.M. Wilson' — CMac SCog
N - 'Campbellii' — CDoC
- 'Campsii Alba' — SMer
- 'Can Can' — CBcs CDoC CTrG SCam SCog
- 'Canon Boscawen' — CTrG
- 'Cara Mia' — CBcs SCam
- 'Carolina Beauty' — CDoC
- 'Carter's Sunburst' ♀H4 — CBcs CTrh ELan ENot EPfP SBrw SCam SCog SPoG WGob
- 'Chandleri Elegans' — see *C. japonica* 'Elegans'
- 'Charlotte de Rothschild' — CTrh CTri GLld NPri
- 'Cheryll Lynn' — CTrh
- 'Christmas Beauty' — SCam
- 'Cinderella' — SCog
- 'Clarise Carleton' — CTrh GGGa LHyd MBri
- 'Clarissa' — NPri SCam
- 'Colonel Firey' — see *C. japonica* 'C.M. Hovey'
- 'Commander Mulroy' ♀H4 — CTrh MBri SCam
§ - 'Comte de Gomer' — ELan EPfP SBrw SCam SCog
- 'Conspicua' — CBcs
§ - 'Coquettii' ♀H4 — CBcs CDul
- 'Coral Beauty' — WFar
- 'Coral Pink Lotus' — SCam
- 'Coral Queen' — SCam
§ - 'Dahlohnega' — CTrh
- 'Daikagura' — CBcs
- 'Dainty' — CBcs SBrw
- 'Daitairin' — see *C. japonica* 'Dewatairin'
- 'Dark of the Moon' **new** — CDoC
- 'Dear Jenny' — CBcs CTrG
- 'Debutante' — CBcs CDoC CMac CTrh LHyd LRHS MAsh SCam
- 'Desire' ♀H4 — CBcs CMHG CTrh ENot GLld MDun SBrw SCam SPoG WGob
- 'Devonia' — CBcs EPfP LHyd SCog

§ - 'Dewatairin' (Higo) — CBcs SCam SCog
- 'Dixie Knight' — CDoC MGos SCam SCog
- 'Dobreei' — CMac
- 'Doctor Burnside' — CBcs CDoC CMHG CTrh SCam SCog
- 'Doctor Olga Petersen' — SCog
- 'Doctor Tinsley' ♀H4 — CDoC GLld LRHS MAsh NPri SCam
- 'Dolly Dyer' **new** — CDoC
- 'Dona Herzilia de Freitas Magalhaes' — SCam SCog
- 'Dona Jane Andresson' — SCam
- 'Donckelaeri' — see *C. japonica* 'Masayoshi'
- 'Donnan's Dream' — CTrh
- 'Doris Ellis' — CMHG
- 'Double Rose' (d) — NBlu SCog
- 'Drama Girl' ♀H2 — CBcs CDoC CTrw SBod SBrw SCam SCog
- 'Duc de Bretagne' — ISea SCog
- 'Duchesse Decazes' — CBcs MBri
- 'Edelweiss' — CDoC MGos SCam SCog
- 'Effendee' — see *C. sasanqua* 'Rosea Plena'
§ - 'Elegans' ♀H4 — CBcs CDoC CMac CTrG ENot EPfP ISea MAsh NBlu SBod SBrw SCam SCog SHBN SPer SReu SSta WFar
- 'Elegans Splendor' — CDoC
- 'Elegans Supreme' — CDoC
- 'Elegant Beauty' — see *C. x williamsii* 'Elegant Beauty'
- 'Elisabeth' — WFar
- 'Elizabeth Arden' — SBrw
- 'Elizabeth Dowd' — CBcs SCog
- 'Elizabeth Hawkins' — CTrh GLld LHyd MAsh SBrw
- 'Ella Drayton' — SCog
- 'Ellen Sampson' — GLld
- 'Emmett Barnes' — LHyd SCam
- 'Emmett Pfingstl' — SCam
- 'Emperor of Russia' — CBcs LHyd LRHS
- 'Erin Farmer' — CBcs
- 'Eugène Lizé' — SCam
- 'Evelyn' — SCam
- 'Eximia' — NBlu SCam
- 'Faith' — CBcs
- 'Fanny' — SCam
- 'Fashionata' — SCam
§ - 'Faustina' — MAsh
§ - 'Fimbriata' — CDoC SCam
- 'Fimbriata Alba' — see *C. japonica* 'Fimbriata'
- 'Finlandia Variegated' — SCam SCog
- 'Fire Dance' — CTrh
- 'Fire Falls' ♀H4 — CMHG
- 'Firebird' **new** — CBcs
- 'Flame' — CBcs
- 'Flashlight' — EPfP
§ - 'Fleur Dipater' — SCam SPoG
- 'Flowerwood' — SCam SCog WFar
- 'Forest Green' — ELan
- 'Fortune Teller' — CBcs
- 'Frans van Damme' — CBcs LHop
- 'Fred Sander' — CBcs CDoC CWSG GLld SCam SCog SMer
- 'Frosty Morn' — CBcs ELan
- 'Furo-an' — MAsh SCam
- 'Geisha Girl' — SCam SCog
- 'Général Lamoricière' — CDoC
§ - 'Gigantea' — NBlu SBrw SCam
- 'Giuditta Rosani' — CDoC
- 'Giuseppina Pieri' — LHyd
- 'Gladys Wannamaker' — SCog
- 'Glen 40' — see *C. japonica* 'Coquettii'
- 'Gloire de Nantes' ♀H4 — NBlu SBrw SCam SCog
- 'Gold Tone' — SCam
- 'Grace Bunton' — CBcs CDoC MGos SCam SCog
- 'Granada' — SCog
- 'Grand Prix' ♀H4 — CDoC CTrh CTrw GLld LHyd LRHS MGos SCam SCog

- 'Grand Slam' ♀H2	CBcs CBrm CDoC CDul CMac CTrh EPfP LRHS SCam SCog
- 'Guest of Honor'	CBcs CTbh
- 'Guilio Nuccio' ♀H4	CBcs CDoC CTbh CTrG EPfP IArd LRHS MGos NPri SCam SCog SMer SPer SPur
- 'Gus Menard'	SCam
- 'Gwenneth Morey'	CBcs CDoC CTbh ELan EPfP SCam
- 'H.A. Downing'	SCam
§ - 'Hagoromo' ♀H4	CBcs CDoC CTrh ELan EPfP MAsh SCog SHBN SPer WFar
§ - 'Hakurakuten' ♀H4	CMHG CTrh EHol GLld IArd ISea SBrw SCam SCog
- 'Hanafúki'	MAsh MGos SCam SCog
- 'Hanatachibana'	SCam
- 'Hatsuzakura'	see *C. japonica* 'Dewatairin'
- 'Hawaii'	CSBt CTrh MGos SCam SCog
- Herme	see *C. japonica* 'Hikarugenji'
- 'High Hat'	CBcs LHyd SCog
§ - 'Hikarugenji'	MGos SCog
- 'Hime-otome'	SCam
- 'Hinomaru'	CMac
- 'Holly Bright'	CTrh GLld
- HTB 10	SCam
- HTB 4	SCam
§ - 'Imbricata'	CBcs ENot ISea MAsh SCog
- 'Imbricata Alba'	SCam
- 'Incarnata'	SCam
- 'Italiana Vera'	MAsh
- 'J.J.Whitfield'	CMac
- 'Jack Jones Scented'	CMHG
- 'Janet Waterhouse'	CBcs WFar
- 'Jean Clere'	CTrG GLld MGos MWea SCog
- 'Jingle Bells'	CBcs
- 'Joseph Pfingstl' ♀H4	CCtw CDoC GLld MAsh NPri SCam SCog
- 'Joshua E.Youtz'	LHyd SCog
- 'Jovey Carlyon'	CBcs CDoC
- 'Joy Sander'	see *C. japonica* 'Apple Blossom'
§ - 'Julia Drayton'	LRHS MAsh
- 'Julia France'	SCog
- 'Juno'	CBcs SBrw SCam
I - 'Jupiter' Paul ♀H4	CBcs CDoC CMac CTbh CTrh CTri CTrw EPfP ISea LHyd LSRN MGos SBrw SCog SHBN
- 'Justine Heurtin'	SCam
§ - 'K. Sawada'	SCam SCog
- 'Katie'	MDun SCog
- 'Kellingtoniana'	see *C. japonica* 'Gigantea'
- 'Kenny'	CBcs
- 'Kentucky'	SCam
- 'Kewpie Doll'	CTrh
- 'Kick-off'	CBcs CTrh SCog
- 'Kimberley'	CBcs CCtw CDoC EPfP GLld SCog
- 'King Size'	CDoC SCam
- 'King's Ransom'	CMac MAsh
§ - 'Kingyo-tsubaki'	SSta
- 'Kitty Berry'	CTrh
- 'Kokinran'	SCam
§ - 'Konronkoku' ♀H4	CBcs CCtw CDoC CTrh SCog
- 'Kouron-jura'	see *C. japonica* 'Konronkoku'
- 'Kramer's Beauty'	SCog SPoG
- 'Kramer's Supreme'	CBcs CBrm CCCN CDoC CTrG CWSG MAsh MGos NBlu NLar SBod SBrw SCam SCog WFar
- 'La Graciola'	see *C. japonica* 'Odoratissima'
- 'La Pace Rubra'	SCam
- 'Lady Campbell'	CTri NBlu SCam
- 'Lady Clare'	see *C. japonica* 'Akashigata'
- 'Lady Erma'	CBcs
- 'Lady Loch'	CTrh MAsh MBri MGos SBrw SCam
- 'Lady McCulloch'	SBrw SCam
- 'Lady Vansittart'	CBcs CBrm CDoC CSam CTbh CTrG ELan ENot EPfP GLld ISea LHyd LRHS MAsh MGos NBlu SBrw SCog SPer WGob
§ - 'Lady Vansittart Pink'	NBlu SCam SHBN
- 'Lady Vansittart Red'	see *C. japonica* 'Lady Vansittart Pink'
- 'Lady Vansittart Shell'	see *C. japonica* 'Yours Truly'
- 'Latifolia'	GLld SBrw SCam
- 'Laurie Bray'	SCog WFar
§ - 'Lavinia Maggi' ♀H4	CBcs CTbh CTrG CTrh ELan ENot EPfP GLld LHyd LPan LRHS MAsh MGos NBlu SBrw SCam SCog SHBN SMer SPer SPoG SReu SRms SSta WGob
- 'Lavinia Maggi Rosea'	SCam
- 'L'Avvenire'	SCog
§ - 'Le Lys'	SCam
- 'Lemon Drop'	CTrh SCam
- 'Leonora Novick' **new**	CDoC
- 'Lily Pons' ♀H4	CTrh GLld LHyd
- 'Lipstick'	LHyd
- 'Little Bit'	CBcs CDoC CMHG CTrh SCam SCog SPer
- LOR 280	SCam
- 'Lovelight' ♀H4	CTrh
- 'Ludgvan Red'	SBrw SCam
- 'Lulu Belle'	SCog
- 'Ma Belle'	CMHG
- 'Mabel Blackwell'	SCam
- 'Madame de Strekaloff'	CMac SCam
- 'Madame Lebois'	SCam
- 'Madame Martin Cachet'	CMHG SCog
- 'Madge Miller'	LRHS MAsh
- 'Magic Moments'	SCam
- 'Magnoliiflora'	see *C. japonica* 'Hagoromo'
- 'Magnoliiflora Alba'	see *C. japonica* 'Miyakodori'
- 'Maiden's Blush'	CMac
- 'Margaret Davis'	CCCN CDoC CSBt CTbh CTrG ELan ENot EPfP GLld IMGH LHyd LSRN MAsh MGos MWea SBrw SCam SPoG SCog SPer SSta
- 'Margaret Davis Picotee' ♀H4	CBcs CMHG CTbh CTrh CTrw SCog SPer SSta
- 'Margaret Rose'	SCam
- 'Margaret Short'	CDoC
- 'Margherita Coleoni'	CBcs LHyd SHBN
- 'Marguérite Gouillon'	CBcs ISea LHyd SCam
- 'Marian Mitchell'	SCam
- 'Mariana'	SCog
- 'Marie Bracey'	CBcs SCam
- 'Marinka'	CBcs
- 'Marjorie Magnificent'	LRHS MAsh
- 'Mark Alan'	CDoC
- 'Maroon and Gold'	CDoC SCog
- 'Mars' ♀H4	CBcs MGos SBrw SCam SCog WFar
- 'Mary Alice Cox' **new**	CDoC
- 'Mary Costa'	CTrh WFar
- 'Mary J.Wheeler'	CTrw
§ - 'Masayoshi' ♀H4	CSBt CTrG GLld LHyd SCog
§ - 'Mathotiana Alba' ♀H4	CBcs CDoC CMac CSBt ELan EPfP LSRN MAsh SBrw SCam SCog SPer
- 'Mathotiana Purple King'	see *C. japonica* 'Julia Drayton'
§ - 'Mathotiana Rosea' ♀H4	CBcs CMac SCam SHBN SPer
- 'Mathotiana Supreme'	CDoC SCam SCog
- 'Matterhorn'	CTbh CTrh
- 'Mattie Cole'	LHyd SCam WGob
- 'Maui' **new**	CDoC
- 'Mercury' ♀H4	CBcs CMac COtt CTrG CWSG GGGa SCog SHBN
- 'Mercury Variegated'	CMHG
- 'Mermaid' **new**	CDoC
- 'Midnight'	CDoC CMHG GLld SBrw SCam WFar WGob
- 'Midnight Magic'	CTrh
- 'Midnight Serenade'	CCtw SCam
- 'Midsummer's Day'	CBcs

- 'White Swan'   CMac COtt CSBt GLld MAsh
- 'Wilamina' ♀H4   CDoC CMHG CTrh GLld
- 'Wildfire'   SCam
- 'William Bartlett'   CTrh
- 'William Honey'   CTrh
- 'Winter Cheer'   SCog
- 'Wisley White'   see *C. japonica* 'Hakurakuten'
§ - 'Yours Truly'   CBcs CMac CTrh LHyd MDun
    SBrw SCam SCog
§ - 'Yukibotan'   CBcs
§ - 'Yukishiro'   CTrw
'John Tooby'   COtt LBuc
'Jury's Yellow'   see *C. x williamsii* 'Jury's Yellow'
'Lasca Beauty' (*reticulata*   SCam
    x *japonica*)
'Lavender Queen'   see *C. sasanqua* 'Lavender Queen'
'Leonard Messel' (*reticulata*   CBcs CDoC CDul
    x *williamsii*) ♀H4   CMHG CTrG CTrh ENot EPfP
    GGGa LHyd MAsh MDun MGos
    NBlu SBrw SCam SCog SHBN SMer
    SPer SReu
'Liz Henslowe' **new**   CDoC
lutchuensis   CDoC CTrh SCam
'Madame Victor de   see *C. japonica* 'Le Lys'
    Bisschop'
'Maud Messel' (x *williamsii*   SCam
    x *reticulata*)
'Milo Rowell'   SCam
'Mimosa Jury' **new**   CDoC
'Nicky Crisp' (*japonica* x   GLld LHyd
    pitardii)
'Nijinski' (*reticulata* hybrid)   CDoC
'Nonie Haydon' (*pitardii*   CDoC
    hybrid) **new**
oleifera   NLar SBrw SCam SCog WFar
'Paolina Guichardini'   NLar
'Paradise Little Liane' PBR   CBcs SCam SCog
'Pink Spangles'   see *C. japonica* 'Mathotiana Rosea'
pitardii   SCog
- 'Snippet' **new**   CDoC
'Polar Ice' (*oleifera* hybrid)   CDoC SCam SCog
'Polyanna'   CDoC SCog
'Quintessence' (*japonica* x   CDoC GLld SCog
    lutchuensis)
reticulata 'Arch of   CTrG
    Triumph'
- 'Captain Rawes'   SCam
- 'Mary Williams'   NBlu
rosiflora 'Roseaflora   CDoC
    Cascade' **new**
'Royalty' (*japonica* x   CTrG
    reticulata) ♀H3
rusticana 'Arajishi'   see *C. rusticana* 'Beni-arajishi'
    misapplied
§ - 'Beni-arajishi'   CDul CMac COtt SCam SCog SCoo
    WFar
saluenensis 'Exbury   CCtw
    Trumpet'
- 'Trewithen Red'   CTrw
'Salutation' (*reticulata* x   ISea SCam
    saluenensis)
sasanqua Thunb.   CDul CSBt CSam ISea LPan
- 'Baronesa de Soutelinho'   SCam SCog
- 'Ben'   SCog
- 'Bettie Patricia'   SCog
- 'Bonanza'   see *C. hiemalis* 'Bonanza'
- 'Borde Hill form'   SCam
- 'Cleopatra'   LPan
- 'Crimson King' ♀H3   CTbh GQui SCam SHBN
- 'Dazzler'   see *C. hiemalis* 'Dazzler'
- 'Early Pearly' **new**   CDoC
- 'Flamingo'   see *C. sasanqua* 'Fukuzutsumi'
- 'Fragrans'   SCog
- 'Fuji-no-mine'   CTrh SCog
§ - 'Fukuzutsumi'   CSBt CTrG SBrw SCam SCog
    WCwm

- 'Gay Sue'   CTrh LHyd SCam
- 'Hiryû'   SCam
- 'Hugh Evans' ♀H3   CBcs CTrh CTri LHyd SBrw SCam
    SCog SSta
- 'Jean May' ♀H3   CDoC ENot EPfP GLld LHyd SCam
    SCog SPer SSta WGob
- 'Kenkyô'   MGos SCam SCog SSta
§ - 'Lavender Queen'   SCam
- 'Little Pearl'   LHyd
- 'Lucinda'   SCog
- 'Maiden's Blush'   CSBt ISea SCam SCog WFar
- 'Mignonne'   CTrh
- 'Narumigata'   CBcs CDoC CMac CTbh CTrh
    CTrw ENot EPfP LHyd SCam SCog
    SPoG SSta WGob WSHC
- 'Navajo'   CDoC
- 'New Dawn'   SCam
- 'Nyewoods'   CMac
- 'Papaver'   SCam SCog
- 'Paradise Blush'   CBcs SCam SCog
- 'Paradise Glow'   GLld SCam SCog
- 'Paradise Hilda'   CBcs SCog
- 'Paradise Pearl'   CBcs SCam SCog
- 'Paradise Petite' PBR   SCog
- 'Paradise Venessa' PBR   CBcs SCog
- 'Peach Blossom'   CBcs LHyd
- 'Plantation Pink'   CBrm CSBt CTrh ENot GKev SCam
    SCog SPer
- 'Rainbow'   CTrG CTrh GLld ISea SBrw SCam
    SCog SSta WFar WGob
- 'Rosea'   SCam
§ - 'Rosea Plena'   CBcs CMac CTrw SCog
- 'Sasanqua Rubra'   CMac
- 'Sasanqua Variegata' (v)   SCam SCog SSta
- 'Setsugekka'   CDoC SCam SCog
I - 'Shishigashira'   CTrh SCam
- 'Snowflake' *   SCam SCog SSta
- 'Sparkling Burgundy'   see *C. hiemalis* 'Sparkling
    Burgundy'
- 'Tanya'   CDoC
- 'Winter's Joy'   SCam
- 'Winter's Snowman'   CDoC SCam SCog
'Satan's Robe' (*reticulata*   CDoC MGos NBlu SCam SCog
    hybrid)   WFar
'Scented Sun'   CTrh
'Scentuous' (*japonica* x   CDoC
    lutchuensis)
'Shiro-wabisuke' (wabisuke)   CDoC
'Show Girl' (*sasanqua* x   LHyd SBod SCam SCog
    reticulata)
§ - 'Shôwa-wabisuke'   CDoC CTrh
    (wabisuke)
§ *sinensis*   CCCN CTrG CTrh EShb LPan NLar
    SBrw SCam SDEP
'Sir Victor Davis' **new**   CDoC
'Snow Drop' (*pitardii* x   CDoC
    fraterna) **new**
'Snow Flurry' (*oleifera*   CDoC SCam SCog
    hybrid)
'Spring Festival' (*cuspidata*   CDoC CMHG CTrh
    hybrid) ♀H4   ENot LHyd SCam WMoo
'Spring Mist' (*japonica* x   CDoC CMHG CTrh LHyd SCam
    lutchuensis)
'Strawberry Parfait'   NPri SPoG
'Sugar Dream' **new**   CDoC
'Swan Lake' (hybrid)   CTrG ISea SCam SCog
'Sweet Emily Kate'   CDoC
    (*japonica* x
    lutchuensis) **new**
'Tarôkaja' (wabisuke)   SCam
thea   see *C. sinensis*
'Tinsie'   see *C. japonica* 'Bokuhan'
'Tiny Princess' (*japonica* x   CBcs
    fraterna)
'Tom Knudsen' (*reticulata*   CDoC CTrh SCam
    x *japonica*) ♀H3

'Tomorrow Supreme' — see *C. japonica* 'Tomorrow Variegated'
transnokoensis — CCtw ISea SCam
'Transtasman' **new** — CDoC
'Tricolor Sieboldii' — see *C. japonica* 'Tricolor'
'Tristrem Carlyon' — CBcs CCtw CDoC CTrG SPoG
(*reticulata* hybrid) ♀H4
tsaii — CDoC CPLG
'Valley Knudsen' — SCog
(*saluenensis* x *reticulata*)
x *vernalis* 'Hiryû' — SCog
- 'Star Above Star' — CMHG
- 'Yuletide' — GLld SCam
'Volcano' **new** — CDoC
x *williamsii* 'Anticipation' — More than 30 suppliers
♀H4
- 'Anticipation Variegated' — CBcs GGGa
- 'Ballet Queen' — CDoC CSBt MGos SCam SPoG WFar
- 'Ballet Queen Variegated' — CDoC SCog
- 'Bartley Number Five' — CMac
- 'Beatrice Michael' — CMac
- 'Blue Danube' — CBcs
- 'Bow Bells' — CDoC CDul CMac CTrh LHyd LRHS NBlu SBrw SCam SSta
- 'Bowen Bryant' ♀H4 — CTrw GGGa SCog
- 'Bridal Gown' — LHyd
- 'Brigadoon' ♀H4 — CBcs CDoC CMHG CTrG CTrh CTrw EPfP GGGa GLld LHyd MBri MDun MGos SCog
- 'Burncoose' — CBcs
- 'Burncoose Apple Blossom' — CBcs
- 'Buttons 'n' Bows' **new** — CDoC SCog
- 'C.F. Coates' — CDoC SCog SSta
- 'Caerhays' — CBcs
- 'Carnation' — MAsh
- 'Carolyn Williams' — CBcs SCam
- 'Celebration' — CBcs
§ - 'Charity' — GLld
- 'Charlean' — SCam
- 'Charles Michael' — CBcs
- 'China Clay' ♀H4 — CTrG EPfP LHyd LRHS SBrw SCog
§ - 'Citation' — CBcs CMac CTrw
- 'Contribution' — CTrh
- 'Crinkles' — CDul SBrw SCam SSta
- 'Daintiness' ♀H4 — LHyd SCam SCog
- 'Dark Nite' — CMHG
- 'Debbie' ♀H4 — More than 30 suppliers
- 'Debbie's Carnation' — CMHG
- 'Donation' ♀H4 — More than 30 suppliers
- 'Dream Boat' — CBcs LHyd
- 'E.G. Waterhouse' — CBcs CDoC CMHG CSBt CTrG CTrh CTri CTrw ENot EPfP LHyd MAsh NBlu SBrw SCam SCog SPoG SSta WCot WGob
- 'E.T.R. Carlyon' ♀H4 — CBcs CCtw CDul CTrh CTri ENot EPfP GLld LHyd LRHS MAsh NLar SCam SCog SPoG WBVN
§ - 'Elegant Beauty' ♀H4 — CBcs CSBt CTrG CTrh CTrw CWSG GLld MDun SBod SBrw SCam SCog SPur WBVN
- 'Elizabeth Anderson' — CTrh SCam
- 'Elizabeth de Rothschild' — SCam
- 'Ellamine' — CBcs
- 'Elsie Jury' ♀H3 — CBcs CDoC CMac CSBt CTrG CTri CTrw CWSG GLld GQui LHyd MGos NBlu SBod SBrw SCam SCog
- 'Exaltation' — SCam SCog
- 'Francis Hanger' — CBcs CDoC CTrh LHyd MDun SBrw SCam SCog
- 'Free Style' — SCam
- 'Galaxie' ♀H4 — CBcs ISea SCog
- 'Garden Glory' — GGGa

- 'George Blandford' ♀H4 — CMHG CMac SCam
- 'Glenn's Orbit' ♀H4 — CBcs CDoC CTrw SCam SCog
- 'Golden Spangles' (v) — CBcs CDoC CMac CSBt CTrG CTrh ELan EPfP LHyd LRHS MGos SBrw SCam SPer SReu SSta WGob
- 'Grand Jury' — SCam
- 'Gwavas' — CBcs CCCN CDoC GLld LHyd SBrw SCam SCog
- 'Hilo' — CTrw
- 'Hiraethlyn' — LHyd SCam
- 'J.C. Williams' ♀H4 — CBcs CMac CSam CTri CTrw CWSG ENot EPfP ISea LHyd SCog
- 'Jamie' **new** — CDoC
- 'Jean Claris' — SCog
- 'Jenefer Carlyon' — CCtw CDoC
- 'Jill Totty' — CTrh
- 'Joan Trehane' ♀H4 — CTrw
- 'Julia Hamiter' ♀H4 — CBcs CTrw SCog
§ - 'Jury's Yellow' ♀H4 — CBcs CCCN CDoC CSBt CTbh CTrG CTrh CTri CTrw ELan ENot EPfP GGGa GQui LHyd LRHS LSRN MAsh MGos NPri SBrw SCam SCog SHBN SPoG SSta WBVN WFar
- 'Laura Boscawen' — CTrG CTrh LHyd SCam
- 'Les Jury' ♀H4 — CDoC CMHG CSBt CTbh CTrh LSRN MWea SCog SPer
- 'Margaret Waterhouse' — CBcs CDoC COtt SCam SCog
- 'Mary Christian' ♀H4 — CBcs EPfP LHyd SBrw SCam SSta
- 'Mary Jobson' — CBcs CDoC SCam
- 'Mary Phoebe Taylor' ♀H4 — CBcs CDoC CTrG CTrw CWSG EBee ENot GLld NLar SCam SCog SHBN
- 'Mildred Veitch' — CSBt
- 'Mirage' — CTrh SCam
- 'Moira Reid' — CDoC
- 'Monica Dance' — CBcs
- 'Muskoka' ♀H4 — CBcs CMHG CTrh WCwm
- 'New Venture' — CBcs
- 'November Pink' — CBcs EHol
- 'Phillippa Forward' — CMac
- 'Red Dahlia' — CBcs SCam
- 'Rendezvous' — CDoC SCam SCog
- 'Rose Parade' — LHyd
- 'Rose Quartz' — MAsh
- 'Rosemary Williams' — CBcs SCam
- 'Ruby Bells' — CMHG
- 'Ruby Wedding' — CBcs CDoC CSBt CTbh CTrh ENot GLld GQui LHyd MAsh MWea NLar SCog SPer SPoG WBVN
- 'Saint Ewe' ♀H4 — CBcs CDoC CSBt CTbh CTrG CTrh CTri CTrw EPfP GGar GKev GLld ISea LHyd MBri MGos SBrw SCam SCog SHBN SMer SPer SPoG WGob
- 'Saint Michael' — CDoC
- 'Sayonara' — CBcs SBrw SCog
- 'Senorita' ♀H4 — CDoC CTrh LHyd SBrw SCam SCog
- 'Simon Bolitho' — CBcs CTbh LHyd SBrw
- 'Taylor's Perfection' — CTrw
- 'The Duchess of Cornwall' — CCtw CDoC SBrw
- 'Tiptoe' — CDoC CTrh LHyd MBri
- 'Tregrehan' — GLld
- 'Twinkle Star' — CDoC
- 'Waltz Time' — SCam
- 'Water Lily' ♀H4 — CBcs CDoC CTrh CTrw EPfP GLld MGos SCam SPur
- 'Wilber Foss' ♀H4 — CBcs CDoC CMHG CTrh GLld LHyd SCam SCog
- 'William Carlyon' — CWSG GLld
- 'Wynne Rayner' — SBrw SCam
- 'Yesterday' — NBlu
'Winelight' **new** — CDoC
'Winter's Charm' (*oleifera* x *sasanqua*) — SCog

'Winter's Dream' (*hiemalis* x *oleifera*) — SCog

'Winter's Interlude' (*oleifera* x *sinensis*) — CDoC SCam SCog

'Winter's Joy' — SCog

'Winter's Toughie' (*sasanqua* hybrid) — SCam SCog

'Winton' (*cuspidata* x *saluenensis*) — CBcs CDoC SCam

'Wirlinga Belle' — SCam SCog

'Yoimachi' (*fraterna* x *sasanqua*) — CDoC CTrh

'Yukihaki' — see *C. japonica* 'Yukishiro'

Campanula ✿ (*Campanulaceae*)

from Iran — EBee EPPr NBre

abietina — see *C. patula* subsp. *abietina*

§ *alliariifolia* — More than 30 suppliers

- 'Ivory Bells' — see *C. alliariifolia*
- 'Minor' **new** — GKev

allionii — see *C. alpestris*

§ *alpestris* — ECho NLAp

alpina — MDKP NBur

americana — SPav

ardonensis — NSla

argaea — EChP NSfd WLin

argyrotricha — NBur

armena — CNic CSec EBur ELan EWin NLar NSfd

arvatica — CGra CLyd ECho EPot ETow GMaP LRHS MDKP NMen NSfd WAbe WPat

- 'Alba' — CLyd ECho GMaP NMen NSla WPat

aucheri — see *C. saxifraga* subsp. *aucheri*

§ 'Balchiniana' (v) — WEas

barbata — CGra EBee EDAr GBin GKev ITim LHop MMHG NBur NLAp NWCA SMar WMoo WPer

- var. *alba* — GAbr NBur

bellidifolia — NBir NBre

§ *betulifolia* ♀H4 — CSam EPot ITim NBur WFar WLin

- JCA 252.005 — SBla

'Birch Hybrid' ♀H4 — CMHG CNic EAEE ECho ECtt EDAr ELan EPfP GMaP LBee LRHS NBlu NJOw NSfd WFar WTel

bononiensis — GBBs LTwo MHar NBre NSfd SPoG SRms

'Bumblebee' — CGra EHyt SBla WAbe

'Burghaltii' ♀H4 — CDes CElw CHar CMil CPom EBee EBrs ECha EHrv ELan EMon GMac LRHS MLHP MSte SBch SBla SWat WCot WFar WOut WPer WWhi

calaminthifolia — EBur

'Cantata' **new** — CGra

§ *carnica* — ECho MSte NSfd

carpatha — SBla

carpatica ♀H4 — ECho EPfP GKev ITim MBar MWgw NBre NBro NGdn SBch SPlb SRms SWat

- f. *alba* — EAEE GKev MWgw NBre NFor NGdn SPlb SWat

- - 'Bressingham White' — SBla

§ - - 'Weisse Clips' — COfd EAEE EBee ECho ECtt ELan ENot EPfP GGar GMaP LAst LHop MDun NGdn NJOw SPer SPla SPoG SRms SWvt WFar WPat WPer WWeb

§ - 'Blaue Clips' — More than 30 suppliers

- blue — MRav
- Blue Clips — see *C. carpatica* 'Blaue Clips'
- 'Blue Moonlight' — EAEE EBur LRHS SMer
- 'Blue Uniform' **new** — NSfd
- 'Chewton Joy' — CTri EAEE LRHS WLin
- dwarf — EPot
- 'Karpatenkrone' — EBee

- 'Kathy' — GBuc
- 'Maureen Haddon' — LRHS

* - var. *pelviformis* **new** — SMHy WCot

- 'Queen of Somerville' — NJOw
- 'Silberschale' — NBre
- 'Suzie' — SBla
- var. *turbinata* — ECho EHyt SRms
- - 'Foerster' — GBuc LRHS MTho SBla SMer WHoo
- - 'Georg Arends' — CNic
- - 'Isabel' — CSpe EAEE LRHS
- - 'Jewel' — EAEE EHyt LRHS
- - 'Wheatley Violet' — LRHS SBla
- White Clips — see *C. carpatica* f. *alba* 'Weisse Clips'
- 'White Uniform' **new** — NSfd

§ *cashmeriana* — CGra EBur EHyt NBur

- SEP 386 — EHyt
- 'Blue Cloud' — CWib MBri

cephallenica — see *C. garganica* subsp. *cephallenica*

cervicaria — EBee

§ *chamissonis* — EBee ECho NBur NSla SBla WPat

§ - 'Major' — CPBP EDAr EPot EWes LBee NBur

- 'Oyobeni' — NBur NLAp WLin

§ - 'Superba' ♀H4 — EBur ECho ELan MTho NBur NMen NSla

choruhensis — CGra ITim NBur NSla

§ *cochleariifolia* ♀H4 — CSpe CTri EBee ECho EDAr ELan EPfP EPot GMaP LRHS MDun MTho NJOw SSvw STre WFar WHoo WLin WPer WTel WWhi

- var. *alba* — CNic CSpe EDAr GMaP LRHS MHer MMuc NRya NSfd SBch SBla SRms WAbe WHoo WLin WPer

- - 'Bavaria White' — CBrm ECho ITim LBMP WFar WGwG

- - double white (d) — WPat

- - 'White Baby' (Baby Series) — EAEE ECho ECtt EPfP GAbr GGar NSfd SPoG

- 'Annie Hall' **new** — ECho

- 'Bavaria Blue' — CBrm ECho ITim LBMP NLRH NSfd NWCA WGwG WRHF

- 'Blue Baby' (Baby Series) — ECho ECtt EPfP GGar MHer NBlu NPro SBch SPoG SRms

- 'Blue Tit' — GBuc
- 'Blue Wonder' — COtt
- 'Cambridge Blue' — EAEE LRHS NBur NSfd WAbe WFar
- 'Elizabeth Oliver' (d) — More than 30 suppliers
- 'Flore Pleno' (d) — ECtt NLAp
- 'Miss Willmott' — CLyd EBur MTho NBir
- 'Oakington Blue' — EAEE LRHS SBla
- var. *pallida* 'Miranda' — LRHS WIvy
- - 'Silver Chimes' — ECho ITim
- 'Tubby' — CLyd EAEE ECho GKev LRHS MHer MTho NJOw SRms
- 'Warleyensis' — see *C.* x *haylodgensis* W. Brockbank 'Warley White'

collina — CTri GSki LTwo NBre NBur NJOw NSfd WCFE WPer

'Covadonga' — CMea CPBP EAEE ECGP ECho LHop LRHS LTwo

cretica — EMag GKev NSfd

'Crystal' — ECtt MAvo MNrw SUsu

dasyantha — see *C. chamissonis*

dolomitica — EBee LTwo NLAp

'E.K.Toogood' — CElw CPBP EBee ECho ECtt GKev MWat NBro NLAp NVic SBla SMac SRms

'Elizabeth' — see *C. takesimana* 'Elizabeth'

ephesia — CSec

eriocarpa — see *C. latifolia* 'Eriocarpa'

excisa — CPBP WAbe

§ 'Faichem Lilac' — EBee LSou LTwo NChi NLar NPro NRnb NSfd STes

fenestrellata — ITim MTho NBro NJOw NLAp SRms WAbe WFar

finitima — see *C. betulifolia*

'Flashing Lights' **new** — ERou MBnl

foliosa — ECtt NBur WPer

formanekiana ♀H2-3 — EBee EBur EChP EMag GBBs NBur NSfd

fragilis — CGra EBur ECho EHyt

- subsp. *cavolinii* — EHyt

- 'Hirsuta' — ECho

garganica ♀H4 — ECho EGra EPfP GAbr GBBs GMaP GSki MDKP MRav NBlu NFor NSfd SMar SWvt WFar WMoo WPer

- 'Aurea' — see *C. garganica* 'Dickson's Gold'

- 'Blue Diamond' — ECho ELan LHop NBlu SBla WAbe WFar

§ - subsp. *cephallenica* — CElw NBro NJOw

§ - 'Dickson's Gold' — More than 30 suppliers

- 'Erinus Major' **new** — NSfd

- 'Hirsuta' — ECho

- 'Major' — ECho IHMH LAst NJOw SPoG WFar WRHF

- 'W.H. Paine' ♀H4 — CLyd ECho ECtt LRHS MDKP NMen NSla WAbe WFar WHoo

'Gaven' **new** — IPot

§ 'Glandore' — NPro

glomerata — CBgR CElw CEnt CRWN EGra LSRN MBNS MBrN NBid NBro NLan NMir NSfd SPet SRms STes SWal WBrk WFar WWye

- var. *acaulis* — CPrp CStu CWan EBee EPfP ERou GAbr LRHS MBNS NJOw NLar NSfd NVic NWCA SPet SPla WFar WPer WWeb

- var. *alba* — CBcs CBgR EBee EChP ELan EMFW EPfP ERou EShb GMaP GSki LRHS MNFA MRav MTis MWat NBro NHol NRnb SPer SPla SPlb STes SWat WCAu WFar WGwG WMnd WPer WWeb

§ - - 'Alba Nana' — LAst

§ - - 'Schneekrone' — EBee ECha EPfP ERou NBre SMrm WFar

- 'Caroline' — More than 30 suppliers

- Crown of Snow — see *C. glomerata* var. *alba* 'Schneekrone'

- var. *dahurica* — CTri EBee NBre NLar SMar SPet WPer

- 'Joan Elliott' — CBgR EChP ECha GBuc LRHS MRav MWat NGdn WAul WCra

- 'Nana Alba' — see *C. glomerata* var. *alba* 'Alba Nana'

- 'Purple Pixie' — LRHS

- 'Superba' ♀H4 — More than 30 suppliers

grossekii — EChP EHrv EWll GMac LTwo MFOX NBre NEgg NJOw NRnb WHrl WLin WOut

hakkiarica — CGra

'Hallii' — LRHS NSfd NWCA

'Hannah' — LRHS

Hannay's form — CHar

x *haylodgensis* misapplied — see *C. x haylodgensis* 'Plena'

§ x *haylodgensis* — CCge CGra CMea CPBP EDAr NSfd SBla WAbe WCot WHoo
W. Brockbank 'Marion Fisher' (d)

§ - 'Plena' (d) — EBee ECho EDAr ELan EPot LAst LBee LHop LRHS NBro NMen NSfd NWCA SBla SRms WAbe WCot WEas WFar WHoo WKif WPat

§ - 'Warley White' (d) — CStu EBur ECho ELan

- 'Yvonne' — EDAr LAst NEgg NSfd SPoG WFar

'Hemswell Starlight' — CLyd NPro

hercegovina 'Nana' — CPBP EHyt WAbe

'Hilltop Snow' — CGra CPBP EHyt NSfd

hofmannii — CWan EBur ELan GKev MWhi NLar NSfd SYvo WFar WRha

hypopolia — EPfP

§ *incurva* — CDMG CSpe EBee EBur EMan EPot GAbr GBBs MNrw MWea NOak NRya NSfd NSti WGwG WLin WPer

integrifolia 'Bells' **new** — LSou

isophylla ♀H2 — ECho MBri SPet

- 'Alba' ♀H2 — ECho

- 'Flore Pleno' (d) — EBur

- 'Mayi' ♀H2 — CSpe

- 'Mayi' misapplied — see *C.* 'Balchiniana'

- 'Variegata' — see *C.* 'Balchiniana'

jaubertiana — CGra EHyt

'Joe Elliott' ♀H2-3 — CStu ECho LRHS WAbe

kemulariae — NBur NJOw NSfd SRms WPer

- *alba* — ITim

'Kent Belle' ♀H4 — More than 30 suppliers

khasiana **new** — NSfd

'Kifu' (v) — ENot LRHS

lactiflora — More than 30 suppliers

- *alba* — see *C. lactiflora* white-flowered

N - 'Alba' ♀H4 — EBee EBla EChP EGle ERou GAbr GMaP MAvo MDKP MNFA SMrm STes WCMO

- 'Avalanche' — EBrs

- 'Blue Avalanche' — EBee NSfd SMrm

- 'Blue Cross' — COtt EBee EBrs EMag LRHS NBre NLar WTel

- 'Blue Lady' — EBee EChP NBre WFar

- 'Dixter Presence' — IPot NDov SMHy

- dwarf pink — SHar SPet WCot

- 'Favourite' — CFir CSpe EBee ERou MNrw NCGa NGdn NLar STes

- 'Loddon Anna' ♀H4 — More than 30 suppliers

- 'Pink Star' **new** — SMrm

- 'Pouffe' — CWCL EAEE EBee EBla EChP ECtt EGle ELan EPfP GMaP GMac LRHS MDKP MRav NBro NCGa NDov NGdn SPer SPet SPla SWat SWvt WFar

- 'Prichard's Variety' ♀H4 — More than 30 suppliers

- 'Senior' — EMil MDKP

- 'Superba' ♀H4 — EBee

- 'Violet' — EBee SWat WPer

- 'White Pouffe' — EAEE EBee EChP EGle ELan EPfP GKev GMaP GMac GSki LRHS MDKP MRav NCGa NChi NLar SAga SMer SMrm SPer SPla SPoG STes SWat WFar WLin

§ - white-flowered — ECha LAst NBir NBur SPer SWat WPer

lanata — CSec

lasiocarpa — CGra LRHS WFar

§ *latifolia* — CArn EChP ECha GAbr GBBs LRHS MWgw NBid NFor NMir NOrc NSfd NSti NVic SBla SMer SPer SRms WCAu WCra WFar WMoo

- var. *alba* — ELan GAbr GBBs MAvo MBri MSte NGdn SBla SPav SPer SRms WFar WHal WPer

- - 'White Ladies' — NBur NSfd

* - 'Amethyst' — SDnm SPav WMnd

- 'Brantwood' — EBee EChP ECtt EDAr ENot ERou GAbr GMac MRav MWat MWhi NChi NOak NSfd SDnm SMer SPav SPer SRms STes SWat WMnd

- 'Buckland' — CHea SBla SPav

§ - 'Eriocarpa' — NBur NSfd

- 'Gloaming' — EBee ERou NBur NSfd SMeo

- var. *macrantha* — EBee ELan EPfP ERou GMaP LHop LRHS MBri MGos MHar MHer MSte NBPC NCGa NGdn NJOw NRnb NSti SPav SPoG SSvw SWat SWvt WCAu WMoo WPer WWeb WWye

- - 'Alba' — CAby CMMP ECha ECtt ERou EShb GMaP LHop LPhx LRHS MRav

	MSte NCGa NRnb NSfd SPoG WCAu WCot WLin WMoo WPer
- 'Misty Dawn'	WCot WFar
- 'Roger Wood'	MWgw
§ *latiloba*	CElw CMHG SBch WBrk WCot WFar
- 'Alba' ♀H4	CBre CElw EBee EGle ELan EPPr EPfP GAbr GCal GMaP GMac MDKP NChi NGdn SBch SGar SSvw WBrk WEas WLin WOut WRHF
- 'Hidcote Amethyst' ♀H4	More than 30 suppliers
- 'Highcliffe Variety' ♀H4	CHea CSpe EBee EChP EGle ELan EPfP GBuc MFOX MNFA MRav MWat NCGa NSfd NSti SPla WCAu WCMO WCot WEas WKif WMnd
* - 'Highdown'	MLLN WFar
- 'Percy Piper' ♀H4	CSam EBee ELan EWsh GBuc LRHS MAvo MFOX MRav NBre NBro NFor NLar WFar WLin WOut
- 'Splash'	CElw CFee EBee ECtt MAvo WCot
linifolia	see *C. carnica*
longestyla	WCot
'Lynchmere'	ETow
makaschvilii	EBee ECtt EDAr GKev GMac IGor LRHS MSph MWhi MWrn NBur NCGa NLar NRnb NSfd SAga SBod SPoG STes WCHb WCMO WCot WHrl WLin WPer
'Marion Fisher'	see *C.* x *haylodgensis* W. Brockbank 'Marion Fisher'
massalskyi	EHyt
medium	LAst NRnb NSfd
- 'Alba'	NSfd
§ - var. *calycanthema*	ERou
- 'Cup and Saucer'	see *C. medium* var. *calycanthema*
- 'Rosea' **new**	NSfd
'Milkshake' **new**	EBee NBro
mirabilis 'Mist Maiden'	CLyd EPot ETow LRHS WFar
'Monic' **new**	NBlu
morettiana	NSla
muralis	see *C. portenschlagiana*
'Mystery Blue'	EPfP
nitida	see *C. persicifolia* var. *planiflora*
- var. *planiflora*	see *C. persicifolia* var. *planiflora*
'Norman Grove'	CLyd EPot
ochroleuca	CMea CPom EBee EChP GBBs GCal LRHS NBur NCGa SHGN SPoG STes SWat WCFE WCot WHrl WMoo
- 'White Beauty'	CWib
- 'White Bells'	MWhi NRnb WGwG WMnd
odontosepala	CElw EMon
'Oliver's Choice'	WHrl
olympica misapplied	see *C. rotundifolia* 'Olympica'
§ *ossetica*	CElw CSpe EBee ECtt ELan EMan GKev MLHP NCiC
pallida subsp. *tibetica*	see *C. cashmeriana*
parviflora Lam.	see *C. sibirica*
patula	NLar NSfd
§ - subsp. *abietina*	NBre NLar
'Paul Furse'	EBee ECtt LRHS MDKP MLLN NBre NLar NSfd STes WCAu WCMO WCot WHal WLin WTin
pelviformis	MNrw
§ *pendula*	CSec CWan EBee EChP EPfP EWes GBuc GKev MNFA NJOw NLar NSfd NSph WFar WWeb
persicifolia	More than 30 suppliers
- var. *alba*	More than 30 suppliers
§ - 'Alba Coronata' (d)	CFir EMon GAbr GBri LRHS NBir WCAu WEas WFar
- 'Alba Plena'	see *C. persicifolia* 'Alba Coronata'
- 'Amethyst' **new**	EBrs
- Ashfield double ice blue (d)	NBre
- 'Beau Belle'	EBee EChP EMan ERou LSou MBNS NLar NMoo STes WSan
§ - 'Bennett's Blue' (d)	More than 30 suppliers
- blue- and white-flowered	WHil
- 'Blue Bell'	MWat
- 'Blue Bloomers' (d)	CElw CHar CHea CLAP CMil EBee EChP EGle EMon EWes GBri GMac LLWP MAvo MNFA MRav MSph WCot WWeb
- blue cup-in-cup (d)	EBla MBnl MDKP WFar WLin
- blue-flowered	IFoB LAst MBow MRav NRnb SPlb WEas WFar
- 'Boule de Neige' (d)	CMMP CWCL EBee EBla ECtt LAst NOak NSfd WCMO WEas WSan
- 'Caerulea Coronata'	see *C. persicifolia* 'Coronata'
* - 'Caerulea Plena' (d)	EWsh MBNS
§ - 'Chettle Charm' PBR ♀H4	More than 30 suppliers
§ - 'Coronata' (d)	ECtt NEgg
- 'Cristine'	MDKP
- cup and saucer blue (d)	CAby
§ - cup and saucer white (d)	CElw EBla ELan GMaP WFar WPer WWye
§ - double blue (d)	EGle NBir NBro NSfd WEas
- double white (d)	ELan NChi WMoo
- 'Eastgrove Blue'	NCob
- 'Fleur de Neige' (d) ♀H4	CSam EBee ECtt LRHS MLLN NBre NCob NOak WAul WCMO WCot WHoo WLin
- 'Flore Pleno'	see *C. persicifolia* double blue
- 'Frances' (d)	CLAP EMon
- 'Frank Lawley' (d)	LRHS NSfd
- 'Gawen'	CWCL EBee GMaP GMac MAvo MNFA NBre NHol NLar WCMO WCot
- 'George Chiswell' PBR	see *C. persicifolia* 'Chettle Charm'
- 'Grandiflora'	NBre
- 'Grandiflora Alba'	GBuc LBMP NBre NSfd SMrm
- 'Grandiflora Caerulea'	NBlu NLar
§ - 'Hampstead White' (d)	EChP ECtt EGle EHrv ERou GBuc LAst LHop LRHS NBro NSti SBch SPla STes WCAu WEas WHer WLin WMnd
- 'Hetty'	see *C. persicifolia* 'Hampstead White'
- 'Kelly's Gold'	More than 30 suppliers
- 'Kent Blue'	CSec
- 'La Belle'	EBee EChP EMan EPyc ERou MTis NLar STes WHil
- 'La Bonne Amie' **new**	EBee
- 'Moerheimii' (d)	EBee EShb MAvo MBnl MDKP MWea NBir NFla STes WCAu
- var. *nitida*	see *C. persicifolia* var. *planiflora*
- 'Peach Bells'	MBNS NOak
- 'Perry's Boy Blue'	NPer
§ - var. *planiflora*	CPBP EBee ETow ITim SBla
§ - - f. *alba*	CMea SBch
- 'Powder Puff' (d) **new**	WCot
- 'Pride of Exmouth' (d)	CCge CHar CHea CMMP CSam EBee EChP ECtt EHrv ELan EMan EShb GBuc LAst LRHS MArl MBri MCCP MNFA MWgw NOak NSfd WBrk WCFE WCMO WCot WCra WHoo WLin WMnd
- 'Rearsby Belle' (d)	MDKP
- subsp. *sessiliflora*	see *C. latiloba*
I - 'Snowball' **new**	NSfd
- 'Snowdrift'	ELan SRms
- 'Telham Beauty' misapplied	CFwr CHea COtt CSBt CWCL EBee ECtt ELan ENot EPfP ERou EShb GAbr LRHS MRav MSte NHol NRnb SMer SMrm SPer SPla SRms SWvt WMnd WPer WWeb
- 'Telham Beauty' D. Thurston	NSfd
- 'Tinpenny Blue'	WTin
- 'White Bell'	MWat NEgg

- 'Superba'	ECho
- 'White Gem'	LBMP NBre NSfd SSvw WOut WPtf
'Royal Wave' **new**	NBhm
rupestris	EBur LTwo
'Samantha'	EBee EBla EMan ERou LAst LSou MCCP NSfd SBch SHar SMrm SPoG SRGP SVil WCot
'Sarastro'	More than 30 suppliers
sarmatica	CSec EBee EMag EMan EMon GAbr MBrN MSte MWhi NBid NJOw NOak NRnb NSfd NSti SMad SRms STes WCHb WMnd WPer
sartorii	EBur ITim
saxifraga	EBur NBur NMen
§ - subsp. *aucheri*	EBur GEdr NLAp WAbe
scabrella	CGra
seraglio **new**	NSla
shetleri	CGra
§ *sibirica*	NBHF NBre NBur NSfd SSvw WPer
- white	NLar
siegizmundii	GMac NBur NSfd
'Sojourner'	CGra EHyt
speciosa	EBee EChP MWhi NBHF NBre NSfd WLin WPer
sporadum	EHyt
'Stansfieldii'	CGra EAEE EBur NMen WPat
stevenii	CGra WPer
'Summer Pearl'	CStu ERou LAst MBNS NEgg WLin
§ 'Swannables'	CPou EBee ECtt EGle EMan EWsh GMac LTwo MNFA NCGa NChi NSfd
§ *takesimana*	More than 30 suppliers
- B&SWJ 8499	WCru
I - 'Alba'	EBee EBla EBrs EShb MDKP NBre NEgg SHar SSvw WMoo
- 'Beautiful Trust'^PBR	CBgR CElw CLAP CSpe EBee EBla ECtt ERou GMac LAst NBPC NBhm NLar NSfd NSti SHar SPoG SRGP WCMO WCru WOVN WPGP
§ - 'Elizabeth'	More than 30 suppliers
- 'Elizabeth II' (d)	MAvo MTho WCMO WCot WLin
teucrioides	NWCA
thyrsoides	EBee EMag EWll NBre NBur NRnb NSfd NSti SDnm SPav WPer
- subsp. *carniolica*	SGar
'Timsbury Perfection'	CGra
tommasiniana ♀^H4	EHyt LRHS NBur NSfd SBla WAbe
trachelium	CBgR CMHG EBee EBrs EChP EMag EPfP GAbr MBNS MNrw MRav NBPC NEgg NJOw NLan SAga SGar WFar WHer WMnd WMoo WPer
- var. *alba*	CLAP EBee EChP GAbr LRHS MMHG MNrw MWhi STes WBrE WCot WFar WMnd WMoo WPer
- 'Alba Flore Pleno' (d)	CBgR CDes CFir CHar CHea CLAP CMil EBee SBch SBla STes WCot WFar
- 'Bernice' (d)	More than 30 suppliers
- lilac-blue	NRnb
- 'Snowball'	EBee ERou EShb LAst LSRN MBnl
tridentata	GKev
troegerae	LRHS SBla
'Tymonsii'	CPBP EBur ECho EHyt LRHS LTwo NBir NJOw NMen WFar
'Van-Houttei'	CElw CHar CMil EBee EMon GMac NLar SAga SBch WCMO WCot WFar WLin WPer
versicolor	NBre
- G&K 3347	EMon
vidalii	see *Azorina vidalii*
waldsteiniana	CPBP LRHS LTwo NBur NWCA WAbe WFar
wanneri	CBcs CSec EBur EChP EMan EPfP LRHS NLar

'Warley White'	see *C.* x *haylodgensis* W. Brockbank 'Warley White'
'Warleyensis'	see *C.* x *haylodgensis* W. Brockbank 'Warley White'
x *wockei* 'Puck'	EAEE EBee EBur ECho ECtt EHyt LRHS LTwo NLar NSfd NWCA WAbe WPat
zangezura	CDes CSec CWan EBee EBur EChP EMan EPPr EShb GEdr GKev MLLN NGdn NSfd SGar SHGN SSvw WCra WLin
'Zierlotte'	NJOw
zoysii	EAEE LRHS NSla SBla

Campanula x *Symphyandra* see *Campanula*

Campanumoea see *Codonopsis*

Camphorosma (*Chenopodiaceae*)
monspeliaca	XPep

Campsis (*Bignoniaceae*)
RCB/Arg L-8	WCot
atrosanguinea	see *Bignonia capreolata* 'Atrosanguinea'
grandiflora	CArn CBcs CPIN CSPN EBee ELan ENot EPfP GSki IMGH LRHS MAsh SPer SWvt WCFE XPep
radicans	CArn CBcs CBrm CDul CMac CRHN CSBt CWib EBee ECrN ELan EPfP LAst LPan LRHS LSRN MAsh MSwo SHBN SLon SPer SPlb WBVN WBrE WDin XPep
- 'Atrosanguinea'	EPfP
- 'Flamenco'	CDoC CFRD EBee EHol ELan EShb GKev GQui GSki LAst LRHS MAsh SAdn SBod SBra SCoo SHGC SLim SPoG SWvt WCot WFar
§ - f. *flava* ♀^H4	CBcs CDoC CFRD CHEx CPIN EBee ELan ENot EPfP IMGH LHop LRHS MAsh MCCP MGos NBlu NPal NSti SBra SLim SPer SPoG SSta SWvt XPep
- 'Indian Summer'	CBcs ENot EPfP LRHS MAsh MBlu MBri MGos NLar SHFr SLim SPoG WCot
- 'Yellow Trumpet'	see *C. radicans* f. *flava*
x *tagliabuana* Dancing Flame = 'Huidan'^PBR	MGos NLar SPer
- 'Madame Galen' ♀^H4	More than 30 suppliers

Camptosema (*Papilionaceae*)
rubicundum	CPIN

Camptosorus see *Asplenium*

Campylandra see *Tupistra*

Campylotropis (*Papilionaceae*)
macrocarpa	NLar

Canarina (*Campanulaceae*)
canariensis ♀^H1	CPIN CStu WCot WPGP
eminii	CPIN

Canavalia (*Papilionaceae*)
gladiata **new**	CPLG

Candollea see *Hibbertia*

Canna ✿ (*Cannaceae*)
'Adam's Orange'	CHEx
'Aida' (Grand Opera Series)	MBri MJnS
'Alberich'	CSam SHaC
altensteinii	XBlo
'Ambassador'	EShb MBri MOak WHil

	'America'	WCMO WCot
	'Angel Pink'	MJnS
	'Annaeei' ♀H3	EAmu MOak SChr SHaC
	'Anthony and Cleopatra' (v)	WCot
I	'Aphrodite' van Klaveren ♀H3	SHaC
	'Apricot Dream'	SHaC
	'Apricot Ice'	MOak SHaC
	'Aranyálom'	SHaC
	'Argentina'	SHaC
	'Aristote'	SHaC
	'Assaut'	SHaC
	'Atlantis'	XBlo
I	*aurea*	CHEx
	'Australia'	CBos CHen EZes LAst LSou MJnS MOak SHaC WCot WGwG WHil XBlo
	'Black Knight'	CFir CHen CSpe CTbh EAmu EBee EChP ELan EWll IBal LAst MJnS MOak MSte MTis SPet WCMO WMul WWlt XBlo
	'Bonfire'	CHEx
	'Bonnezeaux'	SHaC
	brasiliensis	CHll CRHN WCMO WCot
	'Brillant'	ELan SHaC WDyG
	'Caballero'	EAmu EBee SHaC
	'Caliméro'	SHaC
	'Canary'	XBlo
	'Carnaval'	SHaC
	'Centenaire de Rozain-Boucharlat'	CHEx SHaC
	'Cerise Davenport'	CFir
	'Champigny'	SHaC
	Chaumes = 'Turcacha'	SHaC
	'Cherry Red' Schmid	SHaC
	'Chinese Coral' Schmid	CHEx
	'Chouchou'	SHaC
I	'Citrina'	XBlo
§	'City of Portland'	ELan MOak SChr SHaC
*	'Cleopatra'	CFir EAmu EBee MJnS SHaC SPet WCMO WGwG WHil
*	'Cléopâtre'	SHaC
	coccinea	EZes MOak
§	'Colibri'	SHaC WHil
	'Conestoga'	MOak
	'Confetti'	see C. 'Colibri'
	'Corail'	SHaC
	'Corrida'	SHaC
	'Creamy White'	CHEx XBlo
	'Crimson Beauty'	LAst MOak SHaC
	Crozy hybrids	LRav
	'Delaware' ♀H3	MOak
	'Délibáb'	CSam EChP MBri MJnS SHaC SPet WCMO WDyG
	'Di Bartolo'	SHaC XBlo
	'Dollar'	SHaC
	'Dondo' new	SHaC
	'Dondoblutrot'	SHaC
	'Durban' ambig. new	EZes
	'Durban' Hiley, orange-flowered	see C. 'Phasion'
	'E. Neubert'	SHaC
	edulis	CHEx MOak
	- green-leaved	EZes
	- purple-leaved	EZes MOak
§	x *ehemanii* ♀H3	CKob CRHN CSev EBee MJnS MOak SChr SDix SHaC WCMO WMul WPGP
	'Emblème'	SHaC
	'En Avant'	CHEx MBri SHaC SPlb WCMO
	'Endeavour'	CDWL CHEx EShb LPJP MOak SHaC WMAq WMul WWpP
	'Erebus' ♀H3	CDWL EZes MOak SDix SHaC WMAq
	'Ermine'	WCMO WCot
	'Étoile du Feu'	SHaC XBlo
	'Eureka'	MOak
	'Evening Star'	MBri SHaC
	'Extase'	SHaC
	'Fatamorgana'	SHaC WHil
	'Felix Ragout'	SHaC
*	'Felix Roux'	SHaC
	'Feuerzauber'	SHaC
	Firebird	see C. 'Oiseau de Feu'
	flaccida	CDWL EZes SHaC WMul
	'Flame'	XBlo
	'Flammèche'	SHaC
§	'Florence Vaughan'	SHaC
	'Fournaise'	SHaC
	'Gaicty'	MOak
	Gamay = 'Turcagram'	SHaC
	'General Eisenhower' ♀H3	SHaC WCMO
	x *generalis*	SHaC
	- - hybrids	SHGC
	- 'Corsica' new	SHaC
	- 'Pink Princess' new	SHaC
	- 'Skyhawk' new	WCMO
	glauca	EZes SDix SHaC WWpP
	'Gnom'	SHaC
	'Golden Girl'	SHaC
	'Golden Lucifer'	CHEx ELan MJnS
	'Gran Canaria'	EAmu SHaC
	'Grand Duc'	MOak SHaC
	'Grande'	CFir ITer MJnS MOak SHaC
	'Heinrich Seidel'	CHEx
	'Hercule'	CHEx SHaC
	'Horn'	SHaC
	hybrids	ELan
	'Ibis'	SHaC
§	*indica*	CHEx CHen CPLG CSev EFul EShb EZes MGol MOak SAPC SArc SHaC SPlb SYvo WHil
	- 'Purpurea'	CHEx EZes LEdu MOak SChr SDix SHaC SPlb WCot WDyG WHil WMul WPGP
	- 'Red King Rupert' new	CCCN
	- 'Russian Red' ♀H3	EZes SHaC WHil
	'Ingeborg' ♀H3	SHaC
	'Intrigue'	MOak SHaC WSPU
	iridiflora misapplied	see C. x *ehemanii*
	iridiflora Ruiz & Pav.	CDWL CHEx CSpe
	'Italia'	EAmu SHaC WHil
	'Jivago'	SHaC
	'Journey's End'	SHaC
	'King City Gold'	MOak SHaC
I	'King Humbert' (blood-red)	CBcs CHEx EPfP LAst MBri MGol MJnS MOak SYvo WCMO WCot WHil XBlo
	King Humbert (orange-red)	see C. 'Roi Humbert'
	'King Midas'	see C. 'Richard Wallace'
	'Königin Charlotte'	SHaC
	'La Gloire'	SHaC
	'La Quintinie'	SHaC
	'La Source'	SHaC
	'La Traviata'	CHen MOak
	'L'Aiglon'	SHaC
	'Lenape' ♀H3	MOak
	'Lesotho Lill'	CHll
	'Libération'	EAmu SHaC
	'Liberté'	see C. 'Wyoming'
	'Lippo's Kiwi'	MOak
	'Lolita'	SHaC
	'Louis Cayeux' ♀H3	SDix SHaC
	'Louis Cottin'	CBcs CCCN CHEx EBrs EChP EPfP SHaC WCMO
	'Lucifer'	CBcs CCCN CHEx CSpe EAmu EPfP LAst LRHS MBri MJnS MLan

	NPer SHaC SPet SPlb SYvo WBrE WCMO WHil	
lutea	CHEx XBlo	
'Madame Angèle Martin'	EAmu EShb MOak SHaC XBlo	
'Madame Paul Casaneuve'	SHaC	
'Maggie'	SHaC	
'Malawiensis Variegata'	see *C.* 'Striata'	
'Marabout'	SHaC	
'Margaret Strange'	SHaC	
'Marvel'	LAst	
'Meyerbeer'	SHaC	
'Monet'	ECho EPfP WCMO	
'Montaigne'	SHaC	
'Mrs Oklahoma'	MOak SHaC	
'Musifolia' ♀H3	CHEx CHen CKob EAmu EZes LPJP MJnS MOak SChr SDix SHaC WCMO WDyG WMul XBlo	
'Mystique' ♀H3	MOak SDix SHaC	
'Ointment Pink'	XBlo	
§ 'Oiseau de Feu'	SHaC	
'Oiseau d'Or'	MJnS SHaC	
'Orange Beauty'	EAmu MOak	
'Orange Perfection'	CFir CHEx CSam LAst MBri MOak SHaC	
'Orange Punch'	SHaC WCot	
'Orchid'	see *C.* 'City of Portland'	
'Osric'	CSpe	
'Pacific Beauty'	LSou WCot	
'Pallag Szépe'	SHaC	
'Panache'	CHEx EZes ITer MOak SHaC WCot WDyG WMul	
'Panama'	SHaC	
'Passionata'	SHaC	
'Pearlescent Pink'	XBlo	
'Perkeo'	LAst MJnS SHaC SPet	
'Petit Poucet'	SHaC	
§ 'Pfitzer's Salmon Pink'	CHEx SHaC	
§ 'Phasion' (v) ♀H3	More than 30 suppliers	
'Picadore'	SHaC	
'Picasso' ♀H3	CBcs CCCN CHEx CPLG EAmu EPfP EShb LAst MGol MJnS MLan SHaC SPet SYvo XBlo	
'Pink Beauty'	MOak	
'Pink Champagne'	XBlo	
'Pink Futurity' (Futurity Series)	MJnS MOak SHaC	
'Pink Perfection'	SHaC	
'Pink Sunburst' (v)	CBow CKob CSpe EZes LAst MJnS NGdn SPlb WCMO	
'Plantagenet'	SHaC	
'Plaster Pink'	XBlo	
'President'	CHEx CRHN CSut EBrs ECho EPfP LAst MOak SHaC SPet SPur WBrE XBlo	
'President Carnot'	SHaC	
'Pretoria'	see *C.* 'Striata'	
'Primrose Yellow'	SHaC	
'Prince Charmant'	SHaC	
'Princess Di'	CMdw SHaC	
'Pringle Bay' (v)	XBlo	
'Puck'	SHaC	
'Ra' ♀H3	CDWL MOak SHaC WHil WMAq	
'Red Futurity' (Futurity Series)	MJnS MOak	
'Red Wine'	MOak SHaC	
§ 'Richard Wallace'	CPLG CSam CSut LAst MJnS MOak SHaC SPlb SYvo WCMO WCot WHil WMul XBlo	
'Robert Kemp'	EAmu SHaC	
§ 'Roi Humbert'	CSam MSte SHaC WMul	
'Roi Soleil' ♀H3	CHEx SHaC	
'Roitelet'	CHEx SHaC	
'Rosa'	SHaC	
Rosalind = 'Turcaros'	SHaC	
'Rose Futurity' (Futurity Series)	MOak SHaC	

'Rosemond Coles'	CHEx CSam CSut EPfP MJnS MLan MOak SHaC SYvo WCMO WMul
'Saladin'	SHaC
'Salmon Pink'	see *C.* 'Pfitzer's Salmon Pink'
'Salsa'	SHaC
'Saumur'	SHaC
Savennières = 'Turcasaw'	SHaC
'Schwäbische Heimat' ♀H3	SHaC
'Sémaphore'	EBee MBri SHaC WCMO
'Shenandoah' ♀H3	SHaC
'Singapore Girl'	MOak SHaC
'Snow-white'	XBlo
speciosa	XBlo
'Stadt Fellbach'	MOak SHaC
'Strasbourg'	CSam NPer SHaC WMul
'Strawberry Pink'	XBlo
'Striata' misapplied	see *C.* 'Stuttgart'
§ 'Striata' (v) ♀H3	CHEx CKob CSev CSpe EBee EShb EZes LAst LPJP MJnS MOak MTis NGdn NMoo NScw NVic SAga SHBN SHaC SPet SYvo WCMO WCot WDyG WHal WMul WSPU XBlo
'Striped Beauty' (v)	CCCN CDWL EAmu EShb EZes MOak SHaC
§ 'Stuttgart' (v)	CHen CSpe EAmu EPfP EShb EZes IBal MJnS MOak NMoo SHaC WCMO WCot WHal WHil WMul
'Summer Gold'	XBlo
'Sundance'	SHaC
'Sunset' **new**	WCot
'Südfunk'	EAmu SHaC
'Tafraout'	SHaC
'Talisman'	SHaC XBlo
'Taney'	CDWL SHaC WMAq
'Tango'	SChr
'Taroudant'	SHaC
'Tchad'	SHaC
'Tirol'	MBri MOak WMul
'Tricarinata'	CHEx
'Triomphe'	SHaC
'Tropical Rose'	CPLG LRHS SRms WCot
Tropicanna	see *C.* 'Phasion'
'Vainqueur'	SHaC
'Valentine'	WCot
'Vanilla Pink'	XBlo
* 'Variegata' (v)	LRHS WCMO WCot WMul
'Verdi' ♀H3	CSpe MJnS SChr SHaC
'Viva'	SHaC
warscewiczii	CPLG EZes MOak SYvo WCot WHil
'Whitehelm Pride' ♀H3	SHaC
'Wine 'n' Roses'	SHaC
'Woodbridge Pink'	XBlo
§ 'Wyoming' ♀H3	CBcs CCCN CHEx CHen CSam EWll LAst MBri MCCP MJnS MOak MSte MTis NVic SEND SHaC SYvo WCMO WCot WMul XBlo
'Yara' **new**	EBrs
'Yellow Futurity' (Futurity Series)	MJnS
'Yellow Humbert' misapplied	see *C.* 'Richard Wallace', *C.* 'Cleopatra', *C.* 'Florence Vaughan'
'Yellow Humbert'	LAst MBri MGol MOak SHaC

Cannomois (Restionaceae)

congesta **new**	CBig
virgata	CBig

Cantleya (Icacinaceae)

* *robusta* **new**	NPal

Cantua (Polemoniaceae)

buxifolia	CAbb CBcs CFee CPLG CPle ECre EShb SOWG WCMO WCot WPGP

Capnoides see *Corydalis*

Capparis (*Capparaceae*)
spinosa	CCCN XPep
- var. **inermis**	XPep

Capsicum (*Solanaceae*)
annuum	CCCN CSim MBri
- var. **annuum** (Longum Group) cayenne	LRav
- - - jalapeno	LRav
- - 'Oda'	LRav
- - 'Othello'	LRav
- - 'Purple Prince'	LRav
- - 'Purple Tiger'	LRav
baccatum	CSim
chinense	CSim
- Habanero Group	LRav
frutescens	CSim
- Tabasco Group	LRav
pubescens	CSim EUnu

Caragana (*Papilionaceae*)
CC 3945 **new**	CPLG
arborescens	CAgr CDul EPfP MBar MGol NWea SBLw SEND SPer SPlb WBVN WDin XPep
- 'Lorbergii'	CEnd CLnd EPfP GBin IMGH MBlu SCoo SPer WFoF
- 'Nana'	NLar
- 'Pendula'	CLnd CWib ELan ENot EPfP LAst MAsh MBar MBlu NEgg NHol NPri SBLw SCoo SLim SPer SPoG WDin
- 'Walker'	CBcs CEnd CWib EBee ELan ENot EPfP LPan LRHS MAsh MBar MBlu MBri MGos NEgg NHol SBLw SCoo SLim SPer WOrn
aurantiaca	MBar
frutex 'Globosa'	NBlu
jubata	NLar
microphylla	WNor

carambola see *Averrhoa carambola*

caraway see *Carum carvi*

Cardamine ✿ (*Brassicaceae*)
alba	WEas
asarifolia misapplied	see *Pachyphragma macrophyllum*
asarifolia L.	CLAP EBrs
bulbifera	CLAP EBee EPPr GBuc GEdr IBlr LEdu NRya WBri WCMO WCru WSHC
californica	EBee EMan EPPr NRya WCru WMoo
concatenata	CLAP EBee NLar SWat WCru WHal
diphylla	CLAP EBee LEdu MLLN NLar WCot WCru WFar
- 'Eco Cut Leaf'	CDes WCMO WCru WPGP
enneaphylla	CLAP GBuc IBlr LEdu NDov NGby WCru
glanduligera	CDes CElw EBee EGle EPPr LEdu NDov SCnR WCru WPGP WSHC
§ **heptaphylla**	CLAP EBee ECha ELan GBin GBuc IBlr MBri MRav SWat WBri WCru
- Guincho form	CDes CLAP EBee GBin IBlr WPGP
- white-flowered	CLAP GCal
§ **kitaibelii**	CLAP EBee ECha GBin GBuc IBlr LEdu NPol SCnR SIng WCru
latifolia Vahl	see *C. raphanifolia*
lineariloba	IBlr
macrophylla	CAby CLAP EBee NLar SDys SWat WCMO WCot WCru WFar
- 'Bright and Bronzy' **new**	WCru

maxima	LEdu WCru
§ **microphylla**	CLAP EHyt GCrs LEdu NDov WAbe WCru
pachystigma	EBee
- NNS 98-149	WCot
pentaphylla ♀H4	CPom CSpe EBee EGle ELan EMar EPPr EPla ERos GBBs GBuc GCrs GEdr GGar IBlr MBri MDun MNFA MRav NBir NDov WCot WCru WPnP WTin
- bright pink	CLAP NPol WCot
pratensis	CArn CHrt CRWN EBee EMFW ENot EWTr MBow MHer NLan NMir NPri SIde SWat WFar WHer WMoo WPtf WSFF WShi WWpP WWye
- 'Edith' (d)	CDes CLAP EBee GBin GBuc MNrw NChi WPrP
- 'Flore Pleno' (d)	CBre CFee CWan EBee ECha ELan EMan IFro ITer MFOX MHer MNrw MTho NBid NBir NBro NLar SBch SBla SWat WEas WFar WHoo WMoo WOut WSFF WSHC WWhi
- 'Improperly Dressed'	CNat
- 'William' (d)	CMea EBee EMan EPPr GBuc MNrw SHar WFar WMoo WPnP WPrP
quinquefolia	CDes CElw CLAP CMea CPom EBee ECha EGle EHrv EMan EMar GBuc IBlr NDov SBch SBla SDys SUsu WBrk WCMO WCot WCru WFar WLin WPGP WRha WWye
§ **raphanifolia**	CBre CDes CLAP CPom CRow EBee ECha EMan GAbr GBuc GCal GGar IBlr LEdu MRav NBid NBro SWat WBor WMoo WPGP WPnP WPtf WTin
trifolia	More than 30 suppliers
* - **digitata**	MTho
waldsteinii	CAby CDes CElw CLAP CPom CSpe EBee ECho EGle EHrv GBuc LToo NCGa NDov SBla SCnR SRot WAbe WCMO WCru WHoo WIvy WWhi
yezoensis	CDes IBlr
- B&SWJ 4659	WCru

cardamon see *Elettaria cardamomum*

cardoon see *Cynara cardunculus*

Cardiandra (*Hydrangeaceae*)
alternifolia	CLAP
- B&SWJ 5719	WCru
- B&SWJ 5845	WCru
- B&SWJ 6354	WCru
formosana	CLAP
- B&SWJ 2005	WCru
- B&SWJ 3632	WCru
- 'Hsitou' **new**	WCru

Cardiocrinum (*Liliaceae*)
cathayanum	EBee ITer MDun WCot WPGP
cordatum	WCMO
- B&SWJ 4841	WCru
- var. **glehnii**	EBee GBuc GEdr WWst
- - B&SWJ 4758	WCru
- red-veined	EBee GBuc GEdr
giganteum	CBcs CBct CBro CHEx EBee ECho EPot GAbr GBuc GEdr GGar GKev GMaP IBlr MBri MDun NLAp SMad WBVN WCMO WCot WCru WFar WHer WMul WPGP
- B&SWJ 2419	WCru
- HWJK 2158 from Nepal **new**	WCru

- var. *yunnanense*	CPom EBee EPfP GAbr GBuc GEdr GGGa GGar IBlr NBid NLar SMad WCMO WCru WPGP
- - CD&R 2491	WCru

Carduus (Asteraceae)

benedictus	see *Cnicus benedictus*

Carex (Cyperaceae)

RBS 0214	MAvo
from Uganda	GCal MMoz
acuta	CBig NBlu NBre
acutiformis	CBig CRWN NBHF NBre NSco
alba	CBig EPPr WDyG
albida	CHrt EBrs EHul EMan LRHS SWal
albula	MMoz WHoo
appressa	CBig
arenaria	CBig EPPr GBin NBHF NBre NNor
* *arundinacea* **new**	LAst
atrata	CCol CHrt EBee EHoe EKen EPPr EPla LRHS WDyG WHrl
aurea	CBig EPPr IFoB NBre NHol
baccans	CBig EPPr GCal LRav NOak WDyG
bebbii	EPPr
berggrenii	EBee EChP ECou ECrN EHoe EHul ELan GSki ITim LEdu LPBA LRHS MBnl NBro NCob NHol NWCA SPer SPlb SWal SWat WMoo WPer WTin WWye
binervis	CRWN
boottiana	EWes
brunnea	EHoe EWes
- 'Jenneke'	CBrm CKno CPen EBee EPPr LRHS MAvo MBar SPoG WMoo
- 'Variegata' (v)	CBrm CPLG EHoe EPPr MMoz
buchananii ♀H4	More than 30 suppliers
- 'Viridis'	EHoe ELan EMan GBin LRHS WHer
bushii	NCob
caryophyllea	EBee EChP EGoo EHoe EPPr EPla
'The Beatles'	MMoz NBir NBro NHol
chathamica	CAby CBig CRez EMan MMoz
'China Blue'	CRez EPPr MMoz WMoo
comans	COlW CWCL EFul EHoe EMon EPPr EShb GCal GQui GSki LRHS NBro NHol NPol
- bronze	More than 30 suppliers
- 'Bronze Perfection'	GBin WCMO WFar
- 'Dancing Flame'	CPrp CWCL EBee EWsh LBBr SVil SWal
- 'Frosted Curls'	More than 30 suppliers
- Red **new**	LAst
- 'Small Red'	see *C. comans* 'Taranaki'
§ - 'Taranaki'	EBee EMan EPPr MBNS MMoz NGdn NHol SWal WPtf
conica 'Hime-kan-suge'	see *C. conica* 'Snowline'
- 'Kiku-sakura' (v)	NHol
§ - 'Snowline' (v)	More than 30 suppliers
coriacea	CBig
- from Dunedin, New Zealand	EPPr
crinita	EPPr MNrw WWpP
cristatella	EBee EPPr
crus-corvi	EPPr
curta	CRWN
dallii	EBee ECou EKen EWes GBin MMoz NLar WWeb
davisii	EPPr
demissa	CRWN EBee EHoe EPPr
depauperata	CRWN EHoe EMon WWye
digitata	CRWN WWye
dioica	CRWN
dipsacea	More than 30 suppliers
- 'Dark Horse' **new**	CTrC EBee GCal WPtf
dissita	CBig LEdu
divulsa subsp. *divulsa*	CRWN
- subsp. *leersii*	EPPr

dolichostachya	CAby CMil CPen CRez EBee EBrs
'Kaga-nishiki' (v)	EMan EMon EPPr LAst LBBr LEdu LRHS MMoz WCot WPnP WPrP WPtf
duthiei	EBee GCal
- KEKE 494	MMoz WPGP
echinata	CRWN
§ *elata*	EPPr
§ - 'Aurea' (v) ♀H4	More than 30 suppliers
- 'Bowles' Golden'	see *C. elata* 'Aurea'
- 'Knightshayes' ♀H4	CKno CPen EBee EMan EWes GBin MMoz WCot
'Evergold'	see *C. oshimensis* 'Evergold'
fascicularis	CBig
firma 'Variegata' (v)	MWat NMen NWCA SIng WAbe
§ *flacca*	CBgR CBig CRWN EHoe EMan EPPr EWin GBin NBre SWal WGwG WPer
- 'Bias' (v)	CNat EBrs EMan EMon EPPr EPla LRHS MMoz WDyG WRHF
§ - subsp. *flacca*	EBee EWes MMoz NHol NSti WPGP WWye
flagellifera	More than 30 suppliers
- 'Auburn Cascade'	EBee EPfP GCal NHol NPro
- 'Coca-Cola'	CKno CPen EBee GCal MAvo NOak
- 'Rapunzel'	EBee EPPr MMoz WPGP
flava	CBig EBee EHoe EPPr SMar
fortunei	see *C. morrowii* Boott
fraseri	see *Cymophyllus fraserianus*
fraserianus	see *Cymophyllus fraserianus*
geminata	CBig
glauca Scopoli	see *C. flacca* subsp. *flacca*
glauca Bosc. ex Boott	CBig CKno CWCL EPla WPGP
granularis	EPPr
grayi	CBgR CBig CFwr EBee EHoe EMon EPla GBuc GCal LBuc LEdu LRHS MBlu MTho NCGa NOak WCot WDyG WPer WSan WWye
§ *hachijoensis*	EMon LAst LRHS WFar
- 'Evergold'	see *C. oshimensis* 'Evergold'
halleriana	XPep
'Happy Wanderer'	SLPl
hirta	CRWN EPPr NSco
hispida	CBig EPPr MCCP MMoz WMoo WPtf WRos
hordeistichos	EBee EPPr
hostiana	CRWN
§ 'Ice Dance' (v)	CMea EBee EGle EPPr EPla GGar GKev GQue MMoz NCGa NHol NLar NOak SBch SWvt WCot WPGP WPrP WWpP
kaloides	EBee EHoe EMan EMon LRHS MAvo
'Kan-suge'	see *C. morrowii* Boott
longebrachiata	CBig
lucida **new**	EShb NNor
lupulina	CPen GBin
lurida	CBig CKno CPen EPfP GBin MAvo MBNS NBre NLar WWpP
macloviana	EPPr
macrocephala	EPPr NBre
'Majken'	EBee NBre
maorica	CBig LEdu
maritima	CRWN
Milk Chocolate = 'Milchoc'PBR (v)	CHar CKno CPen EBee WCMO WLeb
* *mimosa*	EPPr
molesta	EPPr
montana	EBrs LRHS
morrowii misapplied	see *C. oshimensis*, *C. hachijoensis*
§ *morrowii* Boott	GKev MWhi
- 'Evergold'	see *C. oshimensis* 'Evergold'
- 'Fisher's Form' (v)	CKno CTri EBee EHoe EPPr EPla EPot EWsh LEdu LHop LRHS MMoz MRav NGdn NHol NMir

	SMac SWvt WCot WFar WPGP WPer WWye
- 'Gilt' (v)	EAEE EBee EMon EPPr LRHS MBNS NHol
- 'Nana Variegata' (v)	CTri NBir WPGP
- var. *temnolepis* 'Silk Tassel'	EPPr WCot
N - 'Variegata' (v)	CMHG EChP EHoe EHrv EHul ELan EMon EPPr EPfP EPla GMaP LAst LPBA LRHS MBar MMoz MRav NBir NFor NHol NSti SGar SHFr SLPl SMac SRms WCot WFar WPnP
muehlenbergii	EPPr
multifida	EPPr
muricata subsp. *muricata*	EPPr
muskingumensis	More than 30 suppliers
- 'Ice Fountains' (v)	EBee EPPr ERou LIck MAvo
- 'Little Midge'	CKno EBee EBrs EMan EPPr GBin LRHS WWpP
- 'Oehme' (v)	CKno CWCL EBrs EMan EPPr EPla EPyc EShb GBin GCal LEdu LRHS MAvo NBid SUsu WCot WDyG WPtf WTin
- 'Silberstreif' (v)	CBrm CKno CPen CRez EBee GBin GGar NLar
nigra	CRWN EHon EPPr GSki NBHF NLar WWpP
§ - 'On-line' (v)	EBee EHrv EPPr MMoz NBlu NHol WBrk WMoo WWpP
- 'Variegata'	see *C. nigra* 'On-line'
No 1, Nanking (Greg's broad leaf)	MMoz
No 4, Nanking (Greg's thin leaf)	EPPr MAvo
normalis	EPPr
obnupta	EPPr
obtrubae	CRWN
ornithopoda	EGle
- 'Aurea'	see *C. ornithopoda* 'Variegata'
§ - 'Variegata' (v)	CBrm ECtt EHoe EHul EPla EPot MBrN MMoz MWhi NBro NGdn NHol SBch WCot WFar WMoo WTin WWye
§ *oshimensis*	WCot
§ - 'Evergold' (v) ♀H4	More than 30 suppliers
- 'Evergold Compact'	SMac
- 'Variegata' (v)	EPot IHMH NBir
ovalis	CRWN SWal WRos
pallescens	EPPr WWye
- 'Breckland Frost' (v)	EPPr
- 'Wood's Edge' (v)	CNat
panicea	CKno CRWN CWCL EBee EHoe EPPr EPla MMoz NBlu WFar WMoo WWpP
paniculata	CBig CRWN NBre NSco
pendula	More than 30 suppliers
- 'Cool Jazz' (v)	EPPr MAvo
- 'Moonraker' (v)	CWCL EBee EHoe EPPr EPla LEdu MAvo MBNS WCot WLeb WMoo WWpP
petriei	CWCL ECha EMag EWes GBuc LAst LLWP MAvo MBNS MMoz NVic SWal SYvo WCot WFar WHoo WPer WTin
phyllocephala	EHoe EShb WCot WDyG WRos
- 'Sparkler' (v)	More than 30 suppliers
pilulifera 'Tinney's Princess' (v)	CNic EBrs EMan LRHS NHol WCMO
plantaginea	CAby EBee EBrs EHoe EMon EPPr EPla GBin LEdu WCot WDyG WFar WHil WMoo WPGP
platyphylla	WWye
praegracilis <u>new</u>	CKno
projecta	EPPr

§ *pseudocyperus*	CBgR CRWN EHoe EHon EPPr EPla GBin GlBF LPBA MBow MMoz MNrw NBlu NNor NPer SRms SWat WFar WLeb WMoo WPer WPnP WWpP WWye
pulicaris	CRWN
reinii	WPrP WWpP
remota	CBig CRWN EPPr LRHS NBre WPer WWye
riparia	CBig CRWN EMFW LPBA MBow MMoz MWhi NHol NPer NSco SWal SWat WFar WRos WShi
- 'Bowles' Golden'	see *C. elata* 'Aurea'
- 'Variegata' (v)	CBen CBgR CDWL CRow EBee EGra EHoe EHon EMFW EMag EMon EPla EShb GCal GMaP LPBA LRHS MAvo MMoz NBro NHol SAga WAbb WCMO WCot WFar WHal WMoo WPnP WWpP
rostrata	CRWN MBow
saxatilis 'Ski Run' <u>new</u>	EBee
* - 'Variegata' (v)	EHoe EMan
secta	CBig ECou EHoe EPPr GGar GMaP LRav MNrw NBre WDyG WMoo WPer
- from Dunedin, New Zealand	EPPr
- var. *tenuiculmis*	see *C. tenuiculmis*
shortiana	EPPr
siderosticha	EShb SLPl WPGP WPer
- 'Elaine West' (v)	EBee WCot
- 'Golden Fountains'	WCot
- 'Kisokaido' (v)	EBee EMan WCot
- 'Old Barn'	EBee EPPr
- 'Shima-nishiki' (v)	CBcs CElw CHrt CPen CPrp EBee EGle EHoe EMan EPPr EPfP EPla EShb LAst LEdu MMoz NCGa NPro NScw SMad SPoG WBor WCot WLin
- 'Variegata' (v)	More than 30 suppliers
'Silver Sceptre' (v)	More than 30 suppliers
'Silver Sparkler' <u>new</u>	NBir
solandri	CPen CSam EChP ENot EWsh LEdu MAvo NLar SWal WMoo WPtf WWpP
spissa	MAvo MNrw
sprengelii	EPPr
stipata	EPPr
stricta Gooden.	see *C. elata*
stricta Lamarck	CBrm EPla
- 'Bowles' Golden'	see *C. elata* 'Aurea'
sylvatica	CBig CRWN EPfP WWye
tasmanica	CBig
§ *tenuiculmis*	CBrm CKno CWCL EBee EBrs EChP EHoe EMan EMon EPPr EShb EWsh GBin GWCH LRHS MAvo MWhi NHol NSti SBch SWal WTin
tereticaulis	WCwm
testacea	More than 30 suppliers
- 'Old Gold'	CPrp EPPr EWes LBBr MBri NOak SMad SMer SPlb SVil WBrE WFar WLeb
texensis	EPPr
trifida	CHEx CHrt CKno EBee EKen GCal GGar LRHS MMoz MNrw MTis SMad WCot WFar WMoo WPnP WWye
- 'Chatham Blue'	CKno CMHG EChP GBin NBPC NBir SEND
typhina	EPPr
umbrosa	CBig
- subsp. *sabynensis* 'Thinny Thin' (v)	EBee EMon EPPr
uncifolia	ECou
utriculata	EPPr
virgata	CBig

viridula subsp. | EBee
brachyrrhyncha new |
- subsp. *viridula* | CRWN
vulpina | CBig EPPr NBre
vulpinoidea | EPPr
'Yellow Tassels' | ITer

Carica (Caricaceae)
goudotiana | CKob EUnu
x *heilbornii* (F) | CKob
quercifolia | CKob EUnu

Carissa (Apocynaceae)
grandiflora | see *C. macrocarpa*
§ *macrocarpa* (F) | ERea EShb

Carlina (Asteraceae)
acanthifolia | ECho
- subsp. *cyanara* | NWCA
 JJA 274.101 |
acaulis | CArn CMea ECho ELan EPfP GEdr GKev MNHC NEgg NJOw NPri NWCA SDnm SMer SPav SPlb SRms WFar WPer
- subsp. *acaulis* | GPoy
- bronze | CAby CSam EMan EWll LDai LPhx MCCP NLar
- var. *caulescens* | see *C. acaulis* subsp. *simplex*
§ - subsp. *simplex* | EChP ECha EMan EShb GBuc GGar GMaP LRHS NPri SMar WFar WJek WPer
- - bronze | CBow EBee LPhx NBre NChi NSla SMad
vulgaris | NBre WPer
- 'Silver Star' | LPhx

Carmichaelia (Papilionaceae)
'Abundance' | ECou
'Angie' | ECou
angustata 'Buller' | ECou
appressa | ECou GGar
- 'Ellesmere' | ECou
§ *arborea* | ECou
- 'Grand' | ECou
astonii | ECou
- 'Ben More' | ECou
- 'Chalk Ridge' | ECou
australis | ECou WSHC
- 'Bright Eyes' | ECou
- 'Cunningham' | ECou
- Flagelliformis Group | ECou
- 'Mahurangi' | ECou
- Ovata Group | ECou
- 'Solander' | ECou
'Charm' | ECou
'Clifford Bay' | ECou
corrugata | ECou
'Culverden' | ECou
curta | ECou
enysii | CCCN EHyt
exsul | ECou
fieldii 'Westhaven' | ECou
flagelliformis 'Roro' | ECou
glabrata | CHEx CPLG CPle
'Hay and Honey' | ECou
juncea Nigrans Group | ECou
kirkii | ECou
'Lilac Haze' | ECou
monroi | ECou
- 'Rangitata' | ECou
- 'Tekapo' | ECou
nana | ECou
- 'Desert Road' | ECou
- 'Pringle' | ECou
- 'Waitaki' | ECou
nigrans 'Wanaka' | ECou

odorata | CPLG ECou
- Angustata Group | ECou
- 'Green Dwarf' | ECou
- 'Lakeside' | ECou
- 'Riverside' | ECou
ovata 'Calf Creek' | ECou
'Parson's Tiny' | ECou
petriei | ECou SMad
- 'Aviemore' | ECou
- 'Lindis' | ECou
- 'Pukaki' | ECou
- Virgata Group | ECou
'Porter's Pass' | ECou
'Spangle' | ECou
'Tangle' | ECou
uniflora | ECou
- 'Bealey' | ECou
'Weka' | ECou
williamsii | ECou
'Yellow Eyes' | ECou

x *Carmispartium* (Papilionaceae)
astens | see x *C. hutchinsii*
§ *hutchinsii* | ECou
- 'Butterfly' | ECou
- 'County Park' | ECou GCal
- 'Delight' | ECou
- 'Pink Beauty' | ECou
- 'Wingletye' | ECou

Carpenteria (Hydrangeaceae)
californica ♀H3 | CMCN CPMA CSBt ELan ENot EPfP GQui IMGH LHop MBri MGos MLan MWat NPal NSti SBrw SGar SHBN SHGC SMur SPer SPla SReu SSpi SSta WAbe WDin WHCG WPat WSHC
- 'Bodnant' | CDul ELan LRHS MBri MGos MWea SBra SBrw SPoG SSpi WGer WPGP
- 'Elizabeth' | CAbP CPMA ELan EPfP LRHS MAsh MBri SBrw SMur SSpi SSta WDin WPGP WPat
- 'Ladhams' Variety' | CBcs CPMA EPfP LRHS MGos MRav NEgg NLar SBra SBrw WKif WSPU

Carpinus ✿ (Corylaceae)
betulus ♀H4 | More than 30 suppliers
* - 'A. Beeckman' | SBLw
- 'Columnaris' | CLnd CTho SBLw
* - 'Columnaris Nana' | CMCN
§ - 'Fastigiata' ♀H4 | CBcs CCVT CDoC CDul CEnd CLnd CMCN CSBt CTho CWib EBee ECrN ELan ENot EPfP LBuc LPan MBar MGos NBee NWea SBLw SPoG WDin WFar WOrn
- 'Frans Fontaine' | CDoC CDul CMCN CTho EBee IArd LAst LPan LRHS MBlu MBri MGos NBlu SBLw SCoo SIFN SLim SPer SPoG SSta
- 'Horizontalis' | CMCN
- 'Pendula' | CDul CEnd CLnd CTho EBee LPan MBlu SBLw SIFN WDin
- 'Purpurea' | CBcs CDul CEnd MGos NLar SBLw
- 'Pyramidalis' | see *C. betulus* 'Fastigiata'
- 'Quercifolia' | CDul SBLw
caroliniana | CLnd CMCN NEgg WNor
caucasica | SIFN
cordata | CMCN SBir SIFN WCwm WDin
coreana | CLnd CMCN CTho WDin WNor
fangiana | CEnd CLnd CTho SIFN WPGP
fargesii | see *C. viminea*
henryana | CMen SBir SIFN WDin WHCr WNor

japonica ♀H4	CEnd CMCN CMen CTho EPfP IDee LPan MBlu SIFN SMad WDin
laxiflora	CMen SIFN WFar WNor WPGP
- var. *longispica* B&SWJ 8772	WCru
- var. *macrostachya*	see *C. viminea*
orientalis	CMCN WNor
polyneura	CMCN SBir WNor
pubescens	SIFN WPGP
* *schisiensis*	CDul
x *schuschaensis*	SIFN
shensiensis	CMCN
tschonoskii	CMCN
turczaninowii ♀H4	CDul CMCN CMHG CMen CTho IDee LNar NPal NWea SBir SHGN SIFN STre WDin WNor
§ *viminea*	CEnd CMCN CTho WNor

Carpobrotus (*Aizoaceae*)

§ *edulis*	CAgr CCCN CDoC CHen CHrt CTbh EShb EUnu EWin SAPC SArc SChr SEND WHer
- var. *edulis*	CHEx
- var. *rubescens* **new**	CCCN
- - pink-flowered	CHEx
muirii	CCCN EShb EWin
rossii	GGar

Carpodetus (*Escalloniaceae*)

serratus	CBcs CTrC

Carthamus (*Asteraceae*)

tinctorius	MNHC MSal SPav

Carum (*Apiaceae*)

carvi	CArn CBod CHrt CWan GPoy GWCH MHer MNHC NPri NVic SIde WHer WJek WPer WSel
copticum	EUnu MSal
petroselinum	see *Petroselinum crispum*
roxburghianum	EUnu

Carya ✿ (*Juglandaceae*)

aquatica	CTho
cordiformis	CMCN CTho EPfP
glabra	CMCN
N *illinoinensis* (F)	CAgr CBcs CMCN SSpi
- 'Carlson No 3' seedling	CAgr
- 'Colby' seedling	CAgr
- 'Cornfield' **new**	CAgr
- 'Lucas' **new**	CAgr
laciniosa (F)	CTho EGFP EPfP SSpi
- 'Henry' (F)	CAgr
- 'Keystone' seedling (F)	CAgr
ovalis	EGFP
ovata (F)	CAgr CLnd CMCN CTho EPfP MBlu SSpi WDin WWes
- 'Grainger' seedling (F)	CAgr
- 'Neilson' seedling (F)	CAgr
- 'Weschke' seedling (F)	CAgr
- 'Yoder no 1' seedling (F)	CAgr
pallida	CMCN
tomentosa	EPfP

Caryophyllus see *Syzygium*

Caryopteris ✿ (*Verbenaceae*)

x *clandonensis*	EBee ECtt ENot MGan MWat NBir WCFE WDin WFar WHCG WHar WSHC WTel WWye
- 'Arthur Simmonds' ♀H4	CSam CTri EBee ECha EPfP LHop SPer WGor
- 'Blaue Donau'	EBee LAst SPoG
- 'Dark Night'	CHar LRHS MSph SMac SPoG SPur
- 'Ferndown'	CDoC CWib EBee ECrN EPfP EWTr LHop LRHS MGos NLar SPer SPla SReu SRms WWeb
- 'First Choice' ♀H3-4	CAbP CSpe EBee ECrN ELan EPfP LHop LRHS LSRN MAsh MBri MGos NLar SMad SMur SPer SPoG SRkn SWvt WOVN
- Grand Bleu = 'Inoveris'PBR	CSBt EBee ELan EMil EShb EWTr LBuc LSRN MAsh MBNS MRav MSwo NCGa SPoG SPur
- 'Heavenly Baby'	MAsh
- 'Heavenly Blue'	More than 30 suppliers
- 'Kew Blue'	More than 30 suppliers
- 'Longwood Blue'	ELan EPfP LRHS
- 'Moody Blue' (v)	EPfP SPoG
- 'Pershore'	MWgw WSPU
- 'Summer Gold'	MRav SPoG
- 'Summer Sorbet' (v)	CBcs CBow CDoC EBrs ELan EMil EWes LBuc LRHS MAsh MGos MNHC SCoo SPoG
- 'Worcester Gold' ♀H3-4	More than 30 suppliers
divaricata	EBee EMon
- 'Electrum'	EMan EMon LSou MDKP
- 'Jade Shades'	EBee EMon LSou WSHC
- variegated (v)	CBow
§ *incana*	CMCN CPle CWoW ECrN EPfP MWhi SLon SPer SPoG WOut WSHC XPep
- 'Autumn Pink' **new**	CBgR
- 'Blue Cascade'	MRav
- 'Jason'PBR	ENot MGos
- weeping	EBee ELan GBuc GCal MSte MTis NLar SAdn WLeb WPat
mastacanthus	see *C. incana*
mongolica	XPep
odorata	EShb

Caryota (*Arecaceae*)

'Hymalaya'	CRoM LPal WMul
mitis ♀H1	EAmu LPal SBig WMul
obtusa	LPal
ochlandra	LPal
urens	LPal

Cassandra see *Chamaedaphne*

Cassia (*Caesalpiniaceae*)

corymbosa Lam.	see *Senna corymbosa*
grandis	CSec
marilandica	see *Senna marilandica*
obtusifolia	see *Senna obtusifolia*

Cassinia (*Asteraceae*)

aculeata	GGar
leptophylla	GGar SPer
- subsp. *fulvida*	CBcs ECou EHoe GGar IFro MBar SPer
- subsp. *vauvilliersii*	CDoC CPLG GGar SPer
- - var. *albida*	CBcs SPer
- - 'Silberschmelze'	SOWG
N *retorta*	ECou
'Ward Silver'	CPLG ECou EHoe EWes GSki

Cassinia x *Helichrysum* (*Asteraceae*)

* hybrid	WKif WSHC

Cassiope ✿ (*Ericaceae*)

'Askival Arctic Fox'	GCrs
'Askival Snowbird'	GCrs ITim
'Askival Snow-wreath'	see *C.* Snow-wreath Group
'Askival Stormbird'	GCrs
'Badenoch'	ECho GCrs GEdr NDlv NLAp
'Bearsden'	CMHG MBar NDlv
'Edinburgh' ♀H4	CMHG ECho EPfP GCrs GEdr MBar NDlv NHol

fastigiata Askival strain	GCrs
x *wardii*	
'Kathleen Dryden'	GCrs
lycopodioides ♀H4	MBar
- 'Beatrice Lilley'	ECho GEdr ITim LTwo MBar NDlv
	NLAp SRms WPat
- 'Jim Lever'	GCrs ITim WAbe
- *minima*	GEdr
- 'Rokujō'	NHol
'Medusa'	NHol WPat
mertensiana	ECho GCrs MBar NDlv NJOw
	NLAp SRms
- var. *californica*	GCrs
- var. *gracilis*	CMHG GEdr NHol
'Muirhead' ♀H4	CMHG ECho GCrs GEdr MBar
	MDun NDlv NHol NRya SRms
	WAbe
pectinata new	GIBF
'Randle Cooke' ♀H4	CMHG ECho GCrs GEdr MBar
	MDun NDlv NHol NLAp SRms
selaginoides	GIBF
- LS&E 13284	GCrs WAbe
§ Snow-wreath Group	GCrs
tetragona	MBar NLar SRms
wardii 'George Taylor'	GGGa

Castanea ✿ (*Fagaceae*)

'Bouche de Betizac' (F)	CAgr LPan
crenata	CAgr
henryi	CBcs
'Layeroka' (F)	CAgr LRHS NWea
'Maraval'	CAgr LRHS NWea
'Maridonne' (F)	CAgr
'Marigoule' (F)	CAgr SKee
'Marlhac' (F)	CAgr
'Marsol' (F)	CAgr
mollissima	CBcs CMCN ISea
x *neglecta*	CTho
'Précoce Migoule' (F)	CAgr
pumila	CAgr CMCN
'Rousse de Nay' (F)	CAgr
sativa ♀H4	More than 30 suppliers
§ - 'Albomarginata' (v) ♀H4	CDoC CDul CEnd CTho EBee EPfP
	IMGH MBlu MBri MDun MGos
	NBea SBLw SCoo WDin WOrn
	WPat WWes
- 'Anny's Red'	MBlu
- 'Anny's Summer Red'	CDul LRHS
- 'Argenteovariegata'	see *C. sativa* 'Albomarginata'
- 'Aspleniifolia'	CBcs CDul MBlu
- 'Aureomarginata'	see *C. sativa* 'Variegata'
- 'Belle Epine' (F)	CAgr
- 'Bournette' (F)	CAgr
* - 'Doré de Lyon'	CAgr
- 'Herria' (F)	CAgr
- 'Laguépie' (F)	CAgr
- 'Marron Comballe' (F)	CAgr
- 'Marron de Goujounac' (F)	CAgr
- 'Marron de Lyon' (F)	CAgr CDul CEnd CLnd CTho EMui
	EPfP MBlu MCoo NWea SKee
- 'Marron de Redon' (F)	CAgr
- 'Numbo' (F)	CAgr
- 'Pyramidalis'	WDin
§ - 'Variegata' (v)	CBcs CLnd CMCN ECrN ELan
	EMil EPfP EWTr LPan MAsh
	MGos
- 'Verdale' (F)	CAgr
seguinii	LEdu
'Simpson'	CAgr
'Vignols' (F)	CAgr

Castanopsis (*Fagaceae*)

chinensis new	CAgr CBcs
cuspidata	CBcs
orthacantha new	CBcs

Castanospermum (*Papilionaceae*)

australe new	CArn

Castilleja (*Scrophulariaceae*)

christii	GKev
hispida new	WAbe
miniata	WAbe

Casuarina (*Casuarinaceae*)

cunninghamiana	ECou

Catalpa ✿ (*Bignoniaceae*)

bignonioides ♀H4	More than 30 suppliers
- 'Aurea' ♀H4	More than 30 suppliers
- 'Nana'	ECrN LRHS MBri SBLw WDin
- 'Purpurea'	see *C.* x *erubescens* 'Purpurea'
- 'Variegata' (v)	CTho EPfP LRHS MAsh MRav SSta
	WCMO WPat
bungei	CLnd CTho EGFP LPan MGos
	MJnS SAPC SArc SHGN WNor
- 'Purpurea'	ELan
x *erubescens*	SBLw
§ - 'Purpurea' ♀H4	More than 30 suppliers
fargesii	CLnd
- f. *duclouxii*	CDul CTho EPfP MBlu NLar
	WPat
ovata	CMCN CTho EGFP WBVN
- 'Slender Silhouette' new	NLar
speciosa	CBcs CDul CLnd CMCN CTho
	EPfP SBLw SPer
- 'Pulverulenta' (v)	CDoC CDul CEnd CMCN EMil
	LPan MAsh MDun MGos NLar SBig
	SPer WOrn

Catananche (*Asteraceae*)

caerulea	More than 30 suppliers
- 'Alba'	CMea COIW EBee EBla EChP ECha
	EPfP ERou IFoB LRHS NBid NBir
	NPri SPer SPoG WCAu WMoo
	WMow WPer
- 'Amor White'	CSim LRav
- 'Bicolor'	CMMP ECrN EMan MHer MNrw
	SHGN STes SWal WFar WHoo
	WMoo
- 'Major' ♀H4	EChP ECrN LDai LRHS SRms WEas
caespitosa	SBla

Catha (*Celastraceae*)

edulis	CArn CKob GPoy MGol WJek

Catharanthus (*Apocynaceae*)

roseus ♀H1	GPoy MBri MSal
- Ocellatus Group	MBri

Caulophyllum (*Berberidaceae*)

thalictroides	CArn CDes CLAP GBBs GBuc
	GEdr LEdu MGol MSal NLar WCot
	WCru WFar WMoo WPnP WSHC
- subsp. *robustum*	CLAP WCru

Cautleya ✿ (*Zingiberaceae*)

cathcartii	CLAP LEdu
- B&SWJ 2281	WCru
- B&SWJ 2314	CBct
- 'Tenzing's Gold'	CLAP WCru
§ *gracilis*	CBct CKob CLAP EBee EZes IBlr
	LEdu MOak SBig WMul
- B&SWJ 7186	WCru WDyG
- CC 1751	WCot
lutea	see *C. gracilis*
spicata	CBct CDoC CHEx CKob EBee
	ECho EZes GBin IBlr SBig WCot
- B&SWJ 2103	WCru
- 'Crûg Canary'	CLAP WCru
* - var. *lutea*	CBct CHEx CPne MOak

- 'Robusta'	CHEx CLAP CMdw CPne EAmu EBee EBrs EMan EShb GCal IBlr LEdu MGol MTis SMad WBor WCot WCru WMul WPGP

Cayratia (Vitaceae)

§ **thomsonii**	CDul CPlN WCru
- BWJ 8123	WCru

Ceanothus ✿ (Rhamnaceae)

'A.T. Johnson'	CDul EBee ECrN LAst MWya SHBN SLim SPer SRms
americanus	CArn CPle MSal
arboreus	SAPC SArc
- 'Owlswood Blue'	LRHS
- 'Trewithen Blue' ♀H3	More than 30 suppliers
'Autumnal Blue' ♀H3	More than 30 suppliers
'Basil Fox'	LRHS
'Blue Buttons'	LRHS
* 'Blue Carpet'	CWSG
'Blue Cushion'	CBcs CDoC CPMA CWSG EBee GGar LHop LRHS MGos MRav NLar SLon SMer SWvt WRHF
'Blue Dreams'	WFar
'Blue Jeans'	EBee ELan IArd LRHS MWea WAbe WLeb
* 'Blue Moon'	LRHS
'Blue Mound' ♀H3	More than 30 suppliers
'Blue Sapphire'PBR	CBcs CBgR CDoC CFwr CRez CSBt CWSG EBee ELan EMil EPfP LAst LHop LRHS MBlu NLar SHBN SPer SPoG SWvt
'Burkwoodii' ♀H3	CBcs CDoC CDul CSBt CTri CWSG ENot EPfP LAst LRHS MAsh MDun MGan MGos MRav NHol SHBN SPer SPoG SWvt WFar
'Cascade' ♀H3	CBcs CTri CWSG EBee ENot LRHS MGos MWat NSti SCoo SLon SPer SPlb WHCG XPep
'Centennial'	LRHS
'Concha' ♀H3	More than 30 suppliers
§ **cuneatus** var. **rigidus**	EHol LRHS NHol SRms WAbe WSHC
- - 'Snowball'	ELan EPfP LRHS
'Cynthia Postan'	CAbP CBcs CMHG CSBt CWSG EBee ECrN EPfP IArd ISea LRHS MBlu MRav MWat NHol NLar SCoo SDix WWeb
'Dark Star' ♀H3	CBcs CBrm CDoC CMHG CPMA CSPN CTbh CWSG EBee EPfP LRHS MAsh MBlu NSti SEND SOWG SPla SPoG SSta SWvt
'Delight'	CBcs EBee ELan EPfP EPla EWTr LRHS MGos MRav NBlu NLar WDin WFar
x **delileanus**	CBcs
- 'Gloire de Versailles' ♀H4	More than 30 suppliers
- 'Henri Desfossé'	EHol ELan LRHS MRav NCGa NLar SOWG SPer WDin WKif
- 'Indigo'	WKif
- 'Topaze' ♀H4	CBcs CRez CWSG EBee ELan EMil EPfP LRHS MRav NLar SLon SOWG WDin WHar WKif
dentatus misapplied	see *C. x lobbianus*
dentatus Torr. & A.Gray	ENot GBin SPer SPlb
- var. **floribundus**	CDul CSBt ELan LRHS SDix
* - 'Superbus'	EBee
'Diamond Heights'	see *C. griseus* var. *horizontalis* 'Diamond Heights'
divergens	EBee
'Edinburgh' ♀H3	EBee EPfP GBin LRHS MGos WFar
'El Dorado' (v)	SPoG
'Eleanor Taylor'	EBee SLon
'Fallen Skies'	LRHS
foliosus var. **austromontanus**	CTrw

'Frosty Blue'	LRHS
gloriosus	EBee EWes
- 'Anchor Bay'	EBee ELan EPfP IArd LRHS SLon SOWG WWeb
- 'Emily Brown'	CBcs CDoC CSPN EBee ELan GGar LAst MRav NHol NLar WFar
- 'Hearts Desire' **new**	LRHS
- 'Popcorn' **new**	LRHS
§ **griseus** var. **horizontalis** 'Diamond Heights' (v)	MAsh MGos NPri SPer WFar
- - 'Hurricane Point'	WFar
- - 'Silver Surprise'PBR (v)	CBcs CSPN EBee ELan EMil ENot EPfP LRHS MGos NLar NPri SHBN SLim SPer SPoG WOVN
- - 'Yankee Point'	CBcs CDoC CSBt CWib EBee EMil ENot EPfP GGar ISea LRHS MAsh MGos MRav MSwo SCoo SHBN SLim SMer SPer SPlb SPoG SWvt WDin WFar XPep
impressus	CBcs CMHG CSBt CTri ECrN ELan EPfP LRHS MAsh MGos MRav SMer SPer SPla SWvt WCFE WFar WWeb XPep
- 'Victoria'	EGra LBuc NLar SRGP XPep
N 'Italian Skies' ♀H3	CBcs CDoC CMac CSBt CWSG EBee ELan EMil EPfP LAst LRHS MDun MGos MLan MRav MSwo MWgw NPri SCoo SLim SLon SMer SPer SPlb SPoG SWvt WDin WFar XPep
'Joan Mirov' **new**	LRHS
'Joyce Coulter'	CBcs
'Julia Phelps'	CMHG EBee WEas WSPU
'Ken Taylor'	LRHS
'Kurt Zadnik' **new**	LRHS
§ x **lobbianus**	CBcs CDul CTri EHol MRav NJOw SPlb WDin WFar
- 'Russellianus'	MWya SHBN
maritimus 'Frosty Dawn' **new**	LRHS
x **pallidus** 'Marie Simon'	CBcs CBrm CWib EBee ECrN EHol ELan EMil EPfP LAst LHop LRHS MGos NJOw SCoo SPer SPoG SRms SWvt WCFE WDin WFar WKif WWeb
- 'Marie Simon Variegated' (v)	CPMA
- 'Perle Rose'	CBcs CMac CPle EBee EPfP LAst LRHS LTwo MGos SHBN SOWG SPer SPla WKif WSHC
papillosus var. **roweanus**	CPle
§ 'Pershore Zanzibar'PBR (v)	CBcs CBgR CSBt CSPN CWSG EBee EHoe ELan ENot EPfP LAst LBuc LRHS MGos MRav MSwo MWgw MWya NPri SAdn SHBN SPer SPoG SSto SWvt WBrE WSPU WWeb
'Pin Cushion'	CDoC CWSG CWib EPfP LRHS MWgw NHol WSPU
'Point Millerton'	see *C. thyrsiflorus* 'Millerton Point'
'Popcorn' **new**	MGos
prostratus	CPle GIBF MAsh SHBN SMad WAbe
'Puget Blue' ♀H4	More than 30 suppliers
purpureus	CPle LRHS WWeb
'Ray Hartman'	SMad XPep
repens	see *C. thyrsiflorus* var. *repens*
rigidus	see *C. cuneatus* var. *rigidus*
'Sierra Blue'	EBee SHGC
'Snow Flurries'	see *C. thyrsiflorus* 'Snow Flurry'
'Southmead' ♀H3	CDoC CTri EBee EGra ELan EMil EPfP GBuc LRHS MAsh MGos MSwo MWat NEgg NHol WBrE WDin WFar WHCG WMoo

thyrsiflorus	CBcs CMac CTri CWSG CWib EPfP LRHS MAsh NHol SHBN SPer SRms SWvt WDin WFar WHar WTel
§ - 'Millerton Point'	CDul CWSG EBee EMil EPfP LAst LRHS MBlu MGos MWea NLar SCoo SLim SPoG WGwG XPep
§ - var. *repens* ♀H3	More than 30 suppliers
§ - 'Skylark' ♀H3	CDoC CDul CWSG ELan ENot EPfP GGar LHop LRHS MAsh MBri MGos MLHP NPri SDix SLim SReu SSpi SSta WDin WFar WPat WWeb
§ - 'Snow Flurry'	CBcs CWib EPfP MSwo WFar
'Tilden Park'	LRHS
x *veitchianus*	CMac CSBt EBee ELan LRHS MAsh MBar MDun NHol SPer
velutinus	MSal
'White Cascade'	EHol LRHS
'Zanzibar'PBR	see *Ceanothus* 'Pershore Zanzibar'

Cedrela (Meliaceae)

sinensis	see *Toona sinensis*

Cedronella (Lamiaceae)

§ *canariensis*	CArn CBod CHby CHrt CSec CSev EShb EUnu GBar GGar GPoy ILis MBow MHer MNHC MSal NGHP NTHB Slde SOWG SWat WCHb WGwG WHer WPer WSel WWye XPep
mexicana	see *Agastache mexicana*
triphylla	see *C. canariensis*

Cedrus (Pinaceae)

atlantica	CDul CLnd CMen CSBt ECrN EHul EWTr LCon MBar NWea SEND WBVN WEve WMou WWes
- 'Aurea'	CDul CMac LCon LLin MBar MGan MGos NLar SSta WDin WHar
- 'Fastigiata'	CDoC CDul CMac EHul LCon MBar MBri MGan MGos NLar SCoo SLim SPoG WEve
- Glauca Group ♀H4	More than 30 suppliers
- - 'Glauca Fastigiata'	CKen CMen ECho WEve
- - 'Glauca Pendula'	CDoC CDul CMen ECho ECrN EHul EOrn EPfP IMGH LCon LPan LRHS MBar MBlu MBri MGan MGos NBlu NEgg SBLw SHBN SLim SMad SPoG SSta WDin WEve WFar WOrn
- - 'Saphir Nymphe'	ECho NLar
- - 'Silberspitz'	CKen
- - 'Pendula'	CMac ECho GBin MAsh SHBN
brevifolia	ECho LCon LLin LPan MBar MGos NLar STre WEve
- 'Epstein'	ECho LCon MBar MGos
- 'Hillier Compact'	CKen GTSp
- 'Kenwith'	CKen ECho LCon NLar
deodara ♀H4	More than 30 suppliers
- 'Albospica' (v)	LLin SWvt
- 'Argentea'	MBar MGos
- 'Aurea' ♀H4	CDoC CDul CSBt CTho ECho ECrN EHul EOrn EPfP GBin IMGH LCon LLin LPan LRHS MBar MBri MGan MGos MWya NEgg SBLw SLim WDin WEve WFar WOrn
I - 'Aurea Pendula'	ECho
- 'Blue Dwarf'	CKen ECho LLin NLar WEve
* - 'Blue Mountain Broom'	CKen
- 'Blue Snake'	CKen NLar
- 'Blue Triumph'	LPan
- 'Cream Puff'	CSli ECho LLin MAsh MBar MGos
- 'Dawn Mist' (v)	ECho LLin
- 'Devinely Blue'	CKen SLim
- 'Feelin' Blue'	CDoC CKen COtt CRob CSli ECho EHul EPla IMGH LBee LCon LLin LRHS MAsh MBar MBlu MBri

	MGos MLan NHol SCoo SHBN SLim SPoG SWvt WEve WFar
- 'Gold Cascade' new	SLim
- 'Gold Cone'	ECho MGos
- 'Gold Gowa'	MGos NLar
- 'Gold Mound'	CKen CSBt ECho MAsh WEve
- 'Golden Horizon'	CDoC CKen CMen CRob CSBt ECho EHul EOrn EPla IMGH ISea LBee LCon LLin LPan LRHS MAsh MBar MBlu MBri MGos NBlu SCoo SHBN SLim SPoG SWvt WDin WEve WFar
- 'Karl Fuchs'	CDoC MAsh MBri NBlu NLar SCoo SMad WGor
- 'Kashmir'	CSli NLar
- 'Kelly Gold'	LPan NLar
- 'Klondyke'	MAsh
- 'Mountain Beauty'	CKen
- 'Nana'	CKen
- 'Nivea'	CKen
- 'Pendula'	CDoC CKen ECho EHul LCon LPan MBar MGos WEve WGor
- 'Polar Winter'	SMad
- 'Pygmy'	CKen
- 'Raywood's Prostrate'	CKen
- 'Robusta'	SBLw WEve
- 'Roman Candle'	CSli ECho EOrn SHBN WEve
- 'Scott'	CKen
- 'Silver Mist'	CKen MGos
- 'Silver Spring'	MGos NLar
libani ♀H4	More than 30 suppliers
- 'Comte de Dijon'	ECho EHul LCon LLin LRHS NLar SLim SPoG
- 'Fontaine'	NLar
- 'Home Park'	CKen NLar
- Nana Group	CKen ECho
- 'Pampisford'	ECho NLar
- 'Saint Catherine' new	NLar
- 'Sargentii'	CDoC CKen ECho EHul EOrn IMGH LCon LLin MBar MBlu MGos NLar SHBN SLim WEve
- 'Taurus'	MBar NLar

Celastrus (Celastraceae)

angulatus	GIBF
orbiculatus	CBcs CDoC CFwr CMac CPIN EBee ELan LRHS MBri MGol MRav NSti SBrw SHGC SLon SPer SReu SSta WBor WFar WSHC
- 'Diana' (f)	NBea NLar SSta
- 'Hercules' (m)	NBea NLar
- Hermaphrodite Group ♀H4	CBrm CSam GSki SBra SDix
- var. *papillosus* B&SWJ 591	WCru
- var. *punctatus* B&SWJ 1931	WCru
rosthornianus	GIBF
scandens	CMac EBee IMGH NLar NScw SMur SPlb WDin
- (f)	CPIN
- (m)	CPIN

Celmisia ✿ (Asteraceae)

allanii	IBlr WLin
alpina	IBlr
- large-leaved	IBlr
angustifolia	EPot GCrs GEdr IBlr
- silver-leaved	IBlr
argentea	ECho GCrs IBlr NDlv NLAp WAbe
armstrongii	ECho IBlr
asteliifolia	IBlr
Ballyrogan hybrids	IBlr
bellidioides	ECho EWes GCrs GEdr IBlr MDKP
bonplandii	GEdr IBlr
brevifolia	IBlr

coriacea misapplied	see *C. semicordata*
coriacea Raoul	see *C. mackaui*
coriacea (G. Forst.) Hook. f.	GCal IBlr MDun NLAp
costiniana	IBlr
dallii	IBlr
'David Shackleton'	IBlr
densiflora	GCrs GKev IBlr
– silver-leaved	IBlr
discolor	IBlr
durietzii	IBlr
glandulosa	IBlr
gracilenta	GCrs IBlr NLAp NSla SRot
– CC 563	NWCA
graminifolia	ECho IBlr
haastii	IBlr
'Harry Bryce'	IBlr
hectorii	GCrs IBlr
hectorii × *ramulosa*	WAbe
holosericea	IBlr
hookeri	GCal IBlr
inaccessa	IBlr
incana	GCrs IBlr
Inshriach hybrids	IBlr NHar
insignis	IBlr
Jury hybrids	IBlr
latifolia	IBlr
– large-leaved	IBlr
longifolia	GGar
– large-leaved	IBlr
– small-leaved	IBlr
§ *mackaui*	GGar IBlr
markii	IBlr
monroi	IBlr
morganii	NLAp
petiolata	GKev
prorepens	GKev IBlr
pugioniformis	IBlr
ramulosa	GEdr GGar ITim NLAp SIng
§ – var. *tuberculata*	GCrs IBlr NSla
saxifraga	IBlr ITim WAbe
§ *semicordata*	GBuc IBal IBlr ITim NLAp NSla
– subsp. *aurigans*	IBlr
– subsp. *stricta*	IBlr
sericophylla	IBlr
– large-leaved	IBlr
sessiliflora	IBlr ITim NWCA
– 'Mount Potts'	IBlr
spectabilis	CTrC ECho IBlr MDun WAbe WCot
– 'Eggleston Silver'	NEgg WCMO
– subsp. *magnifica*	IBlr
– subsp. *spectabilis* var. *angustifolia*	IBlr
spedenii	IBlr
tomentella	IBlr
traversii	IBlr NLAp WWeb
verbascifolia	IBlr
viscosa	IBlr NLAp
§ *walkeri*	GGar GKev IBlr NLAp
webbiana	see *C. walkeri*

Celosia (Amaranthaceae)

argentea var. *cristata*	MBri
– – Plumosa Group	MBri
– 'Venezuela' <u>new</u>	NBlu

Celsia see *Verbascum*

× *Celsioverbascum* see *Verbascum*

Celtica see *Stipa*

Celtis (Ulmaceae)

australis	CAgr CBcs EGFP LEdu LPan MGos SBLw
bungeana	CMCN IDee NLar

caucasica	NLar
julianae	IArd NLar WCwm WNor
occidentalis	CAgr CDul CTho ELan GIBF IArd NBlu WBVN
– var. *pumila*	WNor
sinensis	CMen LEdu NLar WNor

Cenolophium (Apiaceae)

denudatum	CDes CHrt EBee ECha NChi WPGP WTMC

Centaurea ✿ (Asteraceae)

from Turkey	WPGP
HH&K 271	NBid
alba	EBee
alpestris	CMHG EChP ECho NBre NEgg NLar
atropurpurea	EDAr LPhx NDov NLar SMar SPoG WHal WHil WMnd WOut
bella	More than 30 suppliers
– 'Katherine' (v)	MAvo
benoistii	CAby CDes CHad CKno CPom EBee LPhx MRav NDov SMHy SUsu WHrl WPGP
'Blue Dreams'	EMon MLLN
cana	see *C. triumfettii* subsp. *cana*
candidissima misapplied	see *C. cineraria*
'Caramia'	EBee SMeo SSvw SUsu
cheiranthifolia	CDes CElw EBee EChP ECha EMon EPPr NBir WFar WPGP
§ – var. *purpurascens*	EMon
§ *cineraria*	EBee EMan MOak SRms WEas
– subsp. *cineraria* ♀[H3]	EBee WCot
I 'Copper Hybrid' <u>new</u>	SMHy
cyanus	CArn GWCH MBow MHer MNHC NPri WFar WJek
– 'Black Ball'	CSpe
dealbata	CEnt COIW CPrp CTri CWib EBee EPfP GAbr IFoB IHMH LAst LRHS NBPC NBlu NBro NMir NOrc SECG SMer WBor WCot WFar WMoo WPer WWeb WWhi
– 'Steenbergii'	CAbP EBee EChP EGle ELan ERou GCal GGar LRHS MNFA NBid NOak NPer NSti SBch SPer SPoG WAbb WCAu WCot WFar WHoo WMnd
fischeri Willd.	CDes EBee EMon WPGP
glastifolia	EBee EMon GCal MLLN NBre WCot WPGP
gymnocarpa	see *C. cineraria*
'Hoar Frost'	CDes CMil EMon
hypoleuca <u>new</u>	NBid
– 'John Coutts'	More than 30 suppliers
jacea	CSam EShb GAbr MBow NBid NLar SYvo WAul WCot WPer
'Jordy'	CFwr EBee IPot
kotschyana	CDes EBee NBid NBre WPGP
macrocephala	More than 30 suppliers
marschalliana	NBid
mollis	NBid
montana	More than 30 suppliers
– 'Alba'	More than 30 suppliers
§ – 'Carnea'	CCVN CElw CPom CSam EBee EChP ECha EGle EMon GMaP LLWP LPhx MNFA NChi NLar SAga SMeo STes WCAu WFar WMoo WBVN
– 'Coerulea'	WBVN
– 'Gold Bullion'	CDes EBee EBrs ECGP ECtt EGle ELan EMon EPPr EWes GBuc LDai MAvo MBri MCCP NBid NBir NSti SMad SPoG SSvw WBor WCAu
– 'Gold Strike' <u>new</u>	EBee
– 'Grandiflora'	EBee
– 'Horwood Gold'	LHop
– 'Joyce'	CDes CElw EMon NLar

- 'Lady Flora Hastings' — CBre CDes CElw CKno CMdw CSam CSpe EBee GMac SBla WPGP
- 'Ochroleuca' — EGoo EMon GBuc MLLN NBre
- 'Parham' — CElw CMHG CPrp CSev EBee ELan EMan ERou GCal LHop LLWP LRHS MNFA MRav NBid NEgg NFla NSti SPer SPla SPlb SWat WMnd
- 'Purple Prose' — EMon
- 'Purpurea' — CAby CDes CPom EBee
- 'Rosea' — see *C. montana* 'Carnea'
* - *violacea* — IBlr
- 'Violetta' — CPom NBir WFar WMoo

nervosa — see *C. uniflora* subsp. *nervosa*

nigra — CArn CHrt COld CRWN EBee GIBF MBow NBre NLan NMir NNor NPri NSco SECG WMoo WSFF

- var. *alba* — CArn CBre NBid WWye
- subsp. *rivularis* — ECha MNFA NBid NBre

orientalis — CMdw CSam CSpe EAEE EBee EChP EMar EWes LPhx MHar MMHG MNFA NBre NDov NLar WHal WOut WPer

pannonica subsp. *pannonica* — CPom NBid WSHC

pestalozzae — EHyt

phrygia — COIW EBee GAbr NBid NBre NLar WPer WRos

- subsp. *pseudophrygia* — NBid

pulcherrima — COIW EBee EChP ECha EMan EMon GCal MAvo MLLN NBre NLar NOak NSti WPer XPep

'Pulchra Major' — see *Stemmacantha centaureoides*

rhapontica — see *Stemmacantha rhapontica*

rhenana — WOut

rigidifolia — EGle

rothrockii — LDai

rupestris — CMHG EBee EChP EDAr LPhx NBre NDov NEgg NJOw NLar SAga SGar SMHy WPer WWeb

ruthenica — CHea EChP LPhx MNFA MSte NBre NBow NGdn NLar SBch SMad SPlb WCot WLin WMnd

* - 'Alba' — MSte

scabiosa — CArn CRWN CWib EBee EMag GWCH MBow MHer MWhi NBid NBre NDov NJOw NLan NMir NPri NSco SECG SPoG WPer

- f. *albiflora* — CBgR EBee EMon LRHS MWgw NDov NFla STes

simplicicaulis — CDes CNic CSam EBee ECrN EGle EMan GAbr GBri MTho SAga SBch SBla SRms WEas WHoo WPer WSHC WWhi

thracica — EBee LPhx WCot

§ *triumfettii* subsp. *cana* 'Rosea' — CBrm NJOw SBla WBrk

- subsp. *stricta* — CBgR CDes CKno CPrp EBee EMon GAbr GBuc MSte NBre

uniflora <ins>new</ins> — EBee

§ - subsp. *nervosa* — NBid NBre NBro WPer

Centaurium (Gentianaceae)

erythraea — CArn GPoy MHer MSal NLar NWCA WWye

* *littorale* 'Album' — CSec

scilloides — CStu MTho NLAp NMen NSla NWCA WAbe

Centella (Apiaceae)

§ *asiatica* — CArn EOHP GPoy ILis MSal WJek

Centradenia (Melastomataceae)

floribunda — SYvo

---

inaequilateralis — CHal ECtt EMan EWin MBri SHFr SPet

'Cascade' —

Centranthus (Valerianaceae)

§ *ruber* — More than 30 suppliers

* - 'Alba Pura' — EWTr NBPC

§ - 'Albus' — More than 30 suppliers

- 'Atrococcineus' — ECha EMan SPoG WPer

- var. *coccineus* — More than 30 suppliers

- mauve — LPhx NDov XPep

- 'Roseus' — NEgg WMoo WOVN

- 'Rosy Red' — EDAr

- 'Snowcloud' — COIW CSev EKen

- 'Swanage' — CNat

'White Cloud' — WJek

Centratherum (Asteraceae)

punctatum <ins>new</ins> — EAro

Cephalanthera (Orchidaceae)

falcata — EFEx GEdr WWst

longibracteata — EFEx GEdr

Cephalanthus (Rubiaceae)

occidentalis — CBcs CPle CWib EBee EMil IDee IMGH LRav MBNS MBlu MGos NBlu NLar SBrw SPer SPoG SSpi WBVN WFar

Cephalaria (Dipsacaceae)

HWJ 695 — LPhx

§ *alpina* — COIW EBee EBla EBrs ECho EDAr EHrv EMan EPfP IBal IHMH LRHS MHer MNrw NEgg NHol NLar NRnb SBch SRms SWat WFar WPer

- 'Nana' — CMil EMon NMen NWCA

ambrosioides — MLLN

dipsacoides — CAby CEnt CFee CKno CSec CSpe EBee EBla EChP ECha GQue LDai LPhx MFOX MGol MHer NBre NLar NRnb SMHy SPoG WCMO WHal WMoo WRHF

§ *flava* — NBre

galpiniana — SPlb

- subsp. *simplicior* — CSec EBee

§ *gigantea* — More than 30 suppliers

graeca — see *C. flava*

leucantha — CHea COIW EMan GBuc MLLN MSph NBre NLar STes WMoo

litvinovii — CElw EMon

oblongifolia — NRnb SPoG

radiata — CSam EBee GBin NDov

tatarica — see *C. gigantea*

tchihatchewii — EBee MLLN

Cephalotaxus (Cephalotaxaceae)

fortunei — CDoC CDul SLon

- 'Prostrate Spreader' — EHul

harringtonii — ECho LEdu SMur

- B&SWJ 5416 — WPGP

- var. *drupacea* — CDoC GIBF LCon

- 'Fastigiata' — CBcs CDoC CDul CKen EHul EOrn IArd IDee LCon LLin LPan LRHS MAsh MBar MBri SBLw SCoo SLim SPoG WDin WFar WGer

- 'Gimborn's Pillow' — IDee MBar

- 'Korean Gold' — CKen LCon NLar SLim

- 'Prostrata' — MBar

Cephalotus (Cephalotaceae)

follicularis — SHmp

Cerastium (Caryophyllaceae)

alpinum — ECho SRms

- var. *lanatum* — ECho ETow EWes GMac MDKP NJOw NLar

arvense	NDlv
candidissimum	EWes NLar XPep
grandiflorum	EShb
tomentosum	CBrm CHal CTri ECho EPfP GAbr
	GWCH IHMH NBlu NDlv NFor
	NJOw NPri SPer SPet SPlb SPoG
	WFar WPer XPep
- var. *columnae*	CNic ECha ECho EHoe EPfP EWes
	SIng WCot
- 'Yo Yo' **new**	SBch

Ceratoides (*Chenopodiaceae*)
lanata	see *Krascheninnikovia lanata*

Ceratonia (*Caesalpiniaceae*)
siliqua	ELau MSal XPep

Ceratophyllum (*Ceratophyllaceae*)
demersum	CBen CRow EHon EMFW EPfP
	LNCo NSco SLon SWat WMAq
	WWpP

Ceratostigma ✿ (*Plumbaginaceae*)
abyssinicum	ELan
'Autumn Blue'	EPfP
griffithii	CBcs CDoC CFwr CHll CPle CSBt
	CWSG EBee ECtt EGra ELan EPfP
	LAst LRHS MCCP MRav MSwo
	SPer SPla SPoG WBrE WDin WFar
	WGwG WKif WSHC XPep
- SF 149/150	ISea
§ *plumbaginoides* ♀H3-4	More than 30 suppliers
willmottianum ♀H3-4	More than 30 suppliers
- Desert Skies =	CBcs CFwr CSBt EBee ELan EPfP
'Palmgold'PBR	GBuc LAst LHop LRHS MBri MGos
	MWgw NLar SCoo SHop SMac
	SMad SPer SPoG SSta SSto SWvt
	WWeb
- Forest Blue = 'Lice'PBR	CAbP CBcs CDoC CFwr CSBt
	CWSG EBee EGra ELan ENot EPfP
	LHop LRHS LSRN MAsh MBri
	MRav NPri NSti SCoo SHBN SMac
	SMer SPer SPla SPoG SReu WPat
	WWeb

Cercidiphyllum ✿ (*Cercidiphyllaceae*)
japonicum ♀H4	More than 30 suppliers
- 'Boyd's Dwarf'	NLar
- 'Herkenrode Dwarf' **new**	NLar
- 'Heronswood Globe'	CMCN CPMA EPfP MBlu NLar
§ - f. *pendulum* ♀H4	CBcs CDul CEnd CLnd CMCN
	CPMA CWSG EBee EPfP LRHS
	MAsh MBlu MGos NBea NEgg
	NLar SCoo SHBN SLim SPer SPoG
	SSpi WDin WOrn WWes
- - 'Amazing Grace'	CTho LRHS MBlu
- Red Fox	see *C. japonicum* 'Rotfuchs'
§ - 'Rotfuchs'	CBcs CEnd CMCN CPMA CTho
	EBee EPfP LRHS MAsh MBlu
	MDun MGos NEgg NLar NPal SIFN
	SLim SMad SSpi WPGP
- 'Ruby'	CPMA MBlu NLar
- 'Strawberry'	EBee EPfP MBlu NLar
- 'Tidal Wave' **new**	NLar
magnificum	CBcs CDul CEnd CMCN EPfP MBri
	NLar WPGP
- f. *pendulum*	see *C. japonicum* f. *pendulum*

Cercis (*Caesalpiniaceae*)
canadensis	CAgr CBcs CDul CHEx CLnd
	CMCN EPfP GIBF MGos NHol
	SBrw SLim SPer WMul WNor
- f. *alba*	LRHS
- - 'Royal White'	EPfP IArd MBlu NLar
- 'Appalachian Red'	MBlu MBri NLar
- 'Covey'	MBri NLar

- 'Flame'	MBri
- 'Forest Pansy' ♀H4	More than 30 suppliers
- 'Lavender Twist'	NLar
§ - var. *occidentalis*	CAgr LRav NLar SOWG
- 'Pauline Lily'	NLar
- 'Rubye Atkinson'	MBri NLar
- 'Tennessee Pink' **new**	NLar
chinensis	CBcs IFro LRHS NLar SPer SSta
	WDin WMoo
* - f. *alba*	CLnd
- 'Avondale'	CBcs CDoC CEnd CPMA CWib
	EBee EMil EPfP EWes IArd LRHS
	LSRN MBlu MGos NEgg NLar SBrw
	SCoo SLim SMur SPoG SSpi SWvt
	WPGP
gigantea	IArd NLar
griffithii	EGFP IArd NLar
occidentalis	see *C. canadensis* var. *occidentalis*
racemosa	IArd NLar
reniformis 'Oklahoma'	CBcs CPMA EBee MBlu NLar
- 'Texas White'	CBcs CPMA IArd NLar SLim
siliquastrum ♀H4	More than 30 suppliers
- f. *albida*	EPfP LPan LRHS LTwo SBrw SSpi
- 'Bodnant'	EBee EPfP LAst MBlu MBri NLar
yunnanensis	NLar

Cercocarpus (*Rosaceae*)
montanus var. *glaber*	NLar

Cerinthe (*Boraginaceae*)
glabra	NBre NJOw SPlb
major	LEdu WEas WSan
- 'Kiwi Blue'	CHll LEdu MDKP
- 'Purpurascens'	CHad CHrt CMea CSpe EBee EChP
	EGoo EHrv ELan ENot EPfP IFoB
	LIck LRHS MWat MWgw NLar
	SGar SMad SMrm SPer SPoG SUsu
	WWhi
- 'Yellow Gem'	NLar
minor	CSec WGwG
retorta	CSec LDai

Ceropegia (*Asclepiadaceae*)
barklyi	CHal
fusca **new**	EShb
linearis subsp. *woodii*	CHal EShb MBri SRms
♀H1	
pubescens GWJ 9441	WCru

Ceroxylon (*Arecaceae*)
alpinum	CPHo LPJP LPal
ventricosum	LPal

Cestrum (*Solanaceae*)
aurantiacum	ERea EShb
auriculatum	SOWG
x *cultum*	CHll
- 'Cretan Purple'	CHll CPle EPfP ERea LHop SMur
	SUsu
§ *elegans*	CHEx CHal CHll CPLG CSev IDee
	LRHS MOak SLon SOWG WCot
	WDin WWlt
fasciculatum	CBcs EShb SMad SOWG SUsu
'Newellii' ♀H2	CBcs CHEx CMHG CPLG CSev
	CWib EBak ELan EPfP ERea EShb
	MWea SDnm SEND SGar SOWG
	SSpi WBor WPic WSHC
nocturnum	CBcs CDoC CHal CHll CPIN CPle
	EBak ERea EShb LRHS SDEP SHBN
	SOWG XPep
parqui ♀H3	More than 30 suppliers
- 'Orange Essence'	WCot
psittacinum	CPLG
purpureum misapplied	see *Iochroma cyaneum* 'Trebah'
purpureum (Lindl.) Standl.	see *C. elegans*
roseum	CPLG CSev

- 'Ilnacullin'	CFee CPLG CSec ERea
* *splendens*	SOWG
violaceum misapplied	see *Iochroma cyaneum* 'Trebah'

Ceterach (Aspleniaceae)

officinarum	see *Asplenium ceterach*

Chaenomeles (Rosaceae)

x *californica*	CAgr CTho EPfP EPla WHer
cathayensis new	LEdu NLar
§ *japonica*	ECrN MBar MLHP NFor SMer WDin WFar XPep
- 'Cido'	NEgg
- 'Orange Beauty'	NEgg WFar
- 'Sargentii'	CBcs CMac NEgg NLar
'John Pilger'	LHop NHol NPro
lagenaria	see *C. speciosa*
'Madame Butterfly'	CDoC CEnd COtt EBee MGos SMad SPer SPoG WLeb
maulei	see *C. japonica*
sinensis	see *Pseudocydonia sinensis*
§ *speciosa*	CMen CSam ISea MBar MGan NFor NWea WNor
- 'Apple Blossom'	see *C. speciosa* 'Moerloosei'
- 'Aurora'	LRHS
- 'Brilliant'	EPfP
- 'Contorta'	CDoC SPoG
- 'Falconnet Charlet' (d)	MRav
- 'Geisha Girl' ♀H4	More than 30 suppliers
- 'Grayshott Salmon'	NCiC NHol NPro WFar
§ - 'Moerloosei' ♀H4	More than 30 suppliers
- 'Nivalis'	More than 30 suppliers
- 'Port Eliot'	WWeb
- 'Rosea Plena' (d)	SPoG
- 'Simonii' (d)	CBcs EBee EHol EPfP LRHS MGos MRav NEgg NHol NWea SPer WFar
- 'Snow'	CSBt MRav MSwo NHol NPro WCot
- 'Umbilicata'	SPer SRms XPep
- 'Winter Snow'	ENot
- 'Yukigoten'	LRHS NLar
x *superba*	NFor STre
- 'Boule de Feu'	CTri CWib ECtt MCoo
- 'Cameo' (d)	CAbP CEnd EBee ECrN EPfP LHop LRHS MBri MRav NLar SLPl SPoG WWeb
- 'Crimson and Gold' ♀H4	More than 30 suppliers
- 'Elly Mossel'	CBcs CMac CSBt CWib NBlu SMer WFar
- 'Ernst Finken'	EBee
- 'Fascination'	NLar
- 'Fire Dance'	CDul CMac CWib EBee ECrN ECtt IMGH MRav MSwo NHol SPer SPoG
- 'Hollandia'	MGos
- 'Issai White'	EBee LRHS
- 'Jet Trail'	CBcs CSBt EBee ELan EPfP LAst LRHS MGos MRav MSwo NBlu NPro SLPl SMac SPoG SSta WFar
- 'Knap Hill Scarlet' ♀H4	CDoC CDul EBee ECot EPfP LHop LRHS MAsh MGos MRav NEgg NHol SEND SLim SPer SPoG SRms WDin WFar
- 'Lemon and Lime'	EBee ELan EPfP MAsh MGos MRav NLar NSti SLon SPer
- 'Nicoline' ♀H4	CBcs CDoC EBee EPfP LRHS MBri MRav NLar NPri SBra SPoG WDin WFar
- 'Pink Lady' ♀H4	More than 30 suppliers
- 'Red Joy'	NLar SPoG
- 'Red Trail'	MRav
- 'Rowallane' ♀H4	EBee ECrN ELan EPfP IMGH MNHC MRav SHBN WRHF
- 'Salmon Horizon'	MGos
- 'Tortuosa'	LHop MBNS MWea SPoG

- 'Vermilion'	MAsh MBNS

Chaenorhinum (Scrophulariaceae)

§ *origanifolium*	CNic ECho EShb GKev MBrN MWgw NBlu NEgg NWCA SBch SPlb XPep
- 'Blue Dream'	CEnt CSpe EBee ECho ECtt EMan NBur NLAp NVic SPet SPoG SWvt WFar WMoo WPer WRHF WWeb
- 'Summer Skies'	NPri

Chaerophyllum (Apiaceae)

azoricum	EBee
hirsutum	CRow ELan
- 'Roseum'	More than 30 suppliers

Chamaebatiaria (Rosaceae)

millefolium	NLar

Chamaecyparis ✿ (Cupressaceae)

formosensis	CKen
funebris	see *Cupressus funebris*
lawsoniana	CDul CSBt EHul LCon MBar NWea WBVN WDin WMou
- 'Albospica' (v)	ECho EHul MBar SBod WFar
- 'Albospica Nana'	see *C. lawsoniana* 'Nana Albospica'
- 'Albovariegata' (v)	ECho EHul MBar
- 'Allumii Aurea'	see *C. lawsoniana* 'Alumigold'
- 'Allumii Magnificent'	CBcs ECho MAsh NLar
§ - 'Alumigold'	CDoC CSBt CWib ECho LCon MAsh MBar MGos SCoo SMer SPoG WDin
- 'Alumii'	CMac CTri ECho EHul MAsh MBar MGos NWea SPoG
- 'Annesleyana'	NEgg
- 'Argentea'	see *C. lawsoniana* 'Argenteovariegata'
§ - 'Argenteovariegata' (v)	CDoC CMac ECho SLim SPoG
- 'Aurea'	CDul
I - 'Aurea Compacta'	ECho
- 'Aurea Densa' ♀H4	CFee CKen CMac CNic CRob CSBt CTri ECho EHul EOrn EPfP MAsh MBar MGos NEgg SPoG STre WEve WGor
- 'Aureovariegata' (v)	MBar
§ - 'Barabits' Globe'	MBar
- 'Barry's Gold'	EOrn
§ - 'Bleu Nantais'	CKen CMac CRob CSBt ECho EHul LBee LCon LRHS MAsh MBar MGos MWat SCoo SHBN SLim SPoG WCFE WEve WFar
- 'Blom'	CKen EHul MBri
- 'Blue Gem'	NHol
§ - 'Blue Gown'	ECho EHul LBee MBar MGos SRms
§ - 'Blue Jacket'	MBar NWea
- Blue Nantais	see *C. lawsoniana* 'Bleu Nantais'
- 'Blue Surprise'	CKen EHul MBar WFar
- 'Brégéon'	CKen NLar
- 'Broomhill Gold'	CBrm CDoC CMac CRob CSBt ECho EHul ENot LCon LLin LRHS MAsh MBar MBri MGos MWat NHol SCoo SLim SPer SPla SPoG WCFE WDin WEve
- 'Buckland Gold'	CDoC
* - 'Burkwood's Blue'	MBar
- 'Caudata'	CKen MBar NLar
- 'Chantry Gold'	ECho EHul
§ - 'Chilworth Silver' ♀H4	CRob CSBt CTri ECho EHul EOrn LBee LRHS MAsh MBar NBlu SCoo SHBN SLim SPer SPoG SRms WBVN WDin WFar
- 'Chingii'	ECho EHul
- 'Columnaris'	CBcs CDoC CMac ECho EPfP LBee LRHS MBar MBri MGos NBlu NEgg

		NWea SCoo SHBN SLim SPoG
		WCFE WFar
	- 'Columnaris Aurea'	see *C. lawsoniana* 'Golden Spire'
N	- 'Columnaris Glauca'	CSBt CWib ECho EHul EOrn LCon
		MAsh MGos NEgg SBod SPer WDin
		WFar WTel
	- 'Crawford's Compact'	CMac
	- 'Cream Crackers'	ECho EHul
	- 'Cream Glow'	CDoC CKen CRob ECho LRHS
		MGos NLar SCoo SLim SPoG WFar
		WGor
	- 'Croftway'	EHul
	- 'Dik's Weeping'	CDoC LCon WEve
	- 'Dorset Gold'	CMac
	- 'Drinkstone Gold' **new**	ECho
	- 'Duncanii'	ECho EHul
	- 'Dutch Gold'	EHul MAsh
	- 'Dwarf Blue'	see *C. lawsoniana* 'Pick's Dwarf
		Blue'
	- 'Eclipse'	CKen
	- 'Elegantissima' ambig.	CKen CMac ECho MGos
	- 'Ellwoodii' ♀H4	CDul CMac CSBt CTri CWib ECho
		EHul EPfP LCon LRHS MAsh MBar
		MGos NBlu NEgg NWea SCoo
		SLim SMer SPer SPoG WCFE WDin
		WFar WMoo WTel
I	- 'Ellwoodii Glauca'	EGra SPlb
	- 'Ellwood's Empire'	EHul LRHS MBri NHol WEve
	- 'Ellwood's Gold' ♀H4	More than 30 suppliers
	- 'Ellwood's Gold Pillar'	CRob CSBt ECho EHul EOrn LBee
		LCon MAsh MGos NEgg NHol
		SCoo SLim SPla SPoG WFar
§	- 'Ellwood's Nymph'	CKen CRob ECho EOrn LLin MAsh
		MBar SCoo SHBN SLim SPoG WFar
		WGor
	- Ellwood's Pillar = 'Flolar'	CDoC CMac CRob CSBt ECho
		EGra EHul EOrn EPfP LBee LCon
		LRHS MAsh MBar MBri MGos
		MWat NEgg NHol SLim SPla SPoG
		WCFE WDin WFar
	- 'Ellwood's Pygmy'	CMac ECho MBar NHol
	- 'Ellwood's Silver'	ECho MAsh WFar
*	- 'Ellwood's Silver Threads'	CMac ECho NHol
*	- 'Ellwood's Treasure'	ECho
	- 'Ellwood's Variegata'	see *C. lawsoniana* 'Ellwood's
		White'
§	- 'Ellwood's White' (v)	CKen CMac CSBt ECho EHul EPfP
		LRHS MBar NBlu SHBN WFar
		WMoo
I	- 'Emerald'	CKen MBar NHol
	- 'Emerald Spire'	CMac MAsh NHol
	- 'Empire'	WFar
	- 'Erecta Argenteovariegata'	WEve
	(v)	
	- 'Erecta Aurea'	ECho EHul LBee MGos
	- 'Erecta Filiformis'	MBar
§	- 'Erecta Viridis'	CMac CTrG MBar NEgg NWea
		WDin WFar
	- 'Ericoides'	EHul NEgg
	- 'Erika'	ECho MBar
	- 'Filiformis Compacta'	ECho EHul
	- 'Fleckellwood'	CRob CWib ECho EHul MAsh
		MBar SMer SPoG
	- 'Fletcheri' ♀H4	CBcs CMac CWib EHul LBee LCon
		MAsh MBar NWea SBod SHBN
		SMer SPer SPoG WDin WFar
	- 'Fletcheri Aurea'	see *C. lawsoniana* 'Yellow
		Transparent'
	- 'Fletcher's White'	ECho EHul MBar
	- 'Forsteckensis'	CKen CSli ECho EHul EOrn LLin
		MBar NLar NWea SPoG SRms
		WEve WFar WGor
	- 'Fraseri'	MBar NWea WDin
	- 'Gimbornii' ♀H4	CDoC CMac ECho EHul LBee
		LCon MAsh MBar SBod SCoo SLim
		SPoG SRms WCFE WFar
	- 'Glauca'	CDul
	- 'Glauca Spek'	see *C. lawsoniana* 'Spek'
	- 'Globosa'	MGos
	- 'Globus'	see *C. lawsoniana* 'Barabits'
		Globe'
	- 'Gnome'	CDoC CMac CRob ECho EHul
		ENot EOrn GEdr LLin MBar MGos
		NHol SCoo SLim SPoG
	- 'Gold Flake'	MBar MGos
	- 'Gold Lace'	SPoG
	- 'Gold Splash'	MBar
	- 'Golden King'	ECho MBar NWea
§	- 'Golden Pot'	CDoC CRob CSBt CWib ECho
		EGra EHul ENot EOrn LBee LCon
		LRHS MBar MGos MWat NBlu
		NHol SCoo SMer SPoG WDin WFar
§	- 'Golden Queen'	ECho EHul
	- 'Golden Showers'	ECho EHul
§	- 'Golden Spire'	ECho LRHS MBar NEgg NLar WFar
	- 'Golden Triumph'	EHul
	- 'Golden Wonder'	ECho EHul LBee LCon LRHS MBar
		MGos NEgg NWea SCoo SPoG
		SRms WDin WEve WFar
	- 'Goldfinger'	CDoC
	- 'Grant's Gold'	EHul
	- 'Grayswood Feather'	CDoC CRob CSBt ECho EGra EHul
		LBee LRHS MAsh MBar MGos NBlu
		SLim WEve
	- 'Grayswood Gold'	ECho EHul EOrn LBee MBar WEve
	- 'Grayswood Pillar' ♀H4	CDul CMac ECho EHul EOrn LRHS
		MBar MGos
*	- 'Grayswood Spire'	CMac
	- 'Green Globe'	CDoC CKen CRob CSBt CSli ECho
		EHul EOrn LBee LCon LLin LRHS
		MAsh MBar MGos SAga SCoo SLim
		SPoG WDin WEve
§	- 'Green Hedger' ♀H4	CMac CSBt CTri EHul LBuc MBar
		NBlu NEgg SRms WFar
§	- 'Green Pillar'	CBrm CRob CSBt CWib ECho
		LBee LCon LRHS MBar NEgg
		SHBN
	- 'Green Spire'	see *C. lawsoniana* 'Green Pillar'
	- 'Hillieri'	MBar
	- 'Hogger's Blue Gown'	see *C. lawsoniana* 'Blue Gown'
	- 'Howarth's Gold'	MBri
	- 'Imbricata Pendula'	CKen LCon NLar SLim
	- 'Intertexta' ♀H4	EHul WEve
	- 'Ivonne'	ECho EHul MGos NBlu NEgg WEve
		WOrn
	- 'Jackman's Green	see *C. lawsoniana* 'Green Hedger'
	Hedger'	
	- 'Jackman's Variety'	see *C. lawsoniana* 'Green Pillar'
	- 'Jeanette' **new**	MGos
	- 'Kelleriis Gold'	EHul MBar NEgg
	- 'Kilmacurragh' ♀H4	ECho MAsh MBar MGos NWea
		WCFE
	- 'Kilworth Column'	CDoC CRob ECho LLin MGos NLar
		NWea SPoG
	- 'Kingswood'	LRHS MGos WEve
	- 'Knowefieldensis'	CMac ECho EHul ENot LLin
	- 'Lane' hort.	see *C. lawsoniana* 'Lanei Aurea'
	- 'Lanei'	CSBt CWib ECho LCon MAsh
		MGos NEgg SCoo WDin
§	- 'Lanei Aurea' ♀H4	CMac ECho EHul MBar MGos
		NWea WFar
	- 'Lemon Pillar'	SPoG WDin WEve
	- 'Lemon Queen'	CSBt ECho EGra EHul LBee LRHS
		WEve
	- 'Limelight'	EHul MGos
	- 'Little Spire' ♀H4	CDoC ECho EOrn LBee LCon LLin
		LRHS MBar MBri MGos NHol SCoo
		SLim SPoG WEve WGor
	- 'Lombartsii'	ECho EHul LCon WFar
	- 'Lutea' ♀H4	CMac ECho EHul MGos NWea
§	- 'Lutea Nana' ♀H4	CMac ECho EHul MAsh MBar
		MGos NLar

	Name	Suppliers
§	– 'Lutea Smithii'	MBar NWea
	– 'Luteocompacta'	LBee LRHS SHBN
	– 'Lycopodioides'	ECho EHul MBar SPoG
*	– 'MacPenny's Gold'	CMac
	– 'Magnifica Aurea'	ECho
	– 'Miki'	WEve
	– 'Milford Blue Jacket'	see *C. lawsoniana* 'Blue Jacket'
§	– 'Minima'	ECho MBar NEgg SRms WCFE
	– 'Minima Argentea'	see *C. lawsoniana* 'Nana Argentea'
	– 'Minima Aurea' ♀H4	More than 30 suppliers
	– 'Minima Densa'	see *C. lawsoniana* 'Minima'
	– 'Minima Glauca' ♀H4	CDul CMac CSBt ECho EHul ENot EPfP LCon LRHS MAsh MBar MGos NEgg NHol NWea SBod SCoo SHBN SLim SPer SPla SPoG WDin WEve WFar
	– 'Moonlight'	MBar MGos
	– 'Moonshine'	ECho SPoG
*	– 'Moonsprite'	ECho LCon LLin LRHS SLim WEve
	– 'Nana'	ECho MBar
§	– 'Nana Albospica' (v)	CBrm CRob ECho EGra EHul EOrn LBee LCon LRHS MBar SCoo SLim SPoG WFar WGor
§	– 'Nana Argentea'	CKen CMac ECho EHul EOrn EPfP WFar WGor
	– 'Nana Lutea'	see *C. lawsoniana* 'Lutea Nana'
	– 'New Silver'	MGos SPoG
	– 'Nicole'	CDHC ECho MAsh SLim SPoG WGor
	– 'Nidiformis'	ECho EHul LBee LRHS MBar NWea SCoo SRms
	– 'Nyewoods'	see *C. lawsoniana* 'Chilworth Silver'
	– 'Nymph'	see *C. lawsoniana* 'Ellwood's Nymph'
	– 'Parsons'	CDoC
§	– 'Pelt's Blue' ♀H4	CDoC CKen CSBt ECho EGra EHul ENot LBee LCon LRHS MBar MBri MGos NEgg NLar SCoo SHBN SLim SPoG WDin WFar WOrn
	– 'Pembury Blue' ♀H4	CDoC CDul CMac CSBt CWib ECho EHul EPfP LBee LCon LRHS MAsh MBar MGos MWat NWea SBod SCoo SHBN SLim SPer SPoG WDin WFar
	– 'Pendula'	CDoC ECho MBar
§	– 'Pick's Dwarf Blue'	ECho EHul MBar MBri NHol SPoG WGor
	– 'Pot of Gold'	see *C. lawsoniana* 'Golden Pot'
	– 'Pottenii'	CMac CSBt ECho EHul LBee LCon LRHS MAsh MBar MGos NWea SHBN SPoG WDin WEve WFar
	– 'Pygmaea Argentea' (v) ♀H4	CKen CMac CWib ECho EGra EHul ENot EOrn EPfP LBee LCon LLin LRHS MAsh MBar MBri MGos NBlu NEgg NHol SPoG SRms WCFE WDin WFar
	– 'Pygmy'	CNic ECho EHul LCon MBar NHol NLar SCoo SLim
	– 'Rijnhof'	EHul LBee LLin SLim
	– 'Rogersii'	ECho MBar SRms WFar
	– 'Romana'	MBri NBlu
	– 'Royal Gold'	ECho EHul NBlu
	– 'Silver Queen' (v)	CKen MBar NWea
	– 'Silver Threads' (v)	CMac CRob ECho EGra EHul LBee LRHS MAsh MBar NBlu NHol SPoG WBVN WFar
	– 'Silver Tip' (v)	ECho EHul SCoo SLim
	– 'Slocock'	SHBN
	– 'Smithii'	see *C. lawsoniana* 'Lutea Smithii'
	– 'Snow Flurry' (v)	ECho EHul ENot WFar
	– 'Snow White'PBR (v)	CDoC CRob ECho EHul ENot LBee LCon LRHS MAsh MBar MBri MGos NHol SCoo SLim SPla SPoG WFar WGor WRHF
	– 'Somerset'	CMac MBar MGos
§	– 'Spek'	CBcs MBar
	– 'Springtime'PBR	CDoC CRob ECho EHul EOrn LBee LCon LRHS MAsh SCoo SLim SPoG WGor
	– 'Stardust' ♀H4	CDoC CDul CMac CRob CSBt CTri CWib ECho EHul ENot LCon LPan LRHS MAsh MBar MBri NBlu NEgg SBod SCoo SHBN SLim SPer SPoG WDin
	– 'Stewartii'	CDul CTri MBar NEgg NWea SBod SCoo SHBN SMer
	– 'Stilton Cheese'	MBar
*	– 'Summer Cream'	EHul
	– 'Summer Snow' (v)	CBcs CDoC CDul CMac CPne CRob ECho EHoe EHul ENot EPfP LBee LLin LRHS MAsh MBar MGos NBlu NEgg NHol SCoo SLim SPla SRms WEve WFar
	– 'Sunkist'	ECho SLim WFar
	– 'Tamariscifolia'	CDoC ECho EHul MBar SBod SPoG WCFE WDin WFar
	– 'Tharandtensis Caesia'	EOrn MBar WFar
	– 'Tilford'	EHul
	– 'Treasure' (v)	CRob CSli ECho EHoe EHul EPfP LBee LCon LRHS MAsh MBar NHol SCoo SLim SPoG WFar WRHF
	– 'Triomf van Boskoop'	MBar
	– 'Van Pelt's Blue'	see *C. lawsoniana* 'Pelt's Blue'
	– 'Versicolor' (v)	MBar
	– 'Westermannii' (v)	CMac EHul LCon LLin SCoo SLim
	– 'White Edge'	WFar
	– 'White Spot' (v)	ECho EHul LBee LRHS MBar MBri NBlu NEgg SLim SPoG WBVN WFar
	– 'White Wonder' **new**	MGos
	– 'Winston Churchill'	CBcs CSBt ECho MBar MGos NWea SBod
	– 'Wisselii' ♀H4	CDoC CKen CMac CRob CTrG ECho EGra EHul LBee LLin MBar NLar SRms WDin WFar
	– 'Wisselii Nana'	CKen ECho EHul
	– 'Wissel's Saguaro'	CDoC CKen EBrs LCon NLar SLim
	– 'Witzeliana'	CSBt ECho EOrn LRHS MBar MGos NLar SCoo WOrn
	– 'Wyevale Silver'	MBar
	– 'Yellow Cascade'	ECho
	– 'Yellow Queen'	see *C. lawsoniana* 'Golden Queen'
	– 'Yellow Success'	see *C. lawsoniana* 'Golden Queen'
§	– 'Yellow Transparent'	CMac ECho LBee MBar SBod SHBN SPoG WEve
	– 'Yvonne'	CRob ECho LLin LRHS MAsh MBar MGos NHol SCoo SLim SPoG WEve
	leylandii	see x *Cupressocyparis leylandii*
	nootkatensis	CDul ECho MBar
	– 'Aurea'	ECho SCoo WDin WEve
	– 'Aureovariegata' (v)	EHul SLim
	– 'Compacta'	CDul CTri MBar
	– 'Glauca'	CTho LCon MBar NWea
	– 'Gracilis'	EHul
	– 'Green Arrow'	CKen EBrs ECho LCon NLar SLim
	– 'Jubilee'	LCon SCoo SLim
	– 'Lutea'	CTri MBar NWea SLim
	– 'Nidifera'	MBar
	– 'Nordkroken' **new**	NLar
	– 'Pendula' ♀H4	CDoC CDul CKen ECho ELan EOrn EPfP LCon LLin LPan LRHS MAsh MBar MBri MGan MGos NBlu NWea SLim SPer WCFE WDin WEve WFar WMou WOrn
	– 'Strict Weeper'	CKen NLar SLim
	– 'Variegata' (v)	LRHS MBar SLim
	obtusa 'Albospica' (v)	ECho EHul
	– 'Albovariegata' (v)	CKen ECho
	– 'Arneson's Compact'	CKen
	– 'Aurea'	CDoC

	– 'Aureovariegata'	see *C. obtusa* 'Opaal'
	– 'Aurora'	CKen ECho EOrn LCon MGos SPoG WEve
*	– 'Autumn Gold'	MBar
	– 'Bambi'	CKen EOrn LCon LLin MGos NLar WEve
	– 'Barkenny'	CKen
	– 'Bartley'	CKen
	– 'Bassett'	CKen
	– 'Bess'	CKen
	– 'Brigitt'	CKen
	– 'Buttonball'	CKen
	– 'Caespitosa'	CKen
	– 'Chabo-yadori'	CDoC ECho EHul EOrn LBee LCon LLin LRHS MBar MGos NHol SCoo SLim SPoG WFar
	– 'Chilworth'	CKen LCon MBar MGos NLar
	– 'Chima-anihiba'	CKen
	– 'Chirimen'	CKen MGos NLar SBla
	– 'Clarke's Seedling'	CDoC NLar
	– 'Confucius'	CDoC CRob EHul NHol
	– 'Contorta'	EOrn MBar NLar
§	– 'Coralliformis'	CMac ECho EOrn LLin MBar NHol SMur
§	– 'Crippsii' ♀H4	CBcs CDoC CDul ECho EHul EOrn GBin LCon LLin LRHS MBar MGos NHol SCoo SLim
	– 'Crippsii Aurea'	see *C. obtusa* 'Crippsii'
	– 'Dainty Doll'	CKen EOrn LCon NLar
	– 'Densa'	see *C. obtusa* 'Nana Densa'
	– 'Draht'	CDoC MBar NLar SCoo SLim SPoG WEve
	– 'Draht Hexe'	CKen NLar
	– 'Elf'	CKen NLar
	– 'Ellie B'	CKen EOrn
	– 'Ericoides'	CKen ECho EOrn
	– 'Erika'	ECho EOrn
	– 'Fernspray Gold'	CDoC CKen CMac CRob CTri ECho EHul ENot EOrn LCon LLin MAsh MBar NEgg NHol SBod SCoo SLim SPla WFar
	– 'Flabelliformis'	CKen LCon
	– 'Gnome'	CKen
	– 'Gold Fern'	CKen WFar
	– 'Gold Tip'	ECho EOrn
	– 'Golden Fairy'	CKen EOrn LCon WEve
	– 'Golden Filament' (v)	CKen
	– 'Golden Nymph'	CKen EOrn MGos NLar
	– 'Golden Sprite'	CDoC CKen MGos NLar WEve
	– 'Goldilocks'	ECho EHul
	– 'Gracilis Aurea'	CKen ECho
	– 'Graciosa'	see *C. obtusa* 'Loenik'
	– 'Green Diamond'	CKen
	– 'Hage'	CKen EOrn LCon
	– 'Hypnoides Nana'	CKen EOrn
	– 'Intermedia'	CDoC CKen EOrn MGos
	– 'Ivan's Column'	CKen
	– 'Junior'	CKen
	– 'Juniperoides'	CKen ECho EOrn
	– 'Juniperoides Compacta'	CKen
	– 'Kamarachiba'	CDoC CKen ECho LCon LLin LRHS MAsh NLar SCoo SLim SPoG WEve WFar
	– 'Kanaamihiba'	MBar NLar
	– 'Kerdalo' **new**	NLar SLim
	– 'Konijn'	ECho EHul EOrn
	– 'Kosteri'	CDoC CKen CMac CRob ECho EHul ELan EOrn LBee LLin MAsh MBar NDlv NEgg NHol SCoo SHBN SLim WEve
	– 'Laxa'	LCon
	– 'Leprechaun'	NLar
	– 'Little Markey'	CKen EOrn
§	– 'Loenik'	ECho EOrn MBar NHol
	– 'Lycopodioides'	ECho EOrn MGos
	– 'Lycopodioides Aurea'	SLim
	– 'Marian'	CKen MGos NLar
§	– 'Mariesii' (v)	CKen EHul EOrn LBee SHBN
	– 'Minima'	CKen MGos NEgg SMer
	– 'Nana' ♀H4	CDoC CKen CRob ECho LBee LCon LRHS MBar MGos NHol WEve
	– 'Nana Albospica'	ECho
	– 'Nana Aurea' ♀H4	CDoC CRob ECho EHul EOrn EPfP MAsh MBar MGos NHol SHBN SMer SPla WBrE WFar
	– 'Nana Compacta'	EOrn NHol
I	– 'Nana Confucius' **new**	MGos
§	– 'Nana Densa'	CDoC CKen CMac NLar WEve
§	– 'Nana Gracilis' ♀H4	CDoC CDul CKen CMen CSBt CSli ECho EHul ELan ENot EOrn EPfP IMGH LCon LLin MAsh MBar MBri MGos NBlu NHol SHBN SLim SMer SPla SPoG STre WDin WEve WFar
I	– 'Nana Gracilis Aurea'	EHul SMur WEve
I	– 'Nana Lutea'	CDoC CKen CRob CSBt ECho EHul EOrn EPfP LBee LCon LLin LRHS MAsh MBar MGos NHol SCoo SLim SPla SPoG WGer
	– 'Nana Pyramidalis'	ECho LBee
	– 'Nana Rigida'	see *C. obtusa* 'Rigid Dwarf'
	– 'Nana Variegata'	see *C. obtusa* 'Mariesii'
§	– 'Opaal' (v)	ECho MBar
	– 'Pygmaea'	CNic CSBt ECho EHul EOrn LCon LLin MBar MGos NHol SCoo SLim SPoG WEve
	– 'Pygmaea Aurescens'	MBar NEgg
	– 'Reis Dwarf'	ECho LLin
	– 'Repens'	ECho
§	– 'Rigid Dwarf'	CDoC CKen ECho EHul EOrn IMGH LBee LCon LRHS MBar NLar SCoo SPoG WEve
	– 'Saffron Spray'	CKen SLim
	– 'Snowflake' (v)	CDoC CKen CRob ECho EOrn SPoG WEve WFar WGor
	– 'Snowkist' (v)	CKen
	– 'Spiralis'	CKen MBar
	– 'Stoneham'	CKen LCon MBar
	– 'Suirova-hiba' **new**	SLim
	– 'Tempelhof'	CKen CSBt ECho EHul EOrn LCon LLin LRHS MAsh MBar MGos NDlv NEgg NLar SBod SCoo SLim SMer WEve
	– 'Tetragona Aurea'	CBcs CBrm CMac ECho EHul EOrn IMGH LCon LLin LRHS MBar MGos SCoo SLim SPer SPoG WEve
	– 'Tonia' (v)	CDoC CKen ECho EHul EOrn LCon MAsh NHol NLar SCoo SLim SPoG WEve WGor
	– 'Topsie'	CKen
	– 'Torulosa'	see *C. obtusa* 'Coralliformis'
	– 'Tsatsumi Gold'	CDoC CKen ECho NLar SLim
	– 'Verdon'	CKen
	– 'Winter Gold'	WEve
	– 'Wissel'	CKen EOrn
	– 'Wyckoff'	CKen
	– 'Yellowtip' (v)	CKen ECho EHul MBar MGos NLar WEve
	pisifera 'Aurea Nana' misapplied	see *C. pisifera* 'Strathmore'
	– 'Avenue'	ECho EHul
	– 'Baby Blue'	CKen ECho EPfP LCon LLin SCoo SLim WEve
	– 'Blue Globe'	CKen EOrn
	– 'Boulevard' ♀H4	More than 30 suppliers
	– 'Compacta'	ECho EOrn NDlv
	– 'Compacta Variegata' (v)	ECho EHul EOrn MBar NDlv
	– 'Curly Tops'	CRob ECho LCon LLin MGos SCoo SLim SPoG WEve
	– 'Devon Cream'	CRob ECho LBee LCon LRHS MAsh MBar NEgg WFar

	- 'Filifera'	CMac CSBt ECho MBar SCoo SLim SPoG WFar
	- 'Filifera Aurea' ♀H4	CKen CMac CSBt CWib ECho EGra EHul EOrn LBee LCon LLin LRHS MAsh MBar MGos NEgg NHol NWea SCoo SPoG SRms WCFE WDin WEve WFar
	- 'Filifera Aureovariegata' (v)	CMac ECho EHul LLin MBar SCoo SLim SPoG
	- 'Filifera Nana'	ECho EHul ELan EOrn MBar NDlv SLim SPoG STre WDin WFar
	- 'Filifera Sungold'	see *C. pisifera* 'Sungold'
	- 'Fuiri-tsukomo'	CKen
*	- 'Gold Cascade'	MGos
	- 'Gold Cushion'	CKen
	- 'Gold Dust'	see *C. pisifera* 'Plumosa Aurea'
	- 'Gold Spangle'	ECho EHul MBar NEgg WFar
	- 'Golden Mop' ♀H4	CKen ECho EHul MAsh NDlv
	- 'Green Pincushion'	CKen
	- 'Hime-himuro'	CKen ECho
	- 'Hime-sawara'	CKen EOrn
	- 'Margaret'	CKen
	- 'Nana'	CKen ECho EHul EPfP LLin MAsh MBar NBlu NDlv NHol SMer WFar WRHF
I	- 'Nana Albovariegata' (v)	CDoC CNic ECho EOrn LLin LRHS MAsh MBar SPoG WFar
§	- 'Nana Aureovariegata' (v)	CDoC CMac CRob CSBt ECho EGra EHul IMGH LBee LCon LLin LRHS MAsh MBar NDlv NEgg NHol SCoo SLim SPoG WEve WFar
I	- 'Nana Compacta'	CMac ECho SRms
	- 'Nana Variegata' (v)	ECho LBee LRHS MBar SCoo SLim WFar
I	- 'Parslorii'	CKen
	- 'Pici'	CKen
	- 'Plumosa Albopicta' (v)	ECho MBar
§	- 'Plumosa Aurea'	CKen EHul MBar NWea WDin WFar
	- 'Plumosa Aurea Compacta'	CKen CMac ECho NDlv
	- 'Plumosa Aurea Compacta Variegata' (v)	CMac NEgg
	- 'Plumosa Aurea Nana'	CRob ECho MBar MGos NBlu NDlv NHol WFar WRHF
I	- 'Plumosa Aurea Nana Compacta'	CMac
§	- 'Plumosa Aurescens'	CDoC CMac
§	- 'Plumosa Compressa'	CDoC CFee CKen CRob ECho EHul EOrn GEdr LBee LCon MAsh MBar NDlv NEgg SCoo SLim SPoG WFar WGor
	- 'Plumosa Densa'	see *C. pisifera* 'Plumosa Compressa'
	- 'Plumosa Flavescens'	ECho EHul LRHS MBar MGos SCoo
I	- 'Plumosa Juniperoides'	CKen ECho EHul EOrn LLin MBar NBlu NDlv SLim WFar WGor
	- 'Plumosa Purple Dome'	see *C. pisifera* 'Purple Dome'
I	- 'Plumosa Pygmaea'	ECho MGos NDlv WGor
§	- 'Plumosa Rogersii'	CRob ECho EHul EOrn LRHS MBar NHol WGor
	- 'Pompom'	CRob
§	- 'Purple Dome'	CRob ECho EHul EOrn MBar
I	- 'Pygmaea Tsukumo' **new**	MGos
	- 'Rogersii'	see *C. pisifera* 'Plumosa Rogersii'
	- 'Silver and Gold' (v)	ECho EHul MBar
	- 'Silver Lode' (v)	CKen EOrn
	- 'Snow' (v)	CKen CMac EOrn MBar WRHF
	- 'Snowflake'	CKen ECho EHul
	- 'Spaan's Cannon Ball'	CKen
§	- 'Squarrosa'	MBar WDin WFar
	- 'Squarrosa Dumosa'	CKen EHul MBar
I	- 'Squarrosa Dwarf Blue'	SPoG
	- 'Squarrosa Intermedia'	EHul MBar
I	- 'Squarrosa Lombarts'	CMac CSBt ECho EHul EOrn LBee MBar
	- 'Squarrosa Lutea'	CKen MBar
	- 'Squarrosa Sulphurea'	CSBt ECho EGra EHul EOrn EPfP LBee LCon LRHS MAsh MBar NEgg SLim SPla STre WBVN WDin WFar
	- 'Squarrosa Veitchii'	see *C. pisifera* 'Squarrosa'
§	- 'Strathmore'	CKen EHul LLin MBar NHol WDin
§	- 'Sungold'	CDoC CKen CRob CSBt CTri ECho EGra EHul ENot LCon LLin LRHS MAsh MBar NBlu NDlv NEgg NWea SCoo SLim SPla SPoG WEve
	- 'Tama-himuro'	CKen ECho
	- 'Teddy Bear' **new**	ECho NLar
	- 'True Blue' **new**	ECho
	- 'White Beauty' (v)	LCon SLim
*	- 'White Brocade'	CMac
	- 'White Pygmy'	EOrn
	thyoides 'Andelyensis'	CMac CRob CSBt ECho EHul EOrn LLin MBar SCoo SPoG WFar WRHF
	- 'Andelyensis Nana'	CKen
	- 'Aurea'	EHul MBar
	- 'Conica'	CKen
	- 'Ericoides' ♀H4	CKen CMac CRob CTri ECho EHul EOrn LBee LLin MBar MWat SPlb SPoG WDin WEve WFar
§	- 'Glauca'	EOrn
	- 'Kewensis'	see *C. thyoides* 'Glauca'
	- 'Little Jamie'	CKen
	- 'Red Star'	see *C. thyoides* 'Rubicon'
§	- 'Rubicon'	CKen CMac CRob CSBt ECho EHul ENot EOrn EPfP LBee LCon LLin LRHS MAsh MBar MGos NBlu NEgg SLim SPla SPoG WEve WFar WGer
	- 'Top Point'	CDoC CRob ECho ENot EOrn LBee LCon MAsh SCoo SLim SPoG
	- 'Variegata' (v)	ECho EHul MBar
	- 'Winter Wonder'	EHul SPoG

Chamaecytisus (Papilionaceae)

§	**albus**	GQui WDin
§	**hirsutus**	WLin WPGP WWeb
	- subsp. **hirsutissimus**	WLin
	palmensis	CSec
	prolifer	CPLG
§	**purpureus**	CBgR CSBt CWCL EGra ELan EPfP LRHS MAsh MBar MRav MSwo NWea SBod SHBN SPer WBVN WDin WFar WPat
	- f. **albus**	CBcs EPfP MBar SHBN SPer
§	- 'Atropurpureus' ♀H4	CBcs NHol SPer WTel
	- 'Incarnatus'	see *C. purpureus* 'Atropurpureus'
	- 'Lilac Lady'	MAsh
§	**supinus**	CPLG SRms

Chamaedaphne (Ericaceae)

§	**calyculata**	CBcs LRHS SPer WSHC
	- 'Angustifolia'	NLar
	- 'Nana'	CMHG EBee MBar NLar SBrw

Chamaedorea (Arecaceae)

	elegans ♀H1	LPal MBri
	erumpens	see *C. seifrizii*
	glaucifolia	WMul
	linearis	LPal
	metallica misapplied	see *C. microspadix*
	metallica O.F. Cook ex H.E. Moore ♀H1	EAmu LPal SBig
§	**microspadix**	CPHo CRoM CTrC EAmu LPJP LPal WMul
	oblongata	WCot
	radicalis	CBrP CPHo EAmu LPJP LPal WMul
§	**seifrizii** ♀H1	LPal

Chamaelirium (Melanthiaceae)

	luteum	CArn

Chamaemelum (Asteraceae)

§ **nobile** CArn CHby CHrt CPrp CSev CWan ECho EDAr ELau EPfP GBar GMac GPoy IHMH MBow MBri MHer MNHC MWat NGdn NJOw SPlb SRms WBor WJek WPer WSel WWye
- dwarf GBar
- dwarf, double-flowered GBar NLRH (d)
- 'Flore Pleno' (d) More than 30 suppliers
- 'Treneague' More than 30 suppliers

Chamaenerion see *Chamerion*

Chamaepericlymenum see *Cornus*

Chamaerops (Arecaceae)

excelsa misapplied see *Trachycarpus fortunei*
excelsa Thunb. see *Rhapis excelsa*
humilis ♀H3 More than 30 suppliers
- var. **arborescens** new EZes
§ - var. **argentea** CBrP CPHo CTrC EAmu LPJP LPal MGos NPal SAin SChr WMul
- var. **cerifera** see *C. humilis* var. *argentea*
- 'Vulcano' EAmu EZes MBri MGos SAin WMul

Chamaespartium see *Genista*

Chamaesphacos (Lamiaceae)

ilicifolius misapplied see *Siphocranion macranthum*

Chambeyronia (Arecaceae)

macrocarpa LPal

Chamelaucium (Myrtaceae)

axillare SOWG
uncinatum EShb SOWG

Chamerion (Onagraceae)

§ **angustifolium** ECho GBar GWCH NSco SPer SWat WSFF
§ - 'Album' More than 30 suppliers
- 'Isobel' CSpe MLLN MRav WAbb WCot
- 'Stahl Rose' CMea CPom EBee EWes LPhx SMrm SSvw WHil WPGP WSHC
§ **dodonaei** ELan EMan LHop LPhx MTho NEgg WEas WFar
§ **fleischeri** CNic

Chasmanthe (Iridaceae)

aethiopica CPLG CPou EBee ERea LBow SYvo
bicolor CPou CStu EBee IDee LBow
floribunda CHEx ERea LBow LRHS
- var. **duckittii** EBee ECho EPfP LBow LRHS WPGP

Chasmanthium (Poaceae)

§ **latifolium** More than 30 suppliers

Cheilanthes (Adiantaceae)

RCB/Arg P-28 new WCot
RCB/Arg X-5 new WCot
acrostica new WAbe
argentea CLAP WAbe
distans SRms
eatonii WAbe
- f. **castanea** WAbe
eckloniana WAbe
lanosa CLAP EBee EWes NMyG SRms WBor WCot
lindheimeri WAbe WCot
myriophylla WAbe

§ **nivea** WAbe
sieberi WAbe
siliquosa NNS 00-83 WCot
sinuata CLAP
tomentosa CLAP SRms WAbe WCot

Cheiranthus see *Erysimum*

Cheiridopsis (Aizoaceae)

cigarettifera new EShb
derenbergiana EMan WCot
peculiaris ♀H1 new EShb

Chelidonium (Papaveraceae)

japonicum see *Hylomecon japonica*
majus CArn CRWN GPoy MGol MHer MNHC MSal WCHb WHbs WHer WWye
- 'Chedglow' (v) CNat
- 'Flore Pleno' (d) CBre EMag MGol NBid NBro WBor WCHb WHer
- var. **laciniatum** EMon GBar WCot
- 'Laciniatum Flore Pleno' EMar IBlr (d)

Chelone (Scrophulariaceae)

barbata see *Penstemon barbatus*
§ **glabra** More than 30 suppliers
lyonii EBee EChP LAst LEdu MBow MDKP NBre NGdn NLar NRnb SHFr WMoo WPer WSan WShi
- 'Hot Lips' WCot
obliqua More than 30 suppliers
- var. **alba** see *C. glabra*
- 'Forncett Foremost' GQui
- 'Forncett Poppet' NBre
- 'Ieniemienie' EMon
- 'Pink Sensation' EBee MBri NBre
* - **rosea** CHar EBee LRHS MLLN MMHG WGwG

Chelonopsis (Lamiaceae)

moschata CDes CLAP CPom EBee ECha EMan MHar NGby WMoo WPGP WPrP
yagiharana CBod EBee EWTr GGar MBri MCCP MDKP MMHG MWea NBPC NBhm NBid NLar NSti SPoG WHil WMoo

Chenopodium (Chenopodiaceae)

ambrosioides EUnu
bonus-henricus CAgr CArn CBod CHby CWan EUnu GBar GPoy GWCH ILis MHer MNHC NTHB SIde WCHb WHer WSel WWye
botrys MSal
giganteum ILis MNHC WJek

cherimoya see *Annona cherimola*

cherry, duke see *Prunus* x *gondouinii*

cherry, sour or Morello see *Prunus cerasus*

cherry, sweet see *Prunus avium*

chervil see *Anthriscus cerefolium*

chestnut, sweet see *Castanea*

Chiastophyllum (Crassulaceae)

§ **oppositifolium** ♀H4 More than 30 suppliers
- 'Frosted Jade' see *C. oppositifolium* 'Jim's Pride'
§ - 'Jim's Pride' (v) More than 30 suppliers
simplicifolium see *C. oppositifolium*

Chiliotrichum (Asteraceae)
diffusum — CWib GAbr GGar GSki
- 'Siska' — CBcs IArd SMad WCot

Chimonanthus (Calycanthaceae)
fragrans — see *C. praecox*
nitens — GIBF NLar
§ **praecox** — More than 30 suppliers
- 'Brockhill Goldleaf' — LHop SBra SBrw
- 'Grandiflorus' ♀H4 — CEnd EPfP LRHS MAsh MBri SPoG SSpi SSta WPat
- 'Luteus' ♀H4 — CEnd CPMA ELan ENot EPfP LRHS MAsh MBri MRav NLar SMur SPer SSpi SSta WPat
- 'Trenython' — CEnd
yunnanensis — NLar

Chimonobambusa (Poaceae)
falcata — see *Drepanostachyum falcatum*
hejiangensis — EPla
hookeriana (Munro) Nakai — see *Himalayacalamus falconeri* 'Damarapa'
macrophylla f. **intermedia** — EPla
§ **marmorea** — CAbb EPla ERod LPal MMoz MWht NPal SBig WDyG WJun WMul WPGP
- 'Variegata' (v) — EFul EPla ERod SLPl WJun WPGP
§ **quadrangularis** — CBcs CDoC CHEx CTrG EBee EFul EPfP EPla ERod LEdu MAsh MMoz MWht NPal SBig WJun WPGP
- 'Nagaminea' (v) — EPla
- 'Suow' (v) — EPla WPGP
- 'Tatejima' — EPla
§ **tumidissinoda** — CAbb CMCo EPla ERod MMoz NPal SBig WDyG WJun WPGP

Chinese chives see *Allium tuberosum*

Chiogenes see *Gaultheria*

Chionanthus (Oleaceae)
foveolatus — EShb
retusus — CBcs CMCN EPfP IDee LRHS MPkF NLar SBrw SLon SSpi WDin
virginicus — CBcs CDoC CDul CEnd CMCN CPMA ELan EPfP EWTr IArd IDee IMGH LRHS MBlu MBri MMuc SBrw SMad SSpi SSta WDin WHCG WOrn WPGP

Chionochloa (Poaceae)
conspicua — CBig CKno EBee EChP EKen EMan GCal GIBF GSki LEdu MAvo NBir NFor NLar NOGN WPGP
- subsp. **conspicua** — GGar WCot
- subsp. **cunninghamii** — CPLG
- 'Rubra' — see *C. rubra*
flavescens — EHoe GSki ITer
flavicans — CAby CHrt CKno EChP EMan EWsh SMar WCot
pallens — CBig
§ **rubra** — More than 30 suppliers
- subsp. **cuprea** — EBee GBin GGar

Chionodoxa ✿ (Hyacinthaceae)
cretica — see *C. nana*
§ **forbesii** — CBro CFFs CMea CNic EBrs ECho ENot EPfP EPot GAbr LRHS NBPC NBir NJOw SBch SPer SRms WPer WShi
- 'Alba' — ECho NBPC
- 'Blue Giant' — ECho EPot LRHS WDav
- 'Rosea' — ECho
- Siehei Group — see *C. siehei*

gigantea — see *C. luciliae* Gigantea Group
luciliae misapplied — see *C. forbesii*
luciliae Boiss. ♀H4 — CAvo CBro EPfP EPot MBri NBlu SBch SPer
- 'Alba' — CBgR CBro CFwr CRez EBrs ECho LPhx LRHS SPer WLin
§ - Gigantea Group — CHar ECho ELan EPot GKev LPhx NJOw
- - 'Alba' — EPot GCrs GKev
§ **nana** — ECho
'Pink Giant' — CAvo CBgR CBro CFFs EBrs ECho ELan ENot EPfP EPot EWTr GKev LHop LRHS MMHG WCot WDav WHil
sardensis ♀H4 — CBgR CBro CRez ECho EPot LHop LRHS MMHG SBch SGar WLin WRHF WShi
§ **siehei** ♀H4 — CBro

Chionographis (Melanthiaceae)
japonica — EFEx WCru

Chionohebe (Scrophulariaceae)
§ **densifolia** — GAbr GCrs ITim NLAp
pulvinaris — GCrs ITim NSla WAbe

x *Chionoscilla* (Hyacinthaceae)
§ **allenii** — ECho EPot SUsu

Chirita (Gesneriaceae)
'Aiko' — LRHS WDib
'Chastity' — CSpe LRHS WDib
'Diane Marie' — LRHS WDib
dielsii — CFir
heterotricha — LRHS WDib
'Keiko' — LRHS WDib
* **latifolia** x **linearifolia** — WDib
linearifolia — EShb LRHS WDib
linearifolia x **sinensis** — EShb LRHS WDib
longgangensis — LRHS WDib
'New York' — CSpe LRHS WDib
sinensis ♀H1 — CHal LRHS WDib
- 'Hisako' — CSpe LRHS WDib
'Stardust' — LRHS WDib
tamiana — CSpe LRHS WDib

x *Chitalpa* (Bignoniaceae)
tashkentensis — CBcs CEnd CMCN CTho EBee EPfP IDee IMGH MBlu MWya NLar SCoo WPGP XPep
- 'Pink Dawn' **new** — IArd NLar
- 'Summer Bells' — CDoC EBee LRHS SBig

chives see *Allium schoenoprasum*

Chlidanthus (Amaryllidaceae)
fragrans — CStu ECho EShb

Chloranthus (Chloranthaceae)
fortunei — CDes CLAP LEdu SBla WCot WCru
japonicus — CLAP WCru
oldhamii — CLAP LEdu
- B&SWJ 2019 — WCru WPrP
serratus — CLAP LEdu WCru

Chloris (Poaceae)
distichophylla — see *Eustachys distichophylla*
virgata — CWCL

Chlorogalum (Hyacinthaceae)
pomeridianum — WCot

Chlorophytum (Anthericaceae)
bowkeri — EShb
comosum — EShb SEND
- 'Mandanum' (v) — CHal

- 'Variegatum' (v) ♀H1+3   CHal CHen LRHS MBri SRms
- 'Vittatum' (v) ♀H1+3   CHEx EShb NBlu SRms SWal
intermedium B&SWJ 6447   WCru
krookianum   CFir WCMO WCot
macrophyllum   EShb
§ *majus*   WCMO WCot
nepalense   WCot
- B&SWJ 2393   WCru
orchidastrum new   EShb

Choisya (*Rutaceae*)
'Aztec Pearl' ♀H4   More than 30 suppliers
dumosa   LHop
Goldfingers = 'Limo'PBR   More than 30 suppliers
ternata ♀H4   More than 30 suppliers
- 'Brica'PBR   see *C. ternata* Sundance = 'Lich'
- Moonshine =   EBee LRHS NLar SLon SPoG
  'Walcho'PBR
- MoonsleeperPBR   see *C. ternata* Sundance = 'Lich'
§ - Sundance = 'Lich'PBR   More than 30 suppliers
  ♀H3

Chondropetalum (*Restionaceae*)
* *elephantinum* new   CBig
hookerianum   CBig
mucronatum   CBcs CBig CCtw CTrC EAmu
    WPGP
tectorum   More than 30 suppliers
- dwarf new   WPGP

Chondrosum (*Poaceae*)
gracile   see *Bouteloua gracilis*

Chonemorpha (*Apocynaceae*)
fragrans   CPIN

Chordospartium (*Papilionaceae*)
muritai   ECou
- 'Huia Gilpen'   ECou
- 'Ron Feron'   ECou
- 'Wayne Nichols'   ECou
stevensonii   CPle ECou EPfP NLar SMad WBVN
- 'Duncan'   ECou
- 'Kiwi'   ECou
- 'Miller'   ECou

Chordospartium x *Corallospartium*
(*Papilionaceae*)
C. stevensonii x *C.* sp.   ECou
C. stevensonii x   ECou
    C. crassicaule,
    'Coral Spears'

Chorisia (*Bombacaceae*)
speciosa   EAmu WMul

Chorizema (*Papilionaceae*)
cordatum ♀H1   CSec ECou
dicksonii   CSec
ilicifolium   CAbb CBcs CSPN CSec EMil ERea

Chronanthus see *Cytisus*

Chrysalidocarpus see *Dypsis*

Chrysanthemopsis see *Rhodanthemum*

Chrysanthemum ✿ (*Asteraceae*)
'Agnes' new   WOFF
'Agnes Ann' (29K)   MNrw
'Albert's Yellow' (29Rub)   WOFF
'Alexandra'   NHal
'Allouise' (25b) ♀H3   NHal
alpinum   see *Leucanthemopsis alpina*
'Amber Gigantic' (1)   NHal
'Amber Matlock' (24b)   NHal

'Anastasia' (28b)   ECtt EMon EPPr GMac MNrw
    MRav NSti SRms WCot WFar WOFF
    WPer
N 'Anastasia Variegated'   EMon
  (28/v)
'Anastasia White' (28)   SSvw WCot WIvy
'Anne, Lady Brocket'   EMon EWsh GBuc MNrw NCGa
'Annie Lea' (25b) ♀H3   NHal
'Apollo' (29K)   EMon EWll LPhx SSvw
'Apricot' (29Rub)   CPrp EBee EChP EPPr MNrw
    MRav SSvw
'Apricot Chessington' (25a)   NHal
'Apricot Courtier' (24a)   NHal
'Apricot Enbee Wedding'   see *C.* 'Bronze Enbee Wedding'
  (29d)
arcticum L.   see *Arctanthemum arcticum*
argenteum   see *Tanacetum argenteum*
'Astro'   NHal
'Aunt Millicent' (29K)   MNrw
'Balcombe Perfection' (5a)   NHal
balsamita   see *Tanacetum balsamita*
Barbara = 'Yobarbara'PBR   EPfP NHal
  (22)
'Beacon' (5a) ♀H2   NHal
'Bernadette Wade' (23a)   NHal
'Bethanie Joy' (25b)   NHal
'Betty' (29K)   MNrw
'Big Wheel'PBR (22)   LAst
'Bill Wade' (25a)   NHal
* 'Billy Bell' (25a)   NHal
'Blenda'   CHrt
'Bo-peep' (28)   EMon
Bravo = 'Yobra'PBR (22c)   EPfP MNrw NHal
  ♀H3
* 'Breitner's Supreme'   MNrw WCAu
'Brennpunkt'   WHil WMnd
'Bright Eye' (28)   WMnd WOFF WPer
'Brightness' (29K)   SUsu
'Bronze Beauty' (25b)   WFar
'Bronze Cassandra' (5b)   NHal
  ♀H2
'Bronze Dee Gem' (29c)   NHal
§ 'Bronze Elegance' (28b)   CSam EMon ENot MLLN NBir
    NGdn NSti SPla SRms WEas WIvy
    WMnd
§ 'Bronze Enbee Wedding'   NHal
  (29d) ♀H3
'Bronze Margaret' (29c)   NHal
  ♀H3
'Bronze Matlock' (24b)   NHal
'Bronze Max Riley' (23b)   NHal
  ♀H3
'Bronze Mayford   NHal
  Perfection' (5a) ♀H2
'Bronze Mei-kyo'   see *C.* 'Bronze Elegance'
'Bruera' (24b)   NHal
'Carlene Welby' (25b)   NHal
'Carmine Blush' (29Rub)   EBee MNrw WBrk WCot
'Cassandra' (5b) ♀H2   NHal
'Cherry Chessington' (25a)   NHal
'Christopher Lawson'   NHal
  (24b)
cinerariifolium   see *Tanacetum cinerariifolium*
'Clapham Delight' (23a)   NHal
'Clara Curtis' (29Rub)   More than 30 suppliers
coccineum   see *Tanacetum coccineum*
'Conjora' (22c)   LAst
'Contralto' (22)   WCot
'Copper Margaret' (29c)   CHrt
'Cornetto' (25b)   NHal
'Corngold' (5b)   NHal
corymbosum   see *Tanacetum corymbosum*
'Cottage Apricot'   CHea EChP EWoo GMac LHop
    MBNS MNrw WEas
'Cottage Pink'   see *C.* 'Emperor of China'
'Cottage Yellow'   MSte WCot WHoo

'Courtier' (24a) — NHal
'Cream Patricia Millar' (14b) — NHal
Dana = 'Yodana' (25b) ♀H3 — NHal
'Daniel Cooper' (29Rub) — MNrw WOFF
'Darren Pugh' (3b) — NHal
Debonair = 'Yodebo'[PBR] (22c) ♀H3 — EPfP
'Dee Gem' (29c) ♀H3 — NHal
'Denise' (28b) ♀H3 — WOFF
§ 'Doctor Tom Parr' (28b) — EBee ELan EMon IGor LHop LPhx SUsu WPtf
'Doreen Statham' (4b) — NHal
'Dorothy Stone' (25b) — NHal
'Dorridge Crystal' (24a) — NHal
'Duchess of Edinburgh' (29Rub) — CPrp CSam EBee EBrs EChP ECtt ELan EMon LRHS MRav MTis NCGa SSvw WCAu WMnd WOFF
'Duke of Kent' (1) — NHal
'Ed Hodgson' (25a) — NHal
'Edelgard' — WWhi
'Edelweiss' (29K) — EMon GMac WCot
'Egret' (23b) — NHal
'Elaine Johnson' (3b) — NHal
'Elizabeth Lawson' (5b) — NHal
'Elizabeth Shoesmith' (1) — NHal
'Ellen' (29c) — CHrt NHal
* 'Emma Jane' (25a) — NHal
§ 'Emperor of China' (29Rub) — CAby CElw CSam EChP ECha EMon ENot EPPr GCal IGor LPhx LRHS MNrw MRav MSte NCGa SSvw WBor WCot WFar WMnd WOFF
'Enbee Wedding' (29d) ♀H3 — NHal
'Esther' (29Rub) — EMon MNrw
'Fairie' (28a) ♀H3 **new** — MNrw
* 'Fairy Rose' (29K) — MNrw
foeniculaceum misapplied — see *Argyranthemum foeniculaceum* misapplied
foeniculaceum (Willd.) Desf. — see *Argyranthemum foeniculaceum* (Willd.) Webb & Sch.Bip.
'Foxtrot'[PBR] — LAst
'Fred Raynor' **new** — MNrw WOFF
frutescens — see *Argyranthemum frutescens*
'Gala'[PBR] (22) ♀H3 — LAst
'Gambit' (24a) — NHal
'Geof Brady' (5a) — NHal
'Geoff Sylvester' (25a) **new** NHal
'George Griffiths' (24b) ♀H3 — NHal
'Gladys' (24b) — EChP ELan EWoo
'Gladys Emerson' (3b) — NHal
'Gloria' (29K) — MNrw
§ 'Gold Margaret' (29c) ♀H3 NHal
'Golden Cassandra' (5b) ♀H2 — NHal
'Golden Courtier' (24a) — NHal
'Golden Gigantic' (1) — NHal
'Golden Margaret' — see *C.* 'Gold Margaret'
'Golden Mayford Perfection' (5a) ♀H2 — NHal
'Golden Plover' (22) — NHal
'Golden Seal' (7b) — EMon GBuc WSPU
'Goldengreenheart' (29Rub) — MNrw
'Goldmarianne' (29K) **new** GBin
'Gompie Bronze' — NHal
'Gompie Red' — NHal
I 'Gompie Rose' — NHal
'Grace Wade' (25b) — NHal
'Grandchild' (29c) — MNrw
§ x *grandiflorum* — SRms
'Hanenburg' — NHal

haradjanii — see *Tanacetum haradjanii*
'Harold Lawson' (5a) — NHal
'Harry Gee' (1) — NHal
'Harry Woolman' (13b) — NHal
'Hazy Days' (25b) — NHal
'Heather James' (3b) — NHal
'Heide' (29c) ♀H3 — NHal
'Hesketh Knight' (5b) — NHal
Holly = 'Yoholly' (22b) ♀H3 — NHal
'Honey Enbee Wedding' (29d) — NHal
'Horningsea Pink' (19d) — WBor
hosmariense — see *Rhodanthemum hosmariense*
'Imp' (28) — MNrw
'Innocence' (29Rub) — CSam EChP ELan EMon IGor MNrw MRav NCGa NGdn NSti SAga SPla
'Janice'[PBR] (7a) — LAst
'Jante Wells' (28) — EMon WEas WOFF WTel
'Jessie Cooper' — see *C.* 'Mrs Jessie Cooper'
'John Harrison' (25b) — NHal
'John Hughes' (3b) — NHal
'John Wingfield' (14b) — NHal
'Joyce Frieda' (23b) — NHal
'Julia' (28) — GMac
'Julie Lagravère' (28) — WPtf WWhi
'Kay Woolman' (13b) — NHal
'Kenneth Roy' (15a) — NHal
x *koreanum* — see *C.* x *grandiflorum*
'Lady in Pink' (29Rub) — GBuc
'Lakelanders' (3b) — NHal
'Le Bonheur Red' — NHal
'Lemon Margaret' (29c) ♀H3 — NHal
'Leo' (28) — EMon
leucanthemum — see *Leucanthemum vulgare*
'Lilac Chessington' (25a) — NHal
'Lindie' (28) — WHil
'Little Dorrit' (29K) — WOFF
'Long Island Beauty' (6b) ♀H2 — WTel
'Lorna Wood' (13b) — NHal
'Lucy' (29a) ♀H2 — NHal
'Lucy Simpson' (29K) — MNrw WOFF
'Lundy' (2) — NHal
'Luv Purple' — NHal
'Lynn Johnson' (15a) — NHal
Lynn = 'Yolynn'[PBR] (22c) ♀H3 — NHal
macrophyllum — see *Tanacetum macrophyllum* (Waldst. & Kit.) Sch.Bip.
'Malcolm Perkins' (25a) — NHal
'Mancetta Comet' (29a) — NHal
'Mandarin' (5b) — NCGa
maresii — see *Rhodanthemum hosmariense*
'Margaret' (29c) ♀H3 — NHal
'Mark Woolman' (1) — NHal
'Mary' (29K) — MNrw
'Mary Stoker' (29Rub) — More than 30 suppliers
'Matador' (14a) — NHal
'Matlock' (24b) — NHal
mawii — see *Rhodanthemum gayanum*
'Max Riley' (23b) ♀H3 — NHal
maximum misapplied — see *Leucanthemum* x *superbum*
maximum Ramond — see *Leucanthemum maximum* (Ramond) DC.
'Maxine Johnson' (25b) — NHal
'May Shoesmith' (5a) ♀H2 — NHal
'Mayford Perfection' (5a) ♀H2 — NHal
'Mei-kyo' (28b) — CMea EBee EMon ENot IGor LBBr MLLN MRav MWgw SPla SRms WBor WFar WHil
'Membury' (24b) — NHal
'Mermaid Yellow' ♀H2 — LAst

'White Cassandra' (5b)   NHal
'White Enbee Wedding'   NHal
  (29d)
'White Gloss' (29K)   LRHS
'White Margaret' (29c)   NHal
  ♀H3
'White Skylark' (22)   NHal
'White Tower'   MNrw
'Wilder Charms'   WHil
'Winning's Red' (29Rub)   EMon LHop LPhx MNrw MSph
                    SMad
'Wizard'PBR **new**   LAst
'Woolman's Star' (3a)   NHal
'Woolman's Venture' (4b)   NHal
'Yellow Billy Bell' (15a)   NHal
  new
§ 'Yellow Courtier' (24a)   NHal
'Yellow Egret' (23b)   NHal
'Yellow Ellen' (29c)   NHal
'Yellow Enbee Wedding'   NHal
  (29d) **new**
'Yellow Hazy Days' (25b)   NHal
'Yellow Heide' (29c) ♀H3   NHal
'Yellow John Hughes' (3b)   NHal
  ♀H2
'Yellow John Wingfield'   NHal
  (14b)
'Yellow May Shoesmith'   NHal
  (5a)
'Yellow Mayford   NHal
  Perfection' (5a) ♀H2
'Yellow Pennine Oriel'   NHal
  (29a) ♀H3
'Yellow Ralph Lambert'   NHal
  (1)
'Yellow Rylands Gem'   NHal
  (24b) **new**
'Yellow Starlet' (29f/K)   MNrw
'Yellow Whitby' (5b)   NHal
§ *yezoense* ♀H4   CSam CStu ELan WEas
- 'Roseum'   CSam NSti WBor
§ *zawadskii*   NWCA WFar

Chrysocoma (Asteraceae)
ciliata JJH 9401633   NWCA
coma-aurea   EMan

Chrysogonum (Asteraceae)
australe   EBee
virginianum   CHal CMea EAEE EBee EBrs ECha
                    EMan EMar EShb EWes LRHS MRav
                    SBch WFar WMoo

Chrysopogon (Poaceae)
gryllus   CBig EBee GCal WPGP

Chrysopsis (Asteraceae)
§ *mariana*   EMon WOld
villosa   see *Heterotheca villosa*

Chrysosplenium (Saxifragaceae)
alternifolium   EMFW IHMH MCCP NHol
davidianum   CBre CPLG CSam EBee ECha EMan
                    EPot GEdr GKev ITer MNFA NBir
                    NSla WBor WCot WCru WGer
                    WMoo WPrP WPtf
- SBEC 231   NHol
forrestii   GIBF
lanuginosum var.   WCru
  formosanum
  B&SWJ 6979
macrophyllum   CDes WCot WCru
macrostemon var.   EPot
  shiobarense
- - B&SWJ 6173   WCru
oppositifolium   EBee WHer WShi

Chrysothemis (Gesneriaceae)
pulchella ♀H1   CHal

Chusquea ✿ (Poaceae)
breviglumis misapplied   see *C. culeou* 'Tenuis'
breviglumis Phil. **new** NMoo
coronalis   WJun
culeou ♀H4   More than 30 suppliers
- 'Breviglumis'   see *C. culeou* 'Tenuis'
- 'Purple Splendour' **new**   WPGP
§ - 'Tenuis'   EPla ERod WJun WNor
cumingii   WJun
gigantea   EPla LEdu MMoz MWht SBig WMul
                    WPGP
macrostachya   EBee EPla WPGP
montana   EPla
pittieri   WJun
quila   MMoz WPGP
sulcata   WJun
uliginosa   WJun
valdiviensis   EPla WJun WPGP

Cicerbita (Asteraceae)
B&SWJ 5162   WCru
B&SWJ 6588   WCru
BWJ 7891 from China   WCru
§ *alpina*   MSph NBid NLar SGar SPlb
macrorhiza B&SWJ 2970   WCru
plumieri   EMan EWes WCMO WCot WFar
                    WPtf WRos

Cichorium (Asteraceae)
intybus   More than 30 suppliers
- f. *album*   CBod CPrp EBee EBla EChP ECha
                    EDAr EGle EMag EMan EPfP GMac
                    LHop LRHS MRav NCGa NGdn
                    NSti SBch SPoG SWat WCAu
                    WCHb WHil
- var. *foliosum* **new**   EBee
- 'Roseum'   CBod CHad CPrp CSpe EBee EBla
                    ECGP EChP ECha ECot EGle ELan
                    EMag EPfP EWTr GMac LHop
                    LRHS MAvo MBow MRav NCGa
                    NGdn SBch SPer SPoG SWat WCAu
                    WCHb

Cimicifuga see *Actaea*
americana   see *Actaea podocarpa*
foetida   see *Actaea cimicifuga*
ramosa   see *Actaea simplex* 'Prichard's
                    Giant'
rubifolia   see *Actaea cordifolia*

Cineraria (Asteraceae)
maritima   see *Senecio cineraria*
saxifraga   EShb

Cinnamomum (Lauraceae)
camphora   CBcs CHEx CPLG CTrG
japonicum   WPGP
micranthum   WPGP
verum   SDEP

Cionura (Asclepiadaceae)
oreophila   CFir CPfN GCal SPoG WPGP
                    WSHC

Circaea (Onagraceae)
lutetiana   MSal NSco WHer
- 'Caveat Emptor' (v)   CBow EBee EMan NBid WCot
                    WHer

Cirsium (Asteraceae)
acaule   NBre
arvense **new**   WSFF

*	*atroroseum*	SWat
	ciliatum new	EBee
	diacantha	see *Ptilostemon diacantha*
	eriophoroides new	WCot
	eriophorum	LDai NLar
	falconeri	NBur
	helenioides	see *C. heterophyllum*
§	*heterophyllum*	CDes CPom EBee EChP EMan EMon GBri LDai LEdu LPhx NBre NBur NEgg NLar SHar WCot WPGP WTin
	japonicum 'Early Pink Beauty'	LDai NBre
	- 'Early Rose Beauty'	NBre
	- 'Pink Beauty'	LHop NEgg
	- 'Rose Beauty'	EWTr LRHS NBlu NPri SPur
	kamtschaticum	GIBF
	'Mount Etna'	CSam EBee EBla ECGP EMar GBri LHop LRHS MWgw NFla SPoG
	oleraceum	LEdu NBid NBre NLar
	purpuratum	EMan MNrw WCot WPGP
	- JCA 4.192.500	CDes
	rivulare new	CSam
	- 'Atropurpureum'	More than 30 suppliers
	tuberosum new	LPhx
	vulgare	WSFF

Cissus (Vitaceae)

	adenopoda	CPIN
	antarctica ♀H1	CTrC MBri
	discolor	CHal CPIN EShb
	pedata B&SWJ 2371	WCru
	rhombifolia ♀H1	MBri SEND
	- 'Ellen Danica' ♀H1	CHal
§	*striata*	CBcs CDoC CHEx CPLG CTrC CWCL EBee EMil EShb IMGH LRHS MRav SBra SLim SWvt WCru WSHC WWeb

Cistus ✿ (Cistaceae)

	x *aguilarii*	CBcs CPLG CSBt CTri EPfP EWTr LAst WSHC XPep
	- 'Maculatus' ♀H3	CDoC CHar CSam EBee ELan EPfP EWTr GGar LRHS LSRN MAsh MSwo NCGa SLPl SLdr SPer SPla SPoG WAbe WBrE WCFE WGer WHCG WKif WWeb XPep
	albanicus	see *C. sintenisii*
	albidus	CArn EGoo LRav WKif XPep
	- f. *albus*	XPep
	algarvensis	see *Halimium ocymoides*
	'Ann Baker'	SLPl SUsu XPep
	'Anne Palmer'	see *C.* x *fernandesiae* 'Anne Palmer'
	x *argenteus* 'Blushing Peggy Sammons'	CDoC CSBt EBee MAsh MWgw WSPU XPep
	- Golden Treasure = 'Nepond' (v)	EBee EPfP SLim
	- 'Paper Moon'	EBee LSRN XPep
§	- 'Peggy Sammons' ♀H3	CBgR CDoC EBee ECha EGra ELan EPfP EWTr IMGH LAst LHop LRHS LSRN MAsh MGos MRav SLim SMer SPer SPoG SWat SWvt WBrE WFar WHar WSHC WTel XPep
	- 'Silver Ghost'	CDoC EWTr XPep
	- 'Silver Pink' ambig.	More than 30 suppliers
	- 'Stripey'	XPep
	atriplicifolius	see *Halimium atriplicifolium*
	'Blanche'	see *C. ladanifer* 'Blanche'
	x *bornetianus* 'Jester'	CSBt EBee SHop SPla WAbe XPep
	'Candy Stripe' (v)	EBee MBNS
	x *canescens*	XPep
	- f. *albus*	CWib EBee WEas WHCG WKif XPep
	'Chelsea Pink'	see *C.* 'Grayswood Pink'
	chinamadensis	XPep

x	*chnoodophyllus*	XPep
x	*clausonis*	XPep
§	*clusii*	CBgR MAsh SPla XPep
	- subsp. *multiflorus*	XPep
x	*corbariensis*	see *C.* x *hybridus*
	creticus	CDoC LAst MAsh MGos MLHP SGar SLon SPoG WBVN WPGP
	- subsp. *corsicus*	XPep
§	- subsp. *creticus*	EBee ELan EPfP LRHS MSte SCoo SPer WGer XPep
	- - f. *albus*	XPep
§	- - - 'Tania Compton'	WAbe
*	- - - 'Ano Moulia'	XPep
	- - - 'Bali'	XPep
	- - - 'Lasithi'	WAbe
	- subsp. *eriocephalus*	XPep
*	- - - 'Michel Valantin'	XPep
§	- subsp. *incanus*	WHCG
	- var. *tauricus*	XPep
x	*crispatus*	XPep
§	- 'Warley Rose'	SHBN SHop WKif WWeb XPep
§	*crispus* L.	EBee EGoo WEas XPep
	- 'Prostratus'	see *C. crispus* L.
	- 'Sunset'	see *C.* x *pulverulentus* 'Sunset'
§	x *cyprius* ♀H4	CArn CBrm CDul ECtt ELan EPfP LHop MGos MNHC MRav MWat SDix SEND SRms WBrE WDin WFar WWeb XPep
	- f. *albiflorus*	MSte XPep
	- var. *ellipticus* f. *bicolor*	XPep
	- - 'Elma' ♀H3	EBee ELan EPfP LHop LRHS MAsh SPer SPla WEas WGer WHCG WPGP XPep
§	x *dansereaui*	CHar CMHG CSBt CSam CWib EBee ENot EPfP MRav MSte WFar XPep
	- 'Albiflorus'	see *C.* x *dansereaui* 'Portmeirion'
	- 'Decumbens' ♀H4	CBcs CBrm CMHG CTbh CTri ELan EPfP MAsh MBNS MDun MRav MSwo MWgw NCGa NFor SArc SCoo SEND SHBN SMer SPla SPoG WAbe WDin WGer WHCG XPep
	- 'Jenkyn Place'	CDoC EBee MBNS MBri MGos SLPl SPoG SUsu WKif XPep
	- 'Little Gem'	XPep
§	- 'Portmeirion'	WFar XPep
x	*dubius*	XPep
x	*escartianus*	XPep
x	*fernandesiae*	XPep
§	- 'Anne Palmer'	CBgR CDoC EBee EPfP LSRN MWea SPoG WFar
x	*florentinus* misapplied	see x *Halimiocistus* 'Ingwersenii'
§	x *florentinus* Lam.	CAbP XPep
*	- 'Béziers'	XPep
	- 'Fontfroide'	EBee WSPU WWeb
*	- 'Tramontane'	XPep
	formosus	see *Halimium lasianthum* subsp. *formosum*
x	*gardianus*	XPep
	'Gordon Cooper'	EBee WSPU XPep
§	'Grayswood Pink' ♀H4	More than 30 suppliers
	x *heterocalyx* 'Chelsea Bonnet'	EBee MSte SCoo SLim SPoG WPGP WSPU WWeb XPep
	heterophyllus	XPep
	hirsutus Lam. 1786	see *C. inflatus*
	- var. *psilosepalus*	see *C. inflatus*
x	*hybridus*	More than 30 suppliers
*	- 'Donadieu'	XPep
	- Gold Prize = 'Wyecis' (v)	ELan MBri WLeb
	incanus	see *C. creticus* subsp. *incanus*
	inflatus	CPLG SEND WHar WHer XPep
	ingwerseniana	see x *Halimiocistus* 'Ingwersenii'
	'Jessamy Beauty'	SHop SLPl SUsu WAbe XPep
	'Jessamy Bride'	SLPl XPep
	'Jessamy Charm'	XPep

ladanifer misapplied	see *C.* x *cyprius*
ladanifer L. ♀H3	CDoC CSBt CTri ECha ECrN ELan EPfP EWTr IMGH LEdu LRHS MRav MSal MSwo NEgg SECG SGar WEas WFar WHar WSHC WTel XPep
- var. *albiflorus*	CBcs XPep
* - - 'Bashful'	XPep
§ - 'Blanche'	EBee LRHS SHop WKif XPep
- 'John Hardy'	NLar
§ - 'Paladin'	SHop XPep
- Palhinhae Group	see *C. ladanifer* var. *sulcatus*
- 'Pat'	EBee ELan EPfP LRHS LSRN MAsh SPoG
- var. *petiolatus*	XPep
- - f. *immaculatus*	XPep
§ - var. *sulcatus*	CDoC CHar CPle EBee EPfP LHop MSte WFar
- - f. *bicolor*	EBee XPep
- - f. *latifolius*	XPep
- var. *tangerinus*	XPep
lasianthus	see *Halimium lasianthum*
laurifolius ♀H4	CDoC CHar EBee ENot EPfP LRav MGos MNrw MRav NBir NEgg NSti SLPl SLon SPer SPoG WHar WOut XPep
- subsp. *atlanticus*	XPep
§ x *laxus* 'Snow White'	CAbP CDoC EPfP LAst LHop LRHS MDun MGos MSte MWgw NPer NPro SLPl SLim SLon SPer SPoG SUsu WKif WLeb XPep
x *ledon*	SLPl WWeb XPep
libanotis	CPle XPep
x *longifolius*	see *C.* x *nigricans*
x *loretii* misapplied	see *C.* x *dansereaui*
x *loretii* Rouy & Foucaud	see *C.* x *stenophyllus*
x *lucasii*	XPep
x *lusitanicus* Maund	see *C.* x *dansereaui*
'May Snow'	MAsh MBNS SPoG
'Merrist Wood Cream'	see x *Halimiocistus wintonensis* 'Merrist Wood Cream'
x *mesoensis*	XPep
monspeliensis	CAbP EBee EPfP GGar LRHS SPer SPoG SSpi WFar XPep
- CMBS 62	WPGP
- Densifolius Group	XPep
- 'Vicar's Mead'	CBgR CCCN CDoC EBee MBNS SPla SPoG XPep
munbyi	XPep
§ x *nigricans*	EBee ELan EWin WCot XPep
x *oblongifolius*	XPep
x *obtusifolius* misapplied	see *C.* x *nigricans*
x *obtusifolius* Sweet	CAbP EPfP EWes SLPl WEas XPep
§ - 'Thrive'	MBri MGos SCoo
ochreatus	see *C. symphytifolius* subsp. *leucophyllus*
ocymoides	see *Halimium ocymoides*
osbeckiifolius	XPep
'Paladin'	see *C. ladanifer* 'Paladin'
palhinhae	see *C. ladanifer* var. *sulcatus*
parviflorus misapplied	see *C.* 'Grayswood Pink'
parviflorus Lam.	WCFE WSHC XPep
x *pauranthus*	XPep
* - 'Natacha'	XPep
'Peggy Sammons'	see *C.* x *argenteus* 'Peggy Sammons'
x *penarcleusensis*	XPep
x *picardianus*	XPep
x *platysepalus*	LPhx SHop SLPl XPep
populifolius	CMHG ECha LTwo SPer WHer WPGP
- var. *lasiocalyx*	see *C. populifolius* subsp. *major*
§ - subsp. *major* ♀H3	CBgR CPle EBee EPfP LSRN WPGP XPep
- subsp. *populifolius*	XPep
pouzolzii	XPep
psilosepalus	see *C. inflatus*
§ x *pulverulentus*	CPLG CTri ECha EPfP MMHG WAbe WDin WSHC
* - Delilei Group	XPep
* - - 'Fiona'	XPep
§ - 'Sunset' ♀H3	More than 30 suppliers
- 'Warley Rose'	see *C.* x *crispatus* 'Warley Rose'
§ x *purpureus* ♀H3	More than 30 suppliers
- 'Alan Fradd'	CBcs CTbh EBee ENot EPfP LAst LHop LRHS LSRN MAsh MDun MGos MSwo MWgw SCoo SEND SLim SMrm SPla SPoG WBor WFar WGer XPep
- var. *argenteus* f. *stictus*	EBee LSRN WAbe WSPU XPep
- 'Betty Taudevin'	see *C.* x *purpureus*
- var. *holorhodos*	XPep
x *ralletii*	EBee XPep
- f. *subcreticus*	XPep
x *rodiaei* 'Jessabel' **new**	WAbe WLeb
- 'Jessica'	CDoC EBee LAst NLar WAbe WSPU XPep
rosmarinifolius	see *C. clusii*
'Ruby Cluster'	CCCN CDoC MWea WLeb XPep
sahucii	see x *Halimiocistus sahucii*
salviifolius	CAbP CArn CCCN ISea LRHS SSpi WCFE WFar WHCG WWeb XPep
- 'Avalanche'	CRez EBee MAsh MRav WAbe
- 'Gold Star'	EBee SPoG XPep
* - 'Ivoire'	XPep
- 'Prostratus'	ELan LPhx LRHS SPoG WHCG WPGP
* - 'Sirocco'	XPep
* - 'Villeveyrac'	XPep
salviifolius x *monspeliensis*	see *C.* x *florentinus* Lam.
x *sammonsii* 'Ida'	XPep
'Silver Pink' misapplied	see *C.* 'Grayswood Pink'
§ **sintenisii**	XPep
§ x *skanbergii* ♀H3	CBcs CBgR CHar CSBt CTri CWib EBee ELan ENot EPfP LHop LRHS MGos MLHP MRav MWat NBir NSti SCoo SDix SHBN SPer SPla SPoG WEas WFar WLin XPep
* - 'Akamas'	XPep
§ 'Snow Fire' ♀H4	CAbP CBgR CCCN CDoC CSBt EBee ENot EPfP EWTr LRHS LSRN MAsh MBri MGos NPro SCoo SHop SLPl SPla SPoG SSpi SUsu WAbe WGer WLeb WSPU XPep
§ x *stenophyllus*	CWib EBee EGra SPer XPep
- f. *albiflorus*	XPep
* - - 'Mistral'	XPep
* - 'Elise'	XPep
symphytifolius	WPGP XPep
§ - subsp. *leucophyllus*	XPep
- - MSF 98.019	WPGP
'Tania Compton'	see *C. creticus* subsp. *creticus* f. *albus* 'Tania Compton'
x *tephreus*	XPep
'Thornfield White'	EBee
'Thrive'	see *C.* x *obtusifolius* 'Thrive'
tomentosus	see *Helianthemum nummularium* subsp. *tomentosum*
x *verguinii*	EBee EWin LHop XPep
- f. *albiflorus* misapplied	see *C.* x *dansereaui* 'Portmeirion'
- f. *albiflorus*	XPep
* - 'Salabert'	XPep
villosus	see *C. creticus* subsp. *creticus*
wintonensis	see x *Halimiocistus wintonensis*

Citharexylum (Verbenaceae)

spicatum	CPLG

citrangequat see x *Fortucitroncirus*

x *Citrofortunella* (*Rutaceae*)

hybrid **new**	CCCN
floridana 'Eustis' (F)	ERea
- 'Lakeland' (F)	ERea
ichangquat	EZes
ichangquat 6-7-2 **new**	EZes
lemonquat (F)	EZes
§ *microcarpa* (F) ♀H1	CCCN CDoC EMui EPfP ERea MBri SPoG WBVN WMul
§ - 'Tiger' (v/F) ♀H1	EPfP ERea
- 'Variegata'	see x *C. microcarpa* 'Tiger'
mitis	see x *C. microcarpa*
'Nippon' **new**	EZes
swinglei 'Tavares' (F)	ERea

x *Citrofortunella* x *Microcitrus* (*Rutaceae*)

x *C. floridana* 'Eustis' x *M. australasica* **new**	EZes
x *C. mitis* x *M. australasica* **new**	EZes

x *Citroncirus* (*Rutaceae*)

citrandarin	MJnS
citremon	EZes MJnS
'Curafora'	EZes
'Swingle' (F)	EZes
'US119'	EZes MJnS
'Venasca'	EZes
webberi 'Benton'	EZes
- 'Carrizo'	CAgr
- 'Morton'	EZes MJnS
- 'Rusk'	EZes MJnS
- 'Troyer'	EZes

Citrullus (*Cucurbitaceae*)

colocynthis	CArn

citron see *Citrus medica*

Citrus ✿ (*Rutaceae*)

§ *amblycarpa* Djeruk lime (F)	ERea
§ *aurantiifolia* (F)	CCCN
- Indian lime (F)	ERea
- key lime (F)	CDoC
aurantium 'Bouquet de Fleurs'	CCCN CKob ERea
- var. *myrtifolia* 'Chinotto' (F)	ERea
- 'Seville' (F)	ERea
bergamia bergamot	CKob ERea
calamondin	see x *Citrofortunella microcarpa*
'Fukushu' **new**	CCCN
hystrix	CCCN CKob ERea EZes SDEP
Ichang lemon (F)	EZes MJnS
ichangensis (F)	EZes
japonica	see *Fortunella japonica*
junos	CAgr EZes
'Kulci' **new**	CCCN SDEP
kumquat	see *Fortunella margarita*
'La Valette'	CKob EPfP ERea SDEP
latifolia (F/S)	CCCN EPfP ERea
* x *latipes*	EZes
limetta **new**	CCCN EZes
limettoides (F)	CArn EZes
limon (F)	CHEx LPan SPoG WMul
- 'Fino' (F)	EPfP
- 'Four Seasons' **new**	CCCN
§ - 'Garey's Eureka' (F)	CDoC CKob EPfP ERea
- 'Imperial' (F)	ERea
- 'Lemonade' (F)	ERea
- 'Lisbon' (F)	ERea
- 'Mosquito' (v) **new**	CHll
- 'Quatre Saisons'	see *C. limon* 'Garey's Eureka'
- 'Toscana'	EPfP ERea
- 'Variegata' (F/v) ♀H1	CCCN EMui ERea EZes
- 'Villa Franca' (F)	ERea
x *limonia* 'Rangpur' (F)	ERea
'Lipo' **new**	CCCN SDEP
madurensis	see *Fortunella japonica*
maxima (F)	ERea EZes
medica (F)	EZes SDEP
- 'Cidro Digitado'	see *C. medica* var. *digitata*
§ - var. *digitata* (F)	CKob ERea EZes SDEP
- 'Ethrog' (F)	ERea
- var. *sarcodactylis*	see *C. medica* var. *digitata*
§ x *meyeri*	CHEx MJnS
- 'Meyer' (F) ♀H1	CBcs CCCN CHll CKob EPfP ERea GTwe LRHS MJnS SPer
microcarpa Philippine lime	see x *Citrofortunella microcarpa*
mitis	see x *Citrofortunella microcarpa*
x *nobilis* 'Ellendale' (F)	EPfP
- 'Murcott' (F)	EPfP
- Ortanique Group (F)	EPfP
- 'Silver Hill Owari' (F)	ERea
- Tangor Group (F)	ERea
x *paradisi* (F)	CCCN SPoG
- 'Foster' (F)	ERea
- 'Golden Special' (F)	ERea
- 'Star Ruby' (F/S)	EMui ERea
'Ponderosa' (F)	ERea
'Pursta' **new**	CCCN
reticulata (F)	CCCN WMul
- Mandarin Group (F)	CBcs CDoC
- - 'Clementine' (F)	CDoC ERea
- - 'Encore' (F)	ERea
- 'Miyagawa'	see *C. unshiu* 'Miyagawa'
- Satsuma Group	see *C. unshiu*
- 'Variegata' (F/v)	WMul
sinensis (F)	CCCN ERea LPan SLon SPoG WMul
- 'Egg' (F)	ERea
- 'Embiguo' (F)	ERea
- 'Jaffa'	see *C. sinensis* 'Shamouti'
- 'Lane Late' (F)	EPfP
- 'Malta Blood' (F)	ERea SDEP
- 'Moro Blood' (F)	ERea
- 'Navelina' (F/S)	CDoC ERea SDEP
- 'Parson Brown' (F)	ERea
- 'Prata' (F)	ERea
- 'Ruby' (F)	ERea
- 'Saint Michael' (F)	ERea
- 'Sanguinelli' (F)	ERea SDEP
§ - 'Shamouti' (F)	ERea
- 'Thomson' (F)	ERea
- 'Valencia' (F)	ECot EMui
- 'Valencia Late' (F)	ERea
- 'Washington' (F/S)	EPfP ERea GTwe
sudachi **new**	EZes
x *tangelo* 'Seminole' (F)	ERea
§ *unshiu* (F)	ERea
§ - 'Miyagawa'	CCCN ERea
- 'Okitsu' (F/S)	EZes
wilsonii **new**	EZes

Citrus x *Eremocitrus*

C. x *meyeri* 'Meyer' x *E. glauca* **new**	EZes

Cladium (*Cyperaceae*)

mariscus	NLar

Cladothamnus see *Elliottia*

Cladrastis (*Papilionaceae*)

§ *kentukea*	CArn CBcs CDul CLnd CMCN ELan EPfP IMGH MBlu NHol NLar SHBN SSpi WBVN WDin WNor

§ - 'Perkins Pink'   CMCN MBlu SSpi
   - 'Rosea'   see *C. kentukea* 'Perkins Pink'
   lutea   see *C. kentukea*
   sinensis   CBcs CMCN EPfP IDee MBlu SSpi
                             WPGP

Clarkia (Onagraceae)
* *repens*   CSpe

Clausia (Brassicaceae)
   aprica   CPBP

Clavinodum (Poaceae)
§ *oedogonatum*   EPla WJun

Claytonia (Portulacaceae)
   alsinoides   see *C. sibirica*
   australasica   see *Neopaxia australasica*
   caroliniana   EBee NLar
§ *nevadensis*   EMar
   parvifolia   see *Naiocrene parvifolia*
§ *perfoliata*   CArn CPLG GPoy ILis WCHb WHer
§ *sibirica*   CAgr CArn CElw CNic CSec EMag
                             EMan LSou NBid WGHP WHen
                             WRHF WWye
   - 'Alba'   CElw NBid WMoo
   virginica   EHrv WFar WMoo

Clematis ✿ (Ranunculaceae)
   B&SWJ 599   WCru
   BWJ 7630 from China   WCru
   BWJ 8169 from China   WCru
   CC 4427   CPLG MGol
   CC 4478   MGol
   CC 4513   CPLG MGol WCot
   CC 4710   CPLG MGol
   WJS 8910 from Japan   WCru
   'Abundance' (Vt) ♀H4   CBgR CDoC CElw CFRD CRHN
                             CSPN CWCL EPfP ERob ESCh
                             ETho LRHS MBri MRav NBea NHol
                             NTay SBod SBra SDix SHBN SPer
                             SPet SPoG WBGC WTel
   acuminata var.   WCru
   sikkimensis
   B&SWJ 7202 **new**
   addisonii   CBcs CSPN CWoW EBee ERob
                             ESCh NHaw WBGC
   aethusifolia   CSPN ERob
   afoliata   CBcs CSPN CStu EBee ECou ERob
                             ETho WBGC
   afoliata x *forsteri*   ECou
   'Aino' (Vt)   ERob
   'Akaishi' (EL)   CFRD EBee ERob ESCh ETho NTay
   akebioides   CPLG EHyt LRHS SHBN SLim
                             WCru
   'Akemi' (EL)   ERob
   Alabast = 'Poulala'PBR   CSPN CWoW EBee ERob ESCh
   (EL) ♀H4   ETho MAsh MWgw NBea NHaw
                             NTay SBra SCoo SLim SMDP SPoG
                             WBGC
   'Alba Luxurians' (Vt) ♀H4 More than 30 suppliers
   'Albatross'   ENot ERob ESCh
   'Albiflora' (A)   CSPN ECtt ESCh NSti WBGC
   'Albina Plena' (A/d)   ESCh ETho SLim SMDP WBGC
   'Aleksandrit' (EL)   ERob NHaw
   'Alice Fisk' (EL)   CFRD CSPN ERob ESCh ETho
                             LSRN MSwo NBea NHaw NTay
                             SBra SHBN SPoG WBGC WGor
   'Alionushka' (I) ♀H4   More than 30 suppliers
   'Allanah' (LL)   CFRD CRHN EPfP ERob ESCh
                             ETho LAst LSRN MGos MSwo
                             NHaw NTay SBra SCoo SLim SPoG
                             WBGC WFar
§ *alpina* ♀H4   CMac ECtt EPfP ESCh GKev GSki
                             MBar MDun MWhi NHaw NPer
                             SHBN SLim SPlb WBVN WFar

   - 'Albiflora'   see *C. sibirica*
   - 'Columbine White'   see *Clematis* 'White Columbine'
   - 'Jan Lindmark'   see *Clematis* 'Jan Lindmark'
I - 'Odorata' (A)   CSPN ERob LBuc MGos NBea
                             NHaw
I - 'Pamela Jackman' (A)   CDoC CFRD CSPN CWSG EBee
                             ElAn ESCh LAst LRHS MAsh MDun
                             MGos NBea NCGa NEgg NHol NSti
                             NTay SBra SCoo SDix SLim SPer
                             SPoG SWvt WBGC WFar
   - pink-flowered **new**   GKev
   - subsp. *sibirica*   see *C. sibirica*
   'Alpinist' (LL)   ERob
   alternata **new**   ESCh ETho
   'Amelia Joan' (Ta)   ERob MWat
   'Ameshisuto' (EL)   ETho
   'Amethyst Beauty' (A)   ERob
   'Anders' (A/d)   ESCh
   'André Devillers'   see *C.* 'Directeur André Devillers'
   'Andromeda' (EL)   CSPN EBee ERob ESCh ETho
                             NHaw NTay WFar
   Angelique = 'Evipo017'   ESCh
   new
   angustifolia **new**   ETho
   'Anita' (Ta)   ERob ESCh ETho NHaw SBra SLim
                             SPoG WBGC
   'Ann Thomson' **new**   EBee
   'Anna' (EL)   ERob ESCh NTay
   'Anna Carolina'   ESCh
   'Anna Herman' (EL)   ERob
   Anna Louise =   CSPN CWoW EBee ERob ESCh
   'Evithree'PBR (EL) ♀H4   ETho LRHS MBri NTay SBra SCoo
                             SLim SPoG SWCr WBGC
   'Annabel' (EL)   CSPN ERob
   'Annemieke' (Ta)   ERob ESCh MGos SBra WBGC
   'Annie Treasure'   ERob WBGC
   Anniversary = 'Pynot'PBR ENot ERob ESCh LSRN SCoo
   (EL)
   anshunensis   see *C. clarkeana*
   'Anti' (LL)   ESCh
   'Aotearoa' (LL)   ERob ESCh ETho
   'Aphrodite'   CRHN ERob ESCh WBGC
   apiifolia   ERob MWhi
   - B&SWJ 4838   WCru
   'Apple Blossom' (Ar) ♀H4 More than 30 suppliers
   'Apulejus' (A)   ESCh
   'Arabella' (I) ♀H4   More than 30 suppliers
   Arctic Queen =   CSPN EBee ENot ESCh ETho LRHS
   'Evitwo'PBR (EL) ♀H4   LSRN MBNS NPri NTay SCoo SLim
                             SPer SPoG SWCr WBGC WFar
   armandii   More than 30 suppliers
   - 'Enham Star' (Ar)   LBuc LRHS MBri MGos
§ - 'Little White Charm' (Ar) CSPN ERob MBlu NLar SHBN
                             SPoG
   - 'Meyeniana'   see *C. armandii* 'Little White
                             Charm'
§ - 'Snowdrift' (Ar)   CBcs CSBt CSPN CSam CWSG
                             ElAn EPfP ERob ESCh ETho LRHS
                             MGos MLan NSti NTay SHBN SPer
                             SPoG SRms WBGC WCMO
   x *aromatica*   CBcs CElw CPrp CSPN EAEE EBee
                             ElAn EPfP ERob ESCh ETho LAst
                             LFol LRHS MBNS MWgw NBea
                             NSti NTay SBla SBra SCoo SPoG
                             SWCr WBGC
§ 'Asagasumi' (EL)   ERob ESCh ETho NTay
   'Asao' (EL)   CElw CFRD CFir CRHN EBee ElAn
                             EPfP ERob ESCh ETho LAst LRHS
                             MGos MRav NBea NTay SBra SLim
                             SPer SPet SPoG SWCr WBGC
                             WOrn
   'Ascotiensis' (LL)   CBcs CElw CSPN EBee EPfP ESCh
                             ETho LRHS NBea NHaw NPri NTay
                             SBra SDix SLim SPer SPoG SWCr
                             WBGC WFar
   'Ashva'   ESCh ETho

§ 'Aureolin' (Ta) CSPN CWSG EPfP ERob ESCh ETho LRHS MBar NHol NPri SBra SCoo SLim SPoG WBGC WPGP

australis ERob

§ 'Bagatelle' (EL) CFRD CRHN CSPN ERob ESCh MAsh NHaw SCoo SLim SMDP WBGC WFar WGwG

'Bal Maiden' (Vt) **new** CRHN

§ 'Ballerina in Blue' (A/d) ERob ESCh NHaw

'Ballet Skirt' (A/d) ERob ESCh LRHS MGos NHaw NLar SLim SPoG SWCr WBGC

'Baltyk' (EL) CSPN ERob ESCh

'Barbara' (LL) ESCh ETho NHaw NTay

'Barbara Dibley' (EL) CFRD CTri CWSG ERob ESCh LRHS MAsh MBNS MSwo NBea NTay SBra SCoo SDix SLim SPoG WBGC

'Barbara Harrington'[PBR] (LL) ENot ESCh NHaw

'Barbara Jackman' (EL) CFRD CSam EBee ECtt ENot ERob ETho LRHS LSRN MAsh MBar MGos MSwo NBea NEgg NTay SBra SCoo SLim SPer SPoG SWCr WBGC WFar WFoF

'Barbara Wheeler' ERob

barbellata EHyt ERob

'Basil Bartlett' (Fo) ECou ERob ESCh

'Beata' (LL) ESCh ETho

'Beauty of Richmond' (EL) CWSG ERob ESCh

'Beauty of Worcester' (EL) CFRD CFir CSPN CWSG ELan EPfP ESCh ETho LAst LRHS LSRN MAsh MBar MSwo MWgw NBea NHaw NTay SBra SCoo SDix SLim SPer SPoG WBGC WFar WWeb

'Bees' Jubilee' (EL) More than 30 suppliers

'Bella' (EL) EBee ERob ESCh ETho NHaw SMDP

'Belle Nantaise' (EL) CElw ERob ESCh LRHS NBea SBra SCoo SPet WBGC

'Belle of Woking' (EL) CElw CFRD CPou CRHN CSPN CWSG EBee ECtt ELan EPfP ERob ESCh ETho LRHS MBar NBea NEgg NTay SBra SDix SHBN SLim SPer SPet SPoG SWCr WBGC WOrn

'Benedictus' (EL) ESCh

'Bessie Watkinson' ERob

§ 'Beth Currie' (EL) CFRD CSPN ERob ESCh LBuc SCoo SPoG

'Betina' see *C.* 'Red Beetroot Beauty'

'Betty Corning' (Vt) ♀H4 CFRD CHad CRHN CSPN EBee ELan EPfP ERob ESCh ETho LFol LRHS MBri MGos MWgw NBea SBra SLon SWCr WBGC WTel WWhi

'Betty Risdon' (EL) ERob ESCh ETho MAsh

'Big Bird' (A/d) ERob ESCh LBuc

§ 'Bill MacKenzie' (Ta) ♀H4 More than 30 suppliers

Black Madonna see *C.* 'Czarna Madonna'

'Black Prince' (Vt) CFRD CHad CRHN ELan ERob ESCh ETho NHaw NTay SBra WBGC

'Black Tea' (LL) ERob ESCh NHaw

§ 'Błękitny Anioł' (LL) ♀H4 CElw CFRD CRHN CSPN CWoW ERob ESCh ETho GMac LRHS MGos MWgw NBea NPri NTay SBra SCoo SPer SPet SPoG SWCr WBGC WFar

Blue Angel see *C.* 'Błękitny Anioł'

'Blue Belle' (Vt) CElw CFRD CPou CRHN ELan LRHS NBea NSti NTay SBra SMDP SPet SPoG SWCr WBGC WFar

'Blue Bird' (A/d) CBcs CFRD CPIN CWCL CWSG EBee ECtt ESCh MAsh NBea NCGa SLim SPer SPoG WBGC

'Blue Boy' (I) see *C.* x *diversifolia* 'Blue Boy' (I)

'Blue Boy' (L/P) see *C.* 'Elsa Späth'

'Blue Dancer' (A) CElw CFRD EPfP ERob ESCh EShb ETho IBal MGos NBea NTay SPet SWCr WBGC

'Blue Eclipse' (A) CSPN ERob ESCh MAsh WBGC

'Blue Eyes' (EL) CFRD CSPN EBee ERob ESCh NHaw NTay

'Blue Gem' (EL) ERob SLim SPoG

'Blue Light'[PBR] (EL/d) CSPN ELan ENot ERob ESCh ETho LBuc MGos NLar NTay SBra WBGC WFar

Blue Moon = 'Evirin'[PBR] (EL) ENot ESCh ETho LAst LRHS LSRN MAsh MBNS MWgw NBea NLar NPri NTay SBra SCoo SWCr WFar

Blue Pirouette = 'Zobluepi' ESCh ETho NLar

Blue Rain see *C.* 'Sinee Dozhd'

'Blue Ravine' (EL) EBee EPfP ERob ESCh ETho MGos NLar NTay SCoo WBGC

'Blue Stream' (A) ESCh

'Blue Tapers' (A) ERob ESCh NHaw

§ 'Blushing Ballerina' (A/d) CFRD ERob ESCh ETho

§ x *bonstedtii* 'Campanile' (H) ERob ESCh NBir

– 'Crépuscule' (H) ERob ESCh GCal NTay SRms WBGC WCot

'Boskoop Beauty' (EL) ERob ESCh NHaw NTay

'Bowl of Beauty' (Ar) ERob MGos

'Bracebridge Star' (EL) ECtt ERob ESCh

brachiata ESCh SMDP

brachyura ERob

'Bravo' (Ta) ERob WBGC

brevicaudata GIBF

'Brocade' (Vt) CFRD CRHN CSPN ERob ESCh ETho SMDP

'Broughton Bride' CSPN ERob ESCh ETho

'Broughton Star' (M/d) ♀H4 More than 30 suppliers

§ 'Brunette' (A) CSPN EBee ELan EPfP ERob ESCh ETho MAsh MGos NHaw NTay SMDP SPoG SWCr WBGC

buchananiana Finet & Gagnep. see *C. rehderiana*

buchananiana DC. CPLG EBee ERob

– B&SWJ 8333a WCru

'Buckland Beauty' (V) **new** ESCh ETho

'Buckland Longshanks' (H) **new** SMDP

'Burford Bell' (V) ERob WBGC

'Burford Princess' (Vt) ERob

I 'Burford Variety' (Ta) ERob ESCh WBGC

'Burford White' (A) CSPN EBee EPfP ERob NLar NTay WBGC

'Burma Star' (EL) CElw CFRD EPfP ERob ESCh ETho NBea NHaw NTay SMDP WBGC

'C.W. Dowman' (EL) ERob ETho

'Caerulea Luxurians' (Vt) CRHN ERob ESCh NTay WBGC

calycina see *C. cirrhosa* var. *balearica*

§ *campaniflora* CFRD CMea CNic CRHN CSPN EHyt ERob EShb MWhi NBea NWCA SBra SDix SMDP WBGC WPGP

– 'Lisboa' (Vt) ERob SBra SPoG

'Campanile' see *C.* x *bonstedtii* 'Campanile'

'Candida' (EL) CFRD ESCh

'Candleglow' (A) CElw CSPN EBee MAsh SMDP

'Candy Stripe' EBee ERob ESCh MAsh NTay SCoo SLim

'Capitaine Thuilleaux' see *C.* 'Souvenir du Capitaine Thuilleaux'

'Cardinal Wyszynski' see *C.* 'Kardynal Wyszynski'

'Carmencita' (Vt) CRHN CSPN EBee ERob ESCh ETho NHaw NTay SBra SCoo WBGC WFar

'Carnaby' (EL) CFRD CRHN CSPN CWSG EBee ELan EPfP ERob ESCh ETho LAst LRHS MBar MBri MGos NBea NTay

	SBra SCoo SLim SPet SPoG SSto SWCr WBGC WPGP
'Carnival Queen'	CSPN CWSG ERob ESCh
'Caroline' (LL)	CSPN EBee ERob ESCh ETho NBea NHaw NTay SBra SMDP WBGC
'Caroline Lloyd' (Vt)	ERob
* x *cartmanii* hort. (Fo)	CSam
§ - 'Avalanche'PBR (Fo/m) ♀H3	CSPN ELan ERob ESCh ETho GBin LBuc LRHS MGos NLar NPri NTay SBla SHBN SLim SMur SPoG WCot
- 'Joe' (Fo/m)	More than 30 suppliers
- 'Snow Valley'PBR (Fo)	SBla
- 'White Abundance'PBR (Fo/f)	ESCh ETho SBla SPoG
x *cartmanii* hort. 'Joe' x *marmoraria* (Fo)	ECho MGos
- - x *petriei* (Fo)	ECho
Cezanne = 'Evipo023' **new**	ESCh
'Chacewater' (Vt) **new**	CRHN
'Chalcedony' (EL)	CSPN ERob ESCh ETho MGos NTay SBra SBGC
'Charissima' (EL)	CBcs CSPN CSam EPfP ERob ETho MGos NBea NTay SBra SCoo SPet WBGC WFar
'Charlie Brown' **new**	ERob
chiisanensis	CBcs CSPN EHyt ERob NEgg WBGC WHrl
- B&SWJ 4560	WCru
- B&SWJ 8706	WCru
- 'Lemon Bells' (A)	ELan LRHS MAsh SMur SPoG SWCr
- 'Love Child' (A)	CBcs CElw CSPN EBee ELan ERob ESCh ETho MBlu NTay SBra SCoo SLim SMDP SPer WBGC WCot
chinensis misapplied	see *C. terniflora*
chinensis Osbeck	ERob
- RWJ 10042	WCru
Chinook = 'Evipo013'	ESCh LRHS
'Christian Steven' (LL)	CSPN ERob ESCh
chrysantha var. *paucidentata*	see *C. hilariae*
chrysocoma misapplied	see *C. spooneri*, *C.* x *vedrariensis*
N *chrysocoma* Franch.	EPfP ERob MBar NHol NLAp SMDP WCru
- ACE 1093	CPou
- B&L 12237	NBea
'Cicciolina' (Vt)	ERob ETho NHaw NTay
§ *cirrhosa*	CTri ELan LRHS MAsh MGos MWhi NTay SArc SWCr WBGC
§ - var. *balearica*	More than 30 suppliers
- 'Ourika Valley' (C)	EBee ERob ESCh ETho MAsh NLar SMDP WFar
- var. *purpurascens*	More than 30 suppliers
'Freckles' (C) ♀H3	CElw CRHN EBee EPfP ERob ESCh ETho LRHS MAsh NHaw NHol NTay SBra SCoo SLim SMur SPoG SWCr WBGC WCMO WFar
- - 'Jingle Bells' (C)	
- - 'Lansdowne Gem' (C)	CBgR CSPN CWib SMDP
- subsp. *semitriloba*	ERob
- 'Wisley Cream' (C) ♀H3	More than 30 suppliers
'Citra'	see *C.* 'Claudius'
'Claire de Lune' **new**	EBee
§ *clarkeana*	ETho
§ 'Claudius' (A)	EBee ERob ESCh NTay SMDP
'Clochette Pride' (A/d)	ERob ESCh
coactilis	ERob
'Colette Deville' (EL)	ERob ESCh NTay
columbiana	ERob
§ - var. *tenuiloba*	SBla
- - 'Ylva' (A)	EHyt WAbe
'Columbine' (A)	CFRD CWSG EBee ETho LBuc MAsh MBar MSwo NBea NHol SBra SCoo SDix SLim SPoG WBGC
'Columella' (A)	ERob ESCh ETho NHaw NLar

'Comtesse de Bouchaud' (LL) ♀H4	More than 30 suppliers
confusa HWJK 2200	WCru
connata	CPIN ERob ESCh GQui SMDP
- GWJ 9386	WCru
- HWJCM 132	WCru
aff. *connata* HWJK 2176 from Nepal	WCru
- GWJ 9431 from West Bengal	WCru
'Constance' (A) ♀H4	CElw CFRD CRHN CSPN CWoW EBee EPfP ERob ESCh ETho LRHS NHaw NSti NTay SBra SCoo SPer SRms SWCr WBGC WBor WPGP
'Continuity' (M)	EBee ERob ETho MAsh NTay SDix SLim SPla
'Corona' (EL)	CFRD CSPN ELan EPfP ERob ETho LAst LRHS MAsh MBar NBea NHaw NTay SBra SCoo SLim SPet SPoG WBGC WFar
'Corry' (Ta)	ERob ESCh NLar
'Côte d'Azur' (H)	CFwr ERob GCal MAvo MCCP NLar WBGC
'Cotton Candy'	ERob
'Countess of Lovelace' (EL)	CBcs CFRD CSPN CWSG EBee ELan EPfP ERob ESCh ETho LRHS MAsh MBar MBri MGos MWgw NBea NEgg NTay SBra SCoo SDix SLim SPer SPet SPoG SWCr WBGC WFar
County Park hybrids (Fo)	ECou
'Cragside' (A)	ETho SGar
crassifolia B&SWJ 6700	WCru
§ 'Crimson King' (LL)	ERob ESCh ETho NHaw SBod WGor
§ *crispa*	CPou CSPN CWoW EHyt ERob ESCh MWhi NBea WSHC
* - 'Cylindrica'	ERob
Crystal Fountain	see *C.* 'Fairy Blue'
x *cylindrica*	CSPN EBee ESCh WBGC
§ 'Czarna Madonna' (EL)	ERob
'Danae' (Vt)	CRHN ERob WBGC
'Daniel Deronda' (EL) ♀H4	More than 30 suppliers
'Dark Secret' (A)	CSPN EBee EPfP ERob ESCh MAsh
'Dawn' (EL)	CCCN CFRD CSPN ERob ESCh ETho LRHS MAsh NBea NTay SBra SCoo SLim SPoG SWCr WBGC WGwG
'Débutante' (EL)	ESCh NHaw
delavayi var. *limprichtii* BWJ 7727	WCru
'Denny's Double' (EL/d)	CSPN CWSG ERob ESCh ETho MAsh NRib NTay SBra WBGC
'Diana' (LL)	ERob ESCh ETho
dioscoreifolia	see *C. terniflora*
§ 'Directeur André Devillers' (EL)	ERob
§ x *diversifolia*	CElw CFRD CRHN EBee ESCh LRHS MAsh MBNS MGos MSte NHaw NHol SBra SDix SGar SHBN SPer SPet WBGC
- 'Amy' (I)	ERob
§ - 'Blue Boy' (I)	CBgR CElw CFRD CRHN CSPN CSam EBee EPfP ERob ESCh ETho MGos NHaw NTay SBra SPet WBGC
- Floris V' (I)	ERob ESCh NTay SHar
- 'Heather Herschell' (I)	CBgR CElw CFRD CRHN CSPN EBee ERob ESCh ETho NHaw NLar SBra SMDP SPet WBGC
§ - 'Hendersonii' (I)	More than 30 suppliers
- 'Lauren' (I)	ERob
§ - 'Olgae' (I)	CFRD CSPN ESCh ETho MDKP NBea NTay SBra SLim SMDP WBGC

'Docteur Le Bêle' (LL) — ERob NTay
'Doctor Penelope' (M) **new** — SPur
'Doctor Ruppel' (EL) — More than 30 suppliers
'Doggy' (Vt) — ERob
'Dominika' (LL) — CSPN ERob ESCh ETho NHaw NTay WBGC
'Dorath' — ERob ESCh WBGC
'Dorota' (EL) — ERob
'Dorothy Tolver' (EL) — ERob ESCh ETho WBGC
'Dorothy Walton' — see *C.* 'Bagatelle'
'Dovedale' (M) — ESCh
'Dubysa' — ESCh
'Duchess of Albany' (T) — More than 30 suppliers
'Duchess of Edinburgh' (EL) — More than 30 suppliers
'Duchess of Sutherland' (EL) — CFRD ERob ESCh LRHS MGos NHaw SDix SPet WBGC
'Dulcie' — NHaw
x *durandii* ♀H4 — CBcs CFRD CRHN CSPN EBee ELan ENot EPfP ESCh ETho LRHS LSRN MBar MBri MWhi NBea NHol NSti SBra SDix SLim SPer SPla SPoG SWCr WBGC WCot WFar WTel
'Dusky Star' (M) **new** — EKen
'Early Sensation' (Fo/f) — More than 30 suppliers
'East Malling' (M) — ERob ESCh NHaw
'Edith' (EL) ♀H4 — ECtt EPfP ERob ESCh ETho NBea NHaw NTay SLim WBGC WGor
'Edomurasaki' (EL) — ERob ESCh ETho WBGC
'Edouard Desfossé' (EL) — ERob ESCh SBra
'Edward Prichard' — CFRD CSPN EBee EPfP ERob ESCh ETho NBea NHaw SBra SMDP WBGC
'Eetika' (LL) — ERob ESCh ETho
'Ekstra' (LL) — CFRD EBee ERob ESCh ETho
'Eleanor' (Fo/f) — ECou ESCh ETho
Eleanor of Guildford = 'Notpy'PBR (EL) — ENot ERob ESCh
'Elfin' (Fo/v) — ECou
'Elizabeth' (M) ♀H4 — More than 30 suppliers
§ 'Elsa Späth' (EL) — More than 30 suppliers
'Elten' (M) — CSPN ERob ESCh
'Elvan' (Vt) — CBgR CFRD CRHN ERob ESCh NHaw NLar SPet WBGC
'Emajõgi' (LL) — ESCh
'Emerald Stars' — ESCh
'Emilia Plater' (Vt) — CFRD CRHN CSPN ERob ESCh ETho NBea NHaw NTay SBra WBGC
'Empress of India' (EL) — ERob ESCh WBGC
'Entel' (Vt) — ERob ETho NHaw WBGC
'Erik' (A) — ESCh
x *eriostemon* — see *C.* x *diversifolia*
'Ernest Markham' (LL) ♀H4 — More than 30 suppliers
'Esperanto' (LL) — EBee ESCh SMDP
'Essex Star' **new** — ECou
'Etoile de Malicorne' (EL) — ERob ESCh NTay WBGC WGor
'Etoile de Paris' (EL) — ERob ESCh ETho MWgw WBGC
Etoile Nacrée — see *C.* 'Sakurahime'
'Etoile Rose' (Vt) — CRHN CSPN CTri CWoW ELan EPfP ERob ESCh ETho LAst LRHS LSRN MAsh MWgw NBea NHol NTay SBra SCoo SDix SLim SMur SPer SPoG SWCr WBGC WFar WPGP WSHC
'Etoile Violette' (Vt) ♀H4 — More than 30 suppliers
'Europa' (EL) — ERob
'Eva' (LL) — ERob ESCh
Evening Star = 'Evista'PBR — EPfP ERob ETho NTay SLim SPoG WFar
'Eximia' — see *C.* 'Ballerina in Blue'
'Fair Rosamond' (EL) — CFRD EBee EPfP ERob ESCh LRHS MAsh NBea NHaw NTay SBra SDix SLim SPoG WBGC

'Fairy' (Fo/f) — ECou
§ 'Fairy Blue' (EL/d) — ESCh ETho LRHS NPri SCoo
'Fairy Queen' (EL) — ERob ESCh
fargesii var. *souliei* — see *C. potaninii* var. *potaninii*
x *fargesioides* — see *C.* 'Paul Farges'
fasciculiflora — CMHG CRHN CSPN ERob IDee LRHS SMDP SSpi
– L.657 — WCru WPGP
'Fascination'PBR (I) — EPfP ESCh ETho LRHS MAsh SBra
fauriei — ERob
finetiana misapplied — see *C. paniculata* J.G. Gmel.
'Firefly' (EL) — ERob ESCh
'Fireworks' (EL) — CFRD COtt CSPN CWoW EBee ECtt ENot EPfP ESCh ETho LAst LRHS LSRN MAsh MBri MGos NBea NPri NTay SBra SLim SPoG SWCr WBGC WFoF WGor
'Flamingo' (EL) — CWSG ERob
flammula — More than 30 suppliers
– var. *flavescens* — ERob
– 'Ithaca' (F/v) — ERob
– 'Rubra Marginata' — see *C.* x *triternata* 'Rubromarginata'
§ 'Floral Feast' (A/d) — CFRD CSPN ESCh NBea NTay SCoo SLim
'Floralia' (A/d) — see *C.* 'Floral Feast'
florida — CSPN ERob ESCh ETho
– 'Bicolor' — see *C. florida* var. *sieboldiana*
– var. *flore-pleno* (d) — CFir CSPN EBee ELan ENor EPfP ESCh ETho LAst LRHS MAsh NBea NEgg NHol NRib NTay SBod SBra SHBN SMad SPer SPla SPoG SWCr WBGC WCMO WCot WFar
– Pistachio = 'Evirida'PBR (LL) — CFir CSPN EBee EMil EPfP ESCh ETho IBal LBuc MAsh MBNS NLar NTay SBra SLim SMDP SPer SPoG SRkn SWCr WCMO WFar
§ – var. *sieboldiana* (d) — More than 30 suppliers
foetida — CBcs CSPN
foetida x 'Lunar Lass' (Fo) — ECho ECou
foetida x *petriei* — ECho ECou
'Fond Memories' (EL) — ETho
'Forever' — NHaw
forrestii — see *C. napaulensis*
§ *forsteri* — CBcs CSPN ERob ESCh ETho IDee LFol SBra WPGP
forsteri x *indivisa* — WCru
'Foxtrot' (Vt) — CRHN ERob ESCh WBGC
'Foxy' (A) ♀H4 — ERob ESCh NHaw NTay SLon WBGC
'Fragrant Joy' (Fo/m) — ECou ESCh
'Fragrant Spring' (M) — CSPN ECtt ERob ETho MGos NHaw NLar SBra SLim SMDP WBGC WFar
'Frances Rivis' (A) ♀H4 — More than 30 suppliers
'Francesca' (A) — ESCh MGos
'Frankie' (A) ♀H4 — CSPN ELan ENot ERob ESCh ETho LRHS NTay SCoo SLim SPer SWCr WBGC
Franziska Marie = 'Evipo008' (EL) **new** — ESCh MAsh NPri
'Frau Mikiko' (EL) — ERob ESCh ETho
'Frau Susanne' (EL) **new** — ETho
'Freda' (M) ♀H4 — More than 30 suppliers
'Fryderyk Chopin' (EL) — CSPN ERob ESCh ETho NHaw NLar NTay
'Fuji-musume' (EL) ♀H4 — CFRD CSPN ERob ESCh ETho NBea NHaw NLar NTay SBra SCoo SLim SPet WBGC WFar
'Fujinami' (EL) — ERob
fusca misapplied — see *C. japonica*
fusca Turcz. — CPIN CWoW ERob WIvy
– B&SWJ 4229 — WCru
§ – var. *fusca* — ESCh ETho GIBF
– var. *kamtschatica* — see *C. fusca* var. *fusca*

- var. *umbrosa* B&SWJ 700	WCru	
fusijamana	ERob	
'Fuyu-no-tabi' (EL) **new**	ETho	
'G. Steffner' (A)	ERob ESCh	
'Gabrielle' (EL)	CSPN ERob ESCh NHaw NTay SBra SLim WBGC	
Gazelle = 'Evipo014'	ESCh LRHS	
'Gekkyuuden'	ERob	
'Gemini'	ENot ERob ESCh	
'Generał Sikorski' (EL)	CBcs CElw CFRD CMac CRHN CSPN CSam CWSG ECtt ELan EPfP ESCh ETho LAst LRHS LSRN MBri MGos NBea NTay SBra SCoo SDix SHBN SLim SPer SPet SPoG SWCr WBGC	
gentianoides	ERob WAbe WCot	
'Georg' (A/d)	ERob ESCh MGos NHaw WBGC	
'Georg Ots' (LL)	ERob ESCh	
Giant Star = 'Gistar' (M)	ESCh MGos NCGa NLar NPer	
'Gillian Blades' (EL) ♀H4	CFRD CRHN CSPN CWoW EBee ELan ENot EPfP ERob ESCh ETho LAst LRHS MAsh NBea NHaw NPri NTay SBra SCoo SLim SPer SPoG SWCr WBGC	
§ 'Gipsy Queen' (LL) ♀H4	More than 30 suppliers	
'Gladys Picard' (EL)	ERob ESCh NHaw NTay SLim WBGC WFar	
glauca Turcz.	see C. *intricata*	
glaucophylla	CPIN	
'Glynderek' (EL)	ERob ESCh SBra	
'Golden Harvest' (Ta)	ERob ESCh NHol NLar SBra WBGC WFar	
Golden Tiara = 'Kugotia'PBR (Ta) ♀H4	CSPN ERob ESCh ETho LRHS MBri MGos MWgw NBea NPri NTay SBra WBGC WCot	
'Gornoe Ozero' (EL)	ERob	
'Gothenburg' (M)	EBee ERob ESCh NBea NHaw WBGC WFar	
gouriana	ERob	
- subsp. *lishanensis* B&SWJ 292	WCru	
'Grace' (Ta)	CRHN CSPN EBee ERob ESCh ETho NHaw NLar SMDP WBGC	
gracilifolia	ERob ESCh NLar WBGC	
- var. *dissectifolia*	ERob	
I 'Grandiflora' (F)	WFar	
'Grandiflora Sanguinea' (Vt)	ERob SLim	
'Grandiflora Sanguinea' Johnson	see C. 'Södertälje'	
grata hort.	see C. x *jouiniana*	
grata Wall.	CElw CPLG CWoW EHyt ERob	
- B&SWJ 6774	WCru	
'Gravetye Beauty' (T)	More than 30 suppliers	
§ 'Grażyna'	ESCh	
'Green Velvet' (Fo/m)	CPIN ECou	
grewiiflora	SMDP	
- B&SWJ 2956	WCru	
'Guernsey Cream' (EL)	CFRD CSPN CSam CWSG EBee EMil ESCh ETho LAst LRHS MAsh MBri MWgw NBea NEgg NTay SBra SCoo SDix SHBN SLim SPet SPoG SWCr WBGC WFar WWeb	
'Guiding Star' (EL)	ERob ETho NHaw SBra	
'H.F.Young' (EL)	CElw CSPN CWSG EBee ELan EPfP ERob ESCh ETho LRHS MBar MBri MGan MGos MWgw NBea NTay SBra SDix SHBN SLim SPer SPet WBGC WTel	
'Hagley Hybrid' (LL)	More than 30 suppliers	
'Hainton Ruby' (EL)	ERob	
'Haku-ōkan' (EL)	CFRD CSPN CWoW EBee EPfP ERob ESCh ETho LRHS MAsh NBea SBra SCoo SLim SPoG WBGC	
'Hakuree' (I)	ESCh ETho SMDP	
'Hanaguruma' (EL)	CFRD CSPN ERob ESCh ETho NBea NHaw NTay SBra WBGC WFar	
'Hanajima' (I)	EHyt ERob ESCh ETho SBla	
'Hania'	ESCh ETho	
Harlow Carr = 'Evipo004'PBR	ESCh ETho LRHS MAsh MBri SBra SWCr	
'Harmony' (EL/d)	ERob ESCh	
'Haru Ichiban' (EL) **new**	ETho	
'Haruyama' (EL)	ESCh	
Havering hybrids (Fo)	ECou	
'Helen Cropper' (EL)	ERob ESCh ETho MAsh	
'Helios' (Ta)	CSPN CSpe ENot EPfP ERob ESCh ETho LRHS MGos NBea NSti NTay SBra SCoo SPoG WBGC WCot WGwG	
'Helsingborg' (A) ♀H4	CBcs CFRD CSPN EBee ECtt ELan EPfP ERob ESCh ETho LAst LRHS MAsh NBea NEgg NHol NPri NSti NTay SBra SCoo SPla SPoG SWCr WBGC WTel	
I 'Hendersonii' (I)	CFRD CSam ERob ETho LRHS LSRN MSte NHol NTay SPet SPla SWCr WBGC	
hendersonii Henderson	see C. x *diversifolia* 'Hendersonii'	
hendersonii Koch	see C. x *diversifolia* 'Hendersonii'	
hendersonii Stand.	see C. x *diversifolia*	
'Hendersonii Rubra' (Ar)	CSPN	
'Hendryetta'PBR (I)	EPfP ESCh ETho NTay SPoG	
henryi	CDul CPIN ENot LSRN MWgw NLAp	
- B&SWJ 3402	WCru	
'Henryi' (EL) ♀H4	More than 30 suppliers	
henryi var. *morii* B&SWJ 1668	WCru	
heracleifolia	CAby CBcs CBgR CDul CPou EChP ECtt EDAr EGra EHol ESCh GAbr GIBF GSki MAsh NHol NLar SWCr WBGC WMoo WPer	
- Alan BloomPBR	see C. *tubulosa* Alan Bloom = 'Alblo'	
- 'Blue Dwarf'	ESCh ETho MGos	
- 'Cassandra' (H)	EAEE EDAr EHyt EMar EPfP ESCh ETho GCal MAvo NOrc SBla SMDP	
- 'China Purple' (H)	CPen EBee ERob IPot MBNS NLar	
- var. *davidiana*	see C. *tubulosa*	
- 'Pink Dwarf' (H) **new**	ESCh ETho	
- 'Roundway Blue Bird' (H)	ESCh LHop LRHS MAvo NHaw	
'Herbert Johnson' (EL)	CFRD ESCh	
hexapetala misapplied	see C. *recta* subsp. *recta* var. *lasiosepala*	
hexapetala Forster	see C. *forsteri*	
hexasepala	see C. *forsteri*	
'Hikarugenji' (EL)	CSPN ERob ESCh NHaw NTay	
§ *hilariae*	ERob	
§ *hirsutissima*	GIBF WIvy	
- var. *scottii*	EBee ERob WIvy	
'Honora' (LL)	CSPN ERob ESCh NTay SBra WBGC	
'Horn of Plenty' (EL)	ERob ESCh LRHS NBea NHaw SBra SLim SPoG WBGC	
'Huldine' (LL) ♀H4	CBcs CElw CHad CRHN CSPN CSam EBee ELan EPfP ESCh ETho LAst LRHS MBar NBea NEgg NSti SBra SDix SLim SPer SPet SPoG SWCr WBGC WTel WWhi	
'Huvi' (LL)	ERob ESCh ETho NHaw	
'Hybrida Sieboldii' (EL)	CRHN EBee ERob ESCh NBea NTay SBra SLim WBGC WCot	
Hyde Hall = 'Evipo009'	ESCh ETho LRHS MAsh MBri SBra SWCr	
'Hythe Chiffchaff' (Fo)	EHyt	
'Hythe Egret' (Fo)	ECho EHyt ESCh ITim LTwo SIng	
ianthina	CPIN EHyt ERob ESCh WPGP WSHC	
- var. *ianthina* **new**	ETho	

- var. **kuripoensis**	ERob	
- - B&SWJ 700	WCru	
'Ice Maiden' (EL)	ESCh	
'Ice Queen'	ESCh MAsh	
'Ideal' (EL)	ERob	
'Ilka' (EL)	ERob ESCh	
'Imperial' (EL)	ERob ESCh ETho NHaw	
indivisa	see *C. paniculata* J.G. Gmel.	
'Inglewood' (EL)	ERob NTay	
Inspiration = 'Zoin'PBR (I)	CFRD CSPN EBee ELan ERob ESCh ETho MGos NTay SBra SCoo WBGC	
integrifolia	More than 30 suppliers	
I - 'Alba'	More than 30 suppliers	
- 'Budapest' (I)	ERob ESCh MWgw NHaw NTay SBra WBGC	
- 'Hendersonii' Koch	see *C. x diversifolia* 'Hendersonii'	
- var. **latifolia**	ERob ESCh	
- 'Olgae'	see *C. x diversifolia* 'Olgae'	
- 'Ozawa's Blue' (I)	CPrp EAEE EBee EDAr EMar ESCh MBNS MSte NSti	
§ **intricata**	CBcs CFRD CPLG CSPN EBee EHyt EPfP ERob MGos	
- 'Harry Smith' (Ta)	ERob ESCh	
'Iola Fair' (EL)	CSPN ERob ESCh ETho NHaw NTay	
'Ishobel' (EL)	ERob	
ispahanica new	CWoW	
'Iubileinyi-70' (LL)	EBee ERob ESCh	
'Ivan Olsson' (EL)	CFRD CSPN ERob ESCh ETho	
'Jackmanii' (LL) ♀H4	CBcs CMac CRHN CTri EBee ENot EPfP ERob ESCh ETho LRHS LSRN MAsh MGos NBea NEgg NWea SBod SBra SCoo SLim SPer SPet SPoG SWCr WBGC WBor WFar WTel	
'Jackmanii Alba' (EL)	CFRD ELan EPfP ERob ESCh ETho LAst LRHS LSRN MBar NBea NTay SCoo SLim SPet SPoG SWCr WBGC	
'Jackmanii Rubra' (EL)	ERob ESCh ETho NBea SBra SLim WBGC	
'Jackmanii Superba' ambig. (LL)	More than 30 suppliers	
'Jackmanii Superba' misapplied	see *C.* 'Gipsy Queen'	
'Jacqueline du Pré' (A) ♀H4	CBcs CElw CFRD CSPN EBee ELan EPfP ERob ESCh ETho MGos NBea NHaw NTay SBra SMDP SPet WBGC	
'Jacqui' (M/d)	ERob ESCh ETho LRHS MGos NHaw NLar SBra SCoo SLim SPoG	
'James Mason' (EL)	CSPN ESCh ETho NBea NHaw NTay SBra SCoo WBGC	
'Jan Fopma' (I) new	ESCh ETho	
§ 'Jan Lindmark' (A/d)	CBcs CFRD EBee ERob ESCh ETho LRHS MAsh MGos NBea NBir NHol NSti NTay SCoo SLim SMDP SWCr WBGC WCru WFar	
§ 'Jan Paweł II' (EL)	CFRD CWSG CWoW EBee ECtt ELan EPfP ESCh ETho LRHS NBea SBra SCoo SLim SPer SPet SPoG WFar	
'Jānis Ruplēns Number 1'	ERob	
§ **japonica**	CPlN CSPN CSec ERob ESCh ETho NHaw SMDP WBGC	
- B&SWJ 5017	WCru	
§ - var. **obvallata** B&SWJ 8900	WCru	
'Jasper'	ERob ESCh	
'Jefferies' (Ar)	ESCh NLar	
'Jenny Caddick' (Vt)	CFRD CSPN ERob ESCh ETho NHaw NTay SMDP	
'Jenny Keay' (M/d)	EBee ERob ESCh ETho MGos NHaw NLar SBra SCoo SMDP SPoG	
'Jim Hollis' (EL)	ERob	
'Joan Baker' (Vt)	ERob	

'Joan Gray' (EL)	ERob ESCh	
'Joan Picton' (EL)	CFRD CWSG ESCh MAsh NBea NRib NTay SBra	
'John Gould Veitch' (EL)	ERob	
'John Gudmundsson' (EL)	ERob ESCh	
'John Huxtable' (LL) ♀H4	CDoC CRHN ENot EPfP ERob ESCh ETho LRHS NBea NHaw NPri NTay SBra SCoo SLim SPoG SWCr WBGC WGor	
John Paul II	see *C.* 'Jan Pawel II'	
'John Treasure' (Vt)	CRHN ETho WBGC	
'John Warren' (EL)	CFRD CWSG EBee ERob ESCh ETho LRHS MAsh NHaw NTay SBra SCoo SLim SPer WBGC WFar	
'Jorma' (LL)	ERob	
Josephine = 'Evijohill'PBR (EL) ♀H4	COtt CSPN EBee EPfP ESCh ETho LAst LRHS LSRN MAsh MBNS NLar NPri NTay SBra SCoo SPer SPoG SRkn SWCr WFar	
§ x **jouiniana**	CBgR CPLG EBee ERob ESCh MBlu MWya NHol WBGC WGwG WSHC	
- 'Chance' (H)	ESCh NTay	
'Julka' (EL)	ESCh ETho NHaw	
'June Pyne'	ESCh ETho LRHS NPri	
'Justa' (Vt) new	ESCh	
'Juuli' (I)	ERob ESCh ETho	
'Kaaru' (LL)	CRHN CSPN ERob ESCh ETho WBGC	
'Kacper' (EL)	CSPN ESCh ETho MGos NHaw NTay	
'Kaiu' (V)	ERob ESCh	
§ 'Kakio' (EL)	CElw CFRD EBee ENot ERob ESCh ETho LAst LSRN MGos NBea NTay SBra SLim SPer SPet SWCr WBGC WFar	
'Kalina' (EL)	ERob ESCh ETho NHaw	
'Kamilla' (EL)	ERob ESCh	
§ 'Kardynał Wyszyński' (EL)	CFRD EBee ERob ESCh ETho MGos NBea SBra SCoo SMDP WBGC	
§ 'Kasmu' (Vt)	ERob ESCh WBGC	
'Kasugayama' (EL)	ERob	
'Katharina' (EL)	ERob ESCh	
'Kathleen Dunford' (EL)	CFRD ERob ESCh LAst LRHS LSRN NBea NHaw NTay SCoo SLim SMDP WBGC	
'Kathleen Wheeler' (EL)	ERob ETho NTay SDix SLim WBGC	
'Kathryn Chapman' (Vt)	ESCh	
'Keith Richardson' (EL)	ERob ESCh NTay WBGC	
'Ken Donson' (EL) ♀H4	CElw CFRD CWoW EBee EPfP ERob ESCh MGos NTay SPet	
'Kermesina' (Vt) ♀H4	More than 30 suppliers	
'Ketu' (LL)	ERob	
'Kiev' (Vt)	ERob ESCh NHaw	
'Killifreth' (Vt) new	CRHN	
'King Edward VII' (EL)	EBee EPfP ERob ESCh LRHS MAsh NBea NTay WBGC WGor	
'King George V' (LL)	ERob ESCh	
'Kinokawa' (EL)	ERob	
'Kiri Te Kanawa' (EL)	CSPN EBee ERob ESCh ETho LAst LSRN NBea NHaw NTay SBra SLim SMDP WBGC	
kirilovii	ERob ESCh	
'Kirimäe' (LL)	ERob ESCh	
'Kjell' (EL)	ERob ESCh	
'Klaara' (EL)	ERob	
'Kommerei' (LL)	ERob ESCh ETho NHaw	
'Königskind' (EL)	CFRD CSPN ERob ESCh ETho NBea NTay WBGC	
koreana	ERob NHol SMDP WCru WSHC	
- var. **lutea**	CElw EBee ESCh SMDP	
'Kosmicheskaia Melodiia' (LL)	CFRD CSPN ERob ESCh NTay	
'Kotkas' (LL)	ERob	
'Kuba' (LL)	ERob ESCh	
'Küllus' (LL)	ERob ESCh ETho NTay	

ladakhiana	CFRD CSPN CWoW ESch ETho GQui MWhi NBea NBir NHaw SBra SMDP SPoG WCru WPtf
'Lady Betty Balfour' (LL)	CElw CFRD CSPN CWSG ERob ESch ETho LRHS MBNS NTay SBra SCoo SDix SGar SLim SPet SPoG WBGC WFar
'Lady Bird Johnson' (T)	CWoW EBee ERob ESch ETho NTay SBra SCoo SLim SPoG WBGC
'Lady Caroline Nevill' (EL)	ERob ESch NBea NTay SWCr WBGC
'Lady Catherine' (EL/d)	ERob
'Lady Londesborough' (EL)	CFRD EBee EPfP ERob ESch LRHS NBea NHaw NTay SCoo SDix SLim WBGC
'Lady Northcliffe' (EL)	CSPN CTri CWSG EPfP ERob ESch ETho LRHS NBea NTay SBra SDix SLim SPoG SWCr WBGC
'Lambton Park' (Ta) ♀H4	CFRD CFir CRHN CWoW EBee EPfP ERob ETho LRHS NBea NHaw NTay SBra SMDP WBGC
lasiandra	CPlN ERob NHaw SMDP
- B&SWJ 6775	WCru
- white-flowered	ERob
lasiantha B&SWJ 6252	WCru
'Last Dance' (Ta)	CRHN ERob
'Lasting Love'	see *C.* 'Grażyna'
'Lasurstern' (EL) ♀H4	More than 30 suppliers
'Laura' (LL)	ERob ESch NHaw
'Laura Denny' (EL)	ESch ETho SMDP
'Lavender Lace'	ERob ESch
'Lawsoniana' (EL)	CElw CFRD CRHN CWSG ETho LAst MBar NTay SLim SPet SSto WBGC
'Leione'	ESch
'Lemon Chiffon' (EL)	CSPN EBee EMil ERob ESch ETho NHaw NTay SBra
Liberation = 'Evifive'PBR (EL)	ERob ESch ETho LAst LRHS MAsh NTay SCoo SLim SPoG SWCr WBGC
§ ***ligusticifolia***	ERob GSki NHaw
'Liisu' (LL)	ESch
'Lilacina Floribunda' (EL)	CBcs CFRD CWoW EBee LRHS MBNS MBar NHaw SBra WBGC
'Lilactime' (EL)	ERob ESch ETho NHaw NTay SBra
'Lincoln Star' (EL)	CFRD CRHN CWoW EPfP ERob ESch LAst LRHS MBar MGos NBea NEgg NPri NTay SBra SCoo SDix SLim SPer SPet SPoG WBGC
'Lincolnshire Lady' (A)	NTay
'Little Bas' (Vt)	CRHN CSPN ERob ESch NHaw NLar NTay
'Little Butterfly' (Vt)	CRHN ERob ESch NHaw NTay
'Little Nell' (Vt)	CCCN CElw CFRD CRHN CSPN CWoW ELan ERob ESch ETho LRHS MWgw NBea NHol NTay SBra SCoo SDix SLim SPer SPet SPoG WBGC WFar
'Lord Herschell'	CElw ERob ETho SMDP
'Lord Nevill' (EL)	CRHN CWSG EPfP ERob ESch ETho LRHS NBea NTay SBra SDix SSto WBGC WFar
'Louise Rowe' (EL)	EBee ELan ERob ESch ETho LRHS MGos NBea NHaw SBra SCoo SLim SPet SPoG WBGC
loureiroana HWJ 663	WCru
'Love Jewelry'	ESch ETho NHaw
'Lucey' (LL)	ESch
'Lucie' (EL)	NBea WBGC
'Lunar Lass' (Fo/f)	CRez CStu ECho EHyt EPfP ESch ITim LBee NLAp NSla SIng WAbe WPGP
I 'Lunar Lass Variegata' (Fo/v)	ECho
'Luther Burbank' (LL)	CFRD ERob ESch NTay
§ 'M. Johnson' (A)	ERob ESch
§ 'M. Koster' (Vt)	CDoC CElw CFRD CRHN CSam CWoW EBee EPfP ESch ETho LRHS MSwo NBea NHaw NTay SBra SLim SPer SPet SPoG WBGC ERob
'Macrantha' (F)	
macropetala (d)	CBcs CElw CFRD CSBt EBee ELan ENot EPfP ERob ESch ETho LAst LRHS MBar MGan MGos NBea SDix SGar SLim SPer SPet SWCr WBGC WBrE WFar WOrn
- 'Alborosea'	see *C.* 'Blushing Ballerina'
- 'Blue Lagoon'	see *C. macropetala* 'Lagoon' Jackman 1959
§ - 'Chili' (A/d)	ERob
- 'Harry Smith'	see *C. macropetala* 'Chili'
- 'Lagoon' ambig.	NTay
- 'Lagoon' Jackman 1956	see *C. macropetala* 'Maidwell Hall' Jackman
§ - 'Lagoon' Jackman 1959 (A/d) ♀H4	CSPN EBee ERob ETho LRHS LSRN MAsh MSwo MWgw NBea NSti SBra SCoo SLim SMur SPoG SWCr WBGC WCru
§ - 'Maidwell Hall' Jackman (A/d)	CFRD CSPN CTri CWSG EBee ECtt EPfP ERob ESch ETho LRHS LSRN MAsh MGos NBea NHol SBra SHBN SPet SWCr WBGC WCru WPGP WSHC WTel
- 'Maidwell Hall' O.E.P.Wyatt (A)	SCoo
- 'Wesselton' (A/d)	CSPN EPfP ERob ESch ETho MAsh MBri MGos NHaw NHol WBGC WFar
- 'White Moth'	see *C.* 'White Moth'
'Madame Baron-Veillard' (LL)	CFRD ECtt ESch LAst LRHS MBar MWgw NTay SBra SCoo SDix SLim SWCr WBGC WFar
'Madame Edouard André' (LL)	CFRD CRHN CSPN EPfP ERob ESch LRHS MAsh NBea NTay SBra SCoo SDix SLim SPet SPoG SWCr WBGC WFar
'Madame Grangé' (LL) ♀H4	CRHN CSPN EPfP ESch ETho LRHS NBea NHaw NTay SBra SCoo SLim SPoG SWCr WBGC
'Madame Julia Correvon' (Vt) ♀H4	More than 30 suppliers
'Madame le Coultre'	see *C.* 'Mevrouw Le Coultre'
'Madame van Houtte' (EL)	ERob ESch
'Madeleine' (A) **new**	ESch
'Magnus Johnson'	see *C.* 'M. Johnson'
'Majojo' (Fo)	ESch GEdr
'Mammut' (EL)	ERob
§ ***mandschurica***	CPLG ERob ETho GCal NLar SBra WCru
- B&SWJ 1060	WCru
'Marcel Moser' (EL)	ERob ESch NTay SDix
'Margaret Hunt' (LL)	CSPN ELan ERob ESch ETho LRHS NBea NHaw NTay SBra SPla
'Margaret Jones' (M/d)	EBee ERob ESch NHaw WBGC
'Margaret Wood' (EL)	ERob ESch
'Margot Koster'	see *C.* 'M. Koster'
'Maria Louise Jensen' (EL)	ESch NTay SBra WBGC
'Marie Boisselot' (EL) ♀H4	More than 30 suppliers
'Marinka' (H) **new**	ESch
'Märjamaa' (LL) **new**	ESch
'Marjorie' (M/d)	More than 30 suppliers
'Markham's Pink' (A/d) ♀H4	More than 30 suppliers
marmoraria ♀H2-3	CStu EAEE ECho EHyt EPot ESch GCrs LHop LRHS SBla SIng WAbe WFar
- hybrid (Fo)	ITim WThu
marmoraria × ***petriei*** (f)	EHyt
marmoraria × ***marmorata***	ECho
'Marmori' (LL)	ERob ESch ETho NHaw
'Mary Whistler' (A)	ESch

'Mary-Claire' (EL/d) — ERob ESch
§ 'Maskarad' (Vt) — CSPN ERob ESch SWCr WBGC
Masquerade (Vt) — see C. 'Maskarad'
I 'Masquerade' (EL) — ETho LRHS MBri NTay SMur
'Matilda' (EL) — ESch
§ 'Matka Siedliska' (EL) — CSPN ERob NTay
§ 'Matka Teresa' (EL) — ERob
'Matka Urszula Ledóchowska' (EL) — ERob
'Maureen' (LL) — CSPN CWSG ETho MAsh
mauritiana — ERob
maximowicziana — see C. *terniflora*
'Mayleen' (M) ♀H4 — CElw CFRD CHad CPou CSBt CWSG EBee ECtt EPfP ERob ESch ETho LRHS MBri MGos NBea NPri NTay SAga SBra SHBN SLim SPer SPet SPoG SSto SWCr WBGC WFar

Medley = 'Evipo012' — ESch LRHS
'Meeli' (LL)) — EBee ESch
'Meloodia' (LL) — NBea WBGC
'Memm' (A/d) — ERob
§ 'Mevrouw Le Coultre' (EL) **new** — MGan NBlu
'Mia' (EL/d) — ERob
'Michelle' (I) — ERob
microphylla — ECou
'Mikelite' (Vt) — ERob ESch ETho NHaw
'Mikla' (LL) — ERob
'Miniseelik' (LL) — CFRD ERob ESch ETho NTay SMDP
'Minister' (EL) — CFRD ESch ETho
'Minuet' (Vt) ♀H4 — CFRD CHad CRHN CSPN EPfP ERob ESch ETho LRHS MSwo NBea NHol NTay SBra SCoo SDix SLim SPer SPla SPoG SWCr WBGC WTel
'Miriam Markham' (EL) — CFRD ERob ESch NBea NHaw SPoG WBGC
'Miss Bateman' (EL) ♀H4 — More than 30 suppliers
'Miss Christine' (M) **new** — ESch ETho
'Miss Crawshay' (EL) — CFRD ERob NHaw SLim WBGC
'Moniuszko' (EL) **new** — ESch
N *montana* — CBcs CElw CPLG CSBt EBee ECtt ESch MAsh MBar MGos NBea NHol SBod SBra SDix SHBN SLim SPet SPoG SSta WBGC WFar
- B&SWJ 6930 — WCru
- BWJ 8189b from China — WCru
- HWJK 2156 from Nepal — WCru
- B&SWJ 6724 from Taiwan — WCru
- *alba* — see C. *montana*
- 'Alexander' (M) — CPou CWSG ERob LRHS MBNS MGos SCoo SWCr WCru
- var. *grandiflora* ♀H4 — More than 30 suppliers
I - 'Lilacina' (M) — ESch MAsh
- 'Peveril' (M) — CSPN ERob ESch ETho
- var. *rubens* E.H. Wilson — More than 30 suppliers
- - 'Brookfield Clove' (M) — ERob
I - - 'Odorata' (M) — EBee EPfP ERob ESch ETho GSki LFol MGos MWgw NTay SCoo SLim SPoG WBGC WGor
- - 'Pink Perfection' (M) — CDoC CElw CFRD CWSG EBee ECtt ELan EPfP ERob ESch LAst LRHS LSRN NBea NBlu NHol NTay SBra SCoo SLim SPer SPet SPoG SSto SWCr WBGC WFar
- - 'Tetrarose' (M) ♀H4 — More than 30 suppliers
I - 'Rubens Superba' (M) — CFRD CMHG CWSG EBee ECtt ESch LBuc MGan NCGa SHBN SLim WBVN WFar
- var. *sericea* — see C. *spooneri*
I - 'Veitch's Form' (M) — ESch
§ - var. *wilsonii* — More than 30 suppliers
'Monte Cassino' (EL) — CRHN CSPN EBee ERob ESch ETho SMDP SPet WBGC

'Moonbeam' (Fo) — CFRD CPrp EAEE EBee ECou EHyt ELan EMar EPot ESch GEdr ITim LAst MSte NLAp NOrc NSla NTay SBla SLon WAbe WCot
§ 'Moonlight' (EL) — CElw CSPN ERob ESch LAst NTay WBGC
'Moonman' (Fo) — EHyt ETho SIng
'Moonshadow' **new** — CPIN
Morning Cloud — see C. 'Yukikomachi'
Mother Theresa — see C. 'Matka Teresa'
'Mrs Bush' (LL) — ERob LRHS WBGC
'Mrs Cholmondeley' (EL) ♀H4 — More than 30 suppliers
'Mrs George Jackman' (EL) ♀H4 — CSPN ERob ESch ETho MGos NBea NTay SBra SCoo SLim SPla WBGC
'Mrs Hope' (EL) — ERob ESch WBGC
'Mrs James Mason' (EL) — CFRD ERob ESch ETho NBea NHaw NTay SBra SLim SMDP WBGC
'Mrs N. Thompson' (EL) — More than 30 suppliers
'Mrs P.B. Truax' (EL) — ERob ESch ETho LRHS NBea NTay SBra SCoo SDix SLim SMDP WBGC
'Mrs P.T. James' (EL) — ERob ESch
'Mrs Robert Brydon' (H) — CBgR CFRD CPLG EPfP ERob IPot MBNS MWgw NEgg NHol NSti NTay SCoo SLim SPur SRGP STes WBGC WCot WFar WWye
'Mrs Spencer Castle' (EL) — CSPN ERob ESch ETho NBea NTay WBGC
'Mrs T. Lundell' (Vt) — CFRD CSPN EBee ERob ESch ETho NTay
'Multi Blue' (EL) — More than 30 suppliers
'Muran Rouge' **new** — ESch
'My Angel'PBR (Ta) — CSPN ELan ESch MGos NHaw NLar NTay SPer WBGC
'Myōjō' (EL) — CSPN EBee ERob ESch LRHS SBra SCoo SLim SPoG WBGC
'Myōkō' (EL) — SLim
'Nadezhda' (LL) — CFRD ERob ESch ETho SMDP
§ *napaulensis* — CBcs CPIN CSPN CSec ERob ESch ETho LFol LRHS NTay SLim SPoG WBGC WCru WFar WGwG
I 'Natacha' (EL) — CElw EBee ERob ESch NBea NHaw NTay SBra SCoo SLim SPet WBGC
'Natascha' (EL) **new** — ETho SPoG
'Negritianka' (LL) — CSPN ERob ESch LBuc NHaw NTay WBGC
'Negus' (LL) — ERob ESch
'Nelly Moser' (EL) ♀H4 — More than 30 suppliers
'New Dawn' (M) — CSPN ERob ESch NEgg NHaw WBGC
'New Love'PBR (H) — CSPN EGle ERob ESch ETho LAst LBuc LHop MBlu MGos NBPC NHaw NLar NSti NTay SBra WWye
New Zealand hybrids (Fo) — ECou
'Night Veil' (Vt) **new** — ETho
'Nikolai Rubtsov' (LL) — CSPN ERob ESch ETho NTay SMDP
'Niobe' (EL) ♀H4 — More than 30 suppliers
'Norfolk Queen' (EL) — ESch
'North Star' — see C. 'Põhjanael'
'Nuit de Chine' (EL) — ERob ESch
obscura — see C. *japonica* var. *obvallata*
obvallata — see C. *japonica* var. *obvallata*
§ *occidentalis* — NEgg
- var. *dissecta* — EHyt GIBF
- subsp. *grosseserrata* — EHyt
'Ocean Pearl' (A) **new** — ETho
ochotensis — CSPN ERob SDys
- 'Carmen Rose' (A) — ERob
'Odoriba' (V) — ESch ETho
'Ola Howells' (A/d) — ERob ESch
'Olga' (M) — ERob ESch
'Olimpiada-80' (EL) — ERob ESch

'Omoshiro' (EL) — ESCh ETho NHaw NTay
'Oonagare' — ESCh
Opaline — see *C.* 'Asagasumi'
orientalis misapplied — see *C. tibetana* subsp. *vernayi*
orientalis L. — CPLG EBee ESCh GSki LRHS NHol SBra SCoo SReu WFar
- 'Orange Peel' — see *C. tibetana* subsp. *vernayi* var. *vernayi* 'Orange Peel' LS&E 13342
- var. *orientalis* — ERob
- var. *tenuifolia* — ERob
- var. *tenuiloba* — see *C. columbiana* var. *tenuiloba*
'Otto Fröbel' (EL) — CSPN ERob ESCh NTay
'Paala' (EL) — CFRD ERob
'Paddington' (EL) — ERob
'Pagoda' (Vt) ♀H4 — CDoC CElw CFRD CRHN EBee EPfP ESCh ETho LAst LRHS MBri MWgw NBea NHol NSti NTay SBra SCoo SLim SPla SPoG SRms SWCr WBGC
'Päkapikk' (LL) — ERob
'Pamela' (F) — CSPN ERob ESCh ETho LBuc NHaw NTay WBGC
'Pamela Jackman' — see *C. alpina* 'Pamela Jackman'
'Pamiat Serdtsa' (I) — ERob ESCh ETho SBra WBGC
'Pamina' (EL) — ETho
'Pangbourne Pink' (I) ♀H4 — CElw CFRD CHad CSPN CWoW EBee EPfP ERob ESCh ETho GBuc LRHS MAsh MWgw NBea NHaw NTay SBra SCoo SLim SPoG SWCr WBGC WCru
paniculata Thunb. — see *C. terniflora*
§ *paniculata* J.G. Gmel. — CSPN ESCh GGar LRHS WPGP WSHC
- (f) — ETho
- var. *lobata* — MWgw NLar WBGC
'Paola' (EL/d) — ESCh
'Paradise Queen' (EL) — ESCh LBuc MWgw NLar
'Parasol' (EL) — CSPN ERob ESCh NTay
parviflora DC. — see *C. campaniflora*
parviflora ambig. — ERob
parviloba var. *bartlettii* — WSHC
- - B&SWJ 6788 — WCru
'Pastel Blue' (I) — ERob ESCh ETho NBea SMDP
'Pastel Pink' (I) — ERob ESCh ETho SMDP WBGC
'Pastel Princess' (EL) — CFRD ERob NHaw NTay
'Pat Coleman' (EL) — ETho
patens from China — ERob
- from Japan — ERob
- 'Korean Moon' (EL) — WCru
§ - 'Manshuu Ki' (EL) — More than 30 suppliers
- 'Nagoya' (EL) — ESCh
- 'Sanda' (EL) — ESCh
- 'Yukiokoshi' (EL) — ERob ESCh ETho
Patricia Ann Fretwell = 'Pafar' (EL) — CSPN ERob LRHS
§ 'Paul Farges' (Vt) ♀H4 — CBcs CFRD CSPN CStu CWoW EBee ERob ETho MBlu NHol NSti NTay SBra SLim SMDP WBGC WTel WWeb
'Pauline' (A/d) — CBcs CWSG EBee ERob ESCh ETho LRHS NBea NTay SBra SCoo SLim SWCr WBGC
'Pearl Rose' (A/d) — CWSG ERob
'Pendragon' (Vt) — ERob ESCh NHaw
'Pennell's Purity' (LL) — ERob ETho NHaw NTay
'Perle d'Azur' (LL) — More than 30 suppliers
'Perrin's Pride' (Vt) — ERob ESCh LRHS MGos NTay SBra SWCr WBGC
'Peter Pan' (EL) — ERob
peterae — ERob
- var. *trichocarpa* — ERob
Petit Faucon = 'Evisix'PBR (I) ♀H4 — CFRD EBee ECtt ENot EPfP ERob ETho IBal LAst LRHS LSRN MBNS MBri MWgw NBea NPri NTay SBra SCoo SLim SPer SPoG SRkn SWCr WBGC WPGP

petriei — ECou
- 'Princess' (Fo/f) — ECou
- 'Steepdown' (Fo/f) — ECou
'Peveril Peach' — ESCh
'Peveril Pearl' (EL) — CElw ERob ESCh ETho NTay
'Phoenix' (EL) — ESCh
Picardy = 'Evipo024' — ESCh LRHS
I 'Picton's Variety' (M) — CTri EBee ERob ESCh ETho NHaw NHol SHBN WBGC WFar
pierotii — ERob
'Piilu' (EL) — CFRD CSPN ELan ERob ESCh ETho LBuc LRHS MAsh MBNS MBri MWea NHaw NPri NTay SBra SCoo SLim SMDP SPoG WBGC
'Pink Celebration' **new** — ESCh ETho
'Pink Champagne' — see *C.* 'Kakio'
'Pink Fantasy' (LL) — CFRD CRHN CSPN CTri CWSG ERob ESCh ETho LRHS MBar NBea NTay SBra SCoo SLim SPoG SRkn SWCr WBGC
'Pink Flamingo' (A) ♀H4 — CElw CFRD CMHG CSPN EBee ECtt ELan ENot EPfP ERob ESCh ETho LRHS MWgw NEgg NPri NSti NTay SCoo SLim SMur SPet SPoG SRkn SWCr WBGC WBrE
'Pink Ice' (I) **new** — ESCh
'Pink Pearl' (I) — ESCh NTay
'Pink Starlight' (M) **new** — SPur
'Pirko' (Vt) — ERob ESCh
§ *pitcheri* — CPLG ERob ESCh ETho
'Pixie' (Fo/m) — CElw CSPN CTbh ECou EHyt ELan ENot EPfP ESCh ETho GGar LRHS MAsh MGos MWgw NHaw NHol NLar NTay SBra SCoo SPet SPoG SWCr WBGC
I 'Pleniflora' (M/d) — CFRD ESCh MGos NHaw
§ 'Plum Beauty' (A) — CSPN ERob ESCh NHaw WBGC
§ 'Põhjanael' (LL) — CSPN CWSG ERob ESCh ETho MGos NBea SLim WBGC
'Pointy' (A) — ESCh NTay
'Polish Spirit' (LL) ♀H4 — More than 30 suppliers
§ *potaninii* — CCge ERob CSPN CWoW ECtt EPPr EShb GIBF MTis MWhi NEgg WPtf WSHC
§ - var. *potaninii* — CFRD EHyt ERob NTay SDix
- var. *souliei* — see *C. potaninii* var. *potaninii*
'Praecox' (H) ♀H4 — More than 30 suppliers
* 'Prairie' — LRHS
'Prairie River' (A) — ERob
Pretty in Blue = 'Zopre'PBR (F) — ESCh ETho NTay SBra SHBN
'Pribaltika' (LL) — ERob ESCh WBGC
'Primrose Star'PBR — see *C.* 'Star'
'Prince Charles' (LL) ♀H4 — CElw CFRD CHad CPou CRHN CSPN CTri EBee ELan EPfP ESCh ETho LRHS LSRN NBea NBir NTay SBra SCoo SDix SLim SPer SPet SPoG SWCr WBGC WSHC
'Prince Philip' (EL) — ERob ESCh ETho NTay SBra WFar
§ 'Princess Diana' (T) ♀H4 — CBcs CBgR CFRD CHad CRHN CSPN CWSG EBee ELan ERob ESCh ETho LBuc LSRN MBlu MGos MSwo MWgw NBea NHol NTay SBra SLim SPer SPet SPoG SWCr WBGC WCMO WFar
§ 'Princess of Wales' (EL) — CSam EPfP ERob ESCh LRHS LSRN MBNS NLar NPri SBra WBGC WFar WSHC
'Prins Hendrik' (EL) — ERob WGor
'Prinsesse Alexandra'PBR — EBee ESCh ETho NTay
'Propertius' (A) — EBee ERob ESCh ETho NHaw SMDP
'Proteus' (EL) — CFRD CSPN ELan EPfP ESCh ETho LAst LRHS MAsh MBNS NBea NTay SBra SCoo SDix SLim SPer SPet SPoG WBGC

'Pruinina'	see *C.* 'Plum Beauty'	
psilandra	SMDP	
'Pulmapäev' (LL)	ERob	
'Purple Haze' (Vt)	CRHN	
'Purple Spider' (A/d)	CBcs CElw CFRD CSPN EBee	
	ERob ESCh ETho LBuc MAsh MBlu	
	MWgw NHaw NHol NTay SBra	
	SCoo SLim SMDP SPer SPet SPoG	
	WBGC WWhi	
'Purple Treasure' (V)	ESCh	
'Purpurea Plena Elegans'	More than 30 suppliers	
(Vt/d) ♀H4		
quadribracteolata	ECou	
- 'Nancy's Lookout'	ECou	
'Queen Alexandra' (EL)	ERob	
'Radar Love' (Ta)	NLar WBrE	
'Radost' (EL)	ERob	
'Ragamuffin' (EL/d)	ENot ERob ESCh	
'Rahvarinne' (LL)	ERob ESCh ETho	
'Ramona' (LL) **new**	ETho MAsh	
ranunculoides	WCru	
CD&R 2345		
recta	CFRD CFee CSPN CWoW EChP	
	ECtt EPfP ERob ETho GSki LRHS	
	MLLN MNrw MWhi NBea NEgg	
	NLar SPer WBGC WPer WTin	
	WWye	
§ - 'Lime Close' (F)	MSte SMrm	
I - 'Peveril' (F)	CFRD CPrp ERob ESCh LAst MSte	
	NFla SCoo SMDP WBGC	
- 'Purpurea' (F)	More than 30 suppliers	
§ - subsp. *recta* var.	CSPN ERob	
lasiosepala		
- Serious Black	see *C. recta* 'Lime Close'	
- 'Velvet Night' (F)	CSpe ERob ESCh GAbr LAst LHop	
	LSou MDun MTis NEgg NHol	
	SMDP SPoG WBGC	
'Red Ballon' (Ta)	ERob ESCh LBuc SMDP	
§ 'Red Beetroot Beauty' (A)	CSPN ERob ESCh LBuc	
'Red Cooler'	see *C.* 'Crimson King'	
'Red Pearl' (EL)	ERob ESCh ETho MGos NTay	
rehderiana ♀H4	More than 30 suppliers	
- BWJ 7700	WCru	
- CC 3601	CPLG	
'Reiman' (LL)	ERob	
repens	see *C. montana* var. *wilsonii*	
- DJHC795 **new**	EHyt	
reticulata	ERob	
I 'Rhapsody' B. Fretwell (EL)	CFRD CSPN ENot EPfP ERob ETho	
	LRHS LSRN MAsh MGos NBea	
	NHaw SBra SCoo SPoG WBGC	
	WFar	
'Richard Pennell' (EL) ♀H4	EBee ERob ESCh ETho LRHS MAsh	
	NBea NPri NTay SBra SDix SLim	
	SWCr WBGC	
'Ristimägi' (LL)	ERob	
'Rodomax' (A)	ERob ESCh	
'Roko' (A)	ERob	
'Roko-Kolla' (LL)	CFRD CSPN EBee ERob ESCh	
	ETho NBea SBra	
'Romantika' (LL)	CFRD CSPN EBee ELan ERob ESCh	
	ETho NBea NHaw NTay SBra SCoo	
	SLim SPer SPoG WBGC	
'Roogoja' (LL)	ERob ESCh	
'Rooguchi' (I)	CFRD EBee ERob ESCh ETho LRHS	
	SBra SMDP SPoG	
'Rooran' (EL) **new**	ETho	
'Rosa Königskind' (EL)	ERob ESCh ETho	
'Rose Supreme' (EL)	ESCh ETho	
I 'Rosea' (I) ♀H4	CBcs CPrp CSPN EAEE EBee EMar	
	EPfP ERob ESCh EShb ETho LAst	
	LHop LSRN MSte MSwo MTho	
	MWgw NBea NChi NSti NTay	
	SCoo SLim WBGC	
'Rosea' (Vt)	ERob	
Rosebud = 'Robud' (M/d)	CFRD EBee ESCh NCGa NLar NPer	

Rosemoor = 'Evipo002'	ETho LRHS MAsh MBri SBra SWCr	
'Rosy O'Grady' (A) ♀H4	EBee ELan ESCh ETho MBar MBri	
	MGos NBea NHol NLar NSti SCoo	
	SLim SPer WBGC	
'Rosy Pagoda' (A)	EBee ELan EPfP ERob ESCh LRHS	
	MBri NBea NBir NHaw WBGC	
	WTel	
'Rouge Cardinal' (LL)	More than 30 suppliers	
'Royal Velours' (Vt) ♀H4	More than 30 suppliers	
I 'Royal Velvet' **new**	LSRN	
Royal Velvet =	CSPN CWoW EPfP ESCh ETho	
'Evifour'PBR (EL)	LAst MBri MWgw NTay SCoo SLim	
	WBGC	
'Royalty' (EL) ♀H4	CElw CFRD CSPN ELan EPfP	
	ERob ESCh LRHS LSRN NBea	
	NBir NPri NTay SBra SCoo	
	SDix SLim SPer SPet SPoG	
	SWCr WBGC	
'Rozalia' (EL)	ESCh	
'Ruby' (A)	CFRD CMHG CSPN CWSG	
	EBee ELan EPfP ESCh ETho	
	LRHS MAsh MGos NBea NEgg	
	NHol NSti NTay SBra SCoo	
	SDix SHBN SLim SPer SPet	
	SPoG WBGC WTel	
'Ruby Glow' (EL)	CFRD EPfP ERob ESCh MAsh NTay	
	SCoo WBGC	
'Rüütel' (EL)	CFRD ERob ESCh ETho NBea	
	NHaw NTay SBra SCoo SLim SMDP	
	SPoG WBGC	
'Saalomon' (LL)	ERob ETho	
'Sakala' (EL)	ERob ESCh	
§ 'Sakurahime' (EL)	EBee ERob ESCh	
'Sally Cadge' (EL)	CFRD ERob ESCh	
'Salmon Blush' (A/d)	ESCh	
'Samantha Denny' (EL)	CSPN ERob ESCh ETho MAsh	
	NHaw NRib WBGC	
'Sander' (H)	CSPN ERob ESCh ETho WBGC	
'Sandra Denny' (EL)	ETho	
'Sano-no-murasaki' (EL)	ESCh	
'Satsukibare' (EL)	CFRD ERob ESCh MGos WBGC	
I 'Saturn' (LL)	CFRD ERob ESCh NBea SPla	
	WBGC	
'Saturn' (EL)	ESCh	
'Scartho Gem' (EL)	CFRD EPfP ERob ESCh MAsh NBea	
	NPri NTay SCoo WBGC	
'Sealand Gem' (EL)	CFRD ERob ESCh ETho LAst NBea	
	NHaw NTay SBra SLim WBGC	
'Seeryuu' (I)	ETho	
'Semu' (LL)	CSPN ERob ESCh ETho NHaw	
'Serenata' (EL)	ERob ESCh	
serratifolia	CElw CFRD CWoW EHyt ERob	
	ESCh ETho GIBF MDKP MLLN	
	MWhi NTay SDix SMDP WBGC	
	WBVN WFar	
- B&SWJ 8458 from Korea	WCru	
'Sheila Thacker' (EL)	ETho	
I 'Sherriffii' (Ta)	ERob	
'Shin-shigyoku' **new**	ESCh	
'Shirayukihime' (LL)	CSPN ESCh	
§ 'Shiva' (A)	CElw ERob MAsh	
'Shorty' (Ta)	ERob	
'Sho-un' (EL)	EBee ERob ESCh NTay SBra	
'Shropshire Blue'	ERob WBGC	
'Sialia' (A/d)	ERob ESCh	
§ *sibirica*	CBcs EBee ERob SPla WBVN	
- var. *tianschanica* 'Riga'	ERob WBGC	
(A)		
'Signe' (Vt)	see *C.* 'Kasmu'	
'Siirus' (EL)	ERob	
'Silmakivi' (EL)	ERob ESCh	
'Silver Lady'	SPoG	
'Silver Moon' (EL)	CSPN ERob ESCh ETho NBea NTay	
	SBra WBGC	
§ 'Simplicity' (A)	CBgR CSPN EBee ERob ESCh	
	MAsh SPet	

simsii Small	see *C. pitcheri*
simsii Sweet	see *C. crispa*
§ 'Sinee Dozhd' (I)	CSPN ERob ESch SMDP WBGC
'Sinee Plamia' (LL)	ERob ESch NHaw
'Sir Eric Savill' (M) **new**	ESch
'Sir Garnet Wolseley' (EL)	ERob ESch MAsh SDix WBGC
'Sir Trevor Lawrence' (T)	CFRD CSPN CWoW EBee ERob ESch ETho LAst LRHS NBea NHaw NHol NSti NTay SBra SCoo SDix SLim SPer SPoG SWCr WBGC
'Sizaia Ptitsa' (I)	ERob ESch ETho
'Snow Queen' (EL)	CElw CFRD CSPN EBee EPfP ESch ETho GMac LRHS MAsh MBri MGos MSwo NBea NTay SBra SPet WBGC WTel
'Snowbird' (A/d)	CSPN ERob ESch MAsh NHaw NHol SBra
'Snowdrift'	see *C. armandii* 'Snowdrift'
§ 'Södertälje' (Vt)	CFRD CRHN ERob ESch ETho NBea SBra SCoo SPoG
'Solweig' (EL)	ERob
songarica	CWoW ERob ESch ITim NHol NTay WHil
'Souvenir de J.L. Delbard' (EL)	CFRD ERob ESch
§ 'Souvenir du Capitaine Thuilleaux' (EL)	CFRD CWoW ESch LAst MAsh MGos NBea NTay SLim SPoG WBGC
'Special Occasion' (EL)	CFRD CSPN EBee ENot ERob ESch ETho LBuc MBNS NBea NHaw NLar NPri NTay SBra SCoo SLim WBGC WFar
§ *spooneri*	CElw CFRD CTri CWSG ECtt ELan ERob ESch GQui MAsh MGan MWgw SCoo SLim SLon SRms WCru WFoF
§ 'Spooneri Rosea' (M)	CTbh CTrw ERob
'Sputnik' (I)	CSPN ERob ESch NHaw NTay
'Stanislaus' (H) **new**	ETho
stans	CHea CPLG CPou EHyt ERob ESch ETho GSki IFro ITer LRHS NLar SIng SMDP WBGC
- B&SWJ 4567	WCru
- B&SWJ 6345	WCru
- 'Rusalka' (H)	ERob
§ 'Star'[PBR] (M/d)	CDoC COtt CSPN EBee EPfP ERob ESch LAst LBuc LRHS MBlu MGos MSwo MWgw NHol NLar NPri SBra SCoo SPer SPoG WBGC WFar WWhi
'Star of India' (LL)	CElw CFRD CRHN EBee EPfP ERob ESch ETho LRHS MAsh MGos NBea NTay SBra SCoo SDix SLim SPer SPoG SSto SWCr WBGC WFar
'Starfish' (EL)	ERob ESch NHaw NTay
'Stasik' (LL)	ERob ESch NHaw
'Stephanie' **new**	ESch
'Strawberry Roan' (EL)	ESch
Sugar Candy =	ERob ESch LAst MBri NPri NTay
'Evione'[PBR] (EL)	SBra SCoo SLim WBGC
Summer Snow	see *C.* 'Paul Farges'
'Sundance'	CSPN EBee ERob ESch
'Sunrise'[PBR] (M/d)	COtt CSPN EBee ESch ETho LBuc MSwo MWgw NHaw NLar SBra SPoG WFar
'Sunset' (EL) ♡[H4]	CFRD CWoW ERob ESch LRHS MBri NBea NEgg NTay SBra SMur SWCr WBGC
'Sunstar' **new**	SWal
'Suruga' (EL)	ESch
'Susan Allsop' (EL)	ERob ESch WBGC
'Swedish Bells' (I) **new**	ETho
'Sylvia Denny' (EL)	CFRD CWSG CWoW EBee ELan EPfP ERob ESch ETho LAst LRHS

	MBar NBea NRib NTay SCoo SLim SPer SPoG WBGC
'Sympatia' (LL)	ERob ESch NHaw NTay WBGC
'Syrena' (LL)	ESch NHaw
szuyuanensis	WCru
B&SWJ 6791	
§ 'Tage Lundell' (A)	CBgR CElw CFRD CSPN EBee EPfP ERob ETho MGos NBea NTay SMDP SPet WBGC
'Tango' (Vt)	CElw CFRD CRHN EBee ERob ESch SBra SMDP WBGC
§ *tangutica*	More than 30 suppliers
- subsp. *obtusiuscula*	ERob
'Gravetye Variety' (Ta)	
'Tapestry' (I)	ERob SBra SMDP
'Tartu' (EL)	CSPN ERob ESch
tashiroi	ERob ESch ITer SMDP
- B&SWJ 1423	WCru
- B&SWJ 7005 purple-flowered	WCru
- 'Yellow Peril'	WCru
'Tateshina' (EL)	NTay
'Teksa' (LL)	ERob
'Tentel' (LL)	ERob ETho
tenuiloba	see *C. columbiana* var. *tenuiloba*
§ *terniflora*	CBcs CPIN CWoW EBee EHol EPfP ESch ETho LFol LRHS NHaw NSti SBra SLim SPer WCru
- B&SWJ 5751	WCru
- Caddick's form	CFRD
- var. *mandshurica*	see *C. mandshurica*
- var. *robusta*	see *C. terniflora* var. *terniflora*
- var. *terniflora*	ERob LFol
'Teruko'	ERob
'Teshio' (EL)	CSPN EBee ERob ESch ETho LBuc NHaw SBra SLim SPoG WBGC
texensis	CBcs IFro
- 'The Princess of Wales'	see *C.* 'Princess Diana'
'The Bride' (EL)	CSPN ERob ESch ETho NBea NHaw NTay SBra SLim WBGC
'The Comet' (EL)	ERob
'The First Lady' (EL)	CSPN ERob ESch ETho LBuc NTay SLim WBGC
'The President' (EL) ♡[H4]	More than 30 suppliers
'The Princess of Wales'	see *C.* 'Princess of Wales' (L)
'The Princess of Wales' (T)	see *C.* 'Princess Diana' (T)
'The Vagabond' (EL)	CFRD CSPN CWSG ELan ENot ERob ESch ETho MAsh MGos NBea NHaw NTay SBra WBGC
'The Velvet' (EL)	ERob
'Theydon Belle' (EL)	ESch
thunbergii misapplied	see *C. terniflora*
thunbergii Steud.	see *C. triloba*
'Thyrislund' (EL)	CSPN EBee ESch ETho
'Tibetan Mix' (Ta)	CSPN ERob ESch SMDP
§ *tibetana*	MBar MNrw NEgg NHaw SCoo SLim SPer
- CC 4167	MGol
§ - subsp. *vernayi*	CMHG EHyt ERob MSte NSti SBra SWCr WCru
- - var. *laciniifolia*	ERob ESch NHol WBGC
§ - - var. *vernayi*	CBcs CDoC CElw CFRD ENot EPfP ERob ESch ETho GMac LAst LBuc LRHS NHol SBra SGar SLim SPer SPoG WBGC WFar
'Orange Peel' LS&E 13342	
Timpany NZ hybrids (Fo)	ITim
'Tinkerbell'	see *C.* 'Shiva'
'Titania' (EL)	ERob ESch
'Toki' (EL)	ESch
tongluensis	CPIN
- GWJ 9358	WCru
- HWJCM 076	WCru
- HWJK 2368	WCru
tosaensis B&SWJ 8922	WCru
'Treasure Trove' (Ta)	CSPN NHol SMDP WBGC
'Trianon' (EL)	ERob ESch

'Triibu' (LL)	ESCh
'Triinu' (Vt)	ERob
'Trikatrei' (LL)	ESCh
§ *triloba* new	ETho
§ x *triternata*	More than 30 suppliers
'Rubromarginata' ♀H4	
'Tsuzuki' (EL)	CFRD CSPN ERob ESCh ETho NBea
§ *tubulosa*	CPle CSPN EBee ESCh ETho MGos NHol SMDP SRms
§ - Alan Bloom = 'Alblo'PBR (H)	EBrs LRHS NLar
I - 'Alba' (H)	ERob
- 'Wyevale' (H) ♀H4	CSPN EChP ELan ENot EPfP ERob ETho LHop LRHS MAvo MBlu MRav MWat MWgw NHol NTay SBra SCoo SDix SLim SMad SPer SPla WBGC WCot WEas WHil
'Tuchka' (EL)	ERob
'Twilight' (EL)	CFRD CSPN ESCh ETho NTay SCoo SLim SPoG WBGC WFar
'Ulrique' (EL)	ERob
uncinata	ERob SDix
- B&SWJ 1893	WCru
- var. *ovatifolia*	ERob
'Unity' (M)	ESCh
urophylla	CPlN ERob
- 'Winter Beauty'	CBgR ESCh MGos NTay SHBN SPoG
urticifolia	ESCh
- B&SWJ 8640	WCru
- B&SWJ 8651	WCru
'Valge Daam' (LL)	ERob ESCh ETho NHaw NTay SLim
'Vanessa' (LL)	CFRD CRHN ERob ESCh
'Vanilla Cream' (Fo)	ECou
x *vedrariensis* 'Hidcote' (M)	ERob ESCh NHaw SBra WBGC
- 'Highdown' (M)	ERob
- 'Rosea'	see *C.* 'Spooneri Rosea'
veitchiana	ERob
'Velutina Purpurea' (LL)	ERob
'Venosa Violacea' (Vt) ♀H4	CBgR CElw CFRD CRHN CSPN CSam EBee ELan EPfP ERob ESCh EShb ETho LAst LRHS LSRN MAsh NBea NHol NSti SBra SCoo SDix SPer SPet SPla SWCr WBGC WFar
'Vera' (M)	CElw CFRD CSPN EBee ECtt ERob ESCh ETho LRHS NBir NTay SBra SCoo SLim SPet SPla SPoG WBGC WCru
vernayi	see *C. tibetana* subsp. *vernayi*
'Veronica's Choice' (EL)	CFRD CRHN CSPN ELan ERob ESCh LRHS MGos NBea NHaw NTay SBra WBGC
versicolor	ERob ESCh WIvy
verticillaris	see *C. occidentalis*
'Vetka' (LL)	ERob
Victor Hugo = 'Evipo007'	ESCh ETho NLar
N 'Victoria' (LL) ♀H4	CRHN CSPN ERob ESCh ETho LAst LRHS NBea NHaw NTay SBra SCoo SDix SLim SPoG SWCr WBGC
'Ville de Lyon' (LL)	More than 30 suppliers
'Vince Denny' (Ta)	ESCh ETho
Vino = 'Poulvo'PBR (EL)	CFRD ERob ESCh LRHS NHaw NTay SCoo SPoG WBGC
I 'Viola' (LL)	CFRD CSPN EBee ERob ESCh ETho MBri NBea NHaw NTay WBGC WFar
'Violet Charm' (EL)	CWSG ERob ESCh NTay
'Violet Elizabeth' (EL)	ESCh SBra
'Violet Purple' (A)	ERob ESCh MGos NHaw
'Violetta' (EL)	ERob ESCh
viorna	CPlN CWoW EHyt ERob ESCh WIvy WSHC

virginiana misapplied	see *C. vitalba*
virginiana Hook.	see *C. ligusticifolia*
virginiana L. new	ELau
§ *vitalba*	CArn CRWN ERob ESCh ETho MBar MHer NHaw SECG WGwG WHer
viticella ♀H4	CElw CFRD CWib ERob ESCh ETho MBri NBea NHaw SBra SDix WBGC WTel
§ - 'Flore Pleno' (Vt/d)	CRHN ERob ESCh LAst NHaw SBra WBGC
- 'Hågelby Pink' (Vt) new	ETho
- 'Hågelby White' (Vt)	ERob ETho
- 'Hanna' (Vt)	ERob ESCh ETho
- 'Mary Rose'	see *C. viticella* 'Flore Pleno'
Vivienne	see *C.* 'Beth Currie'
'Vivienne Lawson' (LL)	ERob ESCh
'Voluceau' (Vt)	CFRD CPou CRHN ELan ERob ESCh LAst MAsh MGos NBea NTay SBra SLim SPer WBGC
'Vostok' (LL)	ERob ESCh
'Vyvyan Pennell' (EL)	More than 30 suppliers
'W.E. Gladstone' (EL)	CRHN ERob ESCh ETho LRHS NBea NTay SBra SDix WBGC
'W.S. Callick' (EL)	CFRD ERob
'Wada's Primrose'	see *C. patens* 'Manshuu Ki'
'Walenburg' (Vt)	CRHN ERob ESCh NHaw SBra
'Walter Pennell' (EL)	CBcs CWSG EBee ESCh ETho NBea NTay SBra SCoo SLim WBGC WGor
'Warszawska Nike' (EL) ♀H4	CElw CFRD CRHN EBee ELan ENot EPfP ERob ESCh ETho LAst MAsh MBri MGos MWgw NBea NTay SBra SCoo SHBN SPer SPet SPoG WBGC WGwG
'Warwickshire Rose' (M)	CElw CFRD CRHN CSPN CWSG ECtt ERob ESCh ETho LSRN MAsh MGos MWgw NBea NHaw NHol NTay SBra SPoG WBGC WCMO WCot WFar WPGP WSHC WWeb WWhi
'Waterperry Star' (Ta)	ERob
'Wedding Day' (EL) new	ETho
'Wee Willie Winkie' (M) new	SBra
'Western Virgin' (Vb)	ERob NTay
'Westerplatte' (EL)	CFRD CSPN EPfP ERob ESCh ETho LAst LBuc LRHS MAsh NBea NHaw NScw NTay SBra SMDP SPoG WBGC WFar
'Whirlygig' new	CSPN
§ 'White Columbine' (A) ♀H4	EBee EPfP ERob ESCh ETho LAst NBea NSti SPet WBGC
'White Lady' (A/d)	EPfP ERob ESCh NHaw NTay WBGC
§ 'White Moth' (A/d)	CElw CSPN CWSG EBee ELan EPfP ESCh ETho LRHS MAsh MGos MRav NEgg NHaw NHol NTay SBra SLim SPer SPet SPla SPoG SRms WTel
§ 'White Swan' (A/d)	CSPN EPfP ERob ESCh LRHS MBri MGos NBea NHol NPri NSti SCoo SDix SLim SPer SPla SPoG WBGC WFoF
'White Tokyo' (A/d)	MGos
'White Wings' (A/d)	CBcs EBee ERob ESCh ETho LAst MWgw SWCr
'Wilhelmina Tull' (EL)	CSPN ERob ESCh
'Will Goodwin' (EL) ♀H4	CBcs CFRD CWoW EBee ELan EPfP ERob ESCh ETho GMac LAst LRHS MBri NBea NPri SBra SLim SWCr WBGC
'William Kennett' (EL)	CSam CWSG CWoW EBee ELan EPfP ESCh ETho LAst LRHS MBNS MBar MBri MGan MGos MWgw

	NTay SBod SBra SDix SLim SPet SPoG SWCr WBGC
williamsii	CFRD ESCh
'Willy' (A)	More than 30 suppliers
Wisley = 'Evipo001'	CBcs ESCh ETho LRHS MAsh MBri SBra SPer SWCr
'Xerxes' misapplied	see *C.* 'Elsa Späth'
'Yaichi' (EL)	ESCh
'Yatsuhashi'	ERob
'Yellow Queen' Holland	see *C. patens* 'Manshuu Ki'
'Yellow Queen' Lundell/ Treasures	see *C.* 'Moonlight'
'Yorkshire Pride' (EL)	ERob ESCh
§ 'Yukikomachi' (EL)	CFRD CSPN ERob ESCh ETho NHaw NTay SPoG WBGC
'Yuki-no-yoso'oi' (EL)	ERob
yunnanensis	ERob
'Yvette Houry' (EL)	ERob ESCh NHaw NLar NTay WBGC
'Zingaro' (Vt)	ERob
'Zolotoi Iubilei' (LL)	ERob

Clematopsis see *Clematis*

Clementsia see *Rhodiola*

Clerodendrum (Verbenaceae)

bungei	More than 30 suppliers
- 'Herfstleu'	MGos
- 'Pink Diamond'[PBR] (v)	ENot EPfP LBuc LRHS MGos NSti SMad SPer SPoG WCot WFar
§ *chinense* var. *chinense* (d) ♀[H1]	CCCN ERea
- 'Pleniflorum'	see *C. chinense* var. *chinense*
fragrans var. *pleniflorum*	see *C. chinense* var. *chinense*
* *mutabile* B&SWJ 6651	WCru
myricoides 'Ugandense' ♀[H1]	CCCN CHll CKob CMdw CPIN CRHN CSpe ELan ERea EShb MJnS SOWG
philippinum	see *C. chinense* var. *chinense*
speciosissimum	EShb
x *speciosum*	CPIN ERea SOWG
splendens ♀[H1]	SOWG
thomsoniae ♀[H1]	CPIN ELan LRHS MBri MJnS SOWG
trichotomum	More than 30 suppliers
- B&SWJ 4896A	WCru
- 'Carnival' (v)	CAbP CBcs CDul CPMA EBee ELan EPfP EWes IArd LRHS MAsh MBlu MBri NLar SBrw SLim SLon SMad SMur SPer SPoG SSta WPat
- var. *fargesii* ♀[H4]	More than 30 suppliers
- 'Hopleys' (v)	LHop
- 'Purple Haze' **new**	MBri
- white calyx B&SWJ 4896	WCru
wallichii	EShb SOWG

Clethra ✿ (Clethraceae)

acuminata	EPfP NLar
alnifolia	CBcs CBrm CDul CEnd CMCN CMHG CPLG CSBt CTbh CTrG ECrN EPfP IDee MBar SMur SPer SRms WBor WCFE WDin WFar
- 'Anne Bidwell'	MBri NLar
- 'Creel's Calico' (v)	NLar
- 'Fern Valley Pink'	MBri NLar
- 'Hokie Pink'	MBri NLar
- 'Hummingbird'	CEnd EBee ELan EMil EPfP LRHS MAsh MBlu MBri MWgw NLar SBrw SMur SPoG SSpi SWvt WFar WGer
- 'Paniculata' ♀[H4]	CDoC CPLG EPfP SBrw SPoG SPur WFar
- 'Pink Spire'	CBcs CDoC CDul EBee ECrN EPfP EWTr IDee MRav NBlu NEgg NPal SBrw SCoo SPoG WDin WFar WOrn

- 'Rosea'	CTri GQui IMGH MBar MBlu MGos SHBN SPer WFar
- 'Ruby Spice'	CBcs CBrm CEnd CPLG EBee ELan EMil EPfP EWTr IMGH LAst LRHS MAsh MBlu MBri NEgg SBrw SMur SSpi SSta SWvt WBVN
- 'September Beauty'	NLar
- 'Sixteen Candles' **new**	NLar
arborea	CBcs CHEx CMHG CPLG CTrC
barbinervis ♀[H4]	CBcs CMCN CPLG EPfP IDee IMGH MBlu NLar SBrw SPer SPoG WDin WFar WSHC
- B&SWJ 5416	WPGP
- B&SWJ 8915	WCru
delavayi Franch.	CBcs CCCN CDoC CPLG EPfP EWes GGGa GQui NLar
- C&H 7067	GGGa
fargesii	EPfP IMGH MBri MGos NLar
monostachya	NLar
pringlei	NLar
tomentosa	MBri WWes
- 'Cottondale'	MBri NLar

Cleyera (Theaceae)

fortunei	see *C. japonica* 'Fortunei'
- 'Variegata'	see *C. japonica* 'Fortunei'
§ *japonica* 'Fortunei' (v)	CMac CWib SBrw WFar
- var. *japonica*	SBrw WPGP
- var. *wallichii*	WPGP

Clianthus (Papilionaceae)

maximus	ECou
§ *puniceus* ♀[H2]	More than 30 suppliers
§ - 'Albus' ♀[H2]	CBcs CHEx CHll CPLG CTrw CWib EMil EPfP ERea LRHS MWgw SBra SBrw SGar SOWG SPer SPoG WPGP
- 'Flamingo'	see *C. puniceus* 'Roseus'
- 'Kaka King'	CBcs
- 'Red Admiral'	see *C. puniceus*
- 'Red Cardinal'	see *C. puniceus*
§ - 'Roseus'	CBcs CPLG EMil ERea LRHS SBra SBrw SPer SPoG WPGP
- 'White Heron'	see *C. puniceus* 'Albus'

Clinopodium (Lamiaceae)

acinos	see *Acinos arvensis*
ascendens	see *Calamintha ascendens*
calamintha	see *Calamintha nepeta*
grandiflorum	see *Calamintha grandiflora*
§ *vulgare*	CArn CRWN EBee EMag EMan EPPr EUnu GBar MBow MHer NGHP NMir NSco SECG SGar SIde WDyG WFoF WGHP WHer WLin WMoo WOut WPtf

Clintonia (Convallariaceae)

andrewsiana	CLAP GBin GBuc GCrs GEdr GGGa GIBF WCot WCru
borealis	SCnR WCru
HWJK 2339 from Nepal **new**	WCru
udensis	WCru
umbellulata	CLAP WCru
uniflora	CLAP EBee GBuc

Clitoria (Papilionaceae)

ternatea	EMan

Clivia ✿ (Amaryllidaceae)

caulescens	ERea
x *cyrtanthiflora*	ERea
gardenii	ERea
gardenii x *miniata* **new**	WCot
miniata ♀[H1]	CBcs CBgR CHal CSec ECho LRHS MLan MSchr SMur SRms WCMO WCot

- 'Aurea' ♀H1 — CSpe
- var. *citrina* ♀H1 — ECho WSAf
- - 'New Dawn' — ERea
- 'Great Wide Yellow' **new** — WSAf
- hybrids — ERea MBri NPal SEND
- 'Striata' (v) — ERea WCot
nobilis ♀H1 — ERea WCot

Clypeola (*Cruciferae*)
jonthlaspi **new** — WCot

Clytostoma (*Bignoniaceae*)
§ *calystegioides* — CHll CPlN CRHN ERea EShb

Cneorum (*Cneoraceae*)
tricoccon — CKob XPep

Cnicus (*Asteraceae*)
§ *benedictus* — CArn GPoy MHer MSal SIde SPav

Cobaea (*Cobaeaceae*)
pringlei — CPlN ERea WSHC
scandens ♀H3 — CCCN CHen CSpe ELan EWin IFoB LRav SGar SMur SPer
- f. *alba* ♀H3 — EBee ELan SMur SPer

cobnut see *Corylus avellana*

Coccothrinax (*Arecaceae*)
argentata — WMul
argentea (Lodd. ex Schult.f.) Sarg. ex Becc. — EAmu
crinita — LPal

Cocculus (*Menispermaceae*)
§ *orbiculatus* — CPLG CPlN
- B&SWJ 535 — WCru
trilobus — see *C. orbiculatus*

Cochlearia (*Brassicaceae*)
armoracia — see *Armoracia rusticana*
glastifolia — MSal
officinalis — MHer MSal WHer

Cocos (*Arecaceae*)
plumosa — see *Syagrus romanzoffiana*
weddelliana — see *Lytocaryum weddellianum*

Codiaeum ✿ (*Euphorbiaceae*)
variegatum var. — LRHS
pictum 'Excellent' (v)
- - 'Petra' (v) — LRHS MBri

Codonanthe (*Gesneriaceae*)
gracilis — EBak WDib
'Paula' WDib

x *Codonatanthus* (*Gesneriaceae*)
'Golden Tambourine' — WDib
'Sunset' — WDib
'Tambourine' — WDib

Codonopsis ✿ (*Campanulaceae*)
CC 4471 — CPLG
SDR 1867 — GKev
affinis HWJCM 70 — WCru
- HWJK 2151 — WCru
benthamii GWJ 9352 — WCru
bhutanica — EBee MGol WCot
bulleyana — EBee NBre NLar WCot WSan
cardiophylla — EBee GCal GKev NBre NLar
celebica HWJ 665 — WCru
clematidea — CHar CSpe EBee EChP ECha ECho ECtt EPfP GCal GIBF GKev LHop MCCP MDun MTho MWgw NBid

---

NChi SAga SBla SMad SPlb SRms SWvt WCru WFar WKif WLin WSHC
- 'Lilac Eyes' — MCCP NBre NSti
convolvulacea misapplied — see *C. grey-wilsonii*
convolvulacea Kurz — CPne GBuc IGor MTho NSla WCru WHoo WPGP
- B&SWJ 7812 — WCru
- B&SWJ 7847 — WCru
- CC 4471 — MGol
- J&JA 4.220.705 — NWCA
- 'Alba' — see *C. grey-wilsonii* 'Himal Snow'
- Forrest's form — see *C. forrestii* Diels
dicentrifolia — EBee EMan GKev
- HWJCM 267 — WCru
forrestii misapplied — see *C. grey-wilsonii*
§ *forrestii* Diels — CPlN EBee EHyt GKev WCot WCru
- BWJ 7776 — WCru
§ *grey-wilsonii* ♀H4 — CAby CLAP CPlN EChP ECho GCrs GEdr SBla WCMO WCot WIvy
- B&SWJ 7532 — WCru
§ - 'Himal Snow' — CAby CLAP EBee EHyt GCrs GEdr IMGH MDKP SBla WCot WIvy
handeliana — see *C. tubulosa*
§ *javanica* B&SWJ 380 — WCru
- B&SWJ 8145 — WCru
kawakamii — EBee
- B&SWJ 1592 — WCru
§ *lanceolata* — CAby CPlN CPne GCal NSti
- B&SWJ 5099 — WCru
- B&SWJ 562 — WCru
lancifolia B&SWJ 3835 — WCru
macrocalyx — NChi
mollis — EChP ECho GSki NBre NGby NLar WFar
nepalensis Grey-Wilson — see *C. grey-wilsonii*
obtusa — EBee NBre NChi WCot
ovata — CFir Clyd EBee EHyt GBuc MTho NBre NBro NChi SBla SRms
§ *pilosula* — EBee EOHP GPoy MGol MNrw MSal MTho NLar
rotundifolia CC 1770 — WCot
§ - var. *angustifolia* — EBee GKev MDKP WCMO
silvestris — see *C. pilosula*
tangshen misapplied — see *C. rotundifolia* var. *angustifolia*
tangshen Oliv. — CAby CArn GIBF GKev MNrw MSal MTho SHFr
thalictrifolia — GIBF
- MECC 93 — WCru
§ *tubulosa* — EBee LRHS
ussuriensis — see *C. lanceolata*
vinciflora — CPne EHyt GEdr IGor SBla WCot WCru WIvy WSHC
viridis HWJK 2435 — WCru
cf. *viridis* **new** — GIBF

Coffea (*Rubiaceae*)
arabica — CCCN SDEP

coffee see *Coffea*

Coix (*Poaceae*)
lacryma-jobi — CPLG MSal SWal

Colchicum ✿ (*Colchicaceae*)
agrippinum ♀H4 — CAvo CBro CFee CMon ECha ECho EHyt GCal GKev ITim MRav NBir NMen NRya WTin
alpinum — GIBF
'Antares' — ECha NBir
atropurpureum — CBro ECho EPot GEdr
- Drake's form — ECho
'Autumn Herald' — ECho
N 'Autumn Queen' — ECho

§ *autumnale*	CArn CAvo CBro CFee ECho EPot GCal GPoy ITim LRHS NMen NRya WFar WShi
* - 'Albopilosum'	NBir
- 'Alboplenum'	CBro EBrs ECho EPot WTin
- 'Album'	CAvo CBgR CBro EBrs ECho EHyt EPot GAbr GEdr GKev LRHS NBir SPer WFar WGwG WHoo WPnP WShi WTin
- 'Atropurpureum'	ECho
- var. *major*	see *C. byzantinum* Ker Gawl.
- var. *minor*	see *C. autumnale*
§ - 'Nancy Lindsay' ♀H4	CBro EBrs ECho EPot SRot
- 'Pannonicum'	see *C. autumnale* 'Nancy Lindsay'
§ - 'Pleniflorum' (d)	CBgR CBro CSec CStu ECho EPot GEdr GKev
- 'Roseum Plenum'	see *C. autumnale* 'Pleniflorum'
baytopiorum	EHyt GEdr
- PB 224 from Turkey	CMon
'Beaconsfield'	GEdr
§ *bivonae*	CBro ECha
Blom's hybrid	WTin
§ *boissieri*	ERos
- MFF 2192	WCot
bornmuelleri misapplied	see *C. speciosum* var. *bornmuelleri* hort.
bornmuelleri Freyn	CBro EPot GEdr
bowlesianum	see *C. bivonae*
§ *byzantinum* Ker Gawl. ♀H4	CBro ECho EPot GKev LRHS NBir WTin
- *album*	see *C. byzantinum* 'Innocence'
§ - 'Innocence'	CBro CSec EPot
cilicicum	CBro EPot LRHS
- MS&CL 541 from Turkey **new**	CMon
'Conquest'	see *C.* 'Glory of Heemstede'
corsicum	ECho ERos NMen
- from Corsica	CMon
cupanii	EPot SOkd
- from Crete	CMon
davisii	GEdr
'Dick Trotter'	EPot MBri
'Disraeli'	CBro GEdr
'E.A. Bowles'	GEdr LRHS
§ *giganteum*	EBrs EPot GEdr
§ 'Glory of Heemstede'	MBri
'Harlekijn'	GEdr
hungaricum f. *albiflorum*	EPot
illyricum	see *C. giganteum*
'Jolanthe'	WWst
kesselringii	WWst
laetum misapplied	see *C. parnassicum*
laetum Steven	MBri
'Lilac Bedder'	CSec EPot GKev
'Lilac Wonder'	CBro CSec EHyt EPfP EPot GKev LRHS NBPC SPer WCot WFar WHoo
lingulatum	WTin
lusitanum AB&S 4353 from Morocco	CMon
- B&S 469 from Spain	CMon
luteum	WWst
macrophyllum	ECho
- PB 138 from Crete **new**	CMon
micranthum	EHyt
* *neapolitanum* subsp. *micranthum* AB&S 4493 from Morocco	CMon
'Oktoberfest'	EPot
§ *parnassicum*	CBro ECha
peloponnesiacum	CMon
'Pink Goblet' ♀H4	CBro EHyt
procurrens	see *C. boissieri*
psaridis	CMon

pusillum from Crete MS 715	CMon
- - MS 718	CMon
- - MS 833	CMon
'Rosy Dawn' ♀H4	CBro ECha ECho EHyt
sibthorpii	see *C. bivonae*
speciosum ♀H4	CAvo CBro ECho EHyt EPot GEdr LRHS NBir WCot WPnP WTin
- 'Album' ♀H4	CAvo CBro CFee EBla EBrs ECha ECho EHyt EPot ETow GEdr LRHS MBri NBir WCot
- 'Atrorubens'	ECha LRHS MBri
I - var. *bornmuelleri* hort.	GEdr
- var. *illyricum*	see *C. giganteum*
- 'Maximum'	MBri
- 'Ordu'	LEdu
szovitsii Fisch. & B. Mey.	WWst
tenorei ♀H4	CSec ECho EPot GKev NBir WCot
'The Giant'	CBro EBrs EPot LRHS WCot
troodi ambig.	ERos
- from Cyprus	CMon
'Violet Queen'	CBro EPot LRHS
'Waterlily' (d) ♀H4	CAvo CBro CLyd EBrs ECho ELan EPfP EPot GAbr GGar LRHS MBow NBir WCot WGwG WHoo WWFP
'William Dykes'	GEdr
'Zephyr'	ECho

Coleonema (Rutaceae)

album	XPep
§ *pulchellum*	CHEx CSpe NSti XPep
pulchrum misapplied	see *C. pulchellum*
'Sunset Gold'	CPLG CSpe CTrC LHop

Coleus see Plectranthus, Solenostemon

Colletia (Rhamnaceae)

armata	see *C. hystrix*
cruciata	see *C. paradoxa*
§ *hystrix*	CBcs CHEx CTrG CTri EBee GBin GGar SAPC SArc SLon SMad SOWG
- 'Rosea'	CBcs
§ *paradoxa*	CBcs CCCN CHEx CPle EBee IDee LPJP NLar SAPC SArc

Collinsonia (Lamiaceae)

canadensis	CArn EBee ELan EMan MSal WWye

Collomia ♣ (Polemoniaceae)

debilis	EHyt NPol
grandiflora	CSpe EMan NPol WCot
mazama	NPol WLin

Colobanthus (Caryophyllaceae)

canaliculatus	CPBP NMen
§ *quitensis*	ECho

Colocasia (Araceae)

affinis var. *jeningsii*	CKob EAmu EZes MOak
antiquorum	see *C. esculenta*
§ *esculenta* ♀H1	CDWL CHEx CKob EAmu EZes MJnS MOak SDix WMul XBlo
- 'Black Magic'	CDWL CHen EAmu EZes MJnS MOak SBig WCot WMul XBlo
- 'Black Ruffles'	EZes MJnS
- 'Bun-long'	MJnS
- burgundy-stemmed	CHen SBig WMul
- 'Chicago Harlequin' **new**	CDWL EZes
- 'Elepaio Keiki' (v)	EZes MJnS
- 'Fontanesii'	CKob EAmu EZes MJnS WMul
- 'Hilo Beauty'	EZes XBlo
- 'Illustris'	CDWL CKob EZes MJnS
- 'Japanese Cranberry'	MJnS
- 'Nancy's Revenge'	CDWL EZes MJnS

- 'Nigrescens'   EAmu
- 'Palau Keiki'   MJnS
- 'Purple Stem' **new**   EZes
- 'Ruffles' **new**   EZes
- 'Ulaula Kumu-oha'   MJnS
fallax   CDWL CKob EZes WCMO
                             WPrP
formosana   CKob
- B&SWJ 6909   WCru
gigantea   EAmu EZes SBig WMul

Colquhounia (*Lamiaceae*)
coccinea   CArn CHEx CHal CHll CTrC EShb
                             GQui MRav NLar SGar SLon WCru
                             WHil WPGP WSHC WWye
- Sch 2458   WPGP
§ - var. *vestita*   CBcs CPle CWib EBee EPfP GGar
                             IMGH LHop MSte MWea SEND
                             WBor
- - B&SWJ 7222   WCru

Columnea (*Gesneriaceae*)
'Aladdin's Lamp'   CHal WDib
'Apollo'   WDib
x *banksii* ♀H1   CHal EOHP WDib
'Bold Venture'   WDib
§ 'Broget Stavanger' (v)   WDib
'Chanticleer' ♀H1   CHal MBri WDib
I 'Firedragon'   WDib
'Gavin Brown'   WDib
gloriosa   EBak
hirta ♀H1   MBri WDib
- 'Variegata'   see *C.* 'Light Prince'
'Inferno'   WDib
'Katsura'   MBri WDib
I 'Kewensis Variegata' (v)   MBri
   ♀H1
§ 'Light Prince' (v)   WDib
'Merkur'   WDib
microphylla 'Variegata'   MBri
   (v)
I 'Midnight Lantern'   WDib
'Rising Sun'   WDib
'Robin'   WDib
schiedeana   CHal EShb MBri WDib
'Stavanger' ♀H1   CHal WDib
'Stavanger Variegated'   see *C.* 'Broget Stavanger'
Yellow Dragon Group   CHal

Colutea (*Papilionaceae*)
arborescens   CArn CBcs CPLG CWib EBee ELan
                             LHop LRHS MBlu MGos MSal
                             NWea SHBN SLon SPer SPlb SPoG
                             WDin WHer XPep
§ *buhsei*   NLar SLPl SOWG
x *media*   LRav MBlu WGwG
- 'Copper Beauty'   CBcs MGos MRav SPer WPat
orientalis   CCCN LHop XPep
persica misapplied   see *C. buhsei*

Combretum (*Combretaceae*)
grandiflorum **new**   CPlN
microphyllum **new**   CPlN
punctatum **new**   CPlN

Commelina (*Commelinaceae*)
coelestis   see *C. tuberosa* Coelestis Group
communis   EMan
dianthifolia   CEnt EBee EMan GCal GCrs MTho
                             NWCA SHGN SRms WPer
- 'Sapphirino'   EMon
robusta **new**   WCot
tuberosa   ELan EPfP MLan MSte NSti WBrE
                             WCMO
- 'Alba'   ELan MSte WCMO WPer
- 'Axminster Lilac'   WPer

§ - Coelestis Group   CBcs CEnt EBee EBrs EChP ECha
                             EMan EWin IGor SGar SPet SRms
                             WFar WPGP WPer WPtf WSHC
- - 'Hopleys Variegated' (v) CBow EMan

Comptonia (*Myricaceae*)
peregrina   NLar WCru WRos

Conandron (*Gesneriaceae*)
ramondoides   WCru
   B&SWJ 8929

Conanthera (*Tecophilaeaceae*)
campanulata   CMon

Congea (*Verbenaceae*)
tomentosa   CPlN

Conicosia (*Aizoaceae*)
pugioniformis   CTrC

Conioselinum (*Apiaceae*)
morrisonense B&SWJ 173   WCru
schugnanicum   WSHC

Conium (*Apiaceae*)
maculatum   CArn MSal

Conopodium (*Apiaceae*)
majus   CRWN WShi

Conradina (*Lamiaceae*)
verticillata   NLAp WPat

Consolida (*Ranunculaceae*)
§ *ajacis*   MNHC MSal
ambigua   see *C. ajacis*

Convallaria ❀ (*Convallariaceae*)
japonica   see *Ophiopogon jaburan*
keiskei   EBla GIBF
majalis ♀H4   More than 30 suppliers
§ - 'Albostriata' (v)   CBct CBow CFwr CLAP CRow
                             EBee EBla EBrs ECha ECho EHrv
                             ELan EMan EPPr EPfP MRav MTho
                             MWrn NBir SAga SIng WCHb
                             WCMO WCot WCru WEas WHer
                             WPGP
- 'Berlin Giant'   EBee EBla NBre NRya
- 'Blush'   CAvo
- 'Dorien'   CBct CBre CFir EBee EChP MAvo
                             WCMO
- 'Flore Pleno' (d)   CBct EBla EHrv MTho WCMO
- 'Fortin's Giant'   CBct CBro CLAP CMea CRow
                             EBee EBla EMon EPla EPot GEdr
                             MRav NBre NEgg NGby SMad
                             WCMO WCot WPGP WSel
- 'Gerard Debureaux' (v)   see *C. majalis* 'Green Tapestry'
§ - 'Green Tapestry' (v)   CBow CLAP CRow EMon
- 'Haldon Grange' (v)   CLAP EBee EMon
- 'Hardwick Hall' (v)   CAvo CBct CBow CLAP CMdw
                             CRow EBee EBla ECha EHoe
                             EHrv EPla EPot MAvo NBre WCot
                             WSan
- 'Hofheim' (v)   CRow WTMC
- 'Prolificans'   CAby CAvo CBct CBro CFir CLAP
                             CMdw CRow EBee ECho EMon
                             ERos MRav SSvw WCot
- var. *rosea*   More than 30 suppliers
- 'Variegata' (v)   CAvo CRow CHar EBla EPla ERou
                             GCrs LHop MAvo NMen SBch
                             SMad SSvw WHil WSel
- 'Vic Pawlowski's Gold'   CLAP CPLG CRow CStu MAvo SBla
   (v)   WCHb
montana   LRHS NLar
transcaucasica   EBee EPot WCot

Convolvulus (Convolvulaceae)

althaeoides	CHad CHrt CMea CPle ECGP EChP ECho ELan EShb LPhx LRHS NBir SBch SBla SHFr SMad SPer WAbb WEas WPGP WPtf
§ - subsp. *tenuissimus*	CSWP CSpe EBee ECtt EMan EWes WCot
§ **boissieri**	CGra EHyt NWCA SBla WAbe WPat
cantabricus	CHll EChP GCal MDKP NSla WHil
chilensis	LSou
cneorum ♀H3	More than 30 suppliers
- 'Snow Angel'	CSBt EBee GBin LBuc MAsh SPoG SSta SVil SWvt WCot WWeb
elegantissimus	see *C. althaeoides* subsp. *tenuissimus*
floridus	CSec
humilis **new**	ECho
incanus	WCru
lineatus	ECho EHyt EWes LRHS MTho NMen NWCA SMrm
mauritanicus	see *C. sabatius*
nitidus	see *C. boissieri*
oleifolius	XPep
§ **sabatius** ♀H3	CHEx CHal CHrt CSam CTbh ECho ECtt ELan EPfP EPot ERea GKev LAst LHop LRHS MLan NMen NWCA SAga SBla SDix SIng SPet SPoG SYvo WCFE WEas WFar WPGP XPep
- dark	CSpe ECho ELan EMan LIck MOak MSte SMrm SUsu
tricolor **new**	GIBF

x *Cooperanthes* see *Zephyranthes*

Cooperia see *Zephyranthes*

Copernicia (Arecaceae)

alba	LPal SBig
prunifera	EAmu

Coprosma ✿ (Rubiaceae)

acerosa	GGar
- 'Live Wire' (f)	ECou
areolata **new**	GKev
- (m)	ECou
atropurpurea (m)	ECou
- (f)	ECou NWCA
'Autumn Orange' (f)	ECou
'Autumn Prince' (m)	ECou
baueri misapplied	see *C. repens*
'Beatson's Gold' (f/v)	CBcs CBrm CHal CHll CTrG EBee ELan EPfP ERea GGar GQui ISea SBrw SPoG STre WDin WHen WSHC
'Blue Pearls' (f)	ECou
'Brunette' (f)	ECou
§ **brunnea**	CTrC ECho ECou IDee
- 'Blue Beauty' (f)	ECou
- 'Violet Fleck' (f)	ECou
'Bruno' (m)	ECou
'Cappuccino' **new**	CBcs GBin
cheesemanii (f)	ECou
- (m)	ECou
- 'Hanmer Red' (f)	ECou
- 'Mack' (m)	ECou
- 'Red Mack' (f)	ECou
'Chocolate Soldier' (m)	ECou
'Coppershine'	CBcs CPLG CTrC ERea MOak
'County Park Red' **new**	ECou
crassifolia x **repens** (m)	ECou
crenulata	WPic
x **cunninghamii** (f)	ECou
- **macrocarpa** (m)	ECou
'Cutie' (f)	ECou
depressa	ECou
- 'Orange Spread' (f)	ECou
'Evening Glow' 'PBR (f/v)	CBow CCCN CDoC COtt ECou ELan LHop LRHS MAsh MGos SBrw
'Fireburst' **new**	CBcs CCCN CDoC
'Green Girl' (f)	ECou
'Green Globe' **new**	CHll
'Hinerua' (f)	ECou
'Indigo Lustre' (f)	ECou
'Jewel' (f)	ECou
'Karo Red' 'PBR (v)	CDoC COtt CTrC LRHS MAsh MGos SPoG
x **kirkii** 'Gold Edge'	ECou
- - 'Kirkii' (f)	CHll ECou STre XPep
- 'Kirkii Variegata' (f/v)	CBcs CDoC CHal CStu CTrC EBee ECho ECou ERea GQui IFro MOak NScw SBrw SOWG STre WBrE WSHC WWeb
'Kiwi' (m)	ECou
'Kiwi Red' **new**	GGar
'Kiwi-gold' (m/v)	ECou ERea
'Lemon Drops' (f)	ECou
linariifolia (m)	ECou
lucida (f)	ECou
- 'Mount White' (m)	ECou
- 'Wanaka' (f)	ECou
macrocarpa (f)	ECou
- (m)	ECou
'Middlemore'	CDoC
nitida (f)	ECou
parviflora (m)	ECou
- purple-fruited (f)	ECou
- red-fruited (f)	ECou
- white-fruited (f)	ECou
'Pearl Drops' (f)	ECou
'Pearl's Sister' (f)	ECou
'Pearly Queen' (f)	ECou
petriei	ECou WThu
- 'Don' (m)	ECou
- 'Lyn' (f)	ECou
'Pride'	CDoC CTrC CTrG
propinqua	WSHC
- (f)	ECou
- (m)	ECou
- var. *latiuscula* (f)	ECou
- - (m)	ECou
'Prostrata' (m)	ECou
pseudocuneata (m)	ECou
pumila	EPot
'Rainbow Surprise' 'PBR (v)	CCCN COtt CPLG ELan LRHS MAsh MGos SPoG WWeb
§ **repens**	CPLG EShb XPep
§ - (f)	ECou
- (m)	CBcs ECou SEND
- 'Apricot Flush' (f)	ECou
- 'County Park Plum' (v)	ECou
- 'County Park Purple' (f)	ECou ERea
- 'Exotica' (f/v)	ECou
- 'Marble King' (m/v)	ECou
- 'Marble Queen' (m/v)	CBcs CHll ECou EShb MGos WCot WFar
♀H1-2	
- 'Orangeade' (f)	ECou
- 'Painter's Palette' (m)	CBcs EBee ECou WDin
- 'Picturata' (m/v) ♀H1-2	ECou EShb
- 'Pink Splendour' (m/v)	CBcs CDoC ECou ERea EShb LHop WDin
- 'Rangatiri' (f)	ECou
- 'Silver Queen' (m/v)	ECou
- 'Variegata' (m/v)	ECou SBrw
rigida	ECou
- 'Ann' (f)	ECou
- 'Tan' (m)	ECou
robusta	CTrC ECou
- 'Cullen's Point' (f)	ECou
- 'Sally Blunt' (f)	ECou

- 'Steepdown' (f)	ECou
- 'Tim Blunt' (m)	ECou
- 'Variegata' (m/v)	ECou
- 'William' (m)	ECou
- 'Woodside' (f)	ECou
rotundifolia	ECou
'Roy's Red' (m)	CDoC EBee ECou MWea
rugosa (f)	ECou
'Snowberry' (f)	ECou
'Taiko'	CTrC
tenuifolia (m)	ECou
'Translucent Gold' (f)	ECou
'Violet Drops' (f)	ECou
virescens (f)	ECou
'Walter Brockie'	CHll CTrC
'White Lady' (f)	ECou
'Winter Bronze' (f)	ECou
'Yvonne' **new**	MGos SRGP

Coptis (Ranunculaceae)

japonica var. *dissecta*	WCru
B&SWJ 6000	
- var. *major*	CDes WCru
quinquefolia	WCru
B&SWJ 1677	

x *Coralia* (Papilionaceae)

'County Park'	ECou
'Essex'	ECou
'Havering'	ECou

Corallospartium (Papilionaceae)

crassicaule	ECou
- 'Jack Sprat'	ECou
- var. *racemosum*	ECou

Cordyline (Agavaceae)

australis ♀H3	More than 30 suppliers
- 'Albertii' (v) ♀H3	CBcs CCCN LHop MBri NMoo
	NPri SAPC SArc WCot
- 'Atropurpurea'	CDoC ECrN IFoB SSto WDin WFar
- 'Black Night'	CCCN CTrC
- 'Black Tower'	CBcs CDoC CHll ELan MGos
- 'Coffee Cream'	EAmu EBee ELan EPfP LRHS MLan
	NBlu SPer WDin WFar WGer
- 'Olive Fountain' **new**	CCCN
- 'Peko'PBR	CCCN MOak
- 'Pink Champagne'	EMil LRHS MAsh
- 'Pink Stripe' (v)	CBcs CDoC CHen COtt EBee ELan
	ENot EPfP ISea LRHS LSRN MAsh
	MCCP MPRe NBlu NPri NScw
	SHGC SLim SNew SPla SSto SWvt
	WFar
- 'Purple Heart'	CCCN CTrC
- 'Purple Sensation' **new**	CCCN
- Purpurea Group	CBcs CDul CHen CMHG CTbh
	CTrC CWSG EBee ENot EPfP
	ISea LAst LRHS MGos NBlu SBLw
	SEND SGar SHBN SPer SPlb WFar
	WGer
- 'Red Sensation'	CHEx CTrC EGra ISea LRHS MPRe
	SHGC SWvt
- 'Red Star'	CAbb CBcs CDoC COtt CSBt CSam
	CTrC CWSG CWib EBee EChP
	ECrN ENot EPfP LAst LRHS MCCP
	MLan MRav NBlu NPer NPri SNew
	SPoG SWvt WBrE WFar WGwG
	WLin
- 'Sparkler'	CBcs MGos
- 'Sundance' ♀H3	More than 30 suppliers
- 'Torbay Dazzler' (v) ♀H3	More than 30 suppliers
- 'Torbay Red' ♀H3	CAbb CBcs CBrm CDoC CMHG
	COtt CTbh CWSG EBee ELan EPfP
	ISea LHop LPan LRHS LSRN MAsh
	MBri MJnS MWgw SPla SWvt WFar
	WWeb

- 'Torbay Sunset'	CCCN CDoC COtt CTrC ELan
	LRHS
'Autumn'	WFar
banksii	CTrC LEdu WPic
'Dark Star'	CCCN CDoC CHen MCCP MDun
fruticosa 'Atom'	MBri
- 'Baby Ti' (v)	MBri
- 'Calypso Queen'	MBri
- 'Kiwi'	MBri
- 'New Guinea Black'	CTrC EChP ELan NSti WCot
- 'Orange Prince'	MBri
- 'Red Edge' ♀H1	MBri XBlo
- 'Yellow King'	MBri
'Green Goddess'	CBcs CTrC MPRe
§ *indivisa*	CAgr CBrP EAmu EBak GGar IDee
	LPan LRHS MBri NJOw SBig SPlb
	SWal WMul WPGP
- 'Perkeo'	MGos
'Jurassic Jade'	CBcs CTrC
kaspar	CHEx LEdu SAPC SArc
- bronze	CKob
obtecta	CCCN
'Purple Tower' ♀H3	CBrm CDoC CHEx COtt CTrC
	EAmu EBee EChP EMil ENot EPfP
	MAsh MPRe SLim SNew SPoG
	WCot
'Red Bush' **new**	XBlo
§ *stricta*	CHEx MBri
terminalis	see *C. fruticosa*

Coreopsis ✿ (Asteraceae)

auriculata Cutting Gold	see *C. auriculata* 'Schnittgold'
- 'Nana'	EBee NBre WFar
§ - 'Schnittgold'	CWan EBee MWgw NBre NLRH
	WFar WPer
- 'Superba'	LRHS
- 'Zamphir' **new**	EBee MAvo NBhm SPoG
'Baby Gold'	EBee EPfP MBNS NBlu NNor SWvt
	WFar WWeb
Baby Sun	see *C.* 'Sonnenkind'
'Golden Queen' **new**	MBri
'Goldfink'	GSki LRHS MBrN MRav SRms
grandiflora	EBee NBlu SUsu SWat XPep
- 'Astolat'	EAAE EBee EMon MNFA SPer SPet
	SUsu
- 'Badengold'	EBee EMil IHMH
- 'Bernwode' (v)	EBee NLar
- 'Calypso' (v)	EWes LBmB LRHS SCoo SMad
	SPoG WWeb
- 'Domino'	EBee LHop NBre NOak SHGN
- 'Early Sunrise' ♀H4	CSBt EBee ECrN ECtt EGra EPfP
	ERou EShb GMaP LDai LRHS
	MBow MBri MHer MWat NBir
	NEgg NMir NPer SGar SMer SPet
	SPoG SWvt WFar WHen WPer
	WWFP
- Flying Saucers =	EChP GBri LRHS NLar SCoo SPoG
'Walcoreop'PBR	
- 'Heliot' **new**	EBee
- 'Kelvin Harbutt'	ERou
- 'Mayfield Giant'	CSBt EAAE EBee ERou EShb LRHS
	MFOX MNrw MWgw NBre NPri
	SPer SPoG SRms SWat SWvt
- 'Rising Sun' **new**	NPri
- 'Tetra Riesen' **new**	NBre
lanceolata	NBre NSti
- 'Sterntaler'	CFir EBee EMil ERou EShb GAbr
	IHMH LRHS MBri MSph NCGa
	NPri NVic SMad SPet SWvt WMoo
	WPer WWeb
- 'Walter'	MBri MCCP MMHG NBlu
'Limerock Ruby'PBR	EBrs GBri MNrw WFar
maximiliani	see *Helianthus maximiliani*
palmata	MDKP
pubescens	EBee LSou
pulchra	EBee

rosea	NLar WFar WPer
- 'American Dream'	COlW CPrp CSBt EBee EChP ELan
	EMil ENot EPfP EShb GAbr GBBs
	GSki LAst LRHS LSRN MCCP NBPC
	NCGa NEgg SGar SPer SPlb SPoG
	SRms SWvt WBrE WFar WWeb
- 'Heaven's Gate' **new**	EBee EPfP ERou GBri MAvo
- 'Sweet Dreams'^{PBR}	EBrs GBri SPer WFar
§ 'Sonnenkind'	EBee ECtt EMil GMaP IHMH LRHS
	MHer NBre NBro NJOw WPer
Sun Child	see *C.* 'Sonnenkind'
'Sunburst'	COtt EBee GSki LRHS MWgw
	NBre NLRH NOak WPer
'Sunray'	CBcs CDoC COlW CSBt CWib
	EAEE EBee ECtt IHMH LAst LRHS
	LSRN MBri MNrw MWgw NGdn
	NOak SPet SPla SPlb SPoG SRms
	SWvt WFar WMoo WPer WWeb
	WWye
'Tequila Sunrise' (v)	EChP EHoe EMan MBNS NMoo
	SHop
tinctoria	MSal
tripteris	CAby CPou EChP EMon GBin
	LPhx MDKP MSte NBre SAga SHar
	SMad SMar SSvw WMoo WPer
- 'Pierre Bennerup'	EMon
verticillata	EBee EBrs ECha ECrN EHrv ENot
	EPfP IHMH LRHS MBrN MDun
	MHer MWat NPer SDix SRms SWat
	WFar WHal WTin
- 'Golden Gain'	CTri EAEE EBee ECtt EMan EPla
	GBri GSki LHop LRHS MArl MLLN
	NGdn NHol WMnd
- 'Golden Shower'	see *C. verticillata* 'Grandiflora'
§ - 'Grandiflora' ♀^{H4}	CBcs CPrp CTri EBee EBrs ELan
	EPfP ERou GMaP GSki MNFA
	MRav MWgw NCGa NFor
	NGdn NHol NOak NVic SBla
	SMad SPer SPla WCAu WCot WFar
	WMnd
- 'Moonbeam' ♀^{H4}	More than 30 suppliers
- 'Old Timer' ♀^{H4}	SDix
- 'Zagreb' ♀^{H4}	More than 30 suppliers

coriander see *Coriandrum sativum*

Coriandrum (Apiaceae)

sativum	CArn CSev EOHP GPoy ILis LRHS
	MHer MNHC MWat NBlu NVic
	SIde WPer
- 'Leisure'	CBod CSev MBow NPri
- 'Santo'	ELau NGHP WJek

Coriaria ✿ (Coriariaceae)

arborea	WCru
intermedia B&SWJ 019	WCru
japonica	IDee NLar WCot WCru
- B&SWJ 2833	WCru
- subsp. *intermedia*	WCru
B&SWJ 3877	
kingiana	ECou WCru
§ *microphylla*	WCru
- B&SWJ 8999	WCru
myrtifolia	CBcs GSki NLar WCru WFar
	XPep
napalensis	NLar WCru
- BWJ 7755	WCru
pteridoides	WCru
ruscifolia	WCru
- HCM 98178	WCru
sarmentosa	GCal WCru
terminalis var.	CTrG EMan EPfP GBuc GCal LSou
xanthocarpa	NLar WCot WCru WPGP
- - GWJ 9204	WCru
- - HWJK 2112c	WCru
thymifolia	see *C. microphylla*

Coris (Primulaceae)

monspeliensis	EMan XPep

Cornukaempferia (Zingiberaceae)

aurantiflora	MOak

Cornus ✿ (Cornaceae)

alba L.	CCVT CDoC CDul CLnd CTrG
	ECrN ENot EWTr IHMH ISea
	MDun MHer MRav NWea SRms
	WDin WMou
* - 'Albovariegata' (v)	ECho IFoB
- 'Alleman's Compact' **new**	CPMA
- 'Argenteovariegata'	see *C. alba* 'Variegata'
- 'Aurea' ♀^{H4}	More than 30 suppliers
- Chief Bloodgood =	CPMA
'Chblzam' **new**	
- 'Cream Cracker'^{PBR} (v)	MAsh NHol
new	
- 'Elegantissima' (v) ♀^{H4}	More than 30 suppliers
- 'Gouchaultii' (v)	CBcs CPMA EBee ECrN EPfP EWTr
	LPan LRHS MAsh MBar MRav NPri
	SPer SRms WDin WFar
- 'Hedgerow'	MAsh WPat
- 'Hessei' misapplied	see *C. sanguinea* 'Compressa'
- 'Hessei'	MRav
- Ivory Halo =	EBee EMil ENot EPfP LRHS MAsh
'Bailhalo'^{PBR}	MBNS MBri MGos MRav NPri
	NWea SPer SPoG WGer
- 'Kesselringii'	More than 30 suppliers
- 'Red Gnome'	LTwo MAsh WPat
- 'Ruby' **new**	CPMA
- 'Siberian Pearls'	CBcs CPMA EBee ELan MBlu
	MGos NEgg NLar SSta
§ - 'Sibirica' ♀^{H4}	More than 30 suppliers
- 'Sibirica Variegata' (v)	CBow CDoC CMac CPMA EBee
	ENot EPfP EPla EWTr LPan LRHS
	LSRN MAsh MBar MBlu MGos
	NCGa NEgg NPri SHBN SLim SPer
	SPoG SSpi SSta SWvt WFar
- 'Snow Pearls' **new**	CPMA
- 'Spaethii' (v) ♀^{H4}	More than 30 suppliers
- 'Variegata' (v)	CBcs ECho LAst MGos
- 'Westonbirt'	see *C. alba* 'Sibirica'
alternifolia	CMCN CTho EBee ELan GIBF LAst
	MDun SSpi WPat
§ - 'Argentea' (v) ♀^{H4}	More than 30 suppliers
- 'Silver Giant' (v)	CPMA
- 'Variegata'	see *C. alternifolia* 'Argentea'
amomum	CAbP CBcs GIBF NHol NLar WFar
	WWpP
- 'Blue Cloud' **new**	CPMA
- subsp. *obliqua*	WPGP
angustata	GIBF SPer
§ 'Ascona'	CBcs CEnd CPMA ELan EPfP
	IMGH LRHS MBlu MBri NEgg NLar
	SSpi SSta WPat
Aurora = 'Rutban'	CPMA MBlu MPkF NLar
(Stellar Series)	
§ *canadensis* ♀^{H4}	More than 30 suppliers
- RBS 0219	ITer
candidissima Marshall	see *C. racemosa*
capitata	CAgr CBcs CDoC CEnd CHEx
	CMac CPLG CPne CSBt CTho
	CTrG CTri EPfP EShb GIBF LRHS
	MAsh MWya NLar SEND SGar SSpi
	WCru WCwm WFar WPGP WPat
	WPic
- subsp. *emeiensis*	SSpi
§ Celestial = 'Rutdan'	CPMA MPkF NLar
(Stellar Series)	
'Centennial'	LRHS
chinensis	SWvt
'Constellation'	CPMA
(Stellar Series)	

controversa	CBcs CDul CLnd CMCN CTho	
	CTri ECho ECrN ELan EMil EPfP	
	EWTr LPan MBar MBlu MDun	
	SHBN SLPl SPer SReu SSpi SSta	
	SWvt WDin WFar WHCr WHar	
	WOrn WPGP	
§ - 'Frans Type'	CBcs CEnd ELan ERom LSRN MBlu	
	MBri SHBN SReu SSta WDin	
	WHCG WPat	
I - 'Marginata Nord'	CTho NLar NPal	
- 'Pagoda'	EPfP MBlu MBri NBhm NLar NPal	
	SBrw SSpi	
- 'Variegata' (v) ♀H4	More than 30 suppliers	
- 'Variegata' Frans type (v)	see *C. controversa* 'Frans Type'	
- 'Winter Orange'	NLar	
'Eddie's White Wonder' ♀H4	More than 30 suppliers	
florida	CCVT CDul CLnd CMCN CTho	
	EPfP EWTr GIBF ISea LAst LRHS	
	MBar NBlu SBrw SPer WBVN	
	WDin WHCr WNor	
- 'Alba Plena' (d)	CPMA NLar	
- 'Andrea Hart'	CPMA	
- 'Apple Blossom'	CMac CPMA ECho	
- Cherokee Brave =	CPMA CWib ECho LRHS NCGa	
'Comco No 1'	NLar SSpi	
- 'Cherokee Chief' ♀H4	CAbP CBcs CDul CEnd CPMA CTri	
	CWib ECho EPfP IMGH LRHS	
	MGos MPkF NLar SBLw SBrw	
	SHBN SMur SPer WDin WFar	
	WGob WOrn WPat	
- 'Cherokee Daybreak'	see *C. florida* 'Daybreak'	
- 'Cherokee Princess'	CPMA ECho LRHS MAsh MPkF	
	NCGa MSur SSpi	
- 'Cherokee Sunset'	see *C. florida* 'Sunset'	
- 'Cloud Nine'	CBcs CDoC CPMA ECho MGos	
	MPkF MWea NCGa NLar SLdr	
	SPoG WOrn WPat	
* - 'Daniela'	NLar	
§ - 'Daybreak' (v)	CEnd COtt CPMA CWib ECho	
	MBri MGos MPkF SBrw SPer WPat	
- 'First Lady'	CBcs CMac CPMA ECho	
- 'Fragrant Cloud'	ECho	
- 'G.H. Ford' (v)	CPMA	
- 'Golden Nugget'	CPMA ECho	
- 'Junior Miss'	CEnd CPMA EMil	
- 'Junior Miss Variegated'	CPMA	
(v)		
- 'Moonglow'	CPMA	
- 'Pendula'	CPMA	
- f. ***pluribracteata*** (d)	NLar	
- 'Purple Glory'	CPMA ECho MBri NLar SBrw	
- 'Pygmaea' **new**	NLar	
- 'Rainbow' (v)	CAbP CBcs COtt CPMA CWib EPfP	
	LRHS MAsh MBri MGos MPkF	
	NEgg SBod SBrw SHBN SPer SPla	
	SPoG SSta WDin WPat	
- 'Red Giant'	CAbP CPMA ELan LMil LRHS SMur	
	SPer SPoG SSpi	
- 'Royal Red'	CPMA MPkF	
- f. ***rubra***	CBcs CSBt CTri CWib ECho ELan	
	EPfP LAst LRHS MBri MGos MWea	
	SBLw SBrw SPoG SSta WDin WFar	
	WGer WNor	
- 'Spring Day'	ECho	
- 'Spring Song'	CMac CPMA ECho	
- 'Springtime'	CPMA ECho	
- 'Stoke's Pink'	CEnd CPMA ECho	
§ - 'Sunset' (v)	CBcs CEnd CPMA CWib ECho	
	MGos MPkF NLar SBLw SBrw	
	SHBN SWvt WPat	
- 'Sweetwater'	CEnd CPMA EMil	
- 'Tricolor'	see *C. florida* 'Welchii'	
- 'Variegata'	SBLw	
- 'Weaver's White'	ECho MPkF	
§ - 'Welchii' (v)	CEnd CPMA	

- 'White Cloud'	CPMA ELan MBri MPkF	
- 'Xanthocarpa'	MPkF	
'Gloria Birkett'	LRHS SSpi	
'Greenlight'	NPro WGHP	
hemsleyi	EPla	
hessei misapplied	see *C. sanguinea* 'Compressa'	
hongkongensis	IDee	
'Kelsey Dwarf'	see *C. sericea* 'Kelseyi'	
'Kenwyn Clapp'	CPMA	
kousa	CDoC CDul CMCN CPne CTbh	
	CTho EBee ECho ECrN ELan EPfP	
	ERom ISea LAst LRHS MBar MDun	
	MLan NBlu NEgg NFor SBrw SHBN	
	SPer SPlb WDin WFar WHCG WHar	
	WCru	
- B&SWJ 5494	CPMA	
- 'Aget' **new**	CPMA	
- 'All Summer'	CPMA	
- 'Autumn Rose'	CPMA EPfP NLar	
- 'Beni-fuji'	CPMA NLar	
- 'Big Apple'	CPMA	
- 'Blue Shadow'	CPMA	
- 'Bonfire' (v)	LRHS	
- 'Bultinck's Beauty'	LRHS	
- 'Bultinck's Giant'	NLar	
- 'Bush's Pink'	CPMA	
- 'China Dawn' (v)	CPMA	
- var. ***chinensis*** ♀H4	More than 30 suppliers	
- - 'Bodnant Form'	CEnd CPMA WPGP	
- - 'China Girl'	CAbP CBcs CDul CEnd CPMA	
	CWib ELan EPfP EWTr LBuc LMil	
	LRHS MAsh MBlu MBri MGos	
	MSwo MWya SHBN SPer SSpi SSta	
	WDin WOrn WPGP WPat	
- - 'Greta's Gold' (v)	CPMA	
- - 'Milky Way'	CMCN CPMA CWib ECho LBuc	
	MBlu MBri MPkF NLar SHBN	
- - 'Snowflake'	CPMA	
- - Spinners form	CPMA	
- - 'Summer Stars'	CPMA NLar	
- - 'White Dusted'	CPMA EPfP	
- - 'White Fountain'	MBlu MBri MPkF NLar	
- - 'Wieting's Select'	CPMA MBri MPkF	
- - 'Wisley Queen' **new**	CAbP LRHS	
- 'Claudine'	CPMA	
- 'Doctor Bump' **new**	CPMA	
- 'Doubloon'	CPMA ECho SPer	
- 'Dwarf Pink'	CPMA	
- 'Ed Mezitt'	CPMA	
- 'Elizabeth Lustgarten'	CPMA SSta	
- 'Fanfare' **new**	CPMA	
- 'Galilean'	CPMA	
- 'Gay Head' **new**	CPMA	
I - 'Girard's Nana'	CPMA	
- 'Gold Cup' (v)	CPMA MPkF	
- 'Gold Star' (v)	CAbP CEnd CMCN CMac CPMA	
	CWib ECho ELan EMil EPfP LBuc	
	LRHS MBlu MGos NEgg NLar	
	SHBN SPla SPoG SSpi	
- 'Greensleeves' **new**	CPMA	
- 'Heart Throb' **new**	CPMA	
- 'Highland'	CPMA	
- 'John Slocock'	SSpi	
- 'Kreus Dame'	CPMA MBri MPkF	
- 'Little Beauty' **new**	CPMA	
- 'Lustgarten Weeping'	CPMA LRHS NLar	
- 'Madame Butterfly'	CEnd CPMA LRHS MBri SSta	
- 'Milky Way Select'	CPMA ECho LPan MGos	
- 'Minuma'	NLar	
- 'Miss Petty'	MPkF NLar	
- 'Moonbeam'	CPMA MBri MPkF	
- 'Mount Fuji'	NLar	
- 'National'	CPMA ECho MBlu MGos MPkF	
	NLar WPat	
- 'Nicole'	CDoC WDin WGob	
- 'Peve Foggy'	NLar	
- 'Peve Limbo' (v)	CPMA MPkF NLar	

- 'Polywood'	CPMA
- 'Radiant Rose'	CPMA MPkF NLar
- 'Rasen'	CPMA MBri NLar
- 'Rel Whirlwind'	CPMA
- 'Rosea'	CPMA
- 'Samaratin' (v)	CEnd CPMA MBri MPkF
- 'Satomi' ♀H4	More than 30 suppliers
- 'Schmetterling'	CPMA MBri
- 'Snowboy' (v)	CBcs CEnd CPMA LRHS NLar
- 'Southern Cross'	CPMA
- 'Square Dance' **new**	CPMA
- 'Steeple'	CPMA
- 'Summer Fun' **new**	CPMA
- 'Summer Majesty'	CPMA
- 'Sunsplash' (v)	CPMA
- 'Temple Jewel' (v)	CPMA LRHS
- 'Teutonia'	CPMA MBri MPkF
- 'Tinknor's Choice'	CPMA
- 'Trinity Star'	CPMA
- 'Triple Crown'	CPMA
- 'Tsukubanomine'	CPMA NLar
- 'U.S.A.'	MPkF
- 'Vale Milky Way' (v) **new**	NLar
- 'Weaver's Weeping'	CPMA MPkF
- 'Wolf Eyes' (v)	CPMA MBlu MPkF
macrophylla Wall.	CMCN EPfP GIBF WCwm WPGP
mas	More than 30 suppliers
- 'Aurea' (v)	CAbP CPMA EBee ELan EPfP LRHS MAsh MBri MGos MRav NEgg SBrw SLim SPer SPoG SSpi SSta WDin WPat
§ - 'Aureoelegantissima' (v)	CEnd CPMA CWib EBee LRHS MAsh MBri NLar SBrw SPer SSpi WFar WPGP WPat WSHC
- 'Elegantissima'	see *C. mas* 'Aureoelegantissima'
I - 'Flava' **new**	CPMA
- 'Golden Glory' ♀H4	CBcs CPMA EPfP MBlu MBri NLar
- 'Jolico'	CPMA MBlu MBri NLar
- 'Pioneer' **new**	CPMA
- 'Redstone' **new**	CPMA
- 'Spring Glow'	CPMA NLar
- 'Variegata' (v) ♀H4	CBcs CMCN CPMA CTho EBee EPfP LRHS MAsh MBlu MBri MGos NLar NPal SBrw SPoG SSpi WDin WFar WPat
N 'Norman Hadden' ♀H4	CAbP CDoC CDul CEnd CMCN CMac CPMA CSBt CTho ECho EPfP IMGH LAst LRHS MRav MWya SBrw SHFr SPer SSpi SSta WBor WDin WFar WPGP WPat
nuttallii	CTho CTri CWib ECho ECrN ELan EPfP EWTr IMGH ISea LAst LRHS MDun MGos NWea SHBN SWvt WDin WFar WNor
- 'Ascona'	see *C.* 'Ascona'
- 'Barrick'	CPMA
- 'Colrigo Giant'	CPMA MPkF SSpi
- 'Gold Spot' (v)	CMac CPMA ECho EPfP LRHS MGos WPat
- 'Monarch'	CBcs CPMA CTho NLar
- 'North Star'	CPMA MBri NLar
- 'Pink Blush'	MPkF NLar
- 'Portlemouth'	CEnd CPMA LRHS MAsh NLar SSpi WGob WPat
- 'Zurico'	MPkF NLar
officinalis	CMCN CTho EBee EMil EPfP LPan LRHS MBri MWea NLar SPoG WCwm WDin
'Ormonde'	CPMA ECho LRHS NLar SSpi
paucinervis	GIBF
'Pink Blush'	CPMA
'Porlock' ♀H4	CDul CMCN CPMA EPfP IMGH LRHS MBri NLar SSpi WDin
pumila	CPMA NLar WDin
§ *racemosa*	NLar WFar
rugosa	WNor

x *rutgersiensis* Galaxy	see *C.* Celestial = 'Rutdan'
- 'Ruth Ellen'	see *C.* Ruth Ellen = 'Rutlan'
§ Ruth Ellen = 'Rutlan'	CPMA NLar
(Stellar Series)	
sanguinea	CBcs CCVT CDul CLnd CRWN CTri ECrN EPfP LBuc MRav MSwo NFor NWea SPer WDin WHar WMou XPep
§ - 'Anny'	EBee MAsh MBlu
§ - 'Compressa'	EBee EPfP NHol NLar WSPU WWes
- 'Magic Flame'	MAsh MBri
- 'Midwinter Fire'	More than 30 suppliers
§ - 'Winter Beauty'	CBgR CDoC CPMA CSBt CWib EBee EPfP MBlu NEgg SHBN SLon WFar WPat WSPU
- 'Winter Flame'	see *C.* 'Anny'
§ *sericea*	CArn
- 'Budd's Yellow'	LRHS MBri MGos
- 'Cardinal'	LRHS MBri MGos NLar
- 'Coral Red' **new**	CPMA
§ - 'Flaviramea' ♀H4	More than 30 suppliers
- 'Hedgerows Gold'	CPMA SPoG WCot
- 'Isanti' **new**	CPMA
§ - 'Kelseyi'	CBgR CMac CRez EBee EHyt EPla LRHS MBNS MBar MRav NPri NPro SBod SLPl SPer SPoG WDin WWpP
- Kelsey's Gold = 'Rosco'	SLon WPat
- 'Sunshine'	CPMA NPro
§ - 'White Gold' (v) ♀H4	CBow CDoC CPMA EBee EHoe EPla MBri MRav MSwo NPro SLon SPer SPoG WDin WFar WMoo
- 'White Spot'	see *C. sericea* 'White Gold'
* *skangensis* **new**	GIBF
Stardust = 'Rutfan'	CPMA
(Stellar Series)	
Stellar Pink = 'Rutgan'	CPMA CWib MBri MPkF NLar
(Stellar Series)	
stolonifera	see *C. sericea*
- 'White Spot'	see *C. sericea* 'White Gold'
suecica	GIBF
walteri	CMCN NLar WCwm WFar
wilsoniana	GIBF

Corokia (Escalloniaceae)

buddlejoides	CBcs CDoC CMHG CWib ECou GGar SBrw SOWG SPer WCru WFar
'Coppershine'	CMHG
cotoneaster	CAbP CMac CSBt CTri CTrw ECho ECou ELan EMan EPfP EPot LRHS MGos SBod SBrw SLon SMad SMur SPer SPoG WBrE WCMO WCot WFar WPat WSHC WWes
- 'Boundary Hill'	ECou
- 'Brown's Stream'	ECou
- 'Hodder River'	ECou
- 'Little Prince'	GGar
- 'Ohau Scarlet'	ECou
- 'Ohau Yellow'	ECou
- 'Swale Stream'	ECou
- 'Wanaka'	ECou
macrocarpa	CDoC ECou ISea SDix WSHC
x *virgata*	CAbP CBcs CDoC CMHG CMac CTrC CTri EBee ECou ELan EPfP ISea LRHS MBlu MCCP MWhi NScw SAPC SArc SBrw SPer SPlb SWvt WBVN WCru WSHC
- 'Bronze King'	CBrm CDoC CPLG EBee SBrw SPer
- 'Bronze Lady'	ECou
- 'Cheesemanii'	ECou GGar
- 'County Park Lemon'	ECou SOWG
- 'County Park Orange'	ECou
- 'County Park Purple'	ECou
- 'County Park Red'	ECou
- 'Envy'	ECou

- 'Everglades'	ECou
- 'Frosted Chocolate'	CBcs CDoC CTrC EBee ECou EPfP
	LHop LTwo MGos SBrw WDin
	WFar
- 'Geenty's Green'	ECou
- 'Havering'	ECou
- 'Mangatangi'	MGos
- 'Pink Delight'	CDoC ECou EPfP SBrw
- 'Red Wonder'	CBrm CDoC CMHG CMac CPen
	CTrC EBee GGar LRHS MWgw
	SBrw SEND SOWG SPoG WCMO
	WDin
- 'Sandrine'	ECou
- 'Silver Ghost' **new**	ECou
- 'Sunsplash' (v)	CBcs CDoC CTrC ECou LHop
	LRHS LTwo MGos SAga SBrw SPoG
- 'Virgata'	ECou MGos
- 'Wingletye'	ECou
- 'Yellow Wonder'	CBcs CMHG CPen CTrC EBee
	ECot ECou EMan GGar MGos SBod
	SBrw SPoG WDin

Coronilla (Papilionaceae)

comosa	see *Hippocrepis comosa*
emerus	see *Hippocrepis emerus*
glauca	see *C. valentina* subsp. *glauca*
minima	SBla WAbe XPep
valentina	CDMG CDoC CMac CRHN
	CSPN EMil LHop SBra SDix
	XPep
§ - subsp. *glauca* ♀H3	CBgR CDul CFee CMac CSBt
	CWib EBee ELan EPfP ERea LAst
	LRHS MWhi SBrw SGar SPer SPoG
	SRms SUsu WAbe WHCG WPat
	XPep
- - 'Brockhill Blue'	SBra WCMO
- - 'Citrina' ♀H3	More than 30 suppliers
* - - 'Pygmaea'	WCot WWFP
- - 'Variegata' (v)	More than 30 suppliers
§ *varia*	CAgr CArn NBre NLar NPri SHGN
	XPep

Correa (Rutaceae)

alba	CBcs CCCN CDoC CPLG CTrC
	ECou EPfP SBrw SMur WGwG
	XPep
- 'Pinkie' ♀H2	CBcs CPLG ECou SDys SHGN
	SOWG WCot
backhouseana ♀H2	CAbb CBcs CDoC CPLG CPle
	CSam CTrG CTri EBee ECre EPfP
	GGar GQui IDee LHop NLar SAga
	SBod SBrw SGar SLon SOWG SPoG
	WCMO WCot WGwG WPat WSHC
	WSPU
- 'Peaches and Cream'	SRkn
baeuerlenii	CMHG CPLG SOWG
decumbens	CPLG CTrC ECou GSki SDys SMur
	SOWG
'Dusky Bells' ♀H2	CBcs CCCN CDMG CDoC
	CHll CSWP CSam CTrC CTri
	ECou EPfP LHop MOak SAga
	SBra SBrw SMur SOWG WCMO
	WCot
'Dusky Maid'	CCCN CPLG WAbe WCMO
'Federation Belle'	ECou SOWG
glabra	ECou
- red-flowered	ECou
'Gwen'	ECou SOWG
'Harrisii'	see *C.* 'Mannii'
'Inglewood Gold'	ECou
'Ivory Bells'	ECou SDys
lawrenceana	CDoC CTrC ECou GQui SBrw
	SEND WAbe
§ 'Mannii' ♀H2	CBcs CPLG CPom CSev EBee
	ECou EPfP SBrw SOWG SPoG
	WCMO WSHC

'Marian's Marvel' ♀H2	CAbb CCCN CMHG CPLG ECou
	SDys SOWG WAbe
'Peachy Cream'	CDoC EPfP SAga SBrw SMur
	WCMO
'Pink Mist'	ECou
'Poorinda Mary'	ECou SOWG
pulchella ♀H2	CDoC CTri SOWG
§ *reflexa* ♀H2	CDoC CPLG ECou IDee SOWG
	WAbe
- var. *nummariifolia*	WAbe WCot
- var. *reflexa*	CPLG
- var. *scabridula*	SOWG
'Yanakie'	
* - *virens*	CPLG WEas
* *spectabilis*	CPLG
I *viridiflora*	GQui

Cortaderia ✿ (Poaceae)

CB/Arg K2-2	WCot
RCB/Arg Y-1	WCot
argentea	see *C. selloana*
fulvida misapplied	see *C. richardii*
§ *fulvida* (Buchanan) Zotov	CBcs CBig EBee EWes EWin MNrw
	SMad SPur WDin
richardii misapplied	see *C. fulvida* (Buchanan) Zotov
§ *richardii* (Endl.) Zotov	CAby CBcs CBig CKno CMCo
♀H3-4	CSec EBrs EHoe EPPr EPla EWes
	EWsh GAbr GGar GMaP IBlr NVic
	SAPC SArc SMad SWal WCot WCru
	WMnd
- BR 26	GGar
§ *selloana*	CBcs CBig CDul CHEx CSBt
	CTrG CTri EHul EPfP MBar MRav
	NBir NBlu NFor NHol SAPC SArc
	SPlb SWal WBVN WFar WMoo
	WMul
§ - 'Albolineata' (v)	CBcs CBrm CKno EBrs EHoe EMil
	EWes EWsh MAsh MBri MCCP
	MGos MWht NOak SEND SLim
	SPer SPoG SSta SSto SWvt WLeb
	WPat
§ - 'Aureolineata' (v) ♀H3	CBcs CBrm CDoC CMac CSam
	CWCL EBee EHoe ELan ENot EPfP
	EWsh LAst LRHS MAsh MCCP
	MGos MMoz MWhi NLar SLim
	SPer SPoG SSto WFar WLeb WPGP
	WPat
- 'Cool Ice'	CPen
- 'Elegans'	CBig
- 'Gold Band'	see *C. selloana* 'Aureolineata'
- 'Golden Comet'	EBee
- 'Icalma' **new**	CPen EPPr
- 'Monstrosa'	SMad
- 'Patagonia'	EHoe EPPr
- 'Pink Feather'	EPfP SAdn SPer WFar WWeb
- 'Pumila' ♀H4	More than 30 suppliers
- 'Rendatleri'	CBcs CBig CDoC ELan ENot EPfP
	EWsh LRHS MAsh SCoo SLim
	SMad SPer WDin
- 'Rosea'	CBig EPfP IHMH LBMP LRHS MBar
	MGos NBlu NGdn WFar
- 'Senior'	IHMH
- Silver Feather =	ENot
'Notcort'	
- 'Silver Fountain'	ELan EPfP LRHS
- 'Silver Stripe'	see *C. selloana* 'Albolineata'
- 'Splendid Star'PBR (v)	CBcs MAsh MBri NLar SAdn SMad
	SPoG SWvt
- 'Sunningdale Silver' ♀H3	CBcs CBig CDoC CMac EBee
	ECha ECtt EHoe EHul ELan
	ENot EPfP GSki IHMH ISea
	LAst LRHS MAsh MBri MGos
	SHBN SLim SMad SPer SPoG
	SWvt WDin WFar
- 'White Feather'	IHMH MWhi NGdn WFar WMoo
	WWeb

Cortiella (Apiaceae)
aff. *hookeri* HWJK 2291   WCru

Cortusa (Primulaceae)

brotheri	ECho NEgg
- CC 4625	WCot
matthioli	CPom ECho EDAr EPfP GBBs GCrs GGar GKev MBow NEgg NMen NWCA SRms WBVN WFar WRos WWhi
- 'Alba'	EBee ECho GBuc GEdr GKev NEgg NLar NMen NWCA SRms
- subsp. **pekinensis**	CFir CLyd CSec EBee ECho GBuc GKev NJOw NLar NMen SRms
- var. **yezoensis**	EBee
turkestanica	ECho GIBF

Corydalis ✿ (Papaveraceae)

CC 3862 **new**	WCot
from Sichuan, China	CPom MDKP NCot
alexeenkoana subsp. **vittae**	see *C. vittae*
x **allenii**	GCrs
ambigua misapplied	see *C. fumariifolia*
ambigua Cham. & Schldlt.	WWst
angustifolia	NDlv
- white-flowered	WWst
anthriscifolia	CLAP
'Blackberry Wine'	CDes CElw CHll CSpe GBri GBuc LBMP MAvo MDKP NCGa NPri SPur WFar
'Blue Panda'	see *C. flexuosa* 'Blue Panda'
bracteata white	WWst
bulbosa misapplied	see *C. cava*
bulbosa (L.) DC.	see *C. solida*
buschii	CDes CLAP CPom EBee ECho ERos GCrs GEdr NDov NHar NRya SBla SCnR WPGP WPrP WWst
cashmeriana	CLAP CPBP GCrs GEdr NLAp SBla WAbe WHal
cashmeriana x **flexuosa** **new**	CBro EAEE
- 'Kailash'	CLAP EMon GBuc MAvo NLar
caucasica	ERos GBuc NMen
- var. **alba** misapplied	see *C. malkensis*
§ **cava**	CLAP CPom CStu EBee EChP ECho EPot LPhx MWgw NJOw SHGN WAbe WFar WShi
- 'Albiflora'	CLAP ECho EPot LPhx SBla WAbe
- subsp. **cava** **new**	ECho
- subsp. **marschalliana** var. **purpureolilacina**	WWst
chaerophylla	IBlr
- B&SWJ 2951	WCru
cheilanthifolia	More than 30 suppliers
curviflora	EPot
- subsp. **rosthornii**	EWes WCot
- - DJHC 0615	SMHy
I **decipiens** misapplied ♀H4	CPom ECho EPot MWgw WPrP
I **decipiens** misapplied purple-flowered	EBee ECho
decipiens Schott, Nyman & Kotschy	see *C. solida* subsp. *incisa*
§ **densiflora**	WWst
'Early Bird'	EBee EWes
elata	More than 30 suppliers
- 'Blue Summit'	CLAP EBrs EPPr MSte SBla
elata x **flexuosa** clone 1	CLAP CMdw CPom GBin GCrs GEdr WCot WPrP
'Electric Blue' (V) **new**	NBhm
erdelii	WWst

flexuosa ♀H4	CFee CMil CPLG CPne CSpe EBee ECho EDAr EGle EMar EPfP EPot IFro LAst MArl MLHP MNrw MTho NCob NRnb SGar SMac WAbe WBor WFar WSHC
- CD&R 528	EHyt MRav NRya
- 'Balang Mist'	CLAP EGle SBla SUsu
- 'Blue Dragon'	see *C. flexuosa* 'Purple Leaf'
§ - 'Blue Panda'	CElw EBee EGle EPfP EWes GBuc GMaP IBlr LRHS MDun NHar NLar SBla WCMO WCot WFar
- 'Blue Skies' **new**	EBee
- 'China Blue'	More than 30 suppliers
- - CD&R 528c	CAvo CBro CElw CHea CMHG COlW EBee ECha EDAr EHyt EWes LRHS MBri SMad SWat WCot WCru WHer
- 'Golden Panda' (v)	CBct CBow EBee LHop LSou MBNS MCCP MMHG NLar NPri SPoG WCMO WMoo WPrP
- 'Hale Cat' **new**	EPPr
- 'Nightshade'	CElw EBee ECtt GBuc MAvo NBid NCob SWat WBrk WCot WFar WIvy WPrP
I - 'Norman's Seedling'	EBee EPPr WCot WPGP
- 'Père David'	More than 30 suppliers
§ - 'Purple Leaf'	More than 30 suppliers
§ **fumariifolia**	ECho MTho NLAp
glauca	see *C. sempervirens*
glaucescens	WWst
- 'Early Beauty'	EPot
- 'Moonlight Beauty'	EPot
- 'Pink Beauty'	WWst
gorodkovii	GIBF
gracilis	WWst
haussknechtii	EHyt
henrikii	EHyt
incisa	ECho
- B&SWJ 4417	WCru
- f. **pallescens**	NRnb
integra	WWst
jingyuanensis	NLAp
'Kingfisher'	CLAP EWes NHar SBch SBla WAbe WCot WFar
kusnetzovii	EHyt WWst
ledebouriana	NMen
leucanthema	CLAP CPom
- DJHC 752	CDes WPrP
- 'Silver Spectre' (v)	LBMP NSti SOkd SPoG WCMO WLin WTMC
linstowiana	CSec EHyt EMon EPPr LPhx NRnb NWCA
- CD&R 605	CLAP
lopinensis **new**	NLAp
§ **lutea**	CBcs CRWN EBee EChP EDAr EMar EPfP GBuc IBlr IFoB IFro MWgw NCob NPer NVic SEND SHFr SPoG SRms WCot WMoo
lydica	WWst
magadanica	EDAr GIBF
§ **malkensis** ♀H4	CMea EHyt ERos ETow GBin GBuc GCrs NBir NMen SBla SCnR
nariniana	WWst
nobilis	CPom CSec CSpe EBee MLLN
nudicaulis	ECho WWst
ochotensis B&SWJ 3138	WCru
- B&SWJ 917	WCru
§ **ochroleuca**	CDes CElw CRow CSec CSpe EChP EMar EPot GAbr GCrs MTho NJOw NPol SBch WFar WHil WMoo
ophiocarpa	CSec CSpe EBee EGoo EHoe ELan EMan EMar GCal IBlr MBNS MRav MWhi NBur NRnb SPoG SWal WFoF WMoo

oppositifolia **new** — WWst
- subsp. *kurdica* **new** — WWst
ornata — WWst
paczoskii — EAEE EBee ECho EHyt ERos GBuc LRHS NDlv NMen
- RS 12180 — EBee
pallida — NRnb
- B&SWJ 395 — WCru
paschei — EHyt
popovii — GCrs MTho SCnR
pseudofumaria alba — see *C. ochroleuca*
pumila — EPot ETow WLin
repens — WWst
rosea — IBlr
ruksansii — WWst
§ *saxicola* — NPri
scandens — see *Dicentra scandens*
schanginii — WLin
- subsp. *ainii* ♀H2 — ECho
- subsp. *schanginii* — GCrs
scouleri — NBir
seisumsiana — WWst
§ *sempervirens* — EMan GIBF WRos WSan
- 'Alba' — ECho MWgw WFoF
siamensis B&SWJ 7200 — WCru
smithiana — CSec GKev WFar
§ *solida* — CBos CBro CPom CStu EBee EBrs EChP ECho ELan EPot GCrs IBlr ITim LRHS MRav NJOw NMen NRya NWCA WBVN WCot WFar WPnP WShi WTin
- BM 8499 — NHol
- 'Firecracker' **new** — GCrs
- 'First Kiss' — WWst
- 'Harkov' — GCrs
- 'Highland Sunset' — GCrs
§ - subsp. *incisa* ♀H4 — CMea CRez EBee EBrs ECho EHyt GCrs LRHS MNrw MTho WPrP WShi
- 'Maggie Mathew' **new** — SOkd
- 'Margaret' — WWst
- 'Merlin' — WWst
- Nettleton seedlings — EPot
- pink and red shades — CFwr
- 'Snowlark' — WWst
§ - subsp. *solida* — CFwr CLAP CMil CPBP EHyt EPot GCrs NBir NDov NMen NRya WLin WTin
- - from Penza, Russia — EAEE GBuc GCrs LRHS SBla
- - 'Beth Evans' — CMea CRez EBee EBrs ECho EHyt EPot GBin GCrs GEdr GKev IPot LPhx LTwo NHar NMen SCnR SUsu WCot WLin
- - 'Dieter Schacht' ♀H4 — EBee ECho EHyt GCrs NLar NMen WAbe WCot
- - 'George Baker' ♀H4 — CBro CMea CPom CRez EBee EBrs ECho EHyt EPot ETow GBuc GCrs GEdr GKev GSki IPot LBee LPhx LRHS LTwo MTho NDov NMen NSla SOkd SUsu WAbe WCot WWst
- - 'Highland Mist' — GCrs
- - 'Lahovice' — EHyt GCrs NMen WAbe
- - 'Munich Sunrise' — EHyt
- - 'Prasil Sunset' — EHyt
- - 'White Knight' — GCrs
- f. *transsylvanica* — see *C. solida* subsp. *solida*
- 'White Bird' **new** — EPot
- 'White King' — WWst
'Spinners' — CAby CDes CElw CLAP EBee EPPr LPhx SBch SMeo SUsu WPGP WSHC
taliensis — CAby CEnt CPom CSec GKev
- ACE 2443 — EPot
tauricola — GCrs WWst
thalictrifolia Franch. — see *C. saxicola*

tomentella — CSec GEdr GKev SIng
'Tory MP' — CAby CDes CElw CLAP CPne CSam EBee GAbr GEdr MDKP MNrw NBid NChi NHar WHoo WLin WPGP WPrP
trachycarpa — EPot
transsylvanica — see *C. solida* subsp. *solida*
turtschaninovii — WWst
§ *vittae* — ECho EHyt
vivipara — ECho
wendelboi — ECho EHyt GCrs
- subsp. *congesta* — WWst
- - 'Abant Wine' — EPot
wilsonii — EHyt GEdr GKev IBlr NRnb SBla WEas
* *woroshilovii* **new** — WWst
zetterlundii — GBuc NDlv

Corylopsis ✿ (*Hamamelidaceae*)

from Chollipo, South Korea — LRHS
§ *glabrescens* — CPMA GIBF IDee IMGH LRHS NLar SBrw SMur WNor WWes
- var. *gotoana* — EPfP LRHS NLar SMur SSpi SSta
- - 'Chollipo' — MAsh SPoG SSta
glandulifera — NLar
himalayana — CBcs
multiflora — SSpi SSta
pauciflora ♀H4 — More than 30 suppliers
platypetala — see *C. sinensis* var. *calvescens*
- var. *laevis* — see *C. sinensis* var. *calvescens*
sinensis — CLnd EBee GIBF NEgg SBrw WPGP
§ - var. *calvescens* — CBcs CPMA SBrw
§ - - f. *veitchiana* ♀H4 — CBcs CPMA ELan EPfP IDee NLar SBrw SMur SPoG WDin
- - - purple-leaved — CPMA
- 'Golden Spring' — MBri NLar
§ - var. *sinensis* ♀H4 — CBcs CBgR CBrm CDoC CMHG CPMA EBee EPfP IMGH LAst SBrw SLon SReu WDin WFar
- - 'Spring Purple' — CAbP CBcs CEnd CMac CPMA EPfP EWTr LRHS MBri NLar SBrw SPla SPoG SSpi SSta WDin WPGP
spicata — CBcs CPMA CSBt CSam GIBF IDee LRHS MBlu NBlu NEgg SBrw SLim
- 'Red Eye' — NLar
veitchiana — see *C. sinensis* var. *calvescens* f. *veitchiana*
willmottiae — see *C. sinensis* var. *sinensis*

Corylus ✿ (*Corylaceae*)

avellana (F) — CBcs CCVT CDoC CDul CLnd CRWN CTri ECrN EPfP ERea GAbr LAst LBuc LRHS MBar MBow MBri MGos NWea SKee SPer WDin WHar WMou WOrn
- 'Anny's Compact Red' **new** — MAsh NHol
- 'Anny's Red Dwarf' — WPat
- 'Aurea' — CDul CEnd CLnd COtt CSBt CTho EBee ECrN ELan EPfP EWTr LBuc LRHS MAsh MBlu MBri MGos MRav NEgg NHol NWea SIFN SLim SPer SPoG SSta SWvt WDin WFar
- 'Bollwylle' — see *C. maxima* 'Halle'sche Riesennuss'
- 'Casina' (F) — CAgr CTho
- 'Contorta' — More than 30 suppliers
- 'Corabel' (F) — CAgr MCoo
- 'Cosford Cob' (F) — CAgr CDoC CDul CSBt CTho CTri ECrN EMui ERea GTwe LBuc LRHS MBlu MBri MGos SDea SKee SPer
- 'Fortin' (F) — ECrN
§ - 'Fuscorubra' (F) — CBgR ECrN MRav MSwo SIFN
- 'Gustav's Zeller' (F) — CAgr MCoo

§   - 'Heterophylla'   CEnd CTho EPfP GTSp NLar SIFN WMou WWes
  - 'Laciniata'   see *C. avellana* 'Heterophylla'
§   - 'Lang Tidlig Zeller'   CAgr MCoo
  - 'Merveille de Bollwyller'   see *C. maxima* 'Halle'sche Riesennuss'
  - 'Nottingham Prolific'   see *C. avellana* 'Pearson's Prolific'
  - 'Pauetet' (F)   CAgr
§   - 'Pearson's Prolific' (F)   ECrN ENot ERea GTwe LBuc SDea SKee
  - 'Pendula'   LPan MBlu SBLw SCoo SIFN
  - 'Purpurea'   see *C. avellana* 'Fuscorubra'
  - 'Red Majestic'[PBR]   CDul CWib ENot LAst LRHS MAsh MBri MPkF NLar WGer WPat
  - 'Tonda di Giffoni'   CAgr MCoo
  - 'Webb's Prize Cob' (F)   CDoC CDul ECrN ERea GTwe MBlu NLar SBLw SDea SKee WMou
chinensis   EGFP
colurna ♀H4   CAgr CDul CLnd CMCN CTho ECrN EPfP LPan LRHS MGos NBee NWea SBLw SPer WBVN WDin WMou
x ***colurnoides*** 'Laroka' (F)   ECrN
Early Long Zeller   see *C. avellana* 'Lang Tidlig Zeller'
ferox GWJ 9293   WCru
maxima (F)   CLnd ECrN EMui GTwe MSwo NWea SDea WDin
  - 'Butler' (F)   CAgr CTho CTri ECrN ERea GTwe LRHS MBri SKee
  - 'Ennis' (F)   CAgr ECrN ERea GTwe SDea SKee
  - 'Fertile de Coutard'   see *C. maxima* 'White Filbert'
  - 'Frizzled Filbert' (F)   ECrN ENot
  - 'Frühe van Frauendorf'   see *C. maxima* 'Red Filbert'
  - 'Garibaldi' (F)   MBlu
  - 'Grote Lambertsnoot'   see *C. maxima* 'Kentish Cob'
  - 'Gunslebert' (F)   CAgr CSBt CTho ECrN ERea GTwe LRHS MBri SDea SKee
  - Halle Giant   see *C. maxima* 'Halle'sche Riesennuss'
§   - 'Halle'sche Riesennuss' (F)   CAgr ECrN ERea GTwe SEND SKee
§   - 'Kentish Cob' (F)   CAgr CBcs CDoC CDul CSBt CTho CWSG ECrN ENot EPfP ERea GTwe LBuc LRHS MBlu MBri MGan MGos MNHC SDea SFam SKee SPer SRms WHar WOrn
  - 'Lambert's Filbert'   see *C. maxima* 'Kentish Cob'
  - 'Longue d'Espagne'   see *C. maxima* 'Kentish Cob'
  - 'Monsieur de Bouweller'   see *C. maxima* 'Halle'sche Riesennuss'
  - 'Purple Filbert'   see *C. maxima* 'Purpurea'
§   - 'Purpurea' (F) ♀H4   More than 30 suppliers
§   - 'Red Filbert' (F)   CEnd CTho CWSG ENot ERea GTwe LRHS MBlu MBri NLar SCoo SKee SLim SPoG WPat
  - 'Red Zellernut'   see *C. maxima* 'Red Filbert'
  - 'Spanish White'   see *C. maxima* 'White Filbert'
§   - 'White Filbert' (F)   CDoC ENot ERea GTwe MBri SKee WHar
  - 'White Spanish Filbert'   see *C. maxima* 'White Filbert'
  - 'Witpit Lambertsnoot'   see *C. maxima* 'White Filbert'
sieboldiana var. ***mandshurica***   CMCN NLar
'Te Terra Red'   CMCN MBlu MBri SBLw SIFN SMad SSpi WMou

Corymbia see *Eucalyptus*

Corynabutilon see *Abutilon*

Corynephorus (Poaceae)
canescens   CBig EHoe EMan ENot MBar NBir NJOw WHrl

Corynocarpus (Corynocarpaceae)
laevigatus   CHEx ECou MBri

Cosmos (Asteraceae)
§ ***atrosanguineus***   More than 30 suppliers
bipinnatus 'Purity'   CSpe
  - 'Sonata Pink'   SPoG
  - 'Sonata White'   LAst SPoG
§ ***peucedanifolius***   CAvo CHad CSpe SAga
  - 'Flamingo' **new**   GBri NBPC NBhm SPoG
I ***pucidanifolia***   see *C. peucedanifolius*
sulphureus   MSal

costmary see *Tanacetum balsamita*

Costus (Costaceae)
amazonicus   MOak
barbatus   MJnS MOak WMul
curvibracteatus   MOak
erythrophyllus   MOak
speciosus   CKob MOak WMul
I   - 'Variegatus'   MOak
stenophyllus   MOak
villosissimus **new**   MOak

Cotinus (Anacardiaceae)
americanus   see *C. obovatus*
§ ***coggygria*** ♀H4   More than 30 suppliers
  - 'Foliis Purpureis'   see *C. coggygria* Rubrifolius Group
  - Golden Spirit = 'Ancot'[PBR]   CAbP CDoC CDul CHad CRez CSBt CWib EBee ELan ENot EPfP EWTr LAst LBuc LHop MAsh MBri MGos MRav NPri NSti SCoo SLim SPer SPoG SWvt WOVN
  - Green Fountain = 'Kolcot'[PBR] **new**   LBuc SPoG
  - 'Kanari'   EBee EMil NLar
  - 'Notcutt's Variety'   ELan ENot EPfP MGos MRav NSti
  - 'Pink Champagne'   CPMA EPfP MBri NLar WPat
  - 'Red Beauty'   CBcs WPat
  - 'Royal Purple' ♀H4   More than 30 suppliers
§   - Rubrifolius Group   CBcs CDul CMac EBee EPfP EWTr NFor SPer SWvt WDin WFar
  - Smokey Joe = 'Lisjo'   MAsh SSta
  - 'Velvet Cloak'   CAbP CBcs CPMA EBee ELan EPfP LRHS MAsh MBri MGos MRav NLar SLon SPer SPla SWvt WHCG
  - 'Young Lady'[PBR]   EPfP MBlu SPer WDin
'Flame' ♀H4   CAbP CBcs CDul CPMA ELan EPfP EWTr LAst LRHS MAsh MBlu MBri MGos MRav NEgg SLim SPla SPoG SSpi WHCG WPat
'Grace'   More than 30 suppliers
§ ***obovatus*** ♀H4   CMCN CMHG ELan EPfP IArd IDee MBlu MBri MRav NLar SHBN S...

Cotoneaster ✿ (Rosa...
CC&McK 465   N...
acuminatus   S...
acutifolius
adpressus ♀H4
§   - 'Little Gem'
  - var. ***praecox***
  - 'Tom Thumb'
affinis
albokermesi...
amoenus
  - 'Fire Moun...
§ ***apiculatus***
§ ***ascendens***
assadii
assamen...

§ **astrophoros** — MBlu NEgg
atropurpureus — SRms
§ - 'Variegatus' (v) ♀H4 — More than 30 suppliers
boisianus — SRms
bradyi — SRms
brickellii — SRms
§ **bullatus** ♀H4 — CDul CLnd CTri EPfP MGos NFor NLar SEND SPer SRms WCwm WOrn WSHC WTel
- 'Bjuv' — SRms
- 'Firebird' — see *C. ignescens*
- f. *floribundus* — see *C. bullatus*
- var. *macrophyllus* — see *C. rehderi*
- 'McLaren' — SRms
bumthangensis — SRms
buxifolius blue-leaved — see *C. lidjiangensis*
- 'Brno' — see *C. marginatus* 'Brno'
- f. *vellaeus* — see *C. astrophoros*
calocarpus — GIBF
camilli-schneideri — SRms
canescens — SRms
§ **cashmiriensis** ♀H4 — MGos
cavei — SRms
cinerascens — SRms
cinnabarinus — SRms
§ **cochleatus** — CPLG EBee EPot GIBF LAst MBar MGos NEgg NMen SRms WEas WLin
§ **congestus** — CBgR CSBt CWib EBee LRHS MBar MGos MRav MSwo NFor NHol SPer SPlb SRms WDin WHar
- 'Nanus' — CLyd CTri ELan EOrn LRHS MGos NFor NHol NLAp SCoo SIng WBVN WPat
conspicuus — CBcs SRms
- 'Decorus' ♀H4 — CCVT CDoC CSBt CWSG EBee EHol EPfP LRHS MBar MGan MGos MRav MSwo MWhi NEgg NFor NHol NWea SLim SPer SPlb SPoG SWal WBVN WDin WMoo WTel
- 'Flameburst' — LRHS SHBN
- 'Leicester Gem' — SRms
- 'Red Alert' — SRms
cooperi — SRms
cornifolius — SRms
crispii — SRms
cuspidatus — SRms
N **dammeri** ♀H4 — More than 30 suppliers
§ - 'Major' — LAst LBuc NBlu SRms WCFE
§ - 'Mooncreeper' — LRHS MBNS MBri SCoo
- 'Oakwood' — see *C. radicans* 'Eichholz'
- var. *radicans* misapplied — see *C. dammeri* 'Major'
- var. *radicans* C.K.Schneid. — see *C. radicans*
- 'Streib's Findling' — see *C.* 'Streib's Findling'
delavayanus — SRms
dielsianus — GIBF NLar NWea SRms WHrl
distichus var. **tongolensis** — see *C. splendens*
divaricatus — EPfP NWea SLon SRms WFar
duthieanus 'Boer' — see *C. apiculatus*
elatus — SRms
(e)legans — SRms
(...)iensis — SRms
— see *C.* x *suecicus* 'Erlinda'
— SRms
— EBee MGol SRms
— SRms
— CSBt NWea SRms
— SRms
(...)F SRms
(...)CCVT CDul CSBt EBee ECrN (...)EPfP GIBF LBuc LHop (...)Rav MSwo MWat

MWgw NEgg NWea SCoo SLim SPer SPoG SRms WCFE WDin WFar WHar WTel
- var. *sternianus* — see *C. sternianus*
frigidus — CDul NWea SRms WDin
N - 'Cornubia' ♀H4 — CCVT CDoC CDul CSBt CTri EBee EPfP LAst LHop LRHS MAsh MBar MBri MGos MRav MSwo NBlu NEgg NWea SHBN SLim SLon SPer SPla SPoG WDin WJas WOrn
- 'Notcutt's Variety' — ELan ENot EPfP MRav
§ - 'Pershore Coral' — WSPU
- 'Saint Monica' — MBlu
gamblei — SRms WCwm
ganghobaensis — SRms
glabratus — SLPl SRms
glacialis — SRms
glaucophyllus — SEND SRms
§ **glomerulatus** — MBar SRms
gracilis — SRms
granatensis — SRms
harrovianus — NLar SLPl SRms
harrysmithii — GIBF
hebephyllus — NLar
- var. *hebephyllus* — SRms
I **hedegaardii** 'Fructu Luteo' — SRms
henryanus — CDoC SRms
'Herbstfeuer' — see *C. salicifolius* 'Herbstfeuer'
'Highlight' — see *C. pluriflorus*
hillieri — SRms
§ **hjelmqvistii** — LBuc SRms WFar
- 'Robustus' — see *C. hjelmqvistii*
- 'Rotundifolius' — see *C. hjelmqvistii*
hodjingensis — SRms
horizontalis ♀H4 — More than 30 suppliers
- 'Peitz' — SRms
- 'Variegatus' — see *C. atropurpureus* 'Variegatus'
- var. *wilsonii* — see *C. ascendens*
hualiensis — SRms
humifusus — see *C. dammeri*
hummelii — CDul SRms
§ 'Hybridus Pendulus' — More than 30 suppliers
§ **hylmoei** — SLPl SRms
hypocarpus — SRms
ignavus — SLPl SRms
§ **ignescens** — SRms
ignotus — SRms
incanus — SRms
induratus — SLPl SRms
insculptus — SRms
insolitus — SRms
integerrimus — SRms
§ **integrifolius** ♀H4 — CMHG EBee EPfP EPla LRHS MBar MWhi NMen SCoo SRms STre WMoo
kangdingensis — SRms
konishii ETE 233 — GIBF
lacteus ♀H4 — CBcs CDul CTri EBee ELan ENot EPfP EWTr LAst LBuc LRHS MBri MGos MRav NBlu NEgg NWea SCoo SEND SHBN SLon SPer SPla SPoG SRms WCFE WDin WFar XPep
- 'Variegatus' (v) — CEnd
lancasteri — SRms
langei — SRms
laxiflorus — SRms
lesliei — SRms
§ **lidjiangensis** — SRms WCot
§ **linearifolius** — CLyd EHol MWht
lucidus — SPer SRms
ludlowii — SRms
magnificus — SRms
§ **mairei** — SRms
marginatus — MGol SRms

§ – 'Blazovice'	SRms
§ – 'Brno'	SRms
marquandii	EPla SRms
§ *meiophyllus*	SRms
meuselii	SRms
microphyllus misapplied	see *C. purpurascens*
microphyllus Wall.	CTri EBee ENot GIBF MBar MGos
ex Lindl.	NFor NScw NWea SDix SHBN SPer
	SPoG STre WDin WMoo WTel
- var. *cochleatus*	see *C. cashmiriensis*
misapplied	
- var. *cochleatus* (Franch.)	see *C. cochleatus*
Rehd. & Wils.	
'Donard Gem'	see *C. astrophoros*
'Ruby'	SRms
'Teulon Porter'	see *C. astrophoros*
- var. *thymifolius*	see *C. linearifolius*
misapplied	
- var. *thymifolius* (Lindl.)	see *C. integrifolius*
Koehne	
milkedandai	SRms
miniatus	SRms
mirabilis	SRms
moliensis Yu 14196	GIBF
monopyrenus	SRms
'Mooncreeper'	see *C. dammeri* 'Mooncreeper'
morrisonensis	SRms
moupinensis	EBee SRms
mucronatus	SRms
multiflorus Bunge	SRms
§ *nanshan*	EBee NLar SRms WSPU
- 'Boer'	see *C. apiculatus*
newryensis	SRms
niger	GIBF
nitens	SRms
nitidifolius	see *C. glomerulatus*
nitidus var. *parvifolius*	SRms
nohelii	GIBF SRms
notabilis	SRms
nummarioides	SRms
nummularius	SRms
obscurus	SRms
obtusus	SRms
omissus	GIBF SRms
otto-schwarzii	SRms
pangiensis	SRms
pannosus	SLPl SRms WFar
- 'Speckles'	SRms
paradoxus	SRms
parkeri	SRms
pekinensis	SRms
permutatus	see *C. pluriflorus*
perpusillus	SRms WFar
'Pershore Coral'	see *C. frigidus* 'Pershore Coral'
§ *pluriflorus*	SRms
poluninii	SRms
polycarpus	SRms
praecox 'Boer'	see *C. apiculatus*
§ *procumbens*	SLon SRms WDin
- 'Queen of Carpets'	CDoC EBee LRHS LSRN MAsh
	MBNS MGos MRav NHol SCoo
	SLim SPoG SRms SWvt WMoo
- 'Seattle'	SRms
- 'Streib's Findling'	see *C.* 'Streib's Findling'
prostratus	SRms
- 'Arnold Forster'	SRms
przewalskii	SRms
pseudo-obscurus	SRms
§ *purpurascens*	CDul MDun MGos NHol SCoo
	WFar
pyrenaicus	see *C. congestus*
qungbixiensis	SRms
racemiflorus	SRms
§ *radicans*	LRHS MAsh
§ – 'Eichholz'	MGos NHol NLar WDin WWeb
§ *rehderi*	NLar SRms
roseus	GIBF SRms
'Rothschildianus'	see *C. salicifolius* 'Rothschildianus'
rotundifolius	NLar SLon SRms
'Royal Beauty'	see *C.* x *suecicus* 'Coral Beauty'
rufus	SRms
rugosus	SRms
salicifolius	MSwo SEND SPer SRms WDin
	WFar
- Autumn Fire	see *C. salicifolius* 'Herbstfeuer'
§ - 'Avonbank'	CDoC CEnd NLar WSPU
- 'Bruno Orangeade'	SRms
- 'Elstead'	MRav
- 'Exburyensis'	CBcs CDoC EBee EPfP LRHS MAsh
	MBri MGos MRav NLar SCoo
	SHBN SPer SPla WDin WFar WHCG
- 'Gnom'	EBee ELan EPfP LRHS MAsh MBar
	MBlu MGos MRav MWht NBir
	NFor SPer SPoG SRms WDin WFar
	WMoo
§ - 'Herbstfeuer'	EHol LAst MGos MRav MSwo
	SRms WDin WFar WRHF
- 'Merriott Weeper'	CDoC
- Park Carpet	see *C. salicifolius* 'Parktteppich'
§ - 'Parktteppich'	NWea
- 'Pendulus'	see *C.* 'Hybridus Pendulus'
- 'Repens'	CDoC CWib EHol EPfP MGan
	MWhi NScw NWea SPer SPoG
	SRms SSto WDin WFar
§ - 'Rothschildianus' ♀H4	CCVT CDoC CDul CSBt CTri CWib
	EBee ECrN ECtt EMil ENot EPfP
	LAst LRHS MAsh MBar MGos MRav
	MSwo NBlu NEgg SLim SPer SPla
	SPoG SRms SWvt WFar WJas
	WMoo
- var. *rugosus* hort.	see *C. hylmoei*
salwinensis	SLPl SRms
sandakphuensis	SRms
saxatilis	SRms
scandinavicus	SRms
schantungensis	SRms
schlechtendalii	see *C. marginatus* 'Blazovice'
'Blazovice'	
- 'Brno'	see *C. marginatus* 'Brno'
schubertii	SRms
serotinus misapplied	see *C. meiophyllus*
serotinus Hutchinson	CAbP NLar SLPl SRms
shannanensis	SRms
shansiensis	SRms
sherriffii	SRms
sikangensis	GBin SLon SRms
simonsii ♀H4	CDoC CDul CLnd CTri EBee ELan
	EPfP LAst LBuc LRHS MBar MGos
	NHol NScw NWea SCoo SPer SPoG
	SRms WDin WFar WHar
§ *splendens*	GIBF SRms WFar
- 'Sabrina'	see *C. splendens*
spongbergii	SRms
staintonii	SRms
§ *sternianus* ♀H4	EPfP LRHS MBar SLPl SRms
	WHrl
– ACE 2200	EPot
'Streib's Findling'	EBee MAsh MGos
suavis	SRms
subacutus	SRms
subadpressus	SRms
§ x *suecicus* 'Coral Beauty'	CCVT CDoC CTri CWSG CWib
	EBee ELan EPfP GGar LAst LBuc
	LRHS MAsh MBar MGos MSwo
	NBlu NEgg NHol SLim SMer SPer
	SPla SPoG SRms SWal WDin WFar
	WMoo
§ - 'Erlinda' (v)	CEnd CWib EMil NLar SCoo
	SRms
- 'Ifor'	SLPl SRms
- 'Juliette' (v)	CWib LSRN MAsh MBar NBlu NLar
	NPro SCoo SPoG WFar WOrn

- 'Skogholm'	CBcs CSBt CWSG CWib EBee MBar MGos MWat NWea SCoo SPer SRms WDin WFar WHar
taoensis	SRms
tardiflorus	SRms
tauricus	SRms
teijiashanensis	SRms
tengyuehensis	SRms
thimphuensis	SRms
tomentellus	WCFE
tomentosus	SRms
trinervis	SRms
- 'Bruno'	SRms
turbinatus	SRms
uralensis	SRms
uzbezicus	SRms
'Valkenburg'	SRms
vandelaarii	SRms
veitchii	NLar SRms
verruculosus	SRms
villosulus	EHol SRms
vilmorinianus	SRms
wardii misapplied	see *C. mairei*
wardii W. W. Sm.	GIBF SRms
x *watereri*	CCVT CSBt CWib EBee EGra MAsh MSwo NEgg NWea WDin WJas WTel
- 'Avonbank'	see *C. salicifolius* 'Avonbank'
- 'Corina'	SRms
- 'Cornubia'	see *C. frigidus* 'Cornubia'
- 'John Waterer' ♀H4	EPfP LRHS MGos SPoG WFar
- 'Pendulus'	see *C.* 'Hybridus Pendulus'
- 'Pink Champagne'	CAbP
wilsonii	SRms
yakuticus	SRms
yallungensis	SRms
yinchangensis	SRms
zabelii	GIBF SRms

Cotula (Asteraceae)

C&H 452	NWCA
atrata	see *Leptinella atrata*
- var. *dendyi*	see *Leptinella dendyi*
coronopifolia	CSev CWat LPBA NBlu NJOw NPer SWat
§ *hispida*	CBrm CMea CTri EBee ECho ECtt EDAr EPot GAbr GMaP MAvo MBNS MBar MHer MTho MWat NHol NJOw NPer NRya NWCA SBla SPoG SRms WEas WFar WPat WPer WTin WWeb
lineariloba	ECha ECho EWes LBee LRHS
minor	see *Leptinella minor*
'Platt's Black'	see *Leptinella squalida* 'Platt's Black'
potentilloides	see *Leptinella potentillina*
pyrethrifolia	see *Leptinella pyrethrifolia*
rotundata	see *Leptinella rotundata*
sericea	see *Leptinella albida*
serrulata	see *Leptinella serrulata*
squalida	see *Leptinella squalida*

Cotyledon (Crassulaceae)

chrysantha	see *Rosularia chrysantha*
gibbiflora var. *metallica*	see *Echeveria gibbiflora* var. *metallica*
oppositifolia	see *Chiastophyllum oppositifolium*
orbiculata	CHEx CStu SDix
- B&SWJ 723	WCru
- var. *oblonga*	EBee EMan WCot WEas
- var. *orbiculata*	EShb WCMO
simplicifolia	see *Chiastophyllum oppositifolium*
tomentosa subsp. *ladismithensis*	EShb
undulata	WEas

Cowania see *Purshia*

Coxella (Apiaceae)

dieffenbachii	GCal

Crambe (Brassicaceae)

cordifolia ♀H4	More than 30 suppliers
maritima ♀H4	CSev EBee ECGP ECha EMar EPfP GMaP GPoy LAst MAvo MBow MHer MLLN MRav MSal MWgw NFor NSti SMad SPer SWat WBVN WCMO WCot WCru WFar WJek WMnd WPer WWye
- 'Lilywhite'	CAgr ILis WCot
orientalis	WCot
tatarica	NLar SHar WPer

cranberry see *Vaccinium macrocarpon*, *V. oxycoccos*

Craspedia (Asteraceae)

alpina from Tasmania	GGar

Crassula (Crassulaceae)

anomala	SChr
arborescens	see *C. atropurpurea* var. *arborescens*
argentea	see *C. ovata*
arta	EPem
§ *atropurpurea* var. *arborescens*	EShb SRms STre
'Buddha's Temple'	EShb
coccinea	CHEx EShb
columella	EPem
dejecta	EShb
elegans subsp. *elegans*	EPfP
lactea	CHal STre
lycopodioides variegata	see *C. muscosa* 'Variegata'
milfordiae nana new	ECho EDAr
'Morgan's Pride'	EShb
multicava	CHEx
muscosa	EShb SChr SRot STre
§ - 'Variegata' (v)	EShb
obtusa	SRot
orbicularis	EPem
§ *ovata* ♀H1	CHEx CHal EBak EOHP EPem EPfP MBri NBlu NPer SWal
- 'Gollum'	EPem EPfP
- 'Hummel's Sunset' (v) ♀H1	CHal EPem STre SWal
- 'Minima'	EPem
* - *nana*	STre
- 'Variegata' (v)	CHal EBak WCot
pellucida subsp. *marginalis*	CHal
* - subsp. *marginalis* 'Variegata' (v)	CHal
perfoliata var. *falcata* ♀H1	EShb IBlr MBri SRot
perforata	CHal SEND SRot
- 'Variegata' (v)	CHal EWll SRot SVil
portulacea	see *C. ovata*
rupestris ♀H1	EPem MBri
- subsp. *marnieriana*	EPem
§ *sarcocaulis*	CHEx CHal CStu CTri ECho ELan EWll GEdr GMaP ITim MTho NJOw NLAp NMen NVic NWCA SIng SPlb SPoG SRms SRot STre WAbe WEas WPat WSHC
- *alba*	CHal NJOw NLAp SHFr STre WPer
- 'Ken Aslet'	SPet STre
schmidtii	CHal EDAr MBri
sedifolia	see *C. setulosa* 'Milfordiae'

sediformis	see *C. setulosa* 'Milfordiae'
§ *setulosa* 'Milfordiae'	CTri ECho MBar NBir NJOw NLAp
socialis	CHal
tetragona	SEND
* *tomentosa* 'Variegata' (v)	EShb EWin
'Très Bon'	STre

Crataegus ✿ (Rosaceae)

ambigua new	GIBF
arnoldiana	CAgr CEnd CLnd CTho CTri EBee ECrN EPfP IMGH LRHS MAsh MBri MCoo MGos MLan MNHC NWea SCoo SEND SFam SLPl SMad SPer SPoG WOrn
'Autumn Glory'	CEnd CLnd EBee ECrN WFar
azarolus	CAgr EPfP
champlainensis	CLnd CTho
chlorosarca	GIBF
chrysocarpa new	EPfP
chungtienensis	CMCN
coccinea misapplied	see *C. intricata*
coccinea ambig.	NWea
§ *coccinea* L.	CAgr CLnd CTho EPfP MCoo SCoo
coccinioides new	EPfP
cordata	see *C. phaenopyrum*
crus-galli misapplied	see *C. persimilis* 'Prunifolia'
crus-galli L.	CCVT CDoC CDul CLnd CTho EBee ECrN EPfP LAst LBuc SPer WDin WFar WJas
- var. *pyracanthifolia*	CTho
- thornless	MBlu
dahurica new	EPfP
x *dippeliana* new	EPfP
douglasii	EPfP GIBF
dsungarica new	EPfP
x *durobrivensis*	CAgr CLnd CTho EPfP
ellwangeriana	CAgr CLnd CTho ECrN EPfP
eriocarpa	CLnd
flabellata	CEnd GIBF
gemmosa	CEnd MBlu MCoo NLar NWea
greggiana	CLnd EPfP
x *grignonensis*	CBcs CCVT CDul CLnd ECrN EMil MAsh SBLw SEND SPer WJas
intricata new	EPfP
irrasa new	EPfP
jonesiae	EPfP
laciniata Ucria	see *C. orientalis*
§ *laevigata*	CDul NWea
- 'Coccinea Plena'	see *C. laevigata* 'Paul's Scarlet'
- 'Crimson Cloud'	CDoC CEnd CLnd CWSG CWib EBee ECrN ELan EMui ENot EPfP LBuc LRHS MAsh MBri MGos MSwo NWea SCoo SCrf SLim SLon SPer SPoG WJas WOrn WPat
- 'Flore Pleno'	see *C. laevigata* 'Plena'
- 'Gireoudii'	CBcs CDul CEnd CPMA CWib GTSp LAst MAsh MBlu MGos NLar NSti WPat
- 'Mutabilis'	CLnd SBLw
§ - 'Paul's Scarlet' (d) ♀H4	More than 30 suppliers
- 'Pink Corkscrew'	CTho EPfP MAsh MBlu MGos SMad WPat WWes
§ - 'Plena' (d)	CBcs CDoC CDul CLnd CSBt CTho CTri CWib EBee ECrN LAst LRHS MAsh MSwo MWat NBee NWea SBLw SCrf SHBN SLim SPer WDin WOrn
- 'Rosea Flore Pleno' (d) ♀H4	More than 30 suppliers
x *lavalleei*	CCVT CDul CLnd CTri EBee ECrN EPfP GIBF MSwo NEgg NWea SCoo SFam SPer SPur WDin
- 'Carrierei' ♀H4	CDoC CTho EPfP EWTr MAsh MBlu MBri NWea SBLw SCoo WOrn
lobulata new	EPfP

maximowiczii	GIBF
mexicana	see *C. pubescens* f. *stipulacea*
mollis	CAgr CTho ECrN EPfP NWea
monogyna	CBcs CCVT CDoC CDul CLnd CRWN ELan EPfP GWCH LAst LBuc LRHS MBar MBri MGan MGos NBlu NWea SPer WDin WMou
§ - 'Biflora'	CDul CEnd CTho CTri ECrN MAsh MCoo MGos NWea SCoo SLim SPoG WSPU
- 'Compacta'	MBlu NLar
- 'Ferox'	CTho
- 'Flexuosa'	MGos
- 'Praecox'	see *C. monogyna* 'Biflora'
- 'Stricta'	CCVT CDul CLnd CSBt CTho EBee ECrN EPfP MBlu SBLw
- 'Variegata' (v)	CDul ECrN
x *mordenensis* 'Toba' (d)	CDul CLnd CTho EPfP SBLw
neofluvialis	GIBF
nigra new	EPfP
§ *orientalis*	CDul CEnd CLnd CMCN CTho CTri EBee ECrN EPfP IArd LPan LRHS MAsh MBri MCoo MGos NBlu NWea SCoo SHBN SLPl SLim SMad SPer SSpi WJas WMou
oxyacantha	see *C. laevigata*
pedicellata	see *C. coccinea* L.
pentagyna new	EPfP
§ *persimilis* 'Prunifolia' ♀H4	More than 30 suppliers
- 'Prunifolia Splendens'	CCVT IDee MBri SBLw WPat
§ *phaenopyrum*	CDul CLnd CMCN CTho EPfP GIBF MGos SLPl SMad
pinnatifida	EPfP SMad
- var. *major*	CEnd EPfP MCoo NWea SCoo SMad
- - 'Big Golden Star'	CAgr CLnd CTho ECrN MAsh MCoo NLar
'Praecox'	see *C. monogyna* 'Biflora'
prunifolia	see *C. persimilis* 'Prunifolia'
pseudoheterophylla new	EPfP
§ *pubescens* f. *stipulacea*	CDul CLnd EPfP
punctata	CTho SLPl
- f. *aurea* new	EPfP
rhipidophylla new	GIBF
sanguinea	EPfP GIBF
schraderiana	CAgr CDul CLnd CTho EPfP GIBF MCoo NWea SCoo
sorbifolia new	EPfP
succulenta new	EPfP
- var. *macracantha*	EPfP SMad
suksdorfii new	EPfP
tanacetifolia	CAgr CDul CLnd CTho ECrN EPfP MBlu SPer SPoG
turkestanica new	EPfP
uniflora	GIBF
viridis 'Winter King'	CDoC EPfP MAsh MBlu MCoo SLim
wattiana	CTho EPfP

x *Crataemespilus* (Rosaceae)

grandiflora	CDul CEnd CTho

Crawfurdia (Gentianaceae)

speciosa B&SWJ 2138	WCru

Cremanthodium (Asteraceae)

sp.	WCot
angustifolium SDR 3097 new	CSec
bulbiliferum new	GIBF
campanulatum new	GIBF
delavayi new	GIBF
aff. *ellisii* HWJK 2262	WCru
§ *reniforme* GWJ 9407	WCru

Cremastra (Orchidaceae)
variabilis **new**	GEdr WWst

x *Cremnosedum* (Crassulaceae)
'Little Gem' **new**	EPot

Crenularia see Aethionema

Crepis (Asteraceae)
aurea	EBee NJOw
incana ♀H4	CFee CMea CPom ECho EGoo EMan GBri GSki LPhx LRHS MAvo MTho NBid NChi NSla NWCA SIng SRms WAbe WBVN WCMO WCot WPat
- 'Pink Mist'	NLar WWeb
rubra	LRHS

Crinitaria see Aster

Crinodendron (Elaeocarpaceae)
§ *hookerianum* ♀H3	More than 30 suppliers
- 'Ada Hoffmann'	CPLG MBlu MBri NLar
patagua	CBcs CPLG CPle CSam CWib EBee GGar GQui IArd IDee LRHS MBri MDun NLar SBrw SLon SPer WBVN WFar WSHC

Crinum (Amaryllidaceae)
amoenum	EBee ECho MOak
asiaticum var. *sinicum*	CDes
'Big Red' **new**	WCMO
§ *bulbispermum*	CFir EBee ELan LToo WCMO WCot WPic
- 'Album'	EMan
§ *campanulatum*	CMon
capense	see *C. bulbispermum*
'Carolina Beauty'	WCMO WCot
'Elizabeth Traub'	WCot
'Ellen Bosanquet'	CDes CFir CKno WCMO WCot
erubescens	WCMO WCot
'George Harwood' **new**	WCMO
'Hanibal's Dwarf'	CDes WCMO WCot
macowanii	WCot
moorei	CDes CFir CMon EBee ECho LEdu SChr WPGP
- f. *album*	CAvo WCot WMul
§ x *powellii* ♀H3	More than 30 suppliers
- 'Album' ♀H3	CAvo CDes CFFs CHEx CMon CTri EBee ECha ECho ELan EMan EShb EWes LEdu LHop LRHS MBri MOak MRav SSpi WCMO WCot WCru WFar WPGP WPic WViv
- 'Harlemense'	SSpi
- 'Longifolium'	see *C. bulbispermum*
- 'Roseum'	see *C.* x *powellii*
'Regina's Disco Lounge' **new**	WCMO
'Royal White' **new**	WCMO
variabile	WCMO WCot
'White Queen' **new**	WCMO
yemense	CMon WCMO

Criogenes see Cypripedium

Crithmum (Apiaceae)
maritimum	CArn CHrt CWan EMan GPoy MSal NLar NTHB SECG WBri WJek WWye XPep

Crocosmia ✿ (Iridaceae)
'Alistair'	ECtt EGra EMar
'Amberglow'	CElw CFwr CMea CPrp ECho EWoo IBal IBlr MLan NBre NHol NPer WFar WWpP

'Anniversary'	IBlr
'Apricot Surprise' **new**	MAvo
aurea misapplied	see *C.* x *crocosmiiflora* 'George Davison' Davison
aurea ambig.	NBir WCot
aurea Planchon	CPne CPou CSec ECtt IBlr NHol
- JCA 3.100.000	WCot
- var. *aurea*	GCal IBlr
- var. *maculata*	IBlr
- var. *pauciflora*	IBlr
'Auricorn'	IBlr
'Auriol'	IBlr
'Aurora' **new**	CHVG
Bressingham Beacon = 'Blos'	EBee EBrs GGar IBlr LRHS WRHF
'Bressingham Blaze'	CBre CMHG CPrp EBee EBrs GCal IBlr LRHS NBre NHol WCot
Bridgemere hybrid **new**	NHol
'Cadenza'	IBlr
'Carnival'	IBlr
'Cascade'	IBlr
'Chinatown'	IBlr NHol WHil
'Comet' Knutty	EBrs GBuc IBlr NHol WWhi
§ x *crocosmiiflora*	CHEx COIW EBee EGra EPla IBlr LAst NHol NOrc SIng SPlb SRms SWat WBrk WCot WFar WMoo WRHF WShi WWpP WWye
- 'A.E.Amos'	EGra EMar
- 'A.J.Hogan'	CPrp GBin IBal IBlr NHol WHil
- 'African Glow'	ENot
- 'Amber Sun'	IBlr
- 'Apricot Queen'	IBlr NHol
- 'Autumn Gold'	IBlr
- 'Baby Barnaby'	CBos CBre CDes IBlr NHol WPGP
- 'Babylon'	More than 30 suppliers
- 'Bicolor'	CPrp IBal IBlr NHol WHil
- 'Burford Bronze'	CPrp IBal IBlr NHol WHil
- 'Buttercup'	IBlr MLLN NBre NFla WBor WFar
- 'Canary Bird'	CBro CPne CPrp CRow CSam EBee ECho ECtt EGra EMar GAbr GMac IBal IBlr LRHS NBPC NGdn NHol SPer WBrk WHil WRHF
- 'Cardinale'	IBlr
- 'Carmin Brillant' ♀H3-4	More than 30 suppliers
- 'Citronella' J.E. Fitt	CBro CFwr CPLG CPrp CSam CTri EBee EBrs EChP ECha EGra EMar ENot EPfP GKev GMaP ITim LAst LRHS NGdn NHol SAga SPer WBVN WCot WCra WRha
§ - 'Coleton Fishacre'	More than 30 suppliers
§ - 'Columbus'	CAvo CFwr CMMP CPar CPrp EChP EGra EMan EMar ENot GBin IBal IBlr LHop LRHS MWea NHol NRnb SAga SPer WBor WBrk WCot WHil WFar WLin WMnd WWpP
- 'Colwall'	IBlr
- 'Constance'	CBre CBro CElw CFwr CSam EBrs EChP EGra ERou GGar IBal IBlr LRHS MBNS MBri MNrw NBid NGdn NHol NRnb SRGP SRos WFar WHil WSel
- 'Corona'	CPrp IBal IBlr MAvo NCot NHol WHil
- 'Corten'	IBlr
§ - 'Croesus'	EGra GBri IBlr MRav
- 'Custard Cream'	CMil CPrp CSpe GBin IBlr LRHS MAvo NHol SRos WFar WHil
- 'D.H. Houghton'	IBlr
- 'Debutante'	CBos CMil CPrp EBee EBrs ECtt EGra IBal IBlr MAvo NHol WCot WHoo WLin WSHC WWhi
§ - 'Diadème'	CSam NHol WHil
- 'Dusky Maiden'	More than 30 suppliers
§ - 'E.A. Bowles'	CPou CPrp GCal IBlr WCot
- 'Eastern Promise'	CBre CMea CPrp IBal IBlr MAvo NCot SMrm

- 'Elegans' CBre CElw ECtt IBlr
- 'Emberglow' More than 30 suppliers
§ - 'Emily McKenzie' More than 30 suppliers
- 'Etoile de Feu' IBlr
- 'Fantasie' CFwr IBal
- 'Festival Orange' IBlr MAvo
- 'Firebrand' IBlr
- 'Fireglow' ECho ECtt EGra EMar ENot IBlr
WFar WPer
- 'Flamethrower' IBlr
- 'George Davison' see *C.* × *crocosmiiflora* 'Golden
misapplied Glory', 'Sulphurea'
§ - 'George Davison' Davison More than 30 suppliers
- 'Gerbe d'Or' misapplied see *C.* × *crocosmiiflora* 'Coleton
Fishacre'
- 'Gloria' CPen IBlr
- 'Golden Dew' **new** GQue MAvo WCot WGor
- 'Golden Glory' misapplied see *C.* × *crocosmiiflora* 'Diadème'
§ - 'Golden Glory' ambig. CSam CWCL ECho EHrv ELan
GMaP IBal IBlr MAvo MSwo NBir
NChi NEgg NHol SPlb SPoG SRos
WBrE WCot WFar WHil
- 'Goldfinch' IBlr NHol WHil
- 'Hades' CPrp IBal IBlr MAvo
- 'Harlequin' **new** CElw
- 'Harvest Sun' IBlr
- 'His Majesty' CBos CBro CPne CPou CPrp CSam
CSpe IBal IBlr LRHS NHol SDys
WFar WHil WLin WPer WWhi
- 'Honey Bells' CElw WBrk
- 'Honey Angels' More than 30 suppliers
- 'Irish Dawn' CPrp GBin IBal IBlr NBre NHol
§ - 'Jackanapes' CBos CFwr CMil CPne CPrp CRow
CWCL EBee EBrs ECtt EGra EHrv
ELan EPfP GGar IBlr LRHS MBri
MLHP NHol SDys SUsu WCot WHil
WWeb WWhi WWpP WWye
- 'James Coey' J.E. Fitt CHad CHar COlW CPrp CRow
EBee EChP ECha EHrv EPfP ERou
GCal GGar GMac GSki IFoB LRHS
MDun MLHP NDov NGdn NHol
SIng SPer SRGP SWvt WFar WMoo
WViv
* - 'Jesse van Dyke' IBlr
§ - 'Jessie' CElw CFwr EBrs GGar IBlr WHil
WPer WWpP
- 'Kapoor' IBlr
- 'Kiautschou' CAvo EBee EGra GMac IBlr MAvo
NBre NHol SDys WHil
- 'Lady Hamilton' More than 30 suppliers
- 'Lady McKenzie' see *C.* × *crocosmiiflora* 'Emily
McKenzie'
- 'Lady Oxford' CPrp EBrs EGra EMan EMar GGar
IBlr LRHS NHol WHil
- 'Lambrook Gold' CAvo IBlr
- 'Lord Nelson' CPrp
- 'Lutea' EBee ECtt EGra EMar IBlr
- 'Marjorie' WCot
- 'Mars' CElw CFwr CPrp EBee EBla ECtt
EGra EMar EWes EWll GAbr GBuc
GCal GGar GMac IBal IBlr IFoB
LRHS NHol SPlb SRGP WBor
WCMO WFar WOld WPGP WPer
WSel
- 'Mephistopheles' CPrp IBal IBlr MAvo WHil
- 'Merryman' ECtt GMac WWpP
- 'Météore' CFwr CPrp EBee EBrs ECho EMar
GGar IBal MBNS NBre NHol WSel
WWeb
- 'Morgenlicht' CPen ECtt EMar IBal IBlr NHol
WCot WRHF
- 'Mount Usher' CFir CMdw ECtt EGra GAbr GCal
IBlr MAvo NHol WFar
§ - 'Mrs Geoffrey Howard' CBos CDes CMea CPrp CSam EBrs
ECtt EGra GBri IBal IBlr NCGa NHol
SUsu WCru WPGP WPrP WWhi

- 'Mrs Morrison' see *C.* × *crocosmiiflora* 'Mrs
Geoffrey Howard'
- Newry seedling see *C.* × *crocosmiiflora*
'Prometheus'
- 'Nimbus' CPrp EBee GBri IBal IBlr NHol
WCot WHil
§ - 'Norwich Canary' More than 30 suppliers
- 'Olympic Fire' IBlr
- 'Pepper' IBlr
- 'Plaisir' CBos CFwr EBee IBlr WCra WFar
- 'Polo' CFwr
- 'Princess Alexandra' CHVG IBlr SMHy
- 'Prolificans' IBlr
§ - 'Prometheus' CPrp IBal IBlr NHol WHil
§ - 'Queen Alexandra' J.E. Fitt EChP ECha IBlr LHop NCGa NHol
SPer SWat WHal WMoo WPer
- 'Queen Charlotte' CPrp IBal IBlr
- 'Queen Mary II' see *C.* × *crocosmiiflora* 'Columbus'
- 'Queen of Spain' CPrp EBee EBrs GGar IBal IBlr
LRHS MBri MDKP MLLN NHol
SWat WHil WViv
- 'Rayon d'Or' CDes IBlr
- 'Red King' CFwr EBee EBla EPfP ERou IBal
IBlr WFar WHil WLin WRHF
- 'Rheingold' misapplied see *C.* × *crocosmiiflora* 'Diadème'
- 'Rose Queen' IBlr
- 'Saint Clements' IBlr
- 'Saracen' CBcs CHVG CMil CSpe EBee EChP
EMan ERou IBal IBlr IPot LAst
MAvo MBNS MBnl NBre NCGa
NEgg SMrm SPla WCot WFar
- 'Sir Mathew Wilson' CDes EBee EBrs GBri IBal IBlr
WCot
- 'Solfatare' ♀H3 More than 30 suppliers
- 'Solfatare Coleton see *C.* × *crocosmiiflora* 'Coleton
Fishacre' Fishacre'
- 'Star of the East' ♀H3 More than 30 suppliers
- 'Starbright' IBlr
- 'Starfire' ECtt EGra EMar
- 'Sultan' CBro CElw EBee IBlr NCot WCot
WFar WPGP
- 'Venus' CBre CFwr CPen CPou EBee EBrs
ECtt EGra EMar EShb EWll GBuc
IBal IBlr LRHS NBre NHol SRGP
SRos STes WFar WLin WMoo WSel
- 'Vesuvius' W. Pfitzer CElw EBrs GCal IBlr WFar
- 'Vic's Yellow' SGar SMrm
- 'Voyager' CFwr CPrp EBee ECho EPot ERou
IBlr LRHS MAvo MBNS MBri NCot
NFla NHol SIng SWal WCMO WHil
WSel
- 'Zeal Tan' CElw CPen CPrp CSam EBee
ECGP EChP ECtt EGra ELan EMan
EMar EPPr GBin GMac GQue IBlr
LAst MAvo MBNS MBnl MDKP
NEgg SPla WBrk WCMO WCot
WGwG WWhi WWlt

§ × *crocosmioides* IBlr WHil
- 'Castle Ward Late' CBgR CBos CPou CRow ECha
Leichtlin EGra GAbr GBuc GCal IBal IBlr
LRHS MBNS MSte NBre NHol
WMoo WSHC
- 'Mount Stewart Late' IBlr
new
- 'Vulcan' Leichtlin **new** IBlr
'Darkleaf Apricot' see *C.* × *crocosmiiflora* 'Coleton
Fishacre'
'Doctor Marion Wood' EBee NCot
new
'Eclatant' IBlr
'Eldorado' see *C.* × *crocosmiiflora* 'E.A.
Bowles'
'Elegance' IBlr
'Elizabeth' **new** NHol
'Ellenbank Canary' **new** GMac
'Ellenbank Firecrest' GMac MAvo

'Fandango'	IBlr
'Fernhill'	IBlr
* 'Feuerser'	ECtt
'Fire King' misapplied	see *C.* x *crocosmiiflora* 'Jackanapes'
'Fire Sprite'	IBlr
'Firefly'	IBlr NCot NHol
'Flaire'	IBlr
'Fleuve-Jaune' **new**	CPne ECtt
fucata	IBlr
- 'Jupiter'	see *C.* 'Jupiter'
fucata x *paniculata* **new**	NHol
'Fugue'	IBlr
'Fusilade'	IBlr
'Golden Dew' **new**	GAbr LSou MBnl
Golden Fleece Lemoine	see *C.* x *crocosmiiflora* 'Coleton Fishacre'
'Gold Sprite'	IBlr
'Highlight'	IBlr MAvo NHol WHil
'Irish Flame'	NHol
'Irish Sunset'	NHol
'Jennine'	EBrs NCot NHol
Jenny Bloom = 'Blacro'PBR	CMMP EBrs ECtt GBin GBuc LRHS NBir SMHy STes WCMO
'John Boots'	CPen CPrp EBee EChP ECho EHrv GBuc IBlr MBNS NBre NCGa NHol NRnb SMrm SRGP WBor WFar WLin WSel
§ 'Jupiter'	CBre CPou CWCL ECho EGra EMar GBuc GMac IBal IBlr LRHS NChi NHol WCMO WFar WHil WOld
'Kathleen' **new**	EBrs
'Kiaora'	IBlr
'Lady Wilson' misapplied	see *C.* x *crocosmiiflora* 'Norwich Canary'
'Lana de Savary'	CPen CPrp EBee EMan GBin GCal IBal IBlr NCot NHol WCMO WCot WLin
'Late Cornish'	see *C.* x *crocosmiiflora* 'Queen Alexandra' J.E. Fitt
'Late Lucifer'	CHEx CTri GCal IBlr LSRN SDix WCMO
latifolia	see *C.* x *crocosmioides*
'Lucifer' ♀H4	More than 30 suppliers
'Mandarin'	IBlr
§ 'Marcotijn'	EChP ECtt EGra EMan EMar GCal GGar IBlr IGor NHol
§ *masoniorum* ♀H3	More than 30 suppliers
- 'African Dawn' **new**	WCot
- 'Amber'	IBlr
- 'Dixter Flame'	ECtt IBlr IFoB SDix
- 'Firebird'	EBrs GBuc IBlr IGor LRHS MBri NBre NHol SRos WCot
- 'Flamenco'	IBlr
- 'Golden Swan' **new**	ECtt
- 'Moira Reid'	EGra EMar IBlr NHol
- red	IBlr
- 'Rowallane Apricot'	IBlr
- 'Rowallane Orange'	GAbr IBlr NHol
§ - 'Rowallane Yellow' ♀H3-4	CDes CPen EBrs ECha ECtt EGra GBir IGor LRHS MBri NCGa NHol SMHy SRos WCot WHil
- 'Tropicana'	IBlr
mathewsiana	IBlr
'Minotaur'	IBlr
'Mistral'	CFwr CMea CPrp EBee EChP EPfP GBuc IBlr LRHS MAvo MNrw NBre NHol NRnb WBor WCMO WFar WLin WMoo WWpP
'Mount Stewart'	see *C.* x *crocosmiiflora* 'Jessie'
'Mr Bedford'	see *C.* x *crocosmiiflora* 'Croesus'
'Ms Sinkins' **new**	IFoB
'Neptune' **new**	ECtt
Old Hat	see *C.* 'Walberton Red'
'Orange Devil'	CBre ECtt IBlr MBri WWpP
'Orange Lucifer'	NBre NCot WWpP

'Orange Spirit'	WFar
'Orangeade'	EBrs ECtt EGra EMar GBin GBri IBal IBlr NCot NHol SUsu
'Out of the West' **new**	WOut
§ *paniculata*	CElw CHEx COlW CPne CPou EBee EBla EChP ECtt ERou GAbr GGar LBow LRHS MNFA MNrw NBid NHol NOrc SAPC SPet WBrk WCot WMoo WShi WTin
- brown/orange	IBlr
- 'Cally Greyleaf'	GCal
- 'Cally Sword' **new**	GCal
- 'Major'	CTri IBlr
- 'Natal' **new**	CPrp EBee ECtt NHol WFar
- red	CPLG CStu IBlr SWvt
- triploid	IBlr
aff. *paniculata*	ECtt IBlr
pearsei	IBlr
'Phillipa Browne'	EBee GAbr LSou MAvo MBNS SPoG WCMO WCot
§ *pottsii*	CFee CHVG CRow EBrs EChP ECtt EPla GBin GMac IBlr NHol WCot WFar
- CD&R 109	CBre CPou
- 'Culzean Pink'	CHVG CPom CPrp EBee EBrs ECtt EGra GAbr GBin GBuc GCal GMac IBal IBlr MAvo MRav NBir NCob NCot NHol SMrm WCMO WCot WHil WLin WOut WPGP
- deep pink	IBlr IGor
- 'Grandiflora'	IBlr
'Quantreau'	IBlr
'R.W.Wallace' **new**	NHol
'Red Devils'	NHol
'Red Knight'	CMMP GAbr IBlr MAvo NHol WCot
'Roman Gold'	IBlr
rosea	see *Tritonia disticha* subsp. *rubrolucens*
'Rowallane'	see *C. masoniorum* 'Rowallane Yellow'
'Rowden Bronze'	see *C.* x *crocosmiiflora* 'Coleton Fishacre'
'Rowden Chrome'	see *C.* x *crocosmiiflora* 'George Davison' Davison
'Ruby Velvet'	IBlr
'Rubygold'	IBlr
'Sabena'	MAvo
'Saffron Queen'	IBlr
'Saturn'	see *C.* 'Jupiter'
'Scarlatti'	IBlr NHol WHil
'Severn Sunrise' ♀H3-4	More than 30 suppliers
'Shocking'	IBlr
'Son of Lucifer'	WFar
'Sonate'	ECtt NHol SPlb WPer
'Spitfire'	More than 30 suppliers
§ 'Sulphurea'	CPLG CPou CPrp CRow CSam ECtt EGra GGar IBal IBlr NHol SDix SIng WBrk WCMO WCot WEas WHal WHil WPer
'Sunset'	GSki
'Sunzest'	WFar
'Tangerine Queen'	CPen EBrs ECtt EGra EMar GAbr IBal IBlr NHol WCot
'Tiger'	CElw IBlr NCot
I 'Vulcan' A. Bloom	CMdw CPen EBee EBrs ECtt EGra GAbr GGar IBal IBlr LRHS MBri NHol WCot WFar WHil WWhi WWpP
§ 'Walberton Red'	EBrs IBlr MAvo MBri SAga SUsu WCMO WCot
Walberton Yellow = 'Walcroy'PBR	SMHy WCot
'Zeal Giant'	ECtt EGra EMar IBlr NHol WCMO WHil
Zeal unnamed	EBee EGra IBlr NHol

Crocus ✿ (Iridaceae)

abantensis	ERos
adanensis	ERos
alatavicus	WWst
albiflorus	see *C. vernus* subsp. *albiflorus*
§ *ancyrensis*	EPot
- 'Golden Bunch'	EBrs EPfP LRHS WShi
§ *angustifolius* ♀H4	EBrs EPot ERos
asturicus	see *C. serotinus* subsp. *salzmannii*
asumaniae	ECho ERos
aureus	see *C. flavus* subsp. *flavus*
banaticus ♀H4	CBro ECho EHyt ERos GCrs GEdr MSSP WWst
- *albus*	ERos
baytopiorum	ERos
biflorus subsp. *adamii*	ERos
- subsp. *alexandri*	ERos LRHS
§ - subsp. *biflorus*	ERos
§ - - 'Parkinsonii'	EPot ERos
- - 'Serevan' **new**	EPot
- subsp. *crewei*	ERos
- subsp. *isauricus*	ERos
- subsp. *melantherus*	ERos
- 'Miss Vain'	CAvo CFFs EPot GKev LRHS MBri SPer
- var. *parkinsonii*	see *C. biflorus* subsp. *biflorus* 'Parkinsonii'
- subsp. *tauri*	WWst
- subsp. *weldenii* 'Albus'	EPot ERos
- - 'Fairy'	CBgR EPot ERos LRHS
'Big Boy'	EHyt
boryi	ECho EHyt
cambessedesii	ERos SBla SCnR
§ *cancellatus* subsp. *cancellatus*	ECho ERos
- var. *cilicicus*	see *C. cancellatus* subsp. *cancellatus*
- subsp. *mazziaricus*	CNic ERos
- subsp. *pamphylicus*	ERos
candidus var. *subflavus*	see *C. olivieri* subsp. *olivieri*
§ *cartwrightianus* ♀H4	EBrs
- 'Albus' misapplied	see *C. hadriaticus*
- 'Albus' Tubergen ♀H4	EPot ERos
chrysanthus 'Advance'	CBro EPfP EPot LRHS MBri SPer WLin
- 'Alionka'	WWst
- 'Ard Schenk'	EPot GKev LRHS SGar WLin
- 'Aubade'	EPot GKev
- 'Blue Bird'	CBro EPot LRHS MSte
- 'Blue Pearl' ♀H4	CAvo CBro CFFs CMea EBrs EPfP EPot GKev LPhx LRHS MBri MSte NBir SBch SPer WShi
- 'Cream Beauty' ♀H4	CAvo CBro CFFs CMea EBrs EPfP EPot GKev LPhx LRHS MBri MSte NBir SPer
- 'Dorothy'	GKev LRHS
- 'E.A. Bowles' ♀H4	ECho
- 'E.P. Bowles'	CBro EBrs EPot MBri
- 'Early Gold'	WWst
- 'Ego'	WWst
- 'Elegance'	LRHS
- var. *fuscotinctus*	EPot MBri WLin
- 'Gipsy Girl'	CAvo CBro CFFs EPot LRHS MBri SGar
- 'Goldilocks'	EBrs GKev LRHS
- 'Goldmine'	WWst
- 'Herald'	EPot LRHS MSte
- 'Jeannine'	EPot
- 'Ladykiller' ♀H4	CAvo CBro CFFs EPot LRHS MBri MSte
- 'Little Amber'	WWst
- 'Nida'	WWst
- 'Prins Claus'	EPot LRHS MBri SPer
- 'Prinses Beatrix'	EBrs LRHS
- 'Romance'	CAvo CBro CFFs EPot GKev LRHS MBri SBch SPer WLin
- 'Saturnus'	EPot
- 'Skyline'	EPot
- 'Snow Bunting' ♀H4	CAvo CBro CFFs EPfP EPot LPhx LRHS NBir WShi
- 'Spring Pearl'	CBro LRHS
- 'Uschak Orange'	EPot
- 'White Triumphator'	NBir
- 'Zenith'	EPot
- 'Zwanenburg Bronze'	EPfP EPot LRHS MSte WLin
'Cloth of Gold'	see *C. angustifolius*
clusii	see *C. serotinus* subsp. *clusii*
corsicus ♀H4	EPot ERos
cvijicii	WWst
dalmaticus	EPot
- 'Petrovac'	WWst
danfordiae	ERos ETow
'Dutch Yellow'	see *C. x luteus* 'Golden Yellow'
etruscus ♀H4	ERos
- 'Rosalind'	EPot
- 'Zwanenburg'	EPot
§ *flavus* ♀H4	EPot LRHS SBch WShi
fleischeri	EPot ERos
gargaricus	EHyt ERos SCnR
- subsp. *gargaricus*	EPot ERos SOkd
'Golden Mammoth'	see *C. x luteus* 'Golden Yellow'
goulimyi ♀H4	CBro EBrs ECho EPot ERos LRHS NMen WCot
- 'Albus'	see *C. goulimyi* subsp. *goulimyi* 'Mani White'
§ - subsp. *goulimyi* 'Mani White' ♀H4	EHyt ERos SCnR
- subsp. *leucanthus*	EHyt
§ *hadriaticus* ♀H4	ECho ERos
- var. *chrysobelonicus*	see *C. hadriaticus*
imperati ♀H4	ERos
- subsp. *imperati* 'De Jager'	CAvo CBgR CFFs CPBP EPot LRHS
- subsp. *suaveolens*	ERos
'Janis Ruksans' **new**	WWst
x *jessoppiae*	EPot ERos
karduchorum	EPot
korolkowii	CGrW ERos LRHS
- 'Flower of Spring' **new**	LRHS
- 'Golden Nugget'	GCrs
- 'Kiss of Spring'	EPot
- 'Yellow Tiger'	WWst
kosaninii	EPot ERos
kotschyanus ♀H4	ECho NRya SPer
- 'Albus'	ECho EHyt LRHS
§ - subsp. *kotschyanus*	CBro EPot
- var. *leucopharynx*	LRHS
laevigatus 'Fontenayi'	CBro EBrs EHyt EPot GKev
'Large Yellow'	see *C. x luteus* 'Golden Yellow'
longiflorus ♀H4	CBro ERos GEdr
§ x *luteus* 'Golden Yellow' ♀H4	EBrs EPfP WShi
§ - 'Stellaris'	EPot ERos
malyi ♀H2-4	EHyt ERos
- 'Sveti Roc' **new**	EPot
'Mammoth Yellow'	see *C. x luteus* 'Golden Yellow'
mathewii	EPot
medius ♀H4	CBro EPot ERos
michelsonii	WWst
minimus	EHyt EPot ERos LRHS
niveus	CAvo CBro EPot ERos SOkd WCot
nudiflorus	CBro EPot ERos NMen WCot
ochroleucus ♀H4	CBro EPot ERos LRHS MMHG
olivieri	ERos
- subsp. *balansae* 'Zwanenburg'	CMea EPot
§ - subsp. *olivieri*	EHyt EPot ERos
pallasii subsp. *pallasii*	ERos

pestalozzae	EHyt ERos
- var. ***caeruleus***	EPot ERos SCnR
pulchellus ♀H4	CPBP EBrs ECho EPot ERos GCrs MBow NWCA SBch WBor
- *albus*	EPot
'Purpureus'	see *C. vernus* 'Purpureus Grandiflorus'
reticulatus subsp. ***reticulatus***	EPot
rujanensis	ERos
salzmannii	see *C. serotinus* subsp. *salzmannii*
sativus	CArn CAvo CBod CBro EBrs ELan EPfP EPot GPoy LRHS MMHG MSal NBir NGHP SPer
- var. ***cartwrightianus***	see *C. cartwrightianus*
scepusiensis	see *C. vernus* subsp. *vernus* var. *scepusiensis*
§ ***serotinus*** subsp. ***clusii***	EPot EPot
§ - subsp. ***salzmannii***	CBro EPot ERos LRHS SBch
sibiricus	see *C. sieberi*
§ ***sieberi*** ♀H4	EPot ERos
§ - 'Albus' ♀H4	CAvo CBro CFfs ECho EPot LRHS MBri MSte SMeo
- subsp. ***atticus***	EHyt LRHS
- 'Bowles' White'	see *C. sieberi* 'Albus'
- 'Firefly'	CBro EHyt EPot LRHS WLin
- 'Hubert Edelsten' ♀H4	CBgR EHyt EPot ERos
- subsp. ***sublimis*** 'Tricolor' ♀H4	CAvo CBgR CBro CFfs CMea EBrs ECho EHyt EPfP EPot ERos GCrs GKev LRHS MBri NMen SPer
- 'Violet Queen'	CAvo CBro CFfs EPot GKev MBri MSte SPer
speciosus ♀H4	CAvo CBro CMea CPBP EBrs EPot LRHS NBir SPer WCot WHoo WShi
- 'Aitchisonii'	CBro CPBP EPot LRHS
- 'Albus' ♀H4	CBro EPot LRHS
- 'Artabir'	CBro EPot LRHS SBch
- 'Blue Webb' **new**	WWst
- 'Cassiope'	EPot LRHS SBch
- 'Conqueror'	CBro EBrs EPot LRHS WBor
- 'Lakeside Beauty' **new**	WWst
- 'Lithuanian Autumn' **new**	WWst
- 'Oxonian'	EPot LRHS SBch
x ***stellaris***	see *C.* x *luteus* 'Stellaris'
susianus	see *C. angustifolius*
suterianus	see *C. olivieri* subsp. *olivieri*
tommasinianus ♀H4	CAvo CBro CFfs CMea EBrs ECho EPot LLWP MBri MRav NBir SRms WShi
- f. *albus*	EHyt EPot LRHS
- 'Barr's Purple'	EPot LPhx LRHS
- 'Eric Smith'	CAvo CFfs
- 'Lilac Beauty'	EPot SPer
- var. ***pictus***	CAvo CFfs EPot ERos NMen
- var. ***roseus***	CMea EHyt EPot ERos NMen SBch WCot
- 'Ruby Giant'	CAvo CBro CFfs CNic EPfP EPot GKev LPhx LRHS MBri NBir SPer WLin WShi
- 'Whitewell Purple'	CAvo CBro CFfs ECho EPot GKev LPhx MBri NBir WShi
tournefortii ♀H2-4	CBro ERos
§ 'Vanguard'	CAvo CBgR CBro CFfs EBrs EPot
veluchensis	EPot
§ ***vernus*** subsp. ***albiflorus***	EPot ERos
- 'Enchantress'	EPot
- 'Fantasy' **new**	EBrs
- 'Flower Record'	EPfP MBri NBir
- 'Glory of Sassenheim'	EPot
- 'Graecus'	EPot ERos
- 'Grand Maître'	CAvo CFfs MBri
- 'Haarlem Gem'	EPot
- 'Jeanne d'Arc'	CAvo CBro CFfs EBrs EPfP EPot MBri NBir WLin WShi
- 'King of the Striped'	EBrs WLin

- 'Negro Boy'	EPot
- 'Pickwick'	CAvo CFfs EPfP EPot MBri NBir WShi
§ - 'Purpureus Grandiflorus'	CBro
- 'Queen of the Blues'	CAvo CBro CFfs EPot WLin
- 'Remembrance'	EBrs EPfP EPot LPhx NBir WShi
- 'Vanguard'	see *C.* 'Vanguard'
- subsp. ***vernus***	see *C. vernus* 'Purpureus Grandiflorus'
§ - - Heuffelianus Group	CPBP EPot GCrs WWst
- - - 'Brian Duncan' **new**	WWst
- - - 'Dark Eyes'	WWst
- - - 'National Park' **new**	WWst
- - - 'Wildlife' **new**	WWst
- - var. ***neapolitanus***	ERos
- - 'Oradea'	WWst
§ - - var. ***scepusiensis***	EPot ERos
versicolor 'Picturatus'	CBgR EBrs EPot ERos LRHS
vitellinus	WWst
'Yellow Mammoth'	see *C.* x *luteus* 'Golden Yellow'
'Zephyr' ♀H4	CBro EBrs EPot ERos
zonatus	see *C. kotschyanus* subsp. *kotschyanus*

Croomia (Stemonaceae)
heterosepala	WCru

Crossandra (Acanthaceae)
infundibuliformis ♀H1	MJnS

Crowea (Rutaceae)
exalata x ***saligna***	CPLG

Crucianella (Rubiaceae)
maritima	XPep
stylosa	see *Phuopsis stylosa*

Cruciata (Rubiaceae)
§ ***laevipes***	CNat NMir

Cryptanthus (Bromeliaceae)
bivittatus ♀H1	CHal
- 'Roseus Pictus'	CHal
bromelioides	MBri

Cryptogramma (Adiantaceae)
crispa	EFer SRms WHer

Cryptomeria (Cupressaceae)
fortunei	see *C. japonica* var. *sinensis*
japonica ♀H4	CDul CMen ECho ISea LCon NBea STre WEve WNor
- Araucarioides Group	CDoC EHul LCon NLar
- 'Bandai'	LBuc
- 'Bandai-sugi' ♀H4	CKen CMac CMen ECho EHul EOrn EPfP LCon LLin LRHS MBar MGos NDlv SCoo SLim SPla STre WEve WGor WRHF
- 'Barabits Gold'	MBar MGos WEve WWes
- 'Compressa'	CDoC CKen CSli ECho EHul ENot EPfP LBee LCon LLin LRHS MAsh MBar MGos SCoo SLim WGor
§ - 'Cristata'	CBcs CDoC CMac ECho ELan EOrn LAst LCon MBar NEgg NPal SCoo SPoG
* - 'Cristata Compacta'	ECho EOrn
- 'Dacrydioides' **new**	LCon
- Elegans Group	CBcs CBrm CDul CMac CSBt CTri ECho EHul ELan ENot EOrn EPfP LAst LCon LLin LRHS MBar MBri MGos MWat NEgg SHBN SLim SPer SPoG WDin WFar WOrn
- 'Elegans Aurea'	CBcs CDoC CTri ECho EHul LCon LLin MAsh MBar MBri NHol SPoG STre WDin WEve

- 'Elegans Compacta' ♀H4 CDoC CRob CSBt CWib ECho
EHul EOrn GBin IMGH LBee LCon
LRHS MAsh MBNS MBar MBri
SCoo SLim SPoG WBVN WEve
- 'Elegans Nana'   ECho LBee LRHS SRms
- 'Elegans Viridis'   ELan LBuc LRHS MBar SCoo SLim
SPer SPoG
- 'Globosa'   ECho EOrn SLim
- 'Globosa Nana' ♀H4 CDoC ECho EHul ERom LAst LBee
LCon LLin LPan LRHS MAsh MBar
MBri MGos NEgg NLar SCoo SHBN
SLim SPoG WFar WGor
- 'Golden Promise'   CDoC CRob EOrn LBee LLin MAsh
NHol SCoo SLim SPoG WEve
WGor
- Gracilis Group   LCon
- 'Jindai-sugi'   CMac ECho MBar NLar
- 'Kilmacurragh'   CDoC CKen ECho EHul MBar
NWea SLim
- 'Knaptonensis' (v)   CDoC
- 'Kohui-yatsubusa'   CKen ECho
* - 'Konijn-yatsubusa'   CKen
- 'Koshiji-yatsubusa'   EOrn MBar
- 'Koshyi'   CKen NLar
- 'Little Champion'   CDoC CKen LCon NLar SLim
- 'Little Diamond'   CKen
- 'Littleworth Dwarf'   see *C. japonica* 'Littleworth Gnom'
§ - 'Littleworth Gnom'   LLin NLar
- 'Lobbii Nana' hort.   see *C. japonica* 'Nana'
§ - 'Mankichi-sugi'   ECho NHol NLar
§ - 'Monstrosa'   MBar MBri
- 'Monstrosa Nana'   see *C. japonica* 'Mankichi-sugi'
- 'Mushroom'   LCon MGos WFar
§ - 'Nana'   CDoC CMac CTri ECho EHul ENot
EOrn EPfP LCon LLin SLim SPoG
WFar WRHF
- 'Pipo'   CKen NLar
- 'Pygmaea'   ECho LLin MBar MGos SRms
WWes
- 'Rasen-sugi'   COtt ECho LBuc LCon LLin MBar
NEgg NPal SCoo SLim SMad SPoG
- 'Sekkan-sugi'   CBcs CCVN CDul CSli ECho EHul
EOrn LBee LCon LLin LRHS MAsh
MBar MGos NEgg NLar SAga SCoo
SLim SPoG WEve WFar
- 'Sekka-sugi'   see *C. japonica* 'Cristata'
§ - var. *sinensis*   CMCN LAst NOGN
* - - 'Vilmoriniana   ECho EOrn
Compacta'
§ - 'Spiralis'   CDoC CKen CMac CRob ECho
EHul EOrn EPfP LBee LCon LLin
LRHS MAsh MBar MGos NHol
SCoo SLim SPer SPla SPoG WEve
WFar
§ - 'Spiraliter Falcata'   CDoC LBuc MBar NLar
§ - 'Tansu'   CKen ECho EHul EOrn LCon LLin
MBar MGos
- 'Tenzan-sugi'   CDoC CKen LLin MAsh
- 'Tilford Cream'   ECho LAst
- 'Tilford Gold'   ECho EHul ENot EOrn LLin MBar
MGos NBlu NDlv NEgg NHol
WEve WFar
- 'Toda'   CKen
- 'Vilmorin Gold'   CKen EOrn WEve WFar
- 'Vilmoriniana' ♀H4 CDoC CKen CMen CRob CSli CTri
ECho EHul ENot EOrn EPfP IMGH
LBee LCon LLin LRHS MBar MGos
NBlu NHol SCoo SHBN SIng SLim
SPer SPoG WDin WEve WFar
- 'Viminalis'   ECho NHol
- 'Winter Bronze'   CKen
- 'Yatsubusa'   see *C. japonica* 'Tansu'
- 'Yore-sugi'   see *C. japonica* 'Spiralis', 'Spiraliter
Falcata'
- 'Yoshino'   CKen SLim
sinensis   see *C. japonica* var. *sinensis*

Cryptostegia (Asclepiadaceae)
grandiflora new   CCCN

Cryptotaenia (Apiaceae)
canadensis   MRav
japonica   CAgr CPou EUnu GIBF MHer
MNHC MSal NRnb WHer WJek
- f. *atropurpurea*   CArn CFwr CHar CSpe EBee ECha
EHoe EMag EMan GCal GGar
GMac ITer LDai LEdu LPhx MNFA
NSti NVic WCHb WCru WEas WFar
WWhi

Ctenanthe (Marantaceae)
§ *amabilis* ♀H1   CHal
lubbersiana ♀H1   CHal XBlo
§ *oppenheimiana*   LRHS XBlo

Ctenium (Poaceae)
concinnum   CBig

Cucubalus (Caryophyllaceae)
baccifer   CArn EBee NLar WPer WPrP

Cudrania see *Maclura*

cumin see *Cuminum cyminum*

Cuminum (Apiaceae)
cyminum   CArn EUnu SIde

Cunninghamia (Cupressaceae)
§ *lanceolata*   CBcs CDoC CDul CMCN CTho
IArd LCon LLin LRHS MBlu SCoo
SLim SMad SPoG SSta STre WEve
WNor WPGP
§ - 'Bánó'   CMac EOrn
- 'Compacta'   see *C. lanceolata* 'Bánó'
- 'Glauca'   WPGP
- 'Little Leo'   CKen
sinensis   see *C. lanceolata*
unicaniculata   see *C. lanceolata*

Cunonia (Cunoniaceae)
capensis   CPLG CTrC EShb

Cuphea (Lythraceae)
blepharophylla   LRav
caeciliae   CBos CHal MOak
* *compacta* new   LAst
cyanaea   CMHG CPLG MOak SDix SOWG
SUsu
'Harlequin' new   NPri
hirtella   LHop MOak SOWG
aff. *hookeriana*   WCru
B&SWJ 9039
hyssopifolia ♀H1   CHal CHll MOak SOWG SRms STre
SWvt
- 'Alba'   LIck MOak SOWG STre SWvt
- 'Riverdene Gold'   EMan
- 'Rosea'   LIck SWvt
§ *ignea* ♀H1   CBos CDMG CHal CWib ELan
MBri MLLN MOak SOWG SRms
SUsu WWlt
- 'Variegata' (v)   CHal MOak SOWG
§ *llavea* 'Georgia Scarlet'   CCCN EBee EWin LIck LSou MOak
NPri SPoG
- 'Tiny Mice'   see *C. llavea* 'Georgia Scarlet'
macrophylla hort.   CBos CHll MOak
platycentra   see *C. ignea*

x *Cupressocyparis* ✿ (Cupressaceae)
§ *leylandii* ♀H4   CBcs CDoC CDul CMac EHul ENot
EPfP LBuc LCon LPan LRHS MAsh
MBar MBri MGos NBlu NEgg

		NWea SLim SPer SWvt WDin WEve
		WHar WMou
§	- 'Castlewellan'	CBcs CDoC CDul CMac EHul EPfP
		ERom LBuc LCon LPan LRHS
		MAsh MBar MBri MGos NBlu NEgg
		NWea SLim SPer SWvt WDin WEve
		WFar WHar WMou
	- 'Douglas Gold'	CRob
	- 'Galway Gold'	see x *C. leylandii* 'Castlewellan'
	- 'Gold Rider' ♀H4	CDoC EHul ENot LBee LCon LRHS
		MAsh MBar MGos NEgg SCoo
		SLim SPer SWvt WDin WEve WHar
§	- 'Harlequin' (v)	LCon MBar SEND SWvt
	- 'Herculea'	CDoC LPan MAsh
	- 'Hyde Hall'	CTri LBee
	- 'Naylor's Blue'	CMac SEND
	- 'New Ornament'	SMad
	- 'Olive's Green'	EHul LCon SWvt
	- 'Robinson's Gold' ♀H4	CMac EHul GQui LBee LCon LRHS
		MBar NWea SLim WEve WFar
		WHar
	- 'Silver Dust' (v)	SRms WFar
	- 'Variegata'	see x *C. leylandii* 'Harlequin'
	- 'Winter Sun'	WCFE
	notabilis	WCwm
	ovensii	EHul

Cupressus (Cupressaceae)

	arizonica 'Conica Glauca'	ECho MBar
§	- var. *glabra*	ECho WPGP
	- - 'Aurea'	CRob ECho EHul LCon LLin LRHS
		MBar MGos SLim WFar
	- - 'Blue Ice' ♀H3	CBcs CDoC CDul CRob CTho
		ECho EHul EOrn LCon LLin LRHS
		MAsh MBar MGos SCoo SLim SPer
		SPoG SWvt WEve WFar WGer
	- - 'Compacta'	CKen
	- - 'Conica'	CKen SBod
I	- - 'Fastigiata'	CBcs CDoC ECho ECrN EHul
		LCon LPan MBar WEve
	- - 'Glauca'	ECho MBlu NBlu
*	- - 'Lutea'	ECho EOrn SPoG WEve
	- 'Pyramidalis' ♀H3	CMac ECho EPfP SCoo WEve
I	- - 'Sulfurea'	CDoC CKen MAsh NLar WEve
	cashmeriana ♀H2	CBcs CDoC CDul CTho ECho
		ELan EPla EREa LCon LLin LPan
		LRHS SLim WFar WNor WWes
	duclouxiana	WCwm
§	*funebris*	CMCN
	gigantea	CDoC
	glabra	see *C. arizonica* var. *glabra*
	goveniana	MBar
	guadalupensis	CMHG
	lusitanica 'Brice's	CKen SLim
	Weeping'	
	- 'Brookhall'	IDee
	- 'Glauca Pendula'	CKen EPfP LCon WEve
	- var. *lusitanica*	CMCN
	- 'Pygmy'	CKen
	macrocarpa	CCVT CDoC CDul CSBt CTho
		ECho EHul SEND
	- 'Barnham Gold'	SBod SRms
	- 'Compacta'	CKen
	- 'Conybearii Aurea'	MAsh
	- 'Donard Gold'	CMac CSBt ECho EOrn MBar
	- 'Gold Spread'	CDoC CRob ECho EHul EOrn
		LBee LLin LRHS SCoo SLim SPoG
		WFar
	- 'Goldcrest' ♀H3	More than 30 suppliers
	- 'Golden Cone'	CKen CSBt ECho LRHS WEve
	- 'Golden Pillar' ♀H3	CDoC CRob ECho EHul EOrn
		LBee LRHS MAsh MBar NEgg SLim
		SPoG SWvt WDin WFar WGer
	- 'Golden Spire'	WFar
	- 'Greenstead Magnificent'	ECho LCon LRHS MAsh SCoo SLim
	- 'Horizontalis Aurea'	EHul MBar

	- 'Lohbrunner'	CKen
	- 'Lutea'	CDoC ECho WFar
I	- 'Pendula' **new**	ECho
	- 'Pygmaea'	CKen ECho
	- 'Sulphur Cushion'	CKen
	- 'Wilma'	ECho EHul ENot LBee LCon LLin
		LRHS MAsh MGos NEgg SCoo
		SLim SPoG SWvt WEve
	- 'Woking'	CKen
	sargentii **new**	ECho
	sempervirens	CBcs CDul CMCN CPMA ECrN
		EHul ELan ERom ISea LLin LPan
		STop WEve WFar WMul
	- 'Bolgheri' **new**	SBig
	- 'Garda'	CDoC
	- 'Green Pencil'	CKen ECho EPfP LRHS
	- 'Pyramidalis'	see *C. sempervirens* Stricta Group
	- var. *sempervirens*	see *C. sempervirens* Stricta Group
§	- Stricta Group ♀H3	CArn CBcs CKen CMCN CSWP
		ECho EHul EPfP LCon LLin LPan
		MAsh NBlu NLar SAPC SArc SBLw
		SCoo WCFE WEve WOrn
	- 'Swane's Gold'	CBcs CDoC CKen EBrs ECho EHul
		EOrn EPfP LCon LLin LRHS MAsh
		NPal SCoo SLim SPoG WEve WFar
	- 'Totem Pole'	CDoC CKen CSBt CTho ECho
		EHul EOrn EPfP LBee LCon LLin
		LPan LRHS MGos NEgg SCoo
		SEND SLim SPoG WEve WGor
	torulosa	EGFP IDee
	- CC 3687	WHCr

x *Cuprocyparis* see x *Cupressocyparis*

Curculigo (Hypoxidaceae)

capitulata	CKob XBlo
crassifolia B&SWJ 2318 **new**	WCru

Curcuma (Zingiberaceae)

alismatifolia	ECho
amada	CKob MOak
angustifolia	CKob MOak
aromatica	CKob MOak
aurantiaca	MOak
'Blue Top'	CKob
'Cobra'	CKob
cordata	MOak
elata	CKob
gracillima 'Chiang Mai	MOak
Chocolate'	
harmandii	MOak
longa	CKob MOak MSal
ornata	CKob
petiolata 'Emperor' (v)	CKob EZes
'Red Fire'	CKob
roscoeana	MOak
'Ruby'	CKob
'Siam Diamond'	MOak
'Siam Ruby'	MOak
thorelii 'Chiang Mai Snow'	MOak
zedoaria	CKob LRHS MOak WMul

Curcumorpha (Zingiberaceae)

longiflora	MOak

Curtonus see *Crocosmia*

Cuscuta (Convolvulaceae)

chinensis	MSal

Cuspidaria (Bignoniaceae)

convoluta **new**	CPIN

Cussonia (Araliaceae)

gamtoosensis **new**	CKob

paniculata	CHen CKob EShb WMul
- subsp. *sinuata* new	CKob
sphaerocephala new	CKob
spicata	CKob EShb WMul
transvaalensis	CKob EShb

custard apple see *Annona cherimola*

Cyananthus (*Campanulaceae*)

integer misapplied	see *C. microphyllus*
integer Wall. 'Sherriff's Variety'	WIvy
lobatus ♀H4	ECho EMan GBuc GMaP ITim NJOw NSla SBla SIng
- CC 4634	ITim WCot
- 'Albus'	EWes GEdr SBla WAbe WIvy
- dark	WAbe
- 'Dark Beauty'	ECho
- giant	EPot GEdr SBla
lobatus x *microphyllus*	EPot NWCA WAbe WLin
macrocalyx	GEdr ITim SBla WIvy
§ *microphyllus* ♀H4	ECho EPot GEdr GMaP NJOw NLAp NSla SBla WAbe
sherriffii	EPot GEdr WAbe WFar

Cyanella (*Tecophilaeaceae*)

§ *hyacinthoides*	LBow
lutea	CMon ECho
orchidiformis	CMon LBow

Cyanotis (*Commelinaceae*)

somaliensis ♀H1	CHal

Cyathea (*Cyatheaceae*)

australis	EAmu EFtx LPal WFib WMul WPGP
brownii	EAmu WMul
cooperi	CBcs EAmu EFtx WFib
cunninghamii	LRav
dealbata	CAbb CBcs CBrP CTrC EAmu IDee LPal MGos WMul
dregei	SPlb
lepifera	LPal
medullaris	CAbb CBcs CTrC EAmu MGos WMul
milnei	LPal
smithii	CBcs CTrC EAmu EFtx IDee WMul
tomentosissima	EAmu EFtx

Cyathodes (*Epacridaceae*)

colensoi	see *Leucopogon colensoi*
fasciculata	see *Leucopogon fasciculatus*
fraseri	see *Leucopogon fraseri*
juniperina	see *Leptecophylla juniperina*
parviflora	see *Leucopogon parviflorus*
parvifolia	see *Leptecophylla juniperina* subsp. *parvifolia*

Cycas (*Cycadaceae*)

cairnsiana	CRoM
circinalis	CRoM LPal
media	CRoM LPal
panzihihuaensis	CBrP CKob LPal
platyphylla	CRoM
revoluta ♀H1	CAbb CBrP CCCN CDoC CHEx CKob CRoM CTrC EAmu EPfP LPal LRHS LToo MBri MPRe NPal SAPC SArc SChr SEND WMul WNor
revoluta x *taitungensis*	CBrP
§ *rumphii*	CBrP CKob EAmu LPal LRHS
siamensis	LPal
taitungensis	CBrP CRoM
thouarsii	see *C. rumphii*

Cyclamen ❀ (*Primulaceae*)

africanum	CBro CElm CLCN CNic CWCL EAEE ECho EJWh ITim LRHS MAsh NWCA STil WCot
africanum x *hederifolium*	CWCL ECho EHyt
alpinum	CBro CLCN CWCL EAEE ECho EJWh EPot LRHS MAsh STil
balearicum	CBro CElm CLCN EAEE ECho EJWh ITim LRHS MAsh NMen STil
cilicium ♀H2-4	CBgR CBro CElm CLAP CLCN CMea CStu CWCL EAEE ECho EHyt EJWh ERos ITim LRHS MHer MSSP MTho NMen SBla STil WAbe WFar WIvy WNor WPat
- f. *album*	CBro CLCN CWCL CWoo EAEE ECho EHyt EJWh EPot ERos ITim LRHS MAsh STil
- patterned leaf	NBir
colchicum	ECho STil
§ *coum* ♀H4	More than 30 suppliers
- from Meryemana, Turkey	CElm
- from Turkey	ERos
- var. *abchasicum*	see *C. coum* subsp. *caucasicum*
- 'Broadleigh Silver'	CElm
§ - subsp. *caucasicum*	EPot ERos ETow GBuc STil
I - - 'Album'	GBBs NMen
- subsp. *coum*	CBro ECho MAsh
- - f. *albissimum* 'George Bisson'	CElm
- - - 'Golan Heights'	CElm MAsh STil WIvy
- - 'Atkinsii'	CBro
- - f. *coum* Nymans Group	CLAP CWCL MAsh SBla
- - - Pewter Group ♀H2-4	CBel CWCL ECGP ECho ERos MAsh MTho SBla WIvy
- - - - bicoloured	EJWh
- - - - 'Blush'	GBuc STil
- - - - 'Maurice Dryden'	CAvo CBel CBro CLAP CPBP CStu CWCL EAEE ECGP ECho EHrv GBuc GCrs LRHS MAsh STil WCMO WCot WIvy
- - - - red	CLCN GBBs WPat
- - - - 'Tilebarn Elizabeth'	CBel CElm CWCL EHrv MAsh STil WHoo
- - - - white	GBuc MAsh
- - - plain-leaved red	STil
- - - 'Roseum'	CElm CWCL EBrs GBuc STil
- - - Silver Group	CBro CElm CNic CWoo EAEE EBrs ECho EHrv GCrs LRHS MAvo NHol NSla WHoo WPGP
- - - - red	CAvo EPot MTho STil WHoo
- - - - 'Sterling Silver'	CBel
- - magenta	CElm CWCL WHoo
- - f. *pallidum* 'Album'	CAvo CBel CElm EPot ERos ITim MAsh SIng STil WAbe WCot WHoo WNor WPat
- - - 'Marbled Moon'	MAsh STil
- dark pink	CAvo CLAP ECho ITim WHoo
- 'Elm Tree Special'	CElm
- marble-leaved	CBel CWCL ECho ITim LHop WHoo
- 'Meaden's Crimson'	CElm
- plain-leaved	CBel CElm CLAP EBla EPot ITim WAbe
- red	CLAP CStu ECho LPhx
creticum	CLCN CWCL ECho EJWh MAsh STil
creticum x *repandum*	see *C.* x *meiklei*
cyprium	CBro CLCN CWCL EAEE ECho EHyt EJWh ITim LRHS MAsh NJOw STil WCot WIvy
- 'E.S.'	MAsh STil WAbe
elegans	EJWh MAsh STil
europaeum	see *C. purpurascens*

fatrense	see *C. purpurascens* subsp. *purpurascens* from Fatra, Slovakia
graecum	CBro CElm CLCN CStu CWCL CWoo EBla ECho EHyt EJWh EPot LRHS MAsh NMen SRot STil WAbe WCot WIvy
- f. *album*	CBro CElm CWCL EJWh EPot LRHS MAsh STil
- subsp. *anatolicum*	EHyt STil
- subsp. *candicum*	MAsh STil
- subsp. *graecum* f. *graecum* 'Glyfada'	CLCN STil
- silver-leaved	CElm
§ *hederifolium* ♀H4	More than 30 suppliers
- arrow-head	CLAP
- var. *confusum*	MAsh STil WCot
- var. *hederifolium* f. *albiflorum*	More than 30 suppliers
§ - - - 'Album'	CElm EBrs GBBs MWgw WCMO
- - - Bowles' Apollo Group	CLCN GBuc
§ - - - - 'Artemis'	STil
- - - - 'White Bowles' Apollo'	see *C. hederifolium* var. *hederifolium* f. *albiflorum* (Bowles' Apollo Group) 'Artemis'
- - - 'Cotswold White'	WCot
- - - 'Linnett Stargazer'	WCot
- - - 'Nettleton Silver'	see *C. hederifolium* var. *hederifolium* f. *albiflorum* 'White Cloud'
- - - 'Perlenteppich'	CWCL GBBs GBuc GMaP
- - - 'Tilebarn Helena'	STil
§ - - - 'White Cloud'	CBel CElm CLAP EBla EHyt EPot ITim MAsh NEgg NSla STil WIvy
- - f. *hederifolium* Bowles' Apollo Group	CLAP CWCL ECGP GBuc MAsh SBla STil
- - - 'Fairy Rings'	MAsh
- - - red	NEgg
- - - 'Rosenteppich'	CWCL GBBs GBuc GMaP ITim MAsh
- - - 'Ruby Glow'	CBel CElm CWCL GBuc MAsh WCMO WCot WPat
- - - 'Silver Cloud'	CBel CBro CLAP CLCN GBuc MAsh NBir STil WCot WHoo WIvy WPGP WPat WTin
- - - 'Stargazer'	MAsh
- - 'Tilebarn Silver Arrow'	STil
- long-leaved	CElm
- scented	CLCN NHol STil WCot
- silver-leaved	CAby CAvo CWoo EAEE EBla EBrs ECGP ECho EPfP EPot GBBs GBin GCrs LHop LPhx LRHS MAsh SBla SRot STil
x *hildebrandii*	WIvy
ibericum	see *C. coum* subsp. *caucasicum*
intaminatum	CBro CLCN CPBP CWCL CWoo EAEE ECho EJWh EPot ERos LRHS MAsh NMen SChr STil WIvy
- patterned-leaved	CBel CWCL EJWh MAsh STil
- pink	CWCL MAsh NMen STil
- plain-leaved	MAsh STil
latifolium	see *C. persicum*
libanoticum	CBel CBro CElm CLCN CWCL EAEE ECho EJWh ITim LRHS MAsh NMen SBla STil WCot WFar
§ x *meiklei*	CBro CLCN
mirabile ♀H2-3	CBel CBro CElm CLCN CWCL CWoo EAEE EBla ECho EJWh LRHS MAsh NMen STil WAbe WIvy WThu
- 'Tilebarn Anne'	MAsh STil
- 'Tilebarn Jan'	STil
- 'Tilebarn Nicholas'	CBel CElm CWoo EBla MAsh STil
neapolitanum	see *C. hederifolium*
orbiculatum	see *C. coum*
parviflorum	EJWh MAsh STil

peloponnesiacum ♀H2-3	EJWh ERos MAsh
* - subsp. *peloponnesiacum*	CBro CLCN CWCL CWoo STil
- 'Pelops'	CElm
* - subsp. *rhodense*	CLCN MAsh STil
* - subsp. *vividum*	STil
- white-flowered	STil
§ *persicum*	CBro CElm CLCN CStu CWCL ECho EJWh LRHS MAsh NMen SChr STil
- CSE 90560	STil
- var. *persicum* f. *puniceum* from Lebanon	STil
- - - 'Tilebarn Karpathos'	CElm CWCL STil
pseudibericum ♀H2-3	CBel CBro CElm CLCN CWCL CWoo EAEE ECho EJWh LRHS MAsh SBla SIng STil
- 'Roseum'	CLCN MAsh NMen STil
§ *purpurascens* ♀H4	CBro CElm CLCN CWCL EAEE EJWh GBuc LRHS MAsh MSSP NMen SBla STil WHoo WIvy WPat
- f. *album*	SBla
- var. *fatrense*	see *C. purpurascens* subsp. *purpurascens* from Fatra, Slovakia
- 'Lake Garda'	MAsh WPGP
§ - subsp. *purpurascens* from Fatra, Slovakia	EHyt STil
- silver-leaved	CElm STil
- silver-leaved from Limone, Italy	SBla
repandum	CAvo CBro CElm CLCN EAEE ECho EHrv EHyt EJWh ERos LRHS MAsh NMen SBla STil WHer
- subsp. *repandum* f. *album*	CLAP CLCN EJWh MAsh SBla STil
rohlfsianum	CBro CLCN CWCL EAEE EJWh LRHS MAsh STil
x *saundersii*	CLCN EJWh MAsh STil
x *wellensiekii*	MAsh STil

Cydonia ❀ (Rosaceae)

japonica	see *Chaenomeles speciosa*
oblonga 'Agvambari' (F)	SKee
- 'Aromatnaya'	ERea
- 'Champion' (F)	CBcs ECrN SKee WJas
- 'Early Prolific' (F)	ECrN LAst
- 'Ekmek' (F)	SKee
- 'Isfahan' (F)	SKee
- 'Krymsk' (F)	CAgr
- 'Leskovic' (F)	NLar
- 'Ludovic' (F)	WJas
§ - 'Lusitanica' (F)	CDoC CDul ECrN ERea GTwe SKee SPer WJas
- 'Meech's Prolific' (F)	CAgr CLnd CTho CTri ECrN EMil EMui ERea GTwe LRHS MBlu MGos MWat NLar NWea SDea SFam SKee SPer
- pear-shaped (F)	CDul ECrN ENot
- Portugal	see *C. oblonga* 'Lusitanica'
- 'Shams' (F)	SKee
- 'Sobu' (F)	SKee
§ - 'Vranja' (F) ♀H4	More than 30 suppliers

Cymbalaria (Scrophulariaceae)

aequitriloba 'Alba'	GGar
§ *hepaticifolia*	EDAr LRHS NLar WCru WPer
- 'Alba'	CNic
§ *muralis*	ECho ECtt IHMM MBar MHer NJOw NPri SECG WBri WGor XPep
- 'Albiflora'	see *C. muralis* 'Pallidior'
§ - 'Globosa Alba'	CHal EDAr
- 'Kenilworth White'	WMoo
- 'Nana Alba'	NJOw NPri SEND WPer

§ - 'Pallidior' — ECho EWin
- 'Rosea' — WFar
§ **pallida** — CMea CPBP LRHS NSla SBch SBla SPlb WCru WFar WMoo WPer
§ **pilosa** — ECtt EMan NJOw NLar

Cymbopogon (*Poaceae*)

citratus — CArn CBod CCCN CHby CHrt COld CSev CWan EUnu GPoy LRav MNHC MSal NGHP NPri NTHB SHDw SIde WCHb WJek
flexuosus — CBig GWCH MHer WBri
martini — CArn GPoy MSal
nardus — CArn GPoy MSal

Cymophyllus (*Cyperaceae*)

§ **fraserianus** — CDes CHEx EBee GBin

Cynanchum (*Asclepiadaceae*)

sp. — CPLG
acuminatifolium — EMan GCal

Cynara (*Asteraceae*)

§ **baetica** subsp. **maroccana** — LDai
§ **cardunculus** ♀H3-4 — More than 30 suppliers
- ACL 380/78 — SWat
- 'Carciofo Violetto Precoce' (Scolymus Group) new — WHer
* - 'Cardy' — EBee EChP EMan EShb EWin NBre NCGa SMrm SWat WBrE WRHF WWhi
- dwarf — WCot
- var. **ferocissima** new — EBrs
* - 'Florist Cardy' — IGor MFOX MWat NLar WCot
§ - Scolymus Group — More than 30 suppliers
- - 'Carciofo Violetto Precoce'new — WHer
- - 'Gigante di Romagna' — WHer
- - 'Gobbo di Nizza' new — EBee ELau WHer
- - 'Green Globe' — CBod CHar CPrp CSBt CSev EBee ELau IFoB MWat NPer NVic SWal
- - 'Gros Camus de Bretagne' — MAvo WCMO WCot
- - 'Gros Vert de Lâon' — CBcs ECha ELan IBal NBhm SBig WCMO WCot WPGP
- - 'Large Green' — EWin NLar NScw WHil
- - 'Purple Globe' — CArn CPrp CSBt ELau
- - 'Romanesco' — EBee ELau EWin
- - 'Violetto di Chioggia' — CSev EBee ELau MSph WHer WHil
- white-flowered new — WCot
I **hystrix** — see *C. baetica* subsp. *maroccana*
scolymus — see *C. cardunculus* Scolymus Group

Cynodon (*Poaceae*)

aethiopicus — CBig EHoe LPhx SWal
dactylon 'Santana' — XPep

Cynoglossum (*Boraginaceae*)

amabile ♀H4 — GKev NCGa WTMC
- f. **roseum** — CSec WGwG
- - 'Mystery Rose' — WPGP
dioscoridis — CPom EChP NLar WPer
nervosum — CBcs EBee ECtt ELan EMan EMil EPPr EPfP GMac LAst LHop LRHS MLHP MRav MWgw NChi NEgg NGdn NWCA SHGN SPer SPet SWat WCAu WCHb WCot WFar WPnn WTMC
officinale — CArn MHer MSal NSti WCHb WHer WWye

Cynosurus (*Poaceae*)

cristatus viviparous — CNat

Cypella (*Iridaceae*)

§ **coelestis** — CPom EDif EMan
herbertii — CMon CNic CPom EDif
peruviana — CMon CPom EMan WCot
plumbea — see *C. coelestis*

Cyperus (*Cyperaceae*)

§ **albostriatus** — CCCN CHEx CHal MBri
alternifolius misapplied — see *C. involucratus*
alternifolius L. — LPBA WMAq WWpP
- 'Compactus' — see *C. involucratus* 'Nanus'
'Chira' — CSec EChP EKen MBNS WGwG WWpP
§ **cyperoides** — MBri
diffusus misapplied — see *C. albostriatus*
§ **eragrostis** — CArn CHal CMil CPLG CRow CSec EHoe EPPr EPla MCCP NOGN SDix SPlb SWal SWat WAbb WMAq WMoo WWhi WWpP
esculentus — CArn CBig IBlr LRav SWal WDyG
fuscus — EKen MDKP WFar WHal WMoo
§ **giganteus** — CDWL
glaber — EMan EPGN LDai MBar MNHC NBre SMar
haspan misapplied — see *C. papyrus* 'Nanus'
haspan L. new — CDWL
§ **involucratus** ♀H1 — CBen CHEx CHal CPLG CRow CWCL EBak EHon EShb LPBA MBri SArc SWal SWat SYvo WFar WMoo WMul WWpP WWye
- 'Gracilis' — EBak MBri
§ - 'Nanus' — LPBA SWal
- 'Variegatus' (v) — MJnS
longus — CBen CSec EHoe EHon EMFW EMon EPPr GIBF LNCo LPBA MBar MLHP NNor NPer SMad SWal SWat WFar WHal WMAq WPrP WWpP
papyrus ♀H1 — CHEx CHal CKno CMCo EAmu ERea EShb LPan LRHS MBri MJnS SAPC SArc SBig SLdr SMad SUsu WHal WMul XBlo
- 'Mexico' — see *C. giganteus*
§ - 'Nanus' ♀H1 — CDWL CHEx LPal WMul XBlo
- 'Perkamentus'PBR new — EShb
rotundus — CRow EChP MCCP NLar SBch SWal WWpP
sumula hort. — see *C. cyperoides*
ustulatus — CTrC MDKP MMoz
vegetus — see *C. eragrostis*
'Zumila' — WMul

Cyphomandra (*Solanaceae*)

betacea (F) — CHEx CPLG
- 'Goldmine' (F) — ERea
- 'Oratia Red' (F) — ERea
corymbiflora — EUnu

Cyphostemma (*Vitaceae*)

juttae — CRoM LToo

Cypripedium (*Orchidaceae*)

Aki g. — XFro
x **andrewsii** — GCrs XFro
calceolus — EHrv GCrs MDun NLAp WCMO WCot
calcicolum new — NLAp
californicum — WCMO WWst
cordigerum new — WWst
debile — EFEx
Emil g. — XFro
farreri — EFEx NLAp
fasciolatum — EFEx GCrs
flavum — CFir GKev NCGa NLAp WCMO WCot
- white-flowered new — GKev WWst

§ *formosanum*   EBee EFEx WWst
  - dwarf **new**   SOkd
  franchetii   WWst
  Gisela g.   GCrs XFro
  - 'Yellow'   XFro
  - 'Pastel' **new**   WWst
  guttatum   NLAp
  - var. *yatabeanum*   see *C. yatabeanum*
  Hank Small g.   WWst XFro
  henryi   EBee EFEx NLAp WCMO
  himalaicum   EFEx NLAp
  Inge g.   WWst XFro
  Ingrid g.   XFro
§ *japonicum*   EFEx GEdr NLAp WWst
  - var. *formosanum*   see *C. formosanum*
  kentuckiense   CFir WCMO WCot
  lichiangense **new**   NLAp WWst
  macranthos   EFEx EHrv NLAp WCot
  - f. *albiflorum*   NLAp
  - green-flowered   EFEx
  - var. *hotei-*   EFEx
    atsumorianum
  - var. *rebunense*   EFEx
  - var. *speciosum*   EFEx
  margaritaceum   EFEx NLAp
  Michael g.   GCrs XFro
  montanum   EFEx
  parviflorum 'Butterball'   GCrs
    new
  - var. *makasin*   WWst
§ - var. *pubescens*   GCrs
  Philipp g.   XFro
  Pixi g. new   GCrs
  pubescens   see *C. parviflorum* var. *pubescens*
  reginae   CFir CLAP EHrv EPot GCrs GKev
                                  MDun NCGa NLAp SSpi WCot
                                  WWst
  reginae x *tibeticum* **new** WWst
  Sabine g.   XFro
  segawae   EFEx
  tibeticum   EFEx NLAp
  Ulla Silkens g.   EBee GCrs NLAp XFro
  wardii   EFEx
§ *yatabeanum*   EFEx GIBF
  yunnanense **new**   WWst

Cyrilla (Cyrillaceae)
  racemiflora   GIBF NLar

Cyrtanthus (Amaryllidaceae)
  sp. from high altitude **new** WCot
  'Alaska'ᴾᴮᴿ   CBro LRHS WCMO
§ *brachyscyphus*   CDes CMon CSpe EBee ECho ERos
                                  EShb GGar MTis SHFr WCot WSPU
  breviflorus   CDes EBee ECho WPGP
  contractus   CDes
  'Edwina'   ECho EShb SPer
§ *elatus* ♀ᴴ¹   CBro CHal CSev CSpe CStu EBee
                                  EHol EMan ERea EShb LRHS MCCP
                                  NCiC SYvo WCMO WCot WGwG
                                  WHer
  - 'Cream Beauty'   ECho WCMO WCot
  - hybrid   CMon
  - 'Pink Diamond'   CBro LRHS WCot
  'Elizabeth'   ECho SPer
  epiphyticus   WCMO
  falcatus ♀ᴴ¹   CMon EBee WCMO
  flanaganii   CDes
  loddigiesianus   CDes
§ *luteus*   WAbe
  mackenii   CDes CPen CPne EBee ECho
                                  WGwG WPGP
  - var. *cooperi*   CMon WCMO WCot
  - red-flowered **new**   MOak
  - white-flowered **new**   EBee MOak
  montanus   EBee ECho WCot

  obliquus   CMon WCot
  parviflorus   see *C. brachyscyphus*
  purpureus   see *C. elatus*
  sanguineus   CMon ECho WCot WPGP
  - 'Horseshoe Falls'   CMon
  smithiae   CDes WCot
  speciosus   see *C. elatus*

Cyrtomium (Dryopteridaceae)
§ *caryotideum*   CLAP GQui
§ *falcatum* ♀ᴴ³   CFwr CHEx CHal CLAP CMHG
                                  CTrC EBee EFtx ELan EPfP GCal
                                  GMaP IBal MDun NBlu NHol
                                  NMoo NMyG NOrc NSti SEND
                                  SPla SPoG SRms SRot WFar WPnP
* - 'Muricatum'   ELan
  - 'Rochfordianum'   CBcs CCCN WFib
§ *fortunei* ♀ᴴ⁴   CBcs CFwr CHal CLAP CTbh EBee
                                  EFer EFtx EPPr EPfP GBin MAsh
                                  MBnl MDun MGos MWat MWgw
                                  NBid NDlv NHol NVic SHGC SPer
                                  SPoG SRms SRot SSto WCru WFib
                                  WMoo
  - var. *clivicola*   CFwr CPrp CTrC CWCL EBee
                                  EChP EPfP MAsh MBnl MWgw
                                  NDlv NLar NMoo NVic SRot WOut
  lonchitoides   CLAP
  macrophyllum   CLAP WCru

Cystopteris ✿ (Woodsiaceae)
  bulbifera   CLAP GQui
  dickieana   CLAP EBee EMon GBin NVic SRms
                                  WCot WFib
  fragilis   ECha EFer GQui SRms WFib
  - 'Cristata'   CLAP
  moupinensis   WCru
    B&SWJ 6767

Cytisus (Papilionaceae)
  albus misapplied   see *C. multiflorus*
  albus Hacq.   see *Chamaecytisus albus*
  'Amber Elf'   COtt LRHS MBri SPoG
  'Andreanus'   see *C. scoparius* f. *andreanus*
  'Apricot Gem'   MBar MGos NLar SPoG WFar
  ardoinoi ♀ᴴ⁴   ECho
  battandieri ♀ᴴ⁴   More than 30 suppliers
  - 'Yellow Tail' ♀ᴴ⁴   CEnd EBee LRHS MBri WPGP
                                  WSPU
  x *beanii* ♀ᴴ⁴   CPLG EBee ELan EPfP LRHS MBar
                                  NHol SLon SPer SRms SSto WDin
                                  WFar
  'Boskoop Ruby' ♀ᴴ⁴   CDoC CSBt EBee EGra EPfP GGar
                                  LAst LRHS NBlu SPer SPoG SWvt
                                  WFar
  'Burkwoodii' ♀ᴴ⁴   CBcs CDoC CDul CSBt CWSG
                                  EBee EGra ELan ENot EPfP LAst
                                  LRHS LSRN MRav MSwo MWat
                                  MWhi NHol SPoG WFar
  canariensis   see *Genista canariensis*
  'Compact Crimson'   CDoC SPoG
  'Cottage'   EPot WAbe
  'Daisy Hill'   CSBt
  'Darley Dale Red'   EWTr
§ *decumbens*   CLyd NLar SSto WLin
  'Donard Gem'   CDoC LRHS WWeb
  'Dorothy Walpole'   WFar
  'Dukaat'   SHBN
  'Firefly'   CBcs CSBt NBlu NLar
  'Fulgens'   CSBt EPfP LRHS MBar SPer
                                  WWeb
  'Golden Cascade'   CBcs CDoC EBee ELan LAst
                                  LRHS
  'Golden Sunlight'   CSBt ENot EPfP SHBN
  'Goldfinch'   CBcs CDoC CHar CSBt CWSG
                                  EBee ELan MAsh MBri MSwo NPri
                                  WRHF

hirsutus	see *Chamaecytisus hirsutus*
'Hollandia' ♀H4	CBcs CDoC CSBt CWSG EBee EPfP MBar MGos MRav NEgg NPri SHBN SPer WDin WFar
x **kewensis** ♀H4	CSBt CWSG EBee ELan EPfP LRHS MAsh MBar MGos MRav NEgg NHol SHBN SPer SPoG SReu SRms WDin
- 'Niki'	EBee EPfP LRHS MAsh MGos NHol SPer SPoG SSta WGer
'Killiney Red'	ECrN ELan MBri NEgg
'Killiney Salmon'	CTri GGar LSRN MRav SSto WFar
'La Coquette'	CDoC EBee EGra MAsh MBar NBlu SPlb SPoG
'Lena' ♀H4	CDoC CHar CSBt EBee EBrs EGra ENot EPfP GGar LAst LRHS MBar MBri MGos MRav MWat NBlu NEgg NHol NPri SRGP WFar WWeb
leucanthus	see *Chamaecytisus albus*
'Luna'	EBee LRHS NBlu WFar
maderensis	see *Genista maderensis*
'Maria Burkwood'	EPfP MGos NEgg SHBN
'Minstead'	CDoC EBee ELan EPfP GGar SPer SPoG
monspessulanus	see *Genista monspessulana*
'Moyclare Pink'	CMHG
§ **multiflorus** ♀H4	LRav SRms
nigrescens	see *C. nigricans*
§ **nigricans**	ECrN NEgg WPGP
- 'Cyni'	ELan IArd LAst LRHS MAsh SPer SPoG SSpi
'Palette'	LAst LRHS MBar MGan
'Porlock'	see *Genista* 'Porlock'
x **praecox**	CBrm CDul CPSs CSBt EWTr LAst LRHS MGan NBlu NEgg NHol SPlb WFar WWeb
- 'Albus'	CDoC EBee ECrN ELan ENot EPfP EWTr GGar LAst LRHS MBar MGos MRav MWat NBlu NEgg NHol SEND SHBN SPer WFar WWeb
- 'Allgold' ♀H4	More than 30 suppliers
- 'Canary Bird'	see *C.* x *praecox* 'Goldspeer'
- 'Frisia'	CBcs EWTr MBar WFar
§ - 'Goldspeer'	CSBt SEND
- 'Lilac Lady'	LRHS WGer
§ - 'Warminster' ♀H4	EBee ENot EPfP LRHS MAsh MBar MBri MRav MWat NWea SPer SRms
procumbens	NBid
purpureus	see *Chamaecytisus purpureus*
racemosus hort. ex Marnock	see *Genista* x *spachiana*
Red Favourite	see *C.* 'Roter Favorit'
'Red Wings'	NEgg NHol SPer
§ 'Roter Favorit'	EPfP MBar MGos MNHC NScw WGor
scoparius	CAgr CArn CDul CRWN EBee ECrN GWCH MCoo NWea SRms WDin
§ - f. **andreanus** ♀H4	CBgR CDoC ENot EPfP MGos NWea SPer SPoG WFar
- - 'Splendens'	CBcs SSto
- 'Cornish Cream'	CBgR CDoC ECot EPfP SPer WWeb
- 'Jessica'	NBlu SRGP
§ - subsp. **maritimus**	GSki SLPl
- var. **prostratus**	see *C. scoparius* subsp. *maritimus*
x **spachianus**	see *Genista* x *spachiana*
supinus	see *Chamaecytisus supinus*
'Windlesham Ruby'	CDoC CPLG EBee ELan ENot EPfP LAst LRHS MBar MGan NLar SPer WDin WFar
'Zeelandia' ♀H4	CBcs EBee ENot EPfP LAst LRHS MBar MRav MWat NBlu NPri SEND SPer SPoG WFar WWeb

D

Daboecia ✿ (Ericaceae)

§ **cantabrica** f. **alba**	CPLG CSBt EHea MBar MBri NHol SPer SRms
- - 'Alba Globosa'	CCCN EHea EPfP MBar MSwo
- - 'Creeping White'	EHea
- - 'David Moss' ♀H4	EHea MBar
- - 'Early Bride'	EHea
- - 'White Carpet'	EHea
- 'Arielle' ♀H4	EHea
- 'Atropurpurea'	CCCN CNCN CSBt EHea SPer
- 'Barbara Phillips' ♀H4	EHea MBar
- 'Bellita'	EHea
- 'Bicolor' ♀H4	CNCN EHea
- 'Blueless'	EHea EPfP
- f. **blumii** 'Pink Blum'	EHea
- - 'White Blum'	EHea
- 'Bubbles'	EHea
- 'Celtic Star'	EHea
- 'Chaldon'	EHea
- 'Charles Nelson' (d)	EHea MBar
- 'Cherub'	EHea
- 'Cinderella'	CNCN EHea MBar
- 'Cleggan'	EHea
- 'Clifden'	EHea
- 'Covadonga'	EHea MBar
- 'Cupido'	CNCN
§ - 'Donard Pink'	EHea MBar
- 'Eskdale Baron'	EHea
- 'Eskdale Blea'	EHea
- 'Eskdale Blonde'	EHea
- 'Glamour'	EHea
- 'Globosa Pink'	EHea
- 'Harlequin'	EHea
- 'Heather Yates'	EHea
- 'Heraut'	EHea
- 'Hookstone Purple'	CCCN EHea MBar
- 'Irish Shine' **new**	EHea
- 'Johnny Boy' **new**	EHea
- 'Lilac Osmond'	EHea MBar
- 'Pink'	see *D. cantabrica* 'Donard Pink'
- 'Pink Lady'	EHea MBar
- 'Polifolia'	CNCN EHea SRms
- 'Porter's Variety'	EHea MBar
- 'Praegerae'	CCCN CNCN CTri EHea MBar
- 'Purpurea'	EHea MBar
- 'Rainbow' (v)	CNCN EHea MBar
- 'Rodeo' ♀H4	EHea
- 'Rosea'	EHea MBar
- 'Rubra'	EHea
- subsp. **scotica** 'Bearsden'	EHea MBar
- - 'Ben'	EHea
- - 'Cora'	CNCN EHea MBar
- - 'Golden Imp'	EHea
- - 'Goscote'	EHea MGos
- - 'Jack Drake' ♀H4	CNCN EHea MBar MBri NDlv
- - 'Katherine's Choice' **new**	EHea
- - 'Red Imp'	EHea
- - 'Robin'	EHea
- - 'Silverwells' ♀H4	CBcs CNCN EHea MBar MBri NDlv
- - 'Tabramhill'	CNCN EHea MBar
- - 'William Buchanan' ♀H4	CNCN EHea MBar MBri NDlv NHol
- - 'William Buchanan Gold' (v)	CCCN CNCN EHea MBar MBri
- 'Snowdrift'	EHea MBar
- 'Tom Pearce' **new**	CCCN
- 'Waley's Red' ♀H4	EHea GQui MBar
- 'Wijnie'	EHea

Dacrycarpus (Podocarpaceae)
§ **dacrydioides**   ECou LEdu
  - 'Dark Delight'   ECou

Dacrydium (Podocarpaceae)
  bidwillii   see *Halocarpus bidwillii*
  cupressinum   CAbb CBcs CDoC CTrC SMad
  franklinii   see *Lagarostrobos franklinii*

Dactylis (Poaceae)
  glomerata <u>new</u>   WSFF
  - 'Variegata' (v)   CPen EBee EMan EMon ENot EPPr
                           IHMH MBlu MCCP NBid NBro
                           NGdn NHol WFar

Dactylorhiza (Orchidaceae)
  alpestris <u>new</u>   MAvo NLAp
  aristata   EFEx GEdr WWst
  Atlanta g. (*foliosa* x   GEdr
    majalis) <u>new</u>
  x **braunii**   ECha
  - dark   ECha
§ **elata** ♀H4   CDes CLAP EMon GCrs GMaP
                           GQui IBlr LPhx MBri MDun NLAp
                           SMHy WCot
  - 'Lydia'   CLAP GCrs
  Eskimo Nell g.   SBla
§ **foliosa** ♀H4   CBro CDes CFir CLAP ERos ETow
                           GCrs IBlr MDun MTho NLAp WFar
                           WOld
§ **fuchsii**   CHdy CMil CSec EBee EPot ERos
                           GBuc GCrs GKev MAvo MGos
                           MNrw NLAp NMen NRya NSla
                           SCnR SUsu WCot WHer WTin
* - *alba*   NLAp
  - 'Bressingham Bonus'   GCrs
  x **grandis**   IBlr SCnR SMHy
  incarnata   NLAp
  insularis <u>new</u>   NLAp
§ **maculata**   CHdy EBee EChP EHrv ELan EMan
                           ENot EPfP GAbr MDun NCGa
                           NGdn NLAp WCot WFar WHer
  - 'Madam Butterfly'   CBro
  maderensis   see *D. foliosa*
§ **majalis**   CLAP EBrs NLAp WFar
  - subsp. **praetermissa** see *D. praetermissa*
  markusii <u>new</u>   NLAp
  mascula   see *Orchis mascula*
§ **praetermissa**   CFir CFwr CLAP EPot MAvo MDun
                           NCGa NLAp WCot WFar
  purpurella   CLAP NLAp NRya SUsu WCot
                           WFar WSan
  romana x **sambucina** NLAp
    <u>new</u>
* **spagnicola** <u>new</u>   NLAp
  urvilleana   CHdy

Dahlia ✿ (Asteraceae)
  'A la Mode' (LD)   CWGr
  'Abba' (SD)   CWGr
  'Abridge Alex' (SD)   CWGr
  'Abridge Ben' (MinD)   CWGr
  'Abridge Florist' (SWL) CWGr
  'Abridge Fox' (MinD)   CWGr
  'Abridge Primrose' (SWL) CWGr
  'Abridge Taffy' (MinD)   CWGr
  'Adelaide Fontane' (LD) CWGr
  'Admiral Rawlings' (SD) CHad CWGr MAJR WHal WWlt
  'Aimie' (MinD)   CWGr
  'Akita' (Misc)   MBri SPer WAba
  'Albert Schweitzer' (MS-c) CWGr
  'Alden Regal' (MinC)   CWGr
  'Alfred C' (GS-c)   CWGr
  'Alfred Grille' (MS-c)   CWGr EPfP LRHS SPer
  'Alf's Mascot'   WAba

  'Aljo' (MS-c)   CWGr
  'All Triumph' (MinS-c)   CWGr
  'Allan Snowfire' (MS-c) NHal WAba
  'Allan Sparkes' (SWL) ♀H3 CWGr LAyl
  'Alloway Cottage' (MD)   CWGr NHal
  'Alltami Apollo' (GS-c) CWGr
  'Alltami Classic' (MD)   CWGr
  'Alltami Corsair' (MS-c) CWGr
  'Alltami Cosmic' (LD)   CWGr
  'Alltami Ruby' (MS-c)   CWGr
  'Almand's Climax' (GD)   CWGr WAba
                           ♀H3
  'Alpen Beauty' (Col)   CWGr
  'Alpen Fern' (Fim)   CWGr
  'Alpen Flame' (MinC)   CWGr
  'Alpen Mildred' (SS-c)   CWGr
  'Alpen Sun' (MinS-c)   CWGr
  'Alva's Doris' (SS-c) ♀H3 CWGr LAyl
  'Alva's Lilac' (SD)   CWGr
  'Alva's Supreme' (GD) ♀H3 CWGr NHal WAba
  'Amanda Jarvis' (SC)   CWGr
  'Amanjanca' (MinS-c)   CWGr
  'Amaran Candyfloss' (SD) CWGr
  'Amaran Pentire' (SS-c) CWGr
  'Amaran Relish' (LD)   CWGr
  'Amaran Return' (GD)   CWGr
  'Amaran Royale' (MinD)   CWGr
  'Amaran Troy' (SWL)   CWGr
I 'Amazone' (DwB)   LAst
  'Amber Banker' (MC)   CWGr
  'Amber Festival' (SD)   CWGr NHal
  'Amber Vale' (MinD)   CWGr
  'Amberglow' (MinBa)   CWGr LAyl
  'Amberley Jean' (SD)   CWGr
  'Amberley Joan' (SD)   CWGr
  'Amberley Nicola' (SD)   CWGr
  'Amberley Victoria' (MD) CWGr
  'Ambition' (SS-c)   CWGr
  'Amelia's Surprise' (LD) CWGr
  'American Copper' (GD)   CWGr
  'Amethyst' (SD)   CWGr
  'Amgard Coronet' (MinD) CWGr
  'Amgard Delicate' (LD)   CWGr
  'Amgard Rosie' (SD)   CWGr
  'Amira' (SBa)   CWGr NHal WAba
  'Amorangi Joy' (SC)   CWGr
  'Ananta Patel' (SD)   CWGr
* 'Anatol' (LD)   CWGr
  'Anchorite' (SD)   CWGr
  'Andrea Clark' (MD)   NHal
  'Andrew Mitchell' (MS-c) CWGr NHal WAba
* 'Andries' Amber' (MinS-c) LBut
  'Andries' Orange' (MinS-c) CWGr LBut
  'Anja Doc' (MS-c)   CWGr
  'Anniversary Ball' (MinBa) CWGr LAyl
  'Apache' (MS-c/Fim)   CWGr SPer
  'Appetizer' (SS-c)   CWGr
I 'Appleblossom' (Col)   CWGr
  'Apricot Beauty' (MS-c) LAyl
  'Apricot Honeymoon   CWGr WAba
    Dress' (SD)
  'Apricot Jewel' (SD)   CWGr
  'Apricot Parfait' (SS-c) CWGr
  'April Dawn' (MD)   CWGr
  'April Heather' (Col) <u>new</u> NHal
  'Arab Queen' (GS-c)   CWGr
  'Arabian Night' (SD)   More than 30 suppliers
  'Arc de Triomphe' (MD)   CWGr
  'Arlequin' (LD)   CWGr
  'Arnhem' (SD)   CWGr
  'Arthur Godfrey' (GD)   CWGr
  'Arthur Hankin' (SD)   CWGr
  'Arthur Hills' (SC)   CWGr
  'Arthur's Delight' (GD) CWGr
  'Asahi Chohje' (Anem)   CWGr
    ♀H3

'Aspen' (Dwf) **new**   CWGr
'Athelston John' (SC)   CWGr
'Atilla' (SD)   CWGr
'Audacity' (MD)   CWGr LAyl
'Audrey R' (SWL)   CWGr
'Aurora's Kiss' (MinBa)   CWGr LBut NHal
'Aurwen's Violet' (Pom)   CWGr LAyl NHal
australis   EDsa WPGP
'Autumn Choice' (MD)   LAyl
'Autumn Lustre' (SWL)   CWGr
   ♀H3
'Avoca Salmon' (MD)   NHal
'Awaikoe' (Col)   CWGr
'B.J. Beauty' (MD)   CWGr LAyl NHal
'Babette' (S-c)   LBut
'Baby Fonteneau' (SS-c)   CWGr
'Baby Royal' (SD)   CHad
'Babylon' (GD)   EPfP
'Bacchus' (MS-c)   CWGr
'Bach' (MC)   CWGr LRHS
'Bagley Blush' (MinD)   WAba
'Bahama Red' (SD)   CBgR
'Balcombe' (SD)   CWGr
'Ballego's Glory' (MD)   CWGr
'Bambino' (Lil)   CWGr
'Banker' (MC)   CWGr
'Bantling' (MinBa)   CWGr EPfP
'Barb' (LC)   CWGr
'Barbara' (MinBa)   CWGr
'Barbara's Pastelle' (MS-c)   CWGr
'Barbarossa' (LD)   CWGr
'Barbarry Ball' (SBa)   CWGr
'Barbarry Banker' (MinD)   CWGr LAyl
'Barbarry Bluebird' (MinD)   NHal
'Barbarry Cadet' (MinD)   CWGr
'Barbarry Carousel' (SBa)   CWGr WAba
'Barbarry Cascade' (SD)   CWGr
'Barbarry Challenger'   CWGr
   (MinD)
'Barbarry Choice' (SD)   WAba
'Barbarry Clover' (SB)   CWGr
'Barbarry Coronet' (MinD)   WAba
'Barbarry Cosmos' (SD)   CWGr
'Barbarry Dominion'   CWGr
   (MinD)
'Barbarry Flag' (MinD)   CWGr
'Barbarry Gem' (MinBa)   CWGr
'Barbarry Ideal' (MinD)   CWGr
'Barbarry Monitor' (MinBa)   CWGr
'Barbarry Noble' (MinD)   CWGr
'Barbarry Olympic' (SBa)   CWGr
'Barbarry Oracle' (SD)   CWGr WAba
'Barbarry Orange' (SD)   WAba
'Barbarry Pinky' (SD)   CWGr
'Barbarry Polo' (MinD)   CWGr
'Barbarry Red' (MinD)   CWGr
'Barbarry Ticket' (SD)   WAba
'Barbarry Token' (SD)   WAba
'Barbarry Triumph' (MinD)   CWGr
'Barbetta' (MinD)   CWGr
'Barbette' (MinD)   CWGr
'Baret Joy' (LS-c)   CWGr NHal WAba
'Bargaly Blush' (MD)   NHal
'Baron Ray' (SD)   CWGr
'Barry Williams' (MD)   CWGr
'Bart' (SD)   CWGr
'Barton Memory' (S-c)   NHal
'Baseball' (MinBa)   CWGr
'Bassingbourne Beauty'   CWGr
   (SD)
'Bayswater Red' (Pom)   CWGr
I 'Bea' (SWL)   WAba
'Beach Boy' (SD)   CWGr
'Beacon Light' (SD)   CWGr
I 'Beatrice' (MinBa)   CWGr
'Bedford Sally' (MD)   CWGr

'Bednall Beauty'   CBgR CHll CSpe CWCL CWGr
   (Misc/DwB) ♀H3   EBee ECtt EHrv ELan EMan EMil
                               ERou EShb EWes EWin MBri NPri
                               SDnm SDys SPav SUsu SWal WAba
                               WCMO WCot WDyG
'Bell Boy' (MinBa)   CWGr
'Bella S' (GD)   CWGr
'Belle Epoque' (MC)   CWGr
'Belle Moore' (SD)   CWGr
'Bell's Boy' (MS-c)   WAba
'Beretta' (MD)   CWGr
'Berger's Rekord' (S-c)   CSut CWGr EPfP LRHS
'Berliner Kleene'   LRHS
   (MinD/DwB)
'Bernice Sunset' (SS-c)   CWGr
'Berolina' (MinD)   CWGr
'Berwick Banker' (SBa)   CWGr
'Berwick Wood' (MD)   CWGr NHal
'Bess Painter' (SD)   CWGr
'Betty Ann' (Pom)   CWGr
'Betty Bowen' (SD)   CWGr
'Biddenham Cherry' (SD)   CWGr
'Biddenham Fairy' (MinD)   CWGr
'Biddenham Strawberry'   CWGr
   (SD)
'Bill Homberg' (GD)   CWGr WAba
'Bingley' (SD)   CWGr
'Bingo' (MinD)   CWGr
'Bishop of Auckland'   LRHS SPoG WCMO
   (Misc)
'Bishop of Canterbury'   CBgR EBee LRHS MWea NGdn
   (Misc)   NHal SPoG WCMO
'Bishop of Lancaster'   LRHS SPoG WCMO
   (Misc)
'Bishop of Llandaff' (Misc)   More than 30 suppliers
   ♀H3
'Bishop of Oxford' (Misc)   CBgR EBee MWea NGdn WCMO
                               WHoo
'Bishop of York' (Misc)   CBgR CSpe EBee MWea NGdn
                               WCMO
'Bitter Lemon' (SD)   CWGr
'Black Fire' (SD)   CWGr LAyl
* 'Black Knight' (MD)   CWGr
'Black Monarch' (GD)   CWGr NHal
'Black Narcissus' (MC)   CWGr WWlt
'Black Spider' (SS-c)   CWGr
'Black Tucker' (Pom)   CWGr
'Blaisdon Red' (SD)   CWGr
'Blaze' (MD)   CWGr
'Blewbury First' (SWL)   CWGr
'Bliss' (SWL)   CWGr
'Bloemfontein' (SD)   LRHS
'Bloodstone' (SD)   CWGr
'Bloom's Amy' (MinD)   CWGr
'Bloom's Graham' (SS-c)   CWGr
'Bloom's Kenn' (MD)   CWGr
I 'Blossom' (Pom)   CWGr
'Blue Beard' (SS-c)   CWGr
'Blue Diamond' (MC)   CWGr
'Bluesette' (SD)   CWGr
'Bob Fitzjohn' (GS-c)   CWGr
'Bonaventure' (GD)   NHal
'Bonesta' (SWL)   CWGr
'Bonne Espérance' (Sin/Lil)   CWGr
'Bonny Blue' (SBa)   CWGr
'Bonny Brenda' (MinD)   CWGr
'Boogie Woogie' (Anem)   CSut CWGr
'Bora Bora' (SS-c)   CWGr WHlf
'Border Princess'   CWGr
   (SC/DwB)
'Border Triumph' (DwB)   CWGr
'Brackenhill Flame' (SD)   CWGr WAba
'Brackenridge Ballerina'   CSam CWGr LAyl NHal
   (SWL)
'Brandaris' (MS-c)   CWGr
'Brandysnap' (SD)   CWGr

'Brian R' (MD) CWGr
'Brian's Dream' (MinD) NHal
'Bride's Bouquet' (Col) CWGr
'Bridge View Aloha' (MS-c) CWGr EPfP WAba ♀H3
'Bridgette' (SD) CWGr
'Bristol Petite' (MinD) CWGr
'Bronze Glints' (MS-c) WAba
'Brookfield Delight'³ (Sin/Lil) ♀H CWGr SUsu
'Brookfield Dierdre' (MinBa) CWGr
'Brookfield Judith' (MinD) NHal
'Brookfield Rachel' (MinBa) CWGr
'Brookfield Rene' (Dwf MinD) CWGr
'Brookfield Snowball' (SBa) CWGr
'Brookfield Sweetie' (DwB/Lil) CWGr
'Brookside Cheri' (SC) CWGr
'Brookside Snowball' (SB) new CWGr
'Bryce B. Morrison' (SD) CWGr
'Bud Flanagan' (MD) CWGr
* 'Buttercup' (Pom) CWGr
'Buttermere' (SD) CWGr
'By George' (GD) CWGr
'Caer Urfa' (MinBa) WAba
'Café au Lait' (LD) CBgR CWGr EBee NLar SEND SPer
'Calgary' (SD) CWGr
'Camano Ariel' (MC) CWGr
'Camano Choice' (SD) CWGr
'Camano Passion' (MS-c) CWGr
'Camano Poppet' (SBa) CWGr
'Camano Regal' (MS-c) CWGr
'Cameo' (WL) CSam CWGr LBut NHal
'Campos Hush' (SS-c) CWGr
'Campos Philip M' (GD) CWGr
* 'Canary Fubuki' (MD) CWGr
I 'Candlelight' (GD) new NHal
I 'Candy' (SD) new CWGr
'Candy Cane' (MinBa) CWGr
'Candy Cupid' (MinBa) CWGr LBut WAba ♀H3
'Candy Hamilton Lilian' (SD) CWGr
'Candy Keene' (LS-c) NHal
'Capulet' (SBa) CWGr
'Cara Tina' (Misc/DwO) CWGr
'Careless' (SD) CWGr
'Caribbean Fantasy' new CSut SPer
I 'Carolina' (Dwf) new CWGr
'Carolina Moon' (SD) CSam CWGr LAyl NHal
'Carstone Ruby' (SD) NHal
'Carstone Sunbeam' (SD) CWGr
'Carstone Suntan' (MinC) CWGr NHal
'Castle Drive' (MD) CWGr
'Catherine Ireland' (MinD) CWGr
'Cerise Prefect' (MS-c) CWGr
'Cha Cha' (SS-c) CWGr
'Chanson d'Amour' (SD) CWGr
'Chantal' (MinBa) CWGr
'Charles de Coster' (MD) CWGr
'Charlie Briggs' (SBa) new NHal
'Charlie Dimmock' (SWL) NHal new
'Charlie Kenwood' (MinD) CWGr
'Charlie Two' (MD) CWGr NHal WAba
'Charlotte Bateson' (MinBa) CWGr
'Chat Noir' (MS-c) CWGr
'Chee' (SWL) CWGr
'Cheerleader' (GS-c) CWGr
'Cherokee Beauty' (GD) CWGr

'Cherry Wine' (SD) CWGr
'Cherrywood Millfield' (MS-c) CWGr
'Cherrywood Stoddard' (MD) CWGr
'Cherrywood Turnpike' (SD) CWGr
'Cherrywood Wilderness' (MD) CWGr
'Cherubino' (Col) CWGr
'Cherwell Goldcrest' (SS-c) CWGr NHal WAba
'Cherwell Lapwing' (SS-c) NHal
'Cherwell Siskin' (MD) WAba
'Cherwell Skylark' (SS-c) NHal ♀H3
'Chessy' (Sin/Lil) ♀H3 CWGr EPfP LAyl LRHS NHal
'Chic' (MinBa) WWeb
'Chilson's Pride' (SD) CWGr
'Chiltern Amber' (SD) CWGr
'Chiltern Fantastic' (SC) CWGr
'Chiltern Herald' (MS-c) CWGr
'Chiltern Sylvia' (MinS-c) CWGr
'Chimacum Topaz' (MS-c) CWGr
'Chimborazo' (Col) CWGr LAyl SDix
'Chorus Girl' (MinD) CWGr
'Christine' (SD) SPer
I 'Christine' (SWL) new CWGr
'Christmas Star' (Col) CWGr
'Christopher Nickerson' (MS-c) CWGr
'Christopher Taylor' (SWL) CWGr NHal
I 'Cindy' (MinD) WAba
'Clair de Lune' (Col) ♀H3 CBgR CWGr EBee EWin LAst NHal SPav WAba WCMO
'Claire Diane' (SD) CWGr
'Claire Louise Kitchener' (MWL) CWGr
'Clara May' (MS-c/Fim) CWGr
'Clarence' (S-c) CWGr
'Clarion' (MS-c) WCot
'Classic A.1' (MC) CWGr LAyl
'Classic Elise' (Misc) CWGr
'Classic Masquerade'PBR (Misc) CBgR EBee EPfP
'Classic Poème'PBR (Misc) CBgR
'Classic Rosamunde'PBR (Misc) CBgR EBee
'Classic Summertime' (Misc) CBgR CWGr EBee WCMO WWeb
'Classic Swanlake'PBR (Misc) CBgR EBee
'Clint's Climax' (LD) WAba
'Cloverdale' (SD) CWGr
coccinea (B) CBgR CHll CPLG CWGr EBee EDsa EMan EWin LAst MSte NCob SDix SMHy SMad SPav WAba WCMO WCot WDyG WHrl WPGP WSHC
- B&SWJ 9126 WCru
- var. *palmeri* CBgR MCCP
coccinea x *merckii* (B) EMan EWes
coccinea x *sherffii* CHad
'Cocktail' (S-c) CWGr
'Colac' (LD) CWGr
'Color Spectacle' (LS-c) CWGr
'Coltness Gem' (Sin/DwB) CWGr
'Comet' (Misc Anem) CWGr
'Como Polly' (LD) CWGr
I 'Concordia' (SD) CWGr
'Connie Bartlam' (MD) CWGr
'Connoisseur's Choice' (MinBa) CWGr
'Constance Bateson' (SD) CWGr
'Constantine' (MD) CWGr
'Contraste' (Misc) CWGr
'Coral Puff' (DwAnem) LRHS
'Coral Relation' (SC) CWGr

'Coral Strand' (SD) — CWGr
'Cornel' (SBa) — CWGr LAyl LBut NHal WAba
'Cornish Minx' (Pom) — CWGr
'Corona' (SS-c/DwB) — CWGr
'Coronella' (MD) — CWGr
'Corrie Vigor' (SS-c) — NHal
'Corrine' (SWL) — WAba
'Cortez Silver' (MD) — CWGr
'Cortez Sovereign' (SS-c) — CWGr
'Corton Bess' (SD) — CWGr
'Corton Olympic' (GD) — CWGr
'Cottesmore' (MD) — CWGr
'Country Boy' (MS-c) — CWGr
'Crazy Legs' (MinD) — CWGr
'Cream Alva's' (GD) ♀H3 — CWGr
'Cream Delight' (SS-c) — CWGr
'Cream Klankstad' (SC) — CWGr
'Cream Linda' (SD) — CWGr
'Cream Moonlight' (MS-c) — CWGr WAba
'Cream Reliance' (SD) — CWGr
'Crève Coeur' (GD) — CWGr
'Crichton Cherry' (MinD) — CWGr
'Crichton Honey' (SBa) — CWGr
'Crossfield Allegro' (SS-c) — CWGr
'Crossfield Anne' (MinD) — CWGr
'Crossfield Ebony' (Pom) — CWGr
'Crossfield Festival' (LD) — CWGr
'Croydon Jumbo' (GD) — CWGr
'Croydon Snotop' (GD) — CWGr
'Crushed Velvet' (MinD) — CWGr
'Cryfield Bryn' (SS-c) — NHal
'Cryfield Jane' (MinBa) — CWGr
'Cryfield Keene' (LS-c) — CWGr
'Cryfield Max' (SC) — CWGr
'Cryfield Rosie' (SBa) — CWGr
'Curate' (Misc) — CWGr
'Curiosity' (Col) — CWGr LAyl
'Currant Cream' (SBa) — CWGr
'Cyclone' (MD) — CWGr
'Cycloop' (SS-c) — CWGr
'Cynthia Chalwin' (MinBa) — CWGr
'Cynthia Louise' (GD) — CWGr WAba
'Czardas' — GCal
'Daddy's Choice' (SS-c) — CWGr
'Dad's Delight' (MinD) — CWGr
'Daleko Adonis' (GS-c) — CWGr
'Daleko Gold' (MD) — CWGr
'Daleko Jupiter' (GS-c) — CWGr NHal WAba
'Daleko Olympic' (LD) — CWGr
'Daleko Tangerine' (MD) — CWGr
'Dana Champ' (MinS-c) — CWGr
'Dana Dream' (MinS-c) — CWGr
'Dana Iris' (SS-c) — CWGr
'Dana Sunset' (SC) — CWGr
'Dancing Queen' (S-c) — CWGr
'Danjo Doc' (SD) — CWGr
'Danum Cherry' (SD) — CWGr
'Danum Chippy' (SD) — CWGr
'Danum Fancy' (SD) — CWGr
'Danum Gail' (LD) — CWGr WAba
'Danum Julie' (SBa) — CWGr
'Danum Meteor' (GS-c) — CWGr WAba
'Danum Rebel' (LS-c) — CWGr
'Danum Rhoda' (GD) — CWGr
'Danum Salmon' (MS-c) — CWGr
'Danum Torch' (Col) — CWGr
'Dark Desire'^PBR (Sin/DwB) — CAvo CBct CFir CHVG CHar CSpe CWCL EWll MBri SCoo SDnm
'Dark Stranger' (MC) ♀H3 — CWGr
'Darlington Diamond' (MS-c) — CWGr
'Darlington Jubilation' (SS-c) — CWGr
'Davar Hayley' (SC) — CWGr
'Davenport Anita' (MinD) — CWGr

'Davenport Honey' (MinD) — CWGr WAba
'Davenport Lesley' (MinD) — CWGr
'Davenport Sunlight' (MS-c) — CWGr
'Dave's Snip' (MinD) — WAba
'David Digweed' (SD) — CWGr NHal
'David Howard' (MinD) ♀H3 — More than 30 suppliers
'David Shaw' (MD) — CWGr
'David's Choice' (MinD) — CWGr
'Dawn Chorus' (MinD) — CWGr
'Dawn Sky' (SD) — LAyl
'Daytona' (SD) — CWGr
'Dazzler' (MinD/DwB) — CWGr
'Deborah's Kiwi' (SC) — CWGr NHal WAba
'Debra Anne Craven' (GS-c) — CWGr NHal WAba
'Decorette' (DwB/SD) — CWGr
'Decorette Bronze' (MinD/DwB) — CWGr
'Decorette Rose' (MinD/DwB) — CWGr
'Deepest Yellow' (MinBa) — CWGr
'Denise Willow' (Pom) — WAba
'Dentelle de Venise' (MC) — CWGr
'Deuil du Roi Albert' (MD) — CWGr
'Deutschland' (MD) — CWGr
'Devon Joy' (MinD) — CWGr
'Diamond Rose' (Anem/DwB) — CWGr
'Dinah Shore' (LS-c) — CWGr
'Director' (SD) — CWGr
dissecta — CWGr WPGP
— var. *sublignosa* new — WCMO
'Doc van Horn' (LS-c) — CWGr
'Doctor Anne Dyson' (SC) — CWGr
'Doctor Arnett' (GS-c) — CWGr
'Doctor Caroline Rabbitt' (SD) — CWGr
'Doctor John Grainger' (MinD) — CWGr
'Doktor Hans Ricken' (SD) — WAba
'Don Hill' (Col) new — NHal
'Doris Bacon' (SBa) — CWGr
'Doris Day' (SC) — CWGr LBut NHal
'Doris Knight' (SC) — LBut
'Doris Rollins' (SC) — CWGr
'Dottie D.' (SBa) — CWGr
'Dove' (MinC) new — WAba
'Downham Royal' (MinBa) — CWGr
'Drummer Boy' (LD) — CWGr
'Duet' (MD) — CWGr EPfP LRHS
'Dusky Harmony' (SWL) — CWGr LBut
'Dutch Baby' (Pom) — CWGr WAba
'Dutch Boy' (SD) — CWGr
'Dutch Triumph' (LD) — CWGr
'Earl Haig' (LD) — CWGr
'Earl Marc' (SC) — CWGr LBut
'Early Bird' (SD) — CWGr
'Easter Sunday' (Col) — CWGr
'Eastwood Moonlight' (MS-c) — CWGr NHal WAba
'Eastwood Star' (MS-c) — CWGr WAba
'Ebbw Vale Festival' (MinD) — CWGr
'Ebony Witch' (LD) — CWGr
'Edge of Gold' (GD) — CWGr
'Edgeway Joyce' (MinBa) — CWGr
'Edinburgh' (SD) — CWGr SWal WAba
'Edith Holmes' (SC) — CWGr
'Edith Mueller' (Pom) — CWGr
'Edna C' (MD) new — CWGr
'Eileen Denny' (MS-c) — CWGr
'Eisprinzessin' (MS-c) — CWGr
'El Cid' (SD) — CWGr
'El Paso' (SD) — CSut CWGr MBri
'Eleanor Fiesta' (MinS-c) — CWGr

'Elgico Leanne' (MC)   CWGr
'Elizabeth Snowden' (Col)   CWGr WAba
'Ella Britton' (MinD)   CPen EBee LRHS
'Ellen Huston'   CBgR CEnt CPLG CWGr EBee
  (Misc/DwB) ♀H3   LRHS MBri NHal SWal WWeb
'Elma E' (LD)   CWGr NHal WAba
'Elmbrook Chieftain' (GD)   CWGr
'Elmbrook Rebel' (GS-c)   CWGr
'Embrace' (SC)   NHal
'Emile Rose' (MinS-c) new   WAba
'Emma's Coronet' (MinD)   CWGr WAba
'Emmie Lou' (MD)   CWGr
'Emory Paul' (LD)   CWGr
'Emperor' (MD)   CWGr
'Enfield Salmon' (LD)   CWGr
'Engadin' (MD)   CWGr
'Engelhardt's Matador'   CBgR LSou WCot WGwG WHrl
  (MD)
'Enid Adams' (SD)   CWGr
'Eric's Choice' (SD)   CWGr
'Ernie Pitt' (SD)   CWGr
'Esau' (GD)   CWGr
'Eunice Arrigo' (LS-c)   CWGr
'Eveline' (SD)   CBgR CWGr EBrs EPfP LRHS
                                MBri
'Evelyn' (D)   EBee
'Evelyn Foster' (MD)   CWGr
'Evelyn Rumbold' (GD)   CWGr
'Evening Lady' (MinD)   CWGr
excelsa (B)   CHll
'Exotic Dwarf' (Sin/Lil)   CBgR CFir CWGr LSou NHal WCot
                                WGor WGwG
'Explosion' (SS-c)   CWGr
'Extase' (MD)   CWGr LRHS
'Fabula' (Col)   CWGr SPer
'Fairfield Frost' (Col) new   NHal
'Fairway Pilot' (GD)   CWGr
'Fairway Spur' (GD)   LAyl NHal
'Fairy Queen' (MinC)   CWGr
'Falcon's Future' (MS-c)   CWGr
'Fascination' (SWL/DwB)   CBcs CBgR CBos CHVG CHad
  ♀H3   CHar COIW CSam CWCL EBee
                                EBrs ECtt EWll LAyl LSou MAJR
                                MWea NEgg NPri SMeo WHoo
                                WWeb
I 'Fascination' (Misc) new   CWGr
   'Fascination Aus' (Col)   CWGr
   'Fashion Monger' (Col)   CWGr NHal
   'Fata Morgana' (Anem)   CWGr
   'Fermain' (MinD)   CWGr WAba
   'Fern Irene' (MWL)   CWGr
   'Ferncliffe Illusion' (LD)   CWGr
   'Fernhill Champion' (MD)   CWGr
* 'Fernhill Suprise' (SD)   CWGr LBut
   'Festivo' (Dw/Col)   CWGr
   'Feu Céleste' (Col)   CWGr
   'Fidalgo Blacky' (MinD)   CWGr
   'Fidalgo Bounce' (SD)   CWGr
   'Fidalgo Climax' (LS-c/Fim) CWGr
   'Fidalgo Magic' (MD)   CWGr WAba
   'Fidalgo Snowman' (GS-c)   CWGr
   'Fidalgo Splash' (MD)   CWGr
   'Fidalgo Supreme' (MD)   CWGr LAyl
   'Figurine' (SWL) ♀H3   CWGr WAba
   'Fille du Diable' (LS-c)   CWGr
   'Finchcocks' (SWL) ♀H3   CWGr LAyl
   'Fire Magic' (SS-c)   CWGr
* 'Fire Mountain'   NHal
     (MinD/DwB)
   'Firebird' (Sin)   LRHS WAba
   'First Lady' (MD)   CWGr
   'Fleur' (MinD) new   SPer
   'Fleur Mountjoy' (Col)   CWGr
   'Flevohof' (MS-c)   CWGr
   'Floorinoor' (Anem)   CWGr SPer
   'Flutterby' (SWL)   CWGr

'Formby Supreme' (MD)   CWGr
'Forncett Furnace' (B)   GCal
'Forrestal' (MS-c)   CWGr
'Frank Holmes' (Pom)   CWGr WAba
'Frank Hornsey' (SD)   CWGr
'Frank Lovell' (GS-c)   CWGr WAba
'Franz Kafka' (Pom)   CWGr
'Frau Louise Mayer' (SS-c)   CWGr
'Fred Wallace' (SC)   CWGr
'Freelancer' (LC)   CWGr
'Freestyle' (SC)   CWGr
§ 'Freya's Paso Doble'   LAyl
   (Anem) ♀H3
'Freya's Sweetheart'   CWGr
   (Sin) new
'Freya's Thalia' (Sin/Lil)   CWGr LAyl
   ♀H3
'Friendship' (LC)   CWGr
'Fringed Star' (MS-c)   LRHS
* 'Friquolet'   WHlf
'Frits' (MinBa)   CWGr
'Funfair' (MD)   CWGr
'Funny Face' (Misc)   CWGr WAba
'Fusion' (MD) ♀H3   CWGr
'Fuzzy Wuzzy' (MD) new   CSut
'Gala Parade' (SD)   CWGr
'Gale Lane' (Pom)   CWGr
'Gallery Art Deco'PBR   CWGr NHal
   (SD) ♀H3
'Gallery Art Nouveau'PBR   CWGr MBri NHal WCot
   (MinD) ♀H3
'Gallery Cézanne'PBR   CWGr
   (MinD)
'Gallery Leonardo'PBR 3   CWGr
   (SD) ♀H
'Gallery Matisse' (SD)   EPfP SPer
'Gallery Rembrandt'PBR   CWGr
   (MinD)
'Gallery Renoir'PBR 3   CWGr NHal
   (SD) ♀H
'Gamelan' (Dw/Anem)   CWGr
'Garden Festival' (SWL)   CWGr
'Garden Party' (MC/DwB)   CWGr LAyl
   ♀H3
'Garden Princess'   CWGr
   (SC/DwB)
'Garden Wonder' (SD)   EPfP LRHS
'Gargantuan' (GS-c)   CWGr
Gateshead Festival   see *D.* 'Peach Melba' (SD)
'Gaudy' (SD)   CWGr
'Gay Mini' (MinD)   CWGr
'Gay Princess' (SWL)   CWGr LAyl
'Geerlings' Cupido' (SWL)   WAba
§ 'Geerlings' Indian Summer'   NHal
   (MS-c) ♀H3
'Geerlings' Yellow' (SS-c)   CWGr
'Gemma Darling' (GD)   CWGr
'Gemma's Place' (Pom)   CWGr
'Genève' (MD)   CWGr
'Geoffrey Kent' (MinD)   NHal WAba
   ♀H3
'Gerald Grace' (LS-c)   CWGr
'Gerlos' (MD)   CWGr
'Gerrie Hoek' (SWL)   CWGr LBut LRHS
'Gill's Pastelle' (MS-c)   CWGr WAba
'Gina Lombaert' (MS-c)   CWGr LRHS SEND WAba
'Ginger Willo' (Pom)   CWGr
'Giraffe' (Misc)   CWGr
'Giselle' new   SPer
'Gitts Perfection' (GD)   CWGr
'Gitty' (SBa)   CWGr
'Glad Huston' (DwSS-c)   CWGr
'Glenbank Honeycomb'   CWGr
   (Pom)
'Glenbank Paleface' (Pom)   CWGr
'Glenbank Twinkle' (MinC)   CWGr

'Glengarry' (SC) — CWGr
'Glenplace' (Pom) — NHal
'Globular' (MinBa) — CWGr
'Gloria Romaine' (SD) — CWGr
'Glorie van Heemstede' (SWL) ♀H3 — CSam CWGr LAyl LBut LRHS NHal SEND WHrl
'Glorie van Naardwijk' (SD) — SWal
'Glorie van Noordwijk' (Min S-c) **new** — CWGr
'Glory' (LD) — CWGr
'Glow Orange' (MinBa) — CWGr
'Go American' (GD) — CWGr NHal
'Gold Ball' (MinBa) — CWGr
'Gold Crown' (LS-c) — EPfP
'Gold Standard' (LD) — CWGr
'Goldean' (GD) — CWGr
'Golden Emblem' (MD) — CWGr SWal
'Golden Fizz' (MinBa) — CWGr
'Golden Glitter' (MS-c) — CWGr
'Golden Heart' (MS-c) — CWGr
'Golden Horn' (MS-c) — CWGr
'Golden Jubilee' (D) — EPfP
'Golden Leader' (SD) — CWGr
'Golden Scepter' (MinD) — EPfP WAba
'Golden Symbol' (MS-c) — CWGr WAba
'Golden Turban' (MD) — CWGr
'Golden Willo' (Pom) — CWGr
'Goldie Gull' (Anem) — NHal
'Goldilocks' (S-c) — CWGr
'Goldorange' (SS-c) — CWGr
'Good Earth' (MC) — CWGr
'Good Hope' (MinD) — CWGr
'Good Intent' (MinBa) — CWGr
'Goshen Beauty' (SWL) — CWGr
'Goya's Venus' (SS-c) — CWGr
'Grace Nash' (SD) — CWGr
'Grace Rushton' (SWL) — CWGr
'Gracie S' (MinC) — NHal
'Grand Prix' (GD) — CWGr
'Grand Willo' (Pom) — WAba
'Grenadier' (Misc) **new** — CWGr
'Grenadier' (SWL) ♀H3 — CBgR EBee ECtt EMan ERou EWin LSou SDix SDys SPav WAba WCMO WCot
'Grenidor Pastelle' (MS-c) — CWGr NHal WAba
'Gretchen Heine' (SD) — CWGr
'Grock' (Pom) — CWGr
'Gunyun' (GD) — CWGr
'Gurtla Twilight' (Pom) — CWGr NHal
'Gypsy Boy' (LD) — CWGr LAyl
'Gypsy Girl' (SD) — CWGr
'Hallwood Asset' (MinD) — CWGr
'Hallwood Coppernob' (MD) — CBos CWGr
'Hallwood Envoy' (LD) — CWGr
'Hallwood Satin' (MD) — CWGr
'Hallwood Tiptop' (MinD) — CWGr
'Hamari Accord' (LS-c) ♀H3 — LAyl WAba
'Hamari Bride' (MS-c) ♀H3 — CWGr LAyl
'Hamari Girl' (GD) — CWGr NHal
'Hamari Gold' (GD) ♀H3 — CWGr NHal WAba
'Hamari Katrina' (LS-c) — CWGr LRHS WAba
'Hamari Rosé' (MinBa) ♀H3 — CWGr LAyl NHal
'Hamari Sunshine' (LD) ♀H3 — CWGr NHal
'Hamilton Amanda' (SD) — CWGr
'Hamilton Lillian' (SD) ♀H3 — CWGr WAba
'Hans Radi' (Misc) — WAba
'Hans Ricken' (SD) — CWGr
'Happy Caroline' (MinD) — CWGr LRHS

'Haresbrook' (Sin) — EBee EMan ERou EShb EWin LAst MSte NGdn SDys SPav WAba WCMO
'Harvest' (LS-c/Fim) — CWGr
'Harvest Amanda' (Sin/Lil) ♀H3 — CWGr
'Harvest Brownie' (Sin/Lil) — CWGr
'Harvest Dandy' (Sin/Lil) — CWGr
§ 'Harvest Imp' (Sin/Lil) — CWGr LAyl
§ 'Harvest Inflammation' (Sin/Lil) ♀H3 — CWGr NHal
§ 'Harvest Samantha' (Sin/Lil) ♀H3 — CWGr LAyl
§ 'Harvest Tiny Tot' (Misc/Lil) ♀H3 — CWGr
'Haseley Bridal Wish' (MC) — CWGr
'Haseley Goldicote' (SD) — CWGr
'Haseley Miranda' (SD) — CWGr
'Haseley Triumph' (SD) — CWGr
'Haseley Yellow Angora' (SD) — CWGr
'Hayley Jayne' (SC) — CWGr SPer WAba
'Heather Huston' (MD) — CWGr
'Heidi' (SSC) **new** — CWGr
'Helga' (MS-c) — CWGr
'Helma Rost' (SS-c) — CWGr
'Henri Lweii' (SC) — CWGr
'Henriette' (MC) — CWGr
'Herbert Smith' (D) — CWGr SEND
'Hexton Copper' (SBa) — CWGr
'Hi Ace' (LC) — CWGr
'Higherfield Champion' (SS-c) — CWGr
'Highness' (MinS-c) — CWGr
'Hildepuppe' (Pom) — CWGr
'Hillcrest Amour' (SD) — CWGr
'Hillcrest Bobbin' (SBa) — CWGr
'Hillcrest Camelot' (GS-c) — CWGr
'Hillcrest Carmen' (SD) — CWGr
'Hillcrest Contessa' (MinBa) — CWGr
'Hillcrest Delight' (MD) — NHal
'Hillcrest Desire' (SC) ♀H3 — CWGr LAyl WAba
'Hillcrest Divine' (MinD) — WAba
'Hillcrest Fiesta' (MS-c) — CWGr
'Hillcrest Hannah' (MinD) — NHal
'Hillcrest Heights' (LS-c) — CWGr WAba
'Hillcrest Kismet' (MD) — NHal
'Hillcrest Margaret' — WAba
'Hillcrest Pearl' (MD) — CWGr
'Hillcrest Regal' (Col) ♀H3 — CWGr WAba
'Hillcrest Royal' (MC) ♀H3 — NHal SDix
'Hillcrest Suffusion' (SD) — CWGr
'Hillcrest Ultra' (SD) — CWGr
'Hindu Star' (MinBa) — CWGr
'Hit Parade' (MS-c) — CWGr
'Hockley Maroon' (SD) — CWGr
'Hockley Nymph' (SWL) — CWGr
'Homer T' (LS-c) — CWGr
'Honest John' (LD) **new** — CWGr
'Honey' (Anem/DwB) — CWGr LRHS WAba
'Honeymoon Dress' (SD) — CWGr
'Honka' (Misc) ♀H3 — CBgR CWGr LAyl WAba
'Hot Chocolate' (MinD) — CBgR CWGr ECho EPfP NFla NLar WCot
'Hugh Mather' (MWL) — CWGr
'Hulin's Carnival' (MinD) — CWGr
'Hy Clown' (SD) — CWGr
'Hy Fire' (MinBa) — CWGr
'Ice Queen' (SWL) — CWGr
'Ida Gayer' (LD) — CWGr
'I-lyke-it' (SS-c) — CWGr
'Imp' — see *D.* 'Harvest Imp'

imperialis (B)   CHEx CHen CHll CWGr EDsa
                    EMon EShb EWes GCal MJnS
                    MOak SBig WAba WBVN WCMO
                    WDyG WHal WMul
  – B&SWJ 8997   WCru
  – 'Alba' (B)   CWGr
I – 'Tasmania' (B) GCal
'Impression Famosa'   MBri
'Impression Fantastico'   MBri
'Impression Festivo' **new**   MBri
'Impression Flamenco'   CWGr LRHS
  (Col/DwB)
'Impression Fortuna'   CWGr
  (Col/DwB)
'Inca Concord' (MD)   CWGr
'Inca Dambuster' (GS-c)   CWGr NHal
'Inca Matchless' (MD)   CWGr
'Inca Metropolitan' (LD)   CWGr
'Inca Panorama' (MD)   CWGr
'Inca Royale' (LD)   CWGr
'Inca Vanguard' (GD)   CWGr
'Inca Vulcan' (GS-c)   CWGr
'Indian Summer' (SC)   CWGr WAba
'Inflammation'   see *D.* 'Harvest Inflammation'
'Inglebrook Jill' (Col)   CWGr LAyl
'Inland Dynasty' (GS-c)   CWGr
'Inn's Gerrie Hoek' (MD)   CWGr
'Irene Ellen' (SD)   WAba
'Irene van der Zwet' (Sin)   CWGr EPfP
'Iris' (Pom)   WAba
'Irisel' (MS-c)   CWGr
'Islander' (LD)   CWGr
'Ivanetti' (MinBa)   CWGr NHal
'Jack Hood' (SD)   CWGr
'Jackie Magson' (SS-c)   CWGr WAba
'Jackie's Baby' (MinD)   WAba
'Jacqueline Tivey' (SD)   CWGr
'Jake's Coronet' (MinD)   CWGr
  new
'Jaldec Jerry' (GS-c)   CWGr
'Jaldec John' (GD)   CWGr
'Jaldec Joker' (SC)   CWGr
'Jaldec Jolly' (SC)   CWGr
'Jamaica' (MinWL)   CWGr
'Jamie' (SS-c)   CWGr
'Jan Carden'   CWGr
I 'Jan van Schaffelaar'   CWGr
'Janal Amy' (GS-c)   NHal WAba
'Jane Cowl' (LD)   CWGr
'Jane Horton' (Col)   CWGr
'Janet Beckett' (LC)   CWGr
'Janet Clarke' (Pom)   CWGr
'Janet Howell' (Col)   CWGr
'Janet Jean' (SWL)   CWGr
'Japanese Waterlily' (SWL)   CWGr
'Jason' (SS-c)   WAba
'Jazzy' (Col)   CWGr
'Je Maintiendrai' (GD)   CWGr
'Jean Fairs' (MinWL) ♀H3   CWGr LBut
'Jean Marie'^PBR (MD)   CWGr LRHS
'Jean Melville' (MinD)   CWGr
'Jeanette Carter' (MinD)   CWGr
  ♀H3
'Jeanne d'Arc' (GC)   CSut CWGr EPfP
'Jeannie Leroux' (SS-c/Fim)   CWGr
'Jennie' (MS-c/Fim)   CWGr
'Jescot Buttercup' (SD)   CWGr
'Jescot India' (MinD)   CWGr
'Jescot Jess' (MinD)   CWGr LBut
'Jescot Jim' (SD)   CWGr
'Jescot Julie' (O)   CWGr LAyl SMeo
'Jescot Lingold' (MinD)   CWGr WAba
'Jescot Nubia' (SS-c)   CBos CWGr
'Jescot Redun' (MinD)   CWGr
'Jessica' (S-c)   CWGr
'Jessie G' (SBa)   CWGr

'Jessie Ross' (MinD/DwB)   CWGr
'Jet' (SS-c)   CWGr
'Jill Day' (SC)   CWGr LBut
* 'Jill's Blush' (MS-c)   CWGr
'Jill's Delight' (MD)   CWGr
'Jim Branigan' (LS-c)   CWGr NHal WAba
'Jim's Jupiter' (LS-c)   WAba
'Jive' (Anem)   CWGr
'Joan Beecham' (SWL)   CWGr
'Jocondo' (GD)   CWGr NHal
'Johann' (Pom)   CWGr NHal
'John Butterworth' (LD)   CWGr
'John Prior' (SD)   CWGr
'John Street' (SWL) ♀H3   CWGr
'John's Champion' (MD)   CWGr
'Joicie' (MinD) **new**   NHal
'Jomanda' (MinBa) ♀H3   LBut NHal WAba
'Jorja' (MS-c)   CWGr
'Jo's Choice' (MinD)   LBut
'Joy Donaldson' (MC)   CWGr
'Joyce Green' (GS-c)   CWGr
'Joyce Margaret Cunliffe'   CWGr
  (SD)
'Juanita' (MS-c)   CWGr
'Judy Tregidden' (MWL)   CSam
'Julie One' (Misc/O)   CWGr
'Julio' (MinBa)   CWGr
'Jura' (SS-c)   CWGr EPfP
'Just Jill' (MinD)   CWGr
'Juul's Allstar' (Misc) **new**   CWGr
'Kaftan' (MD)   CWGr
'Kaiserwalzer' (Col)   CWGr
'Karenglen' (MinD) ♀H3   LBut NHal WAba
'Kari Blue' (MinWL)   CWGr
'Kari Quill' (SC)   CWGr
'Karma Amanda' (SD)   CWGr WAba
'Karma Bon Bini'^PBR (SC)   WAba
'Karma Corona'^PBR (SC)   CWGr WAba
'Karma Lagoon'^PBR   CWGr WAba
'Karma Maarten Zwaan'^PBR   CWGr WAba
  (SWL)
'Karma Naomi'^PBR   WAba
'Karma Sangria'^PBR   CWGr WAba
'Karma Serena'^PBR   WAba
'Karma Thalia'^PBR   WAba
'Karma Ventura'^PBR (SD)   WAba
'Karma Yin-yang' (SD)   WAba
'Karras 150' (SS-c)   CWGr
'Kate Mountjoy' (Col)   CWGr
'Kate's Pastelle' (MS-c)   WAba
'Kathleen's Alliance' (SC)   NHal
  ♀H3
'Kathryn's Cupid' (MinBa)   CWGr SWal WAba
  ♀H3
'Kathy' (SC)   CWGr
'Katie Dahl' (MinD)   CWGr NHal
'Katisha' (MinD)   CWGr
'Kay Helen' (Pom)   CWGr
'Kayleigh Spiller' (Col)   CWGr
'Keith's Choice' (MD)   CWGr NHal WAba
'Kelsea Carla' (SS-c)   CWGr NHal WAba
'Kelvin Floodlight' (GD)   CWGr EPfP SPer WCMO
'Kenn Emerland' (MS-c)   CSut CWGr EPfP
'Kenora Canada' (MS-c)   CWGr WAba
'Kenora Challenger'   CWGr NHal WAba
  (LS-c)
'Kenora Christmas' (SBa)   CWGr
'Kenora Clyde' (GS-c)   CWGr
'Kenora Fireball' (MinBa)   NHal
'Kenora Jubilee' (LS-c)   NHal
'Kenora Lisa' (MD)   CWGr
'Kenora Macop-B'   CSut
  (MC/Fim) **new**
'Kenora Moonbeam' (MD)   CWGr
'Kenora Ontario' (LS-c)   CWGr
'Kenora Peace' (MinBa)   CWGr

'Kenora Sunset' (MS-c)   CWGr LAyl LBut NHal
  ♀H3
'Kenora Superb' (LS-c)   CWGr NHal
'Kenora Valentine' (LD)   CWGr LAyl NHal
  ♀H3
'Ken's Choice' (SBa)   NHal
'Ken's Coral' (SWL)   CWGr
'Ken's Flame' (SWL)   CWGr
'Ken's Rarity' (SWL)   NHal
'Kidd's Climax' (GD)   ♀H3   CWGr WAba
'Kilmorie' (SS-c)   NHal
'Kim Willo' (Pom)   CWGr
'Kimberley B' (MinD)   CWGr
'Kim's Marc' (SC)   LBut
* 'Kingston' (MinD)   CWGr
'Kismet' (SBa)   CWGr
'Kiss' (MinD)   CWGr
'Kiwi Brother' (SS-c)   CWGr
'Kiwi Cousin' (SC)   CWGr
'Kiwi Gloria' (SC)   NHal WAba
'Klondike' (MS-c)   CWGr WAba
* 'Kogano Fubuki' (MD)   CWGr
'Korgill Meadow' (MD)   CWGr
'Kotare Jackpot' (SS-c)   CWGr
'Kung Fu' (SD)   CWGr
I 'Kyoto' (SWL)   CWGr WAba
'L.A.T.E.' (MinBa)   CWGr NHal WAba
'La Cierva' (Col)   CWGr
'La Gioconda' (Col)   CWGr
'Lady Kerkrade' (SC)   CWGr
'Lady Linda' (SD)   CWGr LBut NHal WAba
'Lady Orpah' (SD)   CWGr
'Lady Sunshine' (SS-c)   CWGr
'L'Ancresse' (MinBa)   CWGr LAyl NHal WAba
'Larkford' (SD)   CWGr
'Last Dance' (MD)   CWGr
'Laura Marie' (MinBa)   CWGr
'Laura's Choice' (SD)   CWGr
'Lauren's Moonlight' (MS-c)   see *D.* 'Pim's Moonlight'
'Lavendale' (MinD)   CWGr
'Lavender Chiffon' (MS-c)   CWGr
'Lavender Freestyle' (SC)   CWGr
'Lavender Leycett' (GD)   CWGr
'Lavender Line' (SC)   CWGr NHal
'Lavender Nunton   CWGr
  Harvest' (SD)
'Lavender Perfection' (GD)   CSut CWGr EPfP
'Lavender Prince' (MD)   CWGr
'Lavengro' (GD)   CWGr
'Le Castel' (D)   CWGr
'Le Patineur' (MD)   CWGr
'Leander' (GS-c)   CWGr
'Lecta' (MS-c)   CWGr
'Lemon' (Anem)   CWGr
'Lemon Cane' (Misc)   CWGr WAba
'Lemon Elegans' (SS-c)   CWGr LBut NHal WAba
  ♀H3
'Lemon Meringue' (SD)   CWGr
* 'Lemon Puff' (Anem)   CWGr
'Lemon Symbol' (MS-c)   CWGr
'Lemon Zing' (MinBa)   NHal
* 'Lenny' (MinD)   CWGr
'Lexington' (Pom)   CWGr
'Leycett' (GD)   CWGr
'Libretto' (Col)   CWGr
* 'Life Force' (GD)   CWGr
'Life Size' (LD)   CWGr
'Light Music' (MS-c)   CWGr
'Lilac Athalie' (SC)   CWGr
'Lilac Shadow' (S-c)   CWGr
§ 'Lilac Taratahi' (SC)   ♀H3   CSam CWGr LAyl NHal
'Lilac Time' (MD)   EPfP LRHS SPer SWal
'Lilac Willo' (Pom)   CWGr
'Lillianne Ballego' (MinD)   CWGr
'Linda's Chester' (SC)   CWGr LBut
'Linda's Diane' (SD)   CWGr

'Lisa'[PBR]   CWGr
'Lismore Canary' (SWL)   CSam WAba
'Lismore Carol' (Pom)   CWGr NHal
'Lismore Moonlight' (Pom)   CWGr LAyl NHal
'Lismore Peggy' (Pom)   CWGr
'Lismore Robin' (MinD)   NHal
'Lismore Sunset' (Pom)   CWGr WAba
'Lismore Willie' (SWL)   LBut WAba
  ♀H3
'Little Dorrit' (Sin/Lil)   CWGr
  ♀H3
'Little Glenfern' (MinC)   CWGr
'Little Jack' (MinS-c)   CWGr
'Little John' (Sin/Lil)   CWGr
'Little Laura' (MinBa)   CWGr
'Little Reggie' (SS-c)   CWGr
'Little Robert' (MinD)   CWGr
'Little Sally' (Pom)   CWGr
'Little Scottie' (Pom)   CWGr
'Little Shona' (MinD)   CWGr
'Little Snowdrop' (Pom)   CWGr
'Little Tiger' (MinD)   CWGr MBri
'Little Treasure'   EPfP
'Liz' (LS-c)   CWGr
'Lois Walcher' (MD)   CWGr
'Lombada' (Misc)   CWGr
'Long Island Lil' (SD)   CWGr
'Longwood Dainty' (DwB)   CWGr NHal
'Loretta' (SBa)   CWGr
'Loud Applause' (SC)   CWGr
'Louis V' (LS-c/Fim)   CWGr
'Louise Bailey' (MinD)   CWGr
'Lucky Devil' (MD)   CWGr
'Lucky Number' (MD)   CWGr
'Ludwig Helfert' (S-c)   CWGr EPfP LRHS SEND
'Lupin Dixie' (SC)   CWGr
'Lyn Mayo' (SD)   CWGr
'Lyndsey Murray' (MinD)   CWGr
'Mabel Ann' (GD)   CWGr LAyl NHal WAba
'Madame de Rosa' (LS-c)   NHal
'Madame Elisabeth Sawyer'   CWGr
  (SS-c)
'Madame J. Snapper'   EShb
'Madame Simone Stappers'   CWGr EBee MMHG
  (WL)
'Madame Vera' (SD)   CWGr LBut
'Madelaine Ann' (GD)   CWGr
'Mafolie' (GS-c) **new**   CWGr
'Magenta Magic' (Sin/DwB)   NHal
'Magic Moment' (MS-c)   CWGr
'Magnificat' (MinD)   CWGr
'Maisie Mooney' (GD)   CWGr
'Majestic Athalie' (SC)   CWGr
'Majestic Kerkrade' (SC)   CWGr
'Majjas Symbol' (MS-c)   CWGr
'Malham Honey' (SD)   CWGr
'Malham Portia' (SWL)   WAba
'Maltby Fanfare' (Col)   CWGr
'Maltby Whisper' (SC)   LAyl
'Mandy' (MinD)   CWGr
'March Magic' (MinD)   CWGr
'Margaret Ann' (MinD)   CWGr LAyl
'Margaret Brookes' (LD)   CWGr
'Margaret Haggo' (SWL)   CSam LAyl NHal
'Marie' (SD)   CWGr
'Marie Schnugg' (Misc)   CWGr LAyl
  ♀H3
'Mariposa' (Col)   CWGr WAba
'Mark Damp' (LS-c)   CWGr
'Mark Lockwood' (Pom)   CWGr WAba
'Market Joy' (SS-c)   CWGr
'Marla Lu' (MC)   CWGr
'Marlene Joy' (MS-c/Fim)   CWGr WAba
'Maroon'[PBR] (Misc)   CWGr
'Mars' (Col)   CWGr
'Marshmello Sky' (Col)   CWGr

'Marston Lilac' (MinD) **new** NHal
'Martin's Red' (Pom) CWGr
'Martin's Yellow' (Pom) NHal WAba
'Mary Eveline' (Col) LAyl NHal
'Mary Jennie' (MinS-c) CWGr
'Mary Magson' (SS-c) CWGr
'Mary Partridge' (SWL) CWGr
'Mary Pitt' (MinD) CWGr
'Mary Richards' (SD) CWGr
'Mary's Jomanda' (SBa) NHal WAba
'Master David' (MinBa) CWGr
'Master Michael' (Pom) CWGr
'Match' (SS-c) CWGr
'Matilda Huston' (SS-c) CWGr NHal
'Matt Armour' (Sin) CWGr
'Maureen Hardwick' (GD) CWGr
'Maureen Kitchener' (SWL) CWGr
'Maxine Bailey' (SD) CWGr
'Maya' (SD) CWGr
'Meiro' (SD) CWGr
'Melanie Jane' (MS-c) CWGr
'Melody Dixie'^PBR (MinD) CWGr
'Melody Dora'^PBR CWGr
'Melody Gipsy'^PBR (SS-c) WWeb
'Melody Swing'^PBR CWGr
'Melton' (MinD) CWGr
merckii (B)   CBgR CHad CMdw CPLG CSpe
                        CWGr EBee EBrs EGoo EWes GCal
                        GMac LAyl LRHS MNrw MSte SAga
                        SMad WAba WDyG WPGP WSHC
- *alba* (B)   CHad CSpe MSte WCru
- compact (B)   CBos EBee EMan WPGP
- 'Edith Eddleman' (B) WCMO
'Meredith's Marion Smith' CWGr
  (SD)
'Mermaid of Zennor' (Sin) CFir CWGr EBee EMan ERou
'Merriwell Topic' (MD) CWGr
'Miami' (SD) CWGr
'Michael J' (MinD) CWGr
'Michigan' (MinD) CWGr
'Mick' (SC) CWGr
'Midas' (SS-c) CWGr
'Midnight' (Pom) CWGr
'Mies' (Sin) CWGr
'Mignon Silver' (DwSin) CWGr
'Millennium' (MS-c) **new** WAba
'Mingus Gregory' (LS-c) CWGr
'Mingus Kyle D' (SD) CWGr
'Mingus Nichole' (LD) CWGr
'Mingus Tracy Lynn' (SS-c) CWGr
'Mingus Whitney' (GS-c) CWGr
'Mini' (Sin/Lil) CWGr
'Mini Red' (MinS-c) CWGr
'Minley Carol' (Pom) ♀H3 CWGr LAyl NHal WAba
'Minley Linda' (Pom) CWGr
'Minnesota' (LD) WAba
'Miramar' (SD) CWGr
'Miss Blanc' (SD) CWGr
'Miss Ellen' (Misc) **new** CWGr
'Miss Rose Fletcher' (SS-c) CWGr
'Miss Swiss' (SD) CWGr
'Misterton' (MD) CWGr
'Mistill Beauty' (SC) CWGr
'Mistill Delight' (MinD) CWGr
'Mom's Special' (LD) CWGr
I 'Mon Trésor' (Min SC) CWGr
'Monk Marc' (SC) CWGr LBut
'Monkstown Diane' (SC) CWGr
'Monrovia' (MinBa) CWGr
'Moonfire' (Misc/DwB) More than 30 suppliers
  ♀H3
'Moonglow' (LS-c) CWGr
'Moor Place' (Pom) NHal WAba
'Moray Susan' (SWL) CWGr WAba
'Moret' (SS-c) CWGr
'Morley Lady' (SD) CWGr

'Morley Lass' (SS-c) CWGr
'Morning Dew' (SC) CWGr
'Mount Noddy' (Sin) CWGr
'Mrs A. Woods' (MD) CWGr
'Mrs Black' (Pom) CWGr
'Mrs George Le Boutillier' CWGr
  (LD)
'Mrs H. Brown' (Col) CWGr
'Mrs McDonald Quill' (LD) CWGr
'Mrs Silverston' (SD) CWGr
'Mummy's Favourite' (SD) CWGr
'Murdoch'   CBgR CPen EBee ECtt EMan EPfP
                         ERou EWin SDys SPav WAba
                         WCMO WCot WHrl
'Muriel Gladwell' (SS-c) CWGr
'Murillo' MBri
'Murray May' (LD) CWGr
'Musette' (MinD) CWGr
'My Beverley' (MS-c)(Fim) LAyl NHal
'My Joy' (Pom) CWGr
'My Love' (SS-c) CSut EPfP LRHS SEND SPer
'My Valentine' (SD) CWGr
'Mystery Day' (MD) CWGr EPfP MBri
'München' (MinD) CWGr
'Nancy H' (MinBa) CWGr
'Nankyoku' (GD) CWGr
'Nargold' (MS-c/Fim) CWGr LAyl
'Natal' (MinBa) CAby CWGr EPfP SPer
'National Vulcan' (MinD) CWGr
'Nationwide' (SD) CWGr WAba
'Neal Gillson' (MD) CWGr
'Nellie Birch' (MinBa) CWGr
'Nellie Geerlings' (Sin) CWGr
'Nenekazi' (MS-c/Fim) CWGr
'Nepos' (SWL) CWGr LBut
'Nescio' (Pom) CWGr EPfP WAba
'Nettie' (MinBa) CWGr
'New Baby' (MinBa) CWGr LRHS
'New Dimension' (SS-c) CWGr EPfP
'New Look' (LS-c) CWGr
'Newsham Wonder' (SD) CWGr
'Nicola' (SS-c) CWGr
'Nicolette' (MWL) CWGr
'Night Life' (SC) CWGr
I 'Night Queen' (Pom) EPfP
'Nijinsky' (SBa) CWGr
'Nina Chester' (SD) CWGr
'Nonette' (SWL)   CBgR CWGr LAst NBPC WAba
                         WCot WGwG
'Norbeck Dusky' (SS-c) CWGr
'Noreen' (Pom) CWGr NHal
'North Sea' (MD) CWGr
'Northland Primrose' (SC) CWGr
* 'Nuit d'Eté' (MS-c) CWGr SEND
Nunton form (SD) CWGr
'Nunton Harvest' (SD) CWGr
'Nutley Sunrise' (MC) CWGr
'Nymphenburg' (SD) CWGr
'Oakwood Diamond' (SBa) CWGr LBut
'Old Boy' (SBa) CWGr
'Omo' (Sin/Lil) ♀H3 LAyl
'Onesta' (SWL) CWGr
'Only Love' (MS-c) CWGr
'Onslow Michelle' (SD) CWGr
'Onslow Renown' (LS-c) CWGr
'Opal' (SBa) CWGr
'Optic Illusion' (SD) CWGr
'Opus' (SD) CWGr
'Orange Berger's Record' CWGr
  (MS-c)
'Orange Fire' (MS-c) CWGr
'Orange Jewel' (SD) CWGr
'Orange Keith's Choice' CWGr
  (MD)
'Orange Mullett' CBos CWGr
  (MinD/DwB)

	'Orange Nugget' (MinBa)	CWGr LRHS
I	'Orange Queen' (MC)	CWGr
	'Orange Sun' (LD)	CWGr
	'Oranjestad' (SWL)	CWGr
	'Orel' (Col)	CWGr WAba
	'Oreti Classic' (MD)	NHal
	'Orfeo' (MC)	CWGr
I	'Orion' (MD)	CWGr
	'Ornamental Rays' (SC)	CWGr LBut
	'Othello' (MS-c)	CWGr
	'Otto's Thrill' (LD)	EPfP
	'Pacific Argyle' (SD)	NHal
	'Paint Box' (MS-c)	CWGr
	'Palomino' (MinD)	CWGr
	'Pamela' (SD)	CWGr
	'Park Princess' (SC/DwB)	CSut CWGr LRHS NHal
	'Parkflamme' (MinD)	CWGr
	'Paroa Gillian' (SC)	CWGr
	'Party Girl' (MS-c/Fim)	NHal
	'Paso Doble' misapplied (Anem)	see *D.* 'Freya's Paso Doble'
	'Pat Mark' (LS-c)	CWGr NHal
	'Pat 'n' Dee' (SD)	CWGr
	'Pat Seed' (MD)	CWGr
	'Patricia' (Col)	NHal
I	'Pattie' **new**	SWal
	'Paul Critchley' (SC)	CWGr
	'Paul's Delight' (SD)	CWGr
	'Peace Pact' (SWL)	CWGr WAba
	'Peach Athalie' (SC)	CWGr
	'Peach Cupid' (MinBa) $\heartsuit$H3	CWGr LBut WAba
§	'Peach Melba' (SD)	NHal
	'Peaches and Cream'PBR	CWGr
	'Pearl Hornsey' (SD)	CWGr
	'Pearl of Heemstede' (SD) $\heartsuit$H3	LAyl NHal
	'Pearl Sharowean' (MS-c)	WAba
	'Pearson's Benn' (SS-c)	CWGr
	'Pearson's Mellanie' (SC)	CWGr
	'Pembroke Pattie' (Pom)	CWGr
	'Pennsclout' (GD)	CWGr
	'Pennsgift' (GD)	CWGr
	'Pensford Marion' (Pom)	WAba
	'Perfectos' (MC)	CWGr
	'Periton' (MinBa)	CWGr
	'Peter' (MinD)	CWGr
I	'Peter' (LD)	LRHS
	'Peter Nelson' (SBa)	CWGr
	'Petit Bôt' (SS-c)	CWGr
	'Petit Byoux' (DwCol)	CWGr
	'Philis Farmer' (SWL)	CWGr
I	'Phoenix' (MD)	CWGr WAba
	'Pianella' (SS-c)	CWGr
§	'Pim's Moonlight' (MS-c)	CWGr NHal WAba
	'Pineholt Princess' (LD)	CWGr
	'Pinelands Pam' (MS-c)	CWGr
	'Pink Attraction' (MinD)	CWGr
	'Pink Breckland Joy' (MD)	CWGr
	'Pink Carol' (Pom)	CWGr
	'Pink Giraffe' (O)	CWGr
	'Pink Honeymoon Dress' (SD)	CWGr
	'Pink Jupiter' (GS-c)	NHal
	'Pink Katisha' (MinD)	CWGr
	'Pink Kerkrade' (SC)	CWGr
	'Pink Loveliness' (SWL)	CWGr
	'Pink Newby' (MinD)	CWGr
	'Pink Pastelle' (MS-c) $\heartsuit$H3	CWGr NHal WAba
	'Pink Preference' (SS-c)	CWGr
	'Pink Robin Hood' (SBa)	CWGr
	'Pink Sensation' (SC) $\heartsuit$H3	LBut
	'Pink Shirley Alliance' (SC)	LAyl
	'Pink Suffusion' (SD)	WAba
	'Pink Sylvia' (MinD)	CWGr
	'Pink Worton Ann' (MinD)	CWGr

	pinnata **new**	CWGr
	'Piperoo' (MC)	CWGr
	'Piper's Pink' (SS-c/DwB)	CWGr LAyl
I	'Pippa' (MinWL)	LBut
	'Playa Blanca'	LRHS
	'Playboy' (GD)	CWGr
	'Plum Surprise' (Pom)	CWGr
	'Poeme' **new**	SPer
	'Polar Sight' (GC)	CWGr
	'Polly Bergen' (MD)	CWGr
	'Polly Peachum' (SD)	CWGr
	'Polventon Supreme' (SBa)	CWGr
	'Polyand' (LD)	CWGr
	'Pontiac' (SC)	CWGr LAyl
	'Pooh' (Col)	NHal
	'Pop Willo' (Pom)	CWGr
I	'Poppet' (Pom)	CWGr WAba
	'Popular Guest' (MS-c/Fim)	CWGr
	'Porcelain' (SWL) $\heartsuit$H3	LBut
	'Potgieter' (MinBa)	CWGr
	'Pot-Pourri' (MinD)	CWGr
	'Prefect' (MS-c)	CWGr
	'Prefere' (Sin)	CWGr LRHS
-	'Preference' (SS-c)	CWGr SHop SWal
	'Preston Park' (Sin/DwB) $\heartsuit$H3	CSam CWGr LAyl NHal
	Pride of Berlin	see *D.* 'Stolz von Berlin'
	'Pride of Holland' (LC)	CWGr
	'Prime Minister' (GD)	CWGr
	'Primeur' (MS-c)	CWGr
	'Primrose Accord' (LS-c)	CWGr
	'Primrose Diane' (SD)	WAba
	'Primrose Pastelle' (MS-c)	NHal WAba
	'Primrose Rustig' (MD)	CWGr
	'Prince Valiant' (SD)	CWGr
	'Princess Beatrix' (LD)	CWGr
	'Princess Marie José' (Sin)	CWGr
	'Pristine' (Pom)	CWGr
	'Procyon' (SD)	CSut CWGr EPfP LRHS
	'Prom' (Pom)	CWGr
	'Promise' (MS-c/Fim)	CWGr
	'Punky' (Pom)	CWGr
	'Purbeck Lydia' (LS-c)	CWGr
	'Purbeck Princess' (MinD)	CWGr
I	'Purity' (SS-c)	CWGr
	'Purper R'O'Sehen' (SD)	CWGr
	'Purpinca' (Anem)	CWGr
	'Purple Cottesmore' (MWL)	CWGr
	'Purple Gem' (SS-c)	CSut CWGr LRHS SPer
	'Purple Joy' (MD)	CWGr
	'Purple Sensation' (SS-c)	CWGr
	'Purple Tai Hei Jo' (GD)	CWGr
	'Pussycat' (SD)	CWGr
	'Quel Diable' (LS-c)	CWGr
	'Quick Step' (Anem)	CWGr
	'Rachel's Place' (Pom)	CWGr
	'Radfo' (SS-c)	CWGr WAba
	'Radiance' (MC)	CWGr
	'Raffles' (SD)	CWGr LAyl
	'Ragged Robin'PBR (Misc)	CAvo CFFs MBri
	'Raiser's Pride' (MC)	NHal WAba
	'Raspberry Ripple' (SS-c)	CWGr
	'Rebecca Lynn' (MinD)	CWGr
	'Red Admiral' (MinBa)	CWGr
	'Red Alert' (LBa)	CWGr
	'Red and White' (SD)	CWGr
	'Red Arrows' (SD)	CWGr
	'Red Balloon' (SBa)	CWGr
	'Red Beauty' (SD)	CWGr
	'Red Cap' (MinD)	CWGr
	'Red Carol' (Pom)	CWGr
	'Red Diamond' (MD)	CWGr NHal
	'Red Highlight' (LS-c)	CWGr
	'Red Kaiser Wilhelm' (SBa)	CWGr
	'Red Majorette' (SS-c)	CWGr

'Red Pimpernel' (SD)	CWGr	
'Red Pygmy' (SS-c)	CWGr MBri	
'Red Riding Hood' (MinBa)	CWGr	
'Red Schweitzer' (MinD)	CWGr	
'Red Sensation' (MD)	CWGr	
'Red Sunset' (MS-c)	CWGr	
'Red Triumph' (SD)	CWGr	
'Red Velvet' (SWL)	CWGr	
'Red Warrior' (Pom)	CWGr	
'Reddy' (DwLil)	CWGr	
'Reedly' (SD)	CWGr LBut	
'Regal Boy' (SBa)	CWGr	
'Reginald Keene' (LS-c)	NHal	
'Reliance' (SBa)	CWGr	
'Rembrandt USA' (Dw/Sin)	CWGr MBri	
'Renato Tozio' (SD)	CWGr	
'Requiem' (SD)	CBos CSut CWGr WAba	
'Reverend P. Holian' (GS-c)	CWGr	
'Rhonda' (Pom)	CWGr NHal	
'Richard Howells' (MinD)	CWGr	
'Richard Marc' (SC)	CWGr	
'Richard S' (LS-c)	NHal	
'Riisa' (MinBa)	CWGr WAba	
'Risca Miner' (SBa)	CWGr WAba	
'Rita Easterbrook' (LD)	CWGr	
'Roan' (MinD)	CWGr	
'Robann Royal' (MinBa)	CWGr	
'Robbie Huston' (LS-c)	CWGr	
'Robert Too' (MinD)	CWGr	
'Robin Hood' (SBa)	CWGr WAba	
'Rockcliffe' (MinD)	WAba	
'Rockcliffe Gold' (MS-c)	CWGr	
'Rokesly Mini' (MinC)	CWGr	
'Rokewood Candy' (MS-c)	CWGr	
* 'Rokewood Opal' (SC)	CWGr	
'Roodkapje' (Sin)	CWGr	
'Rosalinde' (S-c)	CWGr	
'Rose Cupid' (MinBa)	CWGr	
'Rose Jupiter' (GS-c)	CWGr LRHS NHal	
'Rose Tendre' (MS-c)	CWGr	
'Rosella' (MD)	CSut CWGr EPfP LRHS	
'Rosemary Webb' (SD)	CWGr	
'Rossendale Luke' (SD)	CWGr WAba	
'Rosy Cloud' (MD)	CWGr	
'Rothesay Castle' (MinD/DwB)	CWGr	
'Rothesay Herald' (SD/DwB)	CWGr	
'Rothesay Reveller' (MD)	CWGr	
'Rothesay Robin' (SD)	CWGr WAba	
'Rothesay Rose' (SWL)	CWGr	
'Rothesay Snowflake' (SWL)	CWGr	
'Rotonde' (SC)	CWGr	
'Rotterdam' (MS-c)	CWGr	
I 'Roxy' (Sin/DwB)	CBgR CMMP CWGr EBee ECtt ELan EMan EMil ENot EPfP ERou LAst LAyl LRHS MBri MWgw NGdn NVic SPav SPla WAba WCMO WCot WWeb	
'Royal Blood'PBR (Misc)	CAvo MBri	
'Royal Visit' (SD)	CWGr	
'Royal Wedding' (LS-c)	CWGr	
'Ruby Red' (MinBa)	CWGr	
'Ruby Wedding' (MinD)	CWGr	
'Ruskin Andrea' new	NHal	
'Ruskin Belle' (MS-c)	CWGr	
'Ruskin Buttercup' (MinD)	CWGr	
'Ruskin Charlotte' (MS-c)	CWGr LAyl NHal WAba	
'Ruskin Delight' (SS-c)	CWGr	
'Ruskin Diana' (SD)	CWGr LBut NHal WAba	
'Ruskin Dynasty' (SD)	CWGr	
'Ruskin Emil' (SS-c)	CWGr	
'Ruskin Gypsy' (SBa)	CWGr	
'Ruskin Impact' (SD)	WAba	
* 'Ruskin Marigold' (SS-c)	CWGr LAyl LBut NHal	

'Ruskin Myra' (SS-c)	NHal	
'Ruskin Orient' (SS-c)	CWGr	
'Ruskin Petite' (MinBa)	CWGr	
* 'Ruskin Tangerine' (SBa)	NHal	
'Russell Turner' (SS-c)	CWGr	
'Rustig' (MD)	CWGr WAba	
'Rusty Hope' (MinD)	CWGr	
'Rutland Water' (SD)	CWGr SUsu	
'Ryecroft Jan' (MinBa)	NHal	
'Ryedale King' (LD)	CWGr	
'Ryedale Pinky' (SD)	CWGr	
'Ryedale Rebecca' (GS-c)	CWGr	
'Ryedale Sunshine' (SD)	CWGr WAba	
'Safe Shot' (MD)	CWGr	
'Sailor' (MS-c)	CWGr	
'Saint-Saëns' new	SEND	
* 'Saladin' (Misc)	CWGr	
'Salmon Carpet' (MinD)	CWGr	
'Salmon Hornsey' (SD)	CWGr	
'Salmon Jupiter' (LS-c)	WAba	
'Salmon Keene' (LS-c)	WAba	
'Salmon Symbol' (MS-c)	WAba	
'Sam Hopkins' (MWL/SWL)	CSam NHal SMeo	
'Sam Huston' (GD)	LAyl NHal WAba	
'Samantha'	see *D.* 'Harvest Samantha'	
'Sans Souci' (GC)	CWGr	
'Santa Claus' (MD)	CWGr	
'Sarabande' (MS-c)	CWGr	
'Sarah G' (LS-c)	CWGr	
'Sarah Jane' (LD)	CWGr	
'Sarah Louise' (SWL)	CWGr	
'Sarum Aurora' (SD)	CWGr	
'Sascha' (SWL)	CSam NHal	
'Sassy' (MinD)	CWGr	
'Satellite' (MS-c)	CWGr	
'Saynomore' (SWL)	CWGr	
'Scarborough Ace' (MD)	CWGr	
'Scarlet Comet' (Anem)	CWGr	
'Scarlet Rotterdam' (MS-c)	CWGr WAba	
'Scaur Pinky' (MinD)	NHal	
'Scaur Princess' (SD)	CWGr	
'Scaur Snowball' (MinD)	NHal	
'Scaur Swinton' (MD)	CWGr LAyl NHal	
'Schloss Reinbek' (Sin)	CWGr	
'Schweitzer's Kokarde' (MinD)	CWGr	
'Scott's Delight' (SD)	CWGr	
'Scura' (DwSin)	CBgR CWGr	
'Seattle' (SD)	CWGr LRHS	
'Seikeman's Feuerball' (MinD)	WAba	
'Senzoe Brigitte' (MinD)	CWGr	
'Severin's Triumph' (LD)	CWGr	
'Shandy' (SS-c)	CWGr LAyl NHal	
'Shannon' (SD)	CWGr SPer	
'Sharon Ann' (LS-c)	CWGr	
'Sheila Mooney' (LD)	CWGr	
sherffii	CHad CHal CPLG CWGr MCCP MNrw MWea	
'Sherwood Monarch' (GS-c)	CWGr	
'Sherwood Standard' (MD)	CWGr	
'Sherwood Sunrise' (SD)	CWGr	
'Sherwood Titan' (GD)	CWGr	
'Shining Star' (SC)	CWGr	
'Shirley Alliance' (SC)	WAba	
'Shooting Star' (LS-c)	CWGr SPer	
'Shy Princess' (MC)	CWGr	
'Siedlerstolz' (LD)	CWGr	
'Silver City' (LD)	CWGr NHal	
'Silver Slipper' (SS-c)	CWGr	
'Silver Years' (MD)	CWGr	
'Sir Alf Ramsey' (GD)	LAyl NHal WAba	
* 'Sisa' (SD)	CWGr	

'Skipley Spot' (SD)	CWGr	
'Skipper Rock' (GD)	CWGr	
'Sky High' (SD)	CWGr	
'Small World' (Pom) ♀H3	LAyl NHal WAba	
'Smokey'	CWGr EPfP LRHS SEND SPer SWal	
'Smoky O' (MS-c)	CWGr	
'Sneezy' (Sin)	CWGr ELan LRHS	
'Snip' (MinS-c)	CWGr WAba	
'Snoho Barbara' (MS-c)	CWGr	
'Snoho Christmas'	CWGr	
'Snoho Tammie' (MinBa)	CWGr	
'Snow Cap' (SS-c)	CWGr	
'Snow Fairy' (MinC)	CWGr	
'Snow White' (DwSin)	CWGr	
'Snowflake' (SWL)	CWGr WAba	
'Snowstorm' (MD)	CSut	
'Snowy' (MinBa)	CWGr	
'So Dainty' (MinS-c) ♀H3	CWGr LAyl WAba	
'Sondervig' (SD)	CWGr	
'Song of Olympia' (SWL)	CWGr	
'Sonia'	CWGr	
'Sorrento Fiesta' (SS-c)	WAba	
'Sorrento Girl' (SS-c)	WAba	
'Soulman' (Anem)	CWGr	
'Sourire de Crozon' (SD)	CWGr	
'Souvenir d'Été' (Pom)	CWGr	
'Sparkler' new	WHlf	
'Spartacus' (LD)	CWGr NHal	
'Spassmacher' (MS-c)	CWGr	
'Spectacular' (SD)	CWGr	
'Spencer' (SD)	CWGr	
'Spennythorn King' (SD)	CWGr	
'Spikey Symbol' (MS-c)	CWGr	
'Sprinter' (SC)	CWGr	
'Staleen Condesa' (MS-c) new	NHal	
'Star Child' (Misc/O)	CWGr WAba	
'Star Elite' (MC)	CWGr LRHS	
'Star Spectacle' (MS-c)	CWGr	
'Star Surprise' (SC)	CWGr	
'Starry Night' (MinS-c)	CWGr	
'Star's Favourite' (MC)	CWGr	
'Star's Lady' (SC)	CWGr	
'Stefan Bergerhoff' (Dwf D)	CWGr	
'Stella J' (SWL)	CWGr	
'Stella's Delight' (SD)	CWGr	
'Stellyvonne' (LS-c/Fim)	CWGr	
'Stephanie' (SS-c)	CWGr	
'Sterling Silver' (MD) new	CWGr	
§ 'Stolz von Berlin' (MinBa)	EPfP	
'Stoneleigh Cherry' (Pom)	LAyl	
'Stoneleigh Joyce' (Pom)	CWGr	
'Storm Warning' (GD)	CWGr	
'Streets Ahead' (MinD) new	NHal	
'Stylemaster' (MC)	CWGr	
'Sue Mountjoy' (Col)	CWGr	
'Sue Willo' (Pom)	CWGr	
'Suffolk Fantasy' (SD)	CWGr	
'Suffolk Punch' (MD)	CBgR CWGr LAyl LBut SPer	
'Sugartime Sunrise' (MinD) new	NHal	
'Suitzus Julie' (Lil)	CWGr	
'Summer Festival' (SD)	CWGr	
I 'Summer Nights' (SC)	CAby CHad ECGP LAyl NHal SPer WAba	
'Summer's End'	CWGr	
'Summertime' new	SPer	
'Sungold' (MinBa)	CWGr	
'Sunlight Pastelle' (MS-c)	CWGr WAba	
* 'Sunny Boy' (MinD)	CWGr LRHS WAba	
'Sunray Glint' (MS-c)	CWGr WAba	
'Sunray Silk' (MS-c)	CWGr	
'Sunset' (SD)	WAba	
I 'Sunshine' (Sin)	LAyl WWeb	
'Sunshine Paul' (MD)	WAba	

'Sunstruck' (MS-c)	CWGr	
'Super Rays' (MC)	CWGr	
'Super Trouper' (SD)	CWGr	
'Superfine' (SC)	CWGr WAba	
'Sure Thing' (MC)	CWGr	
'Susan Willo' (Pom)	CWGr	
'Susannah York' (SWL)	CWGr	
'Suzette' (SD/DwB)	CWGr	
'Swallow Falls' (SD)	CWGr	
'Swan Lake' (SD)	SPer	
'Swanvale' (SD)	CWGr	
'Sweet Content' (SD)	CWGr	
'Sweet Sensation' (MS-c)	WAba	
'Sweetheart' (SD)	CBgR EBrs LRHS	
'Swiss Miss' (MinBa/O)	CWGr	
I 'Sylvia' (SBa)	EPfP WAba	
'Sylvia's Desire' (SC)	CWGr	
'Symbol' (MS-c)	CWGr	
'Syston Harlequin' (SD)	CWGr	
'Syston Sophia' (MinBa)	CWGr	
'Tahiti Sunrise' (MS-c)	CWGr	
'Tally Ho' (Misc) ♀H3	CBgR CMMP CWGr EBee EMan ENot ERou LRHS MBri MSph MWgw NCob SDys SMad SPav SPla WAba WCMO WCot WWhi	
'Tam Tam' new	SWal	
'Taratahi Lilac'	see *D.* 'Lilac Taratahi'	
'Taratahi Ruby' (SWL) ♀H3	CSam CWGr LAyl LBut NHal WAba	
'Tartan' (MD)	CWGr	
'Teesbrooke Audrey' (Col)	LAyl NHal WAba WCMO	
'Teesbrooke Redeye' (Col) new	NHal	
'Temptress' (SS-c)	CWGr	
'Tender Moon' (SD)	CWGr	
tenuicaulis	CWGr SBig WCMO	
'Thames Valley' (MD)	CWGr	
'That's It!' (SD)	CWGr	
'The Baron' (SD)	CWGr	
'Thelma Clements' (LD)	CWGr	
'Theo Sprengers' (MD)	CWGr	
'Thomas A. Edison' (MD)	CSut CWGr EPfP SWal	
'Thoresby Jewel' (SD)	CWGr	
'Tiara' (SD)	CWGr	
'Tiffany Lynn' (Misc/O)	CWGr	
'Tiger Eye' (MD)	CWGr	
'Tiger Tiv' (MD)	CWGr	
'Tina B' (SBa)	CWGr	
'Tinker's White' (SD)	CWGr	
'Tiny Tot' (Lil)	see *D.* 'Harvest Tiny Tot'	
'Tioga Spice' (MS-c/Fim)	CWGr NHal	
'Toga' (SWL)	CWGr	
'Tohsuikyou' (Misc/O)	CWGr WAba	
'Tommy Doc' (SS-c)	CWGr WAba	
'Tommy Keith' (MinBa)	CWGr	
'Tomo' (SD)	LAyl NHal	
'Top Affair' (MS-c)	CWGr	
'Top Totty' (MinD)	NHal	
* 'Topaz Puff'	LRHS	
'Torra' new	SPer	
* 'Toto' (DwB)	CWGr NHal	
'Tout-à-Toi' (SD) new	CWGr	
'Towneley Class' (SD)	CWGr	
'Tramar' (SC) new	CWGr	
I 'Tranquility' (Col)	NHal	
'Trelyn Kiwi' (SC)	CWGr WAba	
'Trengrove Autumn' (MD)	CWGr	
'Trengrove d'Or' (MD)	CWGr	
'Trengrove Jill' (MD)	CWGr LAyl	
'Trengrove Millennium' (MD)	CWGr NHal	
'Trengrove Tauranga' (MD)	CWGr	
'Trengrove Terror' (GD)	CWGr	
'Trevelyn Kiwi' (S-c)	NHal	
'Trevor' (Col)	CWGr	
'Tropical Sunset' (SD)	CWGr SPer	

'Tsuki-yorine-shisha' (MC)	CWGr	
'Tsuki-ytori-no-shisha' (MC)	WAba	
'Tu Tu' (MS-c)	CWGr	
'Tui Avis' (MinC)	CWGr	
'Tui Orange' (SS-c)	CWGr WAba	
'Tui Ruth' (SS-c)	CWGr	
'Tujays Lemondrop' (SD)	NHal	
'Tula Rosa' (Pom)	CWGr	
'Tutankhamun' (Pom)	CWGr	
'Twiggy' (SWL)	CWGr LRHS	
'Twilight Time' (MD)	CWGr EPfP LRHS	
'Twyning's After Eight' (Sin) ♀H3 **new**	CWGr	
'Twyning's Candy' ♀H3	CWGr	
'Twyning's Chocolate' (Sin)	CWGr	
'Twyning's Peppermint' (Sin) **new**	CWGr	
'Twyning's Pink Fish' (Col) **new**	CWGr	
'Twyning's Smartie' (Sin) **new**	CWGr	
'Uchuu' (GD)	CWGr	
'Union Jack' (Sin)	CWGr WAba	
'United' (SD)	CWGr	
'Utrecht' (GD)	CWGr	
'Vader Abraham' (MinD)	CWGr	
'Vaguely Noble' (SBa)	CWGr	
'Valentine Lil' (SWL)	CWGr	
'Vancouver' (Misc)	CWGr	
I 'Vanity' (MinB/SB) **new**	NHal	
'Vanquisher' (GS-c)	CWGr	
'Variace' (MinBa)	CWGr	
'Vera's Elma' (LD)	CWGr	
'Vesuvius' (MD)	CWGr	
'Vicky Crutchfield' (SWL)	LBut	
'Vicky Jackson' (SWL)	CWGr	
'Victory Day' (LC)	CWGr	
'Vidal Rhapsody' (MS-c)	CWGr	
'Vigor' (SWL)	CWGr	
'Vinovium' (MinBa)	CWGr	
'Violet Davies' (MS-c)	CWGr	
'Vivex' (Pom)	CWGr	
'Volkskanzler' (Sin)	CWGr	
'Vrouwe Jacoba' (SS-c)	CWGr	
'Vulcan' (LS-c)	CWGr	
'Walter Hardisty' (GD)	CWGr	
'Walter James' (SD)	CWGr	
'Wanborough Gem' (SBa)	CWGr	
'Wanda's Aurora' (GD)	NHal	
'Wanda's Capella' (GD)	CWGr NHal WAba	
'Wanda's Moonlight' (GD)	CWGr	
'Wandy' (Pom) ♀H3	CWGr WAba	
'War of the Roses'	WHer	
'Warkton Willo' (Pom)	CWGr	
'Warmunda' (MinBa)	LRHS	
'Waveney Pearl' (SD)	CWGr	
'Welcome Guest' (MS-c)	CWGr WAba	
'Welsh Beauty' (SBa)	CWGr	
'Wendy' (MinBa)	CWGr	
'Wendy Spencer' (MinD)	CWGr	
'Wendy's Place' (Pom)	CWGr	
'Weston Aramac' (SS-c)	CWGr	
'Weston Forge' (SC)	CWGr	
'Weston Miss' (MinS-c)	CWGr NHal	
'Weston Nugget' (MinC)	CWGr WAba	
'Weston Pirate' (MinC) ♀H3	NHal	
'Weston Princekin' (MinS-c)	CWGr	
'Weston Spanish Dancer' (MinC) ♀H3	CWGr LBut NHal WAba	
'Weston Sunup' (MinC) **new**	NHal	
'Wheel' (Col)	CWGr WAba	
'White Alva's' (GD) ♀H3	CWGr LAyl NHal	
'White Aster' (Pom)	EPfP	
'White Ballerina' (SWL)	CSam NHal	
'White Ballet' (SD) ♀H3	CWGr LAyl LBut NHal	
'White Charlie Two' (MD)	NHal	
'White Hunter' (SD)	CWGr	
'White Klankstad' (SC)	CWGr	
'White Knight' (MinD)	NHal	
'White Linda' (SD)	CWGr NHal	
'White Mathilda' (Dw)	CWGr	
'White Merriwell' (SD)	CWGr	
'White Moonlight' (MS-c)	LAyl LBut NHal WAba	
'White Nettie' (MinBa)	CWGr	
'White Pastelle' (MS-c)	WAba	
'White Perfection' (LD)	CSut CWGr EPfP	
'White Polventon' (SBa)	CWGr	
'White Rustig' (MD)	CWGr	
'White Star' (MS-c)	CWGr LRHS	
'White Swallow' (SS-c)	NHal	
'Wicky Woo' (SD)	CWGr	
'Wildwood Marie' (SWL)	CWGr	
'Willemse Glory' (Misc Orch)	CWGr	
'William B' (GD)	CWGr	
'Williamsburg' (SS-c)	CWGr	
'Willo's Borealis' (Pom)	CWGr NHal	
'Willo's Flecks' (Pom)	WAba	
'Willo's Night' (Pom)	CWGr	
'Willo's Surprise' (Pom)	CWGr NHal	
'Willo's Violet' (Pom)	CWGr NHal WAba	
'Willowfield Kay' (MS-c)	WAba	
'Willowfield Matthew' (MinD)	NHal	
'Willowfield Mick' (LD)	CWGr LAyl WAba	
'Winholme Diane' (SD)	CWGr NHal	
'Winkie Colonel' (GD)	CWGr	
'Winnie' (Pom)	CWGr	
'Winsome' (Pom)	CWGr	
'Winston Churchill' (MinD)	CWGr LBut	
'Winter Dawn' (SWL)	CWGr	
'Wise Guy' (GD)	CWGr	
'Wisk' (Pom)	CWGr	
'Wittem' (MD)	CWGr	
'Wittemans Superba' (SS-c) ♀H3	CWGr NHal SDix	
'Wootton Cupid' (MinBa) ♀H3	CWGr LBut NHal WAba	
'Wootton Impact' (MS-c) ♀H3	NHal	
'Wootton Phebe' (SD)	CWGr	
'Wootton Tempest' (MS-c)	CWGr	
'Worton Bluestreak' (SS-c)	CWGr	
'Worton Revival' (MD)	CWGr	
'Worton Superb' (SD)	CWGr	
'Wundal Horizon' (LS-c)	CWGr	
'Yellow Abundance' (SD)	CWGr	
'Yellow Baby' (Pom)	CWGr	
I 'Yellow Bird' (Col)	CWGr	
'Yellow Frank Hornsey' (SD)	WAba	
'Yellow Galator' (MC)	CWGr	
'Yellow Hammer' (Sin/DwB) ♀H3	CWGr LAyl NHal	
'Yellow Linda's Chester' (SC)	CWGr	
'Yellow Pages' (SD)	CWGr	
'Yellow Pet' (SD)	CWGr	
'Yellow Spiky' (MS-c)	CWGr	
'Yellow Star' (MS-c)	CSut CWGr	
'Yellow Symbol' (MS-c)	CWGr LBut	
'Yellow Twist'	CHad	
'Yelno Enchantment' (SWL)	CWGr LAyl	
'Yelno Firelight' (SWL)	CWGr	
'Yelno Harmony' (SD) ♀H3	CWGr LBut	

'Yelno Petite Glory' (MinD)	CWGr
'York and Lancaster' (MD)	CBgR CWGr EMon IGor
'Yorkie' (MS-c)	CWGr WAba
'Yoro Kobi' (DwB)	NHal
'Young Bees' (MD)	CWGr
'Yukino' (Col)	CWGr
I 'Yvonne' (MWL)	WAba
'Zagato' (MinD)	CWGr
* 'Zakuro-fubuki' (MD)	CWGr
'Zakuro-hime' (SD)	CWGr
I 'Zelda' (LD)	CWGr
'Zest' (MinD)	CWGr
'Zing' (LS-c)	CWGr
'Zorro' (GD) ♀H3	CWGr NHal WAba
'Zurich' (SS-c)	CWGr

Dais (Thymelaeaceae)
cotinifolia	CPLG EShb

Daiswa see *Paris*

Dalea (Papilionaceae)
candida	NDov
purpurea	NDov SUsu

Dalechampia (Euphorbiaceae)
dioscoreifolia	CCCN CPIN ERea

Dampiera (Goodeniaceae)
diversifolia	ECou
lanceolata	ECou
teres	ECou

damson see *Prunus insititia*

Danae (Ruscaceae)
§ racemosa	CBcs EBee ELan EMon ENot EPfP EPla ETow GCal IDee LRHS MGos MRav SAPC SArc SBrw SPer SRms SSpi SSta WCot WDin WPat

Danthonia (Poaceae)
californica	CBig

Daphne ✿ (Thymelaeaceae)
acutiloba	CPMA ECho EPot GAbr GKev SAga SBrw SPoG WPGP WSHC
albowiana	CPMA CPle EWes LRHS SAga SBla SCoo WCru
'Allison Carver' (v)	CPMA
alpina	CPMA ECho EHyt GAbr SAga SBla
altaica	CPMA
arbuscula ♀H4	CPMA ECho EPot NMen SBla WThu
- subsp. arbuscula f. albiflora	SBla
- f. radicans	CPMA
arbuscula x cneorum var. verlotii	CPMA
arbuscula x 'Leila Haines'	see *D.* x *schlyteri*
bholua	CAbP CHll CPMA ECho LHop LRHS MGos MWya SPoG SReu SSpi SSta WAbe WCru WPat
I - 'Alba'	CBcs CEnd CLAP CPMA ECho EPfP GAbr ECho LRHS MAsh MGos SBla SCoo SMur SPoG SSpi SSta WCru WPGP
- 'Darjeeling'	CBrm CLAP CPLG CPMA EPfP LRHS MAsh SLon SSpi SSta WPGP
- var. glacialis	WCru
- - 'Gurkha'	CBct CPMA EBee ELan EPfP MAsh SBla SSpi WPGP
- 'Glendoick'	EPfP GGGa MAsh
- 'Jacqueline Postill' ♀H3	More than 30 suppliers

- 'Peter Smithers'	CBct CLAP LRHS MAsh SBla SCoo SReu SSpi SSta
- 'Rupina La'	SBla
blagayana	CBcs CPMA ECho EPot GAbr GCrs GGGa GKev MDun MPRe MWya NEgg SBla SPoG SRms SSpi WCFE WFar
- 'Brenda Anderson'	ITim SBla
blagayana x sericea	CPMA
Collina Group **new**	
'Bramdean'	see *D.* x *napolitana* 'Bramdean'
x burkwoodii ♀H4	CBcs EBee ECho EPot MWya SAga SHBN WDin
- 'Albert Burkwood'	CDul CPMA ECho LRHS LTwo SBla
- 'Astrid' (v)	CBcs CBow CPMA EBee ENot LRHS MGos SCoo SIng SMrm SMur SPoG SSta WDin
- 'Briggs Moonlight' (v)	LRHS
§ - 'Carol Mackie' (v)	CPMA ECho GAbr LHop LTwo MDun MGos SBla
- 'G.K. Argles' (v) ♀H4	CBcs CPMA ECho ERea LAst LRHS MAsh MDun MGos MWya WFar
I - 'Gold Sport'	ECho
- 'Gold Strike' (v)	CPMA ECho
- 'Golden Treasure'	LRHS SBla
- 'Lavenirei'	CPMA
- 'Somerset'	CBcs CDul CPMA ECho ELan ENot EPfP LRHS MGos MSwo NBlu NScw NWea SAga SBla SHBN SLim SPer SPla SPoG SSta WDin WOrn
§ - 'Somerset Gold Edge' (v)	CPMA
§ - 'Somerset Variegated' (v)	LAst WPat
I - 'Variegata' (v)	EBee MGos WPat
- 'Variegata' broad cream edge	see *D.* x *burkwoodii* 'Somerset Variegated'
- 'Variegata' broad gold edge	see *D.* x *burkwoodii* 'Somerset Gold Edge'
- 'Variegata' narrow gold edge	see *D.* x *burkwoodii* 'Carol Mackie'
caucasica	CPMA SAga SBla
circassica	SBla
cneorum	CBcs CPMA ECho ENot EPfP LRHS MGos NMen SMur WDin
- f. alba	CPMA SBla
- 'Blackthorn Triumph'	CPMA SBla
- 'Eximia' ♀H4	CBcs CPMA ECho EPot GAbr LHop LRHS MDun MGos SBla SHBN SIng SRms SUsu
- 'Grandiflora'	see *D.* x *napolitana* 'Maxima'
- 'Lac des Gloriettes'	CPMA
- 'Major' **new**	LHop
- 'Puszta'	CPMA SAga
- var. pygmaea	CPMA EPot SBla
- - 'Alba'	CPMA SBla
- 'Rose Glow'	CPMA ECho
- 'Ruby Glow'	CPMA ECho MWya
- 'Stasek' (v)	CPMA ITim SBla WThu
- 'Variegata' (v)	CPMA ECho EPot MGos NWCA SIng
- 'Velký Kosir'	CPMA SBla WAbe
collina	see *D. sericea* Collina Group
'Fragrant Cloud'	CPMA EWes SBla
genkwa	LRHS SBla
giraldii	CPMA MDun
aff. giraldii	NMen
x hendersonii	CEnd CPMA ECho
- 'Appleblossom'	CPMA ECho
- 'Aymon Correvon'	CPMA SBla
- 'Blackthorn Rose'	CPMA SBla
- 'Ernst Hauser'	CPMA ECho EPot GAbr GEdr GKev LHop LTwo MPRe SBla SUsu WAbe
- 'Fritz Kummert'	CPMA SBla WAbe
- 'Jeanette Brickell' **new**	SBla
- 'Kath Dryden'	CPMA SBla
- 'Marion White'	CPMA SBla

- 'Rosebud' CPMA SBla
'Hinton' **new** CPMA
x *houtteana* CPMA ECho LTwo MDun MGos MWya NBir SPoG
x *hybrida* CEnd CPMA ECho SBla
japonica 'Striata' see *D. odora* 'Aureomarginata'
jasminea CPMA ECho NMen SBla WAbe
jezoensis CPMA LRHS SBla SSta WCru
juliae CPMA SBla
kosaninii CPMA WLin
laureola CPMA CSWP ECho EPfP GKev LRHS MGos MMHG MSte NBir NPer WCFE WGwG WPGP WWye
- 'Margaret Mathew' CPMA MPRe
- subsp. *philippi* CBcs CBgR CPMA CPle CWSG ELan EPfP LRHS MAsh MBri NDlv NMen SBrw SPer SSta WCru WFar
'Leila Haines' CPMA
longilobata CPle NSla
- 'Peter Moore' SBla
x *manteniana* ECho MGos
- 'Audrey Vokins' **new** SBla
- 'Manten' CBcs CPMA ECho GEdr LHop LTwo MDun MWya SPoG
x *mauerbachii* 'Perfume of Spring' CPMA ECho MPRe SBla
'Meon' see *D.* x *napolitana* 'Meon'
mezereum More than 30 suppliers
- f. *alba* CPMA CPle CWib ECho EHyt EPfP GAbr LHop LRHS MBar MDun MGos MPRe NChi NEgg SBla SPer SPoG SRms SWvt WCFE WCru WTin
- - 'Bowles' Variety' CPMA EPot GAbr NBid
- 'Rosea' ECho SRms
- var. *rubra* CBcs CDul CPMA CWSG CWib EBee ECho ELan EPfP EWTr LRHS MGan MGos MSwo NBlu SPer SPoG WCru WDin WFar WGwG WOrn
x *napolitana* ♀H4 CBcs CPMA ECho EPfP EPot GAbr MDun MGos MPRe NLar NMen SHBN SPoG SUsu WAbe WBrE WGob
§ - 'Bramdean' CPMA ECho EPot GEdr MDun MWya SBla WGob
§ - 'Maxima' MGos
§ - 'Meon' CEnd CPMA EBee ECho EPot GEdr LHop LTwo MWya NMen SBla WAbe WPat
odora CBcs CPMA CPle ECho EPot LRHS MGos MPRe MSwo NMen SSta WDin
§ - f. *alba* CCCN CPMA ECho GAbr GEdr GKev ISea LRHS MGos NDlv
I - 'Aureamarginata Alba' (v) CPMA GEdr SBrw
§ - 'Aureomarginata' (v) ♀H3-4 More than 30 suppliers
- 'Clotted Cream' (v) CPMA
- 'Geisha Girl' (v) ELan ERea MAsh MGos SBla WThu
- var. *leucantha* see *D. odora* f. *alba*
- 'Limelight' **new** SBla
- 'Mae-jima' **new** SBla
- 'Marginata' see *D. odora* 'Aureomarginata'
- var. *rubra* CCCN CFir ECho GEdr GKev LRHS LTwo NDlv NLar SBrw WGob
- 'Sakiwaka' CCCN CPMA ECho GEdr LTwo WGob
- 'Walberton' (v) LRHS MGos SPoG
oleoides CPMA EPot GAbr SBla
petraea SBla WAbe
- 'Alba' see *D. petraea* 'Tremalzo'
- 'Grandiflora' GCrs NMen SBla WAbe
- 'Persebee' **new** CPMA

- 'Punchinello' **new** CPMA
§ - 'Tremalzo' SBla
- 'Tuflungo' **new** CPMA
petraea x *sericea* Collina Group SSta WAbe
pontica ♀H4 CBcs CPMA CPle ECho EHyt EPfP LRHS MBri NLar NMen SDix SMad SPoG SSpi SSvw WCru WGwG WPGP
pseudomezereum WCru
retusa see *D. tangutica* Retusa Group
'Richard's Choice' CPMA
rodriguezii x *sericea* **new** CPMA
x *rollsdorfii* 'Arnold Cihlarz' CPMA LRHS WAbe
- 'Wilhelm Schacht' CPMA ECho EPot SBla SMur WGob
'Rossetii' **new** CPMA
'Rosy Wave' CPMA SBla SMur
§ x *schlyteri* CPMA SBla
- 'Lovisa Maria' **new** SBla
§ *sericea* CPMA SBla
§ - Collina Group CPMA EPfP ITim SBla SPoG SRms WThu
sericea Collina Group x (x *susannae* 'Anton Fahndrich') CPMA
striata 'Wolfgang Reich' **new** SBla
sureil GWJ 9200 WCru
x *susannae* 'Cheriton' CPMA ECho EPot GEdr LTwo SBla SMur SSta
- 'Tichborne' CPMA NMen SBla WThu
tangutica ♀H4 More than 30 suppliers
§ - Retusa Group ♀H4 CPMA CSec ECho EHyt EPot GAbr GCrs GGGa ITim LHop LRHS MAsh MBri NEgg NLap NMen NRya SHBN SRms WCru WSHC
- - SDR 3024 GKev
x *thauma* NMen SBla
x *transatlantica* 'Beulah Cross' (v) CPMA SBla
- Eternal Fragrance = 'Blafra' **new** ENot LBuc LRHS MAsh MGos SBla SPer SPoG
- 'Jim's Pride' SBla
'Valerie Hillier' LRHS
velenovskyi SBla
x *whiteorum* 'Beauworth' CPMA ECho LRHS LTwo SBla WAbe
- 'Kilmeston' CPMA ECho EHyt LTwo NMen
- 'Warnford' CPMA

Daphniphyllum (*Daphniphyllaceae*)
calycinum NLar
glaucescens B&SWJ 4058 WCru
- subsp. *oldhamii* var. *kengii* B&SWJ 6872 WCru
- - var. *oldhamii* B&SWJ 7056 WCru
§ *himalaense* subsp. *macropodum* CBcs CCCN CHEx CMCN CWib EBee EPfP MBri NLar SAPC SArc SBrw SDix SLPl SMad SSpi WCru WFar WPGP
- - B&SWJ 2898 WCru
- - B&SWJ 581 WCru
- - B&SWJ 6809 from Taiwan WCru
- - B&SWJ 8763 from Cheju-Do WCru
- - dwarf WCru
humile see *D. himalaense* subsp. *macropodum*
teijsmannii B&SWJ 3805 WCru

Darlingtonia (Sarraceniaceae)
 californica ♀H1   CHew CSWC EFEx ITer MCCP
    SHmp WSSs

Darmera (Saxifragaceae)
§ **peltata** ♀H4   More than 30 suppliers
  – 'Nana'   CCol CHEx EBee ECha GBuc
    LBMP MBri MTis NLar SWat
    WCot WFar WMoo WPnP
    WWpP

Darwinia (Myrtaceae)
 fascicularis   SOWG
 taxifolia   SOWG

Dasylirion (Dracaenaceae)
§ **acrotrichum**   LPan SAPC SArc XPep
 glaucophyllum   EAmu MPRe WMul
 gracile Planchon   see *D. acrotrichum*
 leiophyllum   XPep
 longissimum   CAbb CBrP CTrC EAmu EShb SChr
    WMul XPep
 serratifolium   EAmu
 texanum   CTrC XPep
 wheeleri ♀H1   CBrP CRoM CTrC EAmu EShb
    SChr XPep

Dasyphyllum (Asteraceae)
 diacanthoides   WPGP

date see *Phoenix dactylifera*

Datisca (Datiscaceae)
 cannabina   CAby CArn CDes CFwr EBee ECha
    EMag EMan GCal MGol NBPC
    NLar SMHy SMrm WCot WHil
    WMoo WPGP

Datura (Solanaceae)
 arborea   see *Brugmansia arborea*
 chlorantha   see *Brugmansia chlorantha*
 cornigera   see *Brugmansia arborea*
§ **inoxia** ♀H3   EBak MGol MSal
 metel   MGol
  – 'Belle Blanche'   MGol
 meteloides   see *D. inoxia*
 rosea   see *Brugmansia* x *insignis* pink-
    flowered
 rosei   see *Brugmansia sanguinea*
 sanguinea   see *Brugmansia sanguinea*
 stramonium   CArn MGol MSal
  – var. **chalybaea**   MSal
  – var. **inermis**   MSal
 suaveolens   see *Brugmansia suaveolens*
 versicolor   see *Brugmansia versicolor*
    Lagerh.
  – 'Grand Marnier'   see *Brugmansia* x *candida*
    'Grand Marnier'

Daucus (Apiaceae)
 carota   CArn CHrt CRWN MBow NMir
    NSco SECG WHer
  – 'Ballydowling Lace'   CNat
    new
  – 'Jane's Lace'   CNat

Davallia (Davalliaceae)
§ **mariesii** ♀H3   CMen WAbe WCMO WCot
  – var. **stenolepis**   CMen
 trichomanoides f.   CMen
    barbata

Davidia (Cornaceae)
 involucrata ♀H4   More than 30 suppliers
  – 'Sonoma'   MBlu

  – var. **vilmoriniana** ♀H4   CBcs CDoC EBee ELan EPfP EWTr
    IMGH LRHS MCCP MDun MGan
    MGos NBlu NEgg NPal SHBN SPer
    WCMO WOrn

Daviesia (Papilionaceae)
 brevifolia   SPlb

Decaisnea (Lardizabalaceae)
 fargesii   More than 30 suppliers
  – B&SWJ 8070   WCru
 insignis   CPLG WNor WPGP

Decodon (Lythraceae)
 verticillatus   EMon

Decumaria (Hydrangeaceae)
 barbara   CBcs CMac CPIN EBee EMil GIBF
    LRHS MBri NSti SBra SHBN SLim
    SLon SSta WCru WFar WSHC
  – 'Vicki'   NLar
 sinensis   CPIN EBee EPfP SLon SSpi WCru
    WSHC

Degenia (Brassicaceae)
 velebitica   WLin

Deinanthe (Hydrangeaceae)
 bifida   CDes CLAP CPLG EBee EWes GEdr
    LEdu WCMO WCru WPGP
  – B&SWJ 5012   WCru
  – B&SWJ 5436   GEdr SBig
  – B&SWJ 5655   WCru
 bifida x **caerulea**   CLAP
 caerulea   CDes CLAP CMil EBee GEdr IGor
    LEdu SBla WCMO WCru WPGP
  – pale-flowered   GEdr

Delonix (Caesalpiniaceae)
 regia   CSec SOWG

Delosperma (Aizoaceae)
 LEG 037   CStu
§ **aberdeenense** ♀H1   CHEx
* **album**   EDAr
 ashtonii   CCCN CStu EDAr GEdr WPer
 'Basutoland'   see *D. nubigenum*
 congestum   CStu ECho EDAr EShb EWll GEdr
    NJOw
 cooperi   CCCN CStu EChP ECho ECtt EDAr
    EWll GEdr ITim NJOw NLap SIng
    SPlb WDyG WFar WPat WPer XPep
 ecklonis   EDAr EWin
 esterhuyseniae   EDAr
 lineare   NBir XPep
 lydenburgense   CHEx SChr
§ **nubigenum**   CHEx CHal ECho ECtt EDAr ELan
    EPfP EPot EWin GEdr GGar ITim
    LRHS NBlu NJOw SPoG WAbe
    WFar WPer
 sutherlandii   ECho EDAr EShb EWin EWll GGar
    NJOw
  – 'Peach Star'   EDAr EWin

Delphinium ✿ (Ranunculaceae)
 HWJK 2179 from Nepal   WCru
 HWJK 2263 from Nepal   WCru
 'After Midnight'   CNMi
 'Agnes Brookes'   ERou
 'Ailsa'   CNMi
 'Alice Artindale' (d)   CDes CHad EBee EMon IFoB SBla
    SMrm WCot WPGP WSan
 'Alie Duyvensteyn'   EBee ERou
 'Alison Claire'   CNMi
 ambiguum   see *Consolida ajacis*
 'Angela Harbutt' **new**   CNMi

'Ann Woodfield'	CNMi
'Anne Kenrick'	CNMi
'Anne Page'	ERou
'Apollo'	NRnb
Astolat Group	CBcs CSBt CWib EAEE EBee ELan EPfP EShb EWTr GMaP LRHS MBri MRav MWat NBPC NBir NCob NEgg NFor NLar NPri SMer SPer SPoG WCAu WFar WHil WHoo WWeb
'Atholl' ♀H4	NRnb
'Baby Doll'	CNMi
Belladonna Group	EShb IFoB
- 'Atlantis' ♀H4	EBee ECha ENot ERou SBla SMeo SMrm SPur SWat WCot
- 'Ballkleid'	ERou
- 'Capri'	EBee
- 'Casa Blanca'	EBee EShb GMaP NCGa NLar SBla SMrm SWat WPer
- 'Cliveden Beauty'	EBee GBri LHop MRav MSte MWgw NCGa NChi NLar SBla SPoG SWat WPer
- 'Delft Blue'PBR	EBee MLLN NBre NMoo
- 'Moerheimii'	CBod ERou SMrm SPoG
- 'Piccolo'	ECha ENot ERou SMrm SWat
- 'Pink Sensation'	see *D.* x *ruysii* 'Pink Sensation'
- 'Völkerfrieden' ♀H4	CBod EBrs ERou MRav NCGa NGby NPri NPro SPur
x *bellamosum*	CSim LRHS NCGa NLar SWat WPer
'Berghimmel'	EBee LRHS NGby
'Beryl Burton'	CNMi ERou
Black Knight Group	More than 30 suppliers
'Black Pearl'	ENot
'Blackberry Ice'	CNMi
'Blauwal'	CFir SWat
'Blondie'	CNMi
Blue Bird Group	CBcs CSBt CTri EAEE EBee ELan EPfP GMaP LRHS MNHC MRav MWat NEgg NFor NLar NMir NPri SMer SPer SPla SPoG WCAu WFar WHoo WWeb
'Blue Butterfly'	see *D. grandiflorum* 'Blue Butterfly'
'Blue Dawn' ♀H4	CNMi ERou
Blue Fountains Group	CSBt EPfP LRHS LSRN NBre SPer SPet SPoG SRms
'Blue Hex' **new**	WCot
Blue Jade Group	ERou
'Blue Jay'	CBcs CTri EBee ENot EPfP LRHS LSRN MBow NBir NLar NPri SPer SPoG
'Blue Lagoon'	CNMi
'Blue Mirror'	SRms
'Blue Nile' ♀H4	CNMi ERou
'Blue Oasis'	CNMi
'Blue Skies'	NLar NRnb
Blue Springs Group	NGdn NLar
'Blue Tit'	CNMi ERou
'Bruce' ♀H4	CNMi ERou WCFE
bulleyanum	EBee GIBF
'Butterball'	CNMi MRnb
Cameliard Group	CBcs CSBt EAEE EBee ECtt ELan LRHS MNHC MWat NLar NPri SPer SPoG
'Can-Can' ♀H4	CNMi ERou
cardinale	EHrv NBre
'Carl Topping'	ERou
cashmerianum	ECho GEdr GIBF WSHC
'Cassius' ♀H4	CNMi ERou
caucasicum	see *D. speciosum*
'Centurion Sky Blue' (Centurion Series)	NBHF
ceratophorum var. *ceratophorum* BWJ 7799	WCru

'Chelsea Star'	CNMi ERou
'Cher'	CNMi
'Cherry Blossom'	GAbr NLar
'Cherub' ♀H4	ERou
chinense	see *D. grandiflorum*
'Christel'	EBee ERou
'Circe'	ERou
'Clack's Choice'	CNMi ERou
'Claire' ♀H4	CNMi
Clear Springs Series	LIck NBre
'Clifford Lass'	CNMi NRnb
Connecticut Yankees Group	NBre SRms
'Conspicuous' ♀H4	CNMi ERou
'Constance Rivett' ♀H4	ERou
'Coral Sunset'PBR (d)	EBee ERou NBPC NMoo
'Corinth'	CNMi
'Cream Cracker'	CNMi
'Cressida'	ERou
'Cristella'	ERou
'Crown Jewel'	ERou WCFE
'Cupid'	CNMi ERou
'Darling Sue'	CNMi
'Darwin's Blue Indulgence'PBR	EBee EPfP ERou MLLN SMrm
'Darwin's Pink Indulgence'PBR	EBee ERou MLLN NBPC SMrm SPoG
delavayi	GKev SBla WRos
- B&SWJ 7796	WCru
'Delfy Light Blue'	ENot
'Demavand'	CNMi
'Dolly Bird'	ERou
'Dreaming Spires'	SRms
drepanocentrum	EBee
'Duchess of Portland'	NRnb
'Dunsden Green'	CNMi
'Dusky Maiden' **new**	IFoB
dwarf dark blue	LRHS
dwarf lavender	LRHS
dwarf pink	LRHS
dwarf sky blue	LRHS
'Eelkje'	ERou
'Eileen Joan'	CNMi
elatum	CArn GCal NGdn SRms SSth
'Elisabeth Sahin'	CNMi
'Elizabeth Cook' ♀H4	CNMi
'Elmfreude'	EBee
'Emily Hawkins' ♀H4	CNMi ERou NRnb
'Eva Gower'	ERou
'F.W. Smith'	SSth
'Fanfare'	CNMi ERou NRnb
'Father Thames'	ERou
'Faust' ♀H4	CNMi EBee ERou NRnb
'Fenella' ♀H4	CNMi WCFE
'Filique Arrow'	CFir
'Finsteraarhorn'	ERou IPot NGby WCot
'Florestan'	CNMi
'Foxhill Nina'	CNMi
'Franjo Sahin'	CNMi
Galahad Group	More than 30 suppliers
'Galileo' ♀H4	CNMi
'Gemma'	CNMi
'Gillian Dallas' ♀H4	CNMi ERou NRnb
'Giotto' ♀H4	CNMi
glaciale HWJK 2299	WCru
'Gordon Forsyth'	CNMi ERou
'Gossamer'	CNMi NRnb
§ *grandiflorum*	NCob
§ - 'Blauer Zwerg'	EBee EPfP SHGN SPoG
§ - 'Blue Butterfly'	CSpe EBee EBrs EBur ENot LEdu LRHS SBla SCoo SPer SPlb SPoG WPer WSHC WWeb
- Blue Dwarf	see *D. grandiflorum* 'Blauer Zwerg'
'Grey Wagtail'	CNMi

Guinevere Group	CBcs CSBt CWib EAEE EBee ECtt EPfP EWTr LRHS MBow MBri MNHC MRav MWgw NBPC NBir NFor NLar NPri SPer SPla SPoG WCAu WFar
'Guy Langdon'	CNMi ERou
'Harlekijn'	ERou
'Harmony'	ERou
'Heavenly Blue'	NLar
'Holly Cookland Wilkins'	CNMi
'Hordon Blue' **new**	NBHF
Ivory Towers Group	ECtt
'Jenny Agutter'	CNMi
'Jill Curley'	CNMi
'Joan Edwards'	CNMi
'Joyce Roffey'	ERou
'Kasana'	CNMi
'Kathleen Cooke'	CNMi
'Kennington Calypso'	CNMi
'Kennington Carnival'	CNMi
'Kennington Classic'	CNMi
'Kestrel'	CNMi ERou
King Arthur Group	CBcs CSBt CWCL EAEE EBee ECtt EHol ELan ENot EPfP LSRN MNHC MRav MWat MWgw NBPC NEgg NLar NPri SMer SPer SPoG WBVN WCAu WFar WHoo
'Lady Guinevere'	EBee ERou
§ 'Langdon's Royal Flush' ♀H4	CNMi
'Lanzenträger'	SMeo
laxiflorum **new**	CEnt
'Layla'	CNMi
'Leonora'	CNMi ERou
likiangense	GIBF
'Lillian Basset'	CNMi
'Loch Leven' ♀H4	CNMi ERou
'Loch Lomond'	NRnb
'Loch Nevis'	CNMi
'Lord Butler' ♀H4	CNMi NRnb
'Lorna'	ERou
'Lucia Sahin' ♀H4	CNMi
§ *luteum*	EBee
maackianum	GCal GIBF
Magic Fountains Series	CSam GAbr GMaP IFoB NBlu NCob NJOw NPri SPlb SPoG WFar WGor WHil
- 'Magic Fountains Cherry Blossom'	CBrm EShb NBre SPoG WFar
- 'Magic Fountains Dark Blue'	CBrm EPfP GAbr GMaP LSRN NLar SPoG WFar
- 'Magic Fountains Deep Blue'	CBrm NLar
- 'Magic Fountains Lavender'	CBrm WWeb
- 'Magic Fountains Lilac Pink' **new**	SPoG
- 'Magic Fountains Lilac Rose'	EChP NLar NVic WFar WWeb
- 'Magic Fountains Pure White'	EChP EPfP EShb NBHF NLar WFar WWeb
- 'Magic Fountains Sky Blue'	CBrm EChP EShb LRHS NVic SPoG WFar
'Margaret Farrand'	ERou
'Marie Broan'	CNMi
menziesii	CSec ERos GIBF
'Michael Ayres' ♀H4	CNMi ERou NRnb
micropetalum CNDS 031	WCru
'Mighty Atom'	CNMi ERou NRnb
'Min' ♀H4	CNMi ERou NRnb
'Molly Buchanan'	CNMi ERou
'Moonbeam'	CNMi
'Morning Cloud'	CNMi
'Mother Teresa'	ERou
'Mrs Newton Lees'	EBee ERou

'Mrs T. Carlile'	ERou
'Mulberry Rose'	NBHF WHrl
'Mystique'	ERou
'Ned Rose'	ERou
'Ned Wit'	ERou
New Century hybrids	CBcs LRHS
'Nicolas Woodfield'	CNMi
'Nimrod'	ERou
'Nobility'	ERou
nudicaule	CBod EBee ECho EDAr EPfP LAst MBNS SPoG SRot
- 'Fox' **new**	LSou
- 'Laurin'	ECho NRnb SGar WFar
- var. *luteum*	see *D. luteum*
nuttallianum	GIBF
'Olive Poppleton' ♀H4	CNMi SAga
'Oliver' ♀H4	CNMi NRnb
'Our Deb' ♀H4	CNMi
oxysepalum	CSec WGwG
Pacific hybrids	ENot EPfP LRHS LSRN MHer MLHP NBlu NLar SGar SPet SRms SWal SWvt WFar
'Pagan Purples' (d)	IFoB
'Pandora'	CNMi
'Parade'	ERou
'Patricia Johnson'	CNMi ERou
Percival Group	LRHS NLar
'Pericles'	CNMi NRnb
'Perlmutterbaum'	LPhx SMeo
'Pink Petticoat' (d)	EMon
'Pink Ruffles'	CNMi
'Polar Sun'	NRnb
Princess Caroline = 'Odabar'PBR	CBcs MBri
'Purity'	ERou NRnb
'Purple Ruffles'	EBee EPfP ERou NLar NMRc
'Purple Triumph'	ERou
'Purple Velvet'	CNMi
'Pyramus'	ERou
'Rainbow Select'	NRnb
'Rakker'	EBee ERou
'Red Caroline'	CBcs MBri
requienii	CPom CSec EBee EDsa MWgw NBir SBch WCot WEas WOut
'Rona'	CNMi
'Rosemary Brock' ♀H4	CNMi ERou NRnb
'Royal Flush'	see *D.* 'Langdon's Royal Flush'
'Royal Velvet'	NRnb
§ x *ruysii* 'Pink Sensation'	CFir EBee ERou EWTr GBri NLar NPro SMrm STes WCot WFar WPGP
'Samantha'	ERou
'Sandpiper' ♀H4	CNMi
'Sarita'	EBee ERou NBPC SUsu
'Schildknappe'	EBee
'Sentinel'	CNMi
'Shimmer'	ERou
siamense B&SWJ 7278	WCru
'Silver Jubilee'	CNMi ERou
'Silver Moon'	ERou
'Sir Harry Secombe'	CNMi
'Skyline'	CNMi ERou
'Snowdon'	CNMi
'Solomon'	ERou
'South Seas'	CNMi
* 'Space Fantasy'	SBla
'Special'	SWal
§ *speciosum*	GKev NMen
'Spindrift' ♀H4	CNMi NRnb
stapeliosmum B&SWJ 2954	WCru
staphisagria	CArn ECGP EOHP MSal SSth
'Stardust'	ENot
'Starlight'PBR **new**	ENot
'Starmaker' **new**	EBee
'Strawberry Fair'	CNMi EBee ERou

'Summer Haze'	ERou
Summer Skies Group	CBcs CSBt EAEE EBee ECtt
	ELan EPfP EWTr LHop LRHS
	MBri MNHC MWat MWgw
	NBir NEgg NLar NPri SMer SPer
	SPoG WBrE WCAu WFar WHoo
	WWeb
'Summerfield Diana'	CNMi
'Summerfield Miranda' ♀H4	CNMi
'Summerfield Oberon'	CNMi
'Sungleam' ♀H4	CFir CNMi ERou
'Sunkissed' ♀H4	CNMi
'Susan Edmunds' (d) **new**	EMil SPoG
sutchuenense B&SWJ 7867	WCru
tatsienense	SRms WCru WSHC
- 'Album'	EWes
- 'Blue Ice'	EHyt
tenii B&SWJ 7693	WCru
- BWJ 7906	WCru
'Tessa'	ERou
'Thundercloud'	ERou
'Tiger Eye'	CNMi
'Tiny Tim'	CNMi
tricorne	CLAP
'Turkish Delight'	ERou
'Vanessa Mae'	CNMi
vestitum	GKev NBir SBch
viscosum HWJK 2268	WCru
'Walton Beauty'	CNMi
'Walton Benjamin'	CNMi
'Walton Gemstone' ♀H4	CNMi
'Watkin Samuel'	ERou
'White Ruffles'	CNMi
'Wishful Thinking'PBR	EBee ERou SMrm
Woodfield strain	WHrl
'Yvonne'	ERou

Dendranthema (Asteraceae)
cultivars	see *Chrysanthemum*
nankingense	see *Chrysanthemum nankingense*
pacificum	see *Ajania pacifica*

Dendriopoterium see *Sanguisorba*

Dendrobenthamia see *Cornus*

Dendrocalamus (Poaceae)
asper **new**	XBlo
calostachys **new**	SPlb
giganteus	XBlo
§ *strictus*	XBlo

Dendromecon (Papaveraceae)
rigida	CBcs EPfP LHop LRHS MBri MWea NLar SAga SBrw SMur SSpi WCot WPGP

Dennstaedtia (Dennstaedtiaceae)
punctilobula	CLAP WCMO WCot

Dentaria see *Cardamine*
microphylla	see *Cardamine microphylla*
pinnata	see *Cardamine heptaphylla*
polyphylla	see *Cardamine kitaibelii*

Dermatobotrys (Scrophulariaceae)
saundersii	ECre

Derris (Papilionaceae)
elliptica	CPIN
scandens **new**	CPIN

Derwentia see *Parahebe*

Deschampsia (Poaceae)
cespitosa	CBig CEnt CHrt CKno CNat COIW CRWN EPPr EPfP EWTr LBuc MBar MWat NBre NHol NNor SPlb SPoG SYvo WCFE WDin WGHP WGwG WMoo WPer WPnP WTin
- subsp. *alpina*	LRHS
- Bronze Veil	see *D. cespitosa* 'Bronzeschleier'
§ - 'Bronzeschleier'	CEnt CKno CMea CWCL EBee EBrs EHoe ELan EMag ENot EPla EWsh GBri GCal GMaP LPhx MAvo MBnl MSte MWgw NGdn NHol SPer SPla WGHP WMoo WPtf
- 'Fairy's Joke'	see *D. cespitosa* var. *vivipara*
- Gold Dust	see *D. cespitosa* 'Goldstaub'
- Golden Dew	see *D. cespitosa* 'Goldtau'
- Golden Pendant	see *D. cespitosa* 'Goldgehänge'
- Golden Shower	see *D. cespitosa* 'Goldgehänge'
- Golden Veil	see *D. cespitosa* 'Goldschleier'
§ - 'Goldgehänge'	CSam EHoe EHul EMan EPPr EPfP EPla MMHG NBir NHol NLar NPro SLPl
§ - 'Goldschleier'	CBig CBrm CEnt EBee EBrs ECGP EChP ECha EHoe EMon EPPr EPla EWsh GGar GMaP LPhx NGdn NJOw SWal WMoo WPGP
§ - 'Goldstaub'	EPPr
§ - 'Goldtau'	CBig CHar EBee EHoe EHul EMon EPGN EPPr EPfP EPla GMaP LPhx LRHS MAvo MBnl MMoz MRav MWgw MWhi NGdn NHol NOrc SLPl SMeo SPer SPla SPoG SUsu WCot WGHP
- 'Morning Dew'	EMag WFar
- 'Northern Lights' (v)	More than 30 suppliers
- 'Schottland'	GBin
§ - var. *vivipara*	CBig EBee EHoe EMon EPPr EPla LRHS MWgw NBid NBro NHol NLar NOGN SWal WRos
- 'Willow Green'	GCal MRav SCoo SPoG
elongata	CBig
flexuosa	CBig CBrm COIW CPen EHoe GlBF MWat NBir SMar WPer
- 'Tatra Gold'	More than 30 suppliers
holciformis	CBig

Desfontainia (Loganiaceae)
§ *spinosa* ♀H3	More than 30 suppliers
- 'Harold Comber'	CMac MDun WCru
- f. *hookeri*	see *D. spinosa*

Desmanthus (Mimosaceae)
illinoensis	EBee EMan MGol MSal

Desmodium (Papilionaceae)
callianthum	CMac EBee EPfP LRHS WSHC
canadense	EBee EBrs EMan EShb MGol NLar WCot
§ *elegans* ♀H4	CBcs CHEx CPle EBee ELan EPfP MBri MGol NLar WCru WHer WPGP WSHC
glutinosum	EBee
praestans	see *D. yunnanense*
tiliifolium	see *D. elegans*
§ *yunnanense*	CHEx CPle EPfP LRHS WSHC

Desmos (Annonaceae)
chinensis **new**	CPIN

Desmoschoenus (Cyperaceae)
spiralis	CTrC

Deutzia ✿ (*Hydrangeaceae*)

CC 4548	CPLG MGol
CC 4549	WCot
CC 4550	CPLG
calycosa	GQui
- B&SWJ 7742	WCru
- Farrer 846	SMHy
- 'Dali' SBEC 417	SDys WPGP
chunii	see *D. ningpoensis*
compacta	SLon WFar WPGP
- 'Lavender Time'	EBee GSki MAsh MBNS WCFE
cordatula B&SWJ 6917	WCru
coreana BWJ 8588	WCru
corymbosa	CDoC
crenata 'Flore Pleno'	see *D. scabra* 'Plena'
- var. *nakaiana*	MAsh SIng WPat
- 'Pride of Rochester' (d)	CBcs CMCN CTri CWib EBee
	EHol ENot EWTr MBar MDun
	MRav MTis SLim SLon SPoG
	WDin WHar
aff. *crenata* BWJ 8879	WCru
aff var. *heterotricha*	WCru
BWJ 8896	
discolor 'Major'	CPLG
x *elegantissima*	MRav SRms
- 'Fasciculata'	EPfP SPer WLeb
- 'Rosealind' ♀H4	CBcs CTri EBee ECrN ENot EPfP
	EWTr LHop LRHS MBri MRav
	NEgg NSti SPer SPoG SRGP SRms
	SSpi WCot WKif WLeb WSHC
glabrata B&SWJ 617	GQui WCru
glomeruliflora	WCru
B&SWJ 7748	
gracilis	CDoC CHar CSBt CWoW EBee
	ELan EPfP EWTr GQui MBar
	MNHC MRav MSwo SDix SPer
	SPoG SWal WDin WFar WGwG
	WRHF
- B&SWJ 5805	WCru
- 'Aurea'	CBcs
- 'Carminea'	see *D.* x *rosea* 'Carminea'
§ - 'Marmorata' (v)	CBow CPMA NLar SLon WHCG
- 'Nikko'	CAbP CBcs CPBP CPLG CStu EBee
	ECho EHyt EWes MBar MGos
	MHer NBlu NPro SPlb WDin
	WHCG WKif WSHC
- 'Rosea'	see *D.* x *rosea*
- 'Variegata'	see *D. gracilis* 'Marmorata'
hookeriana	GGGa WFar
- KW 6393	WPGP
x *hybrida* 'Contraste'	CPLG SPer
- 'Joconde'	CPLG MBri WFar WKif
- 'Magicien'	CBrm CDoC CDul CMHG CPLG
	CSBt CSam CWib EBee EPfP GQui
	LHop MAsh MBri MRav MSwo
	NHol SHBN SLon SPer SWvt WFar
	WHCG WHar WKif WPat
- 'Mont Rose' ♀H4	CBrm CDoC CDul CPLG EBee
	ELan EPfP EWTr IMGH LAst LBuc
	LRHS MBar MBri MGos MRav
	MSwo NCGa SLim SMac SPer SPoG
	SWvt WCFE WDin WFar WHCG
	WMoo WSHC
§ - 'Strawberry Fields' ♀H4	CHar CPLG CTri EBee ELan EPla
	EWTr LAst LBuc LRHS LSRN MAsh
	MBar MBlu MBri MDun MGos
	MTis NPro SBod SLon WBVN WKif
	WPGP
'Iris Alford'	SLon
x *kalmiiflora*	CPLG CPMA CSBt CTri EBee EHol
	GQui LRHS MBar MBri MDun
	MNHC MRav MWhi NEgg NFor
	SLPl SPer SPoG SRms
longifolia 'Veitchii' ♀H4	CDul CPle CSBt GQui MRav
	WCFE

§ - 'Vilmoriniae'	MRav
x *magnifica*	CBcs EBee ECrN EHol ELan EPfP
	GQui MBri SRms WDin WHCG
	WHar
- 'Rubra'	see *D.* x *hybrida* 'Strawberry
	Fields'
monbeigii	CPLG WKif
§ *ningpoensis* ♀H4	CAbP CBcs CPLG EBee GQui NHol
	SLPl SPer WPGP
parviflora var.	WCru
barbinervis	
B&SWJ 8427	
'Pink Pompon'	see *D.* 'Rosea Plena'
pulchra	CAbP CHar CMCN CPom ECha
	EPfP IDee MRav NPro SLon SPer
	SSpi WFar WHCG WPGP
- B&SWJ 3870	WCru
- B&SWJ 6908	WCru
aff. *purpurascens*	WCru
BWJ 8007	
§ x *rosea*	CDul CTrw CWib ENot EPfP LAst
	LRHS MBar SHBN SMer SPoG
	SRms WFar WKif
- 'Campanulata'	CPLG EBee EPfP NEgg
§ - 'Carminea'	MDun MRav MSwo NCGa SPlb
	SRms SSta WDin WFar WMoo
§ 'Rosea Plena' (d)	CDoC CPLG CSBt CWib EPfP
	MAsh MDun MGos NBlu NEgg
	SLim SMac SPoG SSta WCFE WFar
	WGwG WPat
scabra	CDul
§ - 'Candidissima' (d)	ECrN GQui MRav NLar SLim SMer
	SPer WCFE
- 'Codsall Pink'	MRav
§ - 'Plena' (d)	CPLG ECtt ELan EPfP IMGH LRHS
	MDun MRav NEgg SHBN SPer SPur
- 'Punctata' (v)	EHoe SRms WFar
- 'Variegata' (v)	SLim
aff. *scabra* B&SWJ 8924	WCru
setchuenensis	EPfP GGGa GQui SSpi WHCG
	WPat WSHC
- var. *corymbiflora* ♀H4	CDoC CDul CSam CTri EPfP EPla
	LRHS MTis NEgg SPoG WFar WKif
	WPGP
taiwanensis	EBee EMil NLar
- B&SWJ 6858	WCru
'Tourbillon Rouge'	EBee WDin
x *wellsii*	see *D. scabra* 'Candidissima'
x *wilsonii*	SRms

Dianella ✿ (*Phormiaceae*)

caerulea	ECou ELan GBuc IFoB IGor NBir
- 'Caspar Blue' **new**	ECou
- 'Cassa Blue' **new**	EPPr
- Breeze = 'Dcnco' **new**	ECou EPPr
- 'Kulnura' **new**	ECou
- Little Jess = 'DCMP01'	ECou EPPr
new	
- var. *petasmatodes*	EBee EMan WCot
- 'Variegata'	see *D. tasmanica* 'Variegata'
intermedia	CTrC IBlr WCot WPic
- 'Variegata' (v)	EBee IBlr
nigra	CBcs CFir CPen CPou CWil EBee
	ECou IFro LEdu NCGa WFar
	WHer
§ - 'Margaret Pringle' (v)	CBcs CPen
- 'Taupo' **new**	ECou
revoluta	CFir CWil ECou IBlr
- 'Baby Blue' **new**	ECou
- Little Rev = 'Dr5000'	ECou EPPr
new	
- 'Hartz Mountain' **new**	ECou
tasmanica	More than 30 suppliers
- 'Aurea' **new**	CPne
- 'Prosser' **new**	ECou
- 'Tas Red' **new**	ECou EPPr

§ - 'Variegata' (v) — CBct CFir CPen CSpe CStu EBee ECou ELan EMan GQui IBlr LHop MSte WCot WOld WWye

Dianthus ✿ (*Caryophyllaceae*)

ACW 2116 — CLyd LBee
'A.A. Sanders' (b) — SAll
acicularis — EHyt
'Adam James' (b) — SAll
'Admiral Crompton' (pf) — CNMi
'Admiral Lord Anson' (b) — WKin
'Alan Titchmarsh' (p) — CCge EAEE EBee ENot EPfP EWll MMHG NEgg NLar SBai SPoG
'Aldridge Yellow' (b) — SAll
'Alfred Galbally' (b) — SAll
'Alfriston' (b) ♀H4 — SAll
'Alice' (p) — EBee EPfP SAll SHay WKin
'Alice Forbes' (b) — SAll SHay
'Alice Lever' (p) — WAbe
'Allegro' (pf) — SHay
'Alloway Star' (p) — EMFP WKin
'Allspice' (p) — CLyd MRav SBch SSvw WEas WHoo WKin WOFF
'Allspice Sport' (p) — WKin
Allwoodii Alpinus Group (p) — CBrm ECho NJOw SRms
'Allwood's Crimson' (pf) — SAll
alpinus ♀H4 — CLyd ECho EHyt GKev ITim LRHS NBlu NEgg NJOw NMen NWCA SPet SRms WPer
- 'Albus' — ECho LRHS WLin
§ - 'Joan's Blood' ♀H4 — ECho GBuc LHop NHol NWCA SBla WAbe WFar WHoo
- 'Millstream Salmon' — CLyd EPot
- 'Rax Alpe' — EPot
'Alyson' (p) — SAll
amurensis — ECho LRHS NDov SSvw WGwG WPer
- 'Andrey' — GCal SHar
- 'Siberian Blue' — GBin
anatolicus — CTri ECho LBee LRHS MHer NDlv NGdn NWCA SSvw WPer XPep
'Andrew Morton' (b) — SAll
'Angelo' (b) — SAll
'Annabelle' (p) — EBee ECho EMFP LRHS
'Anne Jones' (b) **new** — EPfP
'Annette' (pf) — EAEE ECho EWTr EWin LRHS
'Annie Claybourne' (pf) — CNMi
'Anniversay' (p) — CBcs SBai SEND
'Apricot Chace' (b) — SHay
'Apricot Sue' (pf) — CNMi
'Arctic Star' (p) — CMea CTri ECho EMFP GMaP LAst NCGa NEgg NLar SPet SPoG SRot WFar
arenarius — CWoW GKev NEgg NJOw SPlb SSvw WPer
'Argus' — IGor WKin
* 'Arlene' (b) — SAll
armeria — WHer WOut WPer
arpadianus — NHol
'Arthur' (p) — EMFP WKin
'Arthur Leslie' (b) — SAll
§ x *arvernensis* (p) ♀H4 — ECha ECho EPot
- 'Albus' — ECho
'Audrey's Frilly' — WKin WOFF
'Autumn Tints' (b) — SAll
'Auvergne' — see *D.* x *arvernensis*
'Avenarius' (p) — SAll
'Avon Dasset' — LBuc
'Baby Treasure' (p) — ECho NHol SRot
'Badenia' (p) — CLyd LRHS
'Bailey's Celebration' (b) — CBgR EBee ENot SBai SRGP
§ 'Bailey's Daily Mail' (p) ♀H4 — CBcs EBee SBai
'Bailey's Festival' (p) — SBai
barbatus — GWCH

- 'Bodestolz' — LSou
- Nigrescens Group (p,a) ♀H4 — CBre CHad CHrt CMea CSpe GKev LPhx
I - 'Sooty' (p,a) — CAby EBee EChP ELan GBri ITer LSou NDlv NGdn WCFE
- 'Tuxedo Black' **new** — EBee
- 'Woodfall' **new** — GCal
'Barleyfield Rose' (p) — CLyd SIng
'Bath's Pink' — LRHS
§ 'Bat's Double Red' (p) — EMFP IGor SAll SSvw WKin WOFF
'Beauty of Cambridge' (b) — SAll
'Beauty of Healey' (p) — EMFP WKin
'Becky Robinson' (p) ♀H4 — SAll SHay
'Bella' — CPBP
'Belle of Bedfordshire' (b) — SAll
'Belle of Bookham' (b) — SAll
'Berlin Snow' — CLyd CPBP ECho EPot GKev ITim WLin
'Bet Gilroy' (b) — SHay
'Betty Miller' (b) — SAll
'Betty Morton' (p) ♀H4 — CEnt ECtt IFoB MSph MWea SBla SSvw WFar WKif WKin WThu
'Betty Tucker' (b) — SHay
'Binsey Red' (p) — EMFP SSvw WKin
Black and White Minstrels Group — CElw CLyd WKin
Blakeney seedling (p) — WKin
* 'Blue Carpet' — WPer
'Blue Hills' (p) — CLyd ECho GCrs GKev MWea SIng
'Blue Ice' (b) — SAll SHay
'Blush' — see *D.* 'Souvenir de la Malmaison'
'Bobby' (p) — SAll
'Bobby Ames' (b) — SHay
'Bob's Highlight' (pf) — CNMi
'Bookham Fancy' (b) — SAll SHay
'Bookham Grand' (b) — SHay
'Bookham Heroine' (b) — SAll
'Bookham Lad' (b) — SAll
'Bookham Perfume' (b) — SHay
'Bookham Sprite' (b) — SAll
'Border Special' (b) — SAll
'Bourboule' — see *D.* 'La Bourboule'
'Bovey Belle' (p) ♀H4 — CBcs LRHS SBai SHay
'Boydii' (p) — CLyd
'Bransgore' (p) — CLyd
'Bressingham Pink' (p) — ECho ECtt
'Brian Tumbler' (b) ♀H4 — SAll
'Bridal Veil' (p) — EMFP GAbr SAll SBch SSvw WKin
'Brigadier' (p) — ECho
'Brilliance' (p) — ECho MBow
'Brilliant' — see *D. deltoides* 'Brilliant'
'Brilliant Star' (p) ♀H4 — CPBP ECho EMFP LBee SPet WWFP
'Brimstone' (b) — SHay
'Brympton Red' (p) — ECha EMFP MRav SBch SBla SSvw WEas WKin
'Bryony Lisa' (b) ♀H4 — SAll
§ 'Caesar's Mantle' (p) — WKin
caesius — see *D. gratianopolitanus*
'Callander' (b) — SAll
callizonus — EPot GEdr NMen
'Calypso Star' (p) ♀H4 — CPBP ECho ECtt EWin GBuc GMaP NCGa NEgg NLar SPet SPoG STes
'Camelford' (p) — WKin
'Camilla' (b) — CLyd EGoo EMFP SSvw WKin
'Can-can' (pf) — ECho ECtt
'Candy Clove' (b) — SAll
Candy Floss = 'Devon Flavia' (p) **new** — EMFP
'Carlotta' (p) — SHay
'Carmen' (b) — SHay
'Carmine Letitia Wyatt' PBR (p) ♀H4 — EMFP SPoG
'Caroline Bone' (b) — SHay
'Caroline Clove' (b) — SHay

carthusianorum		CArn CBrm CHad CKno EDsa EPot EWTr IGor LDai LPhx MNFA MSte NDlv NDov SAga SGar SMeo SSvw STes SWat WEas WPer XPep
caryophyllus		CArn GBar GWCH WHer WWye
'Casser's Pink' (p)		GBuc
'Catherine Glover' (b)		SAll
* 'Catherine Tucker'		WEas
'Cecil Wyatt' (p)		EAEE EBee EMFP EPfP NEgg NLar SRGP WMnd
§ 'Cedric's Oldest' (p)		WKin
'Charcoal'		WCot
'Charles' (p)		SAll
'Charles Edward' (p)		SAll
'Charles Musgrave'		see *D.* 'Musgrave's Pink'
'Charm' (b)		SHay
'Chastity' (p)		SBla WHoo WKin
Cheddar pink		see *D. gratianopolitanus*
'Cheerio' (pf) ♀H2		SHay
'Cherry Clove' (b)		SAll
'Cherry Moon'		LRHS
'Cherry Pie' (p)		EAEE EBee EPfP NEgg NFla WMnd
'Cherryripe' (p)		SHay
'Cheryl'		see *D.* 'Houndspool Cheryl'
'Chetwyn Doris' (p) ♀H4		SBai
'Chianti' (pf)		NGdn
'China Doll' (p)		SBai
chinensis (p,a)		WHer
'Chomley Farran' (b) **new**		ITer
'Chris Crew' (p) ♀H4		SAll
'Christine Hough' (b)		SAll
'Christopher' (p)		LRHS SAll SHay
'Clara' (pf)		CNMi
'Clara's Lass' (pf)		CNMi
'Clare' (p)		SAll SHay
'Claret Joy' (p) ♀H4		CBcs CFir EMFP EPfP LAst NPri SAll
'Clarinda' (b)		SAll
'Clifford Pink'		WKin
'Clunie' (b)		SAll SHay
§ 'Cockenzie Pink' (p)		EMFP GAbr IGor SAll SSvw WEas WKin
'Constance' (p)		SAll
'Constance Finnis'		see *D.* 'Fair Folly'
'Consul' (p)		SAll
'Conwy Silver'		NHar WAbe
'Conwy Star'		CPBP WAbe
'Copperhead' (b)		SHay
'Corona Cherry Magic' **new**		LRHS
'Coronation Ruby' (p) ♀H4		CBcs SAll SBai SHay
corsicus		XPep
'Coste Budde' (p)		CLyd IGor WEas WKin WSHC
'Cotton Chace' (b)		SHay
'Cranborne Seedling' (p)		WKin
'Cranmere Pool' (p) ♀H4		CBcs CCge CEnt CMea ECtt ELan EPfP LAst LRHS NPri SBai SHay SPoG WFar WMnd
cretaceus		NWCA
'Crimson Ace' (p)		SHay
'Crimson Chance' (p)		NSla
'Crimson Joy' (p) ♀H4		SPoG
'Crimson Tempo' PBR (pf)		SHay
'Crimson Velvet' (b)		SHay
crinitus		NJOw SHFr
'Crompton Classic' (pf)		CNMi
cruentus		LPhx MSte NDov SSvw STes WPer
'Dad's Choice' (p)		SBai
'Dad's Favourite' (p)		CCge CEnt IGor SAll SHay SRms SSvw WEas WHer WKin
'Daily Mail' (p)		see *D.* 'Bailey's Daily Mail'
'Dainty Dame' (p) ♀H4		CPBP CSpe CTri EAEE EBee ECho GBuc GMaP LRHS MNHC MSte MWea NHol NJOw SBla SPoG SRot WFar
'Damask Superb' (p)		IGor WKin
'Daphne' (p)		SAll
'Dark Star' (p)		ECho
'Dark Tempo' (pf)		SHay
'Dartington Double' (p)		ECho
'Dartington Laced'		WKin
'David' (p)		SAll SHay
'David Russell' (b) ♀H4		SAll
'Dawlish Charm' (p)		SBai
'Dawlish Joy' (p)		EMFP SRGP
'Dawn' (b)		SAll SHay
'Dawn' (pf) **new**		ECho
'Delphi' (pf)		SHay
deltoides ♀H4		CArn CElw CEnt CSev ECha ECho ELau EPfP GBar GWCH MBow NSco SHGN SPlb SRms WJek WSel
- 'Albus'		ECha EPfP GBar IHMH MNHC NBlu NEgg NPri SSvw SWat WMoo WPer WRos WSel
- 'Arctic Fire'		CWib ECho MBow NGdn WMoo
- 'Bright Eyes'		CCge ECho
§ - 'Brilliant'		CTri ECho MDun MFOX MNHC NPri NVic SAll SRms SWat WGor
- 'Broughty Blaze'		NRya
- 'Canta Libra' **new**		SWal
- 'Dark Eyes'		EWes
- 'Erectus'		EPfP
- Flashing Light		see *D. deltoides* 'Leuchtfunk'
§ - 'Leuchtfunk'		CHrt EAEE ECho ECtt EPfP GGar LAst LRHS NEgg NMir NNor SPoG SWal WFar WHen WPer WRos
- 'Microchip'		NJOw SPet WFar
- 'Nelli' (p)		ECho SSvw WMoo
- red		NBlu
'Denis' (p)		ELan SAll
'Desert Song' (b)		SAll
'Devon Blush' (p)		EBee
'Devon Charm' (p)		LRHS
'Devon Cream' PBR (p)		CSBt EBee EMFP LRHS NEgg WMnd
'Devon Dove' PBR (p) ♀H4		CMea EAEE EBee EMFP EPfP LAst NEgg NPri WMnd
'Devon General' PBR (p)		CTri EBee ECtt EMFP SPoG
'Devon Glow' PBR (p) ♀H4		EAEE EBee EMFP EPfP LRHS MBNS NEgg NFla SPoG
'Devon Joy' (p)		LRHS
'Devon Magic' PBR (p)		SPoG WFar
'Devon Maid' (p) ♀H4		EBee EPfP
'Devon Pearl' PBR (p)		EBee EMFP LHop WMnd
'Devon Velvet' PBR		EBee NLar
'Devon Wizard' PBR (p) ♀H4		CBgR CHar EMFP ENot LRHS NPri SPoG WCAu WFar
'Dewdrop' (p)		CMea CTri EAEE EBee ECho ECtt EPot EWin LRHS MHer NBir NGdn NPro SAll WAbe WFar WKin WPer
'Diana'		see *D.* Dona = 'Brecas'
'Diane' (p) ♀H4		EAEE ELan EMFP EPfP MBNS NEgg SAll SHay SPla WMnd
'Diplomat' (b)		SAll
'Doctor Archie Cameron' (b)		SHay
§ Dona = 'Brecas' (pf)		LRHS SRGP
'Donnet's Variety'		WEas
'Dora'		LRHS
'Doris' (p) ♀H4		CBcs CHar CMea CTri EAEE EGoo ELan EMFP ENot EPfP ERou LAst LHop LRHS MRav NEgg SAll SBai SHay SPer SPla SPlb SPoG SRGP SRms SSvw WCAu WHlf WMnd WTel
'Doris Allwood' (pf)		CNMi CSBt EMal SAll
'Doris Elite' (p)		SAll
'Doris Galbally' (b)		SAll
'Doris Majestic' (p)		SAll
'Doris Ruby'		see *D.* 'Houndspool Ruby'
'Doris Supreme' (p)		SAll SHay

'Double North' **new**	NWCA
§ 'Dubarry' (p)	CTri CWan ECho ECtt WGor WPer WRHF
'Duchess of Westminster' (M)	EMal SAll
'Duke of Norfolk' (pf)	EMal
'Dusky' (p)	WKin
'E.J. Baldry' (b)	SHay
'Earl of Essex' (p)	EMFP SAll SHay SSvw WKin
'Ebor II' (b)	SAll
'Edenside Scarlet' (b)	SHay
'Edenside White' (b)	SAll
'Edna' (p)	SAll
'Edward Allwood' (pf)	SAll
'Eileen' (p)	SAll
'Eileen Lever' (p)	CPBP EPot SBla WAbe WFar
'Eleanor's Old Irish'	WCot WHoo WTin
'Elfin Star' (p)	ECho MSte SPet
'Elizabeth' (p)	CEnt WEas
'Elizabeth Patrick' (b)	SAll
'Elizabethan' (p)	CAby CFee CStu GAbr GMac SBla WKin
* 'Elizabethan Pink' (p)	CCge SAll
'Emile Paré' (p)	WKin
'Emjay' (b)	SAll
'Emma James' (b)	SAll
'Emperor'	see D. 'Bat's Double Red'
'Empire'	SHay
'Enid Anderson' (p)	WKin
'Enid Burgoyne'	WKin
erinaceus	ECho EHol GKev LRHS NJOw NWCA SIng SRot WAbe
– var. *alpinus*	EPot
'Erycina' (b)	SAll
'Ethel Hurford'	WHoo WKin
'Eudoxia' (b)	SAll
'Eva Humphries' (b)	SAll SHay
'Evening Star' (p) ♀H4	CPBP ECho EMFP EWin LBee MWgw SPet SPoG
'Excelsior' (p)	NFor SSvw
'Exquisite' (b)	SAll
§ 'Fair Folly' (p)	SAll SSvw WEas WKin
'Falcon' (pf)	SHay
'Fanal' (p)	NBir WKin
'Farida'PBR (pf)	SHay
'Farnham Rose' (p)	SSvw
'Fenbow Nutmeg Clove' (b)	CWan WKin WMnd
ferrugineus	MSte
'Fettes Mount' (p)	EWin GAbr GMac SSvw WCot WKin WSPU
'Feuerhexe' (p)	LRHS NPro
'Fiery Cross' (b)	SAll SHay
'Fimbriatus' (p)	WHoo WKin
'Fingo Clove' (b)	SAll
'Fiona' (p)	SAll
'Fireglow' (b)	SAll
'Firestar' (p)	LBee
'First Lady' (b)	ECho SAll
'Flame' (p)	SHay
'Flanders' (b) ♀H4	SAll
'Fleur' (p)	SAll
'Forest Glow' (b)	SAll
'Forest Sprite' (b)	SAll
'Forest Treasure' (b)	SAll
'Forest Violet' (b)	SAll
'Fortuna' (p)	SAll
'Fountain's Abbey' (p)	IGor WKin
'Fragrans' (pf)	NJOw
'Fragrant Ann' (pf) ♀H1	CNMi SHay
* *fragrantissimus*	LRHS
'Frances Isabel' (b)	SAll
'Frances Sellars' (b)	SHay
'Frank's Frilly' (p)	WKin
'Freckles' (p)	SHay
'Freda' (p)	SAll

freynii	CLyd ECho EPot EWes NDlv NLAp SBla WAbe
N fringed pink	see D. *superbus*
'Fusilier' (p)	CElw CEnt CMea CTri EAEE ECho ECtt EDAr EMFP EPfP LAst LHop LRHS MBar MSte MWgw NCGa NEgg NPri NWCA SAll SHay SRot STes WAbe WBVN WFar WKin
'G.W. Hayward' (b)	SHay
'Gail Graham' (b)	SAll
'Garland' (p)	CTri LRHS WGor
'Gaydena' (b)	SAll
'George Allwood' (pf)	SAll
giganteus	CSpe MSte MWea NJOw WKin WSHC
'Gingham Gown' (p)	NBir SBla SPoG
'Gipsy Clove' (b)	SHay
glacialis	ITim MWea SSvw
– subsp. *gelidus*	EHyt
'Gloriosa' (p)	WKin
'Gold Flake' (p)	SHay
'Gold Fleck'	EPot LBee SIng
'Golden Sceptre' (b) ♀H4	SAll
'Grandma Calvert' (p)	SAll
graniticus	EPot
'Gran's Favourite' (p) ♀H4	CBcs CCge CEnt CMea CSBt CTri EBee ECtt EMFP ENot EPfP LAst LRHS NPri SAll SBai SBla SHay SPlb SPoG SRGP SRms WEas WFar WHlf WKin
§ *gratianopolitanus* ♀H4	CArn CTri EPfP EPot GKev LRHS MBow MFOX MHer MNHC MNrw MRav NBid NJOw NWCA SPet SRms WGwG WKin WWye
– 'Albus'	EPot
§ – 'Compactus Eydangeri' (p) **new**	GBin
– 'Flore Pleno' (d)	EMFP SSvw
§ – 'Tiny Rubies' (p)	ECho WKin
'Gravetye Gem' (b)	SRms
'Gravetye Gem' (p)	SHGN WKin
'Green Lanes' (p)	CHll
'Grenadier' (p)	ECho ELan
'Grey Dove' (b) ♀H4	SAll
'Gwendolen Read' (p)	SHay
'Gypsy Star' (p)	EBee ECho EWin GMaP NCGa NEgg SPet SPoG
haematocalyx	NMen NWCA SSvw WAbe WFar WPer WThu
– 'Alpinus'	see D. *haematocalyx* subsp. *pindicola*
§ – subsp. *pindicola*	CGra EHyt ITim LTwo NLAp NMen
'Hannah Louise' (b) ♀H4	SAll
'Hare Hope Clove' (b)	SAll
'Harkell Special' (b)	SAll
'Harlequin' (p)	ECtt EMFP WPer
'Harmony' (b)	SAll SHay
'Harry Oaks' (p)	WKin
'Haytor'	see D. 'Haytor White'
'Haytor Rock' (p) ♀H4	EBee EPfP SHay SPoG
§ 'Haytor White' (p) ♀H4	CWib EBee EPfP LAst LRHS SAll SBai SHay SRms WCFE WCot WEas
'Hazel Ruth' (b) ♀H4	SAll
'Heath' (b)	WKin
'Heidi' (b)	EPfP SHGN
'Helen' (p)	SAll SHay
'Helena Hitchcock' (p)	SAll
'Helix' (pf) **new**	SHay
'Herbert's Pink' (p)	WKin
'Hereford Butter Market'	EBee WKin
'Hidcote' (p)	CLyd CTri EAEE EBee ELan LRHS MWat NMen SBla SHay WFar WKin
'Hidcote Red'	ECho LBee LRHS
'Highland Fraser' (p)	SRms WEas WKif
'Highland Queen' (p)	WKin
'Hoo House' (p)	WKin

'Hope' (p) — EMFP SSvw WKin
'Horsa' (b) — SAll SHay
'Hot Spice'^{PBR} (p) ♀^{H4} — EMFP WHlf
§ 'Houndspool Cheryl' (p) — CBcs CTri EBee EMFP ENot EPfP
  ♀^{H4} — LRHS MBow SAll SRGP SRms WFar
§ 'Houndspool Ruby' (p) — EBee EMFP EPfP SAll SBai WCAu
  ♀^{H4} — WEas
'Ian' (p) — MLHP SAll SBai SHay
'Ibis' (b) — SHay
'Iceberg' (p) — ECho
'Icomb' (p) — CLyd SRms WHoo WKin WPer
'Imperial Clove' (b) — SHay
'Ina' (p) — SRms
'Incas' (pf) ♀^{H1} — SHay
'Inchmery' (p) — EMFP NFor SAll SHGN SHay SSvw
  — WEas WHoo WKin WTin
'India Star'^{PBR} (p) ♀^{H4} — CCge CTri ECho LAst NEgg SPet
  — STes
'Indios' (pf) ♀^{H1} — SHay
'Inglestone' (p) — CTri NHol SBla WLin WPer
'Inshriach Dazzler' (p) — CMea CPBP ECho ECtt EPot EWin
  ♀^{H4} — GAbr GGar GMaP LBee MHer
  — MWea NDlv NHar NHol NRya SBla
  — SIng SPoG SRot WAbe WKin WLin
'Inshriach Startler' (p) — CLyd CMea
'Ipswich Pink' (p) — LRHS MNHC SRms
'Irene Della-Torré' (b) ♀^{H4} — SAll
'Irene Hobbah' (b) — SAll
I 'Ivonne' (pf) — SHay
'Ivonne Orange' (pf) — SHay
'Jack Hodges' (b) — SAll
'Jacqueline Ann' (pf) ♀^{H1} — CNMi
'James Michael Hayward' — SHay
  (b)
'James Portman' (p) — CBgR WMnd
'Jane Austen' (p) — WKin WPer
'Jane Barker' (b) — SAll
'Jane Coffey' (b) — SAll SHay
'Jane Hammond' (b) — SHay
'Janelle Welch' (pf) — CNMi
'Janet Walker' (p) — GMaP
japonicus — CSpe
- f. *albiflorus* — CSec
'Jenny Wyatt' (p) — SHay
'Jess Hewins' (pf) — CNMi SAll
* 'Jewel' **new** — ECho
'Joan Schofield' (p) — CLyd EAEE ECho SPoG
'Joan Siminson' (p) — WKin
'Joanne's Highlight' (pf) — CNMi
'Joan's Blood' — see *D. alpinus* 'Joan's Blood'
'Joe Vernon' (pf) — CNMi
'John Ball' (p) — EMFP SHGN SSvw WKin
'John Grey' (p) — WKin
'Jolene' (b) — SAll
'Joseph Griffiths' (b) — SAll
'Joy' (p) ♀^{H4} — ECho ECtt EMFP EPfP LAst LRHS
  — SAll SHay SPoG
'Julian' (p) — SAll
'Julie Ann Davis' (b) — SAll
'Kathleen Hitchcock' (b) — SAll
  ♀^{H4}
'Kesteven Chamonix' (p) — WPer
'Kesteven Kirkstead' (p) — CSWP MNrw
  ♀^{H4}
'King of the Blacks' (p,a) — CSpe ELan
kitaibelii — see *D. petraeus* subsp. *petraeus*
'Kiwi Far North' **new** — SHGN
knappii — CMea CWoW ELan EPfP LDai
  — LHop NDov NLar NVic SEND
  — SMeo SRms SSvw WMoo WPer
  — XPep
- 'Yellow Harmony' (p,a) — LRHS MBNS MBow SGar
§ 'La Bourboule' (p) ♀^{H4} — CMea CTri EChP ECho EDAr EPot
  — GAbr LBee LRHS MBar MWat NHol
  — NMen NPri SBla SRms WKin WLin
  — WPat

'La Bourboule Albus' (p) — CTri ECho EDAr EPot GCrs ITim
  — NHol SBla WFar WGor
'Laced Hero' (p) — IGor NWCA WKin
'Laced Joy' (p) — SAll SHay
'Laced Monarch' (p) — CBcs CEnt EBee ECtt LRHS NLar
  — SAll SBai SPlb SPoG WKin
'Laced Mrs Sinkins' (p) — MLHP SAll SPer
'Laced Prudence' — see *D.* 'Prudence'
'Laced Romeo' (p) — EMFP SAll SHay WKin
'Laced Treasure' (p) — SAll
'Lady Granville' (p) — CAby IGor SAll SHGN SSvw WKin
'Lady Madonna' (p) **new** — CBgR
'Lady Salisbury' (p) — WKin
§ 'Lady Wharncliffe' (p) — EMFP IGor SBch WKin
'Lancing Monarch' (b) — SHay
langeanus NS 255 — NWCA
'Laura' (p) — SAll SHay
'Lavastrom' — SBla
'Lavender Clove' (b) — SAll
'Lawley's Red' (p) — WKin
'Leiden' (b) — SAll
'Lemsii' (p) ♀^{H4} — ECho ECtt EMFP NMen NVic WPer
'Leslie Rennison' (b) — SAll SHay
'Letitia Wyatt' (p) ♀^{H4} — CMea EBee EMFP ENot SPoG
  — SRGP
'Leuchtkugel' — ECho LTwo NMen
leucophaeus var. — EPot
  leucophaeus
'Liberty' (pf) — SHay
'Lily Lesurf' (b) — SAll
'Lily the Pink' **new** — CBgR
'Linfield Annie's Fancy' — CNMi
  (pf)
'Linfield Dorothy Perry' — SAll
  (p) ♀^{H4}
'Linfield Isobel Croft' (p) — SAll
'Lionheart' (p) — LRHS
'Lipstick' (pf) — SHay
'Little Ben' (p) — SAll
'Little Gem' (pf) — WKin
'Little Jock' (p) — CCge CPBP EAEE ECho EDAr ELan
  — EPot GGar GMaP LBee LRHS MBar
  — MHer MNHC MRav NHol NJOw
  — SAll SBla SHay SIng SPlb SPoG
  — SRms WEas WKin WLin
'Little Miss Muffet' (p) — CHll
'Liz Rigby' (b) — SAll
'London Brocade' (p) — SSvw WKin
'London Delight' (p) — EMFP SHay WKin
'London Glow' (p) — SAll WKin
'London Lovely' (p) — SAll SHGN SSvw WKin
'London Poppet' (p) — NDlv SAll SSvw WKin
'Loveliness' (p) — CBre
lumnitzeri — ECho EHyt GCal LTwo WPer XPep
'Lustre' (b) — SAll SHay
'Mab' — WKin
'Madame Dubarry' — see *D.* 'Dubarry'
'Madonna' (pf) — SHay WKin
'Maisie Neal' (b) ♀^{H4} — SAll
'Malaga' (pf) ♀^{H1} — SHay
'Mambo' (pf) ♀^{H4} — SHay
'Mandy' (p) — SAll
'Manningtree Pink' — see *D.* 'Cedric's Oldest'
'Margaret Stewart' (b) — SAll
'Marion Robinson' (b) ♀^{H4} — SAll
'Marjery Breeze' **new** — SAll
'Marmion' (M) — EMal SAll
'Mars' (p) — ECho ECtt ELan NDlv WAbe
'Marshmallow' (p) — CCge EAEE EBee EMFP MBNS
  — NEgg NFla NLar
'Marshwood Melody' (p) — SBai
'Marshwood Mystery' (p) — WKin
'Mary Simister' (b) — SAll
* 'Mary's Gilliflower' — EMFP WKin
'Matador' (b) — SHay
'Matthew' — WHoo

'Maudie Hinds' (b) SAll
'Maybole' (b) SAll
'Maythorne' (p) SRms
'Mendip Hills' (b) SAll SHay
'Mendlesham Belle' (p) EMFP
  ♀H4
'Mendlesham Frilly' (p) EMFP
'Mendlesham Maid' (p) EMFP
  ♀H4
Mendlesham Minx = EBee ECho EDAr EMFP ENor GBuc
  'Russmin'PBR (p) LBee SAll SPet
'Mendlesham Miss' (p) EMFP
'Mendlesham Saint EMFP
  Helen's' (p)
'Mendlesham Spice' (p) EMFP
'Mendlesham Sweetheart' EMFP ENor
  (p)
'Merlin' CPen
'Merlin Clove' (b) SHay
'Messines Pink' (p) SAll SSvw
'Michael Saunders' (b) SAll
  ♀H4
microlepis CGra ECho EHyt GCrs ITim NGdn
  NWCA SBla WAbe WLin
- f. *albus* CGra EHyt WAbe
* - var. *degenii* NWCA
- 'Leuchtkugel' ECho EHyt WAbe
- var. *musalae* CLyd ECho EHyt LTwo NMen
  WAbe
'Mike Briggs' (b) SAll
'Miss Sinkins' (p) SPet SPla
'Monica Wyatt' (p) ♀H4 EAEE EMFP EPfP LRHS NEgg SBai
  SHay SPoG SRGP
monspessulanus NDlv SSvw WMoo WPer
- subsp. *sternbergii* SBla
'Montrose Pink' see *D.* 'Cockenzie Pink'
'Moortown Plume' WKin
Morning Star = EMFP LBee MWgw
  'Devon Winnie'
'Moulin Rouge' (p) ♀H4 CEnt EBee EMFP ERou MBow
  SHGN SPoG
'Mrs Clark' see *D.* 'Nellie Clark'
'Mrs Gumbly' (p) WKin
'Mrs Holt' (p) EMFP
'Mrs Macbride' (p) SAll WKin
'Mrs N. Clark' see *D.* 'Nellie Clark'
'Mrs Perkins' (b) SAll
'Mrs Roxburgh' WKin
'Mrs Sinkins' (p) More than 30 suppliers
'Murray Douglas' (p) SSvw
'Murray's Laced Pink' (p) WKin WSPU
N 'Musgrave's Pink' (p) ECha MRav SAga SAll SBch SBla
  SHay SSvw WEas WKin
'Musgrave's White' see *D.* 'Musgrave's Pink'
myrtinervius CLyd ECho EHyt GBin GEdr ITim
  NLar NWCA SHGN SRms WPer
- subsp. *caespitosus* EHyt GKev NHar
- - MESE 433 WAbe
'Nan Bailey' (p) SBai
'Nancy Lindsay' (p) SSvw
'Napoleon III' (p) WKif
nardiformis SSvw WPer
'Natalie Saunders' (b) ♀H4 SAll
'Nautilus' (b) SAll SHay
neglectus see *D. pavonius*
§ 'Nellie Clark' (p) CLyd ECho
'Nelson'PBR SHay
'Neon Star'PBR (p) ♀H4 ECho EDAr EMFP GKev SPoG
'New Tempo' (pf) SHay
'Night Star' (p) ♀H4 EChP ECho EMFP EWin GKev LIck
  LSou MNrw NCGa NEgg SPet SRot
  WBVN
nitidus CLyd NBir SSvw WPer
nivalis NWCA
noeanus see *D. petraeus* subsp. *noeanus*
'Nonsuch' (p) WKin

'Northland' (pf) CNMi EMal SAll SHay
'Nyewoods Cream' (p) CMea CTri CWan ECho EMFP EPot
  GAbr LBee LRHS MBar MHer
  MRav NHol NMen NPri SIng WPat
  WPer WTin
§ 'Oakington' (p) CTri LRHS MRav NPri NWCA
  WKin WTel
'Oakington Rose' see *D.* 'Oakington'
'Oakwood Gillian SBai
  Garforth' (p) ♀H4
'Old Blush' see *D.* 'Souvenir de la Malmaison'
'Old Dutch Pink' (p) IGor SSvw WKin
'Old French Red' (pf) new EMal
'Old Fringed Pink' (p) WKin
'Old Fringed White' (p) EMFP
'Old Irish' (p) IGor WKin
'Old Mother Hubbard' (p) CFee CHll
'Old Red Clove' (p) WCot WEas
§ 'Old Square Eyes' (p) MNrw SAll SBla SHay SSvw WEas
  WFar WKin
'Old Velvet' (p) GCal SAll WKin WOFF
'Oliver' (p) SAll
'Orange Maid' (b) SAll
'Oscar' (b) SAll
'Osprey' (b) SHay
'Paddington' (p) SSvw WKin
'Painted Beauty' (p) EMFP NBir
'Painted Lady' (p) CLyd IGor SAll WKin
'Paisley Gem' (p) SSvw WKin WOFF
'Patricia' (b) SHay
'Paul Hayward' (p) SHay
§ *pavonius* ♀H4 CLyd EHyt EWes GKev NGdn NLar
  NWCA WPer
- *roysii* see *D.* 'Roysii'
'Pax' (pf) SHay
'Perfect Clove' (b) SHay
'Peter Wood' (b) ♀H4 SAll
§ *petraeus* EWes
§ - subsp. *noeanus* CLyd LTwo WHal WPer
- - *albus* GCrs
§ - subsp. *petraeus* SSvw WPer
'Petticoat Lace' (p) SAll SHay
'Phantom' (b) SHay
'Pheasant's Eye' (p) EMFP SAll SSvw WHer WKin
'Philip Archer' (b) SHay
* 'Picton's Propeller' (p) GBuc
'Pike's Pink' (p) ♀H4 CCge CTri EAEE EBee ECho EDAr
  ELan EPfP GGar LBee LHop LRHS
  MHer MRav MWgw NHol NMen
  SAll SBla SHay SPet SPoG SRms
  SSvw WAbe WBVN WEas WKin
  WLin WTel
pindicola see *D. haematocalyx* subsp.
  pindicola
pinifolius ITim
'Pink Bizarre' (b) SHay
'Pink Devon Pearl'PBR CBgR
* 'Pink Dona' (pf) SHay
'Pink Fantasy' (b) SAll
'Pink Jewel' (p) CLyd CMea ECho EPot LBee LRHS
  MHer MHNC NHol NMen SAll
  SIng WEas
'Pink Mrs Sinkins' (p) ECha MHer MLHP SAll WKin
'Pink Pearl' (p) SAll SPoG
'Pixie' (b) EPot NHol
'Pixie Star'PBR (p) ♀H4 ECho EPfP SPoG SRot
plumarius NJOw SAll SRms SSvw WGor
  WHer WMoo WPer
- 'Albiflorus' WPer
pontederae NDlv WPer
'Portsdown Fancy' (b) SHay
'Prado' (pf) ♀H4 SHay
'Pretty' LRHS
'Pretty Lady' (p) ECho
'Prince Charming' (p) ECho ELan EPot NEgg NHol NPri
  SIng SRms WPer

'Princess of Wales' (M)	EMal SAll
'Priory Pink' (p)	SAll
'Provence' (pf) **new**	SHay
§ 'Prudence' (p)	SAll WKin
'Pudsey Prize' (p)	CLyd CPBP EHyt EPot WLin
'Pummelchen' (p)	ITim
'Purple Jenny' (p)	SAll
pygmaeus	NBro
* - 'Pink Frills'	NEgg
* *pyrenaicus* 'Cap Béar'	XPep
'Queen of Hearts' (p)	CTri ECho LRHS NWCA SHGN WPer WRHF
§ 'Queen of Henri' (p)	EAEE ECho ECtt GEdr GMaP LBee LRHS MHer SBla SHar WBVN WFar WKin
'Queen of Sheba' (p)	SSvw WKif WKin
'Rachel' (p)	ECtt WPat
'Rainbow Loveliness' (p,a)	CSec SAll SRms
'Ralph Gould' (p)	ECho
'Raspberry Sundae' (p) **new**	CBgR
'Rebecca' (b)	SAll
'Red and White' (p)	WKin
'Red Dwarf' ♀H4	MMHG MSte SPet SPoG SRot
'Red Velvet'	CLyd LRHS
'Reine de Henri'	see *D.* 'Queen of Henri'
'Renoir' (b)	SHay
'Revell's Lady Wharncliffe'	see *D.* 'Lady Wharncliffe'
'Riccardo' (b) ♀H4	SAll
'Richard Gibbs' (p)	MOne
'Richard Pollak' (b)	SAll
'Rivendell' (p)	CLyd ECho NMen WAbe
'Robert Allwood' (pf)	SAll
'Robert Baden-Powell' (b)	SHay
* 'Robin Ritchie'	WHoo WKin
'Robin Thain' (b)	SHay
'Robina's Daughter'	GAbr
'Roodkapje' (p)	SSvw WKin
'Rose de Mai' (p)	CLyd CSam CSev EMFP SAll SBch SSvw WHoo WKin
'Rose Joy' (p) ♀H4	EBee EMFP EPfP SHay
'Rosealie' (p)	SHay
'Roundabout' **new**	SWal
'Royalty' (p)	SHay
§ 'Roysii' (p)	NDlv WPer
'Rubin' (pf)	WEas
'Ruby'	see *D.* 'Houndspool Ruby'
'Ruby Doris'	see *D.* 'Houndspool Ruby'
'Rudheath Pixie' (b)	SAll
'Rudheath Ruby' (b)	SAll
rupicola	CSpe
- subsp. *bocchoriana* **new**	EDsa
'Saint Edith' (p)	WKin
'Saint Nicholas' (p)	EMFP SSvw WKin
'Saint Winifred'	WKin
Salamanca = 'Kosalamana' (pf)	SBai SHay
'Sally Anne Hayward' (b)	SHay
'Sam Barlow' (p)	EGoo SAll SHay SSvw WKin WOFF WWye
sanguineus	NDov SMHy
'Santa Claus' (b)	SAll SHay
Scarlet Beauty = 'Hilbeau' **new**	NBlu
'Scarlet Fragrance' (b)	SHay
'Sean Hitchcock' (b)	SAll
seguieri	EShb SSvw WPer
serotinus	EPot EShb GKev SSvw WCot
Shiplake seedling (p)	WKin
'Shot Silk' (pf)	SAll
'Show Aristocrat' (p)	SAll
'Show Beauty' (p)	SAll
'Show Glory' (p)	SAll
'Show Harlequin' (p)	SAll
'Show Portrait' (p)	NFor
'Show Satin' (p)	SAll
'Shrimp' (b) **new**	CWib
simulans	CLyd EHyt
'Sir Cedric Morris'	see *D.* 'Cedric's Oldest'
'Sir David Scott' (p)	WKin
* 'Six Hills'	NHol WPat
'Snowflake' (p) **new**	ECho
'Snowshill Manor' (b)	WPer
'Solomon' (p)	SSvw WKin
'Solomon's Hat' (p)	WKin
Sonya = 'Avnya' **new**	SHay
'Sops-in-wine' (p)	EChP ECha EMFP GBuc GCal SAll SBch SHay WKin
'Southmead' (p)	ECho
§ 'Souvenir de la Malmaison' (M)	EMal SAll
'Spangle' (b)	SAll
'Spencer Bickham' (p)	MNrw WKin
spiculifolius	EPot NWCA
'Spinfield Volcano' (b)	SAll
'Spirit' (pf)	SHay
'Spring Beauty' (p)	NBir WHer
'Spring Star' (p)	ECtt EWin NLar NPri SRot
'Square Eyes'	see *D.* 'Old Square Eyes'
squarrosus	ECho EPot NWCA
* - *alpinus*	ECho
- 'Nanus'	ECho EHyt ELan EWes LBee LRHS
'Stan Stroud' (p)	SHay
'Starry Eyes'	CMea EMFP GKev NCGa SRot STes WFar
'Storm' (pf)	EMal SAll
'Strathspey' (b)	SAll SHay
'Strawberries and Cream' (p)	CHar CSBt EAEE EBee ECtt EMFP LAst LHop LRHS MBNS NEgg NOrc SHay SPla SPoG WRHF
'Strawberry Kiss'	LRHS WWeb
* *strictus* subsp. *pulchellus*	CPBP EHyt GCrs NSla
§ *subacaulis*	GAbr NGdn NLar
- subsp. *brachyanthus* **new**	NMen
- - 'Murray Lyon'	NHar WThu
suendermannii	see *D. petraeus*
'Summerfield Adam' (p)	SAll
'Summerfield Amy Francesa' (p)	SAll
'Summerfield Blaze' (p)	SAll
'Summerfield Debbie' (p)	SAll
'Summerfield Emma Louise' (p)	SAll
'Summerfield Rebecca' (p)	SAll
(Sunflor Series) 'Sunflor Althea' **new**	NBlu
- 'Sunflor Campari' **new**	NBlu WCot
- 'Sunflor Original' **new**	NBlu
- 'Sunflor Pink Campari' **new**	NBlu
- 'Sunflor Surprise'PBR **new**	NBlu
'Sunray' (b)	SAll SHay
'Sunstar' (b)	SAll
§ *superbus*	CWoW EGoo EShb LPhx MNFA MSal NDov WGwG WHer WKin WMoo WPer
- 'Crimsonia'	CAby CSpe WHrl WPer WPtf
- var. *longicalycinus*	MNrw MSte WHer
I - 'Primadonna'	WBor WPer WPtf
* - 'Rose'	WPer
- 'Snowdonia'	WPer
- subsp. *speciosus*	CSec
'Susan' (p)	SAll
'Susannah' (p)	SAll
* 'Susan's Seedling' (p)	SAll
'Swanlake' (p)	SAll SHay
'Sway Belle' (p)	SBai
'Sway Delight' (p)	SBai

'Sway Sorbet' (p) — SBai
'Sweet Sophie' (pf) — CNMi
'Sweet Sue' (b) — SAll SHay
'Sweetheart Abbey' (p) — EMFP GBuc IGor SSvw WKin
sylvestris — EPot SSvw
'Syston Beauty' (p) — WKin
'Taff Glow' (b) — SAll
'Tamsin' (p) ♀H4 — SBla WKin
'Tamsin Fifield' (b) ♀H4 — SAll
'Tatra Blush' — GCal GMac
'Tatra Fragrance' — CMdw GCal
'Tatra Ghost' — GCal
'Tayside Red' (M) — EMal SAll
'Tempo' (pf) ♀H1 — SHay
'Terranova' — SHay
'Terry Sutcliffe' (p) — WKin
the Bloodie pink — see *D.* 'Caesar's Mantle'
'The Saboteur' (b) — SAll
'Thomas' (p) — SBch
'Thomas Lee' (b) — SAll
'Thora' (M) — EMal SAll
I 'Tickled Pink' — CBgR COtt EMFP LAst WWeb
'Tiny Rubies' — see *D. gratianopolitanus* 'Tiny Rubies'
'Toledo' (p) — WKin
'Tony's Choice' (pf) — CNMi
'Treasure' (p) — ECho SHay
'Trevor' (p) — SAll
'Tundra'PBR (pf) — SHay
turkestanicus — NBir
'Tweedale Seedling' — GBuc
Tyrolean trailing carnations — SAll
'Uncle Teddy' (b) ♀H4 — SAll
'Unique' (p) — EMFP MNrw SAll SSvw WHoo WKin WOFF
'Ursula Le Grove' (p) — IGor SSvw WKin WOFF
'Valda Wyatt' (p) ♀H4 — CBcs EAEE EBee ELan EMFP EPfP LAst LRHS NEgg SAll SBai SHay SPla SPoG SRGP WMnd
'Vectria' (pf) **new** — SHay
versicolor — EHyt
'Violet Clove' (b) — SHay
'W.A. Musgrave' — see *D.* 'Musgrave's Pink'
'W.H. Brooks' (b) — SAll
'Waithman Beauty' (p) — CTri ECtt MBar SAll SBla WHoo WKin WPer WTin WWye
'Waithman's Jubilee' (p) — GMaP SAll SRms
'Warden Hybrid' (p) — CMea CPBP CTri EAEE ECho ECtt EPfP EWin GAbr GKev GMaP LAst LRHS SHGN SHay SPoG WAbe WFar WLin
'Wedding Bells' (pf) — SAll
'Weetwood Double' (p) — CFee WSPU
'Welcome' (b) — SHay
weyrichii — CLyd ECho NMen
'Whatfield Anona' (p) — SAll
'Whatfield Beauty' — EChP ECho ECtt ELan LRHS SAll
'Whatfield Brilliant' (p) — ECho
'Whatfield Can-can' ♀H4 — CMea CPBP EAEE ECho ECtt EMFP EWin GKev GMaP LRHS MNHC NCGa NEgg NJOw NPri SAll SPoG WAbe
'Whatfield Cream Lace' — NWCA
'Whatfield Cyclops' — CLyd ECho LRHS SAll WKin
'Whatfield Dawn' — CLyd ECho
'Whatfield Dorothy Mann' (p) — ECho SAll
'Whatfield Fuchsia' (p) — CLyd SAll
'Whatfield Gem' (p) — CLyd CPBP ECho ECtt ELan EMFP EWin GCal LAst LRHS MNHC MSte MWgw NJOw NPri SAll WBVN WFar WKin WPer
'Whatfield Joy' (p) — CLyd EAEE ECho ECtt ELan EPfP EPot EWin LBee LRHS MHer NMen NPri SAll WFar WPat

'Whatfield Magenta' (p) ♀H4 — CLyd EAEE ECho ELan EPfP EPot LBee LRHS NJOw NWCA SAll SPoG WAbe WEas
'Whatfield Mini' (p) — SAll SRms WPer
'Whatfield Miss' (p) — SAll
'Whatfield Misty Morn' (p) — ECho SAll
'Whatfield Peach' (p) — SAll
'Whatfield Pretty Lady' (p) — ECho SAll
'Whatfield Rose' (p) — ECho EPot
'Whatfield Ruby' (p) — CEnt ECho ELan LAst LRHS NWCA SAll WFar WPer
'Whatfield Supergem' — CLyd ECho ECtt EPot
'Whatfield White' (p) — ECho ECtt LRHS SAll SRms
'Whatfield White Moon' (p) — ECho
'Whatfield Wisp' (p) — CMMP CPBP CTri ECho EWin GEdr MRav NBir NMen NWCA
'White and Crimson' (p) — SAll
'White Joy'PBR (p) ♀H4 — EMFP SPoG
'White Ladies' (p) — ELan EWTr SAll WKin
'White Liberty'PBR (pf) — SHay
'Whitecliff' (b) — SAll SHay
'Whitehill' (p) ♀H4 — ECho MHer NHol NMen NWCA WPat
'Whitesmith' (b) ♀H4 — SAll
'Whitford Belle' (p) — SBai
'Widecombe Fair' (p) ♀H4 — CCge CMea CTri EBee ECtt ELan LRHS MLHP NLar SAll SPoG SRms
* 'Wild Velvet' (p) — WKin
'William Brownhill' (p) — EMFP SSvw WKin
'Winnie Lesurf' (b) — SAll
'Winsome' (p) — SHay
'Yorkshireman' (b) — SHay
'Zebra' (b) — SAll SHay
zederbaueri — NWCA SIng
zonatus **new** — NWCA

Diapensia (Diapensiaceae)
lapponica var. *obovata* — GIBF

Diarrhena (Poaceae)
americana — EPPr
japonica — EPPr EShb LRav SWal WDyG
* *mandschurica* — EPPr
obovata — EPPr

Diascia ❀ (Scrophulariaceae)
anastrepta — ECho
– HWEL 0219 — NWCA
'Appleby Appleblossom' — CElw LSou
'Appleby Apricot' — NDov
'Apricot' — see *D. barberae* 'Hopleys Apricot'
Apricot Delight = 'Codicot' — NPri WFar
  (Sun Chimes Series)
'Baby Bums' — SPoG
barberae — ELan
– 'Belmore Beauty' (v) — CCge ECtt EMan EWes EWin LSou MHer NFla
– 'Blackthorn Apricot' ♀H3-4 — EAEE ECho ECha ECtt EDAr ELan EPfP EShb GBuc IHMH LAst LRHS MBow MHer MSte MWgw NRya SBla SMrm SPav SPer SPlb SPoG SWvt WFar WPer WSHC
– 'Crûg Variegated' (v) — EMan
§ – 'Fisher's Flora' ♀H3-4 — ECho EPyc NDov WFar
§ – 'Hopleys Apricot' — EPfP
§ – 'Ruby Field' ♀H3-4 — CMea ECha ECho ECtt EDAr ELan EPfP LAst LHop LRHS MDun MHer MWgw NBlu NGdn NRya SBla SPer SPla SPoG SRms SWvt WCFE WFar
barberae 'Fisher's Flora' x 'Lilac Belle' — ECho ECtt SHFr
Blue Bonnet = 'Hecbon' — EChP ECtt EMan LSou SWvt WFar
'Blush' — see *D. integerrima* 'Blush'
Blush Delight = 'Codiush' — WFar
  (Sun Chimes Series)

'Coldham'	CMdw ECtt EMan LHop
Coral Belle = 'Hecbel' PBR ♀H3-4	CHar EAEE ECho ECtt EHyt EMan EPfP EWes EWin LAst LHop LRHS LSou MDun MSte NEgg SIng SPav WFar WPer
cordata misapplied	see *D. barberae* 'Fisher's Flora'
cordifolia	see *D. barberae* 'Fisher's Flora'
'Dark Eyes' ♀H3-4	MSte
Eclat = 'Heclat' PBR	ECtt WFar
elegans misapplied	see *D. fetcaniensis*, *D. vigilis*
'Elizabeth' ♀H3-4	WSPU
'Emma'	SWvt
felthamii	see *D. fetcaniensis*
§ *fetcaniensis*	CMHG CPne EPfP EShb EWin LHop NEgg WBVN WBrk WCFE WHal WSPU
- 'Daydream'	LRHS WSPU WWeb
flanaganii misapplied	see *D. vigilis*
flanaganii Hiern	see *D. stachyoides*
'Frilly' ♀H3-4	ECtt MSte
'Hector Harrison'	see *D.* 'Salmon Supreme'
'Hector's Hardy' ♀H3-4	MSte
Ice Cracker = 'Hecrack'	CMea EAEE EChP ECtt EHyt ELan EMan EShb EWin LAst LHop MBow NFla SHGN SPav
Ice Cream = 'Icepol'	CHar CSpe LAst LSou SCoo SMrm SVil
Iceberg = 'Hecice' PBR	CHar CSpe NLar NPri SWvt
§ *integerrima* ♀H3-4	CPne CSam ECha ELan EMan LLWP SGar SPla WCot
- 'Alba'	see *D. integerrima* 'Blush'
§ - 'Blush'	CSam CSpe EGoo EMan MSte NEgg SGar SHGN SMrm
- 'Ivory Angel'	see *D. integerrima* 'Blush'
integrifolia	see *D. integerrima*
'Jack Elliott'	see *D. vigilis* 'Jack Elliott'
'Jacqueline's Joy'	CMea EMan MSte NFla NGdn NPer SBch WBrk WFar
'Joyce's Choice' ♀H3-4	EAEE EWes EWin MSte SBri WFar WHoo
'Kate'	LRHS NDov
'Katherine Sharman' (v)	ECtt EMan EWes EWin LRHS LSou NGdn
'Lady Valerie' ♀H3-4	EWes EWin MSte WPer
'Lilac Belle' ♀H3-4	CCge CMea CPne EAEE ECtt EHyt ELan EPfP LAst LHop LRHS MHar MHer MWgw NEgg NGdn SMrm SPla SPlb SPoG WFar WHoo WPer
'Lilac Mist' ♀H3-4	NPer
lilacina x *rigescens*	CCge
Little Dancer = 'Pendan' PBR	LAst LSou NLar NPri SCoo SGar SIng SMrm WGor
Little Dreamer = 'Pender' **new**	SVil
'Louise'	GBuc
Lucy' x *mollis*	SDys
'Miro'	MBow NLar
patens	CHll
personata	LHop
Pink Delight = 'Codiink'	WFar
Pink Panther = 'Penther' PBR	ECtt NEgg NLar SCoo SPav SPoG SWvt
'Pink Queen'	ECtt SRms
'Pink Spires'	CElw
Prince of Orange = 'Hopor' PBR	EShb GAbr LAst LHop LSou SIng SMrm
'Raspberry Sundae' **new**	EMFP
Red Ace = 'Hecrace' PBR	EChP EPfP EWin LAst NEgg NPer SMrm SPav SPoG SWvt
'Red Delight' **new**	EShb
Redstart = 'Hecstart'	ECtt EPfP EWin LAst LHop NGdn SPet SWvt WFar
rigescens ♀H3	More than 30 suppliers
§ - 'Anne Rennie'	EBee EMan SPoG
- pale	see *D. rigescens* 'Anne Rennie'
'Ruby Field'	see *D. barberae* 'Ruby Field'
'Rupert Lambert' ♀H3-4	EMon GBuc LLWP NDov SBri WLin WPer
§ 'Salmon Supreme'	ECtt ELan EPfP EWin LPhx MWgw NGdn NPer SPoG SRms WFar WMoo WPer
'Selina's Choice'	GBuc
§ *stachyoides*	ELan LHop SBch
Sun Chimes Blush = 'Codiblim' **new**	NPri
Sun Chimes Peach = 'Codipeim'	LAst
Susan = 'Winsue' PBR	WFar
Sydney Olympics = 'Hecsyd'	EMan
tugelensis	WFar
'Twinkle' ♀H3-4	CPBP EAEE ECtt EHyt EPfP EWes GCal LAst NBir NGdn NPer NPri SPet WFar
* 'Twins Gully'	GCal SMrm
§ *vigilis* ♀H3	CFee CMHG CPLG CSam EAEE EChP ECha EDAr EPfP EWin LAst MWgw NBro NEgg SDix SGar
§ - 'Jack Elliott'	EWin MDun SPla WCFE
- - ex JE 8955	LHop
(Whisper Series) Whisper Apricot Improved = 'Balwhisaptim' **new**	SCoo
- Whisper Cranberry Red = 'Balwhiscran' **new**	NPri
- Whisper Cranberry **new**	SCoo
- Whisper Lavender Pink = 'Balwhislapi' **new**	NPri
'White Cloud'	WSPU
(Wink Series) Wink Lavender Pink = 'Balwinlapi' **new**	NBlu
- Wink Strawberry Improved = 'Balwinimstr' **new**	NPri

Dicentra ✿ (*Papaveraceae*)

CC 4450	CPLG
'Adrian Bloom'	CWCL EBee EChP ECho ECtt EHrv EPfP EPla GSki LRHS MBNS MWgw NBid NCob NPri NSti SCoo SWvt WBrE WCra WFar WMnd WMoo WPnP
'Angel Heart'	MBNS NGdn
'Bacchanal' ♀H4	More than 30 suppliers
'Boothman's Variety'	see *D.* 'Stuart Boothman'
'Bountiful'	CMHG EBee GMaP GSki LRHS MLLN MNFA MRav MWgw NGdn NSti SPer SPla SWvt WMnd WRHF
'Brownie'	GBuc
canadensis	CLAP EPot GBuc GSki MAvo MTho NSti WCot WCru
'Candy Hearts'	EBee ELan ENot LBmB NBro NGdn NLar NSti WHlf
'Coldham'	WCru WSHC WTin
cucullaria	CBos CElw CLAP CRow CStu EAEE EBee ECho EHyt EPot ERos ETow GBuc GCrs GEdr GSki LPhx MRav MTho NDov NJOw NMen NSti NWCA SBla WAbe WCot WCru WLin
- 'Pittsburg'	CBos EBee EPPr SCnR WCot
* 'Dark Stuart Boothman'	ECho
'Dragon Heart'	MBNS NGdn
eximia misapplied	see *D. formosa*
eximia (Ker Gawl.) Torr.	CSpe EBee NEgg SWat
- 'Alba'	see *D. eximia* 'Snowdrift'
§ - 'Snowdrift'	CLAP CMMP EBee EChP ECho ECtt EHrv ELan ENot EPfP IHMH MBri MDun MTho NGdn NRnb

	SPoG SRms WFar WHoo WMnd
	WMoo WPnP WPrP
§ **formosa**	More than 30 suppliers
§ - **alba**	CPLG CTri ECha ECho GAbr GMaP
	MLHP MWrn NBir NFor NVic SPla
	SRms STes WCAu WCru WFar WLin
* - 'Aurora'	CBre CWCL EBee EChP ECho
	EWTr GBin GSki LAst LRHS MCCP
	MRav MWgw NBPC NCGa NGdn
	NHol NRnb SPer SPet SPoG SWvt
	WFar WMnd WSan
- 'Cox's Dark Red'	CLAP EWes GBuc GCrs NMen
- dark	WMoo
- 'Furse's Form'	GBin
- subsp. *oregana*	CLAP EBee EPPr GAbr GBuc GCal
	GCrs GGar NBre NChi NMen
	WAbb WCru
- - NNS 00-233	WCot
- - 'Rosea'	EPPr
- 'Spring Gold'	ECha WMoo
'Ivory Hearts'	CLAP EBee ELan ENot GBri LBmB
	NBro NCGa NLar NSti WHlf
'King of Hearts'	More than 30 suppliers
'Langtrees' ♀H4	More than 30 suppliers
lichiangensis	CPlN WCru
- GWJ 9376	WCru
'Luxuriant' ♀H4	More than 30 suppliers
macrantha	CAby CDes CLAP CRow EBee
	ECha EPfP GBuc MTho SBla SMad
	WCru WPGP WSHC
macrocapnos	CBcs CFir CPlN CRow CSec EBee
	EChP EMil EPfP GBuc GQui IDee
	MDKP MTho MWgw NSti SBla
	WBGC WCru
'Paramount'	GBin
'Pearl Drops'	CElw CRow EChP EHrv ELan
	GBuc GGar GMaP LRHS MRav
	NBid NEgg NGdn NOak SPla SRms
	WAbb WEas WHoo WMoo WTin
	WWhi
peregrina	GIBF SOkd WAbe
§ **scandens**	CMHG CRHN CRow CSpe CStu
	ECho EPfP GCal IFro LAst MCCP
	MTho MWgw NCob NLar SHGN
	SMac SPoG SUsu WSHC WSPU
	WWhi
- B&SWJ 2427	WCru
- CC 3223	WRos
- 'Shirley Clemo'	CPLG
'Silver Beads' **new**	ECho
Snowflakes = 'Fusd'	ECho EWes LRHS MCCP MRav
	NBre NDov
spectabilis ♀H4	More than 30 suppliers
- 'Alba' ♀H4	More than 30 suppliers
- 'Gold Heart'PBR	CBow CHad EBee EMan ENot EPfP
	GBri MRav NLar NSti SPer SPoG
	WFar
'Spring Morning'	CElw CMHG CMil CPLG CSam
	EHrv EPPr EPfP NBre NSti WEas
	WRHF
§ 'Stuart Boothman' ♀H4	More than 30 suppliers
thalictrifolia	see *D. scandens*
torulosa B&SWJ 7814	WCru

Dichelostemma (Alliaceae)

§ **capitatum**	EDif ETow
- NNS 95-213	WCot
congestum	CAvo CFFs EBee ECho EMan EPot
	ERos LRHS WCot
§ **ida-maia**	CAvo CBro CFFs EBee ECho ENot
	EPot GAbr GCrs LPhx LRHS NJOw
- 'Pink Diamond'	CBro EBee ECho EPot GCrs
multiflorum	WCot
pulchellum	see *D. capitatum*
volubile	WCot
- NNS 95-220	WCot

Dichocarpum (Ranunculaceae)

| **dalzielii** | WCot |

Dichondra (Convolvulaceae)

argentea 'Silver Falls'	COtt CSpe EShb LSou NPri SCoo
	SPoG WPtf
§ **micrantha**	EShb
repens misapplied	see *D. micrantha*
repens J.R. Forst. &	XPep
G. Forst.	

Dichopogon (Anthericaceae)

| **strictus** | CMon |

Dichorisandra (Commelinaceae)

| * **pendula** **new** | MJnS |
| **thyrsiflora** **new** | MJnS MOak |

Dichroa (Hydrangeaceae)

febrifuga	CAbb CBcs CDoC CHEx CHll
	CKob CMil CPLG CWib EWes
	SBrw SOWG WCMO WCot WCru
	WOVN WPGP
- B&SWJ 2367	WCru
- pink	CHEx
hirsuta from Thailand	CKob
aff. **hirsuta** B&SWJ 8207	WCru
versicolor	CKob
- B&SWJ 6565	WCru
aff. **versicolor** **new**	WPGP

Dichromena see *Rhynchospora*

Dicksonia ❀ (Dicksoniaceae)

antarctica ♀H3	More than 30 suppliers
fibrosa ♀H3	CAbb CBcs CTrC EAmu IDee SChr
	WMul
sellowiana	LPal
squarrosa ♀H2	CAbb CBcs CCCN CTrC LPan
	NBlu NMoo SAPC SArc SPoG
	WMul

Dicliptera (Acanthaceae)

§ **suberecta**	CBcs CDes CHal CHll CMdw EBee
	EHol EMan ERea EShb LHop LSou
	MOak MWea SHFr SOWG SRkn
	WCot WDyG WPGP XPep

Dicranostigma (Papaveraceae)

lactucoides	CPom WLin
- CC 3756	WRos
leptopodum **new**	CSpe

Dictamnus ❀ (Rutaceae)

albus	More than 30 suppliers
§ - var. **purpureus** ♀H4	More than 30 suppliers
* - **turkestanicus**	GCal
caucasicus	CFis EBee EBrs SMHy
fraxinella	see *D. albus* var. *purpureus*
gymnostylis **new**	EBee
tadshikorum **new**	EBee

Dictyosperma (Arecaceae)

| **album** | LPal |

Didymochlaena (Dryopteridaceae)

| **lunulata** | see *D. truncatula* |
| § **truncatula** | CHal MBri |

Dieffenbachia (Araceae)

| 'Camille' (v) ♀H1 | LRHS |
| 'Compacta' (v) | LRHS |

Dierama ❀ (Iridaceae)

| **ambiguum** | CPne CStu SHFr |

argyreum	CElw CFwr EBee EDAr GKev IBlr SAga WCMO WWpP
'Ariel'	IBlr
'Ballerina'	CFir
'Black Knight'	CPen IBlr
'Blush'	IBlr
'Candy Stripe'	CRow GBri GSki MCCP STes
'Castlewellan'	WCra
'Cherry Chimes'	CPen ENot IBal LBuc MGos
cooperi	CElw CFwr CPne CPrp GBri IBlr SPoG WCMO WCot WWpP
'Coral Bells'	CDes GCal
'Donard Legacy'	GBri IBlr
§ *dracomontanum*	More than 30 suppliers
- dwarf pale pink	CMMP WWeb
- Wisley Princess Group	LRHS MBri
dracomontanum x *pulcherrimum*	SMad
dubium	IBlr
ensifolium	see *D. pendulum*
erectum	CLAP EDAr IBlr WLin
'Fairy Bells'	CPen EAEE EBee IPot MBNS NCob NHol
floriferum	CBro EBee IBlr
formosum new	WPGP
galpinii	CLAP CPLG EKen GSki MWrn NLar STes WCMO WCot WLin WPGP
grandiflorum	ECho IBlr WCru
'Guinevere'	More than 30 suppliers
igneum	More than 30 suppliers
- CD&R 278	CPou
'Iris'	IBlr
jucundum	CPne EBee EPot GBri GBuc MLLN WWpP
'Knee-high Lavender'	CDes CSpe SAga
'Lancelot'	More than 30 suppliers
latifolium	CFwr EBee EChP GAbr GSki IBlr SMad WWpP
luteoalbidum	CDes CLAP CStu EBee WPGP
'Mandarin'	CDes IBlr
medium	CMil CPen EBee GSki LRHS SMrm SUsu SWat WPGP WWpP
'Milkmaid'	CPrp IBlr
mossii	CFwr EBee EDAr IBlr MWrn NBre NLar SHom SPlb WLin WPGP
nixonianum	IBlr
'Oberon'	EBee
'Pamina'	CPrp IBlr
'Papagena'	IBlr
'Papageno'	IBlr
pauciflorum	More than 30 suppliers
- CD&R 197	CPBP MDKP
§ *pendulum*	CAvo CBen CBro CFee CPLG CPne EBee ELan ENot EPfP ERou GGar GKev IBlr LAst LRHS LSRN MCCP MNrw MRav NCGa NEgg NHol NLAp SPer SWat SWvt WFar WPnP WWpP
- var. *pumilum*	EShb
pictum	IBlr
Plant World hybrids	MWrn
'Pretty Flamingo'	CPrp IBlr
'Puck'	CDes CPen EBee GCal IBlr IGor ITer MLLN WPGP
pulcherrimum	More than 30 suppliers
- var. *album*	CBro CHar CHea CLAP CMMP CPen CWCL EBee ECha ECho EDAr ELan GBuc GKev GSki IPot ITer MNrw NCGa NCob SPoG STes SUsu WHrl WLin WPGP WRHF WWhi WWpP
- 'Angel Gabriel'	WWpP
- 'Blackbird'	CLAP CMMP CMac CPLG CSam EBee ECho EDAr ELan EPfP EPla GAbr GKev IBlr ITim MCCP MHer
	NCGa NLar SGar SPoG STes SUsu WBVN WCMO WCot WLin WMnd WPGP WWpP
- dwarf	GCal GSki IPot WWhi
- 'Falcon'	IBlr
- 'Flamingo'	IBlr
- 'Flaring Tips' new	IPot
- 'Merlin'	More than 30 suppliers
- 'Miranda'	CPen ERou NCob SDnm WCot WTMC
- 'Pearly Queen'	CRow
- 'Peregrine'	WPGP
- 'Red Orr'	ITim
- 'Redwing'	IBlr
- Slieve Donard hybrids	CLAP CSam EAEE EBee EChP ECho ECtt EMan GBri GCal ITim LHop LRHS MFOX MHer MTis MWrn SPet SPoG WCMO WCot WCra WHrl WMnd WPnP WWpP
pumilum misapplied	see *D. dracomontanum*
'Queen of the Night'	IBlr
reynoldsii	CAbb CBro CFwr CPne EBee EMan GBuc GSki IBlr MCCP MLLN MWrn SGar SMad SPlb STes WCMO WHoo WLin WPGP
'Rich Pink'	CPen
robustum	CLAP CPou GBri GSki IBlr SHom WBVN WPGP
'Sarastro'	CPrp IBlr
'September Charm'	IBlr
sertum	CBro
'Snowgoose'	WCra
'Tamino'	IBlr
'Tiny Bells'	CDes EDAr GCal
'Titania'	CPen IBlr
trichorhizum	CFwr CLAP CPBP CWCL EBee EDAr EKen GAbr GBri GKev GSki IBlr MNrw MWrn NLar STes WLin
'Tubular Bells'	IBlr
'Violet Ice'	IBlr
'Westminster Chimes'	CDes COIW EBee IBlr WPGP

Diervilla ✿ (*Caprifoliaceae*)

lonicera	CHar MTis SLon SMac WFar WHil
middendorffiana	see *Weigela middendorffiana*
rivularis 'Troja Black' new	MBri
§ *sessilifolia*	CBcs CHar CPle ECrN EPfP IDee IMGH LAst MRav SGar SLon WBVN WCot WFar WMoo
x *splendens*	CAbP CCge CMHG CPLG CWib EBee EHoe ELan EPfP LAst LHop LRHS MBNS MBar MRav MSwo NHol SBrw SGar SLPl SMac SPer SPla SPoG SSta WDin

Dietes (*Iridaceae*)

bicolor	CAbb CDes CHEx CMon CPen CPne CTrC EMan ERea EShb LBow LEdu LSou SDnm
* *compacta*	CPen
grandiflora	CAbb CArn CDes CFee CFwr CMdw CMon CPen CPne ECho EDif EMan ERea EShb LBow LEdu NEgg SBch WCot WThu
§ *iridioides*	CDes CNic CPne CSWP CSec EBee ECho EShb GBin LEdu MSte WPGP

Digitalis ✿ (*Scrophulariaceae*)

ambigua	see *D. grandiflora*
apricot hybrids	see *D. purpurea* 'Sutton's Apricot'
cariensis	EShb SPav
ciliata	CFir EChP ELan MHar MLLN SPav

davisiana	EChP GBuc LPhx MNHC MWea MWgw NOak NRnb SPav WCHb WHrl WMoo WPer
dubia	EPfP NBir NLar SBla SDnm SPav WAbe
'Elsie Kelsey'	CSam CSim EBee EShb GBin GKev MBri NRnb SDnm SPav WHil
eriostachya	see *D. lutea*
ferruginea ♀H4	More than 30 suppliers
- 'Gelber Herold'	EBee EChP ERou EWin GMaP LPhx LRHS MDKP MSte NBre NLar NRnb SPoG WGor
- 'Gigantea'	EBee EMan ERou EWTr GCal LRHS MBNS MWgw NEgg NPri NRnb NSti SWat WCMO WSel
- var. *schischkinii*	CPLG CSec EShb GCal NLar NRnb SDnm SPav
'Flashing Spires'	see *D. lutea* 'Flashing Spires'
* *floribunda*	CSec SPav
fontanesii	CEnt EChP EPPr GBuc NBur WOut
'Foxley Primrose'	MBri
x *fulva*	MLLN NBir
'Glory of Roundway'	CDes CPom EBee MEHN MFOX MHer SSvw WCMO WCot WFar
§ *grandiflora* ♀H4	More than 30 suppliers
- 'Carillon'	CHea CSam CWan EBee EChP EShb IFoB LDai LPhx MBNS MSte NBir NGHP NLar NPri WGor WGwG WPer WPtf
- 'Dwarf Carillon'	ECtt
- 'Temple Bells'	EBee EMag SWat WPer
heywoodii	see *D. purpurea* subsp. *heywoodii*
'John Innes Tetra'	CSam EBee EChP EShb LRHS SWat WPGP
kishinskyi	see *D. parviflora*
laevigata	CHar CHrt CSam CSec CWCL EBla EChP ERou EWTr LPhx MNFA MSte MTis NBro NCGa NGHP NRnb SDnm SPav WCHb WMoo WPer
- subsp. *graeca*	WGor
- white-flowered	LPhx NRnb
lamarckii misapplied	see *D. lanata*
lamarckii Ivanina	EBee
§ *lanata*	More than 30 suppliers
- 'Café Crème'	LSou
leucophaea	EMar
§ *lutea*	More than 30 suppliers
§ - subsp. *australis*	EBla LDai SDnm SHFr SPav
§ - 'Flashing Spires' (v)	CBow EKen EMan GBri LSou NBHF NEgg NRnb
- 'Yellow Medley'	WCot
x *mertonensis* ♀H4	More than 30 suppliers
- 'Summer King'	CBcs ECtt MBow NBre NGHP WGor WSel WTMC
micrantha	see *D. lutea* subsp. *australis*
nervosa	SPav
obscura	CEnt EBee EChP ECho EHrv ERou EShb EWTr LAst LRHS MWgw NBir NCob NGHP NPri SBla SDnm SIde SIng SPav WCHb WCMO WGor WGwG WHil WLin WMnd WPer
* - 'Dusky Maid'	NBHF
orientalis	see *D. grandiflora*
§ *parviflora*	More than 30 suppliers
- 'Milk Chocolate'	CBcs CRez ECtt EPfP MHer NBre NEgg NRnb SIde SPet SSvw WPnP WRHF WSel
purpurea	CArn CHrt EBee ECtt EDAr ELau EUnu GPoy MBow MHer MLHP MNHC NBlu NCGa NCob NFor NLRH NLan NMir NPri SECG SIde SPlb SPoG SWal WMoo WPer WWFP WWye
- f. *albiflora*	More than 30 suppliers
- - 'Anne Redetzky'	EBee EChP ECtt ENot GAbr IPot ITer LSou MAvo NBir NSti SPoG WMnd
- - unspotted	CWan EMar
- Camelot Series **new**	NGHP
- - 'Camelot Cream' **new**	NPri
- - 'Camelot Lavender' **new**	NPri
- - 'Camelot Rose' **new**	NPri
- dwarf red	MBNS
- Excelsior Group	CBcs CSBt CSam CTri EBee ENot EPfP ERou GMaP MBri MNHC MWat NMir NVic SMer SPer SPoG SRms SWvt WCMO WFar WGor WWeb
- - primrose	ERou SPer WRHF
- - (Suttons; Unwins) ♀H4	ECtt MRav
- - white	ERou
- Foxy Group	CBgR CWib ECtt EHrv MBNS MWat NJOw SPet SPoG SRms WFar WHen WWeb
- - 'Foxy Apricot'	CBcs SPla SWvt WOVN WPtf
- - 'Foxy Pink'	SPla
- - 'Foxy Primrose'	EChP
- Giant Spotted Group	COtt EBee ECtt EHrv EMag EPfP LHop LRHS SCoo
- Glittering Prizes Group	LRHS SWat
- Gloxinioides Group	EBee ELan ENot EPfP NCob SHFr
- - 'The Shirley' ♀H4	ECtt SGar WGor
§ - subsp. *heywoodii*	CBgR CDes CSec EBee EChP ELan ENot GBuc SBla SDnm SPav SPer WCHb WMoo
- - 'Pink Champagne'	ENot
- - 'Silver Fox'	CSec IPot MBri MHer SMar SPoG WCMO WGor
- 'Jellito's Apricot'	CSam
- 'Pam's Choice'	CPLG CSpe EBee EMag EMar EPyc EWin LAst LRHS MAvo MNFA MWea SPer SRGP SWal WBor WHrl WMnd WPnP WRHF
- peloric	WCHb WCMO
- 'Primrose Carousel'	CSim EBee ECtt EMag EWin LPhx MWat NEgg NLRH SMar
- 'Snow Thimble'	CWoW EBee EBrs EShb EWin GAbr LBMP MNFA NCGa NJOw NLar NVic WCMO WWeb
§ - 'Sutton's Apricot' ♀H4	More than 30 suppliers
* - 'Sutton's Giant Primrose'	CSim EMan EWll
- 'Tinkerbell'	EMag
purpurea x *thapsi* **new**	WGwG
sibirica	CSec EBee EChP GBuc LPhx MHar NEgg NRnb WCHb WPer WTMC
* *spaniflora*	EChP LPhx NEgg NLar NRnb WGwG WLin
'Spice Island' **new**	SPoG
* *stewartii*	CDMG CHar CSec CWan EChP ECtt ELan EShb EWTr EWes GAbr GBBs LDai MAvo MBNS MFOX MHar NBur NChi NRnb SBod SPav SPer WLin WMoo
thapsi	CArn CBow CEnt CSec CWan EChP ECtt GKev MBNS MLLN NBPC NBur NPri NWCA SBla SBod SDnm SIde SPav WCHb WMoo WPer WTMC WWFP
- JCA 410.000	EBee
- 'Spanish Peaks' **new**	CWCL
trojana	EBee ECtt GBuc LRHS SGar
- 'Helen of Troy' **new**	IPot
viridiflora	EBee ECtt EDAr EShb LPhx MBNS MDKP NBro SGar SPav SWat WCHb WFar WPer

- 'Moss Green'   NBHF

dill see *Anethum graveolens*

Dionaea (Droseraceae)
muscipula   CSWC LRHS MCCP WSSs
- 'Akai Ryu'   WSSs
- 'Royal Red'   CSWC
- shark-toothed   CSWC
- 'Spider'   CSWC

Dionysia (Primulaceae)
'Aimee' **new**   EHyt
'Annielle'   EHyt
archibaldii   EHyt
aretioides ♀H2   WAbe
- SLIZE 035   EHyt
- 'Bevere'   EHyt WAbe
- 'Gravetye'   ECho
- 'Paul Furse'   EHyt
- 'Phyllis Carter'   ECho EHyt
- 'Susan Tucker'   EHyt
aubretioides T4Z 133   EHyt
   new
bazoftica T4Z 135   EHyt
'Bernd Wetzel' **new**   EHyt
bryoides ENF 96-5   EHyt
- H 1986   EHyt
- SLIZE 236   EHyt
- T4Z 092   EHyt
- 'Esselmont' **new**   EHyt
- 'Kammerlander'   EHyt
   new
- 'Woodside'   EHyt
'Charlson Drew'   EHyt
'Charlson Emma'   EHyt
'Charlson Gem'   EHyt
'Charlson Jake'   EHyt
'Charlson Moonglow'   EHyt
'Charlson Petite'   EHyt
'Charlson Terri'   EHyt
'Chris Grey-Wilson'   EHyt
'Cinderella'   EHyt
curviflora SLIZE 213   EHyt
'Emmely'   EHyt
'Eric Watson'   EHyt
'Ewesley Iota'   EHyt
'Ewesley Kappa'   EHyt
'Ewesley Mu'   EHyt
'Ewesley Theta'   EHyt
'Francesca'   EHyt
gaubae   EHyt
- DZ 0038-1   EHyt
'Gotborg'   EHyt
'Ina'   EHyt
iranshahrii   EHyt
   SLIZE 213
janthina   EHyt
- SLIZE 265   EHyt
khatamii T4Z 013   EHyt
   new
lamingtonii   EHyt
'Liberty'   EHyt
'Luna'   EHyt
lurorum **new**   EHyt
'Lycaena'   EHyt
'Markus'   EHyt
michauxii   EHyt
'Monika'   EHyt WAbe
'Nan Watson'   EHyt
'Nocturne'   EHyt
odora   EHyt
oreodoxa **new**   EHyt
'Orion'   EHyt
revoluta subsp.   EHyt
   canescens **new**

'Rhapsodie'   EHyt
'Schneeball'   EHyt
tapetodes   EHyt WAbe
- ENF 92-5   EHyt
- 'Brimstone'   EHyt WAbe
- farinose   ECho
- 'Sulphur'   EHyt
termeana DZ 0046-4   EHyt
viscidula GWH 1305   EHyt
'Yellowstone'   EHyt
zagrica SLIZE 176   EHyt

Dioon (Zamiaceae)
califanoi   CBrP
caputoi   CBrP
edule ♀H1   CBrP CRoM LPal WMul
- var. *angustifolium*   CBrP
mejiae   CBrP LPal
merolae   CBrP
rzedowskii   CBrP LPal
spinulosum   CBrP EAmu LPal SBig WMul

Dioscorea (Dioscoreaceae)
CC 4701 **new**   MGol
araucana **new**   LSou
batatas   CPiN ELau LEdu MGol MSal
discolor   CPiN
elephantipes ♀H1   EShb
* *galpinii* **new**   CPLG
japonica   CSec EShb ITer WBVN
nipponica   MSal
quinqueloba   WCru
villosa   CArn ELau MSal

Diosma (Rutaceae)
ericoides   SWvt
- 'Pink Fountain'   LBuc SPoG
- 'Sunset Gold'   LBuc SCoo SPoG WPat
hirsuta 'Silver Flame'   LBuc SPoG

Diosphaera (Campanulaceae)
asperuloides   see *Trachelium asperuloides*

Diospyros (Ebenaceae)
austroafricana   SPlb
kaki (F)   CAgr CBcs CMCN CTho EPfP
                                    ERom LPan MPRe NLar WDin
lotus   CAgr CBcs CMCN CTho LEdu
                                    NLar SPlb WFar WPGP
- (f)   CAgr
- (m)   CAgr
lycioides   EShb SPlb
rhombifolia   WPGP
virginiana (F)   CAgr CBcs CMCN CTho EPfP LEdu
                                    NLar SSpi

Dipcadi (Hyacinthaceae)
serotinum   CPLG
- AB&S 4308 from   CMon
   Morocco
- subsp. *lividum*   WPGP
- - AB&S 4311 from   CMon
   Morocco

Dipelta (Caprifoliaceae)
floribunda ♀H4   CBcs CBrm CDul CMCN CPMA
                                    EBee ELan EMil EPfP LHop LRHS
                                    MBlu MBri NLar SBrw SLon SPer
                                    SSpi SSta WPGP
ventricosa   CAbP CBcs CMCN CPMA CPle
                                    EPfP LRHS MAsh MBlu NLar SSpi
                                    WFar WPGP
yunnanensis   CBcs CPLG CPMA CTri ELan
                                    EMil EPfP LBuc LRHS MAsh
                                    MWea NLar SBrw SSpi SSta WPGP
                                    WPat

Diphylleia (Berberidaceae)

cymosa	CLAP ECha EMan GEdr LPhx MSal WCot WCru WTin
grayi	CLAP GEdr WCru
sinensis	CLAP GEdr WCru

Dipidax see *Onixotis*

Diplacus see *Mimulus*

Dipladenia see *Mandevilla*

Diplarche (Diapensiaceae)

multiflora	GIBF

Diplarrhena (Iridaceae)

§ latifolia	CPLG EPot GBBs GGar IBlr WAbe
– Helen Dillon's form	IBlr SUsu
moraea	CAbP CDes CElw CMea CStu CWCL EBee EBrs ECho EGle EMan GCal GMac GSki IBlr IFoB ITim LRHS MDun NCGa NLAp SAga WBrE WCot WPGP WSHC
– minor	GBBs IBlr
– 'Slieve Donard'	IBlr
– West Coast form	see *D. latifolia*

Diplazium (Woodsiaceae)

wichurae	EPPr

Diplolaena (Rutaceae)

dampieri	SOWG

Diplotaxis (Brassicaceae)

muralis	CArn ELau WJek

Dipogon (Papilionaceae)

§ lignosus	CPIN

Dipsacus ❀ (Dipsacaceae)

§ fullonum	CArn CHrt CPrp CWan GBar IFro MBow MBri MHer MNHC NBid NDov NMir NPri NVic SBch SIde SWal WHer WHil WJek WSFF WWye
inermis	CPom EBee ECha EDsa EMon GBar IFro LPhx NBid NDov NLar WFar WHer
japonicus	EBee MSal
– HWJ 695	WCru
pilosus	CPom NDov
sativus	NLar
strigosus	LPhx MWgw NBre
sylvestris	see *D. fullonum*

Dipteracanthus see *Ruellia*

Dipteronia (Aceraceae)

sinensis	CBcs CMCN LRHS MBri NLar SBrw WNor WPGP

Disanthus (Hamamelidaceae)

cercidifolius ♀H4	CAbP CBcs CMCN EPfP IDee IMGH LRHS NEgg NLar SBrw SSpi
– 'Ena-nishiki' (v) **new**	NLar
– 'Liku' **new**	NLar

Discaria (Rhamnaceae)

chacaye	LEdu WPGP

Diselma (Cupressaceae)

archeri	CDoC CKen CNic GTSp MBar NLar SCoo
– 'Read Dwarf'	CKen

Disphyma (Aizoaceae)

crassifolium	SChr

Disporopsis (Convallariaceae)

aspersa	CDes CLAP WCru WPGP
– tall **new**	WCru
fuscopicta	CLAP EBee EHrv EPPr MAvo WCru WTin
longifolia	CLAP
– B&SWJ 5284	WCru
* luzoniensis	EBee
– B&SWJ 3891	WCru
'Min Shan'	CBct
§ pernyi	More than 30 suppliers
– B&SWJ 1490	WFar
– B&SWJ 1864	WCru
– 'Bill Baker'	MAvo
* punctata	SBla
taiwanensis **new**	WCru
B&SWJ 3388	
undulata **new**	WCru

Disporum (Convallariaceae)

bodinieri	CDes LEdu
cantoniense	CDes CFir CLAP CPom EBee GEdr LEdu WCru WFar WPGP WWst
– B&L 12512	CLAP
– B&SWJ 1424	WCru
– DJHC 98485	CDes
I – 'Aureovariegata'	WCMO WCot
– var. **cantoniense** f. brunneum B&SWJ 5290	WCru
– 'Green Giant'	CDes
– var. **kawakamii** B&SWJ 350	WCru
– 'Night Heron' **new**	WCot
flavens	CBct CDes CLAP CPom CStu EBee EBrs ECho EMan EPfP LEdu LPhx MDun NBid SBch SBla SMHy SUsu WFar WPGP WPnP WSHC WTin
– B&SWJ 872	WCru
* flavum	ECho LRHS SOkd
hookeri	CLAP CPom ECho EPot GGar NMen WCot WCru
– var. **oreganum**	EBee GCrs IBlr WCru
lanuginosum	EBee GCrs GEdr WCot WCru
leucanthum B&SWJ 2389	WCru
lutescens	WCru
maculatum	CBct CLAP SBla SMac WCru
megalanthum	CLAP EHrv WCot WCru
– CD&R 2412b	EPPr
nantouense	CStu LEdu WCot WPGP
– B&SWJ 359	CBct EBee WCru
sessile	CAvo ECho NLAp WCru
I – 'Aureovariegatum' (v)	ECho WCru
I – 'Robustum Variegatum' (v)	EBee MAvo WCMO
– 'Variegatum' (v)	CFwr CHEx CRow EBee ECha ECho ELan EPPr EPfP EPla EPot GEdr IFro LEdu LRHS MRav NBid SBla SMac WAul WCot WCru WFar WHil WPGP WPnP WWye
– 'White Lightning' (v)	WCot
shimadae B&SWJ 399	WCru
smilacinum	WCru WPnP
– B&SWJ 713	WCru
* – 'Aureovariegatum' (v)	WCot WCru
– 'Choyo'	WCru
– double-flowered (d)	GCrs GEdr WCru
– pink	WCru
smithii	CBct CPom CStu ECho EPfP EPot ERos GBuc GCrs GEdr GGar ITim LEdu NBir NMen WCot WCru WPGP
taiwanense B&SWJ 1513	WCru

trabeculatum 'Nakafu' WCru
uniflorum LEdu WCru
- B&SWJ 651 WCot WCru
viridescens LEdu WCMO WCru
- B&SWJ 4598 WCru

Distictis (Bignoniaceae)
buccinatoria CPIN

Distylium (Hamamelidaceae)
myricoides CMCN NLar WFar
racemosum CBcs EPfP LRHS MBlu NLar SBrw
SHBN SLon SMur SReu SSta WBVN
WFar WSHC

Diuranthera see *Chlorophytum*

Dizygotheca see *Schefflera*

Dobinea (Podoaceae)
vulgaris B&SWJ 2532 WCru

Dodecatheon (Primulaceae)
alpinum EBee GEdr GKev SRms
- JCA 11744 SBla
- subsp. *majus* NSla
amethystinum see *D. pulchellum*
'Aphrodite'[PBR] EBee EMan MBri NLar WAul
WTMC
austrofrigidum NHar
clevelandii EBee ETow
- subsp. *insulare* EAEE LRHS NWCA
- subsp. *patulum* EAEE EBee GBuc GKev LRHS
NLAp
conjugens CNic CPom
cusickii see *D. pulchellum* subsp. *cusickii*
dentatum ♀H4 CElw CPBP GBuc GEdr LRHS
MDKP MTho NSla NWCA WAbe
WFar
- subsp. *ellisiae* GCrs GKev
frigidum WAbe
§ *hendersonii* ♀H4 CBro CNic GBuc NMen SRms
integrifolium see *D. hendersonii*
§ *jeffreyi* CMHG EAEE EBee EPPr GSki LRHS
MBri NBid NCGa NDlv NLAp NLar
NMen NMyG SBla WAbe WBor
WFar
- 'Rotlicht' SRms WLin WPer
* x *lemoinei* WAbe
§ *meadia* ♀H4 More than 30 suppliers
- from Cedar County WAbe
- f. *album* ♀H4 CBcs CBro CFwr CSWP CStu
CTri EAEE EBee EChP ECho EGle
ELan EPfP EPot GEdr GSki LHop
LRHS MNFA MTho NMen NMyG
SBla SPoG SRms SWvt WPnP
WWhi
- 'Aphrodite' EChP
* - 'Goliath' GSki NLar WMoo
- membranaceous WAbe
- 'Purple Rose' NEgg
- 'Queen Victoria' ECho GSki MAvo NGby SMeo
SRGP WFar WPnP
pauciflorum misapplied see *D. pulchellum*
pauciflorum (Dur.) see *D. meadia*
E. Greene
poeticum ETow SBla
§ *pulchellum* ♀H4 CBro CNic CStu EAEE EBee GCrs
GEdr GKev GSki LHop LRHS
MNrw NLAp NMen SIng
- *album* EAEE GKev
§ - subsp. *cusickii* LRHS NWCA SRms
- subsp. *pulchellum* new EBee
- - 'Red Wings' CFwr CMea ECho EPot ERou GEdr
MDKP NMen NSla NWCA SMeo
WHoo WLin WPnP WSan

- 'Sooke's Variety' CStu WAbe
radicatum see *D. pulchellum*
redolens EBee GIBF GKev NHar
tetrandrum see *D. jeffreyi*

Dodonaea (Sapindaceae)
viscosa CTrC ECou SPlb XPep
- (f) ECou
- (m) ECou
- 'Picton' (f) ECou
- 'Purpurea' (m) ECou
- 'Purpurea' CAbb CBcs CBrm CDoC CPLG
CPne EBee ECou EDsa EMan
EShb ISea LRav LSou SBrw WGer
XPep
- 'Purpurea' (f) ECou
- 'Red Wings' (f) ECou

Doellingeria (Asteraceae)
scabra see *Aster scaber*

Dolichandra (Bignoniaceae)
cynanchoides new CPIN

Dolichos (Papilionaceae)
lignosus see *Dipogon lignosus*
purpureus see *Lablab purpureus*

Dombeya (Sterculiaceae)
burgessiae IDee SOWG

Dondia see *Hacquetia*

Doodia (Blechnaceae)
aspera GQui WPrP
§ *caudata* EFtx
media GQui LTwo MAvo
squarrosa see *D. caudata*

Doronicum (Asteraceae)
austriacum NBid NBre
carpetanum CSam
cataractarum NBre
caucasicum see *D. orientale*
§ *columnae* CBcs GKev
cordatum see *D. columnae*
§ x *excelsum* 'Harpur CPSs CPrp EBee ERou LEdu MLHP
Crewe' MNFA MRav NBre NPer NVic
WCAu WEas WHil
'Finesse' EBee EDAr EPfP EWin LRHS NBre
SPoG SRms WMoo
'Gold Dust' new SWal
'Little Leo' CMea COlW EBee ELan EMan
ENot GKev GMaP LHop LRav
MBow MHer MLHP NCGa NEgg
NLar NVic SPet SPoG SRGP STes
WBVN WBrE WWeb
'Miss Mason' ♀H4 LRHS
§ *orientale* CWan EBee EBrs EChP EPfP LRHS
NBid NBlu NEgg NFla NJOw SPer
SPoG SWat
- 'Goldcut' NBre NGdn
- 'Magnificum' CHrt CSBt CSam EBee EBrs EMar
EPfP GAbr GMaP LAst LRHS MHer
NMir NPri SECG SPoG SRms WFar
WMnd
pardalianches CHrt CMea ECha GCal IHMH NBre
NSco WRHF
plantagineum see *D.* x *excelsum* 'Harpur
Crewe'
'Excelsum'
'Riedels Goldkranz' WCot

Doryanthes (Doryanthaceae)
excelsa CHEx
palmeri CHEx

Dorycnium see *Lotus*

Doryopteris (Adiantaceae)
concolor var. **kirkii**   EFtx
pedata   MBri

Douglasia see *Androsace*
vitaliana   see *Vitaliana primuliflora*

Dovea (Restionaceae)
macrocarpa   CBig CCCN CPne

Dovyalis (Flacourtiaceae)
caffra (F)   CPle XBlo

Doxantha see *Macfadyena*

Draba (Brassicaceae)
* **abchatica new**   WLin
  acaulis   CSec
  aizoides   CSec EAEE ECho ELan LRHS
                                MWat NBlu NPri SIng SPlb SPoG
                                SRms
  aizoon   see *D. lasiocarpa*
  altaica   GIBF
  alticola   EPot
  aurea var. leiocarpa   CSec
  bruniifolia   EBur ECho EWes LRHS NWCA
  - subsp. heterocoma   WLin
    var. nana
  - subsp. olympica   NLar
  bryoides   see *D. rigida* var. *bryoides*
  compacta   see *D. lasiocarpa* Compacta
                                Group
  crassifolia new   ECho
  cretica   ECho NMen
  cuspidata   EPot
  dedeana   ECho EHyt EWes
  densifolia   WLin
  hyperburea   GIBF
  imbricata   see *D. rigida* var. *imbricata*
§ lasiocarpa   NJOw SGar
§ - Compacta Group   ECho NWCA
  longisiliqua ♀H2   EHyt SIng
  - EMR 2551   EPot
  mollissima   EPot NWCA
  oligosperma   NWCA
  - subsp. subsessilis   WLin
  paysonii var. treleasei   CSec WAbe
  polytricha   EHyt WAbe WLin
  rigida   NLar
§ - var. bryoides   ECho EHyt ITim NWCA WAbe
§ - var. imbricata   EHyt
  - - f. compacta   EPot
  rosularis   EHyt
  x salomonii   EPot
  scardica   see *D. lasiocarpa*
  shiroumana   CSec
  sphaeroides   EHyt
  ussuriensis   GIBF
  ventosa   WAbe
  yunnanensis   WLin

Dracaena ✿ (Dracaenaceae)
  congesta   see *Cordyline stricta*
  draco ♀H1   CArn CTrC EShb IDee
  fragrans   MBri
  - (Compacta Group)   MBri
    'Compacta Purpurea'
  - - 'Compacta Variegata'   MBri
    (v)
  - (Deremensis Group)   LRHS MBri
    'Lemon Lime' (v) ♀H1
  - - 'Warneckei' (v)   MBri
    ♀H1

  - - 'Yellow Stripe' (v)   MBri
    ♀H1
* - glauca   MBri
  - 'Janet Craig'   MBri
  - 'Massangeana' (v) ♀H1   MBri
  indivisa   see *Cordyline indivisa*
  'Lemon Lime Tips' **new**   XBlo
  marginata (v) ♀H1   LRHS MBri XBlo
  - 'Colorama' (v)   MBri
  - 'Tricolor' (v) ♀H1   XBlo
  sanderiana (v) ♀H1   LRHS MBri
* schrijveriana   MBri
  steudneri   MBri
  stricta   see *Cordyline stricta*

Dracocephalum (Lamiaceae)
  altaiense   see *D. imberbe*
  argunense   CAby CPBP GEdr GKev LPhx
                                LRHS NLAp SBch SBla SGar SRms
                                WCru WPat WPer
* - 'Album'   GKev NEgg
  - 'Blue Carpet'   CBgR
  - 'Fuji Blue'   CBrm EBee ITim NEgg NLar
  - 'Fuji White'   CBrm CPBP EBee EMan EPPr GEdr
                                LPhx NEgg SBla SHGN WPer
                                WSHC WWeb
  botryoides   CPBP CSec EMan NJOw NLar
                                NWCA SHGN WMoo WPer
  forrestii   EPot
  grandiflorum   CBod CEnt CHar CMHG
                                CMdw CPom EBee EChP
                                GKev LPhx LTwo MMHG
                                NEgg NLar SAga SBla SMad
                                WFar WMoo WWeb
  - 'Altai Blue' **new**   EBrs WHil
  hemsleyanum   EBee LTwo WPat
§ imberbe   MLLN WOut
  isabellae   EBrs NLar
  mairei   see *D. renatii*
  moldavica   CSec EUnu SIde
  nutans   CSec NLar WPer
  peregrinum   CHar
  - 'Blue Dragon' **new**   LBMP NChi
  prattii   see *Nepeta prattii*
§ renatii   CSec GEdr LPhx
  rupestre   GBri MBri NLAp WPat
  ruyschiana   CBcs EBee EChP ELan EMan GEdr
                                LBBr LPhx LRHS MLLN MRav NLar
                                NWCA
  sibiricum   see *Nepeta sibirica*
  tanguticum   NLar WWeb
* tataricum   EBee
  virginicum   see *Physostegia virginiana*
  wendelboi   MLLN NBir

Dracophyllum (Epacridaceae)
  pronum   ITim

Dracunculus (Araceae)
  canariensis   CStu ITer WCot
  muscivorus   see *Helicodiceros muscivorus*
§ vulgaris   CArn CFwr CMea CPom CSec
                                CSpe CStu EBee EBrs ECho EHrv
                                EMan EMon EPot LEdu LRHS
                                MCCP MRav NJOw NWCA SDix
                                SEND SMad WCMO WCot WFar
                                WPnP
  - white-flowered **new**   WCot

Dregea (Asclepiadaceae)
  macrantha   EShb
§ sinensis   CBcs CCCN CHEx CPIN
                                CSam ELan EPfP ERea EShb
                                EWes GQui LRHS SBra SOWG
                                SPer SPoG WCot WCru WFar
                                WPGP WSHC

- 'Brockhill Silver'	SSpi
- 'Variegata' (v)	WCot

Drepanocladus (Amblystegiaceae)
revolvens	EMFW

Drepanostachyum (Poaceae)
§ *falcatum*	CAbb MGos WJun
falconeri	see *Himalayacalamus falconeri*
	'Damarapa'
hookerianum	see *Himalayacalamus*
	hookerianus
§ *khasianum*	EBee EPla WPGP
§ *microphyllum*	EPla WJun

Drimiopsis (Hyacinthaceae)
maculata	CMon CStu LToo WCot
maxima	CMon

Drimys (Winteraceae)
aromatica	see *D. lanceolata*
colorata	see *Pseudowintera colorata*
granatensis	WPGP
§ *lanceolata*	More than 30 suppliers
- (f)	CTrC ECou GGar NCGa
- (m)	CDoC CTrC ECou GGar GTSp
- 'Mount Wellington'	GCal
- 'Suzette' (v)	MBlu MGos
* *latifolia*	CBcs CHEx
winteri ♀H4	More than 30 suppliers
- var. *andina*	CPLG EPfP GGGa WOrn WPGP
§ - var. *chilensis*	CDul CPLG EPfP ISea LRHS SBrw
	SSpi WCru WPGP
- Latifolia Group	see *D. winteri* var. *chilensis*

Drosanthemum (Aizoaceae)
hispidum	CStu ECho EDAr ELan EPfP EPot
	ITim LRHS MTho NMen NWCA
	SIng SPlb SPoG XPep
speciosum	ECho
* *sutherlandii*	ECho

Drosera (Droseraceae)
admirabilis	CHew
aliciae	CSWC SHmp
andersoniana	EFEx
ascendens	CHew
binata	SHmp
§ - subsp. *dichotoma*	CSWC
- 'Multifida'	CHew MCCP
browniana	EFEx
bulbigena	EFEx
bulbosa subsp. *bulbosa*	EFEx
- subsp. *major*	EFEx
callistos	CHew
capensis	CSWC LRHS MCCP SHmp
- 'Albino'	MCCP
- red	CSWC
dichotoma	see *D. binata* subsp. *dichotoma*
dichrosepala	CHew
erythrorhiza	EFEx
- subsp. *collina*	EFEx
- subsp. *erythrorhiza*	CHew EFEx
- subsp. *magna*	EFEx
- subsp. *squamosa*	EFEx
filiformis var. *filiformis*	CSWC
gigantea	EFEx
graniticola	EFEx
heterophylla	EFEx
intermedia 'Carolina Giant'	MCCP
loureiroi	EFEx
macrantha	EFEx
- subsp. *macrantha*	EFEx
macrophylla subsp. *macrophylla*	EFEx

mannii	CHew
marchantii subsp. *prophylla*	EFEx
menziesii subsp. *basifolia*	EFEx
- subsp. *menziesii*	EFEx
- subsp. *thysanosepala*	EFEx
modesta	EFEx
nidiformis	CHew
orbiculata	EFEx
peltata	CSWC EFEx
platypoda	EFEx
ramellosa	EFEx
rosulata	EFEx
rotundifolia	EBla SHmp
salina	EFEx
scorpioides	CSWC
slackii	CHew
stelliflora	CHew
stolonifera subsp. *compacta*	EFEx
- subsp. *humilis*	EFEx
- subsp. *porrecta*	EFEx
- subsp. *rupicola*	EFEx
- subsp. *stolonifera*	EFEx
tubaestylus	EFEx
zonaria	EFEx

Drosophyllum (Droseraceae)
lusitanicum	CHew

Dryandra (Proteaceae)
formosa	EShb SPlb

Dryas (Rosaceae)
ajanensis	GIBF
drummondii	ECho SBla WAbe WFar WLin
grandis	GIBF
§ *integrifolia*	NMen
- 'Greenland Green'	WAbe
octopetala ♀H4	CMea CTri ECho EPfP GKev GMaP
	LHop MWat NChi NFor NLAp
	NVic SBla SIng SPoG SRms WFar
- var. *lanata*	GIBF
- 'Minor' ♀H4	ECho LBee LRHS NMen WAbe
X *suendermannii* ♀H4	EHol EPfP EPot GMaP LRHS MCCP
	NLAp NMen SPoG WBVN WPat
tenella	see *D. integrifolia*

Dryopteris ✿ (Dryopteridaceae)
from Emei Shan, China	WPGP
aemula	SRms
§ *affinis* ♀H4	CBrm CFwr CLAP EBee ECha
	EMFW EMon EPfP ERod GMaP
	LBuc LPBA MAsh MMoz NBlu
	NHol NMoo SPer SRms SSto WFib
§ - subsp. *borreri*	SRms
§ - subsp. *cambrensis*	EFer
- - 'Insubrica'	EFer
- 'Congesta'	CLAP
- 'Congesta Cristata'	CLAP CWCL EBee EDAr EFer EPfP
	GMaP LPBA MAsh MRav NHol NSti
	SPla SRot
- Crispa Group	CLAP EWsh GBin LAst LRHS
	MMoz
- - 'Crispa Barnes'	WPGP
§ - - 'Crispa Gracilis' ♀H4	CFwr CLAP EFer EFtx ELan EPPr
	ERod GBin MCCP NBir
* - - 'Crispa Gracilis Congesta'	IBal WBor WFib WPat
§ - 'Cristata' ♀H4	More than 30 suppliers
- 'Cristata Angustata' ♀H4	CFwr CLAP CPrp EFer ELan EMon
	GBin MAsh MMoz MWgw NBid
	NDlv NHol SRms WFib WMoo
	WPGP WPrP
- 'Cristata The King'	see *D. affinis* 'Cristata'

- 'Grandiceps Askew' — EFer SRms WFib
- 'Pinderi' — CLAP EBee EFer ELan GBin SEND SRms
- Polydactyla Group — CLAP GQui MDun MRav SPer WFar
- - 'Polydactyla Dadds' — CFwr CLAP EFtx SMac WBor WOut
- - 'Polydactyla Mapplebeck' ♀H4 — CLAP GBin LPBA NBid NHol SRms
- 'Revolvens' — CLAP EFer SRms
atrata misapplied — see *D. cycadina*
atrata (Wall. ex Kunze) Ching **new** — NMoo
x *australis* — CLAP CRez
austriaca — see *D. dilatata*
blanfordii — WPGP
borreri — see *D. affinis* subsp. *borreri*
buschiana — CLAP EBee EFtx NBlu NLar
carthusiana — CLAP EBee EFer GBin NLar SRms WPtf
championii — CLAP
clintoniana — CAby CFwr CLAP EFer MAsh WPGP
x *complexa* 'Ramosissima Wright' — CLAP
- 'Stablerae' — CFwr CLAP EFtx GBin WFib WPGP
- 'Stablerae' crisped — WFib
coreanomontana — MAsh
crassirhizoma — CLAP
crispifolia — NVic
cristata — CFwr CLAP EBee EMon EPfP MLan WCru WMoo
§ *cycadina* ♀H4 — More than 30 suppliers
dickinsii — EBee EMon
§ *dilatata* ♀H4 — CBgR CRWN ECha EFer EFtx ELan EMon EPfP ERod MAsh MSte MWgw NHol SRms WFib WHal WShi WWye
- 'Crispa Whiteside' ♀H4 — CBgR CFwr CLAP CPrp CWCL EBee EFer EFtx EMon ERod IBal MAsh MBnl MBri NHol NLar NMyG SMac SPlb SRms WFib WPGP
- 'Grandiceps' — CLAP CMHG CWil EFer EMon NHol WFib
- 'Jimmy Dyce' — CLAP
- 'Lepidota Crispa Cristata' — CLAP LRHS MWgw
- 'Lepidota Cristata' ♀H4 — CFwr CLAP CMHG CWCL EFtx ELan EMon ERod GBin IMGH MAsh NHol NVic SMac SRms WCru WFib WMoo WPrP
- 'Lepidota Grandiceps' — CFwr CLAP
* - 'Recurvata' — CLAP CRez
erythrosora ♀H4 — More than 30 suppliers
- 'Brilliance' **new** — CLAP CRez
I - 'Prolifera' — see *D. erythrosora* var. *prolifica*
§ - var. *prolifica* ♀H4 — CLAP EChP EFtx GCal IBal MAsh MBnl MSte NBir NDlv NHol NMyG NRib NSti SPla WCot WFib WPat
expansa — EMon
filix-mas ♀H4 — CSBt CTbh CTri CWCL EBee ECha EMFW EPfP ERod GMaP LEdu LPBA LRHS MAsh MBow MMoz MRav MWat NHol NMoo SGar SPer SRms SSto WBrk WFar WShi WWye
- 'Barnesii' — CFwr CLAP EFer ERod GBin MAsh MAvo MSte NDlv NLar NMoo SPlb SPoG
- 'Crispa' — CLAP EHon NHol SRms WFib
- 'Crispa Congesta' — see *D. affinis* 'Crispa Gracilis'
- 'Crispa Cristata' — CBgR CFwr CLAP CPrp EFer EFtx ELan EMon ERod GMaP MAsh MBnl MDun MWgw NBid NBir NHol NSti SPoG SRms SWat WBor WFib WGor WWye

- 'Crispatissima' — NVic
- 'Cristata' ♀H4 — CFwr CLAP EFer EHon ELan MMoz NOak NOrc SRms SWat WMoo
- Cristata Group — EFer
* - - 'Cristata Grandiceps' — EFer
- - 'Cristata Jackson' — CLAP SPlb
- - 'Cristata Martindale' — CFwr CLAP NBid NHol SRms WFib WWye
- - 'Fred Jackson' — CLAP NHol WFib
- 'Depauperata' — CLAP WPGP
- 'Euxinensis' — CLAP
* - 'Furcans' — CLAP
- 'Grandiceps Wills' ♀H4 — EMon NBid NHol WFib
- 'Linearis' — CMHG EFer EHon ELan EMon EWsh LPBA MGos NEgg SRms
- 'Linearis Congesta' — WPGP
- 'Linearis Polydactyla' — CBgR CBrm CFwr CLAP CPrp CWCL EBee EFer EFtx EPfP GBin IMGH MAsh MMoz MWgw NBlu NHol NMoo NMyG SLdr SPoG WAbe WFar WIvy WMoo WPtf
- 'Parsley' — CLAP
* - Polydactyla Group — MGos MRav
- 'Rich Beauty' — WBor
goldieana — CFwr CLAP CMHG EBee EFer EFtx EWTr GBin GMaP MAsh NBir NCob NEgg NLar NMyG SPoG WCru WFar WMoo WPat WPnP
hirtipes — see *D. cycadina*
'Imperial Wizard' — CFir
marginalis — CFwr CLAP EBee EKen GBin GCal MMoz NHol NLar NOGN SPoG WCru WMoo
oreades — SRms WAbe
pacifica — CLAP
paleacea — CLAP
pseudofilix-mas — CRez
pseudomas — see *D. affinis*
x *remota* — SRms
sieboldii — CFwr CHEx CLAP EBee ELan EMon ERod GCal IMGH MAsh MAvo MSte NDlv NHol NOGN SMac SMad SRms WAbe WCot WCru WFib WMoo WPGP
stewartii — CLAP
tokyoensis — CDes CFwr CLAP CRez EBee GBin GCal NEgg NHol NLar
uniformis — CLAP ELan EMon LPBA
- 'Cristata' — CLAP
wallichiana ♀H4 — More than 30 suppliers

Duchesnea (Rosaceae)

chrysantha — see *D. indica*
§ *indica* — CAgr CBgR CPLG CSWP CSec EUnu GAbr IGor ITer LEdu MRav NHol WBrk WMoo WOut
§ - 'Harlequin' (v) — CPLG EMag GBar ITer MCCP MTho
* - 'Snowflake' (v) — CRow WMoo
- 'Variegata' — see *D. indica* 'Harlequin'

Dudleya (Crassulaceae)

abramsii subsp. *affinis* — WCot
  NNS 01-156
cymosa — ETow WLin
- JCA 11777 — CNic
- subsp. *paniculata* — WCot
  NNS 98-221
- subsp. *pumila* — WCot
edulis **new** — WCot
farinosa — CHEx
lanceolata — EMan WCot
saxosa subsp. *aloides* — WCot
  NNS 99-141
verityi NNS 01-159 — WCot

Dugaldia (Asteraceae)

hoopesii	see *Hymenoxys hoopesii*

Dunalia (Solanaceae)

australis	see *Iochroma australe*
- blue	see *Iochroma australe* 'Bill Evans'
- white	see *Iochroma australe* 'Andean Snow'

Duranta (Verbenaceae)

§ *erecta*	EShb LRHS
- 'Geisha Girl'	CCCN
plumieri	see *D. erecta*
repens	see *D. erecta*

Duvernoia see *Justicia*

aconitiflora	CPLG

Dyckia (Bromeliaceae)

frigida **new**	WCot
marnier-lapostellei **new**	WCot
'Morris Hobbs'	EMan WCot
remotiflora	SChr
velascana	CHEx

Dymondia (Asteraceae)

margaretae	CFee SBla WAbe
* *repens*	XPep

Dypsis (Arecaceae)

§ *decaryi*	CCCN EAmu LPal WMul XBlo
decipiens	CBrP WMul
lutescens ♀H1	LPal LRHS MBri

Dysosma see *Podophyllum*

E

Ebenus (Papilionaceae)

cretica	XPep

Ecballium (Cucurbitaceae)

elaterium	CArn LEdu MSal SIde WPGP

Eccremocarpus (Bignoniaceae)

scaber	CBcs CHrt CPLG CRHN CTrG EBee ELan ENot EPfP GKev LIck MBri MEHN MNrw MWgw NPer SBrw SGar SLim SRms SYvo WBrE
- apricot-flowered	EMar
- 'Aureus'	EPfP GKev MAsh NLar SLon SPoG
- 'Carmineus'	CBrm EBee EPfP EWin GGar MAsh MFOX NLar SGar SPoG
- coral red-flowered **new**	WOut
- orange-flowered	EBee MAsh
I - 'Roseus'	SPoG
- 'Tresco Cream'	CSpe EWin

Echeveria ♣ (Crassulaceae)

affinis	MBri
* *agavoides* 'Metallica'	MBri
* 'Black Knight'	WCMO
* 'Black Prince'	CBow EMan GKev NPer SRot WCot WDyG WFar
* *cana* **new**	CBct SRot
'Crûg Ice'	WCru
x *derosa*	EPfP
- 'Worfield Wonder' ♀H1	WEas
'Duchess of Nuremberg'	SRot
elegans ♀H1	CHEx CHal EPfP EWin MBri SAPC WBrE WDyG WGwG

---

§ *gibbiflora* var. *metallica*	EPfP WEas ♀H1
glauca Baker	see *E. secunda* var. *glauca*
harmsii ♀H1	CHal CSWP
'Hens and Chicks'	CHEx
'Mahogany'	MAvo SUsu
'Meridian'	CHEx
'Paul Bunyon'	CHal MAvo
peacockii	EPfP EWin SPet SPoG SWal WRos
'Perle d'Azur'	CHEx WCot
pulidonis ♀H1	EPfP
pulvinata ♀H1	CHal
rosea	WCMO WCot
runyonii 'Topsy Turvy'	CHEx EPfP SRot
secunda	CAbb STre SWal
§ - var. *glauca* ♀H1	CHEx CStu ELan EPfP EShb EWin LPJP MAvo NBir NBlu SArc STre SUsu WCot WGwG
* - - 'Gigantea'	NPer
setosa ♀H1	EPfP
- var. *ciliata*	EShb
shaviana **new**	SRot

Echinacea ♣ (Asteraceae)

angustifolia	CArn CBod CCge CWCL EBee EBla EChP EMan EMar EPPr EPfP GPoy LPhx LRHS MBNS MHer MLLN MNFA MNHC MSal MWgw NGHP NSti STes WBri WCAu WCot WSel WWye
'Art's Pride'	More than 30 suppliers
pallida	More than 30 suppliers
paradoxa	More than 30 suppliers
- 'Yellow Mellow' **new**	EPfP IBal NLar SPer
§ *purpurea*	More than 30 suppliers
- 'Alba'	CCge EBla EShb IHMH LBMP MBri MNHC
- 'Augustkönigin'	CKno EBee EHrv GSki MBnl MSph MSte NBir NCob NDov NEgg NLar NRnb WWlt WWpP
- Bressingham hybrids	EBee EBla EBrs ELan EMar LRHS MRav MTis MWgw SPer WFar GBBs LPhx SAga
- dark-stemmed	GBBs LPhx SAga
- 'Doppelgänger' **new**	CHll EBee EDAr GWWP ITim LBmB LBMP LPhx MDKP NChi NGHP SMad WHil WHlf WPer
- 'Fancy Frills' **new**	CHar CKno ERou MBnl MDKP NBhm WCMO WCot WHlf
- 'Fragrant Angel' **new**	ERou IPot MBnl MDKP WCMO WCot WHlf
- 'Green Eyes' **new**	NBhm
- 'Indiaca'	CAby CBrm EBee EMan MBNS MBri NGHP SMar
- 'Jade' **new**	EBee IBal MBNS NLar
- 'Kim's Knee High'[PBR]	More than 30 suppliers
- 'Kim's Mop Head'	More than 30 suppliers
- 'Leuchtstern'	CBrm EBee NBir NBre NDov NGdn NLar NRnb SWat WHal WPer
- 'Little Giant'	CKno MBnl NBhm
- 'Magnus' ♀H4	More than 30 suppliers
- 'Maxima'	EBee EBrs EHrv LRHS MBnl MLLN MNFA NCob NDov SMad WBVN WCot
- 'Monty Python'	EBee
- 'Pink Flamingo'	WWhi
- 'Prairie Frost' (v) **new**	CKno MBnl WCMO WHlf
- 'Primadonna Deep Rose'	CEnt MWea NBre
- 'Razzmatazz'[PBR] (d)	CKno EBee EPfP IPot MBri MNrw NGdn NMoo NSti SPoG SUsu WSan
- 'Robert Bloom'	EBee EBla EBrs EHrv GBBs LHop MBNS MLLN MNFA MSph NCob NRnb SWat WCAu WCMO WCot WWhi

- 'Rubinglow'	CBgR CElw CWCL EBee EBla EChP ECtt EHrv IBal LAst LHop MBNS MBnl MSph MSte NBir NCGa NCob NDov NGHP NLar NRnb SPoG SWvt WCAu
- 'Rubinstern' ♀H4	More than 30 suppliers
- 'Ruby Giant' ♀H4	More than 30 suppliers
- 'Sparkler' (v) **new**	MBnl WCMO WCot
- 'The King'	CKno EBee IBal LRHS NRnb SRGP WWeb
- 'Verbesserter Leuchtstern'	EBee NBre NGHP NLar
- 'Vintage Wine'PBR	CElw CWCL EBee GBri IBal IPot MLLN NCob NGHP NLar NSti SPoG
- 'White Lustre'	CElw EBee EChP ECha EPfP GSki MBNS NBre NDov NGHP NLar NMoo SHBN SPav WCMO WCot WFar WWhi
- 'White Swan'	More than 30 suppliers
'Ruby Glow'	IBal IPot LAst MDKP
simulata	SUsu
tennesseensis	CArn CBrm CDes EBee GPoy MNFA WHrl
- 'Rocky Top'	More than 30 suppliers
'Vintage Wine'	ELan ERou IPot MBNS NCob SHBN

Echinops (Asteraceae)

RCB/TQ H-2	WCot
albus	see *E.* 'Nivalis'
§ *bannaticus*	CSec EBee GSki NBid SMar WFar WTel
* - 'Albus'	EBee EPfP EWll LAst LRHS NBre NGdn SPoG
§ - 'Blue Globe'	CMHG COIW CWCL CWan EBee EChP EMan EPfP ERou EShb GCal GMaP GSki IBal LAst LRHS LSRN MBri NCGa NChi SCoo STes WBrE WCAu WCMO WFar WMnd WPer WWeb
- 'Blue Pearl'	CMMP GMac WCot
- 'Taplow Blue' ♀H4	More than 30 suppliers
commutatus	see *E. exaltatus*
§ *exaltatus*	EBee MWgw NBir NBre
maracandicus	GCal WCot
microcephalus HH&K 285	CPom
§ 'Nivalis'	CBre EBee ERou LBMP MWgw SEND
ritro misapplied	see *E. bannaticus*
§ *ritro* L. ♀H4	More than 30 suppliers
- 'Moonstone'	CRow
- subsp. *ruthenicus* ♀H4	ECGP EGra ELan GBuc IGor MHar NBre WCot WPGP
- - 'Platinum Blue'	CElw CKno CWCL EBee EMan MBNS NLar SPet WMnd
- 'Veitch's Blue' misapplied	see *E. ritro* L.
- 'Veitch's Blue'	More than 30 suppliers
setifer B&SWJ 8416	WCru
sphaerocephalus	EMan GQue IBlr NBid NBre NBur SBla SPlb WPer WWpP
- 'Arctic Glow'	More than 30 suppliers
strigosus	EBee NBre
tjanschanicus	CWCL EBee EDAr EWll GIBF LDai MHar NBPC NLar NMoo WMnd

Echinospartum see *Genista*

Echium (Boraginaceae)

aculeatum **new**	XPde
amoenum	CFir
boissieri	CCCN CPLG CSec ELan WHil WOut XPde
brevirame	XPde

§ *candicans* ♀H2-3	CAbb CBcs CCCN CCtw CFir CHEx COIW CPLG CSec CTbh CTrC EAmu ECre EShb IDee MPRe NBur SAPC SArc SChr WCHb WFar WGwG XPde
decaisnei	CSec
fastuosum	see *E. candicans*
gentianoides **new**	XPde
- 'Maryvonne' **new**	XPde
- 'Pablina' **new**	XPde
handiense **new**	XPde
italicum	CCCN CHen CPLG CSec CTbh MWgw NLar SIde WHil XPde
lusitanicum subsp. *polycaulon*	CSec EDsa GBBs MSph NEgg NLar WHil WOut XPde
nervosum	EBee
onosmifolium **new**	XPde
§ *pininana* ♀H2-3	More than 30 suppliers
- 'Pink Fountain'	CTbh ECre ELan LSou NLar NRnb XPde
- 'Snow Tower'	CCCN CEnd CTbh ECre ELan EUnu ITer NRnb XPde
pinnifolium	see *E. pininana*
plantagineum **new**	XPde
rossicum	GIBF SPlb
rosulatum **new**	XPde
russicum	CBcs CCCN CFir CPLG CSam CSec EBee EChP EDAr EMan EShb EWll IFro LPhx MNFA NBPC NCGa NChi NLar NSti SDnm SGar SIde SPav WAul WCHb WCot WGwG WWeb XPde
x *scilloniense*	SYvo
simplex	CSec XPde
sordidum	CPLG
strictum	XPde
tuberculatum	CFir EBee EChP LPhx NLar SBod WHil WMoo WOut XPde
vulgare	CArn CCCN EChP EGoo ELan EOHP MBow MHer MNHC MSal NLar NMir NPri NSco SBch SECG SIde WBrE WCHb WGwG WHer WJek WPnn WSel WWye
- Drake's form	CCge MSph SGar
wildpretii ♀H2-3	CBow CHen CTbh EWll ITer XPde
- subsp. *trichosiphon*	CSec
- subsp. *wildpretii*	CSec SPav

Eclipta (Asteraceae)

alba	see *E. prostrata*
§ *prostrata*	MSal

Edgeworthia (Thymelaeaceae)

§ *chrysantha*	CBcs CFwr CPMA CWib EPfP LBuc LPan SBig SBrw SMur SPer SPoG WSHC
- B&SWJ 1048	WCru
I - 'Grandiflora'	CPMA NLar
§ - 'Red Dragon'	CBcs CPMA LBuc NLar
- f. *rubra* hort.	see *E. chrysantha* 'Red Dragon'
gardneri	CFwr NLar WCot
* *grandiflora* **new**	CFwr
papyrifera	see *E. chrysantha*

Edraianthus (Campanulaceae)

croaticus	see *E. graminifolius*
dalmaticus	EPot SBla
dinaricus	NMen NSla
§ *graminifolius*	ECho EPot GKev NLAp NMen WFar WPer
- *albus*	see *E. graminifolius* subsp. *niveus*
§ - subsp. *niveus*	CSec
§ *pumilio* ♀H4	CGra CLyd ECho GKev LRHS NMen NSla NWCA SBla SRms WLin

§ *serpyllifolius* — ECho NMen SBla
§ - 'Major' — NMen SBla WAbe
tenuifolius — NJOw

Ehretia (Boraginaceae)
dicksonii — CHEx CPLG WPGP

Ehrharta (Poaceae)
thunbergii — EPPr

Eichhornia (Pontederiaceae)
crassipes — CBen CWat EMFW LPBA SCoo
- 'Major' — NPer

Elaeagnus ✿ (Elaeagnaceae)
angustifolia — CAgr CBcs CDul ECrN EPfP MBar MBlu MCoo MGos MRav NLar SHBN SPer SRms WBVN WDin WFar XPep
- Caspica Group — see *E.* 'Quicksilver'
argentea — see *E. commutata*
§ *commutata* — CAgr CBcs CMCN EBee ECrN EGra EHoe EPfP IMGH LEdu LHop MBlu MTis MWgw MWhi NFor NLar SMur SPer WDin
§ x *ebbingei* — More than 30 suppliers
- 'Coastal Gold' (v) — CAbP CBcs CDoC CDul EBee LRHS LSRN MAsh MGos SLim SRms
- 'Gilt Edge' (v) ♀H4 — More than 30 suppliers
* - 'Gold Flash' — MGos
- Gold Splash = 'Lannou' (v) — CDoC CDul CWSG EBee EGra EPfP LRHS MAsh MBri SArc SPoG SWvt
- 'Limelight' (v) — More than 30 suppliers
- 'Salcombe Seedling' — CCCN EBee NLar
glabra — EPfP
- 'Reflexa' — see *E.* x *reflexa*
macrophylla — EPfP NFor SSpi WMoo
multiflora — CDul GIBF IDee MCoo NLar SPer WPGP
parvifolia — CCCN EBee EPfP
pungens — ERom EWTr NBir
- 'Argenteovariegata' — see *E. pungens* 'Variegata'
- 'Aureovariegata' — see *E. pungens* 'Maculata'
- 'Dicksonii' (v) — CBcs CBow CTrC CWib EBee LRHS NLar SLon SPer SRms WFar
- 'Forest Gold' (v) — CAbP ELan EPfP LRHS MAsh
- 'Frederici' (v) — CBcs CBrm CDoC CMHG CMac CTrC EBee EHoe ELan EPfP EPla EWTr LHop LRHS MAsh MRav SHBN SLim SPer SPla SPoG WBor WDin WHCG WPat WWeb
- 'Goldrim' (v) ♀H4 — EBee EPfP MGos SHBN SLim WDin
- 'Hosuba-fukurin' (v) — LRHS LTwo MAsh SPoG
§ - 'Maculata' (v) — More than 30 suppliers
§ - 'Variegata' (v) — CBcs CMac CPLG NBir SHBN SPer WGer WHCG
§ 'Quicksilver' ♀H4 — More than 30 suppliers
§ x *reflexa* — CBcs WHCG WPGP
x *submacrophylla* — see *E.* x *ebbingei*
umbellata — CAgr CBcs CBrm CPLG CPle CTho EBee ECrN EPfP MBlu MBri NLar SMad SPer WHCG WRHF WSHC XPep
- var. *borealis* 'Polar Lights' **new** — MBri

Elatostema (Urticaceae)
repens var. *pulchrum* ♀H1 — CHal MBri
- var. *repens* — CHal

rugosum — CHEx

elderberry see *Sambucus nigra*

Elegia (Restionaceae)
capensis — CAbb CBct CBig CBrm CCtw CDoC CFir CFwr CHEx CPLG CPen CPne CTrC CWil EBee EShb GGar IDee SPlb WDyG WMul WNor WPGP
cuspidata — CBig EShb LRav
equisetacea — CBig WNor
filacea — CBcs CBig
fistulosa — CBig
grandis — CBct CBig
grandispicata — CBig
persistens — CBig
racemosa — CCtw
spathacea — CBig CFir
thyrsoidea **new** — CBig

Eleocharis (Cyperaceae)
sp. — LNCo
acicularis — ELan EMFW EPfP IHMH WWpP
dulcis variegated (v) — CRow WWpP
palustris — CRWN EMFW
sphacelata — GGar

Elettaria (Zingiberaceae)
cardamomum — CArn EAmu EShb GPoy LEdu MBri MSal SHDw WJek WMul

Eleutherococcus (Araliaceae)
hypoleucus B&SWJ 5532 — WCru
nikaianus B&SWJ 5027 — WCru
pictus — see *Kalopanax septemlobus*
sciadophylloides B&SWJ 4728 — WCru
senticosus — GIBF GPoy
- B&SWJ 4528 — WCru
septemlobus — see *Kalopanax septemlobus*
sessiliflorus — GIBF
- B&SWJ 8457 — WCru
§ *sieboldianus* — CBcs MGos MRav WDin WFar
§ - 'Variegatus' (v) — CBcs EBee ECrN EGra EHoe ELan EPfP LAst MBlu MGos MRav NEgg NLar SMur SPoG WHer WSHC
trifoliatus RWJ 10108 **new** — WCru

Elingamita (Myrsinaceae)
johnsonii — ECou

Elisena (Amaryllidaceae)
longipetala — see *Hymenocallis longipetala*

Elliottia (Ericaceae)
bracteata — see *Tripetaleia bracteata*
* *paniculata latifolia* — NLar
pyroliflorus — CStu

Ellisiophyllum (Scrophulariaceae)
pinnatum — WMoo
- B&SWJ 197 — WCru WDyG WPrP

Elmera (Saxifragaceae)
racemosa — MGol WPtf

Elodea (Hydrocharitaceae)
canadensis — EHon EMFW WMAq
crispa — see *Lagarosiphon major*

Elsholtzia (Lamiaceae)
ciliata — CArn MSal
fruticosa — CArn WWye

stauntonii	CArn CBcs CPLG EBee ECha EDsa EMan EOHP EPPr GPoy IDee MFOX MHer MTis SBrw SLPl SPer WAul WBor WWye XPep
- 'Alba'	CArn CBcs IDee LRav WWye

Elymus (Poaceae)

arenarius	see *Leymus arenarius*
californicus	CBig
canadensis	CBig CRWN CWCL EHoe EPPr NBre SWal
- f. *glaucifolius*	CFir GCal SLim
cinereus from Washington State, USA	CDes EPPr
giganteus	see *Leymus racemosus*
glaucus misapplied	see E. *hispidus*
§ *hispidus*	CBod CBrm CWCL EBee EGoo EHoe EPPr LRHS MBlu MBri MMoz MPRe MWrn NDov NHol NSti SPer SPla SPoG SUsu WCFE WCMO WCot WPrP WRos WWhi
N *magellanicus*	More than 30 suppliers
- 'Blue Sword'	NBPC SSvw WPtf
repens subsp. *repens* 'Julie Ann' new	WCot
riparius	EPPr
§ *scabrus*	SMrm
sibiricus	EPPr SWal
solandri	EWes GBin GGar LRav MAvo NNor WHrl
- JCA 5.345.500	WPGP
villosus	EPPr
- var. *arkansanus*	EPPr NOGN
virginicus	EBee EPPr

Embothrium ✿ (Proteaceae)

coccineum	CPLG CPne CSec CTrG EPfP LRHS MGos MPRe SPlb SPoG SPur SReu WBrE WNor WPGP WPat
- Lanceolatum Group	CDoC EEnd CSBt ELan EPfP GGar ISea LRHS MBlu MDun MLan NPal SAPC SArc SBrw SHBN SPer SPoG SSpi SSta WDin WFar WPic
- - 'Inca Flame'	CBcs CCCN CDoC COtt CPMA CSBt ELan EPfP ISea LRHS MDun NLar SBrw SMur SPoG SSta SWvt WPat
- - 'Ñorquinco' ♀H3	CBcs CDoC GGar LRHS
- Longifolium Group	CCCN CDul IArd IBlr ISea SBrw

Eminium (Araceae)

spiculatum	WCot

Emmenopterys (Rubiaceae)

henryi	CBcs CCCN CMCN EBee EPfP IArd IDee NLar SBrw SMad SPoG SSpi WPGP

Empetrum (Empetraceae)

luteum	MBar
nigrum	GIBF GPoy MBar NLar
- 'Bernstein'	NHol
- var. *japonicum*	NLAp

Encelia (Asteraceae)

farinosa	XPep

Encephalartos ✿ (Zamiaceae)

altensteinii	CBrP
caffer	CBrP
cycadifolius	CBrP LPal
friderici-guilielmi	CBrP
ghellinckii	LPal
horridus	CBrP
kisambo	LPal
lanatus	CBrP
lebomboensis	CBrP
lehmannii	CBrP LPal
natalensis	CBrP LPal
senticosus	LPal
umbeluziensis	CBrP
villosus	CBrP LPal

Endymion see *Hyacinthoides*

Enkianthus ✿ (Ericaceae)

campanulatus ♀H4	More than 30 suppliers
- var. *campanulatus* f. *albiflorus*	LRHS NLar SMur
I - 'Hollandia'	CPMA
- var. *palibinii*	EPfP GGGa LRHS MGos NLar SBrw SSta WBrE WNor
- 'Red Bells'	CBcs CDoC EPfP GBin LRHS MBri MDun MGos NEgg SBrw SSpi SSta SWvt WFar
- 'Red Velvet' new	NLar
- 'Ruby Glow' new	NLar
- var. *sikokianus*	EPfP GGGa LRHS MDun NLar
- 'Tokyo Masquerade'	CPMA MBri NLar
* - 'Variegatus' (v)	LRHS MAsh SPoG
- 'Venus' new	NLar
- 'Wallaby'	MBri NLar
cernuus f. *rubens* ♀H4	EPfP GGGa GIBF LRHS NBea NEgg NLar SSpi WDin WNor WPic
chinensis	EPfP GGGa IMGH LRHS MAsh SBrw SPoG WNor
deflexus	CDul LRHS WPGP
- GWJ 9225	WCru
perulatus ♀H4	EPfP NEgg SBrw SPoG WFar

Ennealophus (Iridaceae)

fimbriatus RCB/Arg P-16	WCot

Ensete (Musaceae)

glaucum	CKob EAmu EShb EZes MJnS WMul
- from China	CKob
- from Thailand	CKob
perrieri new	CKob
superbum	CKob MJnS WMul
- from Thailand	CKob
§ *ventricosum* ♀H1+3	CCCN CDoC CHrt CKob EAmu EZes LPal MJnS SAPC SArc WMul XBlo
- B&SWJ 9070	WCru
§ - 'Maurelii'	CBrP CHEx CKob CSpe EAmu EShb EZes MJnS NScw SAPC SArc SDix WCMO WCot WMul WPGP
- 'Montbeliardii'	CKob
- 'Rubrum'	see E. *ventricosum* 'Maurelii'

Entelea (Tiliaceae)

arborescens	CHEx ECou EShb

Eomecon (Papaveraceae)

chionantha	CDes CHEx CMCo CPLG CSam CSpe EBee EChP ECho EMar EPot ERos GAbr GCal GEdr GSki LEdu LRHS MRav MWhi NBid SMad WCMO WFar WHer WMoo WPnP WTMC WWye

Epacris (Epacridaceae)

longiflora	SOWG
paludosa	ECou GCrs GGGa
petrophila	GCrs GGGa
serpyllifolia	ECou

Ephedra (Ephedraceae)

americana var. *andina*	EMil
chilensis 'Mellow Yellow' new	WCot

- 'Quite White' **new**	WCot
distachya	GPoy MSal NFor WWye
equisetina	IFro MSal
gerardiana	GEdr IFro
- var. *sikkimensis*	CStu EPla NLar WOld WPer
intermedia	GIBF
- RCB/TQ K-1	WCot
§ *major*	WHer
minima	GEdr NWCA
nebrodensis	see *E. major*
nevadensis	GPoy MSal
sinica	MSal
viridis	CArn MSal

Epigaea (Ericaceae)

gaultherioides	GGGa
repens	GGGa

Epilobium (Onagraceae)

angustifolium	see *Chamerion angustifolium*
- f. *leucanthum*	see *Chamerion angustifolium* 'Album'
- 'Starl Rose' **new**	SWat
californicum misapplied	see *Zauschneria californica*
canum	see *Zauschneria californica* subsp. *cana*
§ *chlorifolium*	EBee
- var. *kaikourense*	see *E. chlorifolium*
crassum	GBuc WGwG
dodonaei	see *Chamerion dodonaei*
fleischeri	see *Chamerion fleischeri*
garrettii	see *Zauschneria californica* subsp. *garrettii*
N *glabellum* misapplied	CSpe ECtt EMan GMaP LRHS NBir SUsu WAbe WEas WWhi WWlt
hirsutum	SWat
- 'Album'	SPoG
- 'Cheryl's Blush' **new**	CRow
- 'Pistils at Dawn'	CNat
- *roseum*	WRha
- 'Well Creek' (v)	MLLN NBid WCHb WCot WHrl
luteum B&SWJ 9558	WCru
microphyllum	see *Zauschneria californica* subsp. *cana*
obcordatum	CStu NEgg
parviflorum **new**	CArn
rosmarinifolium	see *E. dodonaei*
septentrionale	see *Zauschneria septentrionalis*
villosum	see *Zauschneria californica* subsp. *mexicana*
'White Wonder Bells'PBR	MWea WRHF
wilsonii misapplied	see *E. chlorifolium*

Epimedium ✿ (Berberidaceae)

from Jian Xi, China	CFwr
from Yunnan, China	CPom
acuminatum	CDes CElw CLAP EBee EFEx EHyt MDun MNFA SMac WPGP WSHC
- L 575	EHrv MSte SBla
- 'Galaxy'	CLAP CPom EBee
'Akebono'	CDes CLAP EBee NLar
alpinum	CFis CMac EPPr GBBs GBuc NHol WMoo WSHC
'Amanagowa'	CLAP CPMA SBla
Asiatic hybrids	CElw CLAP EBee WHal WPnP
'Beni-chidori'	EBee
'Beni-kujaku'	CPMA EBee GBuc
brachyrrhizum	CDes CMil CPMA CPom EBee WPGP
brevicornu	CLAP CPMA CPom EBee
- f. *rotundatum*	CDes CLAP CPMA WPGP
- - Og 82.010	SBla
'Buckland Spider'	CDes CLAP SBla
campanulatum	CPMA EBee

x *cantabrigiense*	CBro CMac CPom ECtt EPPr EPla GGar LRHS MRav NBre NHol SMac
chlorandrum	CDes CLAP WPGP
creeping yellow	GBin STes
cremeum	see *E. grandiflorum* subsp. *koreanum*
davidii	CDes CPMA EBee ECha GBri GCrs MDun MNFA MSte NLar SMac WFar WHal WHoo WPGP WSHC
- EMR 4125	CElw CLAP EHrv SBla
diphyllum	CFwr CPom CPrp EHrv SAga WBVN WHal
dolichostemon	CElw CLAP CPMA EGle MSte
ecalcaratum	CDes CLAP CPMA CPom EBee WPGP
- Og 93.082	SBla
elongatum	CFwr CLAP
'Enchantress'	CLAP CPMA CPom EGle EHrv GBuc MSte SAga SMHy WHal WHoo
epsteinii	CBos CDes CLAP CPMA CPom EBee WPGP
fargesii	CDes CFwr CMil EHrv WPGP
- 'Pink Constellation'	CLAP CPMA CPom SBch SBla
flavum	CDes CLAP CPMA EDAr EHrv CPom
franchetii	CPom
- 'Brimstone Butterfly'	CDes CLAP CPMA EBee MDun SBla WPGP
'Golden Eagle'	CBow
§ *grandiflorum* ♀H4	CBcs CElw CFis CMac CTri EBee EHrv ELan EPfP EWTr GEdr LBMP MNFA NBir NLAp NLar NMen SAga SBla SPer WBor WCAu WFar WPnP
- 'Album'	CLAP
- 'Crimson Beauty'	CLAP CPMA GBuc MRav SMac SUsu WHal WHoo WSHC
- 'Crimson Queen'	CBow CDes EBee WPGP
- 'Freya'	CBos EBee
- 'Jennie Maillard'	SUsu
- 'Koji'	EGle WSHC
§ - subsp. *koreanum*	CLAP ECha EFEx
- - 'La Rocaille'	CDes CLAP
- lilac	CLAP WFar WHal
- 'Lilacinum'	CDes SBla
- 'Lilafee'	More than 30 suppliers
- 'Mount Kitadake'	CLAP
- 'Nanum' ♀H4	CBos CDes CLyd CPMA CPom EBee ECho EHrv ETow NMen NWCA SAga SBla WAbe WPGP
- pink	EHrv
- 'Queen Esta'	CDes SBla
- 'Red Beauty'	CLAP GAbr MSte
- 'Rose Queen' ♀H4	CBos CMMP EBee EChP ECha EHrv EHyt ELan EPfP GBuc GGar GMaP LRHS MAvo MBri MRav NSti SBla SPoG SWvt WBVN WCAu WMoo WSan
§ - 'Roseum'	CFwr CLAP GBri NMen WSHC EBee GMaP NHol WOVN
- 'Rubinkrone'	EBee GMaP NHol WOVN
- 'Saturn'	CDes CPMA SBla
- 'Shikinomai'	CPMA EGle
- 'Sirius'	CDes CPMA EBee SBla
- f. *violaceum*	CFir CLAP CPMA SAga SBch SBla SMac WSHC
- 'White Beauty'	EGle WSHC
- 'White Queen' ♀H4	CFir CPMA EChP EHrv NOak SBla WHal
- 'Yellow Princess'	CDes CLAP CPMA SBla
higoense	WHal
ilicifolium	CDes
- Og 93020	SBla
'Kaguyahime'	CBow CDes CLAP EHrv MSte SBla
latisepalum	CDes CLAP CMil CPMA CPom EBee EHrv WPGP

leptorrhizum	CDes CLAP CPMA EBee EGle EHrv EMon GBuc GCrs MNFA SWat WHal WSHC
- Og Y 44	EHyt SAga SDys
- 'Mariko'	SBla
lishihchenii	CDes
- Og 96.024	SBla
'Little Shrimp'	CLAP CLyd CPMA CTri EGle GBuc LTwo MNFA NLar WPat
macranthum	see *E.* grandiflorum
membranaceum	CLAP CPMA CPom WHal
myrianthum	CDes CPMA
ogisui	CDes CLAP CPMA CPom EBee EGle EHrv MSte WPGP
§ x *omeiense* 'Akame'	CDes CLAP CMil CPMA WPGP
- 'Emei Shan'	see *E.* x omeiense 'Akame'
- 'Pale Fire Sibling'	CPom
- 'Stormcloud'	CDes CLAP CPMA CPom SMac WPGP
pauciflorum	CPMA CPom EBee
x *perralchicum* ♀H4	CBro CMac CPMA CTri EBee GBuc GKev MNFA NLar SGar SLPl WBVN WPnP WSHC
- 'Frohnleiten'	More than 30 suppliers
- 'Lichtenberg'	CDes CFwr EBee
- 'Nachfolger'	CFwr EBee
- 'Wisley'	CElw CPMA CSam EHrv EWes SBla
perralderianum	CHEx CSam EBee EGle ELan GMaP MDun SRms WHal WHen WPnP WViv
'Pink Elf'	SPla
pinnatum	ECho GMaP MDun WHal WRha
§ - subsp. *colchicum* ♀H4	More than 30 suppliers
- - L 321	SBla
- - 'Black Sea'	CLAP EBee EHrv LHop NLar SAga
- *elegans*	see *E. pinnatum* subsp. *colchicum*
platypetalum	CDes CLAP CPMA EBee NLAp
- Og 93.085	EGle
pubescens	CPMA EHrv SAga
pubigerum	CFwr CPMA EBee ECha EGle GAbr GBuc GEdr MLan MNFA NEgg NHol NPri WCAu WHal WLin
rhizomatosum	CLAP CPom EBee EHyt WPGP
- Og 92.114	CPMA
x *rubrum* ♀H4	More than 30 suppliers
sagittatum	CLAP EFEx
'Sasaki'	GBuc WHlf
sempervirens	CLAP CPMA EBee WHal
- var. *sempervirens*	CLAP
x *setosum*	CPMA EBee ECha EHrv EHyt MDun MSte NLar SMac WHal WSPU
'Sohayaki'	EBee
stellulatum 'Wudang Star'	CDes CLAP CPom EBee EHrv EHyt EWes MDun SMac WPGP WSPU
'Tama-no-genpei'	CPMA CPom
x *versicolor*	CPLG LAst WMoo
- 'Cupreum'	CPom SMHy SMac
- 'Neosulphureum'	CBro CDes CLAP CMMP EBee EMon EPPr SAga SBla WThu WViv
- 'Sulphureum' ♀H4	More than 30 suppliers
- 'Versicolor'	CLAP CPom EHrv SAga SBla SMHy
x *warleyense*	More than 30 suppliers
- 'Orangekönigin'	CPom EBee EGle GBuc MRav NLar NSti SLPl SPla WBor WCAu WHal WMoo WPnP
wushanense	CLAP CPMA
- 'Caramel'	CDes CLAP CPMA CPom EBee EHrv SBla WPGP
x *youngianum*	CBcs CMac EGle MNFA
- 'Merlin'	CFir CLAP CPMA EBee ECha EHrv EPfP NLar NMyG NSti SBch SBla WCAu WHal WSHC

- 'Niveum' ♀H4	More than 30 suppliers
§ - 'Roseum'	More than 30 suppliers
- 'Tamabotan'	CBow CDes GBuc SBla
- 'Typicum'	CLAP EGle EHyt WSHC
- white	NMen WLin
- 'Yenomoto'	CLAP CPMA
zhushanense	EBee

Epipactis (Orchidaceae)

gigantea	More than 30 suppliers
- 'Enchantment'	CHdy
- 'Serpentine Night'	IBlr
gigantea x *veratrifolia*	see *E.* Lowland Legacy g.
§ **Lowland Legacy g.**	WCMO
- 'Irène' **new**	WWst
palustris	CBod CHdy EBee EBla EMan EMar GEdr IPot NLAp NLar NMyG SSvw WHer
'Renate'	WWst
royleana	SBla
Sabine g.	CHdy WCMO
* - 'Frankfurt'	NMen SBla
thunbergii	EFEx GEdr WWst
veratrifolia **new**	CHdy WWst

Epipremnum (Araceae)

§ *aureum* ♀H1	EBak MBri
§ *pinnatum*	LRHS MBri
- 'Marble Queen' (v)	CHal LRHS

Episcia (Gesneriaceae)

'Country Kitten'	CHal
cupreata	CHal
§ *dianthiflora*	CHal SRms WDib
'Pink Panther'	CHal
'San Miguel'	CHal WDib

Equisetum ✿ (Equisetaceae)

arvense	CArn MSal
'Bandit'	CBgR CBow CNat CRow EMon SMad
x *bowmanii*	CNat
* *camtschatcense*	CBgR CDes CMCo CNat CRow IDee ITer SBig SMad
x *dycei*	CNat
fluviatile	CNat NLar
hyemale	CBrm CDWL CHEx CKno CMil CNat CTrC EBla EPfP EPla NPer NSti SPlb WCMO WCot WDyG WFar WMoo WPrP WWhi WWpP
§ - var. *affine*	CBgR CNat CRow EBee ELan EMan EMon EPla LEdu LSou MBlu NLar SMad SPur WMAq WOld WWye
- var. *robustum*	see *E. hyemale* var. *affine*
palustre	GWCH
ramosissimum **new**	CNat
- var. *japonicum*	EMFW LPBA MCCP NFor WWpP
scirpoides	CDWL CMCo CNat CPen CTrC EBee EFer EMFW EMon EPfP EPla LPBA MCCP NBlu NPer SPlb WMAq WMoo WPrP WWpP
sylvaticum	CNat
telmateia	CNat
variegatum	EBee NVic WCot

Eragrostis (Poaceae)

RCB/Arg S-7	WCot
airoides	CHar CKno CSam CWCL EBee EChP EKen EMan EWsh GQui LAst MWat NPro SMad SPoG SUsu WHrl WMoo WPnP WRos
chloromelas	EBee EMan EPPr LPhx MSte WGHP WPGP
curvula	More than 30 suppliers

- S&SH 10 — MSte WPGP
- 'Totnes Burgundy' — CAby CBig CDes CKno CPen CWCL EBee ECha EPPr MAvo MMoz MNrw NOak SUsu WHrl WPGP WPrP
elliottii — CBrm EBee EMan EPPr WOut
gummiflua — CBig EMan
'Silver Needles' — see *Agrostis canina* 'Silver Needles'
spectabilis — CBig CBrm CFir CFwr CKno EBrs EPPr GKev LDai LPhx MAvo . MDKP NBHF NChi NLar SSvw WHil
trichodes — CBig CBrm CFir CKno CPen CWCL EBee EGoo EMan LDai LPhx NBre SMar WPer

Eranthemum (*Acanthaceae*)
pulchellum ♀H1 — ECre

Eranthis (*Ranunculaceae*)
§ *hyemalis* ♀H4 — CBct CBro CMea EBrs ECho EHrv ELan EMon EPfP EPot GAbr GBBs GKev LPhx LRHS MBri NJOw SPer WBVN WCot WFar WGwG WRHF WShi
§ - Cilicica Group — CBro ECho EHrv ELan EMon EPot GKev IBal LHop NJOw WCot WRHF
 - 'Orange Glow' — EHyt
 - (Tubergenii Group) — CBro ECho EHyt EPot GCrs LRHS 'Guinea Gold' ♀H4
pinnatifida — EFEx GCrs

Ercilla (*Phytolaccaceae*)
volubilis — CBrm CFee CPLG CPiN CRHN EBee EMil NSti NVic SBrw WCot WCru WSHC

Eremophila (*Myoporaceae*)
bignoniiflora — SOWG
§ *debilis* — ECou
glabra 'Burgundy' — SOWG
'Kilbara Carpet' — SOWG
maculata — CPLG ECou
 - var. *brevifolia* — SOWG
 - pale pink-flowered — SOWG
 - 'Peaches and Cream' — SOWG
* 'Summer Blue' — SOWG
'Yellow Trumpet' — ECou

Eremurus (*Asphodelaceae*)
aitchisonii 'Albus' — WCot
altaicus JCA 0.443.809 **new** — WCot
* *brachystachys* — CMon
* 'Brutus' — EBee ERou IPot LRHS MSte
bungei — see *E. stenophyllus* subsp. *stenophyllus*
'Emmy Ro' — EBee ERou LRHS MSte SPur
'Helena' — EBee SPur
himalaicus — CAvo CMea EBee EBrs EHrv ELan EPot ERou EWTr LPhx LRHS MHer MSte SMad SPer WCMO WCra WHil WWst
'Image' — EBee ERou LRHS MBNS
x *isabellinus* 'Cleopatra' — More than 30 suppliers
 - 'Obelisk' — CMea EBee ELan ERou LRHS WCMO WCot
 - 'Pinokkio' — EBee EBrs EPot ERou LRHS MHer NFor WViv
 - Ruiter hybrids — CMea CSWP EBee EBrs EChP ECot ELan EMon ENot EPfP ERou GKev LAst LRHS MLLN MNFA MWat SPer SPet WAul WBVN WFar WViv

---

- Shelford hybrids — CBcs CBct CFFs EBee EBrs ELan EMon EWTr EWsh GKev LBMP LRHS MLLN MNrw WFar
 - 'Tropical Dream' — EChP WViv
'Jeanne-Claire' — EBee NLar SPur
'Joanna' — EBee NLar
lactiflorus — WCot
'Moneymaker' — CPLG EBee EPot ERou LRHS WViv
'Oase' — CAvo CFFs CMea EBee EChP EHrv ELan ERou EWTr LRHS MSte NLar SPer WCMO WCot WCra
'Rexona' — EBee ERou LRHS
robustus ♀H4 — CAvo CBcs CMea CSpe EBee EBrs EHrv ELan EMon ENot EPot ERou EWTr LPhx LRHS MAvo MHer MSte NLar SPer SPlb SWat WAul WBVN WCMO WCot WCra WFar WWFP
'Roford' — EBee ERou NMoo
'Romance' — CAvo CFFs CMea EBee EMon EPot ERou LRHS MSte WLin WViv
sogdianus JCA 0.444/090 **new** — WCot
stenophyllus ♀H4 — CBgR CBro CFFs CWib EBrs EChP EPot ERou LBMP LHop LRHS MAvo MWat SMrm SPoG WCMO WCot WFar WViv
§ - subsp. *stenophyllus* — CAvo CBcs CMea EBee EHrv EMon ENot EPfP ERou GMaP MHer MLLN MNrw MRav NFor NPer NPri SPer WBVN WCra WFar WLin
'Yellow Giant' — EBee ERou WCMO WCot

Erianthus see *Saccharum*

Eriastrum (*Polemoniaceae*)
densifolium 'Tetra Riesen' **new** — NWCA

Erica ♣ (*Ericaceae*)
'African Fanfare' — EHea
x *afroeuropaea* — EHea
alopecurus — SPlb
arborea — CNCN CTrG SLon SPlb
§ - 'Albert's Gold' ♀H4 — CBcs CNCN CSBt CTri EHea ELan EPfP LRHS MAsh MBar MBri MGos MSwo NHol SBrw SPla SPoG
 - var. *alpina* ♀H4 — CDoC CNCN CTri EHea ENot EPfP LRHS MBar NHol SBrw SPer SPoG SRms
 - 'Arbora Gold' — see *E. arborea* 'Albert's Gold'
 - 'Arnold's Gold' — see *E. arborea* 'Albert's Gold'
 - 'Estrella Gold' ♀H4 — CDoC CNCN CSBt CTri EHea ELan EPfP LRHS MAsh MBar MGos NHol SBrw SPla SPoG SRms
 - 'Picos Pygmy' — EHea
 - 'Spanish Lime' — EHea
 - 'Spring Smile' — EHea
australis ♀H4 — CBcs LRHS MBar
 - 'Castellar Blush' — CNCN EHea SBrw
 - 'Holehird' — EHea
 - 'Mr Robert' ♀H3 — CNCN EHea EPfP MBar
 - 'Riverslea' ♀H4 — CNCN CTri EHea MBar SBrw
caffra — CTrC IDee SPlb
canaliculata ♀H3 — CBcs EHea SBrw
carnea — ELan
 - 'Accent' — EHea
 - 'Adrienne Duncan' ♀H4 — CNCN EHea MBar MBri NDlv NHol WTel
 - 'Alan Coates' — CNCN EHea MBar
 - 'Alba' — EHea
 - 'Altadena' — CNCN EHea MBar
 - 'Amy Doncaster' — see *E. carnea* 'Treasure Trove'
 - 'Ann Sparkes' ♀H4 — CNCN CSBt CTri EHea EPfP MBar MBri MSwo NHol SPla SRms
 - 'Atrorubra' — CNCN EHea MBar NHol

- 'Aurea'   CNCN CSBt EHea MBar NDlv NHol SRms
- 'Barry Sellers'   EHea NHol
§ - 'Bell's Extra Special'   EHea WMoo
- 'Beoley Pink'   CNCN EHea
- 'Carnea'   CNCN EHea MBar NHol
- 'Catherine Kolster'   EHea
- 'Cecilia M. Beale'   CNCN EHea MBar NHol
- 'Challenger' ♀H4   CNCN EHea EPfP MBar MGos NHol SCoo SPer SPla SRms
- 'Christine Fletcher'   EHea
- 'Christmas Parade' **new**   EHea
- 'Clare Wilkinson'   CNCN EHea
- 'David's Seedling'   EHea
- 'December Red'   CBcs CNCN CSBt EHea EPfP MBar MBri MSwo NHol SPer SPla SRms
- 'Dommesmoen'   EHea
- 'Dwingeloo Pride'   EHea
- 'Early Red'   EHea
- 'Eileen Porter'   CNCN EHea MBar
- 'Eva' **new**   EHea
- 'Foxhollow' ♀H4   CBrm CNCN CSBt CTri EHea EPfP IArd MBar MBri MGos MSwo MWat NHol SPer SPla SRms WMoo WTel
- 'Foxhollow Fairy'   CBcs CNCN EHea MBar SRms
- 'Gelber Findling'   EHea
- 'Gelderingen Gold' **new**   EHea
- 'Golden Starlet' ♀H4   CBrm CNCN CTri EHea EPfP MBar MGos NBlu NHol SPer SPla SRms
- 'Gracilis'   EHea MBar NDlv NHol
- 'Hamburg'   EHea
- 'Heathwood'   CNCN EHea MBar NHol SCoo SPla SRms
- 'Hilletje'   CNCN EHea NHol SRms
- 'Ice Princess' ♀H4   CBrm CNCN EHea EPfP NHol SCoo SPer SPla SRms
- 'Isabell' ♀H4   CNCN EHea EPfP LRHS SCoo SPla SRms
- 'Jack Stitt'   EHea MBar
- 'James Backhouse'   CNCN CTri EHea NHol
- 'January Sun'   EHea NHol
- 'Jason Attwater'   EHea
- 'Jean'   CNCN EHea NHol
- 'Jennifer Anne'   CNCN EHea MBar
- 'John Kampa'   CNCN EHea MBar NHol
- 'John Pook'   EHea
- 'King George'   CNCN CSBt CTri EHea MBar NHol SPer WTel
§ - 'Kramer's Rubin'   EHea
- 'Kramer's Weisse'   EHea
- 'Lake Garda'   EHea NHol
- 'Late Pink'   EHea
- 'Lesley Sparkes'   CSBt EHea MBar
- 'Little Peter'   EHea
- 'Lohse's Rubin'   EHea NDlv
- 'Lohse's Rubinfeuer'   EHea
- 'Lohse's Rubinschimmer'   EHea
- 'Loughrigg' ♀H4   CNCN CSBt CTri EHea MBar NHol SPla SRms WTel
- Madame Seedling   see *E. carnea* 'Weisse March Seedling'
- 'March Seedling'   CNCN EHea EPfP MBar MBri NHol SPer SRms WTel
- 'Margery Frearson'   EHea
- 'Martin'   EHea
- 'Moonlight'   EHea
- 'Mrs Sam Doncaster'   CNCN EHea MBar
- 'Myretoun Ruby' ♀H4   CBcs CNCN CSBt CTri EBrs EHea EPfP MBar MBri MGos NBlu NDlv NHol SPer SPla SRms WTel
- 'Nathalie' ♀H4   CNCN EHea LRHS MSwo NHol SCoo SRms
- 'Netherfield Orange'   EHea
- 'Orient'   EHea SRms
- 'Pallida'   EHea

- 'Pink Beauty'   see *E. carnea* 'Pink Pearl'
- 'Pink Cloud'   CNCN EHea
- 'Pink Mist'   EHea LRHS SPer SRms
§ - 'Pink Pearl'   CNCN EHea MBar
- 'Pink Spangles' ♀H4   CBcs CNCN CSBt CTri EHea MBar MBri MGos MSwo NHol SRms WMoo WTel
- 'Pirbright Rose'   CNCN EHea MGos SRms
- 'Polden Pride'   EHea
- 'Porter's Red'   EHea LRHS MBar
- 'Praecox Rubra' ♀H4   CBcs CNCN EHea EPfP MBar NHol
- 'Prince of Wales'   CNCN CSBt EHea NHol
- 'Queen Mary'   CNCN EHea
- 'Queen of Spain'   EHea
- 'R.B. Cooke' ♀H4   CBrm CNCN EHea EPfP MBar SCoo SPla SRms
- 'Red Rover'   EHea
- 'Robert Jan'   EHea
- 'Romance'   EHea
- 'Rosalie' ♀H4   CBcs CNCN EHea EPfP IArd LRHS MSwo NHol SCoo SPer SPla SRms WMoo
- 'Rosalinde Schorn'   EHea NHol
- 'Rosantha'   EHea NHol SRms
- 'Rosea'   SPlb
- 'Rosy Gem'   CNCN EHea MBar
- 'Rosy Morn'   EHea
- 'Rotes Juwel'   EHea
- 'Rubinteppich'   CNCN EHea SRms
- 'Ruby Glow'   CNCN EHea MBar MSwo NDlv NHol SPla WTel
- 'Scatterley'   EHea
- 'Schatzalp'   EHea
- 'Schneekuppe'   EHea NHol
- 'Schneesturm'   EHea SRms
§ - 'Sherwood Creeping'   EHea MBar
- 'Sherwoodii'   see *E. carnea* 'Sherwood Creeping'
- 'Smart's Heath'   CNCN EHea NHol
- 'Sneznik'   EHea
- 'Snow Prince'   EHea
- 'Snow Queen'   CNCN EHea MBar WMoo
- 'Snow White'   EHea
- 'Spring Cottage Crimson'   EHea MBar
- 'Spring Day'   EHea MSwo
- 'Springwood Pink'   CBcs CBrm CNCN CSBt CTri EHea MBar MBri NHol SRms WMoo WTel
- 'Springwood White' ♀H4   CBcs CNCN CSBt CTri EBrs EHea EPfP MBar MBri MGos MSwo MWat NHol SPer SPla SRms WMoo WTel
I - 'Startler'   EHea LRHS MBar NHol
- 'Sunshine Rambler'   CNCN EHea MBar NHol
    ♀H4
- 'Thomas Kingscote'   CNCN EHea MBar
§ - 'Treasure Trove'   EHea NHol
- 'Tybesta Gold'   CNCN EHea NHol
- 'Urville'   see *E. carnea* 'Vivellii'
- 'Viking'   CNCN EHea NHol
§ - 'Vivellii' ♀H4   CNCN CSBt CTri EHea MBar MBri MWat NDlv NHol SRms WTel
- 'Vivellii Aurea'   EHea
- 'Walter Reisert'   CNCN EHea
- 'Wanda'   EHea MBar
§ - 'Weisse March Seedling'   EHea
- 'Wentwood Red'   EHea
- 'Westwood Yellow' ♀H4   CNCN CSBt EHea MBar MBri MGos NHol SPer SPla SRms WMoo
- Whisky   see *E. carnea* 'Bell's Extra Special'
- 'Whitehall'   EHea LRHS NHol SRms
- 'Winter Beauty'   CNCN EHea MGos NDlv NHol
- 'Winter Gold'   EHea
- 'Winter Melody'   EHea
- Winter Rubin   see *E. carnea* 'Kramer's Rubin'
- 'Winter Snow'   EHea SCoo SRms WMoo
- 'Winter Sport'   EHea

- 'Winterfreude'	EHea NHol
- 'Wintersonne'	CBcs EHea EPfP NHol SRms
ciliaris 'Aurea'	CNCN EHea MBar SRms
- 'Bretagne'	EHea
- 'Camla'	EHea MBar
- 'Corfe Castle'	CNCN EHea MBar
- 'David McClintock'	CNCN EHea MBar
- 'Globosa'	EHea
- 'Maweana'	EHea
- 'Mrs C.H. Gill' ♀H4	CNCN EHea
- 'Ram'	EHea
- 'Rotundiflora'	EHea
- 'Stapehill'	EHea
- 'Stoborough' ♀H4	CNCN EHea MBar
- 'White Wings'	CNCN EHea
- 'Wych'	EHea
cinerea f. *alba* 'Alba Major'	CNCN CSBt EHea MBar
- - 'Alba Minor' ♀H4	CNCN EHea MBar MBri NHol
- - 'Celebration'	EHea MBar
- - 'Doctor Small's Seedling'	EHea
- - 'Domino'	CNCN EHea MBar
- - 'Godrevy'	EHea
- - 'Hookstone White' ♀H4	CNCN EHea MBar NDlv
- - 'Jos' Honeymoon'	EHea
- - 'Marina'	EHea
- - 'Nell'	EHea MBar
- - 'Snow Cream'	EHea MBar
- - 'White Dale'	EHea MBar
- 'Alette'	EHea
- 'Alfred Bowerman'	EHea
- 'Alice Ann Davies'	EHea
- 'Angarrack'	EHea
- 'Anja Bakker'	EHea
- 'Anja Blum'	EHea
- 'Anja Slegers'	EHea
- 'Ann Berry'	CNCN EHea MBar
- 'Apple Blossom'	EHea
- 'Apricot Charm'	CNCN CSBt EHea MBar MSwo
- 'Aquarel'	EHea
- 'Ashdown Forest'	EHea
- 'Ashgarth Garnet'	EHea MBar
- 'Atropurpurea'	CNCN EHea MBar NDlv
- 'Atrorubens'	EHea MBar SRms
- 'Atrorubens, Daisy Hill'	EHea
- 'Atrosanguinea'	CNCN MBar
- 'Atrosanguinea Reuthe's Variety'	EHea
- 'Atrosanguinea, Smith's Variety'	EHea
- 'Baylay's Variety'	EHea MBar
- 'Bemmel'	EHea
- 'Blossom Time'	EHea MBar
- 'Bucklebury Red'	EHea
- 'C.D. Eason' ♀H4	CBcs CNCN CSBt CTri EHea EPfP MBar MBri NHol SRms
§ - 'C.G. Best' ♀H4	CNCN ECho EHea MBar
- 'Cairn Valley'	EHea
- 'Caldy Island'	EHea MBar
- 'Carnea'	EHea
- 'Cevennes'	CNCN EHea MBar
- 'Champs Hill' ♀H4	EHea
- 'Cindy' ♀H4	CNCN EHea MBar NHol
- 'Coccinea'	CNCN EHea
- 'Colligan Bridge'	EHea MBar
- 'Constance'	EHea MBar
- 'Contrast'	EHea MBar
- 'Crimson Glow'	EHea
- 'Daphne Maginess'	CNCN
- 'Discovery'	EHea
- 'Duncan Fraser'	CNCN EHea MBar
- 'Eden Valley' ♀H4	CNCN EHea MBar NHol SRms
- 'Eline'	EHea
- 'England'	EHea
- 'Felthorpe'	EHea
- 'Fiddler's Gold' ♀H4	CNCN EHea MBar NDlv NHol
- 'Flamingo'	EHea
- 'Foxhollow Mahogany'	EHea MBar
- 'Frances'	EHea
- 'Frankrijk'	EHea
- 'Fred Corston'	EHea
- 'G. Osmond'	EHea MBar
- 'Geke'	EHea
- 'Glasnevin Red'	EHea MBar
- 'Glencairn'	EHea MBar NHol
- 'Golden Charm'	CNCN EHea NHol
- 'Golden Drop'	CNCN CSBt EHea MBar MBri MSwo NHol
- 'Golden Hue' ♀H4	CNCN EHea MBar NDlv NHol
- 'Golden Sport'	EHea
- 'Golden Tee'	EHea
- 'Goldilocks'	EHea
- 'Graham Thomas'	see *E. cinerea* 'C.G. Best'
- 'Grandiflora'	EHea
- 'Guernsey Lime'	EHea MBar
- 'Guernsey Pink'	EHea
- 'Guernsey Plum'	EHea
- 'Guernsey Purple'	EHea
- 'Hardwick's Rose'	CNCN EHea MBar
- 'Harry Fulcher'	CNCN EHea
- 'Heatherbank'	EHea
- 'Heathfield'	EHea
- 'Heidebrand'	EHea MBar
- 'Hermann Dijkhuizen'	EHea
- 'Honeymoon'	EHea MBar
- 'Hookstone Lavender'	EHea
- 'Hutton's Seedling'	EHea
- 'Iberian Beauty'	EHea
- 'Jack London'	CNCN EHea
- 'Janet'	EHea MBar
- 'Jersey Wonder'	EHea
- 'Jiri'	EHea
- 'John Ardron'	EHea
- 'John Eason'	EHea
- 'Jos' Golden'	EHea
- 'Joseph Murphy'	CNCN EHea MBar
- 'Josephine Ross'	EHea MBar
- 'Joyce Burfitt'	CNCN EHea
- 'Katinka'	CNCN EHea MBar MSwo NHol
- 'Kerry Cherry'	EHea
- 'Knap Hill Pink' ♀H4	CNCN EHea MBar
- 'Lady Skelton'	EHea MBar
- 'Lavender Lady'	EHea
- 'Lilac Time'	EHea MBar
- 'Lilacina'	EHea MBar
- 'Lime Soda' ♀H4	CNCN EHea
- 'Little Anne' **new**	EHea
- 'Lorna Anne Hutton'	EHea
- 'Maginess Pink'	CNCN
- 'Michael Hugo'	CNCN EHea
- 'Miss Waters'	EHea MBar
- 'Mrs Dill'	EHea MBar
- 'Mrs E.A. Mitchell'	CNCN EHea NHol SPlb
- 'Mrs Ford'	EHea MBar
- 'My Love'	CNCN EHea MBar
- 'Newick Lilac'	EHea MBar
- 'Next Best'	EHea MBar
- 'Novar'	EHea
- 'Old Rose'	EHea
- 'P.S. Patrick' ♀H4	CNCN EHea MBar
- 'Pallas'	EHea
- 'Pallida'	EHea
- 'Patricia Maginess'	CNCN
- 'Paul's Purple'	EHea
- 'Peñaz'	EHea
- 'Pentreath' ♀H4	CNCN EHea MBar
- 'Pink Foam'	EHea MBar
- 'Pink Ice' ♀H4	CNCN CTri EHea EPfP MBar MBri MSwo NDlv NHol
- 'Plummer's Seedling'	EHea MBar

- 'Promenade' EHea
- 'Prostrate Lavender' EHea
- 'Providence' EHea
- 'Purple Beauty' CNCN EHea MBar
- 'Purple Robe' EHea
- 'Purple Spreader' EHea
- 'Purpurea' EHea
- 'Pygmaea' EHea MBar
- 'Robert Michael' EHea
- 'Rock Pool' EHea MBar NHol
- 'Rock Ruth' EHea
- 'Romiley' EHea MBar
- 'Rose Queen' EHea
- 'Rosea' EHea
* - 'Rosea Splendens' EHea
- 'Rosy Chimes' CNCN EHea MBar
- 'Rozanne Waterer' EHea
- 'Ruby' CNCN EHea MBar
- 'Sandpit Hill' EHea MBar
- 'Schizopetala' CNCN EHea MBar
- 'Screel' EHea
- 'Sea Foam' CNCN EHea MBar
- 'Sherry' CNCN EHea MBar
- 'Smith's Lawn' EHea
- 'Spicata' EHea
- 'Splendens' CNCN EHea
- 'Startler' EHea MBri
- 'Stephen Davis' ♀H4 CNCN EHea MBar MBri NHol
- 'Strawberry Bells' EHea
- 'Sue Lloyd' EHea
- 'Summer Gold' CNCN EHea LRHS NDlv
- 'Summer Wonder' EHea
- 'Tilford' EHea
- 'Tom Waterer' EHea MBar
- 'Underwood Pink' EHea
- 'Uschie Ziehmann' EHea
- 'Velvet Night' ♀H4 CNCN CSBt EHea MBar MBri NHol SRms
- 'Victoria' EHea MBar
- 'Violacea' EHea
- 'Violetta' CNCN EHea
- 'Vivienne Patricia' EHea MBar
- 'W.G. Notley' EHea
- 'West End' EHea
- 'Windlebrooke' ♀H4 CNCN EHea MBar NHol
- 'Wine' EHea
- 'Yvonne' EHea
curviflora EHea SPlb
x *darleyensis* WTel
- 'Ada S. Collings' CBrm CNCN EHea MBar
- 'Alba' see *E.* x *darleyensis* 'Silberschmelze'
- 'Archie Graham' EHea
- 'Arthur Johnson' ♀H4 CBcs CNCN CSBt CTri EHea MBar NHol SRms
- 'Aurélie Brégeon' CBcs EHea SRms
- 'Cherry Stevens' see *E.* x *darleyensis* 'Furzey'
§ - 'Darley Dale' CBcs CNCN CSBt EHea EPfP MBar MBri NBlu NHol SCoo SPer SRms WGwG WMoo
- 'Dunreggan' EHea
- 'Dunwood Splendour' MBar
- 'Epe' EHea
- 'Erecta' EHea
- 'Eva'PBR **new** SRms
- 'Eva Gold' **new** EHea
§ - 'Furzey' ♀H4 CNCN CSBt EHea EPfP MBar MBri MGos NDlv NHol SCoo SPer SRms WTel
- 'George Rendall' CBrm CNCN CSBt CTri EHea EPfP NHol SCoo SPla
- 'Ghost Hills' ♀H4 CBcs CNCN CSBt EHea EPfP MBar MSwo NHol SCoo SPer SRms
- 'J.W. Porter' ♀H4 CBcs CNCN EHea EPfP MBar NDlv SCoo SEND SPla SRms WTel

§ - 'Jack H. Brummage' CNCN CSBt CTri EHea IArd MBar MBri MGos MSwo NHol SPla SRms WTel
- 'James Smith' EHea MBar
- 'Jenny Porter' ♀H4 CNCN CSBt EHea EPfP MBar MBri
- 'Kramer's Rote' ♀H4 CDul CNCN CSBt CTri EBrs EHea EPfP MBar MBri MGos NBlu NDlv NHol SPla SRms WGwG
- 'Margaret Porter' CBcs CNCN CSBt EHea EPfP SPla WTel
- 'Mary Helen' CBcs CBrm CNCN CSBt EHea EPfP LRHS NBlu NHol SCoo SPer SPla SRms
- Molten Silver see *E.* x *darleyensis* 'Silberschmelze'
- 'Mrs Parris' Red' EHea
- 'N.R. Webster' CNCN EHea
- 'Pink Perfection' see *E.* x *darleyensis* 'Darley Dale'
§ - 'Silberschmelze' CBcs CNCN CSBt EHea EPfP MBar MBri MGos MSwo NBlu NDlv NHol SPer SRms WMoo WTel
- 'Spring Surprise'PBR EHea EPfP
- 'W.G. Pine' EHea
- 'White Fairy' EHea
- 'White Glow' CNCN CSBt CTri EHea NHol SPla
- 'White Perfection' ♀H4 CBcs CNCN CSBt EPfP IArd MBar NHol SCoo SPla SRms WGwG WMoo

discolor EHea
erigena 'Alba' EHea MBar
- 'Brian Proudley' CNCN EHea MBar
- 'Brightness' CBcs CNCN CSBt EHea EPfP MBar MBri MSwo MWat NDlv NHol SCoo WTel
- 'Coccinea' EHea
- 'Ewan Jones' CNCN EHea MBar
- 'Glauca' EHea
- 'Golden Lady' ♀H4 CNCN CSBt EHea MBar MBri MSwo NHol SCoo
- 'Hibernica' EHea
- 'Hibernica Alba' EHea MBar
- 'Irish Dusk' ♀H4 CNCN CSBt CTri EHea EPfP MBar MGos NHol SCoo SPer SPla SRms
- 'Irish Salmon' CNCN CSBt EHea MBar NDlv
- 'Irish Silver' EHea MBar
- 'Maxima' EHea
- 'Mrs Parris' Lavender' EHea
- 'Mrs Parris' White' EHea
- 'Nana' EHea
- 'Nana Alba' CNCN EHea MBar
- 'Nana Compacta' EHea
- 'Rosea' EHea MBar
- 'Rosslare' EHea
- 'Rubra' EHea NDlv
- 'Superba' CNCN EHea MBar MGos SRms WMoo
- 'Thing Nee' EHea
- 'W.T. Rackliff' ♀H4 CBcs CNCN CSBt EHea EPfP MBar MGos MSwo NBlu NHol SCoo SPla SRms
- 'W.T. Rackliff Variegated' EHea (v)
x *garforthensis* 'Tracy Wilson' EHea
glauca var. *glauca* **new** SPlb
x *griffithsii* 'Ashlea Gold' EHea
- 'Elegant Spike' EHea
§ - 'Heaven Scent' CNCN EHea LRHS
- 'Jaqueline' EHea SPla SRms
- 'Valerie Griffiths' EHea LRHS MBar NHol SCoo WMoo
'Heaven Scent' see *E.* x *griffithsii* 'Heaven Scent'
'Helène' EHea
x *hyemalis* 'Ghislaine' EHea
x *krameri* EHea

lusitanica ♀H3	CBcs CNCN CTrG EHea MBar SBrw	
- 'George Hunt'	CNCN EHea ELan EPfP LRHS NHol SBrw SPla SPoG	
- 'Sheffield Park'	EHea ELan LRHS SPer SPoG	
mackayana subsp. *andevalensis*	EHea	
- - f. *albiflora*	EHea	
- 'Ann D. Frearson' (d)	CNCN EHea	
- 'Doctor Ronald Gray'	CNCN EHea MBar	
- 'Donegal'	EHea	
- 'Errigal Dusk'	EHea	
- 'Galicia'	CNCN EHea	
- 'Lawsoniana'	EHea	
- 'Maura' (d)	EHea	
- 'Plena' (d)	CNCN EHea MBar	
- 'Shining Light'	EHea SDys	
- 'William M'Calla'	EHea	
mammosa	SPlb	
manipuliflora	MBar	
- 'Aldeburgh'	CNCN EHea	
§ - 'Cascades'	EHea	
- 'Corfu'	EHea	
- 'Don Richards'	EHea	
- 'Ian Cooper'	EHea	
- 'Korčula'	EHea	
- 'Waterfall'	see *E. manipuliflora* 'Cascades'	
multiflora	XPep	
- 'Formentor'	EHea	
I *oatesii* 'Winter Fire'	EHea	
x *oldenburgensis* 'Ammerland'	EHea	
- 'Oldenburg'	EHea	
patersonia	SPlb	
x *praegeri*	see *E.* x *stuartii*	
racemosa	EHea	
scoparia	SBrw	
- subsp. *azorica*	EHea	
- subsp. *maderincola* 'Madeira Gold'	EHea	
- subsp. *platycodon*	EHea	
§ - subsp. *scoparia* 'Minima'	EHea MBar SBrw	
- - 'Pumila'	see *E. scoparia* subsp. *scoparia* 'Minima'	
spiculifolia	ITim MBar	
- f. *albiflora*	EHea	
- 'Balkan Rose'	CStu EHea	
straussiana	SPlb	
§ x *stuartii*	MBar	
- 'Connemara'	EHea	
- 'Irish Lemon' ♀H4	CNCN CSBt EHea EPfP MBar MSwo NHol	
- 'Irish Orange'	CBcs CNCN CSBt EHea MBar NBlu NHol	
- 'Irish Rose'	EHea	
- 'Nacung'	EHea	
- 'Pat Turpin'	EHea	
§ - 'Stuartii'	CNCN EHea	
subdivaricata	CTrC EHea	
§ *terminalis* ♀H4	CNCN MBar SRms	
- 'Golden Oriole'	EHea	
- *stricta*	see *E. terminalis*	
- 'Thelma Woolner'	CNCN EHea MBar SBrw	
tetralix	SRms	
- 'Alba'	EHea	
- 'Alba Mollis' ♀H4	CNCN CSBt EHea MBar MBri NHol	
- 'Alba Praecox'	EHea	
- 'Allendale Pink'	EHea	
- 'Ardy'	EHea	
- 'Bala'	CNCN EHea	
- 'Bartinney'	EHea MBar	
- 'Con Underwood' ♀H4	CNCN CSBt EHea MBar MSwo NHol SRms	
- 'Curled Roundstone'	EHea	
- 'Dänemark'	EHea	
- 'Daphne Underwood'	EHea	
- 'Darleyensis'	EHea	
- 'Dee'	EHea	
- 'Delta'	EHea MBar	
- 'Derry Gold' **new**	EHea	
- 'Foxhome'	EHea MBar	
- 'George Fraser'	EHea	
- 'Gratis'	EHea	
- 'Hailstones'	EHea MBar	
- 'Helma'	EHea	
- 'Helma Variegated' (v)	EHea	
- 'Hookstone Pink'	CNCN EHea MSwo	
- 'Humoresque'	EHea	
- 'Jos' Creeping'	EHea	
- 'Ken Underwood'	CNCN EHea MBar	
- 'L.E. Underwood'	EHea MBar NHol	
- 'Mary Grace'	EHea	
- 'Melbury White'	CNCN EHea MBar	
- 'Morning Glow'	see *E.* x *watsonii* 'F. White'	
- 'Pink Glow'	EHea	
- 'Pink Pepper'	EHea NLAp	
- 'Pink Star' ♀H4	CNCN EHea MBar NHol	
- 'Renate'	EHea	
- 'Riko'	EHea SRms	
- 'Rosea'	EHea	
- 'Rubra'	EHea	
§ - 'Ruby's Variety'	EHea MBar	
- 'Ruby's Velvet'	see *E. tetralix* 'Ruby's Variety'	
- 'Ruth's Gold'	CNCN EHea MBar NHol	
- 'Salmon Seedling'	EHea	
- 'Samtpfötchen'	EHea	
- 'Silver Bells'	CSBt EHea MBar	
- 'Stikker'	EHea	
- 'Swedish Yellow'	EHea	
- 'Terschelling'	EHea	
- 'Tina'	CNCN EHea	
- 'Trixie'	EHea	
- 'White House'	EHea	
umbellata	CNCN EHea MBar	
- 'Anne Small'	EHea	
- 'David Small'	EHea	
vagans 'Alba Nana'	see *E. vagans* 'Nana'	
- f. *anandra*	EHea	
- 'Bianca'	EHea	
- 'Birch Glow' ♀H4	CNCN EHea EPfP	
- 'Carnea'	EHea	
- 'Charm'	EHea	
- 'Chittendenii'	EHea	
- 'Cornish Cream' ♀H4	CNCN EHea EPfP MBar NHol	
- 'Cream'	CNCN EHea	
- 'Diana Hornibrook'	CNCN EHea MBar	
- 'Diana's Gold'	EHea	
- 'Fiddlestone'	CNCN EHea MBar	
- 'French White'	CNCN EHea MBar	
- 'George Underwood'	EHea MBar	
- 'Golden Triumph'	EHea MBar NHol	
- 'Grandiflora'	CNCN EHea MBar	
- 'Holden Pink'	CNCN EHea	
- 'Hookstone Rosea'	EHea MBar	
- 'Ida M. Britten'	EHea MBar	
- 'J.C. Fletcher'	EHea	
- 'Kevernensis Alba' ♀H4	EHea MBar	
- 'Leucantha'	EHea	
- 'Lilacina'	CNCN EHea MBar	
- 'Lyonesse' ♀H4	CNCN CTri EHea MBar MBri MGos MSwo NHol SRms	
- 'Miss Waterer'	EHea MBar	
- 'Mrs D.F. Maxwell' ♀H4	CBcs CNCN CSBt CTri EHea MBar MBri MGos MSwo NHol SRms	
- 'Mrs Donaldson'	EHea	
§ - 'Nana'	EHea MBar	
- 'Pallida'	CNCN	
- 'Peach Blossom'	EHea MBar	
- 'Pyrenees Pink'	CNCN EHea MBar	
- 'Rosea'	EHea	
- 'Rubra'	CNCN EHea MBar	

- 'Saint Keverne'	CNCN CSBt CTri EHea IArd MBar NHol
- 'Summertime'	CNCN EHea MBar
- 'Valerie Proudley' ♀H4	CNCN CSBt EHea MBar MBri MGos MWat NHol SRms
- 'Valerie Smith'	EHea
- 'Viridiflora'	CNCN EHea MBar
- 'White Lady'	EHea MBar
- 'White Rocket'	CNCN MBar
- 'White Spire'	EHea
- 'Yellow John'	CBcs CNCN EHea MBar
x *veitchii* 'Brockhill'	EHea
- 'Exeter' ♀H3	CDul CNCN CSBt EHea ELan EPfP LRHS MBar NHol SBrw SPoG WFar
- 'Gold Tips' ♀H4	CNCN CSBt EHea EPfP MBar MBri NHol SBrw
- 'Pink Joy'	CNCN EHea MBri SBrw
versicolor	SPlb
verticillata	CTrC EHea
viridescens	EHea
x *watsonii* 'Cherry Turpin'	EHea
- 'Dawn' ♀H4	CNCN EHea MBar
- 'Dorothy Metheny'	EHea
- 'Dorset Beauty'	EHea
§ - 'F.White'	EHea MBar
- 'Gwen'	CNCN EHea MBar
- 'H. Maxwell'	CNCN EHea
- 'Mary'	EHea
- 'Morning Mist'	EHea
- 'Pink Pacific'	EHea
- 'Rachel'	EHea
- 'Truro'	EHea
x *williamsii* 'Cow-y-Jack'	EHea
- 'Croft Pascoe'	EHea
- 'David Coombe'	EHea
- 'Gew Graze'	EHea
- 'Gold Button'	EHea MBar
- 'Gwavas'	CNCN EHea MBar
- 'Jean Julian'	EHea
- 'Ken Wilson'	EHea
- 'Lizard Downs'	EHea
- 'Marion Hughes'	EHea
- 'P.D. Williams' ♀H4	CNCN EHea MBar

Erigeron ✿ (*Asteraceae*)

from Bald Mountains	NWCA
from Big Horn	NLAp NMen
'Adria'	EBee EChP ECtt GBuc LRHS LTwo MBNS NEgg NGdn SPla WMnd
§ *alpinus*	EHol LRHS NLAp SPoG
aurantiacus	EBee EDAr EHol EPfP MBNS MHer MWgw NBre NBro NJOw NNor NOak NPri
§ *aureus*	NSla WAbe
- NNS 96-87	NWCA
§ - 'Canary Bird' ♀H4	CPBP EHyt EPfP EPot NBir NMen WAbe WFar WLin
* 'Azure Beauty'	EBee EPfP LRHS
Azure Fairy	see *E.* 'Azurfee'
§ 'Azurfee'	CSBt ELan EPfP GMaP MBNS MWat NBir NEgg NOak NPri SGar SPer SPla SPoG SWvt WHen WMoo WPer
Black Sea	see *E.* 'Schwarzes Meer'
'Blue Beauty'	LRHS SRms
'Charity'	LRHS MRav WBrE
chrysopsidis var. *brevifolius*	CPBP
- 'Grand Ridge'	EAEE EHyt EPfP EPot LHop LRHS LTwo NMen NWCA SBla WAbe
compositus	CPBP CTri ITim SRms WLin WPer
§ - var. *discoideus*	EBur NBre NJOw NMen SPlb WPer
- 'Rocky'	ECho GQue SPoG SRot WRHF
Darkest of All	see *E.* 'Dunkelste Aller'
deep pink	CHEx

'Dignity'	EBee EGle EKen ELan LHop LTwo MWat NBro WCot WFar
'Dimity'	CMea ECha EDAr MBri NBre SAga WAbe WBrk WFar WHal
§ 'Dunkelste Aller' ♀H3	CSam EBee ECtt ELan ENot EPfP ERou GMaP LHop LRHS MBri MRav MWgw NGdn SBch SMer SPoG SRms SWvt WBrE WCAu WCMO WEas WFar WMnd
elegantulus	CMea
* *ereganus*	NBre
'Felicity'	ERou
flettii	NJOw NLAp
'Foersters Liebling' ♀H4	EBee EPfP LRHS NGdn SPet WCAu WCMO WCot
foliosus var. *hartwegii*	EPPr
NNS 00-288 **new**	
formosissimus	GBin
'Four Winds'	EBee ECtt ELan EWes LHop LRHS MRav NGdn NJOw NMen WPer
'Gaiety'	NBre
glaucus	CBrm CHrt CSBt EBee EHol EWll GAbr GGar IHMH MWgw NBre SIng SMad WBrk WCot WFar WHoo WWeb
- 'Albus'	EBee EGoo EShb EWll LHop LRHS WMow WPer
- 'Elstead Pink'	CTri EChP ELan NEgg SAga SPla WFar WMow WSHC
- pink	SPla
* - 'Roger Raiche'	SMrm
- 'Roseus'	CBcs CHal ERou
- 'Sea Breeze'	COIW LHop MBNS NBre NEgg NLar NPri SPoG WCot
howellii	EBee NBre WCot
§ *karvinskianus* ♀H3	More than 30 suppliers
- 'Stallone' **new**	NPri
leiomerus	LBee LTwo
'Lilofee' **new**	NGby
linearis	LTwo NBre NMen
'Mrs F.H. Beale'	EBee LRHS SRGP
mucronatus	see *E. karvinskianus*
multiradiatus	WFar
'Nachthimmel'	CSam EBee ECGP ECtt EMan LAst NBre NFla NGdn SPet
nanus	NWCA WPer
oreganus	EBrs
§ *peregrinus*	NOak
philadelphicus	CElw IGor NBir NBro WSHC
'Pink Beauty'	ECtt
Pink Jewel	see *E.* 'Rosa Juwel'
pinnatisectus	NWCA WFar WPer
'Profusion'	see *E. karvinskianus*
pyrenaicus misapplied	see *E. alpinus*
'Quakeress'	CSam EBee EBrs ECtt EMan EPfP GMaP GMac LAst LRHS MRav NBro SMrm SUsu WCMO WCot WEas WFar WTel
radicatus **new**	LTwo
§ 'Rosa Juwel'	CSBt CTri EBee ECtt ELan ENot EPfP GMaP IBal LAst LRHS MBNS MRav NBir NEgg NJOw NOak NPri SEND SPer SPla SPoG SRms SWvt WHen WMnd WMoo WPer WWeb
'Rotes Meer'	EBee ECtt ELan LRHS WCot WFar
rotundifolius 'Caerulescens'	see *Bellis caerulescens*
salsuginosus misapplied	see *Aster sibiricus*
salsuginosus (Richardson) A. Gray	see *E. peregrinus*
§ 'Schneewittchen'	CMMP EBee EChP ECtt ELan EMan EPfP GMac LHop MRav MWat MWgw NCGa NVic SPet SPla SPoG SWvt WCAu
§ 'Schwarzes Meer'	ERou LRHS NGdn WCMO WCot WFar

scopulinus	CPBP ITim LRHS NJOw
simplex	CPBP EAEE LRHS
'Sincerity'	WFar
'Snow Queen'	WFar
Snow White	see *E.* 'Schneewittchen'
'Sommerabend'	EBee GBin
'Sommerneuschnee'	ECha GBin WMnd
speciosus	SMer
- 'Grandiflora'	NBre
'Strahlenmeer'	CPrp EBee LRHS NBre WMnd
trifidus	see *E. compositus* var. *discoideus*
uncialis var. *conjugans*	CGra
uniflorus	LTwo SRms
vagus	CPBP LTwo
'White Quakeress'	CMea EGle ERou GBuc MRav MWrn WCot WRHF
'Wuppertal'	EBee LRHS MRav NBro NEgg NFla NGdn WMnd
* *zionicus* new	EBee

Erinacea (Papilionaceae)
§ *anthyllis* ♀H4	SIng SOkd XPep
pungens	see *E. anthyllis*

Erinus (Scrophulariaceae)
alpinus ♀H4	CMHG CMea CSec CTri ECho ECtt EPfP GKev GMaP MLHP MWat NFor NHol NLAp SBch SIng SPet SPoG SRms WEas WFar WPer
- var. *albus*	CNic ECho MAvo NLAp NLar NMen SRms WHoo WLin WPer
- 'Doktor Hähnle'	CNic ECho EDAr LRHS MAvo MCCP NLAp NLar NMen SIng SRms WHoo WPer

Eriobotrya (Rosaceae)
deflexa	CHEx IDee
- 'Coppertone'	SBLw SCoo
§ *japonica* (F) ♀H3	More than 30 suppliers

Eriocapitella see *Anemone*

Eriocephalus (Asteraceae)
africanus	SPlb WJek

Eriogonum (Polygonaceae)
KM 0135 new	CDes
cespitosum	CGra NLAp SBla
compositum var. *leianthum*	WLin
corymbosum new	EBee
flavum	GEdr WPer
jamesii	NLAp WPat
kennedyi new	CGra
niveum subsp. *niveum*	WLin
ochrocephalum	NWCA
ovalifolium var. *nivale*	GKev SBla WLin
torreyanum new	NWCA
umbellatum	ECho EShb LRHS NLAp
- var. *haussknechtii*	see *E. umbellatum* var. *polyanthum*
- var. *humistratum*	SBla WLin WPat
§ - var. *polyanthum*	WLin
- var. *porteri*	NWCA
- var. *torreyanum*	CMea NLAp WLin WPat
- var. *umbellatum*	LBee
wrightii	WLin

Eriophorum (Cyperaceae)
angustifolium	CBen CRWN CWat EGle EHoe EHon EMFW ENot EPla LPBA MCCP SPlb SWat WHer WMAq WMoo WPer WPnP WSFF WWpP
latifolium	LPBA WWpP
vaginatum	CAby CRow EHoe NSco WSFF WWpP

Eriophyllum (Asteraceae)
lanatum	CFis EBee ECha EPfP EShb LPhx MDKP MEHN NBid NBre SAga SBla WWeb

Eriophyton (Lamiaceae)
wallichianum from Sikkim new	GIBF

Eritrichium (Boraginaceae)
§ *canum*	CSec
howardii	CGra
rupestre	see *E. canum*
- var. *pectinatum*	NSla
sericeum	GIBF
* *sibiricum*	EDif EMan LRav
strictum	see *E. canum*

Erodium ✿ (Geraniaceae)
absinthoides	EAEE LRHS
- var. *amanum*	see *E. amanum*
§ *acaule*	NCiC NLar WFar
§ *amanum*	EBee EWes LRHS WAbe
'Ardwick Redeye'	GCal
balearicum	see *E.* x *variabile* 'Album'
§ 'Bidderi'	MOne NChi NLAp WAbe
'Carmel'	WAbe
'Caroline'	WHoo
carvifolium	CElw EBee EWsh GKev LHop LRHS NFla NLAp NWCA SBch WFar
§ *castellanum*	EBee ETow GCrs LTwo NBre NBro NFla NMen NSti SBch SBla SRms WFar
- 'Dujardin'	LPhx
'Catherine Bunuel'	MOne
celtibericum	NLAp
'Cézembre'	MOne
chamaedryoides	see *E. reichardii*
cheilanthifolium 'David Crocker'	EPot
chrysanthum	More than 30 suppliers
- pink	CSpe ECha LPhx NMen SBla SMrm SRot SUsu
corsicum	CNic EBur ECho EHyt ETow MTho NMen NWCA SRot XPep
- 'Album'	ECho LAst LTwo NMen WAbe
§ 'County Park'	CMea ECha ECou MLHP MOne NRya SBla SHar SRms
daucoides misapplied	see *E. castellanum*
'Eileen Emmett'	EPot WAbe
§ *foetidum*	EGle ETow NMen NSla XPep
- 'Pallidum'	see *E.* 'Pallidum'
- 'Roseum'	GCal MWat
'Fran's Choice'	see *E.* 'Fran's Delight'
§ 'Fran's Delight'	CMea CSpe GMaP MLHP NLAp NMen WHoo WSHC
'Fripetta'	MOne
'Géant de Saint Cyr'	ECtt EMan
N *glandulosum* ♀H4	ECho EPfP GCal LHop MHer MWea SBla SRms SRot WFar WKif WPat
gruinum	EDAr EMan LPhx
guttatum misapplied	see *E.* 'Katherine Joy'
N *guttatum* (Desf.) Willd.	CDes EBee EChP ECho EPot EWTr MWat SIng SRms WPer
x *hybridum* Sünderm.	WAbe
hymenodes L'Hér.	see *E. trifolium*
'Julie Ritchie'	CMea WHoo
§ 'Katherine Joy'	CLyd CNic EBee EWes MHer MOne NDlv NLAp NRya SRot WAbe
x *kolbianum*	NDlv SMHy SMrm WAbe WFar WHoo WKif

- 'Natasha'	CMHG CNic EPot EWes GMaP LBee LRHS MHer NChi NHol NMen SPoG SWat WAbe WFar WKif
'Las Meninas'	SUsu
'Lilac Wonder'	MOne
x *lindavicum*	NChi
macradenum	see *E. glandulosum*
manescaui	More than 30 suppliers
'Maryla'	WAbe
'Merstham Pink'	GMaP MTis NChi NDlv NLAp NLar SBla SMHy SRms WLin
moschatum	ECho
'Nunwood Pink'	MOne NWCA
§ 'Pallidum'	CSam
pelargoniiflorum	CPom CSpe EBee EDAr EPfP GSki LPhx MTho NBro NChi NDov NJOw NLar NRnb SBod SEND SRms STes SWal WEas WFar WKif WPer WWFP
'Peter Vernon'	NWCA
petraeum subsp. *glandulosum*	see *E. glandulosum*
- subsp. *petraeum*	MHer SBla
'Pickering Pink'	NDlv NLAp NMen SRot SWat
'Pippa Mills'	CElw
'Princesse Marion'	MLHP
* 'Purple Haze'	CSpe NEgg SPoG SRms SRot WFar
§ *reichardii*	EAEE ECho ECtt GSki LRHS MHer MTho NLAp NWCA SPet SPoG SRms SWat WAbe WFar WTel
- 'Album'	CEnt ECho EHyt EWTr MWgw NEgg NJOw SPet SPoG WFar WHoo
- 'Bianca'	EBee EChP WRHF
- 'Pipsqueak'	SRot WAbe
* - 'Rubrum'	CElw ECho
'Robertino'	MLHP
'Robespierre'	LPhx
'Robin'	NLAp
rodiei	EBee EWes
romanum	see *E. acaule*
§ *rupestre*	EBee ECho ECtt MOne MWea NDlv SBla SRms SRot
'Spanish Eyes'	MOne NChi SMrm SRot SUsu WAbe WCMO WCot
'Stephanie'	CFis CLyd ECho EWes GMaP LBee LRHS MHer NChi NDlv NHol SMHy SRot SWal
supracanum	see *E. rupestre*
'Tiny Kyni'	WAbe WFar
tordylioides	EBee
trichomanifolium L'Hér.	EWes LBee LRHS MHer NJOw
§ *trifolium*	CHrt ECho ELan EPfP LPhx MHer NCiC NSla NSti SBri SGar SIng WCru WTMC XPep
§ x *variabile*	CBrm ECtt EHyt NLAp
§ - 'Album'	ECho EDAr EPot EWin GBuc GKev LBee MBar MHer MTho NEgg NPri NWCA SBla SHFr SRms SRot WAbe WBrk WFar WPat WPer WTel
I - 'Bishop's Form'	More than 30 suppliers
- 'Candy' **new**	SRot
- 'Derek'	ECho
- 'Flore Pleno' (d)	CStu EBee ECho EDAr EHyt ELan EWes NJOw NLAp NMen NWCA SHFr SIng SRms SRot WFar WPer
- 'Red Rock'	EWes SIng
- 'Roseum' ♀H4	CNic EAEE ECho ECtt EDAr ELan EPfP GSki LBee LRHS NLAp NWCA SIng SRms WBrk WFar WPer
I 'Westacre Seedling'	EWes
'Whitwell Beauty'	NWCA
'Whitwell Superb'	CDes CNic NWCA
x *willkommianum*	NWCA

Erpetion see *Viola*

Eruca (Brassicaceae)

vesicaria	CWan MBow MNHC
- subsp. *sativa*	CArn CSpe ELau GPoy MBow MHer MNHC MSal NGHP SIde WJek WSel

Eryngium ✿ (Apiaceae)

CD&R	EWes
CDPR 3076	WPGP
PC&H 268	EKen MLHP MSph NLar
RB 94054	ITer MSph
RCB/Arg R-5	WCot
RCB/TQ A-3	WCot
§ *agavifolium*	More than 30 suppliers
alpinum ♀H4	More than 30 suppliers
- 'Amethyst'	GBuc IPot LPhx LRHS MBri MSte NBro NLar SWat
- 'Blue Jacket'	NSti WBrE WCot
- 'Blue Star'	More than 30 suppliers
- 'Holden Blue'	EBee GMac
- 'Slieve Donard'	see *E.* x *zabelii* 'Donard Variety'
- 'Superbum'	CMea CSpe EBee ECtt EDAr EHrv ERou GAbr GBri GBuc GSki MBnl MBri MNFA MNrw NCob NEgg NLar SBla SGar SPer SPla SPoG SRms SWat WCot WGwG WSan WViv
amethystinum	CMdw EBee EChP EDAr EHrv EMan GSki MNrw NChi SPla WBVN WHil WPer WSHC
biebersteinianum	see *E. caeruleum*
'Blue Jackpot'	CWCL EBee EHrv EWes IBal LHop MAvo MBNS MBri MLLN MTis NBPC NBhm NMoo NOrc SBig SCoo SMrm SPoG SWat WCMO
'Blue Steel' **new**	More than 30 suppliers
- 'Oxford Blue' ♀H4	CSpe CWCL EHrv GMac GSki LAst MHer NLar SAga SGar SPer STes SWvt WEas WHoo WOld
- 'Picos Amethyst'	EBee EKen ENor GBri LPhx LSRN NBPC NLar NSti SHar SPoG SVil WOVN
- 'Picos Blue'[PBR]	CMHG EBee EBla EHrv IPot LHop LPhx LSRN NLar SMrm SPoG SVil SWat SWvt WCra WHoo WPGP
bromeliifolium	see *E. agavifolium*
misapplied	
§ *caeruleum*	GBuc GMac MGol MNrw NChi NEgg WOut
campestre	CAgr EWll MDKP MHer NChi NGby NLar WFar WPer
carlinae	NDov
caucasicum	see *E. caeruleum*
creticum	NBir NBrc NBro NChi
cymosum B&SWJ 8989 **new**	WCru
Delaroux	see *E. proteiflorum*
dichotomum	NChi
ebracteatum	CHad EBee EBla LPhx MWrn WCot
- CDPR 3139B	CHad
- var. *poterioides*	LPhx SMad
§ *eburneum*	CKno CSec EBee ECha EDAr EMag EPfP EWes GBuc GMaP LPhx LRHS MWgw MWrn NBro NChi NEgg NSti WCot WCru WFar WPic
aff. *eburneum*	WPGP
foetidum	CArn GPoy
§ *giganteum* ♀H4	More than 30 suppliers
- 'Silver Ghost' ♀H4	More than 30 suppliers
glaciale	WLin
- JJA 461.000	NWCA
horridum	EBee EWes GCal GKev LEdu LRHS MEHN MNrw NChi SAPC SArc

	SPoG WCAu WFar WMnd WPGP WWhi WWye
- HCM 98048	WCru
'Jos Eijking' PBR	EBrs EMan ENot GMac LRHS MRav NLar
maritimum	CArn CPou EBee EDAr EGoo GPoy LEdu LPhx MAvo MHer MWgw NLar SECG SPlb WCot WFar WSel
Miss Willmott's ghost	see *E. giganteum*
monocephalum	EBee WPGP WTin
x *oliverianum* ♀H4	CBcs CHad CHar CMea CPrp EBla ECGP EHrv ELan EPfP GBuc GMac LRHS MAvo MLHP MNFA MTis NCGa NChi NDov SBch SDix SMad SPer SPoG SUsu SWat WCAu WCot WWhi
palmatum	EBee NChi
§ *pandanifolium*	CHEx CHrt CMHG CSec CTrG EBee EPfP EWes EWll GCal GWWP ITer NDov SAPC SArc SGar SMad SPav SPoG SWvt WCMO WMnd WPGP
- 'Physic Purple'	CAby LPhx SDix SMHy
paniculatum	EBee WPGP
pectinatum B&SWJ 9109	WCru
petiolatum	MNrw
planum	More than 30 suppliers
- 'Bethlehem' ♀H4	EBee LRHS MBNS MBri NBro
§ - 'Blauer Zwerg'	CKno LHop LRHS SPla SWat WFar WHlf
- 'Blaukappe'	CFir CHar COlW CWCL EBee EBrs EDAr ERou GBBs GBri GMac LDai LPhx LRHS NLar SMrm WAul WBrE WFar WGwG WHil WMnd WViv WWhi
* - 'Blue Candle'	WFar
- Blue Dwarf	see *E. planum* 'Blauer Zwerg'
- 'Blue Ribbon'	CSam EBee LAst LRHS LSou MBNS NEgg SWat
- 'Flüela'	CBct CKno CMMP EBee ECtt EShb EWes GMaP LRHS MWgw NBid NBro SBch SPla SWat WFar WHrl WTin
- 'Hellas'	EBee MAvo MBNS MSph NBid NLar SBig WSan
- 'Seven Seas'	CFir CMMP EBee LRHS MBri MRav MWgw NBro NFla SPla SWat WCot WPer
- 'Silverstone'	EBee GMaP LDai LRHS MDKP NBre NBro NOrc NPri NSti SPoG WCAu
- 'Tetra Petra'	CBcs EBee MAvo NBPC NEgg SRkn WHil WPer
- 'Violet Blue'	GCal NBre
§ *proteiflorum*	CAby COlW EDAr EWll GCal GKev GMac GSki ITer LPhx LRHS MAvo MDKP MSph MWrn NCGa NDov SPlb WAul WCot WGwG
serbicum	GCal
serra	CAby EBee EBrs EDAr EWes GBuc LDai LRHS WBor
- RB 90454	MDKP
spinalba	GSki LPhx MAvo
tricuspidatum	EBee EBrs ECtt GSki LRHS WPer
x *tripartitum* ♀H4	More than 30 suppliers
* - 'Electric Blue'	EBee
* *umbelliferum*	EDAr GCal MAvo MDKP NChi
variifolium	More than 30 suppliers
venustum	CDes LPhx
yuccifolium	CArn CBct CHEx EBee EChP EMag ERou EWes GCal LEdu LPhx NVic SDix SDnm SPav SPlb SWvt WBrE WFar WHoo WMnd WTin
x *zabelii*	CBos CKno ECha ELan ETow GCal GMac LPhx MAvo NBir NBre NChi NDov SMrm WEas WPGP

§ - 'Donard Variety'	CDes GCal GMac IBlr IPot ITim LRHS MBri MDKP MNFA NPri SWat WHil
- 'Forncett Ultra'	CDes CKno GMac SMHy WPGP
- 'Jewel'	CDes CMdw MAvo SMHy SUsu SWat
- 'Violetta'	CBos ECha ELan GBuc GMac IGor MBri MSte NGby SMHy SWat WFar WHoo

Erysimum (Brassicaceae)

from Madeira	CPLG
alpinum misapplied	see *E. hieraciifolium*
'Anne Marie'	ELan
'Apricot Delight'	COtt EPfP EShb EWin MBri SCoo SPoG
'Apricot Twist'	More than 30 suppliers
arkansanum	see *E. helveticum*
§ *asperum*	IFro
'Bowles' Mauve' ♀H3	More than 30 suppliers
'Bowles' Purple'	EChP LAst NCob SRms SWvt WBVN
'Bowles' Yellow'	GBuc NLar SMer
'Bredon' ♀H3	CBgR EBee EChP EPfP EWin LRHS LSou MAsh NBlu NPer NPri SBch WHil WHoo WKif
'Butterscotch'	CFee CSam ECtt MMHG NCob SAga WEas WHoo WTin WWhi
'Butterscotch Variegated' (v)	GBri NCob WCot
candicum	XPep
capitatum	CLyd
- 'Chilli Pepper Red'	LTwo
cheiri	CArn GWCH MBow MHer NSco WCot
- 'Bloody Warrior' (d)	CElw EChP ELan GBri GBuc NPer WEas
- 'Harpur Crewe' (d)	CBgR CEnt CFee CTri EChP ECtt ELan EPfP ERou EShb GMaP LRHS MTho NPer SRms WPnn
- 'Jane's Derision'	CNat
'Chelsea Jacket'	EBee EChP EHol EPfP ERou EWin GBri LDai LHop MWgw SAga WEas
concinnum	see *E. suffrutescens*
'Constant Cheer'	More than 30 suppliers
'Cotswold Gem' (v)	More than 30 suppliers
'Cream Delight'	EWin
'Dawn Breaker'	CElw LSou MBNS MEHN NCob NDov SUsu WCMO WCot
'Devon Gold'	see *E. 'Plant World Gold'*
'Devon Sunset'	CElw GBri SAga WWhi
'Dorothy Elmhirst'	see *E. 'Mrs L.K. Elmhirst'*
dwarf lemon	WHoo
'Ellen Willmott'	CEnt GBin
* *gelidum* var. *kotschyi*	NWCA SBla
* 'Gingernut'	NPer
'Golden Gem'	EWin IHMH NBlu NDlv SPoG WFar WPer
'Golden Jubilee'	ECho ERou GGar
§ *helveticum*	CEnt ECho IFro NPri SRms
§ *hieraciifolium*	CNic EHol
'Jacob's Jacket'	CStu ECtt EPyc MBNS NPer WEas
'Jaunty Joyce'	GBri
'John Codrington'	CElw CSam GBri GBuc LHop MHer NFor NGdn NPer SUsu WKif
'Joseph's Coat'	CElw
'Jubilee Gold'	EWll
'Julian Orchard'	CHll CSpe NCiC SSth
kotschyanum	CGra CLyd CPBP ECho ECtt EHyt ETow LBee MOne NLAp NMen NWCA SRms WPat
'Lady Roborough'	CFee GBuc
linifolium	EBur EMag SRms WBVN WGor XPep

§	– 'Variegatum' (v)	CArn CBrm CSBt ECtt ELan EPfP EPot ERou LAst LRHS NPer SPer SPoG SRot WHoo WPGP
	'Little Kiss'	SECG
	'Mayflower'	NCob
	menziesii subsp. *yadonii*	WLin
	'Miss Hopton'	WEas WLin
	'Moonlight'	CSam ECtt EPot GAbr GBuc GMaP LBee MHer MTho NCGa NDov NFla NFor SBla SRms WBVN
§	'Mrs L.K. Elmhirst'	MDKP MMHG NPer WCMO WCot
	mutabile	CBgR CTri EGoo LPhx MAsh MRav NBir SIde WHal
	– 'Variegatum' (v)	WEas
	'Orange Flame'	CMea CNic ECho ECtt EPot ERou EWin GGar LAst LBee LSou MBar MHer NPer NWCA SAga SPoG WFar WPer WRHF WSan
	'Orange Queen'	WWeb
	'Parish's'	CBgR CMdw CSpe EChP ECtt EWTr LSou MRav MSph SAga
	'Pastel Patchwork' **new**	CSpe
	perofskianum	WEas
	Perry's hybrid	NPer
	'Perry's Peculiar'	NPer
	'Perry's Pumpkin'	NPer
§	'Plant World Gold'	CElw
	'Plant World Lemon'	CElw EBee ERou EWin LIck LSou MBnl MBri MEHN SDnm SPoG SRkn SRot WCot WSan
§	*pulchellum*	ECha SRot
	– 'Variegatum' (v)	CBow GGar WBrE WSFF
	pumilum DC.	see *E. helveticum*
	rupestre	see *E. pulchellum*
	'Rushfield Sunrise'	CElw
	'Ruston Royal'	EBee EWin
	'Sissinghurst Variegated'	see *E. linifolium* 'Variegatum'
	'Sprite'	CLyd CTri ECho ECtt EDAr EPot IHMH NPer
§	*suffrutescens*	XPep
	'Sweet Sorbet'	CHrt EBee EChP ENor EPfP ERou EWin LAst MBri MSte NBPC NLRH NPri SPav SPoG SRkn WSan
	'Turkish Bazaar'	ECho
	'Variegatum' ambig. (v)	CBcs CRez
	Walberton's Fragrant Sunshine = 'Walfrasun'	COtt LRHS SCoo SPoG
	'Wenlock Beauty'	LDai NDov NFor NGdn SRms WHoo WMnd WWhi
	wheeleri	EMag
	'Winter Joy' **new**	CHar ERou MBnl STes
	witmannii	SSth

Erythraea see *Centaurium*

Erythrina (Papilionaceae)

	caffra	WMul
*	*cordifolia* **new**	SBrw
	crista-galli	CAbb CBcs CCCN CHEx CHen CPle CSpe ELan ERea GQui LRHS MLan MPRe MWea SBrw SMur SOWG SPlb WCMO WCot WMul WPat
	– 'Compacta'	SMad
	flabelliformis	MGol

Erythronium ✿ (Liliaceae)

	albidum	CAby CLAP EBee ECho EPot GBuc GCrs IBlr NMen SGar
	americanum	CAby CArn CLAP CWoo EBee ECho EPot GBuc GCrs GEdr GKev IBlr MLLN MSSP NLAp NMen WCru WWst
	'Beechpark'	IBlr
	'Blush'	GBuc IBlr
	'Californian Star'	IBlr

	californicum ♀[H4]	CAby CLAP CWoo ECho EHyt GBuc SCnR WAbe WCru
	– J&JA 1.350.209	CWoo
	– J&JA 13216	CLAP
	– Plas Merdyn form	IBlr
§	– 'White Beauty' ♀[H4]	More than 30 suppliers
	caucasicum	CLAP
	citrinum	CWoo GBuc NMen
	– J&JA 1.350.410	CWoo
	– J&JA 13462	CLAP CWoo
	– subsp. *citrinum* **new**	GIBF
	citrinum x *hendersonii*	IBlr
	'Citronella'	CBro CLAP EChP EHrv GBuc IBlr ITim LRHS MSSP NDlv NJOw NMen NMyG WAbe WCru WFar WLin WPnP WTin
	cliftonii hort.	see *E. multiscapoideum* Cliftonii Group
	dens-canis ♀[H4]	More than 30 suppliers
	– JCA 470.001	CLAP
	– from Slovenia	CLAP
	– WM 9615 from Slovenia	MPhe
	– 'Charmer'	EBee GEdr WWst
	– 'Frans Hals'	CLAP EBee ECho ERos GBuc GCrs GEdr GGar MNFA MTho WAbe WCru
	– 'Lilac Wonder'	EBee ECho EPot GEdr LEdu LRHS MTho NHol WWst
*	– 'Moerheimii' (d)	GEdr IBlr WWst
	– var. *niveum*	ERos IBlr
	– 'Old Aberdeen'	CLAP IBlr
	– 'Pink Perfection'	EBee ERos GCrs GEdr GGar LRHS NHol WCru
	– 'Purple King'	EBee ECho EPot ERos GEdr MDun NLar SPur WAbe WCru
	– 'Rose Queen'	CAby CAvo CBro CFwr CPLG EBee EBrs ECho EPot ERos EWTr GAbr GBuc GGar LRHS MAvo MDun MTho NLAp WHal WLin
*	– 'Semi-plenum' (d)	IBlr
	– 'Snowflake'	CLAP CMea EBee EBrs ECha ECho EPot ERos GBuc GCrs GEdr GGar LRHS MDun MNFA NBir NMen WAbe WCMO WCru WDav
	– 'White Splendour'	CBro ECho ERos IBlr
	elegans	ECho SBla SOkd WWst
	'Flash'	IBlr
§	*grandiflorum*	EBee ECho EPot GBuc GCrs GEdr NMen
	– M&PS 007	CLAP
	– M&PS 96/024	NMen
	– subsp. *chrysandrum*	see *E. grandiflorum*
	– var. *grandiflorum* **new**	GIBF
	helenae	CLAP CWoo GEdr IBlr
	– J&JA 11678	WWst
	hendersonii	CLAP CWoo EHyt GIBF MSSP WAbe WCot
	– J&JA 1.351.301	CWoo
	– J&JA 12945	CLAP CWoo
	– JCA 11116	CLAP
	howellii	CLAP GCrs
	– J&JA 13428	WWst
	– J&JA 13441	CLAP
	japonicum	CBcs EBee ECho EFEx EPot GBBs GBuc GCrs NMen SPer WCru WFar IBlr
	'Jeanette Brickell'	IBlr
	'Jeannine'	GBuc GEdr IBlr WCru
	'Joanna'	GBuc IBlr NMen
	klamathense **new**	GIBF
	'Kondo'	More than 30 suppliers
	'Margaret Mathew'	IBlr
	'Minnehaha'	WWst
	montanum **new**	GIBF
§	*multiscapoideum*	CLAP CWoo ECho GIBF WCot
	– NNS 99-163	WWst
§	– Cliftonii Group	CLAP MPhe

- - J&JA 13525 — CLAP
oregonum — CLAP CWoo ECho ETow GBuc IBlr MSSP SBla WCot WCru WDav
- subsp. *leucandrum* — CLAP MPhe
- - J&JA 13494 — CWoo
- subsp. *oregonum* **new** — GIBF
'Pagoda' ♀H4 — More than 30 suppliers
pluriflorum — GIBF
purdyi — see *E. multiscapoideum*
revolutum ♀H4 — CAby CAvo CBro CFir CLAP CMea CWoo EPot GBuc GCrs GGar GKev GMaP IBlr ITim MNrw MSSP SBla SCnR SOkd SRot SUsu WAbe WCFE WCru
- from God's Valley **new** — WWst
- 'Guincho Splendour' — IBlr
- Johnsonii Group — CNic CWoo EBrs WAbe WCru
- 'Knightshayes Pink' — CLAP GBuc IBlr
- 'Pink Beauty' — WNor
- Plas Merdyn form — IBlr
- 'Rose Beauty' — NMen
- 'White Beauty' — see *E. californicum* 'White Beauty'
'Rippling Waters' — IBlr
'Rosalind' — IBlr
sibiricum — EBee ECho GCrs NMen SPer
- from Siberia **new** — MPhe
- from Ussuri — GIBF
- white — WWst
'Sundisc' — ECha ECho EHyt IBlr MSSP MTho NMen WAbe
tuolumnense ♀H4 — CBro CLAP CMea EBee ECho EHrv EPot ERos GBuc GEdr GGar GMaP IBlr LEdu MCCP MSSP NJOw NMen SUsu WAbe WCot WDav
- EBA clone 2 — WAbe
- 'Spindlestone' — IBlr WWst
umbilicatum — GCrs IBlr

Escallonia ✿ (*Escalloniaceae*)

'Alice' — SLPl SPer
'Apple Blossom' ♀H4 — More than 30 suppliers
'Bantry Bay' — CBcs
§ *bifida* ♀H3 — CDoC CDul CFee CPle WFar WSHC
'C.F. Ball' — CBcs CSBt CTri EBee EHol ELan GGar LBuc MGan MSwo NBlu NEgg NScw NWea SEND SRms WBVN WDin WFar WMoo WTel
'Compacta Coccinea' — CBcs
'Dart's Rosy Red' — NHol SLPl
'Donard Beauty' — SRms WFar
'Donard Radiance' ♀H4 — More than 30 suppliers
'Donard Seedling' — More than 30 suppliers
'Donard Star' — CSBt CWib ENot EPfP LAst MRav NWea SLPl WCFE
'Donard Surprise' — NFor
'Edinensis' — CBcs EPfP MBar MRav NLar SBch SEND SLim WDin WFar WGer WMoo
'Erecta' — EPfP SHGN
x *exoniensis* — SRms
'Gwendolyn Anley' — CMHG SLPl SPer WFar
'Hopleys Gold'PBR — see *E. laevis* 'Gold Brian'
illinita — SPoG
'Iveyi' ♀H3 — More than 30 suppliers
§ *laevis* — CTrw WFar
§ - 'Gold Brian'PBR — CDul CMHG CSBt EBee EHoe ELan ENot EPfP GGar LRHS LSRN MAsh MGos MWat NScw SCoo SHop SMer SPer SWal WFar WHar
- 'Gold Ellen' (v) — CBcs CTri CWSG EBee ELan EPfP LAst LRHS MAsh MGos MRav MSwo NHol SAga SCoo SEND SLim SPer SPla SPoG SWvt WCot WMoo WWeb

Lanarth No 1 — CBcs
'Langleyensis' ♀H4 — CBcs CPLG CSBt CTri CWib NWea WDin WFar WHar
'Little Treasure' **new** — ENot MGos SPoG
mexicana — WFar
x *mollis* — SPer
montevidensis — see *E. bifida*
'Newry' — SPer
organensis — see *E. laevis*
'Peach Blossom' ♀H4 — CBcs CDoC CDul CSam CWib EBee ECrN ELan EMil EPfP GGar LRHS MAsh MBNS MBri MLHP MSwo NBir NCGa NEgg SCoo SHBN SLPl SLim SPer SPoG SSto WFar
'Pink Elf' — MSwo NHol
'Pride of Donard' ♀H4 — CBcs CDoC CSBt EBee EPfP GGar LRHS MAsh MGan NCGa NPri SRms SSto WBrE
punctata — see *E. rubra*
'Red Dream' — CWSG CWoW EBee LAst LRHS MAsh MBri MGos MSwo NBlu NHol NLar SAga SCoo SPoG SRms SWvt WFar WGer
'Red Dwarf' — WAbe
'Red Elf' — EBee ECrN ELan ENot EPfP GGar LAst LRHS MAsh MBar MBri MGos MRav MSwo MWat NEgg NHol SCoo SGar SLPl SPer SPlb SPoG SRms SWvt WBVN WFar WHen WWeb
'Red Hedger' — CDoC CSBt CTrG CWib LRHS MTis SCoo
'Red Robin' — CBcs SPoG
resinosa — CBcs CPLG CPle IFro SAPC SArc WHCG WJek
§ *rubra* — MLHP
- 'Crimson Spire' ♀H4 — CBcs CBrm CDul CSBt CTri CWSG CWib ENot EPfP GGar LRHS LSRN MAsh MBNS MGos MRav MWat NBir NJOw SBod SEND SHBN SLim SPer SPlb SPoG SRms WHen WMoo WWeb
- 'Ingramii' — CDul CSBt CWib NWea SHBN
§ - var. *macrantha* — CBcs CDoC CDul CSBt CWSG CWib ECrN EGra EPfP GGar IArd LAst LRHS MHer NBir NBlu NEgg NWea SCoo SLim SMer SPer SPoG WAbe WDin WFar WGer WMoo WWeb XPep
* - - *aurea* — NScw
- 'Pygmaea' — see *E. rubra* 'Woodside'
§ - 'Woodside' — ECho EHol EPfP LTwo MLHP NHol SRms SSto WHCG
'Saint Keverne' — CBcs
'Silver Anniversary' — MSwo
'Slieve Donard' — CBcs EBee ENot EPfP MRav NEgg NHol NWea SLPl SLim SLon SRms WFar

Eschscholzia (*Papaveraceae*)

I *caespitosa* 'Sundew' — CSpe ENot
californica ♀H4 — XPep
- 'Ivory Castle' **new** — LRav
- 'Jersey Cream' — CSpe
- var. *maritima* — XPep
lobbii — CSpe

Eucalyptus ✿ (*Myrtaceae*)

acaciiformis — LRav
aggregata — GTsp LRav SAPC SArc SPer WCel WMul
alpina — LRav SPlb
amygdalina — GGar
approximans subsp. *approximans* — LRav WCel

archeri	CCVT CDoC EBee ECrN EPfP GQui GTSp LRHS MBNS WCel WOVN WPGP
baeuerlenii	LRav
barberi	LRav
§ *bridgesiana*	CMCN LRav MHer
caesia	SPlb
calycogona	LRav
camaldulensis	LRav SPlb
camphora	CTho LRav WCel
cinerea	GQui LRav SBig SPlb WCel
citriodora	CWib GQui LRav MHer MNHC NGHP SPlb WCel WNor
coccifera	CBcs CCVT CDoC CDul CSBt CTho ELan EPfP GGar LRHS MCCP MLan NBea NBlu NPer NPri SBig SEND SPlb SPoG WCel WDin WMul WNor WPGP
cordata	CCVT LRav NEgg WCel
crenulata	CTrC GQui LRav WCel
crucis subsp. *crucis*	SPlb
cypellocarpa	CMCN SPlb
dalrympleana ♀H3	CAbb CBcs CCVT CDoC CDul CMHG EBee ECrN ELan ENot EPfP EWes LRHS MGos MSwo NBea NEgg NPer SBig SCoo SLim SPer SPoG SRms WBrE WCel WDin WMul WPGP WWeb
dalrympleana x *fraxinoides*	LRav
deanei	WCel
debeuzevillei	see *E. pauciflora* subsp. *debeuzevillei*
delegatensis	CMHG GTSp LRav NPer WCel WMul
- subsp. *tasmaniensis*	GGar WNor
divaricata	see *E. gunnii* subsp. *divaricata*
dives	LRav
elata	CMCN
erythrocorys	SPlb
eximia	SPlb
forrestiana	LRav
fraxinoides	LRav SPlb WCel
gamophylla	SPlb
glaucescens	CCVT CMHG CTho EPfP EWes GQui LRHS LRav NEgg NPri SAPC SArc SPer WCel WGer WMul WPGP
globulus	CHEx LRav MNHC MSal SBLw WCel WFar WMul
goniocalyx	EPfP WCel
§ *gregsoniana*	CCVT CDoC CTho LRav SPlb WCel WPGP
gunnii ♀H3	More than 30 suppliers
§ - subsp. *divaricata*	CCVT EPfP GQui LRHS LRav MBri WCel WGer
- 'Silver Rain'	LRav
johnstonii	CDul CMHG EBee ECrN LRav SPer WCel
kitsoniana	GGar LRav WCel
kruseana	SPlb
kybeanensis	CCVT CDul GQui GTSp LRav WCel
§ *lacrimans*	GTSp WCel WPGP
lehmannii	SOWG
leucoxylon	WCel
- subsp. *megalocarpa*	SPlb
- 'Rosea'	EBee
ligustrina	LRav WCel
'Little Boy Blue'	CWib
macarthurii	LRav WCel
macrocarpa	SPlb
macroryncha	SPlb
mannifera subsp. *elliptica*	LRav WCel
- subsp. *praecox*	LRav
mitchelliana	LRav WCel WDin
moorei	WCel
* - *nana*	LRav MHer MWat WNor
neglecta	EPfP LRav WCel
nicholii	CAbb CBrm CCVT CDul EBee EPfP EWes GQui GTSp LHop LRHS MGos SCoo SPoG WCel WGer WMul WOVN WPGP
niphophila	see *E. pauciflora* subsp. *niphophila*
nitens	CCVT CHen EBee EGFP LRav SAPC SArc SBig SCoo SPlb WCel WMul
§ *nitida*	CMHG GGar WCel WNor
nova-anglica	CMHG CTho LRav
obliqua	GGar
ovata	GGar
parviflora	EGra
parvifolia ♀H4	CBcs CCVT CDoC CDul CLnd EBee EPfP EShb LRHS LRav MWea NEgg SCoo SEND WCel WMul WPGP
pauciflora	CCVT CDoC CSBt CTho ELan EPfP MGos NEgg NHol NLar SEND SPer WBrE WCel WMul WNor
- subsp. *acerina*	WCel
§ - subsp. *debeuzevillei*	CBrm CCVT CDoC CDul CLnd CMHG CTho EBee EPfP EWes GQui LPan LRHS MGos SAPC SArc SBig WCel WMul WPGP WWeb
- subsp. *hedraia*	WCel
- var. *nana*	see *E. gregsoniana*
§ - subsp. *niphophila* ♀H4	More than 30 suppliers
- - 'Pendula'	see *E. lacrimans*
- subsp. *pauciflora*	LRav
perriniana	CCVT CDul CLnd CMHG CSBt EBee ECrN ELan EPfP LPan LRHS MBri MGos NEgg SBig SCoo SLim SPer SPlb SPoG WCel WDin WFar WMul WNor WOrn WPGP
phoenicea	SOWG
pulchella	LRav
pulverulenta	CDul CEnd EBee GTSp LRHS LRav SPlb WGer
- 'Baby Blue'	LRav WCel
regnans	GGar WMul
risdonii	GGar LRav WNor
rodwayi	GGar LRav
rubida	CMHG LRav WCel
scoparia	LRav
sideroxylon	SPlb
- 'Rosea'	SPlb
simmondsii	see *E. nitida*
stellulata	LRav NEgg WCel
stricklandii	LRav
stricta	LRav
stuartiana	see *E. bridgesiana*
sturgissiana	LRav
subcrenulata	CCVT CMHG EBee EPfP GGar GQui GTSp LHop LRav MBNS WCel
tenuiramis	LRav
tetraptera	LRav SPlb
torquata	SPlb
urnigera	CCVT CDoC EBee LHop LRHS MBNS SCoo WCel WDin
vernicosa	CBrm CCVT GGar WCel
viminalis	CArn CHEx GGar LRav WCel WDin
youmanii	LRav

Eucharidium see *Clarkia*

Eucharis (Amaryllidaceae)

§ *amazonica* ♀H1	ECho EShb LRHS MLan MOak SPav
grandiflora misapplied	see *E. amazonica*

Eucodonia (Gesneriaceae)
'Adele'	WDib
andrieuxii 'Naomi'	WDib
§ *verticillata*	CSpe

Eucomis ✿ (Hyacinthaceae)
autumnalis misapplied	see *E. zambesiaca*
§ *autumnalis* (Mill.)	CAbb CAvo CBro CFfs CHEx CPne
Chittenden ♀H2-3	CPou CRHN CSWP EBee EBrs
	ECho EPot GBin GSki LRHS MAvo
	MCCP MDun MWgw SDnm SPav
	SPer SPlb WBrE WHil WPGP WTin
- subsp. *amaryllidifolia*	CPen WPGP
- subsp. *autumnalis*	WPGP
- - 'Peace Candles' **new**	CPen
- subsp. *clavata*	EBee
- 'White Dwarf'	CStu ECho EShb SPer
bicolor ♀H2-3	More than 30 suppliers
- 'Alba'	CAvo CFfs EAmu EBee EBrs ECho
	EPot GSki LBow LRHS SDnm
- 'Stars and Stripes'	WCru
'Cabernet Candles' **new**	CPen
§ *comosa*	CAvo CBrm CBro CFfs CHEx CHll
	CPne CPrp CRHN CSam EChP
	ENot EShb GAbr LBow LEdu LRHS
	MDun SDnm SMad SPav SYvo
	WCru WEas WHil WTin
- 'First Red'	CDes CPou WPGP
- purple-leaved	SBla
- 'Sparkling Burgundy'	More than 30 suppliers
'Frank Lawley'	EBee
'Joy's Purple'	CBro CPen LRHS
montana	CAvo CCtw WPGP
pallidiflora ♀H4	CDes CHEx CPen LEdu WPGP
pole-evansii	CBro CDes CFir CHEx CPLG CPen
	CRHN EAEE EBee EBrs ECGP EDAr
	EMar EShb GCal LRHS MLLN
	MMHG SMrm SPla WCMO WCot
	WCru WPGP
- bronze	CPne
- 'Burgundy'	EBla
- 'Purpurea'	GCal LEdu
punctata	see *E. comosa*
regia	CPLG LToo WCot
* *reichenbachii*	CHen WCMO
'Royal Burgundy'	SPer
'Swazi Pride'	EBee
undulata	see *E. autumnalis*
vandermerwei	CAvo CPLG CPen EBee IPot LRHS
- 'Octopus' **new**	CPen
§ *zambesiaca*	CPen EBee GBin GCal LBow
	WCMO
'Zeal Bronze'	CAbb CBcs CDes CDoC CMHG
	CRHN EBee EPfP GCal MWgw
	NSti WCot WCru WPGP

Eucommia (Eucommiaceae)
ulmoides	CBcs CCCN CDul CMCN EPfP
	NLar SMad WPGP

Eucrosia (Amaryllidaceae)
stricklandii	CMon

Eucryphia ✿ (Eucryphiaceae)
'Castlewellan'	ISea
cordifolia	CAbP CMac CTho CTrw CWib
	GGar GTSp ISea SSpi WDin
- Crarae hardy form	GGGa
§ *cordifolia* x *lucida*	CBcs CCCN ELan ISea NEgg NPen
	SPer SRot WDin WPGP WFar
glutinosa ♀H4	CBcs CCCN CDul CTho ELan EPfP
	IMGH LRHS MBar MBri MDun
	NBea NBir NEgg SBrw SPer SSpi
	SSta WDin WFar WNor WOrn
x *hillieri* 'Winton'	CMHG GQui

x *intermedia*	CTho CTrC CTrG CWSG ELan
	EPfP GGGa LRHS NPal NPri NVic
	SBrw SHBN SPer SRms SRot SSpi
	WDin WFar WPat
- 'Rostrevor' ♀H3	CBcs CDul CMHG CPMA CSBt
	CWib ELan EPfP GAbr GQui IArd
	IMGH ISea LHyd LRHS LSRN
	MDun MGos NCGa SBrw SLon
	SReu SSta WFar WPGP WPat WSHC
lucida	CCCN CDoC CTrC ELan EPfP
	GGar GSki GTSp IArd IMGH ISea
	SBrw WFar WNor
- 'Ballerina'	CPMA GGar ISea LRHS MGos NLar
	NVic SCoo SPoG SRot SSpi SSta
	WFar
- 'Dumpling' **new**	WPGP
- 'Gilt Edge' (v)	ISea LTwo SBrw SHBN
- 'Leatherwood Cream' (v)	IArd ISea SBrw
- 'Pink Cloud'	CBcs CDoC CDul CEnd CPMA
	ELan EPfP EWTr GQui IMGH ISea
	LHop LHyd LRHS LSRN MDun
	NPri SBrw SDnm SLon SMur SPer
	SPoG SRot SSpi SSta SWvt WFar
	WPGP
- 'Pink Whisper'	ISea
- 'Spring Glow' (v)	EMil ISea LTwo SBrw SHBN
milliganii	CAbP CDoC CDul CPMA CTrC
	EPfP GAbr GGar GQui ISea LHop
	MBlu MDun NPal SBod SBrw
	SHBN SPer SRms SSpi SSta WPGP
moorei	CBcs CCCN ELan GQui ISea SBrw
x *nymansensis*	CTrG CWib ECrN EMil MLan NEgg
	SAPC SArc SDnm SReu SRkn SRms
	SSpi WBVN WFar WHCG
- 'George Graham'	GGGa IArd IMGH ISea
- 'Mount Usher'	ISea
- 'Nymansay' ♀H3	More than 30 suppliers
'Penwith' misapplied	see *E. cordifolia* x *lucida*
'Penwith' ambig.	CDoC CPMA GQui NEgg NLar
	SBrw SPer WBrE WDin WFar WGer
	WMoo

Eugenia (Myrtaceae)
australis	CMen IDee
myrtifolia	ERom

Eumorphia (Asteraceae)
prostrata	EBee

Eunomia see *Aethionema*

Euodia (Rutaceae)
daniellii	see *Tetradium daniellii*
hupehensis	see *Tetradium daniellii*
	Hupehense Group

Euonymus (Celastraceae)
B&L 12543	EPla EWes
B&SWJ 4457	WPGP
CC 4522	CPLG
alatus ♀H4	More than 30 suppliers
- B&SWJ 8794	WCru
- var. *apterus*	EPfP
- Chicago Fire	see *E. alatus* 'Timber Creek'
- 'Ciliodentatus'	see *E. alatus* 'Compactus'
§ - 'Compactus' ♀H4	More than 30 suppliers
§ - 'Fire Ball'	EPfP
- Little Moses = 'Odom'	MBlu
* - 'Macrophyllus'	EPfP
- 'Rudy Haag'	CPMA EPfP
- 'Select'	see *E. alatus* 'Fire Ball'
- 'Silver Cloud' **new**	EPfP
§ - 'Timber Creek'	CPMA EPfP MBlu MBri NLar
americanus	EPfP GIBF MBlu NLar
- 'Evergreen' **new**	EPfP
- narrow-leaved	EPfP NLar

atropurpureus — EPfP
'Benkomoki' **new** — MGos
bungeanus — CMCN EPfP EPla NLar
- 'Dart's Pride' — CPMA EPfP NLar
- 'Fireflame' — EPfP NLar
* - var. *mongolicus* — EPfP
- 'Pendulus' — EPfP MBlu SIFN
- var. *semipersistens* — CPMA EPla
carnosus — EPfP NLar
'Copper Wire' — EMil SPoG
cornutus var. — CPMA EPfP LPan MBlu NBhm NLar
  quinquecornutus — SIFN SPoG WPGP WPat
'Den Haag' — EPfP MBri
echinatus — EPfP EPla
- BL&M 306 — SLon
europaeus — More than 30 suppliers
- f. *albus* — CPMA CTho EPfP LTwo NLar
- 'Atropurpureus' — CMCN CTho EPfP MBlu MBri NLar SIFN
- 'Atrorubens' — CPMA
- 'Aucubifolius' (v) — EPfP
* - 'Aureus' — CNat
- 'Brilliant' **new** — EPfP
* - f. *bulgaricus* — EPfP
- 'Chrysophyllus' — EPfP MBlu NLar
- 'Howard' — EPfP
- var. *intermedius* — ENot EPfP MAsh MBlu NLar
- 'Miss Pinkie' — CEnd CMCN
- 'Pumilis' **new** — EPfP
- 'Red Cascade' ♀H4 — More than 30 suppliers
- 'Scarlet Wonder' — CPMA EPfP MBri NLar
- 'Thornhayes' — CTho EPfP
I - 'Variegatus' **new** — EPfP
farreri — see *E. nanus*
fimbriatus — EPfP
fortunei Blondy = — More than 30 suppliers
  'Interbolwi'PBR (v)
- 'Canadale Gold' (v) — CDoC EBee EPla LRHS MAsh MGos MWhi NHol WCFE WDin
- 'Coloratus' — EBee EHol EPfP MBar MSwo NHol SHBN SLon SPer WDin
- 'Dart's Blanket' — CDul ECrN ELan EPla MRav MWhi NScw SLPl SSta WDin WFar
- 'Emerald Cushion' — EBee SPer
- 'Emerald Gaiety' (v) ♀H4 — More than 30 suppliers
* - 'Emerald Green' **new** — IFoB
- 'Emerald 'n' Gold' (v) — More than 30 suppliers ♀H4
- 'Emerald Surprise' (v) ♀H4 — EPfP MBri NHol
- 'Gold Spot' — see *E. fortunei* 'Sunspot'
- 'Gold Tip' — see *E. fortunei* Golden Prince
§ - 'Golden Pillar' (v) — EHoe EHol EPla NHol WFar
§ - 'Golden Prince' (v) — EPfP EPla LRHS MBar MRav MSwo NHol NPro SLim SRms WGor
- 'Harlequin' (v) — CBcs COtt CSBt CWSG EBee EHoe ELan ENot EPfP EPla LAst LBuc LRHS LSRN MAsh MBar MGos MRav NPro SAga SHBN SLim SPer SPla SRms SWvt WCot WFar
- 'Highdown' — WWye
- 'Kewensis' — CWib EBee EPfP MBar MRav MWhi NVic SAPC SArc SBod SLon SPoG WCru WFar
- 'Minimus' — CDul CTri EPla MGos NHol NPro WFar
* - 'Minimus Variegatus' (v) — ECho SPlb
§ - var. *radicans* — CPlN MGan
- - 'Variegatus' (v) **new** — MAsh
- 'Sheridan Gold' — CTri EHoe EPla MRav NHol SHBN
- 'Silver Gem' — see *E. fortunei* 'Variegatus'
- 'Silver Pillar' (v) — CPLG ECrN EHoe ENot LRHS NHol WFar
- 'Silver Queen' (v) — More than 30 suppliers
- 'Sunshine' (v) — CAbP ELan LRHS MAsh MGos NEgg NHol

§ - 'Sunspot' (v) — CBcs CMHG CWSG ECrN EGra ELan EPla IFoB LAst MBar MGos MSwo NHol SLim SPer SRms WDin WFar WHar WTel
- 'Tustin' ♀H4 — EPla SLPl
§ - 'Variegatus' (v) — CMHG MBar NFor NSti SPer SRms STre WCot WDin
- var. *vegetus* — EPla
frigidus — EPfP GIBF WPGP
grandiflorus — CPMA CPle EPfP GIBF MBlu NLar SIFN SSpi WFar
- 'Red Wine' — CPMA CTho EBee EPfP MBri NLar WPat
- f. *salicifolius* — CPMA EPfP MBri NLar
hamiltonianus — CMCN EPfP SSpi WFar
I - 'Calocarpus' — MBlu SIFN
- 'Coral Chief' — SLon
- 'Fiesta' — EPfP MBri
I - 'Harlequin' **new** — CPMA
- subsp. *hians* — see *E. hamiltonianus* subsp. *sieboldianus*
- 'Indian Summer' — CPMA EPfP LRHS MAsh MBlu MBri MWea NLar SBrw SIFN SPur SSpi SSta
- 'Koi Boy' — CPMA LRHS MAsh MGos SIFN SPoG
- 'Miss Pinkie' — CDul CPMA EPfP LRHS MAsh MGos NLar SCoo SIFN SSpi SSta
- 'Pink Delight' — CPMA EPfP MBri
- 'Poort Bulten' — EPfP MBlu MBri NLar
- 'Popcorn' — CPMA EPfP MBlu
- 'Rainbow' — CPMA EPfP MBri NLar
- 'Red Chief' — EPfP
- 'Red Elf' — CPMA EPfP MBri
- 'Rising Sun' — EPfP MBlu MBri NLar
§ - subsp. *sieboldianus* — CDul CMCN CPMA CTho EBee EPfP GIBF MBri MRav SLPl WFar
- - 'Calocarpus' — EPfP MBri NLar
- - 'Coral Charm' — CPMA EPfP MBri NLar SMur
- - Semiexsertus Group — EPfP MBri
* - - var. *yedoensis* f. — EPfP
  koehneanus
- 'Snow' — EPfP MBlu NLar WPat
- 'Winter Glory' — CPMA EPfP LRHS MBlu MBri NLar WPat
- var. *yedoensis* — see *E. hamiltonianus* subsp. *sieboldianus*
hibarimisake — see *E. japonicus* 'Hibarimisake'
japonicus — CDoC CDul ECrN EPfP LRHS SAPC SArc SPer STop WDin XPep
- 'Albomarginatus' — CBcs CTri MBar NBlu SEND SRms STop
- 'Aureopictus' — see *E. japonicus* 'Aureus'
- 'Aureovariegatus' — see *E. japonicus* 'Ovatus Aureus'
§ - 'Aureus' (v) — CBcs CBrm CDoC CDul CMHG CSBt CWib EBee ECrN EGra ENot LRHS SCoo SHBN SLon SPer SSto WDin WHar WTel WWeb
- 'Benkomasaki' **new** — EPfP
- 'Bravo' — CDoC CDul EBee ECrN EGra EHoe EMil LAst LPan LRHS MGos MWea NHol NLar SCoo SPer SPoG SWvt WDin WFar
- 'Chollipo' ♀H4 — ELan EPfP EPla LRHS MAsh
- 'Compactus' — SAPC SArc SCoo
- 'Duc d'Anjou' misapplied — see *E. japonicus* 'Viridivariegatus'
- 'Duc d'Anjou' Carrière (v) — CBcs CHrt EHoe ELan EPla EWes LPan MRav NHol SEND SPoG
- 'Francien' (v) — SPoG
- 'Golden Maiden' — ELan EPfP LRHS MAsh SLim SPoG SWvt
- 'Golden Pillar' — see *E. fortunei* 'Golden Pillar'
- 'Green Spider' — SPoG
- 'Grey Beauty' — EBee NLar SCoo
§ - 'Hibarimisake' — EPfP EPla SBla
- 'Kathy'PBR — SPoG

§ - 'Latifolius Albomarginatus'	CDul EHoe EHol ELan EPfP EPla LRHS MRav MSwo SPer SPoG WDin WWeb
- 'Luna'	see *E. japonicus* 'Aureus'
- 'Macrophyllus Albus'	see *E. japonicus* 'Latifolius Albomarginatus'
- 'Maiden's Gold'	COtt CSBt EBee
- 'Marieke'	see *E. japonicus* 'Ovatus Aureus'
- 'Microphyllus'	CDoC CMac STre WFar WGwG
§ - 'Microphyllus Albovariegatus' (v)	More than 30 suppliers
§ - 'Microphyllus Aureovariegatus' (v)	CDoC CMea EGra EHyt EMil EPfP MGos MWhi NLar WCFE WCot WPat
- 'Microphyllus Aureus'	see *E. japonicus* 'Microphyllus Pulchellus'
§ - 'Microphyllus Pulchellus' (v)	CBcs CDoC CMHG CSBt CWSG EBee ECrN EPfP EPla LHop MBar MRav NHol NJOw SPoG SWvt WDin WHCG WWeb
- 'Microphyllus Variegatus'	see *E. japonicus* 'Microphyllus Albovariegatus'
§ - 'Ovatus Aureus' (v) ♀H4	CDoC CDul CMHG CPLG CSBt CTri CWSG EBee ECrN ENot EPfP LAst LRHS MBar MGos MRav MSwo NBlu SLim SPer SPlb SPoG SRms STop SWvt WCot WDin WFar WRHF WTel
- 'Président Gauthier' (v)	CDoC EBee ECrN MGos MWea SCoo SWvt WDin
- 'Pulchellus Aureovariegatus'	see *E. japonicus* 'Microphyllus Aureovariegatus'
I - 'Pyramidatus' **new**	EPfP
- 'Robustus'	EPfP EPla
- 'Royal Gold'	SPoG
- 'Silver Krista' (v)	SPoG
- 'Silver Princess = 'Moness'	SHBN WRHF
- 'Susan'	EPla NHol
§ - 'Viridivariegatus' (v)	LRHS MAsh
kiautschovicus	EPfP EPla
- 'Berry Hill'	EPfP NLar
- 'Manhattan'	EPfP NLar
latifolius	CMCN CPMA CTho EPfP NLar WDin
maackii	EWTr GIBF
macropterus	CPMA EPfP GIBF NLar
maximowiczianus	EPfP GIBF MBlu MBri NLar
morrisonensis	EPfP
- B&SWJ 3700	WCru
myrianthus	CPMA EPfP MBlu NLar SIFN
nanus	CNic CWib EHol EPfP EPla NHol NLar WSHC
- var. *turkestanicus*	EPfP EPla LHop MBri SLon SRms WFar
obovatus	EPfP
occidentalis	EPfP
oresbius	CPMA EPfP
oxyphyllus	CMCN CPMA CTho EPfP MBri NLar WCru WDin
- 'Angyo Elegant' (v) **new**	EPfP
- 'Waasland'	CPMA EPfP MBri NLar
pauciflorus	EPfP
§ *pendulus*	CHEx CHll CPLG
phellomanus ♀H4	CDul CEnd CTho CWSG EBee EHol EPfP EWTr GIBF LHop LRHS MAsh MBar MBlu MBri MRav NLar SBrw SHBN SIFN SPoG WDin WFar WPGP WPat
- 'Silver Surprise' (v)	CPMA EPfP MBri NLar SBrw WPat
Pierrolino = 'Heespierrrolino'PBR	SCoo SPoG
§ *planipes* ♀H4	More than 30 suppliers
- 'Dart's August Flame'	EPfP MBri NLar
- 'Gold Ore'	EPfP NLar
- 'Sancho'	EPfP MBri NLar

quelpaertensis **new**	EPfP
radicans	see *E. fortunei* var. *radicans*
'Rokojō'	CLyd
rongchuensis	EPfP MBri
rosmarinifolius	see *E. nanus*
sachalinensis misapplied	see *E. planipes*
sachalinensis (F. Schmidt) Maxim. from Ussuriland	GIBF
sacrosanctus	EPfP
sanguineus	CPMA CTho EPfP MBri NLar SSpi
spraguei **new**	EPfP
tanakae	GIBF
tingens	EPfP GIBF SIFN
trapococcus **new**	EPfP NLar
vagans	EPfP
- L 551	EPla SLon
velutinus	EPfP NLar
verrucosus	CPMA EPfP EPla GIBF MAsh MBri NLar SIFN
vidalii	EPfP
yedoensis	see *E. hamiltonianus* subsp. *sieboldianus*

Eupatorium (Asteraceae)

B&SWJ 9052 from Guatamala	WCru
RCB/Arg P-1	WCot
RCB/Arg Q-2	WCot
§ *album*	NBid WPer
- 'Braunlaub'	CPrp EChP EMan EMon LRHS NBre NGdn NSti WCAu WHrl WMnd
altissimum	MSal SRms
arnottianum	WCot
- RCB/Arg L-2	WCot
aromaticum	CRow CSev EBee MLLN MRav MWgw NBre NBro SWat WCHb WPer WSFF WWye
atrorubens	CCCN CKob EBee ERea EShb GCal
cannabinum	CArn EBee EHon ELan EMFW GBar GGar GPoy IFoB LPBA MBNS MBow MHer MRav MSal NBir NGHP NMir NPer NRnb SECG SPav SWat WGwG WPer WSFF WWpP WWye
- 'Album'	EMon LPhx NDov SMHy
- 'Flore Pleno' (d)	More than 30 suppliers
- 'Not Quite White'	LNCo
- 'Spraypaint'	CNat EPPr WWpP
* - 'Variegatum' (v)	CBow EBee EMan MDKP WCot
capillifolium	EShb LSou MLLN SDix SMrm WCot WDyG WPGP
- 'Elegant Feather'	CAby CHea CSpe ECtt EMan EWes EWin LHop LPhx MDKP SAga SHar SMad SUsu WHil
coelestinum	EBee EMan EShb EWes GCal LHop MDKP SMad WFar WHil WSFF WWpP
* *cyclophyllum*	EBrs EMan NBre
* *fistulosum*	CSec MGol NGdn
* - 'Atropurpureum'	CKno CMea EShb IBal NJOw WPer WWeb
fortunei	CArn
* - 'Variegatum' (v)	CBow CKno EBee EMan LSou WCot WPGP
glechonophyllum	MDKP
§ *ligustrinum* ♀H3	CBcs CDoC CPLG CPle CRHN CSam CTbh CTri CWib EBee ECha ELan EMan EPfP IDee ISea LRHS NCGa SAga SBrw SDix SLim SPer WCHb WFar WHCG WMnd WPat WSFF WSHC
lindleyanum	EBee
maculatum	see *E. purpureum* subsp. *maculatum*
madrense	WBor

'Massive White'	GCal
micranthum	see *E. ligustrinum*
occidentale NNS 94-53	WCot
perfoliatum	CAgr CArn GPoy MNrw MSal NBre
	NLar SPav WPer WWye
purpureum	More than 30 suppliers
- 'Album'	EPPr LPhx MLLN WWpP
- 'Bartered Bride'	EBrs ECtt EWes GCal
§ - subsp. *maculatum*	CAby EBee ECGP EHrv EMon
	MDKP NGHP NGdn NLar SBri
	STes WFar WHil WHrl WOut WPer
	WWpP
- - 'Album'	EBee EMon GBin NBir NDov NSti
	SMad
- - 'Atropurpureum' ♀H4	More than 30 suppliers
- - 'Berggarten'	GCal
- - 'Gateway'	CRow EBrs ECtt WTin
- - 'Glutball'	EBee EBrs GCal MNrw NChi SMad
	WWpP
- - 'Riesenschirm'	CKno CSam EBee ECGP EWes
	GCal IBal LPhx LRHS MSte SWat
	WCAu
- 'Purple Bush'	CHad CKno CSam EBee ECha
	LPhx MDKP NBre NDov NEgg
	SMad SSvw WGHP WSFF WWpP
rugosum	EBee ELan EPfP GBar GIBF LPhx
	MGol MWgw NLar SPav SPer
	WCHb WTin
- *album*	see *E. album*
- 'Brunette'	EHrv
- 'Chocolate' ♀H4	More than 30 suppliers
* 'Snowball'	SMrm
triplinerve	MSte
* *variabile* 'Variegatum' (v)	EMan EWes MDKP SMad WCot
	WWpP
weinmannianum	see *E. ligustrinum*

Euphorbia ✿ (*Euphorbiaceae*)

RCB/TQ J-4	WCot
'Abbey Dore'	MAvo WCot WSHC
altissima	MSte
amygdaloides	CNic ECtt NBlu SWat
- 'Bob's Choice'	EWes
- 'Brithembottom'	CSam
- 'Craigieburn'	CDes CSam EBee EChP EGle EMan
	EWes GBri GCal LRHS MBNS
	NDov NSti SUsu WCMO WCra
	WPGP WWeb
- 'Mark's Red' **new**	WCot
§ - 'Purpurea'	More than 30 suppliers
- 'Red Shank'	CMea SBla
§ - var. *robbiae* ♀H4	More than 30 suppliers
- - dwarf	EPot EWes GCal
- - 'Pom Pom'	CDes EBee EMan LSou WPGP
- - 'Redbud'	EBee EMan EPla EWes LSou SLPl
- - 'Rubra'	see *E. amygdaloides* 'Purpurea'
- 'Signal'	EMon
- 'Variegata' (v)	GBuc SMad
- 'Welsh Dragon'	EBee
- 'Winter Glow'	CSpe
- yellow-leaved	WCot
aureoviridiflora	LToo
baselicis	CBow CSpe EDAr EKen EMan
	EWll GBBs LSou MGol
biglandulosa	see *E. rigida*
Blackbird = 'Nothowlee'	ENot LBuc LRHS MGos NSti SPoG
new	
'Blue Haze'	CBct SBla
'Blue Lagoon' **new**	NBhm
brittingeri	NWit
- Baker's form	EPPr
broteroi	WCot
bulbispina	LToo
canariensis	EPfP
capitata	CLyd
capitulata	ELan EPot EWes MTho NWit

ceratocarpa	CFis CFwr EBee EPPr EWes EWin
	GBuc MAvo MBri NWit SMad
	WCMO WCot WPGP WSHC
characias	CBcs CHEx CoIW EAEE EBee ECtt
	EPfP MDun MRav NChi NEgg
	NOak NPer NPri NVic SPer SRms
	WCot WFar WHen WMnd WPer
	XPep
- Ballyrogan hybrids	IBlr
- 'Black Pearl'	CBcs CHrt CMHG CTbh EBee
	EChP EPfP IPot LAst MBNS MCCP
	MDun MSte NCGa NEgg NSti
	SDnm SHop SMer SPav SPoG SWvt
	WFar WOVN
- 'Blue Wonder'	CRez CSpe EBee EPfP GCal GMaP
	LHop LRHS MAvo MCCP MDun
	MSte NEgg NLar NWit SDnm SPav
	SPoG WCMO WCot WGer WWeb
- subsp. *characias*	CBow EBee EHrv GMaP LBBr
	MGos SMHy SPoG WCru
- - 'Blue Hills'	ECtt EGle GBin GBuc GCal MSph
	NWit SMrm
- - 'Burrow Silver' (v)	CBcs CFir CFwr CPen EBee ELan
	LDai MBNS MCCP MRav NBPC
	NCGa NEgg SCoo SDnm SLim SPav
	WCMO WCot WWhi
- - 'Green Mantle'	IBlr
- - 'H.E. Bates'	NBir
- - 'Humpty Dumpty'	More than 30 suppliers
- - 'Perry's Winter Blusher'	ECtt NWit
- dwarf	SMrm
- 'Forescate'	CSWP EBee ECGP EGle EMil EPfP
	EWin MNFA MRav MSte NCGa
	NWit SDnm SPav WFar WMnd
- 'Giant Green Turtle'	CMil
- 'Goldbrook'	EGle EHoe EMan LHop LRHS
	MBNS MNFA MRav MSph MSte
	MWgw SHBN
- 'Portuguese Velvet' ♀H4	CBct CDes CSam CSpe EChP ECha
	EGle EGra EHrv ELan EMar EWTr
	EWsh LHop LPhx MNFA MRav
	NCGa NDov SPav WCMO WCot
	WMnd WSHC WWFP WWeb WWhi
- Silver Swan =	ELan EMan ENot EPfP LBuc MGos
'Wilcott'PBR (v)	NSti SBra SHGC SPoG
- 'Sombre Melody'	IBlr
- 'Spring Splendour'	EWes NWit
- 'Starbright'	EBee NWit
- 'Whistleberry Gold'	EGle
- 'Whistleberry Jade'	EGle NWit
- subsp. *wulfenii* ♀H3-4	More than 30 suppliers
- - 'Bosahan' (v)	CBcs NWit
- - 'Emmer Green' (v)	CBow CDes CPen CSpe EBee EHrv
	EWes GBri GMaP NWit SBla SWat
	WCMO WCot WFoF
- - 'Jayne's Golden Giant'	SMad
- - 'Jimmy Platt'	EGle MTho SRms WBrE WCMO
	WCot WPic
§ - - 'John Tomlinson' ♀H3-4	EBee EGra EHrv EShb EWes GBin
	GMaP MFOX MNFA MRav NEgg
	WCMO WCot
- - Kew form	see *E. characias* subsp. *wulfenii*
	'John Tomlinson'
- - 'Lambrook Gold' ♀H3-4	CSam EBee ECtt EGle EPfP LRHS
	MRav MWat NPer SMad SPer
	WCMO WFar WGer WMnd
- - 'Lambrook Gold'	see *E. characias* subsp. *wulfenii*
seed-raised	Margery Fish Group
- - 'Lambrook Yellow'	EBee EWsh GBuc SMur WSPU
§ - - Margery Fish Group	EGle LRHS NBir SPer
- - 'Perry's Tangerine'	EWes NPer NWit
§ - - 'Purple and Gold'	CMMP CRez CSpe EBee EWes
	GMaP NWit SWvt WCMO WCot
- - 'Purpurea'	see *E. characias* subsp. *wulfenii*
	'Purple and Gold'
- - var. *sibthorpii*	WCMO

- - 'Silver Shadow'	SBla	
- - 'Thelma's Giant'	NWit	
clavarioides	EHyt	
- var. *truncata*	WCot	
cognata	NWit	
- CC&McK 607	EWes	
- CC&McK 724	EBee GBin	
'Copton Ash'	CSpe EBee EWTr EWes MAvo	
	NWit	
corallioides	ECha EMan EShb IBlr LRHS NBPC	
	NDov NPer NSti SHFr SPav SRms	
	WBrE WHer WPnD XPep	
§ *cornigera* ♀H4	CElw CFwr CHad EBee ECha EPfP	
	GBBs GBin GCal GMac IBlr LRHS	
	MNFA MRav NBid NCGa NDov	
	NGdn NLar NSti SWat WCot WHoo	
	WLin WPGP	
- 'Goldener Turm'	EChP	
corollata	EShb	
croizatii	LToo	
cylindrifolia var.	LToo	
tubifera		
cyparissias	CArn CBcs CHrt EBee EChP ECha	
	EDAr ELan GAbr LRHS MLHP	
	MRav NBir NFor NGdn NJOw	
	NMen NSti NVic SPav SRms WEas	
	WFar WFoF WPer WTin XPep	
- 'Baby'	WFar	
- 'Betten'	see *E.* x *gayeri* 'Betten'	
- 'Bushman Boy'	GBri IBlr	
- 'Clarice Howard'	see *E. cyparissias* 'Fens Ruby'	
- clone 2	WCot	
§ - 'Fens Ruby'	More than 30 suppliers	
- 'Orange Man'	CWan EAEE EBee EChP EDAr	
	EMon EPPr EPfP ERou EWes GBin	
	GBri IBlr LRHS MWgw NBro NHol	
	NSti SPla SWat SWvt WFar	
- 'Purpurea'	see *E. cyparissias* 'Fens Ruby'	
- 'Red Devil'	CBre IBlr NWit	
- 'Tall Boy'	EMon EWes GBri IBlr XPep	
deflexa **new**	GKev	
dendroides	WCot	
denticulata	SBla	
'Despina'	NLar	
Diamond Frost =	CCVN LSou SVil WOVN	
'Inneuphe' **new**		
§ *donii*	EBee EGle EWes GGar IBlr NDov	
	NWit SDix SMHy WCru WFar WPer	
- 'Amjilassa'	SAga SUsu	
dulcis	CBre CStu ECtt NBro NOak NWit	
	WEas WHen	
- 'Chameleon'	More than 30 suppliers	
'Efanthia'	CCVN CEnd CRez CSpe ERou	
	EWes GKev LSou MBri MSph NLar	
	NPri SMrm SPoG STes	
enopla	EPem EPfP	
epithymoides	see *E. polychroma*	
esula Baker's form	NWit	
Excalibur = 'Froeup' PBR	CBgR COIW CSpe EBee ELan	
♀H4	EMan GBin GBuc LHop LPhx	
	LRHS MAvo MBNS MBri MCCP	
	MRav MSte MWgw NBir NCGa	
	NSti SHBN SPoG WFar WSHC	
	WWhi	
fragifera	EBee NWit	
'Garblesham Enchanter'	EPPr NWit	
§ x *gayeri* 'Betten'	EBee EMan GCal	
glauca	CFee CFir CPLG ECou NWit	
'Golden Foam'	see *E. stricta*	
gottlebei	LToo	
griffithii	CHll MLHP NBro SPav SWat WFar	
	WGer WMoo WTel	
- 'Dixter' ♀H4	More than 30 suppliers	
- 'Dixter Flame'	EGra NWit	
- 'Fern Cottage'	CElw EBee EHrv EWes GAbr NBre	
	SMrm SUsu WMnd	

- 'Fireglow'	More than 30 suppliers	
- 'King's Caple'	EBee MBNS NWit SPoG WCru	
- 'Wickstead'	EBee EMar GAbr MLHP WViv	
hyberna	CFis EBee GBri IBlr LTwo MLLN	
	NMen NWit SWat	
iharanae	LToo	
jacquemontii	ECha EMan GIBF MLLN MNrw	
	MRav NChi NDov NWit	
'Jade Dragon'	CFwr CSpe NBre SPoG	
'Jessie'	WCot	
jolkinii	EBee	
'Kalipso' **new**	ERou	
x *keysii*	MBri	
lactea 'Grey Ghost'	LToo	
lambii **new**	EShb	
lathyris	CArn CBgR CBre EMar MDun	
	MHer MLHP NBid NLar NPer	
	NRnb SRms WEas WWye	
longifolia misapplied	see *E. cornigera*	
longifolia D. Don	see *E. donii*	
longifolia Lamarck	see *E. mellifera*	
margalidiana	EWes	
x *martini* ♀H3	More than 30 suppliers	
- 'Aperitif'	EPfP IBal MBNS NLar WCot	
- 'Baby Charm'	CPen LRHS	
- dwarf	CFir GCal	
- 'Red Dwarf'	CMil MSph	
- 'Tiny Tim' **new**	SPoG	
§ *mellifera* ♀H3	More than 30 suppliers	
milii ♀H1	CHal EBak LToo SHFr	
- 'Koenigers Aalbäumle'	MBri SHFr	
* - 'Variegata' (v)	CHal	
- yellow-flowered	CHal	
myrsinites ♀H4	More than 30 suppliers	
nereidum	EWes NWit	
nicaeensis	CDes EBee EMan EMon GCal LPhx	
	NWit SMad WCot WPGP XPep	
- subsp. *glareosa*	NWit	
oblongata	EBee EMan EWes GBuc IBlr LRHS	
	NWit	
'Orange Grove' **new**	NBhm	
pachypodioides	LToo	
palustris ♀H4	More than 30 suppliers	
- 'Walenburg's Glorie'	CAby CMHG EBee EChP ECha	
	ELan EWTr GBin LRHS MBri	
	MNrw MRav NCGa NSti NWit	
	SMad SWat WCra WRHF	
- 'Zauberflöte'	CHrt LPBA SRms WFar WWpP	
x *paradoxa*	NWit	
paralias	WCot WHer XPep	
x *pasteurii*	CBgR CFir CKob CPLG CPom	
	EBee EWes LSou MAvo SMHy	
	WMul WPGP	
- 'John Phillips' **new**	WPGP	
pekinensis	MSal NWit	
pilosa 'Major'	see *E. polychroma* 'Major'	
piscatoria	WPGP	
pithyusa	CBgR CNic CSam CSpe EBee EChP	
	ECha ECtt ELan EMan EPfP EWTr	
	LRHS MArl NGdn SHBN XPep	
§ *polychroma* ♀H4	More than 30 suppliers	
§ - 'Candy'	CHar CSam EBee EChP ECha	
	EHrv ELan EPfP GCal LRHS	
	MAvo MCCP MDun NCGa SEND	
	SPla WCot WFar WHoo WLin	
	WMnd	
- 'Emerald Jade'	GBri IBlr NWit WPGP	
§ - 'Lacy' (v)	CDoC CElw EBee ECtt EGle EHoe	
	EHrv ELan EMan ERou EWes LAst	
	MCCP MRav NBir NCob NEgg	
	NGdn NWit SMad SPla SPoG WCot	
	WGwG WHil	
§ - 'Major' ♀H4	CMHG CPLG GCal LPhx SAga	
	WCot WEas	
- 'Midas'	CFee EGle MAvo MNrw NWit	
	SMrm SUsu	

- 'Purpurea'	see *E. polychroma* 'Candy'
* - 'Senior'	EMil EWTr LBmB MAvo NWit WMnd
- 'Sonnengold'	EWes GCal
- 'Variegata'	see *E. polychroma* 'Lacy'
portlandica	CNic MBri NWit WHer
§ x *pseudovirgata*	CFis EMan IBlr NWit
pugniformis	MBri
pulcherrima	LRHS MBri
'Purple Preference'	EPPr NWit
Redwing = 'Charam'PBR ♀H4	EBee ELan EMan ENot EPfP GBBs LRHS MGos MRav NLar SBra SCoo SHGC SPer SPoG
reflexa	see *E. seguieriana* subsp. *niciciana*
§ *rigida*	CBro CDes CKno EBee EChP EGle EGoo EHrv ELan EMan EPfP EPyc EWes GCal GMaP LPhx MAvo MLLN NDov NSti SBla SUsu WCot WFar WHoo WKif WPGP WSHC
- 'Sardis'	NWit
robbiae	see *E. amygdaloides* var. *robbiae*
'Rosies Surprise'	LTwo MAvo MTho NWit
rothiana GWJ 9479a	WCru
sarawschanica	EBee ECha EMan GBin LPhx NWit WCot
schillingii ♀H4	More than 30 suppliers
seguieriana	ECha EMan GBin NBir NLar WPer
§ - subsp. *niciciana*	CBow EBee EMan EMon EWsh GBin MArl NBir SBla SUsu WCra WHoo
serrata	XPep
serrulata	see *E. stricta*
sikkimensis ♀H4	CFee CMHG CMea CPLG CSam CSpe CWCL EBee ECha EGra ELan GAbr GBBs MAvo NBid NEgg SMrm SPav SRms WCMO WCot WCru WEas WFar WWye
- GWJ 9214	WCru
soongarica	MSte NWit
spinosa	NWit XPep
stracheyi **new**	GIBF
§ *stricta*	EBee EMan GBri IBlr MCCP WRos WTin
stygiana	CAby CFir CSam EBee EPla LEdu LPhx MAvo MSte NWit SAga WCru WPGP WSHC
- 'Devil's Honey'	NWit WCot
* *submammillaris*	MBri
'Variegata' (v)	
terracina	WCot
tirucalli	EShb
umfoloziensis	LToo
uralensis	see *E.* x *pseudovirgata*
valdevilloscarpa **new**	EDAr WLin
viguieri ♀H1	LToo
villosa	NWit
§ *virgata*	EWes NSti NWit SPav WCot
x *waldsteinii*	see *E. virgata*
wallichii misapplied	see *E. donii*
wallichii Kohli	see *E. cornigera*
wallichii Hook. f.	CPLG CSam EBee EMan GCal IBlr LRHS MBri NBid NOrc WHil WPGP WSHC
- 'Lemon and Lime'	CWib LSou MWhi

Euptelea (Eupteleaceae)

franchetii	see *E. pleiosperma*
§ *pleiosperma*	CMCN EPfP IArd NLar SSpi
polyandra	CMCN EPfP NLar WPGP

Eurya (Theaceae)

japonica	WPGP
- 'Moutiers' (v) **new**	WPat
- 'Variegata' misapplied	see *Cleyera japonica* 'Fortunei'

Euryops (Asteraceae)

§ *acraeus* ♀H4	CHea CMea CPle CSBt EAEE ECho ELan EPot LHop LRHS MDun MWat NFor NMen NWCA SAga SIng WAbe WFar WLin
candollei	NWCA WAbe
§ *chrysanthemoides*	CHEx ERea EShb MSte
- 'Sonnenschein'	CHal EBee EWin SPet
decumbens	CNic NJOw WLin
evansii	see *E. acraeus*
linearis	GGar WWFP
pectinatus ♀H2	CBcs CCCN CDoC CHEx CHen CPLG CSam CTbh CTrC CTrG CTri EBee ERea EShb GGar MNrw MRav SGar SHBN SOWG WCFE WHer WWye XPep
speciosissimus	LEdu
tysonii	CPle CStu EBee GCal GEdr GGar SPlb WCMO WCot
virgineus	CBcs CBrm CTrC CTrG EBee GGar IDee WGer WWFP

Euscaphis (Staphyleaceae)

japonica	NLar

Eustachys (Poaceae)

§ *distichophylla*	EBee EPPr MAvo WCMO WCot WPrP

Eustephia (Amaryllidaceae)

darwinii	CMon

Eustoma (Gentianaceae)

§ *grandiflorum*	LRHS MBri
russellianum	see *E. grandiflorum*

Eustrephus (Philesiaceae)

latifolius	ECou

Eutaxia (Papilionaceae)

obovata	ECou

Euterpe (Arecaceae)

edulis	LPal

Euthamia (Compositae)

§ *gymnospermoides*	EWes

Evolvulus (Convolvulaceae)

convolvuloides	ERea
§ *glomeratus* 'Blue Daze'	ERea
pilosus 'Blue Daze'	see *E. glomeratus* 'Blue Daze'

Ewartia (Asteraceae)

planchonii	NLAp

Exacum (Gentianaceae)

affine ♀H1+3	LRHS MBri
- 'Rococo'	MBri

Exochorda (Rosaceae)

giraldii	CPle WGwG
- var. *wilsonii*	CSam EBee EPfP EWTr GBin IMGH LHop MAsh MBNS MBlu NLar SBrw SLim SPoG SSta SWvt
x *macrantha*	EBee MNHC
- 'The Bride' ♀H4	More than 30 suppliers
racemosa	EHol EPfP ISea MGos NBlu NLar SHBN SPer WDin WHCG
serratifolia	EPfP NLar SBrw
- 'Northern Pearls'	CPMA
- 'Snow White'	CPMA EBee LBuc MBlu MDun NLar

F

Fabiana (Solanaceae)

imbricata CAbP EMil EPfP GGar GQui LRHS
SAga SBra SBrw SLon SPer SPoG

- 'Prostrata' EBee EPfP GCal LRHS SBrw SSpi
WSHC

- f. *violacea* ♀H3 CBcs CFee CPLG CSBt CTri EBee
EHol EPfP GQui LRHS MAsh MBar
SBrw SPer WKif XPep

Fagopyrum (Polygonaceae)

cymosum see *F. dibotrys*
§ **dibotrys** EBee ECha ELan EPPr LEdu MGol
NSti WMoo

Fagus ✿ (Fagaceae)

§ **crenata** CMCN CMen WDin WNor
- 'Mount Fuji' SBir
engleriana CMCN SBir SIFN
grandifolia CMCN
- subsp. *mexicana* SBir
japonica CMCN
lucida CMCN
orientalis CMCN CTho ECrN
sieboldii see *F. crenata*
sylvatica ♀H4 More than 30 suppliers
§ - 'Albomarginata' (v) CLnd CMCN
- 'Albovariegata' see *F. sylvatica* 'Albomarginata'
- 'Ansorgei' CEnd CLnd CMCN CTho MBlu
SCrf WPat
N - Atropurpurea Group More than 30 suppliers
- 'Aurea Pendula' CEnd CMCN MBlu SBLw
- 'Bicolor Sartini' MBlu
- 'Birr Zebra' CEnd
- 'Black Swan' CEnd CMCN ECrN ENot LPan
MBlu SBLw SBir SMad WGor
- 'Bornyensis' SBir
- 'Brathay Purple' MBlu
- 'Cochleata' CMCN
- 'Cockleshell' CDul CMCN CTho MBlu SBir
SHBN
- 'Comptoniifolia' see *F. sylvatica* var. *heterophylla*
'Comptoniifolia'
- 'Cristata' CMCN MBlu
§ - 'Dawyck' ♀H4 CBcs CCVT CDoC CDul CLnd
CMCN COtt CSBt CTho EBee
ECho ECrN ELan EMil ENot EPfP
LAst LPan MBar MBri MGos MRav
NWea SBLw SLim SPer WDin
WOrn
- 'Dawyck Gold' ♀H4 More than 30 suppliers
- 'Dawyck Purple' ♀H4 More than 30 suppliers
- 'Fastigiata' misapplied see *F. sylvatica* 'Dawyck'
- 'Felderbach' MBlu SBir
- 'Franken' (v) MBlu
- 'Frisio' CDul CEnd CMCN
- 'Grandidentata' CMCN LPan SLon
- 'Greenwood' CDul CMCN MBlu
* - 'Haaren' CMCN
- var. *heterophylla* CLnd CSBt CTho ECho NWea
WOrn
- - 'Aspleniifolia' ♀H4 CDoC CDul CEnd CMCN COtt
ECrN ELan EMil ENot EPfP IMGH
LPan LRHS MBar MBri MGos NEgg
SBLw SBir SCoo SHBN SPer SPoG
WDin WMou WNor
§ - - 'Comptoniifolia' SBir
- - f. *laciniata* CMCN MBlu
- 'Horizontalis' CMCN
- f. *latifolia* SBLw
- 'Leith' **new** SBir
- 'Luteovariegata' (v) CEnd CMCN NLar

- 'Mercedes' CMCN MBlu SBir WPat
- 'Miltonensis' CDul LPan SMad
N - 'Pendula' ♀H4 CBcs CCVT CDoC CDul CEnd
CLnd CMCN CSBt CTho EBee
ECho ECrN ELan EWTr IMGH
LPan MBar MGos MRav MSwo
NWea SBLw SBir SCrf SHBN SPer
WDin WHar WMou WOrn
- 'Prince George of Crete' CDul CEnd CMCN CTho SBir
- 'Purple Fountain' ♀H4 CDoC CDul CEnd CMCN COtt
EBee ELan EMil LAst LPan LRHS
MAsh MBar MBlu MBri MGos
SBLw SIFN SLim SPer SPoG WOrn
- Purple-leaved Group see *F. sylvatica* Atropurpurea
Group
- 'Purpurea Nana' CMCN
- 'Purpurea Pendula' More than 30 suppliers
§ - 'Purpurea Tricolor' (v) CDoC CDul CEnd CMCN ECrN
MBar MBri MGos MWya NBea
NBlu NEgg SBir SCoo SCrf SHBN
SPer WDin WOrn
- 'Quercifolia' CMCN MBlu
I - 'Quercina' CMCN
- 'Red Obelisk' see *F. sylvatica* 'Rohan Obelisk'
- 'Riversii' ♀H4 More than 30 suppliers
- 'Rohan Gold' CDul CEnd CLnd CMCN MBlu
§ - 'Rohan Obelisk' CDul CEnd CMCN EBee ELan IArd
MBlu MBri MGos SBir WOrn
I - 'Rohan Pyramidalis' CDul CEnd CMCN
- 'Rohan Trompenburg' CMCN MBlu
- 'Rohan Weeping' MBlu
- 'Rohanii' CAbP CBcs CDoC CDul CEnd
CLnd CMCN CTho CTri EBee
ECho ECrN ELan EPfP IMGH LPan
NEgg SCrf SHBN WDin WFar
WOrn
- 'Roseomarginata' see *F. sylvatica* 'Purpurea Tricolor'
- 'Rotundifolia' CDoC CDul LPan MBlu
- 'Silver Wood' CMCN
- 'Spaethiana' CMCN EWTr
- 'Striata' CMCN SBir SIFN
- 'Tortuosa Purpurea' CMCN CTho MBlu
- 'Tricolor' (v) CBcs CLnd CSBt CWib EBee ELan
LPan MAsh SBLw SHBN WDin
- 'Tricolor' misapplied see *F. sylvatica* 'Purpurea Tricolor'
- 'Viridivariegata' (v) CMCN
- 'Zlatia' CBcs CDoC CDul CLnd CMCN
CSBt CTho CWib ELan EPfP MBar
MGan MGos MSwo NBee NEgg
SBLw SBir SHBN SPer SPoG WDin
WOrn

Falkia (Convolvulaceae)

repens CFir

Fallopia (Polygonaceae)

aubertii see *F. baldschuanica*
§ **baldschuanica** More than 30 suppliers
- Summer Sunshine = MCCP
'Acofal'PBR
baldschuanicum NPri
'Pink Flamingo'
x *bohemica* 'Spectabilis' CBow CRow EMon
(v)
§ *japonica* var. *compacta* CRow NBre NLar NPri WFar
WMoo
- - 'Fuji Snow' see *F. japonica* var. *compacta* 'Milk
Boy'
§ - - 'Milk Boy' (v) CBow CRow EMan EShb EWes
EWin ITer SMad
- - f. *rosea* CSpe
- - 'Variegata' see *F. japonica* var. *compacta* 'Milk
Boy'
- 'Crimson Beauty' CRow SMHy
§ **multiflora** CArn EBrs EOHP MSal
- var. *hypoleuca* EBee GCal MCCP SPoG

- - B&SWJ 120	WCru
sachalinensis	CRow EBee EWes NLar

Faradaya (Verbenaceae)
splendida	CPIN

Farfugium (Asteraceae)
§ *japonicum*	CHEx MTho
- B&SWJ 884	WCru
- 'Argenteum' (v)	CFir CHEx SMad WCMO WCot WFar WSan
- 'Aureomaculatum' (v) ♀H1	CAbb CFir CHEx CKob EBee EChP EHoe EMan EPfP MBNS MCCP MTho SBig SDnm SMad SPav SWat WCMO WFar WHal WHer WMul WSan
- 'Crispatum'	More than 30 suppliers
- var. *formosanum* B&SWJ 7125	WCru
- var. *giganteum*	CHEx WCMO WCot
- 'Kagami-jishi' (v)	WCot WHil
- 'Kinkan' (v)	WCot WHil
I - 'Nanum'	CHEx
- 'Ryuto'	WCMO WCot
I - 'Tsuwa-buki'	WCot
tussilagineum	see *F. japonicum*

Fargesia (Poaceae)
from Jiuzhaigou, China	MBri WJun
angustissima	EPla MWht WPGP
contracta	EPla
denudata	ENBC EPla MBri SBig WJun
- L 1575	MMoz MWht WPGP
dracocephala	CAbb CDoC EBee EPfP EPla GBin LEdu MAvo MBrN MBri MMoz MWht NGdn SBig SEND SLPl SPoG WJun WMoo WMul WNor WPGP
ferax	EPla WJun WPGP
fungosa	EPla WJun WPGP
§ *murielae* ♀H4	More than 30 suppliers
- 'Amy'	NLar NMoo
- 'Bimbo'	CHEx EPfP GBin LAst MWht NPal WJun WMoo WMul WPGP
- 'Grüne Hecke'	MWht
- 'Harewood'	CWSG EBee GBin MBri MMoz MWgw MWht NMoo SWvt WFar WPGP
- 'Joy'	NLar WMoo WPnP
- 'Jumbo'	CAbb CHEx CSBt CWSG EAmu EBee ELan ENBC EPfP EPla EWsh GAbr GBin LPal LPan LRHS MAvo MBNS MBri MMoz MWht NGdn NPri SBig SPoG SSto SWvt WFar WJun WMul
- 'Lava' **new**	MBri
- 'Little John'	ENBC
- 'Kranich'	NLar
- 'Mae'	MWht
- 'Novecento'	ELan MBri
- 'Pinocchio' **new**	MBri
- 'Simba' ♀H4	More than 30 suppliers
- 'Vampire' **new**	MBri
- 'Willow'	MBri
§ *nitida*	More than 30 suppliers
* - from Jiuzhaigou, China	EPla MWht WPGP
- 'Anceps'	EPla MWht
- 'Eisenach'	CAbb EPla LRHS MBri MMoz NGdn WFar WMoo
- Gansu 2	EBee EPla
- 'Great Wall'	MBri
- 'Nymphenburg' ♀H4	CEnd CFwr CPMA CTbh ENBC EPla LRHS MBar MBri MMoz MWhi MWht NLar NMoo NPri SBig WFar WMoo WMul WPGP
- 'Wakehurst'	EPla MWht NLar

robusta	CAbb CEnd EFul ENBC EPfP EPla LPal MBrN MBri MMoz MWht NGdn NLar NMoo SBig SLPl WJun WMul WNor
- 'Pingwu'	MBri MWht NLar
- 'Red Sheath'	EPla ERod MMoz MWht NPal SEND WJun WPGP
- 'White Sheath'	ENBC
- 'Wolong'	CDoC MWht
rufa	CAbb CEnt ENBC ENot EPfP EPla EShb MAvo MBar MBrN MBri MCCP MMoz MWht NLar NPal SBig WJun WMul WNor WPGP
spathacea misapplied	see *F. murielae*
utilis	CAbb EPla ERod LEdu MAvo MBri MMoz MWht NLar NPal SEND WJun WNor WPGP
yulongshanensis	EPla MWht

Farsetia (Brassicaceae)
clypeata	see *Fibigia clypeata*

Fascicularia (Bromeliaceae)
andina	see *F. bicolor*
§ *bicolor*	More than 30 suppliers
§ - subsp. *canaliculata*	EOas IBlr LEdu SChr WPGP
kirchhoffiana	see *F. bicolor* subsp. *canaliculata*
pitcairniifolia (Verlot) Mez	see *Ochagavia* sp.
pitcairniifolia misapplied	see *F. bicolor*

x *Fatshedera* (Araliaceae)
lizei ♀H3	CBcs CDoC CDul CHEx EBee EGra EPfP EPla EWTr GQui IDee LRHS MPRe MRav MWat NPal SAPC SArc SBra SDix SMac SPer SPla SPlb SPoG SWvt WCFE WDin WFar
§ - 'Annemieke' (v) ♀H3	CBow CDoC CHEx EBee EPfP LHop MPRe MRav SBra SMac SMad SPer SPoG WCMO
§ - 'Aurea' (v)	EHoe ELan EPfP LRHS SBra SEND
- 'Aureopicta'	see x *F. lizei* 'Aurea'
- 'Lemon and Lime'	see x *F. lizei* 'Annemieke'
- 'Maculata'	see x *F. lizei* 'Annemieke'
* - 'Silver Prusca'	EPla
- 'Variegata' (v) ♀H3	CAbb CBcs CHEx EBee ELan EPfP LAst LRHS MPRe NPal SBra SEND SHGN SMac SMer SPer SPla SPoG SWvt WDin WFar

Fatsia (Araliaceae)
§ *japonica* ♀H4	More than 30 suppliers
- 'Golden Handshake' **new**	CBow
- 'Moseri'	CABP CMdw CSam CTrC EChP ECtt IBal LHop MSte NGdn NLar SMad SWvt WCMO WCot WGwG WWhi
- 'Murakumo-nishiki' (v)	NPal
- 'Spider's Web' (v) **new**	CBow NBhm WCot
- 'Variegata' (v) ♀H3	CBcs CDul ENot EPfP LRHS MBri MGos MRav NPal SArc SPer WCMO
papyrifera	see *Tetrapanax papyrifer*
polycarpa	CHEx
- B&SWJ 7144	WCru

Faucaria (Aizoaceae)
tigrina ♀H1	EPfP

Fauria see *Nephrophyllidium*

Feijoa see *Acca*

Felicia (Asteraceae)
§ *amelloides*	CAby CHEx CHal ERea EShb LAst LRHS MLan SGar SPlb

- 'Astrid Thomas' — CSpe
- 'Read's Blue' — CSpe EWin LIck SDnm XPep
- 'Read's White' — ERea EWin MOak SDnm SPet
§ - 'Santa Anita' ♀H3 — CHal CTri ECtt ERea LIck
§ - variegated (v) — CHal ECtt ERea EWin IHMH LAst
  LIck MBri MOak MSte NBlu NPer
  NPri SHFr SPet
- variegated, white- — EWin LIck
  flowered (v)
§ *amoena* — CTri MOak SRms
- 'Variegata' (v) — CTri
capensis — see *F. amelloides*
- 'Variegata' — see *F. amelloides* variegated
coelestis — see *F. amelloides*
drakensbergensis — ETow
erigeroides — CHal GFai
filifolia — CMdw WWFP XPep
fruticosa — CHll
natalensis — see *F. rosulata*
pappei — see *F. amoena*
§ *petiolata* — EBee EMan EWin MOak NSti SGar
  WCot WEas WWFP
§ *rosulata* — CPBP ECho EHyt EMon GCrs
  MBrN MHer MTho NBro NJOw
  SRms SRot
uliginosa — ECho EDAr EWes GEdd GGar
  IHMH LRHS MTho WFar

fennel see *Foeniculum vulgare*

fenugreek see *Trigonella foenum-graecum*

Ferraria (Iridaceae)
§ *crispa* — LBow
- var. *nortieri* — CMon
ferrariola — CMon
uncinata — CMon
undulata — see *F. crispa*

Ferula (Apiaceae)
assa-foetida — CArn EBee LDai LEdu MSal NDov
chiliantha — see *F. communis* subsp. *glauca*
§ *communis* — CArn CMea CSpe CWCL EBee
  ECGP ECha ELan EShb IDee LEdu
  MEHN NBid NLar NSti SDix SDnm
  SMad SPav SPlb SPoG SUsu WCAu
  WCot WEas WJek WPGP WPrP
  WSHC
- 'Gigantea' — see *F. communis*
§ - subsp. *glauca* — EMan EWes LPhx SDix SGar WCot
  WPGP XPep
'Giant Bronze' — see *Foeniculum vulgare* 'Giant
  Bronze'
tingitana — LDai SMad
- 'Cedric Morris' — ECha LPhx SDix SMHy WCot
  WSHC

Festuca (Poaceae)
actae — CBig LEdu SGar WHrl
amethystina — CBig CBrm CHrt CKno CWCL
  EHoe EMon GIBF LEdu LRHS MBnl
  MNHC MNrw MWhi NBlu NCiG
  NGdn NHol NNor NOak SPer SWal
  WMoo WPer WRos WTin
- 'Aprilgrün' — EHoe EPPr
arundinacea — CRWN
californica — CBig EBee EPPr
coxii — EHoe MAvo
curvula subsp. — EPla EShb NHol
  crassifolia
'Eisvogel' — EBee
elegans — EPPr
erecta — EHoe
eskia — CKno CWan EAEE EBee EHoe
  EHul EPPr LRHS MWhi NHol SPer
  SPla WDyG WPer

filiformis — EHoe
'Fromefield Blue' — EChP EHul
§ *gautieri* — CBrm GBin GCal MBar NBre
  NGdn WFoF
- 'Pic Carlit' — EMon GBin
gigantea — CBig NBre
glacialis — EHoe
glauca — More than 30 suppliers
I - 'Auslese' — CPLG EPPr LBMP NGdn
- 'Azurit' — CBig CPrp EChP EGra EHoe EPPr
  EWes EWsh LAst MBnl NHol NLar
  SIng SPoG
§ - 'Blaufuchs' ♀H4 — More than 30 suppliers
§ - 'Blauglut' — CBig EAEE EBee EBrs EHoe EHul
  ENot EPfP EPla GSki LRHS MWgw
  NHol WCra
- Blue Fox — see *F. glauca* 'Blaufuchs'
- Blue Glow — see *F. glauca* 'Blauglut'
- 'Elijah Blue' — More than 30 suppliers
- 'Golden Toupee' — CBcs CBig CWCL CWSG EBee
  EChP ECha ELan ENot EPfP EWes
  LAst LRHS MBar MBlu MGos
  MMoz MRav MWgw NBir NHol
  NSti SLim SPer SPlb SWvt WCMO
  WDin WFar
- 'Harz' — CBrm EHoe EHul EPla LBuc MBar
  NBea NCGa
* - *minima* — CCCN IHMH
- 'Pallens' — see *F. longifolia*
- Sea Urchin — see *F. glauca* 'Seeigel'
§ - 'Seeigel' — CBig EBee EHoe EPPr MBnl MMoz
  NHol NPro
- 'Seven Seas' — see *F. valesiaca* 'Silbersee'
- 'Silberreiher' — EPPr
- 'Uchte' — CWCL
'Hogar' — EHoe
idahoensis — CBig EShb
§ *longifolia* — EBee EPPr
mairei — CKno EHoe EPPr LRHS NBHF
  SWal WDyG
novae-zelandiae — CPen CWCL EBee NNor
ovina — CWan EHoe NBre NGdn WPer
  WSFF
- var. *duriuscula* — CRWN
I - 'Kulturform' — NNor
- 'Söhrewald' — EPPr WMoo
* - 'Tetra Gold' — SWvt
paniculata — CKno EGle EHoe EPPr EPla EWsh
  WMoo
pulchella — CBig
punctoria — EHoe EWsh WMoo
rubra — CBig CRWN WSFF
- var. *nankotaizanensis* — WCru
  B&SWJ 3190
scoparia — see *F. gautieri*
'Siskiyou Blue' — CKno
tatrae — CBrm EBee GBin WCot
valesiaca — NOak WFar WHil
- var. *glaucantha* — CBig EBee EPPr EWll GWCH
  MWhi NBre NGdn NLar XPep
§ - 'Silbersee' — CBig EAEE EBee ECha EHoe
  ENot EPot EWsh LRHS MBar
  MBnl MNrw MSte NHol SRms
  WFar
- Silver Sea — see *F. valesiaca* 'Silbersee'
violacea — EBee EChP EHoe EMan EPPr
  MBNS NLar NNor NOak SIng SPer
  SWal WRos
vivipara — CNat CPrp EGoo EHoe EMon LEdu
  NBid NHol SBch WRos WWhi
* 'Willow Green' — CBod SLim SPlb

Fibigia (Brassicaceae)
§ *clypeata* — SGar
- 'Select' — CSpe
triquetra — GKev

Ficus ✿ (Moraceae)

afghanistanica	ERea
australis misapplied	see *F. rubiginosa* 'Australis'
benghalensis	MBri WMul
benjamina ♀H1	CHal LRHS MBri SRms
- 'Exotica'	CHal LRHS MBri
- 'Golden King' (v)	LRHS MBri
- 'Starlight' (v) ♀H1	LRHS MBri SMur
capitola 'Long'	ERea
carica (F)	EGra LPan MBri MPRe SArc
- 'Abbey Slip' (F)	CHEx
* - 'Acanthifolia'	XPep
- 'Adam' (F)	ERea
- 'Alma' (F)	ERea
- 'Angélique' (F)	ERea
- 'Archipel' new	ERea
- 'Beall' (F)	ERea
- 'Black Ischia' (F)	ERea
- 'Black Mission' (F)	ERea
- 'Bourjassotte Grise' (F)	ERea SDea
- 'Brown Turkey' (F) ♀H3	More than 30 suppliers
- 'Brunswick' (F)	CAgr CWib EMui ERea GTwe
	LRHS MCoo NGHP SLim SPoG
	WCot
- 'Castle Kennedy' (F)	ERea GTwe
- 'Conandria' (F)	ERea
- 'Dalmatie' new	WCMO
I - 'Digitata' new	MBlu
- 'Drap d'Or' new	ERea
- 'Figue d'Or' (F)	ERea
- 'Goutte d'Or' (F)	ERea SDea
- 'Grise de Saint Jean' (F)	ERea
- 'Kaape Bruin' (F)	ERea
* - 'Kadota' (F)	ERea
* - 'Laciniata' (F)	SMad
- 'Lisa' (F)	ERea
- 'Little Yellow Wonder' new	ERea
- 'Longue d'Août' (F)	ERea
- 'Malcolm's Giant' (F)	ERea
- 'Malta' (F)	ERea GTwe
- 'Marseillaise' (F)	ERea GTwe SDea
- 'Negro Largo' (F)	ERea
- 'Newlyn Coombe'	CHEx
- 'Newlyn Harbour' (F)	CHEx
- 'Noir de Provence'	see *F. carica* 'Reculver'
- 'Noire de Carombe' new	see *F. carica* 'Reculver'
- 'Osborn's Prolific' (F)	ERea SWvt
- 'Panachée' (F)	ERea
- 'Pastilière' (F)	ERea
- 'Peter's Honey' (F)	ERea
- 'Petite Grise' (F)	ERea
- 'Pied de Boeuf' (F)	ERea
- 'Pittaluse' (F)	ERea
- 'Précoce de Dalmatie'	ERea WPGP
- 'Précoce Ronde de Bordeaux' (F)	ERea
§ - 'Reculver' (F)	ERea
- 'Rouge de Bordeaux' (F)	ERea SDea
- 'Saint Johns' (F)	ERea
- 'San Pedro Miro' (F)	ERea
- 'Snowden' (F)	ERea
- 'Sollies Pont' (F)	ERea
- 'Sugar 12' (F)	ERea
- 'Sultane' (F)	ERea
- 'Tena' (F)	ERea
- 'Trojano' (F)	ERea
- 'Verte d'Argenteuil' (F)	ERea
- 'Violette Dauphine' (F)	ERea
- 'Violette de Sollies' (F)	ERea
- 'Violette Sepor' (F)	ERea
- 'White Genoa'	see *F. carica* 'White Marseilles'
- 'White Ischia' (F)	ERea

§ - 'White Marseilles' (F)	CWib ECrN EDsa EHol EMui EPfP
	ERea LRHS MBri MCoo NGHP
	SDea SKee SPoG
cyathistipula	MBri
deltoidea var. **diversifolia**	MBri
elastica	LRHS
- 'Doescheri' (v) ♀H1	NScw
- 'Robusta'	MBri
foveolata Wallich	see *F. sarmentosa*
lyrata ♀H1	MBri
microcarpa	STre
- 'Hawaii' (v)	CHal
pubigera new	CPLG
pumila ♀H1	CHEx CHal EBak LRHS MBri XPep
- 'Minima'	CFee
- 'Sonny' (v)	MBri
- 'Variegata' (v)	CHEx CHal MBri
radicans 'Variegata'	see *F. sagittata* 'Variegata'
religiosa	WMul
§ **rubiginosa** 'Australis'	MBri
- 'Variegata' (v) ♀H1	CHal
§ **sagittata** 'Variegata' (v)	MBri
§ **sarmentosa**	MBri

fig see *Ficus carica*

filbert see *Corylus maxima*

Filipendula ✿ (Rosaceae)

alnifolia 'Variegata'	see *F. ulmaria* 'Variegata'
camtschatica	CFir CMCo CRow EBee ELan GIBF
	MDun NBid NLar NMir NPol WFar
	WMoo WPGP
- RBS 0224	MGol
- 'Rosea'	LHop SMad
digitata 'Nana'	see *F. multijuga*
formosa B&SWJ 8707	WCru
hexapetala	see *F. vulgaris*
- 'Flore Pleno'	see *F. vulgaris* 'Multiplex'
- 'Kahome'	More than 30 suppliers
kiraishiensis B&SWJ 1571	EBee WCru
§ **multijuga**	CRow EBee GCal GGar IFoB WBor
	WFar WMoo
palmata	ECha GCal GSki MBri MLHP NBre
	WFar WMoo WWpP
- 'Digitata Nana'	see *F. multijuga*
- dwarf	CLAP GSki MLHP SBla
- 'Elegantissima'	see *F. purpurea* 'Elegans'
- 'Nana'	see *F. multijuga*
- *purpurea*	see *F. purpurea*
- 'Rosea'	ERou IBlr NBir WCHb
- 'Rubra'	CTri GSki MRav NGdn WGwG
- *rufinervis* B&SWJ 941	WCru
- - B&SWJ 8611	WCru
§ **purpurea** ♀H4	CKno CRow CSBt EPfP GGar
	GSki LPBA LRHS MBri MWrn
	WBVN WCru WFar WMoo
	WPnP
- f. *albiflora*	MBri NPri WMoo WPnP WWpP
	WWye
§ - 'Elegans'	CHea CRow EChP ECha EMan
	EMil ERou EWsh GCal GGar GMac
	LAst MLHP MSte NBid NHol NPri
	NSti SWat WFar WMoo
- 'Nephele'	EBee GMac SMHy
- 'Pink Dreamland'	EBee EPPr LPhx SAga WWpP
* - 'Plena' (d)	NLar
- 'White Dreamland'	EBee
'Queen of the Prairies'	see *F. rubra*
§ **rubra**	CRow GAbr LAst LSRN NBid
	WBVN WCra WFar WWpP
§ - 'Venusta' ♀H4	More than 30 suppliers
- 'Venusta Magnifica'	see *F. rubra* 'Venusta'
§ **ulmaria**	More than 30 suppliers
- 'Aurea'	More than 30 suppliers

- 'Flore Pleno' (d)	CBre CRow EBee EBrs GSki LAst
	LHop LRHS MRav NBid NBre NFla
	NGdn SIde SPer SWat WCAu WFar
	WPnP WTin
- 'Rosea'	CDes EBee IBlr WPGP WWpP
§ - 'Variegata' (v)	More than 30 suppliers
§ *vulgaris*	CArn CFee CRWN CTri CWan ECtt
	GBar LAst LPBA MBow MDun
	MLHP MNHC MSal MWgw NBlu
	NBro NMir NNor NPri SECG SWat
	WPer WWpP WWye
- 'Alba'	EBee
- 'Devon Cream'	SBla
- 'Flore Pleno' (d)	see *F. vulgaris* 'Multiplex'
- 'Grandiflora'	EPPr
§ - 'Multiplex' (d)	More than 30 suppliers
- 'Plena'	see *F. vulgaris* 'Multiplex'
- 'Rosea'	EBee NBre

Firmiana (Sterculiaceae)
simplex	CHEx EShb WMul

Fittonia (Acanthaceae)
albivenis Argyroneura	CHal LRHS
Group ♀H1	
- - 'Nana'	CHal
- Verschaffeltii Group ♀H1	CHal

Fitzroya (Cupressaceae)
cupressoides	CBcs CDoC CMac CTho IArd IDee
	LCon LRHS MBar SCoo SLim SPoG

Fockea (Asclepiadaceae)
edulis **new**	EShb

Foeniculum (Apiaceae)
vulgare	CAgr CArn CHby CPrp CWan
	EAEE EChP ECha ELan ELau EPfP
	GBar GMaP GPoy MBow MHer
	MNHC MSal MWat NGHP NPri
	SIde SPer SPlb WMoo WPer WScl
	WWye XPep
- 'Bronze'	see *F. vulgare* 'Purpureum'
- var. *dulce*	CSev SIde
§ - 'Giant Bronze'	EBee ELan LPhx WHen
§ - 'Purpureum'	More than 30 suppliers
- 'Smokey'	ECha MRav

Fontanesia (Oleaceae)
phillyreoides	CBcs CMCN

Fontinalis (Sphagnaceae)
sp.	LPBA
antipyretica	WFar

Forestiera (Oleaceae)
neomexicana	see *F. pubescens*
§ *pubescens*	CBcs

Forsythia ✿ (Oleaceae)
'Arnold Dwarf'	ECrN NLar SRms
'Beatrix Farrand' ambig.	CTri CWSG EBee LRHS MGos
	NEgg NFor NHol NWea SPer SRms
	WRHF WTel
'Beatrix Farrand' K. Sax	IMGH
new	
§ Boucle d'Or =	COtt SLim
'Courtacour'	
'Fiesta' (v)	CWSG EBee EPfP LAst LRHS MAsh
	MBar MGos MRav MSwo MTis
	NBlu NEgg NWea SLim SPer SPoG
	WCot WDin WFar
giraldiana	EBee MSwo SLon SRms
Gold Curl	see *F.* Boucle d'Or = 'Courtacour'
Gold Tide[PBR]	see *F.* Marée d'Or = 'Courtasol'
'Golden Bells'	CDul

'Golden Nugget'	ELan EPfP LRHS MAsh MBri SCoo
	SLon SMer SPoG WCFE
'Golden Times' (v)	CBcs EHoe EWes LBuc LSRN MAsh
	MGos NHol NLar NPro SCoo SPoG
	SWvt WCot WDin WFar
x *intermedia*	ECrN
- 'Arnold Giant'	MBlu
- 'Densiflora'	NWea
- 'Goldraush' **new**	MBri
- 'Goldzauber'	NJOw NWea
- 'Lynwood' variegated	CWib
- 'Lynwood Variety' ♀H4	More than 30 suppliers
- Minigold = 'Flojor'	EPfP LAst LRHS MGos MSwo
	MWat NBlu NEgg NHol SRms
	WBVN WRHF WTel
- 'Spectabilis'	CDul EPfP LBuc MAsh MBar MGan
	NWea SCoo SPer WDin WFar WTel
- 'Spectabilis Variegated' (v)	CBow MBNS NPro
- 'Spring Glory'	MHer
- 'Variegata' (v)	NSti NWea SPer WGwG
- Week-End =	CWSG ECrN EPfP LBuc MAsh MBri
'Courtalyn'[PBR] ♀H4	MGos NWea SEND SLim SLon
	SMer SPlb SPoG WDin WFar
koreana 'Ilgwang' (v)	CPMA
§ Marée d'Or =	COtt CWSG LRHS MBri MGos
'Courtasol'[PBR] ♀H4	MRav NLar SMer SPoG WDin
Mêlée d'Or =	LRHS SCoo SPer
'Courtaneur'	
Melissa = 'Courtadic'	NLar NWea
'Northern Gold'	EPfP
ovata 'Tetragold'	CBcs MBar NEgg
'Paulina'	NLar
spectabilis 'Yosefa'	ELan
suspensa	CArn CBcs CTri CWib EOHP EPfP
	LRHS MBar MSal MWat NVic NWea
	SHBN SPer SPlb WTel
- f. *atrocaulis*	CDul CPle
- var. *fortunei*	MBri NEgg
- 'Nymans'	EPfP MBri MRav NSti SLPl WMoo
§ - 'Taff's Arnold' (v)	CPLG CPMA WSPU
- 'Variegata'	see *F. suspensa* 'Taff's Arnold'
'Swingtime' (v)	EGra
'Tremonia'	ECrN NFor SLon WGwG
viridissima	NFor NWea
- 'Bronxensis'	ECho EHyt EPot GEdr NBir NLar
	NVic WAbe
- 'Weber's Bronx'	NLar

x *Fortucitroncirus* (Rutaceae)
'Sinton' **new**	EZes
'Thomasville'	EZes MJnS

Fortunearia (Hamamelidaceae)
sinensis	NLar

Fortunella (Rutaceae)
'Fukushu' (F) ♀H1	ERea
§ *japonica* (F)	SLon
§ *margarita* (F)	CDoC MBri

Fothergilla (Hamamelidaceae)
gardenii	CBcs CPMA ELan EPfP EWTr MBlu
	MBri NEgg NLar SPer SSpi WDin
- 'Blue Mist'	CAbP CDoC CEnd CPMA CWSG
	ELan EPfP LRHS SBrw SLim SMad
	SPer SPla SReu SSta WDin WFar
	WPat
- 'Suzanne'	MBri NLar
'Huntsman'	SBrw
major ♀H4	CBcs CDul CEnd CPMA CSam
	CWib CWoW EBee ELan EPfP
	EWTr LRHS MBri MGos MLan
	NBlu NEgg SHBN SPer SPoG SReu
	SSpi WDin WFar WNor WPat
- 'Bulkyard' **new**	MBri

- Monticola Group	CDoC CEnd CPMA CSBt CWSG EBee ELan EPfP IMGH LRHS MAsh MBar MDun MGos MMuc NPal SBrw SHBN SLim SPer SRkn SSpi SSta SWvt WBrE WFar
'Mount Airy'	CMCN CPMA EPfP IMGH MBri NLar SBrw SSpi

Fragaria (Rosaceae)

from Taiwan	WHer
alpina	see *F. vesca* 'Semperflorens'
x *ananassa* 'Alice'[PBR] (F)	CSut EMui
- 'Aromel' (F) ♀H4	CSBt CWSG GTwe LRHS SDea
- 'Bogota' (F)	LRHS
- 'Bolero'[PBR] (F)	CSut EMui MBri
- 'Calypso'[PBR] (F)	CSBt EMui LRHS SDea SKee
- 'Cambridge Favourite' (F) ♀H4	CSBt CTri CWSG EMui GTwe LRHS MBri MCoo MGan SDea SKee
- 'Cambridge Late Pine' (F)	CWSG EMui LRHS
- 'Cambridge Rival' (F)	LRHS
- 'Cambridge Vigour' (F)	CWSG GTwe LRHS SDea
- 'Challenger' (F)	EMui
- 'Darselect'[PBR] (F)	EMui
- 'Elsanta'[PBR] (F)	CSBt CWSG EMui GTwe IArd LRHS MGan NPri SDea SPer
- 'Elvira' (F)	EMui
* - 'Emily' (F)	GTwe NPri
- 'Eros'[PBR] (F)	EMui GTwe NPri SKee
- 'Florence'[PBR] (F)	CSBt EMui GTwe LRHS MBri SKee SPer
- 'Fraise des Bois'	see *F. vesca*
- 'Hampshire Maid' (F) **new**	LRHS
- 'Hapil' (F) ♀H4	EMui GTwe LRHS NPri
- 'Honeoye' (F) ♀H4	CSBt EMui GTwe LRHS MBri SKee SPer
- 'Korona'[PBR] (F)	EMui
- 'Kouril' (F)	LRHS
- 'Mae' (F) **new**	CSut
- 'Maxim' (F)	EMui
- 'Pantagruella' (F)	LRHS
- 'Pegasus'[PBR] (F) ♀H4	CSBt CTri EMui GTwe LRHS MAsh
- Pink Panda = 'Frel'[PBR] (F)	CBcs EAEE EBee EChP ECtt EGra ELan EWsh LBuc MRav NEgg NHol NLar SHFr SIng SPer SPoG SSto WCAu WEas WFar WWFP
- pink-flowered	CFee EMui
- Red Ruby = 'Samba'[PBR]	EAEE EBee EChP MNrw NEgg NGdn NLar SIng SPer SPoG WCAu
- 'Redgauntlet' (F)	GTwe LRHS
- 'Rhapsody'[PBR] (F) ♀H4	GTwe LRHS
- 'Rosie'[PBR] (F)	EMui SDea
- 'Royal Sovereign' (F)	GTwe LRHS MGan
- 'Serenata' (F)	NBur
- 'Sophie'[PBR] (F)	LRHS
- 'Symphony'[PBR] (F) ♀H4	EMui MBri SKee
- 'Tamella' (F)	EMui LRHS
- 'Tenira' (F)	EMui
- 'Totem' (F)	GTwe
§ - 'Variegata' (v)	CArn CSev EBee EMan EMon ENot EPPr EPla LDai LHop MCCP MHar MRav MWgw NHol SMar SPer SPoG WMoo WRha
- 'Viva Rosa' (F)	EMui LRHS
'Bowles' Double'	see *F. vesca* 'Multiplex'
chiloensis (F)	CAgr EMon ILis LEdu
- 'Chaval'	ECha EGoo EHrv EMon EPPr MRav MWgw WMoo
- 'Variegata' misapplied	see *F.* x *ananassa* 'Variegata'
indica	see *Duchesnea indica*
'Lipstick'	EWsh NLar WRos
moschata	CAgr
nubicola	GPoy
'Variegata'	see *F.* x *ananassa* 'Variegata'
§ *vesca* (F)	CAgr CArn CRWN CWan EMag EPfP EWTr GPoy LRHS MBow
	MHer MNHC NGHP NMir NPri SECG SIde SPlb WGHP WGwG WJek WPer WSFF WShi WWye
- 'Alexandra' (F)	CArn CBod CPrp ELau EWin GAbr IHMH LRHS MBow NVic SECG SIde WCHb
- 'Flore Pleno'	see *F. vesca* 'Multiplex'
- 'Fructu Albo' (F)	CAgr CArn CBgR CBre CRow EBee IHMH NLar WMoo WPer WWpP
- 'Golden Alexandra'	ELau EMag EWes LRav LSou WHer
- 'Imuricata' **new**	CBre
- 'Mara des Bois'[PBR] (F)	EMui GTwe MBri
- 'Monophylla' (F)	CRow EMon IGor SIde WHer
§ - 'Multiplex' (d)	CBgR CDes CRow CSev EMon GAbr ILis MRav NGHP NHol NLar SMac WCHb WHer WOut WWye
§ - 'Muricata'	CPou CRow EOHP IGor ILis ITer LEdu WHer WWye
* - 'Pineapple Crush'	
- 'Plymouth Strawberry'	see *F. vesca* 'Muricata'
- 'Rügen' (F)	IGor
§ - 'Semperflorens' (F)	ILis
- 'Variegata' misapplied	see *F.* x *ananassa* 'Variegata'
* - 'Variegata' ambig. (v)	EHoe EHrv GAbr NGHP SMac SMar WFar WHrl WPer WSel
virginiana	CAgr
- subsp. *glauca* **new**	EPPr
viridis	CAgr

Francoa (Saxifragaceae)

appendiculata	CAbP CRez EBla EMan GQui MDKP NBre SGar WFar WHer WMoo WPic WPnP
- red-flowered	CKno EBee
Ballyrogan strain	IBlr
'Confetti'	CDes CKno CPLG EBee ELan EMan EPPr ERou GBin LAst MAvo MFOX MNrw NCob NEgg SPoG SWal WCot WCra WFar WGwG WPGP WTMC
'Purple Spike'	see *F. sonchifolia* Rogerson's form
§ *ramosa*	CCVN CMCo CTri EChP EHrv EMan GBuc IBlr LRHS MBow MLan MNrw MWat NBro NEgg SAga SDix SHGN SPav SWal WCru WFar WMoo
* - 'Alba'	CSpe
sonchifolia	More than 30 suppliers
- 'Alba'	MDKP NRnb SMrm SUsu WFar WMoo
- 'Cally Dwarf Purple' **new**	GCal
- 'Culm View Lilac' **new**	CCVN
- 'Doctor Tom Smith'	WCot
- 'Molly Anderson'	EBee MAvo
§ - Rogerson's form	More than 30 suppliers

Frangula (Rhamnaceae)

alnus	CArn CBgR CCVT CDul CLnd CRWN ECrN LBuc MBlu MBow NWea STre WDin WFar WMou WSFF
- 'Aspleniifolia'	CTho EBee ENot EPfP LBuc MBlu MBri MMuc MRav NLar SMur WDin WFar
- 'Columnaris'	EMil SLPl
caroliniana	NLar

Frankenia (Frankeniaceae)

laevis	CTri SRms WRHF XPep
thymifolia	CBrm CNic ECho GGar LRHS MBar MHer MWat SPlb WFar WPer WTel WTin XPep

Franklinia (Theaceae)

alatamaha	CBcs CPMA EPfP LHyd MBlu MBri WFar WNor

Fraxinus ✿ (*Oleaceae*)

americana	CDul CMCN EPfP SBLw WDin
- 'Autumn Purple'	CDul CEnd CTho ECrN EPfP LRHS MAsh MBlu SBLw
- 'Rosehill'	CTho
§ *angustifolia*	CMCN EGFP
§ - subsp. *oxycarpa*	GIBF
- 'Raywood' ♀H4	CBcs CCVT CDoC CDul CEnd CLnd CTho CTri CWib EBee ECrN ELan EPfP EWTr MAsh MBlu MGos MSwo NEgg NWea SBLw SMHT SMad SPer SPoG WDin WFar WJas WOrn
* - 'Variegata' (v)	MGos
anomala	GIBF
bungeana	CMCN EGFP
chinensis	CLnd CMCN GIBF
- subsp. *rhyncophylla*	GIBF
elonza	CLnd
excelsior	CBcs CCVT CDoC CDul CLnd CRWN CSBt CTri CWib ECrN EPfP LAst LBuc LPan MBar MGos NBee NWea SBLw SHBN SHFr STre WDin WMou WOrn
- 'Allgold'	CEnd
- 'Aurea'	SBLw
- 'Aurea Pendula'	CDul CEnd CMCN CWib ECrN EPfP LRHS MAsh MBlu MGos SBLw SPoG
- 'Crispa'	MBlu NEgg NLar SBLw
- f. *diversifolia*	CDul CLnd
- 'Globosa'	SBLw
- 'Jaspidea' ♀H4	More than 30 suppliers
- 'Nana'	EMon SBLw WPat
- 'Pendula' ♀H4	CCVT CDoC CDul CEnd CLnd CTho EBee ECrN ELan EPfP LAst LPan LRHS MBlu MBri NBee NEgg NWea SBLw SHBN SLim SPer SPoG WDin WJas WMou WOrn
- 'R.E. Davey'	CDul CNat
- variegated (v)	ECrN
- 'Westhof's Glorie' ♀H4	CCVT CDoC CLnd EBee ECrN NEgg SBLw WDin WFar WJas WOrn
insularis var. *henryana*	CDul CMCN WPGP
§ *latifolia*	GIBF
longicuspis	GIBF
mariesii	see *F. sieboldiana*
nigra	CMCN
- 'Fallgold'	CEnd
ornus ♀H4	CCVT CDul CLnd CMCN CTri ECrN ELan EPfP EWTr IMGH MBri MSwo NWea SBLw SPer WDin WFar WMoo WOrn
- 'Arie Peters'	CDul LPan SBLw
- 'Mecsek'	MBlu
- 'Obelisk'	MBri SMad
- 'Rotterdam'	SBLw
oxycarpa	see *F. angustifolia* subsp. *oxycarpa*
paxiana <u>new</u>	GIBF
pennsylvanica	CDul CLnd CMCN GIBF
- 'Summit'	CTho
- 'Variegata' (v)	CLnd EBee MAsh MBri SSta WPat
quadrangulata	WDin
§ *sieboldiana*	CDoC CDul CLnd CMCN CPMA EPfP MBlu NLar SSpi WPGP WPat
velutina	CDul CLnd SLPl
xanthoxyloides var. *dumosa* <u>new</u>	WPGP

Freesia (*Iridaceae*)

alba Watson	see *F. caryophyllacea*
alba (G.L. Mey.) Gumbl.	CMon LBow
andersoniae	CMon LBow

§ *caryophyllacea*	CMon
'Cinderella' <u>new</u>	CAvo
corymbosa <u>new</u>	LBow
elimensis	LBow
laxa	see *Anomatheca laxa*
leichtlinii	LBow
'Oberon'	CAvo
'Seagull' <u>new</u>	CAvo
sparrmannii <u>new</u>	LBow
xanthospila	LBow

Fremontodendron (*Sterculiaceae*)

'California Glory' ♀H3	More than 30 suppliers
californicum	CSBt CTri EBee ELan EMil MBri MLan MWat NBlu SHBN SLim SOWG SPlb WCFE WDin WFar WNor WOrn
mexicanum	NLar XPep
'Pacific Sunset'	CDul CPMA ENot EPfP LHop MGos MRav SBra SBrw SMur SPer SPoG
'Tequila Sunrise'	CBcs CBrm CPMA EBee GBin ISea MRav MSph NLar SBrw SPoG SRkn

Freylinia (*Scrophulariaceae*)

cestroides	see *F. lanceolata*
densiflora <u>new</u>	GFai
§ *lanceolata*	CBcs CCCN CTrC EShb
tropica	CHll GFai
visseri <u>new</u>	GFai

Fritillaria ✿ (*Liliaceae*)

acmopetala ♀H4	CAvo CBro CFFs CFwr CPom EBee ECho EPot ERos GBuc GCrs GEdr GIBF LRHS MSSP MSte MTho NJOw NMen NWCA WBVN WCot WCra WLin WSel
- LB 410 from Greece	CMon
- 'Brunette'	EBee ECho MSte WCot WWst
- subsp. *wendelboi*	ECho EHyt EPot GKev LPhx WCot WDav
- - KPPZ	EBee
§ *affinis*	ECho GBuc GCrs GIBF GKev MSSP NMen SBla WCot
- 'Limelight'	ECho
- 'Sunray'	GCrs GEdr
- var. *tristulis*	ERos NMen
- 'Vancouver Island'	ECho EPot WWst
alburyana	EHyt
arabica	see *F. persica*
assyriaca	EPot
atropurpurea	GIBF
aurea	ECho EHyt MSSP NMen
- 'Golden Flag'	CBgR CFwr ECho EPfP GKev LTwo WDav
biflora	ECho GCrs GEdr GIBF WCot
- 'Martha Roderick'	CFwr ECho EHyt MSSP NMen SBla WWst
§ *bithynica*	CFwr CStu EBrs ECho GEdr ITim MSSP
- from Turkey PB 316	CMon
bucharica	EBee GKev
- 'Nurek Giant'	WWst
camschatcensis	CAvo CBro CFwr CMea EBrs ECha ECho EFEx EHyt EPfP EPot GBBs GCrs GEdr GIBF LPhx LRHS MSSP MTho NBir NDov NHar NJOw NMen NWCA SPer WAbe WCru WDav WLin
- from Alaska	GCrs
I - *alpina aurea*	GCrs GEdr
- 'Aurea'	GBuc NMen WWst
- black-flowered	ECho GBuc
- double-flowered	CFir NMen
- f. *flavescens*	ECho EFEx GEdr
- green-flowered	NMen WDav

carduchorum	see *F. minuta*
carica	ECho EHyt GEdr MSSP NMen
- brown-flowered	ECho
- subsp. *serpenticola*	EHyt
caucasica	EHyt GIBF NMen
cirrhosa	EPot GEdr WWst
- brown-flowered	GEdr NMen
- green-flowered	EHyt GEdr NMen WWst
citrina	see *F. bithynica*
§ *collina*	ENot GCrs NMen WWst
conica	GCrs NMen WCot
crassicaulis new	WCot
crassifolia	GIBF MSSP
- subsp. *crassifolia*	CGra EHyt
§ - subsp. *kurdica*	EHyt EPot GCrs GIBF NMen
davisii	CBgR CFwr EBrs ECho EHyt EPot GBuc GCrs GEdr GKev NBPC NJOw NMen WDav
delavayi new	NLAp
delphinensis	see *F. tubiformis*
eastwoodiae	GIBF
eduardii	ECho GIBF GKev WWst
ehrhartii	SBla
elwesii	EBee ECho EHyt EPot GEdr NMen WCot
ferganensis	see *F. walujewii*
forbesii from Turkey	CMon
frankiorum	WWst
glauca	GIBF MSSP WCot
* - 'Golden Flag'	ECho
- 'Goldilocks'	ECho EPot LRHS NMen WCot WCra WDav
graeca	CBgR CBro CFwr ECho EPot GBuc GCrs GEdr GIBF MTho NMen WDav WLin
- subsp. *graeca*	EHyt
- subsp. *ionica*	see *F. thessala*
gussichiae	GCrs MSSP NMen
hermonis subsp. *amana*	CFwr EBrs ECho EHyt EPot GCrs GEdr GIBF GKev ITim LTwo NJOw NMen NWCA WCot WLin
- - - yellow-flowered	EHyt EPot
hispanica	see *F. lusitanica*
imperialis	ECGP MBri WBVN WTin
- 'Aurora'	EBee EBrs EPot GBBs GKev LPhx LRHS NGHP NLar NPer SPer WFar WHil
- 'Garland Star' new	EBee
- var. *inodora*	EBee GCrs
- 'Lutea'	CAby CAvo CSam EBrs ELan ENot EPfP LRHS MSte NFor SMeo WFar
- 'Lutea Maxima'	see *F. imperialis* 'Maxima Lutea'
- 'Maxima'	see *F. imperialis* 'Rubra Maxima'
§ - 'Maxima Lutea' ♀H4	CBro EBee ELan EPfP EPot MNFA NLar SPer
- 'Orange Brilliant'	EBee LRHS MSte
§ - 'Prolifera'	EBee ECho MNFA NLar WCot WHer
- 'Rubra'	EBee ECho ENot GBBs GKev NBir NLar SMeo SPer WFar WHil
§ - 'Rubra Maxima'	CAby CBro EBee EBrs ELan EPfP EPot LRHS MSte
- 'Slagzwaard'	EBee
- 'Sulpherino'	EBee
- 'The Premier'	EBee ECho EPot LRHS
- 'William Rex'	CAvo CFFs EBee EPot ERou
- yellow-flowered new	CFFs
involucrata	EHyt MSSP
ionica	see *F. thessala*
japonica var. *koidzumiana*	EFEx GEdr WWst
karadaghensis	see *F. crassifolia* subsp. *kurdica*
kittaniae	EHyt
kotschyana	ECho EHyt EPot GCrs GEdr NMen
lanceolata	see *F. affinis* var. *tristulis*
latakiensis	ECho EPot GCrs GEdr

§ *latifolia*	GEdr GIBF
- var. *nobilis*	see *F. latifolia*
§ *lusitanica*	MSSP NMen SBla
lutea Bieb.	see *F. collina*
maximowiczii	ECho
meleagris	More than 30 suppliers
- var. *unicolor* subvar. *alba* ♀H4	CAvo CBro CFFs EBee ECho GBri GBuc GIBF LRHS MBri MSSP MWat MWgw NLAp SPer WAul WPnP WShi
- - - 'Aphrodite'	EPot GBuc NBir
meleagroides	WWst
§ *messanensis*	EHyt GCrs MSSP SBla
- subsp. *gracilis*	EHyt GCrs MSSP
- subsp. *messanensis*	CBro
michailovskyi ♀H2	CBro CFFs CFwr CMea CTri EBrs EPfP EPot GBuc GEdr GGar GIBF GKev LRHS MNrw MTho MWgw NBPC NJOw NLAp NMen NWCA SRms WAbe WFar WLin WPnP WSel
§ *minuta*	CFwr CStu ECho EHyt EPot GCrs NMen
montana	EBrs ECho EHyt NMen
nigra Mill.	see *F. pyrenaica*
obliqua	EHyt WCot
olivieri	GCrs
§ *orientalis*	ECho EHyt WWst
pallidiflora ♀H4	CAvo CBro CFwr CLAP CMea EBee EBrs ECho EHyt EPot ERos GBuc GEdr GIBF GKev LPhx MNFA MSSP MSte MTho NBir NMen NSla SUsu WBVN WCra WCru WLin WPnP
§ *persica*	CSam ECha ECtt EHrv EPfP EPot GBBs GIBF GKev LHop LPhx LRHS MAvo MBri MLan MWgw NJOw NMen SGar SPer WCra WFar WGwG WSel
- 'Adiyaman' ♀H4	CAvo CBro CFFs EBee EBrs ELan LPhx WDav
- 'Ivory Bells'	EPot LPhx
- 'Ivory Queen' new	CBro
pinardii	ECho EHyt EPot GCrs GEdr GIBF NMen
pinetorum new	GIBF
pontica	CAvo CBgR CBro CFFs CLAP CMea ECho EHyt EPot ERos GBuc GCrs GEdr LPhx LRHS MLLN MSSP MTho NLAp NMen NSla SBla SMeo SPer SUsu WAbe WCot WCru WLin WPnP
* - 'Aurea' new	WDav
- subsp. *substipilata*	GIBF
pudica	EBrs ECho EHyt GBuc GCrs GEdr ITim LRHS MSSP MTho NBPC NJOw NMen SUsu WLin
* - 'Fragrant'	NMen
- 'Giant'	ECho EPot WWst
- 'Richard Britten'	EHyt GCrs NMen
purdyi	ECho GIBF MSSP
§ *pyrenaica* ♀H4	CLAP CMea CNic ECho EHyt ERos ETow GCrs GEdr GIBF LPhx MSSP NMen NSla SBla WCot WCru WDav WTin WWst
- 'Lutea'	EHyt NSla WCot
raddeana	EBrs ECho EPot LPhx WDav
recurva	GEdr GIBF
rhodocanakis	ECho EHyt NMen
- subsp. *argolica*	NMen
rubra major	see *F. imperialis* 'Rubra Maxima'
ruthenica	ECho ERos GCrs GIBF GKev MSSP NMen SBla
sewerzowii	EPot GCrs WWst
sibthorpiana	CBro
spetsiotica	EHyt

	sphaciotica	see *F. messanensis*
	stenanthera	ECho EHyt EPot GCrs NMen
	tachengensis	see *F. yuminensis*
	tenella	see *F. orientalis*
§	*thessala*	EHyt GBuc GIBF LPhx MSSP MTho NMen WDav
	thunbergii	EBee ECho EHyt GCrs GEdr NLAp NMen WAbe WCot WDav
	tortifolia	NMen
§	*tubiformis*	EHyt GEdr WWst
	unibracteata new	NLAp
§	*uva-vulpis*	CBro CMea CSam EAEE EBrs EChP ECrN ECtt EHyt EMar ENot EPot GBuc GEdr GKev LEdu LHop LPhx LRHS MBow MNrw MTho NBir NJOw NMen SPer WAbe WCot WCru WFar
	verticillata	CBro CMea EBee ECha EHrv EPot GEdr GIBF LPhx MTho NLAp NMen WCru
	wabuensis new	NLAp
§	*walujewii*	EPot GEdr NLAp WCot
	whittallii	ECho EPot GCrs MSSP NMen
§	*yuminensis*	ECho WCot
	- var. *roseiflora*	GEdr
	zagrica	EHyt

Fuchsia ✿ (*Onagraceae*)

	'A.M. Larwick'	CSil EBak EKMF
	'A.W. Taylor'	EBak
	'Aad Franck'	WPBF
	'Aadenken Bert Pelgrims'	WPBF
	'Aalt Groothuis'	WPBF
	'Aart Verschoor' new	WPBF
	'Abbé Farges' (d)	CDoC CLoc CSil CWVF EBak EKMF EPts MWhe NDlv SLBF SPet SWal WRou
	'Abigail'	EKMF LCla WPBF WRou
	'Abigail Storey'	CSil
	'Abundance'	CSil
	'Acapulco' new	WPBF
	'Acclamation' (d)	WPBF
	'Achievement' ♀H4	CDoC CLoc CSil EKMF LCla MJac NDlv SPet WPBF
	'Adagio' (d)	CLoc
	'Adelaide Hoodless' new	WRou
	'Adinda'	CDoC EKMF LCla MWar SLBF WPBF
	'Admiration'	CSil EKMF
	'Adrienne'	SVil
	'Ahehee' (d)	WPBF
	'Aiguillette' new	WPBF
	'Ailsa Garnett'	EBak
	'Aintree'	CWVF
	'Airedale'	CWVF
	'Aisen' new	WRou
	'Aladna's Sanders'	CWVF WPBF
	'Alan Ayckbourn'	CWVF
	'Alan Titchmarsh' (d)	CDoC EKMF EPts LCla MWar SLBF
	'Alaska' (d)	CLoc EBak EKMF WPBF
	'Albertina'	WRou
	'Albertus Schwab'	LCla
	'Albion'	WPBF
	'Alde'	CWVF
	'Alderford'	SLBF WPBF
	'Alf Thornley' (d)	CWVF MWhe WPBF
	'Alfred Rambaud' (d)	CDoC CSil
	'Ali' (d)	EKMF
	'Ali Harder'	WPBF
	'Alice Ashton' (d)	EBak EKMF
	'Alice Blue Gown' (d)	CWVF
	'Alice Doran'	CDoC CSil EKMF LCla
	'Alice Hoffman' (d) ♀H3-4	More than 30 suppliers
	'Alice Mary' (d)	EBak EMan
	'Alice Sweetapple'	CWVF

	'Alice Travis' (d)	EBak
	'Alipat'	EBak EKMF
	'Alison Ewart'	CLoc CWVF EBak EKMF MJac MWhe SPet WRou
	'Alison Patricia' ♀H3	CWVF EBak EKMF EMan LAst LCla MJac MWar SLBF SRGP WRou
	'Alison Reynolds' (d)	CWVF
	'Alison Ruth Griffin' (d)	MJac
	'Alison Ryle' (d)	EBak
	'Alison Sweetman' ♀H1+3	CSil CWVF EKMF MJac MWhe
	'Allure' (d)	CWVF
	'Alma Hulscher'	CWVF
	Aloha = 'Sanicomf' PBR (Sunangels Series)	SLBF
§	*alpestris*	CDoC CSil EBak LCla
	- Berry 64-87	EKMF
	'Alton Water' (d/v)	MWar
	'Alwin' (d)	CWVF MWar MWhe WPBF
	'Alyce Larson' (d)	CWVF EBak MJac
	'Amanda Bridgland' (d)	EKMF
	'Amanda Jones'	EKMF MWhe
	'Amazing Maisie' (d)	MWar WPBF
	'Ambassador'	EBak SPet
	'Ambriorix'	WPBF
	'Amelie Aubin'	CLoc CWVF EBak EKMF WPBF
	'America'	CWVF
	'American Flaming Glory' (d)	WPBF
	'Amethyst Fire' (d)	CSil
	'Amigo'	EBak
§	*ampliata*	CDoC EKMF LCla
	'Amy'	MJac
	'Amy Lye' (d)	CLoc CSil EBak EKMF
	'Amy Ruth'	CWVF
§	'Andenken an Heinrich Henkel'	CDoC CLoc CWVF EBak EKMF MOak MWhe WRou
	'André Le Nostre' (d)	CWVF EBak
	'Andreas Schwab'	LCla
	andrei	CDoC LCla
	- Berry 4637	EKMF
	'Andrew'	CDoC EBak EKMF
	'Andrew Carnegie' (d)	CLoc
	'Andrew George'	MJac
	'Andrew Hadfield'	CWVF EKMF MWar WRou
	'Andrew Simmons'	WPBF
I	'Andromeda' De Groot	CSil
	'Andy Jordens'	WPBF
	'Angela Leslie' (d)	CLoc CWVF EBak EKMF
	'Angela Rippon'	CWVF MJac
	'Angel's Flight' (d)	EBak
	'Anita' (d)	CLoc CSil CWVF EKMF EPts LAst MJac MWar MWhe SLBF WGor WRou
	'Anjo' (v)	CWVF SLBF
	'Ann Howard Tripp'	CDoC CLoc CWVF MBri MJac MWhe WPBF WRou
	'Ann Lee' (d)	EBak
	'Anna'	WPBF
	'Anna Louise'	EKMF SLBF WPBF
	'Anna of Longleat' (d)	CWVF EBak EMan MJac SPet
	'Annabel' (d) ♀H3	CDoC CLoc CTri CWVF EBak EKMF EMan EPts LAst LCla MBri MJac MWar MWhe SLBF SPet SRGP WRou
	'Annabelle Stubbs' (d)	LAst SRGP
	'Annchen' new	WPBF
	'Anneke de Keijzer'	LCla
	'Annie Earle'	EKMF
	'Annie MG Schmidt' new	WPBF
	'Anniek Geerlings'	WPBF
	'Another Storey'	CSil
	'Anthea Day' (d)	CLoc
	'Anthony Heavens'	WPBF
	'Antigone'	SLBF WPBF
	'Anton Schreuder' (d)	WPBF
	apetala	EKMF

- DG 1044	EKMF
'Aphrodite' (d)	CLoc CWVF EBak
'Applause' (d)	CLoc CWVF EBak EKMF EPts LVER SPet
'Apple Blossom'	EKMF
aprica misapplied	see *F. x bacillaris*
aprica Lundell	see *F. microphylla* subsp. *aprica*
'Aquarius'	MWhe
'Aquillette'	WPBF
'Arabella'	CWVF MWhe
'Arabella Improved'	CWVF EKMF
arborea	see *F. arborescens*
§ *arborescens*	CBcs CDoC CHEx CLoc CSil CWVF EBak EKMF EPts EShb LCla LRHS SWal SYvo WRou WWlt
'Arcadia Gold' (d)	CWVF MWhe
'Arcady'	CLoc CWVF
'Ariel'	CDoC CSil WRou
'Arlendon'	CWVF
'Army Nurse' (d) ♀H4	CDoC CLoc CSil CWVF EKMF EPts MWhe NBir NDlv SLBF SPet SWal WPBF
'Aronst Hoeck'	WPBF
'Art Deco' (d)	WPBF
'Arthur Baxter'	EBak
'Arthur Horning' new	WPBF
'Ashley'	CDoC LCla WPBF
'Ashley and Isobel'	CWVF
'Ashtede'	SLBF
'Athela'	EBak
'Atlantic Star'	CWVF EKMF MJac
'Atlantis' (d)	CWVF MJac
'Atomic Glow' (d)	EBak
'Aubergine'	see *F. 'Gerharda's Aubergine'*
'Audrey Hepburn'	CWVF EKMF
'August Cools'	WPBF
'August Siebert' new	WPBF
'Augustin Thierry' (d)	EKMF MWhe
'Aunt Juliana' (d)	EBak
'Auntie Jinks'	CDoC CWVF EBak EKMF LAst LCla MJac MWhe SPet WRou
'Aurora Superba'	CLoc CWVF EBak EKMF WRou
'Australia Fair' (d)	CWVF EBak
§ *austromontana*	EBak
'Autumnale' ♀H1+3	CDoC CHEx CLoc CWVF EBak EKMF EMan EPts LAst LCla LRHS LVER MWhe NVic SLBF SMrm SPet SPoG WPBF WRou
'Avalanche' (d)	CDoC CLoc CSil EBak EKMF SLBF SWal WPBF
'Avocet'	CLoc EBak
'Avon Celebration' (d)	CLoc
'Avon Gem'	CLoc CSil
'Avon Glow'	CLoc
'Avon Gold'	CLoc
ayavacensis	CDoC LCla
- Berry 3601	EKMF
'Azure Sky' (d)	EKMF MJac
'Babette' (d)	EKMF
'Baby Blue Eyes'	CDoC CSil CWVF EKMF
'Baby Blush'	CSil
'Baby Bright'	CDoC CWVF EPts MWar SLBF WPBF WRou
'Baby Chang'	LCla WPBF
'Baby Girl'	WPBF
'Baby Pink' (d)	CWVF
'Baby Thumb' (d)	CSil EPts
§ x *bacillaris*	CBrm CDoC CDul CEnt CSil EBak EWes EWin ITim MBlu SIng SLBF SPoG SRms
§ - 'Cottinghamii'	CDoC CSil EKMF IDee WSHC
§ - 'Oosje'	see F. 'Oosje'
§ - 'Reflexa'	CAbP CTrC GQui LAst LSou WPBF
'Bagworthy Water'	CLoc
'Baker's Tri'	EBak
'Balcon Queen'	MWhe
'Bali Hi'	WPBF
'Balkon'	CWVF
'Balkonkönigin'	CLoc EBak
'Ballerina'	CDoC
'Ballerina Blue'	LAst
'Ballet Girl' (d) ♀H1+3	CHrt CLoc CWVF EBak EKMF SLBF SPet
'Bambini'	CWVF EPts
'Banks Peninsula'	GQui
'Barbara'	CLoc CSil CWVF EBak EKMF EPts MJac MWar MWhe SPet WEas WRou
'Barbara Evans'	MWar WRou
'Barbara Pountain' (d)	CWVF
'Barbara Windsor'	CWVF EPts LAst MJac
'Baron de Ketteler' (d)	CSil EKMF
'Barry M. Cox'	WPBF
'Barry's Queen'	CSil EBak SPet
'Bart Comperen'	WPBF
'Bartje' new	WPBF
'Bashful' (d)	CDoC CSil EPts LCla LRHS NDlv SPet
'Beacon'	CDoC CLoc CSil CWVF EBak EKMF EMan EPts LAst LCla MBri MJac MWhe NDlv SPet SPoG SRGP SWal WRou WTel
'Beacon Rosa'	CDoC CLoc CSil CWVF EKMF EMan EPts MBri MJac MWhe NDlv SLBF SPet SPoG SWal WPBF WRou
'Beacon Superior'	CSil
'Bealings' (d)	CDoC CLoc CWVF EMan MBri WPBF
'Beau Nash'	CLoc
'Beautiful Bobbie' (d)	SLBF
'Beauty of Bath' (d)	CLoc EBak
'Beauty of Cliff Hall'	EKMF
'Beauty of Clyffe Hall'	CSil EBak
'Beauty of Exeter' (d)	COtt CWVF EBak EKMF
'Beauty of Prussia' (d)	CDoC CLoc CSil CWVF
'Beauty of Swanley'	EBak
'Beauty of Trowbridge'	CWVF LCla
'Becky'	WPBF
'Becky Jane'	CSil
'Bel Cinette'	WPBF
'Belijn'	WPBF
'Belinda Jane'	WPBF
'Bella Forbes' (d) ♀H1+3	CLoc CSil EBak EKMF
'Bella Rosella' (d)	CWVF EKMF EPts LAst MJac SCoo SLBF
'Belsay Beauty' (d)	CWVF MJac
'Belvoir Beauty' (d)	CLoc
'Ben de Jong'	CDoC LCla MJac WPBF WRou
'Ben Jammin'	CDoC CLoc CSil CWVF EPts LAst LCla LSou MJac MWar WGor WRou
I 'Béranger' Lemoine 1897 (d)	CSil EBak EKMF
'Berba's Happiness' (d)	CWVF
'Berba's Trio'	WPBF
'Bergnimf'	WRou
'Berliner Kind' (d)	CSil CWVF EBak EKMF
'Bermuda' (d)	CWVF
'Bernadette' (d)	CWVF
'Bernie's Big-un' (d)	MJac
'Bernisser Hardy'	CDoC CSil EKMF EPts LCla WPBF
'Bert de Jong'	WPBF
'Bertha Gadsby'	EKMF
'Bert's Kristof' (d) new	WPBF
'Beryl Shaffery'	WPBF
'Berys'	EKMF MWar
'Berys Elizabeth'	WPBF
'Bessie Kimberley'	CDoC EKMF LCla MWar
'Beth Robley' (d)	CWVF
'Betsy Ross' (d)	EBak
'Bettina Stubi'	WPBF
Betty = 'Goetzbet' (Shadowdancer Series)	LAst NEgg

'Betty Jean' (d) — MWar WPBF
'Beverley' — CSil CWVF EBak EKMF EPts SPet
'Bewitched' (d) — EBak
'Bianca' (d) — CWVF WPBF
'Bicentennial' (d) — CDoC CLoc CWVF EBak EKMF EPts LAst LSou LVER MJac MWar MWhe SPet
'Big Slim' — WPBF
'Bilberry Sorbet' — WPBF
'Billy'PBR **new** — SRGP
'Billy Green' ♀H1+3 — CDoC CLoc CWVF EBak EKMF EPts LCla LRHS MJac MWar MWhe SLBF SPet SWal WPBF WRou
'Bishop's Bells' (d) — CWVF
'Black Beauty' (d) — CWVF
'Black Prince' — CDoC CSil CWVF MWar
'Blackmore Vale' — CWVF
'Blacky' — EBak LAst
I 'Blanche Regina' (d) — CWVF MJac MWhe
'Bland's New Striped' — CDoC EBak EKMF EPts SLBF
'Blauer Engel' — WPBF
'Blaze Away' (d) — MBri
'Bliss' **new** — WPBF
'Blood Donor' (d) — EKMF MJac
'Blowick' — CDoC CWVF EMan MBri MJac MWhe SPet
'Blue Beauty' (d) — CSil EBak EKMF
'Blue Boy' — WPBF
'Blue Bush' — CSil CWVF EKMF EPts MJac NDlv
'Blue Butterfly' (d) — CWVF EBak
'Blue Eyes' (d) — CDoC SPet
'Blue Gown' (d) — CDoC CLoc CSil CWVF EBak EKMF LRHS LVER MWhe NDlv SPet SWal WRou
'Blue Hawaii' — WPBF
'Blue Ice' — MWhe
'Blue Lace' (d) — CSil
'Blue Lagoon' ambig. (d) — CWVF
'Blue Lake' (d) — CWVF LVER
'Blue Mink' — EBak
'Blue Mirage' (d) — CLoc CWVF EKMF MJac
'Blue Mist' (d) — EBak
'Blue Pearl' (d) — CWVF EBak
'Blue Pinwheel' — EBak
'Blue Satin' (d) — COtt MWhe WPBF
'Blue Tit' — CSil LCla
'Blue Veil' (d) — CLoc CWVF EKMF LVER MJac MWar SCoo SVil
'Blue Waves' (d) — CLoc CSBt CWVF EBak MJac MWar MWhe SPet
'Blush o' Dawn' (d) — CLoc CWVF EBak EKMF EPts LVER SPet WPBF
'Blythe' (d) — SLBF
'Bob Pacey' — CWVF
'Bobby Boy' (d) — EBak
'Bobby Dazzler' (d) — CWVF EKMF
'Bobby Shaftoe' (d) — EBak MWhe WPBF
'Bobby Wingrove' — EBak
'Bobby's Girl' — EPts
'Bobolink' (d) — EBak
'Bob's Best' (d) — CWVF EPts MJac
'Boerhaave' — EBak
boliviana 'Alba' — see *F. boliviana* Carrière var. *alba*
boliviana Britton — see *F. sanctae-rosae*
§ *boliviana* Carrière — CDoC CHEx CLoc CSil CWVF EBak EKMF LCla MOak SHFr SYvo WRou
§ - var. *alba* ♀H1+3 — CDoC CLoc CSil EBak EKMF EPts LCla MOak SChr WPBF WRou
- var. *boliviana* — CRHN LRHS
- f. *puberulenta* Munz — see *F. boliviana* Carrière
'Bon Accorde' — CLoc CWVF EBak EKMF EPts SLBF WRou
'Bon Bon' (d) — CWVF EBak
'Bonita' (d) — CWVF MJac WPBF
'Bonnie Lass' (d) — EBak

'Bonny' (d) — CLoc
'Bora Bora' (d) — CWVF EBak EKMF WPBF
'Borde Hill' (d) — EPts SLBF
'Border Princess' — EBak
'Border Queen' ♀H3-4 — CDoC CLoc CSil CWVF EBak EKMF EMan EPts LCla MJac MWar SPet WRou
'Border Raider' — MWar SLBF WPBF
'Border Reiver' — EBak
'Börnemann's Beste' — see *F.* 'Georg Börnemann'
'Boswinning' **new** — WPBF
'Botanischer Garten Berlin' **new** — WPBF
'Bouffant' — CLoc WPBF
'Bougie Humpary' — WPBF
I 'Bountiful' Munkner (d) — CLoc CWVF EKMF MWhe SPet
'Bouquet' (d) — CDoC CSil EKMF
'Bow Bells' — CDoC CLoc CWVF MJac MWhe SPet
'Boy Marc' — LCla WPBF
'Braamt's Glorie' — WPBF
bracelinae — CDoC CSil EKMF
'Brancaster' — SLBF WPBF
'Brandt's Five Hundred Club' — CDoC CLoc EBak SPet
'Brechtje' — WPBF
'Breckland' — EBak
'Bree Vis Nobilis' **new** — WPBF
'Breeders' Delight' — CSil CWVF MBri WPBF
'Breeder's Dream' (d) — EBak WPBF
'Breevis Blauwtje' — WPBF
'Breevis Evelien' **new** — WPBF
'Breevis Homerus' — WPBF
'Breevis Iris' — WPBF
I 'Breevis Jordani' — WPBF
'Breevis Karna' — WPBF
I 'Breevis Lowi' — WPBF
'Breevis Luna' **new** — WPBF
'Breevis Natalica' **new** — WPBF
I 'Breevis Paradoxa' — WPBF
'Breevis Selene' **new** — WPBF
'Brenda' (d) — CLoc CWVF EBak
'Brenda White' — CDoC CLoc CWVF EBak EPts WRou
'Brentwood' (d) — EBak
brevilobis — CSil WPBF
- Berry 4445 — EKMF
'Brian C. Morrison' — EKMF LCla WPBF
'Brian G. Soanes' — EBak
'Brian Hilton' — MWar
'Brian Kimberley' — EKMF LCla MWar WPBF
'Bridal Veil' (d) — EBak
'Bridesmaid' (d) — CWVF EBak SPet
'Brigadoon' (d) — CLoc EBak
'Bright Lights' — EKMF WPBF
'Brightling' — WPBF
'Brighton Belle' — CDoC CWVF WPBF
'Brilliant' ambig. — CWVF NDlv SWal
I 'Brilliant' Bull — CDoC CHrt CLoc CSil EBak EKMF LCla MWhe
'Briony Caunt' — CSil EKMF
'British Jubilee' (d) — CWVF EKMF WPBF
'Brixham Orpheus' — CWVF
'Brodsworth' — CSil EKMF NDlv
'Bronze Banks Peninsula' — CSil EKMF
'Brookwood Belle' (d) — CWVF EPts LCla MJac SLBF
'Brookwood Dale' — MWhe
'Brookwood Joy' (d) — CWVF MJac SLBF
'Brookwood Lady' — MWhe
'Brutus' ♀H4 — CDoC CLoc CSil CWVF EBak EBee EKMF EMan EPts LAst LRHS MHar MWat MWhe NDlv SPet SPoG SWal
'Bryan Breary' — LCla
'Bubba Jack' — SLBF
'Buddha' (d) — EBak

'Bugle Boy' — EPts LCla MWar SLBF
'Bunny' (d) — CWVF EBak
'Burnt Hill' — WPBF
'Burstwick' — CSil
'Burton Brew' — MJac
'Buster' (d) — EKMF LCla SLBF WPBF
'Buttercup' — CLoc CWVF EBak
'C.J. Howlett' — CSil EBak EKMF
'Caballero' (d) — EBak
'Caesar' (d) — CWVF EBak
'Caitlin' **new** — WPBF
'Caitlin Isabelle' — WPBF
'Caledonia' — CSil EBak EKMF
'California' — WPBF WRou
'Callaly Pink' — CWVF
'Cambridge Louie' — CWVF EBak MBri MWar MWhe SPet
'Cameron Ryle' — WPBF
campii — EKMF LCla
campos-portoi — CDoC CSil LCla
 – Berry 4435 — EKMF
'Candlelight' (d) — CLoc EBak
'Candy Stripe' — CLoc
canescens Benth. — EKMF
canescens misapplied — see *F. ampliata*
'Canny Bob' — MJac WPBF
'Canopy' (d) — CWVF
'Capri' (d) — CWVF EBak
'Caprice' — WPBF
'Cara Mia' (d) — CLoc CWVF SPet
'Caradela' — CLoc EKMF MJac MWar WPBF
'Cardinal' — CLoc EKMF WPBF
'Cardinal Farges' (d) — CLoc CSil CWVF EKMF SLBF SPet WPBF
'Careless Whisper' **new** — WPBF
'Carillon van Amsterdam' — MWhe
'Carioca' — EBak
'Carisbrooke Castle' (d) — EKMF
'Carl Drude' (d) — CSil
'Carl Wallace' (d) — EKMF SLBF
'Carla Johnston' ♀H1+3 — CDoC CLoc CWVF EKMF EPts LCla LVER MBri MJac MWar MWhe WRou
'Carleton George' — MWar
'Carmel Blue' — CDoC CLoc LAst LCla LSou MWar MWhe NBlu SPet WGor WPBF WRou
'Carmen' Lemoine (d) — CDoC CSil EKMF WPBF
'Carmine Bell' — CSil EKMF WPBF
'Carnea' — CSil CWib
'Carnoustie' (d) — EBak
'Carol Grace' (d) — CLoc
'Carol Lynn Whittemore' (d) — WPBF
'Carol Nash' (d) — CLoc
'Carol Roe' — EKMF
'Caroline' — CLoc CWVF EBak EKMF EPts MWhe WPBF WRou
'Caroline's Joy' — MJac MWar MWhe SCoo SPet SVil
'Cascade' — CDoC CLoc CWVF EKMF EMan EPts MBri MJac MWhe SPet WBVN
'Caspar Hauser' (d) — CWVF SLBF WPBF
'Catharina' — LCla
'Catherine Bartlett' — CWVF EKMF
'Cathie MacDougall' (d) — EBak
'Cecil Glass' — CSil EKMF
'Cecile' (d) — CDoC CWVF EKMF EPts LAst LCla MJac MWhe SLBF SRGP WRou
'Celadore' (d) — CWVF LVER
'Celebration' (d) — CLoc CWVF
'Celebrity' — WPBF
'Celia Smedley' ♀H3 — CDoC CLoc CSil CWVF EBak EKMF EPts LAst LCla LVER MBri MJac MWar MWhe SLBF SPet WRou
'Celine' — MWar

'Centerpiece' (d) — EBak
'Ceri' — CLoc
'Chameleon' — CDoC SPet
'Champagne Celebration' — CLoc
'Chancellor' — CWVF
'Chandleri' — CWVF EKMF SLBF
'Chang' ♀H1+3 — CLoc CWVF EBak EKMF LCla LRHS MWar MWhe SLBF WPBF
'Chantry Park' — LCla
'Charles Edward' — CSil EKMF WPBF
'Charles Welch' **new** — EPts
Charlie Dimmock = 'Foncha'PBR — CLoc LAst MWhe
'Charlie Gardiner' — CWVF EBak MWhe
'Charlie Girl' (d) — EBak
'Charm of Chelmsford' **new** — LCla
'Charming' — CDoC CLoc CSil CWVF EBak EKMF MJac MWar NDlv SPet WRou
'Chase Delight' (v) — CDoC
'Chatt's Delight' **new** — EKMF
'Checkerboard' ♀H3 — CLoc CSil CWVF EBak EKMF EPts LCla LVER MJac MWar MWhe SLBF SPet
'Cheeky Chantelle' (d) — SLBF WPBF
'Cheers' (d) — CWVF EKMF MWhe
'Chelsea Louise' — EPts
'Chenois Godelieve' — WPBF
'Cherry'PBR Götz — LAst WPBF
'Chessboard' — CLoc
'Cheviot Princess' — WPBF
'Chillerton Beauty' ♀H3 — CLoc CSil CTri CWVF EKMF EPts LCla LRHS MJac MWhe SLBF SPer SPet WMnd WRou
'China Doll' (d) — CWVF EBak MWhe
'China Lantern' — CLoc CSil CWVF EBak EKMF
'Chor Echo' — WPBF
'Chris' — WPBF
'Chris Nicholls' — CSil EKMF
'Christ Driessen' — WPBF
'Christine Bamford' — CDoC CSil CWVF
'Christine Shaffery' (d) — WPBF
'Churchtown' — CWVF
cinerea — LCla
 – Berry 004-86 — EKMF
'Cinnabarina' — CLoc SLBF
* 'Cinnamon' — WPBF
'Cinque Port Liberty' (d) — MWar SLBF
'Cinvenu' — LCla
'Cinvulca' — LCla
'Circe' (d) — CWVF EBak EKMF
'Circus' — EBak
'Circus Spangles' (d) — CLoc COtt EKMF LAst MWar
'Citation' — CDoC CLoc CWVF EBak
'City of Adelaide' (d) — CLoc MWhe
'City of Leicester' — CWVF LCla SPet
'City of Liverpool' **new** — WPBF
'Claire' **new** — WRou
'Claire de Lune' — CDoC CWVF EBak WPBF WRou
'Claire Evans' (d) — CLoc CWVF
'Claire Oram' — CLoc
'Clare Dawson' **new** — WPBF
'Clare Frisby' — EKMF WPBF
'Claudia' (d) — LAst LCla MJac MWar WRou
'Cliantha' (d) — LCla MJac MWhe WRou
'Clifford Gadsby' (d) — EBak
'Cliff's Hardy' — CSil EKMF LCla SPet
'Cliff's Unique' (d) — CWVF EPts
'Clifton Beauty' (d) — CWVF MJac
'Clifton Belle' — CWVF
'Clifton Charm' — CSil EKMF EPts LCla MJac
'Clipper' — CSil CWVF
'Cloth of Gold' — CLoc CWVF EBak MJac MWhe SPet
'Cloverdale Jewel' (d) — CDoC CWVF EBak MWhe SPet

	'Cloverdale Joy'	EBak
	'Cloverdale Pearl'	CWVF EBak EKMF EMan ENot EPfP MWhe SPet SPoG WPBF
	'Cloverdale Star'	WPBF
	'Coachman' ♀H4	CLoc CWVF EBak EKMF EMan EPts LCla MWar MWhe SLBF SPet WBVN WRou
	coccinea	CDoC CSil EKMF EPts LCla
	'Codringtonii'	CSil
	x *colensoi*	CDoC CSil ECou EKMF LCla SHFr
	'Collingwood' (d)	CLoc CWVF EBak
	'Colne Fantasy' (v)	EKMF EPts
	'Come Dancing' (d)	CDoC CWVF LCla SPet
	'Comet' Banks	CWVF
I	'Comet' Tiret (d)	CLoc EBak SPet
	'Comperen Libel'	WPBF
	'Conchilla'	EBak
	'Condor'	SLBF WPBF
	'Connie' (d)	CSil EBak EKMF WPBF
	'Conspicua'	CSil CWVF EBak EKMF WPBF
	'Constable Country' (d)	CWVF
	'Constance' (d)	CDoC CLoc CSil CWVF EKMF EPts LCla MJac MWar MWhe NDlv SLBF SPet SWal WPBF WRou
	'Constance Comer'	MJac
	'Constellation' ambig.	CWVF
I	'Constellation' Schnabel (d)	CLoc EBak
	'Contramine'	WPBF
	'Coombe Park'	MJac
	'Copycat'	CSil
	'Coq au Vin' (d)	WPBF
	'Coquet Bell'	CWVF EBak
	'Coquet Dale' (d)	CWVF EBak WPBF
	'Coral Baby'	LCla
	'Coral Cluster' **new**	MWhe
	'Coral Seas'	EBak
§	'Coralle'	CDoC CLoc CWVF EBak EKMF EMan EPts LCla MJac MWar MWhe SLBF WPBF WRou
	'Corallina'	CDoC CLoc CSil EBak EHol EKMF MWhe SPet WFar
I	'Corallina Variegata' (v)	CSil
*	*cordata* B&SWJ 9095	WCru
	cordifolia misapplied	see *F. splendens*
	cordifolia Benth.	CBcs EBak EKMF MOak WPBF WRou
	'Core'ngrato' (d)	CLoc CWVF EBak
	coriacifolia	EKMF LCla
	'Cornelia Smith'	LCla WPBF
	'Cornwall Calls' (d)	EBak
	'Corrie Palm'	WPBF
	'Corsage' (d)	CWVF
	'Corsair' (d)	EBak
	corymbiflora misapplied	see *F. boliviana* Carrière
§	*corymbiflora* Ruíz & Pav.	CDoC EBak EKMF EPts
	- Berry 4688	EKMF
	- *alba*	see *F. boliviana* var. *alba*
	'Cosmopolitan' (d)	EBak
	'Costa Brava'	CLoc EBak
	'Cotta 2000'	EKMF LCla
	'Cotta Bright Star'	CWVF EKMF LCla
	'Cotta Carousel'	EKMF LCla
	'Cotta Christmas Tree'	CDoC EKMF LCla SLBF
	'Cotta Fairy'	CWVF EKMF
	'Cotta Vino'	EKMF
	'Cottinghamii'	see *F. x bacillaris* 'Cottinghamii'
	'Cotton Candy' (d)	CLoc CWVF LCla MWhe
	'Countdown Carol' (d)	EPts WPBF
	'Countess of Aberdeen'	CLoc CSil CWVF EBak EKMF SLBF
	'Countess of Maritza' (d)	CLoc CWVF
	'County Park'	ECou EWes
	'Court Jester' (d)	CLoc EBak
	'Cover Girl' (d)	EBak EPts LAst MWhe SPet
	'Coxeen'	EBak

	'Crackerjack'	CLoc EBak
	crassistipula	LCla
	- Berry 3553	EKMF
	'Crescendo' (d)	CLoc CWVF
	'Crinkley Bottom' (d)	EPts LVER MJac SLBF WRou
	'Crinoline' (d)	EBak
	'Crosby Serendipity'	CLoc
	'Crosby Soroptimist'	CWVF MJac MWar MWhe WRou
	'Cross Check'	CWVF EMan MBri MJac
	'Crusader' (d)	CWVF
	'Crystal Blue'	EBak
	'Cupid'	CSil EBak
	'Curly Q'	EBak SPet
	'Curtain Call' (d)	CLoc CWVF EBak
	x *cuzco*	EKMF
	cylindracea misapplied	see *F. x bacillaris*
	cylindracea Lindl.	CSil LCla WPBF
	- (m) BRE 43908	EKMF
	'Cymon' (d)	CWVF MWhe
	cyrtandroides	CSil
	- Berry 4628	EKMF
	'Dainty'	EBak
	'Dainty Lady' (d)	EBak
	'Daisy Bell'	CDoC CLoc CWVF EBak EKMF LCla MJac SPet WRou
	'Dalton'	EBak
	'Dana Samantha'	EPts
	'Dancing Bloom'	EPts
	'Dancing Elves'	WPBF
	'Dancing Flame' (d) ♀H1+3	CHrt CLoc CWVF EBak EKMF EMan EPts LAst LCla LVER MBri MJac MWar MWhe SLBF SPet
	'Daniel Lambert' **new**	WPBF
	'Danielle'	LAst WPBF WRou
	'Danielle Frijstein'	WPBF
	'Danielle's Dream' (d)	WPBF
	'Danish Pastry'	CWVF SPet
	'Danny Boy' (d)	CLoc CWVF EBak EKMF MWhe WPBF
	'Danny Kaye' (d)	WPBF
	'Daphne Arlene'	WPBF
	'Dark Eyes' (d) ♀H4	CLoc CSil CWVF EBak EKMF EMan LAst LCla MJac MWhe NBlu SLBF SPet SSea
	'Dark Lady'	MWhe
	'Dark Mystery' (d)	WPBF
	'Dark Night' (d)	CSil
	'Dark Secret' (d)	EBak
	'Dark Treasure' (d)	CDoC EKMF SWal
	'Darreen Dawn' (d)	WPBF
	'Daryn John Woods'	CDoC LCla WPBF
	'Dave's Delight'	EKMF WPBF
	'David'	CDoC CLoc CSil CWVF EKMF EOHP EPts LAst LCla LSou MWhe NDlv SLBF WGor WRou WSPU WWeb
	'David Alston' (d)	CLoc CWVF EBak
	'David Lockyer' (d)	CLoc CWVF
	'David Savage' (d)	LCla
	'Dawn'	EBak
	'Dawn Carless' (d)	WPBF
	'Dawn Fantasia' (v)	CLoc EKMF EPts MWar SLBF WPBF
	'Dawn Redfern'	CWVF
	'Dawn Sky' (d)	EBak
	'Dawn Star' (d)	CWVF LAst MJac MWhe
	'Day by Day'	CSil
	'Day Star'	EBak
	'De Groot's Beauty' (d)	WPBF
	'De Groot's Dikbuil' **new**	WPBF
	'De Groot's Moonlight'	WPBF
	'De Groot's Night' **new**	WPBF
	'De Groot's Parade' (d)	WPBF
	'De Groot's Pipes'	WPBF
	'De Groot's Regenboog'	WPBF
	'De Groot's Tricolore'	WPBF
	'De Groot's Vulkaan' **new**	WPBF

'De Vondeling'		WPBF
'Debby' (d)		EBak
'Deben Petite'		LCla
'Deborah Street'		CLoc
§ *decussata* Ruíz & Pav.		CDoC EBak LCla
– Berry 3049		EKMF
'Dee Copley' (d)		EBak
'Deep Purple' (d)		CDoC CLoc CWVF EKMF LAst MJac SCoo SLBF
'Delilah' (d)		CWVF
'Delta's Angelique'		WPBF
'Delta's Bride'		SLBF WPBF
'Delta's Dream'		CWVF WPBF
'Delta's Groom'		LCla WPBF
'Delta's Matador'		LAst
'Delta's Night'		WPBF
'Delta's Paljas'		WPBF
'Delta's Parade' (d)		EPts WPBF
'Delta's Pim'		WPBF
'Delta's Pride' **new**		WPBF
'Delta's Robijn'		WPBF
'Delta's Sara' (d) **new**		WPBF
'Delta's Song'		WPBF
'Delta's Symphonie' (d)		CWVF WPBF
'Delta's Wonder'		CSil WPBF
'Demi van Roovert'		WPBF
§ *denticulata*		CDoC CLoc CWVF EBak EKMF EPts LCla MOak SLBF WRou
dependens		CDoC EKMF
'Derby Imp'		CWVF
'Desire'		WPBF
'Desperate Daniel'		EPts
'Devonshire Dumpling' (d)		CDoC CLoc CWVF EBak EKMF EMan EPts LAst LCla LVER MBri MJac MWar SLBF SPet
'Diablo' (d)		EBak
'Diamond Celebration' (d)		EKMF MWar
'Diana' (d)		EBak
'Diana Wills' (d)		CWVF MWhe
'Diana Wright'		CSil EKMF MWgw WSPU
'Diane Brown'		CWVF EKMF MWhe
'Diane Marie'		EKMF
§ 'Die Schöne Wilhelmine'		WPBF
'Dilly-Dilly' (d)		CWVF
'Dimples' (d)		CSil MBri
'Dipton Dainty' (d)		CLoc EBak
'Dirk van Delen'		MWhe
'Display' ♀H4		CDoC CLoc CSil CWVF EBak EBee EKMF EMan EPts LAst LCla LVER MBri MJac MWhe NDlv NPer SLBF SPet SPoG SSea WFar WPBF WRou
'Doc'		CDoC CSil EPts NDlv SPet
'Doctor'		see E 'The Doctor'
'Doctor Foster' ♀H4		CDoC CLoc CSil CTri EBak EKMF ENot EPfP EPts NDlv WEas
'Doctor Mason'		CWVF
'Doctor Olson' (d)		CLoc EBak
'Doctor Robert'		CWVF EPts MBri MJac MWhe
'Doctor Topinard'		CLoc EBak EKMF
'Dodo'		WPBF
§ 'Dollar Princess' (d) ♀H4		CDoC CLoc CSil CWVF EBak EBee EKMF EMan EPts LAst LCla MAsh MBri MJac MWar MWhe NBlu NDlv NPer SLBF SPet SPlb SWal WBVN WFar
'Dolly Daydream' (d)		EKMF
'Dominique' (d)		EKMF
'Dominyana'		CSil EBak EKMF LCla
'Don Peralta'		EBak
'Donicetto' **new**		SLBF
'Dopey'		CDoC CSil EPts SPet
'Doreen Redfern'		CLoc CWVF MJac SPet WRou
'Doreen Stroud'		CWVF
'Doris Coleman' (d)		EMan
'Doris Deaves'		SLBF
'Doris Hobbs'		WPBF
'Doris Joan'		SLBF
'Dorothea Flower'		CLoc CSil CWVF EBak EKMF
'Dorothy'		CSil EKMF LCla SLBF SPet
'Dorothy Ann'		SLBF WPBF
'Dorothy Cheal'		CWVF
'Dorothy Day' (d)		CLoc
'Dorothy Hanley' (d)		CBgR CLoc CSil EKMF EPts LAst LSRN LSou MAsh MBri MJac MWhe SLBF SPoG WGor WPBF WRou WWeb
'Dorothy Shields' (d)		CWVF MJac
'Dorrian Brogdale'		LCla WPBF
'Dorset Delight' (d)		CWVF WPBF
'Dot Woodage'		WPBF
'Dove House'		EKMF
'Drake 400' (d)		CLoc
'Drama Girl'		CWVF
'Drame' (d)		CDoC CSil CWVF EBak EKMF LCla NDlv SPet WRou
'Drum Major' (d)		EBak
'Du Barry' (d)		EBak
'Duchess of Albany'		CLoc EBak
'Duchess of Cornwall' (d)		CSil EPts
I 'Duke of Wellington' Haag (d)		CLoc
'Dulcie Elizabeth' (d)		CWVF EBak MJac SPet
'Dunrobin Bedder'		CSil
'Dusky Beauty'		CWVF WPBF WRou
'Dusky Rose' (d)		CLoc CWVF EBak MJac MWhe
'Dusted Pink' (d)		CWVF
'Dutch Kingsize'		WPBF
'Dutch Mill'		CLoc CWVF EBak
'Duyfken'		CWVF
'Dying Embers'		CLoc
'Dymph Werker van Groenland'		LCla MWar
'East Anglian'		CLoc EBak
'Easter Bonnet' (d)		CLoc CWVF
'Ebanflo'		EBak MWar
'Ebbtide' (d)		CLoc EBak WPBF
'Echo'		CLoc CWVF LRHS
'Ector's Isle Cora'		WPBF
'Ectors Nursery'		WPBF
'Ed Largarde' (d)		EBak EKMF
'Eden Lady'		CDoC CLoc SPet WRou
'Eden Princess'		CWVF MJac
'Eden Rock' (d) **new**		SRGP
'Eden's Delight' **new**		WPBF
'Edit van Kessel' **new**		WPBF
'Edith' ambig.		NDlv WRou
'Edith' Brown (d)		CSil EKMF LCla SLBF
'Edith Emery' (d)		SPet
'Edna May'		CWVF
'Edna W. Smith'		CWVF
'Edwin J. Goulding'		WPBF
'Edwin J. Jones' **new**		SLBF
'Eileen Drew'		SLBF WPBF
'Eileen Raffill'		EBak
'Eileen Saunders'		CSil EBak
'Eileen Storey'		EKMF WPBF
'Eisvogel'		WPBF
'El Camino' (d)		CWVF WBVN
'El Cid'		CLoc CSil EBak EKMF
'Elaine Ann'		EPts MJac
'Elaine Taylor' (d)		MJac
'Eleanor Clark'		WPBF
'Eleanor Leytham'		CWVF EBak EKMF LCla WRou
'Eleanor Rawlins'		CSil EBak EKMF
'Elf'		CSil
'Elfin Glade'		CLoc CSil CWVF EBak EKMF WMnd
'Elfrida' (d)		CDoC CSil EKMF NDlv
'Elfriede Ott'		CLoc EBak LCla MWhe WPBF
'Elizabeth' Tiret (d)		WPBF
I 'Elizabeth' Whiteman		EBak EKMF
'Elizabeth Broughton'		EKMF

'Elizabeth Haverkamp' **new**	LCla WPBF
'Elizabeth Tompkins' (d)	MJac
'Elizabeth Travis' (d)	EBak
'Ellen Morgan' (d)	CWVF EBak
'Ellie Jane'	EPts
'Elma'	CDoC LCla
'Elsa' (d)	CWVF LRHS SPet
'Elsie Maude' (d)	CWVF
'Elsie Mitchell' (d)	CWVF MWhe SPet WRou
'Elsstar'	WPBF
'Elysée'	CSil EKMF
§ 'Emile de Wildeman' (d)	EBak EKMF LVER SPet
'Emile Zola'	CSil
'Emily'	WPBF
'Emily Austen'	CWVF EKMF
'Emma Alice' (d)	CWVF
'Emma Louise' (d)	CWVF
'Emma Margaret'	SLBF WPBF
'Empress of Prussia' ♀H4	CDoC CLoc CSil CWVF EBak EKMF EMan EPts LAst LRHS NDlv SLBF SPet SWal MWnd WRou
'Enchanted' (d)	CWVF EBak MWar
'Enchanting Emma' (d) **new**	SLBF
encliandra subsp. *encliandra*	CDoC EKMF LCla WBor WRou
* - var. *gris*	CSil LCla
- subsp. *microphylloides* Berry & Brako 7592	EKMF
§ - subsp. *tetradactyla*	EKMF
§ 'Enfant Prodigue' (d)	CDoC CLoc CSil EKMF SDix SLBF SMrm WMnd
'English Rose' (d)	CWVF
'Enid Carter' (d) **new**	WPBF
'Enstone'	see *F. magellanica* var. *molinae* 'Enstone'
'Erecta'	NPri
'Erica Julie' (d)	MWhe
'Eric's Everest' (d)	EKMF WPBF
'Eric's Majestic' (d)	EKMF MJac
'Erika Borz' (d) **new**	WPBF
'Erika Köth'	LCla WPBF
'Ernest Rankin'	CSil
'Ernie'PBR **new**	SRGP
'Ernie Bromley'	CSil CWVF SLBF
'Ernie Wise' (d) **new**	MJac SCoo
'Errol' (d)	CLoc
'Esmerelda' **new**	WPBF
'Estelle Marie'	CLoc CWVF EBak MBri MWar MWhe SLBF SPet WRou
'Eternal Flame' (d)	CWVF EBak EPts MBri MWhe
'Ethel May'	MJac
'Ethel Wilson'	CSil
'Eureka Red' (d)	CWVF LAst WPBF
'Eurydice' (d)	CLoc
'Eusebia' (d)	MJac
'Eva Boerg'	CLoc CSil CTri CWVF EBak EKMF EMan LAst LCla MBri MWar SPet SWal WKif
'Evelyn Stanley' (d)	CWVF
§ 'Evelyn Steele Little'	EBak
'Evening Sky' (d)	EBak
'Evensong'	CLoc CWVF EBak MWhe WPBF
excorticata	CBcs CDoC CPLG CPle CSil CTrw EKMF SPlb
'Exmoor Woods'	CSil
'Fabian Franck'	CDoC LCla WPBF
'Fairy Falls' **new**	WRou
'Falklands' (d)	CSil SLBF
'Falling Stars'	CLoc CWVF EBak MWhe
'Fan Dancer' (d)	EBak
'Fancy Free' (d)	MBri
'Fancy Pants' (d)	CLoc CWVF EBak
'Fanfare'	CDoC EBak EKMF LCla WPBF WRou
'Fascination'	see *F.* 'Emile de Wildeman'
'Fashion' (d)	EBak
'Favourite'	EBak
'Felicity Kendal' (d) **new**	MJac SCoo
'Feltham's Pride'	CWVF
'Femke Comperen' **new**	WPBF
'Fenman'	CWVF EPts
ferreyrae **new**	LCla
'Festival' (d)	MWhe WPBF
'Festival Lights'	SLBF
'Festoon'	EBak
'Fey' (d)	CWVF EKMF WPBF
'Ffion'	EPts
'Fiery Spider'	EBak WPBF
'Finn'	CWVF EPts
'Fiona'	CLoc CWVF EBak SPet
'Fire Mountain' (d)	CLoc
Firecracker = 'John Ridding'PBR (v)	CHEx CLoc SPoG
'Firelite' (d)	EBak
'Firenza' (d)	CWVF WRou
'First Kiss'	CWVF
'First Lady' (d)	CWVF
'First Lord'	CWVF
'First Success'	CDoC CWVF EKMF LCla LHop WRou
'Flair' (d)	CLoc CWVF
'Flame'	EBak
'Flamenco Dancer' (d)	CLoc CWVF LAst WPBF
'Flash' ♀H3-4	CLoc CSil CTri CWVF EBak EKMF EPts LCla MAsh MJac MWhe NDlv SLBF SPet WRou
'Flashlight'	CDoC CSil CWVF LAst LSou MJac NDlv WPBF
'Flashlight Amélioré'	CSil
'Flat Jack o' Lancashire' (d)	CSil EKMF SLBF
'Flavia' (d)	EBak
'Fleur de Picardie'	WPBF
'Flirt'	WPBF
'Flirtation Waltz' (d)	CLoc CWVF EBak EKMF EMan EPts LVER MJac MWhe SPet
'Flocon de Neige'	CSil EBak EPts
'Floral City' (d)	CLoc EBak
'Florence Mary Abbott'	EMan WPBF
'Florence Taylor'	CWVF
'Florence Turner'	CSil EBak EKMF MWhe
'Florentina' (d)	CLoc CWVF EBak EKMF
'Florrie's Gem' (d)	SLBF
'Flowerdream'	CWVF
'Flyaway' (d)	EBak
'Fly-by-night' (d)	CWVF
'Flying Cloud' (d)	CLoc CSil CWVF EBak EKMF MBri
'Flying Scotsman' (d)	CDoC CLoc CWVF EBak EKMF EPts MJac SCoo SVil WRou
'Fohnhimmel' (d)	WPBF
'Fokko's Katrien' **new**	WPBF
'Folies Bergères' (d)	EBak
'Foolke'	CSil EBak EPts
'Forfar's Pride'	CSil MWar
'Forget-me-not'	CLoc CSil CWVF EBak EKMF WPBF
'Fort Bragg' (d)	CWVF EBak
'Fort Royal' **new**	WRou
'Forward Look'	CDoC MWhe WPBF
'Fountains Abbey' (d)	CWVF EMan
'Four Farthings' (d)	EKMF WPBF
'Foxgrove Wood' ♀H3-4	CSil CWVF EBak EKMF EPts SLBF
'Foxtrot'	CWVF
'Foxy Lady' (d)	CWVF EKMF WPBF
'Frances Haskins'	CSil MWhe WRou
'Frank Saunders'	CWVF LCla WPBF
'Frank Unsworth' (d)	CHrt CWVF EKMF EPts MJac SPet
'Frankie's Magnificent Seven' (d)	EPts

'Frau Hilde Rademacher' (d)	CDoC CSil CWVF EBak EKMF EMan EPts SLBF SWal
'Fred Hansford'	CSil CWVF SLBF
'Fred Swales'	WPBF
'Fred's First' (d)	CDoC CSil EKMF SWal
'Freefall'	EBak
'Friendly Fire' (d)	CLoc
'Frosted Flame'	CDoC CLoc CWVF EBak EKMF LCla MJac MWar MWhe SPet SSea
'Frozen Tears'	WPBF
'Frühling' (d)	CSil EBak EKMF
'Fuchsiade' **new**	WRou
'Fuchsiade '88'	CLoc CSil CWVF EBak EKMF MWhe WPBF
'Fuchsiarama '91'	CWVF WPBF WRou
'Fuji-San'	CDoC EPts WPBF
'Fuksie Foetsie'	CDoC CSil
fulgens ♀H1+3	CDoC EKMF GCal IFro LCla MOak MWhe WRou
* – var. *minuata*	EKMF
* – 'Variegata' (v)	CDoC CLoc CSil EKMF EPts LCla WPBF WRou
'Fulpila'	LCla WPBF
furfuracea	EKMF
'Für Elise' (d)	EBak
'Gala' (d)	EBak
'Galadriel'	WPBF
'Ganzenhof' **new**	LCla
'Garden News' (d) ♀H3-4	CDoC CLoc CSil CWVF EKMF EPts LAst LCla LRHS LVER MJac MWar MWhe NDlv NPer SLBF SPet SWal WFar WRou
'Garden Week' (d)	CWVF MWhe WPBF
'Gartenmeister Bonstedt' ♀H1+3	CDoC CLoc CWVF EBak EKMF EPts LCla LRHS NBlu SPet SSea
'Gary Rhodes' (d)	EBak MJac SCoo
'Gay Fandango' (d)	CLoc CWVF EBak SPet
'Gay Future'	EKMF
'Gay Parasol' (d)	CLoc LAst MJac WRou
'Gay Paree' (d)	EBak WPBF
'Gay Senorita'	EBak
'Gay Spinner' (d)	CLoc
gehrigeri	EBak EKMF LCla
gehrigeri × *nigricans*	EKMF
'Gemma Fisher' (d)	EPts
Gene = 'Goetzgene'[PBR] (Shadowdancer Series)	LSou SCoo WPBF
'Général Charles de Gaulle'	WPBF
'Général Monk' (d)	CDoC CSil CWVF EBak EKMF EMan EPts LAst MBri SRGP SWal
'Général Voyron'	CSil
'Genii' ♀H4	More than 30 suppliers
'Geoffrey Smith' (d)	CSil EKMF EPts
§ 'Georg Börnemann'	CLoc CWVF EBak WPBF
'Georgana' (d)	MWhe WPBF
'George Barr'	EKMF LRHS WPBF
'George Bartlett'	CLoc
'George Johnson'	CDoC SPet
'George Travis' (d)	EBak
'Georges Remy'	WPBF
'Gerald Drewitt'	CSil
§ 'Gerharda's Aubergine'	CDoC CLoc CSil CWVF EKMF WPBF
'Gerharda's Kiekeboe'	WPBF
§ 'Gesneriana'	CDoC CLoc EBak WWlt
'Giant Pink Enchanted' (d)	CLoc EBak
'Gilda'	CWVF MJac
'Gillian Althea' (d)	CDoC CWVF SRGP
'Gilt Edge' (v)	CLoc
l 'Gina' **new**	SLBF WPBF
'Gina Bowman'	LCla SLBF
'Gina's Gold' (d)	WPBF
Ginger = 'Goetzginger'[PBR] (Shadowdancer Series)	LSou NEgg SCoo SVil
'Gipsy Princess' (d)	CLoc
'Girls' Brigade'	CWVF EKMF

'Gitana'	WPBF
'Gladiator' (d)	EBak EKMF LCla
'Gladys Godfrey'	EBak
'Gladys Lorimer'	CWVF EPts
'Gladys Miller'	CLoc
glazioviana	CDoC CSil CWVF EKMF LCla SLBF SWal WPBF WRou
'Glenby' (d)	CWVF
'Glendale'	CWVF
'Glitters'	CWVF EBak EPts
§ 'Globosa'	CAgr CSil EBak EKMF
'Gloria Johnson'	EKMF
'Glororum' **new**	WPBF
'Glow'	CSil EBak EKMF WPBF
'Glowing Embers'	EBak
Glowing Lilac (d)	EMan EPts
'Glyn Jones' (d)	EKMF
'Gold Brocade'	CSil MBri SPet SPoG SWal
'Gold Crest'	EBak WPBF
'Gold Leaf'	CWVF
'Golden Anniversary' (d)	CLoc CWVF EBak EKMF EMan LVER MJac WPBF
'Golden Arrow'	CDoC LCla WPBF
'Golden Border Queen'	CLoc
'Golden Dawn'	CLoc CWVF EBak SPet
'Golden Eden Lady' (v)	MWhe
'Golden Girl'	SLBF
'Golden Herald'	CSil SLBF
'Golden La Campanella' (d/v)	CLoc MBri
'Golden Lena' (d/v)	CSil CWVF EMan
'Golden Margaret Roe' (v)	CSil
'Golden Marinka' (v) ♀H3	CLoc EBak EKMF LAst LRHS LSou MBri SPet
'Golden Melody' (d)	CSil
'Golden Monique'	WPBF
'Golden Pater' **new**	WPBF
'Golden Swingtime' (d)	CHrt EPts MBri MJac SPet SSea WPBF
'Golden Treasure' (v)	CLoc CSil CWVF EKMF MBri MWar
'Golden Vergeer' (v)	SLBF
'Golden Wedding'	EKMF
'Goldsworth Beauty'	CSil LCla
'Golondrina'	CSil CWVF EBak WPBF
'Goody Goody'	EBak
'Gooseberry Hill'	WPBF
'Gordon Boy' (d)	CSil
'Gordon Thorley'	CSil EKMF MWhe
'Gordon's China Rose'	LCla
'Gorgeous Gemma' (d)	WPBF
'Gottingen'	EBak EKMF WPBF
'Governor Pat Brown' (d)	EBak
'Grace Darling'	CWVF EBak MWhe
gracilis	see *F. magellanica* var. *gracilis*
'Graf Witte'	CDoC CSil CWVF EKMF EPts NDlv SPet
'Grand Duchess'	WPBF
'Grand Duke' (d)	CWVF
'Grandad Hobbs' (d)	LCla
'Grandma Hobbs'	LCla
'Grandma Sinton' (d)	CLoc CWVF EMan MBri MWhe
'Grandpa George' (d)	LCla
'Grandpa Jack' (d)	SLBF
'Grayrigg'	CDoC CSil EKMF EPts LCla NDlv
'Great Ouse' (d)	EPts
'Great Scott' (d)	CLoc
'Green 'n' Gold'	EBak
'Greenpeace'	EKMF SLBF WPBF
'Greta'	MWar WRou
'Gretna Chase'	MBri MWhe
'Grey Lady' (d)	CSil
'Grietje'	WPBF
'Groene Boelvaar' (d)	WPBF
'Grumpy'	CDoC CSil EPts LRHS MLan MWhe SPet

'Gruss aus dem Bodethal'	CLoc CWVF EBak EKMF EPts WPBF	
'Guinevere'	CWVF EBak	
'Gustave Doré' (d)	CSil EBak EKMF	
'Guy Dauphine' (d)	EBak	
'Gwen Burralls' (d)	EKMF	
'Gwen Dodge'	LCla WPBF	
'Gypsy Girl' (d)	CWVF	
* 'H.C. Brown'	LCla	
'H.G. Brown'	CSil EBak EKMF MWhe	
'Halsall Beauty' (d)	MBri	
'Halsall Belle' (d)	MBri	
'Halsall Pride' (d)	MBri	
'Hampshire Beauty' (d)	MJac	
'Hampshire Blue'	CDoC CWVF	
'Hampshire Prince' (d)	LVER	
'Hanau'	WPBF	
'Hanna' (d)	SRGP WPBF	
'Hannah Gwen' (d)	EKMF	
'Hannah Louise' (d)	EPts	
'Hannah Rogers'	MWar	
'Hans Callaars'	SLBF WPBF	
'Happy'	CDoC CSil CWVF EPts LCla SPet	
'Happy Anniversary'	CLoc	
I 'Happy Anniversary' (d/v)	EKMF	
'Happy Fellow'	CDoC CLoc CSil EBak NDlv	
'Happy Wedding Day' (d)	CDoC CLoc CWVF EKMF EPts LAst MJac MWhe SCoo SPet SRGP	
'Hapsburgh'	EBak	
'Harbour Lites'	MWar SLBF WPBF WRou	
'Harlow Car'	CDoC CWVF EKMF EPts	
'Harlow Perfection'	EKMF	
I 'Harmony' Niederholzer	EBak	
'Harnser's Flight'	CSil	
'Harrow Pride' (d)	CSil	
'Harry Dunnett'	EBak	
'Harry Gray' (d)	CLoc CWVF EBak EMan EPts LAst MBri MJac MWhe SPet SRGP SSea	
'Harry Pullen'	EBak	
'Harry Taylor' (d)	EPts	
'Harry's Sunshine'	SLBF	
'Hartis Phönix'	WPBF	
'Hartis Schwarzer'	SLBF	
hartwegii	CDoC CSil EKMF LCla	
'Harvey's Reward' **new**	SLBF WPBF	
'Hathersage' (d)	EBak	
'Hathor'	WPBF	
hatschbachii	CDoC CSil EPts LCla	
– Berry 4464	EKMF	
– Berry 4465	EKMF	
'Haute Cuisine' (d)	CLoc EMan MWhe	
'Hawaiian Sunset' (d)	CLoc CWVF EPts LCla SLBF WPBF	
'Hawkshead' ♀H3-4	More than 30 suppliers	
'Hazel' (d)	MWhe	
'Heart Throb' (d)	EBak	
'Heavenly Hayley' (d)	SLBF	
'Hebe'	EBak MWhe	
I 'Hedens Montana'	WPBF	
'Heidi Ann' (d) ♀H3	CDoC CHrt CLoc CSil CWVF EBak EKMF EMan EPts LAst MBri MWhe NDlv SLBF SPet SWal	
'Heidi Blue' (d)	SLBF	
'Heidi Joy'	CSil	
§ 'Heidi Weiss' (d)	CDoC CLoc CSil CWVF MBri SPet	
'Heinrich Henkel'	see *F.* 'Andenken an Heinrich Henkel'	
'Heinzelmännchen'	WPBF	
'Heirloom' (d)	EKMF	
'Helen Clare' (d)	CLoc EBak	
'Helen Elizabeth' (d)	EKMF	
'Helen Nicholls' (d)	EKMF WPBF	
'Helen Spence' (d)	EKMF	
'Helena Rose' **new**	EKMF	
'Hella'	WPBF	
'Hellen Devine'	CWVF	
'Hello Dolly'	CLoc	

'Hemsleyana'	see *F. microphylla* subsp. *hemsleyana*	
'Henkelly's Apmist' **new**	WPBF	
'Henkelly's Benjamin' **new**	WPBF	
'Henkelly's Dikbuik'	WPBF	
'Henkelly's Elegantie'	WPBF	
'Henkelly's Meuleke' (d) **new**	WPBF	
'Henkelly's Sam'	WPBF	
'Henkelly's Stippelke'	WPBF	
'Hennie Bouman' (d)	WPBF	
'Henning Becker'	CWVF WPBF	
'Henri Poincaré'	EBak EKMF	
'Herald' ♀H4	CDoC CSil CWVF EBak EKMF MHar NDlv SLBF SWal WPBF	
'Herbé de Jacques'	see *F.* 'Mr West'	
'Heritage' (d)	CLoc CSil EBak EKMF	
'Herman de Graaff' (d)	EKMF WPBF	
'Hermiena'	CLoc CWVF EPts MWar MWhe SLBF WPBF	
'Hermienne' **new**	WRou	
'Heron'	CSil EBak EKMF	
'Herps Bonang'	WPBF	
'Herps Buikorgel' **new**	WPBF	
'Herps Pierement' **new**	SLBF	
'Hertogin van Brabant' (d)	WPBF	
'Hessett Festival' (d)	CWVF EBak	
'Heston Blue' (d)	CWVF EKMF	
'Het Halens Helmpje'	WPBF	
'Hettenheuvel'	WPBF	
'Hetty Blok' (d)	WPBF	
'Heydon'	CWVF	
'Hi Jinks' (d)	EBak	
hidalgensis	see *F. microphylla* subsp. *hidalgensis*	
'Hidcote Beauty'	CDoC CLoc CWVF EBak MWhe SLBF SPet	
'Hidden Treasure'	MWar WPBF	
'Highland Pipes'	CSil EKMF LCla	
'Hilda Fitzsimmons'	WPBF	
'Hilda May Salmon'	CWVF	
'Hilke'	WPBF	
'Hindu Belle'	EBak	
'Hinnerike'	CSil CWVF EPts LCla WPBF WRou	
'Hiroshige'	LCla	
'His Excellency' (d)	EBak	
'Hobo' (d)	CSil WPBF	
'Hobson's Choice' (d)	CWVF SLBF	
'Hokusai'	WPBF	
'Holly's Beauty' (d)	CDoC CLoc EKMF EPts LAst MWar SRGP SVil WPBF	
'Hollywood Park' (d)	EBak	
'Hot Coals'	CLoc CWVF EKMF EPts LCla MJac MWar MWhe WRou	
'Howerd Hebden'	EKMF SLBF WPBF	
'Howlett's Hardy'	CDoC CLoc CSil CWVF EBak EKMF EPts LRHS NLar SWal WMnd WPBF WRou	
'Hula Girl' (d)	CWVF EBak EKMF MJac MWar MWhe SPet	
'Humboldt Holiday' (d)	EKMF	
'Huntsman' (d)	CDoC LAst MWhe	
'Ian Brazewell' (d)	CLoc	
'Ian Leedham' (d)	EBak EKMF	
'Ian Storey'	CSil EKMF	
'Ice Cream Soda' (d)	EBak	
'Ice Maiden' ambig. (d)	WPBF	
'Iceberg'	CWVF EBak	
'Icecap'	CWVF EKMF MBri	
'Iced Champagne'	CLoc CWVF EBak MJac	
'Ichiban' (d)	CLoc WPBF	
'Icicle' (d)	WPBF	
'Ida' (d)	EBak	
'Igloo Maid' (d)	CLoc CWVF EBak EKMF MWhe SPet	
'Illusion'	WPBF	

'Impala' (d) — CWVF
'Imperial Fantasy' (d) — CWVF
'Impudence' — CLoc EBak SPet
'Impulse' (d) — CLoc
'Indian Maid' (d) — CWVF EBak LVER WPBF
inflata — EKMF
'Ingleore' — WPBF
'Ingrid van der Sande' **new** WPBF
'Insulinde' — CDoC CFee CWVF EPts LCla MJac MWar SLBF WPBF
'Interlude' (d) — EBak
'Iolanthe' — CWVF
'Irene L. Peartree' (d) — CWVF LCla
'Irene Sinton' (d) — MJac SVil
'Iris Amer' (d) — CDoC CLoc CWVF EBak
'Irish Dawn' — MWar
'Irving Alexander' (d) — WPBF
'Isabel Erkamp' — WPBF
'Isabel Ryan' — CSil
'Isis' ambig. — WPBF
'Isis' Lemoine — CSil
'Isle of Mull' — CDoC CSil SPet WPBF
'Italiano' (d) — CWVF MJac
'Ivana van Amsterdam' — SLBF WPBF
'Ivy Grace' — CSil
'Jack Acland' — CWVF
'Jack Shahan' ♀H3 — CDoC CHrt CLoc CSil CWVF EBak EKMF EMan LAst LCla MBri MJac MWar MWhe NBlu SPet SRGP
'Jack Stanway' (v) — CWVF EKMF EPts MWar
'Jack Wilson' — CSil
'Jackie Bull' (d) — CWVF EBak
'Jackpot' (d) — EBak
'Jackqueline' — CWVF
'Jadas Mam' — WPBF
'Jam Roll' (d) — LVER
'Jamboree' (d) — EBak
'James Lye' (d) — CWVF EBak EKMF SWal
'James Shaffery' **new** WPBF
'James Travis' (d) — CDoC CSil EBak EKMF LCla
'Jan Lokhorst' — SLBF WPBF
'Jan Murray' **new** SLBF
'Jan van Erp' — WPBF
'Jandel' — CWVF
'Jane Humber' (d) — CWVF EKMF
'Jane Lye' — EBak
'Janet Williams' (d) — CSil
'Janice Ann' — EKMF LCla MWar WPBF
'Janice Perry's Gold' (v) — CLoc MJac
'Janie' (d) — MAsh
'Janjopiet Driessen' **new** WPBF
'Jap Vantveer' — LCla WPBF
'Jasper's Vlammetje' **new** SDEP WPBF
'Jaunty Jack' — SLBF
'Javelin' — WPBF
'Jean Baker' — CSil
'Jean Campbell' — EBak
'Jean Clark' — WPBF
'Jean Frisby' — CLoc
'Jean Temple' **new** WPBF
'Jeane' — EKMF NEgg
'Jeangil' — WPBF
'Jennifer' — EBak
'Jennifer Hampson' (d) — CSil
'Jennifer Lister' (d) — CSil EKMF
'Jenny Brinson' (d) — WPBF
'Jenny May' — CLoc EPts WPBF
'Jenny Sorensen' — CWVF EKMF WRou
'Jess' — LCla SLBF WPBF
'Jessie Pearson' — CWVF
'Jessimae' — CWVF SPet
'Jester' Holmes (d) — CLoc CSil
'Jet Fire' (d) — EBak
'Jezebel' — WPBF
'Jiddles' — EKMF LCla SLBF WRou
'Jill Harris' — WPBF

'Jill Whitworth' — CDoC
'Jim Coleman' — CWVF MWhe
'Jim Dodge' (d) — EPts WPBF
'Jim Hawkins' — EBak
'Jim Muncaster' — CWVF EKMF
'Jim Watts' **new** CDoC EKMF WPBF
jimenezii — CDoC EKMF LCla WPBF
  – hybrid — EKMF
'Jimmy Carr' (d) — EKMF
'Jimmy Cricket' — CDoC LCla
'Jingle Bells' — MWhe
'Jinlye' — EKMF
'Jo Tamerus' (d) **new** WPBF
'Joan Barnes' (d) — CDoC CWVF
'Joan Cooper' — CLoc CSil CWVF EBak EKMF SLBF
'Joan Goy' — CWVF EKMF EPts MJac MWhe
'Joan Jones' (d) — MJac
'Joan Knight' — CLoc
'Joan Leach' — CSil
'Joan Margaret' (d) — MJac
'Joan Morris' — SLBF
'Joan Pacey' — CWVF EBak EKMF
'Joan Paxton' (d) — LCla
'Joan Smith' — EBak
'Joan Waters' (d) — CWVF
'Joanne' **new** WPBF
'Jo-Anne Fisher' (d) — EPts
'Joan's Delight' — WPBF
'Joe Kusber' (d) — CWVF EBak
'Joe Nicholls' (d) — EKMF
'Joel' — CLoc WPBF
'John Bartlett' — CLoc
'John E. Caunt' — CSil EKMF
'John Green' — EKMF SLBF WPBF
'John Grooms' (d) — CLoc WRou
'John Lockyer' — CLoc CWVF EBak
'John Maynard Scales' — CDoC CWVF LCla MJac MWhe WPBF WRou
'John Quirk' (d) — SLBF
'John Stephens' — EPts
'John Suckley' (d) — EBak
'John Wright' — CSil EKMF LCla
'Johnny' (d) — CLoc
'Joke's Othello' (d) **new** WPBF
'Jomam' ♀H3 — CLoc CWVF MWar WPBF
'Jon Oram' — CLoc CWVF
'Jon Vincent' (d) — SLBF
'Jonne Comperen' **new** WPBF
'Jopie' (d) — WPBF
'Jorma van Eijk' (d) **new** WPBF
'Joseph Holmes' **new** WPBF
'Jose's Joan' (d) — CWVF
'Joy Bielby' — EKMF
'Joy Patmore' — CLoc CWVF EBak EKMF EPts MBri MWar MWhe SLBF SPet
'Joyce' — WPBF
'Joyce Adey' (d) — CWVF
'Joyce Sinton' — CWVF EMan MBri
'Joyce Wilson' (d) — EPts LCla
'Jubilee Quest' — EKMF MWar WPBF
'Judith Coupland' — CWVF
'Juella' — WPBF
'Jules Daloges' (d) — EBak EKMF
'Julia' (d) — EKMF WPBF
'Julie Ann' — MWar
'Julie Horton' (d) — WPBF
'Julie Marie' (d) — CWVF MJac
'June Gardner' — CWVF EKMF
'Jungle' — LCla WPBF
'Juno' Kennett — EBak
juntasensis — EKMF WPBF
'Jupiter Seventy' — EBak
'Justin's Pride' — CDoC CSil EKMF
'Jülchen' — CWVF WPBF
'Kaboutertje' — EKMF
'Kaleidoscope' (d) — EBak

'Kallinga'	WPBF
'Karen Isles'	CDoC LCla WRou
'Karen Louise' (d)	CLoc
'Karin Siegers'	CSil
'Kate Taylor' (d)	SLBF WPBF
'Kate Wylie'	MWar
'Kath Kirk' **new**	EKMF
'Kath van Hanegem'	EPts SLBF WPBF WRou
'Kathleen Muncaster' (d)	EKMF WPBF
'Kathleen Smith' (d)	EKMF
'Kathleen van Hanegan'	CLoc MWar
'Kathryn Maidment'	WPBF
'Kathy Louise' (d)	EMan WPBF
'Kathy's Pipes'	EKMF
'Kathy's Prince'	EKMF
'Kathy's Sparkler' (d)	EKMF
'Katie Elizabeth Ann' (d)	MWar
'Katie Rogers'	EPts
'Katie Susan' **new**	LCla SLBF
'Katinka'	CWVF EPts LCla
'Katjan'	CSil EKMF EPts LCla SLBF
'Katrien Michiels'	WPBF
'Katrina' (d)	CLoc EBak
'Katrina Thompsen'	CLoc CWVF EKMF EPts MWar
'Katy James'	EKMF MWar
'Katy M'	WPBF
'Keepsake' (d)	CLoc EBak
'Keesje'	WPBF
'Kegworth Carnival' (d)	CWVF
'Kelly's Dream' (d)	WPBF
'Kelsey's Kisses'	WPBF
'Ken Goldsmith'	CWVF EPts SWal
'Ken Jennings'	CWVF
'Kenny Dalglish' (d)	CSil EKMF
'Kenny Holmes'	CWVF
'Kenny Walkling'	SLBF WPBF
'Kernan Robson' (d)	CLoc CWVF EBak
'Kerry Anne'	EPts
'Keteltje' **new**	WPBF
'Kevin R. Peake' (d)	MWar
'Keystone'	EBak
'Kim Nicholls'	CDoC EKMF
'Kim Wright' (d)	MWhe
'Kimberly' (d)	EBak
'King of Bath' (d)	EBak
'King of Hearts' (d)	EBak
'King's Ransom' (d)	CLoc CWVF EBak LRHS MWhe SPet
'Kiss 'n' Tell'	CWVF MJac MWhe
'Kit Oxtoby' (d)	CDoC CHrt CWVF EKMF EMan LCla LVER MJac SVil
'Kiwi' (d)	EBak
'Knockout' (d)	CWVF EKMF
'Kolding Perle'	CWVF EKMF SPet
'Königin der Nacht'	WPBF
'Kon-Tiki' (d)	CLoc SPet
'Koralle'	see *F* 'Coralle'
'Krimar'	WPBF
'Krommenie'	WPBF
'Kwintet'	CWVF EBak MJac SPet
'Kyoto'	CWVF
'La Bianca'	EBak
'La Campanella' (d) ♀H3	CDoC CHrt CLoc CWVF EBak EKMF EMan EPts LAst LCla LSou MBri MJac MWar MWhe NBlu NVic SPet
'La Fiesta' (d)	EBak
'La France' (d)	EBak EKMF
'La Neige' ambig.	CWVF
'La Neige' Lemoine (d)	EBak EKMF
'La Porte' (d)	CLoc CWVF
'La Rosita' (d)	EBak SLBF
'La Traviata' ambig.	WPBF
I 'La Traviata' Blackwell (d)	EBak
'La Violetta' (d)	MWhe
'Lace Petticoats' (d)	EBak EKMF
'Lady Bacon' **new**	SLBF
'Lady Boothby'	CDoC CHEx CPLG CSil CWVF EBak EKMF EShb LRHS SLBF SMrm SPet SPoG
'Lady Framlingham' (d)	EPts
'Lady Heytesbury'	EKMF
'Lady in Grey' (d)	EKMF LAst MJac WPBF
'Lady Isobel Barnett'	CDoC CLoc CWVF EBak EKMF MBri MJac MWar MWhe SPet
'Lady Kathleen Spence'	CWVF EBak MWhe SPet WRou
'Lady Lupus' **new**	EPts
'Lady Patricia Mountbatten'	CWVF EKMF EMan MJac WRou
'Lady Ramsey'	EBak
'Lady Rebecca' (d)	CLoc
'Lady Thumb' (d) ♀H3	More than 30 suppliers
'Lady's Smock'	EKMF
§ 'Laing's Hybrid'	CWVF EBak WPBF
'Lakeland Princess'	EBak
'Lakeside'	EBak
'Laleham Lass'	EKMF
'Lambada'	LAst MWar MWhe WPBF WRou
'Lancambe'	CSil
'Lancashire Lad' (d)	LAst MWar WPBF
'Lancashire Lass'	CWVF MBri
'Lancelot'	EBak
'Land van Beveren'	MWar SLBF WPBF
'Lange Lander' **new**	WPBF
'Lark'	CWVF EPts WPBF
'Lassie' (d)	CDoC CLoc CWVF EBak
'Laura' ambig.	CWVF WRou
I 'Laura' (Dutch)	CLoc EPts LCla MWar SLBF
I 'Laura' Martin (d)	EKMF MWhe WPBF
'Laura Cross'	MWar
'Lavender Kate' (d)	CLoc CWVF EBak
'Lavender Lace'	MWhe
'Lazy Lady' (d)	CWVF EBak
'Le Postier'	WPBF
'Lea de Smedt'	WPBF
'Lea's Aubergine'	WPBF
'Lechlade Apache'	CDoC LCla MWar
'Lechlade Chinaman'	CDoC EKMF LCla
'Lechlade Debutante'	CDoC LCla
'Lechlade Fire-eater'	CDoC LCla WPBF
'Lechlade Gorgon'	CDoC CWVF EKMF LCla SLBF WPBF
'Lechlade Magician'	CDoC CSil EBee EKMF EPts LCla MWgw SLBF WSPU
'Lechlade Maiden'	CWVF LCla
'Lechlade Martianess'	LCla
'Lechlade Potentate'	LCla
'Lechlade Tinkerbell'	LCla
'Lechlade Violet'	CDoC CSil EKMF LCla
lehmanii	LCla
'Leicestershire Silver' (d)	MJac
'Leila' (d)	WPBF
'Lemmeke' **new**	WPBF
'Len Bielby'	CDoC CWVF LCla
'Lena' (d) ♀H3	CDoC CLoc CSil CTri CWVF EBak EKMF EPts LAst MBri MJac MWhe NDlv SPer SPet SRGP SSea SWal WEas WPBF
'Lena Dalton' (d)	CLoc CWVF EBak MWhe
'Leonhart von Fuchs'	WPBF
'Leonora'	CDoC CLoc CSil CWVF EBak EKMF MBri MWhe SLBF SPet WRou
'Lesley'	CWVF LCla
'Lett's Delight' (d)	CWVF EPts
'Letty Lye'	EBak
'Leverhulme'	see *F* 'Leverkusen'
§ 'Leverkusen'	CDoC CLoc EBak LCla MJac MWhe SWal WRou
'Li Kai Lin'	CSil
'Liebesträume' ambig.	WPBF

I 'Liebesträume' Blackwell (d) — EBak

'Liebriez' (d) ♀H3-4 — CSil EBak EKMF EPts NDlv SPet SWal

'Liemers Lantaern' — CWVF

'Lieze Brantze' — WPBF

'Likalin' — CWVF

'Lilac' — CSil EBak

'Lilac Dainty' (d) — CSil

'Lilac Lustre' (d) — CLoc CWVF EBak SPet

'Lilac Princess' — MJac

'Lilac Queen' (d) — EBak

'Lilian' — EKMF WPBF

'Lillian Annetts' (d) — CDoC CWVF EKMF LAst LCla MJac MWar SLBF WRou

'Lillibet' (d) — CLoc CWVF EBak

'Lime Lite' (d) — MJac

'Linda Goulding' — CWVF EBak MWhe WRou

'Linda Grace' — EKMF EPts MJac MWar

'Linda Mary Nutt' — MWar

'Linda Rosling' (d) — CDoC EKMF

'Lindisfarne' (d) — CLoc CWVF EBak EKMF MJac SPet WPBF

'L'Ingénue' — WPBF

'Linlithgow Lass' — MWar SLBF

'Lionel' — CSil

'Lisa' (d) — CDoC EPts SPet WPBF

'Lisa Jane' — MWhe

'Lisa Rowe' (d) — WPBF

'Lisi' — WPBF

'Little Annie Gee' — MWar

'Little Baby' — EKMF

'Little Beauty' — CDoC CSil CWVF EKMF MWhe WPBF

'Little Boy Blue' — EPts

'Little Brook Gem' — SLBF

'Little Catbells' — SLBF

'Little Chris' **new** — WPBF

'Little Cracker' — EBee

'Little Gene' — EBak

'Little Jewel' — SPet

'Little Nan' — SLBF WPBF

'Little Orphan Annie' — LCla

'Little Ouse' (d) — CWVF MWhe

'Little Snow Queen' — WPBF

'Little Witch' — EKMF SLBF

'Liz' (d) — CSil EBak EKMF

Liza = 'Goetzliza'PBR (Shadowdancer Series) — CDoC LAst LSou

'Lochinver' (d) — CWVF

'Loeke's Marie-Lou' — WPBF

'Loeky' — CLoc CWVF EBak SPet WPBF

'Logan Garden' — see F. *magellanica* 'Logan Woods'

'Lolita' (d) — CWVF EBak

'London 2000' — LCla MJac SLBF WPBF

'London in Bloom' — SLBF WPBF

'Lonely Ballerina' (d) — CLoc CWVF

'Long Distance' — LCla

'Long Wings' — EKMF LCla

'Lonneke' — WPBF

'Lord Byron' — CLoc EBak EKMF

'Lord Derby' — CSil

'Lord Jim' — CDoC LCla

'Lord Lloyd Webber' (d) **new** — MJac

'Lord Lonsdale' — CWVF EBak EPts LCla MWhe WPBF WRou

'Lord Roberts' — CLoc CSil CWVF SLBF

'Lorelei' — EPts

'Lorna Fairclough' — MJac

'Lorna Swinbank' — CLoc CWVF

'Lottie Hobby' ♀H1+3 — CDoC CLoc CSil CWVF EKMF EPfP EPts EShb ISea LCla LRHS MHar MLHP MOak MWhe SPet WPBF WRou

'Louise Emershaw' (d) — CWVF EBak MJac

'Louise Nicholls' — EKMF MJac SLBF

'Lovable' (d) — EBak

'Loveliness' — CLoc CWVF EBak EKMF MWhe

'Lovely Blue' (d) — WPBF

'Lovely Linda' — SLBF

'Love's Reward' ♀H1+3 — CLoc CWVF EKMF EPts MJac MWar MWhe SLBF WRou

'Lower Raydon' — EBak

I 'Loxensis' — CDoC CWVF EBak EKMF LCla

loxensis misapplied — see F. 'Speciosa', F. 'Loxensis'

loxensis Knuth Berry 3233 — EKMF

– DG 1001 — EKMF

'Loxhore Calypso' — EKMF

'Loxhore Descent' **new** — CSil

'Loxhore Fairy Dancer' — CSil LCla

'Loxhore Herald' — CSil

'Loxhore Lullaby' — CSil LCla

'Loxhore Mazurka' — CSil WPBF WRou

'Loxhore Minuet' — CSil LCla WRou

'Loxhore Operetta' — CSil

'Loxhore Overture' **new** — CSil LCla

'Loxhore Posthorn' — CSil LCla

'Lucinda' — CWVF

'Lucky Strike' (d) — CLoc EBak

Lucy = 'Goetzlucy'PBR (Shadowdancer Series) — EBak

'Lucy Locket' — MJac

'Lukas' — WPBF

'Lunter's Klokje' **new** — WPBF

'Lunter's Trots' (d) — WPBF

'Lunterse Zon' **new** — LCla

'Luscious Lisa' — WPBF

'Lustre' — CWVF EBak

'Lutz Bogemann' — WPBF

§ *lycioides* Andrews — EBak EKMF

I 'Lycioides' — LCla

'Lye's Elegance' — CSil EKMF

'Lye's Excelsior' — EBak

'Lye's Own' — EBak SPet

'Lye's Perfection' — EKMF

'Lye's Unique' ♀H1+3 — CDoC CHrt CLoc CSil CWVF EBak EKMF EPts LCla MJac MWar MWhe SLBF SPet WRou

'Lynda' (d) **new** — WPBF

'Lynette' (d) — CLoc

'Lynn Ellen' (d) — CDoC CWVF EBak

'Lynne Marshall' — CSil

'Lyric' — WPBF

'Maartje' — WPBF

'Mabel Greaves' (d) — CWVF WPBF

'Mac Wagg' **new** — WRou

'Machu Picchu' — CLoc CWVF EKMF EPts LCla WPBF WRou

macrophylla — CDoC WMoo

– BEA 922539 — EKMF

– Berry 3080 — EKMF

– Berry 80-539 — EKMF

– Berry 80-541 — EKMF

macrostigma — CSil EKMF

'Madame Aubin' — CSil EKMF

'Madame Butterfly' (d) — CLoc

'Madame Cornélissen' (d) ♀H3 — More than 30 suppliers

'Madame Eva Boye' — EBak

'Madeleine Sweeney' (d) — MBri

'Madleina' (d) **new** — WPBF

'Maes-y-Groes' — CSil EKMF

magdalenae — EKMF WPBF

magellanica — CAby CDoC COld CSil CTrG CWib EKMF GGar NChi NFor NPer NWea SPer WFar WPnn WRha

– Dahl, S. — EKMF

– 'Alba' — see F. *magellanica* var. *molinae*

I – 'Alba Aureovariegata' (v) — CBgR CDoC EPfP LAst MBri SPer WFar

– 'Alba Variegata' (v) — CSil ENot NPol

- 'Americana Elegans' — CDoC CSil
- 'Comber' — CSil
- var. **conica** — CDoC CSil EKMF
- var. **discolor** — CSil MAsh
- 'Exmoor Gold' (v) — CSil
- 'Fire Gold' — CDoC LRHS
§ - var. **gracilis** ♀H3 — CDoC CHEx CLoc CSil CTri CWVF EKMF LRHS MLHP MWhe SCoo WPnn
  - -'Aurea' — CDoC CSil CWVF EHoe EKMF ELan ENot EPfP GAbr GQui ISea LAst LCla LRHS MRav MWhe SAga SCoo SDix SLBF SPer SPet SPla SPoG WFar WHen WRou
§ - -'Tricolor' (v) — CBgR CDoC CSil EHol EKMF EPts EWes EWin GAbr LCla LRHS SLBF SRms WCFE WPnn WRou
  - -'Variegata' (v) ♀H3 — CBgR CSil EBak EBee EKMF ENot EPfP LCla LRHS LSou MGos MRav SAga SDix SIng SPer SPet SPoG WBVN WPnn
  - 'Lady Bacon' — CDoC CSil EHol EKMF MSte
§ - 'Logan Woods' — CDoC CSil EKMF GCal ISea SLBF
  - 'Longipedunculata' — CDoC CSil EKMF
  - var. **macrostema** — CSil EKMF
§ - var. **molinae** — More than 30 suppliers
§ - -'Enstone' (v) — CBrm CSBt EHoe EKMF EMil EPts
  - -'Enstone Gold' — EKMF
  - -'Golden Sharpitor' (v) — CBgR LAst LSou MDKP WAbe WHen
§ - -'Sharpitor' (v) — More than 30 suppliers
  - var. **myrtifolia** — CDoC CSil EKMF
* - var. **prostrata** — CSil
  - var. **pumila** — CBgR CDoC CSil EShb ETow EWes GCal ITim LAst MLHP SBla SHGN SIng SMHy SRot WAbe WBor
§ - 'Thompsonii' — CDoC CSil ECGP EKMF GCal SBch SMHy
§ - 'Versicolor' (v) — More than 30 suppliers
- 'Magenta Flush' — CWVF
- 'Magic Flute' — CLoc CWVF MJac
- 'Maharaja' (d) — EBak
- 'Maharini' (d) **new** — WPBF
- 'Major Heaphy' — CDoC CWVF EBak EKMF MWhe WPBF
- 'Malibu Mist' (d) — CWVF WPBF
- 'Mama Bleuss' (d) — EBak
- 'Mancunian' (d) — CWVF
I 'Mandarin' Schnabel — EBak
- 'Mandi' — LCla MWar
- 'Mantilla' — CDoC CLoc CWVF EBak EKMF LCla MJac MWhe
- 'Maori Maid' — WPBF
- 'Maori Pipes' — LCla
- 'Marcia'PBR (Shadowdancer Series) — LAst LSou
- 'Marcus Graham' (d) — CLoc CWVF EBak EKMF MWar MWhe SCoo WPBF WRou
- 'Marcus Hanton' (d) — CWVF EKMF LCla
- 'Mardi Gras' (d) — EBak
- 'Margam Park' — LCla
- 'Margaret' (d) ♀H4 — CDoC CDul CLoc CSil CTri CWVF EBak EKMF ENot EPts ISea LCla LVER MWar MWhe NDlv SLBF SPet SWal
- 'Margaret Berger' (d) — SLBF
- 'Margaret Bird' **new** — LCla
- 'Margaret Brown' ♀H4 — CDoC CLoc CSil CTri CWVF EBak EKMF LCla MHar MWhe NDlv SLBF SPet SWal WRou
- 'Margaret Davidson' (d) — CLoc
- 'Margaret Ellen' — WPBF
- 'Margaret Hazelwood' — EKMF
- 'Margaret Pilkington' — CWVF MWar
- 'Margaret Roe' — CDoC CSil CWVF EBak EKMF MJac SPet SWal WPBF

- 'Margaret Susan' — EBak
- 'Margaret Tebbit' — LAst MJac WGor
- 'Margarite Dawson' (d) — CSil
- 'Margery Blake' — CDoC CSil EBak
- 'Margrit Willimann' — WPBF
- 'Maria Landy' — CWVF EKMF EMan LCla MJac MWar WRou
- 'Maria Merrills' (d) — EMan
- 'Marie Helene Meus' — WPBF
- 'Marielle van Dummelen' — WPBF
- 'Mariken' — WPBF
- 'Marilyn Olsen' — CWVF EPts
- 'Marin Belle' — EBak
- 'Marin Glow' ♀H3 — CLoc CWVF EBak MWhe SLBF SPet
- 'Marina Kelly' **new** — WRou
- 'Marinka' ♀H3 — CHrt CLoc CWVF EBak EKMF EMan EPts LAst LCla LVER MBri MJac MWar MWhe SLBF SPet SSea
- 'Marion Hilton' — MWar
- 'Mark Kirby' (d) — CWVF EBak EKMF WPBF
- 'Marlies de Keijzer' — LCla SLBF
- 'Martin Beije' — WPBF
- 'Martina' — SLBF
- 'Martin's Inspiration' — LCla MWar
- 'Martin's Midnight' (d) — WPBF
- 'Martin's Umbrella' — WPBF
- 'Martin's Yellow Surprise' — LCla SLBF
- 'Martinus' (d) — WPBF
- 'Marton Smith' — MWhe
- 'Marty' (d) — EBak
- 'Mary' ♀H1+3 — CDoC CLoc CWVF EKMF EPts LCla LRHS MLan MWar MWhe SLBF
- 'Mary Jones' (d) — EKMF
- 'Mary Lockyer' (d) — CLoc EBak
- 'Mary Poppins' — CWVF
- 'Mary Reynolds' (d) — CWVF
- 'Mary Shead' (d) — MWar
- 'Mary Thorne' — CSil EBak EKMF
- 'Mary's Millennium' — CWVF
- 'Masquerade' (d) — CWVF EBak EMan
- **mathewsii** — EKMF
- 'Maureen Ward' — EKMF
- 'Mauve Beauty' (d) — CSil CWVF EKMF NDlv SLBF
- 'Mauve Lace' (d) — CSil
- 'Max Jaffa' — CSil CWVF
I 'Maxima' — EKMF LCla WPBF
- 'Maybe Baby' — LAst WPBF
- 'Mayblossom' (d) — CWVF SPet
- 'Mayfayre' (d) — CLoc
- 'Mayfield' — CWVF MWhe
- 'Mazda' — CWVF
- 'Meadowlark' (d) — CWVF EBak
- 'Mechtildis de Lechy' — WPBF
- 'Meditation' (d) — CLoc CSil
- 'Melanie' — CDoC WPBF
- 'Melissa Heavens' — CWVF
- 'Melody' — EBak MWhe SPet
- 'Melody Ann' (d) — EBak
- 'Melting Moments' (d) — EKMF SCoo WPBF
- 'Menna' — WPBF
- 'Mephisto' — CSil CWVF
- 'Mercurius' — CSil WPBF
- 'Merlin' — CDoC CSil EKMF LCla
- 'Merry Mary' (d) — CWVF EBak EKMF
I 'Mexicali Rose' Machado — CLoc
- 'Michael' (d) — CWVF EPts
- 'Michael Wallis' — EKMF LCla SLBF WPBF
- **michoacanensis** misapplied — see *F. microphylla* subsp. *aprica*
- **michoacanensis** Sessé & Moç. B&SWJ 8982 — WCru
- 'Micky Goult' ♀H1+3 — CLoc CWVF EKMF EPts LCla MJac MWhe SPet WRou
- 'Microchip' — CSil LCla

microphylla	CBcs CBgR CBrd CDoC CElw CLoc CPLG CSil CWVF EBak GCal GGar MLan MWhe STre WBor WCru WEas
– B&SWJ 9101	WCru
§ – subsp. *aprica*	CDoC LCla
– – BRE 69862	EKMF
§ – subsp. *hemsleyana*	CDoC CPLG CSil EKMF LCla MHar MWhe SWal WOut
§ – subsp. *hidalgensis*	CDoC CSil EKMF LCla
– subsp. *microphylla*	CSil EKMF
§ – subsp. *minimiflora*	CTbh
– subsp. *quercetorum*	CDoC CSil EKMF LCla
– 'Sparkle' (v)	WCot
– 'Variegata' (v) **new**	EWes MCCP
'Midas'	CWVF MBri
'Midnight Sun' (d)	CWVF EBak EPts
'Midwinter'	LAst
'Mieke Meursing' ♀H1+3	CLoc CWVF EBak EKMF MJac MWhe SPet
'Mien Kuypers'	WPBF
'Miep Aalhuizen'	CDoC LCla WPBF WRou
'Mike Foxon'	EKMF
'Mike Oxtoby'	CWVF EKMF
'Mikey's Reward'	WPBF
'Mildred Wagg'	MWar
'Millennium'	CLoc EBak EPts MJac SCoo
'Millie Butler'	CWVF
'Ming'	CLoc
'Miniature Jewels'	SLBF
minimiflora misapplied	see *F.* x *bacillaris*
minimiflora Hemsl.	see *F. microphylla* subsp. *minimiflora*
'Minirose'	CDoC CWVF EPts MJac MWar MWhe WRou
'Minnesota' (d)	EBak
'Mipan'	SLBF
'Mischief'	CSil
'Miss California' (d)	CDoC CLoc CWVF EBak MBri MWhe
'Miss Great Britain'	CWVF
'Miss Lye'	CSil EKMF
'Miss Muffett' (d)	CSil EPts
'Miss Vallejo' (d)	EBak
'Mission Bells'	CDoC CLoc CSil CWVF EBak EKMF EPts SPet
'Misty Haze' (d)	CWVF
'Molesworth' (d)	CSil CWVF EBak EKMF MJac MWhe SPet
'Mollie Beaulah' (d)	EKMF WPBF
'Money Spinner'	CLoc EBak
'Monique Comperen'	WPBF
'Monsieur Thibaut' ♀H4	CSil EKMF ENot SPet
'Monte Rosa' (d)	CLoc CWVF
'Monterey'	MWhe
'Montevideo' (d)	CWVF
'Monument' (d)	CSil
'Mood Indigo' (d)	CWVF WPBF WRou
'Moon Glow'	LAst MJac WPBF
'Moonbeam' (d)	CLoc
'Moonlight Sonata'	CLoc CWVF EBak SPet
'Moonraker' (d)	CWVF
'More Applause' (d)	CLoc EKMF MWhe WPBF
'Morecott' (d)	CWVF
'Morning Light' (d)	CLoc EBak SPet
'Morning Mist'	EBak
'Morning Star'	MBri
'Morrells' (d)	EBak
'Morton Martianette' **new**	EKMF
'Moth Blue' (d)	CWVF EBak SPet
'Mountain Mist' (d)	CWVF EKMF
'Moyra' (d)	CWVF EKMF
'Mr A. Huggett'	CLoc CSil CWVF EKMF EPts LCla MWhe SLBF SPet
'Mr P.D. Lee'	MWhe
'Mr W. Rundle'	EBak WPBF
§ 'Mr West' (v)	EHoe EKMF SPet SSto WRou
'Mrs Churchill'	CLoc
'Mrs John D. Fredericks'	CSil
'Mrs Lawrence Lyon' (d)	EBak
'Mrs Lovell Swisher' ♀H4	CWVF EBak EKMF EPts LCla MWhe SPet
'Mrs Marshall'	CWVF EBak SLBF SPet
'Mrs Popple' ♀H3	More than 30 suppliers
'Mrs W. Castle'	CSil
'Mrs W.P. Wood' ♀H3	CDoC CLoc CSil CWVF EKMF EPts MBri WPBF WRou
'Mrs W. Rundle'	CLoc CSil CWVF EBak EKMF LRHS MWhe SLBF SPet
'Multa'	LAst MJac WRou
'Muriel' (d)	CLoc CWVF EBak EKMF
'My Delight'	CWVF
'My Fair Lady' (d)	CLoc CWVF EBak SPet
'My Honey'	CSil
'My Mum'	LCla SLBF WPBF
'My Reward' (d)	CWVF
'Naaldwijk 800'	WPBF
'Nancy Darnley' (d)	EKMF
'Nancy Lou' (d)	CDoC CLoc CWVF EPts LAst LVER MJac MWhe SLBF SPet SRGP WRou
'Nanny Ed' (d)	CWVF MBri
'Naomi Eggli'	WPBF
'Natasha Sinton' (d)	CLoc CWVF EKMF EMan LAst LVER MBri MJac MWhe NBlu SLBF SPet WRou
'Native Dancer' (d)	CWVF EBak WPBF
'Naughty Nicole' (d)	SLBF WPBF
'Nautilus' (d)	EBak
'Navy Blue'	CSil
'Neapolitan' (d)	CDoC EPts MWhe SLBF
'Neil Clyne'	MWhe
'Nell Gwyn'	CLoc CWVF EBak
'Nellie Nuttall' ♀H3	CLoc CWVF EBak EKMF EPts MWar MWhe SLBF SPet
'Neopolitan'	CLoc CSil
'Nettala'	CDoC WPBF
'Neue Welt'	CSil CWVF EBak EKMF
'New Fascination' (d)	EBak
'New Millennium'	LVER
'Nice 'n' Easy' (d)	MBri MJac NBlu
'Nicki's Findling'	CDoC CWVF EKMF EPts LCla MJac WRou
'Nicola'	EBak
'Nicola Jane' (d)	CDoC CSil CWVF EBak EKMF EPts LCla MBri MJac MWhe SHar SLBF SPet SRGP SWal WRou
'Nicola Storey'	EKMF WPBF
'Nicolette'	CWVF MJac
'Nightingale' (d)	CLoc EBak
§ *nigricans*	CDoC EKMF
'Nina Wills'	EBak
'Niobe' (d)	EBak
'Niula'	CDoC EKMF LCla
'No Name' (d)	EBak
'Nonchalance'	LCla
'Nora' (d)	WPBF
'Norfolk Ivor' (d)	WPBF
'Normandy Bell'	CWVF EBak SPet
'North Cascades' (d)	WPBF
'Northern Dancer' (d)	EKMF
'Northumbrian Belle'	EBak
'Northumbrian Pipes'	LCla WPBF
'Northway'	CLoc CWVF MJac MWhe SPet
'Norvell Gillespie' (d)	EBak
'Novato'	EBak EPts
'Novella' (d)	CWVF EBak
'Nuance'	LCla WPBF
'Nunthorpe Gem' (d)	CDoC CSil
obconica	CSil EKMF LCla
'Obcylin'	CDoC EKMF LCla WRou
'Obergärtner Koch'	CDoC EKMF LCla SLBF

'Ocean Beach'	EPts
'Oddfellow' (d)	CDoC
'Oetnang' (d)	CTri SCoo
'Old Dick' **new**	SLBF
'Old Somerset' (v)	CCCN EPts LCla WPBF
'Olive Moon' (d)	WPBF
'Olive Smith'	CWVF EPts LCla MJac MWar MWhe WPBF WRou
'Olympia'	EKMF MWhe
'Olympic Lass' (d)	EBak
'Onward'	CSil EKMF
§ 'Oosje'	CDoC CSil LCla SLBF WRou
'Opalescent' (d)	CLoc CWVF
'Orange Crush'	CLoc CWVF EBak MJac MWhe SPet
'Orange Crystal'	CWVF EBak EKMF MJac MWhe SLBF SPet
'Orange Drops'	CLoc CWVF EBak EKMF EPts MWhe SPet
'Orange Flare'	CLoc CWVF EBak MWhe SLBF WRou
'Orange King' (d)	CLoc CWVF EMan
'Orange Mirage'	CLoc CWVF EBak LAst MWhe SPet WRou
'Orangeblossom'	SLBF
'Oranje van Os'	CWVF MWhe
'Orchid Flame'	WPBF
'Orient Express'	CDoC CWVF LAst MJac MWhe SWal WPBF WRou
'Oriental Flame'	EKMF
'Oriental Sunrise'	CWVF MWhe
'Ornamental Pearl'	CLoc CWVF EBak
'Orwell' (d)	CWVF WPBF
'Oso Sweet'	CWVF
'Other Fellow'	CWVF EBak EKMF EPts LCla MJac MWhe SLBF SPet WRou
'Oulton Empress'	SLBF
'Oulton Fairy'	SLBF
'Oulton Red Imp'	LCla SLBF
'Oulton Travellers Rest'	SLBF
'Our Darling'	CWVF MWhe
'Our Debbie'	MWar
'Our Nan' (d)	MJac
'Our Shep' (d) **new**	SLBF
'Our Ted'	EBak EPts LCla WPBF
'Our William'	SLBF WPBF
'Overbecks'	see *F. magellanica* var. *molinae* 'Sharpitor'
'Overbecks Ruby'	GBuc
'P.J.B.' (d)	SLBF
'Pabbe's Torreldöve'	WPBF
'Pacemaker'	MGos
'Pacific Grove' Greene	see *F.* 'Evelyn Steele Little'
'Pacific Grove' Niederholzer (d)	EBak
'Pacific Queen' (d)	CLoc EBak
'Pacquesa' (d)	CDoC CWVF EBak EPts MWhe SPet
'Padre Pio' (d)	CWVF EBak MJac
'Pallas'	CSil
pallescens	EKMF
'Paloma' PBR	LAst
'Pam Plack'	CSil EKMF LCla SLBF
'Pamela Knights' (d)	EBak
'Pam's People'	LCla
'Pan'	MWar WPBF
'Pan America' (d)	EBak
'Panache' (d)	LCla
'Pangea'	EKMF LCla WPBF
paniculata $\heartsuit$H1+3	CCCN CDoC CEnd CFee CRHN CTbh CWVF EBak EGra EKMF EPts LCla SHFr SLBF WCru
'Panique'	CDoC CSil LCla
'Pantaloons' (d)	EBak
'Pantomine Dame' (d)	CWVF
'Panylla Prince'	CDoC LCla WRou
'Papa Bleuss' (d)	CLoc CWVF EBak
'Papoose' (d)	CDoC CSil EBak EKMF LCla
'Papua' (d)	SLBF WPBF
'Parkstone Centenary' (d)	CWVF
'Party Frock'	CDoC CLoc CWVF EBak LVER SPet
'Party Time' (d)	CWVF
parviflora misapplied	see *F.* x *bacillaris*
parviflora Lindl.	see *F. lycioides*
'Pastel'	EBak
'Pat Meara'	CLoc EBak
'Patatin Pataton' (d)	WPBF
'Pathétique' (d)	CLoc
'Patience' (d)	CWVF EBak SWal
'Patio King'	EBak EKMF
'Patio Princess' (d)	CWVF EPts LAst LSou MBri MWhe NBlu SSea WGor
'Patricia' Wood	CSil EBak
'Patricia Bervoets' (d)	WPBF
'Patricia Hodge' **new**	EPts WRou
'Pat's Smile'	SLBF
'Patty Evans' (d)	CWVF EBak
'Patty Sue' (d)	MBri MWar WRou
'Paul Berry'	CSil EKMF LCla WPBF
'Paul Cambon' (d)	EBak EKMF
'Paul Kennes'	EKMF WPBF
'Paul Roe' (d)	MJac
'Paul Storey'	CDoC CSil EKMF WPBF
'Paula Jane' (d)	CDoC CLoc CWVF LAst LCla MBri MJac MWar MWhe SLBF SRGP WGor WRou
'Pauline Rawlins' (d)	CLoc EBak
'Paulus'	WPBF
'Peace' (d)	EBak
'Peachy' (d)	CDoC CLoc EKMF LAst MJac SCoo WPBF
'Peachy Keen' (d)	EBak WPBF
'Peacock' (d)	CLoc
'Pee Wee Rose'	CSil EBak EKMF
'Peggy Belle G' **new**	EKMF LCla
'Peggy Burford'	LCla
'Peggy Cole'	EPts
Peggy = 'Goetzpeg' PBR (Shadowdancer Series)	LAst LSou SCoo
'Peggy King'	CDoC CSil EBak EKMF MWhe SPet
'Peloria' (d)	CLoc EBak
'Pennine'	MBri
'People's Princess'	MJac
'Peper Harow'	EBak
'Pepi' (d)	CLoc CWVF EBak SPet
'Peppermint Candy' (d)	CWVF EKMF EPts LAst
'Peppermint Stick' (d)	CDoC CLoc CWVF EBak EKMF EMan LRHS MBri MWhe SPet WRou
'Perky Pink' (d)	CWVF EBak EPts MWhe SPet
'Perry Park'	CWVF EBak MBri MJac
'Perry's Jumbo'	NBir NPer
perscandens	CPLG CSil EKMF LCla MWhe
'Personality' (d)	EBak
'Peter Bellerby' (d)	EKMF
'Peter Bielby' (d)	CWVF EKMF MWar
'Peter Boor'	SLBF
'Peter Crookes'	CWVF
'Peter Grange'	EBak
'Peter James' (d)	CSil EKMF
'Peter Pan'	CSil CWVF SIng
'Peter Shaffery' **new**	LCla
petiolaris	CDoC LCla
- Berry 3142	EKMF
'Petit Four'	CWVF WPBF
'Petite' (d)	EBak
'Phaidra'	CDoC LCla
'Pharaoh'	CLoc
'Phénoménal' (d)	CSil CWVF EBak EKMF EPts LRHS WPBF
'Philippe'	WPBF

'Phillip Taylor'   MJac
'Phryne' (d)   CSil EBak EKMF
'Phyllis' (d) ♀H4   CDoC CLoc CSil CWVF EBak
   EKMF EPts LCla MHar MJac MWhe
   NDlv SHar SLBF SPet SRGP WFar
   WRou WTel
'Piet G. Vergeer'   WPBF WRou
'Piet Heemskerk'   WPBF
'Piet van der Sande'   CDoC LCla MWar
'Pijekna Helena' **new**   WPBF
pilaloensis   EKMF
x *pilcopata*   LCla
'Pinch Me' (d)   CWVF EBak LVER SPet
'Pink Aurora'   CLoc
'Pink Ballet Girl' (d)   CLoc EBak
'Pink Bon Accorde'   CLoc CWVF
'Pink Cloud'   CLoc EBak
'Pink Cornet'   LCla
'Pink Darling'   CLoc EBak MWhe
'Pink Dessert'   EBak
'Pink Domino' (d)   CSil EKMF
'Pink Fairy' (d)   EBak SPet
'Pink Fandango' (d)   CLoc
'Pink Fantasia'   CDoC CLoc CWVF EBak EKMF
   EPts LAst LCla MJac MWar MWhe
'Pink Flamingo' (d)   CLoc EBak
'Pink Galore' (d)   CLoc CWVF EBak EKMF EMan
   LAst LCla LVER MBri MJac MWhe
   SPet
'Pink Goon' (d)   CDoC CSil EKMF LCla LRHS NDlv
   SLBF
'Pink Haze' **new**   CSil
'Pink Jade'   CWVF EBak
'Pink la Campanella'   CWVF EBak EMan LAst MBri MWar
   MWhe WBVN WGor
'Pink Lace' (d)   CSil SPet
'Pink Lady' Ryle-Atkinson   MWhe
'Pink Marshmallow' (d)   CDoC CLoc CWVF EBak EKMF
   ♀H1+3   EMan LAst LCla LVER MJac MWar
   SLBF SPet SSea
'Pink Panther' (d)   EKMF MJac
'Pink Pearl' ambig.   SWal
'Pink Pearl' Bright (d)   CSil EBak EKMF LVER
'Pink Poppet' **new**   EKMF
'Pink Profusion'   EBak
'Pink Quartet' (d)   CLoc CWVF EBak SPet
'Pink Rain'   CSil CWVF EKMF EPts MJac WPBF
   WRou
'Pink Slippers'   CLoc
'Pink Spangles'   CWVF EMan MBri
'Pink Temptation'   CLoc CWVF EBak
'Pink Trumpet'   WPBF
'Pinkmost' (d)   EKMF
'Pinto de Blue' (d)   EKMF MWar WPBF
'Pinwheel' (d)   CLoc EBak
'Piper' (d)   CDoC CWVF
'Piper's Vale'   MJac SLBF SWal
'Pippa Rolt'   EKMF EPts
'Pirbright'   CWVF EKMF
'Pixie'   CDoC CLoc CSil CWVF EBak
   EKMF MJac NDlv SLBF SPet
'Playford'   CWVF EBak
'Plenty'   CSil EBak
'Plumb Bob' (d)   CWVF
'Poermenneke'   LCla WPBF
'Pol Jannie' (d) **new**   WPBF
'Pole Star'   CSil
'Polynesia' (d) **new**   WPBF
'Pop Whitlock' (v)   CWVF EKMF SPet WPBF
'Popely Pride' (d)   WPBF
'Poppet'   CWVF
'Popsie Girl'   MWar SLBF WPBF
'Port Arthur' (d)   CSil EBak
'Postiljon'   CWVF EBak MJac SPet
'Powder Puff' ambig.   CWVF MBri SPet
'Powder Puff' Hodges (d)   CLoc LVER

I 'Powder Puff' Tabraham   CSil
   (d)
'Präsident Walter Morio'   WPBF
   new
'Prelude' Blackwell   CLoc CSil
I 'Prelude' Kennett (d)   EBak EKMF
'President'   CDoC CSil EBak EKMF
'President B.W. Rawlins'   EBak
§ 'President Elliot'   CSil EKMF MWhe
'President George Bartlett'   CSil EKMF EPts LAst LCla MJac
   (d)   MWar MWhe SLBF WRou
'President Jim Muil'   SLBF WPBF
'President Joan Morris'   EKMF SLBF
   (d)
'President Leo Boullemier'   CDoC CSil CWVF EBak EKMF LCla
   MJac SPet
'President Margaret Slater'   CLoc CSil CWVF EBak EMan LCla
   MWhe SPet WPBF
'President Moir' (d)   SLBF WPBF
'President Norman Hobbs'   CWVF EKMF MWar
'President Roosevelt' (d)   CDoC WPBF
'President Stanley Wilson'   CWVF EBak EPts SPet
'Preston Guild' ♀H1+3   CDoC CLoc CSil CWVF EBak
   EKMF LRHS MWar MWhe NPer
   SLBF SPet WRou
'Prickly Heat'   WPBF
'Pride of Ipswich' **new**   WPBF
'Pride of Roualeyn' **new**   WRou
'Pride of the West'   CSil EBak EKMF
'Pride of Windsor'   SLBF WPBF
'Prince of Orange'   CLoc CSil CWVF EBak EKMF
   WPBF
'Princess Dollar'   see *F.* 'Dollar Princess'
'Princess of Bath' (d)   CLoc
'Princess Pamela' (d)   SLBF
'Princessita'   CSil CWVF EBak EMan MWhe SPet
procumbens   CBcs CDoC CHEx CLoc CPLG CSil
   CStu CTrC CWVF EBak ECou
   EKMF EPts EShb GGar IDee ITim
   LCla MWhe NWCA SHFr SIng SLBF
   SSea SWal SYvo WDyG WPic WRou
   WWye
– 'Argentea'   see *F. procumbens* 'Wirral'
– 'Variegata'   see *F. procumbens* 'Wirral'
§ – 'Wirral' (v)   CDoC CHEx CLoc CSil CStu EDsa
   EKMF ITim WBor WCot WPrP
'Prodigy'   see *F.* 'Enfant Prodigue'
'Profusion' ambig.   MWhe
'Prosperity' (d) ♀H3   CDoC CLoc CSil CWVF EBak EBee
   EKMF ENot EPfP EPts LCla LRHS
   LVER MJac MWhe NDlv SPet SWal
   WRou
'Pumila'   CPLG CWib EKMF ELan EPfP EPts
   SLBF SPet SWal WRou
'Purbeck Mist' (d)   CWVF EKMF
'Purperklokje'   CSil CWVF EBak WPBF
'Purple Ann'   EKMF
'Purple Emperor' (d)   CLoc
'Purple Heart' (d)   CLoc EBak
'Purple Lace'   CSil
'Purple Patch'   MBri WRou
'Purple Pride'   MBri
'Purple Rain'   CLoc CSil EKMF EPts LCla WRou
'Purple Splendour' (d)   CDoC CSil
'Pussy Cat'   CLoc CWVF EBak WPBF
'Putney Pride'   EPts
'Put's Folly'   CWVF EBak MJac SLBF
putumayensis   CSil EBak EKMF
'Quasar' (d)   CDoC CLoc CWVF EKMF EPts
   LAst LCla LRHS LSou LVER MJac
   MWhe SLBF SPet WBVN WRou
'Queen Elizabeth II'   EKMF LCla
'Queen Mabs'   EBak
'Queen Mary'   CLoc CSil EBak EKMF
'Queen of Bath' (d)   EBak
'Queen of Derby' (d)   CSil CWVF

'Queen Victoria' Smith (d)	EKMF
'Queen's Park' (d)	EBak
'Query'	CSil EBak SWal WPBF
'R.A.F (d)	CLoc CWVF EBak EKMF EPts LCla MWar SLBF SPet
'Rachel Craig' (d)	MWar
'Rachel Sinton' (d)	EMan LAst MBri SRGP WRou
'Radcliffe Beauty'	MWhe
'Radcliffe Bedder' (d)	CSil EKMF
'Radings Gerda'	LCla
'Radings Inge'	LCla
'Radings Karin'	CDoC WPBF
'Radings Michelle'	CSil CWVF LCla
'Rahnee'	CWVF
'Rainbow'	CWVF
'Ralph Oliver' (d)	WPBF
'Ralph's Delight' (d)	CWVF EKMF LAst MJac WPBF
'Rambling Rose' (d)	CLoc CWVF EBak MJac
'Rams Royal' (d)	CDoC
'Raspberry' (d)	CLoc CWVF EBak MWhe
'Raspberry Sweet' (d)	CWVF
'Ratae Beauty'	CWVF
'Ratatouille' (d)	EKMF WPBF
ravenii	CSil LCla
'Ravensbarrow'	CSil WPBF
'Ravenslaw'	CSil EKMF
'Ray Redfern'	CWVF
'Razzle Dazzle' (d)	EBak
'Reading Show' (d)	CSil CWVF EKMF EPts
'Rebecca Williamson' (d)	CWVF MJac MWhe WPBF
'Rebeka Sinton'	CLoc EBak MBri
'Red Ace' (d)	CSil
'Red Imp' (d)	CSil
'Red Jacket' (d)	CWVF EBak
'Red Petticoat'	CWVF
'Red Rain'	CWVF LCla WPBF WRou
'Red Ribbons' (d)	EBak
'Red Rover'	MWar
'Red Rum' (d)	SPet
'Red Shadows' (d)	CLoc CWVF EBak
'Red Spider'	CLoc CWVF EBak EKMF EMan LAst MWar MWhe SCoo SPet WGor
'Red Sunlight'	EPts
'Red Wing'	CLoc
'Reflexa'	see *F.* x *bacillaris* 'Reflexa'
'Reg Gubler'	SLBF
'Regal'	CLoc
regia	CSil EHol
- var. *alpestris*	see *F. alpestris*
- var. *radicans* **new**	CSil
- subsp. *regia*	CDoC CSil EPts LCla
- - Berry 4450	EKMF
- - Berry 77-87	EKMF
- - Berry 87-87	EKMF
- subsp. *reitzii*	CDoC CSil LCla
- - Berry 04-87	EKMF
- - Berry 67A-87	EKMF
- subsp. *serrae*	CDoC CSil
- - Berry 11-87	EKMF
- - Berry 4504	EKMF
- - Berry 49-87	EKMF
'Remember Eric'	CSil EKMF WPBF
'Remembrance' (d)	CSil EKMF EPts LCla SLBF
'Remy Kind' (d)	WPBF
'Rene Schwab'	LCla
'Renee'	WPBF
'Renee-Madeleine'	WPBF
'Rensina'	WPBF
'Requiem'	CLoc
'Reverend Doctor Brown' (d)	EBak
'Reverend Elliott'	see *F.* 'President Elliot'
'Rhapsody' Blackwell (d)	CLoc
'Rhombifolia'	CSil
'Ria V.D. Leest'	WPBF
'Rianne Foks'	WPBF
§ 'Riccartonii' ♀H3	More than 30 suppliers
'Richard John Carrington'	CSil
'Ridestar' (d)	CLoc CWVF EBak EMan MWhe
'Rijs 2001'	MWar SLBF
'Rina Felix'	WPBF
'Ringwood Market' (d)	CSil CWVF EPts MJac SCoo SPet
'Rise and Shine' **new**	WPBF
'Robbie'	EKMF WPBF
'Robin Hood' (d)	CSil NDlv
'Rocket'	WPBF
'Rocket Fire' (d)	CWVF EPts LAst MJac
'Rodeo'	WPBF
'Roesse Algenib' (d) **new**	WPBF
'Roesse Algieba' (d) **new**	WPBF
'Roesse Blacky'	EKMF WPBF
'Roesse Esli'	WPBF
'Roesse Femke'	WPBF
'Roesse Grafias' (d) **new**	WPBF
'Roesse Himalia' (d) **new**	WPBF
'Roesse Marie'	WPBF
'Roesse Naos' **new**	WPBF
'Roesse Nash' (d) **new**	WPBF
'Roesse Peacock' (d) **new**	WPBF
'Roesse Procyon'	WPBF
'Roesse Skat' (d) **new**	WPBF
'Roesse Thurban' (d) **new**	WPBF
'Roesse Titan' (d) **new**	WPBF
'Roesse Tricolor'	WPBF
'Roesse Wega' **new**	WPBF
'Roesse Zibai' (d) **new**	WPBF
'Roger de Cooker'	CLoc SLBF WPBF
'Rohees Alioth' (d)	WPBF
'Rohees Azha'	WPBF
'Rohees Canopus'	WPBF
'Rohees Emperor' (d)	SLBF WPBF
'Rohees Grumiun' (d) **new**	WPBF
'Rohees Heka' **new**	WPBF
'Rohees Izar'	WPBF
'Rohees King'	WPBF
'Rohees Ksora' (d)	WPBF
'Rohees Leada' (d)	SLBF
'Rohees Maasym'	WPBF
'Rohees Metallah'	WPBF
'Rohees Minkar'	WPBF
'Rohees Mintaka' (d)	WPBF
'Rohees Mira'	WPBF
'Rohees Naos'	WPBF
'Rohees Nekkar'	WPBF
'Rohees New Millennium' (d)	SLBF WPBF
'Rohees Nunki'	WPBF
'Rohees Princess' **new**	WPBF
'Rohees Prins' (d) **new**	WPBF
'Rohees Queen'	WPBF
'Rohees Rana'	WPBF
'Rohees Reda' (d)	WPBF
'Rohees Rialto' **new**	WPBF
'Rohees Rotanev'	WPBF
'Rohees Sadir'	WPBF
'Rohees Segin'	WPBF
'Rohees Vega' **new**	WPBF
'Rohees Zaurak'	WPBF
'Rolla' (d)	CWVF EBak EKMF
'Rolt's Bride' (d)	EKMF
'Rolt's Ruby' (d)	CSil EKMF EPts
'Roman City' (d)	CLoc WPBF
'Romance' (d)	CWVF
'Romany Rose'	CLoc
'Ron Chambers Love'	MWar
'Ron Ewart'	EKMF MWhe WRou
'Ronald L. Lockerbie' (d)	CLoc CWVF EKMF
'Ron's Ruby'	CSil LCla MWhe WPBF
'Roos Breytenbach'	CDoC EKMF LAst LCla MJac WPBF WRou

'Rosamunda'	CLoc
'Rose Aylett' (d)	EBak
'Rose Bradwardine' (d)	EBak
'Rose Churchill' (d)	MBri MJac
'Rose Fantasia'	CDoC CLoc CWVF EKMF EPts LAst LCla MJac MWar MWhe SLBF
'Rose Marie' (d)	CLoc
'Rose of Castile'	CDoC CLoc CSil EBak EKMF LCla LRHS MJac MWhe WRou
'Rose of Castile Improved' ♀H4	CSil CWVF EBak EKMF LCla MJac MWar SPet WPBF
'Rose of Denmark'	CLoc CSil CWVF EBak LAst MBri MJac MWar MWhe NBlu SCoo SPet SWal WGor
'Rose Reverie' (d)	EBak
'Rose Winston' (d)	LAst SCoo
rosea misapplied	see *F.* 'Globosa'
rosea Ruíz & Pav.	see *F. lycioides* Andrews
'Rosebud' (d)	EBak WPBF
'Rosecroft Beauty' (d)	CSil CWVF EBak MWhe
Rosella = 'Goetzrose'PBR (Shadowdancer Series)	WPBF
'Rosemarie Higham'	MJac SCoo
'Rosemary Day'	CLoc
'Roslyn Lowe' (d)	CDoC
'Ross Lea' (d)	CSil
'Roswitha'	SLBF WPBF
'Rosy Bows'	CWVF
'Rosy Frills' (d)	CWVF MJac MWhe
'Rosy Morn' (d)	CLoc EBak
'Rosy Ruffles' (d)	EKMF
'Rough Silk'	CLoc CWVF EBak
'Roy Castle' (d)	CWVF
'Roy Sinton'	LAst
'Roy Walker' (d)	CLoc CWVF LVER
'Royal and Ancient'	CWVF WPBF
'Royal Mosaic' (d)	CDoC CWVF LAst MJac WPBF
'Royal Orchid'	EBak
'Royal Purple' (d)	CSil EBak EKMF MBri
'Royal Serenade' (d)	CWVF
'Royal Touch' (d)	EBak WPBF
'Royal Velvet' (d) ♀H3	CLoc CWVF EBak EKMF EMan EPts LAst LCla LVER MJac MWar MWhe NBlu SLBF SPet SWal WPBF WRou
'Royal Welsh' **new**	WRou
§ 'Rubra Grandiflora'	CWVF EBak EKMF LCla SLBF WRou
'Ruby Wedding' (d)	CSil CWVF EKMF SLBF WPBF
'Ruddigore'	CWVF WPBF
'Ruffles' (d)	CWVF EBak
§ 'Rufus' ♀H3-4	CDoC CLoc CSil CTri CWVF EBak EHol EKMF EPts LCla LRHS MHar MJac MWar MWhe NDlv SLBF SPet WFar WRou
'Rufus the Red'	see *F.* 'Rufus'
'Rummens Trots'	WPBF
'Ruth'	CSil
'Ruth Brazewell' (d)	CLoc
'Ruth King' (d)	CWVF EBak
'Sabrina' **new**	WRou
'Sailor'	EPts
'Sally Bell'	CSil
'Salmon Cascade'	CWVF EBak EKMF EMan EPts LCla MJac MWhe SLBF WRou
'Salmon Glow'	CWVF MJac MWhe
'Salmon Queen' **new**	WPBF
'Samba'	LAst
'Samson' (d/v)	EBak
'San Diego' (d)	CWVF
'San Francisco'	EBak WPBF
'San Leandro' (d)	EBak
'San Mateo' (d)	EBak
§ *sanctae-rosae*	CDoC EBak EKMF EPts LCla WPBF
'Sandboy'	CWVF EBak
'Sanguinea'	CSil EKMF
'Sanrina'	CDoC EKMF
'Santa Cruz' (d)	CSil CWVF EBak EKMF MWhe NDlv SLBF SWal WPBF
'Santa Lucia' (d)	CLoc EBak
'Santa Monica' (d)	EBak
'Santorini Sunset'	WPBF
'Sapphire' (d)	EBak
'Sara Helen' (d)	CLoc EBak
'Sarah Eliza' (d)	SCoo
'Sarah Jane' (d)	CSil EBak
'Sarah Louise'	CWVF
'Sarong' (d)	EBak
'Saskia van der Heijden' (d) **new**	WPBF
'Satellite'	CLoc CWVF EBak EKMF SPet WPBF
'Saturnus'	CSil CWVF EBak SPet WPBF
'Scabieuse' **new**	CSil
scabriuscula	CDoC EKMF LCla
scandens	see *F. decussata* Ruíz & Pav.
'Scarcity'	CDoC CSil CWVF EBak EKMF MWhe SPet SWal
'Scarlet Cascade'	EKMF
'Schiller' ambig.	EKMF WPBF
'Schimpens Glorie' (d)	WPBF
'Schlosz Bentheim'	WPBF
'Schneckerl' (d)	LCla
'Schneeball' (d)	CSil EBak EKMF
'Schneewitcher'	CDoC EKMF EPts
'Schneewittchen' ambig.	WPBF
'Schneewittchen' Hoech	CSil EKMF
'Schneewittchen' Klein	CSil EBak
'Schönbrunner Schuljubiläum'	EBak
I 'Schöne Wilhelmine'	see *F.* 'Die Schöne Wilhelmine'
'Scotch Heather' (d)	CWVF
'Sea Shell' (d)	CWVF EBak WPBF
'Seaforth'	EBak EKMF
'Sealand Prince'	CDoC CSil CWVF EKMF LCla WPBF
'Sebastopol' (d)	CLoc
'Senna Krekels' (d) **new**	WPBF
'Seppe'	WPBF
serratifolia Ruíz & Pav.	see *F. denticulata*
serratifolia Hook.	see *F. austromontana*
sessilifolia	EKMF LCla
'Seventh Heaven' (d)	CLoc CWVF LAst MJac SCoo
'Severn Queen'	CWVF
'Shady Blue'	CWVF
'Shangri-La' (d)	EBak WPBF
'Shanley'	CWVF WPBF
'Shannon So Special' (d)	SLBF
'Sharon Allsop' (d)	CWVF MWhe
'Sharon Caunt' (d)	CSil EKMF
'Sharonelle'	EKMF
'Sharpitor'	see *F. magellanica* var. *molinae* 'Sharpitor'
'Shauna Lindsay'	LCla WPBF
'Shawna Ree'	EKMF
'Sheila Crooks' (d)	CWVF EBak EMan MJac WPBF
'Sheila Kirby'	CWVF MJac
'Sheila Mary' (d)	EKMF
'Sheila Steele' (d)	CWVF
'Sheila's Love'	MJac
'Sheila's Surprise' (d)	SLBF WPBF
'Shekirb' (d)	MJac
'Shelford'	CDoC CLoc CWVF EBak EKMF EMan EPts LCla MJac MWar MWhe SLBF WRou
'Shell Pink'	CSil
'Shirley Halladay' (d)	EKMF LCla WPBF
'Shirley'PBR (Shadowdancer Series)	LAst LSou SCoo SVil
'Shooting Star' (d)	EBak
'Showfire'	EBak

'Showtime' (d)	CWVF
'Shy Lady' (d)	SPet
'Siberoet'	LCla WPBF
'Sierra Blue' (d)	CLoc CWVF EBak
'Silver Anniversary' (d)	EKMF
'Silver Dawn' (d)	EKMF EPts
'Silver Dollar'	MWhe
'Silver King'	WPBF
'Silver Pink'	CSil
'Silverdale'	CDoC CSil EKMF EPts MWhe
'Simmari'	WPBF
'Simon J. Rowell'	EKMF LCla
'Simone Delhommeau'	WPBF
simplicicaulis	CDoC EBak EKMF LCla
'Sincerity' (d)	CLoc
'Sint Bartholomeus' (d)	WPBF
'Sinton's Standard'	MBri
'Siobhan'	CWVF
'Siobhan Evans' (d)	MWar
'Sipke Arjen' **new**	WRou
'Sir Alfred Ramsey'	CWVF EBak MWhe
'Sir Matt Busby' (d)	EKMF EPts LAst MJac WPBF WRou
'Sir Steve Redgrave' (d)	MJac
'Sir Thomas Allen' **new**	SLBF
'Siren' Baker (d)	EBak
'Sissy Sue'	WPBF
'Sister Ann Haley'	EKMF EPts
'Sister Sister' (d)	SLBF WPBF
'Six Squadron'	EKMF
skutchiana	CPLG SMrm
'Sleepy'	CSil EPts SPet WPBF
'Sleigh Bells'	CLoc CWVF EBak EKMF MWhe SPet WPBF
'Small Pipes'	CWVF EKMF LCla WPBF
'Smokey Mountain' (d)	MJac MWar
'Smouldering Fires'	WPBF
'Sneezy'	CSil EPts MWhe
'Snow Burner' (d)	CDoC CLoc CWVF LAst WPBF
'Snow White' (d)	CSil SPet WPBF
'Snowbird' (d)	SLBF WPBF
§ 'Snowcap' (d) ♥H3-4	CBgR CDoC CLoc CSil CWVF EBak EKMF EPts LAst LCla MWhe MAsh MBri MGos MJac MWar MWhe NBlu NPer SIng SLBF SPet SPla SWal WFar WRou
'Snowdon' (d)	CWVF
'Snowdonia' **new**	WRou
'Snowdrift' Colville (d)	CLoc
'Snowdrift' Kennett (d)	EBak
'Snowfall'	CWVF
'Snowfire' (d)	CLoc CWVF EKMF MWhe SCoo WPBF
'Snowflake'	EKMF LCla SLBF WBor
'Snowstorm' (d)	SPet
'So Big' (d)	EKMF
'Sofie Michiels'	WPBF
'Softpink Jubelteen'	WPBF
'Son of Thumb' ♥H4	CDoC CLoc CSil CWVF EKMF EMan EPfP EPts LAst MAsh MBar MGos MJac MWhe NDlv SIng SLBF SPet WFar WRou
'Sonata' (d)	CLoc CWVF EBak
'Sophie Louise'	EKMF EPts MWar WPBF WRou
'Sophie's Silver Lining'	MJac
'Sophie's Surprise'	WPBF
'Sophisticated Lady' (d)	CLoc CWVF EBak EKMF EPts SPet
'Soroptimist International'	WRou
'South Gate' (d)	CLoc CWVF EBak EKMF EMan EPts LAst MBri MJac MWar MWhe NBlu SPet
'South Lakeland'	CSil
'South Seas' (d)	EBak
'Southern Pride'	SLBF
'Southlanders'	EBak
'Southwell Minster'	EKMF
'Space Shuttle'	CLoc EKMF LCla MWhe SLBF WPBF
'Sparky'	CDoC CWVF EPts LCla MWar MWhe WPBF WRou
§ 'Speciosa'	CDoC EBak EDsa EKMF LCla MWhe SWal WRou
'Spion Kop' (d)	CDoC CWVF EBak EKMF LAst MWhe NBlu SPet WGor
§ *splendens* ♥H1+3	CAby CCCN CDoC CLoc CSec CSil EBak EKMF EPts IDee LCla NPer SLBF WRou
- 'Karl Hartweg'	CDoC
'Spring Bells' (d)	MWhe
'Squadron Leader' (d)	CWVF EBak EPts LVER
'Stan' **new**	WPBF
'Stanley Cash' (d)	CLoc CWVF EKMF LVER MWar SPet
'Star Wars'	CLoc EPts MBri MJac MWar SVil WPBF WRou
'Stardust'	CWVF EBak MJac MWhe
'Starlite' (d) **new**	WPBF
'Steirerblut'	WPBF
'Stella Ann'	CWVF EBak EPts LCla WPBF
'Stella Didden' (d)	WPBF
'Stella Marina' (d)	CLoc EBak
'Sterretje'	WPBF
'Stewart Taylor'	MJac
steyermarkii DG 1057	EKMF
'Storeytime' **new**	EKMF
'Straat Fiji' **new**	LCla
'Straat Kobi' **new**	LCla
'Straat Magelhaen'	LCla
'Straat Moji' **new**	LCla
'Straat Napier'	WPBF
'Straat of Plenty'	LCla WPBF
'Straat Susanna D Diykman' **new**	LCla
'Straat Van Diemen' **new**	LCla
'Strawberry Delight' (d)	CLoc CWVF EBak EKMF MJac MWhe SPet
'Strawberry Fizz'	WPBF
'Strawberry Sundae' (d)	CLoc CWVF EBak
'Strawberry Supreme' (d)	CSil EKMF
'String of Pearls'	CLoc CWVF EKMF MJac SLBF SPet WPBF
'Stuart Joe'	CWVF EKMF
* *subparamosis* Green 1006 **new**	EKMF
'Sue'	SLBF
'Sugar Almond' (d)	CWVF
'Sugar Blues' (d)	CDoC EBak
'Summer Bells'	WPBF
'Summerdaffodil'	WPBF
'Sunkissed' (d)	COtt EBak
'Sunningdale'	CDoC CWVF LCla
'Sunny'	COtt
'Sunny Smiles'	CSil CWVF EKMF SPet
'Sunray' (v)	CLoc CTbh CWVF EBak EHoe EKMF ENot LRHS MAsh MWar MWat NBlu NEgg NMRc NSti SPla SPoG STes SWal
'Sunset'	CLoc CWVF EBak MWhe SPer
'Sunset Boulevard' (d)	CDoC
'Supernova'	WPBF
'Supersport' (d)	CDoC WPBF
'Superstar'	CWVF EPts WPBF
'Susan' (d)	COtt LAst
'Susan Drew'	SLBF
'Susan Ford' (d)	CWVF SPet
'Susan Gasaway' **new**	WPBF
'Susan Green'	CSil CWVF EBak EKMF EMan MJac MWar MWhe SPet
'Susan McMaster'	CLoc
'Susan Olcese' (d)	CWVF EBak
'Susan Skeen'	MJac WPBF

'Susan Travis' — CLoc CSil CWVF EBak EKMF MWhe SPet

'Swanley Gem' ♀H3 — CLoc CWVF EBak EKMF MWhe SLBF SPet WRou

'Swanley Pendula' — CLoc

'Swanley Yellow' — CWVF EBak

'Sweet Gilly' (d) — SLBF

'Sweet Leilani' (d) — CLoc EBak

'Sweet Sarah' — SLBF

'Sweet Sixteen' (d) — CLoc

I 'Sweetheart' van Wieringen — EBak

'Swingtime' (d) ♀H3 — CLoc CWVF EBak EKMF EMan EPts LAst LCla LVER MGos MJac MWar MWhe NBlu SLBF SPet

'S'Wonderful' (d) — CLoc EBak

sylvatica misapplied — see *F. nigricans*

sylvatica Benth. — LCla

'Sylvia Barker' — CWVF LCla MWar WRou

'Sylvia Noad' — MWar

'Sylvia Rose' (d) — CWVF

'Sylvia's Choice' — EBak

'Sylvy' — MWhe

'Symphony' — CLoc CWVF EBak

'T.S.J.' — LCla

'Taatje' — WPBF

'Taco' — CDoC LCla WPBF

'Taddle' — CWVF EMan SLBF SPet

'Taffeta Bow' (d) — CLoc EKMF LVER

'Taffy' — EBak WPBF

'Tahoe' — WPBF

'Tamerus Dream' (d) **new** — WPBF

'Tamerus Hoatzin' — WPBF

'Tamerus Hop' (d) **new** — WPBF

'Tamerus Toerako' **new** — WPBF

'Tamworth' — CLoc CWVF EBak MJac

'Tangerine' — CLoc CWVF EBak MWhe WRou

'Tanja's Snowball' — WPBF

'Tantalising Tracy' (d) — WPBF

'Tanya' — CLoc EKMF SPet

'Tanya Bridger' (d) — EBak

'Tarra Valley' — LCla MWhe WPBF

'Task Force' — CWVF

'Tausendschön' (d) — CLoc

'Ted Heath' (d) — WPBF

'Ted Perry' (d) — CWVF

'Ted's Tribute' — EKMF WPBF

'Temptation' ambig. — CWVF SPet

'Temptation' Peterson — CLoc EBak

'Teneriffe Magic' **new** — WPBF

'Tennessee Waltz' (d) ♀H3 — CDoC CLoc CSil CWVF EBak EKMF EMan EPts LRHS LVER MJac MWar MWhe SLBF SPer SPet SWal WEas WRou

'Tessa Jane' — CSil

tetradactyla misapplied — see *F.* x *bacillaris*

tetradactyla Lindl. — see *F. encliandra* subsp. *tetradactyla*

'Texas Longhorn' (d) — CLoc CWVF EBak EKMF WPBF

'Texas Star' — WPBF

'Thalia' ♀H1+3 — CDoC CDul CHEx CHrt CLoc CTbh CWVF EBak EKMF EPfP EPts LAst LCla LRHS LVER MBri MJac MOak MWar MWhe NPri SLBF SPet SPla SPoG SWal WEas WRou

'Thamar' — CDoC CLoc CWVF EPts MWhe WPBF WRou

'That's It' (d) — EBak WPBF

'The Aristocrat' (d) — CLoc EBak

§ 'The Doctor' — CLoc CSil CWVF EBak MWhe

'The Jester' (d) — EBak

'The Madame' (d) — CWVF EBak

'The Tarns' — CSil CWVF EBak EKMF NCiC

'Therese Dupois' — CSil

'Théroigne de Méricourt' — EBak EKMF

'Thilco' — CDoC CSil EKMF

'Thistle Hill' (d) — CSil EKMF

'Thomas' (d) **new** — EPts WPBF

'Thomas Ritchie' **new** — LCla SLBF

'Thompsonii' — see *F. magellanica* 'Thompsonii'

'Thornley's Hardy' — CSil EKMF EMan SPet WPBF

'Three Cheers' — CLoc EBak

'Three Counties' — EBak

'Thunderbird' (d) — CLoc CWVF EBak

thymifolia — CWVF EDsa GQui LHop MWgw SHFr SHGN SIng WKif

- subsp. *minimiflora* — CSil EKMF LCla

- subsp. *thymifolia* — CDoC CSil EKMF LCla

'Tiara' (d) — EBak

'Tickled Pink' — MWar

'Tiffany' Reedstrom (d) — EBak

'Tijl Uilenspiegel' — WPBF

'Tilla Dohmen' — WPBF

tillettiana — EKMF

'Tillingbourne' (d) — CSil SLBF

'Tillmouth Lass' — EKMF

Tilly = 'Goetztil' PBR — LAst SVil
(Shadowdancer Series)

'Timlin Brened' — CWVF EBak MWhe

'Timothy Titus' — LCla MWar SLBF

'Tina's Teardrops' (d) — WPBF

'Ting-a-ling' — CDoC CLoc CWVF EBak MWhe SLBF SPet WPBF WRou

'Tinker Bell' ambig. — CDoC

'Tinker Bell' Hodges — EBak

I 'Tinker Bell' Tabraham — CSil EKMF WPBF

'Tintern Abbey' — CWVF

'Tiny Whisper' **new** — WPBF

'Tjinegara' — CDoC LCla

'Toby Bridger' (d) — CLoc EBak

'Tolling Bell' — CWVF EBak EKMF MJac MWhe SPet WPBF WRou

'Tom Goedeman' — LCla

'Tom H. Oliver' (d) — EBak

'Tom Knights' — CDoC EBak MWhe SPet

'Tom Thorne' — EBak

'Tom Thumb' ♀H3 — More than 30 suppliers

'Tom West' misapplied — see *F.* 'Mr West'

'Tom West' Meillez (v) — CBrm CDoC CHEx CLoc CMHG COIW CSBt CSil CWVF CWib EBak EKMF EPts LCla LHop LRHS LVER MAsh MJac MOak MWar MWhe NVic SAga SDix SLBF SSea SWal WFar

'Tom Woods' — CWVF MWhe

'Tony's Treat' (d) — EPts

'Topaz' (d) — CLoc EBak

'Topper' (d) — CWVF EMan

'Torch' (d) — CLoc CWVF EBak

'Torchlight' — CWVF EPts LCla WRou

'Torvill and Dean' (d) — CLoc CWVF EKMF EPts LAst LRHS LVER MJac MWhe SPet WGor WPBF WRou WWeb

'Tosca' — CWVF

'Trabant' — WPBF

'Tracid' (d) — CLoc CSil

'Tracie Ann' (d) — EKMF WPBF

'Trail Blazer' (d) — CLoc CWVF EBak MJac SPet

'Trailing King' — WPBF

'Trailing Queen' — EBak EKMF MJac WPBF

'Trase' (d) — CDoC CSil CWVF CWib EBak EKMF EPts SWal

'Traudchen Bonstedt' — CDoC CLoc CWVF EBak EKMF EPts LCla MWhe SLBF SPet

'Traudens Heil' **new** — SLBF

'Traviata' — see *F.* 'La Traviata' Blackwell

'Treasure' (d) — EBak

'Tresco' — CSil

'Treslong' — WPBF

I 'Triantha' — WPBF

'Tric Trac' **new** — WPBF

'Tricolor' — see *F. magellanica* var. *gracilis* 'Tricolor'

'Tricolorii'	see *F. magellanica* var. *gracilis* 'Tricolor'
'Trientje'	LCla SLBF
'Trimley Bells'	EBak
'Trio' (d)	CLoc
triphylla	EBak EKMF LCla LRHS
- 'Dominica'	WPBF
'Trish's Triumph'	EPts
'Tristesse' (d)	CLoc CWVF EBak
'Trix Brouwer' **new**	WPBF
'Troika' (d)	EBak EKMF
'Troon'	CWVF
'Tropic Sunset' (d)	MBri MWhe
'Tropicana' (d)	CLoc CWVF EBak
'Troubador' Waltz (d)	CLoc
'Troutbeck'	CSil
'Trudi Davro'	LAst MJac SCoo
'Trudy'	CSil CWVF EBak EKMF SPet SWal
'True Love'	WPBF
'Truly Treena' (d)	SLBF
'Trumpeter' ambig.	CDoC CWVF WPBF
'Trumpeter' Reiter	CLoc EBak EKMF EPts LAst LCla MJac MWhe
'Tsjiep'	CDoC
'Tubular Bells'	EKMF LCla WPBF
'Tumbling Waters' (d)	LVER
'Tuonela' (d)	CLoc CWVF EBak MWhe WPBF
'Turkish Delight'	LAst MWar WPBF WRou
'Tutti-frutti' (d)	CLoc
'Twinkletoes'	EPts
'Twinkling Stars'	CWVF MJac WPBF
'Twinney'	CWVF
'Twinny'	EKMF EPts LCla MWar
'Twirling Square Dancer' (d)	WPBF
'Twist of Fate' (d)	CSil EKMF
'Two Tiers' (d)	CSil CWVF EKMF WPBF
'U.F.O.'	CWVF
'Uillean Pipes'	WPBF
'Ullswater' (d)	CWVF EBak
'Ultramar' (d)	EBak
'Uncle Charley' (d)	CDoC CLoc CSil EBak EKMF
'Uncle Jinks'	SPet
'Uncle Steve' (d)	EBak
'University of Liverpool'	CLoc MJac WPBF
'Upright Bob' **new**	WPBF
'Upward Look'	EBak EKMF
'Valda May' (d)	CWVF
'Valentine' (d)	EBak
'Valerie Ann' (d)	EBak SPet
'Valerie Hobbs' (d)	LCla
'Valerie Tooke' (d)	LCla
'Valiant'	EBak
'Vanessa' (d)	CLoc
'Vanessa Jackson'	CLoc CWVF MJac MWhe
'Vanity Fair' (d)	CLoc EBak
vargasiana	CDoC
'Variegated Brenda White' (v)	EKMF
'Variegated la Campanella' (d/v)	MWhe
'Variegated Lottie Hobby' (v)	CSil EKMF EPts LCla
'Variegated Pink Fascination'	WRou
'Variegated Pixie'	CSil EKMF
'Variegated Procumbens'	see *F. procumbens* 'Wirral'
'Variegated Snowcap' (d/v)	MWhe
'Variegated Superstar' (v)	MBri
'Variegated Swingtime' (v)	EBak LAst
'Variegated Vivienne Thompson' (d/v)	MBri
'Variegated Waveney Sunrise' (v)	MBri
'Variegated White Joy' (v)	EKMF

'Vechtweelde' **new**	WPBF
'Veenlust'	EBak LAst MJac WPBF WRou
'Vendeta'	CDoC LCla
'Venus Victrix'	CSil EBak EKMF MWhe SLBF
venusta	CDoC EBak EKMF LCla
'Versicolor'	see *F. magellanica* 'Versicolor'
'Vesuvio'	EKMF
'Vicky'	EKMF
'Victory' Reiter (d)	EBak
'Vielliebchen'	CDoC CSil
'Vincent van Gogh'	WPBF
'Vintage Dovercourt' **new**	LCla
'Violet Bassett-Burr' (d)	CLoc EBak
'Violet Gem' (d)	CLoc
'Violet Lace' (d)	CSil
'Violet Rosette' (d)	CWVF EBak
Violette = 'Goetzviolet' (Shadowdancer Series)	LAst LSou SCoo SVil
'Viva Ireland'	EBak
'Vivien Colville'	CLoc EKMF
'Vobeglo'	CWVF WPBF
'Vogue' (d)	EBak
'Voltaire'	CSil EBak EKMF
'Voodoo' (d)	CDoC CLoc CWVF EBak EKMF EMan EPts LAst LSou SCoo SLBF SPet WRou
'Vrijheid'	WPBF
vulcanica	CDoC EKMF LCla
* - subsp. *hitchcockii*	EKMF
'Vyvian Miller'	CWVF MJac
'W.F.C. Kampioen'	WPBF
'W.P. Wood'	CSil
§ 'Wagtails White Pixie'	CSil EBak
'Waldfee'	CCVN CDoC CSil EKMF LCla MWhe WBor
'Waldis Alina'	SLBF
'Waldis Geisha' (d)	SLBF
'Waldis Lea'	WPBF
'Waldis Lisbeth' **new**	SLBF
'Waldis Ovambo'	SLBF
'Waldis Simon'	LCla
'Waldis Spezi' **new**	CDoC LCla
'Wally Yendell' (v)	WPBF
'Walsingham' (d)	CWVF EBak WPBF
'Walton Jewel'	EBak
'Walz Banjo'	WPBF
'Walz Beiaard'	WPBF
'Walz Bella'	LCla WPBF
'Walz Blauwkous' (d)	CWVF
'Walz Bombardon' **new**	WPBF
'Walz Cello'	WPBF
'Walz Cocktail' **new**	WPBF
'Walz Epicurist'	WPBF
'Walz Fanclub'	LCla WPBF
'Walz Floreat'	WPBF
'Walz Fluit'	LAst MJac WPBF WRou
'Walz Fonola'	WPBF
'Walz Freule'	CWVF EKMF MJac
'Walz Gitaar'	WPBF
'Walz Gong'	WPBF
'Walz Gusla' **new**	WPBF
'Walz Harp'	CDoC CWVF LCla WPBF
'Walz Hoorn'	WPBF
'Walz Jubelteen'	CDoC CLoc CWVF EKMF EMan EPts LCla MJac MWar MWhe SLBF SSea WRou
'Walz Kattesnoor'	WPBF
'Walz Klarinet'	WPBF
'Walz Lucifer'	LCla MWar WPBF
'Walz Luit'	CDoC WPBF
'Walz Mandoline' (d)	CWVF WPBF
'Walz Nugget'	WPBF
'Walz Orgelpijp' **new**	WPBF
'Walz Panfluit'	LCla
'Walz Parasol'	WPBF
'Walz Pauk' (d)	WPBF

'Walz Piano'   WPBF
'Walz Piston'   WPBF
'Walz Polka'   LCla WPBF
'Walz Spinet'   WPBF
'Walz Telescope'   WPBF
'Walz Toorts' **new**   WPBF
'Walz Triangel' (d)   CSil EKMF WPBF
'Walz Trombone'   WPBF
'Walz Trommel' (d)   WPBF
'Walz Tuba'   WPBF
'Walz Ukelele' **new**   WPBF
'Walz Wipneus'   WPBF
'Wapenveld's Bloei'   CDoC LCla SLBF
'War Dance' (d)   MWhe
'War Paint' (d)   CLoc EBak
'War Pipes'   LCla
'Warton Crag'   CWVF
'Water Nymph'   CLoc SLBF WPBF
'Wave of Life'   CWVF EKMF MWhe
'Waveney Gem'   CDoC CWVF EBak EKMF EMan
                                 LCla MJac MWar SLBF SPet
'Waveney Queen'   CWVF
'Waveney Sunrise'   CWVF MJac MWar MWhe SPet
'Waveney Unique'   CWVF
'Waveney Valley'   EBak MJac
'Waveney Waltz'   CWVF EBak
'Welsh Dragon' (d)   CLoc CWVF EBak WPBF
'Wendy' Catt   see *F.* 'Snowcap'
'Wendy Atkinson' (d)   EKMF
'Wendy Harris' (d)   MJac
'Wendy Leedham' (d)   EKMF
'Wendy van Wanten'   EPts WPBF
'Wendy's Beauty' (d)   CLoc EBak EPts MJac SVil WPBF
                                 WRou
'Wentworth'   CWVF
'Wessex Belle' (d/v)   CWVF
'Wessex Hardy'   CSil EKMF
'Westgate'   WPBF
'Westham'   LCla
'Westminster Chimes' (d)   CLoc CWVF MWhe SPet
'Wharfedale'   CSil MJac SLBF
'Whickham Blue'   CWVF MWar
'Whirlaway' (d)   CLoc CWVF EBak EKMF
'White Ann' (d)   see *F.* 'Heidi Weiss'
'White Clove'   CDoC CSil
'White Fairy'   WPBF
'White Galore' (d)   CWVF EBak EKMF EMan LVER
                                 SPet
'White Général Monk' (d)   CDoC CSil
'White Gold' (v)   EBak
'White Heidi Ann' (d)   CSil MWhe
'White Joy'   EBak
'White King' (d)   CLoc CWVF EBak EKMF EMan
                                 LVER MWhe SPet WPBF WRou
'White Lace'   CSil
'White Lady Patricia   EMan
  Mountbatten'
'White Pixie' ♀H3-4   CDoC CSil EKMF EPts LVER MJac
                                 NDlv SLBF SPer SPet
'White Pixie Wagtail'   see *F.* 'Wagtails White Pixie'
'White Queen' ambig.   CWVF
'White Queen' Doyle   EBak MWhe
'White Spider'   CLoc CWVF EBak MWhe SPet
'White Veil' (d)   CWVF
'White Water'   WPBF
'Whiteknights Amethyst'   CDoC CSil EKMF
'Whiteknights Blush'   CDoC CMdw CPLG CSil EPts EWes
                                 GCal GQui SMrm
'Whiteknights Cheeky'   CWVF EBak EPts LCla
'Whiteknights Green   CDoC CSil EKMF
  Glister'
'Whiteknights Pearl'   CDoC CSil CWVF ECha EKMF EPts
  ♀H1+3   LCla SHGN SLBF SMHy SPet
'Whiteknights Ruby'   EKMF LCla WPBF
'Whitton Starburst'   LCla
'Wicked Queen' (d)   CDoC CSil

'Widow Twanky' (d)   CWVF WPBF
'Wiebke Becker'   EKMF
'Wigan Pier' (d)   LCla MWar SLBF
'Wight Magic' (d)   MJac
'Wild and Beautiful' (d)   CWVF EKMF SPet
'Wilf Langton'   MWar
'Wilhelmina Schwab'   CDoC LCla
'Will van Brakel'   WPBF
'William Caunt'   EKMF
'Willie Tamerus'   WPBF
'Willy Winky'   CSil
'Wilma van Druten'   CDoC LCla WPBF
'Wilma Versloot'   WPBF
'Wilson's Colours'   EPts
'Wilson's Joy'   MJac
'Wilson's Pearls' (d)   SLBF SPet
'Wilson's Sugar Pink'   EPts LCla MJac MWhe
'Win Oxtoby' (d)   CWVF EKMF
'Windmill'   CWVF
'Wine and Roses' (d)   EBak
'Wings of Song' (d)   CWVF EBak
'Winston Churchill' (d)   CHrt CLoc CWVF EBak EKMF
  ♀H3   EMan EPts LAst LCla LVER MBri
                                 MJac MWar MWhe NBlu NVic
                                 SCoo SPet SPlb SSea SWal WWeb
'Winter's Touch'   EKMF
'Witchipoo' **new**   SLBF
'Woodnook' (d)   CWVF
'Woodside' (d)   CSil
wurdackii   EKMF
'Ymkje'   EBak
'Yolanda Franck'   CDoC WRou
'Yonder Blue' (d) **new**   WPBF
'Youth'   EKMF
'Yvonne Schwab'   CDoC LCla
'Zara'   MWhe WPBF
'Zellertal'   WPBF
'Zets Alpha' **new**   WPBF
'Zets Bravo'   CDoC
'Ziegfield Girl' (d)   EBak WPBF
'Zifi' **new**   SLBF
'Zulu King'   CDoC CSil
'Zwarte Dit'   WPBF
'Zwarte Snor' (d)   CWVF

Fumana (Cistaceae)
ericoides   XPep
thymifolia   XPep

Fumaria (Papaveraceae)
lutea   see *Corydalis lutea*
officinalis   CArn MSal

Furcraea (Agavaceae)
bedinghausii   CAby CBct CHll CTrC LEdu MAga
                                 WMul WPGP
§ *foetida*   CCCN
gigantea   see *F. foetida*
longaeva   CAbb CCtw CFir CHEx CPen CPne
                                 CTrC EBee MOak SAPC SArc SChr
                                 SDix WCMO WCot WPGP
selloa var. **marginata** (v) CDoC MAga

G

Gagea (Liliaceae)
lutea   EPot
pratensis   EPot

Gahnia (Cyperaceae)
filum   GGar
sieberiana **new**   SPlb
xanthocarpa   GGar

Gaillardia (Asteraceae)

aristata misapplied	see *G.* x *grandiflora*
aristata Pursch	EBee SMar
- 'Maxima Aurea'	EAEE EBee LAst LPhx LRHS NBre WCAu WWeb
'Arizona Sun' **new**	LSou NPri
'Bijou'	CBrm EBee NBre NVic NWCA SWvt
'Bremen'	EBee MBri NMRc NNor NPri
'Burgunder'	More than 30 suppliers
'Dazzler' ♀H4	CSBt EAEE EBee ECtt ELan ENot EPfP ERou LAst LBMP LRHS MWgw NLar NPri NVic SECG SPer SPoG WCAu WGor WPer
'Dwarf Goblin'	LAst SPet
§ 'Fackelschein'	NBre SRms XPep
'Fanfare'	COtt EBee SCoo SPoG
Goblin	see *G.* 'Kobold'
§ 'Goldkobold'	ELan MHer
§ x *grandiflora*	SMar
- 'Aurea'	LRHS
- 'Aurea Plena' (d)	EBee
§ 'Kobold'	More than 30 suppliers
'Mandarin'	LRHS SRms
* new giant hybrids	MWat WFar
'Saint Clements' **new**	SHar
'Sundance Biocolour'	LSou
'Sundance Red'	EMag
'Tokajer'	EBee EPfP NBre NLar
Torchlight	see *G.* 'Fackelschein'
Yellow Goblin	see *G.* 'Goldkobold'

Galactites (Asteraceae)

tomentosa	CBod CHrt CSec CSpe EBee EHrv ELan EMan EMar EPyc EWTr LDai LRHS NBur NDov SDnm SGar SPav WEas WWeb
- white	CBod NBur

Galanthus ✿ (Amaryllidaceae)

x *allenii*	CBro EHyt WIvy
alpinus	CLAP
- var. *alpinus*	CBro EHyt LFox MTho NMen
- - late-flowering	LRHS
- var. *bortkewitschianus*	LFox
§ *angustifolius*	CBro EHyt
antarctica	WThu
'Armine'	CAvo CSna LFox
'Atkinsii' ♀H4	CAvo CBro CElw CLAP EHrv EHyt EMon EPot ETow GCrs GEdr GKev LFox LRHS MAvo MRav NBir SChr WGPG WShi WTin WWye
§ 'Backhouse Spectacles'	WCMO
'Barbara's Double' (d)	CLAP EHyt
'Benhall Beauty'	CBel CSna LFox
'Bertram Anderson'	LFox
'Brenda Troyle'	CBel CBro CLAP EHrv EPot GCrs GEdr IGor LFox NPol WIvy
byzantinus	see *G. plicatus* subsp. *byzantinus*
caucasicus misapplied	see *G. elwesii* var. *monostictus*
- 'Comet'	see *G. elwesii* 'Comet'
- var. *hiemalis* Stern	see *G. elwesii* var. *monostictus* Hiemalis Group
- 'Mrs McNamara'	see *G. elwesii* 'Mrs McNamara'
'Clare Blakeway-Phillips'	CLAP EHyt
'Colesborne'	EHrv
corcyrensis spring-flowering	see *G. reginae-olgae* subsp. *vernalis*
- winter-flowering	see *G. reginae-olgae* subsp. *reginae-olgae* Winter-flowering Group
'Cordelia' (d)	CLAP EHyt EMon LFox LRHS
'Cowhouse Green'	EHrv
'Desdemona' (d)	CBro CLAP EHyt GCrs LFox WCMO WIvy
'Dionysus' (d)	CBgR CBro CLAP EHrv EPot ERos GCrs GEdr LFox MHom NBir WCMO
§ *elwesii* ♀H4	CBro EAEE ECho ELan EMon ENot EPfP EPot ERos ERou GCrs IGor LFox LRHS NBir NPol SRms WBVN WCMO WCot WShi
- 'Cedric's Prolific'	ECha
§ - 'Comet'	CBel CElw EMon
- 'David Shackleton'	EHrv
- Edward Whittall Group	CLAP
- var. *elwesii* 'Fred's Giant'	GCrs
- - 'Kite'	NPol
- - 'Magnus'	CLAP
- - 'Maidwell L'	CAvo CBel CSna EHrv LFox MBri
* - 'Flore Pleno' (d)	EBrs ENot LFox
- 'Helen Tomlinson'	MBri
- (Hiemalis Group) 'Barnes'	EHrv
- 'J. Haydn'	CElw ECho
§ - var. *monostictus* ♀H4	CAvo ECho EHrv EHyt EMon ETow WIvy WLin
- - from Ukraine	MPhe
- - 'G. Handel'	CElw WWst
* - - 'Green Tips'	NPol
- - 'H. Purcell'	CElw ECho
§ - - Hiemalis Group	CBel CBro ECha EHrv EMon GCrs LRHS WCot
- - 'Warwickshire Gemini' **new**	MAvo
§ - 'Mrs McNamara'	CBel
- 'Selborne Green Tips'	EMon
- 'Zwanenburg'	EMon LRHS
'Faringdon Double' (d)	EHrv
fosteri	CBro EHrv EHyt ERou GCrs LRHS SCnR
'Galatea'	CLAP CSna EHrv EMon LFox LRHS MHom WIvy
'Ginns'	CLAP LFox
§ *gracilis*	CBro CLAP ERos ETow GCrs LFox MTho NPol
- 'Highdown'	CAvo CElw CLAP
- 'Vic Horton'	GEdr WThu
graecus misapplied	see *G. gracilis*
graecus Orph. ex Boiss.	see *G. elwesii*
Greatorex double (d)	CLAP
'Greenfields'	CAvo CBel
'Hill Poë' (d)	CBel CBro CElw CLAP EPot GCrs IGor LFox
'Hippolyta' (d)	CAvo CBro CElw CLAP ECha EHrv EPot GCrs GEdr LFox SOkd WIvy
x *hybridus* 'Merlin'	CAvo CBel CElw ETow GCrs IGor LFox MAvo MHom WIvy
- 'Robin Hood'	CAvo CFee CLAP EHrv EHyt ERos GCrs LFox SBla
§ *ikariae* Bak.	CElw EHyt EPot ERos IGor WFar
- subsp. *ikariae* Butt's form	NPol
- Latifolius Group	see *G. platyphyllus*
- subsp. *snogerupii*	see *G. ikariae*
'Imbolc'	CAvo
'Jacquenetta' (d)	CBel CBro CDes CElw CLAP EHrv EHyt GCrs MHom WPGP
'John Gray'	CBel CBro CSna EMon LFox LRHS NPol
'Ketton'	CAvo CBro CElw LFox LRHS WIvy
'Kingston Double' (d)	CAvo CLAP
'Lady Beatrix Stanley' (d)	CAvo CBro CElw CLAP ECha EHrv EMon EPot ERos GEdr LFox LRHS MTho
§ *lagodechianus*	LRHS WCMO WWst
latifolius Rupr.	see *G. platyphyllus*
'Lavinia' (d)	CAvo CElw CLAP EHyt
'Lerinda'	EHrv
'Limetree'	CBel CBgR CLAP EHrv LFox NPol
'Little John'	EHrv

lutescens	see *G. nivalis* Sandersii Group
'Lyn'	EHrv
'Magnet' ♀H4	CAvo CBro CFee CLAP EHyt EMon EPot GCrs GEdr IGor LFox NPol SOkd WPGP WWst
'Mighty Atom'	CBel CDes CFee CLAP EHrv GCrs LFox
'Moccas'	CBgR CElw EPot
* 'Mrs Backhouse'	SOkd
§ 'Mrs Backhouse No 12'	EHrv
'Mrs Thompson'	CBel EHrv WIvy
'Neill Fraser'	LFox
nivalis ♀H4	CBro CNic CTri EBrs ECho ElAn ENot EPfP EPot GKev ITim LFox LRHS MBow MBri MNHC NJOw NRya SHFr SPer SRms WBrk WCot WFar WGwG WShi WWFP
- 'Anglesey Abbey'	CAvo EMon
- var. **angustifolius**	see *G. angustifolius*
- 'April Fool'	LFox MHom
- 'Bitton'	CBro CLAP LFox NPol
- dwarf	LFox
- 'Greenish'	CAvo CDes CSna
- subsp. **imperati**	WBrk
- 'Lutescens'	see *G. nivalis* Sandersii Group
- 'Melvillei'	EMon
- f. **pleniflorus** (d) **new**	GKev
- - 'Blewbury Tart' (d)	CAvo CLAP CSna
- - 'Flore Pleno' (d) ♀H4	CBro CStu CTri EPfP EPla EPot GAbr LFox LHop LRHS NRya SPer SRms WBrk WCot WFar WHen WShi WWye
- - 'Hambutt's Orchard' (d)	LFox
- - 'Lady Elphinstone' (d)	CAvo CBgR CBro CLAP CRow CSna EHrv GCrs LFox MRav MTho NPol WIvy
- - 'Pusey Green Tip' (d)	CAvo CBro CElw CLAP EPot GCrs GEdr LFox WPGP WTin
- Poculiformis Group	CLAP EMon LRHS
§ - Sandersii Group	CAvo CDes EHyt
§ - Scharlockii Group	CAvo CBel CBro EHyt EMon IGor LFox LRHS
- 'Tiny'	GCrs
- 'Tiny Tim'	EHyt NRya
§ - 'Virescens'	CLAP
- 'Viridapice'	CAvo CBro ECha ECho EHyt EMon EPot ERou GEdr LFox LRHS NMen NPol WCot WIvy WPGP WShi
- 'Warei'	LFox
'Ophelia' (d)	CAvo CBel CBro ETow GCrs IGor LFox
'Peg Sharples'	CSna
peshmenii	EPot SCnR WWst
§ **platyphyllus**	CBro LFox
plicatus ♀H4	CAvo CElw CFee ECho EHrv EMon EPot GEdr LFox LRHS NMen WShi WTin
- from Ukraine	MPhe
- 'Augustus'	CAvo CBel CDes CFee CSna EHrv EHyt ERos GCrs LFox WIvy
- 'Baxendale's Late'	CLAP
- 'Bowles' Large'	ERos MHom
§ - subsp. **byzantinus**	CBro EHyt ERos LFox
- - 'Ron Ginns'	LFox
- 'Colossus'	CBel
- 'Edinburgh Ketton'	CSna EHrv
- 'Florence Baker'	EHrv
- large	NPol
- 'Sally Passmore'	CAvo
- 'Sophie North'	CLAP GCrs
- 'The Pearl'	EHrv
- 'Three Ships'	EHrv
- 'Trym'	CLAP
- 'Warham'	CBro EHrv EPot GEdr MAvo WPGP
- 'Wendy's Gold'	EMon GCrs LRHS

reginae-olgae	CAvo CBro EHrv EHyt ERos GCrs MRav WCMO WCot
- WM 9901	MPhe
- WM 9908	MPhe
§ - subsp. **reginae-olgae** Winter-flowering Group	CBro LFox
§ - subsp. **vernalis**	EHyt LRHS
rizehensis	CAvo CLAP EHrv EPot GEdr
'S. Arnott' ♀H4	CAvo CBel CBro CElw CLAP EBrs ECha ECho ElAn EMon EPot GBuc GEdr IGor LFox LRHS MAvo NBir NMen NRya SBla WPGP WTin
'Saint Anne's'	CAvo CDes CElw CSna WIvy
'Sally Ann'	LFox
'Scharlockii'	see *G. nivalis* Scharlockii Group
'Seagull' **new**	CSna
'Shaggy'	EHyt
'Silverwells'	CElw CSna GEdr
§ 'Straffan'	CAvo CBel CBro EPot GEdr IGor LFox LRHS MHom NPol
'The Apothecary'	EHrv
'The Linns'	GCrs
'The O'Mahoney'	see *G.* 'Straffan'
'Titania' (d)	CBro EHrv
'Trotter's Merlin'	CSna
'Tubby Merlin'	CLAP CSna LFox WIvy
'Washfield Warham'	CSna ECha EMon LRHS
'White Wings' **new**	CSna
'William Thomson'	EMon LFox
'Winifrede Mathias'	CLAP LFox
'Wisley Magnet'	ECha
woronowii ♀H4	CBro CElw CLAP EMon ENot ETow GKev LRHS WCMO WCot

Galax (Diapensiaceae)

aphylla	see *G. urceolata*
§ **urceolata**	GCrs IBlr WSHC

Galega (Papilionaceae)

bicolor	IBlr MLLN NBir NBre SRms STes SWat WFar
'Duchess of Bedford'	CFir CFwr EBee MTis SWat
x **hartlandii**	IBlr MRav WCMO WWhi
- 'Alba' ♀H4	CFwr EBee EGle EHrv EMon EWes GBar GBri GCal IBlr LPhx MArl MWgw SAga SMHy SWat WCMO WCot WHoo WPrP WSHC WWhi
- 'Candida'	NBir
- 'Lady Wilson' ♀H4	EBee ECtt EGle EGra EMan EWes MArl MRav WCMO WCot WFoF WHoo
- 'Spring Light' (v)	ECtt EMan EWes LSou
'Her Majesty'	see *G.* 'His Majesty'
§ 'His Majesty'	CBos CKno EBee ECtt EGle EMan GBri MArl MLHP MRav NBre NCob NGby SAga SWat WCMO WCot WFar WHoo WPGP WWlt
officinalis	More than 30 suppliers
- 'Alba' ♀H4	CBgR CBos CPom CPrp EBee ECtt ElAn ELau EMan EPfP MBrN MHer MNHC NCob SPer SWal WAul WCHb WCMO WFar WHer WHil WHrl WMoo WOut WWye
- Coconut Ice = 'Kelgal'PBR (v)	CBow NCob SPer SPoG WHer
orientalis	CDes CFir EBee ECha ECtt GMaP LRHS MArl MLLN MRav SBch SMac SWat WAbb WCot WMoo WPGP WSHC

Galeobdolon see *Lamium*

Galium (Rubiaceae)

aristatum	ECha EMan MLLN SBch
cruciata	see *Cruciata laevipes*

mollugo	CArn CRWN MSal NSco SIde WCHb
§ *odoratum*	More than 30 suppliers
verum	CArn CRWN GPoy GWCH MBow
	MHer MNHC MSal NLan NMir
	NPri NSco SECG SIde WCHb
	WHbs WHer

Galtonia ✿ (*Hyacinthaceae*)

§ *candicans* ♀H4	More than 30 suppliers
princeps	CAvo CBro EBee EBrs ECha ERos
	ERou GBuc
regalis	CPLG ERos GCal GEdr WPGP
viridiflora	CAvo CBcs CBro CFFs CFwr
	CHar CPLG CStu EBee EBrs EChP
	ECha ECho ELan EPot ERos GCal
	GEdr LAst LRHS MNrw MSte MTis
	NBid NChi NWCA SDnm WCMO
	WFar

Galvezia (*Scrophulariaceae*)
speciosa	XPep

Gamolepis see *Steirodiscus*

Gardenia (*Rubiaceae*)

augusta	see *G. jasminoides*
florida L.	see *G. jasminoides*
globosa	see *Rothmannia globosa*
grandiflora	see *G. jasminoides*
§ *jasminoides* ♀H1	CBcs EBak LRHS MBri
- 'Kleim's Hardy'	EBee ELan EPfP EShb EWes LRHS
	MAsh NLar SOWG SPoG SSta
- 'Star'	SOWG
magnifica **new**	SOWG
thunbergia	EShb SPlb

garlic see *Allium sativum*

Garrya ✿ (*Garryaceae*)

congdonii	NLar
elliptica	CAgr CBcs CDul EBee ECrN EMui
	ENot EPfP ISea LPan LRHS LSRN
	MBri MGos MNHC MWgw NEgg
	NFor NHol NWea SPet SPlb SReu
	WFar WHar WPat
- (f)	LAst MSwo SWvt WCMO WPat
- (m)	CCVT CDoC CSBt EHol GGar
	MGan NBlu SLim SPoG WFar
- 'James Roof' (m) ♀H4	More than 30 suppliers
fremontii	NLar
x *issaquahensis*	CAbP CDoC CPMA EBee ELan
'Glasnevin Wine'	EPfP IMGH ISea LRHS MBlu MGos
	NEgg NHol NLar NPal NSti NVic
	SCoo SLim SMur SPoG SSta WFar
- 'Pat Ballard' (m)	CPMA EPfP NHol NLar
x *thuretii*	MGos NLar WDin WFar

Garuleum (*Asteraceae*)
woodii JCA 324000	CPBP

Gasteria ✿ (*Aloaceae*)
batesiana ♀H1	EPem
liliputana	EPem
verrucosa	EShb

x *Gaulnettya* see *Gaultheria*

Gaultheria ✿ (*Ericaceae*)
adenothrix	WAbe
cardiosepala	GEdr
- CLD 1351	GEdr
cumingiana B&SWJ 1542	WCru
cuneata ♀H4	ECho GEdr LRHS MAsh MBar NDlv
	NLAp NLar SPoG
- 'Pinkie'	ECho LRHS
forrestii **new**	CPLG

hispidula	ECho GGGa
hookeri	IBlr
itoana	ECho GEdr MBar NDlv
'Jingle Bells'	MGos SPoG
macrostigma	WThu
- BR 67	GGar
miqueliana	GEdr
mucronata	CBrm CDul EPfP MBar NWea
	WDin WGwG
- (m)	CBcs CDoC CSBt CTri CWSG ENot
	EPfP LAst MAsh MBar MGos NBlu
	SPer SPoG SRms
- 'Alba' (f)	MBar MGos SLon
- 'Atrococcinea' (f)	SMer
- 'Bell's Seedling' (f/m)	CBcs CDoC CDul CTri CWSG EPfP
♀H4	GGar LRHS MAsh NBir NLRH
	SHBN SPer SPoG SReu SSta
- 'Cherry Ripe' (f)	SHBN
- 'Crimsonia' (f) ♀H4	EPfP MAsh MBar MDun SHBN SPer
	SPur SRms
- 'Indian Lake'	NHol
- lilac-berried (f) **new**	NBlu
- 'Lilacina' (f)	CBcs
- 'Lilian' (f)	CSBt CWSG ENot EPfP GSki LAst
	MAsh SHBN SMer SPer
- Mother of Pearl	see *G. mucronata* 'Parelmoer'
- 'Mulberry Wine' (f) ♀H4	CSBt CTri EPfP LRHS MAsh MGos
	NHol SPer SPoG
- 'October Red' (f)	NHol
§ - 'Parelmoer' (f)	CSBt ENot LAst MAsh SPer SPoG
	SPur
- 'Pink Pearl' (f) ♀H4	SRms
- red-berried (f) **new**	NBlu
- 'Rosea' (f)	MBar MGos
- 'Rosie' (f)	SBod
§ - 'Signaal' (f)	CBcs CBrm ENot EPfP GWCH LAst
	LRHS MAsh MGos SPer
- Signal	see *G. mucronata* 'Signaal'
§ - 'Sneeuwwitje' (f)	CBcs CWSG ENot EPfP GSki LAst
	LRHS MGos NBir SHBN SMer SPer
	SPoG SPur
- Snow White	see *G. mucronata* 'Sneeuwwitje'
- 'Thymifolia' (m)	EPfP SHBN SPer
- white-berried (f)	NBlu
- 'Wintertime' (f) ♀H4	CBrm MGos SRms
* *mucronifolia* dwarf	NWCA
§ *myrsinoides*	GKev
nummularioides	GEdr GGGa NHol
'Pearls'	GCrs NHol
'Pink Champagne'	ITim
procumbens ♀H4	More than 30 suppliers
prostrata	see *G. myrsinoides*
- *purpurea*	see *G. myrsinoides*
pumila	GAbr GCrs LEdu MBar NHol NLAp
- 'E.K. Balls'	NHol
schultesii	WThu
shallon	CAgr CBcs CDoC CSBt EPfP GBar
	MBar MDun MGos SBrw SHBN
	SPer SRms SWvt WDin WFar
- 'Snowqualmi Pass'	NLar
sinensis lilac-berried	WThu
tasmanica	ECou GAbr
thymifolia	GEdr
trichophylla	GGGa GIBF
x *wisleyensis*	LRHS SLon SRms SSta
- 'Pink Pixie'	CMHG ECho LRHS MAsh MBar
	NLar SBrw SSta
- 'Wisley Pearl'	CBcs CDoC IBlr IDee MBar NLar
	SBrw SCoo SReu WFar
yunnanensis	SReu

Gaura (*Onagraceae*)
lindheimeri ♀H4	More than 30 suppliers
- Cherry Brandy =	CEnt CSpe EBee ECtt EPfP ERou
'Gauchebra'	EWes EWin EWll LAst LBMP LHop
	MSph NLar SPer SWat WCra WFar

– compact red	WCot
– 'Corrie's Gold' (v)	CBcs CWSG EBee EChP ECha ECtt EHoe ELan EPfP ERou LAst LRHS MHer NBlu NJOw SAga SPav SPer SPet SPoG WMnd XPep
– 'Crimson Butterflies'^{PBR}	CHea COtt CTbh EBee EPfP EShb LAst LRHS SPoG
§ – 'Heather's Delight'^{PBR}	SHar
– 'Heaven's Harmony' **new**	ERou EWin
– In the Pink^{PBR}	see *G. lindheimeri* 'Heather's Delight'
– 'Jo Adela' (v)	ELan EPfP
– Karalee Petite = 'Gauka'	CBrm CSpe CWCL ECtt EPPr LAst NPri SCoo SPoG STes SVil
– Karalee Pink	MBri
– Karalee White = 'Nugauwhite'	CSpe CWCL LAst MBri SCoo SPoG
– 'Madonna' (v)	CBow
– 'My Melody' (v)	CWCL EBee ERou EWin EWll LAst LSou SPoG
– short	LSou SGar
– 'Siskiyou Pink'	More than 30 suppliers
– 'The Bride'	CEnt CSim CTri EAEE EBee LRHS LSou MArl MRav MWat MWgw NGdn SMar SMrm SPav SPet SPla SRGP STes SWal SWvt WBVN WHil WMnd
– 'Val's Pink'	WHoo WSPU
– 'Whirling Butterflies'	CKno CSpe CWCL EBee ECtt ELan EMil EPfP GMaP GQue NBlu NJOw NPer SBod SMad SMrm SPav SPer SPoG SWat WMnd XPep
– 'White Heron'	EChP IBal MNrw
I 'Variegata' (v)	CWCL ENot LIck

Gaussia (Arecaceae)

maya	LPal

Gaylussacia (Ericaceae)

baccata (F)	NLar
brachycera	GGGa

Gazania (Asteraceae)

'Acajou'	CWCL
'Aztec' ♀^{H1+3}	CHal EWin SUsu
'Bicton Cream'	CHal
'Bicton Orange'	CCCN COIW MAJR SCoo
'Blackberry Ripple'	COIW LAst MAJR NCiC SCoo
'Christopher'	CHal GGar MOak MSte SCoo
'Christopher Lloyd'	COIW LAst MAJR
'Cookei' ♀^{H1+3}	CSpe MAJR MSte SAga WCot
'Cornish Pixie'	CHal
cream	CHal NCiC
'Cream Beauty'	MSte
'Cream Dream'	LAst MOak
Daybreak Series	WFar
'Diane'	CWCL
double bronze	CHal
double yellow	see *G.* 'Yellow Buttons'
'Garden Sun'	MLan
* *grayi*	CHal
* 'Hazel'	MSte
(Kiss Series) 'Kiss Bronze Star'	LIck SGar
– 'Kiss Pomegranate'	LIck
– 'Kiss Rose'	SGar
– 'Kiss Yellow'	LIck SGar
krebsiana	XPep
linearis 'Colorado Gold'	CFir
'Magic'	LAst MAJR NPri SCoo
'Northbourne' ♀^{H1+3}	GGar MSte
'Orange Beauty'	CHEx ELan
'Red Velvet'	CHEx MSte
§ *rigens*	LRHS
– var. *uniflora* ♀^{H1+3}	MSte XPep

– 'Variegata' (v) ♀^{H1+3}	CBow COIW ELan LAst LSou MAvo MOak SPoG WCot
'Silverbrite'	CHal
splendens	see *G. rigens*
'Talent'	SEND
'Torbay Silver'	CHEx
§ 'Yellow Buttons' (d)	COIW

Geissorhiza (Iridaceae)

corrugata	CStu
imbricata	CStu

Gelasine (Iridaceae)

azurea	see *G. coerulea*
§ *coerulea*	CMon EBee EMan WCot

Gelidocalamus (Poaceae)

fangianus	see *Drepanostachyum microphyllum*

Gelsemium (Loganiaceae)

rankinii	CPIN NLar WSHC
sempervirens ♀^{H1-2}	CArn CHll CMCN CPIN CRHN CWoW ERea EShb IDee LSRN MSal NCGa SBra SOWG SPoG WBor
– 'Flore Pleno' (d)	CPIN ERea
– 'Pride of Augusta'	CMCN

Genista (Papilionaceae)

aetnensis ♀^{H4}	CBcs CBgR CEnd CHEx CMCN CTri ECrN ELan EPfP LRHS MDun MRav SAPC SArc SDix SHBN SMad SPer SPoG SRms SSpi SSta WBVN WDin WSHC XPep
§ *canariensis*	CPLG CSBt CWib ERea NBlu WBrE
cinerea	WCFE
decumbens	see *Cytisus decumbens*
delphinensis	see *G. sagittalis* subsp. *delphinensis*
'Emerald Spreader'	see *G. pilosa* 'Yellow Spreader'
fragrans	see *G. canariensis*
hispanica	CBcs CCVT CDul CSBt CTri EBee ECrN ELan EPfP GGar LRHS MBar MGos MNHC SHBN SLim SPer SPoG SRms SWvt WCFE WDin WFar WHar WTel XPep
humifusa	see *G. pulchella*
lydia ♀^{H4}	More than 30 suppliers
§ *maderensis*	EWes WPic
monosperma	see *Retama monosperma*
§ *monspessulana*	ECho XPep
pilosa	CTri EPot ISea MBar MDun MWhi NMen
– 'Lemon Spreader'	see *G. pilosa* 'Yellow Spreader'
– var. *minor*	NLar NMen
– 'Procumbens'	CMea MDKP WPat
– 'Vancouver Gold'	CBcs CSBt ELan EPfP MAsh MGos MRav SMad SPer SPoG SRms WDin WFar WGor
§ – 'Yellow Spreader'	CBcs CMHG CSBt EHol EPot GEdr IArd MSwo NJOw
§ 'Porlock' ♀^{H3}	CBcs CBgR CDoC CDul CPLG CSBt CSPN CWSG EBee MAsh MRav SEND SPoG WDin WWeb
§ *pulchella*	CTri EPot SBla
sagittalis	CTri MDKP MWhi NBir NFor NLar NWCA SBla SPer WTin WWFP
§ – subsp. *delphinensis* ♀^{H4}	NMen
– *minor*	see *G. sagittalis* subsp. *delphinensis*
§ x *spachiana* ♀^{H1}	CTri SPoG
tenera 'Golden Shower'	CPLG SLPl
tinctoria	CAgr CArn GBar GPoy GWCH ILis MGol MHer MSal NFor SIde WHer WWye

- 'Flore Pleno' (d) ♀H4	ECho MGos NMen NPro SRot WCot
- 'Humifusa'	EPot GEdr NWCA
- 'Royal Gold' ♀H4	CWSG CWib EPfP MAsh MGos MRav SHBN SPer SPlb SPoG
villarsii	see *G. pulchella*

Gennaria (Orchidaceae)

diphylla	EBee

Gentiana ✿ (Gentianaceae)

§ *acaulis* ♀H4	More than 30 suppliers
- f. *alba*	EPot WThu
- 'Alboviolacea'	NLar
- Andorra form	WAbe
- 'Belvedere'	EPot GCrs NMen WAbe
- 'Coelestina'	EHyt EPot WThu
- 'Dinarica'	see *G. dinarica*
- 'Holzmannii'	WAbe
- 'Krumrey'	EHyt EPot
- 'Max Frei'	CStu GCrs
I - 'Maxima Enzian'	EPot GCrs NHar
- 'Rannoch'	EPot GEdr NMen
- 'Stumpy'	EPot
- 'Trotter's Variety'	EPot WAbe
- 'Undulatifolia'	EPot
- 'Velkokvensis'	EHyt
affinis	GAbr NLAp NWCA
'Alex Duguid'	CWrd GAbr
'Alpha'	see *G.* x *hexafarreri* 'Alpha'
alpina **new**	WAbe
'Altweibersommer' **new**	CWrd
'Amethyst'	CWrd EPot GCrs GEdr GMaP SIng WAbe
andrewsii	NLAp
angustifolia	GCrs WAbe
- 'Rannoch'	GKev
'Ann's Special'	CWrd GEdr
asclepiadea ♀H4	More than 30 suppliers
- var. *alba*	CHea GBuc GGar GMaP IGor MDKP MTho NChi SRms WAbe WCru WTin
- 'Knightshayes'	EBee GKev NLAp
I - 'Nana' **new**	EBee
- pale blue-flowered	WPGP
- 'Phyllis'	CFir EBee GBuc GKev
- 'Pink Swallow'	EDAr GBuc WHoo
- 'Rosea'	CDes GBuc GMaP MDKP MNrw WPGP
- yellow-flowered	ELan
atuntsiensis	GIBF
'Barbara Lyle'	CWrd WAbe
bavarica var.	SPlb
subacaulis	
x *bernardii*	see *G.* x *stevenagensis* 'Bernardii'
bisetaea	SRms
'Bjorn's Love' **new**	CWrd
'Blauer Diamant'	GCrs
'Blue Flame'	GCrs
'Blue Sea'	CWrd
'Blue Shell'	CWrd
'Blue Silk'	CWrd EPot EWes GBuc GCrs GMaP NHar NLAp SBla SIng WAbe
brachyphylla	WAbe
- subsp. *favratii* **new**	WAbe
burseri	CSec
cachemirica ambig.	WPat
'Cairngorm'	CWrd GAbr GCrs GEdr GMaP NDlv
Cambrian hybrids	CWrd
'Cambrian White'	WAbe
x *caroli*	SBla WAbe
chinensis	GIBF
'Christine Jean'	CWrd GCrs SIng
clausa	GIBF
clusii	EPot WAbe
- *alba*	WAbe
'Compact Gem'	CWrd EPot GCrs GEdr NLAp WAbe
'Coronation'	CWrd
crassicaulis	GAbr GCrs
§ *cruciata*	GAbr MMHG MTho SBch
- subsp. *phlogifolia*	GIBF
§ *dahurica*	ECho GAbr LRHS NGdn SBch SBla SSto
'Dark Hedgehog'	GCrs GEdr
decumbens	WPat
dendrologi	WHil
depressa	MTho WAbe
'Devonhall'	CWrd GEdr WAbe
'Devonhall Surprise' **new**	CWrd
§ *dinarica*	CLyd ECho EHyt MTho NLAp
- 'Col. Stitt'	GEdr WThu
- 'Frocheneite'	WThu
Drake's strain	CWrd LRHS
'Dumpy'	CPBP CWrd EPot GEdr NLAp WAbe
'Dusk'	CWrd GCrs
'Eleanor'	GCrs
'Elizabeth'	CWrd GEdr GMaP
'Ettrick'	GEdr
'Eugen's Allerbester' (d)	CWrd GEdr NHar WAbe
'Eugen's Bester'	CWrd NHar
'Excelsior'	NHar
'Expo' **new**	CWrd
'Exquisite' **new**	CWrd
farreri	EWes GCrs NSla WAbe
- 'Duguid'	GEdr
- hybrids	WAbe
'Fasta Highlands'	NBir
fetissowii	see *G. macrophylla* var. *fetissowii*
'Fohnwolke' **new**	CWrd
freyniana	CSec SBla
'Fuchs' **new**	CWrd
'Gigant' **new**	CWrd
Glamis strain	CWrd GEdr NDlv NHar
'Glen Isla'	EWes
'Glen Moy'	GMaP
'Glendevon'	WAbe
'Gloriosa' **new**	CWrd
'Goliath' **new**	CWrd
§ *gracilipes*	ECho LRHS MWat SPlb SRms
- 'Yuatensis'	see *G. macrophylla* var. *fetissowii*
grossheimii	CSec GIBF GKev
x *hascombensis*	see *G. septemfida* var. *lagodechiana* 'Hascombensis'
'Henry'	CWrd WAbe
x *hexafarreri*	CWrd GCrs
§ - 'Alpha'	GMaP
hexaphylla	WAbe
'Indigo'	WAbe
Inshriach hybrids	CWrd GCrs GMaP
'Inverleith' ♀H4	CWrd EDAr EWes GCrs GEdr IHMH NHol NLAp SPlb WGor
'Joan Ward'	CWrd
'John Ward'	CWrd
kesselringii	see *G. walujewii*
'Kirriemuir'	CWrd EWes NDlv
kochiana	see *G. acaulis*
kurroo var. *brevidens*	see *G. daburica*
lagodechiana	see *G. septemfida* var. *lagodechiana*
ligustica	GCrs
lucerna	CWrd GEdr NHol NLAp
lutea	EBee ECho GAbr GCal GIBF GKev GPoy MAvo NBid NChi SDix SRms WAul WBVN WCAu WCot WLin WWye
x *macaulayi* ♀H4	CWrd EDAr GCrs GEdr SIng SRms WHoo
- 'Elata'	CWrd GCrs NDlv NHol

- 'Kidbrooke Seedling'	CTri CWrd EDAr EWes GCrs GEdr GMaP NHol NLAp SPer WAbe WGwG
- 'Kingfisher'	CTri CWrd EDAr GAbr GEdr NBir NFor NLAp SBla SIng WAbe
§ - 'Praecox'	CWrd EDAr GCrs GEdr NDlv NLAp
§ - 'Wells's Variety'	CWrd GCrs GEdr WAbe
§ *macrophylla* var. *fetissowii*	EBee GAbr GKev NLAp
makinoi 'Royal Blue'	CWCL EBee GBin GBri IDee IPot MAvo NChi NSla WHil WMnd
'Margaret'	WAbe
'Maryfield'	GEdr
'Melanie'	NHar
'Merlin'	GCrs
'Multiflora'	CWrd
* *nepaulensis*	GlBF
§ *nubigena*	CSec
§ *occidentalis*	EPot GCrs NLAp
'Oktoberfest' **new**	CWrd
Olga's pale	GCrs
olivieri	EHyt
oreodoxa	CWrd GCrs
paradoxa	CLyd GCrs GKev NDlv NLAp NSla WPat
- 'Blauer Herold'	NCGa
phlogifolia	see *G. cruciata* subsp. *phlogifolia*
phyllocalyx	GlBF
pneumonanthe	SPlb
prolata	GCrs GKev NLAp
przewalskii	see *G. nubigena*
pumila subsp. *delphinensis*	WAbe
punctata	ITim
purdomii	see *G. gracilipes*
'Robyn Lyle'	WAbe
'Royal Highlander'	CWrd
'Saphir Select'	EDAr GEdr
saxosa	EHyt EPot GCrs GEdr GKev ITim NBir NLAp WAbe WLin
scabra	CStu EBee EDAr GCrs NBlu WWye
- 'Ishusuki'	SBla SOkd
- 'Zuikorindo'	NLar
'Sensation'	CWrd GEdr
septemfida ♀H4	EAEE EHyt ELan EPfP EPot GCrs GEdr LBee LHop LRHS MBri MHer MTho MWat NBir NBlu NLAp NRya NWCA SBla SIng SPlb SRms WHoo
- 'Alba'	NBir
§ - var. *lagodechiana* ♀H4	EBee EDAr EHyt GCal SRms WBVN WFar
- - 'Doeringiana'	NMen
§ - - 'Hascombensis'	ECho
'Serenity'	CWrd GEdr WAbe
'Shot Silk'	CPBP CSam CWrd EDAr EWes GCrs GEdr GMaP NBir NHol SPer SUsu WAbe
sikkimensis	GCrs
'Silken Giant'	WAbe
'Silken Seas'	WAbe
'Silken Skies'	GBuc GEdr WAbe
sino-ornata ♀H4	CTri ECho EDAr GCrs GEdr GGar LRHS LSRN MBri NBlu NLAp NMen SIng SPer SRms WAbe WBVN WFar WGwG WPat
- CLD 476B	GEdr
- 'Alba'	CWrd WFar
- 'Angel's Wings'	CWrd GEdr NHol
- 'Autumn Frolic' **new**	CWrd
- 'Bellatrix'	CWrd GEdr NHol
- 'Blautopf'	CWrd
- 'Brin Form'	CWrd SRms WAbe
- 'Downfield'	CWrd GCrs NDlv NHol
- 'Edith Sarah'	CWrd GCrs GEdr NHol SRms
- 'Mary Lyle'	CWrd GEdr WAbe
- 'Praecox'	see *G.* x *macaulayi* 'Praecox'
- 'Starlight'	NHar
I - 'Trotter's Form'	CWrd EWes
- 'Weisser Traum'	CWrd GEdr
- 'White Wings'	CWrd EWes GCrs LRHS NDlv
siphonantha	CSec
'Soutra'	GEdr
x *stevenagensis* ♀H4	CLyd CTri CWrd LRHS NLAp SIng
§ - 'Bernardii'	CWrd GCrs GEdr SIng WAbe
- dark	CWrd WAbe WFar WPat
- 'Frank Barker'	CWrd WAbe
straminea	EBee GCrs GKev LTwo MDKP WCot
'Strathmore' ♀H4	CTri EDAr EHyt EWes GAbr GCrs GEdr GMaP LRHS NHar NHol NLAp NRya SIng SPlb WAbe WGwG
ternifolia 'Cangshan'	GCrs GEdr WAbe
- 'Dali'	GCrs GEdr GKev NBir
tibetica	CArn EBee EDAr EUnu GCal GlBF GPoy MWat NBid SBch WAul WBVN WCAu WEas WGwG WPer WTin WWye
aff. *tibetica* CC 3935	MGol
trichotoma	GCrs GKev
triflora	EPot GBuc WFar WPGP
- 'Alba'	GBuc
- var. *japonica*	GBri GBuc GCal
- 'Royal Blue'	EBee GCal
Tweeddale strain	GCrs
'Ultra Light' **new**	CWrd
veitchiorum	GCrs
venusta CC 4666 **new**	ITim
verna	CPBP CWCL EAEE EBee ECho EHyt EPfP EPot EWes GCrs ITim LHop LRHS LSRN MTho NLAp NMen NRya NSla SBla SIng SPoG WAbe WFar WPat
- 'Alba'	GCrs ITim NLAp WAbe WFar WPat
§ - subsp. *balcanica*	CLyd ELan MTho NLAp SRms WPat
- subsp. *oschtenica*	NSla WAbe WLin
- slate blue	NLAp WPat
§ - subsp. *tergestina*	EDAr NLAp
'Violette'	CWrd GCrs GEdr
waltonii	ECho EWes
§ *walujewii*	GAbr
wellsii	see *G.* x *macaulayi* 'Wells's Variety'
wilsonii **new**	GlBF
wutaiensis	see *G. macrophylla* var. *fetissowii*

Geranium (Geraniaceae)

from Pamirs, Tadzhikistan	EPPr WPnP
from Sikkim	NWCA
aconitifolium L'Hér.	see *G. rivulare*
aconitifolium misapplied	see *G. palmatum*
'Alan Mayes'	CCge CPrp CSev EBee EBla EPPr MNFA MSte NGdn NSti SRGP WCra WWpP
'Alaska'	CBgR
albanum	CBgR CCge CElw EBee EChP EGra EMar EPPr EWsh GAbr GSki LLWP MNrw NSti SDix SRGP SWal WCru WMoo WPtf WTMC WWpP
albiflorum	CCge CMCo EChP EPPr LRHS MNFA SRGP WCru WMoo WPnP WWpP
'Amanda's Blush'	SMrm
anemonifolium	see *G. palmatum*
'Ann Folkard' ♀H4	More than 30 suppliers
'Ann Folkard' x *psilostemon*	LSRN
'Anne Thomson'	More than 30 suppliers
x *antipodeum*	GBuc WCru
'Black Ice'	

- 'Chocolate Candy'PBR	EPfP GBri NBre NLar WFoF WWeb
§ - Crûg strain	CSpe EHrv EMan EPot LRHS MDKP MDun NBPC NGdn SHBN WCru
- 'Elizabeth Wood'	CCge EMan LSou
- (*G. sessiliflorum* subsp. novae-zelandiae 'Nigricans' X *G. traversii* var. *elegans*)	SRms SWat
- 'Kahlua'	EBee EHrv EMan EPfP MBNS
- 'Sea Spray'	CMHG EBee ECtt EMar EWes GBuc GGar IPot LAst LRHS MNrw MSte NBro NGdn NSti SPoG SWat WCru WMnd WTMC WWpP
- 'Stanhoe'	CSpe EBee ECtt SBch SRot WBrk WFar
aristatum	CDes CPou EBee EBla EChP EPPr EWes MNFA MNrw MRav MSph MTis NBir NCot SPav SRGP STes WCru WMoo WPnP WTMC WWpP
- NS 649	NWCA
armenum	see *G. psilostemon*
asphodeloides	CBre CElw EBee EChP GAbr GSki IFro LLWP MBNS MNFA MNrw MWhi NBid NCot NGdn NSti SPav SRGP SWat WBrk WCru WFar WHCG WHen WMnd WMoo WTin WWpP
- subsp. *asphodeloides* 'Prince Regent'	EMan EPPr MNFA SBch WPtf WWpP
§ - - white-flowered	CCge EBla EMan EPPr SRGP WFar WHen WMoo WWpP
- subsp. *crenophilum*	CElw EBee
- 'Starlight'	NBid SBch WPtf
atlanticum Hook. f.	see *G. malviflorum*
'Aussie Gem'	CFwr
'Baby Blue'	see *G. himalayense* 'Baby Blue'
'Bertie Crûg'	CBow CCge CDes COfd CPrp CSpe EBee EBla ECtt EHrv EPPr GAbr LTwo NBPC NBir NEgg NMoo SCoo SIng SPoG SRms SRot SWat SWvt WCru WFar WPat WWpP
biuncinatum	IFro WPnP
Black Beauty = 'Nodbeauty'	CBct CHad CPen EBee ELan ENot EWes IPot LSou MGos MSph NPri SCoo SDnm SPav SPer SPoG WHlf
'Blue Blood' **new**	CFwr IPot NCot
'Blue Cloud' ♀H4	CDes CElw CMea EBee EBla EGra EMar EPPr GMaP GMac LPhx MAvo MTis NBir NCot SMeo SRGP SSvw SUsu WCra WHoo WMoo WPnP WTMC WWpP
'Blue Pearl'	CCge EBee EPPr NBir NSti SRGP SUsu SVil WCra WMoo WPnP WWpP
§ 'Blue Sunrise'	CBow CCge EBee EBla ELan IBal IPot LAst LRHS MCCP MSte NBPC NCot NEgg NLar NSti SAga SPla SPoG SRkn SRms WCra WFar WWpP
'Bob's Blunder'	CCge CElw CSpe EBee EBla ECtt MBNS NCob NEgg SPla SWvt WCot WCru WFar WTMC WWhi WWlt WWpP
bohemicum	CCge EBla GSki MNFA NCot SRGP WBrk WCru WHen WHer WWpP
- 'Orchid Blue'	EPfP EShb LRHS SWvt WFar
'Brookside' ♀H4	More than 30 suppliers
brutium	WHen
brycei	MNrw
'Buckland Beauty'	CDes EBee EPPr SBch SBla
'Buxton's Blue'	see *G. wallichianum* 'Buxton's Variety'
caeruleatum	EBee EBla EMon EPPr SBch SUsu WWpP

caffrum	CCge EBee EMan EShb GBuc GSki NChi NSti SRGP SWal WCru WOut WWpP
californicum	CElw GBuc WCru
canariense	see *G. reuteri*
candicans misapplied	see *G. lambertii*
'Candy Rose' **new**	LSou
§ x *cantabrigiense*	CBrm CNic CSBt ECtt EDAr EMar EShb GAbr GCal IBlr LAst LVER MHer MNrw MWgw NBid NBir NBro NPer NSti SGar SRms WBrk WCru WFar WHCG WLin WMoo
- 'Berggarten'	CDes CElw EBee EPPr SBch SRGP WPtf WWpP
- 'Biokovo'	More than 30 suppliers
- 'Cambridge'	More than 30 suppliers
- 'Karmina'	CElw CMCo EBee EBla EChP EGle EPPr EPla EPot GSki IHMH NRnb SBch WHoo WMoo WPnP WTMC WWpP
- 'Show Time'	CMCo EBla WWpP
- 'St Ola'	More than 30 suppliers
- 'Westray'PBR	CCge EBee EChP EPPr EShb GAbr GKev MCCP MDun MSte NBlu NEgg NGdn SPoG SRms STes SVil SWvt WWeb
cataractarum	CCge MLLN WCru
- subsp. *pitardii*	SRGP
'Chantilly'	CElw CMCo CSam EBee EBla EGra EPPr GBuc MAvo MNrw NBir NPro SBch SUsu WCru WMoo WPnP WPtf WTMC WWpP
christensenianum B&SWJ 8022	WCru
cinereum	CCge CWCL EBla ECho
- 'Album'	ECho NChi WCru
- 'Apple Blossom'	see *G. x lindavicum* 'Apple Blossom'
- 'Ballerina'	see *G.* (Cinereum Group) 'Ballerina'
I - 'Heather'	CCge EBla EChP EPPr LRHS MAvo MBNS MMHG NBro NGdn NSti WCru
- hybrids	COtt LAst LRHS
- 'Janette'	
- subsp. *ponticum*	see *G. ponticum*
- 'Purple Pillow'	More than 30 suppliers
- 'Rothbury Gem'	CCge EBla NLar WCra
§ (Cinereum Group) 'Ballerina' ♀H4	More than 30 suppliers
- 'Carol'	CCge CDes CElw EAEE EBee EBla EChP EHoe EMar EPPr EWes LAst MAvo MBNS MWhe NBro NDov NGdn NLar NSti SVil SWvt WCra WPnP
- 'Laurence Flatman'	More than 30 suppliers
- 'Sugar Babe'PBR	CCge
'Claridge Druce'	see *G. x oxonianum* 'Claridge Druce'
clarkei 'Kashmir Green'	EPPr LPhx NCot SUsu WMoo
- 'Kashmir Pink'	More than 30 suppliers
§ - 'Kashmir White' ♀H4	More than 30 suppliers
- 'Mount Stewart'	WCru WHil
- (Purple-flowered Group) 'Kashmir Purple'	More than 30 suppliers
- 'Coffee Time'	WWpP
collinum	EPPr GAbr GBuc MNrw NBir NBre NCot SRGP WBrk WCru WPnP WTMC WWpP
aff. *collinum*	CDes
'Coombland White'	CBgR CCge CDes CElw CSam CSpe EBee EBla EPPr IFro LAst MBri MEHN MNFA MNrw MWgw NSti SRGP STes SVil WCMO WCot WCra WCru WHoo WMoo WWeb WWhi WWpP

Crûg strain — see *G.* x *antipodeum* Crûg strain

§ 'Cyril's Fancy' — EBee EBla EChP EPPr MAvo MNFA SUsu WPtf WWpP

dahuricum — WCru

dalmaticum ♀H4 — More than 30 suppliers

- 'Album' — CNic EAEE EBla ECho ECtt EDAr EHyt ELan EPPr EPot GBBs MHer MRav MTho MWhe NChi NRya SIng SMer SRGP SRms SRot SWat WAbe WCra WCru WFar WHCG WWpP

- 'Bressingham Pink' — EPPr WPnP WWpP

- 'Bridal Bouquet' — EBee GBri NChi NMen NSla SBla WAbe WHer

dalmaticum x *macrorrhizum* — see *G.* x *cantabrigiense*

delavayi misapplied — see *G. sinense*

delavayi Franch. — CDes EBee WCru

- B&SWJ 7582 — WCru

'Dilys' — CCge CElw EBee EBla EChP EGle EGra ELan EPPr MAvo MLHP MNFA MNrw MSte NBir NCot NGdn NSti SBla SRGP SUsu WCra WCru WFar WHal WHen WMoo WPnP WTMC WWpP

dissectum — CHll MSal

'Distant Hills' — CMCo EBee EBla EPPr SRGP SUsu WPtf WWpP

'Diva' — CElw CSam EBee EBla EPPr GBBs MAvo MBnl MNrw NSti SRGP SVil WCru WPnP WTMC WWpP

donianum — GIBF

- HWJCM 311 — WCru

'Dusky Crûg' — CBod CCge CDes CElw CSpe CWoW EAEE EBee EHrv EMar EPPr LAst MAvo MBNS MNrw MWgw NOrc NSti SPoG WCMO WCot WCru WFar

'Dusky Gem' — SUsu

'Dusky Rose' — ELan ENot EPfP EShb LAst LRHS MBNS MGos SVil

'Eleanor Fisher' — SUsu

'Elizabeth Ross' — EPPr LRHS MAvo MNrw SBch WCru WHoo WRha WTMC WWhi WWpP

'Elworthy Dusky' — CCge

'Elworthy Eyecatcher' — CCge CElw

'Emily' — SRGP WWpP

endressii ♀H4 — More than 30 suppliers

- 'Album' — see *G.* 'Mary Mottram'

- 'Beholder's Eye' — CCge CMCo COlW EBla ECGP EPPr GAbr LBBr MNFA MSte NBre SBch SRGP WPnP WPtf WTMC WWpP

- 'Betty Catchpole' — EPPr

- 'Castle Drogo' — EBee EBla ECtt EPPr MAvo SRGP WTMC WWpP

- dark — GBBs

- 'Prestbury White' — see *G.* x *oxonianum* 'Prestbury Blush'

- 'Priestling's Red' — CMCo EGra EMar

- 'Rose' — WPer WPnP WWpP

- white-flowered — WPtf

erianthum — CCge GAbr GBuc GMaP GMac MLHP NBre NLar SRGP STes WCru WWpP

- 'Calm Sea' — CCge CDes EBla EGle GBuc NCot SUsu WCru WMoo WTMC

- f. *leucanthum* — SUsu

'Undine'

- 'Neptune' — EPPr GMac NCot SUsu WCru WWpP

eriostemon Fischer — see *G. platyanthum*

'Expression' — see *G.* 'Tanya Rendall'

§ *farreri* — CCge EAEE EBla EGle EHyt GBri GBuc GCal GCrs LHop LRHS MNrw NBir NChi SBla SIng WCru WEas

'Fireworks' **new** — LRHS

glaberrimum — SBla WCru

gracile — CCge EChP EPla GBuc GMaP LSou MNrw NBir NBre SRGP WBrk WCru WMoo WPnP WTMC WWpP

- 'Blanche' — CElw EBee EPPr

- 'Blush' — CElw CMCo EBee EPPr WWpP

grandiflorum — see *G. himalayense*

- var. *alpinum* — see *G. himalayense* 'Gravetye'

'Grasmere' — EGra

'Guiseppii' **new** — EShb

'Gwen Thompson' — WOut

gymnocaulon — CCge CMCo CMHG CMMP EBee EBla EPPr LRHS MNFA NSti SRGP WCru WMnd WWFP WWpP

gymnocaulon x *platypetalum* — EBee

'Harmony' — EPPr WWpP

harveyi — CBrm CMea EBee EBla EMan EPPr EWes GSki LPhx WCru WKif WPGP

hayatanum — NCot WTMC

- B&SWJ 164 — CBod WCru WMoo WWpP

'Hilary' **new** — SRGP

§ *himalayense* — More than 30 suppliers

- CC 1957 from Tibetan border — EPPr

- CC&McK 442 — CMCo

- *alpinum* — see *G. himalayense* 'Gravetye'

§ - 'Baby Blue' — CCge CElw EBee EBla EBrs EGle EPPr GBuc GCal IFro MAvo MBri MNFA MNrw NCot NGdn NSti SRGP SUsu WCra WCru WHen WMoo WPnP WTMC WWpP

- 'Birch Double' — see *G. himalayense* 'Plenum'

- 'Derrick Cook' — EPPr NCot SUsu WCra WWpP

- 'Devil's Blue' — EPPr NCot WPtf WWpP

- 'Frances Perry' — SMur

§ - 'Gravetye' ♀H4 — More than 30 suppliers

- 'Irish Blue' — CElw CMCo EBee EBla EChP ECtt EGle EGra EPPr GAbr GBuc GCal GMac IPot MBri MNFA MSte NCot NPol NSti SRGP WAbb WCra WCru WHal WHen WMoo WTMC WTin WWpP

- *meeboldii* — see *G. himalayense*

- 'Pale Irish Blue' — GCal

§ - 'Plenum' (d) — More than 30 suppliers

- 'Spiti Valley' **new** — NCot

himalayense x *pratense* — NEgg

hispidissimum — CFee

ibericum ambig. — CPne

ibericum misapplied — see *G.* x *magnificum*

ibericum Cav. — CCge CNic CPne CSBt CTri EBla EPla NBre NLar SMac SPav SRGP STes WFar WPtf WWpP

- 'Blue Springs' — ECtt EGra

- subsp. *ibericum* — EBee EPPr MTis

- subsp. *jubatum* — CElw EBla EPPr GCal GMac MNFA MNrw NCot NSti SRms WCru WPnP WTMC WWpP

- - 'White Zigana' — CDes CFwr NCot

- subsp. *jubatum* x *renardii* — GCal SWvt

- var. *platypetalum* misapplied — see *G.* x *magnificum*

- var. *platypetalum* Boissier — see *G. platypetalum* Fisch. & C.A. Mey.

ibericum x *renardii* — NSti

incanum	CCge CHll CSev EBee EMag EMan
	EShb ETow EWes MNrw NBir SGar
	SMrm SRGP WCot WWpP XPep
- var. *multifidum*	EPPr GGar WCru WFar
- white	SRGP
incanum x *robustum*	CMea CSpe MSph WCru
'Ivan'	CCge CElw CMCo EBee EBla EBrs
	EPPr GBuc GMac LRHS MBNS
	NChi NCot SAga SRGP WCru
	WMoo WPnP WWpP
'Jack of Kilbryde'	GBri GCrs
'Jean Armour'	SRGP WCru WTMC WWpP
'Jean's Lilac'	see *G.* x *oxonianum* 'Jean's Lilac'
'Johnson's Blue' ♀H4	More than 30 suppliers
'Jolly Bee' PBR	More than 30 suppliers
'Joy'	More than 30 suppliers
§ 'Kashmir Blue'	CCge EBee EChP EGra EPPr ERou
	EWsh GMaP MAvo MBnl MNFA
	NCot NGdn NSti SBch WCAu
	WMoo WPnP
'Kashmir Lilac'	WHen
§ 'Kate'	EBla EGle EPPr WCru WWpP
'Kate Folkard'	see *G.* 'Kate'
§ 'Khan'	CMCo EBee EBla EPPr IFro MAvo
	MNrw NCot NPro SDys SMHy
	SRGP SUsu WCra WCru WWpP
kishtvariense	CMCo EBee EBla EMag EPPr GCal
	LRHS MNrw MRav NCot NHol
	NSti SBch WCru WPnP WPtf
koraiense	CBod EBla NBre NSti WMoo
	WWpP
- B&SWJ 797	WCru
- B&SWJ 878	EBee WCru
koreanum	CCge CDes EBee EBla GBuc GIBF
	LRHS MNFA SUsu WFar WHil
	WMoo WTMC
- B&SWJ 602	WCru
§ *kotschyi* var. *charlesii*	EBee EBla EPPr
krameri	EBla
- B&SWJ 1142	EBee EBla WCru
§ *lambertii*	CCge EBla EWes GBuc MNrw NBir
	NChi WTMC
- 'Swansdown'	EBla EChP GBuc MNrw WCru
	WPtf WSHC
lanuginosum	EChP
libani	CDes EBee EPPr GBuc GCal LLWP
	MTho MWhe NBid NChi NCot
	NSti WBrk WCMO WCot WCru
	WEas WPnP WTMC WTin WWpP
libani x	CBos CCge CDes EBee IPot
peloponnesiacum	
'Libretto'	WCru
§ x *lindavicum* 'Apple	CLyd CNic EBla EBrs EDAr GBuc
Blossom'	GSki LRHS MSte NChi NMen SBla
	SRGP WAbe WBrE WHCG WLin
- 'Gypsy'	SBla
- 'Lissadell'	SBla
linearilobum subsp.	EPPr SRot WCru WPnP
transversale	
§ 'Little David'	EBee EPPr MAvo SRGP SUsu
	WWpP
'Little Devil'	see *G.* 'Little David'
'Little Gem'	CBrm CCge CDes CMea EBee EBla
	LRHS NChi NDov NLar SUsu WCra
	WCru WFar WTMC WWpP
'Lotusland' **new**	LRHS
lucidum	MSal NSti NVic
'Luscious Linda'	CCge EBee GAbr MBNS MWea
	NSti SPer WCra WFar WPnP WWpP
'Lydia'	SRGP WWpP
§ *macrorrhizum*	More than 30 suppliers
- AL & JS 90179YU	EPPr
- JJH 7003/95	EBee
- 'Album' ♀H4	More than 30 suppliers
- 'Bevan's Variety'	More than 30 suppliers
- 'Bulgaria'	CMCo EPPr WTMC WWpP

- 'Camce' **new**	EPPr
- 'Czakor'	More than 30 suppliers
I - 'De Bilt'	EWes WWpP
- 'Freundorf'	GCal MNFA
- 'Ingwersen's Variety'	More than 30 suppliers
♀H4	
- 'Lohfelden'	CDes EPPr EWes GBuc MNFA
	NChi SRGP WPGP WWpP
- 'Mount Olympus'	see *G. macrorrhizum* 'White-Ness'
- 'Mount Olympus White'	see *G. macrorrhizum* 'White-Ness'
- 'Mytikas' **new**	NCot
- 'Pindus'	CBgR CPrp EAEE EBee EBla EBrs
	EPPr GAbr LRHS MNFA NBre NCot
	NSti SPoG SRGP SUsu WCru WFar
	WPnP WTMC WWpP
- 'Ridsko'	CElw CFee CMCo EPPr GBuc GCal
	MNFA NBro SRGP WCru WHen
	WTMC WWpP
- *roseum*	see *G. macrorrhizum*
- 'Rotblut' **new**	EPPr SRGP
- 'Sandwijck'	CCge CFwr EPPr WWpP
- 'Snow Sprite'	CCge CEnt CMea COlW EBee EPPr
	EPyc GSki LSou MCCP NCot NPro
	SPoG STes WCra WHrl
- 'Spessart'	CCge EBee EBla EChP ELan EPPr
	EPfP GQue LAst LBMP NCGa NPri
	WBVN WCra WCru WFar WOVN
	WTMC WWpP WWye
- 'Variegatum' (v)	CElw EBee EBla EChP ECha EHrv
	ELan GMaP LRHS MDun MNFA
	MTho NBid NBir NSti SPer SPoG
	SRGP SRms WBrk WCMO WCot
	WEas WFar WHen WTMC WWpP
- 'Velebit'	CCge EBee EPPr MSte SRGP WCru
	WTMC WWpP
§ - 'White-Ness'	More than 30 suppliers
macrostylum	CDes CPou EHyt LHop WBVN
	WCot WCru WPer WPnP
- MP 8103D	EBee WCot
- 'Leonidas'	see *G. tuberosum* 'Leonidas'
maculatum	CArn CElw CSev EBee EBrs ECha
	EGra EPfP GCal GPoy LLWP LRHS
	MNFA MRav MSal NSti SMac SWat
	WCra WCru WHal WHen WPnP
	WWpP WWye
- from Kath Dryden	EPPr WWpP
- f. *albiflorum*	CElw CMea EBee EBla EBrs EGle
	EMan EMon EPPr GCal MNrw
	NBid NSti SRGP STes SUsu WBrk
	WCot WCru WMoo WPnP WPtf
	WTMC WWpP
- 'Beth Chatto'	More than 30 suppliers
- 'Elizabeth Ann'	CElw EBee EHrv EPPr EPfP MBNS
	MWea NCot NLar NSti WCot
- 'Espresso'	More than 30 suppliers
- purple-flowered	EPPr WWpP
- 'Shameface'	EBee EPPr MSte SBch SDys SGar
- 'Spring Purple' **new**	NCot
- 'Vickie Lynn'	WWpP
maderense ♀H2	More than 30 suppliers
- white-flowered	ITer LDai WCMO WCot WPnP
§ x *magnificum* ♀H4	More than 30 suppliers
- 'Hylander' **new**	EBee
- 'Peter Yeo'	EBee EPPr NSti SRGP WWpP
- 'Rosemoor'	CBgR CCge CElw COlW EBee EBla
	EChP EHrv ELan EPPr EPfP IPot
	LHop MSte NCot NPro NSti WBrk
	WCot WMnd WPtf WTMC WWpP
- 'Vital' **new**	CWCL NCot
magniflorum	IFro MRav NBid NEgg NGdn SMer
	WCru
§ *malviflorum*	CDes CElw CMHG EBee ECha
	ELan EMar EPPr LLWP LPhx LRHS
	MBow MNFA MNrw MTho SBch
	SBla SMeo SRms WAul WCMO
	WCot WCru WFar WHoo WPnP

– from Spain	EBee EPPr EWes WSHC
– pink-flowered	CDes CMil EBee SBla WCru WMoo WPnP
§ 'Mary Mottram'	CElw CMCo EBee EPPr NBir NCot NSti WEas WWpP
§ 'Mavis Simpson' ♀H4	More than 30 suppliers
maximowiczii	CElw EBee SBch
'Maxwelton'	WTMC
'Menna Bach'	WCru WPnP
'Meryl Anne'	SRGP WPtf
microphyllum	see *G. potentilloides*
molle	NLRH
§ × *monacense*	CMCo EBee EBla ELan EMar EPla GGar GSki LRHS MWgw SBch SMac SWat WBrk WCru WHer WMnd WMoo WPnP WWpP
– var. *anglicum*	CCge EBla EBrs EChP ECtt EPPr GMaP MNFA MRav MWhe WMoo WPnP WWpP
– 'Anne Stevens'	NCot
– 'Breckland Fever'	EBee EPPr WWpP
– 'Claudine Dupont'	CElw EPPr NCot WCot WWpP
– dark-flowered	WMoo
– var. *monacense*	EBla WFar WHen
§ – – 'Muldoon'	CSev EBla EBrs EChP EMag EPPr EPla GSki LRHS MBow MRav NBir NEgg NOak STes WFar WHCG WHen WMoo WPer WPnP WTMC WWpP
'Mourning Widow'	see *G. phaeum* var. *phaeum* black-flowered
multisectum	WCru WTMC
napuligerum misapplied	see *G. farreri*
'Natalie'	CDes CElw EBee EBla EPPr NChi SBch WCra
nepalense	CMCo SRGP SRms WMoo WWpP
'Nicola'	CCge CElw EBee EBla EGle EPPr MNFA NCot SAga SBch WCra WTMC WWpP
'Nicola Jane' **new**	MNFA
'Nimbus' ♀H4	More than 30 suppliers
nodosum	More than 30 suppliers
– dark-flowered	see *G. nodosum* 'Swish Purple'
– 'Julie's Velvet'	CDes MAvo MSte WCra WHoo WPGP WTin WWhi WWpP
– pale-flowered	see *G. nodosum* 'Svelte Lilac'
– 'Pascal'	EBee
– 'Saucy Charlie'	SBch
– 'Silverwood'	SBch
§ – 'Svelte Lilac'	CElw EBee EBla ECGP EGle EPPr EPfP MNFA MSte NFor SRGP SWat WCAu WCot WCru WFar WMoo WPnP WWpP
§ – 'Swish Purple'	CBos CElw CMil EBee EBla EPPr MAvo MNFA MSte NCiC SRGP SWat WCru WFar WHen WMoo WPGP WPnP WWpP
– 'Whiteleaf'	CBos CCge CElw CMea EBee EBla EGle EMag EPPr MAvo MLHP NPro SAga SBch SBla SRGP SUsu SWat WCru WFar WHal WMoo WPnP WTMC WWpP
– 'Whiteleaf' seedling	EBla EGle EMan
'Nora Bremner'	EBee SRGP SUsu WWpP
'Nunnykirk Pink'	EMan EWes MAvo
'Nunwood Purple'	CMCo EBee EPPr MAvo NCot SUsu WPtf WTMC WWpP
ocellatum	CCge
'Oh My God Pass' **new**	WCot
oreganum	CCge
§ *orientalitibeticum*	More than 30 suppliers
'Orion' ♀H4	More than 30 suppliers
'Orkney Blue'	WCru
'Orkney Dawn'	WCru
'Orkney Pink'	More than 30 suppliers
ornithopodon	EBee NCot

'Out of the Blue'	WOut
× *oxonianum*	NCot NEgg WCru WMoo
– 'A.T. Johnson' ♀H4	More than 30 suppliers
– 'Ankum's White' **new**	NLar
– 'Anmore'	SRGP
– 'Breckland Brownie'	CElw EBee EBla EPPr EWes MAvo NCot SRGP WWpP
– 'Breckland Sunset'	EBee EPPr MAvo NCot SRGP WPnP WTMC WWpP
– 'Bregover Pearl'	CBre CElw CMCo EBee EBla EChP EPPr MNFA NCot SRGP WMoo WTMC WWpP
– 'Bressingham's Delight'	CMCo EBla ECtt EWsh LRHS SRGP WCra WTMC WWpP
– 'Buttercup'	EBee EMan EPPr NCot WWpP
I – 'Cally Seedling'	EBee EBla EPPr EWes GCal NPro
§ – 'Claridge Druce'	More than 30 suppliers
– 'Coronet'	CCge EPPr MNFA SRGP WMoo WWpP
– 'David McClintock'	CCge CElw CMCo EBee EPPr GQue MNFA SBch SRGP WFar WMoo WTMC WWpP
– 'Dawn Time'	WWpP
– 'Diane's Treasure'	NCot
– 'Dirk Gunst'	CElw
– 'Elsbeth Blush'	EBee EBla NCot
– 'Elworthy Misty'	CCge CElw CMCo EBee EBla EPPr NCot SBch WWpP
– 'Frank Lawley'	CElw CFis CMCo EBee EBla EChP EPPr GBuc GCal GMac LLWP MNFA NBid NPro NSti SBch SMrm SRGP WBrk WCra WMoo WTMC WWpP
§ – 'Fran's Star' (d)	EBee EBla EGoo WBrk WCru WTMC WWpP
– 'Hexham Pink'	CCge EBee EPPr NChi NPro SBch SRGP WTMC WWpP
– 'Hollywood'	CCge CElw CMCo EBee EBla EChP ELan EPPr GBBs GBuc GMac LRHS MBnl MBri MSte MTho NCot NLar NPer SRGP SRms WBor WBrk WCra WFar WMoo WPnP WPtf WTMC WWpP
I – 'Jean's Lilac'	NCot
– 'Julie Brennan'	CElw EBee EPPr GAbr GBin GCal GMac MNFA NGdn NSti SRGP WCra WWpP
– 'Julie Searle'	SRos
– 'Kate Moss'	EBee EBla EPPr GCai MBnl MNFA NSti SBch SRGP WCra WTMC WWpP
– 'Katherine Adele'	CCge EBee EBla EPPr EWes IPot LSou MBnl MWea NBhm NCot NLar NSti SPoG SRGP
§ – 'Kingston'	CMCo EBee EPPr WWpP
– 'Königshof'	CMCo EBee EPPr NCot WWpP
– 'Kurt's Variegated' PBR (v)	see *G. × oxonianum* 'Spring Fling'
– 'Lace Time'	CBre CCge CElw CMCo CSev EBee EBla EPPr GBBs GMac MBnl MNFA MNrw MTis MWhe NCGa NCot NEgg NGdn NHol NOak SBch SRms WCAu WMnd WMoo WPnP WTMC WWpP
– 'Lady Moore'	CCge CMCo EBee EBla EBrs EPPr EPla GBuc MNrw NBro NCot SRGP WCra WHen WMoo WPnP WTMC WWpP
– 'Lambrook Gillian'	CCge CElw CFis EBee EPPr MNFA NCot SBch SRGP WBrk WPnP WPtf WTMC WWpP
– 'Lasting Impression'	EBee EPPr SRGP WWpP
– 'Miriam Rundle'	CElw EBee EBrs EPPr MNFA MNrw NCot SRGP WCru WMoo WPnP WTMC WWpP
– 'Moorland Jenny'	CElw WMoo WWpP
– 'Moorland Star'	WMoo

- 'Old Rose'	CBrm EGle EPPr GCal LRHS MNFA NCot SBch SRGP WCra WCru WPnP WTMC WWpP
- 'Pat Smallacombe'	CElw EBla EPPr NCot SRGP WCru WMoo WTMC WWpP
- 'Patricia Josephine' **new**	WCAu
- 'Pearl Boland' **new**	EBee SRGP
- 'Phoebe Noble'	CBre CCge CElw CMCo EBee EBla EChP EGle EPPr IFro LRHS MNFA MNrw MWgw NCob NCot NSti SAga SRGP WCra WMoo WPnP WPtf WTMC WWpP
- 'Phoebe's Blush'	EBee EBla EPPr GMac MNFA SBch WTMC WWpP
- 'Pink Lace'	CCge LSou NCot
§ - 'Prestbury Blush'	CBre CElw CMCo EBee EPPr MNFA SRGP WCru WTMC WWpP
- 'Prestbury White'	see *G.* x *oxonianum* 'Prestbury Blush'
- 'Raspberry Ice'	EBee EBla EWes
- 'Rebecca Moss'	CSev EBee EBla EChP EMar EPPr GBuc GMac LRHS MNFA MSte NCot NSti SBch SHBN SRGP WCra WCru WFar WPnP WPtf WTMC WWpP
- 'Red Sputnik'	CMCo EBee EPPr MAvo SRGP WWpP
- 'Rose Clair'	CCge CElw CMCo EBee EBla EGle LAst LRHS MNFA NBir NSti SGar SMer SPet SRGP SRms WBrk WCru WEas WHen WMnd WMoo WPer WTMC WWpP
- 'Rosemary'	SBch WWpP
- 'Rosenlicht'	CBos CElw CSev EBee EBla EPPr LRHS MNFA MRav NLar SRGP WCAu WCra WCru WMnd WMoo WPnP WWpP
- 'Rosewood'	SRos
- 'Sherwood'	CBod CCge EBee EBla EChP ECtt EPPr GCal IFro MTho MWgw NBro NCob NCot NEgg NPro NRnb NVic SGar SRGP WCAu WCra WFar WLin WMoo WPnP WPtf WWpP
§ - 'Spring Fling' **PBR** (v)	CCge CRez EBee EBla EChP EHrv EPPr GSki MBNS NBPC NBre NCot NGdn NSti SPla SPoG SRGP STes WCAu WCMO WCot WWeb
- 'Stillingfleet'	see *G.* x *oxonianum* 'Stillingfleet Keira'
§ - 'Stillingfleet Keira'	NCot NSti SRGP WWpP
- 'Sue Cox' **new**	NCot
- 'Summer Surprise'	CElw CFwr EBee EPPr EWes NLar SRGP WCru WPnP WTMC WWpP
- 'Susan'	EBee EBla EPPr EWes
- 'Susie White'	CElw CMCo EBee EPPr MAvo SRGP WCru WWpP
* - f. ***thurstonianum***	More than 30 suppliers
- - 'Armitageae'	EBee EPPr MNFA NCot SRGP WTMC WWpP
- - 'Crûg Star'	CCge CElw
- - 'Peter Hale'	CMea SAga
- - 'Southcombe Double' (d)	CElw CMCo CSev EBee EBla EGle EHrv EPPr EPfP GBBs IFro IPot MBow MNFA NChi NGdn SRGP SRms SUsu WBrk WCra WCru WFar WHen WMoo WTMC WWpP
§ - - 'Southcombe Star'	EBee EBla EPPr GAbr GCal MBnl MNFA NBro NGdn NSti SRGP WBrk WCru WFar WHen WMoo WPer WPnP WTMC WWpP
- 'Trevor's White'	EBee EBla EChP EGle EPPr MBnl MNFA MNrw NCot SBch SRGP WCru WTMC WWpP

- 'Wageningen'	CBre CElw CMCo EBee EGle GCal GMac LRHS MNFA NCot NGdn NPro SAga SRGP SRms WBrk WCra WCru WHen WHer WMoo WPtf WTMC WWpP
- 'Walter's Gift'	More than 30 suppliers
- 'Wargrave Pink' ♀H4	More than 30 suppliers
- 'Waystrode'	CMCo EBla EPPr SRGP WTMC WWpP
- 'Whitehaven'	EBee NCot
- 'Winscombe'	CElw CMCo EBee EChP GCal LLWP LRHS MRav MTho MWgw NCob WCAu WCru WFar WHen WMnd WMoo WWpP
- 'Winston Churchill' **new**	CFwr
x **oxonianum** x ***sessiliflorum*** subsp. ***novae-zelandiae*** 'Nigricans'	EHrv
'Pagoda'	CCge MNrw
§ ***palmatum*** ♀H3	More than 30 suppliers
palustre	CElw EBla EChP EMar EPPr MBow MNFA MNrw NBro NHol SRGP WFar WHen WMoo WPnP WTMC WTin WWpP
papuanum	SBla WCru
'Patricia'	More than 30 suppliers
peloponnesiacum	EBee EPPr GGar WFar
- NS 660	CElw
phaeum	More than 30 suppliers
- 'Album'	More than 30 suppliers
- 'Alec's Pink'	EBla EPPr LLWP SHar WOut WTMC
- 'All Saints'	EBee EMon SUsu WTMC WWpP
- 'Aureum'	see *G. phaeum* 'Golden Spring'
- black-flowered	see *G. phaeum* var. *phaeum* black-flowered
- 'Blauwvoet'	CFwr NCot WTMC WWpP
- 'Blue Shadow'	CDes CElw EBee EPPr NCot WTMC WWpP
- 'Calligrapher'	CElw EBee EChP EGle EPPr MNFA SBch SRGP SUsu WMoo WTMC WWpP
- 'Chocolate Chip'	CMCo WTMC WWpP
- 'Conny Broe' **new**	NCot
- dark-flowered	CElw SWat
- 'David Bromley'	EMon WCru WPrP WPtf WTMC WTMC
- 'Geele Samobor'	WTMC
- 'George Stone'	EPPr
§ - 'Golden Spring'	CCge CElw EPPr NChi NCot NPro SBch SRGP WTMC WWpP
- 'Hannah Perry'	CElw CHad EBee EPPr LLWP MBnl WTMC
- var. ***hungaricum***	EBee EPPr WCru WTMC WWpP
- 'Klepper'	CFwr CMCo NCot WTMC WWpP
§ - 'Lily Lovell'	More than 30 suppliers
- 'Little Boy'	CMCo EMon EPPr NCot NGdn SRGP WTMC WWpP
- var. ***lividum***	CBgR CBre CElw CFee EBee EBrs EChP EMar EWTr GMaP LLWP LRHS MBow MRav MWgw NCot NEgg NHol SPer SRGP SRms WCAu WCra WFar WHen WPer WPnP WTMC WWhi WWpP
- - 'Joan Baker'	More than 30 suppliers
- - 'Majus'	CCge CElw EBee ECtt EMon EPPr EPfP EPyc LLWP LPhx MNFA MWgw NSti SBch SWat WFar WGHP WMoo WPnP WTMC
- 'Maggie's Delight' (v) **new**	NCot
- 'Marchant's Ghost'	LPhx NGdn SMHy WTMC
- 'Margaret Wilson' (v)	CBos CBow CDes CElw CFir EBee EBla EBla EChP EGle EPPr WBee EBla EChP EGle EPPr MBnl WBee EBla EWes GCal MAvo MBNS NCot SRGP SUsu WCMO WCot WTMC WWpP

	- 'Mierhausen'	CElw CMCo EBee EPPr EShb NCot WPtf WTMC WWpP
	- 'Moorland Dylan'	MAvo MWoo WTMC WWpP
	- 'Mourning Widow'	see *G. phaeum* var. *phaeum* black-flowered
	- 'Mrs Charles Perrin'	CBgR CCge CElw EBee EPPr MAvo STes WTMC WWpP
	- 'Night Time'	EPPr MNFA WWpP
	- 'Our Pat'	NCot
	- var. *phaeum*	SBch
§	- - black-flowered	EChP EGle EPPr EShb GCal MWhe NCob NDov SGar SRGP SRms SWat WCra WCru WHen WMoo WWpP
	- - 'Langthorns Blue'	CCge CDes CElw CMCo CSev EBee ELan EPPr MNFA MNrw NBre SRGP WCra WHen WTMC WWpP
	- - 'Samobor'	More than 30 suppliers
I	- 'Ploeger de Bilt'	EPPr WTMC
	- purple-flowered	MDun
	- 'Rachel's Rhapsody'	EPPr NCot
	- 'Raven'	WTMC
	- red-flowered	MRav WTMC
	- 'Rise Top Lilac'	CCge CMCo EBee NCot WTMC
	- 'Rose Air'	CMCo EBee EChP EGoo EPPr MNFA SRGP WCra WMoo WPnP WTMC WWpP
	- 'Rose Madder'	CBgR CCge CElw CHad CMMP EGle EPPr EPyc GBuc GCal LHop LLWP LPhx MNFA MNrw MSte NChi NCot NMRc SBch WCru WMoo WWpP
	- 'Saturn'	WTMC
	- 'Sericourt' **new**	WCot
	- 'Silver Fox'	WRha
	- 'Small Grey'	EPPr WTMC
	- 'Springtime' PBR	EBee EChP EPPr MAvo NBhm NCot NSti SPoG
	- 'Stillingfleet Ghost'	CBow CElw EBee EBrs EPPr LRHS NBre NCot NPro NSti WTMC
	- 'Taff's Jester' (v)	CCge CElw EBee EWes NHol SMrm SRGP WCMO WCot WTMC WWpP
	- 'Thorn's Blue'	EBrs LRHS
§	- 'Variegatum' (v)	More than 30 suppliers
	- 'Walküre'	EBee EPPr MAvo WTMC WWpP
	- 'Zit Factory'	WTMC
	'Philippe Vapelle'	More than 30 suppliers
	'Pink Delight'	CElw EBee LPhx WWpP
	'Pink Spice' PBR	CCge EBla ECtt MGos MRav
	'Pink Splash'	LSou STes
§	*platyanthum*	CCge EChP EPPr GCal GGar MNrw NBre SBri SRGP WBrk WCru WHCG WHen WMoo WPer WWpP
	- giant	EPPr SGar
	- var. *reinii*	WCru
	- - f. *onoei*	EBee WCru
	platypetalum misapplied	see *G.* x *magnificum*
	platypetalum Franch.	see *G. sinense*
§	*platypetalum* Fisch. & C.A. Mey.	EChP EPPr EWsh LRHS NBid NBir NBre NSti SRGP SRms SWat WCru WPtf WTMC WWpP
	- 'Georgia Blue'	MSte WCru WFar WPtf
	- 'Turco'	GBin
§	*pogonanthum*	CDes EBee GBuc GCal IFro NBir NChi WCru WMoo WPtf
	polyanthes	CFwr GBuc NEgg WTMC
	- CC 3329	WRos
	- HWJCM 276	WCru
	- from China	CFwr
§	*ponticum*	CHar NSti
§	*potentilloides*	CCge EBee GSki NBir SRGP WWpP
	pratense	More than 30 suppliers

	- 'Bittersweet'	CBgR CHar CMCo EBla EChP EMon EPPr WWpP
	- 'Cluden Sapphire'	CAbP EBla MWhi NBre NCot NGdn NHol NPro WCru WFar WWpP
	- 'Flore Pleno'	see *G. pratense* 'Plenum Violaceum'
I	- 'Himalayanum'	NLar
	- 'Hocus Pocus'	CFwr EBee EChP EHrv EPfP ERou MBNS MTis NBhm NBro NLar NMoo NSti SHBN WCAu WCMO WHoo
	- 'Janet's Special'	WHoo
	- 'Lilac Lullaby'	EBee
	- Midnight Reiter strain	More than 30 suppliers
	- 'Mrs Kendall Clark' ♥H4	More than 30 suppliers
	- 'New Dimension'	CFwr EBee ELan ENot EPfP GBin LBuc LRHS MGos MWea NBre NCot NSti WCra
	- 'Okey Dokey'	CElw CFwr EBee
	- pale-flowered	EBee WPnP WWpP
	- 'Picotee' **new**	NCot
	- 'Plenum Album'	NGdn NLar SPoG WCMO WTMC
§	- 'Plenum Caeruleum' (d)	More than 30 suppliers
	- 'Plenum Purpureum'	see *G. pratense* 'Plenum Violaceum'
§	- 'Plenum Violaceum' (d) ♥H4	More than 30 suppliers
	- var. *pratense* f. *albiflorum*	CElw CSam EPPr GMaP IFro MHer MNrw NBid NCot NEgg NOrc SPer WCMO WCra WCru WHen WMnd WMoo WPnP WTMC WWpP
	- - - 'Galactic'	CBgR CCge EBee EChP EPPr LPhx NBir NBre WCra WCru WHen WMoo WPnP
	- - - 'Plenum Album' (d)	CDes EBee EPPr NEgg NLar NSti WCot WPnP
	- - - 'Silver Queen'	CBre CCge CHar EBee EBla EChP ECtt EPPr MBow MNrw NBir NBre SRGP SWal WFar WHen WMoo WPGP WPnP WTMC WWpP
	- - - 'Whimble White'	WWhi
	- 'Purple Heron'	CDes EBee EBla EChP EGle EPPr IBal LAst LSRN MBri MCCP MNrw MSte MTPN NEgg NGdn NLar SPla STes WCMO WFar WGor
	- 'Purple-haze'	CCge EMag GBuc GSki ITer LSou MCCP MWhi NCob NLar WHoo WHrl WMnd
	- 'Rectum Album'	see *G. clarkei* 'Kashmir White'
§	- 'Rose Queen'	CBgR EBee EBla MNrw MRav NBir NEgg NHol NLar SRGP WCMO WCra WCru WHen WPnP WTMC WWpP
	- 'Roseum'	see *G. pratense* 'Rose Queen'
	- 'Splish-splash'	see *G. pratense* 'Striatum'
	- 'Stanton Mill'	NBid
	- var. *stewartianum*	EBee MRav WPnP
	- - 'Elizabeth Yeo'	CCge EBla EPPr NCot NLar SGar SUsu WCru WTMC WWpP
	- - 'Purple Silk' **new**	EPPr
§	- 'Striatum'	More than 30 suppliers
	- 'Striatum' dwarf	WCru
	- 'Striatum' pale	CBre
§	- Victor Reiter Junior strain	More than 30 suppliers
	- 'Wisley Blue'	CMCo EBee EBla EPPr MSte SBch SRGP WHal
	- 'Yorkshire Queen'	CBgR CMCo EBee EPPr NBre NGdn WCru WPtf
	'Prelude'	CCge CDes CElw EBee EPPr IFro NBir NCot NPro SRGP WCra WTMC WWpP
	procurrens	CBre CElw COlW CPLG CSev EBee EChP EMar EPPr EShb GAbr GCal

GGar LLWP LRHS MLLN NBid
NGdn NSti WBrk WCru WFar
WHen WMoo WPnP WPtf WRos
WWpP

§ **psilostemon** ♀H4 — More than 30 suppliers
- 'Bressingham Flair' — CMCo CPrp EBee EBla EBrs EChP
ECtt EGle EGra EPfP GAbr GCal
GSki LHop LRHS MNFA MRav
NBid NChi NGdn NLar SMer SRms
WCAu WCru WFar WMoo WSHC
WTMC
- 'Fluorescent' — MWhi
- 'Goliath' — EPPr SUsu
- hybrid — CElw
- 'Jason Bloom' **new** — EBrs
- 'Madelon' **new** — NCot
pulchrum — CMCo CSpe EMan EPPr GKev
MNrw MWhi SGar SRGP STes
SWat WCot WCru WPer WRos
WWpP
punctatum hort. — see *G.* x *monacense* var.
monacense 'Muldoon'
- 'Variegatum' — see *G. phaeum* 'Variegatum'
pusillum — MSal
pylzowianum — CCge CMCo EBee GGar MRav
NBid NJOw NRya SBch
WCru WFar WHen WMoo
WPnP WTel
pyrenaicum — CCge CRWN CSev EBee EWsh
GAbr MBow NBre NEgg NSti SWat
WBrk WHen WTMC WWpP
- f. **albiflorum** — CCge CHrt EBee EBla EChP
EGra GAbr GBBs LLWP MNFA
MNrw NBir NCot NEgg NSti
SAga SRGP WBrk WPer WPnP
WWpP
- 'Barney Brighteye' — CCge SRGP
- 'Bill Wallis' — More than 30 suppliers
- Gordon's strain — NEgg
- 'Isparta' — CElw EBee EChP EPPr IFro LPhx
SBch SRGP SUsu WBrk
- 'Summer Sky' — CCge EBrs NCot SPav SRGP WPtf
WWpP
- 'Summer Snow' — CCge EBee EPyc NCot NLar SBod
SPoG WCMO WWpP
'Rachel' **new** — CBow
'Rambling Robin' — EBee ECtt EMan EPPr EWes LSou
WCMO WCot WCru XPep
'Ray's Pink' — CCge NPro WWpP
rectum — EPPr NBre WCru
- 'Album' — see *G. clarkei* 'Kashmir White'
'Red Admiral' — CMCo EBee NCot SRGP WCra
'Red Dwarf' — CCge EPPr WMoo
reflexum — CSev EBla EChP EPPr NHol WFar
WTMC WWpP
refractoides — CFwr
refractum — NLAp
- from China — CFwr NLAp
regelii — CCge CElw CMCo CSam EPPr
GMac MNFA NCot SBch WCra
WCru WMoo WPnP WWpP
renardii ♀H4 — More than 30 suppliers
- 'Beldo' — EBee
- blue — see *G. renardii* 'Whiteknights'
- 'Heidi Morris' — WWpP
- 'Tcschelda' — CMCo EBee EBla EChP ECha EMil
EShb GBBs GCal NCGa NCot SBod
SPla SRms SUsu SWat WCra WFar
WPnP WViv WWhi WWpP
§ - 'Whiteknights' — CElw EBla ECha EGra GBuc MAvo
NBir WCru WEas
- 'Zetterlund' — CElw CMCo EBee EBla ECGP EGle
EHrv EMar EPPr LLWP LRHS MAvo
MLLN MNFA MWat MWhe NPri
SWat WBrk WCAu WCru WFar
WMnd WMoo WTMC

§ **reuteri** — CCge ELan IDee LDai SBod SDnm
SGar SPav SRGP WCru WOut
WPnP
'Richard John' — CCge MNFA
richardsonii — CBos CCge EBee EBla EChP EPPr
GCal MNrw NBir NCot NDov
SRGP SRms WCru WPnP WPtf
WTMC WWpP
x **riversleaianum** — WCru
- 'Mavis Simpson' — see *G.* 'Mavis Simpson'
- 'Russell Prichard' ♀H4 — More than 30 suppliers
§ **rivulare** — CCge CMCo EBee EBla GMac GSki
MNFA NBre NSti WHCG WMnd
WPnP WPtf
- 'Album' — EBla
robertianum — CArn CCge EPPr GWCH MHer
SECG SRms WHbs WHen WWpP
§ - 'Album' — CBgR CBod EBla EPPr SHar SRms
- f. **bernettii** — see *G. robertianum* 'Album'
- 'Celtic White' — CBgR CBre CCge EMag EMon EPPr
GCal GSki MHer NGHP SPav SRGP
WHbs WHen WOut WPnP WWpP
robustum — EPPr GSki IFro MNrw MSph NBro
NChi NCot SMad SPav SRGP STes
WCMO WCot WCru WFar WHal
WPGP WSHC WWpP XPep
- Hannays' form — CCge CSev CSpe EBee
'Rosie Crûg' — CCge EChP EMan NLar SWvt
WCru
rosthornii — WCru
Rozanne = 'Gerwat' PBR — More than 30 suppliers
rubescens — see *G. yeoi*
rubifolium — EMan GGar MNFA NChi NHol
WCru WTMC
§ 'Ruprecht' **new** — SBch
ruprechtii misapplied — see *G.* 'Ruprecht'
ruprechtii (Grossh.) — CCge CElw EBee EMag EPPr GIBF
Woronow — MAvo MNrw NBre SRGP WPer
WWpP WWye
Sabani Blue = 'Bremigo' — LHop MSte SPer SPoG SRkn
new
'Salome' — More than 30 suppliers
sanguineum — More than 30 suppliers
- Alan Bloom = — LRHS SIng WCra WTMC
'Bloger' PBR
- 'Album' ♀H4 — More than 30 suppliers
- 'Alpenglow' — EPPr SBch SRGP WHal
- 'Ankum's Pride' — CBgR CCge CMMP EBee EBla
ECGP EChP EGle EPPr IPot LRHS
MNFA NCot NGdn NHol NSti SBla
SUsu SWat WCra WCru WMoo
WPnP WTMC WWpP
- 'Apfelblüte' — CRez EBee NCot SSvw WFar WPnP
- 'Aviemore' — EPPr NCot SBch WWpP
- 'Barnsley' — CElw CPrp EPPr NBro NPro WHrl
WTMC WWpP
- 'Belle of Herterton' — CMCo EBee EPPr MSte NBid NPro
SBch SUsu WCru WTMC WWpP
- 'Bloody Graham' — EGle EPPr MWhe SBch WMoo
WWpP
- 'Canon Miles' — CElw EBee EPPr IPot NCot
- 'Catforth Carnival' — EPPr
- 'Cedric Morris' — CBow CElw EBla EChP ECha EGle
EGra EPPr MAvo MTho NBid SAga
SRGP SUsu WCru WHen WPnP
WTMC WWpP
- 'Compactum' — CFwr
§ - 'Droplet' — SRGP SUsu WPnP WWpP
- 'Elsbeth' — CBgR CCge CElw CMCo EBee EBla
EChP ECha ECtt EGra EPPr EWTr
EWes GBuc NCot NEgg NGdn
NHol NSti SPoG SRGP WCra WCru
WFar WHal WMoo WPnP WTMC
WWpP
- 'Feu d'Automne' — EPPr
- 'Fran's Star' — see *G.* x *oxonianum* 'Fran's Star'

- 'Glenluce'	More than 30 suppliers
- 'Hampshire Purple'	see *G. sanguineum* 'New Hampshire Purple'
- 'Holden'	CElw CNic EPPr WWpP
- 'Inverness'	CFwr EPPr NCot WWpP
- 'John Elsley'	CCge CElw CMCo CPrp EAEE EBee EBla EChP ECtt EHoe EPPr LLWP LRHS MWhe NBro NCot NGdn NLar NSti SRGP SWat WBVN WCra WMnd WPer WPnP WTMC WWpP
- 'John Innes'	CFwr NCot
- 'Jubilee Pink'	CElw EBla GCal SBla WCra WCru WTMC
- var. *lancastrense*	see *G. sanguineum* var. *striatum*
- 'Leeds Variety'	see *G. sanguineum* 'Rod Leeds'
§ - 'Little Bead'	EBla ECho NJOw NMen WCru WPnP WWpP
- 'Max Frei'	More than 30 suppliers
- 'Minutum'	see *G. sanguineum* 'Droplet'
- 'Nanum'	see *G. sanguineum* 'Little Bead'
§ - 'New Hampshire Purple'	CBgR CBos CCge CPrp EBee EChP ECho EPPr LSou NBro NGdn NLar NSti SSvw WCra WTMC WWpP
- 'Nyewood'	EBee EMon EPPr MLLN SEND SRGP WCra WCru WWpP
I - 'Plenum' (d)	EPPr
- var. *prostratum* (Cav.) Pers.	see *G. sanguineum* var. *striatum*
§ - 'Rod Leeds'	CBgR CBos EBee MSte MWea NCot NPro NSti WHal WPnP WTMC WWpP
- 'Sandra'	WWpP
- 'Sara'	WHen WPnP WWpP
- 'Shepherd's Warning' ♀H4	CBgR CCge CMea CSev EBee EBla ECtt EDAr EPPr LRHS MLLN MRav NBir NLar SEND SRGP SUsu SWat WCra WCru WHCG WHoo WTel WTin WWpP
- 'Shepherd's Warning' seedlings	GCal
- 'Shooting Star' **new**	EBee
§ - var. *striatum* ♀H4	More than 30 suppliers
- - deep pink	CSBt CWCL GBBs MSwo SWvt
- - 'Reginald Farrer'	EBee GBuc WCru
- - 'Splendens'	CCge CElw CSev CWib EBla ELan ENot EPPr ITer LBee LHop MRav NBid NChi NCot WCru WEas WPnP WTin WWhi WWpP
- 'Vision'	CCge CFwr EBla LRHS NCot SGar WPer WPnP WWpP
- 'Vision Light Pink'	WPtf
- 'Westacre Poppet'	EPPr EWes
'Sea Fire'	CCge CWCL MNrw
'Sea Pink'	CElw MNrw
'Sellindge Blue'	NCot WCra WWpP
sessiliflorum	ECou
- subsp. *novae-zelandiae* green-leaved	SWat
I - - 'Nigricans'	CCge EBla ECha ECho EHrv ELan EPfP GAbr GGar MHer NBPC NHol NJOw NMoo NWCA SBch SRGP SWal WBrE WCru WEas WFar WHCG WPnP WTMC WWpP
§ - - 'Porter's Pass'	CBow CMea CWib ECho EHoe EWes GBuc LAst MCCP MNrw NBir SBch SPlb SWat WCra WFar WHoo WTMC WWpP
- - red-leaved	see *G. sessiliflorum* subsp. *novae-zelandiae* 'Porter's Pass'
* - 'Rubrum'	CSec GSki WBVN
'Sheilah Hannay'	CSpe SHar
shikokianum	EBee EChP EShb GKev MCCP NLar SGar SPer SRGP WCra WWpP
- var. *kaimontanum*	EBee EBla WCru
- var. *quelpaertense*	CDes EBee EBla WPtf
- - B&SWJ 1234	WCru
- var. *yoshiianum*	CCge CElw GBuc GKev NChi WMoo WTMC
- - B&SWJ 6147	WCru
'Shocking Blue'	EBee MWea NSti
* Silver Cloak Group	CBow ECre GSki LSou MCCP WCot
'Silver Shadow'	EBee LDai NScw NSti
§ *sinense*	CMHG EBee EBla EChP EPPr GCal LRHS MNFA MNrw NLar NSti SRGP WCra WCru WHer WMnd WMoo WPer WTMC WWhi WWpP
- B&SWJ 7870	WCru
'Sirak' ♀H4	More than 30 suppliers
soboliferum	CBod EBee EBla EBrs ELan EPPr LRHS NBir NDlv NSti SPla SRGP SUsu WCra WCru WMoo WPtf WWpP
- Cally strain	GCal MSte
- 'Starman' **new**	WHil
'Southcombe Star'	see *G.* x *oxonianum* f. *thurstonianum* 'Southcombe Star'
'Southease Celestial' **new**	SMHy SSth
§ 'Spinners'	More than 30 suppliers
stapfianum var. *roseum*	see *G. orientalitibeticum*
'Stephanie'	CDes CElw EBee EPPr EWes GGar MWea NCot WCra WWpP
'Strawberry Frost'	EBla EChP LTwo MBNS
subcaulescens ♀H4	More than 30 suppliers
- 'Guiseppii'	CCge EAEE EBee EBla EChP ECtt EPPr GSki MNFA MNrw MRav MWhe NBPC NBro NCot NDov NHol SMer SPla SRGP SRot WBrE WCra WFar WPnP WWeb
- 'Splendens' ♀H4	CSpe CTri EBee EBla ECtt EDAr EPPr EPfP LHop LRHS MBNS MDun MHer MTis MWhe NPri NSla NSti SHBN SPla SRms SWat WFar WPat WPnP WWpP
* - 'Violaceum'	EPPr NEgg
'Sue Crûg'	More than 30 suppliers
'Summer Cloud'	EBee EBla EPPr NCot SRGP WCra WHrl
Summer Skies = 'Gernic'PBR (d)	CCge CFir EBee EPPr IFro LRHS MBNS MBnl MMHG MWgw NBro NCot NLar NMoo SPoG WCAu WCot WCra WFar WHil WPnP WTMC
suzukii	IFro WPtf
- B&SWJ 016	WCru
swatense	MLLN SWat WCru
sylvaticum	CBgR CMMP CRWN EBee EBla MBow MSal NBid NGdn NLRH WBVN WBrk WHal WHen WMoo WPer WShi WTMC WWpP
- f. *albiflorum*	CBre CCge CElw EBee ELan EMar MWhe NSti SBch WCru
- 'Album' ♀H4	More than 30 suppliers
- 'Amy Doncaster'	More than 30 suppliers
- 'Angulatum'	CElw EBee EPPr MNFA SBch WMoo WWpP
- 'Birch Lilac'	CElw EBee EBla EChP EPPr EPfP EWTr GBuc GCal LRHS MAvo WCra WFar WMoo WPnP WTMC WWpP
- 'Birgit Lion' **new**	EBee NCot
- 'Blue Ice'	EBee EBla EPPr GBin WWpP
- 'Caeruleum'	WLin
* - 'Heron'	CCge
- 'Ice Blue' **new**	NCot
- 'Immaculée'	EPPr MRav
- 'Kanzlersgrund'	CElw EPPr
- 'Lilac Time'	EBla EPPr WWpP
- 'Mayflower' ♀H4	More than 30 suppliers

- 'Meran'	CCge EPPr
- 'Nikita' **new**	EPPr
- f. *roseum*	CCge EBee EBrs EPPr GGar NBre NLar WOut
- - 'Baker's Pink'	CBgR CCge CElw EBee EBla EGle EPPr MNFA MRav NCot SBch SRGP WCra WFar WHCG WMoo WPnP WTMC WWhi WWpP
- 'Silva'	CElw EBee ECtt EPPr MAvo MNFA MRav NCot SWat WCru WWpP
- subsp. *sylvaticum* var. *wanneri*	CCge EBee EPPr MRav SBch WCru WTMC WWpP
§ 'Tanya Rendall' **new**	GAbr GBin MAvo MBNS MWea NBhm NMoo NSti SMer SPer SUsu WBVN WCot WCra WPnP
'Terre Franche'	EBee EPPr LHop MAvo NGby NLar SSvw WFar
'Thorn's Blue'	CCge
§ *thunbergii*	CCge GGar GSki LAst MBow NBid NJOw NOak NSti SRGP WBrk WHen WPer WPnP WWpP
- dark-flowered	CSev EMar
- 'Jester's Jacket' (v)	CCge EKen EPPr GWWP ITer MAvo MCCP NPro NSti SGar SPoG SRGP WBrk WCot WCru WHrl WTMC WWpP
- pink-flowered	EPPr SRGP WCru WTMC
- white-flowered	EPPr SRGP WTMC
thurstonianum	see *G.* x *oxonianum* f. *thurstonianum*
'Tidmarsh'	EBee
'Tinpenny Mauve'	WHoo WTin
'Tiny Monster'	CCge CDes CFwr CMCo EBee EBla EWes LSou MAvo MBNS MBnl MWhi NCot NSti WGer
transbaicalicum	CCge CFwr EPPr GBin MBow MNrw NBre SRGP
traversii	CCge CWib EGle GGar MDKP WRos
- var. *elegans*	CFee CSpe CWib EAEE EBee ECtt GGar LPhx MNrw SAga SRGP WCru WEas WHCG WKif
tuberosum	CBro CElw CHrt EBee EBla ECha ECho ELan EPot EShb EWsh LLWP LPhx LRHS MNFA MTho MWhe NBir NBro NGdn NSti SMeo WFar WPnP
- var. *charlesii*	see *G. kotschyi* var. *charlesii*
§ - 'Leonidas'	EBee LPhx LRHS WCot WPnP
- subsp. *linearifolium*	WCru
- pink-flowered	WCru WHal WHoo
'Ushguli Grijs' **new**	CFwr IPot NCot
'Vera May'	SUsu
'Verguld Saffier'	see *G.* 'Blue Sunrise'
versicolor	CElw CMea COIW CRWN EBee EBla EBrs EChP EMar EPfP GCal GGar GSki LRHS MHer MNFA MNrw MTho MWhe NVic SPet SRms WBrk WCru WFar WHCG WMoo WPnP WWpP
- 'Kingston'	see *G.* x *oxonianum* 'Kingston'
§ - 'Snow White'	CCge CElw CMCo EChP EGoo EPPr MNFA MNrw MWhe NBre NCot NDov SRGP WCra WCru WMoo WPnP WTMC WWpP
- 'The Bride'	CMea EGra EMar
- 'White Lady'	see *G. versicolor* 'Snow White'
'Victor Reiter'	see *G. pratense* Victor Reiter Junior strain
violareum	see *Pelargonium* 'Splendide'
viscosissimum	EBla GSki SRGP WMnd
- var. *incisum*	EWsh MCCP NBre WTMC WWpP
- rose pink-flowered	NBir
wallichianum	CBod CCge CMCo CPou EBee ECGP GCal IFro NBir NChi NSti
	SBla WCot WFar WHen WMoo WTMC
§ - 'Buxton's Variety' ♀H4	More than 30 suppliers
- 'Chadwell's Pink'	CCge EBee NBre NEgg
- 'Chris'	EPPr SRGP SUsu
- 'Martha'	EBee
- pale blue-flowered	CElw
- 'Pink Buxton'	EWes NLar SPoG
- pink-flowered	EBla EMan GBuc GCal NCot WCra WCru WWpP
- 'Rosie'	SRGP
- 'Syabru'	CCge CElw CMea EBee EBla EMar GBuc GSki MNrw NCot NLar NPro WBVN WFar WMoo
'Wednesday's Child'	WFar
'Welsh Guiness'	WCru WTMC
wilfordii misapplied	see *G. thunbergii*
wilfordii Maxim.	CCge
Wisley hybrid	see *G.* 'Khan'
wlassovianum	More than 30 suppliers
- 'Blue Star'	CCge MRav NPro SRGP WFar WTMC WWpP
§ *yeoi*	CSpe EPPr MNrw NBir NBro NDov NSti SRGP WCru WOut WTMC
yesoense	EBla EPPr GGar NBir NSti SRGP SWat WCru WFar
- var. *nipponicum*	WCru
- white-flowered	EBee MNFA
yoshinoi	CPLG EBee EBla EDAr EShb EWes GAbr GIBF GSki LLWP LSou MSte MWhi NLar SGar SRGP SWal SWat WMoo WTMC WWpP
yunnanense misapplied	see *G. pogonanthum*
yunnanense Franchet	IFro
- BWJ 7543	WCru

Gerrardanthus (Cucurbitaceae)

macrorhiza	ERea

Gesneria (Gesneriaceae)

cardinalis	see *Sinningia cardinalis*
x *cardosa*	see *Sinningia* x *cardosa*
* *macrantha* 'Compacta'	EShb

Gethyum (Alliaceae)

atropurpureum	CMon
cuspidatum F&W 8233	WCot

Geum ❀ (Rosaceae)

'Abendsonne'	MAvo
aleppicum	CFee NBre SBri
alpinum	see *G. montanum*
andicola	NBre
'Apricot Beauty'	EBrs
'Beech House Apricot'	More than 30 suppliers
'Bell Bank'	CElw CFee GBri MAvo MFOX MHer MRav NBir NBre NChi NCot NDov NGby NPro WCot WMoo
'Birkhead's Cream'	NBir
'Birkhead's Creamy Lemon'	MAvo SBri
'Blazing Sunset' (d)	CElw EBee EBla ECtt LSou MBNS MDKP MRav MWrn NBre NCob NDlv NPro SHGN WFar WHil WRHF
N 'Borisii'	More than 30 suppliers
- 'Borisii' x *montanum*	LHop
bulgaricum	CElw LRHS MRav NBir NLar NPro NRya WPnP WPrP WTMC WTin
'Caitlin'	EMon
calthifolium	EBee EPPr MCCP MLLN MRav NBre NBro
capense	LSou NBre NPro SHGN SPlb
- JJ&JH 9401271	EBee EWes
§ *chiloense*	EBee EBla LEdu
- P&W 6513	GBri NWCA
- 'Red Dragon' **new**	EBee

'Chipchase'	NChi
coccineum ambig.	EBla WRha
coccineum misapplied.	see *G. chiloense*
coccineum Sibth. & Sm.	EBee
MESE 374	
– 'Cooky'	CSam LRHS LSou NPri SPoG SWal
	WHil WRHF
– 'Eos' **new**	WCot
§ – 'Werner Arends'	CBos CMHG CSev EBee EBla GCal
	MBnl MRav NBro SBri WCot WFar
	WMoo
'Coppertone'	CDes CElw CKno COIW EBee
	EBla ECha ECtt EHrv ELan EMon
	MAvo MNrw MRav NBir NBro
	NChi NRya SBla SBri SPav WAul
	WHoo WMoo WTMC WTin
	WWhi WWpP
'Dingle Apricot'	CFir ECtt EMan GCal MAvo MNrw
	MRav MWgw NBir
'Dolly North'	CFir EBee EMan EPyc GAbr GBri
	GGar LRHS MBNS MBri MNrw
	MRav NBro NGdn WAul WCAu
	WHal WPrP WTMC WTin
I 'Elaine's Variety'	MAvo
elatum	EBee EBla
'Farmer John Cross'	CBre CDes CElw EBee EBla ECtt
	MAvo MHar MNrw NCot NLar SBri
	WCra WHal WMoo
fauriei x *kamtschatica*	EBee EBla
'Feuerball'	NBre NGdn
'Feuermeer'	EBee EBla MSte NLar NPro SBri
'Fire Opal' ♀H4	CAby CDes EBee EWes MAvo
	MNrw NBir NBre SUsu WMoo
	WPGP
'Fireball' **new**	NBhm
'Flames of Passion'PBR	CHar EBee EBla EChP ECtt EMan
	GBin IPot MAvo MBNS MBnl
	MWea NBPC NLar SBri SUsu WAul
	WCAu WCot WCra WHil
'Georgeham'	WWhi
'Georgenburg'	More than 30 suppliers
glaciale album	NBre
'Herterton Primrose'	ECtt LTwo MAvo SBri
* *hybridum luteum*	NSti
x *intermedium*	CBre EBee EBla EGle EMan EMon
	EPPr GBri LRHS MAvo MBnl
	MNrw NGdn NLar NPro SBri
	SHGN WFar WMoo WPtf WTMC
– 'Diane'	MAvo NBre
'Karlskaer'	CElw EBee EBla EChP ECtt EGle
	EPfP EWes GBin GCal MAvo MBnl
	MBri MHar MNrw SAga SBri
	WCMO WCot WHil WLin WMoo
	WPnP WViv
'Kashmir'	CFwr MAvo
'Kath Inman' **new**	MAvo
'Lady Stratheden' ♀H4	More than 30 suppliers
'Lemon Drops'	More than 30 suppliers
'Lionel Cox'	More than 30 suppliers
'Lisanne' **new**	NCot
macrophyllum	EBee EMan GBar NBre
– var. *sachalinense*	GIBF
magellanicum	EBee EBla EWes NBre NLar
'Mandarin'	CFir CMdw EBla GCal SBri SMHy
	WViv
'Marika'	CBre CCVN CRow EBee EBla EBrs
	LRHS MNrw NBre WMoo WOut
'Marmalade'	EBee EBla EChP ECtt GAbr LPhx
	MAvo MBnl MHar MNrw NBre
	NPro SBri SDys SMHy SUsu WCra
	WHrl WMoo WWhi
§ *montanum* ♀H4	CEnt EBla ECho GKev LEdu NBir
	NBro NDlv NGdn NPri NRya SPet
	SRms WMoo WPat WPer
– 'Diana'	EMon NDov NLar SBri
– 'Maximum'	MNrw
'Moorland Sorbet'	MAvo WFar WMoo
'Mrs J. Bradshaw' ♀H4	More than 30 suppliers
'Mrs W. Moore'	CAby CBre CDes EBee ECtt EShb
	GBri LBMP MAvo MBnl MHer
	MLLN MNrw NBir NChi NCot
	NLar NPro SRGP SUsu WMoo
	WTMC
'Nordek'	EMan GMac MAvo SBri WPtf
	WWhi
* 'Orangeman'	MNrw
parviflorum	GGar LEdu MLLN NBre NBro
'Paso Doble'	SBri WRHF WRos WSan
§ *pentapetalum*	GEdr WAbe WFar
– 'Flore Pleno' (d)	WAbe
'Pink Frills'	CElw EBee EBla ECha LBMP NCot
	NDov NLar SBri SMHy STes
ponticum	GIBF WOut
'Present'	EBee EBla MAvo NBre SBri
'Primrose'	NGdn NLar NPro WTMC
'Prince of Orange'	CElw EBla GAbr IGor MNrw NBre
	WFar WMoo WRha
'Prinses Juliana'	More than 30 suppliers
pyrenaicum	EBla NBre
quellyon	see *G. chiloense*
I 'Rearsby Hybrid'	MAvo MRav NChi
'Red Wings'	CMMP EBla EMan GCal MBNS
	MRav NBro SHar SUsu
reptans	see *Sieversia reptans*
x *rhaeticum*	EBee ECtt ETow MNrw WMoo
rhodopeum	EBee NBre
'Rijnstroom'	CElw CFwr EBee EBla EChP ELan
	LDai MWea NBPC NBro SUsu
	WCra WHil WPtf
rivale	More than 30 suppliers
– 'Album'	More than 30 suppliers
– 'Barbra Lawton'	EBla MAvo MDKP
– 'Cream Drop'	EBla NChi NGby NPro SBri WCMO
– cream-flowered, from	CFee
Tien Shan, China	
– lemon-flowered	EMan
– 'Leonard's Double' (d)	CPrp MAvo SHar WFar WMoo
	WTMC
– 'Leonard's Variety'	More than 30 suppliers
– 'Marmalade'	EBla MSph NBPC NChi WCMO
– 'Oxford Marmalade'	CElw
– 'Snowflake'	NChi
roylei	NBre
'Rubin'	CElw CHad EBee EBla ECtt EPPr
	EPyc GBuc MBNS MNrw NBre
	NBro NDov NGdn SBch SBri SMHy
	SUsu WAul WCAu WTMC
'Sigiswang'	CDes EBee GAbr GMac MAvo
	MNrw MRav MSte NBre NPro SBri
	WMoo WPGP WPrP
I 'Starker's Magnificum'	WCot
'Susan Grayer' (v) **new**	CNat
'Tangerine'	EBla GGar LSou MAvo MNrw
	MRav NPro SBri
'Tinpenny Orange'	MAvo WTin WWhi
x *tirolense*	EBee EBla NBre
triflorum	CDes CFwr CPBP EBee EBla EChP
	EHrv EMan EPla LPhx LRHS MCCP
	MNrw MRav MTis NLar SRot WFar
	WLin WPnP WTin WWhi
– var. *campanulatum*	EDAr EHyt ETow GBri NChi NPro
	NRya
urbanum	CArn ELau GBar GWCH IHMH
	MBow NLan NMir NPri NSco
	SECG SWat WHbs WHer WMoo
– from Patagonia	EBla MDKP
– 'Checkmate' (v)	EMon
'Wallace's Peach'	SWal
'Werner Arends'	see *G. coccineum* 'Werner Arends'

Gevuina (Proteaceae)

avellana	CBcs CHEx CTrG CTrw WPGP

Gilia ✿ (*Polemoniaceae*)

aggregata	see *Ipomopsis aggregata*
californica	see *Leptodactylon californicum*
'Red Dwarf'	NPol
tricolor	NPol

Gillenia (*Rosaceae*)

stipulata	CHea CWCL EBee EGle EMon LPhx NDov NLar SUsu
trifoliata ♀H4	More than 30 suppliers
- 'Pixie'	EBee WPGP

Ginkgo ✿ (*Ginkgoaceae*)

biloba ♀H4	More than 30 suppliers
- B&SWJ 8753	WCru
- 'Anny's Dwarf'	SIFN
- 'Autumn Gold' (m)	CBcs CEnd CMCN MBlu MGos SIFN SMad WPGP
I - 'Barabits Nana'	CMCN SIFN SMad
- 'Chotek'	SIFN
- 'Doctor Causton' (f)	CAgr
- 'Doctor Causton' (m)	CAgr
- 'Elsie' **new**	SIFN
- 'Fairmount' (m)	CMCN MBlu SIFN
- 'Fastigiata' (m)	CLnd CMCN EZes LPan MGos SBLw
- 'Golden Globe' **new**	NLar
- 'Hekt Leiden'	CMCN
- 'Horizontalis'	CLnd CMCN CMen LCon MBlu SIFN
- 'Jade Butterflies'	CBcs MPkF NLar SLim
- 'King of Dongting' (f)	CMCN MBlu SIFN WMou
- 'Mariken'	LCon MGos MPkF NLar NPal SIFN SLim
- 'Mayfield' (m)	SIFN
- Ohazuki Group (f)	CAgr SIFN
- Pendula Group	CBcs CEnd CMCN CTho EPfP EZes IDee NPal SIFN SLim
- 'Princeton Sentry' (m)	EZes MBlu SIFN SMad
I - 'Prostrata'	CPMA
- 'Saratoga' (m)	CBcs CDoC CEnd CLnd CMCN CPMA CTho EZes MGos SIFN SLim WPGP
- 'Tit'	CEnd CMCN EPfP MGos NLar SIFN
- 'Tremonia'	CMCN EPfP MBlu NLar SIFN SLim
- 'Troll'	SCoo SIFN
- 'Tubifolia'	CMCN EZes MBlu NLar SIFN SLim SMad
- 'Umbrella'	CMCN SIFN
- Variegata Group (v)	CMCN CPMA EZes MBlu NLar SIFN SLim

ginseng see *Panax ginseng*

Gladiolus (*Iridaceae*)

Sdg 053-04 **new**	MSGs
'About Face' (Min) **new**	MSGs
acuminatus	WCot
'Alba' (N)	CGrW
'Alexander S' (L)	MSGs
'Alexandra' (P)	WCot
'Allosius' (S)	CGrW
'Amsterdam' (G)	CGrW MSGs
'Andre Viette'	EBee EMan WCMO WCot
angustus	CGrW WCot
'Anna Leorah' (L)	MSGs
antakiensis	CPou
'Antique Lace' (L)	CGrW MSGs
'Antique Rose' (M)	CGrW
'Anyu S' (L)	MSGs
'Arabella' (P)	WCMO
'Arctic Day' (M/E)	CGrW
'Atom' (S/P)	CBgR CBro CGrW EBee EBrs WHil
atroviolaceus	WPGP
aureus	WCot
'Bangledesh' (M)	MSGs
Barnard hybrids	CGrW
'Beautiful Angel'	CGrW MSGs
'Beauty Bride' (L)	CGrW MSGs
'Beauty of Holland'ᴾᴮᴿ (L)	CGrW MSGs
'Ben Venuto' (L)	CGrW
'Bizar'	EPfP
'Black Jack' **new**	CSut EPfP SPer
'Black Pearls' (S)	MSGs
'Blackbird' (S) **new**	CGrW
blandus var. **carneus**	see *G. carneus*
'Blue Clouds' (L)	CGrW
'Blue Conqueror' (L)	LRHS
'Blue Tropic'	CSut EPfP
'Blueberry Wine' (L/E)	CGrW
'Bluebird' (S) **new**	CGrW
bonaespei	CDes WCot
'Bono's Memory'	LRHS
'Bradley W' (M)	MSGs
'Breathless' **new**	MSGs
'Brittania' (L) **new**	CGrW
'Burgundy Queen' (M)	WCot
byzantinus	see *G. communis* subsp. *byzantinus*
caeruleus	CGrW CPou
callianthus	CFFs CSWP CStu EBla ECho EPfP MSte NCGa SPet WFar WHil WWhi
cardinalis	CAby CDes CMea CPne CPrp EBla EMan GCal IBlr SAga WCMO WCot WCru WPGP
carinatus	CDes CGrW WCot
carinatus x **orchidiflorus**	EBee WCot
'Carla Gabor' (L)	CGrW
carmineus	CGrW LBow WPGP
§ **carneus**	CGrW CPou EBee EMan GCal LBow LRHS SMeo WPGP
'Carquirenne' (G)	CGrW MSGs
'Carved Ivory' (M)	MSGs
caryophyllaceus	CPou
'Century Mark' (G)	MSGs
ceresianus	WCMO
'Charm' (N/Tub)	CAvo CBro CFFs CPrp EBee EBla
'Charming Beauty' (Tub)	ECho
'Charming Lady' (Tub)	ECho WCMO
'Chinon'ᴾᴮᴿ (L) **new**	CGrW
'Chloe' (M)	MSGs
'Christabel'	LBow
'Christabel' (L)	ERos
'Cindy' (B)	ECho EPfP SPer
citrinus	see *G. trichonemifolius*
'Claudia' (N) **new**	CGrW
'Clemence' (Min)	MSGs
'Cloud Nine' **new**	MSGs
x **colvillii**	CPne IBlr
- 'Albus'	EBrs EPot GKev LPhx NJOw WHil
'Comet' (N)	EBrs GKev WHil WPnP
§ **communis** subsp. **byzantinus** ♀H4	More than 30 suppliers
- subsp. **communis**	WCMO
'Contessa Queen' **new**	MSGs
'Cool Blue' (M) **new**	CGrW
'Coral Dream' (L)	CGrW
'Côte d'Azur' (G)	CGrW MSGs
crassifolius	CFir GBuc WCMO WCot
'Cream of the Crop' (M)	MSGs
'Cream Perfection' (L)	MSGs
'Creamy Yellow' (S)	MSGs
'Crusader' (L) **new**	CGrW
§ **dalenii**	CPou CPrp CSam ERos IBlr WCMO WCot WPGP
- 'Bolivian Peach' **new**	WCMO
- subsp. **dalenii** **new**	IBlr
- green-flowered	CDes IBlr
- hybrids	WCot

– orange-flowered	CDes EBee
* – f. *rubra*	IBlr WCot
– yellow-flowered	CDes EBee WPGP
'Darling Clementine' (L) **new**	CGrW
'Daydreamer' (L)	CGrW
'Day's End' (S) **new**	CGrW
'Desirée' (B)	MSGs SPet
'Dominick C' (S)	MSGs
'Doris Darling' (L)	MSGs
'Drama' (L)	CGrW MSGs
'Early Company' (L) **new**	CGrW
'Early Little Lilac' (S)	CGrW
ecklonii	WHil WPGP
'Elegance' (G)	CGrW MSGs
'Elvira' (N)	EBee EBla ECho WPGP
'Emerald Spring' (S)	WCMO WCot
'Emir' (S)	MSGs
'Esperanto' (M)	MSGs
'Esta Bonita' (G)	CGrW MSGs
'Fabienne' **new**	SPer
'Felicta' (L)	MSGs
'Femme Fatale' (L) **new**	CGrW
'Fineline' (M) **new**	CGrW
'Finishing Touch'[PBR] (L)	CGrW MSGs
'Fireball II' (L)	MSGs
'First Frost' (L) **new**	CGrW
flanaganii	CPBP EBee GCrs WCMO WCot
– JCA 261.000	EBee
'Flevo Amico' (S)	CGrW WCot
'Flevo Candy' (S)	MSGs
'Flevo Cheers' **new**	MSGs
'Flevo Cosmic' (Min)	CGrW GBri MSGs WCMO
'Flevo Eclips'[PBR] (G)	MSGs
'Flevo Eyes'[PBR] (L)	CGrW
'Flevo Fire'[PBR] (M)	CGrW MSGs
'Flevo Junior' (S)	CGrW WCMO
'Flevo Party' (S)	CGrW MSGs
'Flevo Smile' (S)	CGrW MSGs
'Flevo Souvenir'[PBR] (L)	CGrW
'Flevo Sunset'[PBR] (L)	CGrW
'Flevo Touch' (S)	MSGs
'Flevo Vision' (L)	CGrW MSGs
floribundus	EBee
'French Silk' (L)	CGrW
'Friendship' (L)	LRHS
geardii	WCot
'Gillian' (L)	LBow
'Gladiris' (L)	MSGs
'Gold Struck' (L) **new**	CGrW
'Golden Melody' (M)	MSGs
'Golden Sunset' (L)	CGrW MSGs
'Good Luck' (N)	CBro
gracilis	WCot
'Grand Prix'[PBR] (L)	MSGs
grandis	see *G. liliaceus*
'Green Baltic' (G/E) **new**	CGrW
'Green Isle' (M/E) **new**	CGrW
'Green Star' (L)	CGrW CSut MSGs
'Green with Envy' (L)	MSGs
'Green Woodpecker' (M)	EBee LRHS
'Gwendolyn'	MSGs
'Gypsy Rose' **new**	MSGs
'Halley' (N)	CBro ECho
'Hastings' (P)	WCMO
'Henriette' (P)	WCMO
'High Style' (L)	CGrW
'Hi-Lite' (L)	CGrW
hirsutus	CGrW
'Honeydew' **new**	MSGs
'Hotline' **new**	MSGs
'Huron Frost' (L)	CGrW MSGs
'Huron Jewel' (M)	MSGs
'Huron Kisses' **new**	MSGs
'Huron Silk' (L)	CGrW MSGs
'Huron White' (M) **new**	CGrW
huttonii	CGrW
huttonii x *tristis*	CPou
huttonii x *tristis* var. concolor	WCMO WCot
hyalinus	WCot
'Ice Cream' **new**	SPer
'Ice Follies' (L)	MSGs
illyricus	CSam GBuc GCal WBVN WPGP
imbricatus	ERos GBuc GCrs
'Impressive' (N)	EPot GKev SPet WHil
'Irish Blessing' (S) **new**	CGrW
§ *italicus*	CGrW EBee ELan GCal LPhx MSte
'Ivory Priscilla'[PBR] (L)	CGrW MSGs
'Ivory Queen' **new**	MSGs
'Ivory Towers' (G)	MSGs
'Jarni Tani' (L)	MSGs
'Jayvee' (S)	CGrW
'Jean K' (M)	CGrW MSGs
'Jim S' (G)	CGrW MSGs
'Jo Ann' (L)	CGrW
'Jolly Joker' **new**	SPer
'Jupiter' (B)	LRHS
§ *kotschyanus*	EBee GCrs
'Kristin' (L)	MSGs
'Lady Barbara' (P)	MSGs
'Lady Caroline' (P)	MSGs
'Lady Eleanor' (P)	WCot
'Lady in Red' (L)	MSGs
'Lady Lucille' (M)	CGrW MSGs
'Lavender Flare' (S)	CGrW
'Lavender Maiden' (L) **new**	CGrW
'Lavender Rose' (L)	MSGs
'Lemon Drop' (S)	MSGs
'Lemon Zest' (M) **new**	CGrW MSGs
§ *liliaceus*	CDes CGrW LBow WCot
'Lime Green' (P)	LRHS
'Linne' (S)	MSGs
'Little Jude' (P)	MSGs WCot
'Little Rainbow' (P) **new**	WCot
'Little Wiggy' (P)	WCot
'Loulou' (G)	CGrW
'Lowland Queen' (L)	CGrW MSGs
maculatus	WPGP
'Maggie' (S)	CGrW EPfP
'Marj S' (L)	CGrW MSGs
'Mary Housley' (L)	SPer
'Mascagni' (M)	EPfP
meliusculus **new**	WCot
'Mileesh' (L)	CGrW MSGs
'Millennium' (L) **new**	CGrW
miniatus	EBee
'Mirella' (N)	MRav
'Miss America' (M)	MSGs
'Mon Amour'[PBR] **new**	CSut
monticola	EBee
'Moon Mirage' (G)	MSGs
'Moon Shadow' (M/E) **new**	CGrW
mortonius	CMdw GCal WPGP
'Mother Theresa' (M)	MSGs
'Mr Chris' (S)	MSGs
'Mrs Rowley' (P)	GBri
§ *murielae* ♀[H3]	CAvo CBro CFFs CFwr CGrW CMea EBee EBrs EWll SMeo SPer STes SWal WGwG WHal WHoo
'Murieliae'	see *G. murielae*
'Nancy'	LBow
natalensis	see *G. dalenii*
'Nathalie' (N)	CGrW EBee EBrs GKev WHil
'New Elegance' **new**	MSGs
'New Wave'[PBR] (L)	CGrW MSGs
'Nicholas' (S)	MSGs
'Nikita' (P)	MSGs
'Nori' (M) **new**	CGrW

'Nova Lux' (L)	EPfP LRHS SPer
'Nymph' (N)	CAvo CElw CFFs EBee EBla EBrs EChP EPot GKev ITim LDai MBow MDun SPur SWal WHil
'Oasis'^{PBR} (G)	CGrW
'Ocean Breeze' (S)	MSGs
ochroleucus	EBee
'Of Singular Beauty' (G)	CGrW MSGs
'Olympic Torch' (L)	MSGs
§ *oppositiflorus*	CDes CPou EBee WPGP
- subsp. *salmoneus*	see *G. oppositiflorus*
orchidiflorus	CGrW CPou
'Orient Express' **new**	MSGs
'Orlando' (L)	MSGs
'Oscar' (G)	LRHS
palustris	ERos WCot
papilio	More than 30 suppliers
- 'David Hills'	WCMO WCot
§ - Purpureoauratus Group	CBro CSam EBee EMan ERos IBlr SRms
- 'Ruby'	CHad CPen
- yellow-flowered	SMHy SMad SUsu
pappei	CDes EBee WPGP
'Peace' (L)	CGrW
'Peach Cobbler' **new**	CGrW MSGs
'Penelope' (P)	WCMO
'Perky' (Min)	SPer
permeabilis	EBee WPGP
'Perth Ivory' (M)	MSGs
'Perth Pearl' (M)	CGrW MSGs
'Peter Pears' (L)	CSut LRHS
'Phyllis M' (L)	CGrW
Pilbeam hybrids	CGrW
'Pillow Talk' **new**	MSGs
'Pink Elf' (S)	MSGs
'Pink Lady' (L)	CGrW MSGs
'Pink Phantom' (L)	CGrW
'Pinnacle' (L)	CGrW MSGs
'Plum Tart' (L)	LRHS SMeo
'Polar Sunset' **new**	MSGs
'Polar Sunshine' **new**	MSGs
'Pop Art'	LRHS
primulinus	see *G. dalenii*
'Prins Claus' (N)	CBro CGrW EBee EBla GKev LRHS SPet WHil
'Pulchritude' (M)	MSGs
punctulatus var. *punctulatus*	ERos
'Purple Haze' **new**	MSGs
'Purple Prince' (M)	CGrW WCMO WCot
purpureoauratus	see *G. papilio* Purpureoauratus Group
'Raspberry Swirl' (L/E) **new**	CGrW
'Red Alert' (L)	MSGs
'Red Beauty'	LRHS
'Revelry' (S)	MSGs
'Robert S' (L)	MSGs
'Robinetta' (*recurvus* hybrid) ♀H3	CBro CElw CPrp EBee EBla EChP ECho EPfP LDai SPur WHil
rogersii	CDes
'Roma' (L)	MSGs
'Rose Elf' (S)	MSGs
'Rose Laguna' **new**	MSGs
'Route One' (L)	CGrW
'Royal Spire' **new**	CGrW MSGs
'Ruth Ann' **new**	MSGs
'Sabu'	LRHS
'Sailor's Delight' (L)	MSGs
'Salmon Sorbet'	CGrW
'Samson' (L)	MSGs
'San Remo'^{PBR} (L)	CGrW
'Santa Lucia' (L) **new**	CGrW
'Satin 'n' Lace' (L) **new**	CGrW
saundersii	WCot WPGP
'Sceptre' (L)	CGrW
scullyi	LBow

segetum	see *G. italicus*
'Serafin' (Min)	LRHS
sericeovillosus	IBlr
'Show Chairman' (L)	MSGs
'Show Star' (L) **new**	CGrW
'Show Stopper' (G) **new**	CGrW
'Silvana' (S) **new**	CGrW
'Silver Shadow'^{PBR} (S)	EPfP
'Sirael' (L/E)	CGrW MSGs WCot
'Sky High' (M) **new**	CGrW
'Smoky Joe' (L)	MSGs
'Snow Cap' (L) **new**	CGrW
'Snowcap' **new**	MSGs
'Solveiga' (L/E) **new**	CGrW
'Sophie'^{PBR} **new**	CGrW
'Sparkle Plenty' **new**	MSGs
'Spic and Span' (L)	CSut
splendens	CDes CGrW WCot WPGP
'Spontaneous Combustion' **new**	MSGs
'Spring Green'	EPfP
'Spring Thaw' (L/E) **new**	CGrW
'Starfish' (S)	MSGs
'Stromboli' (L)	MSGs
'Sue' (P)	MSGs
'Sunset Fire' (G)	CGrW MSGs
'Super High Brow' (G)	CGrW MSGs
'Sylvia' **new**	MSGs
'Tan Royale' (P)	MSGs
'Tante Ann' (M) **new**	CGrW
teretifolius **new**	WPGP
'Tesoro' (M)	MSGs
'The Bride' (x *colvillii*) ♀H3	CAvo CBro CFFs CHad CMil CPrp EBee EBla ECho ITim LDai MWgw SUsu SWal
'Think Pink' (L) **new**	MSGs
'Tickatoo' (P)	WCot
'Tiger Eyes' (S) **new**	CGrW
'Topaz' (L)	CGrW MSGs
'Trader Horn' (G)	SPer
§ *trichonemifolius*	WPGP
tristis	CBro CElw CGrW CMea CPne CPou EBee ECha ELan EMan GMac LBow NCGa SAga SDix SUsu WAbe WFar WHal WPGP WPrP
- var. *aestivalis*	LBow
- var. *concolor*	CGrW CPLG CPrp EMan ERos LBow WCMO WCot
undulatus	CDes ERos LBow WCot WPGP
usyiae	CPou
'Velvet Eyes' (M)	SPer
venustus	WPGP
'Vesuvio' **new**	MSGs
'Victoria' (M)	LRHS
'Video' (L)	CGrW
'Vienna' (L)	CGrW
'Violetta' (M)	CGrW ECho EMan MSGs SPer
virescens	CPou WCMO WCot
'Visual Arts' (M)	CGrW
'Wandering Eyes' **new**	MSGs
watermeyeri	WPGP
watsonioides	CPou ERos WCot
watsonius	WPGP
'Whistle Stop' (S)	MSGs
'White City' (P/S)	LRHS
'White Ice' **new**	MSGs
'White Out' (M) **new**	CGrW
'White Prosperity' (L)	CSut LRHS

Glandularia see *Verbena*

Glaucidium (Glaucidiaceae)

palmatum ♀H4	EFEx EHyt GCrs GEdr GIBF NSla WAbe WBVN WCru
- 'Album'	see *G. palmatum* var. *leucanthum*
§ - var. *leucanthum*	EFEx GCrs NSla

324 Glaucium

Glaucium (Papaveraceae)

§ *corniculatum*	CAby CSpe EBee EBrs EChP EKen LPhx MLLN MWgw NLar SEND SPav SPoG WCot WEas
flavum	CArn CHrt CSpe ECha EGoo ELan EWsh LRHS MHer NLar SPav XPep
- *aurantiacum*	see *G. flavum* f. *fulvum*
§ - f. *fulvum*	ECha EMan SDix SMHy
- orange-flowered	see *G. flavum* f. *fulvum*
- red-flowered	see *G. corniculatum*
phoenicium	see *G. corniculatum*

Glaux (Primulaceae)

maritima	WPer

Glebionis (Asteraceae)

coronaria	CArn
§ *segetum*	GWCH MBow NPri WHer

Glechoma (Lamiaceae)

hederacea	CArn GBar GPoy MHer NMir NSco SECG WHbs WHer WWye XPep
- 'Barry Yinger Variegated' (v)	EBee WCot
- 'Rosea'	GBar WWye
§ - 'Variegata' (v)	CHal EWin IHMH LRHS MBri NBlu SPet

Gleditsia (Caesalpiniaceae)

caspica	CArn SMad
japonica	EPfP
macrantha	EGFP
sinensis	EGFP NLar
triacanthos	CAgr CDul CWib ECrN LEdu LPan MGol SBLw SPlb WBVN WDin WNor
- 'Bujotii'	SBLw
- 'Calhoun'	CAgr
- 'Elegantissima' (v)	SPer
- 'Emerald Cascade'	CDul CEnd EBee
- f. *inermis*	CAgr SBLw WNor
- 'Millwood'	CAgr
- 'Rubylace'	CBcs CDul CEnd CMCN COtt CTri EBee ECrN ELan EPfP LBuc LPan LRHS MAsh MBar MBlu MDun MGos MRav MSwo NHol SBod SHBN SPer WCMO WCot WDin WFar WOrn
- 'Shademaster'	MRav NLar SBLw
- 'Skyline'	SBLw
- 'Sunburst' ♀H4	More than 30 suppliers

Glehnia (Umbelliferae)

littoralis	GIBF

Globba (Zingiberaceae)

andersonii	CKob MOak
bulbifera **new**	ECho
* *cathcartii*	CKob MOak
'Emerald Isle'	LRHS
marantina	CKob MOak
winitii	LRHS
- 'Golden Dragon'	MOak
- 'Mauve Dancing Girl'	MOak
- 'Pink Dancing Girl'	ECho
- 'Red Leaf'	MOak
- 'Violett'	MOak
- 'White Dragon'	MOak WMul

Globularia (Globulariaceae)

alypum	XPep
bellidifolia	see *G. meridionalis*
bisnagarica	WLin

cordifolia ♀H4	CBrm CNic CTri ECho EPot GEdr LBee LRHS MTho NLAp NMen SBla SIng WFar WHoo
- NS 696	NWCA
incanescens	LRHS
§ *meridionalis*	CFee CLyd CPBP EBee ECho EPot EWes GEdr MWat NLAp NMen SAga SBla WFar WHal WPat
- 'Alba'	NMen
- 'Blue Bonnets' **new**	NHar
- 'Hort's Variety'	CNic CPBP CTri NMen WAbe
nana	see *G. repens*
nudicaulis	SBla
- 'Alba'	WIvy
§ *punctata*	CSpe GMaP LRHS NChi NJOw NWCA SRms
pygmaea	see *G. meridionalis*
§ *repens*	CLyd CNic EHyt EPot MTho NLAp NMen SIng WPat
spinosa	NWCA WLin
trichosantha	CFee ECho SPet SRms WFar WLin WPer

Gloriosa (Colchicaceae)

lutea	see *G. superba* 'Lutea'
rothschildiana	see *G. superba* 'Rothschildiana'
§ *superba* ♀H1	CAby MBri
§ - 'Lutea'	LRHS
§ - 'Rothschildiana'	CBcs CDul CRHN CStu ECho EPfP LBow LRHS MOak SOWG SRms

Glottiphyllum (Aizoaceae)

nelii	CStu

Gloxinia (Gesneriaceae)

sylvatica	CHal CSpe EShb WDib

Glumicalyx (Scrophulariaceae)

flanaganii	CSec EBee GCrs GKev NLAp WAbe
- HWEL 0325	NWCA
montanus	CFee EMan IDee MHar NWCA

Glyceria (Poaceae)

aquatica variegata	see *G. maxima* var. *variegata*
maxima	CRWN EMFW LNCo NPer SPlb
§ - var. *variegata* (v)	More than 30 suppliers
spectabilis 'Variegata'	see *G. maxima* var. *variegata*

Glycyrrhiza (Papilionaceae)

echinata	CAgr CArn CPLG MSal NLar
§ *glabra*	CAgr CArn CBod CCCN CHby CWan ELau EShb GPoy GWCH MHer MNHC MSal NLar NMRc NTHB SECG SIde WHer WJek WWye XPep
glandulifera	see *G. glabra*
uralensis	CArn ELau GPoy MHer MSal

Glyptostrobus (Cupressaceae)

§ *pensilis*	WPGP

Gmelina (Verbenaceae)

philippensis	CPIN

Gnaphalium (Asteraceae)

'Fairy Gold'	see *Helichrysum thianschanicum* 'Goldkind'

Godetia see Clarkia

Gomphocarpus (Asclepiadaceae)

§ *physocarpus*	CArn NLar WCot

Gomphostigma (Buddlejaceae)
virgatum   CDes CMdw CPLG CPle CTrC
                       EBee EMan EPPr EShb LRHS MLLN
                       MSte SPlb SSvw WCMO WCot
                       WHrl WPGP WSHC
- 'White Candy'   SHGN

Goniolimon (Plumbaginaceae)
§ **incanum**   XPep
- 'Blue Diamond'   CMMP EBee NBre
§ **tataricum**   CWoW NBre NLar
§ - var. **angustifolium** EBee NBlu NBre SRms WPer
- 'Woodcreek'   MWgw NBre NLar

Goodenia (Goodeniaceae)
scaevolina   CSec
scapigera   CSec

Goodyera (Orchidaceae)
biflora   EFEx
pubescens   EFEx LRHS WCru
schlechtendaliana EFEx

gooseberry see *Ribes uva-crispa*

Gordonia (Theaceae)
axillaris   CCCN CHll

Gossypium (Malvaceae)
herbaceum   MSal

granadilla see *Passiflora quadrangularis*

granadilla, purple see *Passiflora edulis*

granadilla, sweet see *Passiflora ligularis*

granadilla, yellow see *Passiflora laurifolia*

grape see *Vitis*

grapefruit see *Citrus* x *paradisi*

Graptopetalum (Crassulaceae)
bellum ♀H1   CStu SChr
filiferum new   SRot
§ **paraguayense**   CHal SEND

Gratiola (Scrophulariaceae)
officinalis   CArn CWan EHon EMFW EMan
                       MHer MSal NBlu WSel WWpP
                       WWye

Greenovia (Crassulaceae)
aizoon   ETow

Grevillea ✿ (Proteaceae)
alpina   CFee CPLG CPle EBee GQui SMur
                       SOWG
- 'Olympic Flame'   CBcs CCCN CDoC CPLG CSBt
                       CTbh CTrw CWib LHop LRHS
                       SBrw SOWG SPoG
aquifolium   SOWG
arenaria   SOWG
- subsp. **canescens** SOWG
'Austraflora Copper Crest' see *G.* 'Copper Crest'
australis var. **brevifolia** CPLG
baileyana new   SOWG
banksii   CPLG
- 'Canberra Hybrid'   see *G.* 'Canberra Gem'
- var. **forsteri**   SOWG SPlb
banyabba   SOWG
barklyana   ECou SOWG
baueri   SOWG
beadleana   SOWG

bedggoodiana   SOWG
bipinnatifida   SOWG
'Bonnie Prince Charlie' CPLG SOWG
'Bronze Rambler'   SOWG
§ 'Canberra Gem' ♀H3-4 More than 30 suppliers
'Clearview David'   CCCN CPLG SOWG
confertifolia   SOWG
§ 'Copper Crest'   SOWG
'Cranbrook Yellow'   CDoC CPLG SOWG
crithmifolia   CPLG SOWG SPlb
curviloba   CPLG
diffusa subsp.   SOWG
   evansiana
drummondii subsp. SOWG
   pimeleoides
endlicheriana   SOWG
'Evelyn's Coronet'   SOWG
'Fanfare'   SOWG
fulgens   SOWG
x **gaudichaudii**   SOWG
* 'Honey Eater Heaven' SOWG
'Honey Gem'   SOWG
iaspicula new   ECou
involucrata   SOWG
johnsonii   SOWG
juniperina   CBcs CCCN CPLG GGar
- 'Molonglo'   CPLG
- f. **sulphurea**   CBcs CCCN CDoC CDul CHll
                       CPLG CSBt CTrG CTrw EPfP GQui
                       SBrw SOWG SPer SPlb WAbe
                       WSHC
lanigera   CPLG
I - 'Lutea'   SOWG
- 'Mount Tamboritha'   CBcs CCCN CDoC CMHG CPLG
                       IDee LHop SSto WFar
- prostrate   NLAp SOWG WPat
* **laspicalla**   SOWG
'Lawiggra Pink' new   ECou
'Lawiggra Yellow' new ECou
levis   SOWG
longistyla   SOWG SPlb
'Majestic'   SOWG
'Mason's Hybrid'   SOWG
'Moonlight'   SOWG
nudiflora   ECou SOWG
obtusifolia 'Gingin Gem' SOWG
olivacea 'Apricot Glow' SOWG
'Orange Marmalade'   SOWG
paniculata   SOWG SPlb
'Pink Lady'   ECou SOWG
'Pink Surprise'   SOWG
'Poorinda Elegance'   SOWG
'Poorinda Peter'   CPLG SOWG
'Poorinda Rondeau'   CPLG
pteridifolia new   SOWG
quercifolia   SOWG
repens   SOWG
rhyolitica   SOWG
robusta ♀H1+3   CHal SBLw SBig SBrw SMur SOWG
                       SPlb
'Robyn Gordon'   SOWG
'Rondeau'   CCCN CEnd EShb
rosmarinifolia ♀H3 More than 30 suppliers
- 'Desert Flame'   CPLG
- 'Jenkinsii'   CDoC CPLG CSBt SLim
'Sandra Gordon'   SOWG
'Scarlet Sprite'   SOWG
§ x **semperflorens** CDoC CEnd CPLG CWib SOWG
sericea   SOWG
shiressii   SOWG
'Sid Reynolds'   CPLG
'Splendour'   SOWG
thelemanniana   CPLG ECou
- 'Silver'   CPLG
- Spriggs' form   SOWG
thyrsoides   CBcs CPLG

tolminsis	see *G.* x *semperflorens*
tridentifera	CPLG
venusta new	SOWG
victoriae	ECou SOWG WCot
* – subsp. ***tenuinervis*** new	SOWG
– subsp. ***victoriae***	CPLG
williamsonii	ECou SOWG WPat

Greyia (*Greyiaceae*)
sutherlandii	CKob CTrC EDsa SGar SOWG SPlb

Grindelia (*Asteraceae*)
§ ***camporum***	EBee EChP GBar MSal NBre NLar SPlb WCMO WCot WPer
chiloensis	CAbb ECha LRav SDix SMad WCot
integrifolia	CSam EBee
robusta	see *G. camporum*
'Setting Sun'	WCru
squarrosa	GBar
stricta	CArn

Griselinia (*Griseliniaceae*)
littoralis ♀H3	More than 30 suppliers
– 'Bantry Bay' (v)	CAbP CDoC CWSG EBee EHoe ELan GGar LRHS MAsh MSwo NCGa SAga SEND SLim SPer SPoG SSto SWvt WCru WFar
– 'Brodick Gold'	CPLG EBee GGar GTSp
– 'Crinkles'	CPMA SLon
– 'Dixon's Cream' (v)	CBcs CDul CSBt EPfP GQui IArd IFoB MAsh SAga SLon SPoG WCru
– 'Green Jewel' (v)	CBcs CEnd CPMA CWib NLar SPla SPoG
– 'Variegata' (v) ♀H3	More than 30 suppliers
lucida 'Variegata' (v) new	IFoB
scandens	WSHC

guava, common see *Psidium guajava*

guava, purple or strawberry see *Psidium littorale var. longipes*

Gueldenstaedtia (*Papilionaceae*)
himalaica B&SWJ 2631	WCru

Gunnera (*Gunneraceae*)
arenaria	GGar
chilensis	see *G. tinctoria*
dentata	WGwG
flavida	EBee EShb GGar GSki NWCA WGwG
hamiltonii	CRez CStu EBee EBla ECha ECou GGar NBir NWCA SBch WMoo WWpP
magellanica	More than 30 suppliers
– 'Muñoz Gamero'	WShi
– 'Osorno'	WPGP
manicata ♀H3-4	More than 30 suppliers
monoica	GGar GSki
perpensa new	CDes
prorepens	CBcs CEnt CFee CHEx CStu EBee EBla ECha ECou EShb GEdr GSki NBir NWCA WMoo WWpP WWye
scabra	see *G. tinctoria*
§ ***tinctoria***	CDWL CHEx CMHG CPLG CRow CTbh CTrG CWib EBee EBla ECha EHon ELan EPfP EPla GGar MDun NCot NVic SDix SWat SWvt WBVN WCot WFar WMul WPGP WWpP

Guzmania (*Bromeliaceae*)
'Gran Prix'	MBri
'Surprise'	see x *Niduregelia* 'Surprise'
'Vulkan'	MBri

Gymnadenia (*Orchidaceae*)
conopsea	EFEx

Gymnocarpium (*Woodsiaceae*)
dryopteris ♀H4	CLAP EBee EFer EFtx EMar EMon EPot GGar GKev GMaP MMoz NLar NWCA SRms WFib WNor WPnP
– 'Plumosum' ♀H4	CFwr CLAP CWCL EBee EFtx EPla ERod GBin GQui MAsh MWgw NBid NHol NLar NVic SMac SPoG WFib WHal WMoo
oyamense	CLAP EFer
robertianum	CLAP EFer EFtx

Gymnocladus (*Caesalpiniaceae*)
chinensis	CBcs WNor
dioica	CBcs CDul CLnd CMCN CTho EBee ELan EPfP LEdu LRHS MBlu MBri NEgg SPer SSpi WDin WGer WNor WPGP

Gymnospermium (*Berberidaceae*)
§ ***albertii***	GCrs WCot

Gynandriris (*Iridaceae*)
setifolia	CMon
sisyrinchium	CMon EBee ECho EMan
– purple-flowered AB&S 4447 from Morocco	CMon
* – ***purpurea***	ECho

Gynerium (*Poaceae*)
argenteum	see *Cortaderia selloana*

Gynostemma (*Cucurbitaceae*)
pentaphyllum	CAgr
– B&SWJ 570	WCru

Gynura (*Asteraceae*)
§ ***aurantiaca*** 'Purple Passion' ♀H1	MBri
sarmentosa hort.	see *G. aurantiaca* 'Purple Passion'

Gypsophila (*Caryophyllaceae*)
acutifolia	EBee ELan
aretioides	EAEE ECho EPot LRHS NJOw NMen NWCA WRos
§ – 'Caucasica'	EBur ECho EHyt EPot LTwo NDlv SIng
– 'Compacta'	see *G. aretioides* 'Caucasica'
briquetiana	EPot WPat
cerastioides	CTri ECho ECtt EWTr GBBs GGar LAst LHop LRHS MRav NDlv NLap NMen NWCA SPlb SRms WHoo WPer WPnn
dubia	see *G. repens* 'Dubia'
fastigiata	EBee WPer
– 'Silverstar'	LSou SPoG
(Festival Series) 'Festival'PBR	SPoG
– 'Festival Pink'	EBee GMac LRHS SHar WFar WViv
– Happy Festival = 'Danghappy'	LRHS WViv
– 'Royal Festival'	WViv
– 'White Festival'PBR	EBee NLar WFar WViv
gracilescens	see *G. tenuifolia*
'Jolien' (v)	CBow EBee ELan WHil WWeb
muralis 'Garden Bride'	LIck SWvt
– 'Gypsy Pink' (d)	SWvt
nana 'Compacta'	CLyd
oldhamiana	EBee EShb MLLN
pacifica	EBee ECtt EMag EShb NBre NBro NLar NPri WPer

§ *paniculata* — COfd EBee GWCH LAst NBre NFor NMir SECG SRms SWat

  - 'Bristol Fairy' (d) ♀H4 — CSBt EBee ECha ELan EMan ENot EPfP ERou LRHS MDun NBlu NEgg NLar NOrc SMer SPoG SSto SWvt WCAu

  - 'Compacta Plena' (d) — EAEE EBee EChP ECtt EGle ELan EPfP GCal GMaP LHop MLHP MRav MWgw NDov NEgg NFla NLar NVic SPet SPla SRms WPer

  - 'Flamingo' (d) — CBcs ECha ECot ERou NLar SCoo SPer

  - 'Magic Gilboa' (d) — COtt
  - 'Magic Golan' (d) — COtt
  - 'Pacific Pink' — LAst
  - 'Perfekta' — CBcs SPer

§ - 'Schneeflocke' (d) — EBee EShb EWsh GMaP MWat NBre NLar NPri SRms SSto WPer

  - Snowflake — see *G. paniculata* 'Schneeflocke'

§ *petraea* — EPot GKev

  repens ♀H4 — CBrm ECtt EMil LBee MHer MWat NJOw SBch SHGN SPlb SWvt WFar WPer

  - 'Dorothy Teacher' — CLyd CMea ECho ECtt LBee SIng WEas WGor

§ - 'Dubia' — CLyd ECha ECho ECtt EDAr EHol ELan EPot MHer SPoG SRms WLin WPer WSHC

  - 'Fratensis' — ECho ECtt ELan ITim NMen
  - Pink Beauty — see *G. repens* 'Rosa Schönheit'

§ - 'Rosa Schönheit' — ECha EPot LRHS NLar
  - 'Rose Fountain' — WPat

  - 'Rosea' — CBrm CMea CTri CWib EBee ECho ECtt EPfP EShb GAbr GMaP LAst MWat NFor NOak NWCA SAga SBla SPet SPoG SRms SUsu SWvt WFar WHoo WTin

  - 'Silver Carpet' (v) **new** — LBmB
  - white — CMMP CWib EBee ECho ELan EPfP EWin LAst NFor SPet SWvt WPer WRHF

§ 'Rosenschleier' (d) ♀H4 — CMea EAEE EBee EChP ECha ECtt EGoo ELan ENot EPfP LAst MRav MWat NDov NJOw SAga SPer SRms SUsu SWvt WCAu WEas WHoo WLin WSHC WTin

  'Rosy Veil' — see *G.* 'Rosenschleier'

§ *tenuifolia* — ECho EPot ITim LBee NDlv NHol NMen SBla SIng

  transylvanica — see *G. petraea*
  Veil of Roses — see *G.* 'Rosenschleier'

H

Haberlea (Gesneriaceae)

  ferdinandi-coburgii — CLAP CStu ECho GBuc NMen NWCA

  - 'Connie Davidson' — GBuc NMen

  rhodopensis ♀H4 — CDes CElw CFee CNic CStu EBee ECho EHyt GCrs GEdr GGar MSte MWat NLAp NMen NSla NWCA SBla SIng SRms WAbe WPGP WPat WTin

  - 'Virginalis' — CElw CLAP CStu NMen SBla

Habranthus ✿ (Amaryllidaceae)

  andersonii — see *H. tubispathus*
  brachyandrus — CBro SRms
  gracilifolius — CBro CStu ERos SIng
  martinezii — CBro CMon CStu EHyt WCMO

§ *robustus* ♀H1 — CDes CMon EBee ECho EPot EShb LHop LRHS WCMO WCot WHil WPGP

  texanus — CBro CMon ERos WAbe

§ *tubispathus* ♀H1 — CBro CMon CStu ECho EDif ERos NWCA SIng WCMO WCot WPrP

Hackelia (Boraginaceae)

  floribunda **new** — SBod

Hacquetia (Apiaceae)

§ *epipactis* ♀H4 — More than 30 suppliers

§ - 'Thor' (v) — CBow CDes EBee EMon EWes GCrs LTwo MAvo NMen SBla WPGP

  - 'Variegata' — see *H. epipactis* 'Thor'

Haemanthus (Amaryllidaceae)

  albiflos ♀H1 — CHEx CHal CMon CSpe CStu EOHP ITer LToo SRms WCot

  amarylloides subsp. *polyanthes* — ECho LToo

  barkerae — ECho
  coccineus ♀H1 — CMon ECho LToo
  humilis — ECho
  katherinae — see *Scadoxus multiflorus* subsp. *katherinae*

§ 'König Albert' — CMon
  natalensis — see *Scadoxus puniceus*
  pauculifolius — ECho WCMO WCot
  pubescens subsp. *leipoldtii* — ECho
  sanguineus — ERea

Hakea (Proteaceae)

§ *drupacea* — CTrC EShb
  epiglottis — CTrC ECou
  laurina — SPlb
  lissocarpha — CTrC

§ *lissosperma* — CDoC ECou EPla SPlb WPGP
  microcarpa — SLon
  nodosa — CTrC
  platysperma — SPlb

§ *salicifolia* — CCCN IMGH LRHS SPlb
  - 'Gold Medal' (v) — CTrC
  saligna — see *H. salicifolia*
  scoparia — CTrC
  sericea misapplied — see *H. lissosperma*
  sericea Schrad. & J.C.Wendl. — ECou
  - pink-flowered — SPlb
  suaveolens — see *H. drupacea*
  teretifolia — CTrC

Hakonechloa (Poaceae)

  macra — CAby CEnt CKno EBee EBrs EHoe EPla LPhx MMoz MRav MWgw NOGN SMad SPoG SWal WCot WDyG WPGP

§ - 'Alboaurea' ♀H4 — CBcs CFee CHea CKno CPLG CTbh EBee EBrs EFul EGle EGol ELan ENot EPfP EWsh LAst LPhx LSRN MBow MRav NCGa SPer SPla SPoG STre SYvo WFar WHil WWye

  - 'Albovariegata' — CKno CWan EBee GKev LEdu LHop WDyG

  - 'Aureola' ♀H4 — More than 30 suppliers
*   - 'Mediovariegata' (v) — CWCL EBee EPPr EPla WPGP
  - 'Variegata' — see *H. macra* 'Alboaurea'

Halenia (Gentianaceae)

  elliptica — EBee

Halesia (Styracaceae)

§ *carolina* — More than 30 suppliers
  diptera — CBcs CMCN MBlu
  - var. *magniflora* — MBlu
  monticola — CBcs CLnd CMCN ELan EPfP LRHS SPer SSpi WCMO WFar WNor

- var. *vestita* ♀H4	CAbP CDoC CDul CPMA CTho EBee EPfP EWTr IMGH LRHS MAsh MBlu NLar NVic SBrw SHBN SPer SSpi WDin WFar WHCG WPGP WPat
- - f. *rosea*	CBcs CPLG EPfP MBlu
tetraptera	see *H. carolina*

x *Halimiocistus* (*Cistaceae*)

algarvensis	see *Halimium ocymoides*
§ 'Ingwersenii'	CBcs CDoC ELan EWes LRHS SPer SPoG SRms WPer
revolii misapplied	see x *H. sahucii*
revolii (Coste & Soulié) Dansereau	XPep
§ *sahucii* ♀H4	CDoC CSBt EBee ECha ELan EPfP LAst LRHS MAsh MBNS MRav MSwo MWat SDys SGar SHBN SPer SPoG SWvt WAbe WCFE WDin WFar WWeb XPep
- Ice Dancer = 'Ebhals'PBR (v)	CDoC EBee ENot EPfP LAst MAsh NLar SPer SWvt
'Susan'	see *Halimium* 'Susan'
§ *wintonensis* ♀H3	CBcs CDoC CSBt EBee ELan EPfP LRHS MAsh MRav SHBN SPer SPla SRms WCFE WHar WWeb XPep
§ - 'Merrist Wood Cream' ♀H3	CBcs CBgR CDoC CSBt EBee ELan ENot EPfP EWTr LAst LHop LRHS MAsh MRav MSwo MWgw NBir NSti SPer SPla SSpi SSta SWvt WDin WFar WKif WPat XPep

Halimione (*Chenopodiaceae*)

§ portulacoides	XPep

Halimium ✿ (*Cistaceae*)

§ atriplicifolium	LRav XPep
§ calycinum	CAbP EBee ELan EPfP LRHS MAsh MBri MBlu SCoo SLim SPer SPoG SWvt WAbe WCFE WDin WWeb XPep
commutatum	see *H. calycinum*
formosum	see *H. lasianthum* subsp. *formosum*
halimifolium misapplied	see *H.* x *pauanum, H.* x *santae*
halimifolium Willk.	EBee XPep
§ lasianthum ♀H3	CBcs CHar CPLG CSBt CWib EBee EChP ELan EPfP LRHS MBri MRav SLim WBrE WCFE WEas WKif WLin
- 'Concolor'	CBcs CDoC CWib EMil LRHS MSwo SWvt WDin
§ - subsp. formosum	CHar XPep
- - 'Sandling'	EBee EGoo ELan EPfP LRHS MAsh
- 'Hannay Silver'	EBee SPla
libanotis	see *H. calycinum*
§ ocymoides ♀H3	CBcs CDoC CWib EBee EGoo ELan EPfP LRHS MAsh MMHG MSwo SLon WBrE WHar WKif WLin WWlt XPep
§ x pauanum	EBee LRHS NPro XPep
x santae	XPep
'Sarah'	EBee LRHS MAsh MBNS SPoG XPep
§ 'Susan' ♀H3	CDoC EBee ELan EPfP LHop LRHS LSou MAsh MBNS MMHG SCoo SLim SPer SPoG WAbe
§ umbellatum	EBee LRHS NLar SPer WHCG WKif WPat
verticillatum	XPep
wintonense	see x *Halimiocistus wintonensis*

Halimodendron (*Papilionaceae*)

halodendron	CBcs CDul EBee LRav MBlu NBlu SPer WDin

Halleria (*Scrophulariaceae*)

lucida	CCCN CSec WBor

Halocarpus (*Podocarpaceae*)

§ bidwillii	CDoC ECou

Haloragis (*Haloragaceae*)

erecta	CSev
- 'Rubra'	EBee WCot WPer
- 'Wellington Bronze'	CBow CPLG CSpe EBee ECtt EDAr EMan EUnu EWsh GBBs GGar GSki LEdu LRHS MBNS MCCP MLHP SBod SBri SDys SWal WEas WHer WMoo WSHC

Hamamelis ✿ (*Hamamelidaceae*)

§ 'Brevipetala'	CBcs CEnd NHol
x *intermedia* 'Advent'	NLar
- 'Angelly'	MBlu MBri MGos NLar
- 'Aphrodite'	EPfP LRHS MAsh MBlu MBri MGos NBhm SSpi
- 'Arnold Promise' ♀H4	More than 30 suppliers
- 'August Lamken' **new**	NLar
- 'Aurora'	MAsh MBlu NHol NLar SBrw
- 'Barmstedt Gold' ♀H4	CWib EPfP LRHS MAsh MBlu MBri MGos MRav NHol NLar SBrw SReu SSpi SSta
- 'Carmine Red'	MGos NLar WNor
- 'Copper Beauty'	see *H.* x *intermedia* 'Jelena'
- 'Diane' ♀H4	More than 30 suppliers
§ - 'Feuerzauber'	CMac LBuc MGos MSwo NBlu NLar NScw SPer WDin WOrn
* - 'Fire Cracker'	CSBt SBir WPat
- 'Gingerbread' **new**	LRHS
- 'Girard's Orange'	EPfP
- 'Glowing Embers'	LRHS
- 'Harry'	LRHS MAsh MBri NLar SBir SBrw
- Hillier's clone **new**	NHol
- 'Hiltingbury'	LRHS
§ - 'Jelena' ♀H4	More than 30 suppliers
- 'Lansing' **new**	NLar
- 'Livia'	LRHS MAsh NLar
- Magic Fire	see *H.* x *intermedia* 'Feuerzauber'
- 'Moonlight'	CDul CPMA NLar
- 'Nina'	LRHS MAsh
- 'Orange Beauty'	CBcs MGos NLar WGwG
- 'Orange Peel'	EPfP LRHS MAsh MBri NLar
- 'Pallida' ♀H4	More than 30 suppliers
- 'Primavera'	CWSG LPan MAsh MLan NHol SBrw SPla
- 'Ripe Corn'	EPfP LRHS
- 'Rubin'	LRHS MAsh
- 'Ruby Glow'	CBcs CWib EBee ECho MGos NWea SPer SPoG WDin
- 'Strawberries and Cream'	MAsh
- 'Sunburst'	EPfP MAsh MGos
- 'Vesna'	EPfP LRHS MBlu SSpi
§ - 'Westerstede'	COtt CWSG LPan LRHS MGos MLan MRav NBlu NHol NLar NScw NWea SBrw SLim WDin WHar WFar WNor
japonica	WNor
- 'Arborea'	WNor
- 'Robin'	CDul
mollis ♀H4	More than 30 suppliers
- 'Boskoop'	NLar
- 'Jermyns Gold'	EPfP SBrw
- 'Princeton Gold'	CWib
- 'Select'	see *H.* x *intermedia* 'Westerstede'
- 'Superba'	LRHS MAsh
- 'Wisley Supreme'	ELan LRHS MAsh SPoG
'Rochester'	NLar
vernalis	GIBF WDin
- 'Lombart's Weeping'	CFwr

- purple	CBcs MBlu
- 'Purpurea'	CBcs
- 'Sandra' ♀H4	CBcs CMCN ELan EPfP LRHS MAsh MBri MGos MRav NLar SHBN SLon SPer SPoG SReu SSpi SSta WCot
virginiana	CBcs ECrN GBin GIBF GPoy IDee MDun NWea WDin WFar WHCr
'Yamina' **new**	NLar

Hanabusaya (Campanulaceae)

§ *asiatica*	CHar CPom LPhx NChi NSfd WFar

Haplocarpha (Asteraceae)

rueppellii	CFee NBro SRms SRot WPer

Haplopappus (Asteraceae)

brandegeei	see *Erigeron aureus*
coronopifolius	see *H. glutinosus*
§ *glutinosus*	ECha ECho ECtt EPot GEdr MTho NLar NWCA SEND SPlb SPoG SRms XPep
lanceolatus	see *Pyrrocoma lanceolata*
lyallii	see *Tonestus lyallii*
microcephalus	WPer
prunelloides	GEdr NWCA
- var. *mustersii*	CPBP CStu
- - F&W 9384	WCot
rehderi	EBee NJOw WFar WMoo

Hardenbergia (Papilionaceae)

comptoniana ♀H1	CSec CSpe
- 'Rosea'	ERea
violacea ♀H1	CAbb CBcs CHll CPlN CRHN CSPN CSpe CTrC EBee EHol ELan ERea EShb GQui IDee LRHS SBod SLim SMur WCot
- f. *alba*	CBcs CPlN EBee EShb IDee
§ - - 'White Crystal'	ERea WPGP
- 'Happy Wanderer'	ERea LRHS SOWG WPGP
- f. *rosea*	CBcs EBee

Harpephyllum (Anacardiaceae)

caffrum (F)	XBlo

Harrimanella see *Cassiope*

Hastingsia (Hyacinthaceae)

alba GBuc	
- NNS 98-310	WCot
- NNS 98-311	WCot

Haworthia ✿ (Aloaceae)

attenuata	SWal
'Black Prince'	EPfP
cymbiformis	EPfP
- var. *umbraticola*	EPem
fasciata	EPfP
glabrata var. *concolor*	EPfP
radula	EPfP
reinwardtii ♀H1	CHal
tortusa	EPem

hazelnut see *Corylus*

Hebe ✿ (Scrophulariaceae)

albicans ♀H4	CPLG CWCL ECou ELan ENot EPfP IFoB LAst LRHS MBar MBri MGos MRav MWgw NEgg SCoo SHBN SPer SPoG SSto WFar WHCG WTel
- 'Cobb'	ECou
- 'Cranleigh Gem'	ECou
- prostrate	see *H. albicans* 'Snow Cover'
- 'Red Edge'	see *H.* 'Red Edge'
* - 'Snow Carpet'	CCCN
§ - 'Snow Cover'	ECou EWes

- 'Snow Drift'	see *H. albicans* 'Snow Cover'
- 'Snow Mound'	ECou
§ - 'Sussex Carpet'	ECou
§ 'Alicia Amherst'	EHol SPer SRms SSto SWal
allanii	see *H. amplexicaulis* f. *hirta*
'Amanda Cook' (v)	EHoe MCCP NPer
amplexicaulis	CNic
- clone 4	STre
§ - f. *hirta*	NDlv NHol
§ 'Amy'	LRHS MBri NBur NPer SHBN SHop SPer SPoG WSHC
x *andersonii*	CDul
- 'Andersonii Variegata' (v)	CSpe CWib NBur SPla SRms SWal WCot WRHF
- 'Argenteovariegata'	see *Hebe* x *andersonii* 'Andersonii Variegata'
'Andressa Paula'	CCCN
anomala misapplied	see *H.* 'Imposter'
anomala (Armstr.) Cockayne **new**	CCCN
'Aoira'	see *H. recurva* 'Aoira'
§ *armstrongii*	ECho EHoe GGar MBar MGos SSto WDin WPer
'Arthur'	ECou
astonii	ECho
'Autumn Glory'	CPLG CSBt CWSG ECho ELan EPfP GGar LAst LRHS MAsh MBar MGos MSwo NBir NBlu NWea SBod SGar SHBN SMer SPer SPla SPlb SPoG SWal SWvt WDin WGwG WTel
azurea	see *H. venustula*
'Azurens'	see *H.* 'Maori Gem'
'Baby Blush'PBR	CAbP ELan
'Baby Marie'	CAbP COtt CSBt ECho ECot ECou EHoe ELan EPfP LAst LRHS MAsh MGos MSwo MTis NBlu NHol NMen NPer SCoo SPla SPoG SRms SRot SSto SWvt WGwG
barkeri	ECou
'Beatrice'	ECou NDlv
'Beverley Hills'PBR	LRHS
'Bicolor Wand'	CCCN
§ *bishopiana*	ECou ELan ENot LRHS SBod SCoo SPoG SSto
'Blue Clouds' ♀H3	ECou LAst LRHS MSwo NDlv SPer SSto SWal WCFE
§ 'Blue Gem' **new**	LRHS
'Blue Star'	LRHS MAsh SPoG
bollonsii	GGar MSte
'Boscawenii'	CTrG EWin LRHS MGos
'Bouquet'PBR	SPoG
§ 'Bowles' Hybrid'	CCCN CSBt ECou EWin MSwo NBlu SRms SWal
'Bowles' Variety'	see *H.* 'Bowles's Hybrid'
brachysiphon	CTrC EPfP EWin GWCH MGos SHBN SPer WDin WHCG
brevifolia	ECou
breviracemosa	ECou
buchananii	ECho ECou GGar MBar MGos MHer MTho NDlv NHol NPer WPer
- 'Christchurch'	ECou
§ - 'Fenwickii'	ECho WHoo
- 'Minima'	ECho
§ - 'Minor'	ECho GBin GCrs MBar NBir NDlv NWCA SIng
* - 'Nana' **new**	MGos
- 'Ohau'	ECou
buxifolia misapplied	see *H. odora*
buxifolia (Benth.) Ckn. & Allan	ENot GGar NHol NWea WDin
N 'C.P. Raffill'	ECou
§ 'Caledonia' ♀H3	CCCN CSBt ECou ENot EPfP GGar LRHS MAsh MBri MGos MSte MWhi NDlv NHol NJOw NPer SCoo SPer SPoG WFar

'Candy'	ECou	
§ *canterburiensis*	ECou GGar	
N 'Carl Teschner'	see *H.* 'Youngii'	
'Carnea Variegata' (v)	EShb SBod SPer WOut	
carnosula	EHoe EWin GGar GTSp LRHS	
	MGos NBir SPer WPer	
catarractae	see *Parahebe catarractae*	
'Celine'	MGos SPoG	
I 'Chalk's Buchananii'	SBla	
§ 'Champagne' **new**	CCCN LRHS NHol	
'Champion'	EKen MWea SPoG	
* 'Charming White'	ENot EPfP LRHS SCoo SPoG SWal	
chathamica	CNic ECou GGar	
'Christabel'	EWin	
ciliolata x *odora*	GGar	
'Clear Skies'	CAbP ECou LRHS MAsh SPoG	
'Colwall'	ECho WHen	
'County Park'	ECou EWes NHol NMen WMow	
'Cranleighensis'	SSto	
cupressoides	CBcs MBar NDlv SEND WDin	
- 'Boughton Dome'	CTri ECho EHoe EPfP EWin MAsh	
	MGos MTho NLAp NMen WAbe	
	WEas WHoo WPer WSHC	
- 'Nana'	NJOw	
darwiniana	see *H. glaucophylla*	
'Dazzler' (v)	CAbP CSBt ELan ENot LRHS SPoG	
decumbens	CNic ECou EWes GGar MGos	
	NHol	
'Diana'	ECou	
dieffenbachii	GGar	
diosmifolia	CAbP CDoC CPle ELan WAbe	
- 'Marie'	ECou SWal	
divaricata	ECou	
* - 'Marlborough'	ECou	
- 'Nelson'	ECou	
x *divergens*	NDlv	
'Dorothy Peach'	see *H.* 'Watson's Pink'	
'E.A. Bowles'	ECou	
'E.B. Anderson'	see *H.* 'Caledonia'	
'Early Blue'	CSpe NBir	
'Edinensis'	NJOw WSHC WSPU	
'Edington'	CHal LRHS SPer WCFE	
elliptica	CDul ECou	
- 'Anatoki'	ECou	
- 'Charleston'	ECou	
- 'Kapiti'	ECou	
- 'Variegata'	see *H.* 'Silver Queen'	
'Emerald Dome'	see *H.* 'Emerald Gem'	
§ 'Emerald Gem' ♀H3	CDul ECho ENot EPfP GGar MAsh	
	MBar MBri MGos MHer MSwo	
	MWat MWgw NDlv NHol NMen	
	NWCA SCoo SPer SPlb SPoG WFar	
	WPat	
'Emerald Green'	see *H.* 'Emerald Gem'	
epacridea	ECho EWes NHol	
§ 'Eveline'	CSBt EHol ELan LRHS NBir SPer	
	SPoG WCot WKif	
evenosa	LRHS NDlv	
'Eversley Seedling'	see *H.* 'Bowles's Hybrid'	
'Fairfieldii'	CPLG EHol	
'First Light'PBR	CWSG NEgg SCoo SPoG	
'Fragrant Jewel'	CWib SEND SWal	
x *franciscana*	ECou LAst SWal	
§ - 'Blue Gem' ambig.	ECho GGar LRHS MGos NBir NPer	
	SPer SPlb SRms SSto SWal WGer	
	WHar XPep	
- 'Purple Tips' misapplied	see *H. speciosa* 'Variegata'	
- 'Variegata' (v)	see *H.* 'Silver Queen'	
I - 'White Gem'	SRms	
- yellow-variegated (v) **new**	SPer	
'Franjo'	ECou	
'Garden Beauty' **new**	LRHS	
'Gauntlettii'	see *H.* 'Eveline'	
'Gibby'	ECou	
N *glaucophylla*	SBod	
- 'Clarence'	ECou GGar	

I 'Glaucophylla Variegata' (v)	CNic CTri ECou NBir NDlv NSti	
	SPer SPoG SWal WKif	
'Glengarriff'	NHol	
'Gold Beauty' **new**	LRHS	
'Goldrush' (v)	MGos SPoG	
'Gran's Favourite'	CCCN	
'Great Orme' ♀H3	More than 30 suppliers	
'Green Globe'	see *H.* 'Emerald Gem'	
'Greensleeves'	ECou GGar MBar	
'Gruninard's Seedling'	GGar	
haastii	EPfP NLar	
'Hagley Park'	CSBt EPfP LRHS SAga WHCG	
§ 'Hartii'	LRHS MRav SPer	
'Heartbreaker'PBR (v)	ELan LBuc LRHS MAsh MGos SCoo	
	SPoG	
'Highdownensis'	SSto	
'Hinderwell'	NPer	
'Hinerua'	ECou GGar NJOw NNor	
'Holywell'	SBod SWal	
hookeriana	see *Parahebe hookeriana*	
hulkeana ♀H3	CMdw CWCL EMan EWin LSou	
	MHer NBir SAga WEas WHCG	
	WHoo WKif WPat WTin	
'Ian Young'	ITim	
§ 'Imposter'	CNic SRms SWal	
insularis	ECho ECou	
'Jack's Surprise'	EWin	
'James Stirling'	see *H. ochracea* 'James Stirling'	
'Jane Holden'	WSHC	
'Janet'	SGar	
'Jannas Blue'	EPfP	
'Jean Searle' **new**	LAst	
'Joan Lewis'	ECou	
'Joanna'	ECou	
§ 'Johny Day'	MBNS	
§ 'Judy'	ECou	
'June Small'	CNic	
'Just Judy' **new**	LRHS	
'Karo Golden Esk'	ECou NEgg SPoG	
'Kirkii'	EMil EPfP EWin SCoo SPer	
'Knightshayes'	see *H.* 'Caledonia'	
'La Séduisante'	CDul CSBt ECou MLHP SCoo	
	SEND SHBN WKif WSHC	
'Lady Ann'PBR (v)	SPoG	
'Lady Ardilaun'	see *H.* 'Amy'	
laevis	see *H. venustula*	
laingii	CNic	
latifolia	see *H.* 'Blue Gem'	
lavaudiana	WAbe	
'Lavender Spray'	see *H.* 'Hartii'	
'Lindsayi'	ECou NDlv NJOw	
§ 'Loganioides'	GGar	
'Lopen' (v)	ECou EWes	
'Louise'	SGar	
lyallii	see *Parahebe lyallii*	
lycopodioides	EWes	
- 'Aurea'	see *H. armstrongii*	
mackenii	see *H.* 'Emerald Gem'	
macrantha ♀H3	ECho EPfP GCrs GGar LRHS SPer	
	SRms WAbe	
macrocarpa	ECou EWin LRHS SPoG	
- var. *latisepala*	ECou	
§ 'Maori Gem'	GGar SSto	
'Margery Fish'	see *H.* 'Primley Gem'	
'Margret'PBR ♀H4	COtt CSBt EMil ENot EPfP LAst	
	LRHS MAsh MGos MSwo NMen	
	SCoo SHBN SPer SPoG SSto	
'Marjorie'	CDul CSBt ENot EPfP LRHS MGos	
	MRav MSwo NFor NPer NWea	
	SBod SPer SSto SWal WCFE WDin	
	WTel	
matthewsii	ECou WPat	
'Mauve Queen'	EHol	
'Mauvena'	SPer	
'McCabe'	NJOw	
'Mcewanii'	ECou	

'McKean'	see *Hebe* 'Emerald Gem'
'Megan'	ECou
'Mercury'	ECou SCoo
'Midsummer Beauty' ♀H3	ECou EPfP GGar ISea LAst LRHS MGos MLHP MRav NBir SBod SHBN SPer SPlb SSto SWvt WDin WFar WOut WSFF
'Milmont Emerald'	see *H.* 'Emerald Gem'
* minima 'Calvin'	ECho
'Miss Fittall'	ECou
'Misty' **new**	CCCN
§ 'Mohawk'PBR	COtt LRHS SCoo
'Monica'	NHol
* 'Moppets Hardy'	SPer
§ 'Mrs Winder' ♀H4	More than 30 suppliers
'Mystery'	ECou ELan SWal
'Mystery Red'	ENot LRHS MGos SPoG
'Nantyderry'	CCCN CHal GBri SPla SWal WOut
§ 'Neil's Choice' ♀H4	CCCN ECou LRHS MSte SCoo SPoG SWal
'Netta Dick'	ECou
'Nicola's Blush' ♀H4	More than 30 suppliers
obtusata	ECou SCoo
ochracea	MGos NBlu
§ - 'James Stirling' ♀H4	CBrm CSBt ECho EHoe ELan ENot EPfP GGar LRHS MAsh MBar MBri MGos MSwo MTho NBir NFor NHol NJOw SLim SPer SPlb SPoG STre SWvt WDin WFar
§ odora	ECou EPfP MRav MWhi WCFE
I - 'Nana'	EPfP EWin MBar
- 'New Zealand Gold'	CNic EWin LRHS MAsh MGos NDlv SCoo SEND SLon SSto
- var. patens	WHCG
- 'Stewart Island'	ECou
- 'Summer Frost'	CRez NHol NPri SCoo SPoG
- 'Wintergreen'	MRav
'Oratia Beauty' ♀H4	LRHS MRav MWgw
'Orphan Annie'PBR (v)	CWSG ENot LRHS MGos SCoo SPoG
'Oswego'	ECou
'Otari Delight'	CMHG
parviflora misapplied	see *H.* 'Bowles's Hybrid'
§ parviflora (Vahl) Cockayne & Allan	GGar
- 'Holdsworth'	SDys
- 'Palmerston'	ECou
- var. angustifolia	see *H. stenophylla*
- var. arborea	see *H. parviflora* (Vahl) Cockayne & Allan
'Pascal' ♀H4	CCCN ECou ELan EPfP LRHS MBNS MBri MRav NPri SCoo SPoG
'Pastel Blue'	SPoG SSto
pauciramosa	SRms SWal
'Paula'	CPLG
'Pearl of Paradise'PBR	SPoG
perfoliata	see *Parahebe perfoliata*
'Perry's Rubyleaf'	NPer
'Petra's Pink'	CCCN LRHS
§ 'Pewter Dome' ♀H4	CDoC CSBt ECou EGra EHoe EPfP MGos MRav NDlv NEgg NHol SBod SDix SPoG SRms STre WBrE WHen
'Pimeba'	NHol
pimeleoides	ECou NHol NJOw SSto
- 'Glauca'	NPer
- 'Glaucocaerulea'	ECou
- 'Quicksilver' ♀H4	CSBt CTri ECou EHoe ELan ENot EPfP GGar GMaP LAst LRHS MAsh MBar MGos MRav MSwo NBir NHol NPer SCoo SPer SPoG SWal WCot WFar WPat
- 'Red Tip'	ECho
- var. rupestris	ECou
pinguifolia	ECou NDlv SPlb WFar
- 'Hutt'	ECou
- 'Pagei' ♀H4	More than 30 suppliers
- 'Sutherlandii'	CDoC CNic ECho LEdu LRHS MBar MGos MWhi NDlv SCoo SSto WFar
'Pink Elephant' (v) ♀H3	CAbP CSBt ELan EPfP LAst LBuc LRHS MAsh SCoo SPer SPla SPoG SWvt
'Pink Fantasy'	LRHS MRav NHol
'Pink Goddess'	LRHS
'Pink Lady' **new**	SPoG
'Pink Paradise'PBR	CAbP ELan ENot EPfP LRHS MGos NHol NPri SBod SPoG SSto
'Pink Payne'	see *H.* 'Eveline'
'Pink Pixie'	LSou MBri SCoo
'Porlock Purple'	see *Parahebe catarractae* 'Delight'
§ 'Primley Gem'	CCCN LRHS
propinqua	MHer NLAp NMen
- 'Minor'	NDlv
I 'Prostrata'	CNic CSBt NDlv
'Purple Emperor'	see *H.* 'Neil's Choice'
'Purple Paradise'PBR	EPfP LBuc LRHS MBri SPoG
'Purple Pixie'PBR	see *H.* 'Mohawk'
'Purple Queen'	CSBt ELan EPfP EShb GGar LRHS SHFr SPla SPoG SSto
Purple Shamrock = 'Neprock'PBR (v)	CSBt ENot EPfP LBuc LRHS MAsh MBri MGos SCoo SPer SPoG SWal
'Purple Tips' misapplied	see *H. speciosa* 'Variegata'
rakaiensis ♀H4	More than 30 suppliers
ramosissima	NDlv
raoulii	GBri NWCA SBla WAbe WFar
§ recurva	CNic CSam CTri ECou EPfP GGar LAst LRHS MGos NHol SEND SHFr SPoG SRms WBrE WDin
§ - 'Aoira'	ECou NDlv
- 'Boughton Silver' ♀H3	ELan ENot EPfP LRHS MAsh MBNS MWgw SPoG
- 'White Torrent'	ECou
§ 'Red Edge' ♀H4	More than 30 suppliers
'Red Ruth'	see *H.* 'Eveline'
rigidula	ECou MGos NHol SWal
'Ronda'	ECou
'Rosie'PBR	CBcs EPfP LRHS MWea NMen SCoo SPer SSto
'Royal Purple'	see *H.* 'Alicia Amherst'
salicifolia	CCCN ECou ELan ENot EPfP GGar LAst LRHS MRav NEgg NHol NJOw SHBN SPer SPlb SPoG SRms SSto SWal WFar WHCG WTel
- BR 30	GGar
'Sandra Joy' **new**	CCCN LRHS
'Sapphire' ♀H4	CDoC ECou EPfP GGar LRHS MBar MGos NBlu SCoo SPoG SSto WGer
'Sarana'	CCCN ECou
'Seksti'	SWal
selaginoides hort.	see *H.* 'Loganioides'
'Shiraz'	LRHS SCoo
'Silver Dollar' (v)	CAbP CCCN CMMP CPLG CSBt EHoe ELan ENot EPfP LAst LHop LRHS MAsh MGos NPri SPer SPoG SSto SWvt
§ 'Silver Queen' (v) ♀H2	CSBt ECou EGra ELan ENot EPfP EShb GGar LAst MAsh MBar MGos MNHC MRav NBlu NJOw NPer SPer SSto SWal WHar WOut
'Simon Délaux'	CEnt CSBt ECou LRHS NCiC SAga SPoG SSto SUsu WOut
I 'Southlandii'	ECho
speciosa	ECho
- 'Rangatira'	ECou
§ - 'Variegata' (v)	CHal NPer SSto WEas
'Spender's Seedling' misapplied	see *H. stenophylla*
'Spender's Seedling'	ECou EPfP EWin LRHS SEND SPoG SRms STre
'Spring Glory'	LRHS

§ *stenophylla*	ECou EShb EWes EWin SAPC SArc SDix SHFr SSto SUsu
- 'White Lady'	GGar
stricta	ECou
- var. *egmontiana*	ECou
- var. *macroura*	ECou
subalpina	CSBt ECho ECou NHol
subsimilis	SBla
'Summer Blue'	ENot EPfP EWin LRHS
'Summer Snow'	NBir
'Sussex Carpet'	see *H. albicans* 'Sussex Carpet'
'Sweet Kim' (v)	COtt ENot LBuc LRHS SPoG
'Tina'	ECou NHol
'Tiny Tot'	EHyt MTho
'Tom Marshall'	see *H. canterburiensis*
topiaria ♀H4	CAbP CSBt CSam ECho ECou EMil EPfP GGar LAst LHop LRHS MAsh MBrN MSwo MWgw NHol SCoo SHBN SPer SPla SPoG STre WAbe WFar WGwG
townsonii	ECou EWin LHop SAga SCoo
traversii	ECou MSte NHol SRms SSto
- 'Mason River'	ECou
- 'Woodside'	ECou
'Tricolor'	see *H. speciosa* 'Variegata'
'Trixie'	CCCN CNic ECou
'Twisty'	ELan LRHS LSou MBNS SPoG
urvilleana	ECou
'Valentino'PBR	LRHS SPoG
'Veitchii'	see *H.* 'Alicia Amherst'
§ *venustula*	ECou GGar IArd WPer
- 'Patricia Davies'	ECou
- 'Sky Blue'	ECou
vernicosa ♀H3	CNic ECho ECou EPfP LAst LRHS MBar MGos MHer NDlv NHol NJOw SCoo SPer SPlb SPoG SRot STre WAbe WHCG
'Vogue'	EPfP LRHS SPoG
'Waikiki'	see *H.* 'Mrs Winder'
'Wardiensis'	CMHG
'Warleyensis'	see *H.* 'Mrs Winder'
§ 'Watson's Pink'	ECou GGar MWea SPer WKif
'Whistleberry Sapphire'	SWal
§ 'White Gem'	CCCN ECou MGos NBlu NDlv
(*brachysiphon* hybrid) ♀H4	NPer SPer SWal WBVN WFar
'White Heather'	LRHS NBir
'White Spreader'	EWin
'Willcoxii'	see *H. buchananii* 'Fenwickii'
'Wingletye' ♀H3	CCCN CNic ECho ECou GGar LRHS MWgw MWhi NDlv NEgg NNor WAbe WPer WTel
'Winter Glow'	CCCN COtt EWin LSou NHol SCoo
'Wiri Blush'	SHBN SWvt
'Wiri Charm'	CAbP CBcs CDoC CDul COtt CSBt ENot EPfP GGar LAst LRHS MGos MLan MRav MSwo MTis SHBN SSto WBVN WGwG WOut
'Wiri Cloud' ♀H3	CAbP CSBt EPfP EWin GGar LRHS MSwo MTis SSto SWal WGwG
'Wiri Dawn' ♀H3	CAbP CBcs COtt CSBt ELan EPfP EWes EWin GGar LRHS LSou MGos SCoo SHBN SSto SWvt WHrl
'Wiri Desire' new	CCCN
'Wiri Gem'	EWin LRHS MRav
'Wiri Image'	CBcs CDoC COtt CSBt EWin LRHS
'Wiri Joy'	LRHS SEND
'Wiri Mist'	CBcs COtt CTrC EWin GGar LRHS MGos NBlu SPoG
'Wiri Prince'	EWin LRHS
'Wiri Splash'	CDoC COtt CSBt CTrC EShb EWin GGar LRHS MGos SCoo SHBN SSto WGwG
'Wiri Vision'	COtt CSBt LRHS

§ 'Youngii' ♀H3-4	CSBt ELan ENot EPfP LAst LRHS MAsh MBar MBow MHer MRav MWat NBir NJOw NMen NRya NWCA SBod SPer SPlb SPoG SRms SWvt WCFE WHoo WSHC WTel

Hebenstretia (Scrophulariaceae)

dura	CPBP
* *quinquinervis* new	LSou

Hedeoma (Lamiaceae)

hyssopifolia	LPhx

Hedera ✿ (Araliaceae)

algeriensis	see *H. canariensis* hort.
§ *azorica*	EShb WFar WFib
- 'Pico'	WFib
- 'Variegata' (v)	WCot
§ *canariensis* hort.	CBcs CDoC CDul SAPC SArc WFib WGwG
- 'Algeriensis'	see *H. canariensis* hort.
- var. *azorica*	see *H. azorica*
- 'Cantabrian'	see *H. maroccana* 'Spanish Canary'
§ - 'Gloire de Marengo' (v) ♀H3	More than 30 suppliers
- 'Gloire de Marengo' arborescent (v)	SPer
- 'Marginomaculata' ♀H3	CDoC EPfP EShb LRHS MAsh SMad SPoG WFib WWeb
- 'Montgomery'	LRHS MWht
- 'Ravensholst' ♀H3	CMac NSti WFib
- 'Variegata'	see *H. canariensis* 'Gloire de Marengo'
chinensis	see *H. nepalensis* var. *sinensis*
- typica	see *H. nepalensis* var. *sinensis*
§ *colchica* ♀H4	EPfP LRHS SPer WCFE WDin WFar WFib
- 'Arborescens'	see *H. colchica* 'Dendroides'
- 'Batumi'	MBNS
§ - 'Dendroides'	WCot
§ - 'Dentata' ♀H4	EPla MRav MWhi WFib
- 'Dentata Aurea'	see *H. colchica* 'Dentata Variegata'
§ - 'Dentata Variegata' (v) ♀H4	More than 30 suppliers
- 'My Heart'	see *H. colchica*
- 'Paddy's Pride'	see *H. colchica* 'Sulphur Heart'
§ - 'Sulphur Heart' (v) ♀H4	More than 30 suppliers
- 'Variegata'	see *H. colchica* 'Dentata Variegata'
cristata	see *H. helix* 'Parsley Crested'
§ *cypria*	WFib
'Dixie'	NLar
helix	CArn CCVT CRWN CTri MBar MGos NBlu NWea SHFr WDin WFar WHer WSFF XPep
- 'Abundance'	see *H. helix* 'California'
- 'Adam' (v)	CWib ECrN LAst MBri MTho WFib
- 'Amberwaves'	MBri NBre WFib
- 'Amita'	CHal
§ - 'Angularis'	ECot
- 'Angularis Aurea' ♀H4	EHoe EPfP MWht NBir NHol SHBN WFib
- 'Anita'	CBgR ECrN GBin WFib WGwG
§ - 'Anna Marie' (v)	CMac LRHS MBri WFib
- 'Anne Borch'	see *H. helix* 'Anna Marie'
- 'Annette'	see *H. helix* 'California'
- 'Arborescens'	CNat ENot NPal WCot WDin
- 'Ardingly' (v)	MWhi WFib
- 'Asterisk'	WFib
- 'Atropurpurea'	CNat EPPr EPla GBin MBar WDin WFib
- 'Aurea Densa'	see *H. helix* 'Aureovariegata'
§ - 'Aureovariegata' (v)	CNic
- 'Baby Face'	WFib
- var. *baltica*	WFib
- 'Barabits' Silver' (v)	EGoo EPla

- 'Bill Archer' WFib
- 'Bird's Foot' see *H. helix* 'Pedata'
- 'Blue Moon' WFib
- 'Bodil' (v) SHFr
- 'Boskoop' WFib
- 'Bowles Ox Heart' WFib
- 'Bowles Shield' CNic
- 'Bredon' ECrN
- 'Brigette' see *H. helix* 'California'
§ - 'Brokamp' MWht SLPl WFib
- 'Bruder Ingobert' (v) WHrl
- 'Buttercup' More than 30 suppliers
- 'Buttercup' arborescent MAsh SPoG
§ - 'Caecilia' (v) ♀H4 CBcs ELan EPfP LRHS MSwo NLar
    NSti SLim SPer SWvt WCot WFar
    WFib WWeb
N - 'Caenwoodiana' see *H. helix* 'Pedata'
- 'Caenwoodiana Aurea' WFib
- 'Calico' (v) WFib
§ - 'California' NSti
- 'California Gold' (v) WFib
- 'Calypso' WFib
- 'Carolina Crinkle' CBgR MWhi WFib
- 'Cathedral Wall' WFib
§ - 'Cavendishii' (v) SRms WFib
§ - 'Ceridwen' (v) ♀H4 CRHS EBee MBri SPlb WFib
    WWeb
- 'Chalice' ECrN WFib
- 'Chedglow Fasciated' CNat WFar
- 'Cheeky' WFib
- 'Cheltenham Blizzard' (v) CNat
- 'Chester' (v) WFar WFib
- 'Chicago' CWib WFib
- 'Chicago Variegated' (v) WFib
- 'Chrysophylla' EPla MSwo
- 'Clotted Cream' (v) CBrm LHop LRHS MAsh WFar
    WFib
- 'Cockle Shell' NBre WFib
§ - 'Congesta' ♀H4 EPla MTho MWgw NBir SRms STre
    WFib
- 'Conglomerata' CBcs ELan EPla MBar NBir NBre
    NEgg NFor SRms WDin WFib WTel
- 'Conglomerata Erecta' CSWP NVic SRms WCFE WFib
- 'Courage' WFib WGwG
- 'Crenata' WFib
- 'Crispa' MRav NFor
- 'Cristata' see *H. helix* 'Parsley Crested'
- 'Cristata Melanie' see *H. helix* 'Melanie'
- 'Curleylocks' see *H. helix* 'Manda's Crested'
- 'Curley-Q' see *H. helix* 'Dragon Claw'
- 'Curvaceous' (v) WCot WFib
- 'Cyprus' see *H. cypria*
- 'Dainty Bess' CWib
- 'Dead Again' WCot
§ - 'Dealbata' (v) CMac WFib
- 'Deltoidea' see *H. hibernica* 'Deltoidea'
- 'Discolor' see *H. helix* 'Minor Marmorata',
    H. helix 'Dealbata'
- 'Domino' (v) EWes
§ - 'Donerailensis' CBgR MBlu WFib WPer
- 'Don's Papillon' CBgR CNat
- 'Dovers' WFib
§ - 'Dragon Claw' ECrN EPla WFib
- 'Duckfoot' ♀H4 CBgR CDoC CHal ECrN MTho
    MWhi NSti WFar WFib WOut
- 'Dunloe Gap' see *H. hibernica* 'Dunloe Gap'
- 'Egret' WFib
- 'Eileen' (v) NBre WFib
- 'Elfenbein' (v) WFib
- 'Emerald Gem' see *H. helix* 'Angularis'
- 'Emerald Jewel' WFib
- 'Erecta' ♀H4 CBgR EBee EPPr EPfP EPla LRHS
    MBar MGos MTho MWhi MBlu
    NGHP NHol SHGN SPer SPlb SPoG
    SSto WCot WDin WFar WFib WPat
    WPrP WWye XPep

- 'Ester' (v) LAst SRGP WFib
§ - 'Eva' (v) ECrN NBir WDin WFib
- 'Fanfare' WFib
- 'Fantasia' (v) ECrN MBri NBre WFib
- 'Feenfinger' WFib WGwG
- 'Ferney' WFib
- 'Filigran' ECrN NLar SMad WFib WHer
- 'Flashback' (v) WFib
- 'Flavescens' WFib
- 'Fleur de Lis' ECrN
- 'Fluffy Ruffles' ECrN WFib
I - 'Francis Ivy' WFib
- 'Frizzle' ECrN WFib
- 'Frosty' (v) WFib
- 'Gavotte' EPPr MTho MWht WFib
- 'Ghost' WFib
- 'Gilded Hawke' WFib WGwG
- 'Glache' (v) SHFr WFib
- 'Glacier' (v) ♀H4 More than 30 suppliers
- 'Glymii' EPla WFar WFib WTin
- 'Gold Harald' see *H. helix* 'Goldchild'
- 'Gold Ripple' EHoe NBre SEND
§ - 'Goldchild' (v) ♀H3-4 CBcs CDoC CSam EBee ECrN
    ENot EPfP EPla LAst LRHS MAsh
    MBar MGos MRav MSwo MWhi
    NBir NBlu NHol SAga SHFr SLim
    SPer SPoG SWvt WDin WFib WTel
- 'Goldcraft' (v) WFib
- 'Golden Ann' see *H. helix* 'Ceridwen'
* - 'Golden Arrow' ELan LRHS MAsh SPoG
- 'Golden Curl' (v) EPfP LRHS SCoo WWeb
- 'Golden Ester' see *H. helix* 'Ceridwen'
- 'Golden Gate' (v) ECrN LAst WFib
- 'Golden Gem' NPro
- 'Golden Girl' WFib
- 'Golden Ingot' (v) ♀H4 ECrN ELan EPla MBar MWhi NBre
    WFib WGwG
- 'Golden Kolibri' see *H. helix* 'Midas Touch'
- 'Golden Mathilde' (v) CHal GBin
- 'Golden Pittsburgh' (v) WFib
- 'Golden Snow' (v) WFib
- 'Goldfinch' MBri WFib
- 'Goldfinger' MBri WFib
- 'Goldheart' see *H. helix* 'Oro di Bogliasco'
§ - 'Goldstern' (v) CBgR EHoe MWhi WFib
- 'Gracilis' see *H. hibernica* 'Gracilis'
§ - 'Green Feather' EGoo
- 'Green Finger' see *H. helix* 'Très Coupé'
§ - 'Green Ripple' CBcs CSBt CTri CWib EBee ECrN
    EShb LRHS MAsh MBar MGos
    MRav MSwo MWht NBro SEND
    SLim SPer SPlb WBor WDin WFar
    WFib WHen
- 'Greenman' WFib WGwG
- 'Hahn's Green Ripple' see *H. helix* 'Green Ripple'
- 'Halebob' MBri WFib WGwG
- 'Hamilton' see *H. hibernica* 'Hamilton'
§ - 'Harald' (v) CWib EBee NSti SCoo WDin WFib
* - 'Hazel' (v) WFib
- 'Hedge Hog' WFib
- 'Heise' (v) WFib
- 'Heise Denmark' (v) WFib
- 'Helvig' see *H. helix* 'White Knight'
- 'Henrietta' WFib
- 'Hester' WFib
- subsp. *hibernica* see *H. hibernica*
- 'Hispanica' see *H. maderensis* subsp. *iberica*
- 'Hite's Miniature' see *H. helix* 'Merion Beauty'
- 'Holly' see *H. helix* 'Parsley Crested'
- 'Hullavington' CNat
- 'Humpty Dumpty' CPLG MBar
- 'Ice Cream' MBlu
- 'Ideal' see *H. helix* 'California'
- 'Imp' see *H. helix* 'Brokamp'
- 'Ingelise' (v) WFib
- 'Ingrid' (v) WFib

	- 'Irish Lace'	WFar
	- 'Ivalace' ♀H4	CBcs CNat CRHN EBee ECha ECrN EPfP EPla MGos MNrw MRav MSwo MWhi MWht NBid NSti SRms WDin WFib WTin
	- 'Jake'	CHal MBri WFib
	- 'Jasper'	WFib
	- 'Jersey Doris' (v)	WFib
	- 'Jerusalem'	see *H. helix* 'Schäfer Three'
	- 'Jessica'	SCoo
	- 'Jester's Gold'	ELan ENot EPfP EPla MBri MGos WDin
	- 'Jubilee' (v)	ECrN WCFE WFar WFib
	- 'Kaleidoscope'	WFib
	- 'Kevin'	WFib
	- 'Knülch'	WFib
	- 'Kolibri' (v)	CDoC CFRD CHal CRHN EBee EMil EPfP LAst MBar MBri MWht NBlu WFib
§	- 'Königer's Auslese'	CRHN SPoG WFib
	- 'Kurios'	CNat
	- 'Lalla Rookh'	MRav WFib WGwG WHrl
	- 'Lemon Swirl' (v)	WFib
	- 'Leo Swicegood'	CBgR MWhi NBre WFib
	- 'Light Fingers'	LRHS NBre SPoG WFib WGwG WHrl
	- 'Limey'	WFib
	- 'Little Diamond' (v)	CDoC CTri EHoe ELan EPfP LHop LRHS MAsh MBar MBri MWht NHol SHBN SLon SPoG SWvt WDin WFar WHrl WTin
	- 'Little Silver' **new**	LRHS
	- 'Little Witch'	EPla
	- 'Liz'	see *H. helix* 'Eva'
	- 'Lucille'	WFib
I	- 'Lutzii' (v)	WFib WGwG
§	- 'Luzii' (v)	EBee ECrN EHoe MBar MGos NSti SGar SHBN WFib
	- 'Maculata'	see *H. helix* 'Minor Marmorata'
§	- 'Manda's Crested' ♀H4	CSWP ECrN NLar WFib WGwG
	- 'Maple Leaf' ♀H4	WFib
	- 'Maple Queen'	MBri
	- 'Marginata' (v)	SRms
	- 'Marginata Elegantissima'	see *H. helix* 'Tricolor'
	- 'Marginata Minor'	see *H. helix* 'Cavendishii'
I	- 'Marmorata' Fibrex	WFib
	- 'Masquerade' (v)	WGor
	- 'Mathilde' (v)	EBee LRHS MWht WFib
	- 'Maxi'	LRHS SCoo
	- 'Meagheri'	see *H. helix* 'Green Feather'
§	- 'Melanie' ♀H4	ECha ECrN EPla LRHS WCot WFib WGwG
	- 'Meon'	WFib
§	- 'Merion Beauty'	WFib
§	- 'Midas Touch' (v) ♀H3-4	COtt CWib EPfP MBri NLar WFib
	- 'Midget'	CRow
	- 'Mini Ester' (v)	EPfP MBri
	- 'Mini Heron'	LAst MBri
	- 'Mini Pittsburgh'	LAst
	- 'Minikin' (v)	WFib
	- 'Minima' misapplied	see *H. helix* 'Spetchley'
	- 'Minima' M.Young	see *H. helix* 'Congesta'
	- 'Minima' Hibberd	see *H. helix* 'Donerailensis'
§	- 'Minor Marmorata' (v) ♀H4	CHal WSHC
	- 'Mint Kolibri'	EHoe MBri
	- 'Minty' (v)	EPla LRHS MWht NBre SCoo WFib
	- 'Misty' (v)	WFib
	- 'Needlepoint'	EHoe
	- 'Nena' **new**	NBre
	- 'New Ripples'	MWht
	- 'Niagara Falls' **new**	LRHS
	- 'Nigra Aurea' (v)	WFib
	- 'Norfolk Lace'	EWes
	- 'Obovata'	WFib
N	- 'Oro di Bogliasco' (v)	More than 30 suppliers
	- 'Ovata'	WFib
§	- 'Parsley Crested' ♀H4	CMac CSBt EBee ECrN EPfP MAsh MBar NSti SGar SPer SPoG SRms WBVN WFar WFib WGwG
	- 'Patent Leather'	WFib
N	- 'Pedata'	EPfP MSwo WFib
	- 'Perkeo'	CHal EGoo WFib
	- 'Perle' (v)	NBir
	- 'Persian Carpet'	WFib
	- 'Peter' (v)	WFib
	- 'Peter Pan'	WFib WGwG
*	- 'Pin Oak'	EHoe WDin WFar
	- 'Pink 'n' Curly'	WFib
	- 'Pink 'n' Very Curly'	NBre WCot
§	- 'Pittsburgh'	WFib
	- 'Plume d'Or'	CHal WFib
§	- f. *poetarum*	CNat EPla MBlu WFib
	- - 'Poetica Arborea'	ECha SDix
	- 'Poetica'	see *H. helix* f. *poetarum*
	- 'Preston Tiny'	NBir
	- 'Raleigh Delight' (v)	WCot
	- 'Rambler'	NBir
	- 'Ray's Supreme'	see *H. helix* 'Pittsburgh'
	- subsp. *rhizomatifera*	WFib
	- 'Ritterkreuz'	WFib WGwG
	- 'Romanze' (v)	WFib WGwG
	- 'Russelliana'	WFib
	- 'Rüsche'	EGoo
	- 'Sagittifolia' misapplied	see *H. helix* 'Königers Auslese'
	- 'Sagittifolia' Hibberd	see *H. hibernica* 'Sagittifolia'
§	- 'Sagittifolia Variegata' (v)	CFRD EBee ECrN LRHS MBri NBea WFib WRHF
	- 'Saint Agnes' **new**	LRHS MAsh
	- 'Sally' (v)	WFib
	- 'Salt and Pepper'	see *H. helix* 'Minor Marmorata'
§	- 'Schäfer Three' (v)	CWib WFib
	- 'Shadow'	WFib
	- 'Shamrock'	EPfP MWht WFib
	- 'Silver Butterflies' (v)	WFib
	- 'Silver King' (v)	MRav MWht NBir WFib WGwG
	- 'Silver Queen'	see *H. helix* 'Tricolor'
	- 'Spectre' (v)	WHer
§	- 'Spetchley' ♀H4	CHal CNic EPla EPot GCal MAsh MBar MRav MWhi NPer SMad WCFE WCot WFib WGwG WHrl WPat WPrP WTin
	- 'Spiriusa'	WFib
	- 'Stuttgart'	CWil WFib
	- 'Sunrise'	WFib
	- 'Suzanne'	see *H. nepalensis* var. *nepalensis* 'Suzanne'
	- 'Tamara'	SCoo
	- 'Tango'	ECrN
	- 'Tanja'	WFib
	- 'Teardrop'	ECrN NBre
	- 'Telecurl'	WFib
	- 'Tenerife'	WFib
	- 'Tiger Eyes'	CBcs WFib
	- 'Topazolite' (v)	WFib
§	- 'Très Coupé'	CBcs CBgR CDoC EBee ECrN EGoo ISea LRHS SAPC SArc SCoo SPoG WDin
§	- 'Tricolor' (v)	CBcs CTri EBee EPfP LRHS MGos MWht SBra SHBN WCFE WFib WTel
	- 'Trinity' (v)	WFib
	- 'Tripod'	CBcs WFib WGwG
	- 'Triton'	MBar WFib
	- 'Troll'	WFib
	- 'Tussie Mussie' (v)	WFib
	- 'Ursula' (v)	LPBA NBre WFib
	- 'Very Merry'	LPBA
	- 'White Heart'	MGos
§	- 'White Knight' (v) ♀H4	WFib
	- 'White Mein Herz' (v)	GBin WFib

- 'White Wonder' **new**	LRHS
- 'William Kennedy' (v)	WFib
- 'Williamsiana' (v)	CBcs WFib
- 'Woeneri'	MWht SLPl WFib
- 'Wonder'	WFib
- 'Yab Yum' (v)	CBcs
- 'Yellow Ripple'	LPBA MBri NBre WDin
- 'Zebra' (v)	WFib
§ *hibernica* ♀H4	CBcs CDul CNat CSBt LBuc LRHS MBar MRav MSwo MWhi NBlu NWea SPer SPoG SRms WDin WFib
- 'Anna Marie'	see *H. helix* 'Anna Marie'
- 'Aracena'	EPla SLPl
- 'Betty Allen'	WFib
§ - 'Deltoidea' ♀H4	EPla MWht WFib
I - 'Digitata Crûg Gold'	WCru
§ - 'Dunloe Gap'	EPla
§ - 'Gracilis'	WFib
§ - 'Hamilton'	WFib
- 'Harlequin' (v)	CFRD WFib
- 'Lobata Major'	SRms
- 'Maculata' (v)	EPla SLPl WSHC
- 'Palmata'	WFib
- 'Rona'	WFib WGwG
§ - 'Sagittifolia'	CTri EPfP GBin LRHS MBar SHFr SRms WDin WFar
- 'Sulphurea' (v)	MGos WFib
- 'Tess'	EPla
- 'Variegata' (v)	MBar
maderensis	WFib
§ - subsp. *iberica*	WFib
maroccana 'Morocco'	WFib
§ - 'Spanish Canary'	WFib
nepalensis	WFib
§ - var. *nepalensis* 'Suzanne'	MBar WFib
§ - var. *sinensis*	MWht WFib
- - L 555	EPla
pastuchovii	EShb WFib
- from Troödos, Cyprus	see *H. cypria*
- 'Ann Ala'	WFib WGwG
§ *rhombea*	WCot WFib
- 'Eastern Dawn'	WFib
- 'Japonica'	see *H. rhombea*
I - f. *pedunculata* 'Maculata'	CWib
- var. *rhombea* 'Variegata' (v)	WFib

Hedychium ✿ (Zingiberaceae)

B&SWJ 3110	WPGP
B&SWJ 7155	WPGP
B&SWJ 7171	CKob
CC 4729	CPLG
'Anne Bishop'	CKob MJnS WPGP
aurantiacum	CBct CHEx CPne EAmu EBee EZes LEdu MJnS NPal WCMO WMul WPnP
chrysoleucum	CCCN CHEx EShb MJnS
coccineum ♀H1	CBcs CKob EAmu ECho EShb LRHS MJnS MNrw MOak WMul
- B&SWJ 5238	CKob WCru
- var. *angustifolium*	CRHN EPfP WHal WPGP
- - 'Peach'	MOak
- 'Tara' ♀H3	CBct CDes CDoC CHEx CKob CPne CRHN CSam EAmu EBee EPfP ERea IBlr IGor LEdu LPJP MJnS MNrw MOak MSte SAPC SArc SChr SDix SUsu WCMO WCot WCru WMul WPGP
coronarium	CAvo CBct CDes CHEx CKob EAmu EBee EShb EZes LRHS MJnS MOak MSte SYvo WCMO WCot WMul WPGP
- B&SWJ 8354	WCru
- 'Andromeda'	CKob WCMO WMul
- var. *flavescens*	see *H. flavescens*
- 'Gold Spot'	CKob EZes MOak SChr
- 'Orange Spot'	EAmu
coronarium x *ellipticum* **new**	CKob
coronarium x *gardnerianum*	MJnS WMul
'Dave Case'	CKob MJnS
densiflorum	CBct CBrd CDes CHEx CHen CHll CKob CPne CTbh EAmu EBee ECha EShb EZes IBlr MEHN MLLN MOak SDix SSpi WCru WMul WPGP
- EN 562	CKob
- 'Assam Orange'	CAvo CBct CBrm CDoC CHEx CKob CPLG CPne CRHN CSam EAmu EBee ERea EShb EZes GCal LEdu MAvo MJnS MNrw MOak MSte SChr SDix WBVN WCMO WCru WMul WPGP
- 'Sorung'	CKob
- 'Stephen'	CAvo CBct CDes CHEx CKob EAmu EBee EZes MJnS MNrw MSte SSpi WCMO WMul WPGP
'Doctor Moy' (v)	CHen CKob MJnS MOak
'Double Eagle'	CKob MJnS WPGP
'Elizabeth'	CDes CKob EZes MJnS WCMO WMul WPGP
ellipticum	CHEx CKob CPLG EAmu EBee ERea EZes LEdu MJnS MNrw MOak WMul
- B&SWJ 7171	WCru
- red bracts **new**	CKob
'Filigree'	CDes CFir CKob MJnS WCMO
§ *flavescens*	CBcs CBct CKob CPne EAmu EBee EShb EZes LEdu LRHS MJnS MNrw MOak SChr WCru WMul WPGP WPnP
forrestii misapplied **new**	CKob
forrestii Diels	CDes CHEx CKob CPLG EAmu EShb EZes GCal IBlr ITer LPJP MJnS MNrw MOak MSte SAPC SArc WCru WKif WMul WPGP
- var. *latebracteatum* HWJ 604	WCru
gardnerianum ♀H1	More than 30 suppliers
- B&SWJ 7155	WCru
- var. *pallidum*	CKob
- yellow-flowered **new**	MOak
'Gold Flame'	CDes CFir CKob CMdw EBee MJnS MNrw MOak WCMO WPGP
gracile	CKob EAmu EZes MOak WCMO
greenii	CBcs CBct CDoC CFir CHEx CKob CRHN CSam EBee ECho EShb EZes LEdu LRHS MJnS MNrw MOak MSte SArc SBig SChr SDix SYvo WBor WCMO WCru WMul WPGP WPnP
griffithianum	EBee MJnS MNrw
'Hardy Exotics 1'	CHEx
hasseltii	CKob
horsfieldii	CKob
hybrid from Great Dixter	CKob MJnS
I x *kewense* **new**	CKob MOak
§ 'Kinkaku'	CKob MJnS WDyG WPGP
'Lemon Sherbet'	CFir CKob MJnS
'Luna Moth'	CDes CKob EBee EZes MJnS WMul WPGP
maximum	CKob MJnS WCMO WDyG WMul
'Nikasha-cho'	CKob EBee EZes
'Orange Brush'	CKob
'Pink Flame'	CKob MJnS
'Pink Sparks'	CKob
'Pink V'	CKob WPGP
pink-flowered	CDes CKob
'Pradhan'	CFir CHEx CKob MJnS WCMO

x *raffillii* — CKob MJnS MNrw
'Shamshiri' — CKob MJnS
spicatum — CAvo CBcs CDes CFir CHEx CKob
CMdw CPLG CPne CRHN EBee
EChP EMan EShb GPoy LEdu
MNrw MOak MSte WCFE WCMO
WMul
- B&SWJ 2303 — WCru WPGP
- BWJ 8116 — WCru
- CC 1705 — CKob
- CC 3249 — WCot
- from Salween Valley, — CKob
  China **new**
- var. *acuminatum* — EZes WPGP
  new
- 'Singalila' **new** — WCru
- 'Tresco' — CKob WCMO
stenopetalum **new** — CKob
'Telstar 4' — CKob
thyrsiforme — CKob CPne EAmu EBee ERea
EShb MJnS MOak WCMO WCru
WMul
'Twengwainran' — MOak
villosum — EBee EcHo WMul
wardii **new** — CHEx CKob
yunnanense — CDes CHEx CKob EAmu ERea
LEdu MJnS MNrw SBig WCru
WPGP
- BWJ 7900 — CKob WCru
- L 633 — CKob

Hedysarum (Papilionaceae)
consanguineum **new** — GKev
coronarium — CAby CArn CEnt CPle CSpe EHrv
ELan EPfP MBrN SPet SYvo WCot
WCra WKif
hedysaroides — EDAr
multijugum — CBcs EBee MBlu SPer WCot
nitidum — EBee

Hegemone (Ranunculaceae)
lilacina — GIBF

Heimia (Lythraceae)
salicifolia — CArn CBrm EMan EUnu IDee LRav
MBlu MGol MSal SGar WCMO
WWye
- RCB/Arg P-7 — WCot

Helenium ✿ (Asteraceae)
'Autumn Lollipop' — EBee IBal LSou MBNS NLar NOrc
NSti SBig SPav WMnd
autumnale — CSBt CSam CTri EBee EGoo LDai
LSRN MBNS MLHP MNHC MSal
NChi NEgg NJOw SPet SWvt
WBVN WFar WMoo
- 'All Gold' — EDAr SWvt
- 'Cupreum' **new** — SBch
- Helena Series **new** — LBMP
- - 'Helena Gold' **new** — EBee NBre
- - 'Helena Rote Töne' — EDAr LBMP NBHF
  new
- 'Praecox' — MWrn
- 'Sunset Shades' — GBBs
'Baronin Linden' — CSam
'Baudirektor Linne' ♀H4 — CSam WWpP
'Biedermeier' — CAby CPrp CSam CWCL EBee
EBrs ECtt EShb LAst LHop MAvo
MLLN MNFA MTis NCob NGdn
SPla
bigelovii — CSam
'Blütentisch' ♀H4 — CPrp CSam EBee EChP EMan
GMaP GMac MBnl MNFA MWgw
NCGa NLar NVic SPoG SPur SUsu
WHal WMnd WWpP
'Bressingham Gold' — CElw CSam WWpP

'Bruno' — CAby CHar CWCL EBrs EGle ELan
ERou GMac GSki MArl MRav NRnb
SHop WWpP
'Butterpat' ♀H4 — CHad EBee EBrs EChP ECtt EGra
EHrv EPfP ERou GMaP IBal LRHS
MRav NBPC NCGa NSti SBla SHop
WSan WWpP
'Can Can' **new** — CSam
'Chelsey' **new** — EBee EHrv ERou IBal MBNS MBnl
MLLN NBhm NChi NLar NMoo
NSti SHop SPoG
'Chesney' **new** — MSph
'Chipperfield Orange' — CBgR CElw CHad CSam EGra
ERou GBri LHop MArl MHar MRav
NBre NGdn NVic WOld WWpP
'Coppelia' — EBrs LBMP NBir NGdn WOld WTel
Copper Spray — see *H.* 'Kupfersprudel'
'Crimson Beauty' — CMea ECtt ELan EPfP LRHS MLLN
MRav
Dark Beauty — see *H.* 'Dunkelpracht'
'Dauerbrenner' **new** — CSam
'Die Blonde' — CAby LPhx NBre NDov SMHy
WWpP
§ 'Dunkelpracht' — More than 30 suppliers
'Feuersiegel' ♀H4 — CAby CSam LPhx NBre NDov
WOld WWpP
'Fiesta' — CSam
'Flammendes Käthchen' — CAby CSam EBee EBrs GMac LPhx
LRHS NBre NDov SAga WGHP
WWpP
'Flammenrad' — CSam EBee
'Flammenspiel' — CFwr CSam EBee EBrs EChP ECtt
LRHS MNFA MRav MSph WWpP
flexuosum — EBee EShb MWrn NBre WPer
'Gartensonne' ♀H4 — CSam NBre WWpP
'Gay-go-round' — CSam
'Gold Fox' — see *H.* 'Goldfuchs'
'Gold Intoxication' — see *H.* 'Goldrausch'
Golden Youth — see *H.* 'Goldene Jugend'
§ 'Goldene Jugend' — CElw CMea CSam ECtt ELan MRav
WCot WEas WOld WWpP
§ 'Goldfuchs' — CSam CWCL WCMO WCot WWpP
§ 'Goldlackzwerg' — EBrs NBre
§ 'Goldrausch' — CHar CSam EBee MDKP MWat
NBre WHlf WMow WOld WWpP
'Goldreif' **new** — CSam
'Helena' — EBee MWea MWhi NEgg NLar
NRnb WPer
hoopesii — see *Hymenoxys hoopesii*
'Indianersommer' — More than 30 suppliers
'July Sun' — NBir
'Kanaria' — CAby CBre CHea CPrp EBee EBrs
EMil ERou EWll LRHS MNFA MRav
NCob NLar SPoG SPur WLin
WMnd WOld WWpP
'Karneol' ♀H4 — CSam EBee LHop LRHS NBre
WWpP
'Kleiner Fuchs' — CSam EBee EChP NLar WWpP
'Kokarde' — CSam
'Königstiger' — CFwr CSam EBee EBrs GMac LRHS
NBre WWpP
'Kugelsonne' — NBre WWpP
§ 'Kupfersprudel' — CFwr
'Kupferzwerg' — CAby CSam CWCL IPot NBre
NDov WEas WGHP
'Luc' **new** — CSam
'Mahagoni' **new** — CSam
'Mahogany' — see *H.* 'Goldlackzwerg'
'Margot' — CDes CSam CWCL NBre WWpP
'Meranti' — CSam
'Moerheim Beauty' ♀H4 — More than 30 suppliers
'Orange Beauty' — WHlf
Pipsqueak = 'Blopip' — CHea EBrs ECtt GBri LRHS NBre
'Potter's Wheel' — CDes CKno CSam EBee IPot
WCMO WCot WWpP
puberulum — SPav

'Pumilum Magnificum'	CBgR CDes CHar CPrp CSam CWCL EBee EHol EPfP GSki LEdu LHop LRHS MBnl MNFA MWat SPer WCMO WFar WPGP WTel
'Rauchtopas'	CSam IBal IPot SUsu
Red and Gold	see *H.* 'Rotgold'
'Red Army'	EBee MBri MNrw NCGa NGdn NRnb
'Red Glory'	CFwr EHrv
'Ring of Fire' ♀H4	CSam IPot
'Riverton Beauty'	CSam EBee ERou NChi SUsu WHoo
'Riverton Gem'	CSam CWCL ECtt NBre NChi WHoo
§ 'Rotgold'	CFwr CMea ECtt ENot LSRN MWrn NBre NEgg NJOw NOak NRnb SGar SPoG SRms STes WFar WMoo WPer WWeb
'Rotkäppchen' **new**	CSam
'Rubinkuppel'	CSam LPhx NDov
'Rubinzwerg' ♀H4	More than 30 suppliers
'Sahin's Early Flowerer' ♀H4	More than 30 suppliers
'Septemberfuchs'	EBee GMac LEdu NBre
'Sonnenwunder'	ECha LEdu MLHP NBre WOld WWpP
'Sunshine'	WBrk WSan
'The Bishop'	More than 30 suppliers
'Vivace'	CSam
'Waldhorn'	MSph
'Waltraut' ♀H4	More than 30 suppliers
'Wesergold' ♀H4	EBee EChP LTwo SMHy SPoG
'Wonnadonga'	CFwr
'Wyndley'	More than 30 suppliers
'Zimbelstern'	CDes CElw CFwr CMdw CMil EBee EBrs ECha ECtt ERou LHop LPhx LRHS MNFA MRav NDov WAul WFar WWpP

Heliamphora (Sarraceniaceae)
nutans	SHmp

Helianthella (Asteraceae)
§ *quinquenervis*	CPLG EBee EBrs EMan GCal NLar WCMO WFar

Helianthemum ✿ (Cistaceae)
'Alice Howarth'	CFul WHoo
alpestre serpyllifolium	see *H. nummularium* subsp. *glabrum*
'Amabile Plenum' (d)	CFul GAbr GCal MBNS NLar
'Amy Baring' ♀H4	CFul CTri EAEE GAbr LRHS WPer
'Annabel'	CFul EAEE ECho EPfP GAbr IGor MWya SBla SMer WPer WTel
apenninum	CFul SRms XPep
- var. *roseum*	ECho
'Apricot'	CFul
'Apricot Blush'	CFul WAbe
'Avalanche'	CFul
'Baby Buttercup'	CFul CLyd CMea GAbr
'Banwy Copper'	WBVN
'Beech Park Red'	CFul ECho ECtt LBee LRHS MHer WAbe WFar WHoo WKif WRHF
'Ben Afflick'	CFul EAEE ECho LBee LRHS MBNS SRms
'Ben Alder'	CFul ECho GAbr MHer
'Ben Attow'	CFul
'Ben Dearg'	CFul CMea ECho ECtt GAbr SRms
'Ben Fhada'	CBcs CFul CMea COIW CPBP CTri ECho ECtt EPfP GAbr GEdr GKev GMaP LBee LRHS MHer NEgg NHol NPri SBla SPoG SRms WAbe WBVN WBrE WCFE WFar WPer
'Ben Heckla'	CFul CSam CTri EAEE ECho ECtt EPfP GAbr GEdr IHMH ITim LRHS MSte SBla WPer WTel
'Ben Hope'	CFul ECho ECtt EPfP EWTr GAbr GEdr SRGP
§ 'Ben Ledi'	CBcs CBrm CFul CPBP ECho ECtt EPfP GAbr GBuc GEdr GMaP IHMH LHop LRHS MBar MHer MWgw NChi NHol NPri NSla NVic SPoG SRms WAbe WFar WPer
'Ben Lomond'	CFul ECho GAbr
'Ben Macdhui'	CFul GAbr
'Ben More'	CBcs CFul COIW EAEE ECho ECtt EWin GAbr LHop LRHS MSwo MWat NBir NPri SPoG SRGP SRms WFar
'Ben Nevis'	CFul CTri ECha ECho GAbr GEdr SBla SRms WTel
'Ben Vane'	CFul COIW EAEE GAbr LRHS
'Bentley'	CFul
'Bishopsthorpe'	CFul
'Boughton Double Primrose' (d)	CFul ECho ELan EWes GMaP LHop LRHS SBla SMer WEas WHoo WSHC WSel WTin
'Brilliant'	NBir
'Broughty Beacon'	CFul GAbr WGor
'Broughty Orange'	WSel
'Broughty Sunset'	CFul CSam GAbr NBir WHoo WSel
'Brown Gold' (d)	ECho
'Bunbury'	CFul CMea COIW GAbr IHMH MBrN MWhi NBir SPoG SRms
'Butterball' (d)	CFul
canum	SBla
'Captivation'	CFul EGoo GAbr
caput-felis	XPep
'Cerise Queen' (d)	CFul CTri ECha ECho GAbr GKev LHop LRHS MSwo SDix SRms WBVN WHoo
chamaecistus	see *H. nummularium*
'Cheviot'	CFul CMea ECha GAbr NBir SAga WEas WHoo WPer WSHC
'Chichester'	CFul
'Chocolate Blotch'	CFul CMea CRez EAEE ECho GAbr GEdr LHop LRHS NChi NHol SEND SPla SRms WPer
'Coppernob'	CFul
'Cornish Cream'	CFul ECho GAbr LBee LRHS
croceum	LTwo
cupreum	CFul GAbr
'David'	CFul EGoo
'David Ritchie'	WHoo
'Diana'	CMea SAga
'Die Braut'	CFul
double apricot (d)	GAbr
double cream (d)	ECha ECho
double pink (d)	ECha MWgw
double primrose (d)	GAbr
double red (d)	NChi
'Elisabeth'	CFul EGoo
'Ellen' (d)	CMea
'Etna'	CFul STre
'Everton Ruby'	see *H.* 'Ben Ledi'
'Fairy'	CFul ECho LTwo
§ 'Fire Dragon' ♀H4	CFul CMea EAEE ECha ECho EPfP GAbr GMaP LRHS MWgw NBir NEgg NWCA SAga SBla SEND SPoG SRms WAbe WLin XPep
'Fireball'	see *H.* 'Mrs C.W. Earle'
'Firegold'	WAbe WFar
'Flame'	CFul
'Georgeham'	CFul ECho ECtt EPfP GAbr LBee LHop LRHS NBir SAga SBla SMer SPoG SRms WEas WGor WHoo WPer
'Gloiriette'	CFul
§ 'Golden Queen'	CFul ECho ECtt EPfP GAbr ITim LRHS MBNS MSwo MWhi NLar SPoG WFar WPer

'Henfield Brilliant' ♀H4	CBrm CFul CPBP CPLG CSpe EAEE ECho EPfP GAbr LHop LRHS NBir NHol SMad SMer SPla SPoG SRms WEas WHoo WLin WPer WSHC WSel WTel	
'Hidcote Apricot'	CFul NEgg	
'Highdown'	CFul GAbr SRms	
'Highdown Apricot'	MWea SPoG WFar	
'Highdown Peach'	GAbr	
'Honeymoon'	CFul GAbr SBla WSel	
'John Lanyon'	CFul	
'Jubilee' (d) ♀H4	CFul COfd COlW ECho ECtt ELan EPfP GAbr LAst NBir NChi NHol SBla SDix SPoG SRms WEas WFar WKif WSel WTel	
I 'Jubilee Variegatum' (v)	CFul GAbr	
'Karen's Silver'	WAbe	
'Kathleen Druce' (d)	CFul ECho EWes GAbr MWat SAga WHoo	
'Kathleen Mary'	CMea	
'Lawrenson's Pink'	CFul ECho ECtt EWTr GAbr SRGP	
'Lemon Queen'	CFul	
'Linton Rose'	NBir	
'Lucy Elizabeth'	CFul GAbr	
lunulatum	CFul CLyd CMea EAEE ECtt LRHS NHol NLAp NMen WAbe WPat	
'Magnificum'	CFul EHol MWat	
§ 'Mrs C.W. Earle' (d) ♀H4	CFul COlW CTri EAEE ECGP ECho ECtt ELan GAbr GBuc LAst MBow MWat MWya NPri SBla SDix SRms WFar WSel	
'Mrs Clay'	see *H.* 'Fire Dragon'	
'Mrs Croft'	WPer	
'Mrs Hays'	CFul GAbr	
'Mrs Jenkinson'	CFul WTel	
'Mrs Lake'	CFul GAbr	
'Mrs Moules'	CFul SRms	
mutabile	CEnt CFul LPhx SPlb	
§ *nummularium*	GPoy MBow MHer MNHC NMir NSco SHGN WPat WSFF WWye XPep	
§ - subsp. *glabrum*	CFul CNic EHyt GAbr MNHC NHol NJOw NLAp WPat	
- subsp. *grandiflorum* **new**	NLAp	
§ - subsp. *tomentosum*	CFul GAbr MWat	
oelandicum	GAbr NWCA SRms	
- subsp. *alpestre*	CFul CLyd NJOw NLAp NMen WPer	
- subsp. *piloselloides*	CLyd	
'Old Gold'	CFul GAbr LRHS SRms WAbe WLin WPer WSel WTel	
'Orange Phoenix' (d)	CRez GAbr GKev LSou NEgg WFar	
'Ovum Supreme'	CFul GAbr	
'Pershore Orange'	CFul	
'Pink Double'	EWTr	
'Pink Glow'	CFul WPer	
'Praecox'	CFul CMea CTri ECho GAbr LBee LRHS SRms WHoo WPer WTel	
'Prima Donna'	CFul NBir	
'Prostrate Orange'	CFul SRms	
'Raspberry Ripple'	CBow CFul CHar COfd EAEE ECho ECtt ELan EPfP EPot LAst LHop LRHS MWrn NHol SPoG SRms WAbe WFar WHoo	
'Razzle Dazzle' (v)	CBow CFul LAst SRms WFar	
'Red Dragon'	EPot WAbe	
'Red Orient'	see *H.* 'Supreme'	
'Regenbogen' (d)	ECha GAbr GCal SBla	
§ 'Rhodanthe Carneum' ♀H4	More than 30 suppliers	
§ 'Rosakönigin'	CFul ECho ECtt GAbr MHer WAbe WLin	
'Rose of Leeswood' (d)	CBrm CFul CMea CPBP CTri GMaP LBee LRHS NChi NEgg SAga SBla	

	SPoG SRms WEas WFar WHoo WKif WSHC WSel
Rose Queen	see *H.* 'Rosakönigin'
'Roxburgh Gold'	CFul SRms
'Rushfield's White'	CFul
'Saint John's College Yellow'	CFul CSam EAEE ECho GAbr LRHS
'Salmon Beauty'	CFul
'Salmon Bee'	CFul
'Salmon Queen'	CElw CFul EAEE ECho ECtt GAbr LBee LHop LRHS NHol NPri SRms WPer WSel
* *scardicum*	CFul CMea NLAp
'Schnee' (d)	CFul ECha EGoo
serpyllifolium	see *H. nummularium* subsp. *glabrum*
'Shot Silk'	CFul CPBP ECho EWes
'Snow Queen'	see *H.* 'The Bride'
'Southmead'	CFul ECho GAbr
'Sterntaler'	CFul GAbr SRms
'Sudbury Gem'	CFul EAEE EChP ECha ECho EWin GAbr LRHS NHol SMer WTel
'Sulphureum Plenum' (d)	CFul ECtt EPfP
'Summertime'	CFul
'Sunbeam'	CSam ECho GAbr SRms
'Sunburst'	CFul GAbr
§ 'Supreme'	CFul ECho ELan EPfP EWes LBee LRHS SDix SRms WSel WWeb
'Tangerine'	CFul ECha GAbr
'Terracotta'	CRez
§ 'The Bride' ♀H4	CBcs CFul CMea COfd EAEE ECha ECho ELan EPfP GKev GMaP LHop LRHS MHer MSte MWat MWgw NHol NVic SBla SDix SMer SPoG SRms WAbe WEas WFar WHoo WSel WWeb
'Tigrinum Plenum' (d)	CFul CPBP ECho EWes LRHS SBla
'Tomato Red'	CFul ECha NSla
tomentosum	see *H. nummularium*
umbellatum	see *Halimium umbellatum*
'Venustum Plenum' (d)	CFul WEas
'Voltaire'	CFul ECho EPfP GAbr NPri NVic
'Watergate Rose'	CFul ECho MWat NBir
'Watfield Mist' **new**	CHar
'Welsh Flame'	WAbe WFar
'Windmill Gold'	CFul LBee
'Wisley Pink'	see *H.* 'Rhodanthe Carneum'
'Wisley Primrose' ♀H4	More than 30 suppliers
'Wisley White'	CFul CTri ECha ECho ECtt EGoo EPfP GAbr
'Wisley Yellow'	CBrm SAga
'Yellow Queen'	see *H.* 'Golden Queen'

Helianthus ✿ (*Asteraceae*)

RCB/Arg CC-3	WCot
angustifolius	WFar WPer
atrorubens	EBee LRHS MRav NBro WFar WGHP
'Capenoch Star' ♀H4	CElw CPrp EBee ECha ECtt ERou GBuc GMaP LEdu LRHS MArl MAvo MBri MLLN MRav NBro NLar SDix SMrm SPoG WCAu WCMO WCot WFar WOld WWpP
'Capenoch Supreme'	EBrs
decapetalus	CHar MDKP WHal WWye
- 'Maximus'	SRms
- Morning Sun	see *H.* 'Morgensonne'
divaricatus	NBre
x *doronicoides*	SRms
giganteus 'Sheila's Sunshine'	CBre CElw GBri GMac MAvo MNFA MSte NDov WCMO WOld WWpP
gracilentus	NBre
'Gullick's Variety' ♀H4	CBre CHea EBee ECtt EPfP EShb IBlr LLWP MBnl NBro NChi NEgg NSti SPur STes WBrk WOld WWpP

'Hazel's Gold' — NBre
hirsutus — EBee NBre
x *kellermanii* — CAby EBee EMon LPhx MWgw NBre NDov SAga
§ x *laetiflorus* — EBee ELan GAbr MDKP NBre NLar NOrc
* - 'Superbus' ♀H4 — IBlr
§ 'Lemon Queen' ♀H4 — More than 30 suppliers
'Limelight' — see *H.* 'Lemon Queen'
§ 'Loddon Gold' ♀H4 — CElw CHar EBee EBrs ECtt ELan EPfP ERou EShb IBlr LPhx LRHS MAvo MBri MRav MTis MWat NEgg NVic SAga SRGP WBrE WBrk WCMO WCot WCra WFar WWpP WWye
§ *maximiliani* — EBee EShb LEdu LRHS LRav MDKP MSte SPav SWal WWpP XPep
microcephalus — EBee
'Miss Mellish' ♀H4 — NRnb WCMO WCot WHoo
mollis — EBee EBrs EShb NBre SPav WPer
'Monarch' ♀H4 — CFwr EBee ERou GMac LPhx MDKP MRav MSte MWgw NBre NCGa SDix SMad WCMO WOld WWpP
§ 'Morgensonne' — ECtt EHrv MAvo MDKP MWat NRnb WCMO WCot WFar
x *multiflorus* — MBri
'Anemoniflorus Flore Pleno' **new**
- 'Meteor' — EBee NBre NChi
occidentalis — IBlr LRHS WPer
orgyalis — see *H. salicifolius*
quinquenervis — see *Helianthella quinquenervis*
rigidus misapplied — see *H.* x *laetiflorus*
§ *salicifolius* — CFwr EBee EBrs EGra EMan EMon EPPr EShb LEdu LRHS MBri MSte NCGa SDix SMad SMrm WBVN WCMO WCot WFar WMnd WTin WWye XPep
- 'Hot Chocolate' **new** — WCot
- 'Low Down' PBR — CFwr EBee EBrs GBri LRHS MBNS MNrw NBPC NBro NMoo
scaberrimus — see *H.* x *laetiflorus*
'Soleil d'Or' — EBee ECtt EGra WCAu WCMO WHal
strumosus — WCot
'Triomphe de Gand' — CHea GBri MRav MWat WFar WOld
tuberosus — CArn EBee EUnu GPoy
- 'Dwarf Sunray' — LEdu
- 'Fuseau' — LEdu SWal
- 'Garnet' — LEdu
- 'Sugarball' — LEdu

Helichrysum (Asteraceae)

from Drakensberg Mountains, South Africa — CNic NWCA
acutatum — GCal
adenocarpum — SPlb
alveolatum — see *H. splendidum*
ambiguum — CFis
angustifolium — see *H. italicum*
- from Crete — see *H. microphyllum* (Willd.) Cambess.
arenarium — ECho
§ *arwae* — EHyt EPot WAbe
bellidioides — CTri ECha GAbr GGar LRHS SMer WCru
bellum — NWCA
chionophilum — EPot NWCA
'Coco' — see *Xerochrysum bracteatum* 'Coco'
§ *conglobatum* — XPep
coralloides — see *Ozothamnus coralloides*
'County Park Silver' — see *Ozothamnus* 'County Park Silver'

'Dargan Hill Monarch' — see *Xerochrysum bracteatum* 'Dargan Hill Monarch'
doerfleri — XPep
'Elmstead' — see *H. stoechas* 'White Barn'
fontanesii — SPer WHer XPep
frigidum — CPBP EHyt EPot ITim LRHS
heldreichii — EPot
- NS 127 — NWCA
hookeri — see *Ozothamnus hookeri*
§ *hypoleucum* — GGar WCot WHer
§ *italicum* ♀H3 — CArn CBcs CEnt CPbn CWan EChP ECha EGra ELau EShb GPoy IHMH MBar MBow MHer MLHP MNHC MWat MWgw NBlu NGHP SECG SPet SRms WDin WGwG WHCG WWye XPep
- from Crete — NWCA
- 'Dartington' — CBod EBee EOHP EWin MHer NGHP SIde WJek WSel
I - 'Glaucum' — CWib
- 'Korma' PBR — CAbP EBee ELan ENot EPfP EWTr EWin MAsh NGHP SHGC SIde SLon SPoG WJek
- subsp. *microphyllum* — see *H. microphyllum* (Willd.) Cambess.
- 'Nanum' — see *H. microphyllum* (Willd.) Cambess.
§ - subsp. *serotinum* — EBee EGoo EPfP GGar GPoy MRav NBlu SLim SMer SPla SRms STre SWal SWvt WDin WPer WSel WTel XPep
lanatum — see *H. thianschanicum*
ledifolium — see *Ozothamnus ledifolius*
marginatum misapplied — see *H. milfordiae*
marginatum DC. JJ&JH 9401733 — NWCA
microphyllum misapplied — see *Plecostachys serpyllifolia*
§ *microphyllum* (Willd.) Cambess. — ETow GBar MHer MNHC NBlu SIde SPer WJek WSel XPep
§ *milfordiae* ♀H2-3 — ECho EDAr EPot GEdr NWCA SIng SRms
montanum — NWCA
orientale — EPot SMer SPoG XPep
§ *pagophilum* — CPBP ITim NLAp
§ *petiolare* ♀H2 — EBak ECtt EWin MOak NBlu SGar
- 'Aureum' — see *H. petiolare* 'Limelight'
- 'Goring Silver' ♀H2-3 — MOak NPri SPet
§ - 'Limelight' ♀H2 — CHal ECtt EWin MOak NBlu NPri SPet
- 'Roundabout' (v) — LSou MOak
- 'Variegatum' (v) ♀H2 — CHal ECtt NPri SPet SPoG
petiolatum — see *H. petiolare*
plumeum — ECou EPot
populifolium misapplied — see *H. hypoleucum*
rosmarinifolium — see *Ozothamnus rosmarinifolius*
'Ruby Cluster' — WFar
rupestre — XPep
§ 'Schwefellicht' — EBee ECha EGle EPPr EPfP ERou EShb LRHS MLHP MNFA MWgw NFla NVic SMer SPer SPet SWat WCAu WEas WKif WSHC
selago — see *Ozothamnus selago*
serotinum — see *H. italicum* subsp. *serotinum*
serpyllifolium — see *Plecostachys serpyllifolia*
sessile — see *H. sessilioides*
§ *sessilioides* — EPot ITim NSla WAbe WLin
§ *sibthorpii* — CSev ECho EHyt LRHS NWCA
'Skynet' — see *Xerochrysum bracteatum* 'Skynet'
§ *splendidum* ♀H3 — CStu EHoe EPfP NBro NFor NWCA SLon SPer WBrE WDin WPer XPep
aff. *splendidum* — MWgw
stoechas — CArn XPep
- 'White Barn' — WCot
Sulphur Light — see *H.* 'Schwefellicht'
§ *thianschanicum* — EBee EShb GIBF SRms XPep

- Golden Baby	see *H. thianschanicum* 'Goldkind'
§ - 'Goldkind'	EPfP IHMH NBir NBlu NPri
thyrsoideum	see *Ozothamnus thyrsoideus*
trilineatum	see *H. splendidum*
tumidum	see *Ozothamnus selago* var. *tumidus*
virgineum	see *H. sibthorpii*
woodii	see *H. arwae*

Helicodiceros (*Araceae*)

§ *muscivorus*	CDes CMon EBee WCMO WCot

Heliconia ✿ (*Heliconiaceae*)

angusta 'Holiday'	MJnS
- 'Yellow Christmas'	MJnS
bihai	WMul
bourgaeana	LPal
caribaea 'Purpurea'	XBlo
'Fire and Ice'	WMul
'Golden Torch'	MJnS SBig XBlo
indica 'Spectabilis'	XBlo
latispatha 'Orange Gyro'	MJnS XBlo
- 'Red Gyro'	XBlo
lingulata 'Fan'	LPal
metallica	XBlo
psittacorum	CCCN
- 'Strawberries and Cream' **new**	SBig
rostrata	LPal MJnS XBlo
stricta 'Dwarf Jamaican'	MJnS

Helictotrichon (*Poaceae*)

pratense	EHoe MAvo
§ *sempervirens* ♀H4	More than 30 suppliers
- var. *pendulum*	EBee EMon EPPr GBin MAvo MLLN
- 'Saphirsprudel'	CKno CMdw EBee EPPr GBin WCot WPGP

Heliophila (*Brassicaceae*)

carnosa	SPla
longifolia	CSpe

Heliopsis ✿ (*Asteraceae*)

helianthoides	EBrs EMon LRHS NBre WHil WLin
- 'Limelight'	see *Helianthus* 'Lemon Queen'
- Loraine Sunshine = 'Helhan'PBR (v)	CBow LRHS
- var. *scabra*	EBee MDKP WHil WMnd
- - 'Asahi'	EBee ERou MBri NLar SPoG
- - Ballerina	see *H. helianthoides* var. *scabra* 'Spitzentänzerin'
- - 'Benzinggold' ♀H4	MRav SMrm
- - Golden Plume	see *H. helianthoides* var. *scabra* 'Goldgefieder'
§ - - 'Goldgefieder' ♀H4	EBee EPfP LRHS MBnl NBre NBro WFar
- - Goldgreenheart	see *H. helianthoides* var. *scabra* 'Goldgrünherz'
§ - - 'Goldgrünherz'	EBee MSph NBre
- - 'Hohlspiegel'	GBin NBre
- - 'Incomparabilis'	MWgw WCAu
- - 'Light of Loddon' ♀H4	MWat
- - 'Mars'	CFwr
- - 'Patula' **new**	EBee NBro
§ - - 'Sommersonne'	CSBt ECtt EGra ERou LBMP MRav NBro NJOw NPer SMer SPer SRms STes WCAu WFar WMnd WWeb
§ - - 'Spitzentänzerin' ♀H4	EBee MBri NBre NGby
- - 'Summer Nights' **new**	LBMP LDai MDKP NDov
- - Summer Sun	see *H. helianthoides* var. *scabra* 'Sommersonne'
- - 'Venus'	CFwr EBee ECtt ERou GBri LAst NBhm NBid NLar NRnb NVic WCAu WFar

Heliotropium ✿ (*Boraginaceae*)

§ *arborescens*	CArn EPfP MHom MOak
- 'Chatsworth' ♀H1	CAby CCCN CHad CSev ECre ECtt EHol EMan ERea EShb MAJR MHom MOak MSte SDnm SMad WFar
- 'Dame Alice de Hales'	CHal ERea MAJR MHom MOak
- 'Florence Nightingale' **new**	MAJR
- 'Gatton Park'	CMdw ERea MAJR MHom MOak SMrm
- 'Lord Roberts'	ERea MAJR MHom MOak WWlt
- 'Marine'	ECtt EWin LIck SPav WGor
- 'Mary Fox' **new**	ERea
- 'Mrs J.W. Lowther'	MAJR
- 'Nagano'PBR	EWin
- 'Netherhall White'	ERea
- 'P.K. Lowther'	WEas
- 'President Garfield'	MOak SMrm WFar
- 'Princess Marina' ♀H1	CMdw CSev CSpe EMan ERea LAst LRHS LSou MAJR MSte NLar SPav WEas
* - 'The Queen'	ECtt ERea
- 'The Speaker'	ERea MAJR MHom MOak
- 'White Lady'	CHal CPLG CSev ECtt EHol ERea EShb EWin LSou MAJR MHom MOak NLar
- 'White Queen'	ECtt MAJR MHom
- 'Woodcote' **new**	MAJR
'Chequerboard'	ERea
'Fowa'	ERea
peruvianum	see *H. arborescens*
'Purple Prince' **new**	NBlu
'Seifel'	ERea

Helipterum see *Syncarpha*

anthemoides	see *Rhodanthe anthemoides*
'Paper Cascade'PBR	see *Rhodanthe anthemoides* 'Paper Cascade'

Helleborus ✿ (*Ranunculaceae*)

abschasicus	see *H. orientalis* Lam. subsp. *abchasicus*
§ *argutifolius* ♀H4	More than 30 suppliers
- from Italy	EHrv
- 'Janet Starnes' (v)	MAsh
- 'Little 'Erbert'	MAsh
- mottled-leaved	see *H. argutifolius* 'Pacific Frost'
§ - 'Pacific Frost' (v)	CBow CLAP MAsh NEgg NPro WBVN
- 'Silver Lace'PBR	CBow CFir CMil CPen CTbh CWCL EBee ELan EPfP LDai LHop MCCP MGos MSte NBir NEgg NSti SPer SPoG
atrorubens misapplied	see *H. orientalis* Lam. subsp. *abchasicus* Early Purple Group
atrorubens Waldst. & Kit.	CLCN EBee NEgg
- WM 9805 from Croatia	MPhe
- 'Spotted Fern' **new**	MPhe
- from Slovenia	CBel GBuc
- - WM 9028	MPhe
- - WM 9216	WCru
- - WM 9216	MPhe
- - WM 9617	SSth
x *ballardiae*	CLAP MAsh MPhe WAbe WFar
- double-flowered (d)	CLAP
bocconei subsp. *bocconei*	see *H. multifidus* subsp. *bocconei*
colchicus	see *H. orientalis* Lam. subsp. *abchasicus*
corsicus	see *H. argutifolius*
croaticus	CLCN SSth WFar
- WM 9313	MPhe
- WM 9416	MPhe
- WM 9810 from Croatia	GBuc MPhe

cyclophyllus	EBee EPfP GAbr GBin GBuc GEdr MAsh MHom MPhe WFar
- JCA 560.625	CLCN
dumetorum	CBel CLCN EBee GBuc NLar WCru WFar
- WM 9209 from Hungary	MPhe
- WM 9209 from Slovenia	MPhe
- WM 9627 from Croatia	MPhe
§ x *ericsmithii* ♀H4	More than 30 suppliers
foetidus ♀H4	More than 30 suppliers
- from Italy	GBin MAsh WCot
- from NE Aragon **new**	SSth
- 'Chedglow'	CNat
- 'Curio' (v)	CNat
- 'Gold Bullion'	CBow CSpe
- 'Green Giant'	MAsh MTho SSth WCru
- 'Miss Jekyll's Scented'	ITer
- 'Ruth'	MAsh MPhe
- scented	MHom
- 'Sienna'	MAsh
- 'Sopron'	CLAP EBee MAsh NLar WCru
- 'Tros-os-Montes' **new**	SSth
- Wester Flisk Group	More than 30 suppliers
N x *hybridus*	More than 30 suppliers
- 'Agnes Brook'	WFib
- 'Alys Collins'	WFib
- Anderson's red hybrids	CLCN
- anemone-centred	CLAP EHrv NRar WFar
- 'Angela Tandy'	WFib
- 'Antique Shades'	WFar
- 'Apple Blossom'	EHrv WFar
- apricot-flowered	CLAP CLCN EHrv GBuc SPla WFar WTin
- 'Aquarius'	CLCN
- Ashwood Garden hybrids	CPMA EBrs EHrv ENot EPPr EPfP GWWP LRHS MAsh MGos MRav SCoo SSth WCra
- Ashwood Garden hybrids, anemone-centred	CPMA MAsh
- Ashwood Garden hybrids, double (d)	MAsh
- 'Baby Black'	ECot
- Ballard's Group	CLAP EBee EBrs EChP GEdr ITer MBnl MBri MNFA MNHC NCGa NRar SPoG WCot WCru WFar WMnd
- 'Black Spot' **new**	EWTr
- black-flowered	CBel CLAP CLCN EHrv EPPr GBuc WCru WFar WHoo WTin
- 'Blowsy' seedlings	CLCN
- 'Blue Lady'	COIW CWCL EBee EChP ENot EPfP GBin GEdr IBal LAst MBNS MGos MNFA MNrw MSte MWea NCGa NMoo SMad SPer SPoG STes WBVN WCMO WWeb
- 'Blue Metallic Lady'	CWCL EBee MBNS MNrw SHBN
- blue-grey-flowered	CBel CLCN EHrv
- Blumen Group	MBri
- Bradfield hybrids	EHrv
- Bradfield hybrids, anemone-centred	EHrv
- Bradfield Star Group	EHrv
- Caborn hybrids	LLWP
- 'Carlton Hall'	WFib
- 'Cheerful'	NBir WCru
- 'Cherry Davis'	WFib
- 'Citron'	CLAP
- 'Clare's Purple' **new**	GBin WBor
- cream-flowered	CBel CLAP CPMA MCCP NHol WFar WTin
- dark purple-flowered **new**	SPoG
- 'David's Star' (d)	CFir
- deep red-flowered	CBel CLAP WFar WTin WViv
- 'Double Vision' (d) **new**	CBrm
- double yellow-flowered (d) **new**	GBin
- double, black-flowered (d) **new**	NRar
- double, red-flowered (d)	GBin SPoG
- double-flowered (d)	CBel CLAP GBuc LHop NRar SHBN WCMO WCot WFar WHoo
- 'Dove Cottage Double Pink'	NDov
- Draco strain	CLCN
- 'Dusk'	WCru
- 'Elizabeth Coburn'	WFib
- 'Fibrex Black'	WFib
- 'Fred Whitsey'	WFib
- 'Garnet'	WFar
- 'Gertrude Raithby'	WFib
- 'Gladys Burrow'	WFib
- 'Green Ripple'	WFar
- 'Greencups'	WCru
- green-flowered	CLCN ITer MBNS WCru WFar
- 'Günther Jürgl'	SSth
- 'Hades' seedling	WCru
- Hadspen hybrids	CHad
- 'Harvington Apricots'	SPoG WCMO
- 'Harvington Picotee'	SPoG WCMO
- 'Harvington Pink'	LRHS MHer NLar SPoG
- 'Harvington Pink Speckled' **new**	SPoG
- 'Harvington Red'	LRHS MHer NLar SPoG
- 'Harvington Shades of the Night'	MHer NLar SPoG
- 'Harvington Speckled'	LRHS MHer SPoG
- 'Harvington White'	LRHS MHer NLar SPoG
- 'Harvington Yellow'	LRHS MHer NLar SPoG
- 'Harvington Yellow Speckled'	MHer NLar SPoG
- 'Hazel Key'	WFib
- 'Helena Hall'	WFib
- 'Hidcote Double'(d) **new**	NRar
- 'Ian Raithby'	WFib
- ivory-flowered	CLCN WFar
- 'John Raithby'	WFib
- Joy hybrids	EBee EChP ENot
- Kaye's garden hybrids	EAEE EPfP LAst MWgw WMnd
- Kochii Group	CAvo WCru
- 'Lady Charlotte Bonham-Carter'	WFib
- 'Lady Macbeth'	EWes
- Lady Series	COtt SHBN
- large, pink-flowered	WTin
- 'Le Max Creme'	EBee EChP
- 'Little Black'	ECho ELan EWes
- maroon-flowered	CBel NRar SPla WCru WFar
- 'Mary Petit'	WFib
- 'Maureen Key'	WFib
- 'Mrs Betty Ranicar' (d)	CBro CPen ENot GBin LBuc MBNS MNFA NBPC NLar SHBN SPer SPoG WBVN WCMO WCot
- 'Mystery'	WCru
- nearly black	CBel
- 'Pamina'	EHrv
§ - Party Dress Group (d)	EHrv SBla WFar
- 'Pebworth White'	WFib
- 'Philip Ballard'	WCru
- Picotee Group	CBel SSth
- 'Picotee'	CLAP EHrv GBuc NDov NRar SPla SPoG WCot WCru WFar WHoo
- 'Pink Lady'	EBee ENot GBin MWgw NCGa SHBN SPer WHlf WWeb
- pink-flowered	CLAP CLCN CPMA EGra GBuc MBNS MCCP NEgg NRar SPla SSth WAbe WCru WFar WHoo WTin WViv
- plum-flowered	CBel CLAP CLCN EGra EHrv SSth WFar WTin
- primrose-flowered	CLAP GBuc MBNS NHol NRar SPla SSth WAbe WCru WFar WTin

- 'Purple Haze' **new** — EWTr
- purple-flowered — CBel CLAP CLCN CPMA NHol NRar SSth WAbe WBor WCru WFar WHoo
* - 'Purpurascens' — MCCP
- 'Queen of the Night' — CLAP
- 'Ray Peters' — WFib
- red-flowered **new** — NCGa
- 'Red Lady' — CTbh CWCL EBee ENot EPfP GBin IBal MBNS MGos MSte MWea MWgw NMoo SHBN SPer SPoG WCot WWeb
- 'Red Mountain' — MBNS
- 'Rosina Cross' — WFib
- 'Shades of Night' — EHrv LRHS
- 'Sirius' seedlings — CLCN
- slaty blue-flowered — CBel CLAP EHrv GBuc NRar SSth WCot WCru WFar
- slaty purple-flowered — GBuc NRar WFar WHrl
- 'Smokey Blue' — EWTr NEgg
- smokey purple — WFar
- 'Snow Queen' — EHrv SSth
- 'Speckled Draco' — CPLG
- spotted — CAvo CLAP CLCN EChP EPfP GAbr GBuc LAst MBnl MCCP NCGa NEgg NHol SBla SPer WCot WCru WHoo WTin
- 'Spotted Lady' — ENot GBin MNrw SHBN
- spotted, cream — CBel CLAP NBir SSth WTin
- spotted, green — CLAP SSth WFar WTin
- spotted, ivory — CLAP
- spotted, light purple — LAst
- spotted, pink — CLAP GBuc NBir NDov NHol NRar SEND SPla WFar WHoo WTin
- spotted, pink, double (d) — GBin SPoG
- spotted, primrose — CLAP GBuc WFar WTin
- spotted, white — EChP EBee NBir NDov NRar SPla SSth WAbe WCru WFar WTin
- spotted, white, double (d) — GBin
- 'Sunny' — WCru
- 'Sunny' seedlings — CLCN
- 'Ushba' — CLAP
- 'Ushba' seedlings — CLCN GCal NBir
- 'Victoria Raithby' — WFib
- 'Violetta' — WCru
- white — CBel EGra ITer NRar SSth WCFE WCru WFar WHoo WTin WViv
- 'White Lady' — COIW EBee ENot GEdr IBal MGos MWea NCGa SHBN SPer SPoG WCot WWeb
- 'White Lady Spotted' — CWCL EBee EPfP GMac MSte NGHP SMad SPoG WWeb
- white, double (d) — GBin
- white-veined — EGra WFar
- 'Yellow Lady' — CTbh EBee EChP MNFA MNrw MSte MWea MWgw SPer SPoG WCMO WCot WWeb
- yellow-flowered — CBel NDov SSth WCru WFar WHoo WHrl WTin
- Zodiac Group — CLCN ENot EPfP GBuc LBuc
lividus ♀H2-3 — CAby CBro CHar CLAP CLCN EAEE ECho EHyt ELan EPfP EWes LHop LRHS MAvo MPhe NBir SBla SSth SWat WAbe WCru WFar
- subsp. *corsicus* — see H. argutifolius
Marion White Group — SBla
'Moonshine'PBR — EKen GCai WCot
multifidus — CLCN EBee EPfP NBir NHol SPer WFar
§ - subsp. *bocconei* — CBel CLCN EHrv MAsh MHom WFar
- - WM 9719 from Italy — MPhe
- subsp. *hercegovinus* — EHrv MDun SBla WFar
- - WM 0020 — MPhe
- subsp. *istriacus* — CBro GBuc WFar
- - WM 9225 — WCru

- - WM 9322 — MPhe
- - WM 9324 — MPhe
- subsp. *multifidus* — CBel EHrv MHom SMHy
- - WM 9104 — MPhe
- - WM 9529 — MPhe
- - WM 9748 from Croatia — MPhe
- - WM 9833 — MPhe
niger ♀H4 — More than 30 suppliers
- Ashwood strain — CLAP MAsh
- Blackthorn Group — CBow EHrv LRHS SBla
- 'Christmas Carol' **new** — MAsh
I - 'Crûg Hybrid' — WCru
- double-flowered (d) — LAst
- Harvington hybrids — EHrv LRHS MHer SPoG WCMO
- 'Louis Cobbett' — EHyt
§ - subsp. *macranthus* — EBee MNHC NCGa NGHP NMoo
- *major* — see H. niger subsp. macranthus
- 'Maximus' — CLAP COIW EBee EChP EWes NCGa
- 'Nell Lewis' — MAsh
- pink-flushed **new** — NRar
- 'Potter's Wheel' — CPMA EBee ECho ECot ELan ENot GBuc LRHS MAvo MRav SBla SHBN SPla WCru
- 'Praecox' — CWan EBee ENot EWes SHBN SPur SVil WWeb
- 'Ras Buis' — NMoo
- Sunrise Group WM 9519 — MPhe
- Sunset Group WM 9113 — GBuc MPhe
- 'White Christmas' **new** — LRHS
- 'White Magic' — CBcs CPMA GMaP MGos MNrw SBla WCru
x *nigercors* ♀H4 — EBrs EHrv ETow GBin GEdr MAsh MBri WAbe WCot
- 'Alabaster' — NBir
- double-flowered (d) — CMil EHrv LAst LHop LSou MAvo MBNS NBir NCGa NMyG SPoG WCMO WCot WTMC
- 'Pink Beauty' — SHBN
- 'Vulcan Beauty' — SHBN
x *nigristern* — see H. x ericsmithii
odorus — CAvo CBcs CBel CLCN EHrv MAsh MPhe WFar WPGP
- - WM 0312 from Bosnia — MPhe
- - WM 9202 — WCru
- - WM 9310 — GBuc
- - WM 9415 — MPhe
- - WM 9728 from Hungary — MPhe
N *orientalis* misapplied — see H. x hybridus
orientalis Lam. — CBcs CBel CLCN CPne EWes GKev LAst MPhe NEgg SMer WWeb
§ - subsp. *abchasicus* — EBee GEdr SRms
§ - - Early Purple Group — CAvo CBre CTri GCal WFar
- subsp. *guttatus* — EBee GGar NEgg NHol SMac SPla SRkn WCru
'Pink Beauty'PBR **new** — CPen
purpurascens — CBel CLCN EBee EHrv GBuc GEdr IFoB MBNS MNFA NBir SBla SPer SSth WAbe WBrE WFar WPnP
- from Hungary — WCAu
- WM 9412 — MPhe WCru
- WM 9211 from Hungary — MPhe WCru
Snowdon strain — CSBt EPfP GCai LBuc NEgg SHBN
x *sternii* — More than 30 suppliers
- Ashwood strain — MAsh
- 'Beatrice le Blanc' — MAsh
- Blackthorn Group ♀H3-4 — CBcs CElw CPMA CSpe EHrv ENot EPfP GBuc ITer LAst MBri MRav MSte SBla SMac SPoG SRkn WBrk WCru WFar WHoo WPGP
- Blackthorn dwarf strain — CLAP EBee GBuc SHBN
- Boughton Group — GBin MAsh
- 'Boughton Beauty' — CAvo CLAP EBee EHrv EHyt ELan GBuc LHop MTho
- Bulmer's blush strain — MAsh
'- Cally strain — GCal

– dwarf	WFar
– 'Joy's Purple' **new**	CPen
– pewter	CAby CSpe EDAr
thibetanus	CLAP EFEx EHrv EPot GBuc GEdr GKev MAsh MPhe SBla WCru WViv
– red-flowered	GBin
torquatus	CBel CBro CLCN EBee EHrv MBri MPhe MTho SSth WFar WTin
– WM 9106 from Montenegro	GBuc MPhe WCru
– WM 9745	EHrv
– WM 9820 from Bosnia	MPhe
– Caborn hybrids	LLWP
– 'Dido' (d)	WFar
– double-flowered hybrids (d)	CBos WFar
– double-flowered, from Montenegro (d)	WFar
– hybrids	ECGP EHrv SBla WFar
– Party Dress Group	see *H.* x *hybridus* Party Dress Group
– semi-double (d)	WFar
– Wolverton hybrids	SBla WFar
vesicarius	CDes EBee EHrv EWes
viridis	EBee EBrs ECha EHrv EPfP IFoB SRms WCru WFar WTin
– WM 0444	MPhe
– subsp. *occidentalis*	CBel CBro EHrv MHom
– – WM 9401	MPhe
– – WM 9502 from Germany	MPhe
– subsp. *viridis* WM 9723 from Italy	MPhe
'White Beauty'[PBR]	CPen ENot EPfP SHBN

Helonias (Melanthiaceae)

bullata	EBee GEdr IBlr WCot

Heloniopsis (Melanthiaceae)

acutifolia	GEdr
– B&SWJ 218	WCru
– B&SWJ 6817	WCru
japonica	see *H. orientalis*
§ *kawanoi*	CLAP GEdr NMen WAbe WCru
§ *orientalis*	CBro CLAP EBee ECho EHyt GBuc GCal GCrs GEdr GKev LRHS NMen NSla SOkd WCot WCru
§ – var. *breviscapa*	WCru WPGP
– from Korea	GEdr
– variegated (v)	GEdr WCru
– var. *yakusimensis*	see *H. kawanoi*
umbellata	CDes CLAP GEdr
– B&SWJ 1839	WCru
– B&SWJ 6836	WCru

Helwingia (Helwingiaceae)

chinensis	CPle CSam NLar SSpi
himalaica	WPGP
japonica	EFEx NLar WFar

Helxine see *Soleirolia*

Hemerocallis ✿ (Hemerocallidaceae)

'Aabachee'	CCol
'Absolute Zero'	SDay SRos
'Adah'	SDay
'Addie Branch Smith'	EGol SDay
'Admiral'	CHar WCAu
'Admiral's Braid'	EWoo
'Adoration'	SPer
'Age of Miracles' **new**	SPol
'Alan'	EChP ECtt MNFA MRav WFar
'Alaqua'	CFir EGle IBal LAst MBNS MFOX MNrw NRnb SHBN WSan
'Albany'	CCol
'Alec Allen'	SRos
'Alien Encounter'	SPol
'All American Baby'	EBee MBNS SPol
'All American Plum'	CWCL CWrd EBee EMar EPfP GBin IBal IPot MBNS WAul
'All American Tiger' **new**	SRos
'All Fired Up'	CCol SPol
'Alpine Snow' **new**	EWoo SRos
altissima	CHEx EMon EPla LPhx MNFA MNrw SMrm
'Always Afternoon'	CCol CKel CWrd EChP EMar EWoo GBri GBuc MBNS NCGa SDay SRos WAul WCAu WHrl
'Amadeus'	SDay
'Amazon Amethyst'	WCAu
'Ambassador'	CBgR
'Amber Star'	LPBA WWpP
'American Revolution'	More than 30 suppliers
'Amersham'	EGle GSki MNFA
'Andrea Nicole'	CCol
'Andrew Christian'	SPol
'Angel Artistry'	SDay
'Angel Curls'	EGol
'Angel Unawares'	WTin
'Ann Kelley'	MSte SDay
'Annie Golightly'	SDay
'Annie Welch'	EPla MBNS NBre
'Antique Rose'	CKel SDay
'Anzac'	COlW ECha ECtt EHrv EMar EPla ERou GMac LRHS MNFA NBre NGdn NHol NPri SAga SPav SRos SWvt WFar WLin WMoo WSel WTMC WWpP
'Apache Uprising'	SDay SRos
'Apple Court Damson'	SPol
'Apple Court Ruby'	SPol
'Apple Of My Eye' **new**	EWoo
'Après Moi'	EKen EMar LAst MBNS MLLN NLar WBrE WCAu
'Apricot Beauty' (d)	ECho EMar NPri
'Apricotta'	WCot WPnP
'Arctic Snow'	CBgR CCol EBee EChP EGle EHoe EMar EPfP EWoo LAst MLan MNrw NBPC NLar SDnm SMer SPav SPoG SRos SUsu WAul WSan WSel
'Ariadne'	SBla
'Arriba'	MNFA NBro
'Artistic Gold'	WTin
'Asiatic Pheasant'	CCol
'Aten'	CCol MNFA NPri WAul WWpP
'Atlanta Bouquet'	SRos
'Atlanta Full House'	SDay
'August Orange'	MNFA
'Autumn Minaret'	CCol
'Autumn Red'	EMar MBNS NBir NOak SPol WCot
'Ava Michelle'	SDay
'Avant Garde'	SPol
'Awakening Dream'	SRos
'Awesome Blossom'	CPen CWrd MBNS NMoo
'Awesome Candy' **new**	EWoo
'Aztec Furnace'	SDay
'Baby Blues' **new**	SPol
'Baby Darling'	SDay
'Baby Talk'	CFir GBuc LRHS
'Baja'	MNFA WFar
'Bald Eagle'	CMCo EGle
§ 'Bali Hai'	EBee EMar ENot MBNS NGdn NRnb WHrl
'Ballerina Girl'	SRos
'Ballet Dancer'	ERou
'Bamboo Blackie' **new**	EWoo SPol
'Banbury Cinnamon'	MBNS
'Bandolero' (d)	EBee
'Bangkok Belle'	SDay
'Banned in Boston'	EWoo

'Barbara Mitchell'   CCol EChP MBNS MNFA NCGa
                     NMoo SDay SRos WAul
'Barbary Corsair'   SDay
'Barley Hay'   MSte
'Baronet's Badge'   SPol
'Baroni'   ECha GBin
'Battle Hymn'   WCAu
'Bayou Bride' **new**   CCol
'Bayou Ribbons'   MBNS
'Beat the Barons'   SPol SRos
'Beautiful Edgings' SRos
'Beauty Bright'   WCAu
'Beauty to Behold'   SDay SRos
'Becky Lynn'   CCol EBee ECtt EWoo MBNS
                     WHoo
'Bed of Roses'   MNFA
'Bedarra Island'   SDay
'Bejewelled'   EGol EPla NMoo
'Bela Lugosi'   More than 30 suppliers
'Beloved Returns' ♀H4   WCAu
'Benchmark'   MNFA SRos
'Bengal Bay' **new**   EWoo
'Berlin Lemon' ♀H4   MNFA WWpP
'Berlin Oxblood'   MNFA WAul
'Berlin Red' ♀H4   CPrp ECha EGle EMar EPla LBMP
                     MBNS MNFA NGdn
'Berlin Red Velvet' ♀H4   MNFA
'Berlin Watermelon' MBNS
'Berliner Premiere' MNFA
'Bernard Thompson'   EMar MNFA SRos
'Bertie Ferris'   EBee NLar SRos
'Bess Ross'   CMHG MNFA WCAu
'Bess Vestale'   ENot GBuc MNFA MWat NHol
'Best Kept Secret' **new**   EWoo
'Bette Davis Eyes'   SPol SRos
'Betty Benz'   SRos
'Betty Jenkins' **new**   SRos
'Betty Warren Woods' SRos
'Betty Woods' (d)   SRos
'Big Apple'   SRos
'Big Bird'   CMCo CPar EChP MBNS NCGa
                     SHBN SHar WAul
'Big Blue' **new**   EWoo
'Big Smile'   CWCL EBee EMar IPot MAvo
                     MBNS MNrw NBPC NBro NMoo
'Big Snowbird'   SRos
'Big Time Happy' **new**   SPoG
'Big World'   MNFA
'Bill Norris'   SDay SRos
'Bird Bath Pink'   SPol
'Bitsy'   EGle EGol MNFA MOne MSte SPet
                     WCot WMnd
'Black Ambrosia'   SDay
'Black Emmanuella'   ECho EMar LDai SBch
'Black Eyed Stella' CKel MBNS
'Black Falcon'   SDay
'Black Knight'   NLar SRms
'Black Magic'   CBro CHad CHar CTri EGol ELan
                     EPla ERou GMaP GMac LRHS
                     MNFA MRav MWgw NBir NGdn
                     NHol SPer SPoG WHer WMoo
'Black Plush'   CCol SRos
'Black Prince'   CFir EBee EWll MBNS NBre NBro
                     WAul WMow
'Blackberry Candy'   EWoo GBri MBNS WAul WCAu
'Blaze of Fire'   WCAu
'Blessing'   SRos
'Blonde Is Beautiful' SDay SRos
'Blue Sheen'   CCol CFir EBee ECtt EGle EGol
                     EMar LAst LRHS MBNS MCCP
                     NGdn NOrc NPri WCAu WFar
                     WMoo WWeb
'Blueberry Candy'   EWoo MBNS WAul WSan
'Blueberry Cream' **new**   CWCL EBee EPfP MBNS MWea
'Blushing Belle'   CMil EChP EMar LRHS MBNS
                     MNFA NBro

'Bold Courtier'   CBgR WCAu
'Bold One'   CMHG SRos
'Bold Ruler' **new**   CCol
'Bold Tiger'   SDay
'Bonanza'   More than 30 suppliers
'Boney Maroney'   SRos
'Booger'   SRos
'Booroobin Magic'   EWoo
'Border Lord' **new**   EWoo
'Boulderbrook Serenity' SDay
'Bourbon Kings'   CMHG EBee EGol EMar ERou
                     MBNS NBre SPav
'Bowl of Roses'   WCAu
'Brass Buckles'   see *H.* 'Puddin'
'Brenda Newbold'   SPol
'Bridget'   ELan
'Bright Banner'   WCAu
'Bright Spangles'   SDay SRos WEas
'Brocaded Gown'   CCol ELan SDay SRos
'Brunette'   MHar SAga SHop
'Bruno Müller'   MNFA
'Bubbly'   SDay SRos
'Bud Producer'   SPol
'Buffy's Doll'   EBee EMar MBNS MNFA SDay SRos
                     WGob
'Bumble Bee'   EMar MBNS NBre NRnb
'Buried Treasure'   MNFA
'Burlesque'   SPol
'Burning Daylight' ♀H4   EBee EBrs ECtt EHol EHrv EMar
                     EPfP EPla ERou GSki LRHS MBow
                     MNFA MNrw MRav NBre NHol
                     SPer SRms WCot WFar WSel
'Bus Stop'   SPol
'Butterfly Ballet'   SDay SRos
'Butterscotch'   WFar
'Butterscotch Ruffles' SDay
'Buzz Bomb'   CWat EGle EHrv EMFW EMar
                     GMac GSki LRHS LSRN MHar
                     MNFA MSte NCob NGdn SPer
                     SRos WCAu

'Cabbage Flower' **new**   SDay
'Calico Spider' **new**   SRos
'California Sunshine' SRos
'Call Girl' **new**   SDay
'Camden Gold Dollar' EGol SRos
'Cameroons'   CCol SDay
'Campfire Embers' **new**   GBin
'Canadian Border Patrol' CWCL EMar EPfP EWoo IBal IPot
                     MBNS MNrw NLar SPol SRos
                     WCMO WHil
'Canary Feathers'   SDay
'Canary Glow'   CSBt CTri ERou SRos WFar
'Capernaum Cocktail' SPol
'Captive Audience'   SRos
'Cara Mia'   EMar MBNS WFar
'Caribbean Jack Dolan' EWoo
   new
'Carolicolossal'   SPol
* 'Caroline'   WHrl
'Cartwheels' ♀H4   EBee EGra EHrv EMFW EMar EPfP
                     EPla ERou GBuc GMaP LRHS
                     MBNS MNFA NBro NRnb SBch
                     SPer SPla SRos WCAu WFar WMoo
                     WTin
'Casino Gold'   SRos
'Castle Strawberry   SPol
   Delight'
'Catherine Neal'   CCol SDay SRos
'Catherine Woodbery' More than 30 suppliers
'Cathy's Sunset'   CKel CSam EBee ECtt EMar EPla
                     MBNS MSte MWat MWgw NBre
                     NBro NGdn NHol NRnb SRGP SVil
'Cedar Waxwing'   CHea EGol MSte
'Cee Tee'   SRos
'Cenla Crepe Myrtle' EWoo
'Chance Encounter'   MBNS SDay

'Chantilly Lace'	CMHG NGdn
'Charbonier'	MNFA
'Charles Johnston'	CKel CMMP EChP LAst NRnb SDay SRos WAul WTMC
'Charlie Pierce Memorial'	EWoo SPol SRos
'Chartreuse Magic'	CMHG EGol EPla ERou NHol SPer
'Cherry Brandy'	EWoo
'Cherry Cheeks'	CFir ECtt EGol ELan EPfP ERou LRHS MBNS MBri MHar MRav NFla NHol NRnb SPav SRos SVil WAul WCAu WCot WFar WGob WWeb WWpP
'Cherry Eyed Pumpkin'	SRos
'Cherry Kiss'	SRos
'Cherry Tiger' **new**	MBNS
'Cherry Valentine' **new**	MBNS
'Chesières Lunar Moth'	SPol SRos
'Chester Cyclone'	SDay
'Chestnut Lane'	SRos
'Chewonki' **new**	EMar
'Chic Bonnet'	SPer
'Chicago Apache'	CFif COtt EBee EChP EGle EMar ENot EPfP GBuc MBNS MNFA MSte NBir NCGa NRnb SDay SRos SUsu WAul
'Chicago Arnie's Choice'	WSan
'Chicago Blackout'	CFir CSpe EBee EChP EGol EPfP MBNS NHol NRnb WCAu
'Chicago Cattleya'	CFir EChP EGle EGol LAst MRav NRnb WAul
'Chicago Cherry'	NRnb WWpP
'Chicago Fire'	EBee EGol EPfP MBNS NBhm SHar WWye
'Chicago Heirloom'	CFir EChP EGle EGol NRnb WAul WCAu
'Chicago Jewel'	CFir EGle EGol NRnb NSti WAul WWpP
'Chicago Knobby'	EMar MBNS
'Chicago Knockout'	CFir EGle EGol EPfP EWoo MBNS NRnb SPer WAul WCAu
'Chicago Peach'	EChP IPot NBir WCAu
'Chicago Peach Parfait'	WSan
'Chicago Petticoats'	CWrd EGol NHol SDay
'Chicago Picotee Lace'	EBee EChP EGle EGol EPfP NGdn WCAu
'Chicago Picotee Memories'	EBee EGle MBNS WCAu
'Chicago Picotee Queen'	MNFA
'Chicago Princess'	EGle EGol
'Chicago Rainbow'	IPot MBNS WAul WSan
'Chicago Rosy'	EGol
'Chicago Royal Robe'	CWat EBee EGol EPla ERou EWll LLWP MBNS MNFA MRav MSte NBid NCGa SPer WCMO WCot WTin WWhi
'Chicago Silver'	CFir COIW EGle EGol IPot MBNS WCAu
'Chicago Star'	SRos
'Chicago Sunrise'	CHad CSBt EBee EBrs EGol EMar ENot EPla GMaP IBlr LRHS MBNS MBri MNFA MRav NGdn NHol NMoo NOrc NRnb SPet SRos SWvt WPer WWeb
'Chicago Violet'	WCAu
'Chief Sarcoxie' ♀H4	SRos WCAu
'Children's Festival'	CHad COIW CSBt CSev CSpe CWat ECtt EGle EGol EMil EWoo GMaP GSki LPBA LRHS MBNS MRav MTis NHol SPoG SRos STes SWvt WFar WMoo WPer WPnP WTel WWeb
'China Bride'	EWoo SRos
'China Lake'	EMar
'Chinese Autumn'	SRos
'Chinese Cloisonne'	EMar
'Chorus Line'	SRos

'Christmas Is'	CBgR CCol CWrd EGol EMar LPhx MBNS MBri MNFA NMoo SDay SDnm SPav WAul WCAu WGob
'Christmas Island'	CDWL EMil NBre NCGa WHil
'Churchill Downs'	MNFA
'Ciao'	EMar MHar
'Cimarron Knight' **new**	SPol
citrina	CBgR EDsa ELan GIBF LRHS MNFA MSte NFla NGdn WTin XPep
'Civil Law'	SDay
'Civil Rights'	SRos
'Classic Simplicity'	WCAu
'Cleopatra'	CPar SDay SRos
'Cloth of Gold'	WCot
'Clothed in Glory'	CWCL EWoo MBNS NMoo
'Colonial Dame' **new**	WTin
'Comet Flash' **new**	SPol
'Coming Up Roses'	SRos
'Condilla' (d)	SDay
'Contessa'	CBro EBrs EHon WWpP
'Cool It'	CKel EBee EDsa EGle EMar GBuc IPot LRHS MBNS NBre NCGa NMoo NRnb WCAu
'Cool Jazz'	EMar SDay SRos
'Coral Mist'	CCol CSBt MBNS NBre NRnb
'Corky' ♀H4	More than 30 suppliers
'Corsican Bandit'	CMMP SDay
'Cosmic Hummingbird'	EWoo
'Country Club'	EChP EGle EGol LAst MBNS NHol WCAu WSan WWpP
'Country Fair Winds'	CCol
'Country Melody'	SDay SRos
'Court Magician'	EWoo SRos
'Cranberry Baby'	EGle SDay SRos WHoo WTin
'Crawleycrow' **new**	EMar
'Crazy Pierre'	EMar SPol
'Cream Drop'	CPrp EBee EChP ECtt EGle EGol EMar GMaP GMac LRHS MRav NBro NGdn NOrc NSti SDnm SPav SPer WAul WCAu WCMO WCot WMoo WTMC WTel WTin
'Creative Art'	SRos
'Creative Edge'	ERou EWoo MBNS SDnm SPav WAul
'Crimson Icon'	MSte SDay WTin
'Crimson Pirate'	CBgR CBre CCol EBee EMar EMil EPPr ERou LRHS LSRN MBNS MLan MNFA MSph NBir NBlu NCGa NHol NMoo NOrc NPro SPer SPlb SPoG WHrl WTin
'Croesus'	NHol SRms
'Crystalline Pink'	SRos
'Cupid's Bow'	EGol
'Cupid's Gold'	SDay SRos
'Curls' **new**	SDay
'Curly Cinnamon Windmill' **new**	SRos
'Custard Candy'	CWCL EChP MBNS MBri NBir NMoo SRos SUsu WAul WCAu
'Cynthia Mary'	EGle EMar LRHS MBNS MNFA NBro NFla SRGP WFar
'Dad's Best White'	EMar
'Daily Dollar'	LRHS MBNS NGdn
'Dainty Pink'	EGol
'Dallas Spider Time'	MNFA
'Dallas Star'	SPol
'Dan Tau'	CKel
'Dance Ballerina Dance'	SDay SRos
'Dancing Dwarf'	SDay
'Dancing Shiva'	SDay
'Dancing Summerbird'	SPol SRos
'Daring Deception'	CFir CKel EBee EMar EWoo IPot LAst MBNS MLLN NCGa NMoo WHrl
'Daring Dilemma'	CCol EWoo SPol
'Daring Reflection' **new**	SDay

'Dark Angel'	EWoo
'Dark Elf'	SDay
'David Kirchhoff'	EBee EWoo IPot MBNS WAul WCAu
'Debussy' **new**	EWoo
'Decatur Imp'	EGol
'Delightsome'	SRos
'Demetrius'	MNFA MWea NCGa
'Desdemona'	CMil
'Designer Jeans'	SPol SRos
'Destined to See'	CBcs CFir CMHG CPar CWan EBee EMar EWoo GBin GSki LDai LHop LSou MBNS MDun NBro NCob NCot NEgg SPav SPer WBVN WCMO WCot WHrl WSan
'Devil's Footprint'	SDay SPol
'Devonshire'	SDay SRos
'Dewberry Candy'	SRos
'Diamond Dust'	CKel EBee EChP EGle EMar EPla LPhx LRHS MBNS MNFA MSte NLar SPer WTin
'Dido'	CTri ERou GBuc
'Divertissment'	CCol
'Doll House'	SRos
'Dominic'	CPar EBee EMar MBNS SRos WMoo
'Dorethe Louise'	SDay SPol SRos
'Dorothy McDade'	COIW ENot EWoo
'Double Action' (d)	SPol
'Double Coffee' (d)	SPav
'Double Cream' (d)	WCot
'Double Cutie' (d)	CMCo MBNS NBre NLar SDay WAul
'Double Daffodil' (d)	WCAu
'Double Dream' (d)	EMar GBuc
'Double Firecracker' (d)	CBcs CWrd EMar IBal MBNS NBro NLar NMoo SPoG WCra WHrl WSan
'Double Pompon' (d)	WCAu
'Double River Wye' (d)	CBgR CBos CCol CDWL CFir COIW EChP ECtt EGol EMar EMil IPot MBNS MNrw NGdn NPri SHBN SHar SRos WAul WCMO WCot WHoo WMnd WTin WWye
§ 'Doubloon'	COIW ERou GBuc MWgw NHol
'Dragon Heart' **new**	EWoo
'Dragon King'	SPol
'Dragon Mouth'	EGol
'Dragon's Eye'	CCol EWoo SDay
'Dragon's Orb'	CKel
'Dream Baby'	NBre
'Dreamy Cream'	SRos
'Dresden Doll'	SPer
'Druid's Chant'	EWoo
'Duke of Durham'	SMeo
'Dune Needlepoint'	SPol
dumortieri	CAvo CBro CSam EBrs ECha EGol EGra EHrv ELan EMar EPla GGar MNFA MNrw MRav NBid NBir NHol NSti NVic SPer WCot WTin WWpP
- B&SWJ 1283	WCru
- from Ussuri	GIBF
'Dutch Beauty'	EMar EPla WFar WTMC
'Dutch Gold'	MNrw NBro
'Earlianna'	SPol
'Earth Angel'	SPol
'Easy Ned'	SDay SRos
'Ed Murray'	CSBt EBee MNFA SRos WAul WCAu
'Ed Ra Hansen'	CCol
'Edelweiss'	EWTr SDay
'Edgar Brown'	EWoo MBNS
'Edge Ahead'	CCol MBNS NRnb
'Edge of Darkness'	CKel CWrd EBee EChP EGle EPfP IPot MBNS MWea NLar NSti SDnm SPav WAul WCAu WHil WSan

'Edna Spalding'	EBrs SDay SRos
'Eenie Allegro'	CBro CCol EChP EGle EGol EMar ENot IBal MBNS SPla WMnd
'Eenie Fanfare'	EGle EGol LRHS MBNS MNFA NBir WAul
'Eenie Gold'	LRHS
'Eenie Weenie'	CBgR CBro CFee EBla ECtt EGle EGol EPla ERos IBal LRHS MBNS MHar MNFA NBro NBur SAga SHBN SPer SRms WPer WTMC WWye
'Eenie Weenie Non-stop'	EPPr
'Eggplant Escapade'	SPol SRos
'Egyptian Ibis'	EWoo MBNS
'El Desperado'	More than 30 suppliers
'Elaine Strutt'	EGol MBNS MNFA NCGa NMoo SDay SRos SWvt
'Eleanor Marcotte'	SDay
'Elegant Candy'	CCol CKel CPen ENot MBNS NMoo NRnb SRos WGob WSan
'Elegant Greeting'	ERou MBNS NOak
'Elizabeth Ann Hudson'	MNFA SDay
'Elizabeth Salter'	CWCL EBee MBNS NMoo SRos SUsu WCAu
'Elizabeth Yancey'	EGol
'Elva White Grow'	SDay
'Emerald Lady' **new**	SRos
'Emperor's Dragon'	CCol
'Enchanter's Spell'	SDay
esculenta	SMad
'Etched Eyes'	EWoo
'Eternal Blessing'	SRos
'Evelyn Claar'	EChP
'Evening Glow'	SRos
'Ever So Ruffled'	SRos
exaltata	GIBF
'Exotic Love'	SDay
'Eye Catching'	EWoo
'Eye-yi-yi'	SPol
'Fabulous Prize'	SRos
'Fairest Love'	EBee EMar LDai MBNS
'Fairy Charm'	SDay
'Fairy Tale Pink'	CCol MNFA SDay SPol SRos
'Fairy Wings'	SPer
'Faith Nabor'	EMar SRos
'Fama' **new**	SRos
'Fan Club'	EMar
'Fan Dancer'	EGol
'Fandango'	MNFA SPer
'Farmer's Daughter'	SRos
'Fashion Model'	WPer
'Femme Osage'	SRos
'Festive Art'	EWoo MBNS SRos
'Final Touch'	EBee IPot MAvo MBNS MLLN NBhm NBro WGob
'Finlandia'	MNFA
'Fire Dance'	SRos
'Fire Tree'	SPol
'First Formal'	SPer
'Flames of Fantasy'	SRos
'Flaming Sword'	EBee GBuc LRHS NBlu NHol WRHF
flava	see *H. lilioasphodelus*
'Fleeting Fancy'	SRos
'Floyd Cove'	SDay
'Flutterbye' **new**	SRos
'Fly Catcher'	EMar SRos
'Fol de Rol' **new**	SRos
'Fooled Me'	SRos
'Forbidden Dreams' **new**	EWoo
'Forgotten Dreams' **new**	EBee MBNS MWea SPoG
forrestii	GKev
- 'Perry's Variety'	CCol EMon
'Forsyth Lemon Drop'	SDay
'Forsyth White Sentinal'	SRos
'Fortune's Dearest'	EWoo

Name	Suppliers
'Forty Second Street'	CFir CWrd EBee MBNS MLLN NCGa NMoo WFar WSan
'Fragrant Bouquet'	SRos
'Fragrant Pastel Cheers'	SDay SRos
'Frances Fay'	SRos WAul
'Francois Verhaert' **new**	EWoo
'Frandean'	MNFA
'Frank Gladney'	MNFA SRos
'Frans Hals'	More than 30 suppliers
'French Porcelain'	SDay
'Frozen Jade'	SRos
'Fuchsia Dream' **new**	EMar
'Fuchsia Fashion'	CCol
'Full Reward'	WCAu
fulva	CTri EGra ELan IBlr LRHS MHar MWgw NBir NBre SHBN SRms WBVN WBrk WWpP
N - 'Flore Pleno' (d)	More than 30 suppliers
N - 'Green Kwanso' (d)	CBgR CPLG CSWP ECGP ECha EGra EMon EPla IBlr MHer MMHG NVic SMad SPla WAul WFar WPnP WRha WTin WWpP
* - 'Kwanso' ambig. (d)	EBrs NOrc
- var. *littorea*	EPla
- var. *rosea*	EBrs EMon MNFA SMHy WCMO
§ - 'Variegated Kwanso' (d/v)	CBow CRow EGle ELan EMon EPPr EShb GCal IBlr MAvo MRav MTho NBir SBla SBod SPav WCMO WCot WFar WHer WHoo WWlt
'Funky Fuchsia'	SPol
'Gadsden Goliath'	SPol
'Gadsden Light'	CCol SDay
* 'Garden Plants'	SRos
'Garden Portrait' **new**	CMil
'Gaucho'	MNFA
'Gay Octopus' **new**	CBgR SRos
'Gay Rapture'	SPer
'Gemini'	SRos
'Gentle Country Breeze'	SRos
'Gentle Shepherd'	More than 30 suppliers
'George Cunningham'	CSev ECtt EGle EGol EHrv ELan ERou MNFA MRav NBir SPol SRos SUsu WCAu WFar
'Georgette Belden'	MBri
'Georgia Cream' (d)	MBNS
'German Ballerina'	SPol
'Giant Moon'	CMHG EBrs ELan EPla ERou LRHS SRms WFar WHal
'Gingerbread Man'	MBNS
'Glacier Bay'	CBgR EBee LHop
'Glory's Legacy'	SRos
'Glowing Gold'	WCAu
'Gold Crest'	MNFA
'Gold Dust' **new**	SRos
'Gold Imperial'	EWll NBre
'Golden Bell'	NGdn NHol
'Golden Chance'	WCAu
'Golden Chimes' ♀H4	More than 30 suppliers
'Golden Ginkgo'	LRHS MBri MNFA WSPU
'Golden Nugget'	MBNS
'Golden Orchid'	see *H.* 'Dubloon'
'Golden Peace'	SRos
'Golden Prize'	EPla MNFA NGdn NPri SDay SRos WCot WFar
'Golden Scroll'	SDay SRos
Golden Zebra = 'Malja'PBR (v)	ENot EPfP MGos NLar NSti SDnm SPoG WFar
'Good Looking'	EGol
'Grace and Favour'	SDay SPol
'Graceful Eye'	SRos
'Grand Masterpiece'	CMMP EBee EChP IPot NGdn NRnb SPet WAul
'Grand Palais'	SRos
'Grape Magic'	EGol SRos WTin
'Grape Velvet'	CHar CPar CSpe EGle EGol MBNS MCCP MFOX MHar MNFA NBre
'Green Dolphin Street' **new**	SRos
'Green Dragon'	SDay
'Green Drop'	SAga WFar
'Green Eyed Giant'	MNFA
'Green Eyed Lady'	SDay
'Green Flutter' ♀H4	CSev EChP EPfP GCal LPhx LRHS LSRN MBNS MBri MNFA NBir NBre NCGa NGdn NSti SRos
'Green Glitter'	MNFA
'Green Gold'	CMHG MNFA
'Green Puff'	NBir SDay
'Green Spider'	SDay SRos
'Green Valley'	MNFA
'Grumbly'	ELan WPnP
'Guardian Angel'	WTin
'Gusto'	WCAu
'Hail Mary' **new**	SDay
'Halo Light'	MNFA
'Hamlet'	SDay
'Happy Returns'	CBgR COtt CTri EBee EBrs ECha EGol ELan EMar EWoo IBal IFro LAst MBNS MBri MHar MNFA NEgg NGdn SBla SDay SRGP SRos WCAu WTin
'Harbor Blue'	CCol SDay
'Hawaiian Nights' **new**	EWoo
'Hawaiian Punch'	EGol
'Hawaiian Purple'	EGol
'Hawk'	SPol
'Hazel Monette'	EGol
'Heartthrob'	WCAu
'Heavenly Treasure'	SRos
'Heidi Eidelweiss'	CPLG
'Heirloom Lace'	WCAu WFar
'Helen Boehm' **new**	EMar
'Helle Berlinerin' ♀H4	MNFA SPol
'Her Majesty's Wizard'	EWoo MAvo MBNS NBro SPoG SPol
'Hercules'	NBre
'Heron's Cove' **new**	EWoo
'Hey There'	SDay SRos
'High Tor'	GCal GQui MNFA
'Highland Lord' (d)	SDay
'Holiday Mood'	ELan ERou
'Holly Dancer'	SPol
'Honey Jubilee'	SPol
'Hope Diamond'	CCol SDay WCAu
'Hornby Castle'	CBro EBrs LRHS NHol WPer
'Hot Ticket'	SRos
'Hot Wire'	SRos
'Houdini'	EChP EGle EGol WCAu WMnd WWye
'House of Orange'	SPol
'Howard Goodson'	MNFA
'Humdinger'	SRos
'Hyperion'	CBgR CPrp CSev CTri ECha ECtt EGol EPfP LAst MLan MNFA MRav NGdn NHol SHBN SPer SPla SPoG SRos SUsu WTMC WWye
'Ice Carnival'	CBgR CKel EGle EPfP ERou LDai LRHS MBNS MNFA NBhm NBre NGdn NOrc SPet SVil
'Ice Castles'	CTri
'Ice Cool'	SRos
'Icecap'	WAul WFar WMoo WPnP WWpP
'Icy Lemon'	SRos
'Ida Duke Miles'	SDay SRos
'Ida Munson'	EGol
'Imperator'	EPla LPBA NHol
'Impromptu' **new**	SDay
'In Depth' (d)	EGle EPfP MBNS NBro NCGa NLar WCot
'Inchon' **new**	EMar

'Indian Giver'   CCol
'Indian Paintbrush'   EChP EGle EWoo LHop MBri NBir
                                   SPol WCAu
'Inner View'   EChP ECtt EWoo MBNS NLar
                                   NRnb WMnd
'Inspired Edge'   MBNS
'Inspired Word'   SRos
'Invicta'   SRos
'Invitation to Immortality'   EWoo
  new
'Iridescent Jewel'   SDay
'Irish Elf'   GBuc GMac WTin
'Isle of Capri'   SRos
'Isle of Dreams'   SDay
'Isleworth'   EWoo
'Jake Russell'   MBNS MNFA
'James Clark' **new**   EWoo
'James Marsh'   CBgR CCol CPar EChP EGle EPfP
                                   EWes MBNS MBri MNFA MNrw
                                   NCGa NRnb NSti SRos WAul WCAu
                                   WMnd
'Janet Gordon'   SPol SRos
'Janice Brown'   CCol CKel CWCL EChP EMar
                                   EWoo MBNS MNFA NLar NMoo
                                   SRos
'Jan's Twister'   CCol
'Jason Salter'   EWoo NCGa SDay WAul
'Java Sea'   EBee
'Jean Swann' **new**   CCol
'Jedi Dot Pierce'   SRos
'Jenny Wren'   EMar EPPr EPla EWoo GSki LRHS
                                   MBNS MNFA NBre NBro NEgg
                                   SRGP SUsu WAul WCAu
'Jerusalem'   SRos
'Jo Jo'   WCAu
'Joan Cook'   EGle
'Joan Senior'   More than 30 suppliers
'Jock Randall'   MNFA
'Jockey Club' (d)   EMar MBNS
'John Bierman'   SRos
'Joie de Vivre'   EWoo
'Jolyene Nichole'   SRos
'Journey's End'   SDay
'Jovial'   SDay SRos
'Judah'   SDay SRos
'Justin June'   CCol
'Kate Carpenter'   SRos
'Kathleen Salter'   EWoo SRos
'Katie Elizabeth Miller'   SRos
'Kecia'   MNFA
'Kelly's Girl'   SRos
'Kent's Favorite Two'   SRos
'Kindly Light'   CCol EMar MNFA SRos WCAu
'King Haiglar'   CCol EGol LPhx SRos
'Kiwi Claret'   EWoo
'Klowa Sunset' **new**   EWoo
N 'Kwanso Flore Pleno'   see *H. fulva* 'Green Kwanso'
N 'Kwanso Flore Pleno   see *H. fulva* 'Variegated Kwanso'
    Variegata'
'La Peche'   SDay
'Lace Cookies' **new**   EWoo
'Lacy Marionette'   SPol
'Lady Cynthia'   CKel CSBt
'Lady Fingers'   CBgR CCol MNFA
'Lady Limelight' **new**   SDay
'Lady Liz' **new**   MNFA
'Lady Mischief'   EWoo
'Lady Neva'   CCol SDay SRos
'Ladykin'   SPol SRos
'Lake Effect' **new**   EWoo
'Lake Norman Spider'   MNFA
'Lark Song'   EBrs EGol WFar
'Laughton Tower' **new**   SMHy
'Lauren Leah'   SRos
'Lavender Bonanza'   WCAu WCFE
'Lavender Deal'   EMar

'Lavender Memories'   SDay
'Lavender Silver Cords'   SPol
'Leebea Orange Crush'   EMar
'Lemon Bells' ♀H4   EBee ECha EGle EMFW EMar EPPr
                                   EPfP GMaP GSki MBNS MNFA
                                   MWgw NBro NCGa NGdn SDay
                                   SRos SVil WCAu
'Lemon Dessert' **new**   SRos
'Lemon Mint'   EGol SRos
'Lemonora'   SDay
'Lenox'   SDay SRos
'Leonard Bernstein'   SRos
'Light the Way'   ECha
'Light Years Away' **new**   EWoo
§ *lilioasphodelus* ♀H4   More than 30 suppliers
  - 'Rowden Golden   CRow
      Jubilee' (v)
'Lillian Frye'   EGol
'Lilting Belle'   CCol SRos
'Lilting Lady'   SDay
'Lime Frost'   SRos
'Linda'   ERou EWll MRav NHol SRos
'Linda Agin' **new**   EWoo
* 'Liners Moon'   EGol
'Lines of Splendor' **new**   CCol
'Lipstick Print'   SRos
'Little Audrey'   EGle MHar
'Little Baby Mine'   EWoo
'Little Bee'   MBNS NBre
'Little Beige Magic'   EGol
'Little Big Man'   SDay
'Little Bugger'   MBNS NEgg NGby NLar
'Little Bumble Bee'   CFir COIW EGle EGol EMar MBNS
                                   MNFA WCAu
'Little Business'   EWoo MBNS MNFA SDay WAul
'Little Cadet'   MNFA
'Little Cameo'   EGol
'Little Carpet'   MBNS
'Little Carrot Top'   WCAu
'Little Cranberry Cove'   EGol
'Little Dandy'   EGol
'Little Deeke'   MHar MNFA SDay SRos
'Little Fantastic'   EGol
'Little Fat Dazzler'   SDay SPol SRos
'Little Fellow'   MBNS
'Little Grapette'   CHad CPrp EGle EGol MBNS
                                   MNFA NLar NSti SBod SRos WAul
                                   WCAu WCot WTin
'Little Greenie'   SDay
'Little Gypsy Vagabond'   SDay SRos
'Little Lassie'   MBNS
'Little Lavender Princess'   EGol
'Little Maggie'   MHar MSte SDay
'Little Missy'   CBgR EMar EWoo LAst MBNS
                                   NBre SPet WGob WHoo
'Little Monica'   SDay
'Little Pumpkin Face'   EGol
'Little Rainbow'   EGol
'Little Red Hen'   EMar GBuc LRHS MBNS MNFA
                                   NBro NEgg NGdn NLRH SDay
'Little Show Stopper'   EWoo MBNS NBro NMRc NMoo
                                   SPoG
'Little Sweet Sue'   MNFA
'Little Sweet Talk'   SRos
'Little Tawny'   WCAu
'Little Toddler'   SDay
'Little Violet Lace'   GSki SDay
'Little Wart'   EGol MNFA SDay
'Little Wine Cup'   CMHG COIW CWat EBee EChP
                                   ECtt EGol EMar EPla EWsh GMaP
                                   GMac IBal LAst LRHS MNFA MRav
                                   MTis MWat NBir NGdn NOrc NPri
                                   SPoG SRms WAul WFar WMoo
                                   WPer WTel
'Little Witching Hour'   EWoo
'Little Women'   SDay

'Little Zinger' — SDay
'Littlest Clown' — SDay
'Lochinvar' — ENot GBuc MRav SRos
'Long John Silver' **new** — SRos
'Long Stocking' — SPol SRos
'Longfield Purple Edge' — EBee MBNS
'Longfield's Beauty' — EGle MBNS NCGa
'Longfield's Glory' — CCol MBNS NBre NCGa NMoo WGob
'Longfield's Pride' — ECho MBNS
'Longfield's Purple Eye' — MBNS NCGa NLar NMoo
'Longfield's Twins' — CWrd EBee MBNS NBPC NMoo WCot
longituba — CPLG
  - B&SWJ 4576 — WCru
'Lord of Lightning' — EWoo
'Lori Goldston' **new** — EWoo
'Love Glow' — CFir
'Lucretius' — MNFA
'Lullaby Baby' — CCol EGle EGol ELan MBNS NOrc SDay SPol SRos
luna — NOak
'Lusty Lealand' — CDWL CHea CPar EGle EGol EMar MBNS SRos
'Luxury Lace' — CPrp CSpe CWat EChP ECho ECtt EGle EGol ELan EMar EPfP EPla LRHS MNFA MTis NBir NGdn NPri SPol SRos WAul WCAu WCFE WFar WMoo WPnP WTMC WTin WWhi
'Lydia Bechtold' **new** — CCol
'Lyn Wright' — EWoo
'Lynn Hall' — EGol MBNS
'Lyric Opera' **new** — SDay
'Mabel Fuller' — MRav
'Maggie Fynboe' — SPol
'Magic Carpet Ride' — SPol
'Magic Lace' **new** — EWoo SRos
'Mahogany Magic' — SRos
'Malaysian Monarch' — SRos
'Maleny Bright Eyes' — EWoo
'Maleny Charmer' — EWoo
'Maleny Miter' — EWoo
'Maleny Piecrust' — EWoo
'Maleny Sizzler' — EWoo
'Maleny Tapestry' — EWoo
'Maleny Think Big' — EWoo
'Maleny Tiger' — EWoo
'Mallard' — CWat ECtt EGol EHrv EMar EPla LLWP LRHS MRav MTis SRos SWat WPer WTMC
'Manchurian Apricot' — SRos
'Mandalay Bay Music' **new** — EWoo
'Marble Faun' — SRos
'Margaret Perry' — CFee EMar GBin WAul
'Marion Caldwell' — SPol
'Marion Vaughn' ♀H4 — CSev ECot EGle EGol EHrv ELan EPfP GMaP LHop LRHS MNFA NSti SBch SDix SPer SRGP SRos SSpi WCAu WFar
'Mariska' — SDay SRos
'Marse Connell' — SRos
'Martha Adams' — CCol
'Mary Ethel Anderson' — EWoo
'Mary Todd' — EGle EGol MBNS MNFA WCAu WMnd
'Mary's Gold' — SDay SPol SRos
'Mask Ball' **new** — SRos
'Matador Orange' — EWsh
'Matt' — SRos
'Mauna Loa' — CCol EBee EMar MBNS MNFA MNrw NBre NRnb WAul WCAu WCMO WCot
'May Hall' — CMCo
'May May' — SPol
'Mayan Poppy' — EWoo
'Meadow Mist' — EGle EGol

'Meadow Sprite' — SRos
'Melody Lane' — CMCo EGol MNFA
'Meno' — EGol
'Mephistopheles' — EWoo
'Merlot Rouge' — WAul
'Merry Maker's Serenade' — EWoo
'Metaphor' — SDay
'Michele Coe' — CMMP EBee EGol EHrv EMar LRHS MBNS MNFA NBre NBro NCGa NEgg NGdn SPav SRGP SRos WCAu WMoo
middendorffii — CAvo EBee EBrs EMon GCal GIBF GMaP MNFA NGdn NSti WCAu WFar WPnP WWpP
  - 'Elfin' — EMon
  - var. *esculenta* — EMon
  - 'Major' — CFee
'Midnight Love' — EWoo
'Midnight Magic' — EMar EWoo
'Midnight Raider' — EWoo
'Mikado' — LRHS
'Milady Greensleeves' — CCol SDay SRos
'Milanese Mango' — EWoo SDay
'Mildred Mitchell' — LBuc MBNS WSan
'Millie Schlumpf' — SDay SRos
'Ming Lo' — SDay
'Ming Porcelain' — CMil SDay SRos
'Mini Pearl' — CBgR CMMP EChP EGol EPfP LRHS MBri SDay SRos WPer WWye
'Mini Stella' — CBro ECtt ENot IBal MBNS NBre NOrc WAul WFar WPnP
miniature hybrids — SRms WPer
minor — CBro EBrs EGol EMon GCal NGdn SRms
'Miressa Purple' — EBee
'Missenden' ♀H4 — MNrw SRos
'Mission Moonlight' — EGol MHar WCAu
'Missouri Beauty' — CCol CPar EBee ERou LRHS MBNS NOrc NPri WWeb
'Missouri Memories' — EWoo SRos
'Mister Lucky' — EWoo
'Mokan Cindy' — EMar
'Moment of Truth' — MBNS NBre
'Monica Marie' — SRos
'Moon Witch' — SDay SRos
'Moonlight Masquerade' — EPfP WCMO
'Moonlight Mist' — CCol SRos
'Moonlit Caress' — EBee IPot MBNS SRos WAul
'Moonlit Crystal' — CSpe
'Moonlit Masquerade' — CCol CPen EChP EGle EMar ERou EWoo GBuc MBNS MBri MCCP MLLN NCGa NOrc NRnb SDnm SPav SPer SRos WAul WCAu WGob WHrl WSan
'Mormon Spider' — SPol
'Morning Dawn' — EGle
'Morning Sun' — EMar MBNS NBre WCMO WCot
'Morocco' — SPol
'Morocco Red' — CBro CTri ELan EPla GSki NBre NGdn
'Morrie Otte' — SPol
'Mosel' — SDay
'Mount Joy' — SPer
'Mountain Beauty' — EWoo
'Mountain Laurel' — LDai LRHS MNFA MRav WFar
'Mr Ted' — CCol
'Mrs B.F. Bonner' — WAul
'Mrs David Hall' — CMdw
'Mrs Hugh Johnson' — CHad CSev ECot LAst MSte NHol SHBN WWpP
'Mrs John J. Tigert' — ERou
* 'Mrs Lester' — SDay
multiflora — EMon MNFA NHol SMHy
'My Belle' — SRos
'My Darling Clementine' — SDay SRos
'My Melinda' — SDay

'My Sweet Rose'   SRos
'Mynelle's Starfish'   SPol
'Mysterious Veil'   EGol
'Nacogdoches Lady'   CCol
'Nairobi Dawn'   SRos
'Nairobi Night'   EWoo
nana   CFir EPot
'Nanuq'   SDay SRos
'Naomi Ruth'   EGle EGol LAst MBNS WCAu
   WHoo WTin
'Nashville'   CBro ELan ERou IBlr
'Natural Veil'   SPol
'Neal Berrey'   SRos
'Nefertiti'   CBgR CMCo CMMP EChP LAst
   LHop NBPC NBir SPer WAul WCAu
   WSan
'Neon Rose'   SRos
'New Direction' **new**   EWoo
'New Perspective' **new**   CCol
'Neyron Rose' ♀H4   CHar CHea EGol EPfP EPla ERou
   GSki MBNS MNFA NBre NEgg
   NGdn SRos WCAu WMoo
'Night Beacon'   CBgR ECho ECtt EGol EMar EWes
   EWll EWoo IBal LBBr MBNS MBri
   MLLN MNFA MNrw NCGa NLar
   NMoo SDay SRos WGob WHrl
'Night Embers' **new**   EWoo
'Night Raider'   SDay SRos
'Night Wings' **new**   EWoo
'Nigrette'   LPBA NHol WWpP
'Nile Crane'   CBgR EBee ERou MBNS MNrw
   NCGa SDay SPer WAul
'Nivia Guest'   SDay
'Nob Hill'   CMdw EGol EPla GBin MNFA SRos
'Noble Warrior'   EWoo
'Nordic Night'   CCol
'Norton Orange'   MNFA SAga WFar
'Nosferatu' **new**   SDay
'Nova' ♀H4   CPrp MNFA SRos
'Nuka' **new**   EMar
'Ocean Rain'   SRos
'Old Tangiers'   EMar SRos
'Olive Bailey Langdon'   EGol SRos
'Oliver Billingslea' **new**   EWoo
'Olympic Showcase'   SRos
'Omomuki'   SRos
'Oom Pah Pah'   ECha
'Open Hearth'   CCol SRos
'Orange Dream'   SDay
'Orange Velvet'   SDay SRos
'Orangeman' hort.   EMar EPla GSki LRHS MBNS NGdn
'Orchid Beauty'   ECha MLHP WMoo
'Orchid Candy'   CWrd EWoo MBNS NBir WAul
'Orchid Corsage'   SDay
'Oriental Ruby'   EGol MNFA
'Out of Darkness' **new**   EWoo
'Outrageous'   SRos
'Paige Parker'   EGol
'Paige's Pinata'   EBee MBNS NBPC
'Paintbrush'   CRez
'Painted Lady'   MNFA
'Painted Trillium'   CMil
'Painter Poet' **new**   EMar
'Painters Touch' **new**   SDay
'Palace Garden Beauty' **new**   EWoo
'Palace Guard'   MNFA
'Pandora's Box'   More than 30 suppliers
'Paper Butterfly'   CCol EMar SRos
'Paradise Pink'   NPri
'Paradise Prince'   EGol
'Pardon Me'   CMHG CMMP ECho EGle EGol
   ELan GMaP IBal MBNS MNFA
   NCGa NGdn NHol SRos WAul
   WBor WCAu
'Pastel Ballerina'   SRos

'Pastel Classic'   SRos
'Pastilline'   SPol
'Patchwork Puzzle'   EWoo SRos
'Patricia' **new**   EPfP MBNS SPoG
'Patricia Gentzel Wright'   EWoo
new
'Patsy Bickers'   CCol
'Peach Petticoats'   SRos
'Pear Ornament'   SRos
'Pearl Lewis'   SDay
'Pemaquid Light'   CMHG
'Penelope Vestey'   EBla EGle EMar GBuc LRHS MBNS
   MNFA NCGa NGdn SPol SRGP
   SRos
'Penny's Worth'   EBrs EGol MBNS NOrc WAul WCot
   WFar WHoo
'Persian Princess'   CMCo
'Persian Ruby'   SPol
'Petite Ballerina'   SDay
'Piano Man'   EMar MBNS MWea NMoo WAul
   WGob
'Piccadilly Princess'   SRos
'Pink Ambrosia' **new**   EWoo
'Pink Ballerina'   EGol
'Pink Charm'   COlW EBee EChP ECha EMar
   EWsh GBBs GMaP LPBA LRHS
   MHar MNFA MWgw NBro NGdn
   NHol NOrc SHBN SPla SRos WCAu
'Pink Cotton Candy'   EWoo SRos
'Pink Damask' ♀H4   More than 30 suppliers
'Pink Dream'   EMar LRHS MBNS MNFA NBir
   NBre NHol SPol WCAu
'Pink Glow'   CMMP
'Pink Heaven'   EGol
'Pink Lady'   ERou MNrw MRav NBur SHBN
   SRms
'Pink Lavender Appeal'   EGol WCAu
'Pink Prelude'   EBee EChP EMar LRHS MBNS
   MNFA MWat NBro
'Pink Puff'   ERou MBNS NBir NBre NCGa NLar
   SDay WGob
'Pink Salute'   SRos
'Pink Sundae'   ECha MTis
'Pink Super Spider'   MNFA SRos
'Pinocchio'   MBNS NMoo
'Pirate Treasure'   MBNS
'Pirate's Patch'   SPol SRos
'Pirate's Promise'   EWoo
'Pixie Pipestone'   CCol
'Plum Candy' **new**   EWoo
'Point of Honor' **new**   EWoo
'Pojo'   SDay
'Pompeian Purple'   EGol
'Pony'   EGol SDay SRos
'Ponytail Pink'   EGol
'Prague Spring'   EMar MNFA SRos WCAu
'Prairie Belle'   CBcs CSWP MBNS NBre WCAu
   WFar WWhi
'Prairie Blue Eyes'   CCol EChP ECho EGle EGol LRHS
   MBNS MNFA NMoo NRnb SPlb
   SPol SRos WAul WCAu WCot
   WMnd WTMC
'Prairie Moonlight'   SRos
'Prairie Sunset'   WCAu
'Prelude to Love'   EMar
'Pretty Mist'   MBri
'Pretty Peggy'   MNFA
'Primrose Mascotte'   NBir
'Prince of Midnight' **new**   SDay
'Prince Redbird'   SDay SRos
'Princess Blue Eyes'   SPol
'Princeton Eye Glow' **new**   SDay
'Princeton Silky'   SRos
'Prize Picotee Deluxe'   SRos
'Prize Picotee Elite'   SRos WTin
'Protocol'   SDay

§ 'Puddin'   NHol SDay WAul
'Pumpkin Kid'   SRos
'Puppet Show'   SDay
'Purbeck Silk' **new**   CCol
'Purbeck Sundae' **new** CCol
'Pure and Simple'   SDay SPol
'Purple Bicolor'   CRez
'Purple Pinwheel'   SPol
'Purple Rain'   CHea CWat MBNS MWea SPol
                        SRos SWvt
'Purple Rain Dance'   SPol
'Purple Waters'   CCol EPfP EWll LRHS MBNS
                        MWgw NBre NOrc NPri WAul
                        WPnP
'Pursuit of Excellence' SRos
'Pygmy Plum' **new**   SDay
'Queen of May'   WCot
'Quick Results'   SRos
'Quinn Buck'   SDay
'Ra Hansen'   SDay
'Radiant'   CBcs
'Radiant Greetings' **new** MNFA
'Raging Tiger'   SDay
'Rainbow Candy'   LTwo MBNS NMoo SPoG WSan
'Raindrop'   EGol
'Raining Violets' **new** EWoo
'Rajah'   CBgR EGra EMar MBNS NBro SPer
                        WWeb
'Raspberry Candy'   EChP ECho EMar EWll MBNS
                        MLLN MNrw NBhm NBro NCGa
                        NOrc WAul WCAu WGob WHrl
'Raspberry Pixie'   EGol MNFA SPol
'Raspberry Wine'   MHar
'Real Wind'   CCol MNFA SPol SRos
'Red Admiral' **new**   EBrs
'Red Flag'   CCol
'Red Precious' ♀H4   EGol MNFA MNrw SMHy SRos
'Red Ribbons'   CCol SDay SPol SRos
'Red Rum'   CBgR EWll MBNS MTis NBro
                        WPnP WWhi
'Red Volunteer'   SRos
'Regal Centre'   EWoo
'Respighi'   SRos
'Return Trip'   SPol
'Ribbonette'   EBee MBNS NMoo WSan
'Ringlets'   GSki MNFA
'Robin Coleman'   MNFA
'Rocket City'   ELan SRos
'Roger Grounds'   CCol SPol
* 'Romantic Rose'   EMar MBNS
'Romany'   LPBA
'Root Beer'   SRos WTin
'Rose Corsage' **new**   EWoo
'Rose Emily'   SDay SRos
'Rose Festival'   WCAu
'Rose Fever'   EWoo
'Rose Roland'   NBre
'Rosella Sheridan'   SRos
'Rosewood Flame'   SRos
'Rosewood Snowflakes'   SRos
   new
'Rosy Returns' **new**   MBNS MWea NMoo
'Royal Braid'   CPen EChP EGle ENot EPfP EWoo
                        MBNS MNrw NCGa NLar SPer
                        WCot WSan
'Royal Charm'   SRos
'Royal Corduroy'   SRos
'Royal Robe'   CPLG CTri LPhx
'Royal Saracen'   SDay
'Royalty'   NGdn WWpP
'Ruby Spider'   CCol SDay SRos
'Rudolf Seyer'   MBNS
'Ruffled Antique Lavender' WCAu
'Ruffled Apricot'   CKel LBMP MBNS MNFA NFla
                        SDay SPav SRos WCAu
'Ruffles and Lace'   CCol

'Russell Prichard'   ERou
'Russian Easter'   SRos
'Russian Rhapsody'   CKel SRos
'Rutilans'   CFee
'Sabine Baur'   EBee EMar EWoo IBal IPot MBNS
                        MWea WAul WCMO WCra
'Sabra Salina'   SRos
'Saffron Glow' **new**   SDay
'Saintly'   EWoo
'Salmon Sheen'   MNFA SDay SPer SRos
'Sammy' **new**   SDay
'Sammy Russell'   More than 30 suppliers
'Samuel Bell' **new**   EWoo
'Sandra Elizabeth' **new** SDay
'Sandra Walker'   EGol LAst
'Santiago' **new**   SPol
'Satin Clouds'   EGol
'Satin Glass'   EBrs MNFA
'Satin Glow'   ECha MLHP
'Scarlet Flame'   ECha WMoo
* 'Scarlet Oak'   LRHS MBri MNFA SRos
'Scarlet Orbit'   EWoo SRos
'Scarlet Ribbons'   SPol
'Scarlock'   MNFA
'Scatterbrain'   CKel
'Schoeppinger Anfang'   EBee
'School Girl'   EBrs
'Scorpio'   CBgR CCol MNFA SPol
'Scotland'   IBal
'Searcy Marsh'   EGol
'Sebastian'   SRos
'Secret Splendor'   CCol SPol
'Selma Longlegs' **new** SRos
'Seminole Wind'   EWoo
'Serena Sunburst'   SRos
'Serena Madonna'   CFir
'Serenity Morgan'   EBee EPfP LBuc MBNS
'Shaman'   SRos
'Sherry Lane Carr'   SPol SRos
* 'Shocker' **new**   EWoo
'Shogun'   MBNS
'Shooting Star'   SPla
'Shotgun' **new**   SPol
'Show Amber'   MBNS SRos
'Silent Sentry'   CFir EWoo
'Silken Fairy'   EGol
'Siloam Amazing Grace' SDay SRos
'Siloam Angel Blush'   SDay
'Siloam Baby Talk'   CMMP EChP EGle EGol EMar LAst
                        MNFA NBir SRos WAul WHoo
                        WMoo WPnP WTin
'Siloam Bertie Ferris' MNFA SDay
'Siloam Bo Peep'   CCol EGol MNFA WAul WTMC
'Siloam Brian Hanke'   SRos
'Siloam Button Box'   EBee EChP EGol WAul WSan
'Siloam Bye Lo'   EGol EWoo SDay
'Siloam Cinderella'   EGol SDay SRos
'Siloam David Kirchhoff' EMar EWoo MBNS SDay SRos
'Siloam Doodlebug'   EGol SRos
'Siloam Double Classic' (d) CCol EGol EMar SRos
'Siloam Dream Baby'   EPPr GBri MBNS NCGa
'Siloam Edith Sholar'   EGol
'Siloam Ethel Smith'   EGol MNFA SDay SRos
'Siloam Fairy Tale'   EChP EGol
'Siloam Flower Girl'   SDay
'Siloam French Doll'   CCol MBNS NLar NRnb
'Siloam French Marble' SRos
'Siloam Gold Coin'   SDay
'Siloam Grace Stamile' CFir SRos WGob
'Siloam Harold Flickinger' SRos
'Siloam Jim Cooper'   EWoo SRos
'Siloam Joan Senior'   ECtt EGol MBNS
'Siloam John Yonski'   SDay
'Siloam June Bug'   EGle EGol ELan MNFA WCAu
'Siloam Justine Lee'   MBNS
'Siloam Kewpie Doll'   EGol

'Siloam Little Angel'	EGol
'Siloam Little Girl'	EGol SDay SRos
'Siloam Mama'	SRos
'Siloam Merle Kent'	EMar EWoo MNFA SDay SRos
'Siloam New Toy'	EGol
'Siloam Orchid Jewel'	EGol
'Siloam Paul Watts'	SRos
'Siloam Peewee'	EGol
* 'Siloam Pink'	LAst
'Siloam Pink Glow'	EGle EGol WAul
'Siloam Pink Petite'	EGol
'Siloam Plum Tree'	EGol
'Siloam Pocket Size'	EGol MSte
'Siloam Prissy'	EGol
'Siloam Purple Plum'	EGol
'Siloam Queen's Toy' **new**	SPol
'Siloam Red Ruby'	EGol
'Siloam Red Toy'	EGol MNFA
'Siloam Red Velvet'	EGol
'Siloam Ribbon Candy'	EGol SDay
'Siloam Rose Dawn'	SRos
'Siloam Rose Queen'	SDay
'Siloam Royal Prince'	CMMP EBee EChP EGle EGol EPfP
	MNFA NHol NRnb SDay
'Siloam Shocker'	EGol MNFA
'Siloam Show Girl'	CMCo EGle EGol EWoo MBNS
	NCGa
'Siloam Stinnette's Delight' **new**	CCol
'Siloam Sugar Time'	EGol
'Siloam Tee Tiny'	EGle EGol
'Siloam Tinker Toy'	EGol
'Siloam Tiny Mite'	EGol SDay
'Siloam Toddler'	EGol
'Siloam Tom Thumb'	EGol EMar MBNS WCAu WGob
'Siloam Ury Winniford'	ECho EGol EMar MBNS MCCP
	MNFA NBre NLar NMoo WAul
	WHoo WPnP WTin
'Siloam Virginia Henson'	EGol MNFA SRos WCAu
'Silver Ice'	SRos
'Silver Lance' **new**	SRos
'Silver Quasar' **new**	SRos
'Silver Queen' **new**	GBin
'Silver Trumpet'	EGle EGol
'Silver Veil'	WFar
'Sir Blackstem'	SRos
'Sirius'	NHol
'Sirocco'	EBee EChP WTin
'Slender Lady'	SDay SRos
'Smoky Mountain Autumn'	EMar EWoo MHar SPol SRos
'Snappy Rhythm'	MNFA
'Snowed In'	EWoo SRos
'Snowy Apparition'	EMar EWTr EWll MBNS MNFA
	MSte MWea
'Snowy Eyes'	EGle EGol EMar GBuc IPot MBNS
	NCGa NHol NRnb
'Solid Scarlet'	SRos
'Someone Special'	SDay SPol SRos
'Song In My Heart' **new**	EWoo
'Song Sparrow'	CBro GMac LRHS WPer WWye
'Sovereign Queen'	EGol
'Spacecoast Starburst'	EMar MBNS NBro WCAu
'Spanish Glow'	SRos
'Spider Man'	SDay SRos WCAu
'Spider Miracle'	CCol MNFA SDay
'Spilled Milk'	SPol
'Spinne In Lachs' **new**	SRos
'Spring Willow Song'	SDay
'Squash Dolly' **new**	EWoo
'Stafford'	More than 30 suppliers
'Starling'	CFir CPar EChP EGle EGol MNFA
	MSte NChi WAul WCAu
'Stars and Stripes'	MNFA
'Startle'	CFir EWoo MAvo MBNS MNrw
	SPoG WSan
'Statuesque'	WFar

'Stella de Oro'	More than 30 suppliers
'Stoke Poges' ♀H4	CAvo CBro CSev EBee EChP EGle
	EGoo EMFW EMar EPPr EPfP EPla
	LAst LHop LRHS MBNS MNFA
	NEgg NGdn SAga SDay SPer SRos
	STes SWat WCAu
'Stoplight'	CCol EMar SDay SPol SRos
'Strawberry Candy'	CMMP EChP EMar EMil EPfP EWll
	EWoo LAst LSRN MBNS MBri
	NCGa NGdn NRnb SPer SPet SPoG
	SRos WAul WCAu WHoo WHrl
'Strawberry Fields Forever'	EWoo MBNS SPol
'Strawberry Swirl'	MNFA
I 'Streaker' B. Brown (v)	WCot
'Streaker' McKinney	MNFA
'Strutter's Ball'	CPar EChP EGle EWoo IPot MNFA
	NGdn NRnb SDay SPer SRos SWat
	WAul WCAu WCMO WHoo WMnd
'Sugar Cookie'	EWoo SDay SRos
'Summer Dragon' **new**	EBee MBNS NMoo SPoG
'Summer Interlude'	WCAu WMoo
'Summer Jubilee'	SDay
'Summer Wine'	More than 30 suppliers
'Sunday Gloves'	EGol SRos
'Sunstar'	CCol
'Super Purple'	CKel
'Superlative'	SRos
'Susan Weber'	SRos
'Suzie Wong'	MNFA SRos
'Svengali'	SDay SPol
'Sweet Harmony'	CCol
'Sweet Pea'	EGol SDay
'Sweet Sugar Candy' **new**	EWoo
'Taj Mahal'	SDay WFar
'Tang'	MBNS MNFA NMoo NOrc
	WCAu
'Tangerine Tango'	EWoo
'Tango Noturno'	SPol
'Tapestry of Dreams'	EWoo
'Tasmania'	SPer
'Techny Peach Lace'	SRos
'Techny Spider'	SRos
'Tejas'	CElw EBee MBNS NBre SPer
'Tender Shepherd'	EGol WCAu
'Tetraploid Stella de Oro'	SDay
'Tetrina's Daughter' ♀H4	EPfP NHol SRos
'Texas Sunlight'	WAul
'Theresa Hall'	WFar
'Thumbelina'	ECha MNFA
§ *thunbergii*	CAvo ECha EMon MNFA MNrw
	SMac WCAu
'Tigerling'	EWoo SRos
'Tigger' **new**	CDWL
'Tilly Whim' **new**	CCol
'Time Lord'	SDay
'Timeless Fire'	SRos
'Tinker Bell'	MSte SRos
'Tom Collins'	SDay SRos
'Tom Wise'	SPol SRos
'Tonia Gay'	SPol SRos
'Tootsie'	SDay
'Tootsie Rose'	SRos
'Torpoint'	EMar LRHS MBNS MNFA NCob
'Towhead'	EGol ENot MRav
'Toyland'	CMCo CSev EChP EGol EMar EPfP
	GSki MBNS NBir NGdn NLar NPri
	SUsu
'Trahlyta'	CPar SDay SPol SRos
'Treasure of Love' **new**	EWoo
'Trevi Fountain' **new**	EWoo
'Trond'	SDay
'Troubled Sleep'	EWoo
'True Pink Beauty' **new**	EWoo
'Tuolumne Fairy Tale'	SPol

'Tuscawilla Blackout'	SRos
'Tuscawilla Tigress'	ECho EMar NCGa SRos WAul
'Tutankhamun' **new**	MNFA
'Tuxedo'	SPol
'Twenty Third Psalm'	WTin
'Twist of Lemon' **new**	SRos
'Two Faces of Love'	SPol
'Unforgetable Fire' **new**	EWoo
'Uniquely Different'	SPol
'Upper Class Peach'	SRos
'Uptown Girl'	SRos
'Valiant'	EMar MBNS
'Vanilla Candy'	SRos
'Varsity'	CPLG EBrs EGol NBir SPer SRos WCAu
'Veiled Beauty'	WCAu
'Velvet Shadows' **new**	SDay
'Vera Biaglow'	MNFA SDay SPol SRos
'Vespers'	CAbP WFar
vespertina	see *H. thunbergii*
'Vi Simmons'	SRos
'Victoria Aden'	CBro IBal
'Victorian Lace' **new**	EWoo
'Victorian Ribbons'	SPol
'Video'	SRos
'Vino di Notte'	SRos
'Vintage Bordeaux'	ELan WAul
'Violet Hour'	SDay
'Virgin's Blush'	SPer
'Vohann'	CMdw SRos
'Waiting in the Wings' **new**	SRos
'Walking on Sunshine'	SRos
'War Paint'	SDay
'Water Witch'	CWat EGol
'Watership Down' **new**	EWoo
'Waxwing'	WPer
'Wayside Green Imp'	EGle EGol MNrw MSte
'Wedding Band'	SRos
'Wee Chalice'	EGol
'Welchkins'	WAul
'Welfo White Diamond'	SPol
'Well of Souls'	CCol
'West Coast Blues' **new**	CCol
'Whichford' ♀H4	CBgR CBro CHad CMMP CSam EBee EBrs ECGP ECtt EGol ELan ETow LAst LPhx LRHS MNFA NCob SPer SPla SRos WCAu EMar LRHS LSRN MNFA NBro NEgg
'White Coral'	
'White Dish'	EGol
'White Edged Madonna'	EMar SBch WHrl
'White Pansy'	SDay SRos
'White Perfection' **new**	EWoo
'White Temptation'	CFir CMMP EChP EGol EPfP EWoo MNFA NCGa NGdn SDay SRos WAul WHoo
'White Zone' **new**	EWoo
'Whooperee'	SRos
* 'Wide Eyed'	EPla MNFA
'Wild about Sherry'	SPol
'Wild Mustang'	CCol MBNS
'Wild One'	MNFA
'Wild Welcome'	WCAu
'Wilson Spider'	SPol
'Wind Frills'	CCol SDay
'Wind Song'	SRos
'Window Dressing'	COlW EGol GMac
'Windsor Tan'	WCAu WCFE
'Wine Bubbles'	EGol
'Wine Merchant'	EMar MNFA
'Wineberry Candy'	CPar CWrd EGle EPfP EWoo MBNS MLLN NLar SPoG WAul WCAu
'Winnetka'	WCAu
'Winnie the Pooh'	SDay
'Winsome Lady'	ECha EMar LRHS MBNS WHrl
'Winter Olympics'	SDay
* 'Witch Hazel'	WCAu
'Wood Duck'	EGle
'Xia Xiang'	SRos
'Yabba Dabba Doo'	CCol SPol SRos
'Yellow Explosion'	SRos
'Yellow Lollipop'	MNFA SDay SRos
'Yellow Mantle'	MNFA
'Yellow Ribbon' **new**	CCol
'Yesterday Memories'	SRos
'Young Countess'	CMCo
'Zagora'	WCAu
'Zampa'	SDay

Hemiorchis (Zingiberaceae)

pantlingii	CKob MOak

Hemiphragma (Scrophulariaceae)

heterophyllum	EBee

Hepatica ✿ (Ranunculaceae)

acutiloba	CArn CBgR CBro CLAP ECho EPot GBuc GCrs GEdr MAsh NBir NLar WCru
americana	CLAP EBee ECho EHrv GBuc GCrs MAsh NBir NLar WCru WPnP
angulosa	see *H. transsilvanica*
'Gyousei'	GBuc
henryi	MAsh NLAp WCru
insularis	CLAP MAsh SBla
– B&SWJ 859	WCru
maxima	GEdr
– B&SWJ 4344	WCru
x *media* 'Ballardii'	GBuc IBlr MNFA
– Blackthorn Group	SBla
– 'Harvington Beauty'	CFwr CLAP EHrv GBuc IBlr MAsh NBir WCMO WCot
§ *nobilis* ♀H4	More than 30 suppliers
– var. *asiatica*	MAsh
– blue-flowered	CDes ECho GAbr GBuc GEdr MAsh NSla NWCA SBla SRot WAbe WCru
– 'Cobalt'	CLAP ECho NLAp NSla WAbe
– 'Cremar' **new**	MAsh
– dark blue-flowered	CLAP
– double pink-flowered	see *H. nobilis* 'Rubra Plena'
– var. *japonica*	CArn CBro EBee EPfP EWes GBuc GCrs MAsh NBir SBla WCru
– – f. *magna* **new**	CStu
– 'Landquart Marble'	NLAp WHil
– large, pale blue-flowered	NLAp WHil
– lilac-flowered	MTho SBla
– mottled leaf	ECho EHrv MTho SBla
– Picos strain	CLAP ECho EHyt EPot ETow GCrs MAsh NLar NWCA SBla SIng SOkd SRot
– var. *pubescens*	MAsh
* – var. *pyrenaica*	EHyt GBuc LEdu MAsh
* – – 'Apple Blossom'	CLAP GCrs MAsh NBir
* – 'Pyrenean Marbles'	CLAP
– red-flowered	ECho WHil
– Rene's form	WFar
– var. *rubra*	CLAP ECho NLAp NMen NSla
§ – 'Rubra Plena' (d)	ECha EHyt MAsh MAvo NSla
– 'Tabby' **new**	ECho
– violet-flowered	MAsh SBla
– white-flowered	CLAP ECho EHyt GCrs ITim MAsh NMen NSla SBla SIng SRot WCru WIvy
nobilis var. *japonica* x *yamatutai* **new**	MAsh
'Sakaya'	WHil

§ ***transsilvanica*** ♀H4 — CBro CLAP CMea EBee ECho EHyt GAbr GBuc GCrs LHop LRHS MAsh NMen SBla WAbe WAul WCot WCru WHal WTin
- 'Ada Scott' — WSHC
- 'Blue Jewel' — CBgR CFir CLAP CRez EBee EBrs ECho GBBs GCrs GEdr MAsh NLar NMen SMeo WPnP
- blue-flowered — IBlr MAsh
- 'De Buis' — CBgR CBod CFwr CLAP EBee ECho EPot GCrs GEdr LPhx MAsh MAvo MBow MDun NJOw NLAp NLar LRHS WPnP
- 'Eisvogel' — CLAP ECho GEdr NMen
- 'Elison Spence' (d) — ECha IBlr MAsh SBla
- 'Karpati Krönen' **new** — MAsh
- 'Lilacina' — ECha ECho GEdr
- 'Loddon Blue' — IBlr
- pink-flowered — CLAP SBla
- 'Typ Scharrer' **new** — MAsh
- white-flowered — ECho SBla
- 'Winterfreude' **new** — MAsh
triloba — see *H. nobilis*
yamatutai — MAsh

Heptacodium (Caprifoliaceae)
jasminoides — see *H. miconioides*
§ ***miconioides*** — CAbP CBcs CMCN CPLG CPMA CPle CTri EBee ELan EPfP GQui IArd IDee IMGH LRHS MBlu MBri MCCP MGos NEgg NPal SBrw SMad SPoG WBVN WCMO WCot WMou WPGP WSHC

Heptapleurum see *Schefflera*

Heracleum (Apiaceae)
candicans — EMan
- BWJ 8157 — WCru
dulce — EBee GIBF
lanatum 'Washington Limes' (v) — EBee EMan EPPr WCot
lehmannianum — EBee EMan NSti WCot
minimum 'Roseum' — CPom
moellendorfii — EBee GIBF
sibiricum — GIBF
sosnowskyi — GIBF
- RBS 0231 — ITer
sphondylium pink — CNat
wilhelmsii — GIBF

Herbertia (Iridaceae)
§ ***lahue*** — CDes CStu ECho LRHS WPGP

Hereroa (Aizoaceae)
odorata — EShb EWin

Hermannia (Sterculiaceae)
candicans — see *H. incana*
erodioides JCA 15523 — CPBP
§ ***incana*** — CHal MOak
§ ***pinnata*** — CPBP CSec WAbe
pulchella — CPBP NWCA WAbe
stricta — CPBP NWCA WAbe

Hermodactylus (Iridaceae)
§ ***tuberosus*** — CAby CArn CAvo CBro CFFs CHar CStu CTri EBee EBrs ECGP ECha ECho LEdu LPhx LRHS SBch SMeo STes WCot WTin
- MS 821 — WCot

Herniaria (Illecebraceae)
glabra — CArn GBar GPoy MSal NGHP SIde WWye

Herpolirion (Anthericaceae)
novae-zealandiae — ECou

Hertia see *Othonna*

Hesperaloe (Agavaceae)
funifera — XPep
parviflora — CTrC EBee EMan LEdu SBig SChr WMul XPep

Hesperantha (Iridaceae)
§ ***baurii*** — CLyd CPBP CStu EBee ECho EMan GBuc NLAp NLar NMen WAbe
coccinea — see *Schizostylis coccinea*
cucullata — EBee
* - 'Rubra' — NWCA
falcata **new** — EBee
grandiflora — ECho
huttonii — EBee ECho EMan MWrn NBir NCGa NEgg
mossii — see *H. baurii*
vaginata 'Stanfordiae' — LBow
woodii — CDes CFir

Hesperis (Brassicaceae)
lutea — see *Sisymbrium luteum*
matronalis — More than 30 suppliers
- alba — see *H. matronalis* var. *albiflora*
§ - var. ***albiflora*** — CCge CHar CHrt CMea CPrp CSpe CTri ELau EMar EPfP ERou GMaP LRHS MBow NGHP NPri SGar SIde SPer SPoG SSvw STes SWat WBrk WCAu WFar WMnd WMoo WPer WWye
- - 'Alba Plena' (d) — CAbP CCge CElw CMea ECtt ELan EMan GBuc LRHS LSou MNFA MNrw NBir NCGa NCob NPri WBrk WCot WCra WFar WGwG WWhi
- - 'Edith Harriet' (d/v) **new** — ERou LSou LTwo MBNS SPoG WCot WTMC
- double-flowered (d) — EChP NCob WCMO
- 'Frogswell Doris' — CBow IFro LDai
- 'Lilacina' — CMea SWat
- 'Lilacina Flore Pleno' (d) — CCge NBre
steveniana — SBch SMrm

Heterolepis (Asteraceae)
aliena — GFai SGar

Heteromeles (Rosaceae)
arbutifolia — see *H. salicifolia*
§ ***salicifolia*** — CAgr EShb

Heteromorpha (Apiaceae)
arborescens — SPlb

Heteropappus (Asteraceae)
altaicus — WPer

Heteropolygonatum (Convallariaceae)
roseolum **new** — EBee

Heteropyxis (Myrtaceae)
natalensis — EShb

Heterotheca (Asteraceae)
mariana — see *Chrysopsis mariana*
pumila — NWCA
§ ***villosa*** — EMan
- 'Golden Sunshine' — EBee

Heuchera ✿ (Saxifragaceae)
'Amber Waves'PBR — More than 30 suppliers

§ *americana* — CEnt EBee ECha GBar MRav NBir SMHy

- Dale's strain — IBal IFoB IFro LBBr MNrw NGdn NLar SMar SPlb SPur SWvt WGor WHrl WMnd WPnP WTMC WWeb
- 'Harry Hay' — CDes EPPr MSte NDov WPGP
- 'Ring of Fire' — CBcs CHar COtt EBee EBla EGle EPfP GBri GKev IArd IBal LRHS MAvo MDun MSte NCGa NMyG NPri NSti NVic SDnm SPav SPla SPoG SWvt WCot WFar

'Amethyst Myst' — CMMP COlW EBee ENot EPfP GBBs GSki LRHS MBNS NCob NEgg NLar NMyG NPri SDnm SPav SPoG SRkn SRot WCMO WFar WGor

'Baby's Breath' **new** — ECho

'Beauty Colour' — More than 30 suppliers

'Black Beauty' — CBct CHVG GCai LSou NLar NPri SRot

* 'Black Velvet' — EPfP NBre

'Blackbird' ♀H4 — MBNS NPro SDnm SPav SRkn SSto SWvt WMnd

'Blood Red' **new** — NBhm

'Blood Vein' — CBow MBNS MWrn NBre

'Blushing Bride' — NRnb

Bressingham hybrids — CWib ENot IFoB LBMP LRHS MLHP NBir NBlu NMir SEND SPer SPet SRms WFar WPer

x *brizoides* — IHMH NJOw

'Burgundy Frost' ♀H4 — WCot

'Can-can' ♀H4 — More than 30 suppliers

'Canyon Chimes' — COtt

'Canyon Duet' — COtt LRHS MBNS

'Canyon Pink' — NRnb NSti

'Cappuccino' — CBct EBee EChP ECtt ELan IBal IBal MBnl MBow MLLN NBro NPri NRnb SDnm SPav SWvt WCFE WFar WWeb WWpP

'Caramel' **new** — CBos LSou LTwo MBNS MBnl MWgw NGdn SMad SPer SPoG SUsu WCot

'Cascade Dawn' — EBee ECtt GBuc IBal LAst LBMP LHop LRHS MRav MSte NBir NGdn NLar SPav SPer WBrk WCMO WCot WFar

'Champagne Bubbles'PBR — EBee MBNS NPri SPoG WCot

'Cherries Jubilee'PBR — CAbP CBow CFir CHar EBee EBla EDAr GMaP LRHS MBNS MBnl MGos MLLN MSph NCGa NEgg NPri SHar SPav SWal WBor WBrk WGor

'Chiqui' — SUsu

chlorantha — EBee GCal NBre

'Chocolate Ruffles'PBR — More than 30 suppliers

'Chocolate Veil' ♀H4 — CPen EPfP SHar WWeb

'Color Dream' — IBal

coral bells — see *H. sanguinea*

'Coral Bouquet' — EBee EMan GBri GQue LAst LSou MBNS MLLN SHar WCot WCra WGwG WWhi

'Coral Cloud' — MRav

Crème Brûlé = 'Tnheu041' **new** — CBct GCai LRHS LTwo MGos SDnm SPoG SRot STes SVil WCMO WGor

'Crimson Curls' — LRHS MBnl SWvt

'Crispy Curly' — CBow EMan MBNS MWrn NBre NBur NRnb

cylindrica — EBee MBNS MRav MSte MWgw NBre WPer

- var. *alpina* — EBee NWCA
- 'Brownfinch' — SMHy

§ - 'Greenfinch' — CFee EBee ECha EGle ELan ENot EPfP ERou EWTr GCal IBal IHMH LRHS MLHP MRav MTis NBir

---

NDov NOrc SPav SPer SPoG SWat WCAu WFar WGwG WMnd WPer

- 'Hyperion' — ECtt

'Dennis Davidson' — see *H.* 'Huntsman'

'Diana Clare' — ECtt

'Dingle Mint Chocolate' — ECtt

Ebony and Ivory = 'E and I'PBR — More than 30 suppliers

I 'Eco Magnififolia' — CLAP

'Eden's Aurora' — EBee EChP WMnd

'Eden's Joy' — EChP MBNS

'Eden's Mystery' — ECtt WWeb

elegans — WCot

'Emperor's Cloak' — CBow CEnt CHar ECtt EKen GKev LEdu LSou MGol NBur NDlv NLar SWal SWvt WMoo

'Emperor's Cloak' green — CEnt

'Firebird' — NBir NVic

Firefly — see *H.* 'Leuchtkäfer'

'Fireworks'PBR ♀H4 — CBow CPen EBee EDAr EPPr GAbr GBBs MBNS MBnl MLLN NCob NDov NLar SHar SPer SPla SPoG WBor WBrk WCMO WCot WGor WHoo

'Florist's Choice' — CAbP EBee IBal MBNS MNFA NRnb SHar WCot WHoo

glauca — see *H. americana*

'Green Ivory' — EBee LRHS MRav NGdn NSti SBch

'Green Spice' — CBct CBow EDAr GBin LSou MBNS NPri SPav SPoG SRot

'Greenfinch' — see *H. cylindrica* 'Greenfinch'

grossulariifolia — MBNS WPer

'Helen Dillon' (v) — CBow EBee ECtt EMan GBri IBal LAst MLLN MRav NBir NPri SPla SPoG SWvt WFar WWhi

'Hercules'PBR — EBee EChP ECtt EPfP MBNS

hispida — MSte WPer

'Hollywood' **new** — GCai NBhm WCot

§ 'Huntsman' — EChP ECha ELan GBri GBuc MBNS MRav WFar WMnd

Key Lime Pie = 'Tnheu042' **new** — CBct GCai LRHS MBnl MBri MGos SDnm SPoG SRot STes SVil

'Lady in Red' — MBNS NBre

'Lady Romney' — GCal

§ 'Leuchtkäfer' — More than 30 suppliers

Licorice = 'Tnheu044' **new** — GCai LRHS MBri MGos SDnm SVil WGor

'Lime' **new** — LSou

'Lime Rickey' — CBow GCai NBhm WCMO

'Little Tinker' **new** — EBee LAst LSou MBNS MBnl WBor

'Magic Wand'PBR ♀H4 — CAbP EBee LRHS MBNS SHar SUsu WCot

'Marmalade' — CKno GCai WCMO

'Mars' — EPfP MBNS NSti SPav

maxima — EMon

'Mercury' — EChP MBNS NMoo SPav

'Metallica' — LRav MWrn NLar

micans — see *H. rubescens*

micrantha — EBee GCal SRms

- var. *diversifolia* Bressingham Bronze = 'Absi'PBR — EAEE EBee EBrs EPla LRHS SPla WFar

N - - 'Palace Purple' — More than 30 suppliers

- 'Martha Roderick' — WCot

§ - 'Ruffles' — EBee EPPr LRHS

- 'Mini Mouse' — EBee EWes LBmB

'Mint Frost'PBR — COtt EBee ECtt ELan EMar ENot EPfP EWTr GBri GSki LAst LHop LRHS MGos MLLN MRav NGdn NHol NPri NRnb SDnm SPav SPer SPoG SWvt WCot WFar WWlt

'Monet' — see *H. sanguinea* 'Monet'

'Montrose Ruby' — NBre

'Mother of Pearl' — ECtt

'Neptune' — EBee EChP EPfP MBNS NMoo SPav SPoG

Neueste hybrids	LRav
'Northern Fire'	MBNS
'Oakington Jewel'	CSam EBrs ELan LRHS
'Obsidian'	CHar CPen CRez EBee GBri GCai
	IPot LSRN MBnl MSte MWea NBPC
	NRnb NScw SHar SPer SPoG
	WCMO WCot WFar
'Painted Lady'	GBuc
'Palace Passion'	WBrE
* 'Palace Purple Select'	CTri CWat CWib EDAr IBal LAst
	NJOw SWvt
'Peach Flambé' **new**	CBow GCai NBhm
'Peachy Keen' **new**	CBow GCai NBhm WCot
'Persian Carpet'	CHEx EBee ECha ECtt EMar GSki
	IBal LHop LRHS MDun MLLN
	MWgw NBir NGdn NPri SDnm
	SWvt WBVN WCMO WCot WFar
'Petite Marbled Burgundy'	CBgR COtt EBee ECtt EDAr EGle
	GBri IBal LAst LTwo MNFA MSte
	NDov NGdn NLar NPri NSti SUsu
	SWvt WAul WCMO WCot WFar
	WGwG WWhi
'Petite Pearl Fairy'	CAbP CBct CBow COtt EBee EGle
	EHoe ELan EMil GSki MBri MSte
	NCGa NGdn NLar NSti SPla SWvt
	WCot WFar WGor WHoo WWhi
'Petite Pink Bouquet'	CBct EBee EChP ECtt EMan EPPr
	GSki IBal MBNS NLar NPro SPla
	WCot WWeb
'Petite Ruby Frills'	CBgR WWeb
'Pewter Moon'	CBcs EBee ELan EMil EPfP IHMH
	LAst LRHS MGos MRav NBir NPri
	SDnm SSto WBrE WBrk WFar
	WMnd WPnP WTin
'Pewter Veil'[PBR]	EBee ENot EPfP LAst MBNS NCGa
	NPri SPer SPoG WFar WPnP
pilosissima	EBee NBre
'Pink Lipstick' **new**	GCai
§ 'Pluie de Feu'	CFir CWCL EBrs EChP ECtt EPfP
	GBri LBmB MBNS MRav SSto
'Plum Pudding'[PBR]	More than 30 suppliers
'Prince'	CPen EBee EBrs EKen ENot EPfP
	LSRN MBNS NMoo SMer SPoG
	SRkn SWvt WPtf
'Prince of Silver'	IBal MBNS NMoo
pringlei	see *H. rubescens*
* x *pruhoniciana* Doctor	SRms
Sitar's hybrids	
pubescens	EBee GBri
pulchella	CBow CPBP CSam EAEE EBee
	EDAr IBal ITim LRHS MBNS MHer
	NJOw SRms SUsu
- JCA 9508	NMen
'Purple Mountain Majesty'	EBee MBNS NCGa WCot
new	
'Purple Petticoats' ♀[H4]	CBcs EBee ENot EPfP GCai MDun
	MLHP MLLN NBre NCGa NCob
	NDlv NGdn NLar NPri SHar SPoG
	SRot
'Quick Silver'	CMea EBla GSki MNFA NBir SMer
	SWvt WCMO WFar
'Quilter's Joy' ♀[H4]	NBre
'Rachel'	More than 30 suppliers
Rain of Fire	see *H.* 'Pluie de Feu'
'Raspberry Ice'	NRnb
'Raspberry Regal' ♀[H4]	EBee ECtt EGle GAbr MLLN MRav
	MSph NBir NEgg NSti SWvt WAul
	WFar
'Red Spangles'	EBrs EPfP LRHS MBNS MWrn NBir
'Regina' ♀[H4]	CAbP EBee ECtt EPfP IBal LSRN
	MBNS MBri NBro SHar SPoG SWvt
	WFar WWeb
richardsonii	MNrw
'Robert'	MBNS
Rosemary Bloom =	LRHS
'Heuros'[PBR]	
'Royal Velvet' **new**	WCot
§ *rubescens*	CAbP ECho MTho NBro NMen
	SIng WPer
'Ruby Veil'	EBee SPoG
'Ruffles'	see *H. micrantha* 'Ruffles'
'Sancyl'	SRms
§ *sanguinea*	CAgr CSBt EDAr LRHS NBir NFor
	WGHP WPer
- 'Alba' ♀[H4]	EMon EWTr
- 'Geisha's Fan'	CBow COlW EBee EDAr EKen IBal
	MBnl MTis NBhm NGdn SHar SPer
	SWvt
§ - 'Monet' (v)	CBow EBee EChP ENot MBNS
	MLHP NSti SPoG
- 'Sioux Falls'	EBee EChP EWes NBre WPnP
§ - 'Snow Storm' (v)	CBow EBee ELan EPfP MBar MGos
	MRav SPlb WFar WMnd
- 'Taff's Joy' (v)	EMon EWes
- 'White Cloud' (v)	EBee NBre SRms WPer WPnP
'Saturn'	EBee EChP MBNS NMoo NSti
'Scarlet Flame' **new**	EBee
'Schneewittchen'	EPfP LRHS MRav
'Scintillation' ♀[H4]	ECtt LRHS NBre SRms
'Shamrock'	GCai NBre
'Silver Indiana'[PBR]	LSRN SPoG
'Silver Lode'	NRnb
'Silver Scrolls'[PBR]	More than 30 suppliers
'Silver Shadows'	SHar
'Silver Streak'	see x *Heucherella* 'Silver Streak'
'Snow Storm' (v)	see *H. sanguinea* 'Snow Storm'
'Starry Night' **new**	GCai SHar
'Stormy Seas'	More than 30 suppliers
'Strawberries and Cream'	EHrv WHer
(v)	
'Strawberry Candy'[PBR]	CBow CWCL EBee ENot GBBs
	GCai LSou NCGa NEgg NPri SPoG
	SRkn
'Strawberry Swirl'	CBcs CHar EBee EBla ECtt ENot
	GMaP LAst MLLN MRav MSte NBir
	NDov NLar NPri NSti SPoG SWal
	SWat SWvt WCAu WCot WFar
	WOVN
'Swirling Fantasy'	CBow EChP EPfP EShb IBal MBnl
	NMoo
'Vale of Passion' **new**	NBre
'Van Gogh'	EBee MBNS SMac SPoG
'Veil of Passion'[PBR]	SHar
'Velvet Night'	CBow CKno EBee EBrs EMan EPfP
	EWsh IBal LBBr LRHS MBNS NBir
	NBre NRnb SHar SHop SPoG WFar
	WPtf WRHF WSan
'Venus'	LSou MBNS MTis NMRc SPur SUsu
	WBrE WBrk WCMO WCot WWlt
'Vesuvius'[PBR]	NRnb SHar
villosa	ECha MRav
- 'Autumn Bride'	EWTr LAst WRHF
- var. *macrorhiza*	EShb GCal NBre WMnd
- 'Royal Red'	ECha GBuc
'White Marble'	SHar
'White Spires'	EBrs SHar
'Winter Red'	EAEE EBee LAst MBNS NFla SPur
	WCAu
'Yeti'	WPnP
'Zabelliana'	GBri GCal

x *Heucherella* (*Saxifragaceae*)

alba 'Bridget Bloom'	EBee EBla EBrs EChP ECha ELan
	ENot GMaP MRav NOrc NPri SPer
	SRms WCAu WFar WHoo WMnd
§ - 'Rosalie'	CBow CFee EBla ECha EMar LRHS
	MBNS MBri MRav MSte NBir NBro
	NPro SPlb WBrk WFar WMnd
	WMoo
'Burnished Bronze'[PBR]	CBct CBow EBee EBla GCai GKev
	LSou MBnl MLHP MLLN MSte
	NBro NCGa NEgg NGdn NLar

	SDnm SGar SHar SPav SPoG
	SRot STes SUsu SWvt WCMO
	WFar
'Chocolate Lace'	EBee EKen MLLN NRnb SHar
'Cinnamon Bear'	EBee
'Dayglow Pink'PBR	CBct EBla EPPr EShb GCai GMaP
	NBro NCGa NEgg SHar SRkn SRot
	WFar WGor WSan
Gold Strike =	GCai SVil WGor
'HERTN041' **new**	
'Heart of Darkness'	NRnb
'Kimono'PBR ♀H4	More than 30 suppliers
'Ninja'PBR	see *Tiarella* 'Ninja'
'Pearl Kohl' (v)	CCol
'Pink Frost'	EBla
Pink Whispers =	SVil
'HERTN042' **new**	
'Quicksilver'	CBcs CBct EBee EBla EChP EHrv
	EMil GBuc GMaP LAst MBnl MSte
	NGdn NPri SPer SWvt WCAu
	WCMO WCot WFar WWhi
'Ring of Fire'	EBrs WFar
§ 'Silver Streak'	CBow EBee EBla EChP EPPr GAbr
	GSki MSte MWgw NBro NCGa
	SPla SPoG SWvt WCot WFar WMoo
'Stoplight' **new**	CBow CSpe GCai LAst LSou MBNS
	MBnl MSph MNHC NCGa Ngdn
	NMyG SPer SPoG WCMO WCot
	WCra WGor
'Sunspot' (v)	EKen EMil ENot EPfP GCai LBmB
	LBuc LRHS MGos NMyG SHar
	SPoG WBor WCMO WCot
tiarelloides ♀H4	EMan EPfP LRHS WMnd
§ 'Viking Ship'PBR	More than 30 suppliers

Hexastylis see *Asarum*

Hibanobambusa (*Poaceae*)

'Kimmei'	EBee
tranquillans	CMCo EBee EFul EPla MBrN MMoz
	MMuc WJun WPGP
- 'Shiroshima' (v) ♀H4	CAbb CDoC CHen CPMA EAmu
	EBee ENBC ENot EPla ERod LPal
	MAsh MBrN MCCP MMoz MWhi
	MWht NMoo NPal NVic SBig WJun
	WMul WNor WPGP

Hibbertia (*Dilleniaceae*)

aspera	CBcs CCCN CPLG CPle CRHN
	WFar WSHC
§ *cuneiformis*	CPle MAsh
pedunculata	ECou
procumbens	ITim WAbe
§ *scandens* ♀H1	CBcs CCCN CHEx CHll CRHN
	ECou ELan GQui SOWG WMul
stricta	ECou
tetrandra	see *H. cuneiformis*
* *venustula*	ECou
volubilis	see *H. scandens*

Hibiscus ✿ (*Malvaceae*)

acetosella 'Red Shield'	CSpe EShb LSou
cannabinus	CSec SIde
coccineus	EShb MSte SOWG
fallax	CHll
hamabo	ELan
huegelii	see *Alyogyne huegelii*
leopoldii	SPer SRms
manihot	see *Abelmoschus manihot*
'Moesiana'	MBri
moscheutos	CArn CFir CHEx MSte
- 'Galaxy'	EShb WHil
mutabilis	SOWG
panduriformis	CSec
paramutabilis	EWes
rosa-sinensis	EBak EShb LRHS MBri SOWG

- 'All Aglow'	SOWG
- 'Bimbo'	SOWG
- 'Casablanca'	MBri
- 'Cockatoo'	SOWG
- 'Cooperi' (v) ♀H1	CHal SOWG
- Full Moon = 'Monoon'	SOWG
(d)	
- 'Gina Marie'	SOWG
- 'Great White'	SOWG
- 'Hawaiian Sunset'	SOWG
- 'Holiday'	MBri
- 'Jewel of India'	SOWG
- 'Kardinal'	MBri
- 'Kim Ellen'	SOWG
- 'Kinchen's Yellow'	SOWG
- 'Koeniger'	MBri
- 'Lady Flo'	SOWG
- 'Molly Cummings'	SOWG
- 'Mrs Andreasen'	SOWG
- 'Norman Lee'	SOWG
- 'Pink Mist'	SOWG
- 'Sprinkle Rain'	SOWG
- 'Tarantella'	SOWG
- 'Ten Thirty Seven'	SOWG
- 'Thelma Bennell'	SOWG
- 'Tivoli'	MBri
- 'Wings Away'	SOWG
sabdariffa	MSal
schizopetalus ♀H1	MJnS SBig SOWG
sinosyriacus	EPfP
- 'Autumn Surprise'	SBrw
- 'Lilac Queen'	LRHS SBrw SPoG WPGP
- 'Ruby Glow'	MGos WPGP
syriacus	MNHC SPet WFar WNor
- 'Admiral Dewey' (d)	MGos SPla
- 'Aphrodite'	CPMA EBee LRHS MRav
- 'Ardens' (d)	CEnd CSBt EBee EMui EPfP MGos
	NLar SPer
- Blue Bird	see *H. syriacus* 'Oiseau Bleu'
- 'Boule de Feu' (d)	ELan SEND
- 'Bredon Springs' ♀H4	ENot
- 'Caeruleus Plenus' (d)	MGos
new	
- 'China Chiffon' **new**	ENot
- 'Coelestis'	MGos SPer
- 'Diana' ♀H4	CDul EBee EMil ENot EPfP LRHS
	MGos MRav SLon
- 'Dorothy Crane'	CEnd LRHS MGos MRav SBra
- 'Duc de Brabant' (d)	CSBt EBee EMui EPfP SHBN SPer
- 'Elegantissimus'	see *H. syriacus* 'Lady Stanley'
- 'Hamabo' ♀H4	CBcs CDul CSBt EBee EcHo EMil
	ENot EPfP LAst LPan LRHS LSRN
	MBri MGos MRav MWgw NLar
	NPri SCoo SHBN SLim SPer SPla
	SPlb SPoG SWvt WDin WFar
- 'Helene'	ELan ENot LRHS LSRN MBlu
	MRav
- 'Jeanne d'Arc' (d)	SLon
§ - 'Lady Stanley' (d)	ECho LRHS MGan SCoo SPer
- Lavender Chiffon =	EBee ELan ENot EPfP EWes LRHS
'Notwoodone'PBR	MGos MRav NPri SPer SPoG
♀H4	
- 'Lenny' ♀H4	ENot MGos MRav
- 'Leopoldii'	NBlu
- 'Marina'	EMui EPfP
- 'Meehanii' misapplied	see *H. syriacus* 'Purpureus
	Variegatus'
§ - 'Meehanii' (v) ♀H4	CDul CEnd CSBt ENot EPfP LRHS
	MAsh MBri MGos SCoo SPer SPla
	SPoG SSta
§ - 'Oiseau Bleu' ♀H4	More than 30 suppliers
- Pink Giant = 'Flogi'	CBcs CDul CMHG EBee ECho
	ELan EPfP LRHS MBri MGos MWat
	SLon SPer WDin
§ - 'Purpureus Variegatus'	CSBt LAst MGos SPoG
(v)	

- 'Red Heart' ♀H4 — CEnd CSBt EBee ECho ELan ENot EPfP LAst LRHS MAsh MBri MCCP NBlu NLar NPri SBra SPer SPla SPoG SRms SWvt WCFE WDin
- 'Rosalbane' — EBee
- 'Roseus Plenus' (d) — ECho WDin
- Russian Violet = 'Floru' — CBcs CEnd COtt ELan EPfP LRHS MGos MRav
- 'Speciosus' — EMui MRav SLon SPer
- 'Totus Albus' — CSBt ECho SPoG
- 'Variegatus' — see *H. syriacus* 'Purpureus Variegatus'
- White Chiffon = 'Notwoodtwo'PBR ♀H4 — EBee ELan ENot EPfP EWes LRHS LSRN MGos MRav SPer SPoG
- 'William R. Smith' ♀H4 — EBee ELan LAst MRav MSwo SHBN SLon SPer SSta WDin
- 'Woodbridge' ♀H4 — More than 30 suppliers
trionum — CSpe SBch WKif
- 'Sunny Day' — ELan

hickory, shagbark see *Carya ovata*

Hieracium (Asteraceae)
aurantiacum — see *Pilosella aurantiaca*
britannicum — WOut
brunneocroceum — see *Pilosella aurantiaca* subsp. *carpathicola*
§ *glaucum* — WEas
§ *lanatum* — CSpe ECho EHol MDKP NBir WEas WRos
maculatum — see *H. spilophaeum*
pilosella — see *Pilosella officinarum*
praecox — see *H. glaucum*
scullyi **new** — EPPr
§ *spilophaeum* — EGra EHoe EMag EMar GGar LRHS NBid NPer NWCA WOut WPer WRos
- 'Leopard' — EBee EMan NJOw SGar SMar WWeb WPtf
umbellatum — WOut
villosum — CSpe EBee ECho EHoe LRHS MDun MNFA NBro WHer WLin WRos
waldsteinii — MDKP
welwitschii — see *H. lanatum*

Hierochloe (Poaceae)
occidentalis — CBig
odorata — CBig ELau EMan GAbr GPoy MGol SMar SSvw WPtf
redolens — GAbr

Hieronymiella (Amaryllidaceae)
aurea RCB/Arg M-4 — WCot

Himalayacalamus (Poaceae)
asper — EPla ERod WPGP
§ *falconeri* — CBrm EFul EPfP EPla MAsh MMoz SDix WPGP
§ - 'Damarapa' — EPla MMoz WDyG WJun
§ *hookerianus* — CAbb EPla WJun
porcatus — EBee WPGP

x *Hippeasprekelia* (Amaryllidaceae)
'Red Beauty' — CFwr WCMO

Hippeastrum ✿ (Amaryllidaceae)
BC&W 5154 — CStu
x *acramannii* — CMon GCal WCot
advenum — see *Rhodophiala advena*
'Amigo' **new** — WCMO
'Amputo' **new** — WCMO
'Aphrodite' (d) **new** — WCMO
'Apple Blossom' — MBri SGar

aulicum — CMon
'Bianca' **new** — WCMO
bifidum — see *Rhodophiala bifida*
'Blossom Peacock' (d) — EBrs
'Calimero' — EBrs
'Charisma' **new** — EBrs WCMO
'Chico' **new** — WCMO
'Christmas Gift' — EBrs
'Dancing Queen' **new** — WCMO
'Desire' **new** — WCMO
'Elvas' **new** — EBrs
'Emerald' **new** — WCMO
'Fairytale' — MBri WCMO
'Flaming Peacock' **new** — WCMO
gracile 'Pamela' **new** — CStu WCMO
'Grandeur' **new** — WCMO
'Hercules' — MBri
'Jewel' (d) — EBrs MBri
'Jungle Star' — EBrs
'Lady Jane' — MBri
'Lemon Lime' — EBrs
'Liberty' **new** — WCMO
'Mary Lou' (d) — EBrs
'Merengue' **new** — EBrs WCMO
'Moonlight' **new** — WCMO
'Nagano' **new** — WCMO
papilio ♀H1 — CMon
* - 'Butterfly' — LRHS
'Philadelphia' (d) — EBrs
'Pink Floyd' — WCMO
'Pink Star' **new** — EBrs WCMO
puniceum — CMon
'Red Peacock' **new** — WCMO
'Reggae' **new** — WCMO
reticulatum var. *striatifolium* — CMon
'Royal Velvet' **new** — WCMO
'Ruby Meyer' **new** — WCMO
rutilum var. *fulgidum* — CMon
* 'San Antonio Rose' — CDes WCot
'Showmaster' **new** — WCMO
'Solomon' **new** — EBrs
stylosum — CMon WCMO
'Tango' **new** — WCMO
'Toledo' **new** — WCMO
'Toughie' — CDes CSpe EMan MSph WCMO WCot
'Vera' — WCMO
vittatum — CBgR CMon WCMO
'Yellow Goddess' **new** — EShb

Hippocrepis (Papilionaceae)
§ *comosa* — CRWN XPep
§ *emerus* — CBcs CBgR CCCN CMHG CPLG CTri EBee ELan EPfP LAst LHop MBri MGos NLar SPoG SSto STre WRHF WSHC XPep

Hippolytia (Asteraceae)
§ *herderi* — EMan EOHP EShb

Hippophae (Elaeagnaceae)
rhamnoides ♀H4 — CArn CBcs CBrm CCVT CDul CLnd CRWN CSBt CTri EBee ELan EPfP LBuc MBar MBlu MCoo MRav NWea SPlb SPoG WDin WFar WHCG WMou XPep
- SDR 2849 — GKev
- 'Askola' (f) — MGos
- 'Frugna' (f) — CAgr
- 'Hergo' (f) — CAgr MCoo
- 'Hikal Dafo' (m) — CAgr
- 'Juliet' (f) — CAgr
- 'Leikora' (f) — CAgr ELan MBlu MCoo MGos NLar SPer

- 'Pollmix' (m)	CAgr ELan MBlu MCoo MGos NLar SPer
- 'Romeo' (m)	CAgr
salicifolia	CAgr LEdu
- GWJ 9221	WCru

Hippuris (Hippuridaceae)
vulgaris	CBen EHon EMFW IHMH NPer WFar WMAq WWpP

Hiptage (Malpighiaceae)
benghalensis	CPlN

Hirpicium (Asteraceae)
armerioides	NWCA

Hoheria ✿ (Malvaceae)
§ *angustifolia*	CBcs CTho ECou EPfP SBrw SSpi
'Borde Hill'	CPMA EPfP SBrw SSpi SSta WHCG
glabrata	CBcs ECou EPfP GGar IMGH NPal SBrw WPGP
- 'Silver Stars'	EPfP
'Glory of Amlwch' ♀H3	CAbb CDul CPMA CSam CTho EPfP GCal SBrw SSpi WCru WKif WPGP
'Hill House'	CHll
'Holbrook' **new**	CSam
§ *lyallii* ♀H4	CBcs CCCN CDoC CPLG ECou ELan EPfP IDee LSRN SBrw SHBN SSpi SSta WBor WDin
microphylla	see *H. angustifolia*
populnea	CBcs CCCN
- 'Alba Variegata' (v)	CBcs CDoC CTrC SMad
- 'Moonlight'	CDoC SPoG
- 'Osbornei'	SBrw
- 'Sunshine' (v)	CDoC SBrw SMur SPoG
'Purple Delta'	ECou
sexstylosa	CAbb CDoC CDul CHEx CMHG CTri ELan EPfP IMGH ISea LHop MDun MWea SBrw SPer SPur SSta SWvt WGer
- 'Pendula'	CBcs WDin
- 'Stardust' ♀H4	CAbP CAbb CCCN CDul CEnd CMCN CPLG CPMA CSam CTho CWSG ELan EPfP LRHS MAsh MBri MGos NLar NPal SBrw SMad SMur SPer SPoG SReu SSpi WFar WPGP WPat WSHC
* - 'Starshine'	ERea
* - 'Sunburst'	NEgg

Holarrhena (Apocynaceae)
pubescens **new**	CCCN

Holboellia (Lardizabalaceae)
angustifolia	NLar WCru
chapaensis HWJ 1023 **new**	WCru
coriacea	CBcs CHEx CHll CPlN CRHN CSam EBee EPfP LEdu LRHS MDun MGos SAPC SArc SBra SOWG SPer SSta WCFE WCot WCru
- 'Cathedral Gem' **new**	CPlN
- purple-flowered **new**	WCru
fargesii	CPlN
- DJHC 506	WCru
grandiflora	CPlN
- B&SWJ 8223	WCru
- HWJ 1024	WCru
latifolia	CBcs CBrm CHEx COtt CPlN CRHN CSBt CSam CTrG CTri EBee EPfP ERea LRHS MTPN NLar SAPC SArc SBra SEND SLim SOWG SPer SPoG WFar
- HWJK 2014	WCru
- SF 95134	ISea

Holcus (Poaceae)
lanatus	WSFF
mollis 'Albovariegatus' (v)	More than 30 suppliers
- 'White Fog' (v)	CPen EBee EHul ENot MBlu NHol WFar

Holmskioldia (Verbenaceae)
sanguinea	CPlN EShb

Holodiscus (Rosaceae)
discolor	CAgr CDul CPle EBee ELan EWes GIBF GQui IDee LRHS MBlu MRav NBlu NSti SBrw SHBN SLon SMad SPer SPlb SPoG SSpi SSta WBVN WDin WHCG
- var. *ariifolius*	EPfP
- var. *discolor*	CBcs
dumosus	WPGP

Homalocladium (Polygonaceae)
§ *platycladum*	CHal CPle LEdu

Homalomena (Araceae)
pendula	EAmu

Homeria (Iridaceae)
breyniana	see *H. collina*
- var. *aurantiaca*	see *H. flaccida*
§ *collina*	ECho ERos
§ *flaccida*	ECho LBow
ochroleuca	CMon ECho LBow

Homoglossum see *Gladiolus*

Hordeum (Poaceae)
brachyantherum	CBig
chilense	EBee
jubatum	CBig CHrt CKno CSpe CWCL EChP EGoo EHoe EKen EPla EWes LHop LIck LRHS MAvo MBnl MWat NChi NDov NGdn NHol SEND SIng SPoG SUsu WHil WRos WWye
- from Ussuri	GIBF

Horkeliella (Rosaceae)
purpurascens NNS 98-323 WCot	

Horminum (Lamiaceae)
pyrenaicum	CMHG EBrs ECho ELan EMan GAbr GKev NJOw NLar SBla SRms WFar WMoo WOut WPer WPtf WTin
- pale blue	MDKP MSte

horseradish see *Armoracia rusticana*

Hosta ✿ (Hostaceae)
AGSJ 302	CDes
'A Many-Splendored Thing'	IBal
'Abba Dabba Do' (v)	EGol EMic EPGN LBuc NMyG
'Abby' (v)	EGol EMic EPGN IBal MBNS NMyG WWye
'Abiqua Ariel'	EMic
'Abiqua Blue Crinkles'	EMic NBir
'Abiqua Drinking Gourd'	EBee EGol EMic EPGN GBin GSki IBal MHom MIDC NMyG
'Abiqua Ground Cover'	EGol
'Abiqua Moonbeam' (v)	CFir EMic EPGN IBal MSwo NMyG
'Abiqua Recluse'	EGol
'Abiqua Trumpet'	EGol IBal NGdn NLar NMyG
aequinoctiiantha	EGol
albomarginata	see *H. sieboldii* 'Paxton's Original'
§ 'Albomarginata' (*fortunei*) (v)	CBcs CWib ECho EGol EMic GSki MBar MNrw NBir NMyG SHBN SPer SPoG SWvt WBrE

Name	Suppliers
'Alex Summers'	EBee IBal NBhm
'Allan P. McConnell' (v)	EGol EMic EPGN WHal WIvy
'Allegan Fog' (v)	EGol IBal
'Alligator Shoes' (v)	EGol IBal
'Alpine Aire'	EMic
'Alvatine Taylor' (v)	EGol
'Amanuma'	EGol EMic IBal MHom
'Amber Maiden' (v)	EGol
'Amber Tiara'	EMic
'American Dream' (v)	EGol EMic EPGN IBal NMyG
'American Halo'	EBee EMic IBal MIDC NBPC NLar
'American Sweetheart'	IBal
'Amy Elizabeth' (v)	EGol EMic IBal
'Angel Feathers' (v)	EGol
'Ann Kulpa' (v)	EMic EPGN IBal NMyG
'Anne' (v)	EGol IBal
'Anne Arett' (*sieboldii*) (v)	EPGN
'Antioch' (*fortunei*) (v)	ECho EGol EMic GAbr GQue IBal IHMH MIDC MRav MSte NMyG NRnb WFar WWye
'Aoki' (*fortunei*)	EMic EPGN NHol
'Aphrodite' (*plantaginea*) (d)	CFir EBee EBrs EGol EMic EPGN IBal LSou MBNS MBri MHom MSte NCGa NCob NGdn NLar NMoo SPer SPoG WCMO WCot WGwG NNor
'Apollo' **new**	NNor
'Apple Green'	EMic IBal
'Aqua Velva'	EGol
'Archangel'	EGol
'Argentea Variegata' (*undulata*)	see *H. undulata* var. *undulata*
'Aristocrat' (Tardiana Group) (v)	EGol EMic EPGN IBal NMyG
'August Beauty'	EMic
'August Moon'	More than 30 suppliers
I 'Aurea' (*nakaiana*)	EBrs
aureafolia	see *H.* 'Starker Yellow Leaf'
'Aureoalba' (*fortunei*)	see *H.* 'Spinners'
'Aureomaculata' (*fortunei*)	see *H. fortunei* var. *albopicta*
* 'Aureomarginata' ambig. (v)	CPrp EGra GAbr GKev GSki NEgg
§ 'Aureomarginata' (*montana*) (v)	CSBt EGol EHoe ELan EMic EPGN EWsh GCal GMaP IBal MBri NEgg NHol NLar NMyG SPla SUsu WFar WTin WWpP
§ 'Aureomarginata' (*ventricosa*) (v) ♀H4	CBro ECha EGol EMic EPfP IBal LRHS MBri MIDC MWat MWgw NGdn NVic WFar WTin WWye
'Aureostriata' (*tardiva*)	see *H.* 'Inaho'
'Aurora Borealis' (*sieboldiana*) (v)	EGol
'Austin Dickinson' (v)	EGol EMic IBal LBuc
'Azure Snow'	EGol
'Babbling Brook'	EGol
'Baby Bunting'	EGol EMic EPGN IBal MBNS MIDC NBro NLar NMyG NPro
'Ballerina'	EGol
'Banana Boat' (v)	EGol IBal
'Banyai's Dancing Girl'	EGol EMic
'Barbara Ann' (v)	EMic EPGN IBal MBri
'Barbara White'	EGol
'Beauty Substance'	EGle EGol EMic EPGN NMyG
bella	see *H. fortunei* var. *obscura*
'Bennie McRae'	EGol
'Betcher's Blue'	EGol
'Betsy King'	EBee EGol MRav NHol NMyG
'Bette Davis Eyes'	EGol
'Betty'	EGol
'Big Boy' (*montana*)	EGol NNor
'Big Daddy' (*sieboldiana* hybrid) (v)	More than 30 suppliers
'Big Mama'	EGol IBal LRHS MBNS NBhm NLar
'Bigfoot'	EGol
'Bill Brinka' (v)	EGol
'Bill Dress's Blue'	IBal
'Birchwood Blue'	EGol
§ 'Birchwood Parky's Gold'	CMHG EAEE EGol EMic EPGN EPfP GMaP IHMH LRHS MBNS MIDC NCob NGdn NHol NOak SHBN SMrm WWye
'Birchwood Ruffled Queen'	EGol EMic
'Bitsy Gold'	EGol IBal
'Bitsy Green'	EGol
'Black Beauty'	EGol EPGN
'Black Hills'	CWib EBee EGol IBal MBNS NMyG
'Blackfoot'	EGol
'Blaue Venus'	EGol
§ 'Blonde Elf'	EGol EMic IBal MBNS NEgg NGdn NMyG
'Blue Angel' misapplied	see *H. sieboldiana* var. *elegans*
'Blue Angel' (*sieboldiana*) ♀H4	More than 30 suppliers
'Blue Arrow'	EGol EPGN
'Blue Beard' **new**	IBal
'Blue Belle' (Tardiana Group)	EGol EMic MSte NGdn NLar NPro WHoo WTin
'Blue Blazes'	LRHS
'Blue Blush' (Tardiana Group)	EGol WTMC
'Blue Boy'	EGol EMic EWes NHol NMyG
'Blue Cadet'	CBcs ECho EGol EMic EMil GEdr GSki IBal IFoB IHMH LAst LPBA MBar MLHP NBir NLar NMyG NOak NRnb SBod SHBN SPoG WCAu WCra WFar WMnd WWpP
'Blue Canoe'	IBal
'Blue Chip'	EMic IBal
'Blue Clown' **new**	IBal
'Blue Cup' (*sieboldiana*)	MRav
'Blue Danube' (Tardiana Group)	EGol EMic MHom
'Blue Diamond' (Tardiana Group)	CMHG EGol EMic EPGN WFar
'Blue Dimples' (Tardiana Group)	EGol IBal LRHS MBNS NMoo
'Blue Edger'	NBir
'Blue Heart' (*sieboldiana*)	EMic
'Blue Ice' (Tardiana Group)	EGol EPGN IBal
'Blue Impression'	EMic
'Blue Jay' (Tardiana Group)	EGol
'Blue Lady'	EMic
'Blue Mammoth' (*sieboldiana*)	EGol EMic EPGN LRHS
'Blue Monday' **new**	EMic
'Blue Moon' (Tardiana Group)	EGol EPGN EPfP ERos IBal LPBA MBNS MHom MIDC NHol NMyG WAul
'Blue Mountains' **new**	LBuc
'Blue Mouse Ears'	EGol EMic EPGN IBal
'Blue Seer' (*sieboldiana*)	EGol IBal
'Blue Shadows' (*tokudama*) (v)	EPGN IBal LRHS MIDC MWgw SHBN
'Blue Skies' (Tardiana Group)	EGol MHom
§ 'Blue Umbrellas' (*sieboldiana* hybrid)	ECho EGol ELan EMic EPGN EPfP GSki IBal LRHS MBri MHom MIDC NGdn NHol NLar NMyG
'Blue Vision'	EPGN LRHS
'Blue Wedgwood' (Tardiana Group)	CBro CPrp EBee ECho EGol ELan EMic ENot GSki IBal LAst LPBA MIDC NHol NMyG SPla SPoG WCFE WHil WTMC WWpP
'Bobbie Sue' (v)	EGol
'Bold Edger' (v)	EGol EPGN
'Bold Ribbons' (v)	EGol EMic GAbr WTin
'Bold Ruffles' (*sieboldiana*)	EGol LRHS
'Bonanza'	EMic
'Border Bandit' (v)	EGol

'Borwick Beauty' (*sieboldiana*) (v)	EMic NGdn NLar NMyG
'Bountiful'	EGol EMic
'Bouquet'	EGol
'Brenda's Beauty' (v)	EGol
'Bressingham Blue'	CPrp EBee EBrs ECho ECtt EGol IBal LRHS MIDC MRav MWat NMyG SPoG SWvt WCAu WFar WMnd WTMC WWpP
'Brigadier'	EGol
'Bright Glow' (Tardiana Group)	EGol
'Bright Lights' (*tokudama*) (v)	ECho EGol EMic EPGN GBBs IBal LAst NGdn NMyG WTMC WWye
'Brim Cup' (v)	EBee EGol EMic EPGN EWTr IBal LAst MBNS MBri MIDC NBPC NBro NGdn NMyG NOrc NRnb
'Brooke'	EGol EMic IBal NMyG
'Brother Ronald' (Tardiana Group)	EGol EMic IBal LRHS
'Bruce's Blue'	EGol GSki
'Buckshaw Blue'	EGol EPGN ETow MDKP NBir NGdn NPro WTMC
'Bunchoko'	IBal
'Burke's Dwarf' **new**	IBal
'Butter Rim' (*sieboldii*) (v)	EGol
'Cadillac' (v)	MIDC
'Calypso' (v)	EGol EMic EPGN IBal LBuc
'Camelot' (Tardiana Group)	EGol EMic IBal LRHS NGdn
'Canadian Blue'	EMic WTMC
'Candy Hearts'	CMHG CSam EGol EMic EPGN MHom MWat WTin
capitata B&SWJ 588	WCru
'Captain Kirk' (v)	IBal NMyG
caput-avis	see *H. kikutii* var. *caput-avis*
'Carnival' (v)	EGol EMic EPGN IBal MIDC NCGa NEgg
'Carol' (*fortunei*) (v)	EGol EMic EWsh IBal LAst MBNS MSte NEgg NMyG NNor WHal
'Carolina Blue'	IBal
'Carousel' (v)	EGol
'Carrie Ann' (v)	see *H.* 'Carrie'
§ 'Carrie' (*sieboldii*) (v)	EGol
'Cascades' (v)	EGol EMic EPGN IBal
'Cat's Eyes' (v)	EGol EMic EPGN IBal
'Celebration' (v)	EGol ELan EMic EPGN LRHS MDKP WHal
'Center of Attention'	IBal
'Challenger'	EMic
'Change of Tradition' (*lancifolia*) (v)	EMic
'Chantilly Lace' (v)	EGol EMic IBal NMyG WTin
'Chartreuse Waves'	EGol
'Chartreuse Wiggles' (*sieboldii*)	LRHS NHar
'Cheatin Heart'	EGol IBal
'Chelsea Babe' (*fortunei*) (v)	EGol
'Chelsea Ore' (*plantaginea* hybrid) (v)	CHad
'Cherish'	EGol EMic IBal
'Cherry Berry' (v)	CMHG CPen CRez EBee EGol EMic EPGN IBal MBNS MIDC MWgw NBro NCob NEgg NGdn NMyG NPro NRnb SRGP SVil WAul WBor
'Cherub' (v)	EGol
* 'China' (*plantaginea*)	EMic
'Chinese Sunrise' (v)	EChP EGol EMic EPGN IBal IPot LBuc MBNS MHom NHol NMyG WHal
'Chiquita'	EGol
§ 'Chôkô Nishiki' (*montana*) (v)	EGle EGol EMic EPGN IBal MIDC NGdn NMyG NNor SPoG

'Christmas Candy'	EPGN GAbr IBal NBhm NCob
'Christmas Tree' (v)	CMMP ECho EGle EGol EMic EPGN GBri IBal IFoB IPot LRHS MIDC NBPC NEgg NGdn NMyG NRnb SVil WTMC WWye
'Cinnamon Sticks'	IBal
'Citation' (v)	EGol
'City Lights'	EGol EMic NEgg
clausa var. *normalis*	EGol GQui LRHS NBir NGdn NLar NMyG
'Cody'	IBal
'Collector's Choice'	EGol
'Color Glory' (v)	EChP EGle EGol EPGN GAbr IBal LAst NCGa NEgg NGdn NLar NMyG SPer WAul WTMC
'Colossal'	EGol EMic
'Columbus Circle' (v)	EGol
'Cookie Crumbs' (v) **new**	IBal
'Coquette' (v)	EGol EMic
'Corkscrew' **new**	IBal
'Corona' (v) **new**	EMic
'Cotillion' (v)	EGol IBal
'County Park'	EGol EMic
'Cracker Crumbs' (v)	EGol EMic IBal
'Cream Cheese' (v)	EGol
'Cream Delight' (*undulata*)	see *H. undulata* var. *undulata*
'Crepe Soul' (v)	IBal
'Crepe Suzette' (v)	EGol EPGN LRHS
'Crested Reef'	EGol EMic NMyG
'Crested Surf' (v)	EGol EMic IBal
§ *crispula* (v) ♀H4	EGol EHon EMic EPfP MBar MHom NChi NCob NMyG SHBN WWpP
'Crown Jewel' (v)	EPGN
'Crown Prince' (v)	EGol EPGN
§ 'Crowned Imperial' (*fortunei*) (v)	EMic NHol
'Crusader' (v)	EGol EMic EPGN IBal LRHS NMyG WFar
'Cupid's Dart' (v)	EGol
'Curlew' (Tardiana Group)	EGol
'Dancing in the Rain' (v) **new**	IBal
'Dark Star' (v)	EGol EPGN
'Dawn'	EGol IBal
'Daybreak'	ECho EGol EMic EPGN LAst LRHS MBri NBro WHil WTMC WWye
'Day's End' (v)	EGol
'Deane's Dream'	IBal
decorata	EGol EMic MBar
'Deep Blue Sea'	IBal
'Delia' (v)	EPGN
'Delta Dawn'	IBal
'Devon Blue' (Tardiana Group)	CPrp EGol WWye
'Devon Giant'	EMic
'Devon Green'	EPGN GBri IBal IPot MHom MIDC MLLN MSte NBro NCob NEgg NGdn NLar NMyG NNor NPro WAul WFar WHal
'Dew Drop' (v)	CAby EGol EMic IBal NMyG
'Diamond Tiara' (v)	EGol EMic EPGN GAbr IBal LAst LRHS MBNS MIDC NMyG
'Diana Remembered'	EGol EMic EPGN IBal MBNS WBor
'Dick Ward'	IBal
'Dixie Chick' (v) **new**	IBal
'Domaine de Courson'	EMic IBal WFar
'Don Stevens' (v)	EGol
'Donahue Piecrust'	EGol
'Dorset Blue' (Tardiana Group)	EGol EPGN GSki IBal LRHS
'Dorset Charm' (Tardiana Group)	EGol
'Dorset Flair' (Tardiana Group)	EGol EMic
'Doubloons'	EGol EMic

'Dream Queen' (v)	NMyG
'Dream Weaver' (v)	CWib EBee EGol EMic IBal MNrw NGdn WWye
'Drummer Boy'	EGol EMic
'Duchess' (*nakaiana*) (v)	EGol
'DuPage Delight' (*sieboldiana*) (v)	EGol IBal NGdn NLar
'Dust Devil' (*fortunei*) (v)	EGol IBal
'Earth Angel' (v) **new**	EGol IBal
'Edge of Night'	EGol EMic
'Edwin Bibby'	EPGN
'El Capitan' (v)	EGol EMic EPGN LRHS
'El Niño'PBR (Tardiana Group) (v)	EMic IBal MIDC MNrw MSte NBro NGdn NMyG
§ *elata*	EBee EGol EGra EMic GKev
'Elatior' (*nigrescens*)	EMic IPot
'Eldorado'	see *H.* 'Frances Williams'
'Eleanor Lachman' (v)	EGol EMic IBal
'Elegans'	see *H. sieboldiana* var. *elegans*
'Elfin Power' (*sieboldii*) (v)	EGol
'Elisabeth'	NMyG
'Elizabeth Campbell' (*fortunei*) (v)	EGol EMic IBal MSte
'Ellen'	EMic
'Ellerbroek' (*fortunei*) (v)	EGol EMic GSki
'Elsley Runner'	EGol
'Elvis Lives'	EGol EKen GBin IBal LAst MCCP NGdn NMyG NNor NPro
'Embroidery' (v)	MIDC
'Emerald Carpet'	EGol
'Emerald Necklace' (v)	EGol
'Emerald Skies'	EGol
'Emerald Tiara' (v)	EGol EMic EPGN LRHS MIDC NMyG SVil WTin
'Emeralds and Rubies'	EGol EMic
'Emily Dickinson' (v)	EBee EGol IBal NEgg
'Eric Smith' (Tardiana Group)	EGol EMic EPGN MHom NMyG WFar
'Eric Smith Gold'	ENot EPGN
'Eskimo Pie' (v) **new**	IBal
'Eternal Flame'	IBal
'Evelyn McCafferty' (*tokudama* hybrid)	EGol
'Evening Magic' (v)	EGol
'Eventide' (v)	EGol
'Everlasting Love' (v)	EGol
'Excitation'	EGol
'Fair Maiden' (v)	EGol EPGN IBal
'Faithful Heart' (v) **new**	IBal
'Fall Bouquet' (*longipes* var. *hypoglauca*)	EGol
'Fall Emerald'	EMic
'Fallen Angel' **new**	IBal
'Falling Waters' (v)	EGol IBal
'Fan Dance' (v)	EGol
'Fantabulous' (v)	EPGN IBal
'Fantastic' (*sieboldiana* hybrid)	EGol LRHS
'Fantasy Island' (v) **new**	IBal
'Fascination' (v)	EPGN
'Fatal Attraction'	IBal
'Feather Boa'	EGol EPGN IBal
'Fenman's Fascination'	EMic
'Fire and Ice' (v)	More than 30 suppliers
'Fire Island'	EGol EMic IBal
'Fireworks' (v) **new**	IBal
'First Frost' (v) **new**	IBal
'Five O'Clock Shadow' (v)	IBal
'Five O'Clock Somewhere' (v) **new**	IBal
'Flame Stitch' (*ventricosa*) (v)	EGol EMic
'Floradora'	EGol EMic IBal NMyG
'Flower Power'	EGol

fluctuans	ECho GBBs
'Fool's Gold' (*fortunei*)	EMic IBal
'Forest Fire' **new**	IBal MBNS MIDC
'Forest Shadows'	EMic IBal
'Formal Attire' (*sieboldiana* hybrid) (v)	EGol EMic IBal LRHS
'Forncett Frances' (v)	EGol
'Fortis'	see *H. undulata* var. *erromena*
fortunei	CMMP EGol EMic MIDC NHol NNor WEas WFar WWye
§ - var. *albopicta* ♀H4	More than 30 suppliers
- - f. *aurea* ♀H4	CBos CHad CMHG ECha EGol EHoe ELan EPla LRHS MBar MIDC NLar NMyG SPer SPla SRms WFar WHal WWeb
- - - dwarf	EMic
§ - var. *aureomarginata* ♀H4	More than 30 suppliers
- var. *gigantea*	see *H. montana*
§ - var. *hyacinthina* ♀H4	ECho EGol EMic EPfP GCal IBal LRHS MBar MRav NMyG NOrc NRnb SHBN WFar WPtf WWeb
- - - variegated	see *H.* 'Crowned Imperial'
§ - var. *obscura*	ECho EGol EMic WLin
- var. *rugosa*	EMic
'Fountain'	NHol
'Fourth of July'	EGol
'Fragrant Blue'	ECho EGol EMic GBBs IBal LRHS NBro NMyG SMac SPoG
'Fragrant Bouquet' (v)	CMHG CWib ECho EGol EMic EPGN IBal LRHS MBri NCGa NEgg NGdn NHol NLar NMyG SVil WPtf
'Fragrant Dream'	EMic EPfP IBal NLar
'Fragrant Gold'	EGol
'Fragrant King' **new**	IBal
'Fragrant Star' **new**	IBal
'Fragrant Surprise' (v) **new**	IBal
'Fran Godfrey'	EPGN
'Francee' (*fortunei*) (v) ♀H4	More than 30 suppliers
§ 'Frances Williams' (*sieboldiana*) (v) ♀H4	More than 30 suppliers
'Frances Williams Improved' (*sieboldiana*) (v)	EGol EPfP MWat NEgg
Frances Williams' seedlings	NSti
'Freising' (*fortunei*)	EBee
'Fresh' (v)	EGol EPGN
'Fried Bananas'	EGol EMic
'Fried Green Tomatoes'	EBee ECho EGol EMic MIDC NLar NMyG NOrc
'Fringe Benefit' (v)	EGol EMic GAbr
'Frosted Jade' (v)	CWib EGol EPGN NLar NMyG WTin
'Fujibotan' (v) **new**	EGol
'Fulda'	EGol
'Gaiety' (v)	EGol EPGN
'Gaijin' (v)	IBal
'Gala' (*tardiflora*) (v)	NMyG
'Galaxy'	IBal
'Gay Blade' (v)	EGol
'Gay Feather' (v)	IBal LAst NMyG SPoG
'Gay Search' (v)	EPGN
'Geisha' (v)	EGol EPGN IBal MBNS MCCP NMyG NPro WHal
'Gene's Joy'	EPGN
'Ghost Spirit'	EBee IBal
'Gigantea' (*sieboldiana*)	see *H. elata*
'Gilt By Association'	IBal
'Gilt Edge' (*sieboldiana*) (v)	CWat EMic NMyG
'Ginko Craig' (v)	More than 30 suppliers
glauca	see *H. sieboldiana* var. *elegans*
'Glockenspiel'	EGol
I 'Gloriosa' (*fortunei*) (v)	EGol WFar
'Glory'	EGol

Name	Suppliers
'Goddess of Athena' (*decorata*) (v)	EGol
'Gold Drop' (*venusta* hybrid)	ECho EGol EMic IBal NHol
'Gold Edger'	CBro CPrp EBee EGol ELan EMar EMic EPfP ERos GAbr GMaP LRHS MIDC MRav MSte NBir NEgg NGdn NHol NJOw NMyG NNor NSti SPer SPla WFar WLin WTin
§ 'Gold Haze' (*fortunei*)	EGol EMic EPGN MHom NBir NCGa NHol NMyG
'Gold Leaf' (*fortunei*)	EGol
'Gold Regal'	EGol EMic EPGN MHom MSte NMyG WFar WMnd WWpP WWye
'Gold Rush' [PBR]	ENot NMyG
'Gold Standard' (*fortunei*) (v)	More than 30 suppliers
'Goldbrook' (v)	EGol WTin
'Goldbrook Gaynor' **new**	EGol
'Goldbrook Genie'	EGol
'Goldbrook Ghost' (v)	EGol
'Goldbrook Girl'	EGol
'Goldbrook Glamour' (v)	EGol
'Goldbrook Glimmer' (Tardiana Group) (v)	EGol
'Goldbrook Gold'	EGol
'Goldbrook Grace'	EGol
'Goldbrook Gratis' (v)	EGol
'Goldbrook Grayling'	EGol
'Goldbrook Grebe'	EGol
'Golden Age'	see *H.* 'Gold Haze'
'Golden Anniversary'	NHol WTMC
'Golden Ben'	ITim
'Golden Bullion' (*tokudama*)	EGol GBri
'Golden Decade'	EGol
'Golden Fascination'	EGol
'Golden Friendship'	EGol
'Golden Guernsey' (v)	EMic
'Golden Isle'	EGol
'Golden Meadows' **new**	IBal
'Golden Medallion' (*tokudama*)	CMHG EGol ELan IBal MBNS NEgg NGdn NHol NMyG SHBN WFar
'Golden Nakaiana'	see *H.* 'Birchwood Parky's Gold'
'Golden' (*nakaiana*)	see *H.* 'Birchwood Parky's Gold'
'Golden Prayers'	IBal MIDC NLar WFar WHal
'Golden Prayers' (*tokudama*)	ECtt EGol ELan EPGN ERos GSki LRHS MIDC MRav NBir NBro NGdn NHol NMyG NOrc SPla
'Golden Scepter'	CMHG EGol EMic EPGN NHol NMyG SMer WFar
'Golden Sculpture' (*sieboldiana*)	EGol LRHS WWye
'Golden Spider'	EGol EMic
'Golden Sunburst' (*sieboldiana*)	CPrp EGol EGra ELan EMic GSki IBal NBid NEgg NGdn NHol WFar
'Golden Tiara' (v) ♥[H4]	More than 30 suppliers
'Golden Waffles'	CMHG EBee NEgg
'Goldpfeil'	EMic
'Goldsmith'	EGol
'Good as Gold'	EMic EPGN NMyG
'Gosan Gold Mist'	EMic
'Gosan' (*takahashii*)	EGol
gracillima	EPGN IBal NRya
'Granary Gold' (*fortunei*)	EGol EPGN LRHS
'Grand Finale' **new**	IBal
'Grand Marquee' (v) **new**	IBal
'Grand Master'	EGol IBal MDKP
'Grand Tiara' (v)	EGol EPGN NMyG
'Gray Cole' (*sieboldiana*)	EGol EMic EPGN IBal LBuc NMyG
'Great Expectations' (*sieboldiana*) (v)	More than 30 suppliers
'Green Acres' (*montana*)	EGle LEdu MSte SMeo WFar
'Green Angel' (*sieboldiana*)	EGol
'Green Dwarf'	NWCA WFar
'Green Eyes' (*sieboldii*) (v)	EGol
'Green Fountain' (*kikutii*)	EGol EMic MIDC MSte WHal
'Green Gold' (*fortunei*) (v)	EMic
'Green Piecrust'	EGol
'Green Sheen'	EGol EPGN NMyG
'Green Velveteen'	EGol
'Green with Envy' (v)	EGol
'Grey Ghost'	IBal
'Grey Piecrust'	EGol IBal
'Ground Master' (v)	CMHG COIW COtt ECho ECtt EGol ELan ENot EPfP GAbr GMaP GSki IBal IFoB LPBA LRHS MBri MRav MSwo NBPC NBro NHol NMyG NSti WFar WWeb WWye
'Ground Sulphur'	EGol GCal
'Guacamole' (v)	CBgR EBee EGle EGol EMic EPGN IBal IPot MIDC NLar NMyG SUsu SVil WAul WTin WWye
'Guardian Angel' (*sieboldiana*)	EBee EGol EMic EPGN EWTr
'Gum Drop'	EMic
'Gun Metal Blue'	EMic
'Hadspen Blue' (Tardiana Group)	More than 30 suppliers
'Hadspen Hawk' (Tardiana Group)	EGol NMyG
'Hadspen Heron' (Tardiana Group)	EGol MHom MWat NMyG WCot WHal
'Hadspen Nymphaea'	EGol
'Hadspen Rainbow'	IBal
'Hadspen Samphire'	EGol EMic EPGN MHom NBir
'Hadspen White' (*fortunei*)	EGol EMic
'Hakujima' (*sieboldii*)	EGol
§ 'Halcyon' (Tardiana Group) ♥[H4]	More than 30 suppliers
'Halo'	EGol
'Happiness' (Tardiana Group)	EGol EHoe EMic MHom MRav NMyG
'Happy Hearts'	EGol EMic
'Harmony' (Tardiana Group)	EGol EMic
'Harry van de Laar' **new**	EMic
'Harry van Trier' **new**	EMic
'Hart's Tongue'	IBal
'Harvest Glow'	EGol
'Heart Ache'	EGol
'Heart and Soul' (v)	EGol
'Heartleaf'	EMic
'Heart's Content' (v)	EGol
'Heartsong' (v)	EGol NMyG
'Heideturm'	EBee
'Helen Doriot' (*sieboldiana*)	EGol EMic
helonioides misapplied f. *albopicta*	see *H. rohdeifolia*
'Herifu' (v)	EGol
'Hertha' (v) **new**	EMic
'Hidden Cove' (v)	EGol IBal
'Hi-ho Silver' (v)	ENot EPGN IBal
'Hilda Wassman' (v)	EGol
'Hirao Elite'	IBal
'Hirao Majesty'	EGol
'Hirao Splendor'	EGol NMyG
'Hirao Supreme'	EGol
'Holstein'	see *H.* 'Halcyon'
'Honey Moon'	EGol
§ 'Honeybells' ♥[H4]	More than 30 suppliers
'Honeysong' (v)	EMic EPGN
'Hoosier Harmony' (v)	EGol EMic
'Hope' (v)	EGol EMic IBal
'Hotspur' (v)	EGol
§ 'Hyacintha Variegata' (*fortunei*) (v)	CMHG GBri IHMH NNor
'Hydon Gleam'	EMic
'Hydon Sunset' (*nakaiana*)	CMHG CMMP CMea EGol EMic EPGN IBal MIDC NHol NMyG

	NOak NRya NSti WCMO WHal WMnd WPtf WTin
hypoleuca	EGol WLin
'Ice Cream' (*cathayana*) (v)	EGol
'Illicit Affair'	EMic IBal
'Ilona' (v)	EGol
§ 'Inaho'	EGol EPGN NMyG
'Inca Gold'	EGol
'Independence' (v) **new**	IBal
'Independence Day' (v)	EPGN
'Inniswood' (v)	CWib EGle EGol EPGN EPfP IBal IPot LRHS MBNS MBri NBro NGdn NLar NRnb NSti WMnd
'Invincible'	EGle EGol EMic EPGN IBal LAst LRHS MBNS MIDC NLar NMyG NNor NRnb SVil WTin WWye
'Iona' (*fortunei*)	ECho EGol EMic EPGN NMyG
'Irische See' (Tardiana Group)	EGol
'Iron Gate Glamour' (v)	EGol
'Iron Gate Special' (v)	EMic
'Iron Gate Supreme' (v)	CWat
'Island Charm' (v)	EGol EMic EPGN IBal NBhm
'Iwa Soules'	EGol
'Jack of Diamonds'	IBal
'Jade Cascade'	EGol ELan EMic MSte NBir NEgg NHol NLar NMyG SMrm WLin WOVN
'Jade Scepter' (*nakaiana*)	EGol EMic
'Jadette' (v)	EGol
'Janet Day' (v) **new**	EMic
'Janet' (*fortunei*) (v)	EGol GMaP NGdn NHol WWpP
'Japan Girl'	see *H.* 'Mount Royal'
'Jewel of the Nile' (v)	IBal
'Jim Mathews'	IBal
'Jimmy Crack Corn'	EGol EMic IBal
'Jolly Green Giant' (*sieboldiana* hybrid)	EMic
'Joseph'	EGol EMic IBal
'Josephine' (v) **new**	NNor
'Journeyman'	EBrs EGol EMic
'Joyce Trott' (v) **new**	IBal
'Julia' (v)	EGol EMic IBal
'Julie Morss'	ECho EGol EMic EPGN GMaP IBal MHom MWat NMyG WWpP
'Jumbo' (*sieboldiana*)	EMic
'June'[PBR] (Tardiana Group) (v)	More than 30 suppliers
'June Beauty' (*sieboldiana*)	EWsh
'June Fever' (Tardiana Group) **new**	IBal NBhm NBro NLar NMoo
'Just So' (v)	EGol EMic EPGN IBal
'Kabitan'	see *H. sieboldii* var. *sieboldii* f. *kabitan*
'Karin'[PBR]	EMic
'Katherine Lewis' (Tardiana Group) (v)	EMic IBal
'Kelsey'	EGol EMic
I 'Kifukurin' (*pulchella*) (v)	EGol EMic
'Kifukurin Ubatake' (*pulchella*) (v)	EPGN IBal
kikutii	EGol EMic NWCA WTin
§ - var. *caput-avis*	EGol EMic
- var. *polyneuron*	EGol
- var. *tosana*	EGol
§ - var. *yakusimensis*	CPBP EGol EMic ETow GBin IBal SMad
'King James'	IBal
'Kingfisher' (Tardiana Group)	EGol
§ 'Kirishima'	EPGN
'Kiwi Black Magic'	IBal
'Kiwi Blue Baby'	IBal
'Kiwi Blue Ruffles'	IBal

'Kiwi Blue Sky'	IBal
'Kiwi Canoe'	IBal
'Kiwi Cream Edge' (v)	EMic
'Kiwi Forest'	IBal
'Kiwi Full Monty' (v)	EMic IBal
'Kiwi Gold Rush'	IBal
'Kiwi Jordan'	IBal
'Kiwi Leap Frog'	IBal
'Kiwi Minnie Gold'	IBal
'Kiwi Parasol'	IBal
'Kiwi Spearmint'	IBal
'Kiwi Splash'	IBal
'Kiwi Sunlover'	IBal
'Kiwi Sunshine'	IBal
'Kiwi Treasure Trove'	IBal
kiyosumiensis	GIBF NHol
'Klopping Variegated' (v)	EGol
'Knave's Green'	EPGN
'Knockout' (v)	EBee EGol EPGN IBal MBNS MIDC MNrw NBPC NBro NEgg NGdn NLar NMyG NNor NRnb
'Korean Snow'	IBal
'Koriyama' (*sieboldiana*) (v)	EMic IBal LBuc
'Krossa Regal' ♀[H4]	More than 30 suppliers
'Lacy Belle' (v)	EGol EMic IBal NBro NGdn NMyG NPro NRnb
'Lady Guinevere'	IBal
'Lady Helen'	EMic
'Lady Isobel Barnett' (v)	ECho EMic IBal NMyG
laevigata	EGol
'Lake Hitchock'	IBal
'Lakeside Accolade'	NMyG
'Lakeside April Snow' (v) **new**	EMic
'Lakeside Baby Face' (v) **new**	IBal
'Lakeside Black Satin'	EMic EPGN IBal
'Lakeside Blue Cherub' **new**	IBal
'Lakeside Cha Cha' (v)	EGol EMic
'Lakeside Coal Miner' **new**	IBal
'Lakeside Cupcake' (v) **new**	EMic IBal
'Lakeside Dragonfly' (v) **new**	IBal
'Lakeside Kaleidoscope'	EMic IBal LBuc
'Lakeside Little Gem' **new**	IBal
'Lakeside Little Tuft' (v) **new**	IBal
'Lakeside Lollipop' **new**	EMic
'Lakeside Looking Glass'	EMic ENot IBal
'Lakeside Meter Maid' (v) **new**	IBal
'Lakeside Neat Petite'	EGol IBal
'Lakeside Ninita' (v)	EGol EMic EPGN IBal
'Lakeside Premier'	EGol EMic
'Lakeside Rhapsody' (v) **new**	IBal
'Lakeside Roy El' (v) **new**	IBal
'Lakeside Shoremaster' (v)	IBal
'Lakeside Small Fry' (v) **new**	IBal
'Lakeside Spruce Goose' (v) **new**	IBal
'Lakeside Symphony' (v)	EGol
'Lakeside Zinger' (v) **new**	EMic IBal
§ *lancifolia* ♀[H4]	CBro CMHG CRow ECha ECho EGol EHrv ELan EMic EWTr GMaP MIDC MRav NGdn NHol NMyG NSti SBod SRms WAul WGwG WTin
'Leather Sheen'	EGol EMic EPGN
'Lee Armiger' (*tokudama* hybrid)	EGol
'Lemon Delight'	EGol EMic EPGN NMyG
'Lemon Frost'	IBal

'Lemon Lime'	EGol EMic IBal MHom MNrw NMyG NPro WBrk WIvy WPat WTin WWye
'Lemonade' **new**	GBin
'Leola Fraim' (v)	EGol EMic EPGN IBal NMyG
'Leviathan'	EMic
'Liberty'[PBR] (v)	EGol EPGN IBal
* *lilacina*	WFar
'Lily Pad'	EPGN
'Lime Piecrust'	EGol
'Lime Shag' (*sieboldii* f. spathulata) **new**	MIDC
'Limey Lisa'	EMic IBal
'Little Aurora' (*tokudama* hybrid)	EGol EMic EPGN IBal
'Little Black Scape'	CPen EBee EGol EMic EPGN GBin IBal LSRN MBNS MHom NCob NEgg NGdn NHol NLar NMyG NPro SIng SPoG
'Little Blue' (*ventricosa*)	EGol
'Little Bo Beep' (v)	EGol
'Little Caesar' (v)	EGol EMic EPGN IBal
'Little Doll' (v)	EGol
'Little Jim' (v) **new**	MIDC
'Little Razor'	EGol
'Little Stiffy' **new**	IBal
'Little Sunspot' (v)	EGol EMic IBal
'Little White Lines' (v)	EGol EPGN IBal
'Little Wonder' (v)	EGol
longipes	EGol
longissima	CMHG EBee EGol WCru
'Louisa' (*sieboldii*) (v)	ECha EGol MSte WIvy
'Love Pat' ♥[H4]	CFir EGol EMic EPGN EPfP EWsh GAbr GBin GSki IBal LAst MCCP MIDC MRav NMyG NNor SPla SVil
'Loyalist'[PBR] (v)	EMic EPGN NLar NMyG WFar
'Lucky Charm'	EMic
'Lucy Vitols' (v)	EGol EMic IBal
'Lunar Eclipse' (v)	EGol
'Mack the Knife'	IBal
'Maekawa'	EGol EMic
'Majesty'	EGol IBal NMyG
'Mama Mia' (v)	EGol EMic EPGN GAbr IBal MBNS NBro
'Maraschino Cherry'	EGol EMic IBal NMyG NRnb
'Margin of Error' (v)	EPGN NMyG
'Marginata Alba' misapplied	see *H. crispula*, *H.* 'Albomarginata'
'Marginata Alba' ambig. (v)	ECha LPBA
'Marilyn'	EGol LRHS
'Marquis' (*nakaiana* hybrid)	EGol
'Maruba' (*longipes* var. latifolia)	EGol
'Mary Joe'	EMic
'Mary Marie Ann' (*fortunei*) (v)	EGol EMic EPGN NMyG
§ 'Masquerade' (v)	EGol EPGN IBal NHar WFar WHal
'Mediovariegata' (*undulata*)	see *H. undulata* var. *undulata*
'Medusa' (v)	EGol IBal WCot
'Mentor Gold'	EGol
'Metallic Sheen'	LRHS
'Midas Touch'	NEgg NHol NLar
'Middle Ridge'	NHol
§ 'Midwest Gold'	MHom
'Midwest Magic' (v)	CWib EGol EMic IBal NLar
'Mildred Seaver' (v)	EGol EMic IBal MBri NMyG WWye
'Millennium' **new**	EMic
'Millie's Memoirs' (v)	EGol
'Minnie Bell' (v)	EGol
'Minnie Klopping'	EMic
§ *minor* Maekawa	CBro EBrs EGol EMic EPGN ERos GEdr GGar GIBF GSki MTho NHol NMyG WCot WFar
- from Korea	EGol
- Goldbrook form	EGol
minor misapplied f. *alba*	see *H. sieboldii* var. *alba*

'Minor' (*ventricosa*)	see *H. minor* Maekawa
'Minuteman' (*fortunei*) (v)	EBee ECho EGle EMic ENot EPGN EPfP GAbr GBin IBal IPot LAst LRHS MBNS MIDC MSte NCGa NGdn NMyG NNor NOrc NRnb SHBN SPla WFar WGor WTMC WTin
'Moerheim' (*fortunei*) (v)	ECho EGol EMic EPGN IBal LRHS MBar MBri MIDC NHol WHal WLin WTMC
N *montana*	CWib ECho EGol EMic NHol WBrE WCru
- B&SWJ 4796	WCru
- B&SWJ 5585	WCru
- f. *macrophylla*	EGol
'Moon Glow' (v)	EGol NMyG
'Moon River' (v)	EGol EMic EPGN NMyG
'Moon Shadow' (v)	EGol
'Moon Waves'	EGol
'Moonbeam'	NRnb WTMC
'Moonlight' (*fortunei*) (v)	EChP EGol EMic EPGN GMaP NMyG WWye
'Moonlight Sonata'	EGol
'Moonstruck' (v)	EGol EMic EPGN
'Morning Light'[PBR]	EBee EGol EMic EPGN EPfP IBal MBNS MBri NBhm NBro NGdn NMoo WBor
'Moscow Blue'	EGol LRHS
'Mount Everest'	EMic IBal
'Mount Fuji' (*montana*)	EGol
'Mount Hope' (v)	EGol
'Mount Kirishima' (*sieboldii*)	see *H.* 'Kirishima'
§ 'Mount Royal' (*sieboldii*)	NHol
'Mount Tom' (v)	EGol IBal
'Mountain Snow' (*montana*) (v)	CWat ECho EGol EMic LRHS NMyG WTMC
'Mountain Sunrise' (*montana*)	EGol
'Mr Big'	MBNS
'Mrs Minky' **new**	EBrs EMic
'Myerscough Magic'	MSte
nakaiana	EBee EMic GCal NDlv
'Nakaimo'	NHol
'Nameoki'	NHol
'Nana' (*ventricosa*)	see *H. minor* Maekawa
§ 'Nancy Lindsay' (*fortunei*)	CTri EGol EMic NGdn WTMC
'Nancy Minks'	EMic IBal
'Neat and Tidy'	IBal
'Neat Splash' (v)	EChP NBir NHol
'New Wave'	EGol
'Niagara Falls'	CFir EGol
'Nicola'	EGol EMic EPGN MHom NMyG
'Night before Christmas' (v)	CFir CMMP COtt ECho EGle EGol EPGN IBal IPot LAst MBri MIDC MNrw NBro NCGa NEgg NGdn NHol NMyG NNor NRnb SHBN SPla SRGP WTMC WWeb WWye
nigrescens	EGol EPGN GCal GSki WBVN WWye
- 'Cally White'	GCal
'Nokogiryama'	EGol EMic
'North Hills' (*fortunei*) (v)	EAEE EGol EMic GSki LRHS MWgw NBir NCob NGdn SWvt
'Northern Exposure' (*sieboldiana*)	CFir EGol EMic IBal NGdn NRnb
'Northern Halo' (*sieboldiana*) (v)	ECho EGol EMic
'Northern Lights' (*sieboldiana*)	EGol
'Obscura Marginata' (*fortunei*)	see *H. fortunei* var. *aureomarginata*
'Obsession'	EGol IBal
'Okazuki Special'	EGol
'Old Faithful'	EGol EMic
'Old Glory'[PBR] (v)	EGol IBal
'Olga's Shiny Leaf'	EGol EMic

'Olive Bailey Langdon' (*sieboldiana*) (v)	EMic IBal
'Olive Branch' (v)	EGol
'Olympic Edger'	EMic IBal
'Olympic Glacier' (v) **new**	IBal
'Olympic Sunrise' (v) **new**	EMic
'One Man's Treasure'	EMic IBal
'Ophir'	IBal
'Ops' (v) **new**	IBal
'Orange Marmalade'	IBal
'Oriana' (*fortunei*)	EGol
'Osprey' ('Tardiana Group)	EGol LRHS
'Oxheart'	EMic
pachyscapa	EMic
'Pacific Blue Edger'	CAby CFir CMMP EGol EMic EPGN LAst MBri WAul WWye
'Pandora's Box' (v)	CWib EGol EMic GEdr NHar WCot
'Paradigm' (v)	EBrs EGol EMic EPGN IBal NEgg NMyG
'Paradise Beach' **new**	EMic
'Paradise Joyce'PBR	EGol EMic EPGN IBal MBri MIDC NLar NMyG
'Paradise on Fire' (v)	EMic IBal
'Paradise Power'PBR	EGol EMic IBal
'Paradise Puppet' (*venusta*)	EPGN
'Paradise Red Delight' (*pycnophylla*)	EMic
'Pastures Green'	EGol
'Pastures New'	EGol EMic LPhx MHom NHol NMyG
'Pathfinder' (v)	EGol IBal
'Patricia' **new**	EMic
'Patrician' (v)	EMic EPGN IBal NMyG
'Patriot' (v)	More than 30 suppliers
'Paul Revere' (v) **new**	IBal
'Paul's Glory' (v)	EGle EGol EMic EPGN GBin IBal LAst LRHS MBri NBhm NGdn NMyG SPoG SUsu SVil WTMC WWye
'Peace' (v)	EGol EMic EPGN
'Peanut' **new**	IBal
'Pearl Lake'	EAEE EBee EGol EMic IHMH LPhx LRHS MHom MSte MWat NBir NCob NGdn NHol NLar NMyG SRGP WTin
'Peedee Gold Flash' (v)	NMyG
'Pelham Blue Tump'	EGol EMic
'Peppermint Ice' (v)	EGol
'Permanent Wave'	EGol
'Peter Pan'	EGol EMic
'Phoenix'	EGol GBin
'Photo Finish' (v)	EGle EMic
'Phyllis Campbell' (*fortunei*)	see *H.* 'Sharmon'
'Picta' (*fortunei*)	see *H. fortunei* var. *albopicta*
'Piecrust Power'	EGol
'Piedmont Gold'	EBrs EGol EMic EPGN IBal MSte WTMC
'Pilgrim' (v)	EGol EMic EPGN IBal NBro NMyG SMac SPoG WFar
'Pineapple Poll'	CWat EMic EPGN MIDC NMyG WTin
'Pineapple Upside Down Cake' (v)	EBee EPGN IBal NBhm NLar SPur
'Pizzazz' (v)	EGle EGol EMic EPGN IBal LAst MHom MIDC NGdn NHol NLar NMyG NRnb SHBN WHil WTMC WWye
plantaginea	EGol EMic LEdu LPhx MHom MIDC NMyG SSpi WCru WKif WWye
- var. *grandiflora*	see *H. plantaginea* var. *japonica*

§ - var. *japonica* ♀H4	CAvo CDes CHad CStu EBee ECha EHrv EMic EPGN GSki IBal WCAu WCFE WPGP
'Platinum Tiara' (v)	EMic EPGN IBal NBir NMyG
'Plug Nickel' **new**	IBal
'Pooh Bear' (v)	EGol
'Popo'	EGol IBal
'Potomac Pride'	EPGN NMyG
'Praying Hands' (v)	EGol EMic IBal
'Pretty Flamingo'	EMic IBal
'Prince of Wales'	IBal
'Puck'	EGol
'Purple Dwarf'	EGol EMic NGdn NHol NLar WHal WIvy
'Purple Glory' **new**	EMic
'Purple Passion' **new**	EGol
'Purple Profusion'	EGol EMic
pycnophylla	EGol
'Queen Josephine' (v)	COtt EGol EMic EPGN IBal IPot LAst MBNS MBri MHom MIDC NCGa NEgg NGdn NMyG NPro WFar WTMC WWye
'Quilting Bee'	EGol
'Radiant Edger' (v)	EGol EMic EPGN IBal LRHS NHol
'Radio Waves' **new**	IBal
'Rain Forest' **new**	IBal
'Raleigh Remembrance'	EGol
'Rascal' (v)	EGol EMic LRHS
'Raspberry Sorbet'	EGol EPGN
rectifolia	NHol NNor
'Red Neck Heaven' (*kikutii* var. *caput-avis*)	WTin
'Red October'	CMHG CRez EChP EGol EMic EPGN EPfP GAbr GBin IBal MBNS MBri MCCP NEgg NGdn NLar NMoo NMyG
'Red Salamander'	EGol
'Regal Splendor' (v)	EGol EMFW EMic EPGN GSki IBal LRHS MHom NBro NCGa NHol NMyG SHBN SPla WAul WMnd WWpP WWye
'Remember Me'PBR	EDAr EGol ELan EMic EPGN IBal LAst LSRN MBNS MCCP MDun NCGa NCob NGdn NHol NLar NMyG NNor NRnb SPoG WGor WWeb
'Resonance' (v)	EPGN MBri NGdn NLar NPro WHal WTMC
'Reversed' (*sieboldiana*) (v)	EGol ELan EMic EPGN EPfP EWsh MDKP MIDC MSte NBro NGdn NHol NNor WHal WTMC
'Revolution'PBR (v)	CHad CPen CWib EGle EGol EMic EPGN IBal IPot LSRN MBNS MBri MIDC NBPC NBro NCGa NCob NLar NMyG NOrc NRnb WAul
'Rhapsody' (*fortunei*) (v)	EGol
'Rhapsody in Blue'	EGol
'Richland Gold' (*fortunei*)	EGol EMic EPGN NMyG
'Rippled Honey'	CPen EPGN IBal NCob NMyG NPro
'Rippling Waves'	EGol EMic
'Rising Sun'	EGol
'Risky Business' (v)	IBal
'Robert Frost' (v)	EGol EMic IBal WTin
'Robusta' (*fortunei*)	see *H. sieboldiana* var. *elegans*
§ *rohdeifolia* (v)	EBrs EGol LBuc LRHS
§ - f. *albopicta*	EGol ELan NHol
'Ron Damant' **new**	EPGN
'Rosemoor'	EGol
'Roxsanne' **new**	EMic
'Royal Golden Jubilee'	EPGN NMyG
§ 'Royal Standard' ♀H4	More than 30 suppliers
'Royalty'	EGol
rupifraga	EGol
'Ryan's Big One'	IBal

§ 'Sagae' (v) ♀H3-4	EBee EBrs EChP EGle EGol EMic EPGN EPfP IBal IPot MBri MHom MIDC MNrw MSte NEgg NGdn NMyG SPla SPoG WAul WFar WTMC	
'Saint Elmo's Fire' (v)	EGol EMic IBal NCGa NEgg SPla	
§ 'Saishu Jima' (*sieboldii f. spathulata*)	EPla NHol WCru	
'Saishu Yahite Site' (v)	EGol	
'Salute' (Tardiana Group)	EGol	
'Samurai' (*sieboldiana*) (v)	EGol IBal IPot LAst MRav NBir NBro NEgg NGdn NLar NRnb WWye	
'Sarah Kennedy' (v)	EPGN	
'Satisfaction' (v) **new**	EMic	
'Savannah'	EGol	
'Sazanami' (*crispula*)	see *H. crispula*	
'Scooter' (v)	EGol EMic EPGN NMyG	
'Sea Bunny'	EGol	
'Sea Dream' (v)	EGol EMic EPGN NMyG	
'Sea Drift'	EGol	
'Sea Fire'	EGol	
'Sea Gold Star'	EGol NMyG	
'Sea Gulf Stream'	IBal	
'Sea Hero'	EGol	
'Sea Lotus Leaf'	EGol EMic NLar NMyG	
'Sea Monster'	EGol	
'Sea Octopus'	EGol	
'Sea Sapphire'	EGol	
'Sea Sunrise'	EPGN	
'Sea Thunder' (v)	EGol EMic EPGN IBal	
'Sea Yellow Sunrise'	EGol EMic IBal	
'Second Wind' (*fortunei*) (v)	EMic EPGN NMyG	
'See Saw' (*undulata*)	EGol	
'Semperaurea' (*sieboldiana*)	GSki	
'September Sun' (v)	EGol IBal LRHS NMyG	
'Serendipity'	EGol EMic EPGN MHom	
'Shade Beauty' (v)	EGol	
'Shade Fanfare' (v) ♀H4	EBrs EGol ELan EMic EPGN EPfP GSki IBal LRHS MBNS MBri MIDC MRav MWgw NBir NGdn NLar NMyG NSti SPer WFar WMnd WTin WWye	
'Shade Master'	EGol LAst NHol	
§ 'Sharmon' (*fortunei*) (v)	CWat EGol EMic EPGN IPot MBNS NHol NMyG	
'Shelleys' (v)	EGol	
'Sherborne Profusion' (Tardiana Group)	EMic	
'Sherborne Swift' (Tardiana Group)	EGol	
'Shining Tot'	EGol	
'Shiny Penny' (v)	EGol IBal	
'Shirley Vaughn' (v)	EGol	
'Shogun' (v)	EGol	
'Showboat' (v)	EGol IBal NMyG	
'Showtime'	IBal	
sieboldiana	CMHG ECha ECho EGol ELan EMic EPfP GMaP MRav NChi NFor NHol NJOw SPer SPlb SRms WBVN WFar WGwG WTin WWpP	
§ - var. *elegans* ♀H4	More than 30 suppliers	
- 'George Smith'	IBal	
sieboldii	CBcs CWat NEgg	
§ - var. *alba*	EGol EWTr	
§ - 'Paxton's Original' (v) ♀H4	CWib EGol EHrv IHMH MBar NLar SRms	
§ - var. *sieboldii* f. *kabitan* (v)	EBrs EGol EPGN MIDC NMyG NSti WTin	
- - f. *shiro-kabitan* (v)	EGol EMic EPGN	
'Silk Kimono' (v)	EGol	
'Silver Bowl'	EGol	
'Silver Crown'	see *H.* 'Albomarginata'	
'Silver Lance' (v)	EGol EMic EPGN NMyG	
'Silver Shadow' (v)	NCob NCot NMyG WPtf	

'Silver Spray' (v)	EGol
'Silvery Slugproof' (Tardiana Group)	MWat NMyG
'Sitting Pretty' (v)	EGol EPGN
'Slick Willie'	EGol
'Small Sum'	IBal
'Snow Cap' (v)	EGle EGol EMic IBal MBri MIDC NEgg NGdn NLar NMoo NMyG NNor NPro SHBN WAul WCra WDav
'Snow Crust' (v)	EGol EMic LRHS
'Snow Flakes' (*sieboldii*)	EGol EPGN EPfP EWTr GCal LRHS MBar MBri NBro NGdn NHol NMyG NPro SBod SHBN WFar WGwG WTMC
'Snow White' (*undulata*) (v)	EGol
'Snowden'	CHad CMHG ECha ECho EGol EMic EPGN GMaP IBal MWat NBir NCob NGdn NHol NMyG SSpi WBrk
'Snowstorm' (*sieboldii*)	NHol
'So Sweet' (v)	COIW EGol EMFW EMic EMil EPGN GSki IBal LPBA MBri MHom MIDC MSte MSwo NBro NEgg NGdn NHol NMyG SPoG SRGP
'Solar Flare'	EGol
'Something Different' (*fortunei*) (v)	EGol EPGN
'Sparkling Burgundy'	EGol
'Sparky' (v)	EGol IBal
'Special Gift'	EGol EMic
§ 'Spilt Milk' (*tokudama*) (v)	EGol EMic EPGN IBal WHoo
§ 'Spinners' (*fortunei*) (v)	ECha EGol EMic
'Spinning Wheel' (v)	EGol
'Spritzer' (v)	EGol EMic NMyG
'Squash Casserole'	EGol
'Squiggles' (v)	EGol
'Stained Glass'	IBal
'Starburst' (v)	EGol
§ 'Starker Yellow Leaf'	EMic
'Stenantha' (*fortunei*)	EMic
'Stenantha Variegated' (*fortunei*) (v)	NHol
'Stetson' (v)	EGol
'Stiletto' (v)	EBee EGol EHrv EMic EPGN GEdr IBal IHMH IPot LAst MBNS MHom MIDC NBro NGdn NLar NMoo NMyG NNor NPro NRnb NSti SDnm WAul WPtf WWye
'Striptease' (*fortunei*) (v)	CHen EGol EMic EPGN EWTr GBin GQue IBal LAst MBNS MIDC NGdn NHol NLar NOrc NRnb SHBN SMer SVil WCMO WFar WTMC WWye
'Sugar and Cream' (v)	CMMP CWat ECho EGol EMic EPGN LAst LRHS MWat NGdn NRnb WTMC
'Sugar Plum Fairy' (*gracillima*)	EGol
'Sultana' (v)	EMic IBal
'Sum and Substance' ♀H4	More than 30 suppliers
'Summer Breeze' (v)	EGol IBal
'Summer Fragrance'	EGol EMic EPGN LRHS NMyG
'Summer Music' (v)	EGle EGol EMic EPGN IBal LAst MBNS MBri NMyG
'Summer Serenade' (v)	EGol EMic
'Sun Glow'	EGol
'Sun Kissed' (v) **new**	IBal
'Sun Power'	CPen ECho EGol EMic EPGN EPfP EWTr IBal LRHS MBNS MIDC NBro NLar NMyG NSti
'Sundance' (*fortunei*) (v)	EGol
* 'Sunflower'	NOak
'Super Bowl'	EGol
'Super Nova' (v)	EGol EMic IBal SPoG

'Surprised by Joy' (v)	EGol IBal
'Sweet Bo Beep'	EGol
'Sweet Home Chicago' (v)	EGol IBal
'Sweet Marjorie'	EGol
'Sweet Susan'	EGol EMic MBNS SPer SPoG WWpP
'Sweet Tater Pie'	EGol
'Sweetheart'	EMic
'Sweetie' (v)	EGol EMic IBal
'Swirling Hearts'	EGol
'Swoosh' **new**	EPGN
'Tall Boy'	CSev ECha EGol EPla GCal MWgw NBir NNor WWye
'Tamborine' (v)	EGol EPGN NMyG
'Tango'PBR **new**	EMic IBal
Tardiana Group	CBro ECho EGol ELan MHom NGdn NHol
tardiflora	EGol ERos WCot WPGP
'Tattoo'PBR (v)	EDAr EGol EMic EPGN IBal LSRN MBNS MIDC NLar NMoo NMyG SPoG
'Tea and Crumpets' (v)	EPGN
'Teaspoon' **new**	IBal
'Temple Bells'	EGol
'Tenryu'	EGol
'Terry Wogan' **new**	IBal
'The Twister'	EGol EMic
'Thomas Hogg'	see *H. undulata* var. *albomarginata*
'Thumb Nail'	ECha EGol EMic GSki IBal
'Thumbelina'	IBal
'Thunderbolt' (sieboldiana)	EPGN IBal MBNS NCob
'Thunderbolt' (v)	EGol MIDC
'Tick Tock' (v) **new**	IBal
'Timpany's Own' (sieboldiana)	ITim
'Tiny Tears'	CStu EGol IBal
'Titanic'PBR	IBal
tokudama	CBcs EGol EMic GIBF LRHS MHom NBir NGdn NHol NNor NSti WFar
§ - f. *aureonebulosa* (v)	EGol EMic EPGN IBal IPot LRHS MSte NGdn NMyG NSti WMnd
- f. *flavocircinalis* (v)	CBgR CPrp ECho EGol EMic EPGN IBal LRHS NBPC NBro NMyG WFar WHoo WMnd WWye
'Topscore' **new**	NNor
'Torchlight' (v)	EGol EMic LRHS
tortifrons **new**	IBal
'Tortilla Chip' **new**	IBal
'Tot Tot'	EGol
'Touch of Class'PBR (v)	IBal
'Touchstone' (v)	MBri NMyG SWvt
'Toy Soldier'	IBal
'Trail's End'	EMic
'True Blue'	CBgR EBee EGol EMic GAbr IBal LAst NRnb
'Tutu'	EGol MIDC
'Twilight' (*fortunei*) (v)	CWib EBee EGol EMFW EMic EPGN IBal MBNS NLar NRnb SMer SWvt WRHF
'Twinkle Toes'	EGol
'Twinkles' **new**	MIDC
'Twist of Lime' (v)	EGol
'Ultramarine' **new**	IBal
'Ultraviolet Light'	IBal
'Unchained Melody' **new**	IBal
undulata	ECha MIDC NNor WBrE WFar WWpP
§ - var. *albomarginata*	More than 30 suppliers
§ - var. *erromena* ♀H4	EHon EMic EPfP GMaP LPBA MWgw NBid NHol SPer WWpP
§ - var. *undulata* (v) ♀H4	CBcs EBee ECho EHoe EHon EHrv ELan EMFW EPGN EPfP GMaP IBal IHMH LAst LPBA MRav MSwo

	MTis NBlu NEgg NMyG NVic SPer SPoG WEas WFar WKif WWeb WWpP
- var. *univittata* (v) ♀H4	CBro ECha EGol EPGN EPfP GKev IBal MHom NBir NPro WBrk WFar WKif WMoo
'Urajiro Hachijo'	EGol
'Urajiro' (*hypoleuca*)	EGol
'Valentine Lace'	EBee EGol EMic
'Van Wade' (v)	EGol EMic EPGN
'Vanilla Cream' (*cathayana*)	EGol NMyG
'Variegata' (*gracillima*)	see *H.* 'Vera Verde'
'Variegata' (*tokudama*)	see *H. tokudama* f. *aureonebulosa*
'Variegata' (*undulata*)	see *H. undulata* var. *undulata*
'Variegata' (*ventricosa*)	see *H.* 'Aureomarginata'
'Variegated' (*fluctuans*)	see *H.* 'Sagae'
'Velvet Moon' (v) **new**	IBal
ventricosa ♀H4	CBcs CBro ECho EGol EGoo EMic EPfP GAbr GBBs GMaP LPBA MIDC MRav NHol SGar WBrk WCFE WFar WWye
- BWJ 8160 from Sichuan	WCru
- var. *aureomaculata*	EBrs EGol NBir NSti SPer WWye
I 'Venucosa'	EGol EMic WFar
'Venus Star'	GSki NMyG
venusta ♀H4	CBro CSWP EBee EBrs ECho EGol EMic EPGN ERos GCrs GEdr IBal MHer MRav NBir NJOw NMen NMyG NRya NSti SRot WEas WTMC WTin
- B&SWJ 4389	WCru
- dwarf	CSWP
- 'Kin Botan' (v)	IBal
- *yakusimensis*	see *H. kikutii* var. *yakusimensis*
§ 'Vera Verde' (v)	EPGN GQui IBal MHom NBir NMyG
'Verna Jean' (v)	EGol
'Veronica Lake' (v)	EGol EMic IBal WHal
'Vilmoriniana'	EGol EMic
'Viridis Marginata'	see *H. sieboldii* var. *sieboldii* f. *kabitan*
'Wagtail' (Tardiana Group)	EMic
'Wahoo' (*tokudama*) (v)	EGol
'Warwick Curtsey' (v)	EGol IBal
'Warwick Delight' (v)	EGol IBal
'Warwick Edge' (v)	EGol IBal
'Warwick Essence'	EGol EMic
'Warwick Sheen'	IBal
'Waving Winds' (v)	EGol
'Waving Wuffles'	EMic
'Wayside Blue'	EMic
'Wayside Perfection'	see *H.* 'Royal Standard'
'Weihenstephan' (sieboldii)	EGol EMic
'Weser'	EGol
'Wheaton Blue'	EMic
'Whirlwind' (*fortunei*) (v)	CBgR CWib ECho EGol EPGN GBBs GBin GQue IBal IPot MBri MIDC MNrw MSte NBro NEgg NGdn NMyG NNor NRnb SVil WAul WMnd WTMC WWye
'Whirlwind Tour' (v)	EGol
'Whiskey Sour' **new**	IBal
'White Christmas' (*undulata*) (v)	EGle EGol EPGN
'White Fairy' (*plantaginea*) (d)	IBal NMyG
'White Feather' (*undulata*)	EMic IBal NBir
'White Gold'	EGol EPGN NMyG
'White On' (Montana) **new**	EMic
'White Tacchi'	EMon
'White Triumphator' (*rectifolia*)	EGol EMic EPGN IBal MBri NMyG
'White Trumpets' **new**	EMic EPGN
'White Vision'	EGol

'Whoopee' (v)   EPGN MBNS
'Wide Brim' (v) ♀H4   More than 30 suppliers
'Wind River Gold'   EGol
'Windsor Gold'   see *H.* 'Nancy Lindsay'
'Winfield Blue'   CMHG EGol NEgg
'Winfield Gold'   EGol
'Winsome' (v) **new**   IBal
'Wogon Giboshi'   see *H.* 'Wogon'
§ 'Wogon' (*sieboldii*)   CMMP EPGN GEdr GMaP NDlv
                                NHol NMen NSti
'Wogon's Boy'   EGol EPGN
'Wolverine' (v)   EGol EPGN GAbr GEdr IBal LSou
                                MBNS MHom MIDC NGdn NMyG
                                WCot WLin
'Wrinkles and Crinkles'   EGol
'Wylde Green Cream'   IBal
'Xanadu' (v) **new**   IBal
'Yakushima-mizu'   EGol
  (*gracillima*)
* *yakushimana*   GCrs NMen
'Yellow Boa'   EGol
'Yellow Edge' (*fortunei*)   see *H. fortunei* var.
                                aureomarginata
'Yellow Edge' (*sieboldiana*)   see *H.* 'Frances Williams'
'Yellow River' (v)   ECho EGol EMic EPGN IBal MBri
                                NEgg NGdn NMyG
'Yellow Splash' (v)   ECha ECho GKev LRHS
                                MBNS MHom NMyG
'Yellow Splash Rim' (v)   EGol MBri NCGa NRnb
'Yellow Splashed Edged'   EMic
  (v)
'Yellow Submarine' **new**   IBal
'Yin' (v) **new**   IBal
yingeri   EGol
- B&SWJ 546   WCru
'Zager Blue'   EMic
'Zager Green'   EMic
'Zager White Edge'   EGol EMic NMyG WTin
  (*fortunei*) (v)
'Zounds'   CMHG EBrs EChP ECtt EGol EHoe
                                ELan EPGN EPfP EShb GSki IBal
                                IHMH LRHS MDun MIDC MRav
                                NHol NMyG NOak NOrc NSti
                                SHBN SPla WBor WFar WHil WWye

Hottonia (Primulaceae)
palustris   EHon ELan EMFW EMag LPBA
                                NPer NSco NVic SWat WPnP

Houstonia (Rubiaceae)
caerulea misapplied   see *H. michauxii*
caerulea L.   ECho EDAr
- var. *alba*   ECho IHMH SPlb
§ *michauxii*   SPoG
- 'Fred Mullard'   EWes
serpyllifolia **new**   ECho

Houttuynia (Saururaceae)
cordata   GBar LNCo NEgg SDix SWat WFar
§ - 'Boo-Boo' (v)   EChP EMan EPfP EPla EWin LSou
                                NBro WWpP
§ - 'Chameleon' (v)   More than 30 suppliers
- 'Fantasy' **new**   EBee
- 'Flame' (v)   COfd CWCL MAsh NCGa NPri
                                SMrm
- 'Flore Pleno' (d)   CBen CRow EBee EChP ECha
                                EHon ELan EMFW EPfP EPla GBar
                                LPBA MCCP MRav MWgw NBir
                                NPer SGar SIde SMac SPer SPlb
                                SPoG SRms SWat WFar WPnP WTin
                                WWpP
- 'Joker's Gold'   EBee EMan EPPr EPfP EPla EShb
                                LSou MBNS MWgw NBro NVic
                                SMrm WWpP
* - 'Pied Piper'   CDoC EBee EWin LRHS SAga
- 'Sunshine' **new**   EBee

- 'Tequila Sunrise'   CHEx
- 'Terry Clarke' (v)   see *H. cordata* 'Boo-Boo'
- 'Tricolor'   see *H. cordata* 'Chameleon'
- Variegata Group (v)   EBla EPot GBar LPBA NBro SIng
                                WWpP

Hovenia (Rhamnaceae)
dulcis   CAgr CBcs CMCN EPfP EUnu IArd
                                ITer LEdu MBlu NLar SMur WBVN

Howea (Arecaceae)
§ *belmoreana* ♀H1   LPal
§ *forsteriana* ♀H1   CCCN LPal LRHS MBri NScw
                                WMul

Hoya (Asclepiadaceae)
archboldiana   CPlN
* *australis*   CPlN SOWG
bandaensis   CPlN
bella   see *H. lanceolata* subsp. *bella*
carnosa ♀H1   CBcs CPlN CRHN EBak ELan
                                EOHP GQui MGol SRms SWal
                                WWFP
- 'Compacta'   CHal
* - 'Hindu Rope'   NPer
* - 'Krinkle'   NPer
- 'Red Princess'   MBri SAdn
- 'Tricolor'   NPer
- 'Variegata' (v)   MBri
cinnamomifolia   SOWG
* *compacta* 'Tricolor'   NPer
darwinii misapplied   see *H. australis*
gigas   CPlN
imperialis   CPlN ERea
lacunosa   CCCN LRHS
§ *lanceolata* subsp. *bella*   CHal ERea EShb GQui SRms
  ♀H1
linearis   EShb SOWG
motoskei   ERea
multiflora   SOWG
sussuela **new**   CPlN

Hugueninia (Brassicaceae)
alpina   see *H. tanacetifolia*
§ *tanacetifolia*   NEgg

Humata (Davalliaceae)
tyermannii   CMen WFib

Humea see *Calomeria*
elegans   see *Calomeria amaranthoides*

Humulus (Cannabaceae)
japonicus   MSal
- 'Variegatus' (v)   EUnu
lupulus   CArn CBcs CPlN CRWN EMag
                                EPfP GBar GPoy ILis MNHC MSal
                                NGHP SIde WDin WHer WSel
                                WWye
- 'Aureus' ♀H4   More than 30 suppliers
- 'Aureus' (f)   CRHN GBar GGar MCCP MPRe
                                SPla SPoG WCot WWFP
- 'Aureus' (m)   MCCP
* - *compactus*   GPoy
- 'First Gold'PBR   MNHC
- 'Fuggle'   CAgr GPoy SDea
- 'Golden Tassels' (f)   CBcs CBrm CDul EBee EMui ENot
                                EPfP LHop LRHS MAsh MBNS
                                MCCP MPRe NGHP SBra SLim
                                SMad SPoG SSto WWeb
- (Goldings Group)   SDea
  'Cobbs'
- - 'Mathons'   CAgr SDea
- - 'Hallertauer'   SDea
- 'Hip-hop'   EMon EWes
- var. *neomexicanus*   CPlN EWes

- 'Prima Donna' — CBcs EBee EMui GBin LHop MBNS NLar SIde SPoG SWvt WHil
- 'Taff's Variegated' (v) — EMon EWes WSHC
- 'Wye Challenger' — CAgr GPoy
- 'Wye Northdown' — SDea

Hunnemannia (*Papaveraceae*)
fumariifolia 'Sunlite' ♀H4 — LRav

Huodendron (*Styracaceae*)
tibeticum — WPGP

Hutchinsia see *Pritzelago*
rotundifolia — see *Thlaspi cepaeifolium* subsp. *rotundifolium*

Hyacinthella (*Hyacinthaceae*)
dalmatica — ERos
dalmatica 'Grandiflora' — ECho WWst
heldreichii — ERos
lazuliria — ERos
leucophaea — ECho ERos WWst
lineata — WWst
millingenii — EHyt ERos

Hyacinthoides (*Hyacinthaceae*)
algeriensis AB&S 4337 from Morocco — CMon
§ *hispanica* — CBro EBrs IBlr NBir SPer
- 'Alba' — EBrs SPer
- 'Dainty Maid' — WCot
- 'Excelsior' — LRHS
- 'La Grandesse' — CBro
- 'Miss World' — WCot
- 'Queen of the Pinks' — WCot
- 'Rosabella' — CBro
- 'Rose' — CMea SPer
- 'Rosca' — CPom
- 'White City' — WCot
§ *italica* ♀H4 — CMon SIng WShi
§ *non-scripta* — CArn CAvo CBct CBro CFFs CTri EBrs EPfP EPot IBlr LRHS MBow MHer NBir NMir SHFr SPer SRms WHer WHil WPtf WShi
- S&B 194 from Portugal — CMon
- 'Alba' — NBir WHil
- 'Bracteata' — CNat
- 'Chedglow' new — CNat
§ *vicentina* — ERos
- 'Alba' — ERos

Hyacinthus ✿ (*Hyacinthaceae*)
amethystinus — see *Brimeura amethystina*
azureus — see *Muscari azureum*
comosus 'Plumosus' — see *Muscari comosum* 'Plumosum'
fastigiatus — see *Brimeura fastigiata*
multiflowered blue — CAvo EBrs
multiflowered pink — CAvo EBrs
multiflowered white — CAvo EBrs
'Nereus' — EBrs
orientalis — SMeo WShi
- 'Aiols' new — SPer
- 'Anna Liza' — MBri
- 'Anna Marie' ♀H4 — CAvo CBro EBrs MBri
- 'Blue Festival' new — SPer
- 'Blue Jacket' ♀H4 — CBro EBrs MBri
- 'Carnegie' — CAvo CBro EBrs ENot EPfP SPer
- 'China Pink' new — SPer
- 'City of Haarlem' ♀H4 — CBro EBrs EPfP MBri SPer
- 'Delft Blue' ♀H4 — CAvo CBro EBrs EPfP MBri SPer
- 'Gipsy Queen' ♀H4 — EBrs LSou MBri SPer
- 'Jan Bos' — EBrs EPfP MBri SPer
- 'L'Innocence' ♀H4 — CAvo CBro EPfP SPer
- 'Ostara' ♀H4 — CBro EPfP MBri

- 'Peter Stuyvesant' — EBrs
- 'Pink Festival' new — SPer
- 'Pink Pearl' ♀H4 — EPfP MBri
- 'Splendid Cornelia' — EBrs SPer
- 'White Festival' new — SPer
- 'White Pearl' — CAvo MBri
- 'Woodstock' — EBrs LSou SPer

Hydrangea ✿ (*Hydrangeaceae*)
angustipetala — CSam WPGP
- B&SWJ 3454 — WCru
- B&SWJ 3814 — WCru
- B&SWJ 6038 from Yakushima — WCru
- B&SWJ 7121 — WCru
* - f. *formosa* B&SWJ 7097 — WCru
* - f. *macrosepala* B&SWJ 3476 — WCru
* - f. *obovatifolia* B&SWJ 3487b — WCru
anomala subsp. *anomala* B&SWJ 2411 — WCru
- - BWJ 8052 from China new — WCru
- - 'Winter Glow' — CPIN WCru
- subsp. *glabra* — CPIN
- - B&SWJ 3117 — WCru
§ - subsp. *petiolaris* ♀H4 — More than 30 suppliers
- - B&SWJ 6337 — WCru
- - B&SWJ 6081 from Yakushima — WCru
- - B&SWJ 8497 — WCru
§ - - var. *cordifolia* — EBee MBNS NLar
§ - - 'Brookside Littleleaf' — NLar
- - dwarf — see *H. anomala* subsp. *petiolaris* var. *cordifolia*
- - 'Furuaziai' — WCru
* - - var. *minor* new — MAsh
* - - var. *tiliifolia* — EBee EPfP GCal SHyH WFar WSHC
- - 'Yakushima' — WCru WPGP
* - subsp. *quelpartensis* B&SWJ 8799 — WCru
§ *arborescens* — CArn CPLG MRav WFar WPGP
- 'Annabelle' ♀H4 — More than 30 suppliers
- 'Astrid Lundgren' — MAsh
§ - subsp. *discolor* — WCru WPat
- - 'Sterilis' — SHyH SPla WPGP
- 'Grandiflora' ♀H4 — CBcs ELan EPfP LSRN MRav NBro NEgg SPer WCru WDin WHCG WPGP WSHC
- 'Hills of Snow' — MAsh
- subsp. *radiata* — CABP CMil LRHS MAsh SSpi WFar WPGP
aspera — CHEx CTri GIBF SHyH SLon SSpi SSta WCru WKif WPGP
- from Gongshan, China new — WPGP
- 'Anthony Bullivant' — EBee NLar SSpi SWvt WPat
- Kawakamii Group — CHEx CMil CSpe EPla NLar SSpi WCru WPGP
- - B&SWJ 1420 — WCru
- - B&SWJ 3462 — WCru
- - B&SWJ 6827 — WCru
- - B&SWJ 7025 — WCru
- - B&SWJ 7101 — WCru
- - 'August Abundance' — WCru
- - 'September Splendour' — WCru
aspera Kawakamii Group x *involucrata* — WPGP
§ - 'Macrophylla' ♀H3 — CMil CWib EPfP GCal LRHS MRav NBlu NEgg NPal SBrw SHyH SMad SPer SPoG SSpi WCru WFar WPGP
- 'Mauvette' — CMil MBlu NLar NPal SBrw SHyH SPer WCru WPGP
- 'Peter Chappell' — CMil NLar SSpi WPGP
§ - subsp. *robusta* — SHyH SLPl WCru WPGP

- 'Rocklon'	CMil NLar WCru WPGP
- 'Rosthornii'	see *H. aspera* subsp. *robusta*
- 'Sam MacDonald'	LRHS NEgg NLar SSpi WCMO WPGP
§ - subsp. ***sargentiana*** ♀H3	CBcs CEnd CHEx EBee ELan EPfP IArd LRHS MAsh MBlu MBri MGos MRav NBea NPal SBrw SHBN SHyH SMad SPer SSpi SSta WCMO WCru WDin WFar WKif WPGP
- - large-leaved	WCot
- subsp. ***strigosa***	CMil CPLG EPfP SBrw WCru WPGP
- - B&SWJ 8201	WCru
- 'Taiwan Pink'	EPfP NLar
- 'Velvet and Lace'	LRHS
§ - Villosa Group ♀H3	More than 30 suppliers
cinerea	see *H. arborescens* subsp. *discolor*
glandulosa B&SWJ 4031	WCru
§ ***heteromalla***	CMHG CTrG EPfP SSpi WPGP
- B&SWJ 2142 from India	WCru
- B&SWJ 2602 from Sikkim	WCru
- BWJ 7657 from China	WCru
- HWJCM 180	WCru
- HWJK 2127 from Nepal	WCru
- SF 338	ISea
- Bretschneideri Group	EPfP GQui MBlu SBrw SHyH WCru WFar
- 'Fan Si Pan'	WCru
- 'Morrey's Form'	WCru
- 'Snowcap'	EPfP GQui IArd NLar SBrw SHyH SSpi WCMO WCru
- f. ***xanthoneura*** 'Wilsonii'	WCru WKif WSHC
- 'Yalung Ridge'	WCru
* ***heterophylla***	MGos
hirta B&SWJ 5000	WCru
indochinensis B&SWJ 8307	WCru
integerrima	see *H. serratifolia*
integrifolia	CPIN GGGa WPGP
- B&SWJ 022	WCru
- B&SWJ 6967	WCru
involucrata	CPLG EPfP LRHS MMHG SBrw SPer WCru WDin
- dwarf	WCru
- 'Hortensis' (d) ♀H3-4	CElw CMil CPLG CPle EPfP MGan MRav SBrw SMad SPer SSpi WAbe WCru WKif WPGP WSHC
* - 'Plena' (d)	CLAP CMil GAbr MSte SPoG SSta WCot WCru WFar WPGP WTMC
* - 'Sterilis'	EPfP SSpi
- 'Viridescens'	SSpi WPGP
lobbii	CPLG CPle
- B&SWJ 3214	WCru
longipes	GQui WCru WPGP
- BWJ 8188	WCru
'Love You Kiss' (L)	SCoo SPoG
luteovenosa	IDee WCru WPGP
- B&SWJ 5602	WCru
* ***macrocephala***	SSpi
macrophylla	CTrG
- 'AB Green Shadow'PBR	ENot SPoG
- 'Adria' **new**	SHyH
- 'All Summer Beauty'	MAsh
- Alpen Glow	see *H. macrophylla* 'Alpenglühen'
§ - 'Alpenglühen' (H)	CBcs CPLG CSBt ELan MAsh SHBN SHyH SRms WPGP
- 'Altona' (H) ♀H3-4	CBcs CWSG EPfP IArd ISea LRHS MAsh MGos MRav NBir NPri SBod SHyH SPer WPGP
- 'Amethyst' (H/d)	WPGP
- 'Ami Pasquier' (H) ♀H3-4	CBcs CDoC CMac CSBt EBee EPfP LRHS LSRN MRav MSwo SCoo SGar SHyH SLim SPla SSpi SWvt WGer WPGP WWeb
* - 'Aureomarginata' (v)	EPfP SHyH WCot

- 'Aureovariegata' (v)	ELan SNut
- 'Ayesha' (H)	CBcs CBrm CDoC CDul CEnd CMHG CTrw EBee ECtt ENot EPfP EWTr MAsh MGos MRav NHol SBod SDix SHBN SHyH SNut SPer SPla SPoG SWvt WCFE WDin WPGP WWlt
- 'Ayesha Blue' (H)	CPLG ENot MWgw SWvt
- 'Bachstelze' (L)	SSpi
- 'Beauté Vendômoise' (L)	CMil NLar SSpi WPGP
- 'Benelux' (H)	CBcs CWSG SHyH
§ - 'Blauer Prinz' (H)	CSBt CSam LRHS SHBN SHyH
§ - 'Blaumeise' (L)	ENot MAsh MBri MDKP MRav NBlu SHyH SLon SSpi WGer WPGP
§ - 'Bläuling' (L)	CDoC MGos NEgg SHyH WBVN WWeb
- 'Blue Bonnet' (H)	CSBt EPfP IBal LSRN SPer WHen
- Blue Butterfly	see *H. macrophylla* 'Bläulling'
- 'Blue Dwarf'	ENot MGos
- Blue Prince	see *H. macrophylla* 'Blauer Prinz'
- Blue Sky	see *H. macrophylla* 'Blaumeise'
- Blue Tit	see *H. macrophylla* 'Blaumeise'
- 'Blue Wave'	see *H. macrophylla* 'Mariesii Perfecta'
- Bluebird	see *H. macrophylla* 'Bläuling'
- 'Bluebird' misapplied	see *H. serrata* 'Bluebird'
- 'Bodensee' (H)	CBcs EGra LRHS MBri SBod SPla WBVN
- 'Bouquet Rose' (H)	CWib ECtt MRav NBlu
- 'Bridal Bouquet' (H)	CDoC
- 'Brugg'	WPGP
- 'Brunette' (H)	CMil
- 'Buchfink' (L)	SSpi WPGP
§ - 'Cardinal Red' (H) **new**	ECre
- 'Cordata'	see *H. arborescens*
- 'Deutschland' (H)	CTri
- 'Domotoi' (H/d)	CMil SNut
- Dragonfly	see *H. macrophylla* 'Libelle'
- Dragonfly = 'Hobella'PBR (L)	LBuc
* - 'Dwaag Pink'	MRav
- 'Early Sensation'	MAsh SPoG
- 'Eldorado' (H)	EHol
§ - 'Enziandom' (H)	CBcs CSBt SHyH WPGP
§ - 'Europa' (H) ♀H3-4	CBcs CMac CPLG CTrw CWSG LRHS MGos MWgw NPri SBod SEND WPat
§ - 'Fasan' (L)	WPGP WSPU
- Firelight	see *H. macrophylla* 'Leuchtfeuer'
- Fireworks	see *H. macrophylla* 'Hanabi'
- Fireworks Blue	see *H. macrophylla* 'Jōgasaki'
- Fireworks Pink	see *H. macrophylla* 'Jōgasaki'
- Fireworks White	see *H. macrophylla* 'Hanabi'
- 'Forever Pink'	MAsh WGer
§ - 'Frau Fujiyo' (H)	CPLG LRHS
§ - 'Frau Katsuko' (H)	LRHS SPer
§ - 'Frau Mariko' (H)	LRHS
§ - 'Frau Nobuko' (H)	LRHS
- 'Freudenstein'	CBcs MBri
- 'Frillibet' (H)	CAbP CDoC EPfP LRHS WPGP
- 'Gartenbaudirektor Kuhnert' (H)	SHyH SMer
§ - 'Générale Vicomtesse de Vibraye' (H) ♀H3-4	CBcs CDoC CEnd CMHG CTri CWSG EBee EPfP LRHS MBar NCGa SHBN SHyH SLim SNut SPer SSpi WPGP
- Gentian Dome	see *H. macrophylla* 'Enziandom'
- 'Geoffrey Chadbund'	see *H. macrophylla* 'Möwe'
- 'Gerda Steiniger'	CBcs SHyH
- 'Gertrude Glahn' (H)	CBcs EBee MAsh SHyH WFar
- 'Glowing Embers'	IArd MBNS SEND WPGP
- 'Goliath' (H)	EPfP LRHS
- 'Hamburg' (H)	CBcs CEnd CTri CWSG ECtt ENot EPfP LRHS MGos MRav NEgg SDix SHyH WBrE WFar WWeb

§	– 'Hanabi' (L/d)	CBcs CDoC CFee CLAP CMil ECre MBlu NLar
	– 'Harlequin'	CMil WCot WPGP
	– 'Harry's Pink Topper' (H)	MAsh
	– 'Hatfield Rose' (H)	CBcs
	– 'Hatsushimo'	CFwr NLar
	– 'Heinrich Seidel' (H)	CBcs EBee WBrE WMoo
	– 'Hobergine'PBR (H)	CBcs
	– 'Holstein' (H)	MAsh MDun
§	– 'Hörnli' (H)	LAst
	– 'Izu-no-hana' (L/d)	CBcs CFwr CLAP CMil MAsh MBlu NLar SMHy SSpi SUsu WPGP
	– 'Jofloma'	NLar
§	– 'Jōgasaki'	CBcs CFwr CLAP ECre MAsh MBlu NLar WPGP
§	– 'Joseph Banks' (H)	CBcs
	– 'Kardinal' (H)	see *H. macrophylla* 'Cardinal Red' (H)
	– 'King George' (H)	CBcs CDoC CDul CSBt CWSG EBee LAst LRHS MBar MGos MRav MWat SHyH SLim SPer SPoG SWvt WFar WMoo WTel
	– 'Kluis Superba' (H)	CBcs CTri MRav SHyH
§	– 'Koningin Wilhelmina' (H)	WTel
	– 'Kuro-hime' (L)	CBcs
	– 'La France' (H)	CBcs CTri CWSG LRHS MBar MRav SHyH WFar
	– 'Lady Fujiyo'	see *H. macrophylla* 'Frau Fujiyo'
	– Lady Katsuko (H)	see *H. macrophylla* 'Frau Katsuko'
	– 'Lady Mariko'	see *H. macrophylla* 'Frau Mariko'
	– 'Lady Nobuko'	see *H. macrophylla* 'Frau Nobuko'
	– 'Lady Taiko Blue'	see *H. macrophylla* 'Taiko' blue
	– 'Lady Taiko Pink'	see *H. macrophylla* 'Taiko' pink
	– 'Lanarth White' (L) ♀H3-4	CBcs CBrm CDoC CSBt CTri EBee ELan EPfP EWTr MAsh MRav MSwo SHBN SHyH SLPl SLim SPer SReu SRms SSpi WBor WKif WPGP
	– 'Lemon Wave' (L) **new**	NLar
§	– 'Leuchtfeuer' (L)	ENot LRHS MBri MGos SHyH WGer
§	– 'Libelle' (L)	CBcs CDoC CSBt EPfP MAsh MGos MRav SHyH SLim SNut SPer SPoG SSpi WBVN WKif
	– 'Lilacina'	see *H. macrophylla* 'Mariesii Lilacina'
§	– 'Maculata' (L/v)	EHol ELan GQui SGar WGwG
§	– 'Madame A. Riverain' (H)	CWSG SBod SHyH
§	– 'Madame Emile Mouillère' (H) ♀H3-4	More than 30 suppliers
	– 'Maréchal Foch' (H)	CTri
§	– 'Mariesii' (L)	CMHG CSBt CTri EBee ELan ENot ISea LRHS MSwo NEgg SDix SPer WGwG WKif
§	– 'Mariesii Grandiflora' (L) ♀H3-4	ENot EPfP MAsh MBar NBro NCGa NPri SBod SEND SHBN SHyH SPer SRms WDin WFar WMoo WPGP
§	– 'Mariesii Lilacina' (L) ♀H3-4	EPfP MWhi SEND SLon SPer WKif WMoo WPGP
§	– 'Mariesii Perfecta' (L) ♀H3-4	More than 30 suppliers
	– 'Mariesii Variegata' (L/v)	CWib
	– 'Masja' (H)	CBcs EBee EGra IArd LRHS MGos MSwo NBro SHBN SHyH WWeb
	– 'Mathilda Gütges' (H)	CDoC MAsh SHyH SSpi WPGP WWeb
	– 'Max Löbner'	SHyH
	– 'Merveille Sanguine'	CDoC IArd MRav NLar WCMO WCot WLeb WPGP WPat
	– 'Messalinde'	MGos
	– 'Messelina Teller'	ENot
	– 'Mini Hörnli'	see *H. macrophylla* 'Hörnli'
	– 'Miss Belgium' (H)	CTri
	– 'Miss Hepburn'	CBcs CSBt SHyH SPer
	– 'Mousmée'	IArd SLPl SSpi
§	– 'Möwe' (L) ♀H3-4	CBcs CDoC CEnd CMil CPLG EBee ECtt ENot LHop MAsh NEgg NPri SCoo SDix SGar SHBN SHyH SNut SPer SRms SSpi SSta WPGP
§	– 'Nachtigall' (L)	EBee SNut SSpi
	– 'Niedersachsen' (H)	CBcs CDoC MRav SHyH SMer WPGP
	– Nightingale	see *H. macrophylla* 'Nachtigall'
	– 'Nigra' (H) ♀H3-4	CBcs CMil CPLG CWib ELan EPfP EPla MAsh MBri MGos SDix SHBN SHyH SNut SPer WFar WGwG WPGP WPat
	– 'Nikko Blue' (H)	CBcs CWSG EPfP MBar MDun NBlu NEgg
	– var. *normalis*	CPLG NLar
§	– 'Nymphe' (H)	LRHS
	– 'Papagei'	SPer
	– 'Parzifal' (H) ♀H3-4	CBcs CDul CTrw SHyH WPGP
	– 'Pax' (L)	see *H. macrophylla* 'Nymphe'
	– 'Pfau' (L)	SSpi
	– Pheasant	see *H. macrophylla* 'Fasan'
	– 'Pia' (H)	CBcs CBgR CDoC CPLG CSBt CStu EHyt ELan MAsh MGos MRav NWCA SAga SBod SLim SMad SPer SPla SPoG SRms WAbe WCru WFar WPat
	– Pigeon	see *H. macrophylla* 'Taube'
	– 'Prinses Beatrix'	CBcs SHyH
	– 'Quadricolor' (L/v)	CAbb CMil CPLG EHoe EPfP LRHS MRav SDix SGar SHBN SHyH SLim SNut SPer SPla SPlb SRms WCMO WCot WHCG WSHC WWeb
	– Queen Wilhelmina	see *H. macrophylla* 'Koningin Wilhelmina'
	– 'R.F. Felton'	CBcs
	– 'Ramis Pietis' (L)	CBcs MAsh
	– 'Red Baron'	ENot
	– Redbreast	see *H. macrophylla* 'Rotkehlchen'
	– 'Regula' (H)	CTrw
	– 'Renate Steiniger' (H)	ENot MGos SHyH WGwG
	– 'Rosita' (H)	LRHS MAsh WFar
§	– 'Rotkehlchen' (L)	NBlu
	– 'Rotschwanz' (L)	CMil MAsh SSpi WPGP
	– 'Saint Claire'	CBcs CPLG
	– 'Sandra'	CBcs ENot
	– 'Schwabenland'	NPri
	– 'Sea Foam' (L)	NBlu WCot
	– 'Selina'	CBcs ENot MDKP SPoG
	– 'Semperflorens'	MAsh
	– 'Sheila' (L) **new**	CBcs MBri
*	– 'Shower'	ENot LRHS
	– 'Sibylla' (H)	CBcs WPGP
	– Sister Therese	see *H. macrophylla* 'Soeur Thérèse'
	– 'Snow'	ENot MBri
	– 'Snowball'	ENot MGos
§	– 'Soeur Thérèse' (H)	CBcs CSBt LRHS MAsh MGos SHyH SWvt WGwG WPGP
§	– 'Taiko' blue (H)	LRHS SPer
§	– 'Taiko' pink (H)	LRHS
§	– 'Taube' (L)	CBcs CPLG GQui NBlu
N	– Teller Blau (L)	CDoC COtt CSBt EBee EPfP MRav NSti SCoo SLim SPoG SWvt WDin WWeb
N	– Teller Rosa (L)	CDoC EBee EPfP SCoo SWvt WWeb
N	– Teller Rot (L)	CDoC CSBt EPfP SCoo SPlb SPoG SWvt WDin WWeb
N	– Teller variegated	see *H. macrophylla* 'Tricolor'
N	– Teller Weiss	see *H. macrophylla* 'Libelle'
	– 'Tokyo Delight' (L) ♀H3-4	CDoC CLAP CPLG MAsh SHyH WPGP
§	– 'Tricolor' (L/v)	CBcs CDoC LAst LRHS MGos MTis NEgg SBod SHyH SLon SPer SPoG WFar WKif WMoo

- 'Trophy'PBR	SPoG
- 'Val de Loire'	CWSG
- 'Variegata'	see *H. macrophylla* 'Maculata'
- 'Veitchii' (L) ♀H3-4	CBcs CMHG CMil CPLG CSBt ENot EPfP EWTr MRav MSwo SBod SDix SGar SHyH SPoG SSpi WPGP
- 'Vicomte de Vibraye'	see *H. macrophylla* 'Générale Vicomtesse de Vibraye'
- 'Westfalen' (H) ♀H3-4	IArd SDix SPla
- 'White Lace' (L)	ELan SHyH
- white lacecap (L)	SHyH
- 'White Mop'	CWib
- 'White Wave'	see *H. macrophylla* 'Mariesii Grandiflora'
- 'Zhuni Hito'	NLar
- 'Midori' (L)	CBcs
paniculata	CMCN CTrw LAst
- B&SWJ 3556 from Taiwan	WCru
- B&SWJ 5413 from Japan	WCru
- 'Ammarin' **new**	NLar
- 'Big Ben'	MBri
- 'Black Porch' **new**	NLar
- 'Brussels Lace'	CAbP CMil EBee EWTr LRHS MAsh MBri MRav NLar SHyH SNut SPla SPoG SSpi WCMO WPat
- 'Burgundy Lace'	CBcs MAsh MBlu MBri
- 'D.V.P. Pinky' **new**	NLar
- 'Dart's Little Dot'	WPat
- 'Everest'	CAbP LRHS MAsh SHyH SNut
- 'Floribunda'	EPfP LRHS NEgg WPGP
- 'Grandiflora' ♀H4	More than 30 suppliers
- 'Greenspire'	CBcs LRHS MBlu MBri
- 'Harry's Souvenir' **new**	MBri
- 'Kyushu' ♀H4	More than 30 suppliers
- 'Limelight'PBR	CBcs CHVG CMil EKen GQui LBuc MBlu MBri NLar SNut WBrE WCMO WOVN WPat
- 'Mount Aso'	CMil NLar WPGP
- 'October Bride'	NLar WPGP
- 'Phantom'	MAsh MBlu MDKP WPat
- 'Pink Beauty' **new**	MDKP
- Pink Diamond = 'Interhydia' ♀H4	CAbP CDoC ENot GQui LAst LHop LRHS MAsh MBlu MBri MGos MRav NLar NPri SHyH SPla SSpi SSta WCru WFar WPGP WPat
- 'Pink Jewel'	CWib WPat
- 'Praecox'	GQui SLon SPer WCru WPat
- 'Silver Dollar'	MAsh MBri
- 'Tardiva'	CBcs CDoC EPfP GQui LPan LRHS MAsh MGos MRav NBro NHol SDix SHyH SPer SRms WDin WFar WHCG WKif WPGP WPat WWeb
- 'Unique' ♀H4	CBcs CBgR CBrm CDoC CMil EBee EPfP EWTr GQui LHop LRHS MAsh MBri MRav SHyH SMac SNut SPer SPla SSpi WCru WDin WFar WPGP WPat
- 'Waterfall' **new**	CLAP
- 'White Lace'	MBlu
- 'White Lady'	CBcs
- 'White Moth'	CBcs NLar SHyH SNut
petiolaris	see *H. anomala* subsp. *petiolaris*
§ 'Preziosa' ♀H3-4	More than 30 suppliers
quelpartensis	CBcs CRHN GQui
- B&SWJ 4400	WCru
quercifolia ♀H3-4	More than 30 suppliers
- 'Alice'	EPfP WPGP
- 'Alison' **new**	EPfP
- 'Burgundy'	CBcs CPMA EPfP MBri NLar WPGP
- 'Flore Pleno'	see *H. quercifolia* 'Snow Flake'
- 'Harmony'	CEnd CPMA EBee EPfP EWTr IArd MBri NLar SSta WHCG WPGP WPat
- 'Lady Anne'	CFwr WPGP
- 'Little Honey'	MAsh SPoG
- 'Pee Wee'	CBcs CDoC CMil EPfP LRHS MAsh NLar SHyH SLon SPoG SReu SSpi SSta WPGP WPat
- 'Sike's Dwarf'	CEnd CPMA GCal NLar WPat
- Snow Queen = 'Flemygea'	CBcs CDoC CKno CPMA CSBt CWSG EBee ELan EPfP ISea MAsh MGos MRav MSte NLar SHyH SLim SPer SPla SWvt WFar WGwG WHCG WPGP WPat
§ - Snowflake = 'Brido' (d)	CAbP CBcs CDoC CEnd CHar CMil CPMA CSPN ELan EMil EPfP EWTr LRHS MAsh MGos SLon SMur SPer SPla SPoG SSpi SSta WHCG WPGP WPat
- 'Tennessee Clone'	EBee GCal NLar
'Sabrina'PBR	CBcs ENot MBri SPoG
sargentiana	see *H. aspera* subsp. *sargentiana*
scandens B&SWJ 5523	WCru
- B&SWJ 5893	WCru
§ - subsp. *chinensis*	WFar
- - B&SWJ 1488	WCru
- - B&SWJ 3420	WCru
- - B&SWJ 3423 from Taiwan	WCru
- - BWJ 8000 from Sichuan	WCru
- subsp. *liukiuensis*	WCru
- - B&SWJ 6022	WCru
- 'Splash' (v)	CMil
seemannii	More than 30 suppliers
'Selma' (H) **new**	CBcs
serrata	CPLG CTrw CWib WDin WKif
- B&SWJ 4817	WCru
- B&SWJ 6241	WCru
- 'Acuminata'	see *H. serrata* 'Bluebird'
- 'Aigaku'	CLAP CPLG WPGP
- 'Amagi-amacha'	CMil
- 'Amagyana'	CPLG WPGP
I - 'Aurea'	SLon
- 'Belle Deckle'	see *H. serrata* 'Blue Deckle'
- 'Beni-gaku'	CLAP CMil CPLG MAsh NBro NLar SMer WPGP
- 'Beni-yama'	CMil WPGP
- 'Blue Billow'	MAsh NLar
§ - 'Blue Deckle' (L)	CMHG MAsh MRav SHyH SNut SPla WPGP
§ - 'Bluebird' ♀H3-4	CBcs CDul CSBt CWSG EBee ELan EPfP GQui LRHS MAsh MBar MBlu MBri MGos MWgw NBlu NCGa NEgg SBod SDix SHBN SHyH SLim SNut SPer SSta SWvt WFar WMoo WWeb
- 'Diadem' ♀H3-4	CBos CMil CPLG SDix WPGP WSHC
- dwarf white	WCru
- 'Fuji Snowstorm'	CMil
- 'Fuji Waterfall' (d) **new**	CAbP CMil LSou LTwo NCGa SPoG WBor WCMO WCot WCra
- 'Golden Showers'	CMil
- 'Golden Sunlight'PBR	CBcs CDoC LRHS SLon SMad SPoG SWvt
- 'Graciosa'	CMil WPGP
- 'Grayswood' ♀H3-4	CBcs CEnd CSBt CWSG GQui LRHS MBri MRav SDix SGar SHyH SPer SSpi WKif WPGP
- 'Hakucho'	MAsh
- 'Hallasan' ambig.	CMil
- 'Hime-benigaku'	CLAP CMil
- 'Intermedia'	CPLG NBro
* - 'Jogasaki'	CLAP
§ - 'Kiyosumi' (L)	CDoC CEnd CLAP CMil CPLG GQui SSpi WCru WPGP
- 'Klaveren'	CMil
- 'Koreana' (L)	CMil
- 'Kurenai' (L)	NLar SSpi
- 'Kurenai-nishiki' (v)	CMil
- 'Maiko'	IArd

- 'Miranda' (L) ♀H3-4   CBos CBrd CPLG CSam MAsh NLar SSpi WFar
- 'Miyama-yae-murasaki' (d)   CLAP CMil WPGP
- 'Ō-amacha'   CMil
- 'Preziosa'   see *H.* 'Preziosa'
- 'Professeur Iida'   WPGP
- f. *prolifera*   CMil EBee WPGP
- 'Ramis Pictis'   WPGP
- 'Rosalba' ♀H3-4   CLAP CPLG EPfP MRav SPer SPla WFar WSHC
- 'Shichidanka-nishiki' (d/v)   CBcs CDoC CPLG
- 'Shino-goku'   MAsh
- 'Shinonome'   CLAP CMil GQui WPGP
- 'Shirofuji'   CLAP CMil WPGP
- 'Shirotae' (d)   CMil WPGP
- 'Spreading Beauty'   CMil WPGP
- var. *thunbergii*   CBcs CMHG GQui WFar WPGP
* - - 'Plena' (d)   WCru
- 'Tiara' ♀H3-4   CBos CMil GGGa MAsh MBri NLar SHyH SSpi WPGP WSHC WWes
- 'Uzu Azisai'   WPGP
- 'Woodlander'   MAsh
- 'Yae-no-amacha'   CBcs WPGP
§ *serratifolia*   CHEx CPlN EPfP EPla SBra SBrw SPoG SSpi SSta WCru WFar WGer WPGP

  sikokiana   CLAP
- B&SWJ 5035   WCru
- B&SWJ 5855   WCru
  'Soraya' (L) **new**   CBcs
  'Sunset' (L)   CBcs
  tiliifolia   see *H. anomala* subsp. *petiolaris*
  villosa   see *H. aspera* Villosa Group
  xanthoneura   see *H. heteromalla*
  'Ya-no-amacha'   CBcs

Hydrastis (Ranunculaceae)
  canadensis   CArn COld GBuc GPoy LEdu WCru

Hydrocharis (Hydrocharitaceae)
  morsus-ranae   CDWL CRow EHon EMFW LNCo LPBA NPer NSco SWat WPnP

Hydrocleys (Limnocharitaceae)
  nymphoides   XBlo

Hydrocotyle (Apiaceae)
  asiatica   see *Centella asiatica*
  sibthorpioides **new**   CBow
* - 'Variegata' (v)   CPLG EBee EMan EPPr EShb SIng WCHb WHer WPer
  vulgaris   EMFW

Hydrophilus (Restionaceae)
  rattrayi **new**   CBig

Hydrophyllum (Hydrophyllaceae)
  canadense   CLAP EBee EMar WCru
  virginianum   CLAP CPom EBee MGol MSal

Hylomecon (Papaveraceae)
* *hylomecoides*   WCru
§ *japonica*   CDes CFwr CMea CPom EBee EChP ECho ERos ETow GBBs GBuc GCrs GEdr GKev MSte NBir NDov NMen NRya SHGN WAbe WCru WFar WPnP WTin

Hylotelephium see *Sedum*

Hymenanthera see *Melicytus*

Hymenocallis (Amaryllidaceae)
  'Advance'   ECho LRHS
§ *caroliniana*   ECho

x *festalis* ♀H1   ECho EPfP ERea LRHS MBri SPav WCMO WCot WFar
- 'Zwanenburg'   ECho WCMO
  harrisiana   ECho LRHS WCMO WCot
  littoralis   MOak
- 'Variegata' **new**   MOak
§ *longipetala*   ECho LRHS WCMO WCot
  occidentalis   see *H. caroliniana*
  'Sulphur Queen' ♀H1   CBgR ECho LRHS SPav WCMO WCot

Hymenolepis (Asteraceae)
  parviflora   see *Athanasia parviflora*

Hymenosporum (Pittosporaceae)
  flavum   SOWG

Hymenoxys (Asteraceae)
  acaulis var. *caespitosa*   see *Tetraneuris acaulis* var. *caespitosa*
  grandiflora   see *Tetraneuris grandiflora*
§ *hoopesii*   More than 30 suppliers

Hyophorbe (Arecaceae)
§ *lagenicaulis*   LPal
  verschaffeltii   LPal

Hyoscyamus (Solanaceae)
  albus   CSpe GBar MGol MSal
  niger   CArn GPoy MGol MSal WWye

Hyparrhenia (Poaceae)
  hirta   XPep

Hypericum ❁ (Clusiaceae)
  CC 4131   CPLG MGol
  CC 4543   MGol
  CC 4544   CPLG
  acmosepalum   WPGP WPat
  aegypticum   CLyd ECho EDAr EHyt LBee LRHS MHer NJOw NMen NWCA SBla SRot WFar WOld WPat WPer XPep
  androsaemum   CAgr CArn CRWN EAro ECha ELan ELau ISea MHer MRav MSal MSwo NPer NSco SHFr WDin WMoo WOut
§ - 'Albury Purple'   CElw EShb GBuc LDai MHer MRav MWgw SGar WHrl WMoo
- 'Autumn Blaze'   CBcs MGos
§ - 'Dart's Golden Penny'   SPer
- 'Excellent Flair'   MGos NLar
- 'Orange Flair'   MGos
§ - f. *variegatum*   EAro IFro MWgw NBir NLar NScw
    'Mrs Gladis Brabazon' (v)   NSti SBod SLon SPoG WCot WHrl
  'Archibald'   EBee
  ascyron   EBee
  athoum   CLyd EHyt NBir WPat
  atomarium   EBee WPGP
  balearicum   EHrv IFro MTho WAbe WPGP XPep
  barbatum MESE 371   EBee
  bellum   GCal SLon
- subsp. *latisepalum*   SLon
  calycinum   CBcs CDul ECho ELan EPfP EWTr IHMH LBuc MBar MGos MRav MWat NEgg NWea SHBN SWvt WDin WGwG WMoo WTel
- 'Senior'   EWin
§ *cerastioides*   CTri CWib LBee LRHS SIng SPoG SRms WAbe WFar WPer
  coris   ECho EWes LRHS MTho MWat SRms
  crux-andreae   EBee
  cuneatum   see *H. pallens*

Hypocalymma (Myrtaceae)

Hypocalyptus (Papilionaceae)

Hypochaeris (Asteraceae)

Hypocyrta see *Nematanthus*

Hypoestes (Acanthaceae)

Hypolepis (Dennstaedtiaceae)

Hypoxis (Hypoxidaceae)

hirsuta	ECho
hygrometrica	ECho ECou NMen
krebsii	ECho
parvula	NMen
- var. **albiflora**	WCot
§ - - 'Hebron Farm Biscuit'	CBro CWrd ECho EWes GEdr SAga
	SBla WAbe WFar
* **tasmanica**	EMan
villosa	ECho ERea

Hypoxis x *Rhodohypoxis* see x *Rhodoxis*
H. parvula x **R. baurii**   see x *Rhodoxis hybrida*

Hypsela (Campanulaceae)

sp.	CFee
longiflora	see *H. reniformis*
§ **reniformis**	ECho EDAr EMan LAst LBee LRHS
	MRav NHol NJOw NWCA SIng
	SPoG WFar
- 'Greencourt White'	ECho GBuc

Hypseocharis (Oxalidaceae)
pimpinellifolia new	WCot

Hyssopus ❀ (Lamiaceae)

ambiguus	XPep
officinalis	CArn CBrm CHby CSev ECha ELan
	ELau EPfP EUnu GPoy IHMH LBuc
	LRHS MBNS MBar MBri MHer
	MNHC MRav NGHP SECG SGar
	SIde SPlb WCHb WGHP WGwG
	WPer WWye XPep
- f. **albus**	CSev CWan EBee ECha ELau EPfP
	EWin GPoy MHer MLHP MNHC
	NGHP SBch SHGN SIde SPlb
	WCHb WGwG WJek WPer WSel
	WWye
§ - subsp. **aristatus**	CArn CBod CHrt CWan EBee ECho
	EDAr ELau GPoy LLWP MHer
	MNHC NChi SIde WCHb WEas
	WJek WSel WWye
- 'Blaue Wolke' new	GBin
- subsp. **canescens**	EAro XPep
- 'Roseus'	CBrm CEnt CSev EBee ECha ELau
	EPPr EPfP EWin GPoy LLWP MBNS
	MHer MNHC NGHP SBch SHGN
	SIde WCHb WGwG WJek WKif
	WPer WWye
- white	WEas
* **schugnanicus**	LLWP MHar
seravschanicus	EOHP

Hystrix (Poaceae)

patula	CBrm CHrt CKno CPLG CWCL
	EChP EGra EHoe EMon EPPr
	EShb GCal LLWP LRHS MCCP
	MMoz MNrw MWhi NGdn NHol
	NOak SHFr SPlb SWal WPer
	WRos WTin

Iberis (Brassicaceae)

'Betty Swainson'	CHrt GBri SMrm
candolleana	see *I. pruitii* Candolleana Group
commutata	see *I. sempervirens*
'Correvoniana'	WEas
'Dick Self'	LRHS
gibraltarica	ECho EWin LRav NFor NPri SRms
	WGor
'Golden Candy'	CRez SPoG

§ **pruitii** Candolleana	ECho EHyt WAbe
Group	
saxatilis	EAEE ECho EDAr XPep
- **candolleana**	see *I. pruitii* Candolleana Group
semperflorens	WCFE WSPU XPep
§ **sempervirens** ♀H4	CBcs COfd CTri CWib ECho ELan
	EPfP IFoB IFro LAst MHer MWat
	NBid NBlu NBro NEgg NFor NOrc
	NVic SEND SRms SWal WBrE
	WCFE WFar WPer
- 'Compacta'	ECho
- 'Little Gem'	see *I. sempervirens* 'Weisser
	Zwerg'
- 'Pygmaea'	ECho ECtt NMen SBla
- Schneeflocke	see *I. sempervirens* 'Snowflake'
§ - 'Snowflake' ♀H4	ECho ENot EPfP GAbr IFoB LRHS
	LRav NBlu NHol NJOw NLar SBch
	SIng SPer SPoG SWvt WRHF
§ - 'Weisser Zwerg'	CMea ECha ECho ECtt ELan LAst
	LBee LRHS MHer MRav NMen
	NRya SBla SPoG SRms WHoo

Idesia (Flacourtiaceae)

polycarpa	CAbP CAgr CBcs CDul CMCN
	CTho EPfP IDee LHop NLar
	SSpi WBVN WDin WFar WPGP
	WPat

Ilex ❀ (Aquifoliaceae)

N x **altaclerensis**	SHHo STop
- 'Atkinsonii' (m)	SHHo WWHy
- 'Balearica'	SHHo
- 'Belgica' (f)	SHHo
§ - 'Belgica Aurea' (f/v) ♀H4	CBcs CDoC CSBt CTho EBee EPfP
	LRHS MBar MBri NHol NWea
	SEND SHBN SHHo WFar WWHy
- 'Camelliifolia' (f) ♀H4	CSBt CTho EBee ELan EPfP IFoB
	MBlu MBri MRav MWat NLar
	NWea SHHo SPla STop WFar
	WWHy
- 'Golden King' (f/v) ♀H4	More than 30 suppliers
- 'Hendersonii' (f)	SHHo WWHy
- 'Hodginsii' (m) . ♀H4	CTri ECot MBar MRav SEND SHHo
	WFar WWHy
- 'Howick' (f/v)	SHHo
- 'James G. Esson' (f)	SBir SHHo
- 'Lady Valerie' (f/v)	SHHo WWHy
- 'Lawsoniana' (f/v) ♀H4	CDoC CSBt CSam EBee ELan EPfP
	LRHS MAsh MBar MBri MRav NBlu
	NHol NWea SHBN SHHo SLim
	SLon SPer SPla SPoG SRms SSta
	WBVN WDin WFar WPat WTel
	WWHy
- 'Maderensis'	NRib
- 'Maderensis Variegata'	see *I. aquifolium* 'Maderensis
	Variegata'
- 'Marnockii' (f)	SHHo WWHy
- 'Moorei' (m)	SHHo
- 'Mundyi' (m)	SHHo
- 'Purple Shaft' (f)	MRav SHHo
- 'Ripley Gold' (f/v)	MAsh NHol SCoo SHHo STop
	WWHy
- 'Silver Sentinel'	see *I.* x *altaclerensis* 'Belgica
	Aurea'
- 'W.J. Bean' (f)	SHHo
- 'Wilsonii' (f)	EBee LPan SHHo WWHy
aquifolium ♀H4	More than 30 suppliers
- 'Alaska' (f)	CDoC CMCN EMil ENot LAst LBuc
	MAsh NBlu NHol NLar NSti SBir
	SHHo STop SWvt WFar WWHy
- 'Amber' (f) ♀H4	CTri SHHo SMad WWHy
- 'Angustifolia' (f)	EPla MAsh WCFE WFar
- 'Angustifolia' (m or f)	EPfP MBar MWat NHol SHHo SPoG
	WBVN WFar
§ - 'Argentea Marginata'	More than 30 suppliers
(f/v) ♀H4	

§ - 'Argentea Marginata Pendula' (f/v)	CDoC CTri ECrN ELan EPfP LPan LRHS MAsh NHol NLar SHHo SLim SRms WFar WPat WWHy
- 'Argentea Pendula'	see *I. aquifolium* 'Argentea Marginata Pendula'
- 'Argentea Variegata'	see *I. aquifolium* 'Argentea Marginata'
- 'Atlas' (m)	CBcs CDoC LBuc WWHy
- 'Aurea Marginata' (f/v)	CDul CTho EBee EHoe LBuc MGos NBlu NEgg NHol NWea SBod SCoo SHBN SHHo WCFE WDin WFar WPat
- 'Aurea Marginata Pendula' (f/v)	CDoC MAsh NHol NLar SLim SPer WPat
- 'Aurea Ovata'	see *I. aquifolium* 'Ovata Aurea'
- 'Aurea Regina'	see *I. aquifolium* 'Golden Queen'
- 'Aureovariegata Pendula'	see *I. aquifolium* 'Weeping Golden Milkmaid'
- 'Aurifodina' (f)	IMGH SHHo WWHy
§ - 'Bacciflava' (f)	More than 30 suppliers
- 'Bella' (f) **new**	SHHo
- 'Bokrijk' **new**	SHHo
- 'Bowland' (f/v)	MAsh NHol
- 'Cookii' (f)	SHHo
- 'Crassifolia' (f)	EPla SHHo SMad WWHy
- 'Crispa' (m)	CDul EBee MBlu NHol SBir SHHo WWHy
- 'Crispa Aureomaculata'	see *I. aquifolium* 'Crispa Aureopicta'
§ - 'Crispa Aureopicta' (m/v)	SHHo WWHy
- 'Elegantissima' (m/v)	SCoo SHHo WWHy
- 'Ferox' (m)	CDul ELan EPfP LRHS SHHo SPer STop WDin WGwG WWHy
- 'Ferox Argentea' (m/v) ♀H4	More than 30 suppliers
* - 'Ferox Argentea Picta' (m/v)	LRHS WWHy
- 'Ferox Aurea' (m/v)	CDoC CSBt CWib EBee ELan EPfP LAst MAsh NHol SHHo SPla WWHy
§ - 'Flavescens' (f)	EBee EPfP NHol SHHo
- 'Fructu Luteo'	see *I. aquifolium* 'Bacciflava'
- 'Gold Flash' (f/v)	EBee LRHS MAsh MBri MGos NBlu NHol SHHo WDin WWHy
- 'Golden Hedgehog'	EPfP SPoG WWHy
- 'Golden Milkboy' (m/v)	CDul EBee ELan EPfP MBlu MGos SHHo SPoG WCFE WDin WPat WWHy
- 'Golden Milkmaid' (f/v)	EHol
§ - 'Golden Queen' (m/v) ♀H4	CDoC CWSG CWib EBee LRHS MGos NBir NHol NWea SHHo SPer SRms WPat WWHy
- 'Golden Tears'	SHHo WWHy
- 'Golden van Tol' (f/v)	CBcs CDoC CLnd CSBt CTri EBee ECrN ELan ENot EPfP IMGH LAst LRHS MAsh MBar MBlu MGos MSwo NHol SCoo SHBN SHHo SRms WDin WWHy WWeb
- 'Green Pillar' (f)	EPfP MBar SHHo WWHy
- 'Handsworth New Silver' (f/v) ♀H4	More than 30 suppliers
- 'Harpune' (f)	SHHo WWHy
§ - 'Hascombensis'	CDoC EHol LHop MGos NHol NMen NWea WFar WWHy
- 'Hastata' (m)	CWib IArd WWHy
- 'Ingramii' (m/v)	SBir SHHo WWHy
- 'J.C. van Tol' (f/m) ♀H4	More than 30 suppliers
- 'Latispina' (f)	SHHo WWHy
- 'Laurifolia Aurea' (m/v)	SHHo
- 'Lichtenthalii' (f)	IArd SHHo
- 'Madame Briot' (f/v) ♀H4	More than 30 suppliers
§ - 'Maderensis Variegata' (m/v)	SHHo
- 'Monstrosa' (m)	SHHo
- moonlight holly	see *I. aquifolium* 'Flavescens'
- 'Myrtifolia' (m)	CDoC ELan EPfP LPan MBar MBlu MGos MRav NBlu NLar SCoo SHHo SPoG WCFE WFar WWHy
- 'Myrtifolia Aurea' (m/v)	SPoG SWvt WFar
§ - 'Myrtifolia Aurea Maculata' (m/v) ♀H4	CBgR CBrm CDoC CSam EBee EHoe ELan EPfP IMGH LAst LRHS MAsh MBri MRav NEgg NHol NWea SHHo SMad SPer SPoG SWvt WBVN WFar WPat WWHy
- 'Myrtifolia Aureovariegata'	see *I. aquifolium* 'Myrtifolia Aurea Maculata'
- 'Ovata' (m)	WWHy
§ - 'Ovata Aurea' (m/v)	SHHo WWHy
- 'Pendula' (f)	EPfP SHHo
- 'Pendula Mediopicta'	see *I. aquifolium* 'Weeping Golden Milkmaid'
§ - 'Pyramidalis' (f) ♀H4	CDoC CDul CEnd CSBt CTho CTri EBee ELan IFoB LRHS MAsh MBar MBri MGan MGos MLan MRav NBlu NFor NHol NLar NWea SHHo SPer SRms WDin WFar WMoo WWHy
- 'Pyramidalis Aureomarginata' (f/v)	CDoC LRHS MBri MGos MLan NLar SHHo WBor
- 'Pyramidalis Fructu Luteo' (f) ♀H4	MBar NWea SHHo
- 'Recurva' (m)	WWHy
- 'Rubricaulis Aurea' (f/v)	CBgR NHol SHHo STop WWHy
- 'Scotica' (f)	WWHy
- Siberia = 'Limsi'PBR (f)	EBee SHHo WWHy
- 'Silver King'	see *I. aquifolium* 'Silver Queen'
- 'Silver Lining' (f/v)	SHHo STop
- 'Silver Milkboy' (f/v)	CTho EHoe ELan LRHS MAsh MBNS MBlu MGos WFar WWHy
- 'Silver Milkmaid' (f/v)	CBgR CDoC CWSG EBee EPfP LAst LRHS MBar MRav NEgg NHol SHBN SHHo SLim SPer SPla SPoG SWvt WMoo WWHy
§ - 'Silver Queen' (m/v) ♀H4	More than 30 suppliers
- 'Silver Sentinel'	see *I.* x *altaclerensis* 'Belgica Aurea'
- 'Silver van Tol' (f/v)	CDoC ELan IMGH LAst LRHS NHol NLar NPer NWea SHHo SMer SPoG WFar WWHy WWeb
- 'Somerset Cream' (f/v)	NLar WWHy
§ - 'Watereriana' (m/v)	EHol MAsh SHHo SMur
- 'Waterer's Gold'	see *I. aquifolium* 'Watereriana'
§ - 'Weeping Golden Milkmaid' (f/v)	SHHo WPat
x *aquipernyi*	SHHo
- Dragon Lady = 'Meschick' (f)	LPan NLar SHHo WWHy
- 'San Jose' (f)	CMCN SHHo
x *attenuata*	WFar
- 'Sunny Foster' (f/v)	CMCN ENot EPla LRHS MGos SHHo WFar
§ *bioritsensis*	CMCN CTri NWea
buergeri	CMCN
cassine	CMCN
- var. *angustifolia*	STop
chinensis misapplied	see *I. purpurea*
ciliospinosa	CMCN WPGP
colchica	CMCN SHHo
corallina	CBcs CMCN
cornuta	ERom LPan LRHS SHHo WFar
* - 'Aurea'	SHHo
- 'Burfordii' (f)	SHHo
- 'Dazzler' (f)	LPan SHHo
- 'Fine Line' (f)	SHHo
- 'Ira S. Nelson' (f/v)	SHHo
- 'O. Spring' (f/v)	SHHo
- 'Rotunda' (f)	SHHo
- 'Willowleaf' (f)	SHHo
I *crenata*	CMCN CTri ERom EWTr GBin MBar MGos SAPC SArc SHHo WDin WFar WNor

- 'Akagi'	WFar
- 'Aureovariegata'	see *I. crenata* 'Variegata'
- 'Braddock Heights' (f)	SHHo
- 'Cape Fear' (m)	SHHo
- 'Carolina Upright' (m)	SHHo
- 'Cole's Hardy' (f)	SHHo
- 'Convexa' (f) ♀H4	CBcs EPfP IMGH LPan MBar MBri NBlu NHol NWea SHHo WFar WGwG WPat
- 'Convexed Gold'	MBri
- 'Fastigiata' (f)	CDoC CEnd EBee ECrN EPfP EPla LAst LRHS MAsh MBNS MBar MBri MGos NBlu NLar SCoo SHHo SPer SPoG WFar
- 'Fructo Luteo'	see *I. crenata* f. *watanabeana*
- 'Fukarin'	see *I. crenata* 'Shiro-fukurin'
* - 'Glory Gem' (f)	CBcs LPan SHHo
- 'Gold Tips'	MGos
- 'Golden Gem' (f) ♀H4	More than 30 suppliers
- 'Green Dragon' (m)	EPla
- 'Green Hedge'	LBuc
- 'Green Island' (m)	SHHo
- 'Green Lustre' (f)	SHHo
- 'Helleri' (f)	CMCN EPfP EPla MBar SBla SHHo WPat
- 'Hetzii' (f)	EWTr NLar SHHo
- 'Ivory Hall' (f)	EPla SHHo
- 'Ivory Tower' (f)	SHHo
* - 'Kobold'	SHHo
- 'Korean Gem'	EPla SHHo
- var. *latifolia* (m)	SHHo
- 'Luteovariegata'	see *I. crenata* 'Variegata'
- 'Mariesii' (f)	IMGH MBlu SBla SHHo SIng
- 'Mount Halla' (f)	CMCN
- 'Nakada' (m)	SHHo
- var. *paludosa*	EBee
- 'Pride's Tiny'	SHHo
I - 'Pyramidalis' (f)	NHol NWea
§ - 'Shiro-fukurin' (f/v)	CMCN CMHG ELan EPfP LAst LRHS MAsh NHol SHHo
- 'Sky Pencil' (f)	CMCN
- 'Snowflake'	see *I. crenata* 'Shiro-fukurin'
- 'Stokes' (m)	EBee NLar SHHo
§ - 'Variegata' (v)	CMCN EPla LRHS MBar NHol SHHo SPoG
§ - f. *watanabeana* (f)	SHHo
'Dazzler'	see *I. cornuta* 'Dazzler'
decidua	CMCN
dimorphophylla	CBcs CDoC CMCN SHHo
- 'Somerset Pixie'	SHHo
'Doctor Kassab' (f)	CMCN SHHo
'Drace' (f)	SHHo
'Elegance' (f)	WFar
fargesii	CPne
ficoidea	CMCN
glabra	SHHo
'Good Taste' (f)	SHHo WFar WWHy
hascombensis	see *I. aquifolium* 'Hascombensis'
hookeri	SHHo
'Indian Chief' (f)	MBlu SMad WFar
insignis	see *I. kingiana*
'John T. Morris' (m)	SHHo
§ *kingiana*	WFar WPGP
x *koehneana*	CDul ELan
- 'Chestnut Leaf' (f) ♀H4	CCVT CDoC CLnd CMCN MBri MRav SHHo SMad WFar WLeb WPGP WWHy
latifolia	CBcs CHEx CMCN SHHo SMad WPGP
'Lydia Morris' (f)	CSam SHHo WFar
'Mary Nell' (f)	SBir SHHo
maximowicziana var. *kanehirae*	CBcs CMCN WWHy
x *meserveae*	SHHo
- Blue Angel (f)	CBcs CDoC CDul COtt EBee ELan EMil EPfP IFoB IMGH LPan MBar

	MBri MLan MWat MWgw NBlu NEgg NHol NWea SHHo SPoG SRms WDin WFar WPat WWHy
- Blue Prince (m)	CBcs CBrm CDoC COtt EBee EHol GKev LBuc LPan MBar MBlu NHol NWea SHBN SHHo SLim SPer SPoG WDin WFar WWHy
- Blue Princess (f)	CBcs CBrm COtt ECrN ENot EPfP LBuc LPan MBar MBlu MRav NBlu NHol NSti NWea SCoo SHBN SHHo SLim SPer SPoG WDin WWHy
- Golden Girl = 'Mesgolg' (f)	WWHy
* - 'Red Darling' (f)	CDul
montana **new**	GIBF
myrtifolia	CMCN ECot MLan MRav NEgg NPri
'Nellie R. Stevens' (f)	CDoC EBee LPan NWea SCoo WWHy
opaca	CMCN
paraguariensis **new**	EOHP
pedunculosa	CMCN SHHo
perado latifolia	see *I. perado* subsp. *platyphylla*
- subsp. *perado* **new**	CBcs
§ - subsp. *platyphylla*	CBcs CHEx CMCN MBlu SAPC SArc SHHo WWHy
pernyi	CMCN CTrG EPfP LRHS SHHo SLon WFar WPic WWHy
- var. *veitchii*	see *I. bioritsensis*
§ *purpurea*	CMCN SPla
'Pyramidalis'	see *I. aquifolium* 'Pyramidalis'
rugosa	CMCN
'September Gem' (f)	CMCN
serrata	CMen
'Sparkleberry' (f)	LRHS
suaveolens	CMCN
verticillata	CMCN CPne IMGH NWea WDin WFar
- (f)	EPfP NLar NWea WFar
- (m)	CBcs CDoC EPfP NLar
- 'Christmas Cheer' (f)	WFar
- 'Jim Dandy' (m)	MBlu
- 'Maryland Beauty' (f)	CPMA MBlu
- 'Southern Gentleman' (m)	CPMA MBlu
- 'Winter Red' (f)	CMCN CPMA EBee MBlu MMHG
vomitoria	CMCN ESbh SHHo
x *wandoensis*	CMCN SHHo WWHy
'Washington' (f)	WWHy
yunnanensis	CMCN SHHo

Iliamna see *Sphaeralcea*

Illicium (Illiciaceae)

anisatum	CArn CBcs CFwr EPfP NLar SBrw SSpi WFar WPGP WSHC
floridanum	CBcs CFwr EBee EPfP NLar SBrw SSpi
I - 'Compactum' **new**	WPGP
- 'Halley's Comet'	NLar
- variegated (v)	SSpi
henryi	CMCN CMHG CPLG EPfP NLar SBrw WPGP WSHC
simonsii BWJ 8024	WCru

Ilysanthes see *Lindernia*

Impatiens ✿ (Balsaminaceae)

from China	CLAP CPom CSpe EMan GCal LSou MCCP MDKP MHar WCMO WCot WPGP
apiculata	GCal MDKP
arguta	CDes CFir CLAP CPLG CPom CSpe EBee EMan EShb GCal LSou MCCP MDKP WCru WDyG WPGP

auricoma	EBak SHFr
auricoma x *bicaudata* **new**	WDib
balfourii	EBee EHrv EMan EMon NBir
congolensis	CCCN EPfP
cristata	CPLG
'Diamond Rose'	CHal
double-flowered (d)	EBak
falcifer	CSpe
forrestii **new**	CLAP
(Harmony Series)	LAst
Harmony Dark Red = 'Danhardkrd'	
- Harmony Lavender	LAst
- Harmony Light Pink = 'Danharltpk'	LAst
- Harmony Orange Blaze = 'Danharoblaze' **new**	LAst
- Harmony Margenta = 'Danharmgta'	LAst LSou
- Harmony Raspberry Cream **new**	LAst
- Harmony Salmon = 'Danharsal'	LAst
hawkeri	see *I. schlechteri*
hians	SHFr
'Kalima' x *pseudoviola* **new**	LSou
x *kaskazini* **new**	EBee
keilii **new**	WDib
kerriae B&SWJ 7219	WCru
kilimanjari x *pseudoviola*	CFee CFir CPLG CSpe GCal MDKP
longiloba B&SWJ 6623	WCru
'Madame Pompadour'	CHal
New Guinea Group	see *I. schlechteri*
niamniamensis	CHll EBak ERea EShb WCot WDib
- 'Congo Cockatoo'	CHEx CHal CHen CTbh EOHP GCal NPer SHFr SPoG SRms
- 'Golden Cockatoo' (v)	CHal CHen EBak EShb MCCP MOak
omeiana	CFir CHEx CLAP CPLG CPom CSpe EBee EMan EPPr EShb GCal ITer LHop MAvo MCCP MNrw SBch SBig WBor WCMO WCot WCru WDyG WLin WPGP WSHC
parasitica **new**	WDib
pseudoviola	SDix SHFr
puberula HWJK 2063	WCru
'Raspberry Ripple'	CHal
§ *schlechteri*	EBak MBri NBlu
'Secret Love'PBR	SHFr
sodenii	CSpe EShb SHFr
stenantha	CFir WCMO
sulcata	SHFr
sultani	see *I. walleriana*
tinctoria	CDoC CFir CHEx CHll CKob CPLG CPom CSpe EDsa EMon EShb GCal MCCP MNrw WCMO WCot WCru WMul WPGP WPrP WWlt
- subsp. *elegantissima*	CFee
- subsp. *tinctoria*	IFro
tuberosa **new**	WDib
ugandensis	CKob
uniflora	CDes CFir CPLG CSpe GCal LHop LSou MCCP MDKP
Velvetea	see *I.* 'Secret Love''
violeta B&SWJ 6608	WCru
walkeri	CFee
§ *walleriana*	EBak MBri
- 'Dapper Dan' (Duet Series) (d/v)	CHal
- (Fiesta Series) 'Burgundy Rose'PBR (d)	LAst

- - Fiesta Appleblossom = 'Balfieplos' (d)	LAst NPri SVil
- - Fiesta Blush = 'Balfieblus' (d)	NPri
- - Fiesta Olé Frost = 'Balolefro' (d)	NPri
- - Fiesta Olé Peppermint = 'Balolepep' (d/v)	SVil
- - Fiesta Olé Rose = 'Balolerose'PBR **new**	NPri
- - Fiesta Olé Salmon = 'Balolesal' (d)	NPri
- - Fiesta Olé Stardust = 'Balolestop' (d)	NPri
- - Fiesta Sparkler Cherry = 'Balfiespary' (d)	NPri
- - Fiesta Stardust Lavender = 'Balfiesala'PBR	LAst
- - 'Fiesta White'PBR (d)	NPri
- - 'Lavender Orchid'PBR (d)	NPri
- - 'Pink Ruffle'PBR (d)	LAst
- - 'Salsa Red' (d)	LAst
- - 'Sparkler Rose'PBR (d)	NPri SVil
- (Tempo Series) 'Meloblue'	LAst
- - 'Meloda'	LAst
- - 'Melody)	LAst
- - 'Shocking Pink)	LAst
- 'Peach Ice' (Summer Ice Series) (d/v)	CHal
* - 'Variegata' (v)	CHal

Imperata (Poaceae)

brevifolia	CBrm
cylindrica	CMen MGol MSal
- 'Red Baron'	see *I. cylindrica* 'Rubra'
§ - 'Rubra'	More than 30 suppliers

Incarvillea (Bignoniaceae)

§ *arguta*	EBee EShb MGol SBla
- var. *longipedicellata* BWJ 7875	WCru
brevipes	see *I. mairei*
compacta	MDKP
- ACE 1455	EBee
- BWJ 7620	WCru
cf. *compacta* **new**	GIBF
delavayi	More than 30 suppliers
- 'Alba'	see *I. delavayi* 'Snowtop'
- 'Bees' Pink'	CAby EBee ECho GBuc GCal GKev SHGN
§ - 'Snowtop'	COlW COtt EBee EChP ECho ECrN ELan ENot EPfP EPot ERou GBuc GKev GMaP LAst MDun MLLN NEgg NJOw NLar NRnb SPer SPet SPla SWvt WBrE WFar WPGP
diffusa	SBla
forrestii	EBee ECho GIBF
- KGB 43	EHyt
grandiflora	EHyt ELan GCrs GIBF SBla
himalayensis 'Frank Ludlow'	GBuc
- 'Nyoto Sama'	GBuc
lutea BWJ 7784	WCru
§ *mairei*	CAby EBee ECho EGoo EHyt EMan GCrs GEdr GKev GSki LHop LRHS MLLN NLar WPer
- var. *mairei*	EPot GBuc GIBF
- - CLD 101	GCrs
- - f. *multifoliata*	see *I. zhongdianensis*
- pink	EHyt

§ **olgae** — CBrm EBee EHyt EMan EShb GIBF GSki MLLN NLar NWCA SHGN
przewalskii — GKev LPhx
sinensis 'Cheron' — CSpe LPhx
§ **zhongdianensis** — EBee EPot ERos GBri GBuc GCal GCrs GEdr GIBF GKev LPhx MDKP MGol NWCA SOkd WAbe
- BWJ 7692 — WCru
- BWJ 7978 — WCru
- CLD 233 — EHyt

Indigofera (*Papilionaceae*)
CC 4536 **new** — MGol
amblyantha ♀H4 — CBcs CHar EBee EPfP GCal IDee IMGH MBlu MBri NLar SBrw SEND SLon SPlb SPoG SSpi WDin WKif WSHC
australis — SOWG
balfouriana BWJ 7851 — WCru
cassioides **new** — WCru
cytisoides — GFai
decora f. **alba** — EPfP IDee MBri
dielsiana — EPfP MWea SBrw WKif WPGP
frutescens — CPLG
gerardiana — see *I. heterantha*
hebepetala — CPLG WCru WDin WPGP WSHC
§ **heterantha** ♀H4 — More than 30 suppliers
- CC 4537 — MGol
kirilowii — EPfP IArd MBri SBrw SOWG WPGP WSHC
pendula — EPfP IDee SBrw SSpi WPGP WSHC
- B&SWJ 7741 — WCru
potaninii — EPfP MGol SHBN
pseudotinctoria — CPLG EGFP EPfP LRav MGol NLar SRms WFar
subverticillata — WPGP
tinctoria — CArn MSal

Indocalamus (*Poaceae*)
latifolius — EBee EPPr EPla ERod LPal MMoz MMuc MWht NLar SEND WJun
- 'Hopei' — EPla
longiauritus — EPla
solidus — see *Bonia solida*
tesselatus f. **hamadae** — EPla ERod MMoz MWht WJun
§ **tessellatus** ♀H4 — CAbb CDoC CHEx CMCo EAmu EBee EFul ENBC EPfP EPla ERod MCCP MMoz MWht NGdn NMoo SMad WDyG WFar WJun WMoo WMul WPGP WPnP

Inula ✿ (*Asteraceae*)
acaulis — NJOw WCot
afghanica **new** — EBee
barbata — MLLN NBre
britannica var. **chinensis** — NBre
candida — XPep
crithmoides — WCFE WHer XPep
dysenterica — see *Pulicaria dysenterica*
ensifolia — CBcs ELan EPfP GBBs MLLN MRav MSte MTho NBro NPri SLPl WCAu WFar WPnP WWpP
- 'Compacta' — ECho
- 'Gold Star' — EAEE EBee ECho EMan EPfP MLLN MNFA MWat NBid NBir NFor NJOw SBla SMer SPet WFar WGwG WMnd WMow WPer
glandulosa — see *I. orientalis*
helenium — More than 30 suppliers
- 'Goliath' — MLLN
helianthus-aquatilis — MLLN
hirta — MLLN NBre SLPl WPer
hookeri — More than 30 suppliers
- GWJ 9033 — WCru

macrocephala misapplied — see *I. royleana*
macrocephala Boiss. & Kotschy ex Boiss. — EBee MLLN
magnifica — More than 30 suppliers
- 'Sonnenstrahl' ♀H4 — LPhx
oculus-christi — EBee EWes MLLN NBre WPtf
- MESE 437 — EPPr
* 'Oriental Star' — GAbr WHil
§ **orientalis** — CKno COlW EBee EChP EPPr EPfP GBBs GIBF IHMH LRHS MBri MNFA MWat NBre NVic SHGN SMad SPet SPoG WBrE WCAu WFar WMnd WPGP WPer WSel WWpP
racemosa — EMon EPla EShb EWes GBin GCal IBlr MGol MNFA MNrw MSte NBid NSti SPlb SRms WFar WTin WWpP
- 'Sonnenspeer' — NBre NLar SLPl WPer WPtf
rhizocephala — CSam ECho MDKP NJOw WPer
§ **royleana** — GBuc GCal GMac MDKP MNrw MRav MSte NBre
salicina — EBee
verbascifolia — ECho

Iochroma (*Solanaceae*)
§ **australe** — CBcs CHEx CHll CKob CPle CSec CSpe EDsa LRav MOak SGar SHFr SOWG WCot
§ - 'Andean Snow' — CHll CPLG EShb MOak
§ - 'Bill Evans' — CPLG
cyaneum — CCCN CDoC CKob CPLG ERea SHFr SOWG SYvo
- purple-flowered — CHll
- 'Trebah' — CKob ERea MOak SYvo
gesnerioides 'Coccineum' — CCCN CHll WCot
§ **grandiflorum** — CCCN CDoC CHEx CHll CKob CSev SGar SOWG SYvo
violaceum hort. — see *I. cyaneum* 'Trebah'
warscewiczii — see *I. grandiflorum*

Ipheion (*Alliaceae*)
'Alberto Castillo' — More than 30 suppliers
dialystemon — CMon CStu ECho EPot NMen SBla SOkd WAbe
'Rolf Fiedler' ♀H2-3 — More than 30 suppliers
sellowianum — CMon CPBP ECho NWCA SCnR WCMO WCot
sessile — CMon SOkd
§ **uniflorum** — CAvo CBro CFFs CMea CStu CTri EBee ECha ECho MBri MNrw MRav MWgw NJOw NMen NWCA SIng SPer SRms WAbb WAul WCot WFar WHoo WPer WPnP WTin
- 'Album' — CBro CPom EAEE EBee ECha ECho ELan EPot ERos EWes LPhx LRHS MAsh MRav MTho SBla SIng WCot WPnP
- 'Charlotte Bishop' — More than 30 suppliers
- 'Froyle Mill' ♀H4 — More than 30 suppliers
- 'Wisley Blue' ♀H4 — More than 30 suppliers

Ipomoea (*Convolvulaceae*)
acuminata — see *I. indica*
alba — CCCN
* **andersonii** — CPIN
batatas 'Ace of Spades' — EUnu
- 'Blackie' — EShb EUnu WFar
- 'Margarita' — EUnu
- 'Pink Frost' (v) — EUnu
brasiliensis — see *I. pes-caprae* subsp. *brasiliensis*
§ **cairica** — CPIN CSec
'Cameo Elegance' (v) **new** — LSou
carnea — CCCN SOWG
costata — CSec

§ *indica* ♀H1 — CCCN CHEx CHal CHll CPlN CTbh EPfP ERea EShb ISea MJnS MPRe SOWG SPer SYvo WMul
- 'Betty Mars' — CPlN
- 'Edith Piaf' — CPlN
- 'Tokiko Kato' new — CPlN
- 'Zarah Leander' — CPlN
involucrata new — CPlN
learii — see *I. indica*
§ *lobata* — CSpe LBMP LRHS LSou SGar SUsu SYvo
microdactyla — CPlN
muellerii — CSec
x *multifida* — CSpe
nil — LRav
ochracea — CSec
§ *pes-caprae* subsp. *brasiliensis* — CSec
purpurea 'Kniola's Purple-black' — CSpe SBch
quamoclit — CSpe
tricolor — CSec WGwG
tuberosa — see *Merremia tuberosa*
versicolor — see *I. lobata*

Ipomopsis (Polemoniaceae)
§ *aggregata* — CSec GKev NPol
rubra — EBee

Iresine (Amaranthaceae)
herbstii — CHal EBak ERea SMur
- 'Aureoreticulata' — CHal
- 'Brilliantissima' — CHal MOak SMrm
lindenii ♀H1 — CHal MOak

Iris ✿ (Iridaceae)
AC 4623 from Tibet — GIBF
AGSJ 431 — EWoo
CLD 1399 — NHol
'Abbey Road' (TB) — WCAu
'About Town' new — EFam
'Abracadabra' (SDB) — SMrm
'Abridged Version' (MTB) — NZep
'Acadian Miss' (La) new — WCAu
'Ace of Clubs' (SDB) — NZep
'Acoma' (TB) — EFam EWoo WCAu
'Action Front' (TB) — EAEE EBee EChP EHrv ERou IPot LAst MWgw NEgg NGdn SCoo SDnm SPla WCra WWeb
'Actress' (TB) — EAEE ECGP EChP LBuc LSRN SPet SPla WCra
'Adobe Rose' (TB) — ESgI
'Adrienne Taylor' (SDB) — WCAu ♀H4
'Affluence' (TB) new — MOak
'After the Storm' (TB) new — ECho EFam
'Afternoon Delight' (TB) — ESgI MRav WCAu
'Agatha Christie' (IB) — WCAu
'Agatha Dawson' (Reticulata/v) — EMon
'Aggressively Forward' (TB) new — WCAu
'Agnes James' (CH) ♀H3 — CBro
'Ahead of Times' (TB) — EFam
'Air Up There' (TB) new — CIri
aitchisonii var. *chrysantha* — GKev
'Albatross' (TB) — CKel
albicans ♀H4 — CMea CMon ECho EPot LEdu WCAu
§ *albomarginata* — WWst
'Alcazar' (TB) — EPfP LSRN NMoo SWat WEas WFar WMnd
'Aldo Ratti' (TB) — ESgI
'Alice Harding' (TB) — ESgI
'Alien Mist' (TB) — EFam WCAu

'Alison Elizabeth' new — WAul
'Alizes' (TB) ♀H4 — ESgI EWoo WAul WCAu
'All American' (TB) new — EFam
'All Lit Up' (TB) new — EFam
'All Right' (IB) — NZep
'All that Jazz' new — EKen
'Allegiance' (TB) — WCAu WEas
'Allendale' (BB) — CIri
'Allison Elizabeth' (BB) ♀H4 new — CIri
'Alpine Journey' (TB) — EFam ESgI
'Alpine Lake' (MDB) — NZep WCAu
'Alpine Twilight' (TB) — EFam
'Alsterquelle' (SDB) — WTin
'Altruist' (TB) — EFam WCAu
'Amadora' (TB) — CKel
'Amain' (TB) new — EFam
'Amas' (TB) — WCAu
'Ambassadeur' (TB) — EBee ERou
'Amber Blaze' (SDB) — NZep
'Amber Queen' (DB) — EAEE EBee ECtt ELan ERos MSte MWat MWgw NBir NEgg NMen SPer SPet SPla SPoG WWeb
'Amber Snow' (TB) new — EFam
'Ambroisie' (TB) — ESgI
'American Patriot' (IB) — WCAu
'America's Cup' (TB) — WCAu
'Amethyst Dancer' new — EFam
'Amethyst Flame' (TB) — EAEE ECho ERou ESgI NBre SRms WCAu
'Amherst' (SDB) new — EFam
'Amherst Blue' (SDB) new — SIri
'Amherst Bluebeard' (SDB) — SIri
'Amherst Caper' (SDB) — WCAu
'Amherst Jester' (BB) new — SIri WAul
'Amherst Moon' (SDB) — SIri WCAu
'Amherst Purple Ribbon' (SDB) — SIri WCAu
'Amherst Sweetheart' (SDB) — SIri WCAu
'Amigo' (TB) — ESgI
'Amphora' (SDB) — CBro ERos GBuc
'Andalou' (TB) — CIri ESgI
'Andy Dandy' (La) — CWrd
'Angel Unawares' (TB) — WCAu
'Angelic' (SDB) — WCAu
'Angelic Wings' (TB) — EFam
'Angel's Tears' — see *I. histrioides* 'Angel's Tears'
anglica — see *I. latifolia*
'Anna Belle Babson' (TB) — ESgI
'Anna Marie' (TB) — EFam
'Annabel Jane' (TB) — CKel COIW WCAu
'Anne Elizabeth' (SDB) — CBro ERos
'Annikins' (IB) ♀H4 — CKel
'Anniversary Celebration' (TB) — CKel
'Antarctique' (IB) — ESgI
'Anthology' (TB) new — EFam
'Antigone' — ESgI
'Anvil of Darkness' (TB) — CIri
'Anxious' (TB) new — EFam
aphylla — GIBF WCAu
- subsp. *fieberi* — WCot
'Apollo's Touch' (IB) — NZep
'Appledore' (SDB) — CBro ERos
'Appointer' (SpecHybrid) — CRow GBin
'Apricorange' (TB) ♀H4 — CKel
'Apricot Drops' (MTB) ♀H4 new — CIri WAul WCAu
'Apricot Silk' (IB) — WCMO
'Apricot Skies' (BB) — NZep
'Arab Chief' (TB) — CKel
'Arabi Pasha' (TB) — WCAu
'Arabian Story' new — EFam
* 'Arabic Night' (IB) — WCAu
'Archie Owen' (Spuria) — WCAu

'Arctic Fancy' (IB) ♀H4   CKel MOak
'Arctic Snow' (TB)   WCAu
'Arctic Wine' (IB)   WCAu
'Arden' (BB)   EFam
arenaria   see *I. humilis*
'Argument' **new**   WWst
'Argus Pheasant' (SDB)   ESgI WCAu
'Arlene's Other Love' **new**   EFam
'Armageddon' (TB)   ESgI
'Arnold Velvet' (SDB)   EFam
'Art Deco' (TB) **new**   SIri
'Art School Angel' (TB)   CIri
'Artful' (SDB) **new**   WCAu
'Artistic Gold' (TB)   EFam
'Artist's Whim' (TB)   EFam
'Ask Alma' (IB)   ESgI NZep WCAu
'Asteroid Zone' (TB) **new**   EFam
'Astrid Cayeux' (TB)   ESgI EWoo
* 'Atlantique' (TB)   CKel
'Attention Please' (TB)   CKel ELan
§ *attica*   CBro CPBP EHyt EPPr EPot ERos LBee LEdu LRHS LTwo NJOw NWCA WAbe WLin
   - lemon   CPBP WThu
§ *aucheri* ♀H2   CBro ECho GKev WWst
   aucheri x *bucharica* **new**   EBrs
'Audacious' (BB)   NZep
'Aunt Corley' (TB) **new**   CIri
'Aunt Josephine' (TB) **new**   ESgI
'Aunt Martha' (BB)   MBri WCAu
'Aurean' (IB)   CKel
'Auroralita' (SDB) **new**   EFam
'Austrian Sky' (SDB)   CSam EAEE EBee MBNS NEgg STes WCAu
'Autumn Apricot' (TB) **new**   EFam
'Autumn Bugler' (TB) **new**   EFam
'Autumn Circus' (TB)   EFam WCAu
'Autumn Clouds' (TB)   EFam
'Autumn Echo' (TB) **new**   EFam
'Autumn Encore' (TB) **new**   WHlf
'Autumn Leaves' (TB)   WCAu
'Autumn Maple' (SDB) **new**   EFam ESgI
'Autumn Mists' (TB)   EFam
'Autumn Orangelite' (TB)   EFam
'Autumn Thunder' (TB) **new**   EFam
'Autumn Tryst' (TB)   EFam WCAu
'Avalon Sunset' (TB)   ESgI
'Avanelle' (IB)   ERou MOak NBre
'Az Ap' (IB)   COlW EBee NZep WCAu
'Aztec Sun' (TB)   SIri
'Babbling Brook' (TB)   SPoG
'Baboon Bottom' (BB)   WCAu
'Baby Bengal' (BB)   WCAu
'Baby Bibs' (MTB)   NZep
'Baby Blessed' (SDB)   CBro EFam NZep SRGP WCAu
'Baby Prince' (SDB)   EFam ESgI
'Baccarat' (TB)   WCAu
'Back in Black' (TB)   CKel
'Back Street Affair' (TB)   CIri
'Bahloo' (TB) **new**   EFam
'Bajazzo' (La) **new**   WCAu
bakeriana   ECho
'Bal Masqué' (TB)   ESgI
baldschuanica   WWst
'Ballerina' (TB)   NBir
'Ballerina Blue' (TB)   ERou
'Ballet Lesson' (SDB) ♀H4   CIri
'Ballyhoo' (TB)   WCAu
'Bamba' (SDB) **new**   EFam
'Banana Cream' **new**   EFam
'Banana Frappe' (TB) **new**   MOak

'Banbury Beauty' (CH) ♀H3   CLAP
'Banbury Melody' (CH)   CFee GMac
'Banbury Ruffles' (SDB)   ESgI NMen WCAu
'Bandera Waltz' (TB)   WCAu
'Bang' (TB)   CKel
'Bangles' (MTB) **new**   CIri WCAu
'Bar de Nuit' (TB)   ESgI
'Barbara's Kiss' (Spuria)   CIri
barbatula BWJ 7663 **new**   WCru
'Barletta' (TB)   WCAu
'Barn Dance' (TB) **new**   EFam
'Baroque Prelude' (TB)   CKel
'Batik' (BB)   WCAu WCMO WCot
'Batsford' (SDB)   CBro
'Bayberry Candle' (TB)   ESgI MWea WCAu
'Be a Devil' (TB) **new**   EFam
'Be Mine' (TB) **new**   EFam
'Be My Baby' (BB) **new**   WCAu
'Beauty Mark' (SDB)   NZep
'Becalmed' (IB) **new**   EFam
'Bedford Lilac' (SDB) ♀H4   CIri NZep
'Bedtime Story' (IB)   EBee GBri SWat
'Bee Wings' (MDB)   WEas
'Bee's Knees' (SDB) ♀H4 **new**   CIri WAul
'Before the Storm' (TB)   CKel ESgI WCAu
'Beguine' (TB)   ESgI
'Being Busy' (SDB)   ESgI
'Bel Azur' (IB)   ESgI
'Bellboy' (MTB)   NZep
'Belvi Cloud' (TB)   EFam
'Belvi Queen' (TB)   EFam MNrw
N 'Benton Arundel' (TB)   ECha
'Benton Dierdre' (TB)   SRms
'Benton Nigel' (TB)   WCAu
N 'Benton Sheila' (TB)   CFee
'Berkeley Gold' (TB)   CMea COtt CSBt EAEE EBee ECtt ELan EPfP EWes EWsh GMac NEgg NOrc NVic SCoo SHBN SPer SWat WCAu WCMO
'Berlin Tiger' ♀H4   CRow EPPr WCAu
'Berry Blush' (TB) **new**   EFam
'Bess Bergin' (TB) **new**   EFam
'Best Bet' (TB)   EFam EWoo WCAu
'Best Man' (TB)   EFam
'Bethany Claire' (TB)   EFam ESgI
'Betty Cooper' (Spuria)   WAul WCAu
'Betty Simon' (TB)   CKel ESgI EWoo
'Beverly Sills' (TB)   ERou ESgI IPot LRHS SRGP WCAu
'Bewilderbeast' (TB)   WCAu
'Bianco' (TB)   WCAu
'Bibury' (SDB) ♀H4   EFam EGle WCAu
'Big Dipper' (TB)   EWoo SIri
'Big Melt' (TB)   CKel
'Big Money' (CH) ♀H3   GBuc
'Big Squeeze' (TB) **new**   CIri
biglumis   see *I. lactea*
biliottii   CBro
'Billionaire' (TB) **new**   EFam
'Bishop's Robe' (TB)   SSvw
N 'Black Beauty' (Dut) **new**   EPfP
'Black Beauty' (TB)   SPer WFar
'Black Flag' (TB)   WCMO
'Black Gamecock' (La)   CBgR CFir CWCL CWrd EPPr NBro NMoo WCAu WMAq
'Black Hills' (TB)   EBee ENot WCAu
'Black Ink' (TB)   COlW
'Black Knight' (TB)   EHol NGdn SMer SPoG
'Black Night' (TB)   SRGP STes
'Black Stallion' (MDB) **new**   ESgI
'Black Suited' (TB) **new**   CIri
'Black Swan' (TB)   CHad COtt EChP ECha ECtt ELan EPfP ESgI EShb LAst LBuc LSRN MSte NBre SDnm SHBN SPer SPla

'Black Taffeta' (TB) | WCAu WCMO WCot WCra WEas WWeb
'Black Tie Affair' (TB) | CKel
'Black Tie Affair' (TB) | ESgI EWoo WCAu
'Black Ware' (TB) **new** | EFam
'Black Watch' (IB) | CKel
'Blackbeard' (BB) ♀H4 | CKel WCAu
'Blackcurrant' (IB) **new** | CIri
'Blackout' (TB) | EFam ESgI
'Blast' (IB) | CKel
'Blatant' (TB) | EFam ESgI WCAu
'Blazing Light' (TB) **new** | ESgI
'Blazing Saddles' (TB) | NZep
'Blenheim Royal' (TB) | ESgI WCAu
'Blessed Again' **new** | EKen
'Blessed Again' (IB) | EFam EKen
'Blessed Assurance' (IB) | EFam
'Blitz' (SDB) | EFam NZep
'Blitzen' (IB) **new** | WCAu
'Blood Covenant' (SDB) | NZep
'Blousy Blouse' **new** | EFam
'Blue Ballerina' (CH) ♀H3 | GBuc
'Blue Crusader' (TB) | WCAu
'Blue Denim' (SDB) | CBro CElw ECho ECtt EGle EHyt EPfP GMaP MBNS MRav NBir NBro NMoo SMrm WCAu WHoo WTin
'Blue Eyed Blond' (IB) | MWea WCAu
'Blue Eyed Brunette' (TB) | WCAu
'Blue Fin' (TB) **new** | EFam WCAu
'Blue For You' **new** | EFam
'Blue Hendred' (SDB) | NBir WCAu
'Blue Horizon' (TB) | ERos
'Blue Lamp' (TB) **new** | CKel
'Blue Line' (SDB) ♀H4 | NBre NZep
'Blue Luster' (TB) ♀H4 | ESgI
'Blue Moonlight' (TB) | EFam
'Blue Mystery' **new** | WWst
'Blue Note Blues' (TB) | WCAu
'Blue Pigmy' (SDB) | ERos LBBr MBNS MWat MWgw NEgg NMen NSti SPer SPet WWeb
'Blue Pools' (SDB) | EGle EHyt MBri MSte NBir NZep WTin
'Blue Reflection' (TB) | ESgI
'Blue Rhythm' (TB) | CKel EAEE EChP EFam ELan EPfP ERou GMaP GMac LPhx MRav MSte NBre NMoo SCoo SPer WAul WCAu WMnd
'Blue Sapphire' (TB) | CHad ESgI SHBN WCAu
'Blue Shimmer' (TB) | COtt CSBt EAEE EBee ECha ELan ENot EPfP ESgI MRav NCGa NGdn SCoo SHBN SPer SPet SPla SPoG SWat WCAu WCra WHil
'Blue Staccato' (TB) | CKel ESgI WCAu
'Blue Suede Shoes' (TB) | ESgI
'Blue Velvet' (TB) | WMoo
'Blue Warlsind' | WWst
'Bluebeard' (TB) | EHyt
'Blueberry Filly' (IB) **new** | CIri
'Bluebird Wine' (TB) | WCAu
'Bob Nichol' (TB) ♀H4 | CKel
'Bodacious' (TB) | EFam ESgI
'Bohemian' (TB) | ESgI
'Boisterous' (BB) | CIri WCAu
'Bold Gold' (TB) **new** | EFam
'Bold Look' (TB) | ESgI
'Bold Pretender' (La) | CWrd
'Bold Print' (IB) | EAEE EBee IPot SPoG WCAu WCra
'Bollinger' | see *I.* 'Hornpipe'
'Bonnie Davenport' (TB) | CIri
'Bonny' (MDB) | CBro
'Bonus Bucks' (TB) **new** | CKel
'Bonus Mama' (TB) **new** | EFam
'Boo' (SDB) | CKel NZep WCAu WDav
'Bourne Graceful' | see *I. japonica* 'Bourne Graceful'
'Bouzy Bouzy' (TB) | ESgI
bracteata | CNic GBuc WPer

– JCA 13427 | CLAP
'Braggadocio' (TB) | WCAu
'Braithwaite' (TB) | CKel EAEE EBee ELan ENot ERou MBnl MSte NBre SHBN SPur SRms SWat WAul WCAu
'Brannigan' (SDB) | CBro MBri NBir NSti
'Brasilia' (TB) | NBir NBre
'Brass Tacks' (SDB) | NZep WCAu
'Brassie' (SDB) | CBro ERos IHMH MBNS NBro NMoo SHGN SMrm
'Brave New World' (TB) **new** | CIri
'Breakers' (TB) ♀H4 | CKel ESgI EWoo WCAu
'Breezy Blue' (SDB) **new** | WCAu
§ 'Bride' (DB) | NBlu WMnd
'Bride's Halo' (TB) | EWoo WCAu
'Brigantino' (BB) | ESgI
'Bright Button' (SDB) | CKel ESgI EWoo
'Bright Chic' (SDB) | ESgI
'Bright Child' (SDB) **new** | WCAu
'Bright Fire' (TB) | EWoo SIri
'Bright Moment' (SDB) | EPPr
'Bright Vision' (SDB) | ESgI NZep
'Bright White' (MDB) | CBro CKel ECho ERos MBNS NMen
N 'Bright Yellow' (DB) | MRav
'Brighteyes' (IB) | SRms
'Brilliant Excuse' (TB) | NZep
'Brindisi' (TB) | ESgI WCAu
'Brise de Mer' (TB) | ESgI
'Broadleigh Angela' **new** | CBro
'Broadleigh Ann' (CH) | CBro
'Broadleigh Carolyn' (CH) | CBro
  ♀H3 |
N 'Broadleigh Charlotte' (CH) | CBro
N 'Broadleigh Clare' (CH) | CBro
'Broadleigh Dorothy' (CH) | CBro GGar
'Broadleigh Elizabeth' (CH) | CBro
N 'Broadleigh Emily' (CH) | CBro
N 'Broadleigh Florence' (CH) | CBro
N 'Broadleigh Jean' (CH) | CBro
'Broadleigh Joan' (CH) | CBro
'Broadleigh Joyce' (CH) | CBro
'Broadleigh Lavinia' (CH) | CBro MRav
'Broadleigh Mitre' (CH) | CBro CElw
'Broadleigh Nancy' (CH) | CBro MAvo
'Broadleigh Peacock' (CH) | CBro CElw CNic IBal MAvo MRav
N 'Broadleigh Rose' (CH) | CBos CBro CElw EHrv EPyc GBuc MAvo MBrN MRav SAga SIri SMrm SWal WLin WSHC
'Broadleigh Sybil' (CH) | CBro GCrs
'Broadleigh Victoria' (CH) | CBro GBuc
'Broadway' (TB) | NZep
'Broadway Baby' (IB) | ESgI
'Broadway Doll' (BB) | EFam
'Brom Bones' (SDB) | EFam
'Bromyard' (SDB) ♀H4 | CBro WCAu
'Bronzaire' (IB) ♀H4 | CKel EFam WCAu
'Bronze Beauty Van Tubergen' (*hoogiana* hybrid) | EPfP GBBs NBir SAga SPer WFar
'Bronzed Aussie' (TB) **new** | CIri
'Brother Carl' (TB) **new** | EFam
N 'Brown Chocolate' (TB) | WCAu
'Brown Duet' (TB) **new** | EFam
'Brown Lasso' (BB) ♀H4 | WCAu
'Brown Trout' (TB) | NBir
N 'Brummit's Mauve' (TB) | WCAu
'Bubbly Mood' (TB) **new** | SCoo
bucharica hort. | see *I. orchioides* Carrière
bucharica ambig. | ECho SUsu WBor WHil
§ *bucharica* Foster ♀H3-4 | CBgR CBro CMdw CPom CSam EBee ECho EPfP EPot EWTr GIBF GKev SUsu WCAu
N – 'Sanglok' | WWst
bucharica x *orchioides* | WWst
  new

'Buckwheat' (TB) **new**   EFam SIri
'Buddy Boy' (SDB) **new**   WCAu
'Bugles and Horns' (TB)   EFam
   new
'Buisson de Roses' (TB)   ESgI
bulleyana   ECho GBBs GBin GCrs GIBF GKev
   MGol NEgg NWCA SRms WAbe
   – ACE 1819   GBin
   – ACE 2296   EBee GBuc
   – black-flowered   CSec EBee GKev
   – – SDR 1792   GKev
   – – SDR 2714   GKev
   aff. *bulleyana*   GBBs
'Bumblebee Deelite'   NZep WCAu
   (MTB)   ♀H4
'Burgundy Brown' (TB)   NZep
'Burgundy Bubbles' (TB)   CIri
'Burgundy Party' (TB)   ESgI
'Burnt Toffee' (TB)   ESgI WAul
'Busy Being Blue' (TB)   EFam
   new
'Butter Pecan' (IB)   WCAu
'Buttercup Bower' (TB)   WCAu
'Buttercup Charm' (MDB)   NZep
'Buttered Popcorn' (TB)   SMer
'Buttermere' (TB)   SRms
'Butterpat' (IB)   EFam ESgI NZep
'Butterscotch Carpet'   WCAu
   (SDB)
'Butterscotch Kiss' (TB)   CSBt EAEE EBee ECGP EChP ELan
   ERou MBNS MRav MTis MWgw
   NBir NEgg SCoo SDnm SHBN SPer
'Button Box' (SDB)   NZep
'Bye Bye Blues' (TB) **new**   EFam
'Cabaret Royale' (TB)   ESgI WCAu
'Cable Car' (TB)   CKel ESgI EWoo
'Cahoots' (SDB) **new**   EFam
'Caliente' (TB)   EKen EPfP MRav WCAu
'California Style' (IB)   ESgI NZep
§ Californian hybrids   CAby CBct CElw CPBP CWCL
   ECGP EPot NBir WBor WCFE
   WCMO WCot WWhi
'Calliope Magic' **new**   EFam
'Calm Stream' (TB)   ♀H4   CKel
   new
'Cambridge Blue'   see *I.* 'Monspur Cambridge Blue'
'Camelot Rose' (TB)   WCAu
'Cameo Blush' (BB)   EFam
'Cameo Wine' (TB) **new**   EFam EPfP
'Cameroun' (TB)   ESgI
'Campbellii'   see *I. lutescens* 'Campbellii'
canadensis   see *I. hookeri*
'Canadian Streaker' (TB)   WCot
   (v) **new**
'Canaveral' (TB) **new**   EFam
'Candy Clouds' (TB)   WCAu
'Candyland' (BB)   EFam
'Candylane' (MTB)   CKel
'Cannington Bluebird' (TB)   WCAu
'Cannington Ochre' (SDB)   CBro
'Cannington Skies' (IB)   EFam
'Cantab' (Reticulata)   CAvo CBro CFFs EBrs EPot GBin
   LHop LPhx
'Cantina' (TB)   EFam
capnoides   WWst
'Capricious' (TB)   ESgI
'Capricorn Cooler' (TB)   EFam
   new
'Captain Gallant' (TB)   WCAu
'Caption' (TB)   ESgI
'Captive' (IB) **new**   EFam
'Caramba' (TB)   WCAu
'Carats' (SDB) **new**   EFam
'Carilla' (SDB)   ERos
'Carnaby' (TB)   ESgI IPot MBri WCAu
'Carnival Song' (TB)   WCAu

'Carnival Time' (TB)   EAEE EBee ECGP EChP EShb IPot
   LAst MBNS NFla SPer WAul WCra
'Carnton' (TB)   WEas
'Carolina Gold' (TB)   MOak
N 'Carolyn' (CH)   CFir
'Carolyn Rose' (MTB)   ♀H4   NBre NZep
'Caronte' (IB)   ESgI
'Carriwitched' (IB)   CKel
'Cascade Sprite' (SDB)   SRms
'Cascadian Skies' (TB)   ERou
'Cast A Spell' **new**   EFam
'Cat's Eye' (SDB) **new**   CIri
cedretii from Lebanon   CMon
   LB 391
N 'Cedric Morris'   EWes WEas
'Cee Jay' (IB)   ♀H4   EWoo
'Celebration Song' (TB)   ESgI WCAu
'Celestial Glory' (TB)   WCAu
'Celestial Happiness' (TB)   EFam
   new
'Celsius' (SDB) **new**   EFam
'Certainly Certainly' (TB)   EFam
chamaeiris   see *I. lutescens*
'Champagne Elegance'   EFam EPyc ESgI NBir WCAu
   (TB)
'Champagne Encore' (IB)   ESgI
'Champagne Frost' (TB)   EFam WCAu
   new
'Champagne Music' (TB)   WCAu
'Champagne Waltz' (TB)   EFam
'Chance Beauty'   WCAu
   (SpecHybrid)   ♀H4
   new
'Change of Pace' (TB)   WCAu
'Chanted' (SDB)   EFam EPPr ESgI WCAu
'Chanteuse' (TB)   SWat
'Chantilly' (TB)   EAEE EBee EChP ELan EPfP MRav
   MTis NBir NEgg NGdn NOrc
   SDnm SPer SWat WFoF
'Chapeau' (TB)   WCAu
'Chapel Bells' (TB) **new**   CKel
'Chartreuse Ruffles' (TB)   EWoo
'Char-true' (Spuria)   WCAu
'Chasing Rainbows' (TB)   WCAu
'Chaste White' (TB)   EFam ESgI
'Chatter' (TB) **new**   EFam
'Cheerful One' (TB) **new**   CIri
'Cheers' (IB)   NZep
N 'Cherished' (TB)   EBee GBin SMer
'Cherokee Lace' (Spuria)   WTin
'Cherry Blossom Special'   CIri
   (TB) **new**
'Cherry Garden' (SDB)   CBro CElw CHad CKel EBee ECtt
   EFam EGoo EHrv EHyt ELan EPfP
   EWes IPot LEdu MBNS MBri MRav
   MTis NBPC NBir NMoo NSti
   NWCA SMrm SRGP WCMO WCot
   WEas
'Cherry Glen' (TB)   CIri
'Cherry Orchard' (TB)   NFor
'Cherry Ripe' (TB)   SGar
'Cherry Smoke' (TB)   WCAu
'Cherub Tears' (SDB)   NZep WCAu
'Cherub's Smile' (TB)   ESgI
'Chickasaw Sue' (BB) **new**   EFam
'Chickee' (MTB)   ♀H4   CKel NZep
'Chicken Little' (MDB)   CBro EBee NMoo
'Chief Moses' (TB)   WCAu
I 'Chieftain' (SDB)   MRav
'China Dragon' (TB)   SWat
'China Seas' (TB) **new**   NBre
'Chinese Empress' (TB)   EFam
   new
'Chivalry' (TB)   WTin
'Chocolate Moose' (TB)   CIri
   new

'Chocolate Vanilla' (TB)		ESgI WCAu
'Chorus Girl' (TB)		CKel
'Christmas Angel' (TB)		ERou WCAu
'Christopher Columbus' (TB) **new**		EFam
chrysographes ♀H4		CPrp CWCL EBee EBrs ENor EPfP GIBF GMac GSki IPot MBnl MCCP MLHP MRav MWrn NBPC NSti SHGN SMac SRms SWal WAul WCAu WCFE WFar WHil WPtf WSan WWeb WWhi
	- *alba*	NBir
I	- 'Black Beauty'	CFir ECho EPfP GBBs
I	- 'Black Knight'	CMdw EPfP EWsh GBuc GCal ITim MDun MHer MSte NBid NChi NFor NLar SHGN SWat WMnd WViv
I	- 'Black Velvet'	GAbr
	- black-flowered	More than 30 suppliers
	- crimson-flowered	IBlr
	- 'Ellenbank Nightshade' **new**	GMac
N	- 'Inshriach'	GBuc IBlr LEdu WAbe
N	- 'Kew Black'	CDes ECho MBnl NBir NChi NEgg NHol NWCA WCMO WHer WHil
	- 'Mandarin Purple'	GBuc GCal GMac SPer SWat WMoo
	- red	ECho
	- 'Rob'	ECho
§	- 'Rubella'	CRow ECho GMac MSte WFar WPrP
	- 'Rubra'	see *I. chrysographes* 'Rubella'
N	- 'Tsiri'	NWCA
	- yellow-flowered **new**	EBrs
chrysographes x *forrestii*		CBow NBir WViv
chrysophylla		GBuc
	- JCA 13233	CLAP
'Chubby Cheeks' (SDB)		CKel WCAu
'Chuck Waltermire' (TB)		EFam
'Church Stoke' (SDB)		WCAu
'Cimarron Rose' (SDB)		EPPr ESgI NZep WCAu
'Cinnabar Red' (Spuria)		WAul
'Cinnamon Apples' (MDB) **new**		ESgI
'Cinnamon Roll' (Spuria)		WCAu
'Cinnamon Stick' (Spuria) **new**		CIri
'Circle Step' (TB)		LBmB
I	'City Lights' (TB)	EFam WCAu
'Clara Garland' (IB) ♀H4		EFam WCAu
'Clarence' (TB)		EFam ESgI WCAu
clarkei		GBin GIBF GQue WFar
	- B&SWJ 2122	WCru
	- CC 4181	MGol
'Class Act' (TB) **new**		EFam
'Classic Bordeaux' (TB)		CIri
'Classic Look' (TB)		ESgI
'Classico' (TB) **new**		EFam
'Clay's Caper' (SDB)		NBre
'Clear Morning Sky' (TB) ♀H4		CIri
N	'Cleo' (TB)	CKel NBir NSti
'Cleo Murrell' (TB)		ESgI
'Cliffs of Dover' (TB)		CKel EFam EKen SGar SIri SRms
N	'Climbing Gold'	ECho
'Close Shave' (TB) **new**		CIri
'Close Your Eyes' (TB) **new**		EFam
'Cloud Fire' **new**		EFam
'Cloud Mistress' (IB)		ESgI
'Cloudcap' (TB)		SRms
'Cloudia' (TB) **new**		EFam
'Cloudless Sunrise' (TB)		ERou
'Clyde Redmond' (La)		WMAq
'Coalignition' (TB)		WCAu

'Codicil' (TB)		ESgI EWoo WCAu
'Colette Thurillet' (TB)		ESgI WCAu
collettii		ECho
'Colonial Gold' (TB)		WCAu
'Color Brite' (BB)		EFam
'Colorific' (La) **new**		EPPr NBro NMoo
'Colorwatch' (TB) **new**		EFam
'Combo' (SDB)		CKel
'Come to Me' (TB) **new**		EFam
'Coming Attraction' (TB) **new**		MOak
'Coming Up Roses' (TB)		WCAu
'Compact Buddy' (MDB) **new**		ESgI
'Concertina' (IB) **new**		CIri
confusa ♀H3		CAbP CAby CHEx CSev EBee EShb GBin IFro SAPC SArc SBig SEND WBrk WCMO WDyG WFar WMul WPic WWst
N	- 'Martyn Rix'	CBct CDes CFwr CHEx CHad CLAP CPou CSev EBee EMan EPfP GCal IGor MHer MTis SChr WCMO WCot WDyG WFar WHrl WMnd WPGP WPer WPic WPrP WSHC
'Conjuration' (TB)		EFam ESgI EWoo WCAu
'Connect The Dots' (MTB) **new**		WCAu
'Conspiracy' (TB)		CIri
'Constant Wattez' (IB)		CKel EBee ESgI NLar
'Consummation' (MTB)		NZep
'Cool Treat' (BB) ♀H4		CIri
'Copatonic' (TB)		CIri WCAu
'Copper Classic' (TB)		ESgI NZep WCAu
'Cops' (SDB)		ESgI NZep
'Coquetterie' (TB)		ESgI
'Coral Chalice' (TB)		EFam ERou
'Coral Charmer' (TB) **new**		EFam
'Coral Joy' (TB)		EFam
'Coral Point' (TB)		EFam WCAu
'Coral Strand' (TB)		WCAu
'Coral Wings' (SDB)		NZep
'Cordoba' (TB)		WCAu
'Corn Harvest' (TB)		EFam NZep
'Corps de Ballet' (TB) **new**		CIri
'County Town Red' (TB) **new**		CIri
'Court Magician' (SDB) **new**		SIri
'Cozy Calico' (TB)		ESgI WCAu
'Cradle Days' (MDB)		EBee
'Cranapple' (BB) ♀H4		WCAu
'Cranberry Crush' (TB)		WCAu
'Cranberry Ice' (TB)		EWoo
'Cranberry Sauce' (TB) **new**		CIri
'Cream and Peaches' (SDB) **new**		SIri
'Cream Beauty' (Dut)		SPer
'Cream Cake' (SDB)		NZep
'Cream Pixie' (SDB)		WCAu
'Creative Stitchery' (TB)		EFam
'Creme d'Or' (TB)		EFam ESgI
'Crème Glacée' (TB)		ESgI
cretensis		see *I. unguicularis* subsp. *cretensis*
'Cricket Lane' (SDB)		NZep
'Crimson Tiger' (TB)		EFam
'Crinoline' (TB)		CKel
'Crispette' (TB)		WCAu
cristata ♀H4		CPBP GBuc LEdu NLar NPro SIng SRms WCru
	- 'Alba'	ERos GCal LRHS NWCA WAbe
cristata x *lacustris*		CSec ETow GKev NMen
crocea ♀H4		CPLG GBin MGol
'Croftway Lemon' (TB)		COIW

'Cross Current' (TB) **new**	WCAu
'Cross Stitch' (TB)	EFam NZep
'Crowned Heads' (TB)	CKel WCAu
'Crushed Velvet' (TB)	WCAu
'Crystal Glitters' (TB)	ESgI
cuniculiformis	MGol
– ACE 2224	EHyt GBuc
'Cup Cake' (MDB) **new**	ESgI
'Cup Race' (TB)	WCAu
'Cupid's Cup' (SDB)	ESgI
'Curlew' (IB)	WCAu
'Curtain Up' (TB)	EFam
'Cute Orange Horn' (TB) **new**	EFam
'Cutie' (IB)	ESgI NZep WAul WCAu
'Cyanea' (DB)	ECho EFam
cycloglossa	ECho EPot LEdu LRHS WWst
'Daffodil Cloud' **new**	EFam
'Dance Away' (TB)	ESgI WCAu
'Dance for Joy' (TB) **new**	EFam
'Dancer's Veil' (TB)	CHar ECtt ERou ESgI MRav NBre NVic SMer WCAu
'Dancin'' (IB)	NZep
'Dancing Gold' (MTB)	NZep
'Dandy Candy' (TB) **new**	CIri
danfordiae	CAvo CBcs CBro CFFs EBrs ECho EPfP EPot GKev LRHS SPet WCMO WFar WGwG WLin
'Danger' (TB)	ESgI
'Dante's Inferno' (TB) **new**	EFam
'Dardanus' (AB)	CFwr CMea EBee ECho EPot LEdu
'Dark Avenger' (SDB) **new**	CIri
'Dark Blizzard' (IB)	NZep
'Dark Crystal' (SDB)	EFam ESgI
'Dark Rosaleen' (TB) ♀H4	NBre
'Dark Spark' (SDB)	WCAu
'Dark Twilight' **new**	EFam
'Dark Vader' (SDB)	ESgI WCAu
'Darkling' (SDB) **new**	EFam
'Dash Away' (SDB)	ESgI SIri
'Dashing' (TB) **new**	EFam
'Daughter of Stars' (TB) **new**	CIri
'Dauntless' (TB)	ESgI
'David Guest' (IB)	CKel
'Dawn of Fall' (TB) **new**	EFam
'Dawning' (TB)	ESgI
'Dazzle Me' (SDB) **new**	WCAu
'Dazzling Gold' (TB)	ESgI WCAu
'Death by Chocolate' (SDB) **new**	CIri
§ *decora*	GIBF LEdu NWCA WCot
'Deep Black' (TB)	CKel EBee EChP EHrv ELan EPfP MBNS MRav MSte MWgw NOrc SDnm SHBN SWat WAul WCAu
'Deep Caress' (TB)	ESgI
'Deep Dark Secret' (TB)	CIri
'Deep Pacific' (TB)	MBri WCAu
'Deep Purple' (TB)	LAst
'Deep Space' (TB)	WCAu
'Deft Touch' (TB)	CKel WCAu
'Deity' (TB) **new**	EFam
delavayi ♀H4	CAby ECho EWes GBin GIBF GMaP IBlr MLLN NEgg NLAp
– SDR 50	GKev
N – 'Didcot' **new**	EBrs
'Delicate Lady' (IB) ♀H4	CKel
'Delta Blues' (TB)	EWoo
'Delta Butterfly' (La)	WMAq
'Demon' (SDB)	CKel CMil SMrm
'Denys Humphry' (TB)	CKel WCAu
'Deputé Nomblot' (TB)	ESgI
'Derwentwater' (TB)	SRms WCAu
'Desert Country' (SDB) **new**	EFam
'Desert Dream' ambig.	GAbr GGar
'Desert Song' (TB)	CKel EFam WCAu
'Designer Gown' (TB)	ERou
'Destry Rides Again' (TB) **new**	EFam
'Devil May Care' (IB) **new**	CIri
'Devilry' (SDB)	EHyt
'Diabolique' (TB)	CIri
'Diamond Doll' (BB) **new**	EFam
'Diligence' (SDB) ♀H4	CKel
'Distant Roads' (TB)	WCAu
'Ditto' (MDB)	EFam
'Dixie Darling' (TB)	ESgI
'Dixie Pixie' (SDB)	EGle WCAu WTin
'Doctor No' (TB) **new**	EFam
'Dolce Acqua' (TB) **new**	CIri
'Doll' (IB)	EWoo
'Dolly Madison' (TB)	ESgI
'Don Juan' (TB)	ESgI
'Donegal' (IB) **new**	EFam
'Don't Be Cruel' (TB)	CIri
'Doodads' (TB) **new**	WCAu
'Doodle Strudel' **new**	EFam
'Doozey' (MDB) **new**	ESgI
'Dorcas Lives Again' (TB)	EFam
'Double Byte' (SDB) **new**	EFam
'Double Espoir' (TB)	ESgI
'Double Lament' (SDB)	CBro ERos
'Double Time' (TB)	EFam
douglasiana ♀H4	EChP ECho EShb GBin GKev MLLN NEgg NWCA SMac WFar WTin
– 'Amiguita' (CH)	CFir EBee
'Dovedale' (TB) ♀H4	EFam WCAu
'Dover Beach' (TB)	SGar
'Draco' (TB)	ESgI
'Drama Queen' (TB) **new**	CIri
'Dream Indigo' (IB)	CKel WCAu
'Dreamsicle' (TB)	SIri
'Dresden Candleglow' (IB)	WCAu
'Dress Circle' (Spuria)	CIri
'Drum Song' (IB) **new**	EFam
'Dude Ranch' (TB) **new**	CIri
'Duke of Earl' (TB)	EFam
'Dunlin' (MDB)	CBro EHyt ERos NBir NMen
'Dural White Butterfly' (La) **new**	LAst NCGa
'Dusky Challenger' (TB)	ESgI EWoo SCoo WCAu
'Dutch Chocolate' (TB)	ESgI WCAu
'Dwight Enys' (TB) ♀H4	CKel
dykesii	CRow
'Dynamite' (TB)	CIri
'Eagle Control' (TB) **new**	EFam
'Earl of Essex' (TB)	EFam WCAu
'Early Frost' (IB)	CKel EPPr WAul
'Early Light' (TB) ♀H4	WCAu
'Earthborn' (TB) **new**	CIri
'Earthborne' (TB) **new**	EFam
'East Indies' (TB)	WCAu
'Easter Tide' (La) **new**	WCAu
'Eastertime' (TB)	ESgI
'Echo Beach' (TB) **new**	EFam
'Echo de France' (TB)	ESgI EWoo
'Ecstatic Echo' (TB)	ESgI
'Ecstatic Night' (TB)	WCAu
'Edge of Winter' (TB)	CKel SIri
'Edith Wolford' (TB)	EBee ESgI EWoo GBin MWea SRGP WCAu WCMO WCra WSan
N 'Ed's Blue' (DB)	ELan
'Edward' (Reticulata)	CBro ECho EPfP EPot GKev WCAu WFar
'Edward of Windsor' (TB)	CBos CHad CMil EAEE ELan ERou GMaP NBir NLar NOrc SDnm SRGP WCAu WMnd
'Eggnog' (TB) **new**	EFam
'Eileen Louise' (TB) ♀H4	EFam WCAu
'Elainealope' (TB)	EFam

'Eleanor Clare' (IB) ♀H4 CKel
'Eleanor Hill' (Spuria) **new** WAul
'Eleanor's Pride' (TB) CKel EFam ESgl EWTr WCAu
'Electrique' (TB) WCAu
elegantissima see *I. iberica* subsp. *elegantissima*
'Elizabeth Arden' (TB) CKel
'Elizabeth of England' CWCL GKev LBmB SRGP WHlf
  (TB)
'Elizabeth Poldark' (TB) ESgl WCAu
'Ellenbank Damselfly' **new** GMac
'Ellenbank Sapphire' **new** GMac
'Elsa Sass' (TB) ESgl
N - 'Elvinhall' CBro
'Emmanuel' (TB) **new** EFam
'Empress of India' (TB) EBee EWTr
'Enchanted Gold' (SDB) NZep
'Encircle' (CH) GBuc
'Encre Bleue' (IB) ESgl
'English Charm' (TB) EFam ESgl WCAu
'English Cottage' (TB) COIW EBee EFam GCal MWat
  NLar WCAu WCra WIvy
'English Knight' (TB) EFam
'Ennerdale' (TB) SRms
'Ennoble' (TB) **new** CIri
§ *ensata* ♀H4 More than 30 suppliers
- 'Ack-Countable' CIri
N - 'Activity' CRow CSBt GSki NBro NGby SHar
  WFar WPrP WSan
- 'Alba' ECha MWat
- 'Aldridge Prelude' WAul
- 'Alpine Majesty' **new** CIri
- 'Aoigata' CPrp
- 'Apollo' CBen CRow
- 'Artist' NBro
* - 'Asahi-no-sora' LBmB
- 'August Emperor' **new** CBgR NBhm
- 'Azuma-kagami' CBgR CFir CWrd EBee ELan NCGa
I - 'Azure' CWrd
- 'Barr Purple East' ♀H4 CPrp CRow
- 'Beni-tsubaki' WAul
I - 'Blue King' GSki MBlu NBro
I - 'Blue Peter' CBen CRow
- 'Blue Prince' **new** CBen
N - 'Blush' NBro
- 'Butterflies in Flight' CRow
- 'Caprician Butterfly' ♀H4 CMHG EPfP GSki NBhm NLar
  NMoo SMrm WAul WCAu WSan
N - 'Carnival Prince' CFir NBro SBod WFar WMoo WPnP
- 'Cascade Crest' WAul
- 'Cascade Spice' WAul
- 'Center of Interest' NCGa
  new
- 'Chico Geisho' WAul
- 'Chiyodajō' CKel
- 'Crepe Paper' WFar
N - 'Cry of Rejoice' EBee ECho EWTr GBri NBhm
  NBre NBro SWat WAul WCAu WFar
- 'Crystal Halo' CIri
- 'Dace' CWrd EBee
- 'Dancing Waves' CRow WCMO
I - 'Darling' CPen CRow CSam EBee ECho
  EPfP GSki IBlr MBNS MLHP NBro
  NLar SRGP WAul WCAu WFar
  WMoo WPnP WTMC
- 'Dramatic Moment' CWrd GBuc WCMO WFar
I - 'Dresden China' CRow
N - 'Eden's Blue Pearl' CMMP EBee EChP EGle GBin IPot
  NBro
N - 'Eden's Blush' EBee MLHP WAul WSan
N - 'Eden's Charm' CAby EChP EGle ELan GBin NBro
  NHol SPet SVil WAul WHil WWye
N - 'Eden's Delight' NHol
N - 'Eden's Harmony' EBee EChP NBro WAul WSan
  WTMC
N - 'Eden's Paintbrush' CMil EBee EChP EGle ELan EPfP
  NBro SVil WHil WTMC

N - 'Eden's Picasso' CFir EBee EGle ELan EPfP IPot
  NBro NGdn SVil WHil WSan
  WTMC
N - 'Eden's Purple Glory' EChP EGle GBin NBro WCot WTin
N - 'Eden's Starship' CFir EBee WSan
- 'Electric Rays' CWrd WAul
I - 'Emotion' EBee EWTr NBro NGby WAul WFar
  WPnP
- 'Enkaishu' CWrd
I - 'Fortune' EHrv GBin WAul
- 'Fractal Blue' **new** CIri
- 'Freckled Geisha' CIri
- 'Frilled Enchantment' WAul
- 'Geisha Gown' SWal
- 'Gei-sho-mi' CPrp
N - 'Gipsy' CSpe EBee WAul
- 'Good Omen' CWrd
N - 'Gracieuse' CBgR CPen CPrp CSev EBee EGle
  ELan GBin MBri NBPC NBro NLar
  SUsu SWat WAul WFar WHil WMoo
  WPnP
- 'Gusto' CPen EPfP IPot LDai NBhm NBro
  NMoo WHil WSan
- 'Hana-aoi' IBlr
- 'Happy Awakening' GSki
- 'Haru-no-umi' CKel
- 'Hatsu-shimo' IBlr
- 'Hegira' **new** CIri WAul
- 'Hercule' CHad CPrp CRow EGle GAbr NBir
  WTMC
- Higo hybrids IBlr LPBA
- Higo white SPer
- 'Himatsuri' **new** SPoG
N - 'Hokkaido' CBen CRow IBlr
- 'Hue and Cry' ♀H4 WAul
* - 'Innocence' CKel CWrd EHrv NBre NGby NLar
  SWat WAul WAul WFar WHil
- 'Iso-no-nami' EBee EWll MBlu NBro WAul WPrP
  WTMC
- 'Jitsugetsu' **new** CFir NMoo SPoG
N - 'Jodlesong' EBee WFar
- 'Kalamazoo' WFar
- 'Katy Mendez' ♀H4 WAul
- 'Kiyo-tsura' **new** CKel
N - 'Kogesho' EBee EPfP EWTr GBuc NBro NLar
  NMoo WAul
- 'Koh Dom' SPer
- 'Kongo San' CWrd WFar
- 'Kuma-funjin' CRow IBlr
- 'Kumo-no-obi' CPrp EBee LRHS NBro SWat WAul
  WCAu
N - 'Laced' SPer
- 'Landscape at Dawn' CRow
- 'Lasting Pleasure' ♀H4 CWrd
N - 'Laughing Lion' CPen CRez EBee EBla NBro NOrc
  WAul WFar WMoo WPnP
- 'L'Ideal' CPen
- 'Light at Dawn' CPen EGle EPfP LDai NBPC NBhm
  NBro NLar SPoG WAul WFar WMoo
  WSan
N - 'Lilac Blotch' SPer
- 'Lorenzaccio' **new** CIri
- 'Loyalty' CWrd EBla ECho SRGP WFar
- 'Manadzuru' IBlr
- 'Mancunian' ♀H4 CKel
I - 'Mandarin' CBen CRow
- 'Midnight Stars' WAul
- 'Midnight Whispers' WAul
- 'Midsummer Reverie' CRow
N - 'Momozomo' CWrd LTwo NBhm NLar SPoG
§ - 'Moonlight Waves' CHad CMHG CPrp CRow EBla
  EGle ELan EMFW EPPr EPfP EShb
  EWll GBuc GGar GMaP GMac
  MBri MSte NBro NEgg NGdn SPla
  SVil SWat WAul WCAu WCMO
  WFar WTMC

'Ferrous Fantasy' (TB) **new** CIri
'Festive Skirt' (TB) CKel WCAu
'Feu du Ciel' (TB) ♀H4 ESgI
'Fierce Fire' (IB) ♀H4 CKel
'Fiesta Time' (TB) EWoo
filifolia CMon
- var. *latifolia* SF 332 CMon
  from Morocco
- - MS 437 from Spain CMon
'Film Festival' (TB) ESgI
N 'Fire and Flame' (TB) NBir
'Firebug' (IB) ESgI
'Firecracker' (TB) ERou MRav WCAu
'Fireside Glow' (TB) **new** EFam
'First Interstate' (TB) ESgI WCAu
'First Romance' (SDB) **new** SIri
'First Step' (SDB) NZep
'First Violet' (TB) WCAu
'Flaming Victory' (TB) **new** ESgI
'Flapjack' (SDB) NZep
'Flareup' (TB) WCAu
'Flashing Beacon' (MTB) NZep
flavescens ESgI WCAu
'Flavours' (BB) **new** WCAu
'Flea Circus' (MDB) NZep
'Fleur Collette Louise' (La) CIri
  new
'Flight to Mars' (TB) **new** CIri
'Flirting' (SDB) **new** EFam
'Flirty Mary' (SDB) EGle
'Floorshow' (TB) **new** EFam
§ 'Florentina' (IB/TB) ♀H4 CArn CBro CHby COlW EGoo ESgI
  EWoo GPoy ILis MHer MNHC
  MRav NBid NBir SIde WCAu WPic
  WWye
'Flower Shower' (SDB) EFam
'Flumadiddle' (IB) CBro CKel
§ *foetidissima* ♀H4 More than 30 suppliers
- 'Aurea' WCot
- *chinensis* see *I. foetidissima* var. *citrina*
§ - var. *citrina* CBre CFir CRow EGle EPla GAbr
  GCal GSki IBlr MRav SChr SUsu
  WCot WEas WHoo WWye
- 'Fructu Albo' EBee EChP GSki MBNS NLar WBrk
  WCot WTin
- var. *lutescens* EPPr IBlr
N - 'Moonshy Seedling' CSWP EGol
- 'Variegata' (v) ♀H4 CElw CHar CRow ECtt EGle EHrv
  EPfP GMaP MCCP MRav NBir
  NCob NLar NPer SBch WCAu
  WCMO WCot WHil WMnd WWhi
- yellow-seeded WCot WTin
'Fogbound' (TB) **new** CIri
'Fondation Van Gogh' (TB) ESgI
'Foolish Fancy' (TB) **new** SIri
'For Mary' (TB) **new** CIri
'Forest Light' (SDB) CBro ESgI
'Forever Gold' (TB) **new** EFam
'Forever Yours' (TB) EFam
'Forge Fire' (TB) ESgI
formosana CMon ECho
- B&SWJ 3076 WCru WPrP
forrestii ♀H4 More than 30 suppliers
'Fort Apache' (TB) ESgI EWes EWoo
'Fortunata' (TB) **new** EFam
fosteriana NWCA WWst
'Foxy Lady' (TB) EFam ESgI
'Frank Elder' (Reticulata) CBro CMea ECho EHyt EPot ERos
  GKev LRHS MRav MTho NMen
  WCAu WCot
'Frans Hals' (Dut) MMHG MNrw
'French Rose' (TB) CKel
'Fresh Image' (IB) **new** WCAu
'Fresh Start' (SDB) **new** WAul
'Fresno Calypso' (TB) ESgI WCAu
'Fringe Benefits' (TB) WCAu

'Frison-roche' (TB) ESgI
'Fritillary Flight' (IB) ♀H4 CKel
'Frivolité' (TB) ESgI
'Frontier Marshall' (TB) NMoo
'Frost and Flame' (TB) EAEE EChP ECtt ELan ENot EPfP
  ERou EWll MBri MRav MSte NEgg
  NGdn NLar NOrc SHBN SPer SPla
  SWat WCra
'Frosted Velvet' (MTB) CIri EFam WCAu
'Frosty Jewels' (TB) ESgI
'Full Impact' (TB) **new** CIri
fulva CDes CPom CRow EBee GCal GSki
  IBlr NBir NBro NSti WCMO WCot
  WLin WTin
- 'Marvell Gold' (La) CRow
x *fulvala* ♀H4 CAby CDes CFir CPom EBee EMon
  EPPr EWes GBin IBlr NBir NSti
- 'Violacea' EBee EBrs WCot
'Furnaceman' (SDB) CBro ERos MBri
'Fuzzy' (MDB) ERos
'Gala Gown' (TB) WCAu
'Gallant Moment' (TB) SIri
'Galleon Gold' (SDB) CKel NZep
'Galway' (IB) **new** SIri
'Garden Bride' **new** EFam
'Garden Grace' (TB) **new** EFam
'G'day Mate' (TB) **new** EFam
N 'Gelbe Mantel' (Sino-Sib) CLAP EBee EChP NBir NBro NGdn
  NHol NSti WFar
'Gemstar' (SDB) WCAu
'Gentius' (TB) WMnd
'Gentle' (SDB) **new** WCAu
'Gentle Grace' (SDB) ESgI
'George' (Reticulata) ♀H4 CAvo CBro CFFs EBrs ECho EPot
  ERos GAbr GCrs GKev LHop LRHS
  MMHG MSte WHoo
'Gerald Darby' see *I. x robusta* 'Gerald Darby'
germanica ♀H4 EHol LEdu NFor WCAu
- 'Firebreather' **new** ERou
- var. *florentina* see *I.* 'Florentina'
N - 'Mel Jope' NBir
- 'Nepalensis' EGoo
N - 'The King' WCAu
'Ghost Train' (TB) **new** CIri
'Gibson Girl' (TB) EFam WCAu
'Gilded' (TB) **new** EFam
'Ginger Swirl' (TB) EFam
'Gingerbread Castle' (TB) WCAu
'Gingerbread Man' (SDB) CBro CHad CMea EGle EHrv EHyt
  ERos ESgI MBrN MWea NMen
  SMrm SWal WCAu WHoo WIvy
  WLin
'Gipsy Beauty' (Dut) EBrs MSph SPer
'Glacier' (TB) ECho
'Glacier King' (TB) EFam
'Glad Rags' (TB) ESgI NZep
'Glam' (IB) **new** EFam WCAu
'Glorious Day' (IB) **new** EFam
'Glowing Seraphin' (TB) EFam
  new
'Glowing Smile' (TB) **new** CIri
'Gnu Rayz' (IB) **new** CIri
'Gnus Flash' (TB) WCAu
'Go Between' (TB) WCAu
'Godfrey Owen' (TB) CKel WCAu
'God's Handiwork' (TB) EFam
  new
'Godsend' (TB) CKel EFam WCAu
'Going My Way' (TB) ESgI EWoo SIri STes WCAu
'Gold Burst' (TB) EFam
'Gold Country' (TB) EFam ESgI
'Gold Galore' (TB) EFam
'Gold Mania' (Spuria) CIri
'Gold of Autumn' (TB) CKel SMrm
'Gold Reprise' (TB) **new** EFam
'Goldberry' (IB) WCAu

'Golden Alien' (TB) **new**	CIri	
'Golden Alps' (TB)	SRms WCAu	
'Golden Child' (SDB)	EFam ESgI	
'Golden Ecstasy' (TB) **new**	EFam	
'Golden Encore' (TB)	CKel EFam WCAu	
'Golden Fair' (SDB)	NBir	
'Golden Forest' (TB)	WCAu	
'Golden Inmortal' (TB)	EFam	
'Golden Muffin' (IB)	NZep	
'Golden Panther' (TB) **new**	CIri	
'Golden Planet' (TB)	CKel	
'Golden Ruby' (SDB)	NBre	
N 'Golden Surprise' (TB)	EBee	
'Golden Violet' (SDB)	ESgI	
'Goldkist' (TB) **new**	CIri	
'Gondolier' (TB)	LBmB	
goniocarpa	NLAp	
- var. *grossa*	NLAp	
'Good Fairy' (TB) **new**	EFam	
'Good Looking' (TB)	WCAu	
'Good Show' (TB)	EWoo WCAu	
'Good Vibrations' (TB)	SIri	
'Goodbye Heart' (TB)	ESgI	
'Gordon' (Reticulata)	CSam ECho EPot GKev LRHS WFar	
gormanii	see *I. tenax*	
'Gossip' (SDB)	CBro ESgI	
'Gothic' (TB) **new**	EFam	
gracilipes x *lacustris*	GEdr WAbe	
graeberiana	EBee ECho EPot GKev WWst	
- white fall	LRHS WWst	
- yellow fall	LRHS WWst	
graminea ♀H4	More than 30 suppliers	
- 'Hort's Variety'	GCal	
- var. *pseudocyperus*	CRow NSti SDys	
graminifolia	see *I. kerneriana*	
'Granada Gold' (TB)	ENot SRms	
'Grand Baroque' (TB)	EFam	
'Grape Adventure' (TB) **new**	EFam	
'Grape Jelly' (TB) **new**	WCAu	
'Grape Reprise' (TB)	EFam	
'Grapelet' (MDB)	ERos NZep WCAu	
'Grapeshot' (TB)	CIri	
'Grapesicle' (SDB)	NZep	
'Great Gatsby' (TB) **new**	CKel EFam	
'Great Lakes' (TB)	ESgI	
'Grecian Goddess' (TB)	EFam	
'Grecian Skies' (TB)	ESgI	
'Green and Gifted' (TB)	CIri EFam	
'Green Halo' (DB)	EGle	
'Green Prophecy' (TB)	CIri CKel	
'Green Spot' (SDB) ♀H4	CBro CKel EBee ECtt EHrv EHyt	
	ELan EPfP EWTr GBuc MWat NBir	
	NCob NEgg NHol NLar NMen	
	NWCA SBla SPer SPet WCAu WCFE	
	WEas	
'Green Streak' (TB)	CIri	
'Gringo' (TB)	WCAu	
'Gypsy Boy' (SDB)	NZep	
'Gypsy Jewels' (TB)	CKel ESgI	
'Gypsy Romance' (TB) ♀H4	ESgI WCAu	
'Habit' (TB) **new**	CIri WCAu	
'Hagar's Helmet' (IB)	EFam	
N 'Haizon Bleu'	EWoo	
'Halloween Pumpkin' (TB) **new**	EFam	
'Halo in Pink' (TB)	EFam	
halophila	see *I. spuria* subsp. *halophila*	
'Hand Painted' (TB)	EFam	
'Handshake' (TB)	CIri	
'Happening' (SDB)	NZep	
'Happy Birthday' (TB)	ESgI	
N 'Happy Border' (BB)	EFam	
'Happy Mood' (IB) ♀H4	EFam NBre WCAu	
'Happy Pal' (TB)	EFam	

'Harbor Blue' (TB)	EBee MWat WCAu	
'Harlequinade' (BB)	EFam	
'Harlow Gold' (IB)	ESgI NZep	
'Harmony' (Reticulata)	CAvo CBro CFFs EBrs ECho EPfP	
	EPot GBBs LRHS MBri SPer SPet	
	WFar	
'Harriette Halloway' (TB)	CMil CPen EAEE EBee EShb LSRN	
	MBNS NLar SMrm SPet SRGP	
hartwegii	ECho WLin	
'Harvest King' (TB)	ESgI	
'Harvest of Memories' (TB)	EFam ESgI	
'Haute Couture' (TB) **new**	WCAu	
'Haviland' (TB)	SIri	
'Hawaiian Halo' (TB) **new**	EFam	
'Hazelnut Delight' (TB) **new**	CIri	
'Headcorn' (MTB) ♀H4 **new**	CIri WAul	
'Headlines' (TB)	WCAu	
'Heather Carpet' (SDB)	WCAu	
'Heather Sky' (TB) **new**	CIri	
'Heavenly Days' (TB)	WCAu	
'Heaven's Bounty' (BB)	EFam	
'Helen Boehm' (TB)	ESgI	
'Helen Collingwood' (TB)	ESgI	
'Helen K. Armstrong' **new**	EFam	
'Helen McGregor' (TB)	ESgI	
'Helen Proctor' (IB)	ESgI NZep WCAu	
'Helen Traubel' (TB)	WCAu	
'Helge' (IB)	COIW ECho EPfP NBre SWat	
'Hellcat' (IB)	NZep WAul WCAu	
'Hello Darkness' (TB) ♀H4	ESgI WCAu	
'Hemstitched' (TB) **new**	EFam	
'Here's Heaven' (TB) **new**	EFam	
'Heure Bleue' (TB)	EWoo	
'Hickory Leaves' (Spuria) **new**	CIri	
'High Barbaree' (TB)	WCAu	
'High Blue Sky' (TB)	WCAu	
'High Command' (TB)	CKel EFam	
'High Energy' (TB)	EFam	
'High Ho Silver' **new**	EFam	
'High Roller' (TB) **new**	CIri	
'High Waters' (TB) **new**	EFam	
'Highland Games' (TB) **new**	CIri	
'Highline Amethyst' (Spuria) **new**	WAul	
'Highline Halo' (Spuria)	WCAu	
'Hindenburg' (TB)	EFam	
'Hindu Magic' (TB)	WCAu	
hippolyti **new**	WWst	
'Hissy-Fit' (IB) **new**	CKel	
histrio	EHyt	
- subsp. *aintabensis*	ECho EHyt EPot	
histrioides	ECho WAbe	
§ - 'Angel's Tears'	ECho ERos NMen	
- 'Lady Beatrix Stanley'	ECho NMen	
N - 'Major'	CDes	
N - 'Michael Tears'	WWst	
- 'Reine Immaculée'	ERos	
'Hocus Pocus' (SDB)	EHyt EPPr EWoo WAul	
'Holden Clough' (SpecHybrid) ♀H4	More than 30 suppliers	
x *hollandica* **new**	EBrs	
'Hollywood Blonde' (TB)	EFam	
'Holy Fire' (TB) **new**	CIri	
'Holy Night' (TB)	CKel	
'Honey Glazed' (IB)	ESgI MOak NZep WAul WCAu	
'Honey Scoop' (TB)	EFam	
'Honeyplic' (IB) ♀H4	SIri WAul WCAu	
'Honington' (SDB)	EFam WCAu	
'Honky Tonk Blues' (TB)	CKel ESgI	
'Honorabile' (MTB)	WCAu	
hoogiana ♀H3	EBrs ECho EPot GKev LRHS	
N - 'Gypsy Beauty'	WFar	

	– 'Purpurea'	LRHS
§	*hookeri*	CSam CStu ELan GBBs GEdr GIBF GKev IGor NJOw WAbe
	– Brown 0233	CStu
	hookeriana	WLin
§	'Hornpipe' (TB)	WCAu
	'Hot Fudge' (IB)	EPPr
	'Hot Gossip' (TB) **new**	WCAu
	'Hot Jazz' (SDB)	WCAu
	'Hot Spice' (IB)	WCAu
	'Hotseat' (SDB) **new**	EFam
	'Howard Weed' (TB)	EBee
	'Howdy Do' (TB)	EFam
	'Hugh Miller' (TB)	WCAu
	'Hula Doll' (MDB)	EGle NMen
	'Hula Honey' (TB)	EFam
§	*humilis*	CGra
	'Hurricane Lamp' (TB) **new**	MOak
	hyrcana	ECho EHyt
	'I Bless' (IB)	EFam
	'I Do' (TB)	EFam NZep
	'I Seek You' (TB)	ESgI
§	*iberica*	ECho
	– subsp. *elegantissima*	CMea EHyt
	– subsp. *iberica*	WWst
§	– subsp. *lycotis*	EHyt
	'Ice Dancer' (TB) ♀H4	CKel
	'Ice Wings' (BB) **new**	WCAu
	'Ida' (Reticulata)	GKev
	'Ila Crawford' (Spuria) ♀H4	WCAu
	illyrica	see *I. pallida*
	'Imagine Me' (TB) **new**	EFam
	imbricata	CMon
	'Imbue' (SDB)	EFam ESgI
	'Immortal Hour' (TB)	WCAu
	'Immortality' (TB)	CKel EFam EKen ESgI WCAu
I	'Imperator' (Dut)	ECho
	'Imperial Bronze' (Spuria)	NFor WAul WCAu
	'Impetuous' (SDB) ♀H4	CKel EFam
	'Imprimis' (TB)	ESgI WCAu
	'In a Flash' (IB) **new**	WCAu
	'In Love' (TB) **new**	EFam
	'In the Stars' (TB) **new**	EFam
	'In Town' (TB)	ESgI EWoo
	'Incoscente' (TB)	ESgI
	'Indeed' (IB)	CBgR EFam
	'Indian Chief' (TB)	EMil ESgI GBin SPur WCAu
	'Indian Jewel' (SDB)	EGle EHyt
	'Indian Pow Wow' (SDB)	CSev
N	'Indiana Sunset' (TB)	CKel
	'Indigo Flight' (IB)	CKel
	'Indiscreet' (TB)	EFam WCAu
	'Infernal Fire' (TB)	CIri
	'Infinite Grace' (TB)	ESgI
	'Innocent Heart' (IB) ♀H4	WCAu
	'Innocent Star' (TB) **new**	EFam
	innominata	CWCL EAEE ECha ECho GGar GKev IBlr IBlr LHop LRHS NBir NBro NEgg NPal SAga SMar SRms SWal WBVN
	– JCA 13225	CLAP
	– apricot	CPrp IBlr
	– Ballyrogan hybrids	IBlr
	– yellow	CAvo NRya
	'Inscription' (SDB)	EGle EHyt
	'Interpol' (TB)	ESgI EWoo WCAu WWhi
	'Invitation' (TB)	EFam ESgI
	'Irish Doll' (MDB)	EGle WCAu
	'Irish Moss' (SDB) **new**	WAul
	'Irish Tune' (TB)	ESgI
	'Ishmael' (SDB)	EGle
	'Island Sunset' (TB) **new**	EFam SIri
	'Isoline' (TB)	ESgI
	'Istanbul' (TB)	EFam
	'It's Magic' (TB)	EFam

	'J.S. Dijt' (Reticulata)	CAvo CBro CFFs ECho EPot GKev LRHS MBow MBri NJOw
	'Jabal' (SDB)	SIri WDav
	'Jade Mist' (SDB)	EGle
	'Jan Reagan' (SDB)	NZep
	'Jane Phillips' (TB) ♀H4	More than 30 suppliers
	'Jane Taylor' (SDB)	CBro EGle
	'Janet Lane' (BB)	CKel
	'Jangles' (IB) **new**	WCAu
	japonica ♀H3	CHEx ECho EHrv NPer WAul WFar WOut
	– 'Aphrodite' (v)	WTin
§	– 'Bourne Graceful'	CAby WCAu
	– 'Ledger'	CAvo CHll CKel CPLG CPrp CSpe EBee ECha EHrv ELan EPfP IGor MRav SIri SMad WPGP
I	– 'Purple Heart' **new**	CAvo
N	– 'Rudolph Spring'	GCal
I	– 'Snowflake' **new**	CAvo
§	– 'Variegata' (v) ♀H3	CAvo CBow CHEx CHad CKel CPrp CSpe ECha EHrv GGar LRHS NBro NPer SAPC SAga SArc SMad SPoG WAul WCFE WCMO WEas WFar WHil WPGP WPic
	'Jasper Gem' (MDB)	EGle EHyt ERos NBir
	'Jaunty Jean' **new**	EFam
	'Jay Kenneth' (IB)	CBgR
	'Jazz Festival' (TB)	WCAu
	'Jazz Maid' **new**	EFam
	'Jazzamatazz' (SDB)	ESgI WCAu
	'Jazzed Up' (TB)	WCAu
	'Jean Cayeux' (TB)	ESgI
	'Jean Guymer' (TB)	EFam NBir WCAu
	'Jeanne Price' (TB)	SCoo WCAu
	'Jephthah's Daughter' (TB)	EFam
	'Jeremy Brian' (SDB) ♀H4	WCAu
	'Jersey Lilli' (SDB)	WCAu
	'Jesse's Song' (TB)	EFam ESgI MOak NZep WCAu
	'Jester' (TB)	EFam
	'Jewel Baby' (SDB)	CBro CKel NZep
	'Jeweler's Art' (SDB)	EWoo WCAu
	'Jiansada' (SDB)	CBro
	'Jigsaw' (TB)	ESgI
	'Jitterbug' (TB)	EHrv WCAu
	'Joanna' (TB)	NLar
	'Joanna Taylor' (MDB)	ERos NMen NZep WCAu
N	'Joe Elliott' (CH)	EGle
	'John' (IB)	CKel EFam
	'Joy Boy' (SDB)	ESgI
	'Joyce' (Reticulata)	CBro ECho EPot GKev LRHS MBri SGar SPet
	'Joyce Terry' (TB)	ESgI
	'Joyful' (SDB)	ESgI
	'Jubilant Spirit' (Spuria)	CWrd EBee EWes
	'Jubilé Rainier III' (TB) **new**	CIri
	'Jubilee Gem' (TB)	CKel
	'Juicy Fruit' (TB)	EFam WCAu
	'Julia Vennor' (TB)	CKel
	'July Sunshine' (TB)	EFam
	'June Prom' (IB)	LRHS SRGP WCAu
	'Jungle Fires' (TB)	WCAu
	'Jungle Shadows' (BB)	MRav NBir WCAu
	'Jurassic Park' (TB)	ESgI WCAu
	'Juris Prudence' (TB)	ESgI
	'Just Dance' (IB)	EFam ESgI
	'Just Jennifer' (BB)	WCAu
	'Just Reward' (Spuria)	CWrd
	kaempferi	see *I. ensata*
	'Kaibab Trail' (Spuria)	CIri
	'Kangchenjunga' (TB)	ESgI
	kashmiriana	CBcs CMon
	'Katharine Hodgkin' (Reticulata) ♀H4	More than 30 suppliers
	'Katie-Koo' (IB) ♀H4	CKel WDav
	'Katmandu' (TB) **new**	EFam
	'Katy Petts' (SDB)	ESgI NZep WCAu

'Kayo' (SDB)	EGle	
'Keeping up Appearances' (TB) **new**	CIri WCAu	
'Kelway Renaissance' (TB)	CKel	
kemaonensis	GIBF	
'Kent Pride' (TB)	CHad EAEE EBee EChP ECha EPPr EPfP ERou IPot MRav MSte MWat SGar SHBN SIri SPer SPoG SWat WAul WCAu WCra WTin WWlt	
'Kentucky Bluegrass' (SDB)	WCAu	
§ *kerneriana* ♀H4	ERos GBuc LRHS MLLN NBir NEgg	
'Kernewek' (TB) **new**	EFam	
'Kevin's Theme' (TB)	WCAu	
'Kildonan' (TB)	WCAu	
'Kilt Lilt' (TB)	WCAu	
'King's Rhapsody' (TB) **new**	EFam	
'Kirkstone' (TB)	WCAu	
'Kissing Circle' (TB)	EFam ESgI EWoo	
'Kitt Peak' (Spuria) ♀H4	CIri	
'Kiwi Capers' (SDB)	NZep	
'Kiwi Slices' (SDB)	CKel ESgI	
klattii	see *I. spuria* subsp. *musulmanica*	
'Knick Knack' (MDB)	CBro CPBP EAEE EBee ECho EHyt ELan ERos GAbr GCrs LBee LRHS MRav MSte NEgg NMen SDnm SPla SPoG WHil	
kolpakowskiana	WWst	
'Kona Nights' (BB)	ESgI	
korolkowii	GIBF	
'La Nina Rosa' (BB)	WCAu	
'La Senda' (Spuria)	WCAu WCot	
'La Vie en Rose' (TB)	ESgI	
'Laced Cotton' (TB)	SCoo WCAu	
'Laced Lemonade' (SDB)	MBri	
§ *lactea* ♀H4	NWCA	
lacustris ♀H4	CBro ERos NBro NMen NWCA WAbe	
'Lacy Snowflake' (TB) **new**	MOak	
'Lady Emma' (MTB)	EFam	
'Lady Essex' (TB)	EFam WCAu	
'Lady Friend' (TB)	EFam ERou ESgI EWoo WCAu	
'Lady Ilse' (TB)	WCAu	
'Lady in Red' (SDB)	ESgI	
'Lady Mohr' (AB)	WCAu	
'Lady of Fatima' (TB)	ESgI	
'Lady R' (SDB)	EHyt	
§ *laevigata* ♀H4	CDWL CRow CWat ECha ECho EGle EHon ELan EMFW EPfP GIBF GSki LNCo LPBA MRav NBro NPer SEND SGar SPer SWat WCAu WFar WMAq WMoo WPnP WShi WWpP	
- var. *alba*	CBen CRow ECha ECho EHon ELan EPfP LPBA SWat WAbe WFar WMoo WWpP	
- 'Albopurpurea'	CDWL EMFW WTMC	
- 'Atropurpurea'	CRow IBlr LPBA	
- 'Colchesterensis'	CBen CDWL CRow CWat EMFW LPBA NGdn NPer SWat WCra WHrl WMAq WTMC	
I - 'Dorothy'	LPBA NGdn	
N - 'Dorothy Robinson'	CWat LNCo SWat WPnP	
- 'Elegant'	see *I. laevigata* 'Weymouth Elegant'	
- 'Elgar'	WMAq	
- 'Liam Johns'	CRow	
- 'Midnight'	see *I. laevigata* 'Weymouth Midnight'	
- 'Mottled Beauty'	CRow	
N - 'Plum Purple'	EGle	
- 'Rashomon'	CRow	
- 'Regal'	CDWL CRow	
I - 'Reveille'	EGle	
- 'Richard Greaney'	CRow	
- 'Rose Queen'	see *I. ensata* 'Rose Queen'	

I - 'Snowdrift'	CBen CRow CWat EHon EMFW LNCo LPBA NBir NGdn NPer SWat WCAu WFar WMAq WPnP WTMC WWpP	
- 'Surprise'	see *I. laevigata* 'Weymouth Surprise'	
- 'Variegata' (v) ♀H4	CBen CBow CDWL CMea CRow CWat EAEE ECha ECho EHoe EHon EMFW EPfP EPla LNCo LPBA LRHS NBid NBro NGdn NPer SPer SWat WMAq WMoo WTin WWhi	
- 'Violet Garth'	CRow	
- 'Weymouth'	see *I. laevigata* 'Weymouth Blue'	
§ - 'Weymouth Blue'	CBen CRow	
§ - 'Weymouth Elegant'	CBen CFir CRow	
§ - 'Weymouth Midnight'	CBen CFir CMil CRow EHon LPBA SWat WCMO	
- 'Weymouth Nearly' **new**	CBen	
- 'Weymouth Purity' **new**	CBen	
§ - 'Weymouth Surprise'	CBen	
N 'Langport Chapter' (IB)	CKel	
N 'Langport Chief' (IB)	CKel	
N 'Langport Claret' (IB)	CKel	
N 'Langport Curlew' (IB)	CKel ESgI	
N 'Langport Duchess' (IB)	ESgI WDav WTin	
N 'Langport Fairy' (IB)	CKel	
N 'Langport Finch' (IB)	NBir WIvy	
N 'Langport Flame' (IB)	CKel ESgI WTin	
N 'Langport Flash' (IB)	EFam	
N 'Langport Hope' (IB)	CKel	
N 'Langport Jane' (IB)	CKel	
N 'Langport Lady' (IB)	CKel ESgI	
N 'Langport Lord' (IB)	CKel ESgI	
'Langport Minstrel' (IB)	CKel	
N 'Langport Robe' (IB)	ESgI	
N 'Langport Smoke' (IB)	CKel	
N 'Langport Song' (IB)	ESgI	
N 'Langport Star' (IB)	CKel	
'Langport Storm' (IB)	CHad EAEE EBee EChP EMil MBri NGdn SHBN WAul WDav WIvy WTin	
N 'Langport Sun' (IB)	CKel EFam SMrm	
N 'Langport Swift' (IB)	CKel	
'Langport Sylvia' (IB)	CKel	
N 'Langport Tartan' (IB)	CKel	
N 'Langport Violet' (IB)	CKel	
'Langport Vista' (IB)	CKel	
'Langport Wren' (IB) ♀H4	CBro CKel EFam ESgI LRHS MBri NBir SMrm WEas WTin	
'Larry Gaulter' (TB)	WCAu	
'Las Vegas' (TB)	WCAu	
'Lascivious Dreams' (TB)	EFam	
'Latest Style' **new**	EFam	
§ *latifolia* ♀H4	ECho GIBF GKev	
- from the Pyrenees	CMon	
- 'Duchess of York'	ECho EPot	
- 'Isabella'	EBee EPot SMeo	
- 'King of the Blues'	ECho EPot	
- 'Mansfield'	EBee EPot SMeo	
- 'Mont Blanc'	EBee EPot	
- 'Queen of the Blues' (Eng)	ECho EPot	
'Latin Rock' (TB)	WCAu	
latiphilum	GIBF	
'Laura Louise' (La)	CWrd	
§ *lazica* ♀H4	CAbP CBro CMea CMon CPen CPrp CRow CSpe EBee EBrs ECre EHyt EMan EPPr EPfP EWsh GGar IBlr LRHS MRav MSte NBir NCGa NSti SUsu WCot WEas WPGP	
- 'Joy Bishop'	WCMO WCot	
- 'Richard Nutt' **new**	WCot	
N - 'Turkish Blue'	CPrp IBlr	
'Leah Traded' (BB)	EFam	
'Leda's Lover' (TB)	ESgI	
'Legato' (TB) **new**	EFam	

'Lemon Brocade' (TB)   ESgI EWoo MBri WCAu
'Lemon Dilemma' (Spuria)   CIri
'Lemon Fever' (TB)   ESgI
'Lemon Flare' (SDB)   ECtt EFam MRav SRms WCAu
'Lemon Ice' (TB)   EAEE EBee LBuc SPer
'Lemon Lyric' (TB)   EFam ESgI
'Lemon Mist' (TB)   ESgI
'Lemon Peel' (IB) **new**   CKel
'Lemon Pop' (TB)   WCAu
'Lemon Puff' (MDB)   CBro WCAu
'Lemon Tree' (TB)   WCAu
'Lemon Whip' (IB)   EWoo
N 'Lena' (SDB)   CBro
'Lenna M' (SDB)   CKel ECho
'Lenora Pearl' (BB)   ESgI WCAu
'Lent A. Williamson' (TB)   GMaP
'Lenten Prayer' (TB)   CIri
'Leprechaun Delight'   EFam
   (SDB) **new**
'Leprechaun's Purse'   WCAu
   (SDB) **new**
'Let's Elope' (IB)   ESgI WCAu
'Letter From Paris' **new**   EFam
'Light Beam' (TB) **new**   EFam
'Light Cavalry' (IB)   ESgI EWoo NZep
'Light Laughter' (IB)   WCAu
'Lighten Up' (SDB)   NZep
'Lilac and Lavender' (SDB)   NZep
'Lilac Stitchery' (TB)   EFam
'Lilla's Gloves' **new**   EFam
'Lilla's Stripes' **new**   EFam
'Lilli-white' (SDB)   CKel CWat EBee EGle ELan ENot
   MBNS MRav MWgw NEgg SPoG
   WCAu
'Lilting' (TB) **new**   EFam
'Lima Colada' (SDB)   NBre SMrm
'Limbo' (SpecHybrid)   CRow
'Limelight' (TB)   SRms
'Linesman' (SDB)   NZep
'Lingering Love' (TB)   WCAu
linifolia   WWst
'Liqueur Crème' (TB) **new**   EFam
'Little Amigo' (SDB)   NZep
N 'Little Amoena'   ERos NMen
'Little Annie' (SDB)   NZep
'Little Bev' (SDB) **new**   EFam
'Little Bill' (SDB)   EGle
'Little Black Belt' (SDB)   NZep SIri
'Little Blackfoot' (SDB)   ESgI WCAu WHoo
'Little Blue-eyes' (SDB) **new** ESgI
'Little Bluets' (SDB) **new**   ESgI
'Little Dandy' (SDB)   EGle EHyt WCAu WIvy
'Little Dogie' (SDB)   EGle EHyt
'Little Dream' (SDB)   EGle NZep WCAu
'Little Episode' (SDB)   ESgI NZep WCAu
'Little John' (TB)   WCAu
'Little Pearl' (MDB)   NZep
'Little Rosy Wings' (SDB)   CBro CPBP EFam ERos
'Little Shadow' (IB)   ENot MRav SRms WCMO
'Little Sheba' (AB)   WCAu
'Little Showoff' (SDB) **new** ESgI WAul
'Little Snow Lemon' (IB)   EFam NZep
'Little Tilgates' (CH)   ♀H3   CBos WCot
'Live Jazz' (SDB)   NZep WCAu
'Llanthony' (SDB)   WCAu
loczyi   EBee
'Lodore' (TB)   SRms WCAu
'Logo' (IB)   WCAu
'Lois Parrish' (TB)   CIri
'Lollipop' (SDB)   ESgI SIri
longipetala   GIBF NBir
'Lookin' Good' (IB)   NZep
'Lookingglass Eyes'   CIri
   (Spuria) **new**
'Loop the Loop' (TB)   EBee EGle EPfP EWoo NBre SCoo
   SPoG SWat WBor WCra

'Loose Valley' (MTB)   SIri WCAu
   ♀H4 **new**
'Lord Warden' (TB)   EAEE ECGP EChP SPet WCAu
'Loreley' (TB)   ESgI
'Lorenzaccio de Medecis'   ESgI
   (TB)
'Lorilee' (TB)   ESgI
'Lothario' (TB)   WCAu WFoF
'Loud Music' (TB)   WCAu
'Louis d'Or' (TB)   ♀H4   CIri
Louisiana hybrids   WMAq
'Louvois' (TB)   ESgI
'Love for Leila' (Spuria)   CIri
   ♀H4
'Love the Sun' (TB)   EFam ESgI
'Lovebird' (TB) **new**   EFam
'Lovely Again' (TB)   EFam WCAu
'Lovely Fran' (TB)   EFam
'Lovely Light' (TB)   MBri
'Lover's Charm' (TB)   WCAu
'Love's Tune' (IB)   EAEE SRGP
'Loveshine' (SDB)   MRav NZep
'Low Ho Silver' (IB)   EFam WCAu
'Low Snow' (SDB)   NZep
'Lucky Devil' (Spuria)   CIri
'Lucy's Gift' (BB)   ♀H4   CIri WAul
   new
'Lugano' (TB)   ESgI
'Luli-Ann' (SDB)   ♀H4   CKel
'Lullaby of Spring' (TB)   CKel WCAu
'Lumalite' (SDB) **new**   WAul
'Lumière d'Automne' (TB)   ESgI
'Luminosity' (TB)   EFam
'Luna di Miele' (BB)   ESgI
'Lunar Frost' (IB)   SIri
'Lurid' (TB) **new**   EFam
§ *lutescens*   ♀H4   CMon ECho EPot ERos GEdr GKev
   NSla WAbe XPep
§ - 'Campbellii'   EHyt ERos MSte NMen
- subsp. *lutescens*   WLin
§ - 'Nancy Lindsay'   WCAu
lycotis   see *I. iberica* subsp. *lycotis*
'Lyme Tyme' (TB)   CIri
'Ma Mie' (IB)   ESgI
maackii   GIBF GSki
macrosiphon   GKev
'Madame Maurice Lassailly' (TB)   ESgI
'Madeira Belle' (TB)   EWoo WCAu
'Magharee' (TB)   ESgI
'Magic Bubbles' (IB)   ♀H4   CIri
'Magic Flute' (MDB)   EGle
'Magic Kingdom' (TB)   EFam
'Magic Man' (TB)   EBee
'Magic Memories' **new**   EFam
'Magic Palette' **new**   EFam
magnifica   ♀H3-4   CBro GKev NPri NWCA WWst
N - 'Agalik'   CMea LRHS
'Mahogany Snow' (SDB)   NZep
'Maiden' (TB) **new**   EFam
'Maisie Lowe' (TB)   ESgI
'Making Eyes' (SDB)   ESgI EWoo WCAu
'Mallow Dramatic' (TB)   WCAu
   new
I 'Mandarin' (TB)   ESgI
'Mandarin Purple'   CDes EBee GGar IBlr NGdn NHol
   (Sino-Sib)
mandshurica   GIBF
'Mango Entree' (TB)   CIri
'Mango Kiss' (SDB) **new**   EFam
'Many Moons Tales' (TB)   EFam
'Maple Treat' (TB)   CIri EFam
'Marcel Turbat' (TB)   ESgI
'Marche Turque' (TB)   ESgI
'Marco Polo' (TB)   ESgI
'Margarita' (TB)   WCAu
'Margot Holmes' (Cal-Sib)   GCal

'Margrave' (TB)	SIri WCAu
'Marguerita' (Reticulata) **new**	CBgR ECho
'Marhaba' (MDB)	CBro ERos
'Marilyn Holloway' (Spuria)	WCAu
'Marmalade Skies' (BB)	EFam NZep WCAu
'Maroon Moon' (TB) **new**	CIri
'Martyn Rix'	see *I. confusa* 'Martyn Rix'
'Mary Constance' (IB) ♀H4	CKel
'Mary Frances' (TB)	WCAu
'Mary McIlroy' (SDB) ♀H4	CBro WTin
'Mary Randall' (TB)	WCAu
'Mastery' (TB) **new**	CIri
'Matrix' (TB) **new**	EFam
'Maui Moonlight' (IB) ♀H4	CKel EFam NZep
'Maui Surf' (BB) ♀H4 **new**	CIri WAul
'Mauna Loa Fire' (TB) **new**	CIri
'Mauvelous' (TB) **new**	CIri EFam
'May Melody' (TB)	WCAu
'McKellar's Grove' (TB) **new**	CIri
'Meadow Court' (SDB)	CBro CKel CMMP CRez ERos NBro WCAu WDav
'Media Luz' (Spuria)	WCAu
'Medway Valley' (MTB) ♀H4	SIri WAul WCAu
'Melbreak' (TB)	WCAu
'Melissa Sue' (TB)	EFam
mellita	see *I. suaveolens*
- var. *rubromarginata*	see *I. suaveolens*
'Melon Honey' (SDB)	CKel EGle EHyt NZep WCAu WDav WHoo
'Memo' (IB) **new**	EFam
'Memphis Blues' (TB)	EWoo
'Memphis Delight' (TB)	WCAu
'Men in Black' (TB) **new**	WCAu
'Menton' (SDB)	CKel
'Mer du Sud' (TB) ♀H4	ESgI SCoo
'Merit' (MTB) **new**	EFam WCAu
'Merlot' (TB) **new**	CIri
'Merseyside' (SDB)	EGle
'Mescal' **new**	EFam
'Mesmerizer' (TB)	EFam WCAu
'Metaphor' (TB)	WCAu
'Mezza Cartuccia' (IB)	ESgI
'Michael Paul' (SDB) ♀H4	ESgI
'Michael's Angel' **new**	WWst
'Midday Blues' (IB)	NZep
'Midnight Caller' (TB)	EFam
'Midnight Fire' (TB)	ERou
'Midnight Moonlight' (TB) **new**	CIri
'Midnight Oil' (TB)	WCAu
'Midnight Pacific' (TB)	EFam
'Mil Byers' (TB)	EFam
milesii ♀H4	CDes CPLG CPou CSec GBuc GIBF IGor MSph NBir NEgg WCot WPer WPic
- CC 4590	GKev MGol
'Millennium Falcon' (TB) **new**	CIri
'Millennium Sunrise' (TB)	WCAu
'Ming' (IB) **new**	WCAu
'Mini Big Horn' (IB) **new**	CIri
'Mini Champagne' (BB) **new**	EFam
'Mini Might' (SDB) ♀H4 **new**	EFam
'Mini-Agnes' (SDB)	CBro
'Miss Carla' (IB)	NBre
'Miss Mauve' (IB) **new**	CIri
'Miss Nellie' (BB)	CKel
'Miss Scarlett' (BB)	EFam
'Mission Sunset' (TB)	EHrv WCAu
'Missouri Iron Ore' (Spuria) **new**	CIri

'Missouri Orange' (Spuria) **new**	CIri
'Missouri Rainbows' (Spuria) **new**	CIri
missouriensis ♀H4	IGor NBid SSpi
§ - 'Tollong' ♀H4	MSte
'Mister Roberts' (SDB)	ESgI NZep
'Mistigri' (IB) **new**	WAul
'Mme Chereau' (TB)	ESgI WCAu
'Mme Louis Aureau' (TB)	ESgI
'Modern Classic' (TB)	EWoo
* 'Mohogang Mountain' (TB)	EFam
monnieri	GIBF NLar SDix
Monspur Group	GCal WCot
§ 'Monspur Cambridge Blue' (Spuria) ♀H4	WCAu
'Monty's Sweet Blue' (TB) **new**	EFam
'Moon Journey' (TB) **new**	SIri
'Moon Sparkle' (IB)	CKel
'Moonlight' (TB)	EFam NFor WCot
'Moonlight Waves'	see *I. ensata* 'Moonlight Waves'
'Moonlit Waves' (TB) **new**	CKel
'Moonstruck' (TB)	EWoo
'Morning Show' (IB)	EBee
'Morning's Blush' (SDB) ♀H4	CIri
'Morwenna' (TB) ♀H4	EFam WCAu
'Mote Park' (MTB) **new**	CIri
'Mother Earth' (TB)	ESgI
N 'Mount Stewart Black'	GCal
'Mrs Horace Darwin' (TB)	CFir SWat WMnd
'Mrs Nate Rudolph' (SDB)	EBee EGle MBri MGos SMrm WHoo
'Mrs Tait' (Spuria)	GCal NChi
'Mulberry Rose' (TB)	CFee
'Mulled Wine' (TB)	EFam ESgI
'Murmuring Morn' (TB)	WCAu
'Music Box' (SDB)	NZep
'My Friend Jonathan' (TB)	EFam
'My Ginny' (TB) **new**	CIri
'My Honeycomb' (TB)	WCAu
'My Kayla' (SDB) **new**	ESgI
N 'My Seedling' (MDB)	CBro ERos NMen WIvy
'Mystic Lover' (TB) **new**	EFam
'Naivasha' (TB)	CKel
'Nancy Hardy' (MDB)	CBro EHyt ERos NMen
'Nancy Lindsay'	see *I. lutescens* 'Nancy Lindsay'
'Nanny' (SDB)	SIri
narcissiflora	CFir WCot
'Nashborough' (TB)	WCAu
'Natascha' (Reticulata)	EBrs ECho EPot LPhx WLin WRHF
'Natchez Trace' (TB)	WCMO
'Natural Grace' **new**	EFam
'Navajo Jewel' (TB)	ESgI EWoo WCAu
'Near Myth' (SDB) **new**	WCAu
'Nectar' (IB)	ESgI
'Needlecraft' (TB)	EFam NBre
'Needlepoint' (TB)	ESgI
'Neige de Mai' (TB)	ESgI
'Neon Pixie' (SDB)	NZep
nepalensis	see *I. decora*
nertschinskia	see *I. sanguinea*
N 'New Argument' (Juno)	WWst
'New Centurion' (TB)	WCAu
'New Idea' (MTB)	ESgI WCAu
'New Leaf' (TB) **new**	EFam WCAu
'New Snow' (TB)	WCAu
'Nibelungen' (TB)	EPfP MWea NBre WFar
'Nice n' Nifty' (IB)	NZep WTin
nicolai	WWst
'Nigerian Raspberry' (TB)	WCAu
'Night Edition' (TB)	ESgI
'Night Game' (TB)	WCAu
'Night Owl' (TB)	CKel ELan WHlf
'Night Ruler' (TB)	ESgI WCAu

'Night Shift' (IB) new	NBre
'Nightfall' (TB)	EBee
'Nights of Gladness' (TB)	ESgI
'Nineveh' (AB)	WCAu
'Noces Blanches' (IB)	ESgI
'Noon Siesta' (TB)	ESgI
'Nora Eileen' (TB)	CKel
'Northern Flame' (TB)	EFam
'Northwest Pride' (TB)	WCAu
'Nut Ruffles' (SDB) new	WAul
'O Shenandoah' (TB)	EFam
'Obsidian' (TB) new	CIri
'Ochraurea' (Spuria)	GCal NGdn NSti
'Ochre Doll' (SDB) new	CKel
ochroleuca	see *I. orientalis* Mill.
'O'Cool' (IB) new	CKel
'October' (TB)	EFam
'October Storm' (IB) new	CIri EFam
odaesanensis	EBee
'Off Broadway' (TB) new	EFam
'Oktoberfest' (TB)	EFam ESgI
'Ola Kalá' (TB)	CMMP EAEE ECGP ERou ESgI EWTr GMaP MSte NBre NEgg NLar SPer SPoG SPur WCAu
'Olive Reflection' new	EFam
'Olympiad' (TB)	ESgI
'Olympic Challenge' (TB)	EAEE ESgI WCAu
'Olympic Torch' (TB)	EFam WCAu
'Ominous Stranger' (TB) new	ESgI WCAu
'One Desire' (TB)	NZep WCAu
'Opalette' (IB) new	EFam
'Open Sky' (SDB)	NZep SIri
'Orageux' (TB)	ESgI
'Orange Blaze' (SDB)	CBro
'Orange Caper' (SDB)	EGoo ESgI GBuc MRav MSte MWat NEgg NLar NZep SPet WCAu WWeb
'Orange Dawn' (TB) ♀H4	EFam
'Orange Harvest' (TB)	EFam EWoo
'Orange Order' (TB)	WCAu
N 'Orange Plaza'	ECho NMen
'Orange Popsicle' (TB) new	EFam
'Orange Tiger' (SDB)	NZep WCAu
'Orangerie' new	EFam
'Orchardist' (TB)	CKel
'Orchid Cloud' (TB)	EFam
'Orchidea Selvaggia' (TB)	ESgI
orchioides misapplied	see *I. bucharica* Foster
§ *orchioides* Carrière	CMea CSam EChP ECho EDAr ELan ERos ETow GKev NWCA WLin
N - 'Urungachsai'	EPot WWst
'Oregold' (SDB)	NZep WCAu
'Oregon Skies' (TB)	ESgI EWoo
N 'Oriental Argument' (Juno)	WWst
'Oriental Baby' (IB)	CKel EWoo
'Oriental Beauty' (TB) new	GBri
'Oriental Beauty' (Dut)	SPer WFar
'Oriental Glory' (TB)	WCAu
'Oriental Touch' (SpecHybrid)	CRow
orientalis Thunb.	see *I. sanguinea*
- 'Alba'	see *I. sanguinea* 'Alba'
orientalis ambig.	EPyc
§ *orientalis* Mill. ♀H4	EPPr GIBF IFro LPBA MSte MWgw SGar WCAu WDyG
'Orinoco Flow' (BB) ♀H4	CHar CKel EFam ESgI WCAu
'Orloff' (TB)	ESgI
'Osage Buff' (TB) new	CKel
'Osaka' (TB) new	CIri
'Out Yonder' (TB)	WCAu
'Ovation' (TB)	ESgI
'Overjoyed' (TB)	WCAu

'O'What' (SDB)	ESgI
'Owyhee Desert' (TB)	CIri WCAu
'Oxford Tweeds' (SDB) new	ESgI
'Ozone Alert' (TB)	CIri
'Pacer' (IB)	NZep
Pacific Coast hybrids	see *I.* Californian hybrids
'Pacific Mist' (TB)	WCAu
'Pacific Panorama' (TB)	ESgI
'Pacific Tide' (TB) new	EFam
'Pagan Dance' (TB) new	EFam WCAu
'Pagan Goddess' (TB) new	EFam
'Pagan Princess' (TB)	WCAu
'Pageant' (TB)	WTin
'Paint It Black' (TB)	EWoo
'Painted Clouds' (TB) new	MOak
'Painter's Choice' (Spuria) new	CIri
'Pale Primrose' (TB)	WCAu
'Pale Shades' (IB) ♀H4	CBro CKel ERos
'Palissandro' (TB)	ESgI
§ *pallida*	CHad EBee EGoo GMaP GSki MCCP MRav MSte MWat NFla WBrE WCAu WMnd
- 'Argentea Variegata' (v)	More than 30 suppliers
- 'Aurea'	see *I. pallida* 'Variegata'
- 'Aurea Variegata'	see *I. pallida* 'Variegata'
- var. *dalmatica*	see *I. pallida* subsp. *pallida*
- subsp. *pallida* ♀H4	CKel EAEE EChP ECha ELan MBri MWgw SDix SPer
- 'Variegata' misapplied	see *I. pallida* 'ArgenteaVariegata'
- 'Variegata' hort. (v) ♀H4	More than 30 suppliers
pallida x *tectorum* new	GSki
'Palo Pinto' (TB) new	EFam
'Palomino' (TB)	WCAu
'Paltec' (IB)	CPou EBee
'Pane e Vino' (TB)	ESgI
'Pansy Top' (SDB) new	SIri
'Paprika Fono's' (TB) new	EFam
'Paradise' (TB)	CKel EPfP
'Paradise Bird' (TB) ♀H4	EFam
'Paradise Saved' (TB) new	EFam
paradoxa	WWst
'Paricutin' (SDB)	CBro EGle
'Party Dress' (TB)	EAEE EBee ELan EMan ENot ERou LAst LRHS MBNS MBnl MRav NBir NEgg NGdn NLar NOrc SMer SPer SPoG SRms SWat WCra WWeb
parvula	WWst
'Passion Flower' (TB) new	EFam
'Passionata' new	EFam
'Passport' (BB) new	ECho
'Pastel Charm' (SDB)	CMMP GBin MSte SMrm STes WMnd
'Pastel Delight' (SDB)	NZep
'Patches' (TB)	ESgI
'Patina' (TB)	ESgI EWoo WAul WCAu
'Patterdale' (TB)	NBir NBre NVic WCAu
'Paul Black' (TB) new	CIri
'Pauline' (Reticulata)	CBro EAEE ECho EPfP EPot GBBs GKev LRHS SPer SPet WFar
N 'Peaceful Warden' (TB)	EWoo
'Peaceful Waters' (TB) new	EFam
'Peacetime' (TB) new	WCAu
'Peach Band' (TB)	ERou
'Peach Brandy' (TB) new	EFam
'Peach Everglow' (TB) new	EFam
'Peach Eyes' (SDB)	CBro CKel ERos
'Peach Float' (TB)	WCAu
'Peach Melba' (TB)	ESgI
'Peach Petals' (BB)	NZep
'Peach Picotee' (TB)	EFam ESgI
'Peach Reprise' (BB) new	EFam
'Peach Spot' (TB)	WCAu
'Peaches ala Mode' (BB)	WCAu
'Peacock'	see *I. ensata* 'Peacock'

'Pearls of Autumn' (TB)	EFam WCAu
'Pearly Dawn' (TB)	EAEE EBee EChP ECha MSte MTis
	NBre NEgg SCoo SPer SRGP SSvw
	SWat
'Pegaletta' **new**	EPPr NBro
'Peggy Chambers' (IB)	EFam SMrm
♀H4	
'Pele' (SDB)	EFam ESgl WCAu
'Penny Anne' (BB) **new**	EFam
'People Pleaser' (SDB)	NZep
'Pepper Blend' **new**	EFam
'Peppermint Twist' (SDB)	NZep
'Perfume Counter' (TB)	EFam
'Persian Berry' (TB)	MOak WCAu
'Pet' (SDB)	NZep
'Peter James' (SDB) ♀H4	CIri
new	
'Phaeton' (TB)	CIri
'Pharoah's Daughter' (IB)	SIri WAul
'Pheasant Feathers' (TB)	CIri
'Phil Keen' (TB) ♀H4	CKel EFam
'Picacho Peak' (Spuria)	CIri
N 'Picadee'	EPfP GBuc NCob
'Picante' (TB) **new**	CIri
'Piero Bargellini' (TB)	ESgl
'Pigeon' (SDB)	NZep
'Pigmy Gold' (IB)	EBee ENot ERos
'Pineapple Poll' (TB) **new**	EFam
'Pinewood Amethyst' (CH)	CAby CDes GMac
'Pinewood Delight' (CH)	CDes
'Pink Angel' (TB)	EWoo
'Pink Attraction' (TB)	EFam ESgl
'Pink Bubbles' (BB)	NZep
'Pink Charm' (TB)	EChP EMan LBuc LRHS SPet WCra
'Pink Confetti' (TB)	ESgl
'Pink Fawn' (SDB)	ESgl
'Pink Formal' (TB)	ESgl
'Pink Horizon' (TB)	EPfP NFla WFar
'Pink Kitten' (IB)	NZep WCAu
'Pink Light'	LAst
'Pink Pussycat' (TB)	MBri
'Pink Ruffles' (IB)	CHar
'Pink Swan' (TB)	ESgl
'Pink Taffeta' (TB)	ESgl
'Pinkness' (TB)	EFam
'Pinky Dinky' **new**	EFam
'Pinnacle' (TB)	CKel SWat WCAu
'Piper's Tune' (IB)	SMrm
'Pipes of Pan' (TB)	MRav WCAu
'Piquant Lass' (MTB)	NZep
'Pirate's Patch' (SDB)	ESgl
'Pirate's Quest' (TB)	EFam
'Piroska' (TB) ♀H4	ESgl
'Piu Blue' (TB)	ESgl
I 'Pixie' (Reticulata)	ECho ELan EPot
'Pixie' (DB)	GKev
'Pixie Flirt' (MDB)	ERos
planifolia	WWst
- PB 449 from Spain	CMon
* - f. *alba*	WWst
'Pleased as Punch' (IB)	EFam
'Pledge Allegiance' (TB)	GSki SIri WCAu
plicata	WCAu
'Plickadee' (SDB)	CBro EPot
'Pluie d'Or' (TB)	ESgl
'Plum Lucky' (SDB) **new**	SIri
'Plum Wine' (TB)	CKel
'Poco Taco' (TB) **new**	WAul
'Poem of Ecstasy' (TB)	WCAu
'Poetess' (TB) **new**	WCAu
'Pogo' (SDB)	EChP ECtt EFam EGle ELan ENot
	EPfP EPot EWoo GBuc GMaP
	MBNS MMHG MRav NBir NWCA
	SRms
'Polar Queen' (TB) **new**	EFam
'Pond Lily' (TB)	WCAu

'Pookanilly' (IB)	ESgl
'Port of Call' (Spuria)	CWrd
'Portrait of Amy' (TB) **new**	EFam
'Posh' (IB) **new**	EFam
'Powder Blue Cadillac'	CKel
(TB) **new**	
'Power Surge' (TB)	EWoo
'Presby's Crown Jewel'	CIri
(TB) **new**	
'Presence' (TB) **new**	EFam SIri
'Presumption' **new**	EFam
'Pretender' (TB)	LRHS WCAu
'Pretty Please' (TB)	ESgl
'Prince' (SDB)	EGle
'Prince Indigo' (TB)	ENot
'Prince of Burgundy' (IB)	WCAu
♀H4	
'Prince of Earl' (TB)	EFam
'Princess' (TB)	LEdu
'Princess Beatrice' (TB)	WCAu
'Princess Pittypat' (TB)	EFam
'Princess Sabra' (TB) ♀H4	CKel
'Princesse Caroline de	ESgl
Monaco' (TB)	
'Priscilla of Conrinth'	EFam
(TB) **new**	
prismatica	CMon EBee GIBF GKev WTin
- *alba*	IGor
'Professor Blaauw' (Dut)	EBrs EPfP
♀H4	
'Progressive Attitude' (TB)	EFam WCAu
'Protocol' (IB)	CKel EFam
'Proud Tradition' (TB)	WCAu
'Provencal' (TB)	CKel ESgl WAul WCAu
'Proverb' (Spuria)	WCAu
'Prudy' (BB) ♀H4	CKel
pseudacorus ♀H4	More than 30 suppliers
- B&SWJ 5018 from Japan	WCru
- from Korea	CRow
- 'Alba'	CRow EBee GIBF LAst
- var. *bastardii*	CBgR CRow CWat EBee ECha
	EMFW IGor LPBA NPer SLon
	SMHy SPer WBrk WCMO WFar
	WMoo WTin WWpP
- 'Beuron'	CRow
- cream	EGol NBir WAul
N - 'Crème de la Crème'	GBin
- 'Esk'	GBin GCal
N - 'Flore Pleno' (d)	CBgR CRow EBee ECho EMFW
	EPPr GSki LPBA NLar NPer WBrk
	WCMO WCot WFar
N - 'Golden Daggers'	CRow
I - 'Golden Fleece'	SPer
- 'Golden Queen'	CRow IGor WWpP
- 'Ilgengold'	CRow
N - 'Ivory'	CRow
* - *nana*	CRow LPBA
- 'Roccapina'	GBin
- 'Roy Davidson' ♀H4	CBgR CDWL CKel CPrp CRow
	EMFW GBin IBlr LPBA WFar WPtf
	WTin
N - 'Sulphur Queen'	WCot
- 'Sun Cascade'	CRow
N - 'Tiger Brother'	SIri
- 'Tiggah'	CRow
N - 'Turnipseed'	WTin
- 'Variegata' (v) ♀H4	More than 30 suppliers
pseudopumila	ERos
'Puddy Tat' (SDB) **new**	CIri
'Pulsar' (TB) **new**	EFam
'Pulse Rate' (SDB)	CBro
pumila	CPBP EAEE EDAr EPot GSki LRHS
	MHer NFor NMen NWCA WLin
- 'Alba' (DB) **new**	CPBP
- *atroviolacea*	CKel SMrm WMnd
- subsp. *attica*	see I. *attica*

	- blue-flowered	SWal
N	- 'Gelber Mantel'	NBir
N	- 'Jackanapes'	WEas
N	- 'Lavendel Plicata'	EBee NBro NGdn
	- 'Violacea' (DB)	MBri SRms
	- yellow	GAbr SWal
	'Pumpin' Iron' (SDB)	CKel ESgI MSte WDav
	'Pumpkin Center' (SDB)	NZep
	'Punkin' (TB) **new**	EFam
	'Puppet' (SDB)	EGle
	'Puppy Love' (MTB)	NZep
	purdyi	GBuc
	'Pure Allure' (SDB) ♀H4	CIri NZep
	'Purple Duet' (TB)	EFam
	'Purple Gem' (Reticulata)	ECho EPfP EPot LHop WRHF
	'Purple Landscape' (SDB) ♀H4	NBre
	'Purple Sensation' (Dut)	ECho MSph
	'Quaker Lady' (TB)	ESgI SIri WCAu
	'Quark' (SDB)	CBro CKel NZep
	'Quasar' (TB) **new**	EFam
	'Quechee' (TB)	CHad CPen EAEE EBee EChP EPfP ERou GMaP LBuc MBNS MRav MSte NLar SHBN SWat WAul WCra
	'Queen in Calico' (TB)	ESgI WCAu
	'Queen of May' (TB)	ESgI
	'Queen's Circle' (TB)	CIri
	'Queen's Ivory' (SDB)	WCAu
	'Queen's Prize' (SDB) **new**	SIri
	'Quiet Friendship' (TB) **new**	MOak
	'Quietly' (SDB)	EFam
	'Radiant Angel' (TB) **new**	EFam
	'Radiant Apogee' (TB)	ESgI
	'Rain Dance' (SDB) ♀H4	ESgI NZep WCAu
	'Rainbow Goddess' (TB)	EFam
	'Rainbow Rim' (SDB) **new**	ESgI
	'Rajah' (TB)	CMil EAEE EBee EChP ELan EPfP ERou EShb GMaP MMHG MRav MSte NOrc SCoo SHBN SPer SPet SPla SPoG SPur SUsu WCMO WCra WMnd
	'Rameses' (TB)	ESgI
	'Rapture in Blue' (TB)	EWoo
	'Rare Edition' (IB)	CKel EFam EWoo MBri NBre NZep WAul WCAu
	'Rare Treat' (TB)	NZep WCAu
	'Raspberry Acres' (IB)	WCAu
	'Raspberry Blush' (IB) ♀H4	CHad CKel CPar EFam EPfP EWTr LAst MOak NBre NZep SHBN SWat WCAu
	'Raspberry Fudge' (TB)	WCAu
	'Raspberry Jam' (SDB)	EGle EHyt NZep
	'Raspberry Sundae' (BB)	NZep
	'Raven Hill' (TB)	WCAu
	'Razoo' (SDB)	CKel
	'Real Coquette' (SDB)	SIri
	'Rebecca Perret' (TB)	EWoo
	'Recurring Dream' (TB) **new**	EFam
	'Red Atlast' (MDB) **new**	ESgI
	'Red Canyon Glow' (TB) **new**	CIri
	'Red Duet' (TB)	EFam
	'Red Flash' (TB)	ESgI
	'Red Hawk' (TB)	CIri
	'Red Heart' (SDB)	ESgI GMaP MRav WTin
	'Red Lion' (TB)	NZep
	'Red Oak' (Spuria)	WCAu
	'Red Orchid' (IB)	ELan NBlu NBre WCAu
	'Red Revival' (TB)	EFam WCAu
N	'Red Rum' (TB)	CKel
	'Red Spot' (SDB) **new**	EHyt
	'Red Tornado' (TB)	ESgI
	'Red Zinger' (IB)	ESgI MOak NZep WAul
	'Redelta' (TB)	EFam

	'Redwood Supreme' (Spuria)	CWrd GSki WAul
	'Regal Surprise' (SpecHybrid)	CRow
	'Regards' (SDB)	CBro
§	*reichenbachii*	CPBP EPot ERos LBee LTwo NWCA
	- NS 700	CPou
	'Reincarnation' (TB) **new**	EFam
	'Remember Spring' (TB) **new**	EFam
	'Renown' (TB) **new**	ESgI
	'Repartee' (TB)	ESgI EWoo
	'Response' (Spuria)	CWrd
§	*reticulata* ♀H4	CBcs CBro EBrs ECho ELan EPfP LRHS MBNS SPer SPet WCAu WFar WGwG
	- 'Lovely Liza' **new**	WWst
	- 'Spring Time'	CBgR ECho LRHS
N	- 'Violet Queen'	ECho
	'Return to Bayberry' (TB) **new**	CIri
	'Returning Chameleon' (TB)	EFam
	'Returning Peace' (TB)	EFam
	'Riches' (SDB)	NZep
	'Rime Frost' (TB)	EFam WCAu
	'Ringer' (TB) **new**	ESgI
	'Ringo' (TB)	ESgI WCAu
	'Ripple Chip' (SDB)	NZep WTin
	'Rippling Waters' (TB)	ESgI
	'Ritz' (SDB)	MOak
	'Rive Gauche' (TB)	ESgI
	'River Avon' (TB) ♀H4	WCAu
	'River Pearl' (TB)	CIri
	'Rivulets of Pink' (Spuria)	CIri
§	x *robusta* 'Dark Aura'	WCot WTin
§	- 'Gerald Darby' ♀H4	More than 30 suppliers
	- 'Mountain Brook'	CRow
	'Rock Star' **new**	EFam
	'Rockabye' (SDB) **new**	WAul
§	'Rocket' (TB)	EAEE EChP GMaP IPot LBuc MRav NBir NBre NEgg NGdn SPer
	'Role Model' (TB)	WCAu
	'Roman Emperor' (TB)	EFam
	'Roman Rhythm' (TB)	EWoo WCAu
	'Romance' (TB)	ERou
	'Romantic Evening' (TB) **new**	WCAu
	'Romantic Mood' (TB)	CKel
	'Ron' (TB)	EWoo
	'Roney's Encore' (TB)	EFam
	'Rosalie Figge' (TB)	EFam WCAu
	'Rose Queen'	see *I. ensata* 'Rose Queen'
	'Rose Violet' (TB)	WCAu
	'Rosemary's Dream' (MTB)	NBre SMrm
	rosenbachiana	EPot WWst
I	- 'Sina'	WWst
N	- 'Varzob'	WWst
	'Roseplic' (TB)	ESgI
	'Rosette Wine' (TB)	ESgI WCAu
	rossii	GIBF
	'Rosy Veil' (TB)	ESgI
	'Rosy Wings' (TB)	EHyt ESgI
	'Roulette' (TB)	MBri
N	'Roy Elliott'	NMen SIng
	'Royal Contrast' (SDB) ♀H4	NZep
	'Royal Crusader' (TB)	WCAu
	'Royal Elegance' (TB)	EFam EWoo SIri
	'Royal Intrigue' (TB)	SIri
	'Royal Knight' (TB) **new**	MOak
	'Royal Magician' (SDB)	WTin
	'Royal Satin' (TB)	EWoo
	'Royal Summer' (TB)	EFam

'Royal Tapestry' (TB) **new** — NBre
'Rubacuori' (TB) — ESgl
'Ruban Bleu' (TB) — ESgl EWoo
'Rubistar' (TB) — ESgl
'Ruby Chimes' (IB) — WCAu
'Ruby Contrast' (TB) — CHad WCAu
'Ruby Morn' (TB) **new** — CIri
rudskyi — see *I. variegata*
'Ruffled Canary' (Spuria) — WCAu
'Ruffled Revel' (SDB) — SIri
'Rustic Cedar' (TB) — ESgl WCAu
'Rustic Dream' (TB) **new** — CIri
'Rustic Royalty' (TB) — CIri
'Rustler' (TB) — ESgl WCAu
'Rusty Dusty' (SDB) — NZep
* 'Rusty Red' (La) **new** — WMAq
'Ruth Black' (TB) **new** — WCAu
ruthenica — ECho ERos GBin GIBF NMen
 - var. *nana* — GBin
 -- L 1280 — EPot
'Ryan James' (TB) — CKel
sabina — GIBF
'Sable' (TB) — CHad EAEE EBee EChP EHrv ELan ESgl GMaP MBri MSte NGdn NOrc SCoo SEND SHBN SPer WAul WCAu WCra
'Sable Night' (TB) — CHar CKel ERou
'Sager Cedric' (TB) — WCAu
'Saint Crispin' (TB) — EAEE ERou ESgl EWTr GMaP MRav MSte SPer SPet SPoG WWeb
'Sally Jane' (TB) — WCAu
'Salonique' (TB) — ESgl NBlu NBre NLar WCAu WFar
N 'Saltbox' (SDB) — WIvy
'Saltwood' (SDB) — CBro NBre SIri
'Sam Carne' (TB) — WCAu
'San Francisco' (TB) — ESgl
'San Leandro' (TB) — MBri
'Sand Princess' (MTB) — NBre SIri
'Sandstone Sentinel' (BB) — CIri
'Sandy Caper' (IB) — WCAu WTin
'Sangone' (IB) — ESgl
§ *sanguinea* ♀H4 — GIBF MGol WBVN
§ - 'Alba' — IBlr
§ - 'Nana Alba' — GBin IBlr SIri
§ - 'Snow Queen' — More than 30 suppliers
'Sapphire Beauty' (Dut) — EPfP
'Sapphire Gem' (SDB) — CKel WAul WCAu WDav
'Sapphire Hills' (TB) — WCAu
'Sapphire Jewel' (SDB) — EPPr NZep
'Sarah Taylor' (SDB) ♀H4 — CBro EFam EHyt EWoo WCAu
sari — SBla
'Sass with Class' (SDB) — CKel EFam WTin
'Satin Gown' (TB) — WCAu
'Saturday Night Live' (TB) — CIri
'Saxon' (TB) — EFam
'Saxon Princess' (TB) — EFam
'Scented Bubbles' (TB) — EFam
schachtii purple-flowered — SBla
'Scottish Warrior' (TB) **new** — EFam
'Scribe' (MDB) — CBro NBir WCAu
'Scrimmage' (SDB) — NZep
'Sea Fret' (SDB) — CBro
'Sea Monster' (SDB) — EPPr SIri WDav
'Sea Power' (TB) **new** — CIri
'Sea Wisp' (La) — CWrd EPPr NBro
'Seafire' (SDB) **new** — CIri
'Season Ticket' (IB) **new** — ESgl
'Second Look' (TB) **new** — EFam
'Second Opinion' (MTB) — NZep
'Second Show' (TB) **new** — EFam
'Secretariat' **new** — EFam
'Semola' (SDB) — ESgl
'Seneca Rebound' (SDB) — EFam
'Senlac' (TB) — EWTr NLar SMer WMnd
'Senor Frog' (SDB) **new** — ESgl
'September Frost' (TB) — EFam

'September Replay' **new** — EFam
serbica — see *I. reichenbachii*
'Serene Moment' (TB) **new** — SIri
'Serengeti Spaghetti' (TB) — CIri
'Serenity Prayer' (SDB) — WCAu
'Set To Music' **new** — EFam
setosa ♀H4 — CBro CPne CSec CTri EAEE EBee ECho EGle EHyt EKen EMFW EPfP ERos GBBs GKev IGor ITer LPBA LRHS MHer MLan MNrw NDlv NEgg NGdn NLAp SPer SWal
 - AER 0233 — MGol
 - *alba* — MSte NLar SIng
 - var. *arctica* — EBee EHyt EMon EPot GBuc LEdu NMen NWCA SBla WHoo WPer
 - subsp. *canadensis* — see *I. hookeri*
 - dwarf — see *I. hookeri*
§ - 'Hondoensis' — MSte
 - 'Hookeri' — see *I. hookeri*
 - 'Kirigamini' — see *I. setosa* 'Hondoensis'
 - var. *nana* — see *I. hookeri*
* 'Sevenly Seven' (TB) — EFam
'Severn Side' (TB) ♀H4 — CKel
'Shakespeare's Sonnet' (SDB) **new** — ESgl
'Shameless' (IB) **new** — NBre
'Shampoo' (IB) — CKel SIri WAul WCAu
'Sheer Ecstasy' (TB) — CIri
'Sheila Ann Germaney' (Reticulata) — ECho EHyt EPot NMen
'Shelford Giant' (Spuria) ♀H4 — NBir NEgg
'Shepherd's Delight' (TB) — WCAu
'Sherbet Lemon' (IB) ♀H4 — CKel EFam WCAu
'Sherwood Pink' (TB) **new** — EFam
'Sherwood Primrose' (TB) ♀H4 **new** — EFam
'Shindig' (SDB) **new** — EFam WCAu
'Shoot the Moon' (TB) **new** — EFam
'Short Distance' (IB) — EWoo SIri
'Show Me Yellow' (SDB) — NZep
'Showman' (TB) — ERou
shrevei — see *I. virginica* var. *shrevei*
'Shurton Inn' (TB) — CKel WCAu
'Shy Violet' (SDB) — NZep
sibirica ♀H4 — More than 30 suppliers
 - 'Ann Dasch' — EBee WLin
 - 'Annemarie Troeger' ♀H4 — EBee NBre
 - 'Anniversary' — CDes CLAP CMdw EBee LRHS MBNS WLin
 - 'Atoll' — SIri
 - 'Baby Sister' — CAby CMHG EBee EBla EBrs EGle GAbr GBin LRHS MBri NBre NBro SWat WAul WWFP
 - 'Berlin Bluebird' — LPhx SMHy
 - 'Berlin Ruffles' ♀H4 **new** — CIri
 - 'Berlin Sky' — ESgl
 - 'Bickley Cape' — EBee
 - 'Blaue Milchstrasse' ♀H4 — GBin
 - 'Blaumacher' **new** — GBuc
 - 'Blue Burgee' — ECha
I - 'Blue Butterfly' **new** — SHBN
N - 'Blue Emperor' — EBee
 - 'Blue King' — CKel COtt EBee EBla EChP EGle ELan EPfP GMaP LRHS MBNS MDun MRav NBro NGdn NMoo SPer SPoG WLin WMnd WMoo
 - 'Blue Meadow Fly' — EBee
 - 'Blue Mere' — WLin
 - 'Blue Moon' — CPrp CRez WFar
 - 'Blue Pennant' — CWrd EBee GBin
 - 'Blue Reverie' — CPen EPPr ESgl
N - 'Blue Sceptre' — IBlr
 - 'Blue Seraph' — GBin
 - 'Blueberry Fair' **new** — CIri

	Name	Suppliers
	- 'Bournemouth Beauty' ♀H4	CIri
	- 'Bridal Jig'	CWrd EBee GBin
	- 'Butter and Sugar' ♀H4	More than 30 suppliers
	- 'Caesar'	CRow SDys SRms WLin
	- 'Caesar's Brother'	CBgR CPrp EBee EChP EGle ELan EMil IBlr LRHS MNFA NBro SPer SWal SWat WCAu WCMO WWhi WLin
	- 'Camberley'	
	- 'Cambridge' ♀H4	EBee EBla ECGP MBri MNFA MSte NBre NHol SBch SWat WCAu WFar WOut
	- 'Canonbury Belle'	WLin
	- 'Charming Darlene'	CWrd
	- 'Chartreuse Bounty'	EBee EChP EGle EMan ERou EWes GAbr GQue ITim LAst MAvo MBNS MLLN NBPC NLar NMoo NPri NSti SUsu WWeb
N	- 'Chateuse Belle'	CWrd WBrE
	- 'Circle Round'	CSpe EPPr LPhx
	- 'Clee Hills'	WLin
	- 'Cleedownton' ♀H4	WLin
	- 'Cleve Dodge' **new**	ESgI SIri
	- 'Clouded Moon'	see *I. sibirica* 'Forncett Moon'
	- 'Cool Spring'	WLin
	- 'Coquet Waters'	NBid WLin
	- 'Coronation Anthem'	NEgg WAul WLin
	- cream	see *I. sibirica* 'Primrose Cream'
	- 'Crème Chantilly' ♀H4	WLin
	- 'Dance Ballerina Dance'	CFir CRow CWCL EBee EChP EMan ERou EWTr GBri GQue MLLN MNFA NBPC NCGa NMoo SMrm SUsu SWat WCMO WFar WPtf WSan
N	- 'Dancing Moon'	CWrd
	- 'Dancing Nanou'	NBre SWat
	- 'Dark Circle'	CWrd EBee
I	- 'Dark Delight' **new**	CWrd
	- 'Dear Delight'	EPPr
	- 'Dear Dianne'	CKel ECha NBre
	- 'Dewful'	CWrd WFar WLin
	- 'Dirigo Black Velvet' **new**	CIri
	- 'Double Standards' **new**	CIri
	- 'Dragonfly'	WWhi
	- 'Dreaming Green'	CWrd WLin
	- 'Dreaming Orange'	CWrd
	- 'Dreaming Spires' ♀H4	ESgI SIri
	- 'Dreaming Yellow' ♀H4	CBre CFee EBee ECha EGle EMan EPfP EShb EGac MNFA MRav MWgw NBro NChi NGdn SBch SHBN SPer WCAu WMoo WWhi
	- 'Ego'	COtt ECha GBin GMac GSki LRHS NBro NCGa NGby SWat WLin WMoo WPrP
	- 'Elinor Hewitt'	EWTr
	- 'Ellesmere'	NGdn
	- 'Emma Ripeka' **new**	WAul WLin
	- 'Emperor'	CRow CWat ERou MSte MWgw NBre NBur NSti SMrm SWat WLin
	- 'Eric the Red'	IBlr NBur
	- 'Ever Again'	CWrd
	- 'Ewen'	CBgR CLAP CMdw CPou CRow CSam EBee EGle GBin GBuc IBlr MNFA MNrw NGdn SWat WFar WPrP WWhi WWlt
	- 'Exuberant Encore' ♀H4	CWrd WCAu
	- 'Flight of Butterflies'	More than 30 suppliers
§	- 'Forncett Moon'	GMac WLin
	- 'Fourfold Lavender'	EBee GSki WAul
	- 'Fourfold White'	ESgI GMac LPhx LRHS
	- 'Gatineau'	CDes CLAP EBee GBuc
N	- 'Gerbel Mantel'	GBin GMac SHBN SPet WFar WHil
	- 'Grand Junction' **new**	WLin
	- 'Gull's Wing'	EBee
	- 'Harpswell Hallelujah'	EBee
	- 'Harpswell Happiness' ♀H4	CHVG CLAP CPrp EBee EGle EPfP EPyc GBin MBri SWat WAul WMoo
	- 'Harpswell Haze'	ECha WMoo
	- 'Harpswell Velvet'	CWrd
	- 'Heavenly Blue'	EHon WLin WWpP
	- 'Helen Astor'	CBos CDes CHVG CLAP CMea CRow CSam CTri EAEE EBee EGle EShb LRHS MBNS MHar MRav SWat WLin
	- 'High Standards'	CWrd
N	- 'Himmel von Komi'	GBin
	- 'Hoar Edge'	WLin
	- 'Hubbard'	CMMP CPen EShb GBin MNrw NBro NHol WHrl
	- 'Illini Charm'	CPen EChP GSki NBro SSvw WFar WMoo WWhi
	- 'Isla Serle' ♀H4	WLin
	- 'Jac-y-do'	WLin
	- 'Jewelled Crown'	CPen WFar
	- 'Kabluey' **new**	CIri
	- 'Kathleen Mary' ♀H4	WLin
	- 'Kingfisher'	WLin
	- 'Lady Vanessa'	CPou CWrd EBee EGle EPPr ERou GAbr GBin LBuc MRav NBro NMoo NSti WAul WHil WSan
	- 'Langthorns Pink'	CMdw EGle ELan MRav WLin
	- 'Laurenbuhl'	CPLG WLin
	- 'Lavender Bounty'	EBee EBla EGle NBre NBro SPet WCAu WHil WHoo
	- 'Lavender Light'	WLin
	- 'Leo Hewitt'	WLin
	- 'Limeheart'	CPou CSev EBrs EGle ELan ERou
N	- 'Limelight'	LRHS
	- 'Little Blue'	EBee LRHS
	- 'Little Sister' **new**	GBuc
N	- 'Little Twinkle Star'	CWrd EBee GBin NPro WFar
	- 'Llyn Brianne'	WLin
	- 'Mabel Coday' **new**	WLin
	- 'Mad Magenta' **new**	WCAu
	- 'Maranatha'	NBre
	- 'Marcus Perry'	CRow MSte
	- 'Marilyn Holmes'	EBee EGle NFor WCMO WCot
	- 'Marshmallow Frosting'	WFar
§	- 'Melton Red Flare'	CMHG CPen EBee EBla EHon ELan EMan EPPr EShb GBin LRHS MBNS SBch SDys WCAu WCra WFar WWpP
	- 'Memphis Memory' **new**	CWrd
	- 'Mesa Pearl' **new**	CIri
	- 'Moon Moth'	WLin
	- 'Moon Silk'	CFwr CWrd EBee EPyc GBin WHrl
	- 'Mountain Lake'	CPen CSam EAEE EMan EPPr GBin LRHS SBch SWat WCAu
	- 'Mrs Rowe'	CDes CFee CPou CRow EBee EBla EGle EGra EPPr GBuc LLWP MNFA MRav MSte MWat SWat WCAu WFar WLin WPtf WTin
	- 'Mrs Saunders'	WLin
	- 'My Love'	WLin
	- 'Navy Brass'	EGle GBuc NBre
	- 'Night Breeze'	SIri
	- 'Niklas Sea' **new**	GBin
	- 'Nora Distin'	WLin
	- 'Nottingham Lace'	EBee GMac SWat WLin
	- 'Oban' ♀H4	GBuc WLin
	- 'Orville Fay'	EChP GMac WCMO WCot WFar
	- 'Ottawa'	CPou CRow ECGP ELan ERou LRHS MBNS SWat WFar
	- 'Outset'	EBee GSki SSvw
I	- 'Pageant'	WCot
I	- 'Painted Desert'	CWrd EBee
	- 'Papillon'	CAvo CTri EBee EBla EChP ECtt EGle ELan EPPr ERou GMac LHop LRHS MAvo MNFA NBir NBro NCob NGdn NHol NSti SPer SWat WCMO WFar WLin WPer WPnP

N	- 'Pearl Queen'	CBos MTPN WFar
	- 'Peg Edwards'	EBee
	- 'Percheron'	ESgI SIri
	- 'Perfect Vision' ♀H4 **new**	WLin
	- 'Perry's Blue'	More than 30 suppliers
I	- 'Perry's Favourite'	CFee CRow
	- 'Perry's Pigmy'	GBuc WLin
	- 'Persimmon' misapplied	see *I. sibirica* 'Tycoon'
	- 'Persimmon' ambig.	CFir EAEE EBee EBla ECtt EGle EMFW EMan ERou LRHS MArl MNFA MWat NMoo SWat WFar WMoo
*	- 'Phosphor Flame'	WLin
	- 'Pink Haze'	CHar CRow EBee EGle EMan EPfP ESgI EWTr GBin GQue MLLN MNFA MTis NBro NMoo NSti SPur WAul WHrl WLin
	- 'Pirate Prince'	NPer WCra WHoo
	- Plant World hybrids	CBrm MDKP SWal
	- 'Plissee' ♀H4	GBin WLin
	- 'Polly Dodge'	EBrs
	- 'Pontypool'	WLin
	- 'Pounsley Purple'	CPou
§	- 'Primrose Cream'	WCot WLin
	- 'Prussian Blue' ♀H4	WLin
	- 'Purple Cloak'	MSte
	- 'Purple Mere'	WFar WLin
N	- 'Red Flag'	NHol
	- 'Reddy Maid'	WCAu
	- 'Redflare'	see *I. sibirica* 'Melton Red Flare'
N	- 'Regality'	CWCL EWTr MBNS MMuc NBPC NBro SHBN SHGN
	- 'Regency Belle' ♀H4	SIri
	- 'Regency Buck'	CWrd
	- 'Rikugi-sakura'	EBla EMan LTwo NBPC NBhm NBro WCot WSan
	- 'Roanoke's Choice'	CElw CFwr CWrd EBee GBin NCGa WHrl
	- 'Roaring Jelly'	WCAu
	- 'Roger Perry'	CFee
	- 'Rosseline' ♀H4	WLin
	- 'Royal Blue'	ECha GBuc SWat
	- 'Ruby Wine'	CPen
	- 'Ruffled Velvet' ♀H4	More than 30 suppliers
	- 'Ruffles Plus'	CWrd
	- 'Savoir Faire'	ECha
	- 'Sea Horse'	GBuc WLin
	- 'Sea Shadows'	CBos ESgI MBri NBir WCAu
	- 'Seren Wib'	WLin
	- 'Shaker's Prayer'	CIri CWrd WAul
	- 'Shall We Dance' ♀H4	WAul
	- 'Shirley Pope' ♀H4	CAby CDes EBee EBrs EGle GAbr GBin GMac GQue LPhx LRHS MBri MNFA NCGa NMoo NSti SMeo SUsu WAul WCMO WCot WFar WMoo
	- 'Shirley's Choice'	SIri
	- 'Showdown'	EBee ECtt EGle GMaP LRHS NHol SAga SHBN SWat WCAu WFar
	- 'Shrawley'	WCAu
	- 'Silberkante'	WLin
	- 'Silver Edge' ♀H4	More than 30 suppliers
	- 'Simple Gifts' **new**	CIri
	- 'Sky Wings'	CRow ECha EGle MArl WMoo
	- 'Smudger's Gift' ♀H4	WLin
	- 'Snow Prince'	CWrd
	- 'Snow Queen'	see *I. sanguinea* 'Snow Queen'
	- 'Snowcrest'	CBre SPur WLin
	- 'Soft Blue' ♀H4	CDes EBee NBre SMHy WLin
N	- 'Southcombe White'	COIW CRow GBin GBuc GCal MHar NGdn SIri
	- 'Sparkling Rosé'	More than 30 suppliers
	- 'Splashdown' (Sino-Sib)	SWat
	- 'Star Cluster' **new**	CWrd
	- 'Steve'	CHVG CPar EBee EChP MLLN MNFA NBro NCGa SWat WAul
	- 'Steve Varner'	SIri WFar WLin
	- 'Strawberry Fair' **new**	CIri
	- 'Summer Sky'	CBre SWat WAul WCAu WCMO WCot WLin WTin
	- 'Super Ego'	WTin
	- 'Superba'	WLin
	- 'Taldra'	WLin
	- 'Tal-y-Bont'	WFar WLin
	- 'Tanz Nochmal'	GBin
	- 'Teal Velvet'	ECha GSki SIri WCAu WFar
	- 'Tealwood'	WLin
	- 'Temper Tantrum'	CKel CWrd
	- 'Thelma Perry'	WLin
	- 'Tornado Rose' **new**	CIri
	- 'Tropic Night'	More than 30 suppliers
§	- 'Tycoon'	EAEE EBee EBrs EShb GBin GBuc IBlr LRHS MNFA NChi NHol SBch SPer
	- 'Valda'	EBee
	- 'Vee One'	WLin
	- 'Velvet Night'	WBrE WLin
	- 'Vi Luihn'	CBcs ECha EPPr WMoo
N	- 'Violet Skies'	EBee GBin SUsu
	- 'Visual Treat'	SIri
	- 'Walter'	EBee
	- 'Weisse Etagen'	WLin
	- 'Welcome Return'	CHVG EBee GBin GQue NBro NMoo SUsu SWat WFar WMoo
N	- 'Welfenfürstin'	GBin
	- 'Welfenprinz' ♀H4	WLin
I	- 'White Queen'	EBla ESgI SWat WBrE
I	- 'White Swan'	LAst
	- 'White Swirl' ♀H4	More than 30 suppliers
	- 'White Triangles'	SIri
	- white-flowered	EGle WOut
	- 'Wisley White'	MWgw NBre
	- 'Yankee Consul'	CWrd
	- 'Zweites Hundert' **new**	NBre
§	'Sibirica Alba'	CBrm CRow ECha EDAr EPfP EShb GAbr GBBs LLWP MHer SIng SWat WBrk WCFE WFar WWpP WWye
§	'Sibirica Baxteri'	CFee
	sichuanensis	EPot
	sieboldii	see *I. sanguinea*
	'Sierra Blue' (TB)	ESgI
	'Sierra Grande' (TB)	EFam EWoo WCAu
	'Sign of Leo' (TB)	EFam
	sikkimensis	GIBF
	'Silent Strings' (IB)	MBri
	'Silicon Prairie' (TB)	ESgI
	'Silk Romance' (TB) **new**	EFam
	'Silver Dividends' (TB)	EFam
	'Silver Screen' (TB) **new**	EFam
	'Silverado' (TB)	CKel ESgI WCAu
	'Silvery Beauty' (Dut)	GBBs NBir SPer WFar
	sindjarensis	see *I. aucheri*
	'Sindpers' (Juno) ♀H3	WWst
	'Sinister Desire' (TB) **new**	WCAu
	sintenisii ♀H4	CBro CPBP EHyt NWCA
	- HH&K 172	CMdw
	'Sir Michael' (TB)	ESgI
	'Sissinghurst' (SDB)	WIvy
	'Sister Helen' (TB)	EFam
	'Siva Siva' (TB)	ENot ERou MRav WCAu
	'Skating Party' (TB)	CKel ESgI EWoo
	'Skiers' Delight' (TB)	NBre WCAu
	'Skookumchuck' (TB) **new**	EFam
	'Sky and Sun' (TB) **new**	CIri
	'Skye Blue' (TB) **new**	EFam
	'Skyfire' (TB)	ESgI MWea
	'Skyline' (Juno)	WWst
	'Skyship' (TB) **new**	CIri
	'Slap Bang' (SDB)	ESgI NZep
	'Sleepy Time' (MDB)	NZep
	'Small Sky' (SDB)	CBro
N	'Smart Girl' (TB)	CKel SMrm

	'Smell the Roses' (SDB)	EFam NZep
	'Smokey Dream' (TB)	CKel
	'Sneezy' (TB) **new**	WCAu
	'Snow Cloud' (TB)	EWoo
	'Snow Festival' (IB)	NZep
	'Snow Fiddler' (MTB)	NZep
	'Snow Plum' (IB) **new**	SIri
	'Snow Tracery' (TB)	ENot MBri
	'Snow Tree' (SDB)	NZep
	'Snow Troll' (SDB)	WCAu
	'Snowbrook' (TB)	WCAu
	'Snowcone' (IB)	ESgI
	'Snow-in-Summer' (TB) **new**	EFam
	'Snowmound' (TB)	CKel WCAu
	'Snowy Owl' (TB) ♀H4	CKel WCAu
	'Soaring Kite' (TB)	WCAu
	'Social Event' (TB)	ESgI WCAu
	sofarana from Lebanon LB 400	CMon
	'Soft Breeze' (SDB)	NZep
	'Soft Caress' (TB)	WCAu
	'Solid Mahogany' (TB)	EFam MRav WCAu
	'Solstice' (TB)	EFam
	'Sombrero Way' (TB) **new**	EFam
	'Somerset Blue' (TB) ♀H4	CKel WCAu
N	'Somerset Vale' (TB)	SMrm
	'Somerton Brocade' (SDB)	CKel WDav
	'Somerton Dance' (SDB)	CKel
	'Son of Sun' (Spuria) **new**	CIri
	'Sonata in Blue' (TB) **new**	EFam
	'Song of Norway' (TB)	EPPr ESgI NZep SIri WAul WCAu
	'Sonoran Sands' (IB) **new**	CIri
	'Sonoran Señorita' (Spuria) ♀H4	CIri
	'Sopra il Vulcano' (BB)	ESgI
	'Sostenique' (TB)	ESgI WCAu
	'Soul Power' (TB)	ERou
	'Sound of Gold' (TB) **new**	EFam
	'Southern Clipper' (SDB)	MBri
	'Southern Spy' (TB)	EFam
	'Sovereign Crown' (TB) **new**	EFam
	'Space Mist' (TB)	EFam
	'Spanish Coins' (MTB)	NZep
	'Sparkplug' (SDB) **new**	ESgI
	'Sparks Fly' (SDB) **new**	WCAu
N	'Spartan'	CKel
	'Spatzel' (TB) **new**	EFam
	'Special Feature' (TB) **new**	EFam
	'Speed Limit' (TB)	EFam
	'Spellbreaker' (TB)	ESgI EWoo
	'Spice Lord' (TB)	WCAu
	'Spiced Custard' (TB)	ESgI
	'Spiced Tiger' (TB)	WCAu
	'Spinning Wheel' (TB)	SIri
	'Spirit of Fiji' (TB) **new**	EFam
	'Spirit of Memphis' (TB)	EFam
	'Splash of Red' (SDB)	NZep
	'Splashacata' (TB) **new**	CIri
	'Split Decision' (SDB)	NZep
	'Spot of Tea' (MDB) **new**	ESgI
	'Spreckles' (TB)	ESgI
	sprengeri	SOkd
	'Spring Festival' (TB)	WCAu
	'Spun Gold' (TB)	ESgI
	spuria	CPou ELan GSki NEgg
	- subsp. *carthaliniae*	WPer
§	- subsp. *halophila*	GBin GIBF WCAu
	- subsp. *maritima*	EMan SMHy
§	- subsp. *musulmanica*	GIBF
	- subsp. *ochroleuca*	see *I. orientalis* Mill.
	- subsp. *spuria*	GBuc GIBF
	- var. *subbarbata*	GIBF
	x *squalens*	WCAu
	'Stairway to Heaven' (TB)	WCAu
	'Stapleford' (SDB)	CBro EGle
	'Staplehurst' (MTB) ♀H4 **new**	CIri WAul
	'Star Performer' (TB)	EFam
	'Star Prince' (SDB) **new**	ESgI
	'Star Shine' (TB)	WCAu
	'Starcrest' (TB)	ESgI WAul
	'Starfrost Pink' (TB) **new**	EFam
	'Starring' (TB) **new**	CIri
	'Starship' (TB)	EFam ESgI
	'Starship Enterprise' (TB) **new**	CIri
	'Staten Island' (TB)	ENot ESgI MBri SRms WCAu WTin
	'Status Seeker' (TB)	WCAu
	'Stella Polaris' (TB)	COlW
	'Stellar Lights' (TB)	EWoo WCAu
§	*stenophylla*	EPot SBla
	'Stepping Out' (TB) ♀H4	EBee EPfP ESgI EShb GBin IPot LRHS MWea NBre WAul WCAu
	'Stinger' (SDB) ♀H4	CIri
	'Stingray' (TB)	EFam
	'Stitch in Time' (TB)	EWoo WCAu
	'Stitch Witch' (SDB) **new**	MOak
	'Stockholm' (SDB)	CKel NZep WDav
	stolonifera 'Sina Dark' **new**	WWst
	'Storm Center' (TB)	SIri
	'Stormy Circle' (SDB) **new**	WCAu
	'Stormy Night' (TB)	EFam
	'Strange Child' (SDB)	NZep
	'Strawberry Sensation' (TB)	NZep
	'Strictly Jazz' (TB) **new**	EFam WCAu
	'Striking' (TB)	EWoo
	'Strozzapretti' (TB) **new**	CIri
	'Study In Black' (TB)	WCAu
	stylosa	see *I. unguicularis*
§	*suaveolens*	CBro CPou EHyt NMen SRot WDav WIvy
	- 'Rubromarginata'	ERos NJOw
*	- var. *violacea*	NMen NWCA WLin
	subbiflora	CMon
	subbiflora x *timofejewii*	WCot
	'Sugar' (IB)	NSti WCAu
	'Sugar Blues' (TB) **new**	EFam
	'Sugar Snaps' (IB)	EFam
	'Suky' (TB) **new**	EFam
	'Sultan's Palace' (TB)	CRez ECho ESgI SCoo SMer STes WBor WCMO
	'Sumatra' (TB)	ESgI
	'Summer Falls' **new**	MOak
	'Summer Green Shadows' (TB)	EFam
	'Summer Holidays' (TB)	EFam
	'Summer Luxury' (TB)	NZep
	'Summer's Smile' (TB)	ESgI
	'Sun Dappled' (TB)	ERou
	'Sun Doll' (SDB) ♀H4	EFam NZep
	'Sun King' (TB)	EFam
	'Sunchime' (SDB) **new**	EFam
	'Sundown Red' (IB)	NBir
	'Sunmaster' (TB)	EFam
	'Sunny and Warm' (TB)	CKel
	'Sunny Dawn' (IB) ♀H4	CKel EFam WDav
	'Sunny Disposition' (TB) **new**	EFam
	'Sunny Honey' (IB)	NZep
	'Sunny Red Wine' (Cal-Sib)	GBin
	'Sunny Smile' (SDB) **new**	EFam
	'Sunny Tyke' (MDB)	EFam
	'Sunrise in Sonora' (Spuria) ♀H4	CIri
	'Sunset Colors' (Spuria) ♀H4	CIri
	'Sunset Point' (TB) **new**	CIri
	'Sunshine Boy' (IB) **new**	CKel

'Sunshine Isle' (SDB)	NZep	
'Superstition' (TB) ♀H4	ELan EPPr ESgI GBin SIri SMrm WCAu	
'Supreme Sultan' (TB)	EFam ESgI EWoo WCAu	
'Susan Bliss' (TB)	CRez EBee ELan EPfP ESgI GMaP MBNS NBre WCAu	
svetlanae	WWst	
'Swain' (TB)	ESgI	
'Swaledale' (TB)	WCAu	
'Swazi Princess' (TB)	CKel ESgI WCAu	
'Sweet Kate' (SDB) ♀H4	WCAu	
'Sweet Lena' (TB) **new**	ESgI	
'Sweet Musette' (TB)	EFam WCAu	
'Sweeter than Wine' (TB)	WCAu	
'Sweetheart Ring' (TB) **new**	EFam	
'Swingtown' (TB)	WCAu	
'Sybil' (TB)	GBin	
'Sylvan' (TB) **new**	EFam	
'Sylvia Murray' (TB)	WCAu	
'Symphony' (Dut)	ECho NBir	
'Syncopation' (TB)	ESgI WCAu	
'Tahitian Pearl' (TB) **new**	CIri	
'Talish' (Reticulata)	WWst	
'Talk' (SDB) **new**	EFam	
'Tall Chief' (TB)	EAEE MTis WCAu	
N 'Tanex' **new**	ECho	
'Tang Fizz' (TB) **new**	EFam	
'Tangerine Sky' (TB)	SCoo WCAu	
'Tangfu' (IB)	ESgI	
'Tantara' (SDB)	WTin	
'Tanzanian Tangerine' (TB)	WCAu	
'Tarheel Elf' (SDB)	ESgI WTin	
'Tarn Hows' (TB)	SRms WCAu	
'Tarot' (BB) ♀H4 **new**	EFam	
'Tatiana' (TB) **new**	EFam	
'Taverlae' **new**	EBrs	
'Tea Leaves' (TB)	EFam	
tectorum	CAby CSWP EHol ERos GBin GIBF GKev GSki NWCA	
- 'Alba'	CPBP EPPr ERos	
- 'Variegata' misapplied	see *I. japonica* 'Variegata'	
- 'Variegata' ambig. (v)	EBee EMan EPPr EWTr MRav NSti SPoG WFar	
'Teesdale' (TB) **new**	EFam	
'Tell Fibs' (SDB)	CBro	
'Temple Gold' (TB)	CKel NPer	
'Temple Meads' (IB)	EFam ESgI WCAu	
'Templecloud' (IB) ♀H4	CHar CKel	
'Tempting Fate' (TB)	EWoo	
'Ten' (SDB)	NZep	
§ *tenax*	CLAP CNic CPBP ECho ETow GBuc GEdr GSki NWCA WBVN	
'Tender Years' (IB)	WAul	
'Tennessee Gentleman' (TB) **new**	EFam	
'Tennessee Vol' (TB)	EFam	
'Tennison Ridge' (TB) **new**	EFam WCAu	
tenuissima	GBuc	
- subsp. *tenuissima* **new**	CPBP NMen	
'Terra Rosa' (TB)	CIri	
'Terre de Feu' (TB)	ESgI	
'Thais' (TB)	ESgI	
'That's Red' (MTB) **new**	CIri WCAu	
'The Bride'	see *I.* 'Bride'	
'The Red Douglas' (TB)	ESgI	
'The Rocket'	see *I.* 'Rocket'	
'Theatre' (TB)	ESgI	
'Then Again' (TB) **new**	EFam	
'Third Charm' (SDB)	CBro EFam	
'Third World' (TB)	CBro	
'Thornbird' (TB) ♀H4	EFam ESgI WCAu	
'Thousand Lakes' (SDB)	NZep	
'Three Cherries' (MDB)	CBro ECho EGle	
'Three Seasons' (TB) **new**	EFam	
'Thriller' (TB)	ESgI WCAu	

thunbergii	see *I. sanguinea*	
'Thunder Echo' (TB)	ESgI	
'Tickle Me' (MDB)	WCAu	
'Tide's In' (TB)	ERou EWoo	
'Tiffany' (TB)	WTin	
'Tiffany Time' (TB) **new**	EFam	
'Tiger Butter' (TB)	ESgI	
'Tiger Honey' (TB)	CIri WCAu	
tigridia	WCot	
'Tiki Bird' (Sino-Sib) **new**	CIri	
'Tillamook' (TB)	WCAu	
'Time Piece' (TB) **new**	CKel	
'Time Traveller' (TB) **new**	CIri	
'Ting Tang' (SDB) **new**	EFam	
tingitana var. *fontanesii*	EBee WPGP	
- - AB&S 4452 from Morocco	CMon	
- - AB&S 4521	CMon	
'Tinkerbell' (SDB)	CPBP EGle MSte NBir SPet	
'Tintinara' (TB) ♀H4	CKel	
'Tiny Freckles' (MDB)	NZep	
'Tir Na Nog' (SB)	CIri	
'Titan's Glory' (TB) ♀H4	ESgI MRav WAul WCAu WCot	
'To the Point' (TB)	WCAu	
'Toasted Watermelon' (TB) **new**	CIri WCAu	
'Tol-long' ♀H4	see *I. missouriensis* 'Tollong'	
'Tom Johnson' (TB)	WCAu	
'Tom Tit' (TB)	WCAu	
'Tomingo' (SDB)	WCAu	
'Tomorrow's Child' (TB)	ESgI	
'Toni Lynn' (MDB)	EHyt	
'Toots' (SDB)	EGle WTin	
'Top Flight' (TB)	EChP ELan ERou LAst SHBN SMrm SRms	
N 'Topolino' (TB)	CKel SAga	
'Topsy Turvy' (MTB)	NBre	
'Total Eclipse' (TB)	SRms	
'Total Recall' (TB) **new**	EFam	
'Toucan Tango' (TB) **new**	CIri	
'Touch of Mahogany' (TB) **new**	CIri WCAu	
'Touch of Spring' (TB)	EFam	
'Tracy Tyrene' (TB)	ESgI	
transylvanica	GIBF	
'Travelling North' (TB) **new**	EFam	
'Trenwith' (TB)	CKel	
'Trick or Treat' (TB)	EFam	
'Trillion' (TB)	CIri	
'Triple Whammy' (TB)	EFam ESgI	
trojana	CMon	
'True Navy' (SDB) **new**	WCAu	
'Tu Tu Turquoise' (SDB)	NZep	
tuberosa	see *Hermodactylus tuberosus*	
'Tumbleweeds' (SDB)	NZep	
'Tumultueux' (TB)	ESgI	
N 'Tuscan' (TB)	CMil	
'Tut's Gold' (TB)	ESgI WCAu	
'Tweety Bird' (SDB) **new**	EFam	
'Twice Told' (TB) **new**	EFam	
'Twin' **new**	WWst	
'Two Rubies' (SDB)	NZep	
'Tyke' (MTB)	NZep	
typhifolia	NEgg	
'Tyrian Dream' (IB) **new**	WCAu	
§ *unguicularis* ♀H4	More than 30 suppliers	
- 'Abington Purple'	CBro CPen WCMO WCot	
- 'Alba'	CBro WMnd	
N - 'Bob Thompson'	CBro	
- subsp. *carica* var. *angustifolia*	WSHC	
§ - subsp. *cretensis*	CAby EBee ECho EPPr EPot NMen SHGN WAbe	
- - 'Mount Ida' **new**	SBla	
- - white-flowered	SBla	
- 'Diana Clare'	WCMO WCot	

	- 'Kilndown'	WFar
	- var. *lazica*	see *I. lazica*
N	- 'Marondera'	CAvo
	- 'Mary Barnard' ♀H4	CAvo CBro CFee CHar CPen CPou
		CSam ECGP ECha ECho EHrv
		ENot GEdr IBlr MAvo NBir NMen
		SBla SHBN WCMO WCot WMnd
N	- 'Oxford Dwarf'	CBro ECho
N	- 'Palette'	ELan
§	- 'Walter Butt'	CAvo ECGP ECho NBir SBla SRot
		WFar WLin WSHC
	'Up Dancing' (TB) **new**	EFam
	uromovii	GBuc MArl
	'Vague a l'Ame' (TB)	ESgI
	'Valimar' (TB)	WCAu
	'Vamp' (IB)	CKel EPPr SIri
	'Vandal Spirit' (TB)	ESgI
N	'Vanilla Fluff'	CWrd
	'Vanity' (TB) ♀H4	ESgI WCAu
	'Vanity's Child' (TB)	ERou WCAu
§	*variegata* ♀H4	CMea EGoo GCal GIBF WCAu
		WCot
§	- var. *reginae*	WCAu
	'Vegas Heat' (BB) **new**	CIri
	'Vegas Showgirl' (SDB)	NZep
	'Velvet Toy' (MDB)	EHyt
	'Veneer' (TB)	CIri
	'Verity Blamey' (TB)	CKel
	verna	ERos NHol
	versicolor ♀H4	CArn CBen CDWL CElw CRow
		EBee EHon EMFW EPPr GBin
		GKev GSki IBlr LNCo LPBA LRHS
		MNHC MNrw MSal NGdn SPlb
		SRms SWat WBrk WFar WMAq
		WShi WTin WWpP
	- 'Between the Lines'	CRow
	- 'Candystriper'	SIri
	- 'China West Lake'	CRow
	- 'Claret Cup'	CPou CWrd
	- 'Dottie's Double'	CRow
	- 'Georgia Bay'	CRow
N	- 'Goldbrook'	EGol
	- 'Kermesina'	CDWL CRow CWat EBee ECha
		EGol EHon ELan EMFW GBuc
		GCal GGar IBlr LPBA NBlu NPer
		NSti SRms SWat WBrk WEas WFar
		WMAq WMoo WPnP WWpP
	- 'Mint Fresh'	SIri
	- 'Mysterious Monique'	CDWL CMdw CRow
	- 'Party Line'	SIri
	- purple	GSki
	- var. *rosea*	CRow
	- 'Rowden Allegro'	CRow
	- 'Rowden Aria'	CRow
	- 'Rowden Cadenza'	CRow
	- 'Rowden Cantata'	CRow
	- 'Rowden Concerto'	CRow
	- 'Rowden Fugue'	CRow
	- 'Rowden Lyric'	CRow
	- 'Rowden Mazurka'	CRow
	- 'Rowden Nocturne'	CRow
	- 'Rowden Prelude'	CRow
	- 'Rowden Refrain'	CRow
	- 'Rowden Rondo'	CRow
	- 'Rowden Sonata'	CRow
	- 'Rowden Symphony'	CRow
	- 'Rowden Waltz'	CRow
	- 'Silvington'	CRow
	- 'Whodunit'	CRow
	'Vert Galant' (TB)	ESgI
	'Vibrant' (TB)	WCAu
	'Vibrations' (TB)	ESgI
	vicaria	ECho EPot GKev LEdu WWst
I	- 'Sina'	WWst
	'Victoria Falls' (TB)	EFam ESgI MOak WCAu
	'Vinho Verde' (IB) ♀H4	CKel

	'Vino Rosso' (SDB)	ESgI
	'Vintage Press' (IB)	WCAu
	'Vintage Year' (Spuria)	WCAu
	violacea	see *I. spuria* subsp. *musulmanica*
	'Violet Beauty' (Reticulata)	EPot GKev LPhx LRHS MBow
	'Violet Classic' (TB)	WCAu
	'Violet Icing' (TB) ♀H4	CKel EFam
	'Violet Music' (TB) **new**	EFam
	'Violet Returns' (TB) **new**	EFam
	'Violet Rings' (TB)	WCAu
	'Viper' (IB) **new**	CIri
	'Virginia Bauer' (TB) **new**	EFam
	virginica 'De Luxe'	see *I.* x *robusta* 'Dark Aura'
	- 'Pond Crown Point'	CRow
	- 'Pond Lilac Dream'	CRow
N	- 'Purple Fan'	CRow
§	- var. *shrevei*	CRow WCAu
	'Vitafire'	SIri
	'Vitality' (IB)	ESgI
	'Vive la France' (TB)	ESgI EWoo
	'Vizier' (TB) **new**	WCAu
	'Voila' (IB)	ESgI NZep
	'Volts' (SDB)	CKel
	'Voluminous' (TB) **new**	CIri
	'Volute' (TB)	ESgI
	'Voyage' (SDB)	EWoo
	'Wabash' (TB)	EBee ELan ERou ESgI WCAu WTin
	'Walker Ferguson' (Spuria)	WCAu
	'Walter Butt'	see *I. unguicularis* 'Walter Butt'
	'Waltz Across Texas' (TB) **new**	EFam
	'War Chief' (TB)	ESgI WCAu
	'War Sails' (TB)	SIri WCAu
	warleyensis	WWst
	'Warl-sind' (Juno)	EPot WWst
	'Warranty' (TB) **new**	WCAu
	'Warrior King' (TB)	WCAu
	'Waterboy' (SDB)	NZep
	'Watercolor' (SDB)	NZep
	wattii	CMon GCal MGol
	'Way to Go' (TB) **new**	CIri
	'Webelos' (SDB)	EGle
	'Wedding Candles' (TB)	WCAu
	'Wedding Vow' (TB)	CKel
	'Wedgwood' (Dut)	NBre
	'Well Suited' (SDB)	EWoo
	'Westar' (SDB) ♀H4	CKel NZep
	'Westwell' (SDB)	WCAu
	'What Again' (SDB)	SUsu
	'Wheels' (SDB)	WTin
	'Whispering Spirits' (TB) **new**	CIri
	'White Bridge' (Dut)	MSph
	'White City' (TB)	CHad EAEE EFam EPfP GMaP
		MRav NPer SCoo SDnm SHBN SIri
		SPer SPoG SRms SWat WAul WCAu
		WMnd
N	'White Cliffs of Dover'	NEgg
	'White Excelsior' (Dut)	ECho
	'White Knight' (TB)	EBee ELan ENot EPfP NBre SCoo
		WMnd
	'White Lightning' (TB) **new**	EFam
	'White Reprise' (TB)	ESgI
	'White Superior' (Dut)	NBir
	'White Wine' (MTB)	WCAu
	'Whiteladies' (IB) ♀H4	EFam
	'Whitewater River' (Spuria) **new**	CIri
	'Whoop 'em Up' (BB)	EFam NZep
	'Why Not' (IB)	NZep
	'Widdershins' (TB)	CIri
	'Widecombe Fair' (SDB)	WIvy
	'Wild Jasmine' (TB)	WCAu
	'Wild Ruby' (SDB)	CKel
	'Wild West' (TB)	CKel

willmottiana	WWst
- 'Alba'	ECho WWst
'Willowmist' (SDB)	NZep
wilsonii ♀H4	CAby GBBs GBin GBuc GIBF GKev NEgg SMHy
'Windsurfer' (TB) **new**	EFam
'Winemaster' (TB)	EWoo SIri
winogradowii ♀H4	CAvo CBro ECho EHyt EPot ERos GCrs NMen WAbe
'Winter Olympics' (TB)	CMil EBee ESgI EShb LBuc
'Wirral Gold' (IB) **new**	EFam
'Wisteria Sachet' (IB)	WCAu
'Witching' (TB)	EFam WCAu
'Wizard of Id' (SDB)	EGle NZep WTin
'Wondrous' (TB)	CIri ESgI
'Words and Music' (TB) **new**	EFam
'Worlds Beyond' (TB)	WCAu
'Wow' (SDB)	EGle
'Wyckhill' (SDB)	WCAu
'Wyoming Cowboys' (Spuria) ♀H4	CIri
xiphioides	see *I. latifolia*
xiphium	ECho GIBF
- B&S 411 from Portugal	CMon
'Xmas Fires' (TB) **new**	EFam
'Yaquina Blue' (TB)	EWoo WCAu
'Yellow Court' (Sino-Sib)	CRow
'Yellow Girl' (SDB)	NZep
'Yes' (TB) **new**	WCAu
'Young Blood' (IB) **new**	WCAu
'Youth Dew' (TB) **new**	EFam
'Yo-yo' (SDB)	EPPr SIri
'Yvonne Pelletier' (TB)	WCAu
'Zambezi' (TB) **new**	EFam
'Zantha' (TB)	WCAu
'Zero' (SDB) ♀H4 **new**	CKel
'Zinc Pink' (BB)	WCAu
'Zipper' (MDB)	WCAu
'Zowie' (SDB)	NZep

Isatis (Brassicaceae)

glauca	NDov
tinctoria	CAgr CArn CBod CHby COld CRWN CSev EOHP EUnu GPoy ILis LRHS MHer MNHC MSal NDov NVic SECG SIde SPav WBri WCHb WGwG WHer WJek WSel WWye

Ischyrolepis (Restionaceae)

ocreata	CTrC WNor
§ ***subverticillata***	CBig CCtw CHEx CTrC EAmu WMul

Ismene see *Hymenocallis*

Isodon (Lamiaceae)

serra 'Korean Zest'	EBee EGoo WCru

Isolepis (Cyperaceae)

§ ***cernua***	CBrm CHal EBee EMFW EPfP MBri NOak SCoo WDyG WFar WMAq WPrP

Isoloma see *Kohleria*

Isoplexis (Scrophulariaceae)

canariensis	CAbb CBcs CCCN CCtw CHEx CHen CHll CHrt CPLG CRHN CSec CSpe CTbh ECre EDif EDsa EMan EWll LPhx SAga SHFr SPlb WCFE WCMO
* ***cernua***	NHol
chalcantha	CSec
isabelliana	CCCN EBee EShb LDai MGol WCMO WCot

sceptrum	CBcs CCCN CCtw CHEx CHVG CHll CHrt CPLG CRHN CSec CSpe EBee ECre SAPC SArc SHFr WPGP
- pink	CDes CSpe WPGP

Isopogon (Proteaceae)

anethifolius	SPlb

Isopyrum (Ranunculaceae)

biternatum	GBuc NLar
nipponicum	CLAP WCru
thalictroides	WAbe

Isotoma (Campanulaceae)

sp.	LAst SWvt
§ ***axillaris***	CSpe LIck LRHS MOak NPer SBch SCoo SPet SPoG
- 'Fairy Carpet'	EMan NPri SRms
fluviatilis	CBrm ECou NSfd
- white	ECou
'Sapphire Star' **new**	LRHS

Itea (Escalloniaceae)

chinensis ♀H3	WPGP
ilicifolia ♀H3	More than 30 suppliers
japonica 'Beppu'	MGos SLPl
virginica	CAbP CBcs CMCN CMHG CPle EBee ECrN ELan EPfP EWTr MBlu MRav SLon SPer WBVN WFar WOrn
§ - 'Henry's Garnet'	CDoC CEnd CMCN CPMA CWSG EBee EPfP EWTr GAbr LAst LEdu LRHS MBri MGos MWgw NLar NPri SBra SBrw SLim SPoG SRGP SSpi SWvt WDin WGwG
- Little Henry = 'Sprich'PBR	CBgR EBee LAst NLar
- 'Long Spire'	CPMA MBri NLar WDin
- 'Merlot'	CPMA LRHS NLar
- 'Sarah Eve'	CMCN CPMA NLar SRGP
- 'Saturnalia'	NLar WDin
- Swarthmore form	see *I. virginica* 'Henry's Garnet'
yunnanensis	CPLG

Itoa (Flacourtiaceae)

orientalis SF 92300	ISea

Ixia (Iridaceae)

'Blue Bird'	CFir CPrp ECho WHil
'Castor'	ECho WHil
flexuosa	LBow WCMO WCot
'Giant'	ECho WHil
'Hogarth'	CPrp ECho WHil
'Holland Glory'	ECho WHil
'Mabel'	ECho WCot WHil
maculata	CDes LBow WCMO WCot
'Marquette'	ECho WHil
monadelpha	LBow WCMO WCot
paniculata	LBow WCMO
'Panorama'	ECho WHil
pumilio	WCot
purpureorosea 'Saldanha'	ECho
'Rose Emperor'	ECho WHil
'Spotlight'	ECho WHil
thomasiae	WCot
'Venus'	CFir ECho WHil
viridiflora	CBow LBow NWCA WCMO WCot
'Vulcan'	ECho
'Yellow Emperor'	ECho WCMO WCot WHil

Ixiolirion (Ixioliriaceae)

montanum **new**	CPBP ECho NJOw
pallasii	see *I. tataricum*
§ ***tataricum***	CPrp CStu EBee ECho EMan MBri SBch SMeo WCMO
- Ledebourii Group	CAvo CFFs

Ixora (*Rubiaceae*)
  chinensis 'Apricot Queen' SOWG
  'Golden Ball'   SOWG
  'Pink Malay'   SOWG

J

Jaborosa (*Solanaceae*)
  integrifolia   CDes CFir CPLG CStu EBee ELan
                         GEdr WAul WCMO WCot WCru
                         WPGP WPrP XPep

Jacaranda (*Bignoniaceae*)
  acutifolia misapplied   see *J. mimosifolia*
  acutifolia Kunth   MBri
§ *mimosifolia*   CBcs CHll ELan ERea EShb GQui
                            LRav MGol MPRe SDEP SMur
                            SOWG SPlb WMul

Jacobinia see *Justicia*

Jacquemontia (*Convolvulaceae*)
  pentantha **new**   CPlN

Jamesbrittenia (*Scrophulariaceae*)
§ *jurassica*   EHyt

Jamesia (*Hydrangeaceae*)
  americana   CBcs CPle IDee NLar

Jasione (*Campanulaceae*)
§ *crispa*   MDKP
§ *heldreichii*   CSec EBee GAbr LRHS MWrn SBla
                         SRms WCMO
  jankae   see *J. heldreichii*
§ *laevis*   ECho ECot GAbr IHMH LRHS
                         MDKP MLHP SRms WGwG WWFP
§ - 'Blaulicht'   CBrm CCge CFis CMHG CWib
                         EBee ECha ECrN EPfP LRHS MBNS
                         MBri MLan MNFA MWrn NBPC
                         NBlu NEgg NJOw NLar SPla SPlb
                         SUsu SWal WMoo WWeb
  - Blue Light   see *J. laevis* 'Blaulicht'
  - 'Sangster'   CPLG CSec WCMO
  montana   ECho EDAr MBow WPnn WSFF
  perennis   see *J. laevis*

Jasminum (*Oleaceae*)
  CC 4728 **new**   CPLG
  adenophyllum   CPlN
  angulare ♀H1   CRHN ERea EShb SOWG
  - 'Anne Shelton' **new** CPlN
  auriculatum   CPlN
  azoricum ♀H1   CCCN CPlN CRHN ELan EPfP
                          ERea EShb LRHS NPal WMul XPep
  beesianum   More than 30 suppliers
  bignoniaceum   CPlN WSHC
  decussatum   CPlN
  dispermum   CPLG CPlN CRHN WCot
  floridum   EBee EWes XPep
  fruticans   CMac CPle EBee EPla WCru XPep
  grandiflorum L.   XPep
  - 'De Grasse' ♀H1   CPlN CRHN ERea EShb SOWG
  harmandianum   CPlN
  humile   CEnt CPLG EHol GSki IMGH MGos
                          MHer SDEP SHFr WFar WKif
  - f. *farreri*   WCru
§ - 'Revolutum' ♀H4   More than 30 suppliers
  - f. *wallichianum*   WCru
    B&SWJ 2559
§ *laurifolium* f. *nitidum* CPlN ERea EShb SDEP
  leratii   CPlN

§ *mesnyi* ♀H2-3   CFRD CMac CRHN CSBt CTri
                         CWib EBak ELan EPfP ERea IGor
                         NLar SAga SBra SLim SOWG SPer
                         STre SYvo WCMO WEas WSHC
                         XPep
  molle **new**   CPlN SDEP
  multiflorum   CPlN
  multipartitum   CPlN EShb
  - bushy   CSpe
  nitidum   see *J. laurifolium* f. *nitidum*
§ *nobile* subsp. *rex*   CPlN
  nudiflorum ♀H4   More than 30 suppliers
  - 'Argenteum'   see *J. nudiflorum* 'Mystique'
  - 'Aureum'   EBee ELan EPfP EPla LRHS MAsh
                           MRav NHol NSti SLim SPer SPla
                           SPoG WCot WPat WTel
§ - 'Mystique' (v)   ELan LRHS MAsh NLar SLon SMur
                           SPer SPoG WCMO WPat
  odoratissimum   ERea EShb SOWG
  officinale ♀H4   More than 30 suppliers
  - CC 1709   WHCr
§ - f. *affine*   CBcs CRHN CSPN CSam CTri
                          CWSG CWib ELan ENor ENot EPfP
                          ERea LAst MAsh MGan MRav
                          MWgw NCGa NHol SCoo SDix
                          SLim SPoG SRms WCru WFar
§ - 'Argenteovariegatum' (v) More than 30 suppliers
  ♀H4
  - 'Aureovariegatum'   see *J. officinale* 'Aureum'
§ - 'Aureum' (v)   CDoC CFRD CMac CWSG CWib
                          EBee ECtt ELan EPfP EPla LRHS
                          MAsh MBri MHer MLan MWgw
                          NBir NHol SCoo SHBN SLim SLon
                          SMad SPer SPoG SRms WHCG
                          WMoo WPat
  - 'Clotted Cream'   CBcs CCCN EBee LBuc LRHS
                           LSRN MAsh MBri MGos MWea
                           NLar SBra SMad SPoG WCMO
  - 'Crûg's Collection'   WCru
    B&SWJ 2987
  - double-flowered (d) **new** SDEP
  - Fiona Sunrise =   More than 30 suppliers
    'Frojas'PBR
  - 'Grandiflorum'   see *J. officinale* f. *affine*
  - 'Inverleith' ♀H4   CDoC CWSG EBee ELan EPfP IArd
                          LHop LRHS MAsh MBNS MBri
                          MCCP MLan MRav NEgg SBra
                          SCoo SLim SMac SMad SPer SPoG
                          WFar WSHC
  - 'Variegatum'   see *J. officinale*
                           'Argenteovariegatum'
  parkeri   CBcs CBgR CCVT CFee CMea CTri
                           EBee ECho EHyt EPfP GEdr GMaP
                           IMGH LHop MBNS NLar NMen
                           NRya NWCA SBla SIng SPla SPoG
                           WAbe WFar WPat XPep
  polyanthum ♀H1-2   CArn CBcs CPLG CPlN CRHN
                          CSBt CTri CTrw EBak EBee ELan
                          EPfP ERea ERom EShb LRHS MBri
                          NBlu NPal SBra SDEP SLim SOWG
                          SPer SRms XPep
  primulinum   see *J. mesnyi*
  reevesii hort.   see *J. humile* 'Revolutum'
  rex   see *J. nobile* subsp. *rex*
  sambac ♀H1   CHll CPlN CRHN EHol ELan EPfP
                          EShb SOWG WMul XPep
  - 'Asian Temple' (d) **new** CPlN
  - 'Bangkok Peony' (d) **new** CPlN
  - 'Belle of India' (d) **new** CPlN SDEP
  - 'Grand Duke of Tuscany' CPlN ERea SDEP SOWG
    (d)
  - 'Maid of India'   CPlN
  - 'Maid of Orleans' (d) SDEP SOWG
    ♀H1
  - 'Thai Beauty' (d)   CPlN
  scandens **new**   CPlN

§ **simplicifolium** subsp. CPlN
    australiense
  sinense new CPlN
  x **stephanense** More than 30 suppliers
  syringifolium CPlN
  tortuosum CPlN
  volubile see *J. simplicifolium* subsp.
    australiense

Jatropha (*Euphorbiaceae*)
  podagrica ♀H1 LToo MOak

Jeffersonia (*Berberidaceae*)
  diphylla More than 30 suppliers
  dubia CBro CFir CLAP EAEE ECho EHyt
    EPot ETow EWes GBuc GCrs GEdr
    LEdu LRHS NBir NLAp NMen NSla
    SBla WAbe WCru
  - B&SWJ 984 WCru
  - 'Alba' EHrv SBla

jostaberry see *Ribes* x *culverwellii*

Jovellana (*Scrophulariaceae*)
  punctata CDoC CPLG CPSs CPle EBee IBlr
    ITim MBlu
  repens CFir EBee
  sinclairii CHll CPLG ECou EHyt IBlr WCru
  violacea ♀H3 CAbP CAbb CBcs CDoC CHEx
    CPLG CPSs CPle CSec CTrC CWib
    EMil ERea EShb GCal GGGa IBlr
    ITim SAPC SArc SMad WCru WPGP
    WPic WSHC WWlt

Jovibarba ✿ (*Crassulaceae*)
§ **allionii** CMea CTri CWil EHol EPot
    GAbr LBee LRHS MHer MOne
    NHol NPri SBla SIng STre WAbe
    WFar WHal WHoo WIvy WPer
    WTin
  - 'Oki' CWil MOne
  allionii x **hirta** CWil GAbr MOne NHol NJOw
    NMen SDys
§ **arenaria** CWil EHol GAbr NMen
  - from Passo Monte CWil
    Crocecar Nico
  'Emerald Spring' CWil NMen
§ **heuffelii** ECho LRHS NHol NJOw NMen
    NPri SBch WIvy WPer
  - 'Aga' NHol WIvy
  - 'Aiolos' NHol
  - 'Alemene' NHol
  - 'Almkroon' NHol
  - 'Angel Wings' CWil NHol NMen
  - 'Apache' CWil
  - 'Aquarius' CWil WIvy
  - 'Artemis' NHol
  - 'Aurora' NHol
  - 'Be Mine' CWil
  - 'Beacon Hill' CWil WIvy
  - 'Belcore' CWil WIvy
  - 'Benjamin' CWil NHol
  - 'Bermuda' WIvy
  - 'Bermuda Sunset' NHol
  - 'Big Red' NHol
  - 'Blaze' CWil
  - 'Brandaris' NHol SDys
  - 'Brocade' NHol WIvy
  - 'Bronze Ingot' CWil
  - 'Bronze King' WIvy
  - 'Bulgarien' CWil
  - 'Cameo' WIvy
§ - 'Cherry Glow' CWil NHol
  - 'Chocoleto' WTin
  - 'Cleopatra' NHol
  - 'Copper King' CWil WIvy

  - 'Dunbar Red' NHol
  - 'Fandango' CWil MHom WIvy
  - 'Gento' NHol
  - 'Geronimo' NHol
  - 'Giuseppi Spiny' MHom NHol WIvy WTin
  - var. **glabra** LBee WHoo
  - - from Anabakanak CWil MHom NHol WTin
  - - from Anthoborio CWil NMen WIvy WTin
  - - from Backovo NHol
  - - from Galicica NHol
  - - from Haila, Montenegro/ CWil NHol NMen WIvy
    Kosovo
  - - from Jakupica, CWil WIvy
    Macedonia
  - - from Ljuboten CWil NHol NMen WTin
  - - from Osljak CWil
  - - from Pasina Glava CWil
  - - from Rhodope CWil MHom NHol
  - - from Treska Gorge, CWil NMen WTin
    Macedonia
  - - from Vitse, Greece WIvy
§ - - 'Cameo' NHol
  - 'Gold Rand' NHol
  - 'Grand Slam' CWil
  - 'Green Land' CWil
  - 'Greenstone' CMea CWil MHom NHol NMen
    WIvy WTin
  - 'Harmony' CWil
  - 'Henry Correvon' CWil
  - var. **heuffelii** CWil
  - 'Hot Lips' CWil
  - 'Hystyle' new WIvy
  - 'Ikaros' CWil
  - 'Inferno' MHom NHol
  - 'Iole' WIvy
  - 'Ithaca' NHol
  - 'Iuno' CWil
  - 'Jade' CWil NMen WIvy
  - 'Kapo' WIvy
  - var. **kopaonikensis** CWil LBee MHom NMen
  - 'Mary Ann' MHom WIvy
  - 'Miller's Violet' CWil WIvy WTin
  - 'Mink' CWil
  - 'Minuta' CWil NHol NMen WIvy WTin
  - 'Mystique' CMea CWil LBee NMen WIvy
  - 'Nannette' CWil
  - 'Opele' NHol
  - 'Orion' CWil NHol NMen
  - 'Pink Skies' CWil WIvy
  - 'Prisma' CWil WIvy WTin
  - 'Purple Haze' WIvy
  - 'Red Rose' CWil WIvy
  - 'Serenade' CWil
  - 'Springael's Choice' CWil
  - 'Sundancer' WIvy
  - 'Sungold' NHol
  - 'Suntan' CWil NHol WIvy
  - 'Sylvan Memory' CWil
  - 'Tan' CWil NHol WTin
  - 'Torrid Zone' WIvy WTin
  - 'Tuxedo' CWil
  - 'Vesta' CWil
  - 'Violet' SDys WIvy
§ **hirta** CHal CWil GAbr GKev MOne
    NHol NMen SAga SBla SIng STre
    WPer
  - from Wintergraben SIng SPlb
§ - subsp. **borealis** CWil MOne NDlv NHol
  - subsp. **glabrescens** EPot LRHS
  - - from Belianske Tatry CWil MOne NDlv
  - - from Smeryouka CWil SIng
  - 'Lowe's 66' MOne
  - var. **neilreichii** EAEE LRHS MHom WBVN
  - 'Preissiana' CWil LBee LRHS MOne NDlv
    NHol NMen SIng WIvy
    WTin

§ **sobolifera**   CHEx CWil EPot MOne NHol
                               NJOw NMen SIng SPlb WAbe
                               WHal WIvy WPer
- 'August Cream'   CWil LBee LRHS
- 'Green Globe'   CWil SDys WTin
- 'Miss Lorraine'   CWil

Juania (Arecaceae)
australis   EAmu WMul

Juanulloa (Solanaceae)
aurantiaca   see *J. mexicana*
§ **mexicana**   SOWG

Jubaea (Arecaceae)
§ **chilensis**   CBrP CDoC CPHo CRoM EAmu
                               EZes LPJP LPal NPal SChr WMul
spectabilis   see *J. chilensis*

Juglans ✿ (Juglandaceae)
§ **ailanthifolia**   CDul CMCN CTho ECrN IDee
- var. **cordiformis** 'Brock' CAgr
  (F)
-- 'Campbell CW1' (F)   CAgr
-- 'Fodermaier' seedling   CAgr
-- 'Rhodes' (F)   CAgr
ailanthifolia x **cinerea** see *J.* x *bixbyi*
§ x **bixbyi**   CAgr WGWT
cathayensis (F)   WGWT
- B&SWJ 6778   WCru
cinerea (F)   CMCN EGFP WGWT
- 'Booth' seedlings (F)   CAgr
- 'Craxezy' (F)   CAgr
- 'Kenworthy' seedling   CAgr
§ **elaeopyren**   EGFP WGWT
hindsii   CMCN
x **intermedia**   WGWT
mandschurica   EGFP WGWT
microcarpa   WGWT
- subsp. **major**   see *J. elaeopyren*
§ **nigra** (F) ♀H4   More than 30 suppliers
- 'Emma Kay' (F)   CAgr WGWT
- 'Laciniata'   CDul CMCN CTho MBlu WGWT
- 'Thomas' (F)   CAgr
- 'Weschke' (F)   CAgr
'Paradox'   WGWT
'Red Danube' (F)   WGWT
§ **regia** (F) ♀H4   More than 30 suppliers
- 'Abbotbad' (F)   WGWT
- 'Axel' (F)   WGWT
- 'Broadview' (F)   CAgr CDoC CDul CEnd CTho
                               EMui ERea GTwe LRHS MBlu MBri
                               MCoo MGos MNHC MWat SCoo
                               SDea SKee SPoG WGWT WOrn
- 'Buccaneer' (F)   CAgr CTho ECrN GTwe LRHS
                               SDea SKee WGWT
- 'Coenen' (F)   WGWT
- 'Corne du Périgord' (F)   CAgr
- 'Ferjean' (F)   CAgr LPan
- 'Fernette'PBR (F)   CAgr MCoo
- 'Fernor'PBR (F)   CAgr MCoo
- 'Franquette' (F)   CAgr CDoC GTwe LRHS MCoo
                               WDin
- 'Hansen' (F)   CAgr WGWT
- 'Laciniata'   CMCN WGWT
- 'Lara' (F)   GTwe MCoo WGWT
- 'Leopold' (F)   WGWT
- 'Lu Guang' (F)   WGWT
- 'Mayette' (F)   CAgr WDin
- 'Metcalfe' (F)   WGWT
- 'Meylannaise' (F)   CAgr
- number 16 (F)   WGWT
- 'Parisienne' (F)   CAgr
- 'Pedro' (F)   WGWT
- 'Pendula' (F)   WGWT
- 'Plovdivski' (F)   CAgr CDul WGWT

- 'Proslavski' (F)   CAgr CDul WGWT
- 'Purpurea'   CDul CMCN MBlu WGWT
- 'Rita' (F)   CAgr WGWT
- 'Ronde de Montignac'   CAgr
  (F)
- 'Soleze' (F)   CAgr WGWT
- 'Ssang Sung' **new**   WGWT
- 'Tremlett's Giant' (F)   WGWT
- 'Zhong Lin' (F)   WGWT
sieboldiana   see *J. ailanthifolia*

jujube see *Ziziphus jujuba*

Juncus (Juncaceae)
acutiflorus **new**   NSco
acutus   CPen WWye XPep
* **balticus** 'Spiralis'   CTrC ECho
bulbosus   CNat CRWN
conglomeratus   EHoe
'Curly Gold Strike' (v)   CBgR CKno LBBr SPoG
§ **decipiens** 'Curly-wurly' More than 30 suppliers
- 'Spiralis'   see *J. decipiens* 'Curly-wurly'
I - 'Spiralis Nana' **new**   NWCA
effusus   CHEx CRWN EMFW LNCo LPBA
                               MNHC NPer NSco NSti SWat
                               WMAq WWpP
- 'Gold Strike' (v)   CWCL EMan EPPr EPla EWes EWin
                               LBBr LHop LIck MAvo NOak
                               WWpP
§ - f. **spiralis**   More than 30 suppliers
- 'Yellow Line'PBR (v)   CPen EBee MAvo
ensifolius   CDWL CMea CPen CRow CWat
                               EBee EHoe EMFW EWes LIck
                               LNCo LPBA MAvo MMHG NNor
                               NPer WFar WWpP
filiformis 'Spiralis'   CBgR CBig CBrm CTbh EBee EWin
                               GIBF GKev MAvo NBre
inflexus   CRWN EHon NSco SWat WWpP
- 'Afro'   CBgR CBig CKno CMea EMan
                               EMon EPfP EWin LRHS MAvo
                               MBrN MCCP NBro NOak SPlb
                               WHal
membranaceus   NRya
  HLMS 94.0541
pallidus   EPPr GCal GGar LIck NBid NNor
patens 'Carman's Gray'   CFee CKno CRez CWCL EBrs
                               EMan EPPr EPla GCal GQue LRHS
                               MAvo MCCP MMoz NGdn NNor
                               NOak SAga SPoG WCot WHil
                               WMoo WWpP
- 'Elk Blue'   CKno
'Silver Spears'   EMan MCCP
'Unicorn'PBR   CBgR CPen EBee EPPr EWin MAvo
                               MWgw SPoG
xiphioides   EHoe EPla LRHS NHol NOGN SWal
- JLS 8609LACA   EPPr

Junellia (Verbenaceae)
azorelloides F&W 9344   WAbe
micrantha F&W 9389   WAbe
odonnellii F&W 9271   CPBP
sylvestrii F&W 2705   WAbe
toninii F&W 9332   CPBP
wilczekii   WFar
- F&W 7770   NWCA

Juniperus ✿ (Cupressaceae)
chinensis   CMac CMen SEND
- from Ussuri   GIBF
- 'Aurea' ♀H4   CBcs CKen CMac ECho EHul EOrn
                               LCon MBar MGos SPoG
§ - 'Blaauw' ♀H4   CDoC CMac CMen ECho EHul
                               EOrn LCon LLin MBar MGos SCoo
                               SHBN SLim SPoG STre WEve WFar
- 'Blue Alps'   CDoC ECho EHul EOrn IMGH
                               LCon MBar MBri MGos NEgg NHol

	NLar SCoo SEND SLim SPoG WDin WEve WFar
- 'Blue Point'	MBar MGos
- 'Densa Spartan'	see *J. chinensis* 'Spartan'
- 'Echiniformis'	CKen EOrn
- 'Expansa Aureospicata' (v)	CDoC CKen CMac CRob ECho EHul EOrn EPfP LCon LLin MBar MGos SLim SPoG SRms
§ - 'Expansa Variegata' (v)	CDoC CMac CRob CWib ECho EHul EOrn EPfP IMGH LCon LLin MAsh MBar MGos SCoo SLim SMer SPoG SRms WDin WFar WMoo WTel
- 'Ferngold' **new**	MGos
- 'Globosa Cinerea'	MBar
- 'Japonica'	EOrn MBar SMer
- 'Japonica Variegata' (v)	SLim
§ - 'Kaizuka' ♀H4	CDoC ECho EHul EOrn LBee LCon LRHS MBar SCoo SLim SMad SMer SPoG STre XPep
- 'Kaizuka Variegata'	see *J. chinensis* 'Variegated Kaizuka'
- 'Keteleeri'	MBar
- 'Kuriwao Gold'	see *J.* x *pfitzeriana* 'Kuriwao Gold'
- 'Obelisk' ♀H4	ECho EHul LCon LRHS MBar
- 'Oblonga'	CDoC ECho EHul MAsh MBar STre
§ - 'Parsonsii'	MBar SHBN STre WCFE
- 'Plumosa'	MBar
- 'Plumosa Albovariegata' (v)	EOrn MBar
- 'Plumosa Aurea' ♀H4	EHul EOrn LCon MBar WDin WFar
- 'Plumosa Aureovariegata' (v)	CKen EOrn MBar SLim
- 'Pyramidalis' ♀H4	CBrm CDoC CRob ECho EHul ENot EPfP IMGH LCon LLin SCoo SPoG SRms WDin WFar
- 'Pyramidalis Variegata'	see *J. chinensis* 'Variegata'
- 'Robust Green'	CRob ECho EOrn LCon MBar SCoo SLim SPoG
- 'San José'	CDoC CMen ECho EHul EOrn LLin MAsh MBar SCoo SLim WDin
§ - var. **sargentii**	STre
- 'Shimpaku'	CKen CMen EOrn MBar NLar
§ - 'Spartan'	EHul
§ - 'Stricta'	CSBt EHul LBee LRHS MAsh MBar MGos NBlu SLim SPla WDin
- 'Stricta Variegata'	see *J. chinensis* 'Variegata'
- 'Sulphur Spray'	see *J.* x *pfitzeriana* 'Sulphur Spray'
- 'Torulosa'	see *J. chinensis* 'Kaizuka'
§ - 'Variegata' (v)	MBar SPer SPoG
§ - 'Variegated Kaizuka' (v)	CBrm ECho EHul EOrn LCon MBar SPoG WFar WRHF
communis	CArn CRWN CTrG EHul GPoy MBow MHer MNHC MSal NLar NWea SIde
- (f)	GTSp SIde
- 'Arnold'	CDul MBar MGos
- 'Arnold Sentinel'	CKen
- 'Atholl'	CKen
I - 'Aureopicta' (v)	MBar
- 'Barton'	ECho MBar MGos NHol
- 'Berkshire'	CKen CRob
- 'Brien'	CDoC CKen
- 'Brynhyfryd Gold'	CKen CRob
§ - var. **communis**	ECho MBar NEgg
- 'Compressa' ♀H4	More than 30 suppliers
§ - 'Constance Franklin' (v)	ECho EHul LLin MBar STre
- 'Corielagan'	CKen CNic MBar NLar
- 'Cracovia'	CKen EHul
- var. **depressa**	ECho GPoy MBar
- 'Depressa Aurea'	CKen CMac CSBt ECho EHul LBee LCon LLin LRHS MBar MGos SHBN SPoG WFar WRHF WTel
- 'Depressed Star'	CRob ECho EHul MBar NScw
- 'Derrynane'	EHul
- 'Effusa'	CKen

- 'Gelb'	see *J. communis* 'Schneverdingen Goldmachangel'
- 'Gold Ball' **new**	LBee
§ - 'Gold Cone'	CKen CSli ECho EHul ENot LBee LCon LLin LRHS MAsh MBar MGos NDlv NEgg NHol SLim SMer SPoG WDin WFar
- 'Golden Showers'	see *J. communis* 'Schneverdingen Goldmachangel'
§ - 'Goldenrod'	MGos
- 'Green Carpet' ♀H4	CDoC CKen CRob ECho EHul EOrn EPfP IMGH LBee LBuc LCon LLin LRHS MAsh MBar MBri NEgg NHol SCoo SLim SMer SPoG WCFE WDin WEve
- 'Haverbeck'	CKen
- var. **hemispherica**	see *J. communis* var. *communis*
- 'Hibernica' ♀H4	More than 30 suppliers
- 'Hibernica Variegata'	see *J. communis* 'Constance Franklin'
- 'Hornibrookii' ♀H4	CMac ECho EHul EOrn LLin MBar MGos SBod SHBN SMer SRms STre WDin
- 'Horstmann'	MBar NLar SLim SPoG
I - 'Horstmann's Pendula'	CDoC ECho LCon LLin
- 'Kenwith Castle'	CKen
§ - 'Minima'	SBod
- 'Prostrata'	WFar
- 'Pyramidalis'	SPlb
- 'Repanda' ♀H4	CBcs CDoC CMac CRob CSBt CWib ECho EHul ENot EPfP LAst LCon LLin MAsh MBar MGos NDlv NWea SCoo SLim SMer SPer SPla SPoG SRms WDin WEve WFar
§ - 'Schneverdingen Goldmachangel'	CRob ECho EOrn LLin MBri MGos SLim
- 'Sentinel'	CDoC ECho EHul EPfP LCon LRHS MBar MBri NBlu NEgg NHol SCoo SLim WCFE WDin WEve
- 'Sieben Steinhauser'	CKen
- 'Silver Mist'	CKen
- 'Spotty Spreader' (v)	SCoo SLim SPoG
- 'Suecica Group'	EHul MBar NLar NWea
- 'Suecica Aurea'	EHul EOrn
- 'Wallis' **new**	NHol
- 'Zeal'	CDoC CKen
conferta	see *J. rigida* subsp. *conferta*
- var. **maritima**	see *J. taxifolia*
davurica	EHul
- 'Expansa'	see *J. chinensis* 'Parsonsii'
- 'Expansa Albopicta'	see *J. chinensis* 'Expansa Variegata'
- 'Expansa Variegata'	see *J. chinensis* 'Expansa Variegata'
deppeana 'Silver Spire'	EGra MBar
foetidissima	GIBF
x **gracilis** 'Blaauw'	see *J. chinensis* 'Blaauw'
horizontalis	ECho NWea
§ - 'Andorra Compact'	CNic LPan MBar NHol NLar SCoo
- 'Bar Harbor'	CKen CMac ECho EHul MBar MGos
§ - 'Blue Chip'	CKen CRob ECho EHul ELan ENot EOrn EPfP LBee LCon LLin LRHS MAsh MBar MGos NBir NBlu SCoo SLim SPer SPoG WDin XPep
- 'Blue Moon'	see *J. horizontalis* 'Blue Chip'
- 'Blue Pygmy'	CKen
- 'Blue Rug'	see *J. horizontalis* 'Wiltonii'
- 'Douglasii'	CKen CMac EHol EHul MBar
- 'Emerald Spreader'	CKen ECho EHul ELan LLin MBar WEve
- 'Glacier'	CKen
- 'Glauca Group'	CMac ECho EHul LLin MBar MGos SMer SPer SPoG WDin WEve
- 'Glomerata'	CKen MBar
- 'Golden Carpet'	ECho ELan EOrn EPfP IMGH LBee LBuc LLin MGos NBlu NEgg NHol NLar SLim SPer SPoG WEve

- 'Golden Spreader'	CDoC ECho
- 'Grey Pearl'	CKen ECho EHul SBod
- 'Hughes'	CMac ECho EHul LBee LLin LRHS MBar MGos SBod SCoo SPla
- Icee Blue = 'Monber'	CKen CRob LCon NLar SLim SPoG
- 'Jade River'	CKen ECho EHul GBin LRHS MGos NLar SCoo SLim SPer SPoG
- 'Jade Spreader' **new**	ECho
- 'Limeglow'	CKen ECho NLar SLim
- 'Mother Lode'	CKen NLar
- 'Neumann'	CKen EOrn
- 'Plumosa Compacta'	see *J. horizontalis* 'Andorra Compact'
- 'Prince of Wales'	CRob EHul LLin LPan LRHS MAsh MGos NLar SCoo SLim XPep
- var. *saxatalis* E.Murray	see *J. communis* var. *communis*
- 'Turquoise Spreader'	CKen CRob CSBt ECho EHul LLin MBar SCoo
- 'Variegata' (v)	MBar
- 'Venusta'	see *J. virginiana* 'Venusta'
- 'Villa Marie'	CKen
- 'Webber'	MBar
§ - 'Wiltonii' ♀H4	CDul CKen EHul EOrn MGos NBlu
- 'Winter Blue'	LBee LCon LRHS SLim SPer
- 'Youngstown'	CMac CRob CSWP ECho LLin MBar MGos SBod WFar
- 'Yukon Belle'	CKen
N x *media*	see *J. x pfitzeriana*
§ x *pfitzeriana*	CDul ECho
- 'Armstrongii'	EHul
- 'Blaauw'	see *J. chinensis* 'Blaauw'
- 'Blue and Gold' (v)	CKen ECho EHul LLin MBar NEgg SHBN SLim SPer
- 'Blue Cloud'	see *J. virginiana* 'Blue Cloud'
§ - 'Carbery Gold'	CDoC CMac CRob CSBt CSli ECho EGra EHul ENot EOrn LBee LCon LLin LRHS MAsh MBar MGos NHol SCoo SLim SPoG WEve WFar
- 'Gold Coast'	CDoC CKen CRob CSBt ECho EHul ENot EPfP LBee LRHS MAsh MBar MBri MGos SLim SPer SPla WDin WEve
- Gold Sovereign = 'Blound'PBR	LBee LCon MAsh MGos NHol SMer
- 'Gold Star'	SLim
* - 'Golden Joy'	LCon SCoo SLim SPoG
- 'Golden Saucer'	MBar SCoo
- 'Goldkissen'	CRob MGos NLar
§ - 'Kuriwao Gold'	CMac ECho EHul ENot LBee MBar MGos NHol NLar SCoo SLim SMer STre WEve WFar
- 'Milky Way' (v)	SCoo SLim SPoG
- 'Mint Julep'	CSBt ECho EHul ENot IMGH LAst LBee LCon LLin LPan LRHS MBar MGos NBlu SCoo SLim SPer WBrE WDin WEve WFar WMoo
- 'Mordigan Gold'	WEve
- 'Old Gold' ♀H4	CKen CMac ECho EHul EOrn EPfP IMGH LBee LCon LRHS MAsh MBar MGos NBlu NEgg NHol NWea SBod SCoo SLim SMer SPer SPlb SPoG SRms WDin WEve WFar WTel
- 'Old Gold Carbery'	see *J. x pfitzeriana* 'Carbery Gold'
- 'Pfitzeriana'	see *J. x pfitzeriana* 'Wilhelm Pfitzer'
- 'Pfitzeriana Aurea'	CBcs CDoC CMac CSBt CTri ECho EHul EPfP LCon LRHS MBar MBri MGos NBlu NEgg NWea SHBN SPoG WCFE WDin WEve WFar WOrn
- 'Pfitzeriana Compacta' ♀H4	CMac ECho EHul MBar SCoo SLim
- 'Pfitzeriana Glauca'	EHul IMGH LCon LRHS MBar SCoo SLim
- 'Richeson'	MBar
- 'Silver Cascade'	EHul
§ - 'Sulphur Spray' ♀H4	CSBt CWib ECho EHul ENot EOrn EPla LAst LBee LCon LLin LRHS MAsh MBar MGos NEgg NHol SEND SLim SPer SPla SPoG SRms WBVN WCFE WDin WEve WFar WMoo WTel
§ - 'Wilhelm Pfitzer'	ECho EHul EPfP MBar NWea
phoenicea	XPep
§ *pingii* 'Glassell'	CDoC ECho MBar NLar
§ - 'Pygmaea'	ECho EOrn MBar SPoG
§ - var. *wilsonii*	CDoC CKen ECho EHul EOrn MBar NEgg NLar
procumbens 'Bonin Isles'	LLin LRHS SCoo SLim SPoG
- 'Nana' ♀H4	More than 30 suppliers
recurva 'Castlewellan'	EOrn LCon MGos NLar
- var. *coxii*	CDoC CMac ECho EHul EOrn GGGa LCon LLin MAsh MBar MGos NEgg SRms WCFE WPic
§ - 'Densa'	CDoC CKen ECho EHul EOrn MBar NHol SHBN
- 'Embley Park'	EHul MBar
- 'Nana'	see *J. recurva* 'Densa'
rigida	CMen EHul LLin MBar NLar
§ - subsp. *conferta*	CRob ECho ENot LBee LCon MBar SEND SLim SPer SPoG STre WEve
* - - 'Blue Ice'	CKen ECho EOrn LLin SPoG WFar
- - 'Blue Pacific'	COtt CRob ECho EHul MBar SLim SPoG WFar
- - 'Blue Tosho'	CRob ECho LCon SLim SPoG
- - 'Emerald Sea'	EHul
- - 'Silver Mist'	CKen
sabina	ECho NWea
§ - 'Blaue Donau'	ECho EHul MBar
- Blue Danube	see *J. sabina* 'Blaue Donau'
- 'Broadmoor'	EHul
- 'Buffalo'	EHul
- Cupressifolia Group	MBar
- 'Hicksii'	CBcs CMac MBar
- 'Knap Hill'	see *J. x pfitzeriana* 'Wilhelm Pfitzer'
- 'Mountaineer'	see *J. scopulorum* 'Mountaineer'
- 'Rockery Gem'	ECho EHul EOrn SLim SPla SPoG WEve WGor
- 'Skandia'	CKen
- 'Tamariscifolia'	CBcs CMac CTri CWib ECho ECrN EHul ENot LBee LCon LLin LRHS MAsh MBar MGos NBlu NEgg NWea SHBN SLim SMer SPer SPoG WCFE WDin WEve WFar WTel
- 'Tripartita'	see *J. virginiana* 'Tripartita'
- 'Variegata' (v)	ECho EHul MBar NWea
sargentii	see *J. chinensis* var. *sargentii*
scopulorum	CKen MBar
- 'Blue Arrow'	More than 30 suppliers
- 'Blue Banff'	CKen
- 'Blue Heaven'	ECho EHul MAsh MBar NLar SRms
- 'Blue Pyramid'	EHul
- 'Boothman'	EHul
- 'Moonglow'	EBrs EHul MBar SCoo
§ - 'Mountaineer'	EHul
- 'Mrs Marriage'	CKen
- 'Repens'	MBar MGos
- 'Silver Star' (v)	ECho EHul MBar MGos
- 'Skyrocket'	More than 30 suppliers
- 'Springbank'	EHul LBee LRHS MAsh MBar WCFE
- 'Tabletop'	MBar
- 'Tolleson's Blue Weeping'	SIFN
- 'Wichita Blue'	EBrs EHul EPfP SEND WEve
§ *squamata*	WBVN
- 'Blue Carpet' ♀H4	More than 30 suppliers

	- 'Blue Spider'	CKen ECho LRHS MBar SCoo SLim SPoG
	- 'Blue Spreader'	ECho NEgg
	- 'Blue Star' ♀H4	More than 30 suppliers
	- 'Blue Star Variegated'	see *J. squamata* 'Golden Flame'
	- 'Blue Swede'	see *J. squamata* 'Hunnetorp'
	- 'Chinese Silver'	ECho EHul MBar SLim
	- 'Dream Joy'	CKen LCon SLim
	- var. *fargesii*	see *J. squamata*
	- 'Filborna'	CKen ECho LBee MBar SLim SMer
	- 'Glassell'	see *J. pingii* 'Glassell'
§	- 'Golden Flame' (v)	CKen
	- 'Holger' ♀H4	CBrm CDoC CDul CMac CRob CSBt ECho EGra EHul EOrn EPfP EPla LBee LCon LLin LRHS MAsh MBar MGos SCoo SLim SPoG WCFE WEve
§	- 'Hunnetorp'	ECho EOrn MBar WGor
	- 'Loderi'	see *J. pingii* var. *wilsonii*
	- 'Meyeri'	CTri ECho EHul EOrn IMGH MBar NWea SBod SCoo SPoG STre WDin WFar WTel
	- 'Pygmaea'	see *J. pingii* 'Pygmaea'
	- 'Wilsonii'	see *J. pingii* var. *wilsonii*
§	*taxifolia*	CDoC ECho IMGH LBee SPoG
	virginiana	CAgr CPne
§	- 'Blue Cloud'	EHul MBar SLim WEve WGor
	- 'Burkii'	CDoC EHul
	- 'Frosty Morn'	CKen ECho EHul MBar WFar
	- 'Glauca'	CSWP EHul NWea
	- 'Golden Spring'	CKen
	- 'Grey Owl' ♀H4	ECho EHul ELan EPfP LCon MBar NWea SCoo SLim SLon STre WDin WFar WGor WTel
	- 'Helle'	see *J. chinensis* 'Spartan'
	- 'Hetzii'	CBcs CMac ECho EHul MBar NLar NWea WDin WFar
	- 'Hillii'	MBar
	- 'Hillspire'	EHul
	- 'Nana Compacta'	MBar
	- Silver Spreader = 'Mona'	CKen EHul SCoo
	- 'Staver'	EHul
	- 'Sulphur Spray'	see *J.* x *pfitzeriana* 'Sulphur Spray'
§	- 'Tripartita'	MBar
§	- 'Venusta'	CKen

Jurinea (Asteraceae)

	dolomiaea CC 4268	MGol
	glycacantha	EBrs LRHS
	ledebourii **new**	EBrs

Jurinella see *Jurinea*

Jussiaea see *Ludwigia*

Justicia (Acanthaceae)

	aurea	EShb
§	*brandegeeana* ♀H1	CCCN CHal EShb MBri SOWG
	- 'Lutea'	see *J. brandegeeana* 'Yellow Queen'
	- variegated (v) **new**	MJnS
§	- 'Yellow Queen'	CHal EShb
§	*carnea*	CHal CSev EBak ERea EShb GCal MBri MJnS SDEP SMad SOWG WCot WMul
	guttata	see *J. brandegeeana*
	'Nørgaard's Favourite'	MBri
	ovata	SMad
	'Penrhosiensis'	EShb
	pohliana	see *J. carnea*
	rizzinii ♀H1	CBcs CHll CPle CSev ERea EShb SOWG
	spicigera	ERea EShb
	suberecta	see *Dicliptera suberecta*

K

Kadsura (Schisandraceae)

	sp.	CMac
	japonica	CBcs CMen CPlN EShb MGol WPGP
	- B&SWJ 1027	WCru
	- 'Fukurin' (v) **new**	NLar
	- 'Shiromi'	CPlN EPfP
	- 'Variegata' (v)	CPlN EPfP EShb LRHS SBra SBrw WSHC
	- white fruit	CPlN EPfP NLar

Kaempferia (Zingiberaceae)

	galanga	MOak
	mottled leaf	MOak
	rotunda	CKob MOak

Kageneckia (Rosaceae)

	oblonga	IFro

Kalanchoe (Crassulaceae)

	alticola **new**	EShb
	beharensis ♀H1	CAbb CCCN CHal EShb LToo MBri SBig
	- 'Rusty'	CSpe
	blossfeldiana	LRHS
	- 'Variegata' (v)	CHal
	daigremontiana	CHal EShb SRms
§	*delagoensis*	CHal EShb STre
	fedtschenkoi	CHal EShb STre
	laciniata	EShb
	manginii ♀H1	CDoC
	orgyalis **new**	EShb
	pubescens **new**	EShb
	pumila ♀H1	CHal EMan ERea EShb EWin EWoo SBch SPet WEas
	rhombopilosa	EShb
	sexangularis	EShb
	'Tessa' ♀H1	MBri MLan SPet SRms STre WCot
	thyrsiflora 'Bronze Sculpture' **new**	CBct CHVG EWll
	tomentosa ♀H1	CHal EShb SHFr SPet WEas
	tubiflora	see *K. delagoensis*

Kalimeris (Asteraceae)

§	*incisa*	EWll GMac IHMH MRav WBor WFar WMoo WTin
	- 'Alba'	EBee ECha NLar NRnb SSvw WFar
	- 'Blue Star'	EBee EBrs ECha EMil EWll LHop NLar NRnb WFar
	- 'Charlotte'	EBee EWes NBre NDov NGby
	- 'Madiva' **new**	ECha
*	- 'Variegata' (v)	NBre SPoG
	integrifolia	ECha WMow WTin
	intricifolia	EBee NBre
§	*mongolica*	EBee ECha NBre WFar WPer
§	*pinnatifida*	EBee EChP EPPr WCot
	- 'Hortensis'	CBod NSti WHil
§	*yomena* 'Shogun' (v)	CBow CEnt EBee ECha EGra EHoe ELan EMil EMon ENot EPPr GBri GBuc GEdr MLLN MWgw NBir NPri NRnb SAga SMer SPer WBor WCot WFar WSHC
	- 'Variegata'	see *K. yomena* 'Shogun'

Kalmia ✿ (Ericaceae)

	angustifolia ♀H4	MBar NBlu NLAp SRms WDin WFar
	- f. *rubra* ♀H4	CBcs CBrm CDoC CSBt ELan EPfP ISea LRHS MAsh MGos NDlv NEgg NHol NVic SBrw SHBN SPer SPoG SReu SRot SSta WFar WHar WPat

latifolia ♀H4	CBcs CEnd CPSs CTrG ELan EMil EPfP GIBF MBar MDun MGos MLan NBlu NEgg NWea SBrw SPer SPlb SReu SSta SWvt WBrE WDin WFar WGer WNor
- SDR 2210	GKev
- 'Alpine Pink'	CBrm LRHS NLar SRot
- 'Carousel'	CAbP EBee ECho EPfP GGGa LRHS MGos MLea NDlv SBrw WFar WGob
- 'Elf'	ECho GEdr LRHS MDun MGos MLea NLar SBrw WFar
- 'Freckles' ♀H4	CBcs ECho ELan EPfP GEdr GGGa LRHS MDun MLea NDlv SBrw SPoG WFar
- 'Fresca'	ECho LRHS MDun WGob
- 'Galaxy'	GGGa
- 'Heart of Fire'	GGGa LRHS NDlv SPoG
- 'Keepsake'	GGGa
- 'Little Linda' ♀H4	ECho GEdr GGGa GKev IMGH LRHS NDlv NLar SBrw
- 'Minuet'	CDoC CDul CWSG ECho EPfP GEdr GGGa IMGH ISea LRHS MAsh MDun MGos MLan MLea MWea NDlv SBrw SPoG SSpi SWvt WBrE WFar
- f. *myrtifolia*	ECho GEdr GKev LRHS MLea SBrw WFar WGob
- 'Nancy'	GEdr SBrw WFar
- 'Olympic Fire' ♀H4	CEnd ELan EPfP GGGa LRHS MBri MGos NDlv NHol SSpi
- 'Ostbo Red'	CBcs CDoC CDul CPSs CSBt ECho EMil EPfP GEdr GGGa IMGH ISea LRHS MGos MLea NDlv NHol SBrw SHBN SPer SPoG SReu SSpi SSta SWvt WFar
- 'Peppermint'	GGGa
- 'Pink Charm' ♀H4	ECho ELan GGGa GWCH LRHS NDlv SBrw
- 'Pink Frost'	CBcs ECho GGGa ISea MBri MDun NDlv NHol NLar SBrw WFar
- 'Quinnipiac'	NHol
- 'Raspberry Glow'	GGGa
- 'Richard Jaynes'	ECho GEdr LRHS WBrE WFar
- 'Sarah'	ECho GGGa LRHS MDun NLar SBrw SSpi
- 'Silver Dollar'	GGGa
- 'Snowdrift'	ECho GEdr GGGa LRHS NDlv SBrw SSpi WFar
§ *microphylla*	GGGa
polifolia	CBcs ECho MBar NHol NLAp SPer WPat
- var. *compacta*	WSHC
- 'Glauca'	see *K. microphylla*
- f. *leucantha*	GGGa NLAp WPat

Kalmia x *Rhododendron* (Ericaceae)

K. latifolia x *R. williamsianum*, 'Everlasting'	see *Rhododendron* 'Everlasting'

Kalmiopsis (Ericaceae)

leachiana ♀H4	GCrs SSta
- 'Glendoick'	GGGa LTwo MDun WPat
* - 'Shooting Star'	LTwo WAbe

x *Kalmiothamnus* (Ericaceae)

ornithomma 'Cosdon'	WThu
- 'Haytor'	WAbe

Kalopanax (Araliaceae)

pictus	see *K. septemlobus*
§ *septemlobus*	CBcs CDul CFwr CHEx CLnd ELan EPfP EWTr GBin GIBF NEgg NLar WBVN WOVN
- var. *lutchuensis* B&SWJ 5947	WCru
- var. *maximowiczii*	CDoC EPfP MBlu NBee NLar WCot

Kelseya (Rosaceae)

uniflora	EHyt WAbe

Kennedia (Papilionaceae)

beckxiana	SOWG
coccinea	CBcs CSec
macrophylla	CPlN CTbh
nigricans	CSec EREa EShb SOWG
prostrata	SPlb
rubicunda	CHal CRHN CSec EREa

Kentia (Arecaceae)

belmoreana	see *Howea belmoreana*
forsteriana	see *Howea forsteriana*

Kentranthus see *Centranthus*

Kerria (Rosaceae)

japonica single misapplied	see *K. japonica* 'Simplex'
- (d)	see *K. japonica* 'Pleniflora'
- 'Albescens'	WFar
- 'Buttercup' **new**	MBri
- 'Golden Guinea' ♀H4	CPLG CWSG EBee ECtt ELan EPfP EWTr LRHS MAsh MBri MGos MNrw MRav MSwo SCoo SPer SWal SWvt WDin WFar WWeb
§ - 'Picta' (v)	CDul CWib EBee EHoe ELan ENot EPfP LAst LRHS MBar MGos MRav MSwo SGar SLim SLon SPer SPoG SRms WDin WFar WSHC WTel WWeb
§ - 'Pleniflora' (d) ♀H4	More than 30 suppliers
§ - 'Simplex'	CPLG CSBt EShb NWea WDin WFar WTel
- 'Variegata'	see *K. japonica* 'Picta'

Khadia (Aizoaceae)

sp.	CStu

Kickxia (Scrophulariaceae)

spuria	MSal

Kigelia (Bignoniaceae)

africana	CSec

Kirengeshoma (Hydrangeaceae)

palmata ♀H4	More than 30 suppliers
- dwarf	WCot
§ - Koreana Group	CLAP CPLG EBee EChP EGle EHrv ELan EMan EPfP GCal GSki IPot LAst LPhx MBri MDun MRav NBPC NBir NCGa NRnb SMad SPer WCot WFar WHil WOVN WTMC

Kitaibela (Malvaceae)

vitifolia	CFee CPLG CSpe EBee EDAr ELan EMon EUnu EWTr GCal IFro LRav NBHF NBid NEgg SDnm SGar SPav SPlb WPer WPic WTMC

Kitchingia see *Kalanchoe*

kiwi fruit see *Actinidia deliciosa*

Kleinia (Asteraceae)

articulata	see *Senecio articulatus*
grantii	EREa EShb
neriifolia	CSec
repens	see *Senecio serpens*
senecioides	WEas
stapeliiformis ♀H1	EShb

Knautia (Dipsacaceae)

§ *arvensis*	CArn CBgR CHll CRWN EMag MBow MHer MLLN MNHC MSwo NLan NLar NMir NPri NSco SECG SPer WFar WGHP WHer WMoo WSFF WSHC
- 'Rachael'	CElw
dipsacifolia	NDov SHar SMHy
§ *macedonica*	More than 30 suppliers
- 'Crimson Cushion'	CBcs CSpe ECtt GAbr GBri LSou NPri SPav WCra WFar
- 'Mars Midget'	More than 30 suppliers
- Melton pastels	COlW EBee EChP EGoo EMar ENot EPfP EShb LSRN LSou MGos MWgw MWrn NCob NPer SMar SPav SPet SPoG SRot SWal SWat SWvt WFar WWeb
- pink	CSam WWlt
- red	CWib NCob
- 'Red Dress'	EBee EMon
- short	ECtt EHrv NCob NCot NDov STes WTMC WWlt
- tall, pale	LPhx NDov
sarajevensis	EBee MAvo
§ *tatarica*	NBre

Knightia (Proteaceae)

excelsa	CBcs

Kniphofia ✿ (Asphodelaceae)

'Ada'	CMdw EBrs EWTr EWes MLLN MRav SMrm
'Alcazar'	CBcs CDes EBee EBla EChP ECot ECtt EPfP GGar LRHS LSRN MBri MHer MRav MSte NCGa NOrc NPri SWvt WCMO WCot WFar WMnd WMul WPGP WWeb
* 'Amber'	NBre
'Amsterdam'	MWat
'Apple Court'	NBir
'Apricot'	CMdw EPla SMHy SMrm
'Apricot Souffle'	EBee MLLN WCot WPGP WPrP
'Atlanta'	CPne EMon GCal LRHS
'Barton Fever'	EBee WCot
baurii	WCot
'Bees' Flame'	EBee
'Bee's Gold'	ERou WCAu
'Bees' Lemon'	More than 30 suppliers
'Bees' Sunset' ♀H4	CAvo CDes EBee EGle EPPr GAbr GBri GBuc MNrw MRav MWgw NBir SUsu WCMO WCot WPGP WPrP WTMC
* *bicolor*	ECtt WCMO WCot WPrP
'Border Ballet'	CBrm EAEE EDAr ERou LHop LRHS MRav NBir NBre NBro NJOw NLar SMar SWat WFar
brachystachya	CPou EBee GCal SBig SPlb WCMO WCot
'Bressingham Comet'	EBee EBrs ECtt EMan EPfP LRHS MBri MRav NBir SBla WPGP
'Bressingham Gleam'	EBrs SMrm WCMO WCot
Bressingham hybrids	NBir
Bressingham Sunbeam = 'Bresun'	CPen EBee EBrs GSki NBir WCot
Bridgemere hybrids	WFar
'Brimstone' ♀H4	More than 30 suppliers
buchananii	CDes
'Buttercup' ♀H4	CAvo CMHG CMdw WSHC WTin
'C.M. Prichard' misapplied	see *K. rooperi*
'C.M. Prichard' Prichard	WCot
'Candlelight'	CDes CMdw COlW EBee NBre SDys SUsu WPGP
caulescens ♀H3-4	More than 30 suppliers
- from John May	WCot
- 'Coral Breakers'	EBee MLLN WCMO WCot WTMC

citrina	CFir CFwr CSec EBee EDAr EPfP GKev LAst LRHS NBre NChi NLar SMar WCot
'Cobra'	CDes EBee EBrs LRHS WCMO WCot
'Comet'	ECtt
'Corallina'	EBee WFar
'Dingaan'	CAbb CAvo CPne CPou EBee EChP ECtt EMan EPPr ERou GBBs GBin GCal GQue GSki MNrw NBir NEgg NPri SAga SDnm SPav WCMO WCot WFar WLin
'Doctor E.M. Mills'	CSam
'Dorset Sentry'	More than 30 suppliers
'Dropmore Apricot'	CMMP SPav
'Drummore Apricot'	CKno CMHG EBee EChP ECha EGle EGra ELan EMan EWll LAst LSou MLLN MRav MSte NBir NSti SAga SDnm WCMO WCot WFar WGHP WHoo WHrl WPGP WPrP WTMC WWye
'Earliest of All'	COtt EBee GSki LBmB LRHS MBri
'Early Buttercup'	ECot EPfP GBri MRav WCot WFar
§ *ensifolia*	CPne CPou ECtt EGra GSki NGdn SRms WMnd
'Ernest Mitchell'	MRav SMrm WCot
Express hybrids	NBre NLar
'Fairyland'	LIck WBrk WFar WTin
'False Maid'	SMHy
* 'Fat Yellow'	EMar MWgw
fibrosa	CFir WCot
'Fiery Fred'	CMil EBee EBrs ELan LRHS MRav NBre SMrm WCMO WCot
'First Sunrise'	EBee ERou
'Flamenco'	CFwr EDAr EWll EWsh NBre NEgg NGdn SMac SPet WHil WTMC WWeb
'Flaming Torch'	ECha
foliosa	CPne LRHS SChr SMrm
'Frances Victoria'	WCot
galpinii misapplied	see *K. triangularis* subsp. *triangularis*
galpinii Baker ♀H4	EBee EMar EWTr GBri MRav NBre SPer SRms WHil WTMC
* 'Géant'	XPep
'Gilt Bronze'	EBee WCot
'Gladness'	EBee ECtt GSki MRav NBir NBre WCMO WCot WPrP
'Goldelse'	EBee NBir WCot
'Goldfinch'	CMdw CSam MRav SMHy SUsu
gracilis	LEdu
'Green and Cream'	MNrw
'Green Jade'	CDes CFir CMdw COtt CRow EBee EBrs EChP ECha EPfP ERou GBri GQue MRav NBir NBro NSti SEND SGar WCAu WCMO WCot WFar WTin
'Green Lemon' **new**	NBre
'H.E. Beale'	GCal MRav SMrm WCMO WCot
'Hen and Chickens'	WCMO
hirsuta	CFir CPne CPou CSam EBee ELan EMan EShb ITer MSte WCMO WCot
- JCA 3.461.900	WCot
- 'Traffic Lights'	CBgR ERou EWll LSou MGol MSph NBhm WCMO WHil
'Hollard's Gold'	WCMO WCot
'Ice Queen'	CAvo CFir CPar CSam CSev EBee EBrs ECGP EGle ERou GBri MBri MRav NBro NCGa NChi NGdn NMRc SWvt WBrE WCAu WCMO WCot WTin WWye
ichopensis	CDes GBuc WCMO WCot WPGP
'Ingénue'	EBee WCot
'Innocence'	EBrs NBre
'Jane Henry'	CDes

'Jenny Bloom'	More than 30 suppliers
'John Benary'	More than 30 suppliers
'Johnathan'	WCMO WCot
laxiflora	CPou WPGP
'Lemon Ice'	EBee WCot
'Light of the World'	see *K. triangularis* subsp. *triangularis* 'Light of the World'
linearifolia	CPou CTrC GGar MLLN MNrw SHom SPlb WCMO WCot
'Little Elf'	SBla SDys WSHC
'Little Maid'	More than 30 suppliers
'Lord Roberts'	CPen ECha ENot GBin MRav SMad SPav WCot
'Luna'	SMrm WCot
'Lye End' Pole	SMrm
macowanii	see *K. triangularis* subsp. *triangularis*
'Maid of Orleans'	CRow EBrs WCMO WCot
'Mermaiden'	CMHG CRow CSam EBee EChP ECtt GMac GSki LAst MNrw NCob WCMO WCot WFar
'Minister Verschuur'	EBee EBrs EMar GSki LBmB LRHS MBri NBre WFar
'Modesta'	EBee SBla WPGP
'Molten Lava' **new**	EBee
'Mount Etna'	EBee WCMO WCot WPGP
multiflora	CPne WCMO WCot
'Nancy's Red'	More than 30 suppliers
nelsonii Mast.	see *K. triangularis* subsp. *triangularis*
'Nobilis'	see *K. uvaria* 'Nobilis'
northiae	CFir CHEx CHad CPou GBin GCal IFro LEdu MNrw NBhm SAPC SArc SPlb WCMO WCru WMnd WPGP
'November Glory'	WCMO
I 'Old Court Seedling'	WCMO WCot WPrP
'Orange Torch'	CPou
'Painted Lady'	CAbP CSam CTri EBee GCal GMac MBnl MBri MRav NCGa NPri SMHy WCMO WHoo
parviflora	CPou
pauciflora	CBro CSpe EBee EMan ERos LHop SDys WCot
'Percy's Pride'	More than 30 suppliers
'Perry's White'	WViv
'Pfitzeri'	SRms
porphyrantha	WCot
x *praecox*	CPne GAbr MAvo WCMO WCot
'Primulina'	CPou EBrs EGra EMar LRHS
'Prince Igor'	CFir EBee EBrs EMan EMar MAvo MLHP MWea NBir SMad WCMO WCot
pumila	CPne GSki ITer
'Ralph Idden'	EChP
'Ranelagh Gardens'	SArc
'Regal Splendour' **new**	EBrs
ritualis	EDAr LSou MAvo WCMO WCot WLin WPGP
§ *rooperi*	More than 30 suppliers
I - 'Torchlight'	CAbb CPne WViv
'Royal Caste'	CFwr EBee MRav NBir NEgg NOrc NPri WFar
'Royal Standard' ♀H4	CBcs COtt EBee EBla ELan ENot EPfP ERou EShb GBri GSki LAst LRHS MNrw MRav NPri SHBN SPer SPoG SRms SWvt WCot WFar WWeb
rufa	CPne CPou WCMO
'Safranvogel'	WCMO WCot
'Samuel's Sensation' ♀H4	CFir EBee EBrs EChP ELan GBri GGar GSki LRHS MBnl MNFA MRav NEgg NLar NOrc NSti SHBN WCMO WCot WTMC
sarmentosa	CPne CPou EBee SPlb WCMO WCot WPGP XPep
'September Sunshine'	MRav
'Sherbet Lemon' **new**	EBee EPPr MLLN MNrw
'Shining Sceptre'	CFwr CSam EBee EBrs ECha ECtt ERou LIck LRHS MLLN MRav MWat NCGa NLar SGar SMad SSvw SWvt WAul WCMO WCot WEas WGHP WHil
'Springtime'	WCot
'Star of Baden Baden'	NBir SMad WCAu WCot
'Strawberries and Cream'	CBcs CFwr EBee EBrs ECha EMan EPfP LAst MSte NPri SAga SPer SUsu WCMO WCot
stricta	CTrC WCot
'Sunbeam'	NBir
'Sunningdale Yellow' ♀H4	CDes CMdw COlW CPou EBee EBla ECha EHrv EMan ERou GMaP MLHP MWat SBla SMHy SPer SRms WCot WEas WPGP
'Tawny King'	More than 30 suppliers
'Tetbury Torch' PBR	LRHS SMrm WWeb WWes
thodei	CPou
thomsonii	GCal
- var. *snowdenii* misapplied	see *K. thomsonii* var. *thomsonii*
- var. *snowdenii* ambig.	CPou CSec WPGP WSHC
§ - var. *thomsonii*	CBow CDes CFir CHVG EBee EMan EMar ETow SAga SMHy SUsu WCot WHal WOut WPrP WWlt
- - triploid variety	GSki
'Timothy'	More than 30 suppliers
'Toffee Nosed' ♀H4	More than 30 suppliers
'Torchbearer'	EBee NBre WCot WFar
triangularis	CHad CMHG CPne EBee EPfP GCal GSki LRHS SMar WFar
- subsp. *triangularis*	CBro COlW CWCL EAEE EBee EChP EMar ENot EPfP GBuc ITer LAst LRHS LSRN MRav NBro SRms SWat WBrE WPrP
- - 'Light of the World'	More than 30 suppliers
'Tubergeniana'	WCot
'Tuckii'	SRms
tuckii Baker	see *K. ensifolia*
typhoides	GCal NBir SPlb WCMO
tysonii	SPlb
uvaria	CBig CPne CPou CTrC EBrs GSki ITer LRHS MHer MNHC NBir NPri NVic SECG SRms WBor WCot WHoo WMnd WPnP WTMC
§ - 'Nobilis' ♀H4	More than 30 suppliers
'Vanilla'	CFir EBee EChP EMan GSki LAst MBNS MRav NGdn NLar WAul WCMO WTMC
'Vesta'	EBrs
'Victoria' **new**	EBrs
'Wol's Red Seedling' **new**	CFir LSou NCGa SPoG SUsu WGwG
'Wrexham Buttercup'	CDes CKno CPne CSam EBee EChP ECtt ETow GAbr GBri GCal GMac GSki IPot LSRN MAvo MBnl MLLN MNFA MRav SUsu WBVN WCMO WCot WHal WHoo WPrP WTMC WWlt
'Yellow Cheer'	CPen LRHS
'Yellowhammer'	CSam EBee ECha NBre WFar WPrP
'Zululandii'	WCot

Knowltonia (Ranunculaceae)

filia	CPLG

Kochia see Bassia

Koeleria (Poaceae)

cristata	see *K. macrantha*
glauca	More than 30 suppliers
§ *macrantha*	CBig EMan NBre NLar NNor NOGN
vallesiana	EHoe EMon LRHS MNrw

Koelreuteria (Sapindaceae)

bipinnata	CMCN
* **orientalis**	GIBF
paniculata ♀H4	More than 30 suppliers
- 'Coral Sun'	MBlu NLar
- 'Fastigiata'	EBee EPfP LRHS MBlu MBri NPal SPoG SSpi
- 'Rosseels'	CBcs MBlu MGos NEgg NLar

Kohleria (Gesneriaceae)

'Clytie'	MBri
'Dark Velvet'	CHal EShb WDib
eriantha ♀H1	CHal EShb MBri WDib
'Jester' ♀H1	CHal WDib
* 'Linda'	CHal
'Strawberry Fields' ♀H1	MBri
§ **warscewiczii** ♀H1	CHal EShb LRHS WDib

Kolkwitzia (Caprifoliaceae)

amabilis	CElw CPLG CSBt CTrw ELan EMil EPfP GIBF LPan MGan MGos NFor NWea SPlb SRms WCFE WDin WHCG WHar WMoo WNor WTel
- 'Maradco'	CPMA EBee EPfP LRHS MAsh MRav NLar NPro SCoo SPoG SSta WPat
- 'Pink Cloud' ♀H4	More than 30 suppliers

Krascheninnikovia (Chenopodiaceae)

§ **lanata**	XPep

Kunzea (Myrtaceae)

ambigua	CPLG CTrC ECou IDee SOWG SPlb
'Badja Carpet'	WAbe
baxteri	ECou EUnu SOWG
capitata	SBrw SOWG
ericifolia	SPlb
§ **ericoides**	CTrC ECou GGar SOWG
- 'Auckland'	ECou
- 'Bemm'	ECou
parvifolia	CPLG ECou SOWG
pomifera	ECou

kumquat see *Fortunella*

L

Lablab (Papilionaceae)

§ **purpureus**	SMur
- 'Ruby Moon'	CSpe LRav

+ *Laburnocytisus* (Papilionaceae)

'Adamii'	CDul CLnd CPMA EBee ELan EPfP LBuc LPan MBlu MGos NLar SMad SMHT SPer

Laburnum ❀ (Papilionaceae)

alpinum	CNic EPfP NEgg NWea SPlb
- 'Pendulum'	CDoC CDul CLnd EBee ELan EPfP LPan LRHS LSRN MBar MBri MGos NBlu NEgg SBLw SBod SCrf SLim SPer SPoG WOrn
§ **anagyroides**	CDul CWib ISea NWea SBLw SEND SRms WBVN WDin
- var. **alschingeri**	MBlu MGos
- 'Pendulum'	NEgg
vulgare	see *L. anagyroides*
x **watereri** 'Vossii' ♀H4	More than 30 suppliers

Lachenalia ❀ (Hyacinthaceae)

§ **aloides**	CBcs CStu ECho EShb LBow MBri
- var. **aurea** ♀H1	CMon ECho LBow LRHS MSte SBch WCot
- 'Balfour's' new	LBow
* - var. **bicolor**	ECho WCot
- var. **luteola**	ECho LBow
- 'Nelsonii'	ECho LBow LRHS
- 'Pearsonii'	ECho LBow LRHS
- var. **quadricolor** ♀H1	CBct CGrW ECho GAbr LBow LRHS WCot
- var. **vanzyliae** ♀H1	LBow
- var. **vanzyliae** x **orchioides** var. **glaucina** new	LBow
bachmanii	CMon
§ **bulbifera** ♀H1	ECho LBow MBri
- 'George' ♀H1	LBow
carnosa new	LBow
contaminata ♀H1	CBct CMon ECho LBow LRHS WCot
elegans	ECho
framesii new	LBow
gillettii new	LBow
haarlemensis new	LBow
hirta new	LBow
'Indian Prince' new	LBow
juncifolia	ECho LBow
liliiflora	CMon ECho LBow
mathewsii	LBow
mediana	LBow
mutabilis	ECho LBow LRHS WCot
namaquensis	ECho LBow
neilii	WCot
orchioides ♀H1 new	LBow
- var. **glaucina**	CGrW ECho LBow WCot
- var. **orchioides** new	LBow
orthopetala	LBow WCot
pallida	ECho LBow
peersii new	LBow
pendula	see *L. bulbifera*
purpureocoerulea	CMon
pusilla	CMon ECho
pustulata ♀H1	ECho LBow LRHS WCot
- blue-flowered	ECho
reflexa	CMon ECho LBow WCot
x **regeliana** new	LBow
'Robyn'	ECho WCot
'Rolina'	ECho WCot
'Romand'	ECho WCot
'Romelia' PBR	CBct ECho WCot
'Ronina'	CBct ECho WCot
'Rosabeth'	WCot
rubida	ECho WCot
'Rupert'	ECho WCot
splendida	ECho
tricolor	see *L. aloides*
unicolor	ECho WCot
unifolia	ECho LBow
violacea	ECho LBow WCot
viridiflora ♀H1	CGrW ECho LRHS WCMO

Lactuca (Asteraceae)

alpina	see *Cicerbita alpina*
intricata	EHyt
lessertiana new	EBee
perennis	CWan EBee EMag EMan GSki LSou MTho NDov NLar NSti SPla SPoG WBor WCFE WCMO WCot WGwG WHer WHrl
virosa	CArn MSal

Lagarosiphon (Hydrocharitaceae)

§ **major**	CBen CDWL EHon EMFW EPfP LNCo NBlu WFar WMAq WPnP

Lagarostrobos (Podocarpaceae)

§ **franklinii**	CBcs CDoC CTrG LLin STre WPic

Lagerstroemia (Lythraceae)

indica ♀H1	CMen EPfP ERom EShb NLar SBLw SEND SPlb
- Little Chief hybrids **new**	EShb
- Petite Pinkie = 'Monkie' **new**	MPRe
- 'Red Imperator' **new**	MPRe SEND
- 'Rosea'	CBcs LPan SEND
- 'Rubra' **new**	MPRe
subcostata	CPLG

Lagunaria (Malvaceae)

patersonii	CHll CPLG WPGP XPep
- 'Royal Purple'	ERea

Lagurus (Poaceae)

ovatus ♀H3	CHrt CKno CWCL EGoo MGol SAdn SBch

Lallemantia (Lamiaceae)

§ **canescens**	EMan

Lambertia (Proteaceae)

formosa	ECou
inermis	SPlb

Lamiastrum see *Lamium*

Lamium ✿ (Lamiaceae)

from Turkey	CStu
album	CArn GWCH NMir
- 'Friday' (v)	CBgR CBow EHoe EMan NBir NBre WHer WHil WWye
armenum	WAbe
flexuosum	NBre
§ **galeobdolon**	CArn CNat CTri CWib LBMP MHar MHer MSal NSco SMac SRms WBrE
- 'Hermann's Pride'	CBcs COIW COtt EBee ECtt EHoe EPfP GCal GMaP IHMH LAst LRHS MAvo MBow MBri MWgw MWrn NBir NCob NMir SAga SMad SPer SPla SRms SWvt WFar WHoo WMoo WWye
- 'Kirkcudbright Dwarf'	EBee EWes NBre
§ - subsp. *montanum* 'Florentinum'	CHal CHrt CSBt CWan EBee EChP ECha EHoe ELan EMan EPfP MMuc MRav NVic SPer WBrk WCAu WFar WPer
§ - 'Silberteppich'	ECha ELan EMan EMar MRav MTho
- 'Silver Angel'	EMan NBre SBch
- Silver Carpet	see *L. galeobdolon* 'Silberteppich'
- 'Variegatum'	see *L. galeobdolon* subsp. *montanum* 'Florentinum'
garganicum	WTMC
- subsp. *garganicum*	CDes CPom EWes GBri WPer
- subsp. *pictum*	see *L. garganicum* subsp. *striatum*
- subsp. *reniforme*	see *L. garganicum* subsp. *striatum*
§ - subsp. *striatum*	SBla
luteum	see *L. galeobdolon*
maculatum	CArn CHrt EGoo EPot IHMH SEND SHFr SRms WFar
- 'Album'	EBee ELan EPfP SHar SPer SRms
- 'Anne Greenaway' (v)	CBow EBee GBri MFOX SPet
- 'Annecy'	WWye
§ - 'Aureum'	CArn COIW EBee ECha ECho EHoe ELan IHMH LAst MTho SPet SWvt WEas WFar WPer
- 'Beacon Silver'	More than 30 suppliers
- 'Beedham's White'	EBee NBir NSti
- 'Brightstone Pearl'	EBee EGoo EWes
- 'Cannon's Gold'	EBee ECha ECtt EHoe ELan EPPr EWes EWin GBuc IHMH SPer SWvt WFar
- 'Chequers' ambig.	EBee EWin LRHS NBre SPer SPla
- 'Dingle Candy'	CBgR
- 'Elaine Franks'	CSam
- 'Elisabeth de Haas' (v)	CBow EWes NBre
- 'Forncett Lustre'	CBgR EBee EWin
- 'Forncett White Lustre' **new**	NBre
- 'Gold Leaf'	see *L. maculatum* 'Aureum'
- Golden Anniversary = 'Dellam'PBR (v)	EBee ELan LAst NBro NGdn NOrc SPla SSto WFar
- 'Golden Nuggets'	see *L. maculatum* 'Aureum'
- 'Golden Wedding'	COtt ECho
- 'Hatfield'	EBee GAbr
- 'Ickwell Beauty' (v)	EBee GBri
- 'James Boyd Parselle'	CBgR CBow CSam EBee EGle EWin MLLN NBre WCot WRHF
- 'Margery Fish'	SRms WEas
- 'Pink Nancy'	EGoo SWvt WFar
- 'Pink Pearls'	CHrt CSBt ECho NBre NCiC SHar SMac SPet WFar WMoo
- 'Pink Pewter'	EBee ECGP ECha ECtt EHoe ELan GGar GMaP IHMH LRHS NGdn NSti SPer SPla SPlb SUsu WBrE
- 'Red Nancy'	EBee
§ - 'Roseum'	CWib EBee ELan EPfP GGar GMaP MRav MWat MWgw NChi NFor SGar SPer WCAu WPer
- 'Shell Pink'	see *L. maculatum* 'Roseum'
- 'Silver Shield'	EBee EWes
- 'Sterling Silver'	EBee NBre WPer
- 'White Nancy' ♀H4	More than 30 suppliers
- 'Wootton Pink'	GBuc GCal MBri MHer NBir NLar SSvw SWvt WCra WEas
microphyllum	CPBP EHyt WAbe
orvala	More than 30 suppliers
- 'Album'	CBod CBos EBee EChP EHrv ELan EMon EPPr MSte SGar SHar SMrm WCMO WCot WHer WTin
- 'Silva'	EMan EMon GBin NBre NGby WCMO WCot WSHC
sandrasicum	CPBP CStu EBee EHyt SBla WAbe WPat

Lampranthus (Aizoaceae)

aberdeenensis	see *Delosperma aberdeenense*
auriantiacus	CBcs CHEx SPet
'Bagdad'	CHEx
blandus	CBcs CCCN
'Blousey Pink'	CHEx
§ **brownii**	CBcs CCCN CHEx CHal CStu ECho ELan EWin NBir SEND SPet WPnn
coccineus	SPet
deltoides	see *Oscularia deltoides*
edulis	see *Carpobrotus edulis*
falcatus	CPLG
glaucus	CStu SEND
haworthii	CHal
multiradiatus	GGar SEND
oscularis	see *Oscularia deltoides*
roseus	CCCN CHEx EWin SPet
spectabilis	CBcs CCCN CHal CStu SAPC SArc SMur SPet WBrE
- orange-flowered	CDoC
- Tresco Apricot	CBcs CCCN
- 'Tresco Brilliant'	CBcs CCCN CHEx SPet
- 'Tresco Fire'	CCCN CDoC CHal
- 'Tresco Orange' **new**	CCCN
- 'Tresco Peach'	CCCN CHal CStu CWCL WAbe
- 'Tresco Red'	CBcs CCCN CTbh CWCL
- white-flowered	CStu
'Sugar Pink'	CHEx

Lamprothyrsus (Poaceae)

hieronymi	EBee

Lancea (Scrophulariaceae)
tibetica	NWCA

Lantana (Verbenaceae)
'Aloha' (v)	CHal
camara	CArn ELan EPfP EShb MBri MOak SRms SYvo XPep
- 'Firebrand'	SYvo
- 'Kolibri'	EWin LAst
- orange-flowered	SWal
- pink-flowered	SWal
- red-flowered	SWal
- 'Snow White'	LAst MOak
- 'Sonja'	LAst
- variegated	EShb
- white-flowered	SWal
- yellow-flowered	NPri SWal
'Goldsome'	EWin LAst
'Ingersheimer'	EWin
§ montevidensis	CHal EShb MOak SPet XPep
- RCB/Arg AA-1	WCot
- 'Boston Gold'	CHal
'Schneeflocke'	EWin
selloviana	see L. montevidensis
'Spreading Sunset'	SOWG
violet-flowered new	SEND

Lapageria (Philesiaceae)
rosea ♀H3	CCCN CHll CKob CPLG CPin CPne CRHN CSec EPfP GQui MDun NLar NSla SAdn SBrw SHBN WCMO WGwG WNor WPGP
- var. albiflora	CPIN CRHN SAdn SBrw WCMO
- 'Flesh Pink'	CPLG CRHN
- 'Nash Court'	ECot EMil

Lapeirousia (Iridaceae)
anceps	CStu
cruenta	see Anomatheca laxa
divaricata	CStu
laxa	see Anomatheca laxa

Lapiedra (Amaryllidaceae)
martinezii MS 425 from Spain	CMon

Lapsana (Asteraceae)
communis 'Inky'	CNat EUnu

Lardizabala (Lardizabalaceae)
biternata	see L. funaria
§ funaria	CPIN CTrG

Larix (Pinaceae)
decidua ♀H4	CAgr CBcs CCVT CDoC CDul CMen CRWN CSBt ECho ECrN ELan EPfP LCon MBar NBlu NEgg NWea SHBN SPer WDin WEve WFar WHar WMou NHol
- 'Autumn Gold Weeping'	
- 'Corley'	CKen ECho LLin MBlu
- 'Croxby Broom'	CKen
- 'Globus'	ECho LRHS NHol SLim
- 'Horstmann Recurved'	ECho LLin LRHS NLar SCoo SLim SPoG
- 'Krejci'	NLar SLim
- 'Little Bogle'	CKen ECho MAsh NHol
- 'Oberförster Karsten'	CKen ECho
- 'Pendula'	CBcs ECho WEve
- 'Puli'	CEnd COtt ECho LCon LLin LRHS MAsh MBlu MGos NHol NLar SCoo SLim SPer SPoG WEve

x eurolepis	see L. x marschlinsii
europaea Middend.	see L. sibirica
gmelinii	GIBF
- var. olgensis	NLar
- var. principis-rupprechtii	GIBF GTSp
- 'Tharandt'	CKen ECho
§ kaempferi ♀H4	CDoC CDul CLnd CMen CSBt CTri ECho ECrN ELan EPfP LBuc LCon LPan LRHS MAsh MBar NEgg NScw NWea SCoo SLim SPer STre WDin WEve WFar WMou WNor
- 'Bambino'	CKen
- 'Bingman'	CKen
- 'Blue Ball'	CKen ECho LLin NLar WEve
- 'Blue Dwarf'	CKen COtt ECho LCon LLin LPan LRHS MAsh MBar MGos NBlu SCoo SLim SPoG WEve WOrn
- 'Blue Haze'	CKen
- 'Blue Rabbit'	CKen CTho GTSp WEve
- 'Blue Rabbit Weeping'	COtt ECho LCon LLin MGos NHol SCoo SLim WDin WEve WOrn
- 'Cruwys Morchard'	CKen
- 'Cupido'	ECho LLin NHol SLim
- 'Diane'	CEnd CKen ECho EPfP LCon LLin LRHS MAsh MBar MBlu MGos NHol NLar SBLw SLim SPoG WEve WOrn
- 'Elizabeth Rehder'	CKen ECho NLar
- 'Grant Haddow'	CKen
- 'Green Pearl'	ECho
- 'Grey Green Dwarf'	NHol
- 'Grey Pearl'	CKen ECho LLin NLar
- 'Hanna's Broom'	LCon NLar SLim
- 'Hobbit'	CKen
- 'Jakobsen'	LCon
* - 'Jakobsen's Pyramid'	LLin LRHS MAsh NHol SCoo SLim SPoG
- 'Nana'	CKen ECho GTSp LLin NLar SLim
I - 'Nana Prostrata'	CKen ECho
- 'Pendula'	CDul CEnd EBee ECho ECrN EPfP LLin LRHS MAsh MBar MBlu MGos NHol NLar SBLw SPer SPoG WEve
- 'Pulii'	ECho SBLw
- 'Stiff Weeping'	CTri ECho LCon MAsh MBlu NLar SLim
- 'Swallow Falls'	CKen
- 'Varley'	CKen ECho
- 'Walter Pimven'	NLar
- 'Wehlen'	CKen
- 'Wolterdingen'	CKen EBrs ECho LCon MBlu NLar SLim
- 'Yanus Olieslagers'	CKen
laricina 'Arethusa Bog'	CKen ECho MBlu
- 'Bear Swamp'	CKen ECho
- 'Bingman'	CKen
- 'Hartwig Pine'	CKen ECho
- 'Newport Beauty'	CKen ECho
leptolepis	see L. kaempferi
§ x marschlinsii	CSBt ECho GBin NWea WMou
- 'Domino'	CKen ECho LLin NLar
- 'Gail'	CKen ECho
- 'Julie'	CKen SLim
- 'Newport 17' new	NLar
russica	see L. sibirica
§ sibirica	MBar
'Varied Directions'	SLim

Larrea (Zygophyllaceae)
tridentata	CArn

Laserpitium (Apiaceae)
halleri	EBee
siler	CArn EBee GBin NDov NLar SMHy SPlb WSHC

Lasiagrostis see *Stipa*

Lasiospermum (Asteraceae)
bipinnatum	SPlb

Latania (Arecaceae)
loddigesii	EAmu LPal
verschaffeltii	LPal

Lathyrus ✿ (Papilionaceae)
albus	CEnd
§ articulatus	ELan SBch WCHb
§ aureus	More than 30 suppliers
azureus misapplied	see *L. sativus*
chilensis	EBee EDsa LSou NLar
chloranthus	EDsa SPav WViv
cirrhosus	CDes EBee EMon
clymenum articulatus	see *L. articulatus*
cyaneus misapplied	see *L. vernus*
* cyaneus (Steven) K Koch	MTho SWat
'Alboroseus'	
davidii	CDes EBee EMon EWes WSHC
filiformis	WSHC
fremontii hort.	see *L. laxiflorus*
§ gmelinii	EBee NLar WSan
- 'Aureus'	see *L. aureus*
grandiflorus	CPIN CSev EChP EMon LPhx
	NLar SBla SMrm SSvw SWat
	WCot
heterophyllus	EMon EWsh MNrw NLar
inermis	see *L. laxiflorus*
japonicus	LPhx
laevigatus	NLar
latifolius ♀H4	CAgr CArn CEnt CRHN CRWN
	EChP EPfP GAbr GBar LAst LRav
	MWat NBid NBlu NPer SDnm
	SPoG SRms SWal WBVN WBor
	WBrk WEas WFar WHer WPer
	WWye
§ - 'Albus' ♀H4	EBee ELan EMan LPhx NBHF SPav
	SRms WEas WWye
- 'Blushing Bride'	SPav WCot WSel
- deep pink	MHer NLar NSti WGwG
- pale pink	NSti
- Pink Pearl	see *L. latifolius* 'Rosa Perle'
- 'Red Pearl'	EBee EChP ECtt ELan EPfP ERou
	GAbr MBri MWgw NPri NRnb
	SMar SPav SPer SPlb SPoG SSvw
	WFar WPer WViv WWeb
§ - 'Rosa Perle' ♀H4	CBcs CPIN CTri EChP ECtt EMan
	ERou EShb LAst LHop MBri MLHP
	MNHC MSte NBir NEgg
	NLar NPer NPri NRnb SBla SBra
	SPav SPer SSvw WCAu WMoo
	WViv WWeb
- Weisse Perle	see *L. latifolius* 'White Pearl'
- 'White Pearl'	see *L. latifolius* 'Albus'
misapplied	
§ - 'White Pearl' ♀H4	More than 30 suppliers
§ laxiflorus	CAby CDes CPom EBee EMag
	ETow LHop MCCP MHar MNrw
	MTho NChi NLar WBVN WPGP
	WViv
linifolius	CDes EBee EMon NLar WCot
	WPGP
- var. montanus	WViv
luteus (L.) Peterm.	see *L. gmelinii*
- 'Aureus'	see *L. aureus*
magellanicus	EBee WSHC
maritimus	CSpe WSHC
montanus	EBee GPoy
multiceps new	WCot
§ nervosus	CPIN CSpe EBee EWes MTho SBla
	SRms
neurolobus	CNic CPLG CPom ITer WGwG
niger	CFee CPom EBrs EDAr EMon
	GBuc GMac LSou MHer MLLN
	MSph NLar NRnb SHFr SMar WFar
	WHil
nissolia	ELan
ochrus	WGwG
odoratus	EWll NBlu
- 'America' ♀H4	WGwG
- 'Bicolor'	ELan
- 'Black Knight'	WGwG
- 'Blanche Ferry'	MSph
- 'Captain of the Blues'	WGwG
- 'Cupani'	CHrt SUsu WGwG
- 'Matucana'	CSpe EBee MWat SBch WGwG
palustris	NLar SMar
polyphyllus	NSti
pratensis	MBow NMir NSco WSFF
pubescens	CRHN GBuc WSHC
'Queen Charlotte'	WGwG
roseus	GCal WSHC WViv
rotundifolius ♀H4	CHad EMag LPhx MNrw MTho
	NLar SMar SSvw WCot WFar WHoo
	WViv
- hybrids	LPhx
- 'Tillyperone'	CFwr EMon EPPr WWpP
§ sativus	CSec CSpe ECho ELan SBch WCHb
- var. azureus	see *L. sativus*
sylvestris	CAgr CBgR CPLG EBee EMon
	MHer MLLN MNrw MSte MWat
	NLar SBch WBrk WOut WViv
tingitanus	CRHN WCHb
- 'Roseus'	CRHN EDsa SBch
transsilvanicus	CPom WViv
tuberosus	CAgr EDsa MNrw SMar WCot
	WSHC
'Tubro'	EMon SHar
venetus	EBee MNrw WSHC
venus 'Spring Delight' **new**	EBrs
§ vernus ♀H4	More than 30 suppliers
- 'Alboroseus' ♀H4	More than 30 suppliers
- var. albus	CDes EBee ECho EWes WPGP
- aurantiacus	see *L. aureus*
- 'Caeruleus'	CBos CDes EBee EMon LHop LPhx
	SUsu
* - 'Cyaneus'	SAga SWat WCot WSan WWpP
- 'Flaccidus'	EBee EChP EGle EMon SMeo WCot
	WKif WSHC WTin
* - 'Gracilis'	WViv
- 'Indigo Eyes'	CDes
- 'Rainbow'	CBgR GAbr LBMP NWCA SMar
	WHil
- 'Rosenelfe'	CDes CMea EBee EDAr EMan
	EWin GBuc SBod SMar WCot WHal
	WHil WPGP WSan WViv
- f. roseus	ECha ETow MRav NBir SRms WCot
	WCru
- 'Spring Beauty'	WViv WWpP
- 'Spring Melody'	EBee MRav WCot WPat
- 'Subtle Hints'	EMon

Laurelia (Monimiaceae)
§ sempervirens	CBcs CTrw WPGP
serrata	see *L. sempervirens*

Laurentia see *Isotoma*

Laurus (Lauraceae)
§ azorica	CBcs WFar
canariensis	see *L. azorica*
nobilis ♀H4	More than 30 suppliers
- f. angustifolia	CMCN CSWP EPla GQui MBlu
	MRav NGHP NLar SAPC SArc
	WCHb WPGP WSel
- 'Aurea' ♀H4	CBcs CBrm CDul CSBt EBee ELan
	ELau EMil EPfP GQui LHop LRHS
	MBlu SBLw SHGC SLim SLon SMad

	SPer SPoG SWvt WCHb WDin WFar WJek WMoo WPat WSel
- clipped pyramid	MGos NBlu
- 'Crispa'	MRav
I - 'Laciniata' **new**	WCot
- 'Sunspot' (v)	CBow WCot

Lavandula ✿ (*Lamiaceae*)

'After Midnight'	see *L.*'Avonview'
'Alba' ambig.	CArn CBcs CSev CWib EGra MHrb SAdn SIde SPer SWat WEas WPer
x *allardii*	see *L.* x *heterophylla* Gaston Allard Group
§ *angustifolia*	More than 30 suppliers
§ - 'Alba' misapplied	see *L. angustifolia* 'Blue Mountain White'
- 'Alba Nana'	see *L. angustifolia* 'Nana Alba'
- 'Arctic Snow'	CBcs CWan ENor LAst MHrb MSwo NBPC NGHP NLLv SDnm SPer SPoG WLav
- 'Ashdown Forest'	CWan ECho ELau GBar MAsh MHer MHrb MLHP MNHC MWgw NGHP SAdn SBch SDow SIde WHoo WJek WLav
- 'Beechwood Blue' ♀H4	CWCL MHrb SDow WLav
- Blue Cushion = 'Lavandula Schola'PBR	ENot EPfP LRHS LSRN MAsh MHrb NPri SDow SMer WFar WLav
- 'Blue Ice'	CWSG ENor SDow
- 'Blue Mountain'	CBcs GBar ITim MHer MHrb WLav
- 'Blue Mountain White'	CWan EBee ECho EHoe ELau ENot EPfP GPoy LBuc LSRN MHer MNHC MSwo NGHP NLLv NMen SAll SDow SLon SPlb SSto WDin WFar WLav WSel XPep
- 'Blue River'PBR	WFar WLav
§ - 'Bowles Early'	CSam CWan GBar NGHP SAdn SAga SMer WFar WLav XPep
- 'Bowles Grey'	see *L. angustifolia* 'Bowles Early'
- 'Bowles Variety'	see *L. angustifolia* 'Bowles Early'
- 'Cedar Blue'	CSev CWan ECho EGoo ELau EPfP GBar MHer MWgw NBur NGHP SDow SHDw SIde SPla WFar WLav
- 'Coconut Ice'	LRHS NGHP NLLv NTHB WLav
- 'Compacta'	MHrb SDow
- 'Dwarf Blue'	CRez EBee EWin WFar XPep
I - 'Eastgrove Nana'	WEas
* - 'Erbalunga'	XPep
- 'Folgate'	CArn CBcs CWCL ELau GBar LAst MHer MHrb MNHC NBur NGHP NHHG SAll SDow SIde WFar WHoo WLav WMnd WSel WTel XPep
- 'Fring A'	SDow
- 'Granny's Bouquet' **new**	MAsh
§ - 'Hidcote' ♀H4	More than 30 suppliers
_ - 'Hidcote Blue'	see *L.angustifolia* 'Hidcote'
- 'Hidcote Pink'	CArn CWib EBee ECho GBar LSRN MHer MNHC MRav MWat NFor NGHP SDow SPer WFar WGwG WHen WKif WMnd WPer WSel XPep
- 'Hidcote Superior'	NChi WWeb
- 'Imperial Gem' ♀H4	More than 30 suppliers
- 'Jean Davis'	see *L. angustifolia* 'Rosea'
N - 'Lady'	CWSG NPer SAdn SBch SEND SHDw SSto SWal WPer
- 'Lady Ann'	MHrb NLLv NTHB SDow WLav
- 'Lavenite Petite'	ENor ENot EPfP LRHS LSRN LTwo MAsh MHrb NBPC NGHP NLLv NLar SDow SPoG SVil WLav WWeb
- Little Lady = 'Batlad'PBR	CRez ENor EWTr LSRN MAsh MHer MHrb MSwo NGHP NLLv NLar SAll SSto WLav WPat
- Little Lottie = 'Clarmo' ♀H4	CWCL CWSG EMil EMil LTwo EWin LAst LRHS MAvo MHer SCoo SDow SIde SMer SSto SWvt WLav

- 'Loddon Blue' ♀H4	CEnt ECho GBar LRHS NGHP NHHG SAdn SDow SIde WHoo WLav
§ - 'Loddon Pink' ♀H4	CWan EBee ECho ELan ENot EPfP GBar GMaP LAst LRHS MAsh MLHP MNHC MRav NGHP NPri SAdn SMer SSto WEas WFar WGwG WHoo WLav WPGP
* - 'Lumières des Alpes'	XPep
- 'Maillette'	EWin MHrb NGHP SDow SIde WLav XPep
* - 'Matheronne'	XPep
- 'Melissa Lilac'	ENor MHrb SDow
- 'Middachten'	SAga
- 'Miss Donnington'	see *L. angustifolia* 'Bowles Early'
- 'Miss Katherine'PBR ♀H4	CSBt CWCL EBee ELan ENor EPfP LAst LHop LRHS LSRN MAsh MHrb MNHC NBPC NGHP NLar SDow SMer SPer SPoG SVil WLav WRHF
- Miss Muffet = 'Scholmis' ♀H4	CWCL EMil LTwo MWgw NLLv SDow SPer WLav
- 'Munstead'	More than 30 suppliers
§ - 'Nana Alba' ♀H4	More than 30 suppliers
- 'Nana Atropurpurea'	WSel
- 'No 9'	SDow
- 'Peter Pan'	CBcs CWCL LSRN MHrb NGHP SDow SMer WLav
- 'Princess Blue'	CSBt CWCL ELan ENor EShb GBar LRHS MAsh NPri SAll SDow SIde SMer SSto WFar WLav WPer WWeb XPep
* - 'Rêve de Jean-Claude'	XPep
§ - 'Rosea'	More than 30 suppliers
- 'Royal Purple'	CArn EBee ENor EWes GBar LRHS MHer NGHP NHHG NPri NTHB SAdn SAll SDow SIde SMur SSto SWvt WLav XPep
- 'Twickel Purple'	More than 30 suppliers
- 'Wendy Carlile' ♀H4 **new**	ENor
'Aphrodite'	LRHS MAsh SDow WLav
aristibracteata	MHer WLav
'Avonview'	CBcs CWCL GBar MHer NGHP SDow SPoG WHoo WLav
'Ballerina'	MHrb SDow
'Bee Brilliant'	CWCL NGHP SPoG WLav
'Bee Cool'	CWCL EBee MHrb NGHP NLLv SPoG WCMO WLav
'Bee Happy'	CMea CWCL CWan EPfP MWea NGHP SHGN SPoG WCMO WLav
'Bee Pretty'	CWCL NGHP
'Blue Star'	EBee EWin NGHP SAll WFar WGHP WGwG
'Bowers Beauty'	MAsh WLav
buchii var. *buchii*	SDow XPep
- var. *gracilis*	CSpe
Butterfly Garden = 'Avenue'PBR	ITim
canariensis	CSev ERea EShb MHer MHrb NHHG SDow WCHb WLav XPep
x *chaytorae*	CArn GBar NHHG
- 'Gorgeous'	SDow
- 'Kathleen Elizabeth'	XPep
- 'Richard Gray' ♀H3-4	CArn CCge EBee GBar LRHS LSRN MAsh MHer MHrb MNHC NGHP NPri SAga SDnm SDow SSvw WAbe WLav WMnd XPep
§ - 'Sawyers' ♀H4	More than 30 suppliers
x *christiana*	GBar MHer MHrb NGHP SDow SHDw WGwG WLav WPat XPep
'Cornard Blue'	see *L.* x *chaytorae* 'Sawyers'
dentata	CArn CEnt CSev CTbh EAro EShb GBar MNHC MWat NEgg NGHP NHHG SAdn SMer WAbe WHer WPic WWye XPep

§	- var. **candicans**	CSev GBar LHop MHer MHrb MNHC NHHG NLLv SBch SDow SPer WCHb WLav WWye XPep
	- - 'Pure Harmony'	SDow WLav
	- var. **dentata** 'Dusky Maiden'	CWCL MHrb SDow WLav
	- - 'Linda Ligon' (v)	CBow EWin GBar MHrb NGHP WGwG WHer WJek WLav XPep
	- - 'Monet'	MHrb NGHP WLav
	- - 'Ploughman's Blue'	CWCL MHrb WLav
	- - f. **rosea**	MHrb SDow WLav
	- - 'Royal Crown' ♀H2-3	GBar MHer WFar WLav XPep
	- - 'Royal Standard'	SHBN
	- - 'Silver Queen'	WLav
	- silver	see *L. dentata* var. *candicans*
	'Devonshire Compact'	CHar CSBt CWCL EWin LSou MHer NGHP NTHB SBch WJek
	'Evelyn Cadzow'	CSec WLav
	'Fathead'	More than 30 suppliers
x	**ginginsii** 'Goodwin Creek Grey'	GBar MHrb MNHC NLLv SDow WGwG WJek WLav XPep
	'Hazel'	MAsh WLav
	'Helmsdale'PBR	CEnd CSBt EBee ELan ENot EPfP LAst LHop LRHS LSRN MAsh MBri MHer MLan MRav MSwo MWat MWgw NBPC NGHP SAll SCoo SDow SLim SMer SPer SPla SPoG SVil WJek WLav XPep
x	**heterophylla** Viv. 'Devantville-Cuche'	
§	- Gaston Allard Group	CArn CPLG CSev CWCL EShb EWin GBar MHer NGHP NHHG NLLv SDow WJek WLav WSel XPep
	- - 'African Pride'	GBar SDow XPep
	'Hidcote Blue'	see *L. angustifolia* 'Hidcote'
§	x **intermedia**	EWin SPla WFar
	- 'Abrialii'	GBar NLLv SDow WLav XPep
	- 'Alba' ♀H4	CBcs CMea CWan GBar NHHG SAga SDow SGar SMer WHlf XPep
*	- 'Alexis'	XPep
N	- 'Arabian Night' ♀H4	CBcs COtt ELau MNHC SDow WLav WWeb XPep
	- 'Bogong'	WLav
	- 'Chaix'	GBar
§	- Dutch Group	CArn CSBt CWCL CWan CWib ENot EPfP GBar LRHS MAsh MBar MRav MSwo SAga SCoo SDow SGar SLim SPer SWat WFar WHen WPer XPep
	- 'Edelweiss'	EAro EWin LRHS MHer MRav NBur NGHP NLLv WLav WRHF XPep
	- 'Fragrant Memories'	ELau EPfP EWin GBar MAsh MHrb NPri SAga SDow SIde SMer WLav
*	- 'Futura'	XPep
	- 'Goldburg = 'Burgoldeen'PBR (v)	CBow CSBt ELan ENot EPfP LAst LBuc MCCP MGos MHer MRav NGHP NLLv NPri SCoo SPav SPla SPoG SSto WLav WWeb
	- 'Grappenhall' misapplied	see *L.* x *intermedia* 'Pale Pretender'
	- 'Grey Hedge'	CWan NGHP SAga WLav
	- 'Gros Bleu'	SDow WLav WWeb
	- 'Grosso'	CBcs CEnt COtt CSam CSev CTri EBee ELan ELau EPfP GBar MHer MHrb MNHC MRav NGHP SAdn SAll SCoo SDow SSto SSvw SWvt WDin WFar WJek WSel XPep
	- 'Hidcote Giant' ♀H4	GBar LRHS MHrb NPer SAdn SAga SDow SPer WKif WLav WSel XPep
	- 'Impress Purple'	GBar MNHC SDow WLav XPep
*	- 'Jaubert'	XPep
*	- 'Julien'	XPep
	- 'Lullingstone Castle'	CBod EAro ELau GBar LHop NGHP SAga SDow WGwG WJek WLav WRHF WSPU
	- 'Old English'	GBar MHrb SDow WCFE
	- Old English Group	CArn CBod ELau WHoo WJek WLav WSel
	- 'Pale Pretender'	CArn CEnd CPbn CSBt CSam CTri CWSG EAro EBee ELau EMil EPfP EUnu GBar MHer MRav MWat MWgw NGHP NVic SMer SPer SWal WFar WMnd WPer WPnn WSel XPep
	- 'Seal'	CArn CPrp EAro EBee ELau GBar MHer MHrb MNHC NGHP NHHG SAga SDow SPer SPoG WFar WHCG WMnd WPer XPep
*	- 'Sumian'	XPep
	- 'Super'	XPep
	- 'Sussex'	GBar MHrb NGHP SDow WLav
§	- Walberton's Silver Edge = 'Walvera' (v)	CBow CRez CWCL ENor EShb LRHS MAsh MGos SCoo SDow SIde SPoG
	'Jean Davis'	see *L. angustifolia* 'Rosea'
	lanata ♀H3	CArn ECha GBar GPoy MHer MHrb MWat NHHG NWCA SDow SHFr WEas WLav WWye XPep
§	**latifolia**	CArn XPep
I	'Lavender Lace'	CWSG NGHP SCoo SDow
	'Loddon Pink'	see *L. angustifolia* 'Loddon Pink'
	mairei	XPep
	'Marshwood'PBR	CTri EBee ENot EPfP LRHS MRav SAdn SCoo SDow SIde SLim SMer SPer SPla
	minutolii	MHer MHrb SDow XPep
	multifida	CArn CSev EUnu LDai MHer NLLv SDow WLav XPep
	- 'Blue Wonder'	NGHP
*	- 'Tizi-n-Test'	XPep
	officinalis	see *L. angustifolia*
	'Passionné'	EBee MAsh NGHP WLav
	pedunculata subsp. **lusitanica**	WLav
§	- subsp. **pedunculata** ♀H3-4	More than 30 suppliers
	- - dark-flowered	WLav
	- - 'James Compton'	CPbn CWib EBee ECha LRHS MAsh SLim WLav WTel
	- - 'Wine'	CBcs WLav
	- subsp. **sampaiana**	WLav
	- - 'Purple Emperor'	CWSG LRHS SPoG WLav
	- - 'Roman Candles' **new**	WLav
	- 'Whero Iti' **new**	SDow
§	**pinnata**	CArn CSev CTbh EPfP EShb EWin GBar MHer MHrb MNHC NEgg NHHG NPri SDow SPoG WCHb XPep
	'Pippa White'	NLLv
	'Pretty Polly' **new**	ENor SDow WLav
	pterostoechas pinnata	see *L. pinnata*
	pubescens	XPep
	'Pukehou'	ENor EPfP LRHS MAsh MHrb NLLv SDow WLav WPat
	'Purple Ribbon'	WGHP
	'Regal Splendour'PBR	CWCL ELan ENor EPfP LRHS LSRN MAsh MBri MHrb NBPC NGHP NLLv NPri SDow SPoG WHlf WLav
	'Rocky Road'	CWSG ENor LBuc LRHS LSRN MAsh MHrb NGHP NLLv SDow SPav SPer SPoG WLav
	'Rosea'	see *L. angustifolia* 'Rosea'
	rotundifolia	MHer SDow XPep
	'Roxlea Park'PBR	CWCL ENor MHrb NGHP WLav
	'Saint Brelade'	CWCL CWan EPfP EWin GBar MAsh NGHP NLLv SDow WLav
	'Silver Edge'	see *L.* x *intermedia* Walberton's Silver Edge = 'Walvera'
	'Somerset Mist'	WLav
N	**spica**	see *L. angustifolia, L. latifolia, L.* x *intermedia*
	- 'Hidcote Purple'	see *L. angustifolia* 'Hidcote'

- 'Pink Perfume' **new**	LSou
stoechas ♀H3-4	More than 30 suppliers
- var. *albiflora*	see *L. stoechas* subsp. *stoechas* f. *leucantha*
- 'Blueberries and Cream' **new**	MAsh SCoo
- 'Fragrant Butterfly' **new**	LSou
- 'Lace' **new**	SPoG WLav
- subsp. *luisieri*	GBar WBri
- - 'Tickled Pink'	CBcs CWCL ELan ENor MHrb NGHP SDnm SPav SPer WLav
- subsp. *pedunculata*	see *L. pedunculata* subsp. *pedunculata*
- 'Saint Marc' **new**	EBee
§ - subsp. *stoechas* f. *leucantha*	CArn CCVT CSBt CSev CWCL CWib ECha ELan ELau EPfP GBar LAst LRHS MBri MSwo NChi SDow SPla WAbe WCHb WFar
- - - 'Snowman'	CBcs CSBt CWan EBee ENor ENot EPfP LAst LRHS MHer MHrb MTPN MWat NGHP NPri SAdn SLim SPer SPoG SSto SVil SWvt WDin WFar WWeb
- - 'Liberty'	LRHS NGHP NLLv SDow SPoG WLav
- - 'Lilac Wings'	ENor LRHS LSRN LTwo NGHP SDow WLav
- - 'Provençal'	LRHS
- - 'Purple Wings'	LRHS SVil
- - f. *rosea* 'Kew Red'	More than 30 suppliers
- 'Victory'	SPoG
'Sugar Plum'	SHGN WLav
'Tiara' **new**	ENor MAsh NLLv SDow SVil WLav
'Van Gogh'	MHrb SDow
vera misapplied	see *L.* x *intermedia* Dutch Group
vera DC.	see *L. angustifolia*
viridis	CArn CSev ELan ELau EPfP GBar LRHS MHer MWat NGHP NHHG NLLv NPer SDow SGar SPla SPoG WAbe WCHb WKif WLav WWye XPep
'Willowbridge Calico'PBR	NEgg WLav
'Willow Vale' ♀H3-4	CMea COtt CTri EBee ELan EPfP GBar LPhx LRHS LSRN MAsh MHer MHrb MLHP MWat NCGa NLLv NPri SAdn SAga SDow SPav SWvt WEas WJek WPGP WSPU WWeb

Lavatera (Malvaceae)

arborea	SChr WHer
- 'Rosea'	see *L.* x *clementii* 'Rosea'
- 'Variegata' (v)	CBcs CBow CHen ELan EMan EWin LSou NPer NSti SBod SDix SEND SGar WCHb WCMO WCot WEas WHer
bicolor	see *L. maritima*
cachemiriana	GBuc GCal LSou MWgw NBur NPer WPer
Chamallow = 'Innovera' **new**	EBee
x *clementii* 'Barnsley'	More than 30 suppliers
- 'Barnsley Baby'	LBuc LRHS MAsh NPer NPri
- 'Blushing Bride'	CDoC EBee EPfP LRHS MAsh MBri MGos NLar NPri SBod SPer SPla SPoG WHar
- 'Bredon Springs' ♀H3-4	CDoC CDul CWSG EBee ECha ECtt EMil ENot EPfP GBri LHop LRHS LSRN MAsh MBri MNHC MSwo NBlu NScw SBod SLim SMer SPer SPla SWvt WFar WWeb
- 'Burgundy Wine' ♀H3-4	More than 30 suppliers
- 'Candy Floss' ♀H3-4	EBee EPfP LRHS MAsh MBNS MBar MGos NPer SAdn SIng WDin
- 'Kew Rose'	CDoC CDul CTri EBee EMil EPfP LRHS MAsh MSwo NPer SLim SPla WWeb

- 'Lavender Lady'	EBee ECtt EPPr NPer
- 'Lisanne'	LRHS MAsh MHer MNrw MSwo NPri SEND SMrm
- 'Mary Hope'	LRHS MAsh
- Memories = 'Stelav'PBR	EBee ELan ENor EPfP LRHS MAsh NEgg NLar NPer NPri SLim SPoG
- 'Pavlova'	CDoC CPLG EPfP LRHS SMrm SPoG
- 'Poynton Lady'	MGos
§ - 'Rosea' ♀H3-4	More than 30 suppliers
- 'Shorty'	WFar
§ - 'Wembdon Variegated' (v)	NPer
'Grey Beauty' **new**	MAsh
§ *maritima* ♀H2-3	CDoC CHrt CMHG CPLG CRHN EBee ECtt ELan EPfP IFoB LHop NPri SHBN SPer SPoG SUsu SWvt WCFE WFar WHCG WKif XPep
- *bicolor*	see *L. maritima*
- 'Princesse de Lignes'	MGos XPep
mauritanica	CSec
N *olbia*	CTri LAst SPlb SRms XPep
- 'Eye Catcher'	EBee LRHS MBNS MSwo NEgg NLar SPer SPoG SWal
- 'Lilac Lady'	EBee ECha ELan EPfP LRHS LSou MAsh MBNS MCCP NCGa NLar NMRc SPer WFar WKif WWeb
§ - 'Pink Frills'	EBee LRHS MBar MBri MNrw NPri SMrm SPla SPoG WWlt
'Peppermint Ice'	see *L. thuringiaca* 'Ice Cool'
'Pink Frills'	see *L. olbia* 'Pink Frills'
plebeia	EChP
'Rosea'	see *L.* x *clementii* 'Rosea'
'Shadyvale Star'	NPro
'Summer Kisses'PBR	MBri
'Sweet Dreams'PBR	LRHS MAsh MBri NLar
tauricensis	NLar
N *thuringiaca*	NNor WFar
§ - 'Ice Cool'	ECha ECtt GCal LAst LRHS MBar MGos NPer NRnb SBla WCot WFar WKif WWeb
- 'Red Rum' **new**	LTwo SPoG
'Variegata'	see *L.* x *clementii* 'Wembdon Variegated'
'White Angel'PBR	LRHS MAsh NLar
'White Satin'PBR	LHop MBri NPri SPoG

Lecanthus (Urticaceae)

peduncularis **new**	CHEx

Ledebouria (Hyacinthaceae)

adlamii	see *L. cooperi*
concolor	EShb
§ *cooperi*	CDes CHal CStu ECho EHyt ELan EMan LEdu LHop NCGa NLAp SIng SRot SUsu WPGP WPrP
§ *socialis*	CHal CSWP CSev CSpe CStu EPem ERos EShb LToo NBir SBch
violacea	see *L. socialis*

x *Ledodendron* (Ericaceae)

§ 'Arctic Tern' ♀H4	CDoC CSBt ECho GCrs GGar GQui LMil LRHS MAsh MBar MDun MGos MLea NHol NWCA SLdr WPic

Ledum (Ericaceae)

§ x *columbianum*	NLar
§ *groenlandicum*	MBar MLea SPer WDin WFar WGer WSHC
- 'Compactum'	MAsh NLar SPoG WFar
macrophyllum	CFir
palustre	COld GGGa GIBF GPoy NLar
- subsp. *decumbens*	GCrs GIBF
§ - f. *dilatatum*	GIBF

Leea (*Leeaceae*)

coccinea	see *L. guineensis*
§ *guineensis*	MBri

Leersia (*Poaceae*)

oryzoides	EBee

Leibnitzia (*Asteraceae*)

nepalensis CC 4361	NJOw

Leiophyllum (*Ericaceae*)

buxifolium ♀H4	EPfP GCrs LRHS NLar SBrw
- var. *hugeri*	GBin NLar
- 'Maryfield'	WAbe

Lembotropis see *Cytisus*

Lemna (*Lemnaceae*)

gibba	CWat LPBA NPer
minor	CWat EHon EMFW LPBA NPer SWat
polyrhiza	see *Spirodela polyrhiza*
trisulca	CWat EHon EMFW LPBA NPer SWat

lemon balm see *Melissa officinalis*

lemon grass see *Cymbopogon citratus*

lemon see *Citrus limon*

lemon verbena see *Aloysia triphylla*

Leonotis (*Lamiaceae*)

leonitis	see *L. ocymifolia*
leonurus	CBcs CDMG CHEx CHll CMdw CSec CTbh CTrC ENot EShb EWes LRHS SMad SPoG WSHC
- var. *albiflora*	CPLG EShb LRav
nepetifolia var. *nepetifolia* 'Staircase'	SDnm SPav WRos
§ *ocymifolia*	CPLG CSec EShb LSou WPGP WWye
- var. *ocymifolia*	EMan LEdu SPlb
- var. *raineriana*	CHll

Leontice (*Berberidaceae*)

albertii	see *Gymnospermium albertii*

Leontodon (*Asteraceae*)

autumnalis	NMir
hispidus	MBow NMir
§ *rigens*	EDAr EMan GBri GBuc NBid SDix SMad SMrm WFar WMoo WPrP
- 'Girandole'	CMCo MNrw WRos

Leontopodium (*Asteraceae*)

alpinum	CArn CTri CWan CWib ECho EHyt GAbr IHMH LRHS NFor NJOw NWCA SBla SIng SPlb SPoG SRms WBVN WPer
- 'Mignon'	CMea ECho ENot EWes GEdr WFar WHoo
coreanum	EBee GKev
kamtschaticum	ECho
§ *ochroleucum* var. *campestre*	EShb MDKP NLar NSla WPer
palibinianum	see *L. ochroleucum* var. *campestre*

Leonurus (*Lamiaceae*)

artemisia	see *L. japonicus*
cardiaca	CAgr CArn CWan EGoo EMan EMon GBar GPoy LEdu MHer MSal SECG SIde WBri WGHP WHbs WSel WWye

- 'Crispa'	EMon
§ *japonicus*	CSec MSal WBor WOut
macranthus	EFEx
- var. *alba*	EFEx
sibiricus L.	MSal NDov SHGN SMad SPav

Leopoldia (*Hyacinthaceae*)

comosa	see *Muscari comosum*
spreitzenhoferi	see *Muscari spreitzenhoferi*
tenuiflora	see *Muscari tenuiflorum*

Lepechinia (*Lamiaceae*)

§ *chamaedryoides*	CHll CPLG CSec
floribunda	CPle CSev
ganderi NNS 03-362 **new**	WCot
hastata	CBrd CMdw CPom EBee MWea WCMO WCot WOut XPep
salviae	CDoC CPLG CPne CSec EDsa EMan WBor

Lepidium (*Brassicaceae*)

campestre	CArn
latifolium	MSal
peruvianum	MSal
ruderale	MSal
virginicum	MSal

Lepidozamia (*Zamiaceae*)

hopei	LPal
peroffskyana	CBrP CRoM LPal

Leptecophylla (*Epacridaceae*)

§ *juniperina*	ECou
- 'Nana' **new**	WThu
§ - subsp. *parvifolia*	ECou

Leptinella (*Asteraceae*)

§ *albida*	CStu
§ *atrata*	ECho IHMH
- subsp. *luteola*	EBee ECho MBrN NWCA WAbe
'County Park'	ECho ECou
§ *dendyi*	ECho ECou EDAr EWes GBin MHer NJOw NLap NMen NSla WMAq
dioica	CTrC GBin
filicula	ECou
hispida	see *Cotula hispida*
§ *minor*	ECou WMoo
pectinata var. *sericea*	see *L. albida*
- subsp. *villosa* CC 475	NWCA
§ *potentillina*	CTri ECha ECho EHoe MBNS MWgw NJOw NLar NRya SRms WPer WPtf
§ *pyrethrifolia*	CSec ECho GGar NLAp NMen SIng
- 'Macabe'	ECou
§ *rotundata*	ECou WPer
§ *serrulata*	ECho MBar
§ *squalida*	ECha ECho GBin GGar IHMH MBar NRya NSti STre WPer
* - *minima*	NJOw
§ - 'Platt's Black'	CPBP CStu EBee ECho EDAr EMan EPot EShb EWes GEdr GGar GKev LRHS NLAp NSti NWCA SBch SIng SPet WFar WHoo WMoo WPat WPer WPrP WWFP WWye
traillii	GGar

Leptocarpus (*Restionaceae*)

similis	CTrC
- BR 70	GGar

Leptocodon (*Campanulaceae*)

gracilis HWJK 2155	WCru

Leptodactylon ✿ (*Polemoniaceae*)

§	*californicum*	NPol
	pungens	NLAp

Leptospermum (*Myrtaceae*)

	argenteum	CBcs
	'Centaurus'PBR **new**	MNHC SBrw
	citratum	see *L. petersonii*
*	*compactum*	CPLG
	'Confetti'	ECou
	'County Park Blush'	ECou
	cunninghamii	see *L. myrtifolium*
	'Electric Red' (Galaxy Series) **new**	CBrm MNHC SBrw WCot
	ericoides	see *Kunzea ericoides*
	flavescens misapplied	see *L. glaucescens*
	flavescens Sm.	see *L. polygalifolium*
§	*glaucescens*	CMHG ECou GGar
§	*grandiflorum*	CTrG ELan EPfP GGar ISea LRHS SBrw SOWG SSpi WSHC
	grandifolium	ECou
	'Green Eyes' (*minutifolium* x *scoparium*)	ECou
	'Havering Hardy'	ECou
	humifusum	see *L. rupestre*
	juniperinum	CTrC SPlb
	laevigatum 'Yarrum'	ECou
§	*lanigerum*	CBcs CMHG CPLG CTri ECou EPfP GGar ISea MGol SBrw SLim SOWG SPoG WBVN
	- 'Cunninghamii'	see *L. myrtifolium*
	- 'Wellington'	ECou
	liversidgei	ECou
	macrocarpum	SOWG
	minutifolium	ECou
	morrisonii	ECou
§	*myrtifolium*	CTri ECou EPla EWes GGar SOWG SPer WPat WPic
	- 'Newnes Forest'	ECou
	myrtifolium x *scoparium*	ECou
	nitidum	CTrC ECou GGar SOWG SPlb
	- 'Cradle'	ECou
	obovatum	CMHG SBrw
§	*petersonii*	CArn ECou EOHP EShb EWin MHer SOWG WPic
	- 'Chlorinda'	ECou
	phylicoides	see *Kunzea ericoides*
	'Pink Falls'	ECou
	'Pink Surprise' (*minutifolium* x *scoparium*)	ECou SOWG
§	*polygalifolium*	ECou GGar MGol SPlb SRms
	prostratum	see *L. rupestre*
	pubescens	see *L. lanigerum*
	'Red Cascade'	SWvt
	rodwayanum	see *L. grandiflorum*
	rotundifolium	CTrC ECou
§	*rupestre* ♀H4	CDoC CPne CTri ECou GGar MBar SBrw SPlb SRms WFar WSHC
	rupestre x *scoparium*	ECou
	scoparium	CArn CDul ECou ELau ERom EUnu MGol MNHC SPlb WDin
	- 'Adrianne'	ELan MAsh
	- 'Autumn Glory'	CSBt CWSG EHoe ISea SBrw SLim
	- 'Avocet'	ECou
	- 'Black Robin'	SOWG
	- 'Blossom' (d)	CBcs ECou SBrw SOWG WGer
	- 'Boscawenii'	CBcs SBrw
	- 'Burgundy Queen' (d)	CBcs CSBt ECou SBrw
	- 'Chapmanii'	CMHG CTrG GGar SBrw
	- 'Coral Candy'	CBcs SBrw SOWG WGer
	- 'County Park Pink'	ECou
	- 'County Park Red'	ECou
	- 'Dove Lake'	WAbe

	- 'Elizabeth Jane'	GGar
	- 'Essex'	ECou
	- 'Fantasia'	ECou
	- 'Fred's Red'	NLAp WPat
	- 'Gaiety Girl' (d)	CSBt
	- 'Grandiflorum'	WGer
	- var. *incanum* 'Keatleyi' ♀H3	ECou SOWG
	- - 'Wairere'	ECou
	- 'Jubilee' (d)	CBcs CSBt ISea SBrw
	- 'Kerry'	CAbP LRHS MAsh
	- 'Leonard Wilson' (d)	CTri ECou EWes
	- 'Lyndon'	ECou
	- 'Martini'	CDoC CSBt CTrG LRHS SBrw SOWG WBor WWeb
	- 'McLean'	ECou
	- (Nanum Group) 'Huia'	CBcs SBrw
	- - 'Kea'	CSBt ECou WGer
	- - 'Kiwi' ♀H3	CBcs CCCN CDoC CDul CSBt ECou ELan EPfP EWes GKev GQui LRHS MAsh MDun SBrw SLim SPla WFar WGer WPat
	- - 'Nanum'	ECou NJOw NMen SBod SIng
	- - 'Pipit'	EWes WAbe
	- - 'Tui'	CSBt CTrC
	- 'Nichollsii' ♀H3	CTrC CTri GKev GQui SBrw SOWG WHar WSHC
	- 'Nichollsii Nanum' ♀H2-3	NLAp SRms WPat
	- 'Pink Cascade'	CBcs CBrm CSBt CTri GGar SBrw SLim
	- 'Pink Damask'	SWvt
	- 'Pink Splash'	ECou
	- 'Pom Pom' **new**	LRHS
	- var. *prostratum* hort.	see *L. rupestre*
	- 'Red Damask' (d) ♀H3	CBcs CDoC CDul CPLG CSBt CTrC CWSG ELan ENot EPfP GGar GQui LRHS LSRN MAsh MDun MRav MSwo NPri NVic SBod SBrw SOWG SPlb SPoG SRms SWvt WBrE WFar WSHC
	- 'Red Falls'	CBcs CPLG ECou SOWG
	- 'Redpoll'	ECou
	- 'Rosy Morn'	ISea
	- 'Ruby Glow' (d)	CTri LRHS
*	- 'Ruby Wedding'	ELan LRHS SPla SPoG
	- var. *scoparium*	GGar
*	- 'Silver Spire'	SOWG
	- 'Snow Flurry'	CBcs CTrC ENot SBod SBrw SLim SPoG
	- 'Sunraysia'	CSBt CTrw
	- 'Winter Cheer'	CBcs LRHS SBrw WCot WWeb
	- 'Wiri Joan' (d)	CBcs
	- 'Wiri Kerry' (d) **new**	SRGP
	- 'Wiri Linda'	CBcs
	- 'Wiri Sandra' **new**	SRGP
	- 'Zeehan'	ECou
	sericeum	SOWG
§	'Silver Sheen' ♀H3	CEnd ECou ELan EPfP LRHS SBrw SLon SPoG WPGP
	'Snow Column'	ECou
	spectabile	SOWG
	sphaerocarpum	ECou
	turbinatum	ECou
	- 'Thunder Cloud'	ECou
	'Wellington Dwarf'	ECou

Leschenaultia (*Goodeniaceae*)

	'Angels Kiss'	ECou
	biloba	CSec ECou
	- 'Big Blue'	SOWG
	- 'Sky Blue'	ECou
	'Blue Moon'	ECou
	'Carnival'	ECou
*	'Eldorado'	SOWG
	formosa red-flowered	ECou
	- 'Scarlett O'Hara'	SOWG

- yellow-flowered	ECou
hirsuta	SOWG
pink-flowered	ECou
'Prima'	ECou

Lespedeza (*Papilionaceae*)

bicolor	CAgr CBcs CMen EDif MGol SEND WDin WFar WHCG
- 'Yakushima'	NEgg NLar
buergeri	NLar SMur WSHC
capitata	MSal
floribunda	CMen
japonica	SPlb
thunbergii ♀H4	CBcs CMen CWib EBee EChP ELan EMil EPfP IDee IMGH LHop LRHS MAsh MBlu NBlu SLon SOWG SPer SSpi SSta WDin WFar WHCG WSHC
- 'Albiflora'	EPfP
- 'Summer Beauty'	CDul EPfP MGos
- 'White Fountain'	LRHS
tiliifolia	see *Desmodium elegans*

Leucadendron (*Proteaceae*)

argenteum	CHEx CTbh CTrC SPlb
daphnoides	EShb SPlb
eucalyptifolium	CTrC EShb SPlb
galpinii	CTrC
gandogeri	WSAf
'Inca Gold'	CBcs CTrC
'Maui Sunset'	CTrC
'Mrs Stanley'	CTrC
'Safari Sunset'	CAbb CBcs CCCN CDoC CTrC IDee SBig WGer
salicifolium	IDee
salignum 'Early Yellow'	CAbb CTrC
- 'Fireglow'	CAbb CBcs CDoC CTrC
strobilinum	CDoC CTrC
tinctum	EShb

Leucanthemella (*Asteraceae*)

§ *serotina* ♀H4	More than 30 suppliers
- 'Herbststern'	CFir WDyG

Leucanthemopsis (*Asteraceae*)

§ *alpina*	ECho
hosmariensis	see *Rhodanthemum hosmariense*
§ *pectinata*	NLAp NSla
radicans	see *L. pectinata*

Leucanthemum ✿ (*Asteraceae*)

atlanticum	see *Rhodanthemum atlanticum*
catananche	see *Rhodanthemum catananche*
graminifolium	CABy EBrs NBre WPer
hosmariense	see *Rhodanthemum hosmariense*
mawii	see *Rhodanthemum gayanum*
maximum misapplied	see *L.* x *superbum*
§ *maximum* (Ramond) DC.	NBro NPer
* - *nanus*	WWeb
- *uliginosum*	see *Leucanthemella serotina*
nipponicum	see *Nipponanthemum nipponicum*
§ x *superbum*	EHol EWsh MBow MHer MLHP NBlu NVic SMac WFar
- 'Aglaia' (d) ♀H4	More than 30 suppliers
- 'Alaska'	CAni EBee EBla GMac LAst LHop LRHS NGdn NLRH NOak NPri SPer SPur SWal SWvt WBor WPer WWpP
- 'Amelia'	EBee NBre NLar
- 'Anita Allen' (d)	CAni CElw CFee CPou EBee EBla MAvo NBre WCMO WCot WFar WPer WWpP
- 'Anna Camilla'	CAni
- 'Antwerp Star'	NBre NLar WBrk WWpP
- 'Banwell'	CAni

- 'Barbara Bush' (v/d)	More than 30 suppliers
§ - 'Beauté Nivelloise'	CAni CPrp EBee EBla EChP ECtt EMan GMaP MAvo MDKP MHar MLLN MMuc NBPC NBre NFla NLar SWat WCMO WCot WFar WHlf WPer WPrP WRHF WRha WWpP
- 'Becky'	CElw EBee EChP ECha EPfP GMac MAvo NBre NPro SPoG
- 'Bishopstone'	CAni CSam EBee ELan ERou NBre WEas WPer WWpP
- 'Christine Hagemann'	CAni CPrp EBee LRHS MAvo MDKP MRav WAul WHoo WWpP
- 'Cobham Gold' (d)	CAni CElw EBee EMan NBre NOrc SUsu WWpP
- 'Coconut Ice'	WPer
- 'Colwall'	CAni
- 'Crazy Daisy'	CAni CElw CMMP CTri CWib NBHF NBre NCob NLar SWal WHrl WRHF WWpP
- 'Devon Mist'	CAni
- 'Droitwich Beauty'	CAni CElw EBee MAvo MNrw WBrk WCFE WHoo WSPU WTel
- 'Duchess of Abercorn'	CAni CSam
- 'Dwarf Snow Lady'	NBre
- 'Easton Lady'	CAni
- 'Eclipse'	CAni CBos MAvo
- 'Edgebrook Giant'	CAni MAvo
- 'Edward VII'	CAni
- 'Eisstern'	MAvo
- 'Esther Read' (d)	More than 30 suppliers
- 'Etoile d'Anvers'	XPep
§ - 'Everest'	CAni CSam EBee NBre NOak SRms
- 'Exhibition'	NBre
- 'Fiona Coghill' (d)	CAni CElw CHea CMil EAEE EBee EBla ECGP ECtt EGle GBri MBnl MDKP MLLN NChi NGdn WCMO WCot WHil WHoo WWpP
- 'Firnglanz'	CAni CFwr GBin MAvo
- 'Gruppenstolz'	CAni
- 'H. Seibert'	CAni CElw CEnt CHea EBla MAvo WWpP
- 'Harry'	CAni
- 'Highland White Dream'PBR	WFar WWeb
- 'Horace Read' (d)	CAni CElw CHar CMea CMil ELan ERea NBir SAga SBch WEas WPer WWpP
- 'Jennifer Read'	CAni ERea MAvo WCot WWpP
§ - 'John Murray' (d)	CAni CElw EBee EShb EWes GSki LRHS LSou MAvo NBir SUsu WAbb WCMO WCot WFar WHrl WTel WWpP
- 'Little Miss Muffet'	EAEE EBee EBla LRHS NCob NFla NPro
- 'Little Princess'	see *L.* x *superbum* 'Silberprinzesschen'
- 'Majestic' **new**	CAni
- 'Manhattan'	CAni CFwr CMdw EBee EBla EBrs EWes GBin GBuc LRHS NBre WWpP
- 'Margaretchen'	CAni MAvo
- 'Marion Bilsland'	CAni MBnl NChi
- 'Marion Collyer' **new**	CAni
- 'Mayfield Giant'	CAni CTri ERou WPer
- 'Mount Everest'	see *L.* x *superbum* 'Everest'
- 'Octopus'	CAni EBee MAvo
- 'Old Court'	see *L.* x *superbum* 'Beauté Nivelloise'
- 'Phyllis Smith'	More than 30 suppliers
- 'Polaris'	CFwr EShb NBre NOak WMoo WWpP
- 'Rags and Tatters'	CAni CBos EBee MAvo
- 'Rijnsburg Glory'	NBre
* - 'Schneehurken'	CAni COIW EBee EBla MAvo NBPC STes SUsu

- 'Shaggy'	see *L.* x *superbum* 'Beauté Nivelloise'
§ - 'Silberprinzesschen'	CAni CPrp EBee EBla EChP EPfP IFro IHMH LRHS NMir NOak NPri SPlb SRms WFar WHen WMoo WPer WWpP
- 'Silver Spoon'	WHil WPer
- 'Sleaph' **new**	CBos
- 'Snow Lady'	COIW EShb IHMH LRHS NMir NPer NPri SPet SRms WFar WHen WTel WWeb WWpP
- 'Snowcap'	EBla EBrs ECha ENot EPfP EPla GSki LRHS MBNS MBri MRav NEgg NGdn SBla SPer SPla SWvt WCAu WMow WTin WWpP
- 'Snowdrift'	CAni CMMP EBee EDAr MAvo NBre NPri WCot WPer WWeb
§ - 'Sonnenschein'	More than 30 suppliers
- 'Starburst' (d)	SRms WHen
- 'Stina'	CFwr GBin
- 'Summer Snowball'	see *L.* x *superbum* 'John Murray'
- 'Sunny Killin'	CAni WTin
- 'Sunny Side Up'PBR	CElw EBee EChP ECtt EWes MBNS MLLN NBre NLar
- Sunshine	see *L.* x *superbum* 'Sonnenschein'
- 'T.E. Killin' (d) ♀H4	CElw CHea CKno CPrp CSam EAEE EBee EBla EBrs ECha ECtt EGle EGra EMan EMar EPfP GSki LAst LHop LRHS MBnl NChi SUsu WCAu WCMO WCot WFar WWpP
- 'White Iceberg' (d)	CAni WPer
- 'White Knight'	MWea NBre WBrk
- 'Wirral Pride'	CAni CCVN CHar EBee ERou MBnl NPri WCra WMnd WWpP
§ - 'Wirral Supreme' (d) ♀H4	More than 30 suppliers
'Tizi-n-Test'	see *Rhodanthemum catananche* 'Tizi-n-Test'
§ *vulgare*	CArn CBgR CHrt CRWN EMag EPfP GBar GWCH IHMH MBow MHer MNHC NLRH NLan NMir NPri NSco SBch SECG SIde WBVN WBrk WHen WHer WJek WShi WWye
- 'Avondale' (v)	NGdn
- 'Filigran'	CAby EShb GMac NBre SIde WHil
§ - 'Maikönigin'	CBgR EBee GAbr GCal IHMH NBre NLRH NNor WHrl WWpP
- May Queen	see *L. vulgare* 'Maikönigin'
- 'Sunny'	CBre EBla
- 'White Crystal' **new**	LAst
'White Knight' **new**	MCCP

Leucocoryne (Alliaceae)

alliacea	CMon ECho
'Andes'	ECho
coquimbensis	CMon
hybrids	ECho
ixioides	CMon ECho LBow
* - *alba*	CMon ECho
purpurea ♀H1	CGrW CMon ECho LBow LRHS

Leucogenes (Asteraceae)

grandiceps	NSla WAbe
leontopodium	EPot GGar GKev NLAp NSla WAbe
tarahaoa	NSla WAbe

Leucojum (Amaryllidaceae)

aestivum	CBcs CBgR CFee EBee EChP ECho EPfP EWTr GAbr GBBs GCrs LHop LRHS MDun NHol SPer SRms WBVN WCot WCra WEas WFar WLin WShi WWpP WWye
- 'Gravetye Giant' ♀H4	More than 30 suppliers
autumnale ♀H4	More than 30 suppliers
- 'Cobb's Variety'	WCot

- var. *oporanthum*	ERos ITim MSte
* - - SF 352 from Morocco	CMon
- var. *pulchellum*	CBro ECho ERos
longifolium	ECho ERos
nicaeense ♀H2-3	CLyd CPBP CStu EAEE EBur ECho EHyt ERos ITim MTho SCnR WCMO WCot
roseum	CLyd EBur ERos NWCA SCnR WAbe
tingitanum	CBro ECho EHyt WCMO WCot
trichophyllum	CBro ECho SCnR
- f. *purpurascens*	ECho
* - var. *roseum* SB&L **new**	CMon
valentinum	CBro CMon CPBP ECho EPot SCnR SRot WCMO WCot
vernum ♀H4	CAvo CBgR CBro CPLG CStu EBrs ECho EHrv EHyt ELan EPfP EPot GCrs GKev LRHS MBow MDun MNrw MRav NHol NMen SRms WAbe WCMO WCot WFar WHer WShi
- var. *carpathicum*	CLAP ECha ECho EHrv GEdr MRav NMen
- var. *vagneri*	CLAP ECha EHrv EMon GEdr LFox LHop WTin

Leucophyllum (Scrophulariaceae)

frutescens	SOWG XPep
minus	XPep

Leucophyta (Asteraceae)

§ *brownii*	CStu ECou EMan EShb EWin LAst MRav SMad XPep

Leucopogon (Epacridaceae)

§ *colensoi*	GCrs MBar MBri MGos NLar NWCA SBrw SLon WAbe WPat
ericoides	MBar
§ *fasciculatus*	ECou
§ *fraseri*	ECou GCrs GEdr
§ *parviflorus*	ECou

x *Leucoraoulia* (Asteraceae)

§ hybrid (*Raoulia hectorii* x *Leucogenes grandiceps*)	SIng WAbe
§ *loganii*	CPBP ITim NSla NWCA WAbe

Leucosceptrum (Lamiaceae)

canum	CPLG CTrG
- GWJ 9424	WCru
stellipilum var. *formosanum* B&SWJ 1804	WCru
- var. *tosaense* B&SWJ 8892 **new**	WCru

Leucospermum (Proteaceae)

cordifolium	SOWG WSAf
'Fountain'	WSAf
'Scarlet Ribbon'	CCCN CTrC

Leucothoe (Ericaceae)

axillaris 'Curly Red'PBR	CWSG EBee ENot EPfP LBuc LRHS MAsh MGos SPoG
Carinella = 'Zebekot'	MBri MGos SPoG
davisiae	EPfP NLar SBrw
§ *fontanesiana* ♀H4	EPfP EWTr LRHS NEgg STre WBrE LRHS
- 'Nana'	More than 30 suppliers
- 'Rainbow' (v)	More than 30 suppliers
- 'Rollissonii' ♀H4	MBar SRms
keiskei	EPfP LRHS
- 'Minor'	SSta
- 'Royal Ruby'	CWSG EBee EPfP MGos NCGa NHol NLar SPoG WDin WFar WMoo

Lovita = 'Zebonard'	CEnd CSam GCal LRHS MBri MGos MRav NCGa NLar SCoo SSta
populifolia	see *Agarista populifolia*
racemosa	NLar
Red Lips = 'Lipsbolwi'[PBR]	CDoC EBee ENot MGos NScw
Scarletta = 'Zeblid'	More than 30 suppliers
walteri	see *L. fontanesiana*

Leuzea (Asteraceae)

centaureoides	see *Stemmacantha centaureoides*

Levisticum (Apiaceae)

§ **officinale**	More than 30 suppliers
I - 'Magnus' **new**	ELau

Lewisia ✿ (Portulacaceae)

'Archangel'	NRya
Ashwood Carousel hybrids	CPBP ECho GCrs MAsh NHar NLAp
'Ashwood Pearl'	MAsh
'Ben Chace'	MAsh
Birch strain	CBcs ECho ELan
brachycalyx ♀H2	ECho EWes GKev MAsh MTho WAbe
cantelovii	MAsh
columbiana	MAsh NJOw NLAp NWCA WAbe
- 'Alba'	GCrs MAsh NLAp WAbe
- subsp. **columbiana**	CGra
- 'Rosea'	GCrs MAsh NLAp NSla WAbe WGor
- subsp. **rupicola**	LTwo MAsh NDlv WGor WLin
- subsp. **wallowensis**	EHyt MAsh NMen WGor
congdonii	MAsh
'Constant Comment' **new**	NBhm
cotyledon ♀H4	EAEE ECho LRHS LTwo MNrw MOne NWCA SPet WBrE WFar WPat
- J&JA 12959	NWCA
- f. **alba**	EDAr LHop MAsh NWCA
- 'Ashwood Ruby'	MAsh
- Ashwood strain	CTri CWCL ECho ENot EPfP EWes LBee LRHS LSou MAsh MOne NLAp NRya SRms WGor
- Crags hybrids	SRms
- 'Fransi'	EDAr NLar
- var. **heckneri** ♀H4	WGor
- var. **howellii**	LTwo SRms WGor
- hybrids	ECho EDAr EHol EPot ITim LHop NBlu SIng SPoG WAbe WBVN WGor WLin
- 'John's Special'	GCrs
- magenta	EDAr GAbr MAsh WGor
- 'Praline' **new**	EDAr
§ - 'Regenbogen' mixed	GEdr LAst SSto WGor WPer
- 'Rose Splendour'	WGor
- Sunset Group ♀H4	GKev LAst MHer NJOw NLar NWCA SRms WPer WRHF
- 'White Splendour'	MAsh SIng WGor
'George Henley'	ECho EHyt EPfP EPot EWes MAsh NMen NRya SIng WAbe
glandulosa NNS 02-210 **new**	NWCA
leeana	EHyt MAsh
'Little Peach'	CBrm EDAr GCrs GKev MSte SIng WPer
'Little Plum'	CBrm CMea CPBP EDAr GCrs GKev MDKP MSte NCGa NDlv NHol NLar NRya NSla NWCA SIng WGor WLin
§ **longipetala**	MAsh NSla NWCA
§ **nevadensis**	EAEE ECho ERos GEdr GKev ITim MAsh MNrw MTho NJOw NMen NRya NWCA SRms SRot WHoo WLin WPer
- **bernardina**	see *L. nevadensis*
- 'Rosea'	EPot GCrs GKev MAsh NWCA WAbe
oppositifolia	GCrs MAsh
- 'Richeyi'	EHyt
'Phyllellia'	MAsh
'Pinkie'	CPBP EDAr GCrs IHMH LTwo MAsh NLAp NMen
pygmaea	CGra EAEE ECho EDAr EWes GCrs GEdr ITim LAst LRHS MAsh MHer NBir NJOw NLAp NMen NRya NWCA WGwG WPer
- from Arizona	EHyt
- subsp. **longipetala**	see *L. longipetala*
Rainbow mixture	see *L. cotyledon* 'Regenbogen' mixed
'Rawreth'	LTwo WAbe
rediviva	CGra CPBP ECho EWes GCrs GEdr GKev ITim MAsh NLAp NSla NWCA SOkd WAbe
- Jolon strain	WGor
- subsp. **minor**	CGra GKev WAbe
- var. **rediviva**	EHyt
- white	MAsh
serrata	MAsh
sierrae	MAsh NJOw WPer
stebbinsii **new**	NWCA
tweedyi ♀H2	CGra EAEE EHyt EPfP GCrs GKev ITim LHop LRHS MAsh NBir NJOw NWCA SIng WGor
- 'Alba'	GCrs ITim LRHS MAsh NWCA SOkd
- 'Elliott's Variety'	MAsh WGor
- 'Rosea'	EAEE EHyt LHop LRHS MAsh SIng WGor

Leycesteria (Caprifoliaceae)

crocothyrsos	CABP CArn CBcs CHEx CWib EBee ELan EPfP EShb GQui IFro NBid SLon SMad SPoG WFar WSHC
formosa ♀H4	More than 30 suppliers
- brown-stemmed **new**	IFoB
- Golden Lanterns = 'Notbruce'[PBR]	CDoC CPLG ENot EPfP GTSp IDee LBuc MBri MGos MMHG NPri SCoo SHGC SPoG
- 'Golden Pheasant' (v)	CPMA
- 'Purple Rain'	MBri NLar

Leymus (Poaceae)

from Falkland Islands	EPPr
§ **arenarius**	More than 30 suppliers
condensatus 'Canyon Prince'	CKno
hispidus	see *Elymus hispidus*
'Niveus'	EHul
§ **racemosus**	CHrt LRav MMHG WOut

Lhotzkya see *Calytrix*

Liatris (Asteraceae)

aspera	GSki NBre NLar WPer
elegans	GSki NBre NLar SPlb WPer
lancifolia	EBee
ligulistylis	EBee GSki NBPC NBre NLar WPer
punctata	EBee NBre
pycnostachya	CFis CRWN MHar MLLN NBre NLar SRms WPer
- 'Alexandra'	EBee
scariosa 'Alba'	EBee NBPC NLar WPer
- 'Gracious'	CPLG EWll
- 'Magnifica'	CBcs
§ **spicata**	More than 30 suppliers
- 'Alba'	COIW CPrp CSBt EBee ECha ECtt ELan ENot EPfP EShb GSki IHMH LAst LEdu LSRN MNFA MNrw MTis NEgg NRnb SPer SPlb WBrE WCAu WHoo WPer

- 'Blue Bird'	WViv
- *callilepis*	see *L. spicata*
- 'Floristan Violett'	CBrm EAEE EBee EChP EPPr EPfP GMaP LAst LRHS MHer MTis MWgw MWrn NEgg NLRH SCoo SPlb SPoG SWvt WFar WGwG WMnd WMoo WPer WWeb
- 'Floristan Weiss'	CArn CBrm COIW EAEE EBee EChP ELau EMar EPPr EPfP GBuc GMaP LRHS MHer MRav MWgw MWrn NCGa NLRH NPri SPla SPoG SWvt WFar WGwG WMnd WMoo WPer WWeb
- Goblin	see *L. spicata* 'Kobold'
§ - 'Kobold'	More than 30 suppliers
squarrosa	EBee

Libertia ✿ (Iridaceae)

HCM 98.089	CDes EBee
'Amazing Grace'	CDes EBee IBlr SBch SUsu WPGP
'Ballyrogan Blue'	CDes IBlr
Ballyrogan hybrid	IBlr
* *breunioides*	CPLG IBlr
caerulescens	CCVN CDMG CPLG EBee EChP ECho EMan ERos GSki IBlr IFoB IGor NBir NLar NRnb SBch SGar SMad SMrm WCot WFar WHer WMoo WPGP WSHC WSan WWye
chilensis	see *L. formosa*
elegans	CPLG GBuc IBlr
§ *formosa*	More than 30 suppliers
- brown-stemmed	IBlr IFoB
grandiflora ♀H4	More than 30 suppliers
- stoloniferous	GGar
ixioides	CBcs CElw CKno EBee ECha ECho ECou EMan EShb GMac GSki IBlr NSti SBod WCFE WFoF WPGP WPic WPrP WRHF WWeb
- hybrid	SDix
- 'Tricolor'	GGar IBlr SPer WMoo
'Nelson Dwarf'	IBlr
paniculata	CPLG
peregrinans	More than 30 suppliers
- East Cape form	IBlr
- 'Gold Leaf'	CBcs CBgR CBow CElw CPrp CWil EHrv IBlr LAst SMad WCot WCru WDyG WPic WTMC WViv
* *procera*	CPLG CSpe EBee IBlr WPGP WSHC
pulchella	IBlr
- Tasmanian form	ECho
sessiliflora	CElw CFee EBee ECho IBlr NBir WCot WFar WPGP
- RB 94073	SMad
Shackleton hybrid	IBlr
tricolor	EBee GBuc
* *umbellata*	IBlr

Libocedrus (Cupressaceae)

chilensis	see *Austrocedrus chilensis*
decurrens	see *Calocedrus decurrens*

Libonia see *Justicia*

Licuala (Arecaceae)

grandis	MBri
spinosa	LPal

Ligularia ✿ (Asteraceae)

B&SWJ 2977	WCru
BWJ 7686 from China	WCru
amplexicaulis GWJ 9404	WCru
calthifolia	CRow
'Cheju Charmer'	WCru
clivorum	see *L. dentata*

§ *dentata*	CRow EBee ECho ECtt EPfP GIBF MMuc NBro NEgg NGby NLar SMar SRms SWat WFar WWeb
- 'Britt-Marie Crawford'	More than 30 suppliers
- 'Dark Beauty'	CBcs ERou EWll GSki IBal MWhi NBre SMar WMnd
- 'Desdemona' ♀H4	More than 30 suppliers
- 'Dunkellaubig'	MBNS
- 'Enkelrig'	EMar MBNS
- 'Orange Princess'	EBee NPer WPer
- 'Orange Queen'	NBre SMar WFar WWeb
- 'Othello'	More than 30 suppliers
- 'Sommergold'	ECha GSki WFar
§ *fischeri*	EBee GSki LBMP LEdu NBre NFor WCot WPer
- B&SWJ 1158	WFar
- B&SWJ 2570	WCru
- B&SWJ 4478	WCru
- B&SWJ 5540	WCru
- B&SWJ 5841	WCru
glabrescens	CRow
§ 'Gregynog Gold' ♀H4	CBct CRow EBee EBrs ECha EGle EMFW EPfP ERou GAbr GMaP GSki LRHS MRav MWgw NBro NCGa NCob NEgg NGdn NOrc SDnm SPav WCru WFar WMul
× *hessei*	EBee GMaP GSki NLar SWat WFar WPnP
hodgsonii	CKno CRow EBla EBrs EPPr GSki LEdu MBri MSte WFar WPer
intermedia	WFar
- B&SWJ 606a	WCru
japonica	CHar CRow EBee EBrs ECha GSki LEdu NLar WFar WPnP
- B&SWJ 2883	WCru
- 'Rising Sun'	WCru
aff. *kaialpina* B&SWJ 5806	WCru
- B&SWJ 6185	EBee
kanaitzensis ACE 1968	WCru
- BWJ 7758	WCru
'Laternchen' **new**	EBee IBal NBro NMoo
'Little Rocket'PBR **new**	NBro
macrophylla	CRow MWhi WFar
× *palmatiloba*	see *L.* × *yoshizoeana* 'Palmatiloba'
§ *przewalskii* ♀H4	More than 30 suppliers
- 'Light Fingered' **new**	NBre
sachalinensis	EBee GCal
sibirica	CSam EBee EBrs EChP GAbr GSki NLar SMar WFar WMoo WPer WPnP
- 'Hietala'	CPne
- var. *speciosa*	see *L. fischeri*
smithii	see *Senecio smithii*
speciosa	see *L. fischeri*
stenocephala	EBee EMil NBro NLar SWat WFar
- B&SWJ 283	WCru
'Sungold'	CBct CSam EBee EBla EBrs NCGa WCot WPnP
tangutica	see *Sinacalia tangutica*
'The Rocket' ♀H4	More than 30 suppliers
tsangchanensis	NEgg
tussilaginea	see *Farfugium japonicum*
veitchiana	CBct CHEx CRow EBee EBla EPfP GAbr GCal GGar LAst LEdu MSte NCGa NCob NEgg NGdn SDnm SPav SWat WCAu WFar WPnP WTMC
vorobievii	CHar CMdw EBee EKen GIBF GSki MBNS NLar
'Weihenstephan'	GCal LRHS MBri
wilsoniana	CBct CHEx CRow EBee ECtt MLLN MRav NBre SDnm SPav SWat WCAu WFar

§ x **yoshizoeana** | CFir CHEx EBee EBla EBrs ELan
'Palmatiloba' | EPla GCal GSki LPhx LRHS MRav
| NHol NOak NSti SBla SDnm SPav
| SWat WCMO WCot WFar WPnP
'Zepter' | EBee EBla GBuc GCal MBri NLar
| WCot

Ligusticum (Apiaceae)

hultenii | GIBF
lucidum | CDul CMCN EBee EHol EPfP EWTr
| LPhx MSal SEND WFar WPGP
- subsp. **lucidum** new | CSpe
porteri | MSal
scoticum | CArn ECrN EOHP EWes GBar GIBF
| GPoy ILis MSal NLar NSti WFar
| WLin WOut WPtf
striatum B&SWJ 7259 | WCru

Ligustrum ✿ (Oleaceae)

chenaultii | see *L. compactum*
§ **compactum** | CLnd NLar
§ **delavayanum** | CBcs ERom LPan MBar MGos
| SAPC SArc SBLw WFar
ibota | NLar
ionandrum | see *L. delavayanum*
japonicum | CCVT CHEx EBee ECrN LPan
| SBLw SEND SMur SPer WDin WFar
| XPep
I - 'Aureum' | MGos
- 'Coriaceum' | see *L. japonicum* 'Rotundifolium'
- 'Macrophyllum' | EPfP MAsh
§ - 'Rotundifolium' | CAbP CBcs CDoC CDul CHEx
| CPLG CPle EBee ELan EMil EPfP
| EPla LRHS MAsh MRav SBod SCoo
| SLim SMad SPer SPoG WCFE WFar
- 'Silver Star' (v) | CPMA NLar SLon
§ **lucidum** ♀H4 | NLar
| CDoC CSBt CTho EBee ECrN ELan
| LAst MBar MGos MRav MSwo NLar
| NWea SAPC SArc SBrw SPer SWvt
| WBVN WDin WFar XPep
- 'Aureovariegatum' (v) | NEgg
- 'Excelsum Superbum' (v) | CAbP CBcs CDul CLnd
♀H4 | CPMA ELan EPfP LAst LPan LRHS
| MAsh MBar MGos NBlu SBLw SPer
| SPoG SSpi
- 'Golden Wax' | CAbP CPMA MRav
- 'Tricolor' (v) | CPMA ELan EPfP LRHS SHBN SLim
| SPla SSpi SSta SWvt WDin WFar
obtusifolium 'Darts | SLPl
Perfecta'
- var. **regelianum** | SEND WFar
ovalifolium | CBcs CCVT CDoC CHll CLnd CSBt
| CTri ECrN EPfP IHMH LBuc LRHS
| MAsh MBar MBri MGos MSwo
| NBlu NWea SBLw SLim SPer SWvt
| WDin WGwG WMou
§ - 'Argenteum' (v) | CBcs CDoC CDul CPLG CTri CWib
| EBee ECrN EHoe IHMH LBuc
| LRHS MAsh MBar MBri NBlu NEgg
| NHol SLim SPer SPla SPoG SWvt
| WDin WFar WTel
- 'Aureomarginatum' | see *L. ovalifolium* 'Aureum'
§ - 'Aureum' (v) ♀H4 | More than 30 suppliers
* - 'Lemon and Lime' (v) | EBee EMil MGos SWvt WRHF
- 'Taff's Indecision' (v) | CPMA
- 'Variegatum' | see *L. ovalifolium* 'Argenteum'
quihoui ♀H4 | ECre ELan EPfP MBri SDix SLon
| SMad SPer WFar WHCG WPat
§ **sempervirens** | EPfP NLar SLon SSta
sinense | CMCN EPfP MRav WFar
- 'Multiflorum' | CWib WFar
- 'Pendulum' | CLnd EPla
- var. **stauntonii** new | NLar
- 'Variegatum' (v) | CBgR CPMA EPla EWes LHop
| MRav SPer

- 'Wimbei' | EPla WFar
strongylophyllum | CDoC WFar
texanum | see *L. japonicum* 'Texanum'
tschonoskii | NLar SLPl
undulatum 'Lemon | NLar SPoG WMoo
Lime and Clippers'
'Vicaryi' | CMHG CPMA ELan EPfP EPla
| EWTr IArd LRHS MAsh MBar
| MGos NPro SDix SPer SPla WFar
vulgare | CBcs CCVT CDul CRWN CTri
| CWan ECrN EPfP LAst LBuc MSwo
| NWea SHFr SWvt WBVN WDin
| WMou WSFF XPep
- 'Aureovariegatum' (v) | CNat
new
- 'Lodense' | MBar SLPl

Lilium ✿ (Liliaceae)

Chen Yi 1 | WCot
from China (IX) | CLAP
'Acapulco' (VIId) | LBmB
African Queen Group | CAvo EBrs ECot GBuc SCoo SPer
(VIa) ♀H4 | SPur WFar
- 'African Queen' (VIa) | CBro CFFs CSut ECri EPfP SPer
albanicum | see *L. pyrenaicum* subsp.
| *carniolicum* var. *albanicum*
amabile (IX) | CLAP EBee LRHS WDav
- 'Luteum' (IX) | CLAP EBee LRHS WDav
- 'Amber Gold' (Ic) | CLAP
America = 'Holean' (Ia) | IBal WDav
amoenum (IX) | EPot
'Angela North' (Ic) | CLAP
'Anglia' (VII) new | LBmB
'Apeldoorn' (Ic) | ECri LRHS NNor
'Aphrodite' (Ia/d) | EPot NBir
'Apollo' (Ia) ♀H4 | CBro EBrs GBuc GKev LRHS MBri
'Arena' (VIIb) | EBrs EPfP LRHS SCoo SPer WFar
'Ariadne' (Ic) | CLAP
* Asiatic hybrids (VI/VII) | NGdn SGar
auratum (IX) | EBrs ECho EFEx EPfP GBuc
- 'Classic' (IX) | CLAP
- 'Gold Band' | see *L. auratum* var. *platyphyllum*
§ - var. **platyphyllum** (IX) | ECri GBuc SBch WDav
- Red Band Group (IX) | WFar
- var. **virginale** (IX) | LRHS WDav WWst
'Avignon' (Ia) | ECri LRHS
Backhouse hybrids (II) | CLAP
bakerianum var. **rubrum** | WDav
'Barbara North' (Ic) | CLAP
'Barbaresco' (VII) | SCoo SPer
'Barcelona' (Ia) | MNrw NNor
'Batist' (Ia) | ECri
Bellingham Group (IV) | CLAP GBuc
'Bergamo' (VIId) | EPfP SCoo WFar
'Bianco Uno' | MBri
'Black Beauty' (VIId) | CAvo CBro CFFs CLAP EBee EBrs
| GBuc LBmB LRHS MSte NNor
'Black Dragon' (VIa) | ECri
'Black Jack' ᵖᴮᴿ | IBal
'Blazing Dwarf' (Ia) | MBri
'Bright Pixie' (Ia) | IBal
'Bright Star' (VIb) | ECri
'Brocade' (II) | CLAP
'Bronwen North' (Ic) | CLAP
brownii | EBee ECho ECri
- var. **australe** (IX) | WCru
B&SWJ 4082
bulbiferum | ECho GBuc
- var. **croceum** (IX) | ECho GIBF
Bullwood hybrids (IV) | CLAP
'Bums' (Ia/d) | EMon
buschianum | GIBF
'Butter Pixie' ᵖᴮᴿ (Ia) | IBal LBmB WGor
'Cameleon' | IBal
camtschatcense | GIBF
§ **canadense** (IX) | GBuc

- var. **coccineum** (IX) — CLAP GBuc WWst
- var. *flavum* — see *L. canadense*
'Cancun' (Ia) — ECri EPot LRHS
candidum (IX) ♀H4 — CArn CAvo CBcs CBro CHar CTri EBrs ECha ECri EHrv ELan EPfP EPot EWTr GIBF IBal LRHS MAvo MHer NGHP SPer WBrE WGwG WHil WPnP
- 'Plenum' (IX/d) — EMon
- var. **salonikae** — GIBF
'Casa Blanca' (VIIb) ♀H4 — CAvo CBro CFFs CSut ECri EPfP GBuc GKev IBal SCoo SPer SPur WFar WHlf
§ 'Casa Rosa' (V) — CSWP ECri MDKP NBir SWat
'Centrefold' — NNor
cernuum (IX) — CLAP EBrs ECho ECri LBmB SPer WCot WPrP
* - 'Album' **new** — EBee SPer
chalcedonicum (IX) — SBch
    JCA 633.201
'Chianti' (Ia) — CSut
'Chinook' (Ia) — NNor
'Chippendale' (Ic) — CLAP
'Chris North' — CLAP
'Cinnabar' (Ia) — ECri
Citronella Group (Ic) — CBro EBrs ECho ECri LRHS NNor SPur WFar
columbianum (IX) — CLAP ECho GBuc GCrs GEdr NMen
- B&SWJ 9564 — WCru
- dwarf (IX) — ECho NMen
'Compass' (Ia) — MBri
'Con Amore' (VIIb) — LRHS SCoo SPer WFar
'Conca d'Or' PBR **new** — LBmB
concolor (IX) — WDav
- var. **stictum** — GIBF
'Connecticut King' (Ia) — ECri EPfP
'Coral Butterflies' — CLAP
'Corina' (Ia) — GBuc NNor SGar
'Côte d'Azur' (Ia) — CBro EPot GKev NNor SRms WGor
'Coulance' (VIId) — EBrs
'Crimson Pixie' (Ia) — CBro LBmB
× **dalhansonii** (IX) — CLAP WCot
§ - 'Marhan' (II) — CLAP GCrs
§ **dauricum** (IX) — GCrs GEdr
davidii (IX) — CLAP EBee ECho ECri GEdr GIBF GKev LBmB WCru WDav
- var. **unicolor** — CLAP
§ - var. **willmottiae** (IX) — CLAP GIBF WViv
debile — GIBF
'Denia' (Ib) — IBal SPoG
'Diabora' **new** — GBuc
distichum — GIBF
- B&SWJ 794 — WCru
'Dizzy' **new** — CFwr
'Doeskin' (Ic) — CLAP
duchartrei (IX) — CFwr CLAP EBee ECho GBuc GCrs GEdr GFle NSla SMac WAbe WCMO WCru WDav
- white (IX) — WDav
§ 'Ed' (VII) — EPot NNor
'Eileen North' (Ic) — CLAP GBuc
'Electric' (Ia) — NNor
'Ellen Willmott' (II) — CLAP
'Enchantment' (Ia) — IBal MBri NNor
'Eros' — CLAP
'Eurydike' (Ic) — CLAP
'Evelina' — EBrs LRHS
'Everest' (VIId) — NNor WDav
'Fairest' (Ib-c/d) — CLAP
'Fancy Joy' — MBri
'Farolito' — LRHS MBri SPoG
'Fata Morgana' (Ia/d) ♀H4 — EBrs EPfP LRHS SCoo
'Feuerzauber' (Ia) **new** — SPer
'Fire King' (Ib) — ECGP ECri NBir SCoo WDav WFar
formosanum (IX) — EBee ECho ECri IBal SEND WViv

- B&SWJ 1589 — WCru
- var. **pricei** (IX) — CMea CSam EBee EBrs ECho EDAr ELan ENot EPfP EPot GEdr GGar GIBF LBee LRHS MHer MNrw NJOw NLAp NMen NWCA SBla SCoo SRot WBVN WGwG WHer WPer
- 'Snow Queen' (IX) — EBee EBrs ECri MDKP
- 'White Swan' (IX) — GBuc
'Fresco' (VII) — ECho
'Garden Party' (VII) ♀H4 — LBmB LRHS WFar
'George Slate' (Ic/d) — CLAP
§ 'Gibraltar' (Ia) — CSut ECri
'Glossy Wings' **new** — NNor
'Golden Joy' — MBri
'Golden Melody' (Ia) — ECri
Golden Splendor Group (VIa) ♀H4 — CAvo CFFs CFwr ECri SCoo SMeo SPer SPur SWat
'Gran Cru' (Ia) ♀H4 — EBrs ECri NNor
'Gran Paradiso' (Ia) — ECri SRms
grayi (IX) — CLAP NSla
'Green Magic' (VIa) — ECri NNor
'Hannah North' (Ic) — CLAP
hansonii (IX) — CLAP EBee ECho ECri IBlr LBmB WDav
- B&SWJ 4756 — WCru
henryi (IX) ♀H4 — CAvo CFFs CFwr CLAP CSWP EBee EBrs ECho ECri EPfP GIBF LPhx LRHS SMeo SPur WCMO WCot WCru WDav WPrP
- 'Album' **new** — EBee
- var. **citrinum** — CLAP ECho
henryi × Pink Perfection Group — CLAP
× **hollandicum** — ECri
'Honeymoon' — SPoG WWeb
'Hotlips' — EPfP SPer
'Iona' (Ic) — CLAP
'Ivory Pixie' (Ia) — CBro
'Jacqueline' — CFwr EBrs GKev WDav
§ 'Jacques S. Dijt' (II) — CLAP
japonicum (IX) — EFEx WCru
- 'Albomarginatum' (IX) — GEdr WWst
'Journey's End' (VIId) — GBuc LRHS NNor SPur
§ 'Joy' (VIIb) ♀H4 — ECri NNor
'Karen North' (Ic) — CLAP
§ **kelleyanum** (IX) — CLAP GBuc WCMO
- NNS 98-373 — WCot
kelloggii (IX) — WCMO WCot
'King Pete' (Ib) ♀H4 — LBmB
'Kiss Proof' (VIIb) — LRHS
'Lady Alice' (VI) — CLAP EBee EBrs
§ **lancifolium** (IX) — CArn CHEx GBin GIBF MOak NLAp SSpi WBVN WBrk WFar
- B&SWJ 539 — WCru
* - **album** — WBor
- Farrer's form — WCMO WCot
- var. **flaviflorum** (IX) — CLAP EBee ECri GBuc GCrs MSte
- 'Flore Pleno' (IX/d) — CLAP CMil CSWP CSam EBee EMon EPPr GAbr GBuc GCal GSki ITer LHop LRHS NBir NSti SOkd WCMO WCot WCru WDav WFar WTin
- Forrest's form (IX) — CLAP EBrs
§ - var. **splendens** (IX) ♀H4 — CBro EBee EBrs ECho ECri EPfP GKev LRHS MWgw NNor SPur WBor
'Landini' **new** — CFwr
lankongense (IX) — CLAP EBee GEdr GFle GIBF SOkd WDav
'Last Dance' (Ic) — CLAP
'Le Rêve' — see *L.* 'Joy'
leichtlinii (IX) — CLAP EBee EBrs ECho ECri WDav
- B&SWJ 4519 — WCru
- var. **maximowiczii** (IX) — CLAP WDav
leucanthum (IX) — EPot GIBF

- var. **centifolium** (IX)	CLAP WCru WWst
'Liberation' (I)	NBir
lijiangense	GEdr WWst
'Lollypop' (Ia)	EBrs EPfP IBal LRHS MNrw NNor SCoo
longiflorum (IX) ♀H2-3	EBee ECho ECri LRHS SCoo SPur WCMO
- B&SWJ 4885	WCru
§ - 'Carmel'	IBal
- 'Memories'	MBri SPoG
- 'Mount Carmel'	see *L. longiflorum* 'Carmel'
§ - 'White American' (IX)	CAvo CBro CFFs CSWP EBrs EPfP LBmB LRHS SPer
- 'White Elegance'	WHal
lophophorum (IX)	EPot GIBF WCru WDav
- var. **linearifolium**	GIBF
'Lovely Girl' (VIIb)	EBrs LBmB
'Luxor' (Ib)	ECri EPfP LRHS NBir SPer
mackliniae (IX)	CLAP EChP ECho GBuc GCal GCrs GEdr GFle GGGa GMac IBlr ITim NMen SBla SUsu WAbe WCMO WHal
- robust habit **new**	WWst
x **maculatum** var. **davuricum**	see *L. dauricum*
- Japanese double (IX)	EMon
'Marco Polo' (Ia)	SCoo WFar
'Marhan'	see *L.* x *dalhansonii* 'Marhan'
'Marie North' (Ic)	CLAP
martagon (IX) ♀H4	More than 30 suppliers
- var. **album** (IX) ♀H4	CAvo CBro CFFs CLAP CNic CSWP EBee EBrs ECGP EChP ECha EHrv ELan EPfP GBuc GEdr LPhx LRHS MTho NBir NChi SRms WAbe WCMO WCot WShi WViv
- pink-flowered (IX)	CBos CLAP
- 'Plenum' (IX/d)	EMon WCot
'Maxwill' (Ic)	CLAP
medeoloides (IX)	CLAP ECho EFEx GBuc GCrs GGGa NMen WCot WDav
'Menton'	ECri
michiganense (IX)	CSWP GBuc GCrs
'Milano' (Ia)	ECri
minima	GIBF
'Miss Lucy'PBR (d) **new**	CSut
'Miss Rio' (VII)	LRHS SCoo
'Mona Lisa' (VIIb/d)	EBrs EPfP EPot IBal LAst LRHS MBri MTis NNor WBVN WFar
§ **monadelphum** (IX)	CLAP EBee ECho EPot ETow GBuc GCrs NLar WCMO WDav
- pale yellow-coloured **new**	WWst
'Mont Blanc' (Ia)	NBir
'Montana'	LRHS
'Monte Negro' (Ia)	EBrs IBal WDav
'Mr Ed'	see *L.* 'Ed'
'Mr Ruud'	see *L.* 'Ruud'
'Mrs R.O. Backhouse' (II)	CLAP EBee MSte
'Muscadet'PBR (VII)	CSut EBrs LRHS MTis
§ **nanum** (IX)	ECho EHyt GBuc GCrs GEdr GGGa NLAp NMen NSla WCru WHal
- AGS/ES	WWst
- from Bhutan (IX)	GBuc GCrs GEdr WCru
- var. **flavidum** (IX)	EHyt GEdr NMen WCru
- 'Len's Lilac' (IX)	WCru
nepalense (IX)	CBcs CBro CFwr CLAP CSWP EBee EBla ECho ECri EPot GCrs GEdr GGar GIBF LHop LRHS MDun NCob SBla WCot WCru WFar WPnP
- B&SWJ 2985	WCru
nobilissimum (IX)	EFEx
'Noblesse' (VII)	LRHS
'Novo Cento' ♀H4	ECri
'Odeon'	ECri
'Olivia' (Ia)	EBrs ECri NNor
Olympic Group (VIa)	ECri
'Orange Pixie' (Ia)	ECri EPfP IBal SCoo WGor
'Orange Triumph' (Ia)	EPfP NNor
'Orestes' (Ib)	CLAP
* Oriental Superb Group	NGdn
§ **oxypetalum** (IX)	GCrs GGGa
- var. **insigne** (IX)	CLAP ECho EHyt EPot ETow GBin GBuc GCrs GEdr GGGa GGar GIBF NMen NSla WCMO WCru WHal
'Painted Pixie' (Ia)	IBal
'Pan' (Ic)	CLAP
papilliferum	ECho WCMO
pardalinum (IX) ♀H4	CAvo CLAP EBee EBrs ECho GKev IBlr IFro LBmB LRHS MSte NSla WCMO WCot WCru WDav WHal WPnP WWhi
- var. **giganteum** (IX)	CLAP ECri EPfP EWTr MNrw SPer WDav WTin
- subsp. **pardalinum** (IX)	NNS 00-488WCot
- subsp. **shastense** (IX)	CLAP GCrs NMen WCot
- subsp. **shastense** x **vollmeri** NNS 00-490	WCot
parryi (IX)	GBuc
parvum (IX)	EBee ECho GBuc
'Peach Butterflies' (Ic/d)	CLAP
'Peach Pixie' (Ia)	NBir NNor SCoo
'Peggy North' (Ic)	CLAP
pensylvanicum	GIBF
Petit Pink = 'Hobozi' (Ia)	MBri
philippinense (IX)	EBee EWin
- B&SWJ 4000	WCru
Pink Perfection Group (VIa) ♀H4	CAvo CBro CFFs CSut ECri EPfP EWTr NNor SBch SCoo SPer SPur SWat WFar WHlf
'Pink Pixie'PBR (Ia)	ECri IBal SGar
'Pink Tiger' (Ib)	CLAP ECri GKev LRHS NNor WGor
pitkinense (IX)	SOkd
pomponium (IX)	GCal
primulinum (IX)	WWst
- var. **ochraceum**	CLAP WWst
§ **pumilum** (IX) ♀H4	CBro CFwr CLAP EBee EBrs ECho ECri EPot GBuc GCal GIBF LRHS MSte MTho SMeo WAul WCru WDav WPrP WViv
- 'Golden Gleam' (IX)	WWst
'Purple Rain' **new**	LBmB
pyrenaicum (IX)	CBro CLAP EBrs ECho IBlr IFro LTwo WCMO WCot WDav WPGP WRha WShi WViv
§ - subsp. **carniolicum** var. **albanicum** (IX)	CLAP EBee
§ - subsp. **pyrenaicum** var. **pyrenaicum** (IX)	CLAP
- - var. **rubrum** (IX)	CLAP WCot
'Raspberry Butterflies' (Ic/d)	CLAP
'Red Carpet' (Ia)	ECri LRHS NBir NNor WGor
'Red Dwarf' (Ia)	ELan IBal
'Red Night' (I)	EGoo LRHS
'Red Rum'	MBri
'Red Star'	EBrs
'Red Tiger' (Ib)	CLAP
'Red Twinkle' **new**	CFwr
'Red Velvet' (Ib)	CLAP
regale (IX) ♀H4	More than 30 suppliers
- 'Album' (IX)	CAvo CFFs CSWP EBee ECri LPhx LRHS NNor SBch SCoo SGar SPur WFar
§ - 'Royal Gold' (IX)	ECri EPfP MWgw WDav
'Reinesse' (Ia)	IBal MBri
'Robert Griersbach' **new**	LBmB
'Robert Swanson' **new**	LBmB
'Rodolfa'PBR **new**	LBmB
'Roma' (Ia)	LRHS NBir

'Rosefire' (Ia) | ECri NNor
'Rosemary North' (I) | CLAP
Rosepoint Lace Group (Ic) | CLAP
'Rosita' (Ia) | ECri WFar
rosthornii | CLAP GBuc WCMO WCot WCru WWst
'Royal Gold' | see *L. regale* 'Royal Gold'
rubellum (IX) | EFEx GBuc
* 'Rubina' **new** | WHlf
§ 'Ruud' (VII) | EPfP EPot LRHS
sachalinense | EKen GIBF WWst
- Brown 0235 | CStu
'Salmon Twinkle' | EBrs WFar
'Sam' (VII) ♀H4 | EPfP EPot GBuc LRHS
sargentiae (IX) | CLAP ECri GBuc GCrs GGGa NMen WCMO WCot WCru
'Scentwood' (IV) | CLAP
sempervivoideum (IX) | ECho WDav
shastense | see *L. kelleyanum*
'Shuksan' (IV) | CLAP
'Silly Girl' (Ia) | ECri NNor
§ 'Snow Crystal' (I) | EPfP IBal
'Souvenir'PBR **new** | LBmB
speciosum (IX) | NSla
- B&SWJ 4847 | WCru
- var. *album* (IX) | ECri GBuc LRHS MWgw NBir NNor SBch
- var. *gloriosoides* (IX) | EPot WCot
- var. *roseum* (IX) | GBuc NNor
- var. *rubrum* (IX) | CFwr CLAP EBee EBrs ECha ECri GBuc LRHS NBir NLar SPer SPur WCMO WPrP
§ - 'Uchida' (IX) | ECri NNor SBch WDav
'Sphinx' (Ia/d) | WCot
'Staccato' (Ia) | ECri
'Star Gazer' (VIIc) | CBro CSut ECot ECri ELan IBal LAst LRHS NNor SCoo SPer WFar WGor
'Starfighter' (VIId) | IBal LRHS
'Sterling Star' (Ia) | CLAP ECri EPfP NNor
Stones = 'Holebobo' **new** | NNor
sulphureum | NLAp WWst
'Sun Ray' (Ia) | LRHS
superbum (IX) | CDes CLAP EBee ECho GBuc WCot WCru WDav WPGP
'Sutton Court' (II) | CLAP
'Sweet Surrender' (I) | ECri LRHS NNor
szovitsianum | see *L. monadelphum*
taliense (IX) | ECho GBuc GEdr GIBF WCMO WCru
tenuifolium | see *L. pumilum*
'Theseus' (Ic) | CLAP
Tiger Babies Group **new** | CLAP WSPU
'Tiger White' (Ic) | CLAP
tigrinum | see *L. lancifolium*
'Tinkerbell' (Ic) | CLAP
'Tinos'PBR **new** | CFwr
tsingtauense (IX) | CLAP GIBF WDav
- B&SWJ 519 | WCru
'Uchida Kanoka' | see *L. speciosum* 'Uchida'
'Viva' (Ic) | CLAP
vollmeri (IX) | CLAP GCrs NMen WCru
wallichianum (IX) | EBee ECho EPot GBuc
wardii (IX) | WWst
'White American' | see *L. longiflorum* 'White American'
'White Butterflies' (Ic/d) | CLAP
'White Henryi' (VId) | CLAP
'White Kiss' (Ia/d) | LRHS
I 'White Lace' (Ic/d) | CLAP
'White Mountain' (VIIc) | SPer
'White Paradise' (V) | SCoo
'White Pixie' (I) | see *L.* 'Snow Crystal'
'White Tiger' (Ib) | CLAP
wigginsii (IX) | CLAP GCrs GEdr

willmottiae | see *L. davidii* var. *willmottiae*
xanthellum var. *luteum* | GEdr WWst
Yellow Blaze Group (Ia) | EPfP
'Yellow Bunting' (I) | WWst
'Yellow Star' (Ib) | LRHS NNor

lime see *Citrus aurantiifolia*

lime, djeruk see *Citrus amblycarpa*

lime, Philippine see x *Citrofortunella microcarpa*

Limnanthes (*Limnanthaceae*)
douglasii ♀H4 | CArn CHrt EPfP LRav SIde
- subsp. *nivea* | CSpe

Limnophila (*Scrophulariaceae*)
aromatica | MSal

Limoniastrum (*Plumbaginaceae*)
monopetalum | XPep

Limonium (*Plumbaginaceae*)
bellidifolium | EBee ECha NJOw SBla WEas WHoo WPer WTin XPep
- 'Dazzling Blue' | EChP
binervosum | EBee
'Blauer Diamant' **new** | NBre
caspium | LRav
chilwellii | EAEE EBee ECGP EMan MSte NCGa
cosyrense | CMea CStu MHer NMen WPer
dumosum | see *Goniolimon tataricum* var. *angustifolium*
gmelinii | MLLN SPlb WPer
* - subsp. *hungaricum* | NLar
- 'Perestrojka' | EBee
gougetianum | ETow WPer
latifolium | see *L. platyphyllum*
macrophyllum **new** | CSec
minutum | CNic MNHC NJOw SPoG
perezii | EShb NBre WPer
§ *platyphyllum* | More than 30 suppliers
- 'Robert Butler' | EAEE EBee ECGP EMan GCal LRHS MRav MSte NBre NCGa SPoG SRGP
- 'Violetta' | CTri EBee ECGP ECha ELan EMan EPfP ERou LAst LRHS MBri MMHG MRav MTis NCGa NLar NOrc SPer WCAu WHoo
pruinosum | XPep
speciosum | see *Goniolimon incanum*
'Stardust' | NBre
tataricum | see *Goniolimon tataricum*
vulgare | WHer XPep

Linanthastrum see *Linanthus*

Linanthus (*Polemoniaceae*)
nuttallii subsp. *floribundus* | CPBP

Linaria (*Scrophulariaceae*)
aeruginea | CSpe EChP
- subsp. *nevadensis* 'Gemstones' | LRHS
alpina | CMea CSpe ECho ECtt GGar MTho NJOw NRya SRms WEas WPer
anticaria 'Antique Silver' | CBgR CHea EBee ECha GBBs GBuc LAst LSou MRav NEgg NLar SBch SSvw WPGP WWeb
Blue Lace = 'Yalin' | EBee LAst LSou NPri SMrm SPoG
capraria | CPBP
cymbalaria | see *Cymbalaria muralis*
§ *dalmatica* | CSpe EBee EChP ECha ELan EPPr ERou LPhx MHar MNFA MWhi

	NBid NBro NPri SHGN WCFE
	WCot WKif WMoo WPer
x *dominii* 'Carnforth'	CBre CPom LSou NBre NBro SBch
	WCot
- 'Yuppie Surprise'	CBgR EBee EChP ECtt EMan LAst
	LDai NBir NDov SPer SSvw SWvt
	WCot WCra WPGP
genistifolia	ECtt MDKP
- subsp. *dalmatica*	see *L. dalmatica*
'Globosa Alba'	see *Cymbalaria muralis* 'Globosa
	Alba'
hepaticifolia	see *Cymbalaria hepaticifolia*
japonica	WCot
* *lobata alba*	ECho SPlb
'Natalie'	SBla
nevadensis 'Grenada Sol'	MWea
new	
origanifolia	see *Chaenorhinum origanifolium*
pallida	see *Cymbalaria pallida*
pilosa	see *Cymbalaria pilosa*
platycalyx **new**	EBee
purpurea	CAby CBgR COlW EBee EHrv ELan
	EPfP IFoB LBMP MHer MNHC
	MWgw NBPC NBro NPer NPri
	SECG SRms WCAu WCot WHen
	WMoo WPer WWye
- 'Alba'	see *L. purpurea* 'Springside White'
- 'Canon Went'	More than 30 suppliers
- 'Radcliffe Innocence'	see *L. purpurea* 'Springside White'
§ - 'Springside White'	CBgR CElw COlW CPom EBee
	ECha ECtt EMan GBuc LPhx MSte
	NBid NBir NPri SBch SSvw SUsu
	WAul WCAu WCot WMoo WPer
	WRha
- 'Thurgarton Beauty'	MDKP
repens	CPom MNrw WCot WHbs WHer
reticulata 'Red Velvet'	CSpe
'Toni Aldiss'	LPhx
triornithophora	CElw CEnt CFir CSec CSpe EBee
	ECha EMan GBuc IGor LBMP
	MNFA MWrn NJOw SEND WKif
	WMoo WPer WPtf WRha
	WWye
- 'Pink Budgies'	CDMG LSou
- purple	ELan MHar STes WMoo
tristis **new**	CSec
vulgaris	CArn ELau GWCH LDai MBow
	MDKP MHer MNHC NMir NPri
	NSco SECG WHer WJek
- hemipeloric	CNat
- 'Peloria'	CNat EBee EMon MDKP WCot
'Winifrid's Delight'	EBee EPfP NBre

Lindelofia (Boraginaceae)

anchusoides misapplied	see *L. longiflora*
§ *anchusoides* (Lindl.)	EPPr GBri NBid
Lehm.	
§ *longiflora*	CFir GBuc GCal LRHS MLLN NBid
	WPer

Lindera (Lauraceae)

benzoin	CAgr CBcs CMCN EPfP LRHS MBri
	MSal NLar SSpi WDin
communis	WPGP
erythrocarpa	CBcs CMCN CPLG EPfP NLar
- B&SWJ 6271	WCru
megaphylla	CBcs CHEx
obtusiloba ♀H4	CAbP CPLG CPne EPfP IArd NLar
	SBrw SPoG SSpi WNor
- var. *heterophylla*	ISea
praecox	EPfP NLar WPGP
reflexa	CBcs CMCN EPfP NLar WPGP
strychnifolia	CBcs CMCN EPfP
umbellata var.	WCru
membranaceae	
B&SWJ 6227	

Lindernia (Scrophulariaceae)

grandiflora	ECou

Linnaea (Caprifoliaceae)

borealis	CStu ILis MHar WAbe
- subsp. *americana*	NWCA

Linum ✿ (Linaceae)

africanum	EShb
alexeenkoanum **new**	WLin
alpinum	SHGN
arboreum ♀H4	SBla WKif WPat
- NS 529	NWCA
campanulatum	WThu
- 'Sulphur' **new**	LSou
capitatum	CPBP EBee GKev NSla
flavum	CTri EPfP GKev XPep
- 'Compactum'	ECho EHol GAbr SBla SRms
	WCot
'Gemmell's Hybrid' ♀H4	CDes CLyd CMea ECho EPot EWes
	LRHS MDKP NBir NMen NWCA
	SBla WAbe WPat
kingii var. *sedoides*	WLin
leonii	LRHS WKif
monogynum	CDes CMdw EBee ECou SBla
§ - var. *diffusum*	ECou
- 'Nelson'	see *L. monogynum* var. *diffusum*
narbonense	CMdw CSam CSpe ECGP LBMP
	LDai LRHS MNFA NLar NOak SBch
	SRms WHoo
- 'Heavenly Blue'	ERou WHen
§ *perenne*	CArn CRWN CTri EBee EChP ECha
	ELan EPfP ERou GMaP LRHS MHer
	MNFA MNHC MWgw NFor NMir
	SIde SPer SRms SUsu WCAu WPer
	XPep
- 'Album'	EBee ECha ELan EPfP ERou
	MNFA NLar SPer SUsu WHen
	WPer
- subsp. *alpinum*	CPBP LBee SBla
'Alice Blue'	
§ - 'Blau Saphir'	CBod CTri EBee ECtt EShb LAst
	LRHS MAvo MLLN MRav MWat
	NLar SRms SWal WHen WRHF
	WWeb
- Blue Sapphire	see *L. perenne* 'Blau Saphir'
- 'Diamant'	CBod EBee ECtt EWin LRHS
- 'Himmelszelt'	LBMP NLar SMrm WHal
- subsp. *lewisii*	EBee NBir WAbe
- 'Nanum Diamond'	EShb NLar
- 'White Diamond'	EBee NCob WHen
sibiricum	see *L. perenne*
suffruticosum	CPBP
- subsp. *salsoloides*	EHyt NLap NWCA SBla WAbe
'Nanum'	WPat
- - 'Prostratum'	GBuc
usitatissimum	CRWN MHer SIde

Liparis (Orchidaceae)

coelogynoides	ECou
cordifolia	EFEx
formosana **new**	WWst
fujisanensis	EFEx
krameri var. *krameri*	EFEx
kumokiri	EFEx
makinoana	EFEx
nervosa **new**	GEdr WWst
nigra	EFEx
sootenzanensis	EFEx

Lippia (Verbenaceae)

alba	MSal
canescens	see *Phyla nodiflora* var. *canescens*
chamaedrifolia	see *Verbena peruviana*
citriodora	see *Aloysia triphylla*

dulcis	CArn CFir EAro EOHP EUnu GPoy ILis LRav MSal WJek
nodiflora	see *Phyla nodiflora*
repens	see *Phyla nodiflora*

Liquidambar ✿ (Hamamelidaceae)

acalycina	CLnd CPMA EBee ELan EPfP LPan LRHS MBlu MGos NLar SBir SIFN SSpi SSta WNor WPGP WPat
- 'Burgundy Flush' **new**	CPMA
'Elstead Mill'	LPan
formosana	CEnd CMCN ECrN EPfP IMGH LPan MBlu MGos NPen SBir SPer SSta WNor WPGP
- B&SWJ 6855	WCru
- Monticola Group	CPMA EPfP SBir SIFN SSta
orientalis	CMCN CPMA EPfP LPan SBir SSta
styraciflua	More than 30 suppliers
- 'Andrew Hewson'	CLnd CPMA LRHS MAsh NLar SBir SSpi SSta
- 'Anja'	CPMA MBlu SSta
- 'Anneke'	CPMA LRHS SBir SSta
- 'Aurea'	see *L. styraciflua* 'Variegata'
- 'Aurea Variegata'	see *L. styraciflua* 'Variegata'
- 'Aurora'	CPMA SBir SCoo SLim
- 'Burgundy'	CLnd CPMA CTho NHol SBir SSta WPGP WPat
- 'Fastigiata'	MBlu
- 'Festeri'	CEnd MAsh SBir SSta WPat
- 'Festival'	CPMA MBlu SBLw SSta
- 'Globe'	CPMA
- 'Golden Treasure' (v)	CMCN CPMA LRHS MGos NLar SSpi WPat
- 'Gum Ball'	CEnd CLnd CMCN CPMA EPfP EWes LTwo MAsh MGos NLar SBir SMad SSta WPat
- Happidaze = 'Hapdell'	CEnd MAsh NLar WPat
- 'Jennifer Carol'	CPMA NLar
- 'Kia'	CAbP CEnd CPMA MAsh SBir WPat
- 'Kirsten'	CPMA NLar
- 'Lane Roberts' ♥H4	CDoC CDul CLnd CMCN CTho EBee EPfP LPan LRHS MAsh MBlu MBri MGos MLan NEgg NLar SBir SMad SPoG SReu SSta WDin WPGP WPat
- 'Manon' (v)	CDoC CEnd CPMA LPan NBhm SBir
- 'Midwest Sunset'	MAsh WPGP WPat
- 'Moonbeam' (v)	CEnd CMCN CPMA EBee MAsh NHol NLar SBir SCoo SLim SSta WPat
- 'Moraine'	CMCN CPMA SBLw SBir
- 'Naree'	CMCN CPMA NLar SBir
- 'Oconee'	CEnd EPfP MAsh WPat
- 'Paarl'	CMCN CPMA
- 'Palo Alto'	CEnd CPMA LRHS LTwo MAsh NHol SBLw SBir SMad SSta WPGP WPat
- 'Parasol'	CEnd CPMA SBir SSta
- 'Pendula'	CLnd CMCN CPMA LRHS SBir SSta
- 'Penwood'	CPMA NLar SSpi SSta
- 'Rotundiloba'	CMCN CPMA EPfP SBir SIFN SSpi SSta WPat
- 'Silver King' (v)	CDul CLnd CMCN CPMA EBee ECrN EHoe EPfP IMGH LRHS MBlu MBri MGos NLar SCoo SLim SPer SPoG SSta WPat
- 'Stared'	CEnd CLnd CPMA SBir WPat
- 'Stella'	CLnd LPan WPGP WPat
- 'Thea'	CAbP CPMA LRHS MAsh MBlu SBir SSta
§ - 'Variegata' (v)	CBcs CDul CLnd COtt CPMA EBee ELan EPfP LPan LRHS MAsh MBlu MDun MGos NBee NEgg NHol SHBN SLim SPer SSta WDin WPat
- 'Worplesdon' ♥H4	More than 30 suppliers

Liriodendron ✿ (Magnoliaceae)

'Chapel Hill' **new**	MBlu
chinense	CBcs CDul CMCN CTho EPfP MBlu SSpi WFar WPGP WPat
'Doc Deforce's Delight' **new**	MBlu
'T. Jackson'	NLar
tulipifera ♥H4	More than 30 suppliers
- 'Ardis'	CMCN NLar SSpi
- 'Arnold'	CMCN
- 'Aureomarginatum' (v) ♥H4	More than 30 suppliers
- 'Aureum'	CMCN
- 'Crispum'	CMCN
- 'Fastigiatum'	CBcs CDoC CDul CEnd CLnd CMCN COtt CTho EBee ECrN ELan EPfP IArd IMGH LPan LRHS MBlu MBri MGos NPal SBLw SPer SPoG SSta WOrn WPat
- 'Glen Gold'	CEnd CMCN MBlu MGos NLar
- 'Mediopictum' (v)	CMCN CTho MBlu
- 'Roodhaan'	NLar

Liriope ✿ (Convallariaceae)

from Vietnam **new**	WPGP
'Big Blue'	see *L. muscari* 'Big Blue'
§ *exiliflora*	CEnd CLAP EBee EGle GCal NLar WFar
§ - 'Ariaka-janshige' (v)	SWat
§ *gigantea*	CLAP EBee GSki SWat
graminifolia misapplied	see *L. muscari*
hyacinthifolia	see *Reineckea carnea*
kansuensis	ERos
koreana	EBee EPPr GCal
- B&SWJ 8821	WCru
'Majestic'	CBct CHar EBee EGle ERou GSki MBri SPla WFar WHoo
§ *muscari* ♥H4	More than 30 suppliers
- B&SWJ 561	WCru
- 'Alba'	see *L. muscari* 'Monroe White'
§ - 'Big Blue'	CBct CBrm CKno CLAP CMMP COlW CPrp EBee ENot EPfP EWTr GSki LEdu LHop LRHS MRav NLar SWvt WBor WCFE WMoo
- 'Christmas Tree'	CBct CPrp EPPr WHoo WMoo
- 'Evergreen Giant'	see *L. gigantea*
- 'Gold-banded' (v)	CPrp EGle ENot EPfP GCal MBNS NSti SHBN WFar WViv
- 'Goldfinger' **new**	WPGP
- 'Ingwersen'	CBgR CPrp EBee ECho MSph NMRc SMeo WHoo WLeb WPnP
- 'John Burch' (v)	CBct CLAP CPrp EBee LHop MBNS MCCP NLar SMad WLeb
- 'Lilac Beauty'	CPne
- 'Majestic' misapplied	see *L. exiliflora*
- 'Moneymaker' **new**	EBee
§ - 'Monroe White'	More than 30 suppliers
- 'Okina' (v)	WCMO WCot
- 'Paul Aden'	EPfP WPGP
- 'Royal Purple'	CBct CHar CLAP EBee ENot EPfP GBin GSki NBPC NGdn NLar SPla WLeb
- 'Silver Ribbon'	CLAP CPrp EBee EPfP EShb GSki NSti SMad SPer WPGP
- 'Silvery Midget' (v)	CPrp SUsu
- 'Superba'	WCot
§ - 'Variegata' (v)	More than 30 suppliers
* - 'Variegated Alba' (v)	CBcs CFir ECho
- 'Webster Wideleaf'	GSki MSph
'New Wonder'	EHrv LEdu
platyphylla	see *L. muscari*
'Samantha'	CBct CPrp ECha
§ *spicata*	CBro EBee ECho ERos SWat WWeb

– 'Alba'	CPLG EBee EBrs ECho GCal MTho WTin
§ – 'Gin-ryu' (v)	CBct CBgR CCge CHar CLAP COIW EBee ECho EPPr EWes GBuc GSki LEdu LSRN MCCP MRav MSte SLPl SPer WCFE WCot WPGP WViv
– 'Silver Dragon'	see *L. spicata* 'Gin-ryu'
– 'Small Green'	EBee

Lisianthius (Gentianaceae)

russelianus	see *Eustoma grandiflorum*

Listera (Orchidaceae)

ovata	WHer

Litchi (Sapindaceae)

chinensis **new**	SDEP

Lithocarpus ✿ (Fagaceae)

densiflorus var. *echinoides*	WCot
NNS 00-504	
edulis	CBcs CHEx SArc WPGP
pachyphyllus	CBcs

Lithodora (Boraginaceae)

§ *diffusa*	ECho SGar SRot
– 'Alba'	ECho EPfP GKev LBee LRHS MGos NWCA SGar SPer SPoG WFar
– 'Baby Barbara' **new**	GKev
– 'Cambridge Blue'	ECho SLdr SPer
– 'Compacta'	ECho EWes NWCA WAbe
– 'Grace Ward' ♀H4	ECho GAbr MGos MWya NHol SBod WAbe WPat
– 'Heavenly Blue' ♀H4	More than 30 suppliers
– 'Inverleith'	ECho EWes WFar
– 'Pete's Favourite'	SRGP WAbe
– 'Picos'	CMea CNic ECho GCrs GKev NMen WAbe WFar WPat
– 'Star'PBR	CBcs CMHG EPfP LRHS NLar SBod SCoo SIng SPer SPoG SRot
fruticosa	CArn XPep
graminifolia	see *Moltkia suffruticosa*
x *intermedia*	see *Moltkia* x *intermedia*
§ *oleifolia* ♀H4	ECho EPot NBir NMen SBla WPat
rosmarinifolia	CSpe EHyt LRHS
zahnii	ECho WPat

Lithophragma (Saxifragaceae)

parviflorum	CDes CMea CPom EBee EHyt EMan EMon EPot EWes MSte MTho NBir NRya NWCA WBor WCru WFar WPnP

Lithospermum (Boraginaceae)

diffusum	see *Lithodora diffusa*
doerfleri	see *Moltkia doerfleri*
erythrorhizon	CPLG MSal WWye
officinale	CArn GBar GPoy MSal NMir
oleifolium	see *Lithodora oleifolia*
purpureocaeruleum	see *Buglossoides purpurocaerulea*

Litsea (Lauraceae)

glauca	see *Neolitsea sericea*

Littonia (Colchicaceae)

modesta	CRHN EShb ITer

Livistona (Arecaceae)

australis	CRoM CTrC EAmu LPal WMul
chinensis ♀H1	CBrP CPHo CRoM EAmu LPJP LPal MPRe SAin SBig WMul
decipiens	CPHo CRoM CTrC LPal MPRe WMul

mariae	LPal
nitida	CKob

Loasa (Loasaceae)

RCB/Arg CC-1	WCot
triphylla var. *volcanica*	EMan EWes GCal WSHC

Lobelia (Campanulaceae)

B&SWJ 8220 from Vietnam	WCru
RCB/Arg S-4	WCot
'Alice'	MSph WDyG WFar
anatina	WDyG
angulata	see *Pratia angulata*
bridgesii	CPLG CPle EChP EShb GCal GGar GMac MHar WPGP WRos
cardinalis ♀H3	More than 30 suppliers
– 'Bee's Flame'	CFir CPrp EAEE EBee EMan EMar ERou EShb MLLN MRav MSte MWgw NBre SUsu SWat
§ – 'Elmfeuer'	CFwr CMHG EBee EChP ERou EShb EWin MSte NLar SMrm SPlb SWvt WFar
– 'Eulalia Berridge'	CSam EBee EChP EGle GBuc SMrm WCru WDyG WFar WMoo WSHC
– subsp. *graminea* var. *multiflora*	CFir
– 'Illumination'	GBuc
– 'Queen Victoria' ♀H3	More than 30 suppliers
* – 'Russian Princess' **new**	NBre
'Cinnabar Deep Red'	see *L.* x *speciosa* 'Fan Tiefrot'
'Cinnabar Rose'	see *L.* x *speciosa* 'Fan Zinnoberrosa'
Compliment Blue	see *L.* x *speciosa* 'Kompliment Blau'
Compliment Deep Red	see *L.* x *speciosa* 'Kompliment Tiefrot'
Compliment Purple	see *L.* x *speciosa* 'Kompliment Purpur'
Compliment Scarlet	see *L.* x *speciosa* 'Kompliment Scharlach'
coronopifolia	EShb
dortmanna	EMFW WWpP
erinus Big Blue = 'Weslobigblue'PBR	EShb LAst LSou
– Blue Star = 'Wesstar'PBR	ECtt LAst
– 'Kathleen Mallard' (d)	ECtt LAst SWvt
– 'Richardii'	see *L. richardsonii*
excelsa	CPle EShb LSou MTPN NCGa NRnb NSfd SPav SPoG WFar WPic
– B&SWJ 9513	WCru
Fan Deep Red	see *L. .* x *speciosa* 'Fan Tiefrot'
'Fan Deep Rose'	see *L. .* x *speciosa* 'Fan Orchidrosa'
'Flamingo'	see *L.* 'Pink Flamingo'
'Forncett Merry' **new**	NBre
fulgens Saint Elmo's Fire	see *L. cardinalis* 'Elmfeuer'
x *gerardii*	see *L.* x *speciosa*
gibberoa	CHEx
'Hadspen Purple'	see *L.* x *speciosa* 'Hadspen Purple'
inflata	CArn EBee EOHP GPoy MSal NSfd WCHb
kalmii	EShb
– 'Blue Shadow'	CStu EBla LAst MNrw NBlu NJOw WPtf
'La Fresco' **new**	EBee
laxiflora	EGra MTho SAga SPet
– B&SWJ 9064	WCru
– var. *angustifolia*	CHEx CPrp CSam CSec EShb GCal MDKP MOak MSte SBod SDnm SHFr SMrm SPav SPoG SRms SUsu WHil WPrP WWye XPep
'Lena'	SWat
lindblomii	CFee CStu GSki
linnaeoides	SPlb
'Lipstick'	WWlt
longifolia from Chile	CFee

§ *lutea*	EWin LRav
'Martha'	EBee
pedunculata	see *Pratia pedunculata*
perpusilla	see *Pratia perpusilla*
polyphylla	ECtt EKen EShb GBBs LPhx NCGa NRnb NSfd WPic
preslii	SPlb
regalis	WCHb
§ *richardsonii* ♀H1+3	ECtt LAst NBlu SWvt
seguinii B&SWJ 7065	WCru
- var. *doniana* CC 3673	WRos
sessilifolia	CPLG CSec EBee EGle GBuc LPBA NEgg WGwG WPer WWye
- B&L 12396	EMon
siphilitica	More than 30 suppliers
- 'Alba'	CSam EBee EBla EPfP EShb EWTr LPBA LRHS MLLN NRnb SPav SRms SWat SWvt WCAu WCHb WFar WHoo WHrl WMnd WMoo WPer WSan WWpP WWye
- blue-flowered	NLar SWat SWvt WSan
- 'Rosea'	MNrw
'Sonia'	SWat
§ x *speciosa*	CSam NBre NJOw SMHy SMar SWat WBor WFar WHil WMoo WSHC
- dark	CMHG EBee EGle
- 'Butterfly Blue'	CBcs EChP EGle EWTr GBuc LBBr MTis NEgg SPla
- 'Butterfly Rose'	EGle GBuc SMHy SRot WCHb
- 'Cherry Ripe'	CPrp EMag EPfP LRHS NHol WCHb WEas
- 'Cranberry Crown'	NRnb
- 'Cranberry Crush'	NRnb SHar
- 'Dark Crusader'	CPrp EAEE EBee EBrs ECGP ECtt ELan EMan EMar EShb LBMP LRHS LSou NHol SBch SMrm SPla SWat WCHb WEas WMnd WSan
- 'Eastgrove Pink'	WEas
- 'Fan Burgundy'	CBrm NJOw WHil
§ - 'Fan Orchidrosa' ♀H3-4	EShb NGdn NJOw SRot WHil
§ - 'Fan Scharlach' ♀H3-4	CFwr EShb MGos NJOw NLar SBch SGar SRot SWvt WDyG WHil
§ - 'Fan Tiefrot' ♀H3-4	CBen CBos CBrm CDWL ERou GBuc NBlu NCGa NGdn SBla SMHy SRms SWat SWvt WCHb WOut WPer
§ - 'Fan Zinnoberrosa' ♀H3-4	CBcs CBrm CFir CMMP ERou LAst LRHS MFOX MHar SRms SRot SWvt WCHb WMoo WPer WWlt
- 'Grape Knee-High'	EBee LSRN LSou MBri NCGa NRnb SPoG SRkn
§ - 'Hadspen Purple'	CHad CPen CWCL EBee EBrs ELan EWTr IPot LSRN MBri MCCP MWea NBre NCGa NCob SHar SPoG SWat WOVN
- 'Kimbridge Beet'	CMac
§ - 'Kompliment Blau'	CFir ERou LRHS SWvt WPer
§ - 'Kompliment Purpur'	ERou MNrw SWvt
§ - 'Kompliment Scharlach' ♀H3-4	CBcs CSWP EBee EMil EPfP ERou LHop LRHS MBNS MNrw NHol NPer SWvt WCHb WFar WMnd WPer
- 'Kompliment Tiefrot'	ERou MNrw MWat SWvt WPer
- 'Monet Moment'	EBee EBla ERou EWes LSou NBre NCGa NRnb SPoG
- 'Pauline'	ECtt
- 'Pink Elephant' ♀H4	CSWP CWCL EBee MDKP MSph NBre SBla SHar WFar WRha WWeb
- 'Pink Flamingo'	CBen CMMP CPLG EBee EBla EBrs LRHS MTis SWat WCHb WFar WSHC WShi WWye
- 'Purple Towers'	EBee NBre
- purple-flowered	EWin
- red-flowered	EWin
- 'Rosencavalier'	CBre CPen EBee EMar LRHS NGby WFar

- 'Royal Purple'	WOut
- 'Ruby Slippers'	CBcs CWCL EBee EBrs ECtt ELan EMan IPot LAst LSRN MBri MTis NCGa NLar SPoG SUsu WFar
- 'Russian Princess' misapplied purple-flowered	More than 30 suppliers
- 'Sparkle deVine'	CBow WFar
- 'Tania'	More than 30 suppliers
- Tresahor Series	CHEx
- 'Wildwood Splendor'	NBre WFar
- 'Will Scarlet'	EBrs EWin
§ - 'Vedrariensis'	More than 30 suppliers
tomentosa	EShb
treadwellii	see *Pratia angulata* 'Treadwellii'
tupa	More than 30 suppliers
- JCA 12527	LAst MBnl MTPN WCot
- Archibald's form	CPLG NRnb WGwG
- dark orange	SMrm
urens	WPGP
valida	CSpe EBee EWin LHop LPhx MBow SGar SPet SWvt WFar
vedrariensis	see *L.* x *gerardii* 'Vedrariensis'
White Star = 'Weslowei'PBR **new**	LAst
'Wildwood Splendour'	NBre WFar
'Will Scarlet'	EBrs EWin
'Zinnoberrosa'	see *L.* x *speciosa* 'Fan Zinnoberrosa'

Lobularia (Brassicaceae)

maritima	XPep

Loeselia (Polemoniaceae)

mexicana	CHll

loganberry see *Rubus* x *loganobaccus*

Loiseleuria (Ericaceae)

procumbens from Japan	GCrs

Lomandra (Lomandraceae)

confertifolia	ECou
hystrix	WCot
'Little Con'	CBcs
'Little Pal'	CBcs
longifolia	ECou GCal LEdu SPlb WCot
- 'Kulnura'	ECou
- 'Orford'	ECou
- 'Tanika' **new**	EPPr

Lomaria see *Blechnum*

Lomatia (Proteaceae)

ferruginea	CBcs CDoC CHEx CTrG EPfP SAPC SArc SBrw SSpi WCru
fraseri	EPfP LHop SSpi
longifolia	see *L. myricoides*
§ *myricoides*	CBcs CCCN CDoC CHEx CPSs CTrG CTrw EMil EPfP LRHS NLar SAPC SArc SLon SPoG SSpi WCMO WPGP
silaifolia	CDoC EPfP
§ *tinctoria*	CBcs CDoC CPSs CTrw EPfP LRHS NLar SArc SSpi

Lomatium (Apiaceae)

grayi	EMan
utriculatum	MSal

Lonicera ✿ (Caprifoliaceae)

B&SWJ 2654 from Sikkim	WCru
from China	WCru
KR 2471	EPla
PC&H 17A	SBra
SDR 2708	GKev

§ *acuminata* — CPlN GIBF IArd LEdu LRHS WGwG WPnP WSHC
- B&SWJ 3480 — WCru
alberti — GBin MBNS MRav SLon WGwG WHCG
albiflora — WSHC
alpigena — GIBF
alseuosmoides — CPlN CTrC EBee GBin IArd SAga SBra SLon SPla SPoG WCru WPGP WSHC WWeb
x *americana* misapplied — see *L.* x *italica*
§ x *americana* (Miller) K. Koch — CBcs CHad CRHN CWoW EPfP LRHS MAsh MGos NWea SDix SGar SLim SPla WMoo
§ x *brownii* 'Dropmore Scarlet' — More than 30 suppliers
- 'Fuchsioides' misapplied — see *L.* x *brownii* 'Dropmore Scarlet'
- 'Fuchsioides' hort. — NSti WSHC
caerulea — CMCN MRav STre WHCG
- var. *edulis* — CAgr GIBF LEdu
- subsp. *kamtschatica* — CAgr CMCN NLar
calcarata — CPlN
§ *caprifolium* ♀H4 — CBcs CDoC CFRD CRHN CWoW EBee ECtt ELan EPfP LBuc LFol LRHS MBar MLan NBea SBra SHBN SPer WCot
- 'Anna Fletcher' — CRHN CSPN MBNS NHaw SBra SLim WCFE
- 'Inga' — SBra
- f. *pauciflora* — see *L.* x *italica*
chaetocarpa — CPle
chamissoi — NLar
§ *chrysantha* — CMCN GIBF
'Clavey's Dwarf' — see *L.* x *xylosteoides* 'Clavey's Dwarf'
deflexicalyx — EPfP NLar
demissa — GIBF
'Early Cream' — see *L. caprifolium*
elisae — NLar WPat
etrusca — IDee LAst MRav WWeb XPep
- 'Donald Waterer' ♀H4 — CBgR CRHN EBee EPfP LHop LRHS SBra SCoo SPla WFar WGor
- 'Michael Rosse' — CBgR EBee ELan IArd LRHS MBNS MSte SBra SRms
- 'Superba' ♀H4 — CPlN CRHN EBee ECrN ECtt ELan EPfP LRHS MLLN SBra SEND SLim SPla WFar WSHC
flexuosa — see *L. japonica* var. *repens*
fragrantissima — More than 30 suppliers
gibbiflora Maxim. — see *L. chrysantha*
giraldii misapplied — see *L. acuminata*
giraldii Rehder — CFRD CPlN EBee EPfP MAsh NHol SBra SLim WCru
glabrata — CPlN LEdu SBra SCoo SLPl SLim
- B&SWJ 2150 — SBra WCru
'Golden Trumpet' **new** — EBee
gracilipes — GIBF
gracilis — MBlu
grata — see *L.* x *americana* (Miller) K. Koch
x *heckrottii* — CDoC CFRD CMac CRHN CSBt EBee ECtt MBar MGan MGos NBea NBlu NSti WDin
- 'Gold Flame' hort. — More than 30 suppliers
§ *henryi* — More than 30 suppliers
- B&SWJ 8109 — WCru
- 'Copper Beauty' — CFir COtt LAst MAsh MBlu MGos NCGa SPoG SVil WDin WPGP
- var. *subcoriacea* — see *L. henryi*
hildebrandiana — CPlN EMil ERea EShb SBra SOWG WPGP XPep
'Hill House' — CHll
'Honey Baby'^PBR — EBee EBrs MAsh MBlu MBri MGos MRav NHol SBra SPoG WPat

implexa — EHol MAsh NHol NPro SBra WSHC XPep
insularis — see *L. morrowii*
involucrata — CFee CMCN CMHG CPLG CPMA CPle CWib GQui LHop MBNS MBar MBlu MRav NHol SMac SPoG WCFE WDin WFar
- var. *ledebourii* — CBgR CPle EBee ELan EPfP LAst NHol SDys WTel
x *italica* ambig. — CHad LFol LHop NBea NPer SBra SEND SLPl SReu SSta
x *italica* Tausch ♀H4 — CBcs CBgR CFRD CMac CRHN CSam CWSG ECtt ELan LAst LFol MBri MRav MWgw NPer NSti SBra SLim SPer WDin WFar WPnn WTel
- Harlequin = 'Sherlite'^PBR (v) — CDul CSPN ECtt ELan ENot EPfP LAst LHop LRHS LSRN MGos NBea NCGa NSti SBra SGar SLim SPer SPlb SPoG SWvt WCot WWeb
* *jaluana* — GIBF
japonica — CCVT
- 'Aureoreticulata' (v) — More than 30 suppliers
- 'Cream Cascade' — CWoW EBee LAst MGos MLLN
- 'Dart's Acumen' — CRHN
- 'Dart's World' — CFRD EBee MAsh NHol SPla WFar
- 'Halliana' ♀H4 — More than 30 suppliers
- 'Hall's Prolific' — More than 30 suppliers
§ - 'Horwood Gem' — CFRD CWoW EBee ECrN ECtt LFol MGos NHol NPro SBra SCoo WFar
- 'Mint Crisp'^PBR (v) — CBgR CFwr CSBt EBee ELan ENor EPfP LAst LRHS LSRN MAsh MBri MGos MWgw NLar SHGC SMur SPer SPoG SWvt WDin WFar WMoo
- 'Peter Adams' — see *L. japonica* 'Horwood Gem'
- 'Red World' — EBee
§ - var. *repens* ♀H4 — More than 30 suppliers
- 'Variegata' — see *L. japonica* 'Aureoreticulata'
jarmilae **new** — EHyt
korolkowii — CBgR CPMA CSam CWoW EBee EPfP LRHS MBNS MBri NBir SLon SPla WHCG WLeb WSHC
- var. *zabelii* misapplied — see *L. tatarica* 'Zabelii'
- var. *zabelii* (Rehder) Rehder — ELan
maackii — CHll CMCN CPMA EPfP GIBF MRav MWhi NLar WHCG
* *macgregorii* — CMCN
macrantha **new** — CPlN
'Mandarin' — CDoC CWSG EBee ELan ENot EPfP LRHS MAsh MBNS MBlu MGos MRav MWgw NCGa SBra SCoo SPer SPoG SSta SWvt
maximowiczii — GIBF
- var. *sachalinensis* — NLar
modesta var. *lushenensis* — CPMA
§ *morrowii* — CMCN GIBF
nervosa — GIBF
nitida — CBcs CCVT CDul CSBt CTri ECrN EPfP MRav NBlu NWea SHBN SPer SPoG STre WBVN WDin WFar WHar WHen
- 'Baggesen's Gold' ♀H4 — More than 30 suppliers
- 'Cumbrian Calypso' (v) — NPro
- 'Eden Spring' — NPro
- Edmée Gold = 'Briloni' — MBri
- 'Elegant' — LBuc WDin
- 'Ernest Wilson' — MBar
- 'Fertilis' — SPer
- 'Hohenheimer Findling' — NLar WDin
- 'Lemon Beauty' (v) — More than 30 suppliers
- 'Lemon Queen' — CWib ELan MSwo
- 'Lemon Spreader' — CBcs LBuc

§ - 'Maigrün'	CBcs EGra EMil EPfP LBuc MBri MSwo NPro SPer SWvt WDin WFar
- Maygreen	see *L. nitida* 'Maigrün'
- 'Red Tips'	CWan EBee EHoe EPfP EPla LRHS MBNS MGos NHol WDin WFar WMoo WWeb
- 'Silver Beauty' (v)	More than 30 suppliers
* - 'Silver Cloud'	NHol
- 'Silver Lining'	see *L. pileata* 'Silver Lining'
- 'Silver Queen'	WEas
- 'Twiggy' (v)	CDoC EMil LBuc LHop MAsh MBri NHol NPro WCot WLeb WRHF
nummulariifolia	XPep
periclymenum	CArn CDul CRWN CTri GPoy MDun MHer NFor NSco NWea SHFr SPlb WDin WHCG WPnn WSFF WWye
- 'Belgica' misapplied	see *L. x italica*
§ - 'Belgica'	More than 30 suppliers
- 'Cream Cloud'	SBra
- 'Florida'	see *L. periclymenum* 'Serotina'
- 'Graham Thomas' ♀H4	More than 30 suppliers
- 'Heaven Scent'	CWoW LBuc MNHC SBra WFar WPnn
- 'Honeybush'	CDoC CPMA CPle CSPN MAsh MBlu MTis NHol NPri SLim WMoo WWeb
- 'La Gasnaérie'	SBra SLim WPnn
- 'Munster'	CFRD CWoW MBri SBra WPnn WSHC
- 'Red Gables'	CFRD CSam CWan CWoW EBee MBNS MBri MGos MRav MSte MWgw NHol SBra SCoo SEND SLim SPla WCMO WCot WGor WKif WPat WPnn
- 'Scentsation' new	MAsh MBri
N - 'Serotina' ♀H4	More than 30 suppliers
- - EM '85	ENot
* - *sulphurea*	WFar
- 'Sweet Sue'	CBgR CRHN CSPN CWoW EBee ECtt ELan EPfP GCal LAst LBuc LFol LRHS MAsh MBNS MGos MLHP MLan MSte NCGa NEgg NSti SBra SCoo SPoG SWvt WFar WMoo WPnP WWeb
- 'Winchester'	EBee
pileata	CBcs CCVT CDul CSBt CTri EBee ECrN ELan EPfP LBuc LRHS MBar MRav MSwo NBlu NFor NHol NPer NWea SPer SPoG SRms STre WBVN WCFE WDin WFar WHar WTel
- 'Moss Green'	CDoC EBee
- 'Pilot'	SLPl
§ - 'Silver Lining' (v)	EPla GBuc SAga
- 'Stockholm'	SLPl
pilosa Willd.	CPIN
- CD&R 1216	SBra
x *purpusii*	CBgR CDoC CPSs CRHN CTri CWSG CWib EBee ECrN EPfP EWTr LAst MBNS MBar MGos MSwo NBea SLim SPer SPla SRms WFar WHCG WHar WSHC WTel
- 'Winter Beauty' ♀H4	More than 30 suppliers
pyrenaica	CPle
quinquelocularis f. *translucens*	GIBF MBlu
ramosissima	NLar
rupicola var. *syringantha*	see *L. syringantha*
saccata	CPMA EPfP
sempervirens ♀H4	CPIN CRHN CSBt EBee EPfP MBNS MRav NBea SBra WFar WSHC
- 'Dropmore Scarlet'	see *L. x brownii* 'Dropmore Scarlet'
- 'Leo'	CSPN

N - f. *sulphurea*	CPIN EBee EPfP LRHS NBea SBra WSHC
- - 'John Clayton'	SBra
setifera	CPle
- 'Daphnis'	EPfP
similis var. *delavayi* ♀H4	CPIN CRHN CSPN CSam EBee ECrN ELan EPfP LRHS MAsh MBri MLan MRav NBea NSti NVic SBra SDix SEND SLPl SPla SPoG WCru WFar WPGP WSHC
'Simonet'	EBee SBra
splendida	SBra
standishii	CBcs CTri EBee EHol MGos MRav SPer WDin WFar WHCG WRha
- 'Budapest'	MBlu MBri MGos NEgg WPat
stenantha	NLar
'Stone Green'	MGos SPoG
subequalis	CPIN WPGP
§ *syringantha*	More than 30 suppliers
- 'Grandiflora'	GQui SLon WAbe
tatarica	CMCN CWib EBee MRav MWhi WBVN WFar WHCG WTel
- 'Alba'	CPMA
- 'Arnold Red'	CBcs EBee ELan EMil EPfP EWTr MBlu MHer NBlu WDin WTel XPep
- 'Hack's Red'	CBcs CWib EBee EHol EPfP GQui LHop LSou MRav MWea SAga SWvt WCot WDin WFar WHCG
§ - 'Zabelii'	EPfP MGos
x *tellmanniana*	More than 30 suppliers
- 'Joan Sayer'	EBee MBNS MBri SBra SCoo SLim WCFE WWeb
thibetica	GIBF MBlu SPer WFar
tianschanica	GIBF
tragophylla ♀H4	CBcs CDoC CPIN CSBt EBee ELan EPfP GCal IDee LRHS MAsh MBNS MBlu MBri MRav NSti SBra SCoo SLim SPer SPoG SSpi SWvt WDin WSHC
- 'Maurice Foster'	EBee SBra
* - 'Pharoah's Trumpet'	ERea LRHS MAsh MBri SSpi SSta
trichosantha var. *acutiuscula*	GIBF
webbiana	ELan
x *xylosteoides*	MRav WFar
§ - 'Clavey's Dwarf'	MBlu SLPl
xylosteum	CArn NLar WFar

Lopezia (Onagraceae)
racemosa	CSpe SHFr

Lophatherum (Poaceae)
gracile	CPLG WDyG

Lophomyrtus (Myrtaceae)
§ *bullata*	CAbP ECou GQui IDee SPer WCHb WFar
- 'Matai Bay'	CBcs CTrC EBee
§ *obcordata*	ISea
§ x *ralphii*	IDee MHer SBrw WCHb WPic
- 'Gloriosa' (v)	CDoC CPle SBrw
§ - 'Kathryn'	CBcs CDoC CPLG CPle EBee ISea NLar SBrw SPoG SSpi
- 'Little Star' (v)	CBcs CDoC CTrC GBri LRHS MAsh SBrw SPoG WPat
- 'Multicolor' (v)	CBcs CTrC
- 'Pixie'	CAbP CBcs CDoC CTrC SBrw SPoG WPat
- 'Red Dragon'	CBcs CTrC EBee GBri IDee LSou MAsh SBrw WFar WPat
- 'Red Pixie' new	CDoC
- 'Sundae' (v)	CPLG
§ - 'Traversii' (v)	LRHS SMur SPoG
- 'Tricolor' (v)	CPle WFar
- 'Variegata' (v)	MHer
- 'Wild Cherry'	CBcs CTrC

Lophospermum (Scrophulariaceae)

§ **erubescens** ♀H2-3   CHEx CHal CRHN EBee EUnu MOak MSte MTis SBch SGar SHFr SMur WPtf
   'Magic Dragon'   MCCP WHil
§   'Red Dragon'   CSpe SBch SGar
§ **scandens**   CRHN ELan SMur
§   - 'Pink Ice'   SOWG

loquat see *Eriobotrya japonica*

Loropetalum (Hamamelidaceae)

   chinense   CMCN CPen CWib CWoW SSpi
   - 'Ming Dynasty'   CPen MAsh MPRe
   - f. **rubrum**   CMen CPLG CWib WMul
   - - 'Blush'   CPMA CWoW
   - - 'Burgundy'   CBcs WCMO WCot
   - - 'Daybreak's Flame'   CPMA CPen SBrw SPoG WGob
   - - 'Fire Dance'   CAbP CBcs CDoC CHll CPMA CPen IDee MGos SBrw SPoG SSpi SWvt WBrE WFar WGwG
   - - 'Pipa's Red'   CPen SPoG
   - - 'Zhuzhou Fuchsia'   CMCN CWoW
   - 'Snowdance'   CAbP
   - 'Tang Dynasty'   CPen MPRe SBrw

Lotus (Papilionaceae)

   berthelotii   CCCN CFee CHEx CSpe CWCL ECtt ELan EOHP ERea EWin MOak SBrw SPet SPoG
   - deep red ♀H1+3   LLck SWvt
   - 'Gold Fish'   CHEx
   berthelotii x **maculatus**   EShb EWll LAst NPri
   'Fire Vine'
   corniculatus   CArn GWCH MBow MCoo MHer NLan NMir NSco NTHB SECG SIde WBri WSFF XPep
   - 'Plenus' (d)   MTho NLar WPer
   creticus   SHFr
   cytisoides   XPep
   'Gold Flash'   LAst
§ **hirsutus** ♀H3-4   More than 30 suppliers
   - 'Brimstone' (v)   CWib ECtt EGoo EPPr EWin LHop LRHS LSou SBrw SPer SWvt WCot
   - dwarf   LHop SBrw
   - 'Fréjorgues'   XPep
   - 'Lois'   EBee MDKP MWgw WSPU
   maculatus   CWCL EOHP EWin SHFr SOWG SPet
   maritimus   EBee EWll LPhx SHFr SRot
   mascaensis misapplied   see *L. sessilifolius*
   pedunculatus   see *L. uliginosus*
   pentaphyllus   XPep
   - subsp. **herbaceus**   XPep
§   - subsp. **pentaphyllus**   EChP
   'Red Flash'   LAst
§ **sessilifolius**   ERea
   suffruticosus   see *L. pentaphyllus* subsp. *pentaphyllus*
   tetragonolobus   SRot
§ **uliginosus**   CAgr NMir NSco WSFF

lovage see *Levisticum officinale*

Ludwigia (Onagraceae)

   grandiflora   WDyG WMAq WWpP
   uruguayensis   LPBA

Luetkea (Rosaceae)

   pectinata   NRya

Luma (Myrtaceae)

§ **apiculata** ♀H3   More than 30 suppliers
§ - 'Glanleam Gold' (v)   More than 30 suppliers
   ♀H3

   - 'Variegata' (v)   CMHG CTri ISea SAga SLim WCru WWye
§ **chequen**   CBcs CFee GGar IDee LEdu MHer NLar WBrE WCHb WCwm WFar WJek WMoo WPic XPep

Lunaria (Brassicaceae)

§ **annua**   GAbr GWCH MBow MNHC MWgw SIde SWat WHer WSFF
   - var. **albiflora** ♀H4   MWgw NBir SWat
I   - - 'Alba Variegata' (v)   CCge CSpe EMar MHer MWgw WHil WTin
   - 'Luckington' **new**   CNat
*   - 'Stella'   WHen
   - 'Variegata' (v)   IBlr MCCP MTho NBir SWat WEas WHer WSan
   - violet   NBir WFar
   biennis   see *L. annua*
   rediviva   CCge EBee ECGP ECha EMon EPPr EPla GAbr GCal GGar IBlr IFro LRHS MRav NBid NPer NSti SMeo SUsu WCot WEas WFar WHen WHer WPGP
   - 'Partway White'   CMil

Lupinus ✿ (Papilionaceae)

   'African Sunset'   CWCL
   albifrons   MWgw XPep
   'Amber Glow'   CWCL
   'Approaching Storm'   SMrm
   'Apricot Spire'   CWCL
   arboreus ♀H4   More than 30 suppliers
   - **albus**   CSpe CWib NRnb SHGN
   - 'Barton-on-Sea'   CBgR CSec EWin NLar NRnb SPla SPoG
   - blue   CBgR CBrm CFwr CHar CSec CWCL CWib EBee ECGP ERou EWTr GBBs MCCP MNHC NLar NPri SEND SPer SPlb SPoG SWvt WBVN WFar WHer
   - 'Blue Boy'   ELan SPla
   - cream   ECGP
   - 'Mauve Queen'   CHEx CSec EWin NLar NRnb SHGN SSvw
   - mixed   CArn SPet
   - prostrate   EWin MDKP MMHG
   - 'Snow Queen'   CBrm CFwr CSec CWCL EWin MCCP NBur NLar SPoG
   - 'Sulphur Yellow'   ERou EWin SHGN SWvt
   - white   CWCL CWib WOut
   - yellow **new**   MLHP
   - yellow and blue   SRkn
   arboreus x **variicolor**   WGwG
   arcticus   CSpe EBee GKev
   'Aston Villa'   CWCL
   'Avalon'   CWCL
   'Baby Doll'   CWCL
   Band of Nobles Series   ECtt NJOw WFar
   ♀H4
   'Beryl, Viscountess   EMon
   Cowdray'
   bicolor   CSec
   'Bishop's Tipple'   CWCL EWes
   'Blue Moon'   CWCL
   'Blue Streak'   CWCL
   'Blueberry Pie'   CWCL
   'Bruiser'   CWCL
   'Bubblegum'   CWCL
   'Captain Scarlet'   CWCL
   'Casanova'   CWCL
   'Cashmere Cream'   CWCL
   chamissonis   CHll CSec CSpe CWCL EBee EChP EHrv EMan EWes LHop LRHS MTho MTis SGar SPer SPla SPoG WFar WPtf

'Chandelier'   CBcs CHad CSBt CTri EBee ECtt
                          ELan ENot EPfP ERou LRHS MBri
                          MRav MWat MWgw NBPC NEgg
                          NMir SMer SPer SPoG SWal SWvt
                          WBVN WCAu WFar WHen WMnd
                          WWeb
'Cherry Belle'   CWCL
'Copperlight'   CWCL
'Desert Sun'   CWCL
'Dolly Mixture'   CWCL
'Dreaming Spires'   CWCL
'Dwarf Lulu'   see *L.* 'Lulu'
Gallery Series   CSBt ENot LAst SCoo SPlb WFar
- 'Gallery Blue'   CBrm ECtt EPfP GAbr LSRN LSou
                          NCGa NDlv NLar NNor NPri NVic
                          SCoo SPer SPoG SWal WFar WHil
- 'Gallery Pink'   EPfP LRHS LSou NCGa NDlv NLar
                          NPri NVic SCoo SPer SPla SPoG
                          SWal WFar WHil
- 'Gallery Red'   CBrm ECtt ENot EPfP GAbr LRHS
                          MLHP NBlu NCGa NDlv NLar NPri
                          NVic SCoo SPer SPla SPoG SWal
                          WFar WHil
- 'Gallery Rose'   LSRN
- 'Gallery White'   CBrm ENot EPfP GAbr LRHS NBlu
                          NDlv NLar NPri NVic SCoo SPer
                          SPla SPoG SWal WFar WHil
- 'Gallery Yellow'   CBrm ECtt EPfP GAbr LRHS LSou
                          NBlu NCGa NDlv NLar NPri NVic
                          SCoo SPer SPla SPoG SWal WHil
'Garden Gnome'   LRav WMoo
'Heather Glow'   NLar
'Ivory Chiffon' **new**   CWCL
'Lady Penelope'   CWCL
littoralis   CSec NRnb
§ 'Lulu'   COtt ECtt ENot LAst LRHS MRav
                          MWat NBlu SPer SPoG SWvt WFar
                          WMoo WRHF
'Manhattan Lights'   CWCL
Minarette Group   CBrm CTri ECtt SGar SPet SPoG
                          SRms WFar
'Mrs Perkins'   SMrm
mutabilis   NRnb
'My Castle'   More than 30 suppliers
'Noble Maiden' (Band of   CBcs CSBt CTri EBee EChP ECtt
  Nobles Series)   ELan EPfP ERou LRHS LSRN MBri
                          MRav MWat MWgw MWrn NBPC
                          NBlu NEgg NMir SPer SPoG SWal
                          SWvt WCAu WFar WHen WMnd
                          WMoo WWeb
nootkatensis   EBrs LDai MNFA
'Pauly' **new**   CWCL
perennis   CAgr
'Persian Slipper' **new** CWCL
'Pink Cadillac'   CWCL
'Plum Duff'   CWCL
'Plummy Blue'   EDif LSou MCCP MWea
'Polar Princess'   CWCL ERou EWes SWat
polyphyllus   CSec EBee MWgw WOut
propinquus   CSec
'Queen of Hearts'   CWCL
'Rainbow Select'   NRnb
'Red Arrow'   CWCL
'Red Rum' **new**   CWCL
x *regalis* 'Morello   CWib MWrn WHil
  Cherry'
'Rote Flamme'   EWes
'Ruby Lantern'   CWCL
Russell hybrids   CSBt ELan ENot EPfP LAst LHop
                          MHer MNHC NBlu SECG SPet SPlb
                          SRms SWvt WFar
'Saffron'   CWCL
'Saint George'   CWCL
'Salmon Star' **new**   CWCL
'Sand Pink'   CWCL EWes
'Sherbert Dip'   CWCL

'Silk Rain'   CWCL
'Snowgoose'   CWCL
'Sparky'   CWCL
'Storm'   CWCL
subcarnosus   SRkn
'Tequila Flame' **new**   CWCL
'Terracotta'   CWCL
texensis   CSpe
'The Chatelaine' (Band of CBcs CSBt EBee ECtt ELan EPfP
  Nobles Series)   ERou LRHS LSRN MBri MNHC
                          MRav MWat MWgw NBPC NBlu
                          NEgg NMir SPer SPoG SWal SWvt
                          WBVN WBor WCAu WFar WHen
                          WMnd WMoo WWeb
'The Governor' (Band of   More than 30 suppliers
  Nobles Series)
'The Page' (Band of   CBcs EBee ELan EPfP ERou LRHS
  Nobles Series)   LSRN MBri MNHC MRav MWat
                          MWgw NBPC NEgg NMir SPer
                          SPoG SWal SWvt WBVN WFar
                          WMnd WMoo WWeb
'Thor'   CWCL
'Thundercloud'   SMrm
'Tutti Frutti' **new**   WHil WRos
variicolor   CSpe
versicolor   CSec CSpe EMan GBBs LDai
                          MEHN MHer MLLN WBrk WHoo
                          WPtf
- 'Dumpty'   LSou

Lutzia (Brassicaceae)
cretica   XPep

Luzula ✿ (Juncaceae)
from New Guinea   EWes
alpinopilosa   CBig EPPr GBin
x *borreri*   EPPr
- 'Botany Bay' (v)   ECtt EPPr EPla GBin WMoo
canariensis   WWye
forsteri   CBgR EPPr
lactea   EPPr
luzuloides   CBig GQui NBre NLar WPer
- 'Schneehäschen'   EBrs EMan EMon EPPr GBin GCal
                          MWgw
maxima   see *L. sylvatica*
nivalis   GAbr
nivea   More than 30 suppliers
pilosa   CBgR EPla GCal NNor
- 'Igel'   GBin SLPl
purpureosplendens   EMon
'Ruby Stiletto'   EBee WPtf
rufa   ECou
§ *sylvatica*   CHEx CRWN CRow CSWP ELan
                          EPPr EPfP EPla MBow MLLN
                          MMoz MRav NBro NOrc WDin
                          WFar WHer WPGP WShi
- from Tatra Mountains,   EPPr
  Czechoslovakia
- 'A. Rutherford'   see *L. sylvatica* 'Taggart's Cream'
- 'Aurea'   CHEx CHar CHrt CKno CSWP
                          EBrs ECha ECrN EHul EPGN EPPr
                          EPfP EPla GCal LAst LRHS MBar
                          MBri MMoz MRav NBid NSti SPla
                          STre WCMO WCot WLeb WMoo
                          WPat WWye
- 'Aureomarginata'   see *L. sylvatica* 'Marginata'
I - 'Auslese'   CBig EPPr GBin NNor SMar WMoo
- 'Barcode' (v)   CNat
- 'Hohe Tatra'   More than 30 suppliers
§ - 'Marginata' (v)   More than 30 suppliers
* - f. *nova*   EPPr
- 'Select'   GCal
§ - 'Taggart's Cream' (v) CElw CRow EBee EBrs EHoe EMar
                          EPla GGar MAvo NBid NHol
                          WDyG WLeb WMoo WPrP
- 'Tatra Gold'   SMad

- 'Tauernpass'	CBgR EHoe EPPr EPla GCal NBid NHol SMac
- 'Wäldler'	EHoe EPPr MBNS NHol
- 'Waulkmill Bay'	SLPl
ulophylla	CBig CFir CTrC ECou GEdr NBre NLar NWCA

Luzuriaga (Philesiaceae)

radicans	CFee ERos IBlr WCru WFar WSHC
- MK 92	SSpi

Lychnis (Caryophyllaceae)

alpina	CMHG EBee ECho EPfP GIBF GKev IHMH NBlu NEgg NJOw NNor NPri NVic SBch WFar WPer
- 'Alba'	GKev NBir
- 'Rosea'	NBir
- 'Snow Flurry'	GKev NCGa NLar
- 'Snowflake'	EWTr
§ x *arkwrightii*	ECha ELan NBre NNor SRot WFar
- 'Orange Zwerg'	CBct CBrm EBee LAst LSou NEgg WHal WWeb
- 'Vesuvius'	CBcs EAEE EBee ENot EPfP LAst LRHS MNrw MWgw NBir NBlu NLRH NNor SPav SPer SPoG SRms STes WMnd WPer
* 'Blushing Bride'	ENot
chalcedonica ♀H4	More than 30 suppliers
- var. *albiflora*	CAby EAEE EBee LAst LRHS MBri MWgw NBro SPer WBrk WFar WHen WMoo WPer WWpP
- - 'Snow White'	ECtt SMer
- 'Carnea'	EBrs EShb EWsh GCal NBre WBrk WPer
- 'Dusky Pink'	LSou MBow MWhi WRHF
- 'Dusky Salmon'	EWTr ITer MDKP NBPC NDlv WWpP
- 'Flore Pleno' (d)	EBee ECha ELan ERou EShb GCal IFro MLLN NLar NPri WCot WFar
- 'Morgenrot'	EChP MCCP NLar NNor
- 'Pinkie'	ELan NLar SBod WLin
- 'Rauhreif'	EBee EChP EShb NBre
- 'Rosea'	CAby EBee EBrs EPfP Llck NBir SMHy SMar WFar WHen WHrl WMoo WPer WRHF
* - 'Salmonea'	ECtt GBri MTis NBir SRms WCAu
- salmon-pink	COIW WWhi
- 'Summer Sparkle Pink'	SWal
- 'Summer Sparkle Red'	SWal
- 'Summer Sparkle White'	SWal
cognata	CDes EBee GMac MDKP
- B&SWJ 4234	WCru
§ *coronaria* ♀H4	More than 30 suppliers
- 'Abbotswood Rose'	see *L.* x *walkeri* 'Abbotswood Rose'
- 'Alba' ♀H4	More than 30 suppliers
- 'Angel's Blush'	EBee GAbr MBnl MDKP MRav NBir SPav SPer WMow WRha
- Atrosanguinea Group	CAby CBre EAEE EBee ERou GMaP IBlr LRHS MBnl MRav NCot NEgg NPri SPer SPoG
- 'Cerise'	MArl MDKP NBir
- 'Dancing Ladies'	ENot WMnd
- 'Flottbek'	NLar
- Gardeners' World = 'Blych' (d)	LPhx
- 'Hutchinson's Cream' (v)	NPro WCHb
- Oculata Group	CAby CMHG CSpe EBee ECtt EGoo ERou LEdu MBow MTho NLRH NOak NPri NSti SECG SGar SMer SPav SPlb SPoG SWal WFar WHen WMoo
§ *coronata* var. *sieboldii*	NBre
dioica	see *Silene dioica*
flos-cuculi	More than 30 suppliers
- var. *albiflora*	CBre EBee EMFW EMag GBar LPBA MBow MLLN NBro NLar SSvw WCHb WHer WMnd WMoo WOut WWpP
- Jenny = 'Lychjen' (d)	GBri SPer
* - 'Little Robin'	ECho EDAr NHol
- 'Nana'	CSpe ECho EDAr GAbr NLar NRya WPer
- 'White Robin' **new**	CBod LBMP NPri
flos-jovis ♀H4	CAby CEnt CSec EAEE EBee EPfP EWTr ITim NLar NPri SBch SRms WMoo WPer
- 'Hort's Variety'	EBrs MRav SBla WRos WSHC
- 'Minor'	see *L. flos-jovis* 'Nana'
§ - 'Nana'	IFro NBid NWCA
- 'Peggy'	CMMP EGoo LRHS MCCP NBre NCGa NLar WWeb
fulgens	NBre
gracillima	CSec
x *haageana*	EBee LRHS NBre NLar NWCA SRms
'Hill Grounds'	MAvo WCot
lagascae	see *Petrocoptis pyrenaica* subsp. *glaucifolia*
miqueliana	NBre NLar WGwG WMoo
- 'Variegated Lacy Red' (v)	EBee
'Molten Lava'	CFir EBee ECho LRHS MHer MRav NBre NLar SGar WPer WWeb
nutans	MSal
preslii minor	EBee
* *sikkimensis*	EBee NBre
'Terry's Pink'	EBee MLLN NCGa WFar WHil
§ *viscaria*	CArn CEnt ECha GIBF IHMH LBMP LDai MSal NCiC NFor NNor SBch SGar SHGN WCot WFar WHer WMoo WTin
- 'Alba'	CBrm EBee ECha GCal MLLN NBre NBro NNor WRha
- *alpina*	see *L. viscaria*
§ - subsp. *atropurpurea*	EBee EChP ECtt LRav LSou NBre NJOw NLRH SRms SSvw WHrl WOut
- 'Feuer'	CBrm EBee EBrs NCGa NEgg NLar NVic SPet WMoo WRHF
- 'Firebird'	EWes ITim MWhi NBre NBur
- 'Plena' (d)	EBee EChP MDun NEgg WSan WTin
- 'Schnee'	CPrp EBrs MSte NVic
- 'Splendens'	EPfP IHMH MNFA SPet
- 'Splendens Plena' (d) ♀H4	CAby CHar EBee GMac MArl MWgw NBre NBro SBla WEas WFar
- 'White Cloud'	MSph
§ x *walkeri* 'Abbotswood Rose' ♀H4	GBuc IBlr WBrk
wilfordii	EShb NEgg SHar
§ *yunnanensis*	EBee GKev LPhx MSte NBid NHol NJOw SIng SPav WMoo WPer
- alba	see *L. yunnanensis*

Lycianthes (Solanaceae)

rantonnetii	see *Solanum rantonnetii*

Lycium (Solanaceae)

barbarum	EUnu EWes NBlu SMad
chinense	CArn NLar
cf. *cinereum*	EUnu
europaeum	XPep

Lycopodium (Lycopodiaceae)

clavatum	GPoy

Lycopsis see *Anchusa*

Lycopus (Lamiaceae)

americanus	EBee GPoy MSal

europaeus	CArn EBee ELau GBar GPoy MBow MHer MSal WBri WGwG WHer WWye
lucidus	MSal
virginicus	COld MSal SDys WWye

Lycoris (Amaryllidaceae)

albiflora	ECho WCot
aurea	EBee ECho LRHS MOak WCMO WHil
haywardii	WCot
radiata	EBee ECho GSki LRHS MOak WCMO WHil
sanguinea	ECho LRHS
sprengeri	ECho WCMO WCot
squamigera	EBee ECho LRHS WCMO WHil

Lygodium (Schizaeaceae)

japonicum	NBid WFib

Lygos see *Retama*

Lyonia (Ericaceae)

ligustrina	LRHS NLar
mariana	NLar

Lyonothamnus (Rosaceae)

floribundus subsp.	CAbb CCCN CDoC CPLG CPSs
aspleniifolius	EBee EWTr SAPC SArc SGar SMad SSpi WFar WPGP

Lysichiton (Araceae)

americanus ♀H4	More than 30 suppliers
americanus x *camtschatcensis*	SSpi
camtschatcensis ♀H4	CBcs CBen CFwr CLAP CRow CWat EBee ECha EHon ELan EMFW EPfP GAbr GIBF ITer LNCo LPBA MDun NEgg NOrc NPer SMad SPer SSpi SWat SWvt WCot WFar WPnP

Lysimachia ✿ (Primulaceae)

BWJ 8072 from China	WCru
B&SWJ 8632 from Korea	WCru
atropurpurea	CArn CHad CHar CSpe EAro EBee EChP EGle ELan ENot EPfP EShb LHop LRHS MHer MNFA NSti SMad SMar SPer SPlb SPoG STes WCot WFar WMnd WRos
- 'Beaujolais'	CBod CEnt LSRN MBNS NPri SMeo SPav WSan WWeb WWhi WWlt WWpP
- 'Geronimo'	CSpe
barystachys	CHea CRow EBee GMac MGol MRav MWrn SHar SMac SMer WFar WOut
candida	WCot
ciliata	CMHG CPLG ECha EHoe ELan GMaP MNrw NEgg NFor NGdn NSti SWat WCAu WCot WFar WMnd WPer
§ - 'Firecracker' ♀H4	More than 30 suppliers
- 'Purpurea'	see *L. ciliata* 'Firecracker'
clethroides ♀H4	More than 30 suppliers
- 'Geisha' (v)	EBee MBNS NLar WCot
- 'Lady Jane'	CBrm MWrn NBur SRms
§ *congestiflora*	NPer SHFr SPet
- 'Golden Falls'	LAst NEgg
- 'Outback Sunset'PBR (v)	ECtt EWin LAst NBlu NPri
decurrens	EBee
– JCA 4.542.500	WCot
ephemerum	More than 30 suppliers
fortunei	EBee IHMH MWat SMac
henryi	EWes

hybrida	EBee WCot
japonica var. *minutissima*	CFee CRow CStu NLar
lichiangensis	CPLG EBee GSki MBNS MGol MLLN NRnb SGar SHFr WMoo WPer
lyssii	see *L. congestiflora*
mauritiana	EBee EWin
- B&SWJ 8815	WCru
melampyroides	WCot
minoricensis	CArn EBee EEls EHrv ELan EMan EWin IHMH SWat WPer
nemorum	MBow WPer
- 'Pale Star'	CBgR CBre WWye
nummularia	CHal COfd COlW CSBt CTri CWat ECtt EHon EPfP EShb GPoy IHMH LNCo LPBA MBar MBow NFor SHFr SWat WBrk WCot WWpP WWye
- 'Aurea' ♀H4	More than 30 suppliers
paridiformis	WCot
- var. *stenophylla*	EBee WCot WPGP
- - DJHC 704	CDes
punctata misapplied	see *L. verticillaris*
punctata L.	More than 30 suppliers
§ - 'Alexander' (v)	More than 30 suppliers
- 'Golden Alexander' (v)	CBct EChP EKen MBNS MBnl NEgg NLar SPer SPoG
- 'Golden Glory' (v)	WCot WWpP
- 'Ivy Maclean' (v)	CRez EBee EChP EMan EWin LSou SWvt WCot WWpP
- 'Senior'	EMil
- 'Sunspot'	EBee WWpP
- 'Variegata'	see *L. punctata* 'Alexander'
- *verticillata*	see *L. verticillaris*
pyramidalis new	CPLG
quadrifolia new	EBee
serpyllifolia	ECtt
Snow Candles = 'L9902' new	LAst LSou
taliensis BWJ 7797 new	WCru
thyrsiflora	EBee EHon EMFW IHMH LNCo NPer SWat WCot WHer WMAq WWpP
§ *verticillaris*	WCot
vulgaris	CArn CRWN LPBA MBow NSco SIde WCot WFar WMoo WPer WWpP WWye
- subsp. *davurica*	WCot
yunnanensis	CDMG CPLG EBee EKen EMan EPPr LSou MDKP MGol MHar NRnb SGar WCot WPer WPtf WWpP WWye

Lysionotus (Gesneriaceae)

* *carniolica*	CStu
gamosepalus B&SWJ 7241	WCru
aff. *kwangsiensis* HWJ 643	WCru
'Lavender Lady'	CSpe
pauciflorus	CDes ETow
- B&SWJ 189	WCru
- B&SWJ 303	WCru
- B&SWJ 335	WCru

Lythrum (Lythraceae)

alatum	EShb MGol NBre SMar WWpP
anceps	LPhx NBre NLar SMar
salicaria	More than 30 suppliers
- 'Blush' ♀H4	More than 30 suppliers
- 'Brightness'	CDWL
§ - 'Feuerkerze' ♀H4	CDWL CKno CMea CPrp CRow CSec CWCL EBee ECtt EGle ELan EPfP ERou GCal LAst LHop LRHS

MRav NBir NDov NEgg NHol NSti
NVic SAga SPer SPla WFar WPer
WTel
- Firecandle   see *L. salicaria* 'Feuerkerze'
- 'Happy'   SMrm
- 'Lady Sackville'   CAby CBos CDWL EBee GBuc
                           GMaP LRHS MBNS NDov SSvw
                           SUsu WCAu WTMC WTel
- 'Morden Pink'   EBee EChP EGle LPhx MBri MDKP
                           MSte NCob NGby WFar WPtf
                           WSHC
- 'Prichard's Variety'   CKno EBee WPGP
- 'Red Gem'   NEgg
- 'Robert'   More than 30 suppliers
- 'Robin' **new**   EBee
- 'Rose'   ELan MWgw NBir NEgg SWvt
- 'Rosencaule'   EBee
- 'Stichflamme'   NCob
- 'Swirl'   EBee ECtt MDKP NBre NDov WFar
                           WWpP
- 'The Beacon'   CMHG EBee EMan GCal MDKP
                           SRms
- 'Zigeunerblut'   CMHG EBee EGle LPhx MDKP
                           MRav MSte NGby NLar SWat
                           WWpP
virgatum   CMHG LPhx NDov SMHy SUsu
                           WOut WSHC
- 'Dropmore Purple'   CDWL CHar COlW CSBt EBee
                           EChP ERou LHop LPhx LRHS
                           MBri MDKP MSte NDov SAga
                           SMer WCAu WFar WHlf WPtf
                           WWpP
- 'Rose Queen'   ECha EMan MDKP MRav NDov
                           SMHy WFar WPer
- 'Rosy Gem'   CMMP CWan EBee ECtt EPfP
                           GMaP GMac MBNS MWat MWgw
                           MWhi NBid NBro NOak SECG
                           SRGP SRms SWal SWvt WFar
                           WGHP WHoo WPer WViv WWeb
                           WWpP
- 'The Rocket'   CMMP CSam CTri EAEE EBee
                           EChP EGle EPfP ERou LAst LRHS
                           MRav NBro NDov NEgg NFla SMer
                           SPer SWvt

Lytocaryum (Arecaceae)
§ *weddellianum* ♀H1   LPal MBri

M

Maackia (Papilionaceae)
amurensis   CBcs CMCN ELan EPfP GIBF IDee
                           IMGH LRav MBri MWea SBrw
                           WBVN WNor
- var. *buergeri*   CLnd EBee GBin
chinensis   CBcs CDul CMCN MBlu MBri
                           NLar

Macbridea (Lamiaceae)
caroliniana   CDes EBee WPGP

mace, English see *Achillea ageratum*

Macfadyena (Bignoniaceae)
uncata   SOWG
§ *unguis-cati*   CPIN CRHN CSec EShb XPep

Machaeranthera (Asteraceae)
§ *bigelovii*   NBre WPer

Machaerina (Cyperaceae)
rubiginosa 'Variegata'   CDWL
   (v)

Machilus see *Persea*

Mackaya (Acanthaceae)
§ *bella* ♀H1   CHll ERea EShb SOWG SYvo

Macleania (Ericaceae)
ericae   WCot

Macleaya (Papaveraceae)
cordata misapplied   see *M. x kewensis*
§ *cordata* (Willd.) R. Br. ♀H4   CArn COlW CPrp EBee EChP ELan
                           EMag EMar EPfP EWsh GBBs LHop
                           LRHS MLHP MWgw NBPC NBir
                           NDov NOrc NPri SPer SPlb SRms
                           WCAu WCot WFar WMnd WMoo
                           WPer WWhi
- 'Celadon Ruffles'   GBin
§ x *kewensis*   EBee GAbr MBri WHoo WPGP
- 'Flamingo' ♀H4   EBee ECha GCal MRav NEgg SBch
                           SWvt WCMO WWye
§ *microcarpa*   CDMG MFOX MGol SGar SWat
                           WSel
- 'Kelway's Coral Plume'   CBcs CHad CKno CSam EBee
   ♀H4   ECha ECtt EHrv ELan EPfP ERou
                           GMaP LRHS MRav MTis MWat
                           MWgw NBro NCGa NEgg SPer
                           SPoG SWvt WBrE WCMO WCot
                           WFar WMnd
- 'Spetchley Ruby'   EBee GBin LPhx MRav NBir NDov
                           WCMO WCot
'Plum Tassel'   WCMO WCot

Maclura (Moraceae)
pomifera   CAgr CArn CBcs CMCN IDee
                           MGol NLar SPlb WDin WFar WPGP
                           XPep
- 'Pretty Woman'   NLar
tricuspidata   CAgr CPle

Macrodiervilla see *Weigela*

Macropiper (Piperaceae)
§ *excelsum*   CHEx ECou

Macrozamia (Zamiaceae)
communis   CBrP CKob CRoM LPal WNor
diplomera   CBrP
dyeri   see *M. riedlei*
glaucophylla   CBrP
johnsonii   CBrP
lucida   CBrP
miquelii   CBrP LPal
moorei   CBrP CRoM LPal
mountperiensis   CBrP
§ *riedlei*   CBrP CRoM LPal
spiralis   CRoM

Maddenia (Rosaceae)
hypocleuca   NLar

Madia (Asteraceae)
elegans   NBur

Maesa (Myrsinaceae)
japonica   CPLG
montana   CPLG

Magnolia ✿ (Magnoliaceae)
acuminata   CBcs CDul CLnd CMCN EPfP IDee
                           IMGH NBhm NLar NPal WDin
- 'Golden Glow'   CBcs CMHG
* - 'Kinju'   CEnd NLar
- 'Koban Dori'   CBcs CPMA CTho ECho EMil
§ - var. *subcordata*   CBcs NEgg NLar
§ - - 'Miss Honeybee'   SSpi

'Advance' — CBcs CPMA
'Albatross' — CBcs CDoC CEnd CTho SSpi WPGP
'Alixeed' **new** — CBcs
'Ambrosia' **new** — CPMA
amoena — CBcs CSdC CTho WNor
- 'Multiogeca' — CBcs CWib
'Ann' ♀H4 — CPLG CSdC CTrh MGos NLar SSpi
'Anticipation' — CEnd
'Apollo' — CBcs CEnd CPMA SSpi
ashei — see *M. macrophylla* subsp. *ashei*
'Athene' — CBcs CDoC CMHG COtt CPMA MBri
'Atlas' — CBcs CEnd CMHG CPMA CTho LMil SSpi WPGP
'Banana Split' **new** — SSpi
'Betty' ♀H4 — CBcs CDoC CDul CSdC IDee LPan MGos NLar NScw SBrw SLim SSta WDin WFar WOrn
'Big Dude' — CEnd IArd SSpi
biondii — CBcs CTho NLar WNor WPGP
'Black Tulip' — ENot LRHS MGos NPri SCoo SPoG SSpi
x **brooklynensis** **new** — NPal
- 'Evamaria' — CTho
- 'Hattie Carthan' — WPGP
- 'Woodsman' — NLar SSta
- 'Yellow Bird' — CBcs CEnd CMCN COtt CPMA CTho EBee ENot EPfP IDee LRHS MBlu MDun MGos MLan NLar NPal SBrw WDin WGer
'Butterflies' — CBcs CDoC CEnd CMHG CPMA CTho ELan EPfP GKev ISea LHyd LMil LRHS MDun NLar SBrw SHBN SSpi SSta WBVN WFar WGob WPGP
'Caerhays Belle' — CBcs CPMA ECho MBri NLar SSpi
'Caerhays New Purple' — ECho
'Caerhays Surprise' — CBcs CPMA SSpi
campbellii — CBcs CMCN CTho ELan EPfP ISea LRHS MDun SBrw SHBN SSpi SSta WFar WPic
- Alba Group — CBcs CEnd CTho MGos WFar WPGP
- - 'Ethel Hillier' **new** — CBcs
- - 'Strybing White' — CBcs
I - - 'Trelissick Alba' — CTho
- 'Betty Jessel' — CPMA CTho
- 'Darjeeling' — CBcs CDoC ECho EMil MBri
- 'Lamellan Pink' — CTho
- 'Lamellan White' — CTho
- subsp. mollicomata — CBcs CEnd CHEx CTrw EPfP ISea WFar
- - 'Lanarth' — CBcs CEnd SSpi
- - 'Maharanee' — CBcs
- - 'Peter Borlase' — CDoC CTho
- (Raffillii Group) 'Charles Raffill' — CAbP CBcs CDul CLnd ELan EPfP MAsh MBri MDun MGos MLan SHBN SLim SPer SPoG WDin WHCr WPGP
- - 'Kew's Surprise' — CBcs CDoC CPMA
'Candy Cane' — LPan WPGP
Chameleon — see *M.* 'Chang Hua'
§ 'Chang Hua' — CPMA MBri MDun NLar
'Charles Coates' — CSdC MDun NLar WPGP
China Town = 'Jing Ning' — MDun
* chingii — CBcs
'Columbus' — CPMA CSdC SSpi WPGP
'Coral Lake' — MBri MDun
cordata — see *M. acuminata* var. *subcordata*
- 'Miss Honeybee' — see *M. acuminata* var. *subcordata* 'Miss Honeybee'
cylindrica misapplied — see *M.* 'Pegasus'
cylindrica Wilson — CMCN CPMA EPfP IArd SPoG SSpi SSta
'Daphne' **new** — CBcs

§ 'Darrell Dean' — CPMA CTho WPGP
'David Clulow' — CBcs CPMA CTho ECho SSpi
dawsoniana — CBcs CMCN EPfP IMGH NLar SSpi
'Daybreak' — CBcs MBri SSpi
delavayi — CBcs CBrP CHEx EPfP LRHS SAPC SArc WMul
§ denudata ♀H3-4 — CBcs CDul CMCN CPMA CTho CTrw CWib EMil EPfP ISea LMil LPan LRHS MGos NLar SBrw SMur SSpi SSta WDin WFar WMul WNor
- 'Dubbel' — CBcs MDun
- 'Forrest's Pink' — CBcs
- Fragrant Cloud = 'Dan Xin' — CPMA CWib MBri MDun NLar
- Yellow River = 'Fei Huang' — CDoC CEnd CWib MBri MDun NLar SPoG SSpi WMul WOrn
'Editor Hopkins' — SSpi
'Elizabeth' ♀H4 — More than 30 suppliers
'Eskimo' — MBri SSpi
'Felix Jury' — ENot MAsh
'Fireglow' — CTho
'Frank Gladney' — CPMA CTho
'Frank's Masterpiece' — MBri MDun
'Full Eclipse' — WPGP
'Galaxy' ♀H4 — More than 30 suppliers
'George Henry Kern' — CBcs CDoC COtt EBee IArd IDee ISea LBuc LRHS MBri MSte NLar SBrw SSpi SSta WCFE WDin WFar
globosa — CPLG SBrw WFar WGob WPGP
'Gold Crown' — MBri SSpi
'Gold Star' — CBcs CEnd CMCN CPMA CSdC CTho EBee LPan LRHS MBlu MBri MGos NLar NPal SHBN SSpi WOrn
'Golden Endeavour' — MDun
'Golden Gift' — CPMA SSpi
'Golden Sun' **new** — CPMA NLar
grandiflora — CMCN CPLG CWib EPfP LAst LEdu LRHS MRav MWya NBlu NLar SAPC SArc SBrw SHBN WCMO WDin WFar WGwG WMul WNor WOrn
- 'Blanchard' — CBcs CPMA
- 'Bracken's Brown Beauty' — SSpi
- 'Charles Dickens' — CBcs CPMA
- 'Edith Bogue' — CPMA ECho MAsh MRav NLar WBVN WGob
- 'Exmouth' ♀H3-4 — More than 30 suppliers
- 'Ferruginea' — CBcs CPMA MGos NBea
- 'Francois Treyve' — IDee SBrw
- 'Galissonnière' — CBcs COtt CWib ECrN ERom IMGH LPan LRHS MGos MRav NBlu SBrw SLim SSpi SWvt WCMO WDin WFar WPGP
I - 'Gallissonnière Nana' — LPan SBLw
- 'Goliath' — CBcs CEnd CHEx CPSs ELan EPfP EWTr LPan SBra SBrw SSpi WPGP
- 'Harold Poole' — CBcs CPMA
- 'Little Gem' — CBcs CDoC CPMA EBee EPfP LRHS MGos NLar SBrw SPoG SSpi
- 'Mainstreet' — CBcs CPMA
- 'Monland' **new** — CBcs
- 'Monlia' **new** — CBcs CPMA
- 'Nannetensis' — CPMA
- 'Overton' — CBcs CPMA
- 'Russet' — CBcs CPMA
- 'Saint Mary' — CBcs CPMA
- 'Samuel Sommer' — CPMA SAPC SArc
- 'Symmes Select' — CBcs CPMA
- 'Undulata' — WGer
- 'Victoria' ♀H3-4 — CDoC CDul CPMA CTho EBee ELan EPfP LHyd LRHS MAsh MBlu MGos SBrw SLim SPoG SReu SSpi SSta WFar WPGP
'Green Bee' **new** — CBcs
'Heaven Scent' ♀H4 — More than 30 suppliers

Name	Suppliers
'Helen Fogg'	WPGP
heptapeta	see *M. denudata*
§ 'Hong Yur'	CEnd CPMA MDun WMul
'Hot Flash'	CBcs CPMA
hypoleuca	see *M. obovata* Thunb.
'Ian's Red' new	CBcs CPMA
'Iolanthe'	CBcs CEnd CMCN CMHG CPMA CSdC CTho ECho ELan MBri MGos NBhm NHol NLar SBrw SPer SSpi SSta WFar WPGP
'J.C. Williams'	CDoC CPMA CTho
'Jane' ♀H4	CDoC CSdC ELan EPfP LMil LRHS MAsh MBri MGos NHol SBrw SHBN SLdr SPer
'Jersey Belle'	CBcs CPMA
§ 'Joe McDaniel'	CDoC CPMA CSdC MLan NLar SSpi WGer
'Jon Jon'	CPMA
'Judy'	EMil NEgg NLar
'Kay Paris'	SSpi
kobus	CBcs CDul CLnd CMCN CPLG CSBt CTho EPfP IMGH LPan MAsh MDun MWya NMoo SBLw SBrw SHBN SPer SPoG WDin WFar WGob WNor
- var. *borealis*	CPMA CTho
- 'Janaki Ammal' new	CPMA
- 'Norman Gould'	see *M. stellata* 'Norman Gould'
'Lamellan Surprise'	CTho
'Leda'	CMCN SSpi
'Legacy' new	NLar
§ *liliiflora*	CTrw MBar NBlu WMul
§ - 'Nigra' ♀H4	More than 30 suppliers
- 'Oldfield'	WPGP
* 'Limelight'	CSdC SSpi
x *loebneri*	CBcs GTSp LRHS WNor
- 'Ballerina'	CDoC MBar NLar SBrw
- 'Donna'	CBcs MGos NLar SSpi WGer
- 'Leonard Messel' ♀H4	More than 30 suppliers
- 'Merrill' ♀H4	CBcs CMCN CMHG CTho CTrh CWib EBee ELan EPfP ISea LPan LRHS MAsh MBri MGos MWat NHol SBrw SPer SReu SSpi SSta WBVN WDin WFar WGob WPGP
- 'Snowdrift'	NLar SSta
lotungensis	NLar
macrophylla	CBrP CHEx CMCN EPfP MBlu SAPC SArc WNor
§ - subsp. *ashei*	WNor
'Manchu Fan'	CBcs CDoC CMCN CPMA CSdC ECho EMil IArd MDun NLar SMur SSpi
'Margaret Helen'	CBcs CPMA ECho
'Mark Jury'	CBcs
'Maryland'	CPMA CWib SBrw SSpi SSta
'Maxine Merrill'	IDee SSpi
'Milky Way' ♀H4	CBcs CMHG CPMA CTho LRHS MGos SMur SSpi WPGP
'Nimbus'	CPMA
obovata Diels	see *M. officinalis*
§ *obovata* Thunb. ♀H4	CMCN CPMA CTho EPfP IDee IMGH MDun MGos MLan NLar SBrw SHBN SSpi SSta WDin WPGP
§ *officinalis*	CMCN EPfP NLar WBVN WFar
- var. *biloba*	EPfP NLar SSpi WPGP
'Peachy' new	NLar
§ 'Pegasus'	CEnd SSpi SSta WDin
'Peppermint Stick'	CBcs CSdC ECho MGos SSta
'Peter Smithers'	CPMA CTho WFar
'Phelan Bright'	CSdC
'Phillip Tregunna'	CBcs CTho SSpi
'Pickard's Sundew'	see *M.* 'Sundew'
'Pinkie' ♀H4	EPfP LRHS MBri MGos NLar SBrw SSpi SSta WGer WGob
'Pirouette'	SSpi
'Princess Margaret'	CBcs CDoC CPMA ECho MBri SSpi
x *proctoriana*	CAbP CDoC CPLG CSdC EPfP NLar SBrw WPGP
- Gloster form new	NLar
- 'Proctoriana'	LMil
'Purple Sensation' new	CBcs CPMA
quinquepeta	see *M. liliiflora*
'Randy'	CBcs EPfP MGos
'Raspberry Ice'	CBcs CDoC CMHG COtt CPLG CSam CSdC CTho CTrw EBee EPfP ISea LRHS MAsh NLar SBrw WFar WGob
'Ricki'	CBcs CSdC EMil EPfP LBuc MBlu MGos NLar SBrw SPoG WFar
rostrata	SSpi WPGP
'Rouged Alabaster'	CDoC
'Royal Crown'	CBcs CDoC CSdC EMil MRav NBhm NLar SBrw SLim WGer
'Ruby'	CBcs CPMA ECho MBri MGos SBrw
'Ruth'	CBcs
salicifolia ♀H3-4	CBcs CMCN EPfP ISea LRHS SBrw SSpi SSta
- 'Jermyns'	SSpi
- upright new	WPGP
- 'Wada's Memory' ♀H4	CDoC CMCN CMHG CPMA CTho EBee ELan EPfP LRHS MAsh MBri MLan MSte NBea NLar NVic SBrw SPer SSpi SSta WDin WFar WGob
- 'Windsor Beauty'	SSpi
sargentiana var. *robusta*	CBcs CBrd CEnd CMCN CTho ELan EPfP IMGH ISea MDun MGos SPer SSpi SSta WDin WFar WHCr
- - 'Blood Moon'	SSpi
- - 'Multipetal'	CBrd
- - 'Trengwainton Glory' new	SSpi
'Satisfaction' new	MBri
'Sayonara' ♀H4	CBcs CPMA ECho EPfP MBri SBrw SSpi WDin WPGP
'Schmetterling'	see *M. x soulangeana* 'Pickard's Schmetterling'
'Serene'	CBcs CEnd CMHG CPMA ECho LMil MBri MGos SSpi SSta
'Shirazz'	CBcs CPMA
sieboldii	More than 30 suppliers
- B&SWJ 4127	WCru
- from Korea, hardy	GGGa
- 'Colossus'	MBri SSpi
- 'Genesis'	SSpi
- 'Michiko Renge'	MBri NLar
- subsp. *sinensis*	CBcs CDoC CLnd CMCN CPMA CSam CTho ELan EPfP GGGa IMGH LRHS MBlu MDun MWya SBrw SSpi SSta WCwm WDin WGer
x *soulangeana*	More than 30 suppliers
§ - 'Alba'	CBcs CDoC CEnd CSBt EBee ECrN EPfP LPan LRHS MGos NBlu SBrw SLim SPer WFar WOrn
- 'Alba Superba'	see *M. x soulangeana* 'Alba'
- 'Alexandrina'	CBcs EPfP NLar SBrw
- 'Amabilis'	MLan WGob
- 'Brozzonii' ♀H3-4	CDoC EPfP LRHS NLar SBrw SSpi
- 'Burgundy'	CBcs CDoC ISea LRHS MAsh MBri MGos WFar
- 'Lennei' ♀H3-4	CBcs CDoC CEnd CMCN CSBt EPfP IMGH LRHS MAsh MGos MSwo NBea NHol NPri SBrw SHBN SLim SPer SRms WBVN WFar WNor WOrn
- 'Lennei Alba' ♀H3-4	CDoC CMCN CSdC LRHS SBrw SLdr SPer WFar WGob
- 'Nigra'	see *M. liliiflora* 'Nigra'
- 'Pickard's Ruby'	CBcs MBri MDun WGob

§ - 'Pickard's Schmetterling' CDoC CSdC LMil MAsh SSta
- 'Pickard's Sundew' see *M.* 'Sundew'
- 'Picture' CBcs CDoC MAsh NLar SBrw
WDin WGob
- Red Lucky see *M.* 'Hong Yur'
- 'Rubra' misapplied see *M.* x *soulangeana* 'Rustica
Rubra'
§ - 'Rustica Rubra' ♀H3-4 More than 30 suppliers
- 'San José' CBcs LMil LRHS MAsh MBri MDun
NLar SSta WFar
- 'Verbanica' LMil LRHS MAsh NLar SPoG
'Spectrum' CBcs CEnd CPMA CSdC IArd IDee
LMil MBri MGos NLar SSpi WPGP
sprengeri CWib WNor
- 'Copeland Court' CTho
- var. *diva* CBcs CEnd NLar SSpi WPGP
- - 'Burncoose' CBcs CDoC
- - 'Lanhydrock' CTho SSpi
- - 'Westonbirt' **new** WPGP
- var. *elongata* COtt
- 'Eric Savill' CTho SSpi WPGP
- 'Marwood Spring' CMHG CTho
'Star Wars' ♀H4 CBcs CDoC CEnd CPMA CSdC
CTho ECho EMil ENot EPfP LMil
MAsh MBri MDun MGos MLan
NLar SBrw SMur SSpi SSta WGer
WPGP
'Stellar Acclaim' MDun
§ *stellata* ♀H4 More than 30 suppliers
- 'Centennial' CBcs CDoC CTho MBri NLar SBrw
WFar
- 'Chrysanthemiflora' LMil
- 'Jane Platt' CBcs MBri MDun MGos SSpi
- f. *keiskei* CEnd CSdC
- 'King Rose' CBcs CDoC COtt CSdC EPfP GKev
ISea LAst LRHS MAsh MSte MWat
SPer SPla
§ - 'Norman Gould' CDoC EPfP MBri NLar SBrw SSta
WDin WGer
- 'Pink Perfection' MDun
- 'Rosea' CMCN COtt ECrN ELan LPan LRHS
MBri MDun MGos MSwo NLar
SBrw SHBN SPoG WCMO WDin
I - 'Rosea Massey' CTho WFar
- 'Royal Star' More than 30 suppliers
- 'Scented Silver' **new** CSdC
- 'Waterlily' ♀H4 CBcs CMCN ELan EPfP GKev
IMGH ISea LAst LRHS LSRN MAsh
NLar NVic SBrw SLim SPer SPla
SPoG SSpi SSta WDin WFar WGob
WPGP
'Summer Solstice' CPMA
'Sunburst' CBcs MDun
'Sundance' CBcs CPMA EMil MDun MGos
NLar SBrw
§ 'Sundew' CBcs CDoC CMCN EPfP IArd
MGos NLar SBrw SHBN WBVN
'Susan' ♀H4 More than 30 suppliers
'Susanna van Veen' CBcs MBri
x *thompsoniana* CMCN EPfP IDee NLar SSpi
'Thousand Butterflies' CPMA
'Tina Durio' CDoC
'Todd Gresham' CPMA WPGP
'Tranquility' MDun SSpi
'Trewidden Belle' CEnd
tripetala CBcs CHEx CLnd CMCN CPLG
CPne CTho EPfP GGGa IMGH
LPan MDun MLan SBrw SHBN SSpi
SSta WDin WMul WPGP
x *veitchii* CDoC CDul CSBt EPfP SSta
- 'Isca' CBcs CTho
- 'Peter Veitch' CBcs CTho SSta
virginiana CMCN CPMA CPne CTho EPfP
LRHS SBig SPoG SSpi WDin WPGP
- 'Havener' IArd
- 'Henry Hicks' SSpi

- 'Moonglow' CPMA
- 'Vulcan' CBcs CEnd CMCN CMHG CPMA
CTho MBlu MDun
x *watsonii* see *M.* x *wieseneri*
§ x *wieseneri* CBcs CMCN CPMA CTho ELan
EPfP IDee LRHS MAsh MBlu SSpi
SSta WBVN WFar WGob WPGP
- 'Aashild Kalleberg' CBcs SSpi
wilsonii ♀H4 More than 30 suppliers
- 'Gwen Baker' CEnd
'Yellow Fever' CBcs CMCN CMHG CPMA CTho
ECho EMil MDun SBrw SMur SSta
'Yellow Lantern' CAbP CBcs CEnd CMCN CSdC
EPfP IDee LMil LRHS MAsh MBlu
NBea NLar NPal SPoG SSpi SSta
zenii CMCN CSdC
- 'Pink Parchment' **new** CPMA

x *Mahoberberis* (Berberidaceae)

aquisargentii CPle ECrN EPfP MAsh MRav NHol
SBrw SEND SLon SPoG WFar
WPGP WPat
'Dart's Treasure' EPla WFar
'Magic' MGos NLar
miethkeana MBar SRms WDin

Mahonia ✿ (Berberidaceae)

§ *aquifolium* CAgr CBcs CDul CTrG EBee ECrN
ENot LAst MBar MGan MGos MRav
NBlu NWea SHBN SPer SPlb SReu
WCFE WDin WFar
- 'Apollo' ♀H4 CAgr CBcs CMac CWib EBee ECrN
ELan EMil EPfP LHop LRHS LSRN
MAsh MBar MBlu MBri MGos
MRav NBlu NEgg NPri SCoo SMer
SPer SPoG SReu WDin WPat
- 'Atropurpurea' CBcs ELan EPfP EPla LRHS MAsh
NEgg NLar SPer SPla SPoG WDin
* - 'Cosmo Crawl' MGos
- 'Exception' **new** EBee
- 'Fascicularis' see *M.* x *wagneri* 'Pinnacle'
- 'Green Ripple' CPMA EPfP MBri MGos NLar WFar
- 'Orange Flame' EPfP MBlu NLar
- 'Smaragd' CBcs CDoC CDul CMac EBee ELan
ENot EPfP LRHS LSRN MAsh MBlu
MGos MRav WHCG WPat
- 'Versicolor' EPla MBlu
bealei see *M. japonica* Bealei Group
bodinieri **new** NLar
confusa CDoC EPla NLar SBrw SSpi WCru
WFar WPGP
fortunei EPla IDee NLar
- 'Winter Prince' **new** NLar
gracilipes EBee EPfP EPla MBlu MDun NLar
WPGP WSPU
japonica ♀H4 More than 30 suppliers
§ - Bealei Group CBcs CDul CSBt EBee ELan EPfP
EPla LAst LRHS MAsh MBar MGan
MGos MRav MSwo MWhi NEgg
NPer SCoo SLim SMer SPoG
SWvt WBor WDin WFar WGwG
WWeb
- 'Gold Dust' SPer
- 'Hiemalis' see *M. japonica* 'Hivernant'
- 'Hivernant' MGos NBlu WOrn
leschenaultii B&SWJ 9535 WCru
lomariifolia ♀H3 CBcs CHEx EPfP EWes LRHS SAPC
SArc SBrw SSpi SSta
x *media* 'Buckland' ♀H4 CAbP CBcs CDul CMac CSBt CSam
CTrw CWSG EBee EPfP ISea LAst
LHop LRHS MDun MRav NHol
SDix SPer SRms WPat
- 'Charity' More than 30 suppliers
- 'Charity's Sister' EPla
- 'Faith' EPla
- 'Hope' **new** NLar

- 'Lionel Fortescue' ♀H4   CBcs CBrm CEnd CMac CPSs CSBt CTrw CWSG EBee ELan EPfP ISea LHop LRHS MAsh MGos MRav NCGa SMad SPer SPoG SSpi WFar
- 'Underway' ♀H4   EPfP LRHS NLar SMur
- 'Winter Sun' ♀H4   More than 30 suppliers
- *nervosa*   CBcs EPfP EPla CDee MBlu SBrw SPer SSta WCru WDin WPat
- *oiwakensis* B&SWJ 3660 **new**   WCru
- *pallida*   WCot WPGP
- *pinnata* misapplied   see *M.* x *wagneri* 'Pinnacle'
- *pinnata* ambig.   EPfP EPla MBar
- *pumila*   WCru
- *repens*   EPla NLar
- 'Rotundifolia'   EPla
- x *savilliana*   EPla MBlu WCru WPGP
- 'Commissioner'   CWib
- *trifoliolata* var. *glauca*   CEnd CPMA NLar
- x *wagneri* 'Fireflame'   EPla
- 'Hastings Elegant'   CPMA NLar
- 'Moseri'   EPla NLar SSpi WPat
- § - 'Pinnacle' ♀H4   ELan EPfP EPla LRHS MGos MLan NFor NHol SMur SPer SPoG WDin
- 'Sunset'   CPMA EPla MBlu NLar
- 'Undulata'   EPfP MBlu NEgg NLar SRms WHCG

Maianthemum (*Convallariaceae*)

- *atropurpureum*   CBct WCru
- *bifolium*   CAvo CBct CDes CPLG CRow EBee ECho EMan EPot GBuc LEdu MDun MNrw MTho NBro NMen SRms WCru WPGP WPnP WTin WWye
- from Yakushima   SOkd
- § - subsp. *kamtschaticum*   CAvo CLAP CPom CRow ECha EHrv GIBF LBuc NLar SMac WCot WTin
- - - B&SWJ 4360   WCru WPrP
- * - - var. *minimum*   WCru
- *canadense*   EBee ECho NBid NMen WCru
- * *chasmanthum*   EBrs EPPr LRHS
- *dilatatum*   see *M. bifolium* subsp. *kamtschaticum*
- *flexuosum* B&SWJ 9069   WCru
- *formosanum*   WCot
- - B&SWJ 349   CBct WCru
- *forrestii*   WCru
- *fuscum*   GBin WCru
- *henryi*   WCru
- *japonicum*   CBct LEdu
- - B&SWJ 1179   WCru
- *oleraceum*   GBin GEdr WCot WCru
- - B&SWJ 2148   WCru
- § *racemosum* ♀H4   More than 30 suppliers
- - subsp. *amplexicaule*   CAvo GCal
- - - 'Emily Moody'   CFwr CPou ELan WPGP
- *salvinii*   LEdu
- - B&SWJ 9000   WCru
- *stellatum*   CAvo CBct CHEx CRow EBee ECha EPPr EPla EWTr GBBs GEdr LEdu LHop MDun MLLN MRav NChi NMyG SMac WCru WPnP WTin WWye
- *szechuanicum*   GEdr WCru
- *tatsiense*   WCru

Maihuenia (*Cactaceae*)

- *patagonica* F&W 10241   WCot
- *poeppigii*   EHyt SPlb
- - JCA 2.575.600   WCot

Maireana (*Chenopodiaceae*)

- *georgei*   SPlb

Malacothamnus (*Malvaceae*)

- *fremontii*   EMan MDKP

Malcolmia (*Brassicaceae*)

- *littorea*   XPep

Malephora (*Aizoaceae*)

- *crocea* var. *purpureocrocea*   XPep

Mallotus (*Euphorbiaceae*)

- *japonicus*   CPLG
- - B&SWJ 6852   WCru

Malus ✿ (*Rosaceae*)

- § 'Adirondack'   CDoC CWSG EMui EPfP LRHS MAsh MBri MGos MLan NLar SCoo SLim SPoG
- 'Admiration'   see *M.* 'Adirondack'
- x *adstringens* 'Almey'   ECrN
- - 'Hopa'   CDul CLnd CTho
- - 'Simcoe'   CLnd CTho
- 'Aldenhamensis'   see *M.* x *purpurea* 'Aldenhamensis'
- 'Amberina'   CLnd
- * *arborescens*   CLnd CTho
- x *atrosanguinea*   CTho
- § - 'Gorgeous'   CCAT CDul CLnd COtt CTho CWSG ECrN GTwe LRHS MAsh MGan MGos MSwo NBlu SCoo SKee SLim SPer SPoG WDin WJas WOrn
- *baccata*   CDul CLnd CMCN CTho GTwe NWea SEND WNor
- - W 264   GIBF
- - 'Dolgo'   CCAT CDoC CTho SKee
- - 'Gracilis'   SBLw
- - 'Jackii'   CTho
- - 'Lady Northcliffe'   CLnd CTho SFam
- - var. *mandshurica*   CTho EPfP GIBF
- - var. *sibirica*   GIBF
- aff. *baccata*   MAsh NWea
- - MF 96038   SSpi
- § *bhutanica*   CDul CLnd CTho EPfP GIBF NLar SPer WNor
- *brevipes*   CLnd CTho MBri SCoo
- 'Butterball'   CLnd CTho ECrN EPfP MAsh MBlu SCoo SKee SLim SPoG WDin WJas
- * 'Cheal's Weeping'   ECrN EWTr LAst NBea
- Coccinella = 'Courtarou'   WDin
- 'Comtessa de Paris' **new**   MAsh
- 'Coralburst'   MBri SCoo
- *coronaria* var. *dasycalyx* 'Charlottae' (d)   CDul CLnd EBee EPfP SFam SPer SPur
- - 'Elk River'   LRHS MAsh MBri
- - 'Nieuwlandiana'   GIBF
- 'Crimson Brilliant'   CLnd
- 'Crittenden'   ECrN MRav SMHT
- *denticulata*   GIBF
- * 'Directeur Moerlands'   CCVT CDoC EBee ECrN EGra EMil EPfP SPur WDin WJas
- *domestica* (F)   ECrN WMou
- - 'Acklam Russet' (D)   SKee
- - 'Acme' (D)   MCoo SDea SKee
- - 'Adams's Pearmain' (D)   CCAT CTho ECrN GBut GTwe LRHS SDea SFam SKee WJas WOrn
- - 'Akane' (D)   SDea
- - 'Alfriston' (C)   CAgr SKee
- - 'Alkmene' (D) ♀H4   ECrN SDea SKee
- - 'All Doer' (D/C/Cider)   CTho
- - 'Allen's Everlasting' (D)   GTwe SDea SKee
- - 'Allington Pippin' (D)   CSBt CTho CTri ECrN SDea SKee WJas
- - 'American Mother'   see *M. domestica* 'Mother'
- - 'Ananas Reinette' (D)   ECrN

446 *Malus*

- 'Anna Boelens' (D) — SDea
- 'Annie Elizabeth' (C) — CAgr CCAT CTho CWib ECrN GTwe LAst SDea SFam SKee WJas
- 'Anniversary' (D) — SDea
- 'Api Rose' (D) — SKee WJas
- 'Ard Cairn Russet' (D) — GBut GTwe SDea SKee
- 'Aromatic Russet' (D) — SKee
- 'Arthur Turner' (C) ♀H4 — CCVT CDoC CTri ECrN EMui GBut GTwe LBuc SCrf SDea SFam SKee WJas
- 'Ashmead's Kernel' (D) ♀H4 — CAgr CCAT CSBt CTho CTri CWib ECrN EMui EPfP ERea GTwe LBuc LRHS MRav MWat NWea SCrf SDea SFam SKee WHar WJas WOrn
- 'Ashton Bitter' (Cider) — CCAT CTho GTwe
- 'Ashton Brown Jersey' (Cider) — CCAT CTho
- 'Autumn Pearmain' (D) — SDea WJas
- 'Backwell Red' (Cider) — CCAT
- 'Baker's Delicious' (D) — ECrN SDea SKee
- 'Ball's Bittersweet' (Cider) — CCAT CTho
- 'Balsam' — see *M. domestica* 'Green Balsam'
- 'Banana Pippin' new — CEnd
- 'Barnack Beauty' (D) — CTho SKee
- 'Barnack Orange' (D) — SKee
- 'Baumann's Reinette' (D) — SKee
- 'Baxter's Pearmain' (D) — SDea SKee
- 'Beauty of Bath' (D) — CAgr CCAT CCVT CDoC CDul CTho CTri CWib ECrN EMui GBut GTwe LAst LBuc SCrf SDea SFam SKee WJas
- 'Beauty of Hants' (D) — ECrN SKee
- 'Beauty of Kent' (C) — SDea SKee
- 'Beauty of Moray' (C) — GBut GQui SKee
- 'Bedwyn Beauty' (C) — CTho
- 'Beeley Pippin' (D) — GTwe SDea SKee
- 'Belfleur Kitaika' (D) — SKee
- 'Belfleur Krasnyi' (D) — SKee
- 'Bell Apple' (Cider/C) — CCAT CTho
- 'Belle de Boskoop' (C/D) ♀H4 — CCAT GTwe MCoo SDea SKee
- 'Bembridge Beauty' (F) — SDea
- 'Ben's Red' (D) — CAgr CCAT CEnd CTho
- 'Bess Pool' (D) — SDea SFam WJas
- 'Bewley Down Pippin' — see *M. domestica* 'Crimson King'
- 'Bickington Grey' (Cider) — CTho
- 'Billy Down Pippin' (F) — CTho
- 'Bismarck' (C) — CCAT ECrN SKee
- 'Black Dabinett' (Cider) — CEnd CTho
- 'Black Tom Putt' (C/D) — CTho
- 'Blenheim Orange' (C/D) ♀H4 — CAgr CCAT CCVT CDoC CDul CSBt CTho CTri CWib ECrN EMui ENot EPfP GTwe LAst LBuc LRHS MBri MCoo MRav MWat SCrf SDea SFam SKee SPer WJas WOrn
- 'Blenheim Red' (C/D) — see *M. domestica* 'Red Blenheim'
- 'Bloody Ploughman' (D) — GTwe LRHS SKee
- 'Blue Pearmain' (D) — SDea SKee
- 'Blue Sweet' (Cider) — CTho
- 'Bolero = 'Tuscan'PBR (D/Ball) — ECrN ENot LRHS SDea SKee
- 'Boston Russet' — see *M. domestica* 'Roxbury Russet'
- 'Bountiful' (C) — CAgr CDoC COtt CSBt CTri CWib ECrN EMui GTwe LBuc MBri SDea SKee SPoG WBVN WHar
- 'Braddick Nonpareil' (D) — SKee
- 'Braeburn' (D) — ECrN EMui ERea LAst LRHS MNHC SDea SKee
- 'Braintree Seedling' (D) — ECrN
- 'Bramley's Seedling' (C) ♀H4 — More than 30 suppliers
- 'Bramley's Seedling' clone 20 — CDoC EMui MBri NLar SCoo SDea SPoG
- 'Bread Fruit' (C/D) — CEnd CTho

- 'Breakwell's Seedling' (Cider) — CCAT CTho
- 'Brenchley Pippin' (D) new — SKee
- 'Bridgwater Pippin' (C) — CCAT CTho WJas
- 'Broad-eyed Pippin' (C) — SKee
- 'Brown Snout' (Cider) — CCAT CTho
- 'Brownlees Russet' (D) — CAgr CCAT CTho GTwe NWea SDea SFam SKee
- 'Brown's Apple' (Cider) — CCAT GTwe
- 'Broxwood Foxwhelp' (Cider) — CCAT
- 'Bulmer's Norman' (Cider) — CCAT
- 'Burn's Seedling' (D) — CTho
- 'Burr Knot' (C) — ECrN SKee
- 'Burrowhill Early' (Cider) — CTho
- 'Bushey Grove' (C) — SDea SKee
- 'Buttery Do' — CTho
- 'Byfleet Seedling' (C) — SKee
- 'Calville Blanc d'Hiver' (D) — SKee
- 'Cambusnethan Pippin' (D) — GBut GQui SKee
- 'Camelot' (Cider/C) — CCAT CTho
- 'Cap of Liberty' (Cider) — CCAT
- 'Captain Broad' (D/Cider) — CCAT CEnd CTho
- 'Captain Kidd' (D) — EMui SKee
- 'Captain Smith' (F) — CEnd
- 'Carlisle Codlin' (C) — GTwe SDea
- 'Carswell's Orange' (D) — SKee
- 'Catherine' (D) — ECrN
- 'Catshead' (C) — CAgr CCAT CCVT ECrN GQui SDea SKee WJas
- 'Cellini' (C/D) — SDea SKee
- 'Charles Ross' (C/D) ♀H4 — CAgr CCAT CDoC CMac CSBt CTho CTri ECrN EMui GBut GTwe LAst LBuc LRHS MBri MCoo MGan MRav MWat NBlu NWea SDea SFam SKee SPoG WHar WJas WOrn
- 'Charlotte'PBR (C/Ball) — ENot LRHS MGos SDea SKee
- 'Chaxhill Red' (Cider/D) — CCAT CTho
- 'Cheddar Cross' (D) — CAgr CTri ECrN
- 'Chelmsford Wonder' (C) — ECrN SKee
- 'Chisel Jersey' (Cider) — CCAT CTri
- 'Chivers Delight' (D) — CAgr CCAT CSBt ECrN EMui GTwe MCoo SCrf SDea SKee WJas
- 'Chorister Boy' (D) — CTho
- 'Christmas Pearmain' (D) — CTho ECrN GTwe SDea SFam SKee
- 'Cider Lady's Finger' (Cider) — CCAT
- 'Claygate Pearmain' (D) ♀H4 — CCAT CTho ECrN GTwe MCoo SDea SFam SKee WJas
- 'Cleeve' (D) — SKee
- 'Clopton Red' (D) — ECrN
- 'Clydeside' — GQui
- 'Coat Jersey' (Cider) — CCAT
- 'Cockle Pippin' (D) — CAgr CTho SDea
- 'Coeur de Boeuf' (C/D) — SKee
- 'Coleman's Seedling' (Cider) — CTho
- 'Collogett Pippin' (C/Cider) — CCAT CEnd CTho
- 'Colonel Vaughan' (C/D) — SKee
- 'Comrade' (D) — SKee
- 'Cornish Aromatic' (D) — CAgr CCAT CTho ECrN GTwe LRHS SCrf SDea SFam SKee WJas
- 'Cornish Gilliflower' (D) — CAgr CCAT CTho ECrN LRHS MCoo SDea SFam SKee WJas WOrn
- 'Cornish Honeypin' (D) — CTho
- 'Cornish Longstem' (D) — CAgr CEnd CTho
- 'Cornish Mother' (D) — CEnd CTho
- 'Cornish Pine' (D) — CEnd CTho SDea SKee
- 'Coronation' (D) — SDea SKee
- 'Corse Hill' (D) — CTho

– 'Cortland' (D)	SKee	
– 'Costard' (C)	GTwe SKee	
– 'Cottenham Seedling' (C)	SKee	
– 'Coul Blush' (D)	GBut SKee	
– 'Court of Wick' (D)	CAgr CCAT CTho ECrN SKee	
– 'Court Pendu Plat' (D)	CCAT LBuc MWat NWea SDea SFam SKee WJas WOrn	
§ – 'Court Royal' (Cider)	CCAT	
– 'Cow Apple' (C)	CTho	
– 'Cox's Orange Pippin' (D)	CBcs CCAT CCVT CDul CMac CSBt CTri CWib ECrN EMui ENot GTwe LAst LRHS MWat NBlu NEgg NPri NWea SCrf SDea SFam SKee SPer WJas WOrn	
– 'Cox's Pomona' (C/D)	CTho SDea SKee WJas	
– 'Cox's Rouge de Flandres' (D)	SKee	
– 'Cox's Selfing' (D)	CDoC CWSG CWib EMui EPfP ERea GTwe LBuc MBri MGan MGos MNHC NBlu SCrf SDea SKee SPoG WHar WJas	
– 'Crawley Beauty' (C)	CAgr CCAT GTwe SDea SFam SKee WJas	
– 'Crawley Reinette' (D)	SKee	
– 'Crimson Beauty of Bath'	CAgr	
– 'Crimson Bramley' (C)	CCAT LAst	
– 'Crimson Cox' (D)	SDea	
§ – 'Crimson King' (Cider/C)	CAgr CCAT	
– 'Crimson King' (D)	CAgr	
– 'Crimson Queening' (D)	SKee WJas	
– 'Crimson Victoria' (Cider)	CTho	
– Crispin	see *M. domestica* 'Mutsu'	
§ – 'Crowngold' (D)	EMui GTwe	
– 'Curl Tail' (D)	SKee	
– 'Cutler Grieve' (D)	SDea	
– 'Dabinett' (Cider)	CCAT CTho CTri EMui GTwe SCrf SDea SKee WOrn	
– 'D'Arcy Spice' (D)	CAgr CCAT ECrN EMil EMui EPfP SDea SFam SKee	
– 'Dawn' (D)	SKee	
– 'Deacon's Blushing Beauty' (C/D)	SDea	
– 'Deacon's Millennium'	SDea	
– 'Decio' (D)	SKee	
– 'Delprim' (D)	SKee	
– 'Devon Crimson Queen' (D)	CTho	
– 'Devonshire Buckland' (C)	CEnd CTho	
– 'Devonshire Crimson Queen' (D)	SDea	
– 'Devonshire Quarrenden' (D)	CAgr CCAT CEnd CTho ECrN GBut SDea SFam SKee WJas	
– 'Discovery' (D) ♀H4	CAgr CBcs CCAT CDoC CDul CSBt CTri CWib ECrN EMui EPfP GBut GTwe LAst LBuc LRHS MBri MRav MWat NBlu NWea SDea SFam SKee SPer SPoG WJas WOrn	
– 'Doctor Hare's' (C)	WJas	
– 'Doctor Harvey' (C)	ECrN SFam	
– 'Doctor Kidd's Orange Red'	see *M. domestica* 'Kidd's Orange Red'	
– 'Doll's Eye'	CTho	
– 'Don's Delight' (C)	CTho	
– 'Dove' (Cider)	CTho	
– 'Downton Pippin' (D)	WJas	
– 'Dredge's Fame' (D)	CTho	
– 'Duchess's Favourite' (D)	SKee	
– 'Duck's Bill' (D)	SKee	
– 'Dufflin' (Cider)	CCAT CTho	
– 'Duke of Cornwall' (D)	CTho	
– 'Duke of Devonshire' (D)	CTho GBut SDea SFam SKee WJas	
– 'Duke of Gloucester' (C)	WJas	
N – 'Dumeller's Seedling' (C)	see *M. domestica* 'Dummellor's Seedling'	

§ – 'Dummellor's Seedling' (C) ♀H4	CCAT SDea SKee	
– 'Dunkerton Late Sweet' (Cider)	CCAT CTho	
– 'Dunn's Seedling' (D)	SDea	
§ – 'Dutch Mignonne' (D)	SKee	
– 'Dymock Red' (Cider)	CCAT	
– 'Early Blenheim' (D/C)	CEnd CTho	
– 'Early Bower' (D)	CEnd	
– 'Early Julyan' (C)	GBut GQui SKee WJas	
– 'Early Victoria'	see *M. domestica* 'Emneth Early'	
– 'Early Worcester'	see *M. domestica* 'Tydeman's Early Worcester'	
– 'East Lothian Pippin' (C)	GBut GQui	
– 'Easter Orange' (D)	GTwe SCrf SKee	
– 'Ecklinville' (C)	SDea SKee WJas	
– 'Edith Hopwood' (D)	ECrN SKee	
– 'Edward VII' (C) ♀H4	CDoC GBut GTwe SCrf SDea SFam SKee WJas	
– 'Egremont Russet' (D) ♀H4	More than 30 suppliers	
– 'Ellis' Bitter' (Cider)	CCAT CTho GTwe SKee	
– 'Ellison's Orange' (D) ♀H4	CAgr CCAT CDul CSBt CTri CWib ECrN EMui GBut GTwe LAst LBuc LRHS NEgg NWea SDea SFam SKee WHar WJas WOrn	
– 'Elstar' (D) ♀H4	CWib ECrN EMui GTwe LAst MRav NBlu SDea SKee	
– 'Elton Beauty' (D)	SDea	
§ – 'Emneth Early' (C) ♀H4	CAgr ECrN EMui GBut GTwe LAst SDea SFam SKee WJas WOrn	
– 'Empire' (D)	LAst SKee	
– 'Encore' (C)	SDea	
– 'English Codling' (C)	CTho	
– 'Epicure' (D)	see *M. domestica* 'Laxton's Epicure'	
– 'Ernie's Russet' (D)	SDea	
– 'Eros' (D)	ECrN	
– 'Essex Pippin' (D)	ECrN	
– 'Evening Gold' (C)	SDea	
– 'Eve's Delight' (D)	SDea	
– 'Excelsior' (C)	ECrN SKee	
– 'Exeter Cross' (D)	CCAT SDea SFam	
– 'Exquisite' (D) **new**	SKee	
– 'Fair Maid of Devon' (Cider)	CCAT CEnd CTho	
– 'Fairfield' (D)	CTho	
– 'Falstaff'PBR (D) ♀H4	CAgr CCAT CDoC ECrN EMui EPfP GTwe MGos SCoo SDea SKee WBVN WJas	
– 'Farmer's Glory' (D)	CAgr CTho	
– 'Fiesta'PBR (D) ♀H4	More than 30 suppliers	
– 'Fillbarrel' (Cider)	CCAT CTho	
– 'Fillingham Pippin' (C)	SKee	
– 'Firmgold' (D)	SDea	
– 'Five Crowns' (D)	SKee	
– 'Flame' (D)	SKee	
– 'Flamenco'PBR (D)	see *M. domestica* 'Obelisk'	
§ – 'Flower of Kent' (C)	CCAT SCrf SDea SKee	
– 'Flower of the Town' (D)	SKee	
– 'Forfar'	see *M. domestica* 'Dutch Mignonne'	
– 'Forge' (D)	CAgr SDea SKee	
– 'Fortune'	see *M. domestica* 'Laxton's Fortune'	
– 'Forty Shilling' (D)	GBut	
– 'Foster's Seedling' (D)	SKee	
– 'Frederick' (Cider)	CCAT CTho	
– 'French Crab' (C)	SDea	
– 'Freyberg' (D)	SKee	
– 'Fuji' (D)	SDea SKee	
– 'Gala' (D)	CSBt EMui GTwe LAst MGan NEgg NPri SCoo SCrf SDea SFam SKee	
§ – 'Gala Mondial' (D)	WJas	
I – 'Gala Royal'	see *M. domestica* 'Royal Gala'	
– 'Galloway Pippin' (C)	GBut GQui GTwe SKee	

- 'Garnet' (D)   SKee
- 'Gascoyne's Scarlet' (D)   CCAT SDea SFam SKee
- 'Gavin' (D)   GBut SDea SKee
- 'Genesis II' (D/C)   SDea
- 'Genet Moyle' (C/Cider)   CCAT WJas
- 'George Carpenter' (D)   SDea SKee
- 'George Cave' (D)   CTho ECrN GBut GTwe LAst MCoo SDea SFam SKee WJas
- 'George Neal' (C) ♀H4   CAgr SDea SFam
- 'Gilliflower of Gloucester' (D)   CTho
- 'Gin' (Cider)   CCAT
- 'Ginny Lin' (D)   CTho
- 'Gladstone' (D)   CAgr CTho SKee WJas
§ - 'Glass Apple' (C/D)   CEnd CTho
- 'Gloria Mundi' (C)   SDea SKee
- 'Gloster '69' (D)   GTwe NBlu SDea SKee
- 'Gloucester Royal' (D)   CTho
- 'Gloucester Underleaf'   CTho
- 'Golden Ball'   CTho
- 'Golden Bittersweet' (D)   CTho
- 'Golden Delicious' (D)   CDul CSBt CWib ECrN EMui ENot LAst MGan NBlu NWea SCrf SDea SKee SPer WHar WOrn
- 'Golden Glow' (C)   SDea
- 'Golden Harvey' (D)   CAgr CCAT
- 'Golden Jubilee' **new**   CEnd
- 'Golden Knob' (D)   CCAT CTho SKee
- 'Golden Monday' (D)   GBut
- 'Golden Noble' (C) ♀H4   CAgr CCAT CDoC CTho ECrN GTwe MCoo SDea SFam SKee WOrn
- 'Golden Nugget' (D)   CAgr
- 'Golden Pippin' (C)   CAgr CCAT GBut SKee
- 'Golden Reinette' (D)   GTwe SKee
- 'Golden Russet' (D)   CAgr ECrN GTwe SDea SKee
- 'Golden Spire' (C)   GBut MCoo SDea SKee
- 'Gooseberry' (C)   SKee
- 'Goring' (Cider)   CTho
- 'Grand Sultan' (D)   CCAT CTho
- 'Granny Smith' (D)   CDul CLnd CWib ECrN GTwe LAst NPri SCrf SDea SKee SPer
- 'Gravenstein' (D)   CCAT GQui SDea SFam SKee
- 'Greasy Butcher'   CTho
§ - 'Green Balsam' (C)   CTri
- 'Green Kilpandy Pippin' (C)   GQui
- 'Greensleeves'PBR (D) ♀H4   CAgr CCAT CDoC CSBt CTri CWSG CWib ECrN EMui GTwe LAst MGan MGos NEgg NWea SDea SKee SPoG WHar WJas WOrn
- 'Greenup's Pippin' (D)   GBut
- 'Grenadier' (C) ♀H4   CAgr CDoC CSBt CTri ECrN EMui GBut GTwe LRHS MGos NEgg SDea SKee WJas WOrn
- 'Halstow Natural' (Cider)   CAgr CTho
- 'Hambledon Deux Ans' (C)   SDea SKee
- 'Hambling's Seedling' (C)   SKee
- 'Hangy Down' (Cider)   CCAT CTho
- 'Harragan Payne' (Cider)   CTho
§ - 'Harry Master's Jersey' (Cider)   CCAT CTho CTri SDea
- 'Harvester' (D)   CTho
- 'Harvey' (C)   SDea SKee
- 'Hawthornden' (C)   GBut GQui GTwe SKee
- 'Hereford Cross' (D)   SKee
- 'Herefordshire Beefing' (C)   SKee WJas WOrn
- 'Herefordshire Russet'PBR **new**   EMui LBuc LRHS MCoo
- 'Herring's Pippin' (D)   CTri GTwe SDea SKee
- 'Heusgen's Golden Reinette' (D)   SKee
- 'High View Pippin' (D)   SKee
- 'Hoary Morning' (C)   CCAT CTho SDea SKee

- 'Hocking's Green' (C/D)   CAgr CCAT CEnd CTho
- 'Holland Pippin' (C)   SKee
- 'Hollow Core' (C)   CAgr CTho
- 'Holstein' (D)   CTho SDea SKee
- 'Honey Pippin' (D)   ECrN
- 'Hood's Supreme' (D)   GBut
- 'Horneburger Pfannkuchen' (C)   SKee
- 'Howgate Wonder' (C)   CAgr CCAT CCVT CDoC CDul CSBt CWib ECrN EMui GBut GTwe LAst LBuc LRHS MGan NPri SCrf SDea SFam SKee WBVN WJas
- 'Hubbard's Pearmain' (D)   SKee
- 'Hunt's Duke of Gloucester' (D)   CTho
- 'Hunt's Early' (D) **new**   SKee
- 'Idared' (D) ♀H4   CWib ECrN SDea SKee
- 'Improved Dove' (Cider)   CCAT
- 'Improved Keswick' (C/D)   CEnd CTho
- 'Improved Lambrook Pippin' (Cider)   CCAT CTho CTri
- 'Improved Redstreak' (Cider)   CTho
- 'Ingall's Pippin' (D)   SKee
- 'Ingrid Marie' (D)   SDea SKee WJas
- 'Irish Peach' (D)   CAgr CCAT ECrN GBut GTwe MCoo SDea SFam SKee WJas
- 'Isaac Newton's Tree'   see *M. domestica* 'Flower of Kent'
- 'Isle of Wight Pippin' (D)   SDea
- 'Isle of Wight Russet' (D)   SDea
- 'Jackson's' (Cider)   see *M. domestica* 'Crimson King'
- 'James Grieve' (D) ♀H4   More than 30 suppliers
- 'Jerseymac' (D)   SDea
- 'Jester' (D)   ECrN GTwe SDea SKee
- 'Jimbo' **new**   LRHS
- 'John Standish' (D)   CAgr CCAT CTri GTwe SCrf SDea
- 'John Toucher's'   see *M. domestica* 'Crimson King'
- 'Johnny Andrews' (Cider)   CAgr CCAT CTho
- 'Johnny Voun' (D)   CEnd CTho
- 'Jonagold' (D) ♀H4   CTri CWib ECrN EMui GTwe LAst NWea SCrf SDea SFam SKee SPer WJas
- 'Jonagold Crowngold'   see *M. domestica* 'Crowngold'
§ - 'Jonagored'PBR (D)   ECrN SDea
- 'Jonared' (D)   GTwe
- 'Jonathan' (D)   SDea SKee
- 'Jordan's Weeping' (C)   GTwe SDea WJas
- 'Josephine' (D)   SDea
- 'Joybells' (D)   SKee
- 'Jubilee'   see *M. domestica* 'Royal Jubilee'
- 'Jumbo' **new**   LBuc MCoo SKee
- 'Jupiter'PBR (D) ♀H4   CCAT CDul CSBt CTri CWib ECrN GTwe LAst NPri SCoo SDea SKee WJas WOrn
- 'Kapai Red Jonathan' (D)   SDea
- 'Karmijn de Sonnaville' (D)   SDea SKee
§ - 'Katja' (D)   CAgr CCAT CCVT CDoC CTri CWib ECrN EMui EPfP GBut GTwe LAst LBuc SCoo SCrf SDea SKee SPer SPoG WHar WJas WOrn
- Katy   see *M. domestica* 'Katja'
- 'Kent' (D)   EMui GTwe MCoo NLar SCrf SDea SKee
- 'Kentish Fillbasket' (C)   SKee
- 'Kentish Pippin' (C/Cider/D)   SKee
- 'Kerry Pippin' (D)   GBut SKee
- 'Keswick Codlin' (C)   CTho ECrN GBut GTwe MCoo NLar NWea SDea SKee WJas
§ - 'Kidd's Orange Red' (D) ♀H4   CAgr CCAT CTri ECrN EMui GQui GTwe LAst LBuc LRHS SCrf SDea SFam SKee WJas
- 'Kill Boy'   CTho
- 'Killerton Sharp' (Cider)   CTho

- 'Killerton Sweet' (Cider) CTho
- 'King Byerd' (C/D) CEnd CTho
- 'King Charles' Pearmain' SKee
  (D)
- 'King Luscious' (D) SDea
§ - 'King of the Pippins' (D) CCAT CTho CTri ECrN
   ♀H4 GBut GTwe MCoo SCrf SDea SFam
      SKee WOrn
- 'King Russet' (D) ♀H4 SDea
- 'King's Acre Bountiful' WJas
  (C)
- 'King's Acre Pippin' (D) CCAT SDea SFam WJas
- 'Kingston Bitter' (Cider) CTho
- 'Kingston Black' CCAT CEnd CTho CTri GTwe
  (Cider/C) SDea SKee
- 'Kirton Fair' (D) CTho
- 'Knobby Russet' (D) SKee
- 'Lady Henniker' (D) CCAT CDul CTho ECrN GTwe
    SDea SKee WJas
- 'Lady Isabel' (D) SKee
- 'Lady of the Wemyss' (C) GBut GQui SKee
- 'Lady Sudeley' (D) CTho GBut SDea SKee
- 'Lady's Finger' (C/D) CEnd
- 'Lady's Finger of SKee
  Lancaster' (C/D)
- 'Lady's Finger of Offaly' SDea
  (D)
- 'Lake's Kernel' (D) CTho
- 'Lamb Abbey Pearmain' SKee
  (D)
- 'Lane's Prince Albert' CCAT CDul CSBt ECrN EMui
  (C) ♀H4 GBut GTwe MGos MRav MWat
      NWea SCoo SDea SFam SKee
      WJas WOrn
- 'Langley Pippin' (D) SDea
§ - 'Langworthy' (Cider) CCAT CTho
§ - 'Lass o' Gowrie' (C) GBut GQui SKee
§ - 'Laxton's Epicure' (D) CAgr ECrN GTwe LAst SDea SFam
   ♀H4 SKee WJas
§ - 'Laxton's Fortune' (D) CCAT CMac CSBt CTri CWib ECrN
   ♀H4 EMui GBut GTwe LAst NWea SCrf
      SDea SFam SKee WHar WJas
- 'Laxton's Pearmain' (D) MCoo
- 'Laxton's Rearguard' (D) WJas
- 'Laxton's Royalty' (D) SDea
§ - 'Laxton's Superb' (D) CBcs CCAT CCVT CDoC CSBt CTri
      CWib ECrN EMui ENot GTwe LAst
      LBuc LRHS MCoo MGan NEgg
      NPri SCrf SDea SKee SPer WHar
      WJas WOrn
- 'Leathercoat Russet' (D) CAgr SKee
- 'Leatherjacket' (C) SKee
- 'Lemon Pippin' (C) CCAT ECrN SDea SKee WJas
- 'Lemon Pippin of CTho
  Gloucestershire' (D)
- 'Lewis's Incomparable' SKee
  (C)
- 'Liberty' (D) GBut SDea
- 'Limberland' (C) CTho
- 'Limelight' (D) EMui LRHS MBri SCoo SKee
- 'Linda' (D) SKee
- 'Link Wonder' **new** CEnd
§ - 'Loddington' (C) SKee
- 'Lodi' (C) SDea
- 'London Pippin' (C) CAgr CTho SKee
- 'Longkeeper' (D) CAgr CEnd CTho
- 'Longstem' (Cider) CTho
- 'Lord Burghley' (D) GTwe SDea SKee
- 'Lord Derby' (C) CAgr CCAT CDul CMac CTho
      CWib ECrN EMui GBut GTwe LAst
      MBri SCrf SDea SFam SKee
- 'Lord Grosvenor' (C) GTwe SDea
- 'Lord Hindlip' (D) GTwe SDea SFam WJas
- 'Lord Lambourne' (D) CAgr CCAT CCVT CDoC CDul
   ♀H4 CSBt CTri CWib ECrN EPfP
      GTwe LAst LRHS MCoo MWat

      SCoo SCrf SDea SFam SKee SPer
      WBVN WHar WJas WOrn
- 'Lord of the Isles' (F) CAgr CCAT
- 'Lord Stradbroke' (C) SKee
- 'Lord Suffield' (C) CTri ECrN SKee
- 'Love Beauty' (D) GBut
- 'Lucombe's Pine' (D) CAgr CDul CEnd CTho ECrN
- 'Lucombe's Seedling' CTho
  (D)
- 'Mabbott's Pearmain' (D) SDea
- 'Maclean's Favourite' (D) SKee
- 'Madresfield Court' (D) SDea SKee WJas
- 'Maggie Sinclair' (D) GBut GQui
- 'Major' (Cider) CCAT
- 'Maldon Wonder' (D) SKee
- 'Malling Kent' (D) EMui SDea SFam
- 'Maltster' (D) SKee WJas
- 'Manaccan Primrose' CEnd
  (C/D)
- 'Manks Codlin' (C) GBut
- 'Margil' (D) CCAT GTwe SDea SFam SKee
- 'Marriage-maker' (D) SKee
- 'May Beauty' (D) SKee
- 'May Queen' (D) SDea SFam WJas
- 'Maypole'PBR (D/Ball) LRHS MGos SDea WJas
- 'Maypole 2000' (C/Ball) ENot
- 'McIntosh' (D) SKee
- 'Melba' (D) SKee
- 'Melon' (D) SDea
- 'Melrose' (D) ECrN GTwe
- 'Merchant Apple' (D) CCAT CTho
- 'Mère de Ménage' (C) SFam
- 'Meridian'PBR (D) CAgr CDoC ECrN EMui MBri SDea
      SKee
- 'Merton Knave' (D) GTwe SDea SFam
- 'Merton Russet' (D) SDea
- 'Merton Worcester' (D) ECrN SDea SKee
- 'Michaelmas Red' (D) GTwe SKee WJas
- 'Michelin' (Cider) CCAT CTri GTwe SDea SKee
      WOrn
- 'Miller's Seedling' (D) GTwe SKee WJas
- 'Millicent Barnes' (D) SDea
- 'Mollie's Delicious' (D) SKee
- 'Monarch' (C) CCAT CTri ECrN GBut GTwe SDea
      SFam SKee WJas
I - 'Mondial Gala' see *M. domestica* 'Gala Mondial'
- 'Monidel'PBR ECrN SKee
- 'Morgan's Sweet' CCAT CEnd CTho CTri SDea SKee
  (C/Cider)
- 'Moss's Seedling' (D) SDea
§ - 'Mother' (D) ♀H4 CAgr CCAT CDoC CTri ECrN
      GTwe SDea SFam SKee WJas
§ - 'Mutsu' (D) CCAT CTri ECrN GTwe LAst SCrf
      SDea SKee
- 'Nancy Jackson' (D) **new** SKee
- 'Nanny' (D) SKee
- 'Neild's Drooper' (D/C) SKee
  new
- 'Nemes Szercsika Alma' SKee
  (C)
- 'Nettlestone Pippin' (D) SDea
- 'Newton Wonder' (D/C) CAgr CCAT CDoC CMac CSBt
   ♀H4 CTho CTri CWib ECrN GTwe LAst
      LBuc SCrf SDea SFam SKee WJas
      WOrn
- 'Newtown Pippin' (D) SDea
- 'Nine Square' (D) CTho
- 'Nittany Red' (D) SDea
- 'No Pip' (C) CTho
- 'Nonpareil' (D) SKee
- 'Norfolk Beauty' (C) SKee
- 'Norfolk Beefing' (C) ECrN ERea LRHS SDea SFam SKee
- 'Norfolk Royal' (D) CDoC ECrN ERea GTwe SDea
      SKee
- 'Norfolk Royal Russet' GBut
  (D)

- 'Norfolk Summer Broadend' (C)	SKee	
- 'Norfolk Winter Coleman' (C)	SKee	
- 'Northcott Superb' (D)	CTho	
- 'Northern Greening' (C)	SKee	
§ - 'Northwood' (Cider)	CCAT CTho	
- 'Nutmeg Pippin' (D)	ECrN SDea	
- 'Nuvar Freckles' (D) **new**	SKee	
- 'Nuvar Gold' (D) **new**	SKee	
- 'Nuvar Golden Elf' **new**	SKee	
- 'Nuvar Golden Hills' (D) **new**	SKee	
- 'Nuvar Home Farm' (D) **new**	SKee	
- 'Nuvar Long Harvest' (D) **new**	SKee	
- 'Nuvar Melody' (D) **new**	SKee	
- 'Nuvar Red Gloss' (D) **new**	SKee	
- 'Oaken Pin' (C)	CCAT CTho	
§ - 'Obelisk'[PBR]	ENot NPri SDea	
- 'Old Pearmain' (D)	SDea	
- 'Old Somerset Russet' (D)	CTho	
- 'Opal' (D)	ECrN	
- 'Opalescent' (D)	SKee	
- 'Orleans Reinette' (D)	CAgr CCAT CTho CTri CWib ECrN GBut GTwe LBuc LRHS MWat SCrf SDea SFam SKee WJas	
- 'Oslin' (D)	GBut SKee	
- 'Owen Thomas' (D)	CTri	
- 'Oxford Conquest' (D)	SKee	
- 'Paignton Marigold' (Cider)	CTho	
- 'Pascoe's Pippin' (D/C)	CTho	
- 'Paulared' (D)	SKee	
- 'Payhembury' (C/Cider)	CTho	
- 'Pear Apple' (D)	CAgr CEnd CTho	
- 'Pearl' (D)	ECrN SDea	
- 'Peasgood's Nonsuch' (C) ♀H4	CAgr CCAT CDoC ECrN GTwe MGan SCrf SDea SFam SKee WJas WOrn	
- 'Pendragon' (D)	CTho	
- 'Penhallow Pippin' (D)	CTho	
- 'Peter Lock' (C/D)	CAgr CEnd CTho SKee	
- 'Peter's Pippin' (D)	SDea	
- 'Peter's Seedling' (D)	SDea	
- 'Pig's Nose Pippin' (D)	CEnd	
- 'Pig's Nose Pippin' Type III (D)	CAgr CTho	
- 'Pig's Snout' (Cider/C/D)	CCAT CEnd CTho	
- 'Pine Golden Pippin' (D)	SKee	
- 'Pitmaston Pine Apple' (D)	CCAT CTho CTri ECrN LAst LRHS MCoo SCrf SDea SFam SKee WJas WOrn	
- 'Pitmaston Russet Nonpareil' (D)	SKee	
- 'Pixie' (D) ♀H4	CCAT CWib GTwe LRHS SDea SFam SKee WJas	
- 'Plum Vite' (D)	CAgr CTho CTri	
- 'Plympton Pippin' (C)	CEnd CTho	
- 'Polka = 'Trajan'[PBR] (D/Ball)	ENot LRHS MGos SDea SKee	
- 'Polly' (C/D)	CEnd	
- 'Polly Whitehair' (C/D)	CTho SDea	
- 'Poltimore Seedling' **new**	CTho	
- 'Pomeroy of Somerset' (D)	CCAT CTho SKee	
- 'Ponsford' (C)	CAgr CCAT CTho	
- 'Port Allen Russet' (C/D)	GQui	
- 'Port Wine'	see *M. domestica* 'Harry Master's Jersey'	
- 'Porter's Perfection' (Cider)	CCAT	
- 'Princesse'	ECrN EMui SDea WBVN	
- 'Quarry Apple' (C)	CTho	

- 'Queen' (C)	CAgr CCAT CTho ECrN SKee	
- 'Queen Caroline' (C)	SKee	
- 'Queen Cox' (D)	ECrN EMui SDea SKee	
- 'Queen Cox' self-fertile	CWib EMui SDea	
- 'Queens' (D)	CTho	
- 'Quench' (D/Cider)	CTho	
- 'Radford Beauty'	MCoo	
- 'Rajka' (D)	SKee	
- 'Red Alkmene' (D)	MBri	
- 'Red Belle de Boskoop' (D)	CAgr	
§ - 'Red Blenheim' (C/D)	SKee	
- 'Red Bramley' (C)	CWib	
- 'Red Charles Ross' (C/D)	SDea	
- 'Red Delicious' (D)	SCrf	
- 'Red Devil' (D)	CAgr COtt CTri CWSG ECrN EMui GTwe LAst MBri MGan MNHC NLar SCoo SDea SKee SPoG WJas	
- 'Red Ellison' (D)	CCAT CTho CTri GTwe SCrf SDea	
- 'Red Elstar' (D)	SCrf	
- 'Red Falstaff'[PBR] (D)	CAgr CDoC ECrN EMui ERea LBuc LRHS MBri MCoo NBlu NLar SKee SPoG WBVN	
- 'Red Fuji' (D)	SDea	
- 'Red Jersey' (Cider)	CCAT	
- 'Red Joaneting' (D)	SKee	
- 'Red Jonagold'[PBR]	see *M. domestica* 'Jonagored'	
- 'Red Jonathan' (D)	SDea	
- 'Red Miller's Seedling' (D)	SCrf SDea	
- 'Red Rattler' (D)	CTho	
- 'Red Robin' (F)	CEnd	
- 'Red Roller' (D)	CTho	
- 'Red Ruby' (F)	CTho	
- 'Red Victoria' (C)	GTwe	
- 'Red Windsor'	EMui LRHS SCoo SKee SPoG	
§ - 'Redcoat Grieve' (D)	SDea	
- 'Redsleeves' (D)	CAgr ECrN GTwe SDea SKee	
- 'Redstrake' (Cider)	CCAT	
- 'Reine des Reinettes'	see *M. domestica* 'King of the Pippins'	
- 'Reinette d'Obry' (Cider)	CCAT	
- 'Reinette du Canada' (D)	SKee	
- 'Reinette Rouge Etoilée' (D)	SDea	
- 'Reverend Greeves' (C)	SDea	
- 'Reverend W. Wilks' (C)	CAgr CCAT CDoC CTri ECrN EMui LAst LRHS MWat SCrf SDea SFam SKee WJas WOrn	
- 'Ribston Pippin' (D) ♀H4	CCAT CTho CWib ECrN GBut GTwe LRHS MCoo MWat SCrf SDea SFam SKee WJas WOrn	
- 'Rival' (D)	CAgr SDea WJas	
- 'Rome Beauty' (D)	SDea	
- 'Rosemary Russet' (D) ♀H4	CAgr CCAT CTho GBut GTwe MCoo SCrf SDea SFam SKee	
- 'Ross Nonpareil' (D)	CAgr GTwe SDea SKee	
- 'Rosy Blenheim' (D)	SKee	
- 'Rough Pippin' (D)	CEnd	
- 'Roundway Magnum Bonum' (C)	CAgr CCAT CTho SDea	
§ - 'Roxbury Russet' (D)	SKee	
§ - 'Royal Gala' (D) ♀H4	ECrN EMui LAst SDea	
§ - 'Royal Jubilee' (C)	CCAT SKee	
- 'Royal Russet' (C)	CEnd ECrN SDea	
- 'Royal Snow' (D)	SKee	
- 'Royal Somerset' (C/Cider)	CCAT CTho	
- 'Rubens' (D)	SKee	
- 'Rubinette' (D)	COtt ECrN EMil GTwe MGan MGos SDea	
- 'Saint Ailred' **new**	SKee	
- 'Saint Cecilia' (D)	SDea WJas	
§ - 'Saint Edmund's Pippin' (D) ♀H4	CTho ECrN GTwe SCrf SDea SFam SKee	

- 'Saint Edmund's Russet' — see *M. domestica* 'Saint Edmund's Pippin'
- 'Saint Everard' (D) — SKee
- 'Saint Magdalen' (D) — SKee
- 'Saltcote Pippin' (D) — SKee
- 'Sam Young' (D) — CAgr SKee
- 'Sandlands' (D) — SDea
- 'Sandringham' (C) — ECrN SKee
- 'Sanspareil' (D) — CAgr SKee
- 'Saturn' — CAgr CTri EMui GBut GTwe SDea SKee SPoG
- 'Saw Pits' (F) — CAgr CEnd
- 'Scarlet Nonpareil' (D) — SDea SKee
- 'Scarlet Pimpernel' (D) — SCrf
- 'Scilly Pearl' (C) — WJas
- 'Scotch Bridget' (C) — GBut NBid SCoo SKee WJas WOrn
- 'Scotch Dumpling' (C) — GBut GTwe MCoo
- 'Scrumptious'[PBR] (D) — CAgr CDoC ENot EREa LBuc LRHS MBri MLan NBlu NLar SCoo SKee SPer SPoG WBVN
- 'Seabrook's Red' (D) — ECrN SKee
- 'Sercombe's Natural' (Cider) — CTho
- 'Severn Bank' (C) — CCAT CTho
- 'Shakespeare' (D) — WJas
- 'Sharleston Pippin' (D) — SKee
- 'Sheep's Nose' (C) — CCAT SDea SKee
- 'Shenandoah' (C) — SKee
- 'Sidney Strake' (C) — CAgr CEnd
- 'Sir Isaac Newton's' — see *M. domestica* 'Flower of Kent'
- 'Sir John Thornycroft' (D) — SDea
- 'Slack Ma Girdle' (Cider) — CCAT CTho
- 'Smart's Prince Arthur' (C) — SDea
- 'Snell's Glass Apple' — see *M. domestica* 'Glass Apple'
- 'Somerset Lasting' (C) — CTho
- 'Somerset Redstreak' (Cider) — CCAT CTho GTwe
- 'Sops in Wine' (C/Cider) — CCAT CTho
- 'Sour Bay' (Cider) — CAgr CTho
- 'Sour Natural' — see *M. domestica* 'Langworthy'
- 'Spartan' (D) — CCAT CDoC CSBt CTri CWib ECrN EMui GTwe LAst LRHS MGan MGos NEgg NPri SCoo SCrf SDea SFam SKee SPer SPoG WJas WOrn
- 'Spencer' (D) — CTri ECrN SKee
- 'Spotted Dick' (Cider) — CTho
- 'Stable Jersey' (Cider) — CCAT
- 'Stamford Pippin' (D) — SDea
- 'Stanway Seedling' (C) — SKee
- 'Star of Devon' (D) — CCAT CEnd SDea
- 'Stark' (D) — SDea
- 'Starking' (D) — ECrN
- 'Starkrimson' (D) — SKee
- 'Stembridge Cluster' (Cider) — CCAT
- 'Stembridge Jersey' (Cider) — CCAT
- 'Steyne Seedling' (D) — SDea
- 'Stirling Castle' (C) — CAgr GBut GQui GTwe SKee
- 'Stobo Castle' (C) — GQui SKee
- 'Stockbearer' (C) — CTho
- 'Stoke Edith Pippin' (D) — WOrn
- 'Stoke Red' (Cider) — CCAT CTho
- 'Stone's' — see *M. domestica* 'Loddington'
- 'Stoup Leadington' (C) — SKee
- 'Strawberry Pippin' (D) — CTho WJas
- 'Striped Beefing' (C) — ECrN SKee
- 'Sturmer Pippin' (D) — CCAT CDul CSBt ECrN GTwe MWat SCrf SDea SFam SKee WJas
* - 'Sugar Apple' — CTho
- 'Sugar Bush' (C/D) — CTho
- 'Summer Golden Pippin' (D) — SKee
- 'Summerred' (D) — ECrN EMil
- 'Sunburn' (D) — ECrN SKee

- 'Sunnydale' (D/C) — SDea
- 'Sunrise'[PBR] (D) — EMui SKee
- 'Sunset' (D) ♀[H4] — More than 30 suppliers
- 'Suntan' (D) ♀[H4] — CCAT CWib ECrN EMil GTwe LAst MWat SDea SKee
- 'Superb' — see *M. domestica* 'Laxton's Superb'
- 'Surprise' (D) — GTwe
- 'Sweet Alford' (Cider) — CCAT CTho ECrN
- 'Sweet Bay' (Cider) — CAgr CTho
- 'Sweet Caroline' (D) — ECrN
- 'Sweet Cleave' (Cider) — CCAT CTho
- 'Sweet Coppin' (Cider) — CCAT CTho CTri
- 'Sweet Ermgaard' (D) — ECrN
- 'Sweet Society' (D) — EMui EREa LBuc LRHS SKee
- 'Tale Sweet' (Cider) — CCAT CTho
- 'Tamar Beauty' (F) — CEnd
- 'Tan Harvey' (Cider) — CCAT CEnd CTho
- 'Taunton Cross' (D) — CAgr
- 'Taunton Fair Maid' (Cider) — CCAT CTho
- 'Taylor's' (Cider) — CCAT SDea
- 'Ten Commandments' (D/Cider) — CCAT SDea WJas
- 'Tewkesbury Baron' (D) — CTho
- 'The Rattler' (F) — CEnd
- 'Thomas Rivers' (C) — SDea
- 'Thorle Pippin' (D) — GBut SKee
- 'Tidicombe Seedling' (D) — CTho
- 'Tom Putt' (C) — CCAT CCVT CTho CTri CWib ECrN GTwe LBuc SDea SKee WJas WOrn
- 'Tommy Knight' (D) — CAgr CCAT CEnd CTho
- 'Topaz' (D) — SKee
- 'Totnes Apple' (D) — CTho
- 'Tower of Glamis' (C) — GQui GTwe SKee
- Town Farm Number 59 (Cider) — CTho
- 'Tregonna King' (C/D) — CCAT CEnd CTho
- 'Tremlett's Bitter' (Cider) — CCAT CTho SDea
- 'Twenty Ounce' (C) — CCAT GTwe WJas
§ - 'Tydeman's Early Worcester' (D) — CAgr CLnd CWib ECrN GTwe SDea SKee WJas
- 'Tydeman's Late Orange' (D) — CTri ECrN GTwe LAst LRHS MCoo MGan SDea SFam SKee WOrn
- 'Upton Pyne' (D) — CCAT CTho SDea SKee
- 'Vallis Apple' (Cider) — CTho
- 'Veitch's Perfection' (C/D) — CTho
- 'Venus Pippin' (C/D) — CEnd
- 'Vickey's Delight' (D) — SDea
- 'Vileberie' (Cider) — CCAT
- 'Vista-bella' (D) — ECrN GTwe SDea SKee WJas
- 'Wagener' (D) — ECrN SDea SKee
- 'Waltham Abbey Seedling' (C) — ECrN
- Waltz = 'Telamon'[PBR] (D/Ball) — LRHS MGos SDea SKee
- 'Warner's King' (C) ♀[H4] — CTho CTri SCrf SDea SKee WJas
- 'Warrior' — CTho
- 'Wealthy' (D) — SDea
- 'Wellington' (C) — see *M. domestica* 'Dummellor's Seedling'
- 'Wellington' (Cider) — CTho
§ - 'Wellspur' (D) — GTwe
- 'Wellspur Red Delicious' — see *M. domestica* 'Wellspur'
- 'Welsh Russet' (D) — SDea
- 'West View Seedling' (D) — SKee
- 'White Alphington' (Cider) — CTho
- 'White Close Pippin' (Cider) — CTho
- 'White Jersey' (Cider) — CCAT
- 'White Joaneting' (D) — GTwe
- 'White Melrose' (C) — GBut GTwe LRHS MCoo SDea
- 'White Transparent' (C/D) — SDea SKee
- 'Whitpot Sweet' (F) **new** — CEnd

- 'Wick White Styre' (Cider)	CTho
- 'William Crump' (D)	CCAT CTho ECrN SDea SFam WJas
- 'Winston' (D) ♀H4	CAgr CCAT CCVT CSBt CTri ECrN GTwe NWea SCrf SDea SFam
- 'Winter Banana' (D)	ECrN SDea SKee
- 'Winter Gem' (D)	CAgr CDoC ECrN EMui ERea LBuc LRHS MBri MGan MGos SDea SKee SPoG WBVN
- 'Winter Lawrence'	CTho
- 'Winter Lemon' (C/D)	GQui
- 'Winter Peach' (D/C)	CEnd CTho ECrN
- 'Winter Pearmain' (D)	SKee
- 'Winter Quarrenden' (D)	SDea
- 'Winter Queening' (D/C)	SDea
- 'Winter Stubbard' (C)	CTho
- 'Woodbine'	see *M. domestica* 'Northwood'
- 'Woolbrook Pippin' (D)	CAgr CCAT CDul CTho
- 'Woolbrook Russet' (C)	CCAT CTho ECrN
- 'Worcester Pearmain' (D) ♀H4	CBcs CCAT CCVT CDoC CDul CSBt CTho CTri CWib ECrN EMui ENot EPfP GBut GTwe LAst LBuc LRHS MWat NPri NWea SCoo SDea SFam SKee SPer SPoG WHar WJas WOrn
- 'Wormsley Pippin' (D)	ECrN
- 'Wyatt's Seedling'	see *M. domestica* 'Langworthy'
- 'Wyken Pippin' (D)	CCAT ECrN GBut GTwe SDea SFam SKee WJas
- 'Yarlington Mill' (Cider)	CCAT CTho CTri SDea SKee
- 'Yellow Ingestrie' (D)	SFam SKee WJas
- 'Yellow Styre' (Cider)	CTho
- 'Yorkshire Aromatic' (C)	GBut SKee
- 'Yorkshire Greening' (C)	SKee
- 'Zabergäu Renette' (D)	SKee
'Donald Wyman'	NLar SCoo
'Echtermeyer'	see *M.* x *gloriosa* 'Oekonomierat Echtermeyer'
§ 'Evereste' ♀H4	More than 30 suppliers
florentina	CMCN CTho EPfP GIBF LTwo SCoo SSpi
floribunda ♀H4	More than 30 suppliers
'Fontana' **new**	MGos
'Gardener's Gold'	CEnd CTho
§ x *gloriosa* 'Oekonomierat Echtermeyer'	CCAT SDea WDin WJas
'Golden Gem'	CCAT EPfP GBut GTwe LRHS MAsh MDun SKee
'Golden Hornet'	see *M.* x *zumi* 'Golden Hornet'
'Harry Baker'	EMui ERea LRHS MAsh MBlu NLar SCoo SLim
'Hillieri'	see *M.* x *schiedeckeri* 'Hillieri'
hupehensis ♀H4	CCAT CCVT CDul CEnd CLnd CMCN CSBt CTho EPfP GTwe LRHS MBlu MRav SCrf SFam SHBN SLPl SPer WMou WPGP WPat
'Hyde Hall Spire'	LRHS MBri MGos SCoo
'John Downie' (C) ♀H4	More than 30 suppliers
'Kaido'	see *M.* x *micromalus*
kansuensis	CLnd EPfP GIBF WCwm
'Laura'PBR	COtt CWSG EMui EPfP LRHS MAsh MBlu MGos NLar SCoo SKee SPoG
x *magdeburgensis*	CCVT CDul CLnd CSBt
'Mandarin'	MAsh
'Marshal Ōyama'	CTho MBlu
'Mary Potter'	CTho
§ x *micromalus*	CLnd
x *moerlandsii*	CLnd
- 'Liset'	CCVT CEnd CLnd CWib EBee ECrN MBri MRav NEgg SCoo SFam SPer SPoG WFar WJas
§ - 'Profusion'	CBcs CDul CLnd CTri CWSG EBee ECrN ELan ENot LAst LRHS MBri

	MGan MGos MRav MSwo NEgg NWea SCrf SHBN SPer WBVN WDin WFar WJas
- 'Profusion Improved'	CCAT CEnd COtt CSBt CWSG MAsh MWat SCoo SKee WOrn
niedzwetzkyana	see *M. pumila* 'Niedzwetzkyana'
'Nuvar Carnival' **new**	SKee
'Nuvar Dusty Red' **new**	SKee
'Nuvar Marble' **new**	SKee
'Nuvar Pearl' **new**	SKee
'Nuvar Red Lantern' **new**	SKee
orthocarpa	CLnd
Perpetu	see *M.* 'Evereste'
'Pink Glow'	LRHS MAsh MBlu NLar SCoo SLim SPoG
'Pink Mushroom'	LRHS NLar SCoo
'Pink Perfection'	CDoC CEnd CLnd ENot LRHS MDun SHBN SKee SPer
Pom'Zaï = 'Courtabri'	CDoC
'Prairie Fire'	MAsh MBri SCoo
prattii	CLnd CTho EPfP
'Princeton Cardinal' **new**	EBee
'Professor Sprenger'	see *M.* x *zumi* 'Professor Sprenger'
'Profusion'	see *M.* x *moerlandsii* 'Profusion'
prunifolia 'Fastigiata'	GIBF
- 'Pendula'	MGan
- var. *prunifolia*	GIBF
- var. *rinkii*	GIBF
pumila 'Cowichan'	ECrN
- 'Dartmouth'	CCAT CDul CLnd CSBt CSam CTho CTri ECrN NEgg SFam
- 'Montreal Beauty'	SCoo WJas WOrn
§ - 'Niedzwetzkyana'	CLnd
§ x *purpurea* 'Aldenhamensis'	CCAT CLnd SDea WDin WOrn
- 'Eleyi'	CDul CLnd ECrN LAst MGan MRav NWea WJas
- 'Lemoinei'	CLnd ECrN EWTr
- 'Neville Copeman'	CDoC CDul CLnd CTri ECrN MBlu MGos SMHT SPur WJas
- 'Pendula'	see *M.* x *gloriosa* 'Oekonomierat Echtermeyer'
'R.J. Fulcher'	CLnd CTho
'Ralph Shay'	CLnd
'Red Ace'	CDul
'Red Barron'	CLnd
'Red Glow'	CLnd COtt EBee ECrN MAsh WJas
'Red Jade'	see *M.* x *schiedeckeri* 'Red Jade'
'Red Obelisk'	LRHS MBri SPoG
'Robinson'	MAsh SPoG
§ x *robusta*	CLnd CTri GTwe LRHS LSRN NWea SCrf SLon
- 'Red Sentinel' ♀H4	More than 30 suppliers
- 'Red Siberian'	ECrN SDea SHBN SPer
- 'Yellow Siberian'	CLnd SPer
rockii	GIBF
'Royal Beauty' ♀H4	CDoC CDul CLnd CWib EGra ENot EPfP GTwe LAst LRHS MAsh MBri MGos MRav MSwo SCoo SCrf SMHT SPer WDin WHar WOrn
'Royalty'	More than 30 suppliers
'Rudolph'	CCAT CCVT CDul CLnd EBee ECrN LRHS MAsh MGos MRav SCoo SLim SPer SPoG WJas WOrn
sargentii	see *M. toringo* subsp. *sargentii*
'Satin Cloud'	CLnd
'Scarlett' **new**	LRHS MBri
§ x *scheideckeri* 'Hillieri'	CCAT CDul CLnd ECrN MAsh SFam
§ - 'Red Jade'	More than 30 suppliers
Siberian crab	see *M.* x *robusta*
sieboldii	see *M. toringo*
- 'Wooster' **new**	CLnd
sikkimensis	GIBF WHCr
- B&SWJ 2431	WCru
'Silver Drift'	CLnd

'Snowcloud'	CCAT CDul CEnd CLnd EBee ECrN LRHS MAsh MBlu SHBN SLim SPer WOrn
spectabilis	CLnd
'Street Parade'	CLnd
'Striped Beauty'	CTho
x **sublobata**	CTho
'Sun Rival'	CCAT CDoC CDul CEnd COtt CSBt CWSG EMui EPfP GTwe LRHS MAsh MBri MDun MGos SCoo SFam SLim SPoG WHar WJas
sylvestris	CArn CCVT CDul CLnd CRWN CTri ECrN EPfP LBuc MRav NBee NWea WDin WMou
§ **toringo**	CLnd CTho ECrN EPfP GIBF SCoo SSpi WSHC
- var. **arborescens**	CTho GIBF
§ - subsp. **sargentii**	CDul CLnd CMCN CTho ECrN ENot LAst MBri MGos MRav NWea SFam SPer SPoG WNor
- - 'Tina'	CLnd
toringoides	see *M. bhutanica*
- 'Mandarin'	NLar SCoo
transitoria ♀H4	CCAT CDoC CDul CEnd CLnd CTho EBee ECrN ELan EMil EPfP GIBF LRHS MAsh MBlu MBri NWea SCoo SSpi WPGP
- 'Thornhayes Tansy'	CTho
trilobata	CCAT CLnd CTho EPfP LRHS MBlu MBri MGos NLar SCoo SPoG
- 'Guardsman'	MAsh MBri NLar
tschonoskii ♀H4	More than 30 suppliers
'Van Eseltine'	CCAT CDul CLnd CSBt CWSG CWib ECrN GTwe LRHS MAsh MBri MWat NEgg SFam SPer SPoG WJas WPat
'Veitch's Scarlet'	CDul CLnd CSBt CTho GTwe SFam
§ 'White Star'	CDoC CDul CSBt CWSG ECrN SCoo SLim SPoG
'Winter Gold'	CDoC CDul CLnd SCrf SPoG
'Wisley Crab'	CLnd EMil GTwe SDea SFam SKee
yunnanensis	EPfP GIBF
- var. **veitchii**	CTho GIBF
x **zumi** var. **calocarpa**	CLnd CTho
§ - 'Golden Hornet' ♀H4	More than 30 suppliers
§ - 'Professor Sprenger'	CLnd CSam EPfP

Malva (Malvaceae)

alcea	CAgr EPfP
- var. **fastigiata**	CArn EMan ERou EShb LRHS MBow NBid NBro NBur SPer SRms WPer
bicolor	see *Lavatera maritima*
fastigiata	SMar
'Gibbortello'	CCge NBur
moschata	CAgr CArn CBcs CElw CHrt CPrp CRWN CSev EBee EChP ECtt ELan EPfP ERou MBow MHer MNHC NBlu NMir SECG SIde SPer SPlb SWat WGwG WHer WMoo WWye
- f. **alba** ♀H4	More than 30 suppliers
- - 'Pirouette'	WHen
- 'Pink Perfection'	EBee EShb NPri
- 'Romney Marsh'	see *Althaea officinalis* 'Romney Marsh'
- **rosea**	EPfP GMaP LAst NBlu NCot NEgg NPer SPoG SWvt WWeb
sylvestris	CAgr CArn GWCH MBow MNHC NBro NMir NSco SMad SWat WHer WJek WMoo WWye
- 'Bardsey Blue' **new**	WGwG
- 'Brave Heart'	CMMP EShb GBri NBur NLar SPav SWvt
I - 'Magic Hollyhock' (d)	SGar
- Marina = 'Dema' PBR	ELan NLar
- subsp. **mauritiana**	CHea EBee EPfP GBri NPer WMoo

- - 'Bibor Fehlo'	CSpe EWin NBur WCFE
- 'Mystic Merlin'	CBgR CMMP EBee SPav
- 'Perry's Blue'	NPer
- 'Primley Blue'	CBcs CBgR CElw EBee EChP ECha ECtt ELan EMan EPfP GBri GMaP MRav MTho NBPC NBlu NCot NGdn NPer NSti SMad SPer WBrE WFar
- 'Richard Perry'	NPer
- 'Zebrina'	CMMP GBri LDai LSou NBur NGdn NPer NPri SEND SWvt WBrE WMoo WRha
verticillata 'Crispa'	CAgr

Malvastrum (Malvaceae)

I x **hypomadarum**	see *Anisodontea* x *hypomadara* (Sprague) D.M. Bates
lateritium	More than 30 suppliers

Malvaviscus (Malvaceae)

arboreus	CHll CKob LEdu XPep
- var. **mexicanus**	CKob CPLG ERea SYvo
- pink	CKob

mandarin see *Citrus reticulata*

mandarin, Cleopatra see *Citrus reshni*

Mandevilla (Apocynaceae)

§ x **amabilis**	CCCN
- 'Alice du Pont' ♀H1	CBcs CCCN CPlN CRHN CSpe CTbh ELan ERea EShb SOWG
x **amoena**	see *M.* x *amabilis*
boliviensis ♀H1	ELan SOWG
hirsuta	CPlN
§ **laxa** ♀H2	CHEx CHll CPlN ELan ERea EShb SAga SBrw SHFr SOWG WCMO WCot WCru WHrl WSHC
sanderi	CCCN EShb MBri
- 'Rosea'	CSpe ERea
splendens ♀H1	CPlN EBak EPfP LRHS SOWG
suaveolens	see *M. laxa*

Mandragora (Solanaceae)

autumnalis	CWan GCal ITer LBBr LEdu MGol MSal NJOw NLar SMad
caulescens	CFir
§ **officinarum**	EEls GCal GCrs GPoy LEdu MGol MHer MSal NGHP SMad WCMO

Manettia (Rubiaceae)

inflata	see *M. luteorubra*
§ **luteorubra**	CCCN ELan WCot

Manfreda see *Agave*

Mangifera (Anacardiaceae)

indica new	SDEP

Manglietia (Magnoliaceae)

chevalieri HWJ 533	WCru
conifera	CBcs SSpi WPGP
fordiana	CBcs
insignis	CBcs CHEx SSpi WPGP
yuyuanensis new	CBcs

Manihot (Euphorbiaceae)

esculenta 'Variegata'	CKob EAmu

Mansoa (Bignoniaceae)

hymenaea	CPlN

Maranta (Marantaceae)

leuconeura var. **erythroneura** ♀H1	EShb XBlo
- var. **kerchoveana** ♀H1	CHal LRHS MBri XBlo

Margyricarpus (Rosaceae)
§ **pinnatus**   CFee CPLG CPle CSpe GEdr GGar MMHG NWCA WPer
   setosus   see *M. pinnatus*

Mariscus see *Cyperus*

marjoram, pot see *Origanum onites*

marjoram, sweet see *Origanum majorana*

marjoram, wild, or oregano see *Origanum vulgare*

Marrubium (Lamiaceae)
   candidissimum   see *M. incanum*
   cylleneum   ECha
*   - 'Velvetissimum'   SBla WCHb
   friwaldskyanum   XPep
   'Gold Leaf'   ECha
§   **incanum**   EChP EGoo EMan IFro NCGa WEas
   libanoticum   ECha WPer
   pestalloziae   EBee
   supinum   CArn EBee XPep
   vulgare   CArn CWan ELau GBar GPoy GWCH MHer MNHC SECG SIde WCHb WGHP WHer WPer WSel WWye
   - 'Green Pompon'   ELau NLar

Marshallia (Asteraceae)
   grandiflora   CDes EBee NLar SUsu
   trinerva   EBee SUsu WHil

Marsilea (Marsileaceae)
   quadrifolia   IHMH WWpP

Marsippospermum (Juncaceae)
   gracile **new**   ECou

Mascarena see *Hyophorbe*

Massonia (Hyacinthaceae)
   depressa   CStu
   echinata   CMon CStu
   aff. echinata   CStu
   pustulata   CMon CStu

Matricaria (Asteraceae)
   chamomilla   see *M. recutita*
   maritima   see *Tripleurosperma maritimum*
   parthenium   see *Tanacetum parthenium*
§   recutita   GPoy MNHC
   tchihatchewii   XPep

Matteuccia (Woodsiaceae)
   intermedia   see *Onoclea intermedia*
   orientalis   CLAP ERod EWsh GCal MAsh MWgw NGby NLar NOrc WFar
   pensylvanica   CLAP EMon ITim NHol
   struthiopteris ♀H4   More than 30 suppliers
   - 'Bedraggled Feathers'   EMon
*   - 'Depauperata'   CLAP
   - 'Jumbo'   CLAP

Matthiola (Brassicaceae)
§   **fruticulosa**   EBee EWin
   - 'Alba'   CDes EBee EWin WPGP
   - subsp. perennis   EBee NWCA WHal
   incana   CBos MArl WCMO WGwG WMnd WPer WRHF
   - alba   ELan GBBs LSou NBir SPav WBVN WCMO WCot WPtf
   - purple   LPhx LSou WCMO WCot

   thessala   see *M. fruticulosa*
   white perennial   CArn CHad CHrt CMea CMil CSev CSpe ECGP ERou ETow LPhx LRav MAvo MSte WGwG WPer SEND SMeo SWal WEas

Maurandella (Scrophulariaceae)
§   **antirrhiniflora**   CSec LRHS

Maurandya (Scrophulariaceae)
§   **barclayana**   CHll CSpe ITer MBri SGar WRos
   - alba   CSpe
   'Bridal Bouquet' **new**   LSou
   erubescens   see *Lophospermum erubescens*
   lophantha   see *Lophospermum scandens*
   lophospermum   see *Lophospermum scandens*
   'Pink Ice'   see *Lophospermum scandens* 'Pink Ice'
   'Red Dragon'   see *Lophospermum* 'Red Dragon'
§   'Victoria Falls'   SOWG

Maytenus (Celastraceae)
   boaria   CMCN EPfP LEdu NLar SAPC SArc SLon WFar WPGP
   chubutensis   LEdu
   disticha   LEdu
   magellanica   WFar

Mazus (Scrophulariaceae)
   reptans   EBee ECho EDAr EMan EPfP GEdr NFla NHol NPer NWCA WBVN WPer
   - 'Albus'   EBee ECho EDAr EMFW LAst NHol NJOw SPlb WPer

Mecardonia (Scrophulariaceae)
   'Goldflake' **new**   EWin LSou NPri

Meconopsis ✿ (Papaveraceae)
   aculeata   GGGa
   - CC 4675   GKev
   baileyi   see *M. betonicifolia*
   Ballyrogan form   GEdr IBlr
   x beamishii   GBuc GFle
§   **betonicifolia** ♀H4   More than 30 suppliers
   - var. alba   CSec CWCL EAEE EBee ELan EPfP GAbr GBuc GGGa GGar GKev GMaP GMac ITim NChi NCob NEgg NLar SPer SRms WPnP
   - 'Glacier Blue'   GAbr GGar
   - 'Hensol Violet'   EBee EChP GBuc GCal GCrs GFle GGGa GGar GKev GMac ITim NLar WViv
   - purple   ITim
   cambrica   CHrt CTri EBee EHrv ELan EMar GGar MBow NCot NHol NPri SGar SIng SPer WAbe WBrk WFar WHen WHer WPnP WPtf WWye
   - 'Anne Greenaway' (d)   ELan WCot
   - var. aurantiaca   LSou SBch
   - flore-pleno (d)   GBuc MTho NBid
   - - orange (d)   GKev NBid NBir NPen NPol WAbe WCot WHen
   - - yellow (d)   WCot
§   - 'Frances Perry'   ETow GBuc GCal GKev IBlr SWal WCot WFar WRos
   - 'Muriel Brown' (d)   EBee GKev
   - 'Rubra'   see *M. cambrica* 'Frances Perry'
   chelidoniifolia   GCal IBlr IGor NBid WCru WFar
   delavayi   GGGa
   dhwojii   GBri GKev NEgg
   discigera HWJK 2282   WCru
   (Fertile Blue Group)   see *M.* (Fertile Blue Group)
   'Blue Ice'   'Lingholm'
N   - 'Lingholm'   CAby CLAP CPLG CPne CSam EBee EShb GBBs GBuc GCal GCrs

		GEdr GFle GGar GKev GMaP IPot ITer ITim LHop MDun MWgw NCGa NChi NEgg NGdn WLin WPGP WViv
N	George Sherriff Group	EBee GAbr GBuc GCal GEdr IBlr NBir
N	- 'Ascreavie'	GCrs GMaP
N	- 'Branklyn' ambig.	EBee GAbr GBri IBlr WFar WPGP
N	- 'Huntfield'	GCrs GMaP
N	- 'Jimmy Bayne'	GAbr GBuc GCrs GEdr GGGa GMaP
N	- 'Spring Hill'	GBuc IBlr
N	*grandis* misapplied	see *M.* George Sherriff Group
N	*grandis* ambig.	CHar CPLG CWCL EGle GEdr GGGa ITim MNrw NEgg NSla SBla SPoG SRms WAbe WBVN WHlf WPnP WViv
	grandis Prain	GFle GKev
	- from Sikkim	GCrs GFle
	- GWJ 9275	WCru
	- GS 600	see *M.* George Sherriff Group
	- HWJK 2304	WCru
	- 'Alba'	GAbr
	- Balruddery form	GGGa
	grandis x *regia*	GBuc
	henrici	GGGa
	horridula	GFle GGGa GKev MTho NEgg NLar
	- BWJ 7983	WCru
	- HWJK 2293	WCru
*	- *alba*	GKev
	- var. *racemosa*	see *M. racemosa* var. *racemosa*
N	(Infertile Blue Group) 'Bobby Masterton'	GBuc GCrs
N	- 'Crewdson Hybrid'	EBee EChP GBuc GCrs GMaP NLar
N	- 'Cruickshank'	GCrs
N	- 'Dawyck'	see *M. (Infertile Blue Group)* 'Slieve Donard'
N	- 'Mrs Jebb'	GBuc GCrs GMaP
N	- 'Slieve Donard' ♀H4	GAbr GBri GBuc GCrs GMaP IBlr
	integrifolia	GFle GGGa GGar
	'Keillour'	GKev
	Kingsbarns hybrids	GCrs GGGa
	latifolia	NEgg
	'Mrs McMurtrie'	IBlr
	napaulensis	CPLG CSam EBee ENot GAbr GCrs GEdr GGGa GGar GKev GMaP IBlr LHop LRHS MDun NChi NEgg NLar SPoG WCAu WHil WLin WMoo WPnP
	- GWJ 9264	WCru
	- pink-flowered	CBcs EBee GKev NEgg NGdn WPGP
	- red-flowered	CBcs GBuc ITim MDun WCru
	- white flowered	CSec GKev
	nudicaulis	see *Papaver nudicaule*
	'Ormswell' ambig.	GBuc IBlr
	paniculata	CSec GGGa GKev IBlr ITim MDun NBir NEgg NLAp WAbe WLin
	- from Ghunsa, Nepal	CDes CLAP EGle
	- GWJ 9312	WCru
	- HWJK 2167	WCru
	- HWJK 2315	WCru
	- ginger foliage	GEdr MDun
	pseudointegrifolia	GGGa NEgg
	- B&SWJ 7595	WCru
	punicea	GCrs GGGa
	quintuplinervia ♀H4	CBos CLAP GBri GCrs GEdr GFle GGGa GMaP IBlr IGor NBid NBir NRya NSla WHal
	- 'Kaye's Compact'	GBuc GEdr IBlr
	racemosa	GFle
§	- var. *racemosa*	GFle
	regia	GAbr GKev LHop NLar WLin WMoo
	robusta	CPne GKev

x *sheldonii* misapplied (sterile)	see *M.* Infertile Blue Group
N x *sheldonii* ambig.	CBcs CHar EBee ENot GAbr GBin GBuc GGGa ITim LAst MBri MDun NBPC NBir SPer SPoG SRms WCru WFar WPnP WViv
x *sheldonii* G.Taylor	NPer WHlf
simplicifolia	GGGa NEgg
superba	GBuc GGGa NEgg
villosa	CPLG GBuc GFle GGGa GKev IBlr WCru
wallichii Hook.	CMil GGGa GKev NEgg NLar
- GWJ 9400	WCru
- white-flowered	GKev
'Willie Duncan'	CSec GMaP

Medeola (Convallariaceae)

virginica	WCru

Medicago (Papilionaceae)

arabica new	MBow
arborea	CArn SEND SPlb XPep
sativa	NLar WHer WSFF

Medinilla (Melastomataceae)

magnifica ♀H1	LRHS MBri

medlar see *Mespilus germanica*

Meehania (Lamiaceae)

cordata	CDes CLAP EBee NLar
fargesii new	CLAP
urticifolia	EBee EPPr MHar MSte WSHC WTMC
- B&SWJ 1210	WCru
- 'Wandering Minstrel' (v)	CDes CLAP EBee EMan WCot

Megacarpaea (Brassicaceae)

polyandra	WCot

Melaleuca (Myrtaceae)

acerosa	SOWG
acuminata	SPlb
alternifolia	CArn ECou ELau EOHP EShb GBar GPoy IDee MGol MHer MSal NTHB SOWG SPlb WHer
armillaris	CBcs CBgR CCCN CDoC CTrC IDee SGar SOWG SPlb
- pink	SOWG
bracteata	ECou
citrina	SOWG
coccinea	SOWG
cuticularis	SPlb
decora	SOWG
decussata	ECou SOWG SPlb
elliptica	SOWG
ericifolia	CTri SOWG SPlb
filifolia	SOWG
fulgens	EShb SOWG SPlb
- apricot	SOWG
*	- 'Hot Pink'	SOWG
- purple-flowered	SOWG
gibbosa	CFwr CPLG ECou IArd IDee SOWG WSHC
holosericea misapplied	see *M. smartiorum*
huegelii	SOWG
hypericifolia	CPLG CTrC ECou EDsa SOWG SPlb
incana	SOWG
lateritia	ECou EShb SOWG
leucadendra	MSal
linariifolia	ECou SPlb
nesophila	ECou EShb IDee SOWG SPlb
platycalyx	SOWG
pulchella	EShb SOWG
pungens	SPlb

pustulata	ECou EShb SOWG
radula	EShb SOWG
* rosmarinifolia	SOWG
scabra	EShb
§ smartiorum	SOWG
spathulata	SOWG
squamea	IDee SPlb WBrE
* squarmania	SOWG
squarrosa	CPLG ECou EDsa SOWG SPlb
thymifolia	ECou SOWG SPlb
viridiflora	GQui
wilsonii	ECou IDee SOWG

Melandrium see *Vaccaria*
rubrum	see *Silene dioica*

Melanoselinum (Apiaceae)
§ decipiens	CArn CHEx CSpe EBee EWes ITer LPhx WPGP

Melasphaerula (Iridaceae)
graminea	see *M. ramosa*
§ ramosa	CBre CStu ERos WPrP

Melia (Meliaceae)
§ azedarach	CArn CBcs EDsa ELau EShb LRav WPGP
- B&SWJ 7039	WCru
- var. japonica	see *M. azedarach*

Melianthus (Melianthaceae)
comosus	CBow CHen EShb EUnu EWes GGar LPhx MWgw NLar SPlb WCMO WCot WGwG
elongatus	CPne CSec EShb WOut
major ♀H3	More than 30 suppliers
minor	CFir CHen
villosus	CBod CBow CFir CHen CPle CSec EDsa EShb EUnu MCCP SGar SPlb SPoG WCMO WOut

Melica (Poaceae)
altissima 'Alba'	EHoe MLHP
- 'Atropurpurea'	More than 30 suppliers
ciliata	CBig CHrt COIW EBee EHoe MMoz NHol NLar NNor SMar SSvw WMnd WRos
- subsp. taurica	EPPr
macra	EHoe EPPr
* - 'Purpurea'	EBee
nutans	CBig CBrm CWCL EHoe EPPr EPla EWsh GBin GWCH NHol NWCA SBch SYvo WHil WRos WWye
penicillaris	EBee EPPr WPer
persica	EPPr
transsilvanica	CBig EPPr NBre NNor
- 'Atropurpurea'	EBee EChP NHol SPer
- 'Red Spire'	CBig EShb IBal LRav MBNS MWhi WMoo
uniflora	CBig NBre SEND
- f. albida	ECha EHoe MHar SLPl WCMO WCot
- 'Variegata' (v)	CBre EBee ECha EHoe EPPr EPla EShb GCal LBMP MBri MMoz NGdn WCot WMoo WTin

Melicope (Rutaceae)
ternata	ECou

Melicytus (Violaceae)
alpinus	ECou
angustifolius	ECou EDsa
crassifolius	CPle ECou EPla WFar
obovatus	ECou NLar
ramiflorus	CHEx ECou

Melilotus (Papilionaceae)
officinalis	CArn GPoy NSco SIde WHer WSel

Melinis (Poaceae)
repens	WCot WHrl
roseus	EHul

Meliosma (Meliosmaceae)
cuneifolia	CBcs NLar
myriantha	CBcs
parviflora B&SWJ 8408	-WCru

Melissa (Lamiaceae)
§ officinalis	CAgr CArn CHal CHrt COfd CPbn CPrp CTri EDAr ELau EUnu GMaP GPoy IHMH MBar MBow MBri MHer MNHC MWat NPri SECG SIde SPlb WBrk WPer WWye XPep
- 'All Gold'	CArn CBre CHal CPrp CSev ECha EDAr EHoe ELan ELau EUnu GBar NBid NPri NSti NVic SPoG WMoo WWye
§ - 'Aurea' (v)	More than 30 suppliers
* - 'Compacta'	GPoy MHer
- 'Quedlinburger Niederliegende'	CArn
N - 'Variegata' misapplied	see *M. officinalis* 'Aurea'

Melittis (Lamiaceae)
melissophyllum	CBrm CFir CPom EBee EMan EMon EShb GBBs LSou MGol MRav MSte MTis NMen SRms SSvw WAbb WCAu WCot WWye
- subsp. albida	EBee WCot
- pink	CFwr EMon
- 'Royal Velvet Distinction'PBR	CPen MRav

Melliodendron (Styracaceae)
xylocarpum	CBcs IArd IDee NLar

Menispermum (Menispermaceae)
canadense	CPIN CTri GPoy MGol MSal SHBN
davuricum	MGol MSal NLar

Menstruocalamus (Poaceae)
sichuanensis	WPGP

Mentha ✿ (Lamiaceae)
angustifolia Corb.	see *M.* x *villosa*
angustifolia Host	see *M. arvensis*
angustifolia ambig.	CPbn EOHP SIde
aquatica	CArn CBen CPbn CPrp CRow CWat EHon ELau EMFW EMag EPfP GPoy IHMH LNCo LPBA MBow MHer NPer NSco SIde SPlb SWal SWat WFar WHer WMAq WMoo WPnP WSFF WWpP
- var. crispa	EOHP IHMH SIde
- krause minze	see *M. aquatica* var. *crispa*
- 'Mandeliensis'	CPbn EOHP IHMH
§ arvensis	CArn ELau GIBF IHMH MHer MSal NSco SIde WHer WJek
- 'Banana'	CPbn EOHP LSou MHer MNHC NGHP
- var. piperascens	MSal SIde
§ - - 'Sayakaze'	CArn CPbn ELau
- var. villosa **new**	CPbn EOHP
asiatica	CPbn ELau MHer SIde WHer
'Betty's Slovakian' **new**	CPbn
Bowles' mint	see *M.* x *villosa* var. *alopecuroides* Bowles' mint
* brevifolia	CPbn EOHP IHMH SIde WHer

§ *cervina* CBen CDWL CPbn CWat EMFW EOHP IHMH LPBA MHer NLar SIde SWat WJek WWpP

* - *alba* CDWL IHMH LPBA MHer NLar WMAq WWpP

I 'Chocolate Peppermint' MNHC SECG

citrata see *M.* x *piperita* f. *citrata*

'Clarissa's Millennium' EOHP SIde

cordifolia see *M.* x *villosa*

corsica see *M. requienii*

crispa L. (1753) see *M. spicata* var. *crispa*

crispa L. (1763) see *M. aquatica* var. *crispa*

crispa ambig x CPbn EDAr GBar
 (x *piperita*)

'Dionysus' CPbn EOHP IHMH SIde

x *dumetorum* CPbn EOHP IHMH

'Eau de Cologne' see *M.* x *piperita* f. *citrata*

eucalyptus mint CPbn ELau EOHP GBar MHer NGHP WGwG WRha

gattefossei CArn CPbn ELau

x *gentilis* see *M.* x *gracilis*

§ x *gracilis* CArn CHby CPbn ELau GBar GWCH IHMH MBow NGHP NPri SIde WJek WWye

- 'Aurea' see *M.* x *gracilis* 'Variegata'

§ - 'Variegata' (v) CAgr CHrt CPbn CPrp CSev CWan ECha EHoe ELau EMar EOHP GGar GPoy ILis MBar MHer MNHC NBlu NPri NVic SPlb WFar WGHP WHer WPer WSel

haplocalyx CArn ELau EOHP MSal SIde

* 'Hillary's Sweet Lemon' CPbn ELau EOHP MHer SIde

'Julia's Sweet Citrus' CPbn EOHP MHer SIde

* *lacerata* IHMH SIde

lavender mint CBod CPbn CPrp CWan ELau EMan EOHP GBar GPoy MHer MRav NGHP NTHB WJek WRha

§ *longifolia* CAgr CPbn CPrp CWan ELau EMag EOHP GBar MBow MRav NSti SBch SIde SPlb WEas WHer WJek WPer WSel WWye

- Buddleia Mint Group CArn CPbn EBee ELau EMan EUnu GAbr GGar IHMH MHer MRav NGHP SECG SIde WRha WSel

- subsp. *schimperi* SIde WJek

- short new EOHP

- silver CAgr CArn CPbn ELau GWCH MHer MNHC

* - 'Variegata' (v) CBod CPbn CPrp ELau EMar EOHP NSti WJek

Nile Valley mint CArn CBod CPbn CPrp ELau EOHP SHDw SIde WCHb

x *piperita* CArn CHby CHrt CPbn CSev CWan ECha EDAr EHoe ELau EOHP GBar GPoy ILis LHop MBow MBri MHer NBlu NFor NGHP NPri NVic SPlb WGHP WPer WWye

- 'After Eight' IHMH

* - alba CArn CPbn GBar MHer WGwG

- 'Black Mitcham' CArn CPbn EOHP GBar

- black peppermint CAgr CHby CPbn EOHP EPfP GWCH IHMH MNHC MWat NBlu NGHP NHol NTHB SBch SECG SWal WGHP WGwG

§ - f. *citrata* More than 30 suppliers

* - - 'Basil' CBod CHrt CPbn CPrp CWan ELau EOHP GBar IHMH MHer MNHC MRav NBlu NGHP NHol NTHB SBch SHDw SIde WGHP WGwG WJek WRha

- - 'Bergamot' CPbn EOHP IHMH

- - 'Chocolate' CAgr CArn CPbn CPrp CWan ELau EMan EOHP EPfP EUnu GBar GGar IHMH ILis MHer MNHC NGHP

NPri SHDw SIde WGHP WGwG WJek WMoo WPer

- - 'Grapefruit' CPbn CWan EOHP GBar ILis LFol LSou NGHP SWal WGwG WJek

- - 'Lemon' CPbn CPrp CWan ELau EMan EOHP GAbr GBar IHMH MBow MBri MHer MNHC NGHP SBch SHDw SIde WCHb WGHP WGwG WJek WPer WRha WSel

- - 'Lime' CHrt CPbn CPrp CWan EMan EOHP GBar ILis LSou MBow MHer NGHP NPri SECG SHDw SIde SPlb WCHb WGHP WGwG WJek

- - orange CPbn EOHP EUnu GBar MHer MNHC MWat NGHP WDyG

- - 'Reverchonii' CPbn EOHP IHMH SIde

- - 'Swiss Ricola' EOHP EUnu MHer SIde

* - 'Extra Strong' IHMH

- 'Logee's' (v) CPbn CWan EBee EMan EWes GBar MHer NBlu NGHP NHol NPri NTHB SIde WCHb WHer WJek WRha

§ - 'Multimentha' EOHP

- f. *officinalis* ELau IHMH SIde

- var. *ouweneellii* CPbn EOHP IHMH SIde
 Belgian mint

- 'Reine Rouge' CPbn EOHP IHMH SIde

- 'Swiss' NGHP WGHP

I - Swiss mint CArn CPbn CPrp SECG WGwG

pulegium CAgr CArn CHby CPbn CPrp CRWN CSev CTri CWan EDAr ELau EOHP GBar GPoy IHMH MHer MNHC NVic SECG SIde SPlb SRms SWal WCHb WHer WJek WPer WWye

- 'Upright' CArn CBod CPbn CPrp GBar GPoy MHer MNHC NTHB SHDw SIde WCHb WJek WPer WSel

§ *requienii* More than 30 suppliers

rotundifolia misapplied see *M. suaveolens*

rotundifolia (L.) Hudson see *M.* x *villosa*

rubra var. *raripila* see *M.* x *smithiana*

'Russian' curled leaf new EOHP

'Russian' plain leaf new EOHP

'Sayakarze' see *M. arvensis* var. *piperascens* 'Sayakaze'

§ x *smithiana* CAgr CArn CPbn CPrp CWan ELau EOHP GAbr GBar GPoy IHMH ILis MHer MNHC NBir NBlu NGHP NPri SBch WHer WPer WRha WWye

- 'Capel Ulo' (v) ELau WHer

§ *spicata* CArn CHby CHrt CPbn CPrp CSev CWan EDAr GBar GPoy IHMH ILis LFol MBar MBow MBri MHer MWat NBlu NFor NGHP NHol SPlb SRms SWal WGHP WHer WJek WPer WWye

- Algerian fruity CPbn EOHP EUnu IHMH SIde

- 'Austrian' new CPbn

* - 'Brundall' CPbn ELau EOHP ILis SIde

- 'Canaries' EOHP IHMH

* - var. *crispa* CArn CPbn CPrp CWan ECha EDAr ELau EOHP GAbr GBar GGar IHMH LHop MHer MNHC NHol NHol NPri SIde SPlb WCHb WCot WPer WRha WSel WWye

- - large-leaved IHMH

- - 'Moroccan' CArn CPbn CPrp CSev EDAr ELau EOHP EUnu GAbr GBar GGar GPoy IHMH LEdu MHer MNHC NGHP NPri NVic SECG SHDw SIde STre WCHb WGHP WJek WSel WWye

- - 'Persian' IHMH

- - 'Guernsey' CPbn EOHP SHDw SIde

- 'Kentucky Colonel' **new**	CPbn EOHP
- 'Mexican'	CArn CPbn
- 'Newbourne'	CPbn ELau EOHP SIde
- 'Pharoah'	CArn CPbn
- 'Rhodos'	CPbn EOHP IHMH
- 'Russian'	CPbn EWin NGHP NHol NTHB SIde
- 'Small Dole' (v)	SHDw
- 'Spanish Furry'	CPbn EOHP MHer SIde
- 'Spanish Pointed'	CPbn ELau EOHP SIde
- 'Tashkent'	CArn CHby CPbn ELau EOHP GWCH MHer MNHC NGHP SHDw SIde WCHb WGwG WJek
- subsp. **tomentosa**	CPbn IHMH
* - 'Variegata' (v)	SHDw WGwG
- 'Verte Blanche'	CPbn IHMH
§ **suaveolens**	CAgr CArn CHby CPbn CWan ELau EOHP GBar GMaP GPoy GWCH IHMH ILis MBow MBri MHer MNHC MWat NGHP NLRH NPri SIde SPlb WBrk WGHP WPer WSFF
* - 'Grapefruit'	CPrp EWin IHMH NGHP NPri
- 'Jokka'	CPbn EBee
* - 'Mobillei'	CPbn EOHP SIde WJek
* - 'Pineapple'	EOHP NLRH WGwG
- subsp. **timija**	ELau SIde WJek
§ - 'Variegata' (v)	More than 30 suppliers
'Sweet Pear'	CPbn EOHP EUnu LSou
sylvestris L.	see *M. longifolia*
Thüringer minze	see *M.* x *piperita* 'Multimentha'
* **verona**	EOHP MHer
§ x **villosa**	CArn CPbn EOHP IHMH SIde
§ - var. **alopecuroides** Bowles' mint	CAgr CBre CHrt CPbn CPrp ELau EMan EOHP GBar GGar GPoy IHMH ILis MHer MNHC NGHP NSti SIde STre SWat WGwG WHer WJek WWye
viridis	see *M. spicata*

Menyanthes (Menyanthaceae)

trifoliata	CBen CRow CWat EHon ELau EMFW EMag GBar GPoy LNCo LPBA MCCP NPer NSco NVic WBVN WFar WHal WMAq WPnP WWpP

Menziesia (Ericaceae)

alba	see *Daboecia cantabrica* f. *alba*
ciliicalyx	SSpi
- 'Glendoick Glaucous'	GGGa
- **lasiophylla**	see *M. ciliicalyx* var. *purpurea*
- var. **multiflora**	CStu EPfP GGGa MDun
§ - var. **purpurea**	GGGa
ferruginea	SSta
'Ulva' **new**	GGGa

Mercurialis (Euphorbiaceae)

perennis	GPoy MGol NSco WHer WShi

Merendera (Colchicaceae)

attica	ECho
eichleri	see *M. trigyna*
filifolia	ECho
- PB 422 from Menorca	CMon
- AB&S 4665 from Morocco	CMon
§ **montana**	ERos GKev WIvy
pyrenaica	see *M. montana*
raddeana	see *M. trigyna*
sobolifera	CMon EHyt WFar
§ **trigyna**	ECho

Merremia (Convolvulaceae)

pinnata	MSal
§ **tuberosa**	EShb SOWG

Mertensia (Boraginaceae)

ciliata	CAbP CMdw CPom LRHS MArl MNrw NBid SWat WLin
franciscana	GCal
maritima	CSpe EDsa EWll GIBF GPoy MSal NGby
- subsp. **asiatica**	see *M. simplicissima*
pterocarpa	see *M. sibirica*
pulmonarioides	see *M. virginica*
§ **sibirica**	CLAP CSpe EDAr LPhx NChi NDlv NLar NPri SMrm SPlb
§ **simplicissima**	CMea EBee EBrs ECho EHyt EMan GIBF GKev LPhx MNrw NBir NWCA SBla SGar SMad SPlb SUsu WFar WHoo
§ **virginica** ♀H4	CArn CBos CBro CLAP CPrp EBee ECho ELan EPfP EPot EWTr GBBs GGar GMac NBid NBir NLar NMyG NPri NWCA SMrm SRms STes WCru WFar WSan
viridis	LPhx

Merxmuellera see Rytidosperma

Meryta (Araliaceae)

sinclairii	CHEx WMul

Mesembryanthemum (Aizoaceae)

'Basutoland'	see *Delosperma nubigenum*
brownii	see *Lampranthus brownii*

Mespilus (Rosaceae)

germanica (F)	CBcs CDul CLnd CTri EBee ECrN ELan EWTr IDee MWat NFor NScw SBLw SDnm SHBN SLon WDin WFar WMou WOrn
- 'Bredase Reus' (F)	SKee
- 'Dutch' (F)	SDea SFam SKee
- 'Large Russian' (F)	ERea GTwe
- 'Macrocarpa'	SKee
- 'Monstrous' (F)	SDea
- 'Nottingham' (F)	More than 30 suppliers
- 'Royal' (F)	CAgr SKee
- 'Westerveld' (F)	SKee

Metapanax see Pseudopanax

Metaplexis (Asclepiadaceae)

japonica B&SWJ 8459	WCru

Metarungia (Acanthaceae)

longistrobus **new**	GFai

Metasequoia (Cupressaceae)

glyptostroboides ♀H4	More than 30 suppliers
- 'Emerald Feathers'	ECho WEve
- 'Fastigiata'	see *M. glyptostroboides* 'National'
- 'Gold Rush'	More than 30 suppliers
- 'Green Mantle'	ECho EHul
§ - 'National'	ECho
- 'Sheridan Spire'	CEnd CTho WPGP
- 'Spring Cream'	ECho NLar SLim SPoG WEve
- 'White Spot' (v)	ECho LLin SLim SPoG WEve

Metrosideros (Myrtaceae)

carminea	CTrC
§ **excelsa**	CHEx CHll CTrC CTrG EBak ECou EShb SHFr
- 'Aureus'	ECou
- 'Fire Mountain'	CTrC
- 'Parnell'	CBcs
- 'Scarlet Pimpernel'	SOWG
- 'Spring Fire'	CBcs CCCN
- 'Upper Hut' (v)	CDoC

- 'Vibrance'   CTrC
kermadecensis   ECou
- 'Red and Gold' **new**   CDoC
- 'Variegatus' (v)   CBcs CDoC CTrC EBee ECou ERea
                                MLan
lucida   see *M. umbellata*
'Moon Maiden'   SOWG
'Pink Lady'   CTrC
robusta   CBcs CHEx
- **aureovariegata new**   EShb
x **subtomentosa** 'Mistral'   ECou
'Thomasii'   EShb SOWG
tomentosa   see *M. excelsa*
§ **umbellata**   CBcs CDul CHEx CPLG CTrC
                                ECou GGar SBrw
villosa   SOWG
- 'Tahiti'   CBcs

Meum (*Apiaceae*)

athamanticum   CBos CSev EBee EDAr EGle EHrv
                                EMan GCal GPoy LRHS MAvo
                                MRav MSal MTho NBid NCGa
                                NChi NSti SBla SGar WFar WHil
                                WPer WPrP WTin

Michauxia (*Campanulaceae*)

campanuloides   GKev
tchihatchewii   CSpe EBee GKev WBor

Michelia (*Magnoliaceae*)

cavalerieri   CBcs SSpi WPGP
champaca   ERea
chapensis   CBcs SSpi WPGP
- HWJ 621   WCru
compressa   CCCN EPfP SBrw
doltsopa   CBcs CHEx ECre EMil EPfP GQui
                                SBrw SSpi WCMO WPGP
- 'Silver Cloud'   CBcs SSpi
figo   CAbb CBcs CDoC EPfP ERea GQui
                                MBri SBrw SSpi WPGP
- var. **crassipes**   SSpi
- var. **figo**   SSpi
foveolata   CBcs SSpi
- var. **cinerascens new**   WPGP
macclurei   CBcs SSpi WPGP
martinii   CBcs
maudiae   CAbb CBcs CDoC CPLG EBee EPfP
                                ISea SSpi WPGP
yunnanensis   CBcs SSpi

Microbiota (*Cupressaceae*)

decussata ♀H4   CBcs CDoC CKen CMac CRob
                                CSBt ECho EHul ENot EOrn EPla
                                LBee LCon LLin LRHS MBar MGos
                                MWat NHol SLim SPoG WCFE
                                WEve WFar
- 'Gold Spot'   NLar SLim
- 'Jakobsen'   CDoC CKen
- 'Trompenburg'   CKen

Microcachrys (*Podocarpaceae*)

tetragona   CDoC ECho ECou EHul EOrn
                                LCon LLin MAsh SCoo SIng
                                SPoG

Microcitrus (*Rutaceae*)

australasica var.   EZes
   sanguinea new
virgata new   EZes

Microcoelum see *Lytocaryum*

Microglossa (*Asteraceae*)

albescens   see *Aster albescens*

Microlaena see *Ehrharta*

Microlepia (*Dennstaedtiaceae*)

speluncae   MBri
strigosa   CCCN CLAP LTwo

Micromeria (*Lamiaceae*)

corsica   see *Acinos corsicus*
croatica   ETow
dalmatica   EBee XPep
fruticosa   EWin XPep
graeca   XPep
rupestris   see *M. thymifolia*
§ **thymifolia**   GPoy NMen SPlb
viminea   see *Satureja viminea*

Microseris (*Asteraceae*)

ringens hort.   see *Leontodon rigens*

Microsorum (*Polypodiaceae*)

diversifolium   see *Phymatosorus diversifolius*

Microstrobos (*Podocarpaceae*)

fitzgeraldii   CKen
niphophilus   CDoC ECou

Microtropis (*Celastraceae*)

petelotii HWJ 719   WCru

Miersia (*Alliaceae*)

chilensis   CMon

Mikania (*Asteraceae*)

araucana new   LSou
§ **dentata**   MBri
ternata   see *M. dentata*

Milium (*Poaceae*)

effusum   COld
- 'Aureum' ♀H4   More than 30 suppliers
- var. **esthonicum**   EBee EPPr NHol WWpP
- 'Yaffle' (v)   CBre CFir CKno CNat CRez EBee
                                ECha EGle EMan EPPr GCal LEdu
                                MCCP SPoG SSvw SUsu WCMO
                                WCot WLeb WWpP

Millettia (*Papilionaceae*)

japonica 'Hime Fuji'   NLar
murasaki-natsu-fuji   see *M. reticulata*
§ **reticulata**   CPIN

Milligania (*Asteliaceae*)

densiflora   IBlr

Mimosa (*Mimosaceae*)

pudica   CArn CCCN CHen LRHS SMur

Mimulus (*Scrophulariaceae*)

'A.T. Johnson'   NVic
'Andean Nymph'   see *M. naiandinus*
§ **aurantiacus** ♀H2-3   CElw CFee CHad CHal CPle CSpe
                                EBak EBee ECtt EPot ERea LHop
                                MHar NBir NPer SAga SDnm SGar
                                SHFr SMrm SPet SPlb SPoG SUsu
                                SWal WAbe
§ - var. **puniceus**   CHal CPle CSpe CTri EBee EDif
                                EMan EWin LAst LHop LRHS LSou
                                MHar SAga SHom SMrm SRkn
                                SUsu
- 'Pure Gold'   EDif
- 'Tangerine'   EDif EWTr
x **bartonianus**   see *M.* x *harrisonii*
bifidus   MHar
- 'Tapestry'   CSpe
- 'Tawny'   SAga
- 'Trish'   CSpe SAga
- 'Verity Buff'   CSpe EDif

§ - 'Verity Purple' — EDif SOWG
- 'Wine' — see *M. bifidus* 'Verity Purple'
x *burnetii* — ECho LPBA SRms
cardinalis ♀H3 — CDWL CSec EBee EChP EHon ELan GKev IHMH LPBA MNrw MTho SHFr SPer SPoG WBor WCot WFar WHil WMoo WPer WPnP WWpP
- NNS 95-344 — EMan
- 'Dark Throat' — SGar
- 'Red Dragon' **new** — SHom
cupreus — GKev
- 'Minor' — ECho
- 'Whitecroft Scarlet' ♀H4 — ECho ECtt ELan EPfP LPBA LRHS LSou MHer SRms WPer
'Eleanor' — EMan LSou SHom SMrm SPet SUsu SWal
glutinosus — see *M. aurantiacus*
- *atrosanguineus* — see *M. aurantiacus* var. *puniceus*
- *luteus* — see *M. aurantiacus*
§ *guttatus* — MBow NPer NSco SECG SRms WMoo WPer WPnP WWpP
§ - 'Richard Bish' (v) — CBow CWat EMan EShb GKev MCCP
§ x *harrisonii* — EBee EMan EPfP EWes EWin GMac LSou
'Highland Orange' — ECho EDAr EPfP IHMH MHer NPri SPlb SPoG WGor WGwG WPer
'Highland Pink' — ECho EDAr EPfP NBlu SIng SPlb SPoG WGor WPer
'Highland Pink Rose' — SWal
'Highland Red' ♀H4 — ECho ECtt EDAr EPfP GAbr GGar GKev IHMH LPBA NBlu SIng SPlb SPoG SRms WFar WHen WPer
'Highland Yellow' — ECho ECtt EDAr LPBA MHer NBlu SIng SPlb SPoG WFar WHen WPer
hose-in-hose (d) — CDWL NPer
'Inca Sunset' — EWes
langsdorffii — see *M. guttatus*
lewisii ♀H3 — CHll CSec EShb GGar MTho SPav SPer SRms WPer WRha
luteus — CWat EHon EMFW EPfP IHMH LNCo LPBA MHer NPer NSco SHFr SPlb WBrk WFar WMAq WPnP WWpP
§ - 'Gaby' (v) — LPBA
- 'Variegatus' misapplied — see *M. guttatus* 'Richard Bish'
- 'Variegatus' — see *M. luteus* 'Gaby'
- 'Variegatus' ambig. (v) — NPer
* 'Major Bees' — EPfP LSou
'Malibu Ivory' — MDKP
'Malibu Orange' — EPfP
'Malibu Red' — MDKP
minimus — ECho
moschatus — CRow EBee
§ *naiandinus* ♀H3 — CMMP CPBP CSec EBee GKev LRHS SPlb SRms WFar WGwG
- C&W 5257 — WRos
'Orange Glow' — EPfP IHMH WHal
orange hose-in-hose (d) — NBir
'Orkney Lemon' — NSti
'Popacatapetl' — CHll CSpe EDif EMan LHop LSou MHar MSte SMrm SOWG SUsu WAbe
primuloides — ECho EWes NWCA SIng SPlb
'Puck' — ECho ECtt GMac LRHS
'Quetzalcoatl' — LSou SAga SMrm
Red Emperor — see *M.* 'Roter Kaiser'
ringens — CWat EHon EMFW EPfP GBri LNCo NBir NPer SPlb SRms WFar WMAq WMoo WPer WWpP
§ 'Roter Kaiser' — WRHF
'Threave Variegated' (v) — EBee EMan EWin GBuc GCal MRav NBir WFar
tilingii — ECho EShb SMar
'Western Hills' — MLLN

'Wine Red' — see *M. bifidus* 'Verity Purple'
'Wisley Red' — ECho ECot ELan SRms
'Yellow Velvet' — ECho

Mina see *Ipomoea*

mint, apple see *Mentha suaveolens*

mint, Bowles' see *M.* x *villosa* var. *alopecuroides*

mint, curly see *M. spicata* var. *crispa*

mint, eau-de-Cologne see *M.* x *piperita* f. *citrata*

mint, ginger see *M.* x *gracilis*

mint, horse or long-leaved see *M. longifolia*

mint, pennyroyal see *M. pulegium*

mint, peppermint see *M.* x *piperita*

mint, round-leaved see *M. suaveolens*

mint, spearmint see *M. spicata*

Minuartia (Caryophyllaceae)
capillacea — ECho
caucasica — see *M. circassica*
§ *circassica* — CLyd ETow NWCA WPer
laricifolia — LRHS
parnassica — see *M. stellata*
§ *stellata* — EPot ETow NDlv NMen SIng
- NS 758 — NWCA
§ *verna* — ECho NMen NVic
§ - subsp. *caespitosa* **new** — ECho
- - 'Aurea' — see *Sagina subulata* var. *glabrata* 'Aurea'

Mirabilis (Nyctaginaceae)
jalapa — CArn CPLG CStu ELan EPfP LRHS LRav MBri MSal SBod SEND SHFr SRms SYvo
- 'Buttermilk' **new** — CCCN
- white — CSpe
multiflora — EShb

Miscanthus ✿ (Poaceae)
capensis — CBig SPlb
flavidus B&SWJ 3697 — WCru
floridulus misapplied — see *M.* x *giganteus*
floridulus ambig. — NOak WFar WPrP
- HWJ 522 — WCru
§ x *giganteus* — CFwr CHar CKno CSev EHoe EPPr EWsh GAbr GCal LRHS MAvo MCCP MMoz MMuc NBea NVic SDix SEND SMad SPlb WCMO WCot WFar
- 'Gilt Edge' — CKno EWsh MAvo
- 'Gotemba' — EWes EWsh MAvo
- 'Golden Bar' — GBuc
nepalensis — CBig CBrm CHrt CKno CMil CPLG ECre EHoe EWes LEdu MAvo MWhi SDix SMrm WCMO WPrP
- CC 3619 — WRos
oligostachyus — CBig GCal NGdn
§ - 'Afrika' — CBig CFwr CPen
I - 'Nanus Variegatus' (v) — CKno CRow EBee EBrs EHoe EPPr EWes MMoz WCot WPGP
§ - 'Purpurascens' — CKno CPrp EBrs ECha EHoe EHrv EHul EPla EWsh GSki LAst LRHS LSRN MAvo MBnl MBrN MMoz MWgw NOak SEND SWal WBor WCMO WCot WGHP WTin
sacchariflorus — More than 30 suppliers

sinensis	CBig CHEx CHrt EBla GBin LEdu MGol MMoz MNHC MWrn NLar NOak WDin WMoo WRos XPep
- B&SWJ 6749	WCru
- 'Adagio'	CBig CFwr CKno CPen EBee EBrs EGle EPPr GBin LEdu SMHy WCMO WCot WPrP
- 'Afrika'	see *M. oligostachyus* 'Afrika'
- 'Arabesque'	CBig CBrm CFwr EBee EGle EPPr IPot MMoz NLar
- 'Augustfeder'	CFwr CPen EBee EBrs EGle LRHS
- 'Autumn Light'	CFwr CKno CPen EBrs EPPr IPot
- 'Ballerina'	CFwr CPen
- 'Blütenwunder'	CFwr CKno CPen EGle IPot
- 'China'	CBig CBrm CDes CFir CHar CKno CWCL EBee EBla EBrs EGle EHoe EPGN EPPr EPla EShb EWes GBin IPot LEdu LRHS MLLN NDov NHol NOrc SAga SPoG SWat WPGP
- var. **condensatus**	CBig EPPr
- - 'Cabaret' (v)	CBrm CFwr CHEx CHar CKno CPen CRez CWCL EBee EHoe EPPr EPyc IPot LEdu LSRN MBri NOak NOrc SMad SPoG SRos WCot WHal WMoo
- - 'Central Park'	see *M. sinensis* var. *condensatus* 'Cosmo Revert'
§ - - 'Cosmo Revert'	CBig CKno CPen EBee LEdu MMoz WDyG
- - 'Cosmopolitan' (v) ♀H4	More than 30 suppliers
- - 'Emerald Giant'	see *M. sinensis* var. *condensatus* 'Cosmo Revert'
- 'David'	CPen
- 'Dixieland' (v)	CBig CBrm CFwr CKno EGle EHoe EPPr LEdu MMoz MRav
- 'Emmanuel Lepage'	CFwr CPen EPPr
- 'Etincelle'	EPPr
- 'Ferner Osten'	More than 30 suppliers
- 'Feuergold'	MSte
- 'Flamingo' ♀H4	More than 30 suppliers
- 'Flammenmeer'	CFwr CPen
- 'Gearmella'	CBig EBee EBrs EGle EWsh LEdu LRHS
- 'Gewitterwolke' ♀H4	CBig CFwr CKno EGle LPhx NDov SMHy
- 'Ghana' ♀H4	CFwr CKno CPen EBee EGle GBin SMHy
- 'Giraffe'	CDes CFwr CKno CPen WPGP
- 'Gnome'	CKno CPen EBee
- 'Gold Bar' (v)	CBow CElw CKno CMHG EBee ECha EMil EPPr LBuc LEdu LSou MBNS NCGa SPer SPoG WCMO WCot WGwG WMoo
- 'Goldfeder' (v)	CFwr CPen EHoe
- 'Goliath'	CBig CFwr CPen EHoe EPPr GBin IPot LEdu WFar WPnP WPrP
- 'Gracillimus'	More than 30 suppliers
- 'Graziella'	More than 30 suppliers
- 'Grosse Fontäne' ♀H4	CBig CBrm CKno EBla EBrs EGle EHoe EPGN EPPr EPla EWsh LEdu LRHS NHol SMHy WAul WCMO WMoo
- 'Haiku'	CFwr CKno CPen GBin LPhx WPrP
- 'Helga Reich'	CBig EBee
- 'Hercules'	CBig CPen EPPr MAvo MMoz WCMO
- 'Hermann Müssel'	CFwr CPen EBee GBin LPhx NDov SMHy
- 'Hinjo' (v)	CDes CElw CFwr CKno CSpe EBee EPPr GBin LSou SPoG WCMO WCot WHrl WPGP WPrP
I - 'Jubilaris' (v)	EWes
- 'Juli'	CBig EBrs GBin WPrP
- 'Kaskade' ♀H4	CBig CBrm CFwr CKno CWCL EBrs EGle EHoe EPGN EPPr EPla
	IPot LEdu LRHS MAvo MMoz MSte NOGN SMeo SMrm WFar WMoo
- 'Kleine Fontäne' ♀H4	More than 30 suppliers
- 'Kleine Silberspinne' ♀H4	More than 30 suppliers
- 'Krater'	CBig CFwr CKno EBee EBrs EPPr LEdu MBrN SMeo SWat
- 'Kupferberg'	CFwr
§ - 'Little Kitten'	CBig CDes CFwr CKno CPen EBee EGle EPPr EPla EWsh LEdu MBar MGol SMad SPoG WPGP
- 'Little Zebra' (v) **new**	ENot LBuc LRHS SPoG
- 'Malepartus'	More than 30 suppliers
- 'Morning Light' (v) ♀H4	More than 30 suppliers
- 'Nippon'	CBig CElw CHrt CKno CPrp EBee EBla EBrs EGle EHoe EPPr EBla LEdu LHop LRHS MAvo MCCP MMoz NDov NGdn NHol NOrc SDys SPer WPGP
- 'Nishidake'	CFwr CPen EBee
- 'November Sunset'	CBig EBee EPPr EWes IPot MMoz
- 'Overdam'	WCMO
- 'Poseidon'	EPPr SDys
- 'Positano'	CBig CKno EBee EBrs MMoz WPGP
- 'Professor Richard Hansen'	CFwr CKno CPen GBin
- var. **purpurascens** misapplied	see *M.* 'Purpurascens'
- 'Pünktchen' (v)	CBig CBrm CFwr CKno CPen CWCL EAEE EBee EBrs ECha EGle EPPr EPla GBin LEdu LPhx MAvo MWgw SMHy SMrm WFar WPnP WTin
- 'Rigoletto' (v)	EPPr
- 'Roland'	CBig CFwr CKno CPen EBee GBin LPhx
- 'Roterpfeil'	CFwr CPen SMHy
- 'Rotfuchs'	CFwr CPen EBee EPPr LPhx MGos MSte SAga WFar
- 'Rotsilber'	More than 30 suppliers
- 'Samurai'	CFwr GMaP MAvo
- 'Sarabande'	CBig CBrm CFwr CKno EBee EBrs EGle EHoe EHul EPPr EWsh IPot LRHS SMHy WFar WGwG WMoo
- 'Septemberfuchs'	LEdu
- 'Septemberrot' ♀H4	CFwr CKno COIW CPrp EBee LEdu SPoG
§ - 'Silberfeder' ♀H4	More than 30 suppliers
- 'Silberpfeil' (v)	MSte
- 'Silberspinne'	CBig CMdw EBla EBrs EGle ENot EPla LEdu LRHS MCCP MWat NGdn SAga SDix SMHy SMeo SPlb WAul WCMO WDin
- 'Silberturm'	CFwr CKno COIW EBee MBri SPoG
- Silver Feather	see *M. sinensis* 'Silberfeder'
- 'Sioux'	CBig CFwr CKno EBee EBrs EGle EHoe EPPr EPla EShb GBin LEdu LRHS MBri MMoz WOVN WTin
- 'Sirene'	CBig CFwr CKno EBrs EGle EHoe EPGN EPPr EPla LRHS MBNS MBlu NHol WFar WHal WPrP
- 'Slavopour'	EPla
- 'Spätgrün'	CFwr EPla
- 'Strictus' (v) ♀H4	More than 30 suppliers
- 'Tiger Cub' (v)	CBig CWCL EBee
- 'Undine' ♀H4	CBos CFwr CKno CMea CPrp CSam EAEE EBee EBla EBrs ECha EGle EHoe EHrv ELan EPGN EPla EWsh LEdu LRHS MLLN MMoz NHol SHFr SPla WGHP
- 'Variegatus' (v) ♀H4	More than 30 suppliers
- 'Vorläufer'	CBrm CFwr CKno CPen EBrs EHoe EWsh LEdu SAga
- 'Wetterfahne'	CFwr EGle

§ - 'Yaku-jima' — CFwr CRez CSam EBee ECha EGle SPoG XPep

- 'Yakushima Dwarf' — More than 30 suppliers
- 'Zebrinus' (v) ♀H4 — More than 30 suppliers
- 'Zwergelefant' — CBig CFwr EBrs MMoz SMHy
tinctorius 'Nanus Variegatus' misapplied — see *M. oligostachyus* 'Nanus Variegatus'
transmorrisonensis — CBig CBod CHrt CKno EBee EHoe EPPr GBin LRav MBri MMoz NHol NNor NOak SAdn SWal WHil WWpP
yakushimensis — see *M. sinensis* 'Yaku-jima', *M. sinensis* 'Little Kitten'

Mitchella (Rubiaceae)

repens — CBcs WCru
undulata B&SWJ 4402 — WCru

Mitella (Saxifragaceae)

breweri — CNic CSam EBee GGar MAvo MRav MSte NHol NSti SHFr SMac SRms WEas WFar WMoo WTin WWye
caulescens — EBee ECha NBro NHol WMoo
diphylla — EBee EPPr LBMP
formosana B&SWJ 125 — WCru
japonica B&SWJ 4971 — WCru
kiusiana — CLAP
- B&SWJ 5888 — GEdr WCru
makinoi — CLAP
- B&SWJ 4992 — WCru
ovalis — EBee
pauciflora B&SWJ 6361 — WCru
pentandra — EBee WMoo
stauropetala — EBee
stylosa B&SWJ 5669 — WCru
trifida new — EBee
yoshinagae — GEdr SBch WMoo
- B&SWJ 4893 — WCru WPrP WPtf

Mitraria (Gesneriaceae)

coccinea — CBcs CEnt CMac CPLG CPiN CPle CSec CTrG CTrw CWib ECho ELan EShb IDee MBlu MDun SArc SLon SPer SSpi WCMO WCot WPic
- from Lake Puyehue — CAby CBcs CDoC CFee EBee EMil ERea GAbr GQui LRHS MAsh MGos SBrw SPoG SSta SWvt WAbe WCru WCwm WFar WPGP WSHC
- Clark's form — CSam CTrC EBee GGar LAst MDun NLar WBor
- 'Lake Caburgua' — GCal GGar IArd NSti

Molinia (Poaceae)

altissima — see *M. caerulea* subsp. *arundinacea*
caerulea — CBig COtt CRWN EHul EPPr LAst LPhx MBlu WWpP
§ - subsp. *arundinacea* — CAby CBig CBrm CKno CWCL ECha EPPr GBin MBNS NLar SLPl WPer
- - 'Bergfreund' — CSam EHoe EPPr EWsh GCal LPhx MAvo NDov SMHy SUsu WDyG WGHP WMoo WPrP WTin WWye
- - 'Cordoba' — CBig CKno EPPr GBin LPhx NDov SMHy
- - 'Fontäne' — CBig CPen CSam EBee EHoe EPPr LPhx MSte NDov NNor SMHy
- - 'Karl Foerster' — CKno CSpe EBee EGle EHoe EHul EPPr EPfP GBin GMaP LEdu LPhx MAvo MMoz NBid NDov NHol SUsu SVil SWat SYvo WCAu WCot WFar WGHP WMoo WPnP
- - 'Skyracer' — CBig CFwr CKno COIW CPrp CSam EBee EBrs EGle EHoe EPPr GBri GQue LIck LPhx MAvo MBri

MMoz MWhi NDov SMHy SMad SPoG WCMO WCot WFar WGHP WMoo WWpP
- - 'Staefa' — EHoe
- - 'Transparent' — CHad CKno CMea CSpe CWCL EBrs ECha EGle EHoe EPGN EPPr GBri GCal GMaP LPhx MBri MMoz MSte NDov NNor SMHy SMad SMrm SUsu WGHP WHal WHoo WMoo WPrP
- - 'Windsaule' — CBig CKno EBee EPPr LPhx NDov
- - 'Windspiel' — CKno CRow CSam CWCL EBee ECha EGle EHoe EMil EMon EPGN EPPr EWsh GCal LEdu LPhx MWgw NDov SWal WCAu WCMO WCot WGHP WMoo WPGP WTin
- - 'Zuneigung' — CBig CKno CSam EBrs EHoe EPPr LPhx NDov
- subsp. *caerulea* — CMdw
- - 'Carmarthen' (v) — CElw CNat EBee EPPr MAvo SUsu WGHP WPnP WPrP
- - 'Claerwen' (v) — ECha EPPr GBuc GCal LPhx SMHy WMoo
- - 'Coneyhill Gold' (v) new — EPPr
- - 'Dauerstrahl' — EPPr GBin GCal MAvo NDov NHol WCMO WGHP WWpP
- - 'Edith Dudszus' — CFwr CKno CMMP CWCL EBee ECha EGle EHoe EPPr EWsh LEdu LPhx LRHS MAvo MBrN MBri MMoz NDov NGdn NHol NOGN SMHy SPer SVil WGHP WLeb WMoo WPGP WWeb
- - 'Heidebraut' — CBig CFwr EAEE EBee EGle EHoe EHul EPPr GBin LPhx LRHS MBri MWgw NBro NCGa NDov SVil WFar WMoo WPnP
- - 'Moorflamme' — CBig CBrm CKno CSam EPPr LPhx WWpP
- - 'Moorhexe' — More than 30 suppliers
- - 'Strahlenquelle' — CElw CKno CSam EAEE EBee EGle ELan EMon EPGN EPPr EPla GBin GCal LRHS MAvo MMoz NBro NCGa NDov NOGN WPGP
- - 'Variegata' (v) ♀H4 — More than 30 suppliers
litoralis — see *M. caerulea* subsp. *arundinacea*

Molopospermum (Apiaceae)

peloponnesiacum — CAby CFwr CSpe EBee EMan GCal ITer LEdu LPhx MLLN NLar WCot WCru

Moltkia (Boraginaceae)

§ *doerfleri* — CPle NChi
graminifolia — see *M. suffruticosa*
§ × *intermedia* ♀H4 — CMea SAga SPet WAbe WFar
petraea — WLin
§ *suffruticosa* — NBir

Momordica (Cucurbitaceae)

balsamina — MSal
charantia — MSal

Monadenium (Euphorbiaceae)

lugardae — MBri
'Variegatum' (v) — MBri

Monarda ✿ (Lamiaceae)

'Adam' — EBee GCal LRHS MLLN MSte NBre WCAu WSHC
'Amethyst' — EBee ECtt EWes SIde
'Aquarius' — CWCL EAEE EBee EChP EMar ERou LAst LRHS MSte MWgw NCob NGHP NHol NPro NSti SPla

	SPoG SRGP WAul WCAu WCHb WFar WMnd WWlt
austromontana	see *M. citriodora* subsp. *austromontana*
'Baby Spice'	EBee ENot LRHS NCob WRHF
§ 'Balance'	CSam CWCL EAEE EAro EBee EChP ECtt EMan EPPr LPhx LRHS MRav NBro NCob NDov NGHP NGdn NHol NSti SMeo SPla SPoG SRGP WCAu WCHb WFar WHil WPGP WSHC
'Beauty of Cobham' ♀H4	CHar CPrp EBee ECha ELan EPfP ERou GBBs GMaP LHop LPhx LRHS MAvo MBri MHer MSte NGHP NHol NLar NRnb NSti SMad SPer WBor WCHb WGHP WSan
'Blaukranz'	NBre
§ 'Blaustrumpf'	CElw CFwr ECtt GBBs GBri MSte NCob NLar NOrc SPer WLin
Blue Stocking	see *M.* 'Blaustrumpf'
Bowman	see *M.* 'Sagittarius'
bradburyana	EShb LTwo NBre WCHb
'Cambridge Scarlet' ♀H4	More than 30 suppliers
'Capricorn'	EHol EMar ERou GBuc LRHS MSte NBre WCHb
'Cherokee'	EBee GBri LPhx NCob NHol WCHb WFar
citriodora	CArn ECtt EUnu GPoy LRHS MNHC MSal NSti SIde SPlb SRms SWat WJek WSel
§ - subsp. *austromontana*	EAro EBee EMag MDKP NBir NJOw SBch SGar SIde WFar WPer
'Comanche'	EHrv EPfP EWes NCob NDov WCHb WFar
'Croftway Pink' ♀H4	More than 30 suppliers
I 'Dark Ponticum'	NCob
didyma	CAgr CArn CHar EDAr EPfP MSal NBro NGHP SECG SWat WBrE WBri WJek
- 'Alba'	SMar
- 'Duddiscombe'	CSam CWCL
- 'Goldmelise'	CFwr NBre NGHP SMar WMoo
'Elsie's Lavender'	EGle GBri GBuc LPhx MAvo NDov NLar SAga WAul WCHb
'Fireball'PBR	CHVG CWCL EBee ECtt LTwo MBnl NLar SBig WHil
§ 'Fishes'	CHVG CSam EAEE EBee EChP ECtt EHrv ELan EMar EPPr EWes LAst MRav MSte NCob NDov NGHP NHol NLar NRnb SPla SRGP WCHb WFar WMnd WSHC WWlt
fistulosa	CArn CWan EUnu GPoy MBow MNHC MSal MWrn SMar WHer WJek WMoo WPer
- f. *albescens*	EBee
'Gardenview'	CMdw EWes GCal NSti SMrm WRHF
'Gardenview Scarlet' ♀H4	CWCL EBee EBrs ECtt EGra GBri GQue LPhx LRHS MBri MDKP MWat NCGa NChi NGHP NGby NLar SPoG WCHb WPer WSan
Gemini	see *M.* 'Twins'
'Gewitterwolke' **new**	CSam
'Hartswood Wine'	NHol SMad
'Heidelerche' **new**	EPPr
'Jacob Cline'	GBin NBre NCob
'Kardinal'	EBee EMil GBin NHol
'Lambada'	SPav
Libra	see *M.* 'Balance'
'Lilac Queen'	CBos NCob
'Loddon Crown'	CBos CFwr CHar CHea EBee ECtt EMar LRHS MBri MDKP NCob NGHP NHol NLar SIde SMer WCHb WFar WRha
'Mahogany'	CHar EBee EChP EGle ERou GAbr GBBs GBri GMaP LRHS MHer

	MLHP MRav NCGa NChi NCob NGHP SMad SPer WCHb WSHC WSan
'Marshall's Delight' ♀H4	CElw EBee EChP LSou NCob NGHP NHol NLar NRnb SMrm WCAu WHil WRHF
'Melissa'	EGle EMil NBre WSan
menthifolia	EAro EBee EDsa GCal LSou SMrm
'Mohawk'	CKno CWCL EAEE EBee EChP ECtt EHrv EMan EPPr ERou LRHS MWat MWgw NChi NCob NDov NHol NOrc WCAu WCHb WHil
'Mrs Perry'	EWes NGHP
'Neon'	LPhx NDov
'On Parade'	EBee EMar ENot NCob NHol
'Ou Charm'	EBee EChP EPPr ERou EWes GBri LRHS MHer MLLN MWat MWrn NDov NGHP NLar SMad WCHb WFar WSan
'Panorama'	EAro ECtt MSal NHol NLar SGar SPlb WMoo WPer
'Panorama Red Shades' (Panorama Series)	CFwr CWib EAro MNHC MWrn NGHP WHil
'Pawnee'	WCHb
Petite Delight = 'Acpetdel'PBR	More than 30 suppliers
'Petite Pink Supreme'	EBee EPfP MBnl MLLN WHil
'Pink Supreme'PBR	EMar NLar
'Pink Tourmaline'	CFwr EChP LPhx NDov NGby NHol NMyG SMad SMrm WCHb WFar
Pisces	see *M.* 'Fishes'
'Poyntzfield Pink'	GPoy
Prairie Night	see *M.* 'Prärienacht'
§ 'Prärienacht'	More than 30 suppliers
punctata	CArn CBod EAro EBee EDAr ELan EMan EUnu GSki ITim LPhx LRHS MLLN MNFA MSal MWrn NGdn NJOw SDnm SMrm SPav SWat WCHb WJek WMoo
- 'Fantasy'	CFwr LBuc NGHP NSti
'Purple Ann'	NCGa NDov
'Raspberry Wine'	ECtt GBri
'Ruby Glow'	CAby CWCL EBee EChP EHrv EMan EMar EPPr IPot LPhx LRHS MArl MBri NCGa NDov NHol SAga SMad WCHb WFar
§ 'Sagittarius'	EAEE EBee EChP EGle EKen EMan LRHS MWgw NChi NCob NFla NGdn NHol SPla SPur SRGP WCAu WCHb
'Sahin's Mildew-free'	WCHb
'Saxon Purple'	NDov NLar
§ 'Schneewittchen'	More than 30 suppliers
§ 'Scorpion'	More than 30 suppliers
'Sioux'	EHrv EWes GBuc LRHS WCHb WFar WRha
'Snow Maiden'	see *M.* 'Schneewittchen'
'Snow Queen'	CSam EAEE EAro EBee ECtt EMar EPPr LRHS MWat MWgw NCob NHol NLar NPro SHar SPla SPur STes WMnd
Snow White	see *M.* 'Schneewittchen'
'Squaw' ♀H4	More than 30 suppliers
§ 'Twins'	CMil CPrp CWCL EBee EChP EMar EPPr ERou LRHS MLLN NGHP NHol NRnb SWat SWvt WCAu WCHb WLin WSHC WSan
'Velvet Queen'	EAEE LSou
'Vintage Wine'	CAby CWCL ECtt EGle GBri NCob NDov WCHb WCot WFar WLin
'Violacea'	NHol WCHb WWpP
'Violet Queen' ♀H4	EAro EBee EBrs EChP EMar EWes LBMP LRHS NBre NCob NFla NHol NPro WCAu WHil

Monardella (Lamiaceae)

linoides subsp. **stricta**	CPBP NWCA
macrantha	CPBP SBla
nana subsp. **arida**	CPBP
- subsp. **tenuiflora**	CPBP
odoratissima	CArn EHyt EMag LPhx LRav SBla
	WJek WPtf

Monochoria (Pontederiaceae)

hastata	CDWL

Monopsis (Campanulaceae)

lutea	see *Lobelia lutea*
Midnight = 'Yagemon'[PBR]	LAst

Monsonia ✿ (Geraniaceae)

crassicaulis	LToo
vanderietiae	LToo

Monstera (Araceae)

deliciosa (F) ♀[H1]	MBri SRms XBlo
- 'Variegata' (v) ♀[H1]	MBri SRms

Montbretia see *Crocosmia*

x **crocosmiiflora**	see *Crocosmia* x *crocosmiiflora*
pottsii	see *Crocosmia pottsii*

Montia (Portulacaceae)

australasica	see *Neopaxia australasica*
californica	see *Claytonia nevadensis*
parvifolia	see *Naiocrene parvifolia*
perfoliata	see *Claytonia perfoliata*
sibirica	see *Claytonia sibirica*

Moraea (Iridaceae)

alpina	GCrs
alticola	CPne EBee GCrs WPGP
- CDL 181	CStu
§ **aristata**	CMon WCot
atropunctata	WCMO WCot
§ **bellendenii**	WCMO WCot
bipartita	WCot
comptonii	CPBP WCot
elegans	CPBP
§ **fugax**	CMon IBlr WCMO WCot
gawleri	CMon LBow WCMO WCot
glaucopsis	see *M. aristata*
huttonii	CFir CPBP CSpe EBee EDif EPPr
	GSki SBla SMad WBVN WCot WCru
	WLin WPic WSHC
iridioides	see *Dietes iridioides*
* **lankenensis**	CDes
longifolia Sweet	see *M. fugax*
loubseri	CMon WCot
lurida	LBow WCMO WCot
moggii	CStu
natalensis	SBla
pavonia var. **lutea**	see *M. bellendenii*
polyanthos	CMon EBee WCot
polystachya	LRHS
spathacea	see *M. spathulata*
§ **spathulata**	CAby CBro CMdw CPLG EBee
	EMan ERos GCal GMac WCot
tricolor new	CPBP
tripetala	WCot
tulbaghensis new	WCot
vegeta	CPBP ERea WCot
villosa	CMon LBow WCMO WCot

Moricandia (Brassicaceae)

moricandioides	CSpe

Morina (Morinaceae)

* **afghanica**	GAbr
alba	NChi

Morisia (Brassicaceae)

hypogaea	see *M. monanthos*
§ **monanthos**	IHMH MBar NHol NLAp NWCA
	SRot WFar
- 'Fred Hemingway'	EAEE ECho EHyt GCrs ITim LRHS
	NMen NSla SIng WAbe WPat
	WThu

Morus ✿ (Moraceae)

alba	CAgr CArn CBcs CDul CLnd
	CMCN CMen CTho CWib ECrN
	ELan EPfP ERea GTwe LBuc MGos
	SBLw SHBN WDin WFar
- 'Macrophylla'	CMCN SMad
- 'Pendula'	CBcs CDoC CDul CEnd CLnd
	CTho CTri ECrN ELan EPfP ERea
	GTwe LPan LRHS MAsh MBlu MBri
	MLan NLar SBLw SCoo SHBN SLim
	SPoG WDin WOrn
- 'Platanifolia'	MBlu SBLw
- var. **tatarica**	CAgr LEdu
§ **bombycis**	LPan SBLw
'Illinois Everbearing' (F)	CAgr ECrN
kagayamae	see *M. bombycis*
nigra (F) ♀[H4]	More than 30 suppliers
§ - 'Chelsea' (F)	CAgr CEnd COtt CTho CTri ECrN
	EMui EPfP ERea GTwe LRHS MBri
	MGan MGos MLan MWya NWea
	SCoo SKee SLim SPer SPoG WPGP
- 'Jerusalem' new	MAsh
- 'King James'	see *M. nigra* 'Chelsea'
- 'Large Black' (F)	EMui
- 'Wellington' (F)	CEnd LPan
rubra	NLar
- 'Nana' new	MBri

Mosla (Lamiaceae)

dianthera	EMan GCal MNrw WHil

Mucuna (Papilionaceae)

* **dalbertsii** new	CPlN
macrocarpa	CPlN
novaguineensis new	CPlN
sempervirens	CPlN

Muehlenbeckia (Polygonaceae)

astonii	CBcs ECou
australis	ECou
axillaris misapplied	see *M. complexa*
§ **axillaris** Walp.	CBcs CTri ECou EDsa EPla GCal
	GGar SBig
- 'Mount Cook' (f)	ECou
- 'Ohau' (m)	ECou
§ **complexa**	CBcs CDoC CHEx CPLG CPlN
	CTrC CTri CWib EBee ECou EPla
	EShb LRHS MCCP MWgw NSti
	SAPC SArc SBra SLim SLon SMac
	SWvt WCFE WPGP WSHC XPep
- (f)	ECou
- 'Nana'	see *M. axillaris* Walp.
- var. **trilobata**	CPlN EPla IBlr WCru WDyG
	XPep
- 'Ward' (m)	ECou
ephedroides	ECou
- 'Clarence Pass'	ECou
* - var. **muricatula**	ECou
gunnii	ECou
platyclados	see *Homalocladium platycladum*

longifolia — More than 30 suppliers
- GWJ 9240 — WCru
nepalensis — WLin
persica — CFis EChP EWes GBBs GBuc MHar WHoo
polyphylla — GPoy
- CC 3397 — GKev

Muhlenbergia (Poaceae)

capillaris	CBig CBrm CKno
dubia	CKno
emersleyi	CBrm
japonica 'Cream Delight'	CPen EBee EHoe EMan
(v)	
mexicana	CBig CPen EBee EPPr NBre WPGP
rigens	CBig CKno XPep

Mukdenia (Saxifragaceae)

acanthifolia	CLAP LEdu WCru
§ **rossii**	CLAP EBee EMon EPla GCal IFro
	LEdu MSte NLar NMyG SMac SMad
	WCot WCru WTMC WThu WTin
- 'Crimson Fans' **new**	NBhm
- dwarf	CLAP GCal
- 'Ōgon'	CLAP
- variegated	EMon

mulberry see *Morus*

Murraya (Rutaceae)

* **elliptica**	SOWG
exotica	see *M. paniculata*
koenigii	EOHP GPoy
§ **paniculata**	CArn CPLG ERea SMur

Musa ✿ (Musaceae)

from Tibet **new**	CKob
from Yunnan, China	see *M. itinerans* 'Yunnan'
§ **acuminata**	MBri
- 'Bordelon'	CKob
§ - 'Dwarf Cavendish'	CKob EAmu ELan EPfP MJnS
(AAA Group) (F) ♀H1	MOak NGHP NScw SPoG WMul
	XBlo
- 'Dwarf Red' (AAA Group)	XBlo
(F)	
- 'Igitsiri' (AAA Group) (F)	CKob
- 'Mai'a oa'	CKob
- 'Red Iholena' (AAA Group)	XBlo
(F)	
* - 'Rose' (AA Group) (F)	CKob
- 'Williams' (AAA Group)	EAmu
(F)	
- 'Zebrina' ♀H1+3	CHen CKob EAmu LRHS MJnS
	MOak XBlo
acuminata 'Grand Nain'	EAmu
x **acuminata** 'Zebrina'	
balbisiana	CKob EAmu WMul
- 'Cardaba' (BBB Group) (F)	CKob
basjoo ♀H3-4	More than 30 suppliers
- 'Sakhalin'	CKob SAdn WMul
beccarii	CKob
'Burmese Blue'	CKob
'Butuhan' (*balbisiana* x	CKob
textilis)	
'Cavendish Super Dwarf'	EZes MJnS
'Cavendish Zan Moreno'	MJnS
cavendishii	see *M. acuminata* 'Dwarf
	Cavendish'
§ **coccinea** ♀H1	MJnS XBlo
ensete	see *Ensete ventricosum*
(Fe'i Group) 'Utafan' (F)	MNHC
hookeri	see *M. sikkimensis*
* **itinerans** 'Yunnan'	CKob EAmu ITer MJnS WMul
* 'Kru' (F)	XBlo
§ **lasiocarpa**	CAbb CDWL CDoC CHEx CHen
	CHll CKob EAmu EZes IDee LRHS
	MBri MJnS NPal SBig WMul
laterita	CKob
mannii	CKob WMul
nana misapplied	see *M. acuminata* 'Dwarf
	Cavendish'
nana Lour.	see *M. acuminata*
ornata ♀H1	ERea LPal MJnS WMul XBlo

- 'African Red'	CKob
- 'Macro'	CKob
- 'Purple'	CKob
x **paradisiaca**	MJnS
- 'Ele-ele' (AAB Group) (F)	CKob
- Goldfinger = 'FHIA-01'	CKob
(AAAB Group) (F)	
- 'Hajaré' (ABB Group) (F)	CKob
- 'Malbhog' (AAB Group)	CKob
(F)	
- 'Ney Poovan' (AB Group)	CCCN EAmu MJnS NPal
(F)	
- 'Orinoco' (ABB Group) (F)	CKob EAmu WMul
- 'Pisang Awak' (AAB Group)	CKob
(F)	
- 'Rajapuri' (AAB Group) (F)	CKob EAmu MJnS
'Royal Purple' (*ornata*	CKob
hybrid)	
'Rubinia' **new**	CKob MJnS
'Saba' ambig. (F)	CKob
sanguinea	CKob
siamensis **new**	CKob
§ **sikkimensis**	CDoC CHen CKob EAmu ELan
	EShb EWes EZes IDee LEdu LPJP
	LRHS MJnS MOak NPal SBig SChr
	WMul XBlo
- 'Red Tiger' **new**	CKob EZes
textilis	CKob
'Tropicana'	SMer SSto XBlo
uranoscopus misapplied	see *M. coccinea*
velutina ♀H1+3	CKob EAmu MJnS MOak SBig
	WMul
* 'Violacea' (*ornata* hybrid)	LPal

Muscari ✿ (Hyacinthaceae)

PF	NWCA
ambrosiacum	see *M. muscarimi*
armeniacum ♀H4	CBro EBrs ECho ENot EPfP ERos
	IHMH LRHS MBri NJOw SRms
	WCot WFar WShi
- 'Argaei Album'	ECho EPot
- 'Babies Breath'	see *M.* 'Jenny Robinson'
- 'Blue Eyes'	ECho WCot
- 'Blue Pearl'	ECho GKev LRHS
- 'Blue Spike' (d)	CBro ECho ENot EPfP LRHS MBri
	NBir NBlu SPer WCot WGwG
- 'Cantab'	CMea ECho GKev
- 'Christmas Pearl' ♀H4	CStu ECho WCot
- 'Dark Eyes'	ECho EPfP LRHS MSph SPer WHil
- 'Early Giant'	ECho
- 'Fantasy Creation'	EChP ECho EPot
- 'Heavenly Blue'	ECho
- 'New Creation' **new**	ECho
± 'Saffier' ♀H4	CGrW ECho LRHS WCot
- 'Valerie Finnis'	CAvo CBgR CBos CBre CBro CCge
	CFFs CFwr CMea CStu ECho EPPr
	EPfP EPot EWTr GCrs ITim LPhx
	LRHS MAvo MNrw MSte NBPC
	SAga SPer SUsu WAul WCMO WCot
* **auchadra** **new**	ERos
§ **aucheri** ♀H4	ECho ERos MSte NRya
* - var. **bicolor**	WCot
- 'Blue Magic'	ECho EPot
- 'Mount Hood'	EBrs ECho
§ - 'Tubergenianum'	EBrs ECho
§ **azureum** ♀H4	CAvo CBgR CBro CFFs CHar CNic
	EBrs ECho EHyt ELan EPfP ERos
	LPhx LRHS NJOw NMen NWCA
	WCot
- 'Album'	CBgR CBro EBrs ECho ERos LPhx
	LRHS NJOw WCot
'Baby's Breath'	see *M.* 'Jenny Robinson'
botryoides	ECho ERos LEdu
- 'Album'	CAvo CBro CFFs CMea EChP ECho
	ENot EPfP EWTr LRHS MBri SPer
	SRms WBor WShi

caucasicum	ECho ERos
chalusicum	see *M. pseudomuscari*
§ *comosum*	CArn CBro ECho EPfP LRHS NWCA
* - 'Album'	ECho
- 'Monstrosum'	see *M. comosum* 'Plumosum'
- 'Pinard'	ECho ERos
§ - 'Plumosum'	CAvo CBro ECho EMan EMon EPfP
	EPot ITim LRHS MAvo MBri SBch
	WAul WCot WHil WSan
dionysicum	EBee ECho
- HOA 8965	WCot
grandifolium JCA 689.450	WCot
§ 'Jenny Robinson' ♀H4	CMil ECho EHrv SAga SCnR SMad
	SMrm WCot
latifolium ♀H4	CAvo CBro CFFs CMea ECho EHyt
	ENot GGar ITim LPhx LRHS MLLN
	NChi SBch SPer WCot WHoo WTin
* - 'Blue Angels'	NBir
§ *macrocarpum*	CAvo CBgR CBro CMea EBee EBrs
	ECha ECho EHyt EPot ERos WAbe
	WCot
- 'Golden Fragrance'	CBgR CMil ECho EPot GKev LRHS
mirum	ECho
moschatum	see *M. muscarimi*
§ *muscarimi*	CBgR CBro CStu ECho NWCA
	WCot WWFP
- var. *flavum*	see *M. macrocarpum*
§ *neglectum*	CBgR CSWP ECho ERos SEND
	WShi WWst
pallens	ECho EHyt ERos LRHS NWCA
	WCMO
paradoxum	see *Bellevalia paradoxa*
parviflorum	ECho ERos
§ *pseudomuscari* ♀H4	ECho ERos
- BSBE 842	EHyt
racemosum	see *M. neglectum*
§ *spreitzenhoferi*	ERos
- MS 712 from Crete	CMon
'Superstar'	ECho
§ *tenuiflorum*	ECho WCot
tubergenianum	see *M. aucheri* 'Tubergenianum'
weissii	ERos
'White Beauty'	ECho LRHS

Muscarimia (Hyacinthaceae)

ambrosiacum	see *Muscari muscarimi*
macrocarpum	see *Muscari macrocarpum*

Musella see *Musa*

Mussaenda (Rubiaceae)

erythrophylla new	CPlN
incana	EShb
philippica	CPlN

Musschia (Campanulaceae)

wollastonii	CHEx CPLG

Mutisia (Asteraceae)

clematis	CRHN
decurrens	CPlN
'Glendoick'	GGGa
ilicifolia	LRHS MTPN SBrw WSHC
* *longifolia*	CSec
oligodon	CPlN SBrw

Myoporum (Myoporaceae)

debile	see *Eremophila debilis*
laetum	CDoC CHEx CPLG CTrC IDee
	XPep
parvifolium	XPep

Myosotidium (Boraginaceae)

§ *hortensia*	More than 30 suppliers
- white	EPot ITer ITim NLar WCMO WNor
nobile	see *M. hortensia*

Myosotis (Boraginaceae)

§ *alpestris*	EHyt
- 'Ruth Fischer'	NBir NMen
aquatica new	NSco
arvensis	GWCH MBow
australis	NWCA
capitata	ECou GCrs
colensoi	ECou EDAr NMen NWCA
explanata	NMen
palustris	see *M. scorpioides*
pulvinaris	GEdr
rakiura	ITim NLAp SBch
rupicola	see *M. alpestris*
§ *scorpioides*	CBen CRow CWat EHon EMFW
	EPfP LNCo LPBA MBow NGdn
	SCoo SPlb SRms SWat WEas WMAq
	WMoo WPnP WWpP
- 'Alba'	LPBA
- Maytime = 'Blaqua' (v)	CDWL NBir NGdn
* - 'Mermaid'	CBen CRow CWat ECha EHon
	EMFW EPfP GAbr LPBA LRHS
	NDov SBch SDix SWat WFar WPer
	WPtf WWpP
- 'Pinkie'	CDWL CRow CWat EMFW LPBA
	NGdn SWat
- 'Snowflakes'	CRow CWat EMFW SWat WWpP
sylvatica	CRWN NBlu NMir

Myrceugenia (Myrtaceae)

ovata	CTrG
planipes	CTrG

Myrcia (Myrtaceae)

tomentosa	GIBF

Myrica (Myricaceae)

californica	CPle LEdu WPGP
cerifera	CAgr CArn LEdu NLar
gale	CAgr CRWN EMil GPoy MCoo
	MGos NLar SWat WDin WFar
	WWye
pensylvanica	ELau GIBF GTSp IFro LEdu
	NLar

Myricaria (Tamaricaceae)

§ *germanica*	NLar

Myriophyllum (Haloragaceae)

propinquum	EMFW
* 'Red Stem'	LPBA
spicatum	EHon EMFW NSco WMAq
verticillatum	EHon SCoo

Myrrhidendron (Apiaceae)

donnellsmithii	WCru
B&SWJ 9099	

Myrrhis (Apiaceae)

odorata	More than 30 suppliers
- 'Forncett Chevron'	GCal LEdu

Myrsine (Myrsinaceae)

africana	CPLG CPle CWib SBLw XPep
divaricata	CTrC IDee
nummularia	GGar WLin WThu

Myrteola (Myrtaceae)

nummularia	EPot GAbr ISea NMen WThu

Myrtus (Myrtaceae)

apiculata	see *Luma apiculata*
bullata	see *Lophomyrtus bullata*
capensis new	LEdu
chequen	see *Luma chequen*
communis ♀H3	More than 30 suppliers

*	- 'Alhambra'	XPep
	- 'Baetica'	XPep
*	- 'Cascade'	XPep
	- 'Flore Pleno' (d)	ELau SBrw XPep
	- 'Jenny Reitenbach'	see *M. communis* subsp. *tarentina*
*	- 'La Clape'	XPep
*	- 'La Clape Blanc'	XPep
	- 'Microphylla'	see *M. communis* subsp. *tarentina*
	- 'Nana'	see *M. communis* subsp. *tarentina*
§	- subsp. *tarentina* ♀H3	More than 30 suppliers
	- - 'Compacta'	CStu EAro WSel
*	- - 'Granada'	XPep
§	- - 'Microphylla Variegata'	CBcs CPle GBar GQui MHer NGHP
	(v)	SPer STre WJek WSel
	- - pink-flowered	XPep
I	- - 'Variegata'	CPLG EHol EPla SBLw XPep
*	- - 'Vieussan'	XPep
	- 'Tricolor'	see *M. communis* 'Variegata'
§	- 'Variegata' (v)	More than 30 suppliers
	dulcis	see *Austromyrtus dulcis*
	'Glanleam Gold'	see *Luma apiculata* 'Glanleam Gold'
	lechleriana	see *Amomyrtus luma*
	luma	see *Luma apiculata*
	nummularia	see *Myrteola nummularia*
	obcordata	see *Lophomyrtus obcordata*
*	*paraguayensis*	CTrC
	x *ralphii*	see *Lophomyrtus* x *ralphii*
	'Traversii'	see *Lophomyrtus* x *ralphii* 'Traversii'
	ugni	see *Ugni molinae*
*	*variegata* 'Penlee' (v)	CTrG

N

Nabalus (Asteraceae)

albus	see *Prenanthes alba*

Naiocrene (Portulacaceae)

§ *parvifolia*	CNic

Nananthus (Aizoaceae)

vittatus	WAbe

Nandina (Berberidaceae)

domestica ♀H3	More than 30 suppliers
- B&SWJ 4923	WCru
- 'Fire Power' ♀H3	More than 30 suppliers
- 'Harbor Dwarf'	LRHS WFar
- var. *leucocarpa*	EPla MBlu NLar
- 'Little Princess'	EPla
- 'Nana'	see *N. domestica* 'Pygmaea'
- 'Nana Purpurea'	CDul EPla GCal
- 'Orhime' **new**	NLar
§ - 'Pygmaea'	CMen WDin
- 'Richmond'	CBcs CEnd CPMA CSBt EBee ELan EPfP LRHS MAsh MGos NLar NVic SBod SHBN SPer SPla SPoG SRGP SRkn SSto WFar
- 'Wood's Dwarf'	MGos

Nannorrhops (Arecaceae)

ritchieana	LPal WMul

Napaea (Malvaceae)

dioica	CPLG EBee EMan WCot

Narcissus ✿ (Amaryllidaceae)

	'Abba' (4)	CQua
	'Aberfoyle' (2) ♀H4	GEve
	'Abstract' (11a)	CQua
	'Accent' (2) ♀H4	CQua
	'Achduart' (3)	CQua GEve
	'Achentoul' (4)	CQua
	'Achnasheen' (3)	CQua GEve
	'Acropolis' (4)	CQua EPfP LRHS
	'Actaea' (9) ♀H4	CBro CFen CQua LBmB MBri
	'Acumen' (2) **new**	CQua
	'Adele Thomson' (3)	GEve
	'Admiration' (8)	CQua
*	'Adrem'	CFen
	'Advocat' (3)	CQua
	'Aflame' (3)	CFen
	'African Sunset' (3)	IRhd
	'After All'	CFen
	'Agnes Mace' (2) **new**	IRhd
	'Ahwahnee' (2)	CQua IRhd
	'Aintree' (3)	CQua
	'Aircastle' (3)	CQua
	'Akepa' (5)	CQua
	'Albatross' (3)	CQua
I	*albidus* subsp. *occidentalis* (13)	EHyt ERos
I	- - SF 15 from Morocco	CMon
I	- - SF 270	CMon
	'Albus Plenus Odoratus'	see *N. poeticus* 'Plenus' ambig.
	'Alpine Winter' (1)	IRhd
	'Alston' (2)	IRhd
	'Alto' (2)	IRhd
	'Altruist' (3)	CQua
	'Altun Ha' (2)	CQua IRhd
	'Amazing Grace' (2)	IRhd
	'Amber Castle' (2)	CQua
	'Ambergate' (2)	GEve
	'American Heritage' (1)	CQua IRhd
	'American Robin' (6)	CQua
	'American Shores' (1)	CQua IRhd
	'Amstel' (4)	CQua
	'Andalusia' (6)	ERos
	'Angel' (3)	CQua
	'Angel Face' (3)	IRhd
	'Angelito' (3)	IRhd
	Angel's Tears	see *N. triandrus* subsp. *triandrus* var. *triandrus*
	'Angel's Wings' (2)	CQua
	'Angkor' (4)	CQua
	'An-gof' (7)	CQua
	'Apotheose' (4)	CFen CQua
	'Applins' (2)	IRhd
	'Apricot' (1)	CBro
	'April Love' (1)	CQua
	'April Snow' (2)	CBro CQua
	'Aranjuez' (2)	CFen CQua
	'Arctic Gem' (3)	CQua
	'Arctic Gold' (1) ♀H4	CQua LBmB
	'Ardglass' (3)	GEve IRhd
	'Ardress' (2)	CQua
	'Ardview' (3)	IRhd
	'Areley Kings' (2)	CQua
	'Arid Plains' (3)	IRhd
	'Arish Mell' (5)	CQua
	'Arkle' (1) ♀H4	CQua GEve LBmB
	'Arleston' (2)	IRhd
	'Armada' (2) ♀H4	CFen
	'Armidale' (3)	IRhd
	'Armoury' (4)	CQua
	'Arndilly' (2)	CQua
	'Arpege' (2)	CQua
	'Arran Isle' (2)	IRhd
	'Arthurian' (1)	IRhd
	'Arwenack' (11a)	CQua
	'Ashmore' (2)	CQua IRhd
	'Asila' (2)	IRhd
	'Assertion' (2)	IRhd
§	*assoanus* (13)	CBro CQua ECho EPot ERos LPhx NMen
	'Astropink' (11a)	CQua
§	*asturiensis* (13) ♀H3-4	CSam ECho IBlr LPhx MNrw
	- 'Navarre' (1) **new**	WCot

asturiensis x	NMen
cyclamineus	
'Atricilla' (11a)	IRhd
'Auchrannie' (2) **new**	IRhd
'Audubon' (2)	CQua
'Auntie Eileen' (2)	CQua
'Auspicious' (2)	IRhd
'Avalanche' (8) ♀H3	CQua LRHS
'Avalanche of Gold' (8)	CQua
'Avalon' (2)	CQua
'Ave' (2)	CQua
'Azocor' (1)	IRhd
'Baby Moon' (7)	CMea CQua EPot GKev LEdu LRHS
	LSou MBri SPer
'Badanloch' (3)	CQua
'Badbury Rings' (3) ♀H4	CQua
'Balalaika' (2)	CQua
'Baldock' (4)	CQua
'Ballinamallard' (3)	IRhd
'Ballygarvey' (1)	CQua
'Ballygowan' (3)	IRhd
'Ballymorran' (1)	IRhd
'Ballyrobert' (1)	CQua
'Baltic Shore' (3)	IRhd
'Balvenie' (2)	CQua
'Bambi' (1)	ERos
'Bandesara' (3)	CQua IRhd
'Bandit' (2)	CQua
'Banstead Village' (2)	CQua
'Bantam' (2) ♀H4	CBro CQua ERos
'Barleywine' (2)	IRhd
'Barlow' (6)	CQua
'Barnesgold' (1)	IRhd
'Barnsdale Wood' (2)	CQua
'Barnum' (1) ♀H4	IRhd
'Barrett Browning' (3)	LBmB
'Bartley' (6)	CQua
'Bath's Flame' (3)	CQua
'Bear Springs' (4)	IRhd
'Bebop' (7)	CBro
'Bedruthan' (2)	CQua
'Beersheba' (1)	CQua
'Belbroughton' (2)	CQua
'Belcanto' (11a)	CQua
'Belfast Lough' (1)	IRhd
'Bell Rock' (1)	CQua
'Bell Song' (7)	CAvo CBro CFfs CQua EPfP ERos
	LRHS LSou NHol SPer
'Ben Aligin' (1)	CQua
'Ben Armine' (2)	GEve
'Ben Hee' (2) ♀H4	CQua
'Ben Loyal' (2)	GEve
'Ben Vorlich' (2)	GEve
'Berceuse' (2)	CQua IRhd
'Bere Ferrers' (4)	CQua
'Bergerac' (11a)	CQua
'Berlin' (2)	ERos LBmB
'Bernardino' (2)	CQua
bertolonii from Algeria	CMon
'Beryl' (6)	CBro CQua ERos LRHS
'Best of Luck' (3)	IRhd
'Best Seller' (1)	SPer
'Bethal' (3)	CQua
'Betsy MacDonald' (6)	CQua
'Biffo' (4)	CQua
'Big John' (1)	GEve
'Bikini Beach' (2)	IRhd
'Bilbo' (6)	CBro CQua
'Binkie' (2)	CBro CQua SPer
'Birdsong' (3)	CQua
'Birkdale' (2)	GEve
'Birma' (3)	EFam
'Birthday Girl' (2)	IRhd
'Bishops Light' (2)	CQua
'Blair Athol' (2)	CQua
'Blarney' (3)	CQua

'Blisland' (9)	CQua
'Blossom' (4)	CQua
'Blossom Lady' (4) **new**	CQua
'Blue Danube' (1)	IRhd
'Blushing Maiden' (4)	CQua
'Bobbysoxer' (7)	CBro CQua ERos MTho
'Bobolink' (2)	CQua
'Bodelva' (2)	CQua
'Bodwannick' (2)	CQua
'Bold Prospect' (1)	CQua
'Bolton' (7)	CBro
'Bon Viveur' (11a)	IRhd
'Bosbigal' (11a)	CQua
'Boscastle' (7)	CQua
'Boscoppa' (11a)	CQua
'Boslowick' (11a) ♀H4	CQua
'Bosmeor' (2)	CQua
'Bossa Nova' (3)	CQua
'Bossiney' (11a)	CQua
'Bosvale' (11a)	CQua
'Bouzouki' (2)	IRhd
'Bowles' Early Sulphur' (1)	CRow
'Boyne Bridge' (1)	IRhd
'Brandaris' (11a)	CQua GEve
'Bravoure' (1) ♀H4	CQua LBmB
'Brentswood' (8)	CQua
'Bridal Crown' (4) ♀H4	CBgR CFen EBrs EPfP LRHS SPer
'Bright Flame' (2)	CQua
'Brindaleena' (2)	IRhd
'Brindle Pink' (2)	IRhd
'Broadland' (2)	CQua
'Brodick' (3)	CQua GEve IRhd
'Brookdale' (1)	CQua
'Broomhill' (2) ♀H4	CQua
broussonetii from	CMon
Morocco EKB	
- - SF 269	CMon
'Brunswick' (2)	CFen
'Budock Bells' (5)	CQua
'Budock Water' (2)	CQua
'Bugle Major' (2)	CQua
bulbocodium (13) ♀H3-4	CBro CNic CStu EHyt LBee LPhx
	LRHS NBPC NWCA SBch SMeo
	SPer SRms WLin WPGP
§ - subsp. ***bulbocodium***	CBro
(13)	
§ - - var. ***citrinus*** (13)	EHyt SSpi
- - var. ***conspicuus*** (13)	CArn CBro CHar CNic CPMA
	CQua ECho EHyt EPot ERos GCrs
	GEdr IFro ITim MSSP NMen NRya
	SBch SGar WCot
* - - ***filifolius*** (13)	CBro
§ - - var. ***graellsii*** (13)	NSla
- - var. ***nivalis*** (13)	ECho ERos
- - var. ***pallidus*** (13)	EHyt ERos
§ - - var. ***tenuifolius*** (13)	CNic CStu NMen
- - var. ***bulbocodium*** x	EHyt
'Jessamy'	
- - var. ***tenuifolius*** x	EHyt
triandrus (13)	
§ - 'Golden Bells' (10)	CAvo CBro CFfs CMea CPom
	CQua CSam CWCL EBrs ECho
	EPot LBmB LRHS MBri NHol
	NJOw SPer SUsu
- var. ***mesatlanticus***	see *N. romieuxii* subsp. *romieuxii*
	var. *mesatlanticus*
- subsp. ***praecox*** (13)	ECho
- - var. ***paucinervis*** (13)	GCrs
- subsp. ***romieuxii***	see *N. romieuxii*
I - subsp. ***viriditubus*** (13)	EHyt ERos
- subsp. ***vulgaris***	see *N. bulbocodium* subsp.
	bulbocodium
'Bunchie' (5)	CQua
'Bunclody' (2)	CQua
'Bunillidh Beauty' (2)	GEve
'Bunting' (7) ♀H4	CQua

'Burning Bush' (3)	IRhd	'Centannées' (11b)	EBrs
'Burntollet' (1)	CQua	'Centrefold' (3)	CQua
'Busselton' (3)	IRhd	'Cha-cha' (6)	CBro CQua
'Buttercup' (7)	CBro	'Chanson' (1)	IRhd
'Butterscotch' (2)	CQua	'Chapman's Peak' (2)	IRhd
'Cabernet' (2)	IRhd	'Charity May' (6) ♀H4	CBro CQua
'Cacatua' (11a)	IRhd	'Charleston' (2)	CQua
'Cadgwith' (2)	CQua	'Chasseur' (2)	IRhd
'Cairntoul' (3)	CQua	'Chaste' (1)	CQua IRhd
'Calamansack' (2)	CQua	'Chat' (7)	CQua
calcicola (13)	CWoo ERos	'Cheer Leader' (3)	CQua GEve
- B&S 413 from Spain	CMon	'Cheerfulness' (4) ♀H4	CAvo CFFs CQua ITim LBmB LRHS
'California Rose' (4)	CQua IRhd		MBri
'Camellia' (4)	EFam	'Cheesewring' (3)	CQua
'Camelot' (2) ♀H4	CQua EPfP LBmB SPer	'Cheetah' (1)	CQua IRhd
'Cameo Angel' (2)	CQua	'Chelsea Girl' (2)	CQua
'Cameo King' (2)	CQua	'Cheltenham' (2)	CQua
'Camoro' (10)	EHyt ITim	'Chenoweth' (2)	CQua
'Campernelli Plenus'	see *N.* x *odorus* 'Double	'Chérie' (7)	CBro CQua
	Campernelle'	'Cherish' (2) **new**	CQua
'Campion' (9)	CQua IRhd	'Cherrygardens' (2)	CQua IRhd
'Canaliculatus' (8)	CArn CBro CQua EBrs ECho ERos	'Chesterton' (9) ♀H4	CQua
	GKev LRHS MBri SPer WGwG	'Chickadee' (6)	CBro CQua
canaliculatus Gussone	see *N. tazetta* subsp. *lacticolor*	'Chickerell' (3)	CQua
'Canary' (7)	CQua	'Chief Inspector' (1)	IRhd
'Canarybird' (8)	CBro	'Chiffon'	CFen
'Canasta' (11a)	CQua	'Chiloquin' (1)	CQua
'Canisp' (2)	CQua	'China Doll' (2)	CQua
'Cantabile' (9) ♀H4	CBro CQua	'Chinchilla' (2)	CQua IRhd
cantabricus (13)	ECho EPot LBmB LPhx WPGP	'Chingah' (1)	IRhd
- SF 348 from Morocco	CMon	'Chinita' (8)	CBro CQua
- subsp. *cantabricus* (13)	EHyt ERos	'Chit Chat' (7) ♀H4	CBro CQua EPot ERos LBmB
- - var. *foliosus* (13) ♀H2	ECho EPot NMen SCnR	'Chobe River' (1)	IRhd
- - - SF 172 from Morocco	CMon	'Chorus Line' (8)	IRhd
cantabricus x *romieuxii* ITim		'Churston Ferrers' (4)	CQua
(13)		'Chy Noweth' (2) **new**	CQua
'Canticle' (9)	IRhd	'Cisticola' (3)	IRhd
'Capax Plenus'	see *N.* 'Eystettensis'	*citrinus*	see *N. bulbocodium* subsp.
'Cape Cornwall' (2)	CQua		*bulbocodium* var. *citrinus*
'Cape Helles' (3)	IRhd	'Citron' (3)	CQua
'Cape Point' (2)	IRhd	'Citronita' (3)	CQua
'Capisco' (3)	CQua	'Clare' (7)	CBro CQua IRhd
'Caramba' (2)	CQua	'Clashmore' (2)	GEve
'Carbineer' (2)	CQua EFam	'Claverley' (2)	CQua
'Carclew' (6)	CQua	'Clearbrook' (2)	CQua
'Cardinham' (3)	CQua	'Cloud Nine' (2)	CBro
'Cargreen' (9)	CQua	'Clouded Yellow' (2)	IRhd
'Carib Gipsy' (2) ♀H4	CQua IRhd	'Clouds Hill' (2)	CQua
'Carlton' (2) ♀H4	CQua EBrs EFam LBmB	'Clouds Rest' (2)	IRhd
'Carnearny' (3)	CQua	'Codlins and Cream'	see *N.* 'Sulphur Phoenix'
'Carnkeeran' (2)	CQua	'Coldbrook' (2) **new**	CQua
'Carnkief' (2)	CQua	'Colin's Joy' (2)	CQua
'Carnyorth' (11a)	CQua	'Colleen Bawn'	CAvo
'Carole Lombard' (3)	CQua IRhd	'Colley Gate' (3)	CQua
'Carwinion' (2) **new**	CQua	'Colliford' (2)	CQua
'Cassata' (11)	EBrs EFam EPfP LBmB LRHS NBir	'Colorama' (11a)	CQua
'Castanets' (8)	IRhd	'Colour Sergeant' (2)	IRhd
'Casterbridge' (2)	CQua IRhd	'Colourful' (2)	IRhd
'Castlerock'	CFen	'Columbus' (2)	CQua
'Catalyst' (2)	IRhd	'Colville' (9)	CQua
'Catherine MacKenzie' (3)	GEve	'Comal' (1)	CQua
'Catistock' (2)	CQua	'Compressus'	see *N.* x *intermedius* 'Compressus'
'Causeway Sunset' (2)	IRhd	'Compton Court' (3)	IRhd
'Cavalryman' (3)	IRhd	*concolor*	see *N. triandrus* subsp. *triandrus*
cavanillesii MS&CL 450	CMon		var. *concolor*
from Spain		'Conestoga' (2)	CQua IRhd
- SF 239 from Morocco	CMon	'Confuoco' (2)	EFam
* - *mauretanicus* SF 260	CMon	'Congress' (11a)	CQua
from Morocco		* 'Connie Number 1'	CStu
'Cavendish' (4)	IRhd	* 'Connie Number 2'	EHyt
'Cazique' (6)	CQua	'Conowingo' (11a)	CQua
'Ceasefire' (2)	IRhd	'Cool Autumn' (2)	CQua
'Cedar Hills' (3)	CQua	'Cool Crystal' (3)	CQua
'Cedric Morris' (1)	CBro CDes CElw CLAP ECha EHrv	'Cool Evening' (11a)	CQua IRhd
	NCGa NDov SMrm	'Cool Pink' (2)	CQua
'Celtic Gold' (2)	CQua	'Coolmaghery' (2) **new**	IRhd

'Coombe Creek' (6)	CQua
'Copper Nob' (2)	IRhd
'Copper Rings' (3) **new**	CQua
'Copperfield' (2) **new**	CQua
'Cora Ann' (7)	CBro
'Coral Fair' (2) **new**	CQua
'Corbiere' (1)	CQua IRhd
cordubensis (13)	CBro ECho EHyt EPot
- MS 434 from Spain	CMon
'Cornet' (6)	CQua
'Cornish Chuckles' (12)	CBro CFen CQua
'Cornish Vanguard' (2)	CQua
'Cornsilk' (11a) **new**	CQua
'Corofin' (3)	CQua
'Coromandel' (2)	IRhd
'Cosmic Dance' (3)	IRhd
'Cotinga' (6)	CQua EBrs
'Countdown' (2)	CQua
'Court Martial' (2)	CFen
'Crackington' (4) ♀H4	CQua IRhd
'Craig Stiel' (2)	CQua GEve
'Creag Dubh' (2)	CQua GEve
'Creed' (6) **new**	CQua
'Crenver' (3)	CQua
'Crevenagh' (2)	IRhd
'Crewenna' (1)	CQua
'Crill' (7)	CQua
'Crimson Chalice' (3)	CQua IRhd
'Cristobal' (1)	CQua
'Crock of Gold' (1)	CFen CQua
'Croesus' (2)	CQua
'Crofty' (6)	CQua
'Croila' (2)	CQua
'Crowndale' (4)	CQua IRhd
'Crugmeer' (11a) **new**	CQua
'Cryptic' (1)	CQua IRhd
'Crystal Star' (2)	CQua
'Cuan Gold' (4)	IRhd
cuatrecasasii (13)	ERos
'Cudden Point' (2)	CQua
'Cul Beag' (3)	CQua
'Culmination' (2)	CQua
'Cultured Pearl' (2)	CQua
'Cupid's Eye' (3)	CQua IRhd
'Curlew' (7)	CQua
cyclamineus (13) ♀H4	CBro CDes CPom CWoo EPot MSSP SCnR SRms WAbe WCru WPGP
'Cyclope' (1)	CQua
cypri (8)	CQua
'Cyros' (1)	CQua
'Dailmanach' (2)	CQua IRhd
'Dailmystic' (2)	IRhd
'Dallas' (3)	CQua
'Damson' (2)	CQua
'Dan du Plessis' (8)	CQua
'Dancing Queen' (2)	IRhd
'Dardanelles' (2)	IRhd
'Dateline' (3)	CQua
'David Alexander' (1)	CQua
'David Mills' (2)	CQua
'Davochfin Lass' (1)	GEve
'Dawn Call' (2)	IRhd
'Dawn Run' (2)	IRhd
'Daydream' (2) ♀H3	CQua
'Daymark' (8)	CQua
'Dayton Lake' (2)	CQua
'Debutante' (2)	CQua
'December Bride' (11a)	CQua
'Delia' (6)	IRhd
'Délibes' (3)	LBmB SPer
'Dell Chapel' (3)	CQua
'Delnashaugh' (4)	CQua
'Delos' (3)	CQua
'Delphin Hill' (4)	IRhd
'Delta Flight' (6)	IRhd
'Demand' (2)	CQua
'Demmo' (2) **new**	CQua
'Dena' (3) **new**	IRhd
'Denali' (1)	IRhd
'Derryboy' (3)	IRhd
'Descant' (1)	IRhd
'Desdemona' (2) ♀H4	CQua
'Desert Bells' (7)	CQua
'Desert Orchid' (2)	CQua
'Diatone' (4)	GEve
'Dick Wilden' (4)	CBgR
'Dickcissel' (7) ♀H4	CBro CQua ERos
'Dimity' (3)	CQua
'Dimple' (9)	CQua
'Dinkie' (3)	CBro
'Diversity' (11a)	IRhd
'Doctor Hugh' (3) ♀H4	CQua GEve IRhd
'Doombar' (1)	CQua
'Dora Allum' (2)	CQua
'Dorchester' (4)	CQua IRhd
'Double Campernelle'	see *N.* x *odorus* 'Double Campernelle'
double pheasant eye	see *N. poeticus* 'Plenus' ambig.
double Roman	see *N.* 'Romanus'
'Double White' (4)	CQua
'Doubleday' (4)	CQua IRhd
'Doublet' (4)	CQua
'Doubtful' (3)	CQua
'Dove Wings' (6) ♀H4	CQua
'Dover Cliffs' (2)	CQua
'Downlands' (3) **new**	CQua
'Downpatrick' (1)	CQua
'Dragon Run' (2)	CQua
'Drama Queen' (11a)	IRhd
'Drumbeg' (2)	IRhd
'Drumlin' (1) ♀H4	IRhd
dubius (13)	CBro ECho EPot
- MS 512 from Spain	CMon
'Duiker' (6)	IRhd
'Duke of Windsor' (2)	EFam
'Dulcimer' (9)	CQua
'Dunadry Inn' (4)	IRhd
'Dunkeld' (2)	CQua
'Dunkery' (4)	CQua IRhd
'Dunley Hall' (3)	CQua IRhd
'Dunmurry' (1)	CQua
'Dunskey' (3)	CQua
'Dupli Kate' (4)	IRhd
'Dusky Lad' (2)	IRhd
'Dusky Maiden' (2)	IRhd
'Dutch Delight' (2)	IRhd
'Dutch Master' (1) ♀H4	CQua EBrs LBmB
'Early Bride' (2)	CFen CQua
'Early Splendour' (8)	CQua
'Earthlight' (3)	CQua
'Easter Moon' (2)	CQua
'Eastern Dawn' (2)	CQua
'Eastern Promise' (2) **new**	CQua
'Eaton Song' (12) ♀H4	CBro CQua
'Eddy Canzony' (2)	CFen CQua
'Edenderry' (1)	IRhd
'Edgbaston' (2)	CQua
'Edge Grove' (2)	CQua
'Edward Buxton' (3)	CFen CQua
'Egard' (11a)	CQua
'Egmont King' (2) **new**	CQua
'Eland' (7)	CQua
'Elburton' (2)	CQua
'Electrus' (11a)	IRhd
elegans (13)	ECho
- var. *fallax* AB&S 4301 from Morocco	CMon
- MS&CL 324 from Tunisia	CMon
'Elf' (2)	CBro CQua
'Elfin Gold' (6)	CQua IRhd
'Elizabeth Ann' (6)	CQua

'Elka' (1)	CBro CQua	
'Ella D' (2)	CQua	
'Elphin' (4)	CQua GEve	
'Elrond' (2)	CQua	
'Elven Lady' (2)	CQua	
'Elvira' (8)	CBro CQua	
'Embo' (2)	GEve	
'Emerald Pink' (3)	CQua	
'Emily' (2)	CQua	
'Eminent' (3)	CQua	
'Emperor's Waltz' (6)	CQua IRhd	
'Empress of Ireland' (1) ♀H4	CQua IRhd LBmB	
'Ensemble' (4)	CQua	
'Epona' (3)	CQua	
'Eribol' (2)	GEve	
'Eriskay' (4)	GEve	
'Erlicheer' (4)	CBgR CQua	
'Escapee' (2)	IRhd	
'Estrella' (3)	CQua	
'Ethereal Beauty' (2)	IRhd	
'Ethos' (1)	IRhd	
'Euryalus' (1)	CQua	
'Evelix' (2)	GEve	
'Evening' (2)	CQua	
'Evesham' (3)	IRhd	
'Eyeglass' (3)	IRhd	
'Eyelet' (3)	IRhd	
'Eype' (4)	IRhd	
'Eyrie' (3)	IRhd	
§ 'Eystettensis' (4)	CBro ECha ERos GCrs IBlr	
'Fair Head' (9)	CQua	
'Fair Prospect' (2)	CQua	
'Fair William' (2)	CQua	
'Fairgreen' (3)	CFen CQua	
'Fairlawns' (3)	CQua	
'Fairmile' (3)	CQua	
'Fairy Chimes' (5)	CBro CQua	
'Fairy Footsteps' (3)	CQua IRhd	
'Fairy Island' (3)	CQua	
'Fairy Spell' (3)	IRhd	
'Fairy Tale' (3) new	CQua	
'Falconet' (8) ♀H4	CBgR CBro CQua ERos	
'Falmouth Bay' (3)	CQua	
'Falstaff' (2)	CQua	
'Famecheck Giant'	EFam	
'Famecheck Luck' (2)	EFam	
'Famecheck Silver' (11b)	EFam	
'Far Country' (2)	CQua GEve	
'Farranfad' (2)	IRhd	
I 'Fashion' (11b)	CQua	
'Fastidious' (2)	CQua	
'February Gold' (6) ♀H4	CAvo CBro CFFs EBrs EPfP EPot ERos LBmB LRHS MBri NBir SGar SPer SRms WShi	
'February Silver' (6)	EBrs EPot SMeo	
'Felindre' (9)	CQua	
'Feline Queen' (1)	IRhd	
'Fellowship' (2)	GEve	
'Feock' (3)	CQua	
fernandesii (13)	CBro ECho ERos SCnR	
- B&S 467 from Spain	CMon	
'Ferndown' (3)	CQua IRhd	
'Ffitch's Ffolly' (2)	CQua	
'Filoli' (1)	CQua IRhd	
'Finchcocks' (2)	CQua	
'Fine Gold' (1)	CQua	
'Fine Romance' (2)	CQua	
'Finland' (2)	CFen	
'Finlandia' (1)	CQua	
'Fiona MacKillop' (2)	IRhd	
'Fionn' (2)	GEve	
'Firebrand' (2)	CQua	
'First Born' (6) new	CQua	
'First Formal' (3)	CQua	
'Flambards Village' (4)	CQua	
'Flirt' (6)	CQua	
'Flomay' (7)	CBro	
'Florida Manor' (3)	IRhd	
'Flower Drift' (4)	EPfP	
'Flower Record' (2)	SPer	
'Flycatcher' (7)	CQua IRhd	
'Flying Colours' (4)	IRhd	
'Flying High' (3)	CQua	
'Foresight' (1)	CQua EFam LBmB	
'Forge Mill' (2)	CQua	
'Fortune' (2)	CQua EFam MBri	
'Foundling' (6) ♀H4	CBro CQua GEve	
'Fragrant Breeze' (2)	EBrs	
'Fragrant Rose' (2)	CQua IRhd	
'Francolin' (1)	IRhd	
'Frank' (9) new	IRhd	
'Freedom Rings' (2)	CQua	
'Freedom Stars' (11a) new	IRhd	
'Fresco' (11a)	IRhd	
'Fresno' (3)	IRhd	
'Frogmore' (6)	CQua	
'Front Royal' (2)	CQua	
'Frosted Pink' (2)	IRhd	
'Frostkist' (6)	CBro CQua	
'Frou-frou' (4)	CQua	
'Fruit Cup' (7)	CQua EPfP	
'Fulwell' (4)	CQua	
'Furnace Creek' (2)	IRhd	
'Fynbos' (3)	IRhd	
gaditanus (13)	CBro ERos	
'Gamebird' (1) new	IRhd	
'Garden News' (3)	IRhd	
'Garden Princess' (6)	CBro	
'Gay Cavalier' (4)	CQua	
'Gay Kybo' (4) ♀H4	CQua LBmB	
'Gay Song' (4)	CQua	
'Gay Time' (4)	CFen	
§ *gayi* (13)	CQua	
'Geevor' (4)	CQua	
'Gellymill' (2) new	CQua	
'Gemini Girl' (2)	CQua	
'George Leak' (2)	CFen CQua	
'Georgia Moon'	CFen	
'Georgie Girl' (6)	CQua	
'Geranium' (8) ♀H4	CBro CQua EPfP LBmB LEdu LRHS SMeo SPer	
'Gettysburg' (2)	CQua	
'Gillan' (11a)	CQua	
'Gin and Lime' (1) ♀H4	CQua	
'Gipsy Queen' (1)	CAvo CQua	
'Gironde' (11)	CQua	
'Glacier' (1)	CQua	
'Glen Cassley' (3)	CQua GEve	
'Glen Clova' (2)	CQua GEve LBmB	
'Glen Lorne' (2)	GEve	
'Glencalvie' (2)	GEve	
'Glendermott' (2)	CQua	
'Glenfarclas' (1) ♀H4	GEve LBmB	
'Glenmorangie' (2)	GEve	
'Glenside' (2)	CQua	
'Glissando' (2)	CQua	
'Gloriosus' (8)	CQua	
'Glowing Pheonix' (4)	CQua	
'Glowing Red' (4)	CQua	
'Goff's Caye' (2)	CQua IRhd	
'Golant' (2) new	CQua	
'Gold Bond' (2)	CQua IRhd	
'Gold Charm' (2)	CQua	
'Gold Convention' (2) ♀H4	CQua IRhd	
'Gold Ingot' (2)	IRhd	
'Gold Medallion' (1)	CQua	
'Gold Mine' (2)	IRhd	
'Gold Strike' (1)	GEve	
'Golden Amber' (2)	CQua	
'Golden Anniversary'	CFen	
'Golden Aura' (2) ♀H4	CQua	

'Golden Bear' (4)	CQua
'Golden Bells'	see *N. bulbocodium* 'Golden Bells'
'Golden Cheer' (2)	CQua
'Golden Cycle' (6)	CQua
'Golden Dawn' (8) ♀H3	CQua
'Golden Ducat' (4)	CQua MBri NBir
'Golden Flute' (2) **new**	IRhd
'Golden Gamble' (11a) **new**	IRhd
'Golden Halo' (2)	CQua
'Golden Harvest' (1)	CQua LRHS SPer
'Golden Incense' (7)	CQua
'Golden Jewel' (2) ♀H4	CQua GEve
'Golden Joy' (2)	CQua
'Golden Marvel' (1)	CQua
'Golden Orbit' (4)	CQua
'Golden Phoenix' (4)	WShi
'Golden Quince' (12)	CBro CQua
'Golden Rain' (4)	CQua
'Golden Rapture' (1) ♀H4	CQua LBmB
'Golden Sceptre' (7)	CBro
'Golden Sheen' (2)	CQua
'Golden Splash' (11a) **new**	IRhd
'Golden Spur' (1)	CQua
'Golden Strand' (2)	IRhd
'Golden Topaz' (2)	IRhd
'Golden Torch' (2)	CQua
'Golden Vale' (1) ♀H4	CQua
'Goldfinger' (1) ♀H4	CQua IRhd
'Goldhanger' (2)	CQua
'Goldsithney' (2)	CBro
'Golitha Falls' (2)	CQua
'Good Measure' (2)	CQua
'Goonbell' (2)	CQua
'Gorran' (3)	CQua
'Gossmoor' (4)	CQua
graellsii	see *N. bulbocodium* subsp. *bulbocodium* var. *graellsii*
'Grand Monarque'	see *N. tazetta* subsp. *lacticolor* 'Grand Monarque'
'Grand Opening' (4)	IRhd
'Grand Primo Citronière' (8)	CQua
'Grand Prospect' (2)	CQua
'Grand Soleil d'Or' (8)	CQua
'Grapillon' (11a)	GEve
'Grasmere' (1) ♀H4	GEve
'Great Expectations' (2)	CQua
'Greatwood' (1)	CQua
'Green Island' (2)	CFen
'Green Lodge' (9)	IRhd
'Greenlet' (6)	CBgR CBro CQua LRHS MSte
'Greenodd' (3)	CQua
'Greenpark' (9)	IRhd
'Grenoble' (2)	CQua
'Gresham' (4)	CQua IRhd
'Gribben Head' (4)	CQua
'Groundkeeper' (3)	IRhd
'Grullemans Senior' (2)	EFam
'Gulliver' (3)	CQua
'Gunwalloe' (11a)	CQua
'Gwennap' (1)	CQua
'Gwinear' (2)	CQua
'Hacienda' (1) **new**	CQua
'Halley's Comet' (3)	CQua IRhd
'Halvose' (8)	CBro
'Halzephron' (2) **new**	CQua
'Hambledon' (2) ♀H4	CQua
'Hampton Court' (2) **new**	CQua
'Happy Dreams' (2)	IRhd
'Happy Fellow' (2)	CQua
'Happy Valley' (2) **new**	IRhd
'Harbour View' (2)	IRhd
'Harmony Bells' (5)	CQua
'Harp Music' (2)	IRhd
'Harpers Ferry' (1)	CQua
'Hartlebury' (3)	CQua

* 'Hat' (10)	EHyt
'Hawaii' (4)	SUsu
'Hawangi' (3)	IRhd
'Hawera' (5) ♀H4	CAvo CBro CFFs CMea CQua EBrs ECGP EPfP EPot GKev LBmB LPhx LRHS LSou MBri SPer WHal WLin
'Hazel Rutherford' (2)	GEve
'Heamoor' (4) ♀H4	CQua
hedraeanthus (13)	ECho
– SG 13	WCot
'Helford Dawn' (2)	CQua
'Helford Sunset' (2)	CQua
'Helios' (2)	CQua
hellenicus	see *N. poeticus* var. *hellenicus*
henriquesii	see *N. jonquilla* var. *henriquesii*
'Henry Irving' (1)	CQua
'Hero' (1)	CQua
'Hesla' (7)	CBro
'Heslington' (3)	CQua
'Hexameter' (9)	CQua
'Hexworthy' (3)	CQua
'Hicks Mill' (1)	CQua
'High Life'	CFen
'High Society' (2) ♀H4	CQua IRhd
'Highfield Beauty' (8) ♀H4	CQua
'Highlite' (2)	CQua
'Hilda's Pink' (2)	CQua
'Hilford' (2)	IRhd
'Hill Head' (9)	IRhd
'Hillstar' (7) ♀H4	CMea CQua IRhd
'Hocus Pocus' (3)	IRhd
'Holly Berry' (2)	CFen CQua
'Hollypark' (3)	IRhd
'Holme Fen' (2)	CQua
'Home Fires' (2)	CQua
'Homestead' (2) ♀H4	IRhd
'Honey Pink' (2)	CQua
'Honeybird' (1)	CQua
'Honeyorange' (2)	IRhd
'Honolulu' (4)	CQua
'Hoopoe' (8) ♀H4	CBro CQua
'Horace' (9)	CQua
'Horn of Plenty' (5)	CBro CQua
'Hornpipe' (1)	IRhd
'Hors d'Oeuvre' (8)	CBro
'Hospodar' (2)	CQua
'Hot Gossip' (2)	CQua
'Hotspur' (2)	CQua
'Hugh Town' (8)	CAvo CQua
'Hullabaloo' (2)	IRhd
'Hunting Caye' (2)	CQua
'Huntley Down' (1)	CQua
'Ice Chimes' (5)	CQua
'Ice Dancer' (2)	CQua
'Ice Diamond' (4)	CQua
'Ice Follies' (2) ♀H4	CQua EBrs EFam LBmB MBri NBir SPer
'Ice King' (4)	NBir SPer
'Ice Wings' (5) ♀H4	CAvo CBro CFFs CPBP CQua EPot ERos LBmB MSte WLin WShi
'Idless' (1)	CQua
'Immaculate' (2)	CQua
'Inara' (4)	CQua
'Inca' (6)	CQua
'Inchbonnie' (2) **new**	CQua
'Independence Day' (4)	CQua
'Indian Chief' (4)	EFam
'Indian Maid' (7) ♀H4	CQua IRhd
'Indora' (4)	CQua
'Inner Glow' (2)	IRhd
'Innisidgen' (8)	CQua
'Innovator' (4)	IRhd
'Inny River' (1)	IRhd
'Interim' (2)	CFen CQua
§ x *intermedius* (13)	CBro CQua ERos
§ – 'Compressus' (8)	CQua

'Intrigue' (7) ♀H4 — CQua IRhd SPer
'Invercassley' (3) — CQua GEve
'Inverpolly' (2) — GEve
'Ipi Tombi' (2) — ERos
'Ireland's Eye' (9) — CQua
'Irish Fire' (2) **new** — CQua
'Irish Light' (2) — CQua
'Irish Linen' (3) — CQua
'Irish Luck' (1) — CQua
'Irish Minstrel' (2) ♀H4 — CQua
'Irish Wedding' (2) — CQua
'Isambard' (4) — CQua
'Islander' (4) — CQua
'Ita' (2) — IRhd
'Itzim' (6) ♀H4 — CBro CQua ECho ERos
'Jack Snipe' (6) ♀H4 — CAvo CBro CFFs CNic CQua EBrs ECGP ECho EPfP EPot ERos LBmB LRHS MBri MSte WShi
'Jack Wood' (11a) — CQua
'Jackadee' (2) — IRhd
'Jake' (3) — IRhd
'Jamage' (8) — CQua
'Jamaica Inn' (4) — CQua
'Jambo' (2) — IRhd
'Jamboree' (2) — CQua
'Jamestown' (3) — IRhd
'Jane Frances' (1) — GEve
'Jane MacLennan' (4) — GEve
'Jane van Kralingen' (3) — GEve
'Janelle' (2) — CQua
'Jantje' (11a) — CQua
'Javelin' (2) — IRhd
'Jeanine' (2) **new** — CQua
'Jeanne Bicknell' (4) — CQua
'Jedna' (2) — CQua
'Jenny' (6) ♀H4 — CAvo CBro CFFs CFen CMea CQua EBrs EPot ERos LBmB LEdu LRHS NBir SBch WShi
'Jetage' (6) — CBro
'Jetfire' (6) ♀H4 — CBro CQua EBrs ECho EPfP EPot ERos GEve LBmB LRHS LSou NHol SPer
'Jezebel' (3) — CBro
'Jim's Gold' (2) — CQua
'Jodi's Sister' (11a) — IRhd
'Johanna' (5) — CBro
'John Daniel' (4) — CQua
'John Lanyon' (3) **new** — CQua
'John's Delight' (3) — CQua
x *johnstonii* — CBro
'Joke Fulmer' — CFen
jonquilla (13) ♀H4 — CAvo CBro CPBP CQua EPot ERos LEdu LPhx LRHS WLin WPGP WShi
- B&S 459 from Spain — CMon
§ - var. *henriquesii* (13) — CQua ECho SCnR WPGP
- - MS 419 from Spain — CMon
'Joppa' (7) — CQua
'Joy Bishop' — see *N. romieuxii* 'Joy Bishop'
'Joybell' (6) — CQua
'Juanita' (2) — CFen EPfP SPer
'Jules Verne' (2) — CQua
'Julia Jane' — see *N. romieuxii* 'Julia Jane'
'Jumblie' (12) ♀H4 — CBro CQua EPfP EPot ERos GGar MBri NJOw SPer
juncifolius — see *N. assoanus*
'June Allyson' — CFen
'June Lake' (2) — CQua IRhd
'Kabani' (9) — CQua
'Kalimna' (1) — CQua
'Kamau' (9) — GEve IRhd
'Kamms' (1) — CQua
'Kamura' (2) — CQua
'Kanchenjunga' (1) **new** — CQua
'Kate Fraser' (2) — GEve
'Kathleen Munro' (2) — GEve
'Kathy's Clown' (6) — CQua

'Kaydee' (6) ♀H4 — CQua IRhd
'Kea' (6) — CQua
'Keats' (4) — CBro CQua
'Kebaya' (2) — CQua
'Kehelland' (4) — CBro
'Kenellis' (10) — CBgR CBro CQua EPot GEdr MSte
'Kernow' (2) — CQua
'Kidling' (7) — CQua ECho
'Killara' (8) — CQua
'Killearnan' (9) — CQua
'Killigrew' (2) — CQua
'Killivose' (3) — CQua
'Killyleagh' (3) — IRhd
'Kiltonga' (2) — IRhd
'Kilworth' (2) — CQua EFam
'Kimmeridge' (3) — CQua
'King Alfred' (1) — CQua EPfP SPer
'King Size' (11a) — GEve
'Kinglet' (7) — CQua
'King's Grove' (1) ♀H4 — CQua IRhd
'Kings Pipe' (2) — CQua
'Kingscourt' (1) ♀H4 — CQua
'Kirkcubbin' (3) — IRhd
'Kit Hill' (7) — CQua
'Kitten' (6) — CQua
'Kitty' (6) — CBro ERos
'Kiwi Magic' (4) — CQua IRhd
'Kiwi Solstice' (4) — CQua
'Kiwi Sunset' (4) — CQua
'Knight of Saint John' — CFen
'Knocklayde' (3) — CQua
'Knowing Look' (3) **new** — IRhd
'Kokopelli' (7) ♀H4 — CBro
'Korora Bay' (1) — IRhd
'La Argentina' (2) — EFam
'La Riante' (3) — CQua
'Ladies' Choice' (7) — IRhd
'Ladies' Favorite' (7) — IRhd
'Lady Ann' (2) — IRhd
'Lady Emily' (2) — IRhd
'Lady Eve' (11a) — IRhd
'Lady Margaret Boscawen' (2) — CQua
'Lady Serena' (9) — CQua
'Lake Tahoe' (2) — IRhd
'Lalique' (3) — CQua
'Lamanva' (2) — CQua
'Lamlash' (2) — IRhd
'Lanarth' (7) — CBro
'Lancaster' (3) — CQua IRhd
'Langarth' (11a) — CQua
'Lapwing' (5) — CBro ERos IRhd
'Larkelly' (6) — CBro ERos
'Larkhill' (2) — CQua
'Larkwhistle' (6) ♀H4 — ERos
'Latchley' (2) — CQua
'Lauren' (3) — IRhd
'Lavender Lass' (6) — CQua
'Leading Light' (2) — CQua
'Lee Moor' (1) — CQua
'Lemon Beauty' (11b) — CQua LBmB
'Lemon Drops' (5) ♀H4 — CBgR CBro CQua EPot ERos LBmB LPhx MSte
'Lemon Grey' (3) — IRhd
'Lemon Heart' (5) — CBro
'Lemon Silk' (6) — CBro CMea CQua LPhx
'Lemon Snow' (2) — IRhd
'Lemonade' (3) — CQua
'Lennymore' (2) — CQua IRhd
'Lewis George' (1) — CQua
'Libby' (2) — IRhd
'Liberty Bells' (5) — CBro CQua LRHS MBri
'Liebeslied' (3) **new** — CQua
'Life' (7) — CQua
'Lighthouse' (3) — CQua GEve
'Lighthouse Reef' (1) — CQua IRhd

'Lilac Charm' (6)	CQua IRhd
'Lilac Hue' (6)	CBro
'Limbo' (2)	CQua IRhd
'Limehurst' (2)	CQua
'Limpopo' (3)	IRhd
'Lindsay Joy' (2)	CQua
'Lingerie' (4) ♀H4	NZep
'Lintie' (7)	CBro CQua ERos
'Lisbarnett' (3)	IRhd
'Lisnamulligan' (3)	IRhd
'Lisnaruddy' (3)	IRhd
'Little Beauty' (1) ♀H4	CAvo CBgR CBro CFFs CMea CQua ECho EPot ERos
'Little Dancer' (1)	CBro CQua
'Little Gem' (1) ♀H4	CAvo CBgR CBro CFFs CQua EPot SPer
'Little Jewel' (3)	CQua
'Little Karoo' (3)	IRhd
'Little Rosie' (2)	IRhd
'Little Sentry' (7)	CBro CQua
'Little Soldier' (10)	CQua
'Little Spell' (1)	CBgR
'Little Witch' (6)	CBgR CBro CFFs CQua ECho EPot ERos SUsu WShi
'Littlefield' (7)	CQua
'Liverpool Festival' (2)	CQua
'Lobularis'	see *N. pseudonarcissus* 'Lobularis'
lobularis Schultes	see *N. obvallaris*
'Loch Alsh' (3)	CQua IRhd
'Loch Assynt' (3)	CQua GEve
'Loch Brora' (2)	CQua GEve
'Loch Coire' (3)	CQua
'Loch Fada' (2)	CQua
'Loch Hope' (2)	CQua GEve
'Loch Leven' (2)	CQua
'Loch Lundie' (2)	CQua
'Loch Maberry' (2)	CQua
'Loch Naver' (2)	CQua GEve
'Loch Stac' (2)	CQua
'Logan Rock' (7)	CQua
'Lordship' (1)	CQua
'Lorikeet' (1)	CQua NZep
'Lothario' (2)	MBri
'Lough Bawn' (2)	GEve
'Lough Gowna' (1)	IRhd
'Lough Ryan' (1)	IRhd
'Loveny' (2)	CQua
'Lowin'	CFen
'Lucifer' (2)	CQua WShi
'Lucky Chance' (11a)	IRhd
'Lundy Light' (2)	CQua
'Lyrebird' (3)	CQua
'Lyric' (9)	CQua
'Lysander' (2)	CQua
x *macleayi* (13)	CQua
'Madam Speaker' (4)	CQua
'Magician' (2)	IRhd NZep
'Magna Carta' (2)	CQua
'Mai's Family' (6) **new**	CQua
'Majarde' (2)	EFam
'Majestic Star' (1)	CQua
'Mallee' (11a)	IRhd
'Manaccan' (1)	CQua
'Mangaweka' (6)	CQua
'Manly' (4) ♀H4	CQua LBmB
'Mantle' (2)	CQua
'Marilyn Anne' (2)	CQua
'Marjorie Hine' (2)	CQua
'Marjorie Treveal' (4)	CQua
'Marlborough' (2)	CQua
'Marlborough Freya' (2)	CQua
'Marshfire' (2) **new**	CQua
'Martha Washington' (8)	CBro CQua
'Martinette' (8)	CFen CQua MBri
'Martinsville' (8)	CQua
marvieri	see *N. rupicola* subsp. *marvieri*

'Mary Copeland' (4)	MMHG
'Mary Kate' (2)	CQua IRhd
'Mary Lou' (6)	IRhd
'Mary Schouten' (2)	GEve
'Marzo' (7)	CQua IRhd
'Matador' (8)	CQua IRhd
'Mawla' (1) **new**	CQua
'Max' (11a)	CQua
'Maya Dynasty' (2)	CQua
'Mayan Gold' (1)	IRhd
'Mazzard' (4)	CQua
'Media Girl' (2)	IRhd
x *medioluteus* (13)	CBro CQua
'Medusa' (8)	CBro
'Melancholy' (1)	CQua
'Melbury' (2)	CQua
'Meldrum' (1)	CQua
'Melen'	CFen
'Memento' (1)	CQua
'Menabilly' (4)	CQua
'Men-an-Tol' (2)	CQua
'Menehay' (11a) ♀H4	CQua IRhd
'Mentor' (2)	GEve
'Merida' (2)	IRhd
'Merlin' (3) ♀H4	CQua GEve LBmB
'Merry Bells' (5)	CQua
'Merrymeet' (4)	CQua
'Merthan' (9) **new**	CQua
'Midas Touch' (1)	CQua
'Midget'	CBgR CBro CFFs CMea CStu ECho EPot ERos GEdr GKev NBPC
'Mike Pollock' (8)	CQua
'Millennium' (1)	CBro
'Millennium Sunrise' (2)	CQua
'Millennium Sunset' (2)	CQua
'Milly's Magic' (2) **new**	CQua
'Minicycla' (6)	CBro GCrs
minimus misapplied	see *N. asturiensis*
'Minnow' (8) ♀H3	CAvo CBro CFFs CQua EBrs ECho EPfP ERos GKev ITim LBmB LPhx LRHS MBri NBPC NBlu NJOw SBch SPer WLin
§ *minor* (13) ♀H4	CBro CQua ECha EPot LPhx WShi
– 'Douglasbank' (1)	CBro
– var. *pumilus* 'Plenus'	see *N.* 'Rip van Winkle'
– Ulster form	IBlr MSSP
'Minute Waltz' (6)	CQua
'Miss Muffitt' (1)	CQua
'Mission Bells' (5) ♀H4	CQua IRhd
'Mission Impossible' (11a)	CQua
'Misty Dawn' (3)	IRhd
'Misty Glen' (2) ♀H4	CQua GEve
'Misty Moon' (3)	CQua
'Mite' (6) ♀H4	CBro CMea CQua EHyt EPot ERos GEdr
'Mithrel' (11a) **new**	CQua
'Mitylene' (2)	CQua
'Mockingbird' (7)	IRhd
'Mondragon' (11a)	CQua EFam
'Mongleath' (2)	CQua
'Monksilver' (3)	CQua
'Montclair' (2)	CQua
'Montego' (3)	CQua
'Moon Dream' (1)	CQua
'Moon Ranger' (3)	CQua IRhd
'Moon Rhythm' (4)	IRhd
'Moon Shadow' (3)	CQua
'Moon Tide' (3)	IRhd
'Moon Valley' (2)	GEve IRhd
'Moonstruck' (1) **new**	CQua
'Moralee' (4)	IRhd
§ *moschatus* (13) ♀H4	CBgR CBro CQua ECho EPot WCMO WCot WShi
– 'Cernuus Plenus' (4)	CAvo
'Mother Catherine Grullemans' (2)	EFam

'Motmot'	CQua	
'Mount Fuji' (2)	CQua	
'Mount Hood' (1) ♥H4	EBrs EPfP LBmB NBir SPer	
'Mount Rainier' (1)	CQua	
'Mount Royal' (2)	IRhd	
'Movie Star' (2)	IRhd	
'Mowser' (7)	CQua	
'Mr Julian' (6) **new**	CQua	
'Mrs Langtry' (3)	CQua WShi	
'Mrs R.O. Backhouse' (2)	CQua WShi	
'Muirfield' (1)	GEve	
'Mullion' (3)	CQua	
'Mulroy Bay' (1)	CQua IRhd	
'Murlough' (9)	CQua	
'Muscadet' (2)	CQua	
'Naivasha' (2)	IRhd	
'Namraj' (2)	CQua	
'Nancegollan' (7)	CBro CQua	
'Nangiles' (4)	CQua	
'Nanpec' (7)	CQua	
'Nansidwell' (2)	CQua	
'Nanstallon' (1)	CQua	
'Nederburg' (1)	IRhd	
'Nether Barr' (2)	IRhd	
§ *nevadensis* (13)	SBla	
'New Hope' (3)	CQua	
'New Life' (3)	CQua	
'New Penny' (3)	CQua IRhd	
'New-baby' (7)	CQua	
'Newcastle' (1)	CQua	
'Newcomer' (3) **new**	CQua	
'Night Music' (4)	CQua	
'Nightcap' (1)	CQua	
'Nirvana' (7)	CBro	
'Niveth' (5)	CAvo CFen CQua	
'Nonchalant' (3)	CQua IRhd	
'Norma Jean' (2)	CQua	
'Nor-nor' (2)	CBro ERos	
'North Rim' (2)	CQua	
'Northern Sceptre' (2)	IRhd	
'Noss Mayo' (6)	CBro CQua	
'Notre Dame' (2) ♥H4	CQua IRhd	
'Numen Rose' (2)	IRhd	
Nylon Group (10)	CBro CNic EHyt EPot GEdr	
'Oadby' (1)	CQua	
'Obelisk' (11a)	CQua	
obesus (13)	EHyt ERos WCot	
'Obsession' (2)	CQua	
§ *obvallaris* (13) ♥H4	CArn CAvo CBgR CBro CFFs CQua	
	ECho EPot ERos SBch SGar SMeo	
	SPer WHer WShi	
'Ocarino' (4)	CQua	
'Ocean Blue' (2)	IRhd	
'Odd Job'	CQua	
x *odorus* (13)	WShi	
§ - 'Double Campernelle' (4)	CQua ECho SBch SPer WCot WShi	
- 'Rugulosus'	see *N.* 'Rugulosus'	
'Odyssey' (4)	IRhd	
'Oecumene' (11a)	CQua	
old pheasant's eye	see *N. poeticus* var. *recurvus*	
'Orange Monarch' (2)	EFam	
'Orange Walk' (3)	CQua IRhd	
'Orangery' (11a)	EFam LRHS	
'Orchard Place' (3)	CQua	
'Oregon Pioneer' (2)	IRhd	
'Ormeau' (2) ♥H4	CQua	
'Oryx' (7) ♥H4	CQua IRhd	
'Osmington' (2)	CQua	
'Ottoman Gold' (2)	IRhd	
'Ouma' (1)	CQua	
'Outline' (2)	IRhd	
'Ouzel' (6)	CQua	
'Oykel' (3)	CQua GEve	
'Oz' (12)	CBro CQua ERos	
'Pacific Coast' (8) ♥H4	CBro CQua ECho	
'Pacific Mist' (11a)	CQua	

'Pacific Princess' (3) **new**	CQua	
'Pacific Rim' (2)	IRhd	
'Painted Desert' (3)	CQua	
'Pale Sunlight' (2)	CQua	
§ *pallidiflorus* (13)	ECha	
- var. *intermedius* from France	CMon	
'Palmares' (11a)	CQua	
'Pamela Hubble' (2)	CQua	
'Pampaluna' (11a)	CQua	
'Panache' (1)	CQua	
'Panorama Pink' (3) **new**	IRhd	
'Paper White'	see *N. papyraceus*	
'Paper White Grandiflorus' (8)	CQua MBri SPer	
'Papua' (4) ♥H4	CQua	
§ *papyraceus* (13)	CQua CStu EBrs WCot	
- subsp. *panizzianus*	CQua	
- subsp. *papyraceus*	CMon	
AB&S 4399 from Morocco		
- - PB 442 from Spain	CMon	
- subsp. *polyanthus*	CMon	
SF 116 from Morocco		
'Paradigm' (4)	IRhd	
'Parcpat' (7)	CBro	
'Parisienne' (11a)	SPer	
'Park Springs' (3)	CQua	
'Parkdene' (2)	CQua	
'Party Time' (2)	IRhd	
'Passionale' (2) ♥H4	CQua NBir SPer	
'Pastiche' (2)	CQua	
'Patabundy' (2)	CQua	
'Pathos' (3) **new**	IRhd	
'Patois' (9)	CQua IRhd	
'Paula Cottell' (3)	CBro	
'Pay Day' (1)	CQua	
'Peach Prince' (4)	CQua	
'Peacock' (2)	IRhd	
'Pearl Wedding' (3) **new**	CQua	
'Pearlshell' (11a)	CQua GEve	
'Peeping Tom' (6) ♥H4	CBro ECho ERos LBmB SRms	
'Peggy's Gift' (3)	IRhd	
'Pemboa'	CQua	
'Pencrebar' (4)	CBro CQua EPot ERos NMyG WShi	
'Pend Oreille' (3)	CQua	
'Pengarth' (2)	CQua	
'Penjerrick' (9)	CQua	
'Penkivel' (2)	CQua	
'Pennance Mill' (2)	CQua	
'Pennine Way' (1)	CQua	
'Pennyfield' (2)	CQua	
'Pennyghael' (2)	GEve	
'Penpol' (7)	CBro CFen CQua	
'Penril' (6)	CQua ERos	
'Penstraze' (7)	CQua	
'Pentille' (1)	CQua	
'Pentire' (11a)	CQua	
'Penvale' (7)	CQua	
'Peppercorn' (6)	CQua	
'Pequenita' (7)	CBro	
'Percuil' (6)	CQua	
'Perdredda' (1)	CQua	
'Perimeter' (3)	CQua	
'Peripheral Pink' (2)	CQua	
§ 'Perlax' (11a)	CQua	
'Permissive' (2)	IRhd	
'Perseus' (1)	GEve	
'Personable' (2) **new**	CQua	
'Petit Four' (4)	LBmB	
'Petrel' (5)	CBro CQua EBrs EPot LPhx MSte	
	SUsu WLin	
'Phalarope' (6)	CQua	
'Phantom' (11a)	CQua	
'Pheonician' (2) **new**	CQua	
'Phil's Gift' (1)	CQua	
'Phinda' (2)	IRhd	

'Picoblanco' (2)	CBro CQua	
'Pigeon' (2) **new**	CQua	
'Pincambo' (2) **new**	IRhd	
'Pineapple Prince' (2) ♀H4	CQua	
'Pink Angel' (7)	CQua	
'Pink Champagne' (4)	CQua	
'Pink Evening' (2) **new**	CQua	
'Pink Formal' (11a)	CQua	
'Pink Gilt' (2)	IRhd	
'Pink Glacier' (11a)	CQua	
'Pink Holly' (11a)	CQua	
'Pink Ice' (2)	CQua	
'Pink Pageant' (4)	CQua IRhd	
'Pink Paradise' (4)	CQua IRhd LBmB	
'Pink Perry' (2)	IRhd	
'Pink Sapphire' (2)	CQua	
'Pink Silk' (1)	CQua IRhd NZep	
'Pink Smiles' (2)	CFen SPer	
'Pink Surprise' (2)	CQua	
'Pink Tango' (11a)	CQua	
'Pipe Major' (2)	CQua	
'Pipers Barn' (7)	CQua	
'Piper's End' (3) **new**	CQua	
'Pipestone' (2)	CQua	
'Pipit' (7) ♀H4	CAvo CBro CFFs CQua ECho EPfP ERos ITim LPhx LRHS MBri MNrw NBir SPer WShi	
'Piraeus' (4)	IRhd	
'Pismo Beach' (2)	CQua GEve	
'Pitchroy' (2)	CQua	
'Pixie's Sister' (7) ♀H4	CQua	
poeticus (13)	CAvo LRHS WHer	
§ - var. *hellenicus* (13)	CBro CQua	
- old pheasant's eye	see *N. poeticus* var. *recurvus*	
- var. *physaloides* (13)	CQua ECho LPhx	
N - 'Plenus' ambig. (4)	CBro CQua EPot GQui WCot WShi	
- 'Praecox' (3)	CBro CQua	
§ - var. *recurvus* (13) ♀H4	CArn CBro CFFs CFen CMea CQua EBrs ECGP ECho EPfP EPot LBmB NBir SPer WShi	
'Poet's Way' (9)	CQua	
'Pol Crocan' (2)	CQua IRhd	
'Pol Dornie' (2)	CQua	
'Pol Voulin' (2)	CQua IRhd	
'Polglase' (8)	CBro	
'Polgooth' (2) **new**	CQua	
'Polly's Pearl' (8)	CQua	
'Polnesk' (7)	CBro	
'Polruan' (2)	CQua	
'Poltreen'	CQua	
'Polwheveral' (2)	CQua	
'Pontresina' (2)	LBmB	
'Pooka' (3)	IRhd	
'Poppy's Choice' (4)	CQua	
'Pops Legacy' (1)	CQua IRhd	
'Port Patrick' (3)	IRhd	
'Port William' (3)	IRhd	
'Porthchapel' (7)	CQua	
'Portloe Bay' (3) **new**	CQua	
'Portrush' (3)	CQua	
'Portstewart' (3)	IRhd	
'Potential' (1)	CQua	
'Powerstock' (2)	IRhd	
'Prairie Fire' (3)	CQua IRhd	
'Preamble' (1)	CQua	
I 'Precocious' (2) ♀H4	CQua	
'Premiere' (2)	CQua	
'Presidential Pink' (2)	CQua	
'Pride of Cornwall' (8)	CBro	
'Primrose Beauty' (4)	CFen CQua	
'Princeps' (1)	CQua	
'Princess Zaide' (3)	CQua	
'Princeton' (3)	CQua	
'Prism' (2)	CQua	
'Probus' (1)	CQua	
'Professor Einstein' (2)	EPfP LBmB	
'Prologue' (1)	CQua	
'Prototype' (6)	IRhd	
'Proud Fellow' (1) **new**	IRhd	
pseudonarcissus (13) ♀H4	CBro CQua CRow EBrs MBow WHer WShi	
- subsp. *gayi*	see *N. gayi*	
§ - 'Lobularis'	CArn CAvo CBro CFFs CQua ECho EPot ERos MBri SPer	
- subsp. *moschatus*	see *N. moschatus*	
- subsp. *nevadensis*	see *N. nevadensis*	
- subsp. *pallidiflorus*	see *N. pallidiflorus*	
'Pueblo' (7)	EBrs ERos LRHS WShi	
'Pulsar' (2)	IRhd	
pumilus (13)	ECho EPot ERos LRHS	
'Punchline' (7)	CQua	
'Puppet' (5)	CQua	
'Purbeck' (3) ♀H4	CQua IRhd	
'Quail' (7) ♀H4	CBro CQua EBrs EPfP ERos LBmB LRHS LSou MBri SPer	
'Quasar' (2)	CQua GEve NZep	
Queen Anne's double daffodil	see *N.* 'Eystettensis'	
'Queen Juliana' (1) **new**	CQua	
'Queen's Guard' (1)	IRhd	
'Queensland' (2)	CFen	
'Quick Step' (7)	CQua IRhd	
'Quiet Hero' (3)	IRhd	
'Quiet Man' (1)	IRhd	
'Quiet Waters' (1)	CQua	
'Quince' (12)	CBro CQua EBrs ITim LSou MSte	
'Radiant Gem' (8)	CQua	
radiiflorus var. *poetarum* (13)	CBro	
'Radjel' (4)	CQua	
'Rainbow' (2) ♀H4	CQua SPer	
'Rame Head' (1)	CQua	
'Rameses' (2)	CQua	
'Rapture' (6) ♀H4	CQua IRhd	
'Rashee' (1)	CQua	
'Raspberry Ring' (2)	CQua	
'Ravenhill' (3)	CQua	
'Rebekah' (4)	CQua	
'Recital' (2)	CQua	
I 'Red Coat'	CQua	
'Red Era' (3)	CQua	
'Red Reed' (1)	IRhd	
'Red Socks' (6)	CQua	
'Reference Point' (2)	GEve	
'Refrain' (2)	CQua	
'Regal Bliss' (2)	CQua	
'Reggae' (6) ♀H4	CBro CQua GEve IRhd	
'Rembrandt' (1)	CFen	
'Replete' (4)	CQua EBrs	
'Reprieve' (3)	CQua	
requienii	see *N. assoanus*	
'Ribald' (2)	IRhd	
'Ridgecrest' (3)	IRhd	
rifanus	see *N. romieuxii* subsp. *romieuxii* var. *rifanus*	
'Rijnveld's Early Sensation' (1) ♀H4	CAvo CBro CFFs CFen CMea CQua EBrs ECha ERos LBmB WCot	
'Rikki' (7)	CBro CQua ERos	
'Rima' (1)	CQua	
'Rimmon' (3)	CQua	
'Ring Fence' (3)	IRhd	
'Ringhaddy' (3)	IRhd	
'Ringing Bells' (5)	CQua	
'Ringleader' (2)	CQua	
'Ringmaster' (2)	CQua	
'Ringmer' (3)	CQua	
'Rio Bravo' (2)	IRhd	
'Rio Gusto' (2)	IRhd	
'Rio Lobo' (2)	IRhd	
'Rio Rondo' (2)	IRhd	
'Rio Rouge' (2)	IRhd	

§	'Rip van Winkle' (4)	CBro CQua CSWP EBrs EPot ERos ITim LRHS MBri NBPC NHol WHal WShi
	'Rippling Waters' (5) ♥H4	CBro CQua ECGP EPot ERos LBmB LRHS
	'Ristin' (1)	CQua
	'Rival' (6)	CQua
	'River Dance' (2)	IRhd
	'River Queen' (2)	CQua IRhd
	'Roberta'	CFen
	'Rockall' (3)	CQua
	'Roger' (6)	CBro CQua
	'Romance' (2) ♥H4	LBmB
§	'Romanus' (4)	CQua
§	*romieuxii* (13) ♥H2-3	CBro EPot ERos ITim LRHS SBch SCnR WCot WPGP
	- JCA 805	EHyt EPot
	- subsp. *albidus* (13)	EPot
	- - SF 110	EHyt
	- - var. *albidus* SF 110 from Morocco	CMon
§	- - var. *zaianicus* (13)	EBrs ECho LPhx
	- - - SB&L 82	WCot
	- - - SF 379 from Morocco	CMon
*	- - - f. *lutescens* (13)	EHyt
	- 'Atlas Gold'	EHyt
§	- 'Joy Bishop' (10)	EPot ERos SCnR
§	- 'Julia Jane' (10)	EHyt EPot ERos GEdr SCnR
	- subsp. *romieuxii*	ECho LPhx WCot
	- - SF 126/1 from Morocco	CMon
§	- - var. *mesatlanticus* (13)	CStu EHyt ERos
§	- - var. *rifanus* (13)	LPhx
	- 'Treble Chance' (10)	EPot
	'Rosannor Gold' (11a)	CQua
	'Roscarrick' (6)	CQua
	'Rose Gold' (1)	IRhd
	'Rose of May' (4)	CQua
	'Rose Royale' (2)	CQua
	'Rose Umber' (2)	IRhd
	'Rosedown' (5)	CBro
	'Rosemerryn' (2)	CQua
	'Rosemoor Gold' ♥H4	CBro CFen CQua SPer
	'Roseworthy' (2)	ERos
	'Rosy Trumpet' (1)	CBro
	'Roxton' (4)	IRhd
	'Royal Armour' (1)	CFen
	'Royal Ballet' (2)	CQua
	'Royal Connection' (8)	CQua
	'Royal Dornoch' (1)	GEve
	'Royal Marine' (2)	CQua
	'Royal Princess' (3)	CQua
	'Royal Regiment' (2)	CQua
	'Rubh Mor' (2)	CQua
	'Ruby Rose' (4)	IRhd
	'Ruby Wedding' (2)	IRhd
	'Rubythroat' (2)	CQua
	'Ruddy Rascal' (2)	IRhd
§	'Rugulosus' (7) ♥H4	CBro CQua ECho ERos
*	'Rugulosus Flore Pleno' (d)	EBrs
	rupicola (13)	CBro CQua CWoo ERos GCrs MSSP NSla NWCA SCnR
§	- subsp. *marvieri* (13) ♥H2	ERos
§	- subsp. *watieri* (13)	CBro ERos GCrs LPhx
	'Rustom Pasha' (2)	CQua
	'Rytha' (2)	CQua
	'Saberwing' (5)	CQua
	'Sabine Hay' (3)	CQua LBmB
	'Sabrosa' (7) **new**	CBro
	'Sacajawea' (2)	CFen
	'Saint Agnes' (8)	CQua
	'Saint Budock' (1)	CQua
	'Saint Day' (5)	CQua
	'Saint Dilpe' (2)	CQua
	'Saint Duthus' (1)	GEve

	'Saint Keverne' (2) ♥H4	CQua
	'Saint Keyne' (8)	CQua
	'Saint Magnus' (1)	GEve
	'Saint Patrick's Day' (2)	CFen CQua SPer
	'Saint Piran' (7)	CQua
	'Salakee' (2)	CQua
	'Salmon Trout' (2)	CQua
	'Salome' (2) ♥H4	CQua EPfP LRHS NBir
	'Salute' (2)	CQua
	'Samantha' (4)	CQua
	'Samaria' (3)	CBro
	'Samba' (5)	ERos
	'Sancerre' (11a)	CQua
	'Sandycove' (2)	CQua IRhd
	'Sandymount' (2)	IRhd
	'Santa Claus' (4) **new**	CQua
	'Satsuma' (1)	CQua
	'Saturn' (3)	CQua
	'Savoir Faire' (2)	IRhd
	scaberulus (13)	CBro CStu EPot ERos
	'Scarlet Chord' (2)	CQua
	'Scarlet Gem' (8)	NHol
	'Scarlett O'Hara' (2)	CQua
	'Scented Breeze' (2)	IRhd
	'Scilly Spring' (8) **new**	CAvo
	'Scilly White' (8)	CQua
	'Scorrier' (2) **new**	CQua
	'Sea Dream' (3)	CQua
	'Sea Gift' (7)	CBro
	'Sea Green' (9)	CQua
	'Sea Legend' (2) **new**	CQua
	'Sea Princess' (3) **new**	CQua
	'Sea Shanty' (2)	IRhd
	'Seagull' (3)	CQua ECho WShi
	'Sealing Wax' (2)	CFen CQua
	'Segovia' (3) ♥H4	CBro CQua EPot ERos LBmB SCnR SPer
	'Selma Lagerlöf' (2)	EFam
	'Sempre Avanti' (2)	LBmB MBri
	'Sennocke' (5)	CBro SOkd
	'Seraglio' (3)	CQua
	'Serena Beach' (4)	IRhd
	'Serena Lodge' (4) ♥H4	CQua IRhd
	serotinus (13)	ECho EPot
	- var. *deficiens* SF 169 from Morocco	CMon
*	- subsp. *orientalis* PB 141 from Crete	CMon
	'Sextant' (6)	CQua
	'Shangani' (2)	IRhd
	'Sheelagh Rowan' (2)	CQua IRhd
	'Sheer Joy' (6)	IRhd
	'Shepherd's Hey' (7)	CQua
	'Sherborne' (4)	CQua
	'Sherpa' (1)	IRhd
	'Sheviock' (2)	CQua
	'Shin Falls' (1)	GEve
	'Shindig' (2)	IRhd
	'Shining Light' (2)	CQua
	'Shortcake' (2) **new**	CQua
	'Shrimp Boat' (11a) **new**	IRhd
	'Siam' (2)	EFam
	'Sidley' (3)	CQua IRhd
	'Signorina' (2)	IRhd
	'Silent Valley' (1) ♥H4	CQua
	'Silk Cut' (2)	CQua
	'Silkwood' (3)	CQua
	'Silver Bells' (5)	CQua IRhd
	'Silver Chimes' (8)	CAvo CBgR CBro CFFs CFen CQua ECho EPfP ERos NBir WRHF
	'Silver Convention' (1) **new**	CQua
	'Silver Crystal' (3)	IRhd
	'Silver Kiwi' (2)	CQua
	'Silver Minx' (1) **new**	CQua
	'Silver Moon' (2)	CFen
	'Silver Plate' (11a)	CQua

'Silver Shell' (11a)	CQua	
'Silver Standard' (2)	CQua	
'Silver Surf' (2)	CQua IRhd	
'Silversmith' (2)	CQua	
'Silverthorne' (3)	CQua	
'Silverwood' (3)	CQua IRhd	
'Singing Pub' (3)	IRhd	
'Sir Samuel' (2)	CQua	
'Sir Watkin' (2)	CQua	
'Sir Winston Churchill' (4)	CQua EPfP LBmB SPer	
♀H4		
'Skerry' (2)	CQua	
'Skibo' (2)	GEve	
'Skilliwidden' (2)	CQua	
'Skywalker' (2)	IRhd	
'Slieveboy' (1)	CQua	
'Sligachan' (1)	GEve	
'Slipstream' (6)	IRhd	
'Small Fry' (1)	CQua	
'Small Talk' (1)	CQua	
'Smokey Bear' (4)	CQua	
'Smooth Sails' (3)	CQua	
'Snoopie' (6)	CQua	
'Snow Bunting' (7)	CBro	
'Snowcrest' (3)	CQua	
'Snowshill' (2)	CQua	
'Soft Focus' (2)	IRhd	
'Solar System' (3)	IRhd	
'Solar Tan' (3)	CQua IRhd	
'Solferique' (2)	CQua	
'Soloist' (2)	IRhd	
'Solveig's Song'	EHyt	
'Sonata' (9)	CQua	
'Songket' (2)	CQua	
'Soprano' (2)	CQua IRhd	
'Sorcerer' (3)	CQua	
'South Street' (2)	CQua	
'Spaniards Inn' (4)	CQua	
'Sparkling Tarts' (8)	CQua	
'Sparnon' (11a)	CQua	
'Sparrow' (6)	CQua	
'Special Envoy' (2) ♀H4	CQua IRhd	
'Speenogue' (1)	IRhd	
'Spellbinder' (1) ♀H4	CQua EFam LBmB MBri	
'Spencer Tracy'	CFen	
'Sperrin Gold' (1)	IRhd	
'Spin Doctor' (3) **new**	IRhd	
'Spindletop' (3) ♀H4	IRhd	
'Spirit of Rame' (3)	CQua	
'Split Image' (2)	IRhd	
'Split Vote' (11a)	IRhd	
'Sportsman' (2)	CQua	
'Spring Dawn' (2)	LSou SPer	
'Spring Joy'	ERos	
'Spring Morn' (2)	IRhd	
'Stainless' (2)	EBrs MSte	
'Stanway' (3)	CQua IRhd	
'Star Glow' (2)	CQua	
'Star Quality' (3)	IRhd	
'Starfire' (7)	CQua	
'State Express' (2)	CQua	
'Steenbok' (3)	IRhd	
'Stella' (2)	WShi	
'Step Forward' (7)	ERos	
'Stilton' (9)	CQua	
'Stinger' (2)	CQua	
'Stint' (5) ♀H4	CBro CQua	
'Stocken' (7)	CBro CQua ERos	
* 'Stockens Gib'	EHyt	
'Stoke Charity' (2)	CQua	
'Stormy Weather' (1)	CQua	
'Strathkanaird' (1)	GEve	
'Stratosphere' (7) ♀H4	CQua	
'Strines' (2)	CQua	
'Suave' (3)	CQua	
'Sugar Bird' (2)	IRhd	

'Sugar Cups' (8)	CQua	
'Sugar Loaf' (4)	CQua	
'Sugarbush' (7)	CBro	
'Suilven' (2)	GEve	
'Suisgill' (4)	CQua	
§ 'Sulphur Phoenix' (4)	CQua WShi	
'Summer Solstice' (3)	IRhd	
'Sun Disc' (7) ♀H4	CBro CMea CQua ECho EPot ERos	
	LSou MBri NJOw SPer	
'Sun 'n' Snow' (1)	GEve	
'Sunday Chimes' (5)	CQua	
'Sundial' (7)	CBro CQua ECho EPot ERos LRHS	
'Sunrise' (3)	CQua	
'Sunstroke' (2)	CQua	
'Suntory' (3)	CQua	
'Suntrap' (2)	IRhd	
'Surfside' (6) ♀H4	CBro CQua ERos LRHS	
'Surrey' (2)	CQua	
'Suzie Dee' (6)	IRhd	
'Suzie's Sister' (6)	IRhd	
'Suzy' (7) ♀H4	CBro	
'Swaledale' (2)	CQua	
'Swallow Wing' (6)	IRhd	
'Swanpool' (3)	CQua	
'Swanvale' (1)	CQua	
'Swedish Fjord' (2)	CQua	
'Sweet Blanche' (7)	CQua	
'Sweet Pepper' (7)	CBro GEve	
'Sweetness' (7) ♀H4	CAvo CBro CFFs CFen CMea CQua	
	SPer WShi	
'Swing Wing' (6)	CQua	
'Sydling' (5)	CQua	
I 'Sylph' (1)	CQua	
'Taffeta' (10)	CBro EHyt	
'Tahiti' (4) ♀H4	CFen CQua EBrs EPfP LBmB	
'Tain' (1)	GEve	
'Tamar Fire' (4) ♀H4	CQua	
'Tamar Lad' (2)	CQua	
'Tamar Lass' (3)	CQua	
'Tamar Snow' (2)	CQua	
'Tamara' (2)	CFen CQua SPer	
'Tangent' (2)	CQua	
'Tarlatan' (10)	CBro ERos	
'Tasgem' (4)	CQua	
'Taslass' (4)	CQua	
'Tater-Du' (5)	CQua	
tazetta subsp. *italicus*	CMon	
MS 520 from France		
§ - subsp. *lacticolor* (13)	CQua NJOw WPGP	
§ - - 'Grand Monarque' (8)	CBro CQua	
* - var. *odoratus*	CQua	
- subsp. *papyraceus*	see *N. papyraceus*	
* - subsp. *syriacus*	CMon	
- subsp. *tazetta* MS 719	CMon	
from Crete		
- - MS 752	CMon	
- - LB 328 from Lebanon	CMon	
'Teal' (1)	CQua	
'Tehidy' (1)	CQua	
§ 'Telamonius Plenus' (4)	CBro CQua IGor WShi	
'Temple Cloud' (4)	IRhd	
tenuifolius	see *N. bulbocodium* subsp.	
	bulbocodium var. *tenuifolius*	
'Terracotta' (2)	CQua IRhd	
'Terrapin' (3)	IRhd	
'Tête-à-tête' (12) ♀H4	CAvo CBro CFFs CHar CQua EBrs	
	EPfP EPot ERos LBmB LRHS LSou	
	MBri MNHC NBlu SPer WHal	
'Thalia' (5)	CAvo CBro CFFs CQua EBrs EPfP	
	ERos LEdu LSou MBri MSte NBir	
	NHol SPer WShi	
'The Alliance' (6)	CQua	
'The Grange' (1)	CQua	
'The Knave' (6)	CQua	
'Thistin' (1)	IRhd	
'Thoresby' (3) **new**	CQua	

'Thoughtful' (5)	CBro CQua
'Tideford' (2)	CQua
'Tiercel' (1)	CQua
'Tiffany' (10)	EHyt
'Tiffany Jade' (3)	CQua
'Tiger Moth' (6)	CQua
'Timolin' (3)	CQua
'Tinderbox' (2)	IRhd
'Tiritomba' (11a)	CQua
'Tittle-tattle' (7)	CFen CQua
'Toby' (2)	CBro ERos
'Toby the First' (6)	CBgR CMea CQua EBrs
'Tommora Gold' (2) **new**	CQua
'Tommy White' (2) **new**	CQua
'Top Hit' (11a)	CQua
'Topolino' (1) ♀H4	CAvo CBro CFFs CQua EPot LBmB SBch SGar
'Toreador' (3)	CFen
'Torianne' (2)	CQua
'Torridon' (2)	CQua GEve
'Toscanini' (2)	EFam
'Toto' (12) ♀H4	CAvo CBro CFFs CQua MBri
'Tracey' (6) ♀H4	CBro CQua
'Trebah' (2) ♀H4	CQua
'Treble Two' (7)	CQua
'Trecara' (3)	CQua
'Trefusis' (1)	CQua
'Trehane' (6)	CQua
'Trelawney Gold' (2) **new**	CQua
'Trelissick'	CQua
'Trena' (6) ♀H4	CBro CQua
'Tresamble' (5)	CBgR CBro CQua
'Trevaunance' (6) **new**	CQua
'Treverva' (6)	CQua
'Treviddo' (2)	CQua
'Trevithian' (7) ♀H4	CBro CQua LBmB WLin
'Trewarvas' (2)	CQua
'Trewirgie' (6)	CBro CQua
triandrus (13) ♀H3	NSla WPGP
- var. *albus*	see *N. triandrus* subsp. *triandrus* var. *triandrus*
§ - subsp. *triandrus* var. *concolor* (13)	CBro ECho
§ - - var. *triandrus* (13)	LPhx
'Trident' (3)	CQua
'Tripartite' (11a) ♀H4	CQua GEve LBmB NZep
'Triple Crown' (3) ♀H4	CQua IRhd
'Tristram' (2)	CQua
'Tropic Isle' (4)	CQua
'Tropical Heat' (2)	IRhd
'Trousseau' (1)	CFen CQua
'Troutbeck' (3)	CQua
'Tru' (3) **new**	CQua
'Trueblood' (3)	IRhd
'Trumpet Warrior' (1) ♀H4	CQua IRhd
'Tryst' (2) **new**	CQua
'Tudor Minstrel' (2)	CQua
'Tuesday's Child' (5) ♀H4	CQua ERos
'Tullynagee' (3)	IRhd
'Turncoat' (6)	CQua
'Tutankhamun' (2)	CQua
'Twink' (4)	CQua
'Tyee' (2)	CQua
'Tyrian Rose' (2)	CQua IRhd
'Tyrone Gold' (1) ♀H4	CQua IRhd
'Tyrree' (1)	IRhd
'Ulster Bank' (3)	CQua
'Ulster Bride' (4)	CQua
'Una Bremner' (2)	GEve
'Uncle Duncan' (1)	CQua IRhd
'Unique' (4) ♀H4	CFen CQua
'Unsurpassable' (1)	LBmB
'Upalong' (12)	CQua
'Upshot' (3) **new**	CQua
'Urchin' (2)	IRhd
'Utiku' (6)	CQua
'Val d'Incles' (3)	CQua IRhd
'Valdrome' (11a)	CQua
'Valinor' (2)	CQua
'Van Sion'	see *N.* 'Telamonius Plenus'
'Vanellus' (11a)	IRhd
'Veneration' (1)	CQua
'Verdin' (7)	CQua
'Verger' (3)	MBri
'Vernal Prince' (3) ♀H4	CQua GEve
'Verona' (3) ♀H4	CQua LBmB
'Verran Rose' (2)	IRhd
'Vers Libre' (9)	CQua GEve
'Vice-President' (2)	CQua
'Vickie Linn' (6)	IRhd
'Victorious' (2)	CQua
'Vigil' (1) ♀H4	CQua
'Viking' (1) ♀H4	CQua GEve
'Violetta' (2)	CQua
'Virginia Waters' (3)	CQua
viridiflorus (13)	WCot
'Vulcan' (2) ♀H4	CQua
'W.P. Milner' (1)	CAvo CBgR CBos CBro CFFs CQua EBrs EHyt EPot WCot WLin WRHF WShi
'Wadavers' (2)	CQua
'Waif' (6)	CQua
'Waldon Pond' (3)	CQua
'Waldorf Astoria' (4)	CQua IRhd
'Walton' (7)	CQua
'War Dance' (3)	IRhd
'Warbler' (6)	CQua
'Warleggan'	CFen
'Warmington' (3)	CQua
'Watamu' (3)	IRhd
'Waterperry' (7)	CBro
'Watership Down' (2)	CQua
watieri	see *N. rupicola* subsp. *watieri*
'Wavelength' (3)	IRhd
'Waxwing' (5)	CQua
'Wayward Lad' (3) **new**	IRhd
'Wee Bee' (1)	CQua
'Weena' (2)	CQua
'Welcome' (2)	CQua
'Westward' (4)	CQua
'Whang-hi' (6)	CQua ERos
'Wheal Bush' (4)	CQua
'Wheal Coates' (7) ♀H4	CQua
'Wheal Honey' (1)	CQua
'Wheal Jane' (2)	CQua
'Wheal Kitty' (7)	CQua ERos
'Wheatear' (6)	CQua IRhd LPhx
'Whetstone' (1)	CQua
'White Emperor' (1)	CQua
'White Empress' (1)	CQua
'White Hill' (2)	IRhd
'White Lady' (3)	CAvo CQua WShi
'White Lion' (4) ♀H4	CQua EFam NHol
'White Majesty' (1)	CQua
'White Marvel' (4)	CBgR CQua
'White Nile' (2)	CQua
'White Prince' (1) **new**	CQua
'White Star' (1)	CQua
'Wicklow Hills' (3)	CQua
'Widgeon' (2)	CQua
willkommii (13)	CBro ERos
'Wind Song' (2) **new**	CQua
'Winged Victory' (6)	CQua
'Winholm Jenni' (3)	CQua
'Winifred van Graven' (3)	CFen CQua
'Winter Waltz' (6)	CQua
'Witch Doctor' (3)	IRhd
'Witch Hunt' (4)	IRhd
'Wodan' (2)	EFam
'Woodcock' (6)	CBro CQua
'Woodland Prince' (3)	CQua
'Woodland Star' (3)	CQua

'Woodley Vale' (2)	CQua
'Woolsthorpe' (2)	CQua
'Xit' (3)	CAvo CBro CFFs CQua EHyt SCnR
'Xunantunich' (2)	IRhd
'Yellow Belles' (5)	IRhd
'Yellow Cheerfulness' (4)	EPfP LBmB LRHS MBri ♀H4
'Yellow Minnow' (8)	CQua
'Yellow Xit' (3)	CQua
'York Minster' (1)	CQua IRhd
'Young American' (1)	CQua
'Young Blood' (2)	CQua IRhd
'Yum-Yum' (3)	IRhd
zaianicus	see *N. romieuxii* subsp. *albidus* var. *zaianicus*
- *lutescens*	see *N. romieuxii* subsp. *albidus* var. *zaianicus* f. *lutescens*
'Zekiah' (1)	CQua
'Zion Canyon' (2)	CQua
'Ziva' (8) new	CAvo

Nardostachys (Valerianaceae)
| *grandiflora* | EOHP GPoy |

Nardus (Poaceae)
| *stricta* | CRWN |

Narthecium (Melanthiaceae)
| *ossifragum* | ERea |

Nassella (Poaceae)
cernua	CBig EBee SWal
lepida	CBig
pulchra	CBig
tenuissima	see *Stipa tenuissima*
trichotoma	CHrt CMea EBee EHoe EMan EMon EPPr EWsh LRHS MCCP SLim SPoG WHal WPGP WRos

Nasturtium (Brassicaceae)
| *officinale* | CPrp EMFW SWat WHer |

Natal plum see *Carissa macrocarpa*

Nautilocalyx (Gesneriaceae)
| *pemphidius* | WDib |

nectarine see *Prunus persica* var. *nectarina*

Nectaroscordum (Alliaceae)
bivalve	ERos
§ *siculum*	More than 30 suppliers
§ - subsp. *bulgaricum*	CBro CHad EBee EMar EPfP EPot ERos EWTr GSki IBlr LPhx LRHS MAvo MDun MNrw MWgw NBid NGHP WAbb WBrE WCMO WCot WCra WTin WWhi
tripedale	EBee WCot

Neillia (Rosaceae)
affinis	CDul EBee EPfP LAst LTwo MBri MTis NBid NLar NPro SBrw SCoo SSpi WBVN WDin WHCG
longiracemosa	see *N. thibetica*
sinensis	CMCN CPle MRav
§ *thibetica*	CBcs CDul CPLG CPle ECrN EGra ELan EMil EPfP EWTr IDee MBri MRav NEgg NPri SBrw SGar SLim SLon SMad SPer SSpi SSta SWvt WBor WDin WFar WHar WPat WTel
thyrsiflora var. *tunkinensis* HWJ 505	WCru

Nelumbo (Nelumbonaceae)
'Baby Doll'	CDWL
'Chawan Basu'	CDWL
'Debbie Gibson'	CDWL
'Momo Botan'	CDWL
'Mrs Perry D. Slocum'	CDWL
nucifera	XBlo
- 'Shiroman'	CDWL

Nematanthus (Gesneriaceae)
'Apres'	WDib
'Black Magic'	CHal WDib
'Christmas Holly'	WDib
'Freckles'	WDib
§ *gregarius* ♀H1	CHal EBak WDib
§ - 'Golden West' (v)	CHal WDib
- 'Variegatus'	see *N. gregarius* 'Golden West'
'Lemon and Lime' new	WDib
radicans	see *N. gregarius*
'Tropicana' ♀H1	CHal WDib

Nemesia (Scrophulariaceae)
Amelie = 'Fleurame'	COtt LRHS SPer SPoG
(Aromatica Series) new Aromatica Compact White = 'Balarcomwit'	NPri
- Aromatica True Blue = 'Balartublue' new	NPri
Blue Lagoon = 'Pengoon'PBR (Maritana Series)	LAst LSRN SCoo SMrm SPoG
Bluebird = 'Hubbird'PBR	CHll
Blushing Bride = 'Yablush'PBR	LSou
§ *caerulea*	ECtt MWgw WPer
- 'Joan Wilder' (clonal)	ECtt WEas WSPU
N - 'Joan Wilder' (seed raised)	see *N. caerulea* lilac/blue
§ - lilac/blue	WPer
Candy Girl = 'Pencand'PBR (Maritana Series)	SCoo
Celine = 'Fleurcel' new	SPoG
§ *denticulata* ♀H3-4	CHal CHar ECtt EPfP IHMH LHop LRHS MArl MBNS NFla SCoo SGar SPoG SRms WBrE WFar WFoF WWeb
- 'Celebration'	LRHS WWeb
- 'Confetti'	see *N. denticulata*
'Fleurie Blue' new	LRHS
foetens	see *N. caerulea*
'Fragrant Cloud'PBR	EChP ELan EPfP LRHS LSou MCCP MNrw NEgg SPer SPla
fruticans misapplied	see *N. caerulea*
fruticans Benth.	ETow
'Golden Eye' new	ENor
Honey Girl = 'Penhon'PBR (Maritana Series)	LAst SCoo WGor
'Ice Blue' new	SPoG
'Ice Cool' new	SPoG
Ice Pink = 'Fleuripi' new	SPoG
'Innocence' ♀H3	CHal EBee EMan EWin LAst MArl MHar SCoo
I 'Innocence Improved' new	LSou
Karoo Blue = 'Innkablue'PBR	CSpe LSou SCoo SVil
Karoo Pink = 'Innkapink'PBR	LSou NPri SVil
Melanie = 'Fleuron'PBR ♀H3	EPfP LRHS
'Orchard Blue'	EBee EPfP EWin
'Pensky' new	SCoo
'Pippa Manby'	ECtt LAst
'Rose Wings'	EPfP
Sugar Girl = 'Pensug'PBR (Maritana Series)	LAst LSou SMrm
'Sugar Plum' new	EPfP
(Sunsatia Series) Sunsatia Banana = 'Intraibana' new	LAst SVil

- Sunsatia Blackberry = 'Inuppink'	SCoo SVil
- Sunsatia Coconut = 'Intraiwhi'PBR	NPri SVil
- Sunsatia Cranberry = 'Intraired'	LAst LSou NPri SCoo SVil
- Sunsatia Lemon = 'Intraigold'	LSou SCoo
- Sunsatia Peach = 'Inupcream'PBR	LAst NPri SCoo SVil
- Sunsatia Pineapple = 'Intraiycl' **new**	SVil
- Sunsatia Saffron = 'Innupsaff' **new**	LSou SVil
sylvatica	CSpe
'Tanith's Treasure'	ECtt EMan
umbonata misapplied	see *N. caerulea* lilac/blue
Vanilla Mlst = 'Grega'PBR	EPfP
'White Wings'PBR	EPfP
'Wisley Vanilla'	LRHS

Neodypsis (Arecaceae)
decaryi	see *Dypsis decaryi*

Neolitsea (Lauraceae)
glauca	see *N. sericea*
§ *sericea*	CBcs CHEx SSpi

Neomarica (Iridaceae)
caerulea	CDes WCot
gracilis	WCMO WCot WPGP

Neopanax see *Pseudopanax*

Neopaxia (Portulacaceae)
§ *australasica*	ECou EDAr
- bronze-leaved	see *N. australasica* 'Ohau'
- 'Lyndon'	ECou
§ - 'Ohau'	ECou EDAr

Neoregelia (Bromeliaceae)
carolinae	MBri
§ - (Meyendorffii Group) 'Flandria' (v)	MBri
- - 'Meyendorffii'	MBri XBlo
- f. *tricolor* (v) ♀H1	CHal MBri
Claret Group	MBri
'Hojo Rojo'	XBlo
'Marconfos'	XBlo

Neottianthe (Orchidaceae)
cucullata	EFEx

Nepenthes (Nepenthaceae)
alata	CSWC
alata x *ventricosa*	SHmp
ampullaria	CSWC
x *coccinea*	MBri
fusca	CSWC
fusca x *maxima*	SHmp
§ x *hookeriana*	CSWC
khasiana	SHmp
maxima x *mixta*	SHmp
rafflesiana	CSWC
sanguinea	SHmp
spectabilis	SHmp
stenophylla	SHmp

Nepeta (Lamiaceae)
CC 3766	WCot
CC 4610	MGol WCot
RCB/TQ H-6	WCot
'Blue Beauty'	see *N. sibirica* 'Souvenir d'André Chaudron'
bucharica	GBuc WOut
* *buddlejifolium*	NBre NLar
* - 'Gold Splash' **new**	NBre
camphorata	GBar MLLN MSte NBre SAga SIde
cataria	CArn CPrp CSev EBee ELau EUnu GBar GPoy MBow MHer MNHC MSal MWat NBro NGHP NPri NTHB SECG SIde WHer WMoo WPer WSel WWye XPep
§ - 'Citriodora'	CArn CHar CPrp EAro EBee ELan ELau EUnu GBar GPoy MHer MNHC MSal NGHP NVic SHGN SIde SUsu WCHb WHer WSel
citriodora Dum.	see *N. cataria* 'Citriodora'
clarkei	CEnt EAro EBee EMan EPPr GIBF LEdu MDKP MMHG MSte NDov SBla SBod SEND SIde SWat WMoo WPer WWhi
curviflora	EUnu
'Dropmore'	EBee EWin XPep
§ x *faassenii* ♀H4	More than 30 suppliers
- 'Alba'	EBee ECtt EPfP GBar LAst NBre NGHP NLar SHGN SMar WMnd
- 'Blauknirps' **new**	NBre
- 'Kit Cat'	EBee MSte WHil
glechoma 'Variegata'	see *Glechoma hederacea* 'Variegata'
govaniana	More than 30 suppliers
grandiflora	EBee EWsh MRav NBre SIde WFar WHer WOut
- 'Blue Danube'	NDov
- 'Bramdean'	CMea CPrp CSam EBee EMan EWes EWin LPhx MBri MHar MRav NCGa NDov SBch WKif WOut
- 'Dawn to Dusk'	More than 30 suppliers
- 'Pool Bank'	EBee ECtt EMan LSou NBre NCGa NGby SGar SIde SUsu
- 'Wild Cat'	CSam EBee EPfP EWTr LPhx NBPC
hederacea 'Variegata'	see *Glechoma hederacea* 'Variegata'
italica	EBee SBla SHar SIde
kubanica	EMan
laevigata	EBee
lanceolata	see *N. nepetella*
latifolia	LPhx NBre SIde
'Lilac Cloud'	NBir
* *longipes* hort.	CPrp CSam EBee GMaP LAst LHop MBri MLLN MNFA MRav MSte NCGa NGdn NSti SBla SMrm SPer SPoG SWat WCAu WFar WHal WMnd WOut WPer WTMC XPep
macrantha	see *N. sibirica*
melissifolia	EBee SBch WCHb WPer WWye XPep
mussinii misapplied	see *N.* x *faassenii*
mussinii Spreng.	see *N. racemosa*
§ *nepetella*	EBee GBri LBMP MGol NBir NChi NLar WFar WOut WPer
nervosa	CArn CSpe EBee EChP ECha ELan EPfP ERou LAst LRHS MBri MHer MNHC MRav MSte NBPC NBro NJOw NPri NSti SBla SPer STes SUsu WFar WPer WSHC WWeb
- 'Blue Moon'	NBid
- 'Forncett Select'	CSam EMan NBre SDys SMrm
§ *nuda*	CPom CSam EAro EBee EChP ECha ECtt LDai MDKP MFOX MLLN SIde WFar WMnd XPep
- subsp. *albiflora*	EBee ECha
* - 'Anne's Choice'	MSte
* - 'Grandiflora'	NBre NLar WMoo
* - 'Purple Cat' **new**	LSou LTwo NCGa SUsu WCot
- 'Snow Cat'	LPhx LSou MDKP MSte NCGa SUsu WCot
pannonica	see *N. nuda*
parnassica	More than 30 suppliers
phyllochlamys	CPBP EBee NCGa

'Porzellan'	CPrp EBee EChP EMan EWin LAst MSte NCGa SMrm WOut
§ *prattii*	CSpe EBee EChP EMag ERou MWat NCGa NLar SBod SIde SPla STes WPer WSHC
§ *racemosa* ♀H4	CArn CHby COfd COlW CPbn CSev ELau EPfP GBar LRHS MNHC MRav SIde WMoo WPtf XPep
- *alba*	WFar
- 'Amelia' **new**	WOut
- 'Blue Ice'	GBuc SIde
- 'Grog'	EBee EWin SIde
- 'Leporello' (v)	EPPr
- 'Little Titch'	CBod CPrp EAEE EBee EMan EPPr EPfP EShb GBar GCal LAst LRHS MNFA MSte NLar SAga SIde SMrm SPla SPoG SWat WFar WSHC WWeb
- 'Snowflake'	CBcs CMea CPrp EAEE EBee ELan EPfP EShb GCal GMaP LRHS MHer MSte NBir SAga SIde SMer SPer SPet SPla SPoG SUsu SWvt WCAu WFar WSel XPep
§ - 'Superba'	EMon GBuc NBre WHoo
- 'Walker's Low'	More than 30 suppliers
* 'Rae Crug' **new**	EWes
reichenbachiana	see *N. racemosa*
§ *sibirica*	COlW EBee ECha ELan EPfP GMac LEdu LRHS MHer MRav NBid NBro NCGa NDov NPri SBch WFar WHal WPer WPtf WWhi
§ - 'Souvenir d'André Chaudron'	More than 30 suppliers
sintenisii	CSWP NBre
'Six Hills Giant'	More than 30 suppliers
stewartiana	CPom EAro EChP EWTr GBuc LDai MLLN NCGa NEgg NLar SBla STes WHoo WMoo
- ACE 1611	GBuc
- BWJ 7999	WCru
subsessilis	More than 30 suppliers
- 'Candy Cat'	EBee EHrv MDKP
- 'Cool Cat'	EBee ECGP LPhx MDKP MSte NLar SMrm
- pink	CAby ECha EGle GBuc MAvo MLLN MSte SBla WSHC
- 'Sweet Dreams'	CFwr CHar CKno EAEE EBee EChP ECtt EMil EShb EWin GBri LAst LEdu LPhx MBri MDKP MGol NBPC NGby NLar NSti SHar SSvw WCAu WFar WWeb
tenuifolia	MSal
transcaucasica	CArn WOut
- 'Blue Infinity'	EKen EWTr NBre NLar WMnd WMoo
troodii	EKen MDKP SIde
tuberosa	More than 30 suppliers
yunnanensis	EMan EPPr GKev LEdu LPhx WHil

Nephrolepis (Oleandraceae)

cordifolia	ERea MBri
exaltata ♀H2	EFtx ERea LRHS
- 'Bostoniensis'	MBri
- 'Green Fantasy' **new**	MOak
- 'Smithii'	MBri
- 'Smithii Linda'	MBri
- 'Teddy Junior'	MBri

Nephrophyllidium (Menyanthaceae)

crista-galli	IBlr

Nerine ✿ (Amaryllidaceae)

'Afterglow'	ECho
'Albivetta'	CAby CBgR CFwr EBee ECho EPot
alta	CMon
'Audrey'	WCot

'Aurora' **new**	WCot
'Bennett Poe'	CMon
'Berlioz'	CMon WCot
bowdenii ♀H3-4	More than 30 suppliers
- 'Alba'	CBro CStu ECho ELan EShb LRHS SCoo SMHy
- 'Codora'	CBgR CCCN CPen ECho LHop LSou SPer
- 'E.B.Anderson'	CMon WCMO WCot
- 'Kinn McIntosh'	WCMO WCot
- 'Manina'	CMdw CMon EBee MSte WCMO WCot
- 'Mark Fenwick'	CBcs CBro EBee ECha MSte WCMO WCot WOld
- 'Marnie Rogerson'	CBro MSte SMHy WCMO WCot
§ - 'Mollie Cowie' (v)	EBee EMon GCal IBlr WCMO WCot WCru
- pale pink striped darker	CDes
- 'Pink Triumph'	CAbP CBcs EBee EBla EBrs ECho EShb GBuc GQui IBlr LRHS MSte MWgw SChr SPer SPla WCMO WCot WDav WHoo
- 'Porlock'	EBee
- 'Quinton Wells'	LPhx
- 'Variegata'	see *N. bowdenii* 'Mollie Cowie'
- Washfield form	SMHy
- 'Wellsii'	CDes CMil CMon EBee GSki WCMO WCot
'Brocade'	CMon
'Canasta'	WCot
'Celestial'	CMon
'Coralina'	CMon
corusca 'Major'	see *N. sarniensis* var. *corusca*
crispa	see *N. undulata*
filamentosa	CBro CMon
filifolia	CAvo CMon CPen ECho EHyt EPot ERos GCal GKev ITim MNrw MTho SChr WCMO WCot
flexuosa	CMon CPne GSki MRav WCMO WViv
- 'Alba'	CBgR CBro CMon CStu EBee EBrs ECha EPot EWTr GKev GSki LPhx LRHS MRav MSte WAbe WCot WViv WWhi
'Fucine'	CDes
'Gaby Deslys'	CMon
'Grilse'	CMon
'Hera'	CBro EMon LPhx MSte WCMO WCot
humilis	CMon CStu WCot
- Breachiae Group	CMon CStu SBch
- Tulbaghensis Group	CMon
'Jenny Wren'	WCot
'Kasmir'	CDes
'King of the Belgians'	ECho WCMO WCot
krigei	EBee
'Lady Eleanor Keane'	CMon
'Lady Havelock Allen' **new**	WCot
'Lord Grenfell'	IBlr
'Mansellii'	CBro CMon WCot
'Maria'	WCMO WCot
'Mars'	CMon
masoniorum	CBro CMon CStu EHyt ERos MTho SBch SChr WCot
'Miss Cator'	WCot
'Nikita'	CFwr CPen ECho MSte
'November Cheer'	ECho
peersii	WCMO WCot
'Plymouth'	CMon SChr
pudica	CMon SBch
- pink flowered	WCMO WCot
'Red Pimpernel'	ECho
'Rose Camellia'	CMon
'Rushmere Star'	CDes CMon SChr WCot
sarniensis ♀H2-3	CBro CFwr ECha EPot LRHS MSte WCMO WCot WDav

*	– 'Alba'	WCMO
§	– var. *corusca*	CStu WCMO
	– – 'Major'	LBow SChr WCot
	– var. *curvifolia* f. *fothergillii*	WCMO WCot
	– very late dull red	CDes
	'Sidney Smee'	CMon
	'Stephanie'	CBgR CBro CFwr CMon ECho EShb LHop LRHS LSou SBch SPer WDav WFar
§	*undulata*	CAby CBgR CBro CCCN CMon CPne CSut EBee ECha ECho EPot ERos LRHS LSou MSte SPer WCot WHil WViv
	'Vicky'	WCot
	'Virgo'	ECho GAbr
	'White Swan'	ECho
	'Zeal Candy Stripe'	CFir WCMO
	'Zeal Colour Break' **new**	SChr
	'Zeal Giant' ♀H3-4	CAvo CBro CFir CMon CPne GCal NGby
	'Zeal Grilse'	CDes CPne
	'Zeal Salmon' **new**	CPne
	'Zeal Silver Stripe'	CFir WCMO

Nerium ✿ (Apocynaceae)

	oleander	CAbb CArn CMdw CTri EBak EBee EEls ELan EShb LRHS MJnS MTis SArc SChr SDEP SPer SPoG SRms WMul
	– 'Agnes Campbell'	XPep
*	– 'Alassio'	XPep
	– 'Album'	EEls
	– 'Album Maximum'	XPep
	– 'Album Plenum' (d)	EEls XPep
*	– 'Almodovar'	XPep
	– 'Alsace'	EEls XPep
	– 'Altini'	EEls XPep
	– 'Angiolo Pucci'	EEls XPep
*	– 'Apache'	XPep
*	– 'Aquarelle'	XPep
*	– 'Arad'	XPep
*	– 'Aramis' (d)	XPep
*	– 'Argunista'	XPep
*	– 'Arizona'	XPep
*	– 'Art Déco'	XPep
*	– 'Atlas'	XPep
*	– 'Barcelona'	XPep
	– 'Belle Hélène'	XPep
	– 'Bousquet d'Orb'	EEls
	– 'Calypso'	XPep
*	– 'Campane'	XPep
	– 'Cap Saint Vincent'	XPep
§	– 'Carneum Plenum' (d)	EEls XPep
*	– 'Caro'	XPep
	– 'Cavalaire' (d)	EEls XPep
*	– 'Cheyenne'	XPep
*	– 'Christine'	XPep
*	– 'Clare'	SOWG
*	– 'Claudia'	XPep
	– 'Commandant Barthélemy'	XPep
	– 'Cornouailles'	EEls XPep
*	– 'Dimona'	XPep
	– 'Docteur Golfin'	EEls
	– 'Dottore Attilio Ragionieri'	XPep
	– 'East End Pink'	XPep
	– 'Ed Barr'	XPep
*	– 'Elat'	XPep
	– 'Emile Sahut'	EEls XPep
	– 'Emilie'	EEls
*	– 'Eole'	XPep
	– 'Eugenia Fowler' (d)	XPep
*	– 'Feuille d'Eucalyptus'	XPep
*	– 'Fiesta Pienk'	XPep
*	– 'Fiesta Rodi'	XPep
	– 'Flavescens Plenum' (d)	EEls EShb XPep
	– 'Framboise'	XPep
*	– 'Galipette' (d)	XPep
*	– 'Garlaban'	XPep
	– 'Géant des Batailles' (d)	EEls SOWG
	– 'General Pershing' (d)	XPep
	– 'Grandiflorum'	XPep
*	– 'Haïfa'	XPep
	– 'Hardy Red'	EEls XPep
	– 'Harriet Newding'	XPep
	– 'Hawaii'	EEls XPep
*	– 'Icare'	XPep
*	– subsp. *indicum*	XPep
*	– 'Isabelle'	EEls
	– 'Isle of Capri'	EEls SOWG XPep
	– 'Italia'	XPep
	– 'J.R.'	EEls XPep
*	– 'Jack'line'	XPep
	– 'Jannoch'	EEls XPep
*	– 'Jardin du Luxembourg'	XPep
*	– 'Jordan Valley'	XPep
*	– 'La Fontaine'	XPep
	– 'Lady Kate'	XPep
	– 'Lane Taylor Sealy'	XPep
*	– 'Lisou'	XPep
	– 'Louis Pouget' (d)	EEls XPep
	– 'Madame Allen' (d)	EEls XPep
*	– 'Madame de Billy'	XPep
	– 'Magaly'	XPep
	– 'Maguelone'	XPep
*	– 'Mainate'	XPep
	– 'Maresciallo Graziani'	EEls XPep
	– 'Margaritha'	EEls XPep
	– 'Marie Gambetta'	EEls XPep
	– 'Marie Mauron'	XPep
	– subsp. *mascatense*	XPep
*	– 'Massif de l'Etoile'	XPep
*	– 'Maurin des Maures'	XPep
*	– 'Mer Egée'	XPep
	– 'Minouche'	XPep
*	– 'Mishna'	XPep
	– 'Mont Blanc'	EEls XPep
	– 'Mont Rose'	XPep
*	– 'Monts Saint Cyr'	XPep
	– 'Moshav'	XPep
	– 'Mrs Burton' (d)	XPep
	– 'Mrs Magnolia Willis Sealy' (d)	XPep
	– 'Mrs Roeding'	see *N. oleander* 'Carneum Plenum'
	– 'Mrs Swanson' (d)	XPep
	– 'Mrs Trueheart'	XPep
	– 'Mrs Willard Cooke'	XPep
	– 'Nana Rosso'	EEls XPep
*	– 'Natou'	XPep
	– 'Navajo'	XPep
*	– 'Neguev'	XPep
*	– 'Nomade'	XPep
	– 'Oasis'	EEls XPep
	– subsp. *oleander*	EEls XPep
*	– 'Osiris'	XPep
	– 'Papa Gambetta'	EEls XPep
*	– 'Pasadena'	XPep
	– 'Petite Pink'	EEls MPRe XPep
	– 'Petite Red'	EEls MPRe XPep
	– 'Petite Salmon'	EEls XPep
*	– 'Petite White'	XPep
	– 'Pietra Ligure'	XPep
	– 'Pink Beauty'	XPep
*	– 'Pirate Des Caraïbes'	XPep
	– 'Porto'	XPep
	– 'Professeur Granel' (d)	EEls XPep
	– 'Professeur Parlatore'	XPep
*	– 'Provence' (d)	EEls SOWG XPep
*	– 'Rivage'	XPep
	– 'Rosa Bartolini'	XPep

- 'Rosario' (d)	XPep
- 'Rose des Borrels'	EEls XPep
* - 'Rose des Vents' (d)	XPep
- 'Rosée du Ventoux' (d)	EEls SOWG
- 'Roseum'	EEls
- 'Roseum Plenum' (d)	CRHN EEls XPep
- 'Rosita'	EEls XPep
* - 'Rossignol'	XPep
* - 'Rubis' (d)	XPep
* - 'Sabra'	XPep
* - 'Sainte Beaume'	XPep
* - 'Sainte Victoire'	XPep
* - 'Santa Fe'	XPep
* - 'Sausalito'	XPep
- 'Scarlet Beauty'	XPep
- 'Sealy Pink'	EEls XPep
* - 'Simie'	XPep
* - 'Snowflake'	SOWG
- 'Soeur Agnès' (d)	EEls XPep
* - 'Soeur Elisabeth' (d)	XPep
- 'Soleil Levant'	EEls XPep
* - 'Solfège'	XPep
* - 'Sophie'	XPep
- 'Souvenir d'Emma Schneider'	EEls XPep
- 'Souvenir des Iles Canaries'	EEls XPep
- 'Splendens' (d)	SOWG
- 'Splendens Foliis Variegatis' (d)	XPep
- 'Splendens Giganteum' (d)	EEls XPep
- 'Splendens Giganteum Variegatum' (d/v)	EEls
* - 'Tamouré' (d)	XPep
* - 'Tavira'	XPep
- 'Tiberias'	XPep
- 'Tito Poggi'	EEls XPep
* - 'Toulouse'	XPep
- 'Vanilla Cream'	CBcs
- 'Variegatum' (v) ♀H1+3	EShb
- 'Variegatum Plenum' (d/v)	CBow WCot
* - 'Vénus'	XPep
- 'Villa Romaine'	EEls XPep
* - 'Ville d'Aubagne'	XPep
- 'Ville de Carpentras' (d)	EEls XPep
- 'Virginie'	XPep
* - 'Zoulou'	XPep

Nertera (Rubiaceae)
balfouriana	ECou
granadensis	EShb MBri

Neviusia (Rosaceae)
alabamensis	NLar

Nicandra (Solanaceae)
physalodes	CArn CHby EUnu ILis MSal NVic SUsu SYvo WRos
- 'Splash of Cream' (v)	EMan EUnu EWll LSou
- 'Violacea'	CSpe SRms SWvt

Nicotiana (Solanaceae)
alata	LPhx
- 'Grandiflora'	LRav
glauca	CHll CPLG CSec CSpe EBee EDsa EShb EWes EWin LDai LRav MGol MOak MSte NLar SDnm SPav
'Hopleys' **new**	CSpe
knightiana	CSec CSpe EBee EWin
langsdorffii ♀H3	CHad CSpe EBee EMan EMon EWin GBri LRav SDnm SPav SUsu WEas

- 'Cream Splash' (v)	EBee EChP EWin LSou
mutabilis	CHll CSec CSpe EBee EWin LDai LPhx MWea SBch WBor WPGP
mutabilis x alata	CSec EBee
rustica	EBee MGol
suaveolens	CBre
sylvestris ♀H3	CHEx CHad CHen CSpe CWSG EBee ELan EMan EPfP EWTr MBow MGol MOak SBch SDnm SEND SMrm SPav SWvt WEas WGwG WWhi WWye
tabacum	CArn MGol SPav

Nidularium (Bromeliaceae)
billbergioides	EOas
- 'Persimmon' **new**	EOas
flandria	see *Neoregelia carolinae* (Meyendorffii Group) 'Flandria'
fulgens ♀H1	EOas
innocentii **new**	XBlo

x *Niduregelia* (Bromeliaceae)
§ 'Surprise'	MBri

Nierembergia (Solanaceae)
caerulea	see *N. linariifolia*
frutescens	see *N. scoparia*
hippomanica	see *N. linariifolia*
§ linariifolia ♀H1	CAbP EHrv EMan
§ repens	CFee CStu ECho EDAr LRHS NLar
rivularis	see *N. repens*
§ scoparia	LPhx XPep
- 'Mont Blanc'	LRHS
- 'Purple Robe'	LRHS

Nigritella see *Gymnadenia*

Nipponanthemum (Asteraceae)
§ nipponicum	CDes CNic CWan EBee ECho EWin GCal GMac LAst MNrw NJOw NSti SRms WBrk WCMO WCot

Noccaea see *Thlaspi*

Nolina (Dracaenaceae)
bigelovii	CBrP
longifolia	EAmu
microcarpa	XPep
texana	CTrC NWCA WCot

Nomocharis (Liliaceae)
aperta	CBos CPLG EBee ECho EHyt EPot GBuc GCrs GEdr GFle GGar GKev ITim MLul WCMO WCru
- ACE 2271	GCrs
- CLD 229	GBuc WWst
farreri	ECho WCru
x finlayorum	EBee ECho GBuc GEdr GFle ITim WCMO
mairei	see *N. pardanthina*
meleagrina	ECho EPot GBuc GEdr GIBF GKev NLAp WAbe WCMO WWst
nana	see *Lilium nanum*
oxypetala	see *Lilium oxypetalum*
§ pardanthina	GBuc GGGa GKev GMac NSla WAbe WCMO WCru
- CLD 1490	GCrs
- f. punctulata	GBuc GGGa WCru
saluenensis	ECho GGGa WAbe WCMO WCru

Nonea (Boraginaceae)
lutea	EChP ECtt LSou MLLN NOrc NSti WCHb WHal WRos WWye

Nothochelone see *Penstemon*

Nothofagus ✿ (*Fagaceae*)
§ alpina — CDul CLnd CMCN NWea WDin WMou WNor WPGP
  antarctica — More than 30 suppliers
  cunninghamii — GGGa IArd STre WNor
  dombeyi — CDoC CDul CLnd CTho EPfP LHyd SAPC SArc STre WNor WPGP
  fusca — CBcs CDoC CDul MGos
  menziesii — CBcs CTrC
  nervosa — see *N. alpina*
  obliqua — CDoC CDul CLnd CMCN ECrN NWea WDin WMou WNor
  procera — see *N. alpina*
  solanderi — CAbb CDul
  - var. *cliffortioides* — CBcs

Notholaena see *Cheilanthes*

Notholirion (*Liliaceae*)
  bulbuliferum — EBee ECho EPot GBuc GKev WAbe
  campanulatum — WWst
  macrophyllum — EBee ECho EPot GBuc GCrs GEdr GKev NLar
  thomsonianum — EBee GCrs

Nothopanax see *Polyscias*

Nothoscordum (*Alliaceae*)
  bivalve — CStu
  gracile — CFir CPLG EBee WPrP
  inodorum — EBee GBuc
  neriniflorum — see *Caloscordum neriniflorum*
  strictum new — ECho

Notospartium (*Papilionaceae*)
  carmichaeliae — ECou
  - 'Hodder' — ECou
  - 'Seymour' — ECou
  glabrescens — ECou
  - 'Ben More' — ECou
  - 'Woodside' — ECou
  glabrescens x torulosum — ECou
  'Joy' — ECou
  torulosum — ECou
  - 'Blue Butterfly' — ECou
  - 'Malvern Hills' — ECou

Nuphar (*Nymphaeaceae*)
  advenum — LPBA
  japonica — CDWL
  - var. *variegata* (v) — CRow NLar
  lutea — CRow EHon EMFW LNCo LPBA NSco SCoo SWat WFar WPnP
  - subsp. *advena* — EMFW
  pumila — CDWL

Nuxia (*Buddlejaceae*)
  congesta — EShb
  floribunda — EShb

Nylandtia (*Polygalaceae*)
  spinosa — SPlb

Nymphaea ✿ (*Nymphaeaceae*)
  'Afterglow' (T/D) — CDWL
  alba (H) — CBen CRWN CRow CWat EHon EMFW EPfP LNCo LPBA NSco SCoo SWat WFar WMAq
  'Albatros' misapplied — see *N.* 'Hermine'
  'Albatros' Latour-Marliac (H) — CDWL LNCo LPBA SWat WPnP

* 'Albida' — CDWL WMAq XBlo
  'Amabilis' (H) — CBen CDWL CRow EMFW LPBA SWat WMAq
  'American Star' (H) — CWat EMFW SWat WMAq
  'Andreana' (H) — CDWL CWat LPBA SWat
  'Arabian Nights' (T/D) — CDWL
  'Arc-en-ciel' (H) — CDWL LPBA SCoo SWat WMAq
  'Arethusa' (H) — LPBA
  'Atropurpurea' (H) — CBen CDWL EMFW LPBA SWat WMAq
  'Attraction' (H) — CBen CDWL CRow EHon EMFW EPfP LNCo LPBA NBlu NPer SCoo SWat WMAq XBlo
  'Aurora' (H) — CDWL EMFW LPBA SWat WMAq WPnP
  'Barbara Dobbins' (H) — CDWL LPBA
  'Berit Strawn' (H) — CDWL EMFW
  'Berthold' (H) — CBen
  'Blue Beauty' (T/D) — CBen
  'Blue Horizon' (T/D) — CDWL
  'Brakeleyi Rosea' (H) — LPBA WMAq
  'Burgundy Princess' (H) — CDWL CWat
  candida (H) — CBen EHon EMFW WMAq
  'Candidissima' (H) — CDWL SWat
§ capensis (T/D) — XBlo
  'Caroliniana' (H) — CDWL
  'Caroliniana Nivea' (H) — CBen CDWL EMFW
  'Caroliniana Perfecta' (H) — CBen LPBA SWat
§ 'Charlene Strawn' (H) — CWat EMFW LPBA SWat WMAq
  'Charles de Meurville' (H) — CBen CDWL CRow EMFW LNCo LPBA NPer WMAq
  'Chubby' (H) — EMFW
  'Colonel A.J. Welch' (H) — CBen EHon EMFW LNCo LPBA NPer SCoo SWat WFar WMAq WPnP
  'Colorado' (H) — CDWL
  colorata — see *N. capensis*
  'Colossea' (H) — CBen CWat EHon EMFW LNCo LPBA WPnP
  'Comanche' (H) — CBen EMFW NPer WMAq
  'Conqueror' (H) — EMFW IArd LNCo LPBA SCoo SWat WFar
  'Danieda' — SWat
§ 'Darwin' (H) — CBen CDWL CWat LPBA SWat WMAq
  'David' (H) — CWat
  'Director George T. Moore' (T/D) — CDWL
  'Ellisiana' (H) — CBen CDWL EMFW LPBA SWat
  'Escarboucle' (H) ♀H4 — CBen CDWL CRow CWat EHon EMFW LNCo LPBA NLar NPer SCoo SWat WMAq WPnP XBlo
  'Esmeralda' (H) — SWat
  'Evelyn Randig' (T/D) — CDWL
  'Excalibur' — CDWL
§ 'Fabiola' (H) — CBen CDWL CRow EHon EMFW EPfP LPBA SCoo WFar WMAq
  'Fire Crest' (H) — CBen EHon EMFW LNCo LPBA NBlu SCoo SWat WFar WMAq
  'Froebelii' (H) — CBen CDWL CRow CWat EHon EMFW LNCo LPBA SWat WFar WMAq
  'Galatée' (H) — CDWL
  'Geisha Girl' — CDWL
  'General Pershing' (T/D) — CDWL
  'Georgia Peach' (H) — CDWL
  'Gladstoneana' (H) ♀H4 — CBen CRow CWat EHon EMFW LNCo LPBA NPer SCoo SWat WMAq
  'Gloire du Temple-sur-Lot' (H) — CBen CDWL EMFW SWat WMAq
  'Gloriosa' (H) — CBen CDWL LPBA SCoo SWat WFar
  'Gold Medal' (H) — CBen
  'Golden West' (T/D) — CDWL

'Gonnère' (H) ♀H4 — CBen CDWL CRow CWat EHon EMFW EPfP LNCo LPBA SWat WMAq WPnP
'Graziella' (H) — LPBA SWat WMAq WPnP
'Green Smoke' (T/D) — CDWL
'H.C. Haarstick' (T/N) — CDWL
'Helen Fowler' (H) — CDWL EMFW SWat WMAq
x *helvola* — see *N.* 'Pygmaea Helvola'
§ 'Hermine' (H) — CBen CDWL EMFW SWat WMAq
'Hollandia' Koster (H) — SWat
'Hollandia' misapplied — see *N.* 'Darwin'
'Indiana' (H) — CBen CDWL EMFW LPBA WMAq
'Irene Heritage' (H) — CBen
'James Brydon' (H) ♀H4 — CBen CDWL CRow CWat EHon EMFW EPfP LNCo LPBA NLar NPer SCoo SWat WFar WMAq WPnP
§ 'Joanne Pring' (H) — SWat
'Joey Tomocik' (H) — CBen CDWL CWat LNCo LPBA SCoo WMAq
'June Alison' (T/D) — CDWL
'King of Siam' (T/D) **new** — CDWL
'Lactea' (H) — CDWL
'Laydekeri Alba' — CDWL
'Laydekeri Fulgens' (H) — CBen CDWL EMFW LPBA SWat WMAq
'Laydekeri Lilacea' (H) — CBen CDWL CRow LNCo LPBA SWat WMAq
'Laydekeri Purpurata' (H) — CDWL EMFW LPBA SWat
'Laydekeri Rosea' misapplied — see *N.* 'Laydekeri Rosea Prolifera'
§ 'Laydekeri Rosea Prolifera' (H) — CBen EMFW LPBA
'Lemon Chiffon' (H) — CDWL
'Limelight' — SWat
'Little Sue' (H) — CDWL
'Luciana' — see *N.* 'Odorata Luciana'
'Lucidia' (H) — CBen CDWL EMFW LPBA SWat WMAq
'Madame de Bonseigneur' (H) — CDWL
'Madame Ganna Walska' (T/D) — CDWL
'Madame Wilfon Gonnère' (H) — CBen CDWL CWat EHon EMFW LNCo LPBA SWat WMAq WPnP
'Marliacea Albida' (H) — CBen CDWL CWat EHon EMFW LNCo LPBA SWat WFar WMAq WPnP XBlo
'Marliacea Carnea' (H) — CBen CDWL CRow EHon EMFW EPfP LNCo LPBA NBlu NPer SCoo SWat WFar WMAq
§ 'Marliacea Chromatella' (H) ♀H4 — CBen CDWL CRow CWat EHon EMFW EPfP LNCo LPBA NLar SCoo SWat WFar WMAq WPnP XBlo
'Marliacea Rosea' (H) — EMFW SWat WMAq XBlo
'Marliacea Rubra Punctata' (H) — LPBA
'Masaniello' (H) — CBen CDWL CRow EHon EMFW EPfP LPBA SWat WMAq
'Maurice Laydeker' (H) — CDWL
'Maxima' — see *Nymphaea* 'Odorata Maxima'
'Mayla' — LPBA
§ 'Météor' (H) — CBen CWat EMFW WMAq
'Midnight' (T/D) **new** — CDWL
'Millennium Pink' — CDWL
'Moorei' (H) — CBen CDWL EHon EMFW LPBA SWat WMAq
'Mrs George C. Hitchcock' (TN) — CDWL
'Mrs George H. Pring' (T/D) **new** — CDWL
'Mrs Martin E. Randig' — CDWL
'Mrs Richmond' Latour-Marliac (H) — SWat XBlo
'Mrs Richmond' misapplied — see *N.* 'Fabiola'
'Newchapel Beauty' — WMAq

'Newton' (H) — CDWL SWat WMAq
'Nigel' (H) — EMFW SWat
'Norma Gedye' (H) — CBen CWat LPBA SWat WMAq
'Odalisque' (H) — EMFW
§ *odorata* (H) — CBen CRow EHon LPBA SCoo WMAq
'Odorata Alba' — see *N. odorata*
§ 'Odorata Luciana' (H) — EMFW
§ 'Odorata Maxima' (H) — WMAq
§ *odorata* var. *minor* (H) — CBen CDWL CRow EMFW LPBA SWat WFar WMAq
– 'Pumila' — see *N. odorata* var. *minor*
'Odorata Sulphurea' (H) — CDWL LNCo NBlu SWat WFar WPnP
§ 'Odorata Sulphurea Grandiflora' (H) — CBen CDWL CRow EMFW LPBA SCoo SWat XBlo
odorata subsp. *tuberosa* (H) — CBen LPBA
§ 'Odorata Turicensis' (H) — LPBA
'Odorata William B. Shaw' — see *N.* 'W.B. Shaw'
'Orange Commanche' — CDWL
'Pam Bennett' (H) — CBen
'Pamela' (T/D) — CBen
'Panama Pacific' (T/D) — XBlo
'Patio Joe' — CDWL
'Paul Hariot' (H) — CDWL CWat EHon EMFW LPBA SWat WMAq WPnP
'Peaches and Cream' (H) — CDWL
Pearl of the Pool (H) — SWat
'Perry's Baby Red' (H) — CBen CDWL CWat LNCo SCoo WMAq
'Perry's Double White' (H) — CBen
'Perry's Fire Opal' (H) — CDWL
'Perry's Pink' (H) — SWat WMAq
'Perry's Viviparous Pink' (H) — CBen
'Perry's Yellow Sensation' — see *N.* 'Yellow Sensation'
'Peter Slocum' (H) — CDWL EMFW SWat
'Phoebus' (H) — CDWL SWat
pink hybrid — CDWL
'Pink Opal' (H) — CBen CDWL CWat EMFW LPBA
'Pink Sensation' (H) — CBen CDWL EMFW SWat WMAq
'Pöstlingberg' (H) — LPBA
'Princess Elizabeth' (H) — EHon LPBA
'Pygmaea Alba' — see *N. tetragona*
§ 'Pygmaea Helvola' (H) ♀H4 — CBen CDWL CRow CWat EHon EMFW LNCo LPBA NBlu NLar NPer SCoo SWat WMAq WPnP
'Pygmaea Rubis' (H) — CRow EHon LPBA SWat WMAq
'Pygmaea Rubra' (H) — CBen CDWL CWat EMFW LNCo NBlu NLar NPer SCoo WMAq WPnP
'Ray Davies' (H) — EMFW
'Red Spider' (H) — CWat LPBA
'Rembrandt' misapplied — see *N.* 'Météor'
'Rembrandt' Koster (H) — CDWL LPBA
'René Gérard' (H) — CBen CDWL CWat EHon EMFW LNCo LPBA SWat WFar WMAq WPnP
'Rosanna Supreme' (H) — SWat
'Rose Arey' (H) — CBen CDWL CRow EMFW LPBA SCoo SWat WMAq
'Rose Magnolia' (H) — CDWL SWat
§ 'Rosea' (H) — CBen LPBA
'Rosennymphe' (H) — CBen LPBA SWat WFar WMAq
'Saint Louis Gold' (T/D) — CDWL
'Seignouretti' (H) — EMFW
'Sioux' (H) — CBen CDWL EHon EMFW LPBA NBlu NPer SWat WMAq XBlo
'Sir Galahad' (T/N) — CDWL
'Sirius' (H) — CBen CDWL EMFW LPBA SWat
'Snow Princess' — LPBA WPnP
'Somptuosa' (H) — EPfP
'Splendida' (H) — WMAq
'Sunny Pink' — CDWL

'Sunrise' — see *N.* 'Odorata Sulphurea Grandiflora'
§ *tetragona* (H) — CBen CDWL CRow CWat EHon LNCo LPBA NBlu WFar WMAq
- 'Alba' — see *N. tetragona*
- 'Johann Pring' — see *N.* 'Joanne Pring'
'Texas Dawn' (H) — CDWL WMAq
'Tina' (T/D) — CDWL
'Tuberosa Flavescens' — see *N.* 'Marliacea Chromatella'
'Tuberosa Richardsonii' (H) — EHon EMFW LNCo WFar
tuberosa 'Rosea' — see *N.* 'Rosea'
'Turicensis' — see *N.* 'Odorata Turicensis'
'Vésuve' (H) — CDWL EMFW SWat
'Virginalis' (H) — LPBA SWat WMAq
§ 'W.B. Shaw' (H) — CBen EHon EMFW LNCo LPBA SWat WMAq WPnP
'Walter Pagels' (H) — CDWL EMFW WMAq
'Weymouth Red' (H) — CBen
'White Delight' (T/D) — CDWL
'William Falconer' (H) — CBen CDWL CWat EMFW LPBA SWat
'Wow' (H) — CDWL
'Yellow Commanche' — CDWL
'Yellow Dazzler' (T/D) — CDWL
'Yellow Princess' (H) — CDWL
§ 'Yellow Sensation' (H) — CBen
'Yul Ling' — SWat
'Zeus' — CDWL

Nymphoides (Menyanthaceae)
peltata — CWat EMFW EPfP LNCo NLar NPer NSco SCoo SWat WFar WMAq WPnP WWpP
§ - 'Bennettii' — EHon LPBA

Nyssa (Cornaceae)
aquatica — CTho SBir SSpi SSta
sinensis ♀H4 — CAbP CBcs CDoC CLnd CMCN CPMA CTho ELan EPfP IDee LRHS MBlu NHol SBir SBrw SPer SReu SSpi SSta WNor
- Nymans form — EPfP LRHS SBir
- Savill form — SIFN
sylvatica ♀H4 — More than 30 suppliers
- 'Autumn Cascades' — EPfP MBlu NLar WPGP
- var. *biflora* — CMCN
- 'Jermyns Flame' — CAbP EPfP LRHS MAsh SSpi
- 'Red Red Wine' — EPfP MBlu NLar SBir WPGP
- 'Sheffield Park' — CAbP CMCN EPfP LRHS SSpi
- 'Windsor' — EPfP LRHS SBir SSpi
- 'Wisley Bonfire' — CAbP ECrN EPfP LRHS NLar SBir SPoG SSpi WPGP

O

Oakesiella see *Uvularia*

Ochagavia (Bromeliaceae)
sp. CHEx NPal SAPC SArc
carnea — EOas
elegans — WPGP
* *rosea* — CHEx

Ochna (Ochnaceae)
serrulata — CSec

Ocimum (Lamiaceae)
'African Blue' — CArn CBod ELau EOHP EWin GPoy LSou MHer NBlu SPoG
basilicum — CArn CSev GPoy LRHS MBow MWat NBlu NPri SECG SIde SWat WPer WSel
- 'Anise' — see *O. basilicum* 'Horapha'

* - 'Cinnamon' — LRHS MBow MNHC MSal NGHP SHDw WJek WSel
- 'Genovese' — ELau MHer MNHC NGHP NVic
- 'Glycyrrhiza' — see *O. basilicum* 'Horapha'
- 'Green Globe' — MNHC
- 'Green Ruffles' — EPfP LRHS MNHC WJek WSel
- 'Holy' — see *O. tenuiflorum*
§ - 'Horapha' — CArn CSev MBow MHer MNHC MSal NGHP SIde WJek
* - 'Horapha Nanum' — NGHP WJek
- 'Magic Mountain' new — EWin
- 'Napolitano' — CBod MHer NGHP SIde SWat WJek
- *glabrescens* — CArn CSev MNHC MWat NBlu SIde
- - 'Dark Opal' — CBod MNHC NGHP SHDw WJek WSel
- - 'Purple Ruffles' — EPfP LRav MBow MNHC SIde SWat WJek WSel
- - 'Red Rubin' — LRav MHer MNHC WJek
- *glabrescens* x *kilimandscharicum* — GPoy
- 'Thai' — see *O. basilicum* 'Horapha'
x *citriodorum* — CArn LRHS MBow MNHC MSal NGHP SHDw SIde WJek WSel
- 'Lime' — LSou MNHC NGHP WJek
- 'Siam Queen' — LRHS MHer WJek
gratissimum — ELau MHer
§ *kilimandscharicum* — GPoy
minimum — CArn CBod CSev ELau LRHS MHer MNHC MWat NBlu SIde WJek WPer WSel
sanctum — see *O. tenuiflorum*
'Spicy Globe' — WJek
§ *tenuiflorum* — CArn GPoy LRHS LRav MNHC MSal NGHP SHDw SIde WJek

Odontadenia (Apocynaceae)
macrantha new — CPlN

Odontonema (Acanthaceae)
schomburgkianum new — CCCN
strictum — WMul

Oemleria (Rosaceae)
§ *cerasiformis* — CBcs CPLG CPle EPfP EPla NLar SSpi WCot WEas WHCG WSHC

Oenanthe (Apiaceae)
aquatica — IHMH
- 'Variegata' (v) — EMFW
* *javanica* 'Atropurpurea' — EHoe
- 'Flamingo' (v) — CBen CRow EBee EChP EGra ELan EMan EMon EPfP GGar IHMH LPBA MBNS NBro NJOw SGar WFar WMAq WPer WSHC WWpP

Oenothera ✿ (Onagraceae)
from South America — MTho
§ *acaulis* — CSpe GCal MNrw SBch SBri SGar WRos
- *alba* — MDKP WCot
- 'Aurea' — WPer
§ - 'Lutea' — see *O. acaulis* 'Aurea'
'Apricot Delight' — EBee EChP EMag EMan ENot GBBs LRHS MBrN NBur STes WMnd WMoo WRHF
§ *biennis* — CArn COld CSev CWan EHoe ELan EUnu GPoy LEdu LPhx MBow MDun MHer NBro NGHP SECG SGar SIde WBrk WEas WFar WHer WJek WPer WSFF
caespitosa — EDsa NRib
- subsp. *caespitosa* — NWCA
NNS 93-505
* *campylocalyx* — CSec EChP EMag EShb EUnu LDai NBur WCMO

childsii	see *O. speciosa*
cinaeus	see *O. fruticosa* subsp. *glauca*
'Colin Porter'	CCge CSec EBur NBur NWCA WMoo WPer
'Crown Imperial'	EBee MCCP SHar SPer SPoG SSto
drummondii	XPep
§ *elata* subsp. *hookeri*	NBre WPer
erythrosepala	see *O. glazioviana*
'Finlay's Fancy'	LEdu WCru
§ *fruticosa*	CSam EChP IFro NLar SPlb
- 'African Sun' [PBR]	EBee ECtt EWes SBod SRot
- 'Camel' (v)	EBee EGle EMan LDai LHop MDKP MFOX NEgg NPro SMrm SUsu WCMO WHil WHrl
- Fireworks	see *O. fruticosa* 'Fyrverkeri'
§ - 'Fyrverkeri' ♀H4	More than 30 suppliers
§ - subsp. *glauca* ♀H4	CElw CHrt COlW EBee EPfP ERou GSki MDKP MNrw MWhi NEgg NGHP SPet SRms SYvo WEas WHil WPer
- - 'Erica Robin' (v)	More than 30 suppliers
- - 'Frühlingsgold' (v)	CBct EBee EShb SUsu
- - narrow grey-leaved	SUsu
- - Solstice	see *O. fruticosa* subsp. *glauca* 'Sonnenwende'
§ - - 'Sonnenwende'	CBre CElw CEnt EBee EBrs LRHS MLLN NGHP NLar NPro WLin WMoo WTel
- - 'Sunspot' (v)	GBuc
- 'Lady Brookeborough'	MRav
- 'Michelle Ploeger'	EBee EGle NBre NCGa
- 'Silberblatt' (v)	CBow LSou WAul
- 'Yellow River'	CElw EBee LRHS WBrk WWeb
- 'Youngii'	EBee EPfP ERou MCCP MLLN SSto WPer
glabra Miller	see *O. biennis*
glabra misapplied	ECha NSti SIng SUsu
§ *glazioviana*	CWan EChP EMag EUnu MNHC NBir WFar WHrl WPer WWye
grandis	CSec
hookeri	see *O. elata* subsp. *hookeri*
kunthiana	CSec ECho EMag EMan ERou EShb MDKP MWea NWCA SPet WMnd WMoo WPer
- 'Glowing Magenta'	LSou
lamarckiana	see *O. glazioviana*
'Lemon Sunset'	CSim CWan EBee EMag LHop LSou NBur NGHP SSvw SWat WMoo
linearis	see *O. fruticosa*
'Longest Day'	LRHS MArl MBrN WWeb
§ *macrocarpa* ♀H4	More than 30 suppliers
- subsp. *fremontii* 'Silver Wings' **new**	LBMP
- 'Greencourt Lemon'	LPhx
- subsp. *incana*	CBrm CMea CSam NBre NGHP SMad
macrosceles	NBre
* *minima*	MDKP WLin
missouriensis	see *O. macrocarpa*
muricata	EBee NBre
nana	NJOw
oakesiana	CSec EBee LPhx
odorata misapplied	see *O. stricta*
odorata Hook. & Arn.	see *O. biennis*
odorata Jacquin	CArn GCal
- 'Sulphurea'	see *O. stricta* 'Sulphurea'
organensis	EBee MLLN NBre WPGP
pallida	NGHP SWat
- 'Innocence'	ECtt LRHS MBNS NBre WPer
- 'Wedding Bells'	NPer
parviflora	CSec
'Penelope Hobhouse'	CBct GBuc LSou SUsu
§ *perennis*	CNic NBre NPro SRms WBVN WEas WPer
pumila	see *O. perennis*
rosea	CEnt NBur

§ *speciosa*	CMHG CRWN CSim EBee EWin LAst MRav NBre SEND SMar SPer SWat WCot WPer XPep
* - 'Alba'	EBee XPep
- 'Ballerina'	LHop WCFE
- var. *childsii*	see *O. speciosa*
- 'Pink Petticoats'	ECha ECtt EKen EMag EShb MArl MCCP NGHP NPer SWat
§ - 'Rosea'	EBee ECho EMag LRHS SPlb SWat WPer
- 'Siskiyou'	CHrt COtt CPrp CSpe EBee ENot EPfP GBuc LEdu LRHS MArl NPri SCoo SGar SHar SIng SMad SMrm SPer SPoG SRot SUsu SWat WHer
- Twilight **new**	SPoG
- 'Woodside White'	SMrm
§ - *stricta*	CHar CHrt CMea CSam CSec ECGP EGoo MBri SIng SMar WBrk WCMO WPer WWye
* - 'Moonlight'	SGar
§ - 'Sulphurea'	CHad CHar CMHG CMil EChP EGoo ELan EMag EMan GCal IFro MNFA MWgw NPer SBch SGar SMrm SUsu WAbb WCot WPer
'Summer Sun'	EAEE EBee LRHS MSph MSte NBre SPoG
syrticola	NBre
taraxacifolia	see *O. acaulis*
tetragona	see *O. fruticosa* subsp. *glauca*
- var. *fraseri*	see *O. fruticosa* subsp. *glauca*
- 'Sonnenwende'	see *O. fruticosa* subsp. *glauca* 'Sonnenwende'
versicolor 'Sunset Boulevard'	CHrt CMMP CSec CSpe EChP ECtt GBuc LAst LDai MHer MWrn NGHP SBod SECG SGar SMrm SPer SPoG SWal WMoo WPer WWeb

Olea (Oleaceae)

europaea (F)	More than 30 suppliers
- subsp. *africana* (F)	CTrC WPGP XPep
- 'Aglandau' (F)	CAgr ERea
- 'Bouteillan' (F)	CAgr ERea
- 'Cailletier' (F)	CAgr
- 'Cellina di Nardo' (F) **new**	MCoo
- 'Chelsea Physic Garden' (F)	WPGP
§ - 'Cipressino' (F)	ERea LPan SBLw XPep
- 'El Greco' (F)	CBcs ERea
- subsp. *europaea* var. *sylvestris*	XPep
- 'Frantoio' (F)	CAgr MCoo
- 'Manzanillo' (F)	ERea
- 'Pyramidalis'	see *O. europaea* 'Cipressino'
* - 'Sativa' (F)	EMui

Olearia ✿ (Asteraceae)

albida misapplied	see *O.* 'Talbot de Malahide'
albida Hook. f.	GGar
- var. *angulata*	CBcs CTrC
algida	ECou GGar
arborescens	GGar GSki
argophylla	CPLG ECou GGar
avicenniifolia	CBcs CTrC ECou GGar
canescens	CPne
capillaris	CDoC CPle ECou GGar WCwm
chathamica	CPLG GGar IDee
§ *cheesemanii*	CBcs CDoC CMHG CPLG CPle EBee EGar NLar SPer
coriacea	ECou
'County Park'	ECou
erubescens	CDoC CPLG
floribunda	CPle GGar
frostii	IDee
glandulosa	ECou GGar
gunniana	see *O. phlogopappa*

	x *haastii*	More than 30 suppliers
	- 'McKenzie'	ECou
	hectorii	ECou
§	'Henry Travers'	CBcs CDoC CPLG CPle EPfP GGar GQui IDee MDun NLar
§	*ilicifolia*	CDoC CDul CPle EBee GGar GSki IDee LRHS MDun
§	*ilicifolia* x *moschata*	CPle GGar IDee NLar WKif
	insignis	see *Pachystegia insignis*
	lacunosa	IDee MDun
	ledifolia	GGar
	lepidophylla	ECou
	- silver	ECou
	lirata	ECou GGar
	macrodonta ♀H3	More than 30 suppliers
	- 'Intermedia'	GGar
	- 'Major'	GGar SHBN
	- 'Minor'	CBcs CDoC CTrC ELan EPfP GGar GQui NLar SPlb WFar
	minor	CBcs
	x *mollis* misapplied	see *O. ilicifolia* x *O. moschata*
	x *mollis* (Kirk) Cockayne	CPle GQui WSHC
	- 'Zennorensis' ♀H3	CBcs CCCN CDoC CPLG EPfP GGar IArd IDee ISea MDun SOWG WDin WEas WGer WPGP
	moschata	CPle GGar NLar
	myrsinoides	CPLG
	nummularifolia	CBcs CDoC CHll CTrC CTri ECou EPfP EPla GGar ISea SEND SPer SSto WDin WFar WKif WTel
	- var. *cymbifolia*	ECou WGer
	- hybrids	ECou
	- 'Little Lou'	ECou
	odorata	CPLG ECou ISea NLar WFar WHCG
	oleifolia	see *O.* 'Waikariensis'
	paniculata	CBcs CDoC CMHG CPLG CPle CTrC CTri EDsa EPfP GGar GSki IDee ISea SLon WGer
§	*phlogopappa*	CSBt CTri ECou GGar MTis WBrE
	- 'Comber's Blue'	CBcs CCCN EPfP GGar LRHS MPRe NCGa SBrw SCoo SPer
§	- 'Comber's Pink'	CBcs CBrm CCCN CDoC CPLG EPfP GGar ISea LRHS MPRe NCGa NPer SAga SBrw SCoo SPer WEas WKif WWeb
	- pink	CTrG
	- 'Rosea'	see *O. phlogopappa* 'Comber's Pink'
	- Splendens Group	CAbb CDul WFar
I	- var. *subrepanda*	CPle CTrC GGar LEdu SEND
§	*ramulosa*	CDoC CPLG CPle CTrC
	- 'Blue Stars'	ECou GGar
	- var. *ramulosa*	ECou
	- 'White Stars'	ECou
	rani misapplied	see *O. cheesemanii*
	rani Druce	ISea
	x *scilloniensis* misapplied	see *O. stellulata* DC.
	x *scilloniensis* Dorrien-Smith ♀H3	CCCN CWCL GGar XPep
	- 'Compacta'	CBcs
	- 'Master Michael'	CCCN CDoC CTbh EBee EHol EPfP LRHS NLar SBod SBrw SOWG SPer SPoG WAbe WEas WKif WSHC WWeb
	semidentata misapplied	see *O.* 'Henry Travers'
	solandri	CDoC CHEx CSam EBee ECou EPla GGar IDee LRHS SDix SEND SHFr SPer STre XPep
	- 'Aurea'	CBcs GQui
	stellulata hort.	see *O. phlogopappa*
§	*stellulata* DC.	CBrm CPLG CPle CTrG CWSG CWib EBee ECou ELan EPfP EWTr ISea LRHS MWat SAga SCoo SDix SGar SOWG SPer SPla WDin WEas WFar WHCG WPic WSHC
	- 'Michael's Pride'	CPLG

	- var. *rugosa* new	ECou
§	'Talbot de Malahide'	CDoC EHol GGar
	traversii	CAbb CBcs CDoC CMHG CSBt CTrC EBee GGar LRHS SBrw SEND WGer WHer XPep
§	- 'Tweedledum' (v)	CBow CDoC CTrC CWib ECou EHoe GGar MOak SSto
	virgata	CCCN CHEx ECou GGar GQui GSki GTSp LEdu SBrw WCot XPep
	- var. *laxiflora*	WHer
	- var. *lineata*	CDoC CPLG ECou EDsa GGar NLar SEND SMur WDin WSHC
	- - 'Dartonii'	CBcs CDoC ECou EHol GGar LRHS MBlu SBig SLPl
	viscosa	CPle GGar
§	'Waikariensis'	CMHG CPLG CPle CTrC ECou GGar IDee LRHS MBri SBrw SEND SLon WCFE WDin WGer

Oligoneuron see *Solidago*

olive see *Olea europaea*

Olsynium (Iridaceae)

§	*douglasii* ♀H4	CBro EBee EDAr EHyt ELan EPot ETow GCrs GEdr LTwo NMen NRya SIng WAbe
	- 'Album'	CMea EHyt GCrs GEdr NMen NRya NSla
	- dwarf new	GEdr
	- var. *inflatum*	EWes
§	*filifolium*	NWCA
§	*junceum*	EHyt MDKP SBla WCot WLin WPGP
	- JCA 12289	MTho
	lyckolmii	WCot
	philippii F&W 10675 new	WCot

Omphalodes (Boraginaceae)

	cappadocica ♀H4	CElw EAEE EBee EBrs ECha ECho EPot IFoB LEdu LRHS MAvo NBro NCGa NCob NFor NPer NWCA SGar SPer SRms SWat WBrk
	- 'Alba'	ECho
	- 'Anthea Bloom'	GBuc IBlr NEgg
	- 'Blueberries and Cream' (v) new	WCot
	- 'Cherry Ingram' ♀H4	More than 30 suppliers
	- 'Cherry Ingram' variegated (v)	CFir WCMO
	- 'Lilac Mist'	CElw CLAP EBee LLWP MRav NCob SBch SRms SSvw SWat SWvt WGwG WPnP WTin
	- 'Parisian Skies'	CElw CLAP
	- 'Starry Eyes'	More than 30 suppliers
§	*linifolia* ♀H4	CMea CSpe EMag NMen SBch
	- *alba*	see *O. linifolia*
	lojkae	NSla SBla WLin
	luciliae	CLAP WHoo WThu
	nitida	EMon GGar NRya
	verna	More than 30 suppliers
	- 'Alba'	More than 30 suppliers
	- 'Elfenauge'	CMil EBee EGle EMon EPPr NBir NLar NRya WCot
	- *grandiflora*	WCot

Omphalogramma (Primulaceae)

	delavayi	GFle
	forrestii	NLAp
	vinciflorum	NLAp
	white-flowered new	NLAp

Oncostema see *Scilla*

onion see *Allium cepa*

Onixotis (*Colchicaceae*)

stricta	CPLG
triquetra	WCot

Onobrychis (*Papilionaceae*)

cornuta	EBee
tournefortii	EBee
viciifolia	EBee EMan MGol MSal SECG WSHC

Onoclea (*Woodsiaceae*)

§ ***intermedia***	EMon
sensibilis ♀H4	More than 30 suppliers
- copper	CHEx CRow SBla WPGP

Ononis (*Papilionaceae*)

repens	CArn MBow MSal NMir
rotundifolia	MSal
spinosa	EBee EWin LRav MHer MSal NBre NMir WFar WPer XPep

Onopordum (*Asteraceae*)

acanthium	More than 30 suppliers
arabicum	see *O. nervosum*
bracteatum	WPer
illyricum	WCot
§ ***nervosum*** ♀H4	CArn CSpe MHar NBur SAga SRms WFar

Onosma (*Boraginaceae*)

alborosea	CMdw CSev ECha EGoo GBri GCal GEdr SAga WEas WKif WPGP
helvetica	EMan
rigida new	CMea CPBP
taurica ♀H4	CMdw MOne NBir

Onychium (*Adiantaceae*)

contiguum	WAbe
japonicum	EFer EFtx GQui SBla SRms WAbe
- 'Dali'	SBla

Ophiopogon ✿ (*Convallariaceae*)

BWJ 8244 from Vietnam	WCru
'Black Dragon'	see *O. planiscapus* 'Nigrescens'
bodinieri	CBct ECho ERos EWes LEdu SMac WRHF
- B&L 12505	CLAP EBee EPPr EPla
aff. ***caulescens*** HWJ 590	WCru
chingii	EPla GCal LEdu SCnR
* - 'Crispum' new	CRez
formosanus	CPrp GBin
- B&SWJ 3659	EBee WCru
'Gin-ryu'	see *Liriope spicata* 'Gin-ryu'
graminifolius	see *Liriope muscari*
intermedius	CBct EBee EPla ERos MSte WCot WPGP
- GWJ 9387	WCru
- HWJK 2093	WCru
§ - 'Argenteomarginatus'	ECho ERos EWes WPGP
- ***parviflorus***	NSti
- 'Variegatus'	see *O. intermedius* 'Argenteomarginatus'
§ ***jaburan***	EBee ECho EShb LEdu MSte NHol NLAp WMoo WPnP
- 'Variegatus'	see *O. jaburan* 'Vittatus'
§ - 'Vittatus' (v)	CMHG CPrp CSBt EBee ECho EHoe ELan EPfP EShb EWes GSki LEdu MCCP MGos SAga SYvo WCMO WCot WFar
japonicus	CBro CDes ECho EPPr EPfP EPla EShb GSki LEdu NLAp NSti XPep
- B&SWJ 1842	WCru
- 'Albus'	CLAP ECho NHol
- 'Compactus'	CDoC CStu EBee SMac SPla WPGP WWye
- 'Curly Lady'PBR new	ENot
- 'Kigimafukiduma'	CBgR CPen EBee LEdu MBNS MRav NLar
- 'Kyoto'	GSki NLAp
- 'Minor'	CBct CEnd CKno CSBt EBee EPfP EPla NLar SMac WPGP
- 'Nanus Variegatus' (v)	CDes EBee EMon NChi
- 'Nippon'	CMMP CPrp ECho EHoe EPPr LAst MSph MWgw
- 'Tama-ryu'	EHyt
* - 'Tama-ryu Number Two'	ECho EPPr SIng
- 'Torafu' (v)	WCMO
* - 'Variegatus' (v)	CPrp ECho LEdu SIng SLPl
malcolmsonii B&SWJ 5264	WCru
planiscapus	CEnd CFee CKno CMHG CPLG CSWP CSam CSev CStu EBee ECho EPPr EPla GAbr GCal MNHC MSte MTho NBro SPla STre WBVN WMoo
* - 'Albovariegatus'	SPoG
- 'Green Dragon'	ELan
- ***leucanthus***	EPPr WCot
- 'Little Tabby' (v)	CBow CDes CLAP CSpe EBee ECho EPla MDKP MMoz NPro WCMO WCot WDyG WGwG WPGP WTin
* - ***minimus***	ECho ERos
§ - 'Nigrescens' ♀H4	More than 30 suppliers
- 'Silver Ribbon'	ECho MDKP SGar
scaber B&SWJ 1871	WCru
'Spring Gold'	CMil EBee EMon
'Tama-hime-nishiki' (v)	EMon
wallichianus	CStu EMar EPPr EPla NLar SGar WCMO WCot WPGP
- GWJ 9387	WCru

Ophrys (*Orchidaceae*)

apifera	WCMO WHer
fuciflora new	CHdy
insectifera new	CHdy

Oplismenus (*Poaceae*)

§ ***africanus*** 'Variegatus' (v) ♀H1	CHal EShb

Opuntia ✿ (*Cactaceae*)

compressa	see *O. humifusa*
erinacea var. ***utahensis*** x ***polycantha*** NNS 99-263	WCot
§ ***humifusa***	CHen SChr SMad WMul
microdasys	SWal
- var. ***albospina***	SWal
§ ***polyacantha***	SChr SPlb
rhodantha	see *O. polyacantha*

orange, sour or Seville see *Citrus aurantium*

orange, sweet see *Citrus sinensis*

Orbea (*Asclepiadaceae*)

variegata ♀H1	EShb WCMO

Orchis (*Orchidaceae*)

anthropophora	EFEx
elata	see *Dactylorhiza elata*
foliosa	see *Dactylorhiza foliosa*
fragrans new	NLAp
fuchsii	see *Dactylorhiza fuchsii*
graminifolia new	GEdr
italica new	GKev NLAp
laxiflora	see *Anacamptis laxiflora*
maculata	see *Dactylorhiza maculata*
maderensis	see *Dactylorhiza foliosa*
majalis	see *Dactylorhiza majalis*

§ *mascula*	WHer
militaris	NLAp
morio	see *Anacamptis morio*
olbiensis new	NLAp
provincialis new	NLAp

oregano see *Origanum vulgare*

Oreomyrrhis (Apiaceae)

argentea	CSec NMen

Oreopanax (Araliaceae)

dactylifolius	LEdu

Oreopteris (Thelypteridaceae)

§ *limbosperma*	SRms

Oresitrophe (Saxifragaceae)

rupifraga	WCru

Origanum ✿ (Lamiaceae)

from Santa Cruz	CArn
acutidens	EHyt WCHb XPep
amanum ♀H2-3	CPBP EBee ECho EGle EHyt ETow
	EWes LRHS MDKP NBir NMen
	SBla WAbe WHoo WPat WWye
- var. *album*	ECho SBla WAbe WPat
x *applii*	ELau
'Barbara Tingey'	CPBP CSpe CWCL EBee EChP
	ECho EHyt ELan ETow EWes ITim
	LBee LPhx LRHS MHer MNrw
	MSte MTho NWCA SBla SMeo
	SUsu WAbe WCFE WCru WHoo
'Bristol Cross'	EBee ECha MHer WPat
'Buckland'	EBee ECho EHyt EPot LPhx LRHS
	MHer MSte NMen NWCA SBla
	WAbe WPat
caespitosum	see *O. vulgare* 'Nanum'
§ *calcaratum*	ECho EMan ETow LRHS MTho
	SBla WAbe WPat
creticum	see *O. vulgare* subsp. *hirtum*
dictamnus	CArn ECho EEls EHyt GPoy LRHS
	LTwo MDKP NWCA SBla SHDw
	WAbe WJek XPep
'Dingle Fairy'	CMMP EBee ECho EGoo ELan
	EMan EPot EWes EGar MHer
	MLLN MMHG MNrw MTho NBir
	NWCA SBch SIde SIng SRot WDyG
	WGwG WMoo WWye
'Emma Stanley'	WAbe
'Erntedank'	EBee
'Frank Tingey'	ECho EHyt ELan LTwo SUsu
'Fritz Kummert'	NCGa
'Gold Splash'	EDAr EPfP GBar SIde WMoo
heracleoticum L.	see *O. vulgare* subsp. *hirtum*
'Hot and Spicy'	EOHP EWin NPri
§ x *hybridinum*	SBla WPat
'Ingolstadt'	SAga WWye
'Kent Beauty'	More than 30 suppliers
'Kent Beauty Variegated'	ECho
(v)	
kopetdaghense	XPep
laevigatum ♀H3	CArn CMHG ECho ELan EPfP EPot
	MHar MHer NBro NMir NPer
	NWCA SGar SIde SUsu WMoo
	WPer WSHC WWhi XPep
- 'Herrenhausen' ♀H4	More than 30 suppliers
- 'Hopleys'	More than 30 suppliers
- 'Purple Charm'	EBee MNHC NBre
- 'Springwood'	NWCA WWye
majorana	CArn CSev ELan ELau GWCH
	MHer MNHC MSal SECG SIde SWat
	WJek WPer WSel WWye XPep
- Pagoda Bells =	EDAr SRot SVil
'Lizbell'PBR	
'Marchants Seedling'	SMHy

microphyllum	CFee CMHG EDAr EGle EHyt GBar
	LRHS MTho NMen SBla SIng SMeo
	WCru WWye XPep
minutiflorum	ECho LTwo
'Norton Gold'	CBre EBee EBrs ECha EPot EWin
	GBar GBuc LRHS MBow MHer
	NBre NPer SIde
'Nymphenburg'	CFee CSam EBee EChP EMan LSou
	MHer MSte NCob SIde SMrm
	WCru WHer WWhi
onites	CArn CHby CWan ELau GBar
	IHMH ILis MHer MNHC MSal
	MWat NBlu SIde SPlb WBrk
	WGwG WHer WJek WPer WSel
	WWye XPep
- 'Noa'	EWin
'Pilgrim'	SIde
* *prismaticum*	GBar
pulchellum	see *O.* x *hybridinum*
'Purple Cloud'	NBir
'Rosenkuppel'	More than 30 suppliers
'Rotkugel'	CMHG CPrp EBee EChP EGle
	EWin LPhx LSou MSte WCru
rotundifolium ♀H4	CMea EBee ECho EDAr ELan LEdu
	MDKP MHer NBir SBch SBla WAbe
- hybrid	MDKP
scabrum	CArn WWye
- subsp. *pulchrum*	CStu XPep
- - 'Newleaze'	LHop SBch WHoo
sipyleum	EHyt SBla
syriacum	XPep
'Tinpenny Pink'	WTin
tournefortii	see *O. calcaratum*
tytthanthum	XPep
villosum	see *Thymus villosus*
virens	CArn GBar ILis MCCP
vulgare	CAgr CArn CHrt CRWN CSev
	CWan ECho EDAr EMag GBar
	GMaP GPoy IHMH MBar MBow
	MHer MNHC NBro NLan NMir
	NPri SEND SGar SIde SPlb WHer
	WPer WSFF WWye XPep
- from Israel	ELau
- 'Acorn Bank'	CArn CBod CPrp CWan EBee
	EGoo EGra EShb EUnu EWes EWin
	MHer MNHC NLar SAga SIde
	WCHb WGwG WHer WJek
- var. *album*	CElw MHer WHer
- - 'Aureum Album'	WHer
- 'Aureum' ♀H4	More than 30 suppliers
- 'Aureum Crispum'	CBgR CPrp CWan ECha EDAr
	EGoo ELau GAbr GBar GPoy
	IHMH ILis NBid NBlu NGHP SBch
	SIde SWat WJek WRha WSel WWye
- 'Compactum'	More than 30 suppliers
- 'Corinne Tremaine' (v)	NBir WHer
- 'Country Cream' (v)	More than 30 suppliers
- 'Curly Gold'	MBow
- *formosanum*	WCru
B&SWJ 3180	
§ - 'Gold Tip' (v)	CBgR CMea CSev EBee EHoe ELau
	GBar IHMH ILis MHer MNHC
	NGHP NPri SIde SPlb SWat WCHb
	WFar WHer WWye
- 'Golden Shine'	CMMP EBee EOHP EWes EWin
	NGHP WRha
§ - subsp. *hirtum*	CArn CHby EOHP GPoy LEdu
	MSal SPlb WBri WJek WPer XPep
- - 'Greek'	CAgr CBod CPrp CWan ELau EUnu
	GWCH MBow MHer MNHC NGHP
	SECG WGwG
§ - 'Nanum'	ECho GBar LRHS WJek
- 'Nyamba'	GPoy
- 'Pink Mist'	EBee
- 'Polyphant' (v)	CMHG CSev EBee EChP EDAr
	EGle EMan EOHP GBar LSou

		MLLN NBir WBrE WCHb WJek WMoo WSel WWye
	- 'Thumble's Variety'	CBgR CBod CElw CMea CPrp EAEE EBee EBrs ECha EGle EGoo EHoe EMag EPot GBar IHMH LHop LRHS MBri MHer MRav NCob NHol SIde SSvw SWat WEas WMnd WMoo XPep
	- 'Tomintoul'	GPoy
	- 'Variegatum'	see *O. vulgare* 'Gold Tip'
	- 'Webb's White'	GBar
	- 'White Charm'	EOHP NHol
	'White Cloud'	EBee
	'Z'Attar'	MHer SIde

Orixa (*Rutaceae*)
	japonica	EBee EPfP WFar WPGP
	- 'Variegata' (v)	CBcs EPfP LRHS SPoG

Orlaya (*Apiaceae*)
	grandiflora	CHrt CSpe MAvo SBch SUsu WCot WFar

Ornithogalum (*Hyacinthaceae*)
	arabicum	CBro EChP ECho EPfP LPhx LRHS MBri MLLN MSph SPet WCot WDav
	arcuatum	CMon WCot
	balansae	see *O. oligophyllum*
	caudatum	see *O. longibracteatum*
	chionophilum	EBee
	ciliiferum	CMon
	comosum	ECho
	conicum	WHil
	dubium ♀H1	CBgR EBrs ECho WCot
	exscapum	CStu ECho
	fimbriatum	ECho
	lanceolatum	EHyt WCot
§	*longibracteatum*	CHEx CStu EBee ECho EPem SChr SYvo WGwG WPrP
	magnum	CAvo CFFs CMea EBee EChP ECho LRHS SPur
	montanum	ECho
	'Mount Everest'	ECho
	'Mount Fuji'	ECho
	nanum	see *O. sigmoideum*
	narbonense	EBee ECho GBuc LPhx LRHS WCot WDav
	nutans ♀H4	CAvo CBro CFFs CFwr CMea CStu EBee EBrs ECho EMon EPfP EPot LPhx MAvo MEHN MLLN MNrw NMen NWCA SMeo WAul WBrk WCot WFar WPer
§	*oligophyllum*	CBgR CMea CStu EBee ECho EPfP EPot MNrw NWCA SMeo WCot WDav
§	*orthophyllum*	CStu WCot
	ponticum	ECho ERos
	pyramidale	CDes CSpe EBee EChP ECho EPot LRHS MNrw WCot
	- AB&S 4600 from Morocco	CMon
	pyrenaicum	CAvo CFFs CStu ECha ERos WCot WShi
	reverchonii	CDes EBee ERos
	- AB&S 4400 from Morocco	CMon
	- AB&S 4600 from Morocco	CMon
	saundersiae	ECho WHil
	schmalhausenii	WWst
	sessiliflorum AB&S 4400 from Morocco	CMon
	- AB&S 4619 from Morocco	CMon
	sibthorpii	see *O. sigmoideum*
§	*sigmoideum*	CStu WAbe
	tenuifolium	see *O. orthophyllum*
	- subsp. *aridum*	WWst
	thyrsoides ♀H1	CCCN ECho EPfP LRHS SPet WHil

	umbellatum	CBro CFFs CNic ECho ELan EMon EPfP GAbr GPoy LHop LRHS MBow MBri MNrw NMen SPer SRms WBVN WFar WHil WPer WShi WWye
	unifolium	ECho

Orontium (*Araceae*)
	aquaticum	CBen CDWL CWat EHon EMFW GAbr LNCo LPBA NLar NPer SWat WMAq WPnP WWpP

Orostachys (*Crassulaceae*)
	furusei	EMan WCot WFar
	iwarenge	CStu
§	*spinosa*	CStu EMan ETow NMen WCot WFar WRos

Oroxylum (*Bignoniaceae*)
	indicum	CArn

Orphium (*Gentianaceae*)
	frutescens	CPLG EDsa EShb

Orthrosanthus (*Iridaceae*)
	chimboracensis	CDes CFir EBee EMan MWea NLar WCot WFar WLin WPGP WPer
	- JCA 13743	CPou
	laxus	CFir EBee ERos EWsh GBuc GMac MAvo NEgg SMad WHrl
	multiflorus	CDes CElw CWCL EBee ITim WPGP
	polystachyus	CCVN CPle CPom CRez CSpe EBee EChP EMan ERos MAvo MWea SSvw WHrl WSHC

Oryzopsis (*Poaceae*)
	hymenoides **new**	MAvo
	lessoniana	see *Anemanthele lessoniana*
	miliacea	CBig CHar CHrt CKno CSpe EBee EHoe EMan EPPr EWsh ITer LDai SMHy WCot WHal WPGP
	paradoxa	EPPr EShb

Oscularia (*Aizoaceae*)
§	*deltoides* ♀H1-2	CCCN CStu EWin MRav WCot WEas

Osmanthus (*Oleaceae*)
	armatus	CABP CTri EPfP MWya NLar WFar
§	x *burkwoodii* ♀H4	More than 30 suppliers
§	*decorus*	CBcs CSBt CTri EBee ELan EPfP EWTr MGos MRav NLar SPer SPla SSta WDin WFar
	delavayi ♀H4	More than 30 suppliers
	- 'Latifolius'	EPfP LRHS SLon WFar
	- 'Pearly Gates' **new**	SMad
	forrestii	see *O. yunnanensis*
	x *fortunei*	EPfP MGos SLPl WFar
	fragrans	CTbh SLon
§	*heterophyllus*	CBcs CDul EBee EPfP EWTr MBar MGan MRav MWya NFor NLar SPer SReu SRms SSta WDin WFar XPep
§	- all gold	CABP CDoC EGra LAst MBlu SMer SPer SPla SPoG
	- 'Argenteomarginatus'	see *O. heterophyllus* 'Variegatus'
§	- 'Aureomarginatus' (v)	CBcs CDoC CHar CMHG CSBt EBee EHoe EPfP LRHS MWya SHBN SLon SPer SPoG
	- 'Aureus' misapplied	see *O. heterophyllus* all gold
	- 'Aureus' Rehder	see *O. heterophyllus* 'Aureomarginatus'
§	- 'Goshiki' (v)	More than 30 suppliers
N	- 'Gulftide' ♀H4	CDoC CDul EBee ECrN EPfP LRHS MGos NLar SCoo WFar
	- 'Myrtifolius'	NLar

- 'Ogon' **new**	MBar
- 'Purple Shaft'	CAbP ELan EPfP LRHS MAsh NHol
- 'Purpureus'	CAbP CBcs CBgR CDoC CDul
	CMHG CSam CWib EBee ECrN
	EGra EHoe EPfP LRHS MBri MDun
	MGos MRav MSph NHol SCoo
	SLim SLon SPer SPoG SSpi SWal
	WDin WWeb
- 'Rotundifolius'	CBcs NLar
- Tricolor	see *O. heterophyllus* 'Goshiki'
§ - 'Variegatus' (v) ♀H4	CBcs CBrm CSBt CWib EBee ECrN
	EGra ELan EMil EPfP LAst LHop
	LRHS LSRN MAsh MBar MGos
	MRav NHol SLim SPer SPla SPoG
	SReu SSta WBVN WDin WFar WHar
	WPat
ilicifolius	see *O. heterophyllus*
rigidus **new**	NLar
serrulatus	CAbP NLar WPGP
suavis	EPfP LRHS NLar SPoG
§ *yunnanensis*	CTbh EPfP LRHS MBlu NLar SAPC
	SArc WFar WPGP

x *Osmarea* (Oleaceae)

burkwoodii	see *Osmanthus* x *burkwoodii*

Osmaronia see *Oemleria*

Osmitopsis (Asteraceae)

asteriscoides **new**	GFai

Osmorhiza (Apiaceae)

aristata B&SWJ 1607	WCru

Osmunda ✿ (Osmundaceae)

sp. CCCN	
cinnamomea ♀H4	CFwr CLAP CWCL EFtx EWes
	GBin NBPC NMyG WPGP
claytoniana ♀H4	CLAP CRez EPfP MAsh NBid NHol
	NLar NMyG NOGN NVic WCru
	WWye
lancea	NLar
regalis ♀H4	More than 30 suppliers
§ - 'Cristata' ♀H4	CFwr CLAP CPLG ELan EWTr
	GBin GCal LPBA MRav NBid NHol
	WFib WPGP
- 'Purpurascens'	More than 30 suppliers
- var. *spectabilis*	CLAP
§ - 'Undulata'	ELan GBin LPBA NHol WFib

Osteomeles (Rosaceae)

schweriniae	EMan
- B&L 12360	CPle SAga

Osteospermum ✿ (Asteraceae)

'African Queen'	see *O.* 'Nairobi Purple'
'Almach'PBR (Springstar Series)	LAst LSou
'Antares'PBR (Springstar Series)	LAst
'Arctur'PBR	LAst
Banana Symphony = 'Sekiin47' (Symphony Series)	CCCN EShb LIck LRHS LSou
barberae misapplied	see *O. jucundum*
'Blackthorn Seedling'	see *O. jucundum* 'Blackthorn Seedling'
'Blue Streak'	CCCN NBur
'Brickell's Hybrid'	see *O.* 'Chris Brickell'
'Buttermilk' ♀H1+3	CCCN CHal ELan LRHS SMrm WWlt
'Cannington Katrina'	MOak
'Cannington Roy'	CMHG CSam CTbh ECtt EPfP EWin GAbr LSRN NBur
'Castor' **new**	LAst
caulescens misapplied	see *O.* 'White Pim'
§ 'Chris Brickell'	CHal GCal MOak MSte NBur WHen WHil
'Countryside' (Side Series)	LHop
Cream Symphony = 'Seidacre'PBR (Symphony Series)	CBcs LAst LSou SVil
ecklonis	CHll CTbh EChP GGar GMaP IBlr ISea MHer NBro NGdn WFar WPer
- var. *prostratum*	see *O.* 'White Pim'
'Edna Bond'	WEas
fruticosum	XPep
I - 'Album'	XPep
'Gemma'PBR (Springstar Series)	MBNS SMrm WGor
'Giles Gilbey' (v)	CCCN CHal CPLG MBNS MOak NBur
'Gold Sparkler' (v)	LRHS SMrm
'Gweek Variegated' (v)	CCCN
'Helen Dimond'	COtt WWeb
'Hopleys' ♀H3-4	MHer MWrn SEND
'Irish'	EPot IGor LSou MWrn
'James Elliman'	MOak
'Jewel' (v)	COtt
§ *jucundum* ♀H3-4	CEnt CMHG CMea CPLG CWCL EChP ECha EPfP EWTr LRHS LSRN MBow MLHP MNrw MRav MTis MWgw NBir NChi NEgg NGdn NPer SEND SPlb SRms SWal WHen WWeb
§ - 'Blackthorn Seedling' ♀H3-4	CMea GBuc NFla NGdn SAga SBla
- var. *compactum*	CHEx CLyd CPBP EShb MBri MHar NLar NPer SMrm SPoG SPur WAbe WHen WHoo WLin
- 'Jackarandum'	MDKP
§ - 'Killerton Pink'	WPer
§ - 'Langtrees' ♀H3-4	LHop SMrm
'Keia'PBR (Springstar Series)	CCCN LAst LSou
'Killerton Pink'	see *O. jucundum* 'Killerton Pink'
§ 'Lady Leitrim' ♀H3-4	CCCN CHEx CHrt ECha EPfP GBri GGar IBlr LHop LSRN MArl MBnl MBow MOak MWrn NPer SAga SPoG SSvw WAbe WWeb
'Langtrees'	see *O. jucundum* 'Langtrees'
'Lemon Symphony'PBR (Symphony Series)	CFir LAst LRHS SVil
'Lubango'PBR	SGar
Milk Symphony = 'Seremi' (Symphony Series)	CCCN CFir SVil
'Mirach' (Springstar Series) **new**	CHVG LSou
§ 'Nairobi Purple'	CCCN CDoC CFee CHEx CHal CPLG ELan GGar MOak NBur
Nasinga Cream = 'Aknam'PBR **new**	CCCN
Orange Symphony = 'Seimora'PBR (Symphony Series)	CBcs CCCN EShb LAst LRHS LSou SMrm SVil
Orania Terracotta = 'Akterra'	SGar
'Pale Face'	see *O.* 'Lady Leitrim'
Peach Symphony = 'Seitope'PBR (Symphony Series)	CBcs LAst LRHS SVil
'Peggyi'	see *O.* 'Nairobi Purple'
I 'Pink Superbum'	CHEx
'Pink Whirls' ♀H1+3	CCCN CHal LRHS NBur
'Pollux'PBR (Springstar Series)	MBNS
'Port Wine'	see *O.* 'Nairobi Purple'
'Seaspray'	COtt
'Silver Sparkler' (v) ♀H1+3	CCCN CHen ELan EShb EWin LRHS MBNS MHer MOak NBur SSto WBrE
'Sparkler'	CCCN CHEx MSte
Springstar Series **new**	EShb

'Stardust'PBR	COtt LRHS NPer SCoo SPoG	
'Stringston Gemma'	CHal	
'Sunny Alex'PBR	LRHS	
'Sunny Amanda'PBR **new**	SRGP	
'Sunny Amelia'	LAst SRGP	
'Sunny Cecil'PBR **new**	SRGP	
'Sunny Dark Martha'PBR	LAst	
'Sunny Flora'PBR **new**	SRGP	
'Sunny Martha'PBR	LAst LRHS	
'Sunny Mary' **new**	LAst SRGP	
'Sunny Nathalie'	LAst SRGP SUsu	
'Sunny Philip' **new**	SRGP	
'Sunny Plum Serena'PBR **new**	SRGP	
'Sunny Serena'PBR	LAst SRGP	
'Sunny Stephanie'PBR **new**	LAst	
'Sunny Zara'PBR **new**	SRGP	
* 'Superbum'	CHEx	
I 'Superbum' x 'Lady Leitrim'	CHEx	
'Svelte'	MSte	
'Tauranga'	see O. 'Whirlygig'	
Tradewinds Deep Purple = 'Oste Deeppur' (Tradewinds Series) **new**	SVil	
'Tresco Peggy'	see O. 'Nairobi Purple'	
'Tresco Pink'	CCCN IBlr	
'Tresco Purple'	see O. 'Nairobi Purple'	
'Trewidden Pink' **new**	MBnl	
'Uranus'	SRGP	
'Vega'	LAst	
'Weetwood' ♀H3-4	CCCN CMHG CPLG ECtt EPot EShb EWin LHop MBNS MBri MHer MLHP MSte SAga SBla WAbe WEas WWeb	
§ 'Whirlygig' ♀H1+3	CCCN CHal MHer MOak	
§ 'White Pim' ♀H3-4	CHll CMHG ELan GBuc LRHS NPer SDix SPer SUsu XPep	
'Wildside'PBR (Side Series)	EShb	
'Wine Purple'	see O. 'Nairobi Purple'	
Wisley hybrids	WEas	
'Wisley Pink'	EPyc	
'Zambesi'	LRHS	
'Zaurak'PBR (Springstar Series)	CBcs CCCN EShb LAst LSou	
'Zimba'PBR	ELan LRHS	
'Zulu'PBR	CCCN LRHS MHer	

Ostrowskia (Campanulaceae)

magnifica	MTho

Ostrya (Corylaceae)

carpinifolia	CAgr CBcs CDul CLnd CMCN CTho CWib EBee EPfP LRHS MBar MBlu NLar SBLw WNor WOrn
japonica	CDul CMCN NLar
virginiana	CMCN ECrN EPfP WNor

Otanthus (Asteraceae)

maritimus	XPep

Othonna (Asteraceae)

capensis	CHal
§ *cheirifolia*	CMea CSam EGoo ELan EMan MFOX NBir NFor WBrk WCot WEas WPer XPep

Othonnopsis see *Othonna*

Ourisia (Scrophulariaceae)

caespitosa	GCrs IBlr NMen NRya
- var. *gracilis*	GEdr GGar IBlr NMen
§ *coccinea*	EBee EMan GAbr GBuc GEdr GGar GKev GMac IBlr LRHS NBir NGby NRya NWCA WAbe
crosbyi	GEdr GGar IBlr
crosbyi x *macrocarpa*	IBlr

elegans	see O. *coccinea*	
lactea	IBlr	
'Loch Ewe'	CPLG GAbr GBuc GCrs GEdr GGar IBlr MDun WCru WPGP	
macrocarpa	IBlr	
macrophylla	GBuc GGar GKev IBlr IGor WAbe	
macrophylla x *modesta*	IBlr	
microphylla	CGra NWCA WAbe	
* - f. *alba*	WAbe	
modesta	IBlr	
polyantha F&W 8487	CPBP WAbe	
- 'Cliftonville Scarlet'	CPBP EHyt WAbe WFar	
'Snowflake' ♀H4	GAbr GCrs GEdr IBlr MDun NBir NLAp NMen WAbe	

Oxalis (Oxalidaceae)

F&W 8673	CMon CPBP	
acetosella	CMea CNat CRWN MBow MHer NSco WHer WShi	
- var. *subpurpurascens*	MMHG WCot	
adenophylla ♀H4	More than 30 suppliers	
- 'Brenda Anderson'	SBla	
- dark	MTho	
adenophylla x *enneaphylla*	see O. 'Matthew Forrest'	
anomala	CMon EMan ERos WCMO WCot	
arborescens	CHEx	
§ *articulata*	EMan ETow MTho NPer SEND	
- 'Alba'	ETow LRHS	
- 'Aureoreticulata'	MTho	
- 'Festival'	WCMO WCot	
- 'Beatrice Anderson'	EHyt GCrs MTho NJOw NMen WAbe	
bowiei	CMon CPBP CStu EBee EPot	
- 'Bowles' White'	MTho	
brasiliensis	CPBP CStu ECho EPot MTho NJOw NMen	
brick-orange	WCMO WCot	
chrysantha	IHMH SIng WAbe	
compacta F&W 8011	CPBP	
corniculata var. *atropurpurea*	MTho	
'Dark Eye'	GCrs	
deppei	see O. *tetraphylla*	
§ *depressa*	CMon CStu CTri ECho EPot EWes GEdr GSki LTwo MTho NBir NEgg NJOw NLAp NMen NRya NSla SIng SRms WBrE WCot WFar	
- 'Irish Mist'	CStu EBee ECho	
eckloniana	CMon	
* - var. *sonderi*	WCot	
enneaphylla ♀H4	CElw EAEE ECho EMan EPot GCrs GGar LRHS MTho NMen NRya	
- F&W 2715	CPBP	
- 'Alba'	CGra ECho EHyt ERos ETow GBuc GCrs GGar ITim NMen NSla WAbe WIvy	
- 'Hythe Seedling'	EHyt	
- 'Minutifolia'	EHyt ERos GCrs LRHS LTwo MTho NMen NRya NSla WIvy	
* - 'Minutifolia Rosea'	CGra	
- 'Rosea'	CStu EHyt EPot ERos GKev MTho NRya NSla	
- 'Ruth Tweedie'	CGra CPBP NLAp NSla	
- 'Sheffield Swan'	CGra CStu ECho EHyt EPot NMen NSla SOkd WAbe	
europaea	GWCH	
falcatula	WCot	
'Fanny'	CStu EBee ECho	
flava	CMon NJOw	
floribunda misapplied	see O. *articulata*	
fourcadei	WCot	
geminata	NBir	
gigantea **new**	CSpe	
glabra	CMon CPBP	
'Gwen McBride'	CGra GCrs SBla WAbe	

hedysaroides	CCCN
'Hemswell Knight'	NMen
hirta	CDes CMon CPBP EPot MTho
	NJOw
- 'Gothenburg'	CPBP EBee ECho EMan ERos
	MTho NMen
imbricata	CMon CPBP EHyt EPot LTwo
inops	see *O. depressa*
'Ione Hecker' ♀H4	CGra CLyd ECho EHyt EPot ERos
	GCrs GEdr GGar GKev ITim LRHS
	MTho NJOw NLAp NMen NRya
	NSla NWCA WAbe WIvy WLin
	WPnP
japonica 'Picta' (v)	EBee
* *karroica*	CMon WCMO WCot
§ *laciniata*	CGra EHyt ERos GCrs ITim MTho
	NMen NSla WAbe
- dark	EHyt
- 'Seven Bells'	SBla WAbe
lactea double	see *O. magellanica* 'Nelson'
lasiandra	EPot ERos
§ *lobata*	CBro CMon CNic CPBP CStu EAEE
	EBee ECho EHyt EMan ERos ETow
	EWes LHop LRHS MTho NJOw
	SBch WAbe WFar
loricata	EHyt NMen
magellanica	CMHG CPom CRow CSpe CTri
	ECho GGar LBee MTho SIng SPlb
	WFar WPer
- 'Flore Pleno'	see *O. magellanica* 'Nelson'
§ - 'Nelson' (d)	CNic CPLG CRow CSpe CStu EBee
	ECho EMan EWes GBuc GCal
	GGar GMac IFro LBee LRHS MTho
	NBir NBro NJOw NPer SSvw WCru
	WMoo WPer WPnP WPrP WPtf
massoniana	CMon EBee SBla SIng
§ 'Matthew Forrest'	CPBP NJOw NMen
megalorrhiza	CPLG SChr
§ *melanosticta*	CBro CFee CLyd CMon CNic CPBP
	CStu EDAr EHyt EMan EPot GCrs
	LBow LTwo NJOw NLar SIng
	WAbe
monophylla	CMon
nahuelhuapiensis	CPBP
F&W 8469	
namaquana	CMon WCot
obtusa	CLyd CMon CNic CStu EBee ECho
	EMan ETow MTho SCnR WCMO
	WCot
- apricot	WCot
oregana	CDes CNic CRez CRow EBee
	GBuc GGar GMac WBor WCot
	WCru WPGP WPrP WSHC
- f. *smalliana*	EBee EWes WCru
palmifrons	CMon CPBP EPot LTwo MTho
	NJOw
patagonica	ECho EPot ERos GCrs NMen WPnP
perdicaria	see *O. lobata*
pes-caprae	CMon
- 'Flore Pleno' (d)	CMon
polyphylla	CMon EBee
- var. *pentaphylla* new	EPot
§ *purpurea*	ECho IHMH MWea WAbe
- 'Ken Aslet'	see *O. melanosticta*
regnellii	see *O. triangularis* subsp.
	papilionacea
rosea misapplied	see *O. rubra*
§ *rubra*	EBee WBrE
semiloba	CMon EMan GCal WCMO WCot
speciosa	see *O. purpurea*
squamata	EHyt NLAp WPat
squamosoradicosa	see *O. laciniata*
stipularis	CMon CNic
succulenta	CHll CSpe
'Sunset Velvet'	LAst
'Superstar'	WAbe

§ *tetraphylla*	CAgr CMMP CMon EBee ECho
	GSki LRHS MTho NEgg NPer
	WRha
* - *alba*	EBee ECho
- 'Iron Cross'	CFwr CHEx EBee ECho EMan
	ENot EPot GSki MMHG NBir
	NJOw WBVN WHil
'Tima' new	CPBP
triangularis	CAgr CHEx CStu ECho ENot EOHP
	EShb NBir NBlu NEgg NPer WBrE
	WFar
- 'Birgit'	EBee ECho
- 'Cupido'	EBee ECho GGar WPer
- 'Mijke'	EBee ECho
§ - subsp. *papilionacea*	CMon EBee EMan ENot GSki LRHS
♀H1	MMHG NEgg NJOw
- - 'Atropurpurea'	CSpe EBee LHop WBVN
	WCMO
* - - *rosea*	EBee EMan WCMO WCot
- subsp. *triangularis*	EBee EBrs NJOw
tuberosa	EUnu GPoy ILis LEdu
- 'Fat Red'	EOHP
- 'Fat White'	EOHP EUnu
- pink	EUnu
- red	EUnu
'Ute'	CGra CPBP GEdr NSla SBla SOkd
valdiviensis	EDAr EMan MDKP MWea NBur
versicolor ♀H1	CMon CPBP CStu ECho EHyt
	EMan EPot ERos ITer MTho NMen
	SBla SCnR SUsu WAbe WCMO
	WCot
- 'Clove Ball'	WPtf
vulcanicola	CStu LSou SDix WDyG
zeekoevleyensis	WCMO WCot

Oxera (Verbenaceae)

pulchella	CPlN

Oxycoccus see *Vaccinium*

Oxydendrum (Ericaceae)

arboreum	CAbP CBcs CDoC CEnd CMCN
	EPfP IDee IMGH LEdu LRHS MAsh
	MBri NLar SBrw SPer SPoG SSpi
	SSta WDin WFar WNor WOrn
- 'Chameleon'	EPfP SPoG SSpi SSta

Oxypetalum (Asclepiadaceae)

caeruleum	see *Tweedia caerulea*
solanoides new	CSec

Oxyria (Polygonaceae)

digyna	CAgr EMan GGar NBro NLar WCot
	WHer

Oxytropis (Papilionaceae)

exscerta	GIBF
hailarensis var.	CPBP
chankaensis	
lambertii	LTwo
maydelliana	GIBF
megalantha	EMan NWCA
ochotensis	GIBF
popoviana	GIBF
pumilio	GIBF
purpurea	EMan LTwo WSHC
shokanbetsuensis	EMan LTwo

Ozothamnus (Asteraceae)

§ *coralloides* ♀H2-3	EPot GCrs GGar NDlv NHar NJOw
	NWCA SIng
§ 'County Park Silver'	EWes GEdr GKev ITim MDKP
	NDlv NLAp NWCA WLin WPat
§ *hookeri*	CDoC CMdw EBee ECou GGar
	MBrN NLar NWCA SBrw SPer
	WJek WPat

§ *ledifolius* ♀H4 — CBcs CDoC CMHG CPle EBee ELan EPfP GGar LRHS MBri NBir SBrw SLon SPer SSpi WDin WHCG WHar WPat WSHC

§ *rosmarinifolius* — CBcs CDoC CTrG EBee ELan EPfP GGar IFro LRHS MSwo SBrw SPer WDin WEas WFar WHCG XPep
- 'Kiandra' — ECou
- 'Silver Jubilee' ♀H3 — CBcs CDoC CEnd CHEx CSBt CSam CTrG EBee ECrN ELan EPfP LRHS MAsh MBri MGos MSwo NEgg NSti SBrw SHBN SLon SPer SPlb SPoG SRkn WDin WFar WHCG WKif XPep

scutellifolius — ECou
§ *selago* — ECou NDlv WCot
- var. *intermedium* — GGar
- 'Minor' — ITim NWCA
§ - var. *tumidus* — NSla SIng WThu
'Sussex Silver' — EWin SBrw
'Threave Seedling' — CDoC CSam ELan LRHS SBrw SPer
§ *thyrsoideus* — CPLG WFar

P

Pachyphragma (Brassicaceae)
§ *macrophyllum* — CPom CSev EBee ECGP ECha EGle EHrv ELan GCal IBlr LRHS MNFA MRav NCiC NLar NMRc NSti WCot WCru WEas WPGP WSHC

Pachyphytum (Crassulaceae)
oviferum — SChr

Pachypodium (Apocynaceae)
bispinosum — CRoM
geayi ♀H1 — CRoM
horombense — CRoM
lamerei ♀H1 — CRoM LToo SBig
lealii subsp. *saundersii* — CRoM LToo
namaquanum — LToo
rosulatum var. *gracilius* — CRoM LToo
rutenbergianum var. *meridionale* — CRoM
succulentum — CRoM LToo

Pachysandra (Buxaceae)
axillaris — CLAP GCal
procumbens — CLAP EBee EHrv EPla NLar WCot WCru
stylosa — EPla MRav NLar
terminalis — More than 30 suppliers
- 'Green Carpet' ♀H4 — CBcs CDoC CSam CWib EAEE EBee ECot EGol ELan EPfP IHMH LAst LHop LRHS LSRN MBar MBri MGos MSwo NBlu NPro SMac SPer SPla SPoG SWvt WCAu
- 'Green Sheen' new — ECha MGos
- 'Variegata' (v) ♀H4 — CBcs CDoC CPMA CSBt EBee ECha ECrN EHoe ELan ENot LAst LRHS MBar MGos MSwo NEgg NHol SHBN SLim SPer SPla SPoG SWvt WBrE WCAu WDin WHar WViv WWeb

Pachystachys (Acanthaceae)
lutea ♀H1 — CHal ERea EShb LRHS MBri MJnS

Pachystegia (Asteraceae)
§ *insignis* — EDsa GGar
minor — WCru

Pachystima see *Paxistima*

Packera (Asteraceae)
§ *aurea* — ECha MSal WMoo

Paederia (Rubiaceae)
scandens — CPLG CPIN WCru WSHC
- HWJ 656 — WCru
- var. *mairei* B&SWJ 989 — WCru

Paederota (Scrophulariaceae)
§ *bonarota* — CLyd
lutea — NWCA

Paeonia ✿ (Paeoniaceae)
'Age of Gold' (S) new — WCAu
albiflora — see *P. lactiflora*
'Alice Roberts' — LRHS
'Alley Cat' — WAul
'America' — MBri WCAu
'Angelet' — CKel
'Angelo Cobb Freeborn' — WCAu
anomala — CFir MHom MPhe NSla WCot
- var. *intermedia* — EGle GCal
- subsp. *veitchii* — see *P. veitchii*
'Argosy' new — WCAu
arietina — see *P. mascula* subsp. *arietina*
'Athena' new — GBin
'Auten's Red' — WCAu
bakeri — EBee MBri
banatica — see *P. officinalis* subsp. *banatica*
'Banquet' (S) new — WCAu
beresovskii — EBee
'Black Monarch' — WCAu
'Black Panther' (S) new — WCAu
'Black Pirate' (S) — CKel WCAu
'Blaze' — WCAu WCot
Blue and Purple Giant — see *P. suffruticosa* 'Zi Lan Kui'
'Bridal Icing' — WCAu
broteroi — EBee SSpi
'Buckeye Belle' — CKel EBee GBin MBri MHom MPhe MSte SWat WAul WCAu WHil WWye
'Burma Midnight' — GBin
'Burma Ruby' — GBin WCAu
cambessedesii ♀H2-3 — CAby CBrd CBro CSpe EAEE EGle EHyt EPot ETow GCrs LHop LRHS MTho NBir NMen NSla SBla SRot SSpi SUsu WCMO WCot
'Carol' — WCAu
caucasica — see *P. mascula* subsp. *mascula*
'Cheddar Royal' — GBin LRHS
'Cherry Ruffles' new — WCAu
'China Pink' — MBri
'Chinese Dragon' (S) — CKel WCAu
'Claire de Lune' — GBin MBri WCAu WCMO WCot
'Claudia' — WCAu
'Coral Charm' — GBin MBri WCot
'Coral Fay' — GBin MSte WCAu
'Coral 'n' Gold' — WCAu
'Coral Sunset' new — GBin
'Coral Supreme' — GBin WCot
corallina — see *P. mascula* subsp. *mascula*
coriacea var. *atlantica* — CBro
Crimson Red — see *P. suffruticosa* 'Hu Hong'
'Crusader' — WCAu
'Cytherea' — MHom WCAu
'Dancing Butterflies' — EBee LRHS LSRN WCAu WHil
daurica — see *P. mascula* subsp. *triternata*
'Dawn Glow' new — WCAu
decomposita — MPhe
decora — see *P. peregrina*
'Defender' — WCAu
delavayi (S) ♀H4 — More than 30 suppliers
- BWJ 7775 — WCru
- from China (S) — MPhe
§ - var. *angustiloba* f. *angustiloba* — SSpi

– – ACE 1047	EPot
– var. **atropurpurea**	NEgg NFor
– hybrid (S)	CPLG NEgg
§ – var. **ludlowii** (S) ♀H4	More than 30 suppliers
§ – var. **lutea** (S)	CDul CHad EBee EPfP IFro LEdu
	LRHS MAsh MGos MLan NLAp
	SAga SHBN SLon SPoG SRms STre
	WAul WFar WHar WHoo WTin
– 'Mrs Sarson'	GBin MCCP SWat
– Potaninii Group (S)	see *P. delavayi* var. *angustiloba* f.
	angustiloba
– Trollioides Group (S)	WCAu
delavayi x **delavayi**	ELan
var. **lutea**	
Drizzling Rain Cloud	see *P. suffruticosa* 'Shiguregumo'
'Early Glow' **new**	GBin
'Early Scout'	GBin WAul WCAu WCot
'Early Windflower'	EGle GBin WCAu
'Eastgrove Ruby Lace'	WEas
'Eden's Perfume'	NLar WCot
'Elizabeth Foster' **new**	WCAu
'Ellen Cowley'	WCAu
emodi	CDes WCMO
'Fairy Princess'	GBin MBri WAul WCAu
'Firelight'	WCAu
'Flame'	EBee EWTr GBin MNrw MSte
	NLar SPer WAul WCAu WCot
	WHil
Fragrance and Beauty	see *P. suffruticosa* 'Lan Tian Yu'
§ Gansu Mudan Group (S)	CKel MPhe
– 'Bai Bi Fen Xia' (S)	MPhe
– 'Bai Bi Lan Xia' (S)	MPhe
– 'Bai Zhang Bing' (S) **new**	IPPs
– 'Cheng Xin' (S)	MPhe
– 'Fen He' (S)	IPPs MPhe
– 'Feng Xian' (S)	MPhe
– 'Hei Xuan Feng' (S)	MPhe
– 'Huang He' (S)	MPhe
– 'Lan Hai Yiu Bo' (S)	MPhe
– 'Lan He' (S)	IPPs MPhe
– 'Li Xiang' (S)	MPhe
– 'Lian Chun' (S)	MPhe
– 'Mei Gui Sa Jin' (S) **new**	IPPs
– 'Xue Hai Bing Xin' (S)	IPPs
new	
– 'Xue Hai Dan Xin' (S)	IPPs
new	
– 'Xue Lian' (S)	MPhe
– 'Zi Ban Bai' (S) **new**	IPPs
– 'Zi Guan Yu Zhu' **new** (S)	IPPs
– 'Zi He' (S) **new**	IPPs
'Gaugin' (S) **new**	WCAu
'Gold Standard'	GBin LRHS WAul
'Golden Bowl'	CKel
'Golden Glow'	WCAu
'Golden Isles'	CKel
'Golden Thunder' **new**	CKel
Green Dragon Lying on	see *P. suffruticosa* 'Qing Long Wo
a Chinese Inkstone	Mo Chi'
'Hei Hua Kui'	see *P. suffruticosa* 'Hei Hua Kui'
'Hesperus' (S) **new**	WCAu
'High Noon' (S)	CKel MPhe NBPC SWat WCAu
	WCMO
'Ho-gioku'	GBin
'Hoki'	CKel
'Honor'	WCAu
'Horizon'	GBin
§ 'Huang Hua Kui' (S)	CKel
humilis	see *P. officinalis* subsp.
	microcarpa
'Illini Belle'	GBin
'Illini Warrior'	WAul WCAu
'Isani Gidui'	see *P. lactiflora* 'Isami-jishi'
'Jack Frost'	LRHS
japonica misapplied	see *P. lactiflora*
'Jean E. Bockstoce'	WCAu
'Joseph Rock'	see *P. rockii*
'Joyce Ellen'	GBin WCAu
§ **kavachensis**	EBee GCal GIBF
I **kevachensis**	see *P. kavachensis*
'Kinkaku'	see *P.* x *lemoinei* 'Souvenir de
	Maxime Cornu'
'Kinko'	see *P.* x *lemoinei* 'Alice Harding'
'Kinshi'	see *P.* x *lemoinei* 'Chromatella'
'Kintei'	see *P.* x *lemoinei* 'L'Espérance'
'Kokamon' **new**	CKel
'Kun Shan Ye Guang'	CKel
§ **lactiflora**	EHrv MPhe WBor
– 'A.F.W. Hayward'	CKel
– 'Abalone Pearl' **new**	GBin
– 'Adolphe Rousseau'	CBcs NBlu WCAu
* – 'Afterglow'	CKel
– 'Agida'	EBee GBin
– 'Albert Crousse'	CBcs CKel GBin NBir NBlu SWat
	WCAu
– 'Alexander Fleming'	EBee EChP ECot EWTr MWea
	MWgw NBir SWat WBrE WCAu
	WHoo
– 'Alice Harding'	GBin WCAu
– 'Amibilis'	WCAu
– 'Amo-no-sode'	WCAu
– 'Angel Cheeks'	WCAu
– 'Anna Pavlova'	CKel
– 'Antwerpen'	ERou MBri WCAu
– 'Arabian Prince'	CKel
– 'Argentine'	WCAu
– 'Asa Gray'	CKel
– 'Auguste Dessert'	CKel GBin MBri MWea WCAu
	WCot
§ – 'Augustin d'Hour'	ERou
– 'Aureole'	CKel
– 'Avalanche'	EBee GBin NBPC NLar SMrm SPur
– 'Ballerina'	CKel
– 'Barbara'	CKel WCAu
– 'Baroness Schröder'	ELan
– 'Barrington Belle'	EPfP GBin MBri MSte WAul
– 'Barrymore'	CKel
– 'Beacon'	CKel
– 'Beatrice Kelway'	CKel
– 'Belle Center'	GBin WCAu
– 'Best Man'	WCAu
– 'Bethcar'	CKel
– 'Better Times'	WCAu
– 'Big Ben'	GBin WCAu
– 'Bing Qing' **new**	IPPs
– 'Blaze of Beauty'	EBee
– 'Bluebird' **new**	CKel
– 'Blush Queen'	ELan WCAu
– 'Boule de Neige' **new**	EWll
– 'Bower of Roses'	CKel
– 'Bowl of Beauty' ♀H4	More than 30 suppliers
– 'Bowl of Cream'	EBee GBin NLar SHBN SWat SWvt
	WCAu
– 'Break o' Day'	WCAu
– 'Bridal Gown'	GBin WCAu
– 'Bridal Veil'	CKel
– 'Bridesmaid'	CKel
– 'British Beauty'	CKel
– 'Bunker Hill'	CKel EBee GBin MBri SMur SPer
	SWvt WCAu WHil
– 'Butter Bowl'	GBin MBri WCAu
– 'Canarie'	MBri
– 'Candeur'	CKel
– 'Cang Long'	CKel
– 'Captivation'	CKel
– 'Carnival'	EBee
– 'Caroline Allain'	CKel
– 'Carrara' **new**	GBin
– 'Cascade'	CKel
– 'Catherine Fontijn'	CKel EBee GBin WCAu WHil
– 'Charles' White'	EBee EGle EPfP GBin LRHS NBPC
	WCAu

- 'Charm'	WCAu
- 'Cheddar Charm'	WAul WCAu
- 'Cheddar Cheese'	MBri
- 'Cheddar Gold' ♀H4	MBri
- 'Cherry Hill'	WCAu
- 'Chestine Gowdy'	CKel
- 'Chief Wapello' **new**	GBin
- 'Chun Xiao'	CKel
- 'Claire Dubois'	CKel ERou GBin WCAu
- 'Cornelia Shaylor'	WCAu
- 'Couronne d'Or'	WCAu
- 'Crimson Glory'	CKel
- 'Cringley White'	EBrs
- 'Dandy Dan'	WCAu
- 'Dark Vintage'	CKel
- 'Dawn Crest'	CKel EBee
- 'Dayspring'	CKel
- 'Delachei'	CKel
- 'Desire'	CKel
- 'Diana Drinkwater'	CKel
- 'Dinner Plate'	MBri WCAu WCot
- 'Do Tell'	GBin NLar SPer WCAu
- 'Docteur H. Barnsby'	CKel
- 'Doctor Alexander Fleming'	CKel SRGP SWat SWvt
- 'Dominion'	CKel
- 'Doreen'	CFir EBee GBin SHBN SRGP WCAu
- 'Doris Cooper'	WCAu
- 'Dorothy Welsh'	CKel
- 'Dresden'	CKel WCAu
- 'Duchesse de Nemours' ♀H4	More than 30 suppliers
- 'Duchesse d'Orléans'	WCAu
- 'Duke of Devonshire'	CKel
- 'Eden's Temptation'	SPer
- 'Edouard Doriat'	WCAu
- 'Edulis Superba'	CKel EBee EChP EGle ELan ENot LEdu LRHS MAvo MBNS NMoo NPer SMer SPur WCAu
- 'Elaine'	CKel
- 'Elizabeth Stone'	CKel
- 'Ella Christine Kelway'	CKel
- 'Elma'	CKel
- 'Elsa Sass'	WCAu
- 'Emma Klehm'	GBin WCAu
- 'Emperor of India'	CKel
- 'Enchantment'	CKel
- 'English Princess'	CKel
- 'Ethelreda'	CKel
- 'Ethereal'	CKel
- 'Evelyn Tibbets' **new**	GBin
- 'Evening Glow'	CKel
- 'Evening World'	CKel
- 'Fairy's Petticoat'	WCAu
- 'Fashion Show'	CKel
- 'Fedora' **new**	EBee
- 'Felicity'	CKel
- 'Félix Crousse' ♀H4	CBcs CKel CTri ELan EMil ENot EPfP ERou EWsh GMaP LAst MBNS MSte MWgw NBir SMrm SPer SPoG SPur SRGP SRms SWat WCAu WHil
- 'Felix Supreme' **new**	GBin
- 'Fen Chi Jin Yu'	CKel
- 'Fen Mian Tao Hua'	CKel
- 'Fen Yu Nu'	IPPs
- 'Festiva Maxima' ♀H4	CKel CTri CWCL EBee EChP ECot ELan EPfP ERou GBin LRHS MBri MSte MWgw NEgg NLar SHBN SPla SRms SWat SWvt WAul WCAu WHil WHoo WViv
- 'France'	CKel
- 'Fuji-no-mine'	GBin
- 'Garden Lace' **new**	GBin
- 'Gardenia'	EBee SHBN
- 'Gay Paree'	EBee GBin NLar SPer WCAu

- 'Gayborder June'	CKel EMil MBri WCAu
- 'Gene Wild'	WCAu
- 'Général MacMahon'	see *P. lactiflora* 'Augustin d'Hour'
- 'Germaine Bigot'	CKel WCAu
- 'Gertrude'	GBin
- 'Gilbert Barthelot'	WCAu
- 'Gleam of Light'	CKel MBri
- 'Globe of Light'	EBee GBin
- 'Gloriana'	WCAu
- 'Glory Hallelujah'	WCAu
- 'Glowing Candles'	WCAu
- 'Go-Daigo' **new**	GBin
- 'Golden Fleece'	WCAu
- 'Goodform'	CKel
- 'Green Lotus'	WAul
- 'Grover Cleveland'	CKel
- 'Guidon'	WCAu
- 'Gypsy Girl'	CKel
- 'Hakodate'	CKel
- 'Heartbeat'	CKel
- 'Helen Hayes'	WCAu
- 'Henri Potin'	CKel GBin
- 'Henry Bockstoce' **new**	GBin
- 'Henry Woodward'	CKel
- 'Her Grace'	CKel
- 'Her Majesty'	NBir
- 'Herbert Oliver'	CKel
- 'Hiawatha'	WCAu
- 'Hit Parade'	WCAu
- 'Honey Gold'	ELan GBin SHBN SPoG WAul WCAu
- 'Huang Jin Lun'	CKel IPPs
- 'Hyperion'	CKel
- 'Immaculée'	EBee ENot GBin MBri SMer SPoG
- 'Inspecteur Lavergne'	CKel LAst LRHS MBri MWea SPer WAul WCAu WCMO WCot
- 'Instituteur Doriat'	GBin MBri WCAu
§ - 'Isami-jishi'	GBin
- 'Jacorma'	CFir GBin WHoo
- 'Jacques Doriat'	CKel
- 'James Pillow'	WCAu
- 'Jan van Leeuwen'	CPen EBee EPfP ERou GBin WCAu WCot
- 'Jappensha-Ikhu'	GBin
- 'Jeanne d'Arc'	CKel
- 'Jewel'	CKel
- 'Jin Chi Yu'	CKel
- 'Jin Dai Wei'	CKel IPPs
- 'John Howard Wigell'	WCAu
- 'Joseph Plagne'	CKel
- 'Joy of Life'	CKel
- 'June Morning'	CKel
- 'June Rose'	WCAu
- 'Kansas'	EBee ELan ERou GBin MBri NBPC NMoo WCAu WCot WFar
- 'Karen Gray'	GBin WCAu
- 'Karl Rosenfield'	CKel CSBt EBee EChP ECot EGle ENot EPfP LAst LRHS MSte MWgw NEgg SPer SPla SPoG SRGP SRms SWvt WFar WHil WHoo WViv
- 'Kathleen Mavoureen'	CKel
- 'Kelway's Betty'	CKel
- 'Kelway's Brilliant'	CKel
- 'Kelway's Circe'	CKel
- 'Kelway's Daystar'	CKel
- 'Kelway's Glorious'	EChP EPfP ERou GBin MBNS NLar SMrm SPoG WCAu WCMO
- 'Kelway's Gorgeous'	EBee
- 'Kelway's Lovely'	CKel
- 'Kelway's Lovely Lady'	CKel
- 'Kelway's Majestic'	CKel
- 'Kelway's Queen'	CKel
- 'Kelway's Scented Rose'	CKel
- 'Kelway's Silvo'	CKel
- 'Kelway's Supreme'	CKel SWat
- 'King of England'	GBin

	- 'Kocho-jishi'	CKel
§	- 'Koningin Wilhelmina'	GBin MNrw
	- 'Krinkled White'	EBee GBin MBri MHom MWgw
		NCGa NLar SMeo SUsu WAul
		WCAu WCMO WCot
	- 'La Belle Hélène'	CKel
	- 'La France'	GBin
	- 'La Lorraine'	CKel
	- 'Lady Alexandra Duff'	EChP EPfP GBin MRav MWea SCoo
	♀H4	SRGP SRms SWvt WCAu WHil
	- 'Lady Kate'	WCAu
	- 'Lady Mayoress'	CKel
	- 'Lady Orchid'	WCAu
	- 'Lancaster Imp' **new**	GBin WAul
	- 'Langport Cross'	CKel
	- 'Laura Dessert' ♀H4	EBee EPfP ERou GBin MBri MWea
		MWgw SHBN WCAu
	- 'Le Cygne'	GBin
	- 'Le Jour'	MBri
	- 'Leading Lady'	CKel
	- 'L'Eclatante'	CKel WViv
	- 'L'Etincelante'	GBin
	- 'Legion of Honor'	CKel WCAu
	- 'Lemon Ice'	CKel
	- 'Lemon Queen'	GBin
	- 'Letitia'	EBee
	- 'Lian Tai' **new**	IPPs
	- 'Lights Out' **new**	GBin
	- 'Lillian Wild'	WCAu
	- 'Little Medicineman' **new**	EBee GBin NBhm NLar
	- 'Liukrecija' **new**	GBin
	- 'Lois Kelsey'	WCAu
	- 'Lora Dexheimer'	WCAu
	- 'Lord Calvin'	WCAu
	- 'Lord Derby'	CKel
	- 'Lord Kitchener'	CKel GBin MBri
	- 'Lorna Doone'	CKel
	- 'Lotus Queen'	GBin NLar WCAu
	- 'Louis Barthelot'	WCAu
	- 'Louis Joliet'	EChP ELan MSte
	- 'Lowell Thomas'	WCAu
	- 'Lyric'	CKel
	- 'Madame Calot'	EBee MBri MSph SRms WCAu
	- 'Madame Claude Tain'	MBri WCot
	- 'Madame de Verneville'	CKel WCAu
	- 'Madame Ducel'	CKel WCAu
	- 'Madame Emile	CWCL EBee LBuc NMoo SHBN
	Debatène'	SPoG WCAu
	- 'Madame Jules Dessert'	WCAu
	- 'Madelon'	CKel WCAu
	- 'Maestro' **new**	GBin
	- 'Magic Melody'	CKel
	- 'Magic Orb'	CKel
	- 'Margaret Truman'	CKel WCAu
	- 'Marguérite Gerard'	WCAu
	- 'Marie Clutton'	CKel
	- 'Marie Crousse'	WCAu
	- 'Marie Lemoine'	CKel SMur WCAu WCot
	- 'Marietta Sisson'	WCAu
	- 'Mary Brand'	WCAu
	- 'Masterpiece'	CKel
	- 'Merry Mayshine' **new**	GBin WCAu
	- 'Meteor Flag'	CKel
	- 'Midnight Sun'	MBri WCAu
	- 'Minnie Shaylor'	WCAu
	- 'Mischief'	WCAu
	- 'Miss America'	GBin MBri WCAu
	- 'Miss Eckhart'	CKel EBee ERou GBin WCAu
	- 'Miss Mary' **new**	EPfP
	- 'Mister Ed'	GBin WCAu
	- 'Mistral'	MBri
	- 'Mo Zi Ling'	WCAu
	- 'Monsieur Jules Elie'	CKel EChP EPfP ERou GBin
	♀H4	LAst MBri MHom MPhe NBPC
		SMer SPer SPla WAul WCAu
		WViv
	- 'Monsieur Martin	CFir GBin WCAu
	Cahuzac'	
	- 'Moon of Nippon'	EBee
	- 'Moon River'	EPfP GBin SHBN
	- 'Moonglow'	WCAu
	- 'Mother's Choice'	EBee GBin SHBN WCAu
	- 'Mr G.F. Hemerik'	CKel EBee GBin MBri MPhe WCAu
		WHil
	- 'Mr Thim'	WCAu
	- 'Mrs Edward Harding'	WCAu
	- 'Mrs F.J. Hemerik'	WCAu
	- 'Mrs Franklin	WCAu
	D. Roosevelt'	
	- 'Mrs J.V. Edlund'	WCAu
	- 'Mrs Livingston Farrand'	WCAu
	- 'My Pal Rudy'	GBin WCAu
	- 'Myrtle Gentry'	GBin
	- 'Nancy Nicholls'	WCAu
	- 'Nancy Nora'	NLar SPer
I	- 'Nellie'	CKel
	- 'Newfoundland'	CKel
	- 'Nice Gal'	WCAu
	- 'Nick Shaylor'	GBin WCAu
	- 'Nippon Beauty'	EBee EGle GBin NBPC NLar SPoG
	- 'Nobility'	CKel
	- 'Ornament'	CKel
	- 'Orpen'	CKel
	- 'Othello'	CKel
	- 'Paola'	CKel
	- 'Paul Bunyan' **new**	GBin
	- 'Paul M. Wild'	EChP NLar WCAu
*	- 'Pecher'	CWCL NBPC NMoo NPer SMrm
		WCMO
	- 'Peregrine'	CKel
	- 'Persier'	EBee
	- 'Peter Brand'	CKel GBin NBPC NLar
	- 'Philippe Rivoire'	WCAu
	- 'Philomèle'	WCAu
	- 'Pico'	WCAu
	- 'Pillow Talk'	EBee WCAu
	- 'Pink Cameo'	NBPC NLar SHBN SPoG WCAu
	- 'Pink Giant'	WCAu
	- 'Pink Lemonade'	WCAu
	- 'Pink Parfait'	CKel GBin WCAu WCot
	- 'Pink Princess'	MBri WCAu
	- 'Polar King'	WCAu
	- 'Port Royale'	CKel
	- 'President Franklin	SWat WCAu
	D. Roosevelt'	
	- 'Président Poincaré'	CKel SMur SWat
	- 'President Taft'	see *P. lactiflora* 'Reine Hortense'
	- 'Primevere'	EPfP EWll GBin MAvo MBNS MSte
		NLar NMoo SMrm SPer SPoG SPur
		WCAu
	- 'Qi Hua Lu Shuang'	CKel IPPs
	- 'Qing Wen'	CKel
	- 'Queen of Sheba'	WCAu
	- 'Queen Victoria' **new**	GBin
	- 'Queen Wilhelmina'	see *P. lactiflora* 'Koningen
		Wilhelmina'
	- 'Raoul Dessert'	WCAu
	- 'Raspberry Sundae'	ELan ERou GBin NLar SPer WCAu
	- 'Red Champion'	MBri
	- 'Red Dwarf'	CKel
	- 'Red Emperor'	WCAu
	- 'Red King'	CKel
	- 'Red Sarah Bernhardt'	MBri
§	- 'Reine Hortense'	GBin WCAu
	- 'Renato'	GBin LRHS
	- 'Richard Carvel'	WCAu
	- 'Rose of Delight'	CKel
	- 'Ruth Cobb'	WCAu
	- 'Sante Fe'	WCAu
	- 'Santorb'	CKel
	- 'Sarah Bernhardt' ♀H4	More than 30 suppliers
	- 'Scarlet O'Hara' **new**	GBin

- 'Schaffe' **new** — GBin
- 'Sea Shell' — GBin NLar
- 'Sha Jin Guan Ding' **new** — IPPs
- 'Shawnee Chief' — WCAu
- 'Shen Tao Hua' — CKel
- 'Shimmering Velvet' — CKel SAga
- 'Shirley Temple' — CKel CWCL EBee ELan GBin MRav MSte MWgw SPoG WCAu WCot WHil WViv
- 'Silver Flare' — CKel
- 'Sir Edward Elgar' — CKel
- 'Soft Salmon Joy' **new** — GBin
- 'Solange' — CKel EBee EChP GBin NCGa NLar SPoG WCAu
- 'Sorbet' — CWCL EChP EPfP LRHS NLar NMoo NPer SMrm WCAu WHil
- 'Spearmint' — CKel
- 'Starlight' — WCAu
- 'Surugu' — MBri
- 'Sweet Melody' **new** — GBin WCAu
- 'Sweet Sixteen' — WCAu
- 'Sword Dance' — EBee EGle EWll GBin MPhe SPoG WHil
- 'Tamate-boko' — WCAu
- 'The Mighty Mo' **new** — GBin
- 'Thérèse' — WCAu
- 'Tom Eckhardt' **new** — GBin
- 'Top Brass' — GBin MRav NLar WCAu
- 'Toro-no-maki' — WCAu
- 'Victoire de la Marne' — SMur
- 'Violet Dawson' **new** — GBin
- 'Vogue' — GBin SMur SWvt WCAu
- 'Walter Faxon' **new** — GBin
- 'West Elkton' **new** — GBin
- 'Westerner' — GBin WCAu
- 'White Angel' — EBee SPoG
- 'White Ivory' — MBri WCAu
- 'White Rose of Sharon' — CKel
- 'White Wings' — CBcs CKel EBee EGle ELan EPfP GBin MBri MSte MWea SPer SWat SWvt WAul WCAu WCot WWye
- 'Whitleyi Major' ♀H4 — WCot
- 'Wiesbaden' — WCAu
- 'Wilbur Wright' — GBin WCAu
- 'Wladyslawa' — EBee WCot
- 'Wu Hua Long Yu' — IPPs
- 'Xue Feng' — CKel
- 'Yan Fei Chu Yu' — CKel
- 'Yan Zi Dian Yu' — CKel IPPs
- 'Yu Cui He Hua' **new** — IPPs
- 'Zhu Sha Dian Yu' — CKel
- 'Zi Die Xian Ju' **new** — IPPs
- 'Zi Feng Chao Yang' **new** — IPPs
- 'Zus Braun' — EBee
- 'Zuzu' — GBin WAul WCAu
- x *lagodechiana* **new** — EBee
- 'Late Windflower' — EGle MHom
- x *lemoinei* (S) — WHal
- § - 'Alice Harding' (S) — CKel WCAu
- § - 'Chromatella' (S) — CKel
- § - 'L'Espérance' (S) — SPer WCAu
- § - 'Souvenir de Maxime Cornu' (S) — CKel EMui LRHS MGos MPhe WCAu
- *lithophila* — see *P. tenuifolia* subsp. *lithophila*
- 'Little Joe' — LRHS
- *lobata* 'Fire King' — see *P. peregrina*
- 'Lois Arleen' — WCAu
- *ludlowii* — see *P. delavayi* var. *ludlowii*
- *lutea* — see *P. delavayi* var. *lutea*
- - var. *ludlowii* — see *P. delavayi* var. *ludlowii*
- *macrophylla* — MPhe
- 'Magenta Gem' — WAul
- 'Mai Fleuri' — WCAu
- *mairei* — CFir MPhe WCot
- 'Marchioness' (S) — CKel WCAu

- *mascula* — CBro EPfP GIBF LHop LRHS LTwo NBir
- - from Samos — SSpi
- - from Sicily — MPhe
- § - subsp. *arietina* — MWat WEas WKif
- - - 'Northern Glory' — WCAu
- - subsp. *hellenica* — EBee MHom
- - - from Sicily — MPhe
- § - subsp. *mascula* — CBro EBee EGle GBin GIBF NLar WCot
- - - from Georgia — MPhe WPGP
- § - subsp. *russoi* — CAby EGle GIBF SSpi WCot
- - - from Sardinia — MPhe
- - - 'Reverchoni' **new** — EBee MHom
- § - subsp. *triternata* — CLAP EGle MHom MPhe
- - - from Crimea — WPGP
- 'Mikuhino Akebono' — CKel
- *mlokosewitschii* ♀H4 — CBct CBro CKel CSpe EBee ECha ECho EGle EHyt ETow GCrs GKev LHop LRHS MNrw MPhe MWgw NBir NMen SBla SUsu WCMO WCot WEas WHil WHoo WPGP WTin
- *mollis* — see *P. officinalis* subsp. *villosa*
- 'Montezuma' — MBri WCAu
- 'Moonrise' — WCAu
- Necklace with Precious Pearls — see *P. lactiflora* 'Ying Luo Bao Zhu'
- 'Nymphe' — CKel EBee EChP EPfP LRHS MRav WAul WCAu WHil
- *obovata* ♀H4 — CFir EPot GIBF GKev MPhe MSal SSpi WCot
- - var. *alba* ♀H4 — GBin GCrs GKev WEas WThu
- - var. *willmottiae* — MHom MPhe
- *officinalis* — CMil EWsh GPoy NEgg SBla
- - WM 9821 from Slovenia — MPhe
- - 'Alba Plena' — CPou GMaP MRav MSte NEgg SWvt WCAu WCMO
- - 'Anemoniflora Rosea' ♀H4 — CKel EBee EChP EGle EPfP GBin LRHS MBri MHom SWvt WCAu
- § - subsp. *banatica* — GKev MHom MPhe WCAu
- - 'China Rose' — GBin WCAu
- - subsp. *humilis* — see *P. officinalis* subsp. *microcarpa*
- - 'Lize van Veen' — GBin WCAu
- § - subsp. *microcarpa* — GIBF GKev
- - 'Mutabilis Plena' — EBee IBlr WCAu
- - 'Rosea Plena' ♀H4 — CKel EBee ECtt EPfP GBin GMaP LAst LHop MRav NEgg SPer SWat SWvt WCAu WCMO
- - 'Rosea Superba Plena' — EWTr NEgg SPoG WCAu
- - 'Rubra Plena' ♀H4 — CPou CWCL EBee ECtt EMil EPfP GAbr GBin GMaP LAst LHop MBri MHom NEgg NGdn SHBN SPer SPoG SRms SWat SWvt WAul WCAu WCMO WCot WFar WHil
- - subsp. *villosa* — CKel CMdw EBee ELan GAbr GBin SEND WCAu
- 'Oriental Gold' — CKel
- *ostii* (S) — CFwr CKel MPhe
- *papaveracea* — see *P. suffruticosa*
- *paradoxa* — see *P. officinalis* subsp. *microcarpa*
- 'Paula Fay' — EChP GBin MBri MRav NLar WCAu
- 'Peachy Rose' **new** — GBin
- Peony with the Purple Roots — see *P. suffruticosa* 'Shou An Hong'
- § *peregrina* — ECho GBin GCal GKev MHom MPhe MWgw NSla SBla SSpi WCAu WCot
- - 'Fire King' — GBin
- § - 'Otto Froebel' ♀H4 — GBin WCAu WCot
- - 'Sunshine' — see *P. peregrina* 'Otto Froebel'
- 'Phoenix White' (S) — MBlu
- 'Pink Hawaiian Coral' — GBin WCot

'Postilion'	GBin MBri WCAu	
potaninii	see *P. delavayi* var. *angustiloba* f. *angustiloba*	
'Prairie Moon' **new**	GBin NBPC NLar WCMO	
'Red Charm'	GBin MBri MHom SHBN SPoG WCAu	
'Red Glory' **new**	GBin	
'Red Magic'	NBPC NLar SMrm	
'Red Red Rose'	WCAu	
'Renown' (S) **new**	CKel	
'Requiem'	GBin WCAu	
'Robert W. Auten'	WCAu	
§ ***rockii*** (S)	EPfP MPhe WViv	
- 'Bing Shan Xue Lian' (S)	IPPs MPhe	
- 'He Ping Lian' (S)	MPhe	
- 'Hong Guan Yu Dai' **new**	IPPs	
- 'Hong Lian' (S)	IPPs MPhe	
- 'Hui He' (S)	MPhe	
- hybrid	see *P.* Gansu Mudan Group	
- subsp. ***linyanshani***	MPhe	
- 'Shu Sheng Peng Mo' (S)	MPhe	
- 'Tian Bai Xue' **new**	IPPs	
- 'Zi Die Ying Feng' (S)	MPhe	
'Roman Gold'	CKel	
romanica	see *P. peregrina*	
'Rose Garland'	WCAu	
'Roselette'	GBin WCAu	
Rouge Red	see *P. suffruticosa* 'Zhi Hong'	
'Roy Pehrson's Best Yellow' **new**	GBin	
ruprechtiana	EBee	
russoi	see *P. mascula* subsp. *russoi*	
'Scarlett O'Hara'	SPer SPoG WCAu WCot	
'Shaggy Dog'	LRHS	
Shandong Red Lotus	see *P. suffruticosa* 'Lu He Hong'	
'Shimano-fuji' **new**	CKel	
'Silver Dawn' **new**	GBin	
sinensis	see *P. lactiflora*	
'Smouthii'	MBri	
'Soshi'	GBin	
'Stardust'	WCAu	
steveniana	EBee EGle MHom MPhe	
§ ***suffruticosa*** (S)	CWib EBee ELan IPPs MGos MPhe NBlu SBrw WBVN	
- 'Akashigata' (S)	CKel	
- 'Alice Palmer' (S)	CKel	
- 'Bai Yu' (S)	CBcs	
- 'Bai Yulan' (S)	LTwo MWgw	
- Bird of Rimpo	see *P. suffruticosa* 'Rimpo'	
- Black Dragon Brocade	see *P. suffruticosa* 'Kokuryû-nishiki'	
- Black Flower Chief	see *P. suffruticosa* 'Hei Hua Kui'	
- 'Cang Zhi Hong' (S)	WViv	
- 'Cardinal Vaughan' (S)	CKel	
- Charming Age	see *P. suffruticosa* 'Howki'	
- 'Dou Lu' (S)	CBcs CKel IPPs MPhe	
- Double Cherry	see *P. suffruticosa* 'Yae-zakura'	
- 'Duchess of Kent' (S)	CKel	
- 'Duchess of Marlborough' (S)	CKel	
- 'Er Qiao' (S)	CBcs CKel MPhe	
- Eternal Camellias	see *P. suffruticosa* 'Yachiyo-tsubaki'	
- 'Fen Qiao' (S)	CBcs	
§ - 'Feng Dan Bai' (S)	CFwr CKel EBee GBin IPPs MPhe NBlu WCAu WViv	
- 'Feng Dan Fen' (S) **new**	IPPs	
- 'Feng Dan Zi' (S) **new**	IPPs	
- Flight of Cranes	see *P. suffruticosa* 'Renkaku'	
- Floral Rivalry	see *P. suffruticosa* 'Hana-kisoi'	
- 'Fuji Zome Goromo' (S)	CKel	
* - 'Glory of Huish' (S)	CKel	
- 'Godaishu' (S)	CKel LRHS MPhe	
- 'Guan Qun Fang' (S)	MPhe	
- 'Guan Shi Mo Yu' (S)	MPhe	
§ - 'Hakuojisi' (S)	CKel EBee WCAu	
- 'Hana-daijin' (S)	LRHS WCAu	
§ - 'Hana-kisoi' (S)	CKel MPhe WCAu	
- 'Haru-no-akebono' (S)	CKel	
§ - 'Hei Hua Kui' (S)	IPPs MPhe	
§ - 'Higurashi' (S)	EBee	
§ - 'Howki' (S)	WCAu	
§ - 'Hu Hong' (S)	CFwr EBee WCAu	
- Jewel in the Lotus	see *P. suffruticosa* 'Tama-fuyo'	
- Jewelled Screen	see *P. suffruticosa* 'Tama-sudare'	
- 'Jia Ge Jin Zi' (S)	CKel WViv	
- 'Jitsugetsu-nishiki' (S)	CKel	
- 'Jiu Zui Yang Fei' (S) **new**	IPPs	
- 'Joseph Rock'	see *P. rockii*	
- Kamada Brocade	see *P. suffruticosa* 'Kamada-nishiki'	
§ - 'Kamada-fuji' (S)	CKel WCAu	
§ - 'Kamada-nishiki' (S)	CKel	
§ - 'Kaow' (S)	CKel NBlu WCAu	
- King of Flowers	see *P. suffruticosa* 'Kaow'	
- King of White Lions	see *P. suffruticosa* 'Hakuojisi'	
* - 'Kingdom of the Moon' (s)	LRHS	
- 'Kinkaku'	see *P.* x *lemoinei* 'Souvenir de Maxime Cornu'	
- 'Kinshi'	see *P.* x *lemoinei* 'Alice Harding'	
- 'Kokucho' **new**	CKel	
§ - 'Kokuryû-nishiki' (S)	CKel GBin SPoG	
- 'Koshi-no-yuki' (S)	CKel	
- 'Lan Bao Shi' (S) **new**	IPPs	
- 'Lan Fu Rong' (S)	CBcs MPhe	
- 'Lan Hu Die' (S) **new**	IPPs	
§ - 'Lan Tian Yu' (S)	MPhe	
§ - 'Luo Han Hong' (S)	WCAu	
- Magnificent Flower	WViv	
- Magnificent Flower	see *P. suffruticosa* 'Hana-daijin'	
- 'Mikasayama' (S)	MPhe	
- 'Montrose' (S)	CKel	
* - 'Mrs Shirley Fry' (S)	CKel	
- 'Mrs William Kelway' (S)	CKel	
- 'Nigata Akashigata' (S)	CKel	
- Pride of Taisho	see *P. suffruticosa* 'Taisho-no-hokori'	
- 'Qing Long Wo Mo Chi' (S) **new**	IPPs	
- 'Qing Long Wo Mo Chi' (S)	CKel IPPs WCAu	
- 'Qing Shan Guan Xue' (S)	WViv	
- 'Reine Elisabeth' (S)	CKel	
§ - 'Renkaku' (S)	CKel LRHS NBlu WCAu	
§ - 'Rimpo' (S)	CKel EBee GBin MPhe	
- subsp. ***rockii*** (S)	see *P. rockii*	
- 'Rou Fu Rong' (S)	MPhe WCAu	
- 'Ruan Zhi Lan' (S)	WViv	
§ - 'San Bian Sai Yu' (S)	WViv	
- 'Sheng Hei Zi' (S)	CBcs	
§ - 'Shiguregumo' (S)	CKel	
- 'Shimadaigin' (S)	CKel MPhe NBlu	
- 'Shimane-chojuraku' (S)	CKel	
- 'Shimane-hakugan' (S)	CKel	
- 'Shimane-seidai' (S)	CKel	
- 'Shimanishiki' **new**	SPer	
* - 'Shimanojuji' **new**	SPer	
- 'Shintoyen' (S)	CKel	
§ - 'Shou An Hong' (S)	MPhe	
- 'Sumi-no-ichi' (S)	CKel	
- 'Superb' (S)	CKel	
§ - 'Taisho-no-hokori' (S)	CKel LRHS WCAu	
§ - 'Taiyo' (S)	CKel LRHS MPhe	
§ - 'Tama-fuyo' (S)	CKel	
§ - 'Tama-sudare' (S)	CKel SPer WCAu	
- The Sun	see *P. suffruticosa* 'Taiyo'	
- Twilight	see *P. suffruticosa* 'Higurashi'	
- Wisteria at Kamada	see *P. suffruticosa* 'Kamada-fuji'	
- 'Wu Jin Yao Hui' (S)	CBcs MPhe WCAu	
- 'Wu Long Peng Sheng' (S)	CFwr CKel GBin MPhe WCAu	
- 'Xiao Tao Hong' (S)	CBcs	
- 'Xue Ta' (S)	CKel	
- 'Yachiyo-tsubaki' (S)	CKel WCAu	
§ - 'Yae-zakura' (S)	NBlu WCAu	

- 'Yakumo' (S)   SPer
- 'Yan Long Zi Zhu Pan' (S)   CKel
- 'Yin Hong Qiao Dui' (S)   CKel
§ - 'Ying Luo Bao Zhu' (S)   WViv
- 'Yomo-zakura' (S)   LRHS
- 'Yoshinogawa' (S)   CKel LRHS
- 'Yu Ban Bai' (S) **new**   IPPs
- 'Yu Lu Dian Cui' (S)   WViv
- 'Zha Sha Lei' **new**   GBin
- 'Zhao Fen' (S)   IPPs MPhe NPer
§ - 'Zhi Hong' (S)   CKel
- 'Zhu Sha Lei' (S)   CKel EBee IPPs MPhe
- 'Zi Er Qiao' (S)   CKel IPPs MPhe
- 'Zi Jin Pan' (S)   WViv
§ - 'Zi Lan Kui' (S)   CKel
- 'Sunshine'   see *P. peregrina* 'Otto Froebel'
  tenuifolia   CDes CLAP CSpe EBee GCal GIBF MDun MHom NCGa NMen NSla SPoG SSpi WCAu
- subsp. *carthalinica*   MPhe
§ - subsp. *lithophila*   MHom MPhe WWst
- 'Plena'   EBee MHom NBhm NLar WCMO
  Three-sided Jade   see *P. suffruticosa* 'San Bian Sai Yu'
  'Thunderbolt' (S) **new**   WCAu
  tomentosa   CMil MHom MPhe WWst
  'Vanilla Twist'   WAul
§ **veitchii**   CAby EPfP GBin GIBF GKev MTho NDlv NMen SSpi WCAu WHil
- from China   MPhe
- 'Alba'   LPhx
- var. **woodwardii**   CLyd CMdw CMil ECho ERos GBin GCrs GKev MTho NSla NWCA SOkd SSpi WCAu WCot WHoo
  'Vesuvian'   CKel WCAu
  'Walter Mains'   WCAu
  White Phoenix   see *P. suffruticosa* 'Feng Dan Bai'
  'Wine Angel' **new**   GBin
  wittmanniana   GBin MDun WCAu WCMO
§ 'Yao Huang' (S)   CBcs IPPs MPhe WCAu
  Yao's Yellow   see *P.* 'Yao Huang'
  'Yellow Crown'   GBin MBri WCAu
  'Yellow Dream'   WCAu WCot
  'Yellow Emperor'   WCot
  Yellow Flower of Summer   see *P.* 'Huang Hua Kui'

Paesia (Dennstaedtiaceae)
scaberula   CDes CLAP CWil NBir SSpi WAbe WCMO

Paliurus (Rhamnaceae)
spina-christi   CArn CBcs CPle EDsa IDee NLar SLon XPep

Pallenis (Asteraceae)
§ **maritima**   LIck XPep
- 'Golden Dollar'   NPri

Panax (Araliaceae)
ginseng   EBee GPoy
japonicus   WCru
- BWJ 7932   WCru
quinquefolius   EBee GPoy MSal
sambucifolius   CPLG

Pancratium (Amaryllidaceae)
canariense MS 924   CMon
  from Tenerife
foetidum MS&CL 372   CMon
  from Morocco **new**
maritimum   EBee ECho LRHS MLul WCot
- from Spain   CMon
zeylanicum   WMul

Pandanus (Pandanaceae)
baptistii **new**   EAmu
utilis   EAmu LPal

Pandorea (Bignoniaceae)
jasminoides   CHal CHll CPlN CRHN EBak ECot EPfP EShb LRHS MRav SOWG
- 'Alba'   CPlN EShb
§ - 'Charisma' (v)   CBcs CBow CHll CPlN EHol EMil EPfP EShb LSou SOWG SPoG WCot WSPU
- 'Lady Di'   CHEx ERea SOWG SYvo WCot
- 'Rosea'   MJnS
- 'Rosea Superba' ♀H1   CBcs CHEx CPlN CRHN ERea LRHS SBod WSPU
- 'Southern Sunset'   CPlN
- 'Variegata'   see *P. jasminoides* 'Charisma'
  lindleyana   see *Clytostoma calystegioides*
  pandorana   CPlN CRHN EBee ERea IDee SAdn SLim SYvo WCot
- 'Golden Showers'   CBcs CCCN CMdw CPlN CRHN EBee ERea EShb SLim SOWG SPoG
- 'Ruby Heart'   CPlN

Panicum (Poaceae)
bulbosum   EHoe EPPr EPla
clandestinum   CFwr EBee EHoe EPPr EPla EWes LBBr LEdu MCCP NPro WHil
miliaceum   EBrs EGle
- 'Violaceum'   CBig CSpe EBrs NLar
  'Squaw'   LRHS NOrc WTin
  virgatum   CBig CRWN CTri LRav NBre WMnd WPer XPep
- 'Blue Tower'   EBrs EGle EPPr LPhx SUsu
- 'Cloud Nine'   CBig CKno CPen CRez EBee EBrs EGle EPPr LHop LPhx MAvo NDov NLar SMHy SUsu WCMO WHal
- 'Dallas Blues'   CBig CKno CPen EBee EMan EPPr EWes MSte MWgw NOak SMHy WFar
- 'Hänse Herms'   CBig CKno CRez EGle EHoe EPPr LPhx MAvo SPla SPoG WFar WGHP
- 'Heavy Metal'   More than 30 suppliers
- 'Heiliger Hain'   CFwr MWea NCGa
I - 'Kupferhirse'   CBig EBee EPPr
- 'Northwind'   CBig CKno CPen EBee EPPr MAvo NDov SMHy WFar
- 'Prairie Sky'   CBig CKno CRez CWCL EBee EMan EPPr GBin LEdu LPhx MAvo MWgw NLar SMHy SUsu WPGP
- 'Red Cloud'   CBig CKno EGle
- 'Rehbraun'   CRez CSBt EBrs EGle EHoe EPPr EWsh LEdu LPhx NGdn NOak SAga SWal WCAu WFar WTin
- 'Rotstrahlbusch'   CBig CKno CPrp EBee EGle EHoe EMan EPPr MAvo MSte MWhi NBea NOrc SMad SPer SWal WCMO WCot WGHP WPGP
- 'Rubrum'   CKno CSBt EBrs EChP ECha ECot EHoe ELan ENot EPPr EPfP LRHS MAvo MRav MWgw SDix SHBN SPla STes WMoo WPrP
- 'Shenandoah'   CAbb CBig CBrm CKno CPen CRez CWCL EBee EGle EPPr EShb EWsh GBin IPot MAvo MBNS SMHy WBor WPrP
- 'Squaw'   CHar CKno CPrp CWCL EAEE EBee EBrs EGle EHoe EPPr EWsh IPot MSte MWgw NDov NPro SHBN SMad WCMO WCot WDyG WFar WGHP WHil WPnP WPrP WWeb WWye
- 'Strictum'   CBig EBee EHoe EHul EMan EMil EPPr EWes LEdu LPhx NLar SMHy
- 'Warrior'   CBrm CHar CKno EBee EBrs EGle EHoe EPPr EPfP EWsh LEdu LHop LRHS MWgw MWhi NCGa NDov NGdn NNor SAga SHBN SUsu WFar WLin WMoo WPGP WPnP

Papaver ✿ *(Papaveraceae)*

aculeatum	ECho LPhx
alboroseum	EAEE EHyt GIBF
'Alpha Centauri' (Super Poppy Series)	SWat WHoo
§ *alpinum* L.	CEnt CSpe EAEE ECho LRHS SIng SRms SWat WFar
- 'Famecheck Double Orange' (d) **new**	EFam
- 'Flore Pleno' (d)	NBir
amurense	CHVG GCal NLar SHGN SWat
anomalum album	CSpe
apokrinomenon	ELan
§ *atlanticum*	EBee EMag EMar EWin GBuc LDai MLan MWgw NBre NBro SPlb WPtf
- 'Flore Pleno' (d)	CSam CSpe MCCP NBre NBro WBrk WFar
'Aurora' (Super Poppy Series)	SWat
'Beyond Red' (Super Poppy Series)	SWat
bracteatum	see *P. orientale* var. *bracteatum*
'Bright Star' (Super Poppy Series) **new**	SWat
burseri	SRot
'Cathay' (Super Poppy Series)	SWat
'Celebration' (Super Poppy Series)	SWat
commutatum ♀H4	CSpe ELan SWat WEas
corona-sancti-stephani	SWat
'Eccentric Silk' (Super Poppy Series)	SWat
fauriei	GKev WRos
§ 'Fire Ball' (d)	EChP ECha ETow GCal IGor LHop MLLN NBre NBro NLar SHGN SWat WCot WMnd WRHF
* 'French Grey' **new**	EAEE
'Harlequin' (Super Poppy Series)	SWat
'Heartbeat' (Super Poppy Series)	SWat
heldreichii	see *P. spicatum*
x *hybridum* 'Flore Pleno' (d)	SWat
involucratum	EHyt
* *isaea* **new**	EHyt
'Jacinth' (Super Poppy Series)	SWat WHoo
lateritium	CPou SRms
- 'Fire Ball'	see *P.* 'Fire Ball'
- 'Nanum Flore Pleno'	see *P.* 'Fire Ball'
'Lauffeuer'	SWat
'Medallion' (Super Poppy Series)	SWat WHoo
§ *miyabeanum*	CSec CSpe EAEE ECho ELan GAbr LRHS NBlu WEas WFar WPer WTMC
- *album*	ECho
- *tatewakii*	see *P. miyabeanum*
nanum 'Flore Pleno'	see *P.* 'Fire Ball'
§ *nudicaule*	CSec ELan NEgg WPer
- Champagne Bubbles Group	EWll GWCH LRHS SWat WFar
- Constance Finnis Group	EMon GBuc LRHS
- var. *croceum* 'Flamenco'	LRHS
- Garden Gnome Group	see *P. nudicaule* Gartenzwerg Series
§ - Gartenzwerg Series	COlW CSpe ECho EMil GAbr MBri NBlu NEgg NJOw NLar SPlb SWal WFar WGor WRHF
- 'Kelmscott Giant'	MWgw
- 'Matador'	NEgg
- 'Meadow Pastels'	CSim
- 'Pacino'	EChP EMil EWin EWll GBuc LRHS NLar SPet SPoG SRms WFar WWeb
- 'Solar Fire Orange'	EAEE EWll
- 'Summer Breeze Orange'	NPri
- 'Summer Breeze Yellow'	NPri
- Wonderland Series	EHrv LBMP
- - 'Wonderland Orange'	NPri
- - 'Wonderland Pink Shades'	NPri
- - 'Wonderland White'	NPri
- - 'Wonderland Yellow'	NPri
oreophilum	CSec
orientale	CBcs EPfP IHMH LAst MBow NBlu NNor SRms SWal SWat WBor WBrE WFar WPer
- 'Abu Hassan'	SWat
- 'Aglaja' ♀H4	CElw EBee EChP GAbr GBBs GBin LAst LPhx MNFA MSph MSte NEgg NGdn NRnb NSti SAga SPoG SUsu SWat WCMO WCot WCra WHoo WLin WWhi
- 'Aladin'	NBre NRnb SWat
- 'Ali Baba'	NBre SWat
- 'Alison'	SWat
- 'Allegro'	CMea CSBt EAEE EBee ECtt GAbr GMaP IBal LAst LRHS MBNS MBri MHer MRav NCGa NVic SPer SPlb SWat SWvt WBVN WCAu
- 'Arc de Triomphe' **new**	EBee
- 'Arwide'	NBre SWat
- 'Aslahan'	ECha NBre SWat
- 'Atrosanguineum'	NBre SWat
- 'Avebury Crimson'	MWat SWat
- 'Baby Kiss' **new**	CFwr EBee
- 'Ballkleid'	ECha SWat
- 'Beauty Queen'	CCge EBee ECha ECot EGle GMac LRHS MNFA MRav MWgw NGdn SDix SWat
- 'Bergermeister Rot'	SWat
- 'Big Jim'	EBee NBre SPla SWat
- 'Black and White' ♀H4	CElw CFwr CSpe EBee EChP ECha EGle EHrv ELan EMar EPfP ERou GMaP LRHS MBri MRav SPer SPla SWat WCAu WCMO WHoo WSan
- 'Blackberry Queen'	EMan NBre SWat
- 'Blickfang'	NBre SWat
- 'Bloomsbury'	EChP
- 'Blue Moon'	EBee WHal
- 'Bolero' **new**	NCGa NLar WCot
- 'Bonfire'	CAby CSam EHrv MBri NCob NRnb
- 'Bonfire Red'	EBee LRHS SWat WCAu
§ - var. *bracteatum* ♀H4	EChP ECha NBir NBur SMHy SWat WMoo
- 'Brilliant'	EBee LRHS MWat NBre NBur NLar SMar SWat WFar WMoo
- 'Brooklyn'	CWCL EBee EMan ERou IPot MAvo NBre SWat
- 'Carmen' **new**	MNrw NCGa NLar WCot
* - 'Carneum'	CSim EChP LRHS NBre NLar SPoG WHil
- 'Carnival'	CMil EBee NBre NLar SWat
- 'Castagnette' **new**	NLar WCot
- 'Catherina'	EBee NBre NRnb SWat
- 'Cedar Hill'	EBee EMar EWes GMac LRHS MRav NBre NRnb SWat
- 'Cedric Morris' ♀H4	CHad CSpe EBee ECha EGle ELan EPPr ERou GCal GMac LAst LPhx MRav MSte MWat MWgw NSti SMrm SWat WCot WEas WHoo WMnd WOut WWhi
- 'Central Park' **new**	CFwr EBee

- 'Charming' — CAby CCge CPar EBee EChP EMar LPhx LRHS MBri MNFA MWat NGdn SWat
- 'Checkers' — LRav MLHP SEND
- 'China Boy' — NBre SWat WWeb
- 'Choir Boy' — CEnt EBee ECtt EGle NBur NLRH NLar NRnb SGar SMar SPoG STes WHrl WMoo
- 'Clochard' **new** — EBee SPoG
- 'Coral Reef' — CBow EBee EMar EPyc EWll GBBs MHer MWhi NBur NEgg NFla SAga SMeo SWat WCra WHer WMoo
- 'Corrina' — EBee NBre SWat
- 'Curlilocks' — CPar EChP ECtt ELan EPfP ERou IBal LAst LRHS MBow MRav MWat NRnb SAga SPer SPoG SRms SWat SWvt WCot WHoo WSan
- 'Derwisch' — NBre SWat
- * 'Diana' — SWat
- 'Domino' **new** — EBee MWea NCGa STes
- double orange (d) — IBal
- 'Double Pleasure' (d) — EBee IBal NBre NLar NMoo SPoG SWat WHrl
- 'Doubloon' (d) — ERou NBre NGdn NRnb SWat WFar
- 'Dwarf Allegro' — GBuc NFor WMnd
- 'Effendi' ♀H4 — CHea IPot LPhx NBre SMHy SUsu SWat
- 'Elam Pink' — EGle MLLN MTis NBre SWat WCot
- 'Erste Zuneigung' — ECha EGle LPhx SWat
- 'Eskimo Pie' — SWat
- 'Eyecatcher' — NCGa
- 'Fancy Feathers' **new** — EBee IPot MAvo MWea NBPC NBhm
- 'Fatima' — CDes CMil EBee NBre SWat WWeb
- 'Feuerriese' — SWat
- 'Feuerzwerg' — SWat
- 'Fiesta' — CAby NBre SMeo SWat
- 'Firefly' **new** — WCot
- 'Flamenco' — ECtt NBre SWat
- 'Flamingo' **new** — SWat
- 'Forncett Summer' — CHea EChP EMar ERou GMac LAst NBre NGdn NOrc SPer STes SWat WCAu WCot
- 'Garden Glory' — CPar EBee EChP ECtt GMac LAst LRHS LSRN MBri NBre NBro NOrc NRnb SMrm SWat WCAu WTMC
- 'Garden Gnome' — ENot EPfP SPet
- 'Glowing Embers' — CSpe ERou LRHS NBre SWat
- 'Glowing Rose' — MDKP NBre SWat
- 'Goliath Group' — CElw CMil ECha ELan GMac IBal LRHS MAvo MBri MRav NBro NVic SAga SDix SPer SRms SWat WEas WFar WMnd
- § - - 'Beauty of Livermere' — More than 30 suppliers
- 'Graue Witwe' — CAby CMil EBee EGle GBuc SMHy SWat WTin
- 'Halima' — NBre SWat
- 'Harlem' **new** — CSpe EBee EMar IPot MAvo NLar SWat WCAu WHrl
- 'Harlem Louvre' **new** — SMrm
- 'Harvest Moon' (d) — CAby EBee EChP ERou IBal LRHS MBow NEgg NPer SWat WHal WHil
- 'Heidi' — SWat
- 'Hewitt's Old Rose' — NBre WCot
- 'Hula Hula' — ECha NBre SWat
- 'Indian Chief' — CMHG EChP EPfP ERou GMac IPot LRHS MRav MSte NBPC NBro NGdn NMoo NPer SPoG WCAu WFar WHil WMnd WWhi
- 'Inferno' **new** — WCot
- 'Joanne' — NLar
- 'John III' ♀H4 — EBee LPhx MBri NBre SWat
- 'John Metcalf' — EBee EGle EMan EPPr LRHS MLLN NBre NSti SMrm SWat WCAu WCot

- 'Juliane' — CAby ECha EGle GMac LPhx MNFA MSte MWgw NSti SWat WCMO WCot WTin WWhi
- 'Karine' ♀H4 — More than 30 suppliers
- 'Khedive' (d) ♀H4 — SWat
- 'King George' — GBuc SWat
- 'King Kong' **new** — NCGa NLar
- 'Kleine Tänzerin' — CMil CSam EChP EMan EMar ERou GBri GMac LBmB LRHS MBri MLLN MWgw NBre NGdn NLar NPri NSti SPoG SWat WBor WCAu WCMO WCot WHil WWeb
- 'Kollebloem' — NBre SWat
- 'Lady Frederick Moore' — EBee EBrs GMac LRHS MBow MLLN NBre SWat
- 'Lady Roscoe' — NBre SWat
- 'Ladybird' — EBee ENot ERou LRHS MBri MRav MSte NBre
- 'Lambada' — SWat
- 'Lauren's Lilac' — CAby CMdw LPhx NBre SMeo SWat
- 'Leuchtfeuer' ♀H4 — CDes EBee ECha LPhx NBre SMHy SWat
- 'Lighthouse' ♀H4 — SWat
- 'Lilac Girl' — CElw CMil CSpe EBee EChP ECha ECtt EGle EWTr EWll GMaP LHop LPhx MRav MSte NLar NSti STes SWat WCot WHoo WHrl WWhi
- 'Louvre' **new** — EBee MAvo NLar SPoG
- 'Maiden's Blush' — NBre NGby NSti SWat
- 'Mandarin' **new** — EBee NBhm NMoo
- 'Manhattan' — CAby CSam EBee ECtt EMan ERou EWes GMac IPot LHop LSou MAvo MBri MLLN MNrw NCob NCot NLar SPer SPla SPoG SSvw STes SWat WCMO WCot WCra WHrl WWhi
- 'Marcus Perry' — EBee ENot EPfP ERou EWes GMaP LRHS MRav NEgg NPri NRnb SPoG SWat WCAu WFar
- 'Mary Finnan' — EBee NBre SWat
- 'Master Richard' — SWat
- 'May Queen' (d) — EChP EShb EWes IBlr LAst LRHS MRav NBre NBro NCGa NSti SWat WCot WHrl WPnn
- 'May Sadler' — COIW EBee ENot NBre NRnb SWat
- 'Midnight' — ERou NBre SWat
- 'Miss Piggy' **new** — CFwr EBee IPot
- 'Mrs H.G. Stobart' — SWat
- 'Mrs Marrow's Plum' — see *P. orientale* 'Patty's Plum'
- 'Mrs Perry' — More than 30 suppliers
- 'Nanum Flore Pleno' — see *P.* 'Fire Ball'
- 'Noema' — SWat
- 'Orange Glow' — NBre NCot NMoo NPri NRnb SWat WMoo
- 'Orangeade Maison' — NBre SWat
- 'Oriana' — EHol LRHS NBre NGdn SWat
- 'Oriental' — SWat
- 'Pale Face' — ERou SWat
- 'Papillion' — EBee NSti
- § 'Patty's Plum' — More than 30 suppliers
- 'Perry's White' — More than 30 suppliers
- 'Peter Pan' — CAby MLLN NBre SWat
- 'Petticoat' — EChP ECtt ELan LAst NBre SWat
- 'Picotée' — More than 30 suppliers
- 'Pink Lassie' — NBre SWat
- 'Pink Panda' — SWat
- 'Pink Ruffles'PBR — EBee EMan ERou MBri NCot SPoG SWat
- 'Pinnacle' — CAby CDes CSWP EBee ERou LRHS MBri NGdn NPri SWat WFar WSan
- 'Pizzicato' — CAby CEnt CMea CPar CWib CWoW EChP EHrv ERou EShb GBBs LRHS MBri MNHC NPer SGar SPet SWat WFar WMoo

- 'Pizzicato White' NBre NRnb
- 'Polka' SWat
- 'Prince of Orange' SWat WHil
- Princess Victoria Louise see *P.orientale* 'Prinzessin Victoria Louise'
- 'Prinz Eugen' CMil NBre NOrc SWat
§ - 'Prinzessin Victoria Louise' CSWP EBee EChP EPfP GAbr GBBs GMaP IBal LAst LRHS MDun MLLN NCGa NPri SSvw SWat WBVN WBrk WFar WPer
- 'Prospero' NBre
- 'Queen Alexandra' CSim EBee EHrv NLar
- 'Raspberry Queen' CDes CMea EBee EChP ECtt EGle ELan ERou GMaP GMac LAst LPhx LRHS MArl MRav MTis NCGa NPri NSti STes SWat WCot WCra WFar WHal WHoo WSan WTin
- 'Raspberry Ruffles' LPhx NBre SWat
- 'Rembrandt' CAby ECot EHrv ERou LRHS MDKP NBre NMoo NPri SWat WPer
- 'Rose Queen' NBre WCot
- 'Rosenpokal' EBee EChP LRHS NGdn NRnb SWat
- 'Roter Zwerg' ECha SWat
- 'Royal Chocolate Distinction' CElw CMil CSpe CWCL EBee EChP EPPr EPfP ERou EWTr GBri IPot MAvo MTis MWea NBPC NLar NSti SPoG SWat WHil
- 'Royal Wedding' CCge EAEE EBee EChP ERou EShb IBal LAst LRHS MDun MHer NGdn NLar NPri NRnb SMad SMrm SPer SPla SPoG SSvw SWat WBor WCot WMoo WWeb WWhi
* - 'Saffron' CAby CElw CHad CMil SWat
- 'Salmon Glow' (d) CBcs CRez EChP IBal LAst MHer NRnb SSvw SWat WFar WPer
- 'Salome' SWat
- scarlet MWgw NCot
- 'Scarlet King' EWll LRHS NBre NEgg NOrc SWat
- 'Showgirl' EBee MLLN NBre SWat
* - 'Silberosa' ECha SWat
- 'Sindbad' CAby ECtt GMac LPhx LRHS MAvo MRav NBre NLar NRnb SWat
- 'Snow Goose' CAby LPhx NBre SWat WHoo
- 'Spätzünder' NBre SWat
- 'Springtime' CSpe EChP EWes GMac LAst LRHS MRav NGdn NLar SWat WCAu WHoo WTMC WTin WWhi
- 'Staten Island' **new** EBee
- 'Stokesby Belle' MWgw NBre
- Stormtorch see *P.orientale* 'Sturmfackel'
§ - 'Sturmfackel' EBee ERou IBal NBre SWat
- 'Suleika' NBre SWat
- 'Sultana' ECha ERou GMac MWat SWat WCAu
- 'The Promise' NBre SWat
- 'Tiffany' CBow CMil EBee ERou GMac LBuc LSou MAvo MLLN NCGa NCot NLar SPer SPla SPoG SSvw STes SWat WCMO WCot WCra WWhi
- 'Trinity' **new** SWat
- 'Turkish Delight' More than 30 suppliers
- 'Tutu' ERou IBal SWat
- 'Türkenlouis' CHar CMHG COlW CWCL ECtt ENot EPfP ERou GMaP GMac IBal LAst LRHS SPoG STes SWat WCAu WFar WTin WWlt
- 'Victoria Dreyfuss' SWat
- 'Viola' SWat
- 'Walking Fire' MNrw
- 'Water Babies' SWat
- 'Watermelon' CMil COtt EChP ECtt ERou GBBs IPot LAst LRHS MAvo MBri MLLN MRav NBPC NGdn NPri NSti SMeo STes SWat WBor WCAu WFar WHoo WTMC WWhi
- 'White King' **new** NBre
- 'Wild Salmon' NBre
- 'Wisley Beacon' NBre SWat
- 'Wunderkind' EBee EChP ECtt EMan IBal LAst MNrw SWat WCAu
'Party Fun' CSpe NEgg WWeb
paucifoliatum CDes NBre
pilosum EBee EMan GBuc SRms SWat WTin
* *porphyrantha* **new** EHyt
radicatum subsp. *hyperboreum* CSec
rhaeticum GKev NBre
'Rhapsody in Red' (Super Poppy Series) **new** SWat
rhoeas CArn GPoy MBow WJek
- Angels' Choir Group (d) SWat
- Mother of Pearl Group CSpe SWat
- Shirley Group CHrt
rupifragum CHrt CMCo CSec EChP ECha ECtt GAbr MLLN NPol SGar SWal WCot WEas WFar WHrl WPer WPnn WRha WTMC
- 'Double Tangerine Gem' see *P.rupifragum* 'Flore Pleno'
§ - 'Flore Pleno' (d) CSWP CSpe EMar ENot LRHS LSou MBri NBre NChi WCFE WHen WMoo WWhi
- 'Tangerine Dream' IBal LSRN MCCP MDun NEgg
sendtneri CSec MHer WLin
'Serena' (Super Poppy Series) SWat
'Shasta' (Super Poppy Series) SWat WHoo
somniferum CArn GPoy MSal SWat
- 'Black Beauty' (d) CSpe SWat
- 'Black Paeony' SBch
- 'Flemish Antique' SWat
- (Laciniatum Group) 'Swansdown' (d) CSpe
- var. *paeoniiflorum* (d) SWat
- 'Pink Chiffon' SWat WEas
- 'White Cloud' (d) SWat
§ *spicatum* CMea ECGP ECha EGle EMan GAbr GCal GIBF LHop LPhx MSte NBir STes WCot WMoo
'Tequila Sunrise' (Super Poppy Series) SWat
'The Cardinal' NBre
thianschanicum **new** LPhx
triniifolium CSec CSpe MWea
'Viva' (Super Poppy Series) SWat
'Water Melon' WSan

Parabenzoin see *Lindera*

Parachampionella see *Strobilanthes*

Paradisea (*Asphodelaceae*)

liliastrum ♀H4 EBee EBrs ECho EMan EPPr ERos GEdr GIBF GKev IGor MTis SRms WBVN WHoo WSHC
- 'Major' ECho GSki LPhx
lusitanica CBrm CDes CMHG CSam CSpe EBee EChP ECho ERos GMac IBlr IFro MWgw SMHy WBVN WPGP WThu WTin WWeb

Parafestuca (*Gramineae*)

albida EPPr

Parahebe (*Scrophulariaceae*)

'Betty' GGar
x *bidwillii* MHer NDlv NWCA SRms SRot
- 'Kea' CFee ECou ECtt GEdr MDKP SRot WPer

canescens	ECou
§ *catarractae*	CHar CMHG CPLG CTri CWib
	ECho ECou EPfP GGar MBow
	MLHP MNrw MTis MWat NBro
	NLAp NPri SPoG SUsu WBrE WFar
	WHen WKif WMnd WPer WWhi
- from Chatham Island	EWes
- 'Baby Blue'	CAbP EPfP SPoG
- blue	CHar EPfP SPer
- 'County Park'	ECou
- 'Cuckoo'	ECou NHol
§ - 'Delight' ♀H3	CNic ECho ECou EWes GGar
	GMaP LHop LRHS MHer NEgg
	NHol NPer SDix SHFr SRot STre
	WEas WFar WHen
- subsp. *diffusa*	ECho ECou LRHS MHer NPer NVic
- - 'Annie'	ECou NHol
- - 'Pinkie'	ECou
- garden form	ECha LLWP SBla
- subsp. *martinii*	ECou
- 'Miss Willmott'	ECho NPri NVic SBch SPer SPlb
	WBVN WPer
- 'Porlock Purple'	see *P. catarractae* 'Delight'
- 'Rosea'	CEnt ECho LAst SSto WFar
- white	CPom ECho LHop MLHP NCh
	SUsu WBVN WEas WPer WWhi
decora	CPLG
densifolia	see *Chionohebe densifolia*
§ *formosa*	CPle ECou WHCG
- erect	ECou GGar
'Gillian'	ECho WPer
'Greencourt'	see *P. catarractae* 'Delight'
§ *hookeriana*	GGar ITim NBlu
§ - var. *olsenii*	ECou GGar
'Joy'	ECou EWes
'Julia'	GGar
'June'	GGar
'Lesley'	GGar
linifolia	CTri
- 'Blue Skies'	ECho
§ *lyallii*	EBee ECGP ECho ECou EDAr GMaP
	LAst MBar MHer MMuc MSwo
	MWat NChi NDlv NEgg NHol NPol
	NWCA SBla SPlb SRms WKif
- 'Baby Pink'	EPfP SPoG
- 'Clarence'	ECou EHol
- 'Glacier'	ECho ECou
- 'Julie-Anne' ♀H3	CAbP ECho ECou EPfP GCal GMaP
	LRHS MAsh SPoG
- 'Rosea'	CTri GGar WPer
- 'Summer Snow'	ECou
'Mervyn'	CNic CTri ECho ECtt EDAr MDKP
	NDlv NLRH WHen WPer
olsenii	see *P. hookeriana* var. *olsenii*
§ *perfoliata* ♀H3-4	More than 30 suppliers
- dark blue	GBuc GCal SMad
- 'Pringle'	CAbP EPfP LRHS SPoG
'Snowcap'	CDoC EPfP LRHS SPlb SPoG

Parajubaea (Arecaceae)

cocoides	LPJP LPal

Parakmeria see *Magnolia*

Paranomus (Proteaceae)

reflexus	EShb

Paraquilegia (Ranunculaceae)

adoxoides	see *Semiaquilegia adoxoides*
§ *anemonoides*	GCrs SBla WAbe WLin
grandiflora	see *P. anemonoides*

Paraserianthes (Mimosaceae)

distachya	see *P. lophantha*
§ *lophantha* ♀H1	CHEx CRHN EBak ERea IDee LRav
	SAPC SArc SOWG

Parasyringa see *Ligustrum*

x *Pardancanda* (Iridaceae)

norrisii	CFir EBee EChP EMan EWes GSki
	LIck LRHS MBNS
- 'Dazzler'	EShb MBNS

Pardanthopsis (Iridaceae)

dichotoma	EBee WHrl

Parietaria (Urticaceae)

§ *judaica*	GPoy MSal WHer WSFF

Paris ✿ (Trilliaceae)

Chen Yi 8 **new**	WCot
Chen Yi 14 **new**	WCot
bashanensis	NLAp WCru
chinensis	WCru
- B&SWJ 265 from Taiwan	WCru
cronquistii	CLAP WCot
delavayi	WCru
- var. *petiolata*	NLAp
fargesii	WCru
- var. *brevipetalata*	WCru
- var. *petiolata*	WCru
forrestii	WCru
incompleta	CAvo CLAP GCrs SBla SOkd SSpi
	WCot WCru
japonica	SBla SOkd WCru
lancifolia B&SWJ 3044	WCru
from Taiwan	
mairei	WCru
marmorata	NLAp WCru
§ *polyphylla*	CArn CBct CBro CFir CLAP EBee
	ECho EMar GEdr MNFA MNrw
	WAbe WCMO WCot WCru WFar
	WPnP WWst
- B&SWJ 2125	WCru
- F 5947	ITim
- Forrest 5945	GCal
- HWJCM 475	WCru
- var. *alba*	CFir
- var. *stenophylla*	CFir CLAP GEdr NLAp WCru
- var. *yunnanensis*	NLAp
quadrifolia	CArn CFir CLAP EBee EMar GPoy
	LPhx MDun NMen SSpi WCot
	WCru WHer WPGP WShi WTin
tetraphylla	WCru
thibetica	CFir CLAP WCru
- var. *apetala*	WCru
- var. *thibetica*	GEdr
verticillata	CLAP GEdr NLAp WCru

Parochetus (Papilionaceae)

§ *africanus* ♀H2	EWes GBuc
communis misapplied	see *P. africanus*
communis ambig.	CBcs CFee CPLG NPer WRha
	WWhi
- B&SWJ 7215 Golden	WCru
Triangle	
- HWJCM 526 from	WCru
Himalaya	
- from Himalaya	EBee
* - 'Blue Gem'	CWCL EWin
- dark	GCal

Paronychia (Illecebraceae)

argentea	CLyd NHol NLAp WPat WPer
§ *capitata*	CHal CLyd CNic CTri IFro SRms
	WPer
kapela	ETow SMad SPlb WPer
- 'Binsted Gold' (v)	CBow EMan LRHS WPer
§ - subsp. *serpyllifolia*	GBin NRya XPep
nivea	see *P. capitata*
serpyllifolia	see *P. kapela* subsp. *serpyllifolia*

Parrotia (Hamamelidaceae)

persica ♀H4 — More than 30 suppliers
- 'Burgundy' — CPMA NLar
- 'Felicie' **new** — EPfP NLar
- 'Jodrell Bank' — MBlu MBri NLar
§ - 'Lamplighter' (v) — CPMA
- 'Pendula' — CMCN CPMA EPfP
- 'Vanessa' — CBcs CDoC CMCN CPMA EWes
  MBlu MBri MGos NLar SBrw WDin
  WFar WMou WOrn WPat
- 'Variegata' — see *P. persica* 'Lamplighter'

Parrotiopsis (Hamamelidaceae)

jacquemontiana — CBcs CPMA MBlu NLar NPal SBrw

parsley see *Petroselinum crispum*

Parsonsia (Apocynaceae)

capsularis — CPLG ECou
heterophylla — ECou

Parthenium (Asteraceae)

integrifolium — CArn GPoy MSal

Parthenocissus (Vitaceae)

TH — CHEx
§ **henryana** ♀H4 — More than 30 suppliers
himalayana — CBcs
- CC 4519 — MGol
- 'Purpurea' — see *P. himalayana* var. *rubrifolia*
§ - var. **rubrifolia** — CPIN EBee EDsa ELan LRHS MAsh
  MRav MWgw NEgg NLar SLim
  SLon SPoG WCru WFar
inserta — NLar
laetevirens **new** — NLar
§ **quinquefolia** ♀H4 — More than 30 suppliers
- var. **engelmannii** — CBcs ELAst LBuc MGos NBlu
  SPer WCFE
- 'Guy's Garnet' — WCru
- var. **hirsuta** **new** — CPIN
semicordata — CPIN
- B&SWJ 6551 — WCru
striata — see *Cissus striata*
thomsonii — see *Cayratia thomsonii*
§ **tricuspidata** ♀H4 — CAgr CWib EBee ECtt EHoe EPfP
  LAst MGos NFor SMer SPer SReu
  WDin WFar WWeb
- 'Beverley Brook' — CMac EBee LBuc MBri SBod SBra
  SPer SPla SRms
- 'Crûg Compact' — CPIN WCru
- 'Fenway Park' — LBuc MBlu SPoG
- 'Green Spring' — CBcs CPIN EBee IArd MBri MGos
  NEgg
- 'Lowii' — CFRD CMac EBee ECot EPfP LBuc
  LRHS MBlu MGos MRav SBra SLon
  SPoG
- 'Minutifolia' — EBee SPer
- 'Purpurea' — MBlu
- 'Robusta' — CHEx CPIN LPan MBNS XPep
§ - 'Veitchii' — More than 30 suppliers

Pasithea (Anthericaceae)

caerulea — CMon WCot

Paspalum (Poaceae)

glaucifolium — CElw LEdu WDyG
quadrifarium — EMan EPPr WCot WPrP
- RCB/Arg RA-5-5 — EBee

Passerina (Thymelaeaceae)

montana — NWCA

Passiflora ✿ (Passifloraceae)

RCB/Arg R-7 — WCot
actinia — CPas CRHN SLim

adenopoda — CPas
'Adularia' — CPas
affinis **new** — CPas
alata (F) ♀H1 — CAbb CCCN CPas EBak MJnS
x **alatocaerulea** — see *P.* x *belotii*
allantophylla — CPas
'Allardii' — CCCN CPas CPIN EShb
amalocarpa — CPas
ambigua — CPas
§ 'Amethyst' ♀H1 — CCCN CPas CPIN CRHN CSPN
  EMil EShb LHop LRHS MJnS SBra
  SPet SPla SPoG WFar WPGP WPat
  WWeb
amethystina misapplied — see *P.* 'Amethyst'
§ - Mikan — CBcs CPas CPIN ECre EHol ERea
  LRHS
ampullacea (F) — CPas
'Anastasia' **new** — CPas
'Andy' — CCCN CPas
anfracta — CPas
'Angelo Blu' — CPas
antioquiensis misapplied — see *P.* x *exoniensis*
antioquiensis Karst ♀H2 — CHll
antioquiensis ambig. — CBcs CDoC CPas CPIN CRHN
  EHol ERea GQui LRHS MTis
  SOWG
antioquiensis ambig. x — CDoC CTrC
  mixta
apetala — CPas
arbelaezii — CPas
x **atropurpurea** — CPas
§ x **aurantia** — CPas CPIN
auriculata — CPas
banksii — see *P. aurantia*
'Barborea' — CPas
§ x **belotii** — CCCN CPas EHol EShb LRHS
- 'Impératrice Eugénie' — see *P.* x *belotii*
biflora Lamarck — CPas
'Blue Moon' — CPas
boendeni — CPas
bogatensis **new** — CPas
'Byron Beauty' — CPas
§ **caerulea** ♀H3 — More than 30 suppliers
- 'Clear Sky' — NBlu
- 'Constance Elliott' — More than 30 suppliers
- **rubra** — CPIN CSBt LRHS WFar
I x **caeruleoracemosa** — see *P.* x *violacea*
x **caponii** — ERea
capsularis — CPas CSec
cerasina — CPas
chinensis — see *P. caerulea*
cincinnata — CPas
cinnabarina — CPas CPIN
citrifolia — CCCN CPas
citrina — CPas SOWG
cobanensis **new** — CPas
coccinea (F) — CPas CTbh LRHS
colinvauxii — CPas
x **colvillii** — CHll CPas
conzattiana — CPas
'Coordination' **new** — CCCN
§ **coriacea** — CPas LRHS
costaricensis — CPas
crenata — CPas
cuneata — CPas
§ - 'Miguel Molinari' — CPas
cuprea — CPas
I 'Curiosa' — CPas
cuspidifolia — CPas
§ **cyanea** — CPas
'Debby' — CPas
x **decaisneana** (F) — CPas
dioscoreifolia — CPas
discophora — CPas
'Eden' — COtt EAmu LRHS MBri NLar SCoo

	edulis (F)	CAgr CCCN CPas IDee LRHS MJnS
	- 'Crackerjack' (F)	ERea
	- f. *flavicarpa* (F)	CPas
	eichleriana **new**	CPas
	elegans	CPas
	'Elizabeth' (F)	CPas
	'Empress Eugenie'	see *P.* x *belotii*
	'Excel'	CPas
§	x *exoniensis* ♀H1	CHll CPas CRHN ECre
	exura	CPas
	filipes	CPas
	'Fledermouse'	CPas
	'Flying V' **new**	CPas
	foetida	CPas SOWG
	- var. *galapagensis*	CPas
	- var. *hirsuta* (F)	CPas
	- var. *hirsutissima*	CPas
I	*gabrielliana* **new**	CPas
	garckei	CPas
	gibertii	CPas EShb
	gilbertiana	CPas WFar
	glandulosa	CPas
	gracilis	CPas
	gracillima	CPas
	gritensis	CPas
	guatemalensis	CPas
	hahnii	CPas
	helleri	CPas
	herbertiana (F)	CPas CPIN ITer
	holosericea	CPas
	incana	see *P. seemannii*
	incarnata (F)	CAgr CArn CPas EShb MSal SPlb
	'Incense' (F) ♀H1	CCCN CPas LRHS SLim SPlb WFar
	indecora	CPas
	'Inverleith' **new**	CPas
	jatunsachensis	CPas
	'Jeanette'	CPas
	'Jelly Joker'	CCCN CPas EShb
	jorullensis	CPas
	juliana	CPas
	kalbreyeri	CPas
	karwinskii	CPas
	'Kate Adie'	CPas
	kermesina **new**	CPas
	x *kewensis*	CPas
	'Lady Margaret'	CPas EShb
	lancearia	CPas
	lancetellesis	CPas
	laurifolia (F)	CPas SLim
§	*ligularis* (F)	CPas EShb LRHS
	'Lilac Lady'	see *P.* x *violacea* 'Tresederi'
	lobata	CPas
	loefgrenii **new**	CPas
	lourdesae	see *P. cuneata* 'Miguel Molinari'
	lowei	see *P. ligularis*
	lutea	CPas
	macrophylla	CPas
	maliformis (F)	CHll CPas
	manicata (F)	CPas EShb
	'Maria' **new**	CCCN
	matthewsii	CPas
	'Mavis Mastics'	see *P.* x *violacea* 'Tresederi'
	mayana	see *P. caerulea*
	mayarum	CPas
	membranacea (F)	CPas
	microstipula	CPas
	miersii	CPas
	misera	CPas
	mixta (F)	CPIN
*	- var. *pinanga*	CPas
	mollissima (F) ♀H1	CAgr CBcs CCCN CHll CPas CPIN
		CRHN CSec EBak EPfP ERea EShb
		IDee SOWG SPlb
	moluccana **new**	CPas
	mooreana	CPas
	morifolia	CPas EShb

	mucronata	CPas
	multiflora	CPas
	murucuja	CPas
	naviculata	CPas
	nephrodes	CPas
	'New Incense'	CPas EShb
	nigradenia **new**	CPas
	nitida (F)	CPas
	oblongata	CPas
	obtusifolia	see *P. coriacea*
	oerstedii	CPas
	- var. *choconiana*	CPas
	onychina	see *P. amethystina* Mikan
	organensis	CPas
	ornitheura	CPas
	palmeri	CPas
I	*pardifolia* **new**	CPas
	parritae **new**	CPas
	penduliflora	CPas
	perakensis **new**	CPas
	perfoliata	CPas
	phoenicea	CPas CPIN
	pilosicorona	CPas
	'Pink Jewel'	CPas
	pinnatistipula (F)	EUnu
	x *piresiae*	CCCN CPas
	pittieri	CPas
	platyloba	CPas
*	*pseudo-oerstedii*	CPas
	punctata	CPas
	'Pura Vida'	CPas
	'Purple Haze'	CCCN CPas CRHN EShb NScw
		WWeb
	quadrangularis (F) ♀H1	CCCN CHll CPas CPIN CWSG
		EBak ERea EShb LRHS MJnS
		WGwG WMul
	quinquangularis	CPas
	racemosa ♀H2	CPas CPIN ERea LAst LRHS MNHC
		SOWG
	reflexiflora	CPas
	resticulata	CPas
	retipetala	see *P. cyanea*
	rovirosae	CPas LRHS
	rubra	CCCN CPas SLim
*	*rufa*	CPas
	sagastegui	CPas
	'Saint Rule'	CPas
	sanguinolenta	CPas CPIN LRHS
	'Sapphire'	CPas
	'Sarah Aimee'	CPas
§	*seemannii*	CPas
	serratifolia	CPas
	sexflora	CPas LRHS
	sexocellata	see *P. coriacea*
	'Simply Red'	CPas
	'Smythiana'	CPas EShb
	sprucei	CPas
	standleyi	CPas CPIN
	'Star of Bristol' ♀H2	CPas SBra SLim
	'Star of Clevedon'	CPas
	'Star of Kingston'	CPas
	'Star of Surbiton' **new**	CPas
	stipulata	CPas
	suberosa	CPas
	subpeltata	CPas
	subpurpurea	CPas
	subrotunda **new**	CPas
	'Sunburst'	CHEx CPas CPIN
	talamancensis	CPas
	tenuifila	CPas
§	*tetrandra*	CPLG CPas ECou
	x *tresederi*	see *P.* x *violacea* 'Tresederi'
	trialata	CPas
	tricuspis	CPas
	tridactylites	CPas
	trifasciata	CCCN CPas EShb

triloba new	CPas
tripartita	CPas
trisecta	CPas
tuberosa	CPas
tulae	CPas
umbilicata	CPas WCru
urbaniana	CPas
variolata	CPas
vespertilio	CPas
§ x *violacea* ♀H1	CBrm CDul CPas CRHN CTbh ERea EShb MJnS WFar
- 'Eynsford Gem'	CCCN CPas
- 'Lilac Lady'	see *P.* x *violacea* 'Tresederi'
§ - 'Tresederi'	CPas ELan MAsh WFar
- 'Victoria'	CPas CSBt EBee SLim
viridiflora	CPas
vitifolia (F)	CPas CPlN LRHS SOWG
- 'Scarlet Flame' (F)	CPas
xiikzodz	CPas
yucatanensis	CPas
zamorana	CPas

passion fruit see *Passiflora*

passion fruit, banana see *Passiflora mollissima*

Patersonia (Iridaceae)
occidentalis	SPlb

Patrinia (Valerianaceae)
gibbosa	CSec EMan LRHS MGol WCru WFar WMoo WPnP WWye
- B&SWJ 874	WCru
intermedia	WLin
scabiosifolia	More than 30 suppliers
- 'Nagoya'	MNrw
triloba	ECho EDAr GBuc GCrs GEdr LRHS LSou MGol MRav SMac SUsu WBVN WFar WMoo WPnP
* - 'Minor'	ECho
- var. *palmata*	EBee WDyG WFar WMoo
- var. *triloba*	ETow GCal
villosa	EBee EDAr LPhx NDov NGdn NLar SSvw

Paulownia (Scrophulariaceae)
catalpifolia	CBcs EPla NLar WPGP
elongata	CBcs NLar WPGP
fargesii Osborn	see *P. tomentosa* 'Lilacina'
fargesii Franch.	SLPl
fortunei	CHEx MBlu NPal SPlb WBVN WNor
kawakamii	WPGP
- B&SWJ 6784	WCru
taiwaniana B&SWJ 7134	WCru
tomentosa ♀H3	More than 30 suppliers
- 'Coreana'	CHll WCru
§ - 'Lilacina'	CBcs

Pavonia (Malvaceae)
hastata	EShb
missionum	EShb
multiflora Jussieu ♀H1	ERea

paw paw (false banana) see *Asimina triloba*

Paxistima (Celastraceae)
canbyi	EHyt NLar

peach see *Prunus persica*

pear see *Pyrus communis*

pear, Asian see *Pyrus pyrifolia*

pecan see *Carya illinoinensis*

Pedicularis (Scrophulariaceae)
axillaris	CSec EBee
- SDR 1745	GKev
longiflora var. *tubiformis*	CSec EBee GKev
rex new	EBee
rhinanthoides subsp. *tibetica*	GKev
superba new	EBee GKev

Peganum (Zygophyllaceae)
harmala	CArn EMan MGol MHer MSal

Pelargonium ✿ (Geraniaceae)
'A Happy Thought'	see *P.* 'Happy Thought'
'A.M. Mayne' (Z/d)	WFib
'Abba' (Z/d)	WFib
'Abel Carrière' (I/d)	SKen SPet
abrotanifolium (Sc)	CRHN EWoo MBPg MHer SSea WFib XPep
'Abundance' (Sc)	LDea MBPg
acerifolium misapplied	see *P. vitifolium*
acetosum	MSte SHFr
* - 'Variegatum' (v)	MSte SSea
'Acushla by Brian' (Sc)	MBPg MWhe
'Ada Green' (R)	LDea
'Ada Sutterby' (Dw/d)	SKen
'Adagio' (Dw)	ESul
'Adam's Quilt' (Z/C)	SKen WEas
'Adele' (Min/d)	ESul
'Ade's Elf' (Z/St)	NFir SSea
'Aerosol' (Min)	ESul
'Ailsa' (Min/d)	ESul SKen
'Ainsdale Beauty' (Z)	SSea
'Ainsdale Claret' (Z)	SSea
'Ainsdale Eyeful' (Z)	SSea WFib
'Ainsdale Glasnost' (Z) new	SSea
'Ainsdale Happiness' (Z/d) new	SSea
'Ainsdale Sixty' (Z) new	SSea
'Akela' (Min)	ESul
'Alan West' (Z/St)	SSea
'Alberta' (Z)	SKen
album	EWoo
alchemilloides	CRHN NCiC
'Alcyone' (Dw/d)	ESul SKen WFib
'Alde' (Min)	ESul MWhe NFir SKen SSea WFib
'Aldenham' (Z)	WFib
'Aldham' (Min)	ESul WFib
'Aldwyck' (R)	ESul LDea WFib
'Alex' (Z)	SKen
'Alex Kitson' (Z)	WFib
'Alex Mary' (R)	ESul SSea
'Algenon' (Min/d)	ESul WFib
I 'Alice' (Min)	WFib
'Alice Greenfield' (Z)	NFir SSea
'Alison' (Dw)	ESul
'Alison Wheeler' (Min/d)	MWhe
'All My Love' (R)	LDea
'Alma' (Dw/C)	ESul
'Almond' (Sc)	MBPg
'Almost Heaven' (Dw/Z/v)	MWhe
'Alpine Glow' (Z/d)	MWhe
'Altair' (Min/d)	ESul
I 'Amalfi' (R)	EWoo
'Amari' (R)	WFib
'Amazon' (R) new	ESul
'Ambrose' (Min/d)	ESul WFib
Amelit = 'Pacameli' (I/d) new	LAst LSou WGor
'American Prince of Orange' (Sc)	MBPg
'Amethyst' (R)	ESul LDea SCoo SPet WFib

§ Amethyst = 'Fisdel'PBR   ECtt LDea LVER MWhe NPri SKen
   (I/d) ♀H1+3
'Amour' (R) **new**   ESul
I 'Amy' (Dw)   WFib
'Andersonii' (Sc)   MBPg MHer
'Andrew Salvidge' (R)   LDea
'Androcles' (A)   LDea
'Angel Josie' (A)   LAst
'Angela' (R)   ESul LDea
'Angela Read' (Dw)   ESul
'Angela Thorogood' (R)   ESul
   new
'Angela Woodberry' (Z)   WFib
Angeleyes Bicolour =   LAst
   'Pacbicolour' **new**
Angeleyes Burgundy =   LAst LSou SSea
   'Pacburg'
'Angeleyes Daphne' **new**   LAst
'Angeleyes Josie' **new**   LAst
Angeleyes Light =   LSou
   'Paceyes'
'Angeleyes Light Pink' **new** LAst
Angeleyes Randy (A)   LAst LSou SSea
Angeleyes Series   LAst MWhe SSea
- Angeleyes Viola =   LAst
   'Pacviola' **new**
'Angelique' (Dw/d)   ESul LVER NFir WFib
'Anglia' (Dw)   ESul
'Ann Field' (Dw/d)   ESul
'Ann Hoystead' (R) ♀H1+3   ESul NFir WFib
'Ann Redington' (R)   ESul
'Anna' (Dw)   ESul
'Anna Scheen' (Min)   ESul
'Anne' (I/d)   WFib
'Annsbrook Aquarius' (St)   ESul NFir
'Annsbrook Beauty' (A/C)   ESul MBPg NFir WFib
'Annsbrook Capricorn'   ESul
   (St/d)
'Annsbrook Fruit Sundae'   LDea
   (A)
'Annsbrook Jupitor' (Z/St)   ESul NFir
'Annsbrook Mars' (St/C)   ESul
'Annsbrook Peaches' (Min) ESul
'Annsbrook Pluto' (Z/St)   ESul
'Annsbrook Rowan' (Min)   ESul
'Annsbrook Squirrel' (Min)   ESul
'Annsbrook Venus' (Z/St)   ESul
'Anthony Ayton' (R) **new**   ESul
Anthony = 'Pacan' (Z/d)   LAst WGor
   new
(Antik Series) Antik Orange   LVER
   = 'Tikorg'PBR (Z)
   ♀H1+3 **new**
- Antik Pink = 'Tikpink'PBR   LVER
   (Z) **new**
- Antik Salmon =   LVER
   'Tiksal'PBR (Z) **new**
- Antik Violet =   LVER
   'Tikvio'PBR (Z) **new**
'Antoine Crozy' (ZxI/d)   WFib
'Antoinette' (Min)   ESul
'Antonnia Scammell' (St/d) ESul
   new
'Apache' (Z/d) ♀H1+3   CHal WFib
'Aphrodite' (Z)   ECtt
'Apollo' (R)   ESul
'Apple Betty' (Sc)   EWoo LDea MBPg MHer WFib
'Apple Blossom Rosebud'   CStu ECtt EShb ESul LAst LRHS
   (Z/d) ♀H1+3   LVER MBri MWhe SKen SSea WBrk
                                    WFib WHPP
'Appledram' (R)   LDea
'Apri Parmer' (Min)   ESul
'Apricot' (Z/St)   ESul LAst SKen WGor
'Apricot Queen' (I/d)   LDea
'Apricot Star'   MSte MWhe WHPP
'April Hamilton' (I)   EWoo LDea WFib

'April Showers' (A)   LDea WFib
'Aquarell' (R)   ESul
Arcona 2000 =   LAst LSou
   'Klecona'PBR
'Arctic Frost'   WFib
§ 'Arctic Star' (Z/St)   ESul LRHS LVER NFir SKen SSea
                                    WBrk WFib WHPP
'Ardens'   CSpe EBee ESul EWoo LHop MSte
                                    NCiC NCob NFir NSti SMrm SSea
                                    SUsu SWvt WCot WEas WFib
'Ardwick Cinnamon' (Sc)   ESul EWoo LDea MBPg NFir WFib
'Aries' (Min)   MWhe
'Arizona' (Min/d)   SKen
'Arnside Fringed Aztec' (R) LDea WFib
'Aroma' (Sc)   EWoo LIck MBPg
'Arron Dixon' (A)   NFir
'Arthington Slam' (R)   LDea
'Arthur Biggin' (Z)   MWhe SKen
'Ashby' (U/Sc)   EWoo LVER MBPg NFir SSea
'Ashfield Jubilee' (Z/C)   NFir SKen
'Ashfield Monarch' (Z/d)   MWhe NFir SSea
   ♀H1+3
'Ashfield Serenade' (Z)   SKen SSea WFib
   ♀H1+3
'Ashley Stephenson' (R)   WFib
'Askham Fringed Aztec' (R) ESul LDea SSea WFib
   ♀H1+3
'Askham Slam' (R)   LDea
asperum Ehr. ex Willd.   see *P.* 'Graveolens'
'Asperum'   MBPg
'Astrakan' (Z/d)   SSea
'Athabasca' (Min)   ESul
§ 'Atomic Snowflake' (Sc/v)   CArn CHal ESul GBar LDea MBPg
                                    MHer MSte MWhe SDnm SIde
                                    SKen SPet SSea WFib
'Atrium' (U)   EWoo WFib
'Attar of Roses' (Sc) ♀H1+3   CArn CHal CRHN ESul GBar LAst
                                    LDea LVER MBPg MHer MSte
                                    MWhe NFir NHHG SDnm SIde
                                    SKen SSea WBrk WFib WGwG
                                    WHPP
'Attraction' (Z/Ca/d)   SSea
'Aubusson' (R)   ESul
'Audrey Clifton' (I/d)   SKen
'Auntie Billie' (A)   LDea
'Aurelia' (A) **new**   LDea
auritum subsp. *auritum* NFir
'Aurora' (Z/d)   MWhe SKen SSea
'Aurore' (U)   see *P.* 'Unique Aurore'
australe   CMon CRHN EWoo SBch WFib
'Australian Bute' (R)   ESul LSou LVER
'Australian Mystery'   CSpe ESul MSte NFir SAga WFib
   (R/Dec)   WHPP
'Autumn' (Z/d)   MWhe
'Autumn Colours' (Min)   ESul
'Autumn Haze' (R)   ESul
'Avril'   ESul
'Aztec' (R) ♀H1+3   ESul LDea LVER MSte NFir WFib
'Baby Bird's Egg' (Min)   ESul WFib
'Baby Brocade' (Min/d)   ESul WFib
'Baby Face' (R)   EWoo
'Baby Harry' (Dw/v)   WFib
'Baby Helen' (Min)   ESul
'Baby James' (Min)   ESul
'Baby Snooks' (A)   ESul LDea MWhe
'Babylon' (R)   ESul EWoo NFir SSea
'Badley' (Dw)   ESul
Balcon Imperial   see *P.* 'Roi des Balcons Impérial'
'Balcon Lilas'   see *P.* 'Roi des Balcons Lilas'
'Balcon Rose'   see *P.* 'Hederinum'
'Balcon Rouge'   see *P.* 'Roi des Balcons Impérial'
'Balcon Royale'   see *P.* 'Roi des Balcons Impérial'
I 'Ballerina' (Min)   WFib
'Ballerina' (Z/d)   MWhe
'Ballerina' (R)   see *P.* 'Carisbrooke'
'Bandit' (Min)   ESul

'Banstead Village' (Z)	LVER
'Bantam' (Min/d)	ESul WFib
§ 'Barbe Bleu' (I/d)	ECtt EWoo LDea LVER MWhe NFir SKen SSea WFib
'Barcelona' (R) **new**	ESul
'Barham' (Min/d)	ESul
'Barking' (Min)	ESul NFir
barklyi	CMon
'Barnston Dale' (Dw/d)	ESul NFir
'Barock '96'	NPri
'Bath Beauty' (Dw)	CSpe SKen WEas
'Baylham' (Min)	ESul
Beach = 'Fisbea' (I/d)	NPri
'Beacon Hill' (Min)	ESul
'Beatrice Cottington' (I/d)	SKen WFib
'Beatrix' (Z/d)	LVER
'Beau Geste' (R)	ESul
'Beauty of Diane' (I/d)	LDea
'Beauty of Eastbourne' misapplied	see *P.* 'Lachskönigin'
'Beauty of El Segundo') (Z/d)	SKen
'Beckwith's Pink' (Z)	SKen
'Beidermeier' (R) **new**	ESul
'Belinda Adams' (Min/d) ♀H1+3	MWhe NFir
§ Belladonna = 'Fisopa' (I/d)	ECtt SCoo
'Belvedere' (R)	ESul
'Bembridge' (Z/St/d)	SSea WFib
'Ben Franklin' (Z/d/v) ♀H1+3	ESul MWhe NFir SPet SSea
'Ben Matt' (R)	WFib
'Ben Nevis' (Dw/d)	ESul LVER
'Ben Picton' (Z/d)	WFib
'Bentley' (Dw)	ESul
'Berkswell Carnival' (A) **new**	LDea
'Berkswell Dainty' (A)	LDea
'Berkswell Debonair' (A) **new**	LDea
'Berkswell Gaiety' (A) **new**	LDea
'Berkswell Lace' (A)	LDea
'Berkswell Pixie' (A) **new**	LDea
'Berliner Balkon' (I)	SKen
Bernardo = 'Guiber'[PBR] (I/d)	LAst NBlu WGor WHPP
'Bernice Ladroot'	LDea
'Beromünster' (Dec)	ESul EWoo LDea MSte NFir SAga SSea WFib
'Bert Pearce' (R)	ESul LDea WFib
'Beryl Gibbons' (Z/d)	MWhe
'Beryl Read' (Dw)	ESul
'Beryl Reid' (R)	ESul LDea WFib
'Berylette' (Min/d)	ESul SKen
'Bess' (Z/d)	ESul
'Bette Shellard' (Z/d/v)	MWhe NFir
'Betty Merry' (R)	LDea
'Betty Read' (Dw)	ESul
'Betty West' (Min/d)	ESul
betulinum	EWoo SSea WFib
'Betwixt' (Z/v)	SKen SSea
'Bianca' (Min/d)	ESul
'Bi-coloured Startel' (Z/St/d)	MWhe
'Big Apple' (Sc)	MBPg
'Bildeston' (Dw/C)	ESul NFir WFib
'Bill West' (I)	SSea WFib
'Billie Read' (Dw/d)	ESul
'Bingo' (Min)	ESul
'Bird Dancer' (Dw/St) ♀H1+3	CHal ESul LVER MSte MWhe NFir SHFr SKen SSea SWal WBrk
'Birdbush Andy Pandy' (Sc) **new**	MBPg
'Birdbush Blush' (Sc)	MBPg
'Birdbush Bold and Beautiful' (Sc)	MBPg

'Birdbush Bramley' (Sc)	MBPg
'Birdbush Chloe' (St)	MBPg
'Birdbush Eleanor' (Z)	MBPg
'Birdbush Lemon and Lime' (Sc)	MBPg
'Birdbush Lemonside' (Sc) **new**	MBPg
'Birdbush Matty'	MBPg
'Birdbush Nutty' (Sc)	MBPg
'Birdbush Pinky and Perky' (U) **new**	MBPg
'Birdbush Sweetness' (Sc)	MBPg
'Birdbush Too Too O' (Sc) **new**	MBPg
'Birdbush Velvet' (Sc)	MBPg
'Birthday Girl' (R)	WFib
'Bitter Lemon' (Sc)	ESul MBPg
'Black Butterfly'	see *P.* 'Brown's Butterfly'
'Black Knight' (R)	CSpe EShb EWoo LVER MSte WHPP
'Black Knight' Lea (Dw/d/c)	ESul MSte NFir
'Black Magic' (R)	NPri
'Black Night' (A)	ESul MBPg
'Black Pearl' (Z/d)	LVER
'Black Prince' (R)	EWoo NFir WFib
'Black Top' (R) **new**	ESul
'Black Velvet' (R)	ESul LDea
'Black Vesuvius'	see *P.* 'Red Black Vesuvius'
'Blackdown Delight' (Dw)	NFir
'Blackdown Sensation' (Dw) **new**	NFir
'Blakesdorf' (Dw)	ESul MWhe
Blanca = 'Penwei'[PBR] (Dark Line Series) (Z/d)	LAst LSou LVER NBlu
Blanche Roche = 'Guitoblanc' (I/d)	EWoo LAst LSou NBlu SCoo
§ 'Blandfordianum' (Sc)	EWoo LDea MHer MSte
'Blandfordianum Roseum' (Sc)	LDea
'Blaze Away'	SSea
'Blazonry' (Z/v)	MWhe SKen SSea WFib
'Blendworth' (R)	LDea
'Blooming Gem' (Min/I/d)	LDea
'Blue Beard'	see *P.* 'Barbe Bleu'
'Blue Orchid' (R)	ESul
'Blue Peter' (I/d)	SKen
Blue Sybil = 'Pacblusy'[PBR] (I/d)	LAst LSou LVER
'Blue Wine'	LAst
Blue Wonder (Z)	LAst LSou WGor
'Bluebeard'	see *P.* 'Barbe Bleu'
Blue-Blizzard = 'Fisrain'[PBR] (I)	SCoo
'Blush Petit Pierre' (Min)	ESul
'Blushing Bride' (I/d)	LDea SKen
'Blushing Emma' (Dw/d)	ESul
'Bob Hall' (St)	ESul
'Bobberstone' (Z/St)	LVER WFib
'Bold Appleblossom' (Z) **new**	SSea
'Bold Candy' (R)	WHPP
'Bold Carmine' (Z/d)	NFir
'Bold Dawn' (Z)	NFir
'Bold Flame' (Z/d)	SSea WFib
'Bold Sunrise' (Z/d)	LVER NFir
'Bold Sunset' (Z/d)	LVER NFir WFib
'Bold White' (Z)	NFir
'Bolero' (U) ♀H1+3	EWoo LVER MSte NFir SSea WFib WHPP
'Bon Bon' (Min/St)	WFib
'Bonito' (I/d)	LVER
'Bonnie Austin' (St) **new**	ESul
'Bonny' (Min/St) **new**	ESul
'Bosham' (R)	ESul LDea WFib
'Both's Snowflake' (Sc/v)	EWoo MBPg

	bowkeri	WFib
	'Brackenwood' (Dw/d)	ESul LVER NFir
	♀H1+3	
	'Bramford' (Dw)	ESul
	'Braque' (R)	LDea
	Bravo = 'Fisbravo'ᴾᴮᴿ	LAst MWhe WFib
	(Z/d)	
	'Break o' Day' (R)	LDea WEas
	'Bredon' (R) ♀H1+3	ESul
	'Brenda' (Min/d)	ESul WFib
	'Brenda Hyatt' (Dw/d)	ESul WFib
	'Brenda Kitson' (Z/d)	LVER MWhe
	'Brettenham' (Min)	ESul
	'Briarlyn Beauty' (A)	LDea MBPg MWhe NFir SSea
		WHPP
	'Briarlyn Moonglow' (A)	ESul EWoo LDea SSea
	'Bridesmaid' (Dw/d)	ESul NFir SKen WFib
	'Bridgwater' (R) **new**	ESul
	'Bright Eyes' (Dw)	WFib
	'Brightstone' (Z/d)	WFib
	'Brightwell' (Min/d)	ESul
	'Brilliant' (Dec)	MBPg MHer WFib
	'Brilliantine' (Sc)	ESul EWoo MBPg MHer WFib
	'Bristol' (Z/v)	SKen SSea
	'Britannia' (R)	LDea
	'Brixworth Boquet'	MWhe
	(Min/C/d)	
	'Brixworth Charmer' (Z/v)	MWhe
	'Brixworth Melody' (Z/v)	MWhe
	'Brixworth Pearl' (Z)	MWhe WFib
	'Brixworth Rhapsody'	MWhe
	(Z/v)	
	'Brixworth Starlight' (I/v)	MWhe
	'Brockbury Scarlet' (Ca)	WFib
	'Bronze Corinne' (Z/C/d)	SKen SPet
	'Bronze Queen' (Z/C)	MWhe
	'Bronze Velvet' (R)	LDea
	'Brook's Purple'	see *P.* 'Royal Purple'
	'Brookside Betty'	ESul
	(Dw/C/d)	
	'Brookside Bolero' (Z)	ESul
	'Brookside Candy' (Dw/d)	ESul
	'Brookside Champagne'	ESul
	(Min/d)	
	'Brookside Fiesta' (Min/d)	ESul
	'Brookside Flamenco'	ESul MWhe WFib
	(Dw/d)	
	'Brookside Primrose'	ESul MWhe NFir WFib
	(Min/C/d)	
	'Brookside Rosita' (Min)	ESul
	'Brookside Serenade' (Dw)	ESul WFib
	'Brookside Spitfire' (Dw/d)	ESul
§	'Brown's Butterfly' (R)	ECtt EShb ESul LDea NFir SSea
		WFib
§	'Bruni' (Z/d)	CHal MWhe
	'Brunswick' (Sc)	ESul EWoo LDea MBPg MHer MSte
		SSea WFib
	'Bucklesham' (Dw)	ESul
	'Bullfinch' (R) **new**	ESul
	'Bumblebee' (Dw)	ESul
	'Burgenlandmädel' (Z/d)	LVER SKen
	'Burgundy' (R)	WHPP
	'Burstall' (Min/d)	ESul
	'Bushfire' (R) ♀H1+3	ESul EWoo LDea NFir WFib
	'Butley' (Min)	ESul
	'Butterfly' (Min/v)	ECtt NPri
§	Butterfly = 'Fisam'ᴾᴮᴿ (I)	SCoo
	'Button 'n' Bows' (I/d)	WFib
	'Cal'	see *P.* 'Salmon Irene'
	'Caledonia' (Z)	SKen
	'California Brilliant' (U)	MBPg
	'Cameo' (Dw/d)	MWhe
	'Camisole' (Dw/d)	LVER
	'Camphor Rose' (Sc)	ESul EWoo LDea MBPg MHer NFir
		SSea
	'Can-can' (I/d)	WFib

	'Candy' (Min/d)	ESul
	'Candy Kisses' (D)	ESul
	canescens	see *P.* 'Blandfordianum'
	'Cape Beauty' **new**	EWoo
	'Capel' (Dw/d)	ESul
	capitatum	EWoo MBPg MHer WFib
	'Capri' (Sc)	MBPg WFib
	'Caprice' (R)	EWoo
	'Capricorn' (Min/d)	ESul
	'Captain Starlight' (A)	CRHN ESul EWoo LDea LVER
		MBPg MHer NFir SSea WFib WHPP
	'Caravan' (A)	LDea
	'Cardinal'	see *P.* 'Kardinal'
	'Cardington' (St/Dw)	ESul
	'Carefree' (U)	EWoo MSte NFir WFib
	'Cariboo Gold' (Min/C)	ESul
	♀H1+3	
§	'Carisbrooke' (R) ♀H1+3	ESul LDea SKen SSea WEas WFib
	'Carl Gaffney'	LDea
	'Carmel' (Z)	WFib
	'Carnival' (R)	see *P.* 'Marie Vogel'
	carnosum	CMon
	'Carol' (R)	ESul
	'Carol Gibbons' (Z/d)	LVER MWhe NFir WFib
	'Carol Helyar' (Z/d)	WFib
	'Caroline' (Dec) **new**	ESul
	'Caroline Plumridge' (Dw)	ESul
	'Caroline Schmidt' (Z/d/v)	CHal LAst LRHS LVER MSte MWhe
		NFir SKen SPet SSea WBrk WFib
	'Carolyn' (Dw)	ESul
	'Carolyn Hardy' (Z/d)	WFib
	Cascade Lilac	see *P.* 'Roi des Balcons Lilas'
	Cascade Pink	see *P.* 'Hederinum'
	Cascade Red	see *P.* 'Red Cascade'
	'Catford Belle' (A) ♀H1+3	CHal CSpe ESul LDea MWhe SSea
		WFib WHPP
	'Cathay' (Z/St)	ESul MWhe NFir SSea
	'Catherine Wheels' (Z/St)	LVER
	'Cathy' (R)	NFir
	caucalifolium subsp.	WFib
	convolvulifolium	
	'Cayucas' (I/d)	SKen
	'Celebration' (Z/d)	ESul
	'Cézanne' (R)	ESul GGar LDea LVER WFib
	'Chantilly Claret' (R)	LDea
	'Chantilly Lace' (R)	ESul LDea
	'Charity' (Sc) ♀H1+3	CHal ESul EWoo LDea LIck LVER
		MBPg MHer MSte MWhe NFir SSea
		WBrk WFib WHPP
	'Charlie Boy' (R)	LDea
	'Charlotte Amy' (R)	LDea
	'Charlotte Bidwell' (Min)	ESul
	'Charlotte Bronte' (Dw/v)	WFib
	'Charm' (Min)	ESul
	'Charmay Adonis' **new**	EWoo
	'Charmay Alf' (A)	LDea
	'Charmay Aria' (A)	LDea
	'Charmay Bagatelle' (A)	LDea
	'Charmay Electra' (A) **new**	LDea
	'Charmay Marjorie' (A)	LDea
	'Charmay Snowflake'	ESul MBPg
	(Sc/v)	
	'Chattisham' (Dw/C)	ESul NFir
	'Chelmondiston' (Min/d)	ESul MWhe
	'Chelsea Diane' (Min)	LVER
§	'Chelsea Gem' (Z/d/v)	LRHS LVER NFir SKen SSea WFib
	♀H1+3	
	'Chelsea Morning' (Z/d)	WFib
	'Chelsea Star' (Z/d/v) **new**	LVER
	'Chelsworth' (Min/d)	ESul
	'Chelvey' (R)	LDea
	'Cherie' (R)	ESul LDea
	'Cherie Bidwell' (Dw/d/v)	ESul
	'Cherie Maid' (Z/v)	SSea
	'Cherry' (Min)	WFib
	'Cherry Baby' (Dec)	NFir

'Cherry Cocktail' (Z/d/v)	MWhe NFir
'Cherry Hazel Ruffled' (R)	ESul LDea
'Cherry Orchard' (R)	ESul LDea SSea
'Cherry Sundae' (Z/d/v)	ESul
'Cheryldene' (R)	LDea
'Chew Magna' (R)	WFib
'Chi-Chi' (Min)	ESul
'Chieko' (Min/d)	ESul MWhe WFib
'Chime' (Min/d)	ESul
'China Doll' (Dw/d)	WFib
'Chinz' (R)	CSpe NFir WHPP
'Chocolate Drops' (Z)	LVER
§ 'Chocolate Peppermint' (Sc)	CHal CHrt CRHN CSev CTbh EAro ESul LDea MBPg MHer MNHC MWhe NBur NFir NHHG SIde SSea SYvo WBrk WFib WHPP
'Chocolate Tomentosum'	see *P*. 'Chocolate Peppermint'
'Chrissie' (R)	ESul WFib
'Christina Beere' (R)	LDea
'Christopher Ley' (Z)	LVER SKen
'Cindy' (Dw/d)	ESul WFib
'Citriodorum' (Sc) ♀H1+3	LDea MBPg MHer NHHG SSea WFib
'Citronella' (Sc)	CRHN LDea MBPg MHer MSte MWhe SSea WFib
citronellum (Sc)	EWoo MBPg
'Clara Read' (Dw)	ESul
'Claret Rock Unique' (U)	EWoo LDea MBPg MHer MSte SKen WFib
'Clarissa' (Min)	ESul
'Clatterbridge' (Dw/d)	ESul LVER NFir
'Claude Read' (Dw)	ESul
'Claudette' (Min)	ESul
'Claudius' (Min)	ESul
'Claydon' (Dw/d)	ESul NFir
'Claydon Firebird' (R)	ESul
'Clorinda' (U/Sc)	CHal CHrt CRHN EShb ESul EWoo GBar LVER MBPg MHer MSte NBur SIde SKen SSea WFib
'Clorinda Variegated'	see *P*. 'Variegated Clorinda'
'Clown' (R)	ESul
'Coconut Ice' (Dw)	ESul LVER
§ Coco-Rico (I)	SKen
'Coddenham' (Dw/d)	ESul LVER WFib
§ 'Colonel Baden-Powell' (I/d)	LDea WFib
'Confetti' (R) **new**	ESul
'Conner' (Min)	ESul
'Constance Spry' (Z)	WEas
'Contrast' (Z/d/C/v)	ESul LAst LRHS MBri MWhe NEgg SCoo SKen SPoG SSea WFib
'Cook's Golden Bird's Egg'	EWoo
'Cook's Peachblossom'	WFib
'Copdock' (Min/d)	ESul
'Copthorne' (U/Sc) ♀H1+3	CRHN ESul EWoo LDea LVER MBPg MHer MSte SKen SSea WBrk WFib WHPP
'Coral Frills' (Min/d)	ESul
'Coral Reef' (Z/d)	LVER
cordifolium	CRHN EWoo WFib
coriandrifolium	see *P. myrrhifolium* var. *coriandrifolium*
'Cornell' (I/d)	ECtt WFib
'Corsair' (Z/d) ♀H1+3	MWhe
'Corvina' (R)	WFib
'Cotta Lilac Queen' (I/d)	LVER
'Cottenham Beauty' (A)	ESul EWoo LDea NFir
'Cottenham Belle' (A) **new**	ESul
'Cottenham Bliss' (A) **new**	ESul
'Cottenham Charm' (A)	ESul LDea
'Cottenham Cynthia Haird' (A) **new**	ESul
'Cottenham Delight' (A)	ESul LDea NFir
'Cottenham Gem' (A)	ESul
'Cottenham Glamour' (A)	ESul NFir
'Cottenham Harmony' (A)	ESul LDea

'Cottenham Jubilee' (A)	ESul LDea
'Cottenham Mervyn Haird' (A) **new**	ESul
'Cottenham Star' (A) **new**	ESul
'Cottenham Surprise' (A)	ESul LDea MBPg MSte MWhe NFir
'Cottenham Treasure' (A)	ESul LDea
'Cottenham Wonder' (A) **new**	ESul
'Cotton Candy' (Min/d)	ESul
'Cottontail' (Min)	ESul WFib
cotyledonis	WFib
'Countess Mariza'	see *P*. 'Gräfin Mariza'
'Countess of Scarborough'	see *P*. 'Lady Scarborough'
'Country Girl' (R)	SPet
'Cover Girl' (Z/d)	WFib
'Cowes' (St/Min/d) **new**	ESul
'Cramdon Red' (Dw)	SKen WFib
'Crampel's Master' (Z)	SKen
'Cransley Blends' (R)	ESul LDea
'Cransley Star' (A)	LDea MWhe WFib
'Cream 'n' Green' (R/v)	LSou NFir
'Creamery' (d)	MWhe WFib
§ 'Creamy Nutmeg' (Sc/v)	CArn CHal CHrt EShb ESul EWoo GBar LDea MHer MWhe NBur NFir SSea
'Creeting St Mary' (Min)	ESul
'Creeting St Peter' (Min)	ESul
'Crescendo' (I/d)	ECtt
'Crimson Fire' (Z/d)	MBri MWhe
'Crimson Unique' (U) ♀H1+3	CRHN CSpe EWoo MBPg MHer SKen SSea WFib
§ *crispum* (Sc)	CHrt GBar GPoy LDea MBPg NHHG WRha
§ - 'Golden Well Sweep' (Sc/v)	MBPg NFir WFib
- 'Major' (Sc)	ESul MBPg SKen WFib
- 'Minor' (Sc)	MBPg MHer
- 'Peach Cream' (Sc/v)	CHal ESul MBPg MWhe WFib
- 'Prince Rupert' (Sc)	MBPg
- 'Variegatum' (Sc/v) ♀H1+3	CHal CRHN GGar GPoy LDea LVER MBPg MHer MWhe NFir SIde SPet SSea WFib
crithmifolium	MHer
'Crock O Day' (I/d)	LVER
'Crocketta' (I/d/v)	LVER NFir SSea
'Crocodile' (I/C/d)	ECtt EShb LDea LVER MWhe NFir SKen SSea SWal WFib
'Crowfield' (Min/d)	ESul WFib
'Crowfoot Rose' (Sc)	EWoo MBPg
'Crown Jewels' (R)	LDea
'Crystal Palace Gem' (Z/v)	LAst LRHS LVER MWhe SKen SSea WFib WHPP
'Crystal West' (Min/St) **new**	ESul
cucullatum	ESul EWoo MHer SSea WFib WHPP
- 'Flore Plenum'	WFib
§ - subsp. *strigifolium*	EWoo
'Culpho' (Min/C/d)	ESul
'Cupid' (Min/Dw/d)	WFib
'Cyril Read' (Dw)	ESul
§ 'Czar' (Z/C)	SCoo
'Dainty Maid' (Sc)	ESul EWoo GGar MBPg NFir SAga SSea
'Dale Queen' (Z)	WFib
'Dallimore' (Dw)	ESul
'Danielle Marie' (A)	LDea
I 'Daphne' (Dec) **new**	SKen
'Daphne' (A)	LAst
'Dark Ascot' (Dec)	ESul
'Dark Lady' (Sc)	MBPg
'Dark Red Irene' (Z/d)	MWhe SKen WFib
'Dark Secret' (R)	CSpe ESul EWoo LDea MSte SKen WFib WHPP
'Dark Venus' (R)	ESul EWoo LDea WFib
Dark-Red-Blizzard = 'Fisblizdark' (I)	EWoo NPri
'Darmsden' (A) ♀H1+3	ESul EWoo LDea NFir SSea

'David John' (Dw/d) — ESul
'David Mitchell' (Min/Ca/d) — ESul
'Davina' (Min/d) — ESul MWhe WFib
'Dawn Star' (Z/St) — ESul NFir
'Deacon Arlon' (Dw/d) — ESul LVER MWhe SKen
'Deacon Avalon' (Dw/d) — WFib
'Deacon Barbecue' (Z/d) — ESul MWhe SKen WFib
'Deacon Birthday' (Z/d) — ESul LVER MWhe WFib
'Deacon Bonanza' (Z/d) — ESul LVER MWhe SKen WFib
'Deacon Clarion' (Z/d) — ESul SKen WFib
'Deacon Constancy' (Z/d) — ESul LVER MWhe
'Deacon Coral Reef' (Z/d) — ESul MWhe SKen WFib
'Deacon Delight' (Sc) — EWoo
'Deacon Finale' (Z/d) — ESul LVER
'Deacon Fireball' (Z/d) — ESul LVER MWhe SKen WFib
'Deacon Flamingo' (Z/d) — ESul MWhe WBrk
'Deacon Gala' (Z/d) — ESul MWhe WFib
'Deacon Golden Bonanza' (Z/C/d) — ESul WFib
'Deacon Golden Gala' (Z/C/d) — ESul
'Deacon Golden Lilac Mist' (Z/C/d) — ESul SKen WFib
'Deacon Jubilant' (Z/d) — ESul MWhe SKen
'Deacon Lilac Mist' (Z/d) — ESul LVER MWhe SKen WFib
'Deacon Mandarin' (Z/d) — ESul MWhe SKen WFib
'Deacon Minuet' (Z/d) — ESul MWhe NFir SKen WFib
'Deacon Moonlight' (Z/d) — ESul MWhe
'Deacon Peacock' (Z/C/d) — ESul MWhe WFib
'Deacon Picotee' (Z/d) — ESul MWhe SKen WFib
'Deacon Regalia' (Z/d) — ESul MWhe SKen WFib
'Deacon Romance' (Z/d) — ESul MWhe WFib
§ 'Deacon Summertime' (Z/d) — ESul MWhe WFib
'Deacon Sunburst' (Z/d) — ESul LVER MWhe SKen
'Deacon Suntan' (Z/d) — ESul MWhe SKen
'Deacon Trousseau' (Z/d) — ESul LVER MWhe WFib
'Dean's Delight' (Sc) — LDea MBPg
'Debbie' (A) — MBPg
'Debbie Parmer' (Dw/d) — ESul
'Debbie Thrower' (Dw) — ESul
'Deborah Miliken' (Z/d) — ESul
'Decora Impérial' (I) — LAst LVER
'Decora Lavender' — see *P.* 'Decora Lilas'
§ 'Decora Lilas' (I) — ECtt LAst LVER SPet
'Decora Mauve' — see *P.* 'Decora Lilas'
I 'Decora Pink' — LAst
I 'Decora Red' — LAst
§ 'Decora Rose' (I) — ECtt LAst SPet
'Decora Rouge' (I) — ECtt SPet
'Deerwood Darling' (Min/v/d) — WFib
'Deerwood Don Quixote' (A) — MWhe
'Deerwood Lavender Lad' (Sc) — ESul EWoo LDea MBPg MHer SSea WFib
'Deerwood Lavender Lass' — ESul LDea MBPg MHer
'Deerwood Pink Puff' (St/d) — WFib
'Delightful' (R) — WFib
'Delilah' (R) — LDea
'Delli' (R) — EWoo NPer WFib
'Delta' (Min/d) — ESul
'Denebola' (Min/d) — ESul
denticulatum — EWoo GBar MHer NHHG SKen SSea
§ – 'Filicifolium' (Sc) — CHal CRHN EShb ESul EWoo LVER MBPg MHer MNHC NHHG SSea WFib
'Diana Hull' — MBPg
'Diana Palmer' (Z/d) — SKen
'Diane' (Min/d) — ESul
'Diane Louise' (d) — SSea
'Dibbinsdale' (Z) — ESul NFir
dichondrifolium (Sc) — EWoo LVER MBPg MHer NCiC NFir WFib WHPP

dichondrifolium x **reniforme** (Sc) — ESul NFir
'Diddi-Di' (Min/d) — ESul
'Didi' (Min) — ESul SKen
'Dingley Bell' — MWhe
'Dinky' (Min/d) — ESul
'Display' (Dw/v) — WFib
'Distinction' (Z) — LAst MWhe NFir SKen SPoG SSea WFib WHPP
'Doctor A. Chipault' (I/d) — LDea
'Dollar Bute' (R) — ESul
'Dollar Princess' (Z/C) — SKen
'Dolly Read' (Dw) — ESul
'Dolly Varden' (Z/v) — ESul LDea MWhe NFir SKen SSea WFib
   ♀H1+3
x **domesticum** 'Royalty White' (R) **new** — LAst
'Don Quixote' (A) — WHPP
'Don's Barbra Leonard' (Dw/B) — NFir
'Don's Carosel' (Z/v) — SSea
'Don's Helen Bainbridge' (Z/C) — NFir
'Don's Mona Noble' (Z/C/v) — NFir SKen SSea
'Don's Richard A. Costain' (Z/C) — NFir
'Don's Seagold' — NFir
'Don's Shiela Jane' (Z/C/d) — NFir
'Don's Silva Perle' (Dw/v) — SKen
'Don's Southport' (Z/v) — NFir
'Don's Stokesley Gem' (Z/C) — NFir
'Don's Swanland Girl' (Min) — ESul
'Don's Whirlygig' (Z/C) — NFir
'Dorcas Brigham Lime' (Sc) — CSpe EAro EWoo SAga
'Dorcus Bingham' (Sc) — GBar MBPg
'Doris Frith' (R) — LDea
'Doris Shaw' (R) — ESul
'Dorothy May' (A) — LDea
'Double Bird's Egg' (Z/d) — SKen
'Double Grace Wells' (Min/d) — ESul
'Double Lilac White' (I/d) — SKen
'Double New Life' (Z/d) — CHal
'Double Orange' (Z/d) — SKen
'Dovedale' (Dw/C) — ESul NFir WFib
'Downlands' (Z/d) — WFib
'Dragon's Breath' (Z/St) — LVER
'Dresden China' (R) — ESul LDea
'Dresden Pippa Rosa' (Z) — SKen
'Dresden White' (Dw) — WFib
'Dresdner Amethyst' (I/d) — LAst
Dresdner Apricot = 'Pacbriap'^{PBR} (I/d) — LVER
'Drummer Boy' (Z) — SKen
'Dryden' (Z) — SKen
'Dubonnet' (R) — LDea
'Duchess of Devonshire' (U) — EWoo WFib
'Duke of Edinburgh' — see *P.* 'Hederinum Variegatum'
'Dulcie' (Min) — ESul
'Dunkery Beacon' (R) — ESul WFib
'Dusty Rose' (Min) — ESul
'E. Dabner' (Z/d) — SKen WFib
'Earl of Chester' (Min/d) — WFib
   ♀H1+3
'Earliana' (Dec) — ESul LDea
'Earlsfour' (R) — LDea MSte
'Easter Morn' (Z/St) — SSea
'Easter Promise' (R) **new** — ESul
echinatum — CSpe EWoo MBPg MHer SSea WHPP
– 'Album' — WFib

- 'Miss Stapleton'	see *P.* 'Miss Stapleton'
'Eclipse' (I/d)	MWhe SKen
'Eden Gem' (Min/d)	WFib
'Edith Stern' (Dw/d)	ESul
'Edmond Lachenal' (Z/d)	WFib
'Edward Humphris' (Z)	EWoo SKen
'Edwards Michael' (A) **new**	LDea
'Eileen' (Min/d)	ESul
'Eileen Postle' (R) ♀H1+3	WFib
'Eileen Stanley' (R)	LDea
'Elaine' (R)	LDea
'Elaine Thompson' (R) **new**	LDea
Elbe Silver = 'Pensil' (I)	LAst NFir SCoo
'Electra' (Z/d)	SKen
'Elegance Burgundy' **new**	LAst WGor
'Elizabeth Angus' (R)	SKen SSea WFib
'Elizabeth Read' (Dw)	ESul
'Ella Martin' (St) **new**	ESul
'Elmfield' (St/Min/d) **new**	ESul
'Elmsett' (Dw/C/d)	ESul LVER NFir SSea WFib
'Elna' (Min)	ESul
elongatum	CMon SHFr SSea
'Els' (Dw/St)	ESul LVER SKen WBrk
'Elsi' (I x Z/d/v)	LVER WFib
'Elsie Gillam' (St)	LVER
'Elsie Hickman' (R)	ESul LDea
'Elsie Portas' (Z/C/d)	ESul SKen
'Embassy' (Min)	ESul WFib
'Emerald' (I)	SKen
'Emilia Joy' (A)	MHer
Emilia = 'Pactina' **new**	LAst LSou WGor
'Emma Hössle'	see *P.* 'Frau Emma Hössle'
'Emma Jane Read' (Dw/d)	ESul MWhe NFir WFib
'Emma Louise' (Z)	SKen
'Emmy Sensation' (R)	LDea
'Emperor Nicholas' (Z/d)	MWhe SKen
'Empress' (Z)	SKen
'Ena' (Min)	ESul
'Enchantress' (I)	SKen
'Encore' (Z/d/v)	LRHS LVER MWhe NFir SSea
endlicherianum	CMon NBhm NWCA WCot WWFP
'Endsleigh' (Sc)	MBPg MHer
'Enid Blackaby' (R)	WHPP
'Enid Brackley' (R) **new**	ESul
'Eroica 2000'	LAst
'Erwarton' (Min/d)	ESul NFir
'Escapade' (Min/d)	ESul
'Eskay Gold' (A) **new**	WFib
'Evelyn' (Min)	ESul
Evening Glow = 'Bergpalais'PBR	LAst
'Evka'PBR (I/v)	LAst LVER NBlu NFir SCoo SSea WHPP
'Excalibur' (Z/Min/v)	LVER
'Explosive' (I)	NPri
exstipulatum	EShb EWoo SSea WEas XPep
'Eyes Randy' (A)	LAst
'Fair Dinkum' (Z/v)	ESul MWhe NFir
§ 'Fair Ellen' (Sc)	ESul EWoo LDea MBPg MHer SKen WFib
'Fairlee' (DwI)	WFib
'Fairy Lights' (Dw/St)	ESul NFir
'Fairy Orchid' (A)	ESul LDea SSea WFib
'Fairy Queen'	LDea MHer
'Falkenham' (Min)	ESul
'Falkland Brother' (Z/C/v)	ESul WFib
'Falkland Hero' (Z/v)	NFir
'Fallen Angel' (Z/St) **new**	LVER
'Fandango' (Z)	ESul MWhe NFir WFib
'Fanny Eden' (R)	WFib
'Fantasia' white-flowered (Dw/d) ♀H1+3	ESul MWhe WFib
'Fareham' (R) ♀H1+3	LDea MSte WFib
'Faye Brawner' (Z/St)	LVER
'Feneela' (Dw/d)	ESul
'Fenland' (R) **new**	ESul

'Fenton Farm' (Dw/C)	ESul NFir WFib
'Fern Mint' (Sc)	MBPg
'Festal' (Min/d)	ESul
'Feuerriesse' (Z)	LVER SKen
'Fiat' (Z/d)	SKen
'Fiat Queen' (Z/d)	SKen WFib
'Fiat Supreme' (Z/d)	SKen
'Fiery Sunrise' (R)	ESul EWoo LDea
'Fiesta' (I/d)	LDea
'Fifth Avenue' (R)	CSpe ESul EWoo MSte WFib WHPP
'Filicifolium'	see *P.denticulatum* 'Filicifolium'
'Fir Trees Audrey B' (St)	NFir
'Fir Trees Big Show' (I/v)	NFir
'Fir Trees Echoes of Pink' (A)	EWoo NFir
'Fir Trees Eileen' (St)	NFir
'Fir Trees Ele' (A/v)	NFir
'Fir Trees Flamingo' (Dw)	NFir
'Fir Trees Jack' (Z/Dw)	NFir
'Fir Trees John Grainger' (Z/v)	NFir
'Fir Trees Mark' (R/Dec) **new**	NFir
'Fir Trees Nan' (Dec)	NFir
'Fir Trees Roseberry Topping' (Dw)	NFir
'Fir Trees Ruby Wedding' (C)	NFir
'Fir Trees Silver Wedding' (Z/C/d)	NFir
'Fir Trees Sparkler' (Min/C)	NFir
'Fire Dancer' (R) **new**	ESul
'Fire Dragon' (Z/St/d)	SKen SSea
'Fireball'PBR	LAst LSou WGor
'Firebrand' (Z)	LVER
'Firefly' (Min/d)	ESul
'Firestone' (Dw)	ESul
(Fireworks Series)	SSea
Fireworks Cherry-white = 'Fiwocher'PBR (Z)	
- Fireworks Light Pink = 'Fiwopink'PBR (Z)	LAst
- Fireworks Salmon = 'Fiwosal'PBR (Z)	SSea
- Fireworks White = 'Fiwowit'PBR (Z)	LAst
'First Blush' (R)	WFib
'First Love' (Z)	NFir
'Fistaneon'PBR (Z/d)	LAst
Flair = 'Fisberno' (I)	NPri
'Flakey' (I/d/v) ♀H1+3	ESul LDea NFir SKen WHPP
'Flarepath' (Z/C/v)	NFir SSea
'Flash' (Min)	ESul
'Flecks' (Min/St) **new**	ESul
'Fleur-de-lys' (A)	LDea
'Fleurette' (Min/d)	CHal ESul MWhe SKen
'Fleurisse' (Z)	WFib
§ 'Flirt' (Min)	WFib
'Floria Moore' (Dec)	ESul EWoo NFir SAga SSea
'Flower Basket' (R/d)	ESul EWoo LDea NFir
'Flower of Spring' (Z/v) ♀H1+3	CHal MWhe SKen SSea
'Flowton' (Dw/d)	ESul
'Foxhall' (Dw)	ESul
Fragrans Group (Sc)	CHal CRHN CSev CTbh ESul EWoo GBar GPoy LVER MBPg MHer MNHC MWhe NHHG SDnm SKen SPet SSea WFib XPep
§ - 'Fragrans Variegatum' (Sc/v)	CSev ESul LIck MBPg MWhe NFir SKen WBrk WFib WHPP
- 'Snowy Nutmeg'	see *P.* (Fragrans Group) 'Fragrans Variegatum'
'Fraiche Beauté' (Z/d)	WFib
'Francis Gibbon' (Z/d)	WFib
'Francis James' (Z)	WFib

Name	Sources
'Francis Kelly' (R) **new**	ESul
'Francis Parrett' (Min/d) ♀H1+3	ESul MWhe SKen WFib
'Francis Read' (Dw/d)	ESul
'Frank Headley' (Z/v) ♀H1+3	CHal EShb ESul LAst LRHS LVER MSte MWhe NPer NVic SAga SCoo SDnm SIde SKen SSea WBrk WFib WHPP
§ 'Frau Emma Hössle' (Dw/d)	ESul LVER MWhe WFib
'Freak of Nature' (Z/v)	ESul MWhe NFir SKen SSea WFib
'Frensham' (Sc)	ESul EWoo MBPg MHer WFib
'Freshfields Suki' (Dw)	NFir
'Freshwater' (St/C)	ESul MWhe
'Freston' (Dw)	ESul
'Friary Wood' (Z/C/d)	ESul NFir WFib
'Friesdorf' (Dw/Fr)	ESul LVER MHer MWhe NFir SKen WBrk WFib
'Frills' (Min/d)	ESul MWhe NFir
'Fringed Angel' (A)	CFee
'Fringed Apple' (Sc)	LDea MBPg NBur
§ 'Fringed Aztec' (R) ♀H1+3	ESul LDea LVER NFir SKen SPet SSea WFib WHPP
'Fringed Jer'Ray' (A)	LDea
'Fringed Petit Pierre' (Min)	MWhe
'Fringed Rouletta' (I)	LDea
'Frosty' misapplied	see P. 'Variegated Kleine Liebling'
'Frosty Petit Pierre'	see P. 'Variegated Kleine Liebling'
'Fruity' (Sc)	MBPg
frutetorum	MBPg MHer
fruticosum	EShb EWoo WFib
'Frühlingszauber Lila' (R)	ESul
'Fuji' (R)	NFir
fulgidum	CSpe EShb EWoo MHer NFir WFib
'Funny Girl' (R)	ESul
'Fynn' (Dw)	ESul
'Gabriel' (A)	ESul EWoo LDea LVER MBPg NFir
'Galilee' (I/d) ♀H1+3	LDea LVER SKen
Galleria Sunrise = 'Sunrise' (R)	ESul LDea SKen WEas
'Galway Girl' (Sc)	MBPg
'Galway Star' (Sc/v) ♀H1+3	MBPg MHer WBrk WFib
'Garland' (Dw/d)	ESul LVER
'Garnet' (Z/d)	ESul LVER
'Garnet Rosebud' (Min/d)	ESul WFib
'Gartendirektor Herman' (Dec)	ESul EWoo LAst NFir SSea WFib WHPP
'Gaudy' (Z)	WFib
'Gay Baby' (DwI)	ESul LDea MWhe
'Gay Baby Supreme' (DwI)	ESul
§ 'Gemini' (Z/St/d)	ESul MWhe NFir SSea WFib
'Gemma' (R)	ESul NFir
'Gemma' (Min/C)	LVER
'Gemma Jewel' (R) ♀H1+3	ESul
'Gemma Rose' (R)	LDea
I 'Gemstone' (Min)	ESul
'Gemstone' (Sc) ♀H1+3	EWoo LDea MBPg MHer NFir WBrk
'Genie' (Z/d)	MWhe SKen WFib
'Gentle Georgia' (R)	WFib
'Geofbar' (R) **new**	ESul
'Geoff May' (Min)	ESul
'Georgia' (R)	WFib WHPP
'Georgia Mai Read'	ERea
'Georgia Peach' (R)	ESul WFib
'Georgie' (R)	LDea
'Georgina Blythe' (R) ♀H1+3	WFib
'Geo's Pink' (Z/v)	MWhe
'Geosta'	LAst
'Gerald Portas' (Dw/C)	ESul
'Gerald Wells' (Min)	ESul LVER
'Geraldine' (Min)	ESul
'Gess Portas' (Z/v)	ESul
'Ghost Storey' (Z/C)	NFir
'Giant Butterfly' (R)	ESul
'Giant Oak' (Sc)	ESul MBPg MHer MSte
gibbosum	EWoo MHer SSea WFib
'Gilbert West' (Z)	SKen
'Gilda' (R/v)	LDea NFir
'Gill' (Min/Ca)	ESul
'Ginger Frost' (Sc/v)	WFib
'Ginger Rogers' (Z)	NFir
'Glacier Claret' (Z)	WFib
'Glacier Crimson' (Z)	SKen
'Glacis'PBR (Quality Series) (Z/d)	LAst LSou
'Gladys Evelyn' (Z/d)	WFib
'Gladys Stevens' (Min/d)	ESul
'Gleam' (Z/d)	LVER
'Glen Sheree' (R) **new**	ESul
'Gloria Pearce' (R)	ESul LDea
'Glowing Embers' (R)	ESul LDea
§ *glutinosum*	MBPg MHer WFib
'Goblin' (Min/d)	ESul SKen WFib
'Godfreys Pride' (Sc)	MBPg
'Godshill' (R)	LDea
'Goesta' (Z/d)	LSou
'Gold Star' (Z/St/C)	ESul
'Golden Baby' (DwI/C)	ESul LDea NFir WFib WHPP
'Golden Brilliantissimum' (Z/v)	ESul LRHS MWhe SSea WFib
'Golden Butterfly' (Z/C)	ESul
'Golden Chalice' (Min/v)	ESul MWhe NFir WFib
'Golden Clorinda' (U/Sc/C)	CRHN EWoo LDea MBPg MHer NFir SSea WEas
'Golden Crest' (Z/C)	SKen
'Golden Ears' (Dw/St/C)	ESul MWhe NFir NPer WFib
'Golden Edinburgh' (I/v)	WFib
'Golden Everaarts' (Dw/C)	ESul
'Golden Fleece' (Dw/C/d)	ESul
'Golden Gates' (Z/C)	ESul SKen
'Golden Harry Hieover' (Z/C) ♀H1+3	ESul MBri MHer SSea
'Golden Lilac Gem' (I/d)	WFib
'Golden Mirage' (Z/v)	SSea
'Golden Petit Pierre' (Min/C)	ESul SSea
'Golden Princess' (Min/C)	WFib
'Golden Roc' (Min/C)	ESul
'Golden Staphs' (Z/St/C)	ESul NFir SSea WFib
'Golden Stardust' (Z/St)	ESul LVER
'Golden Wedding' (Z/d/v)	LRHS MWhe NFir SSea
'Golden Well Sweep'	see P. crispum 'Golden Well Sweep'
'Goldilocks' (A)	ESul
'Gooseberry Leaf'	see P. grossularioides
'Gordano Midnight' (R)	EWoo LDea
'Gosbeck' (A)	SSea WFib
'Gossamer Carnival' (Z/d)	NFir
'Gothenburg' (R)	ESul
'Gottweig' (Z) **new**	ESul
'Grace' (A)	LDea
'Grace Thomas' (Sc) ♀H1+3	EWoo LDea MBPg MHer WFib
'Grace Wells' (Min)	ESul WFib
§ 'Gräfin Mariza' (Z/d)	SKen
'Grand Duchess' (R)	LDea
'Grand Slam' (R)	ESul LDea LVER NFir WFib
'Grandad Mac' (Dw/St)	ESul NFir
grandiflorum	EWoo WFib
'Grandma Fischer'	see P. 'Grossmutter Fischer'
'Grandma Ross' (R)	ESul
'Grandma Thompson' (R) **new**	ESul
'Granny Hewitt' (Min/d)	ESul
graveolens	EWoo SBch
§ 'Graveolens' (Sc)	CHal ESul GBar GPoy LVER MBPg MHer MWhe SKen SSea WFib
'Great Bricett' (Dw/d)	ESul
'Green Ears' (Z/St)	ESul
'Green Eyes' (I/d)	SKen

'Green Goddess' (I/d) LDea SKen
'Green Gold Petit Pierre' ESul
  (Min)
'Green Lady' (Sc) MBPg
'Green Silver Galaxy' (St) ESul
  new
'Green Woodpecker' (R) LDea SSea
§ 'Greengold Kleine Liebling' (Min/C/v) ESul SKen
'Greengold Petit Pierre' see *P.* 'Greengold Kleine Liebling'
'Greetings' (Min/v) ESul MBri SSea WFib
'Grey Lady Plymouth' ESul EWoo LDea MBPg MHer NFir
  (Sc/v) WFib WHPP
'Grey Sprite' (Min/v) ESul WFib
§ 'Grossmutter Fischer' (R) LDea
§ *grossularioides* EOHP IFro MBPg MHer
  - B&SWJ 6497 WCru
  - 'Coconut' MBPg
'Grozser Garten' (Dw) ESul
'Grozser Garten Weiss' ESul
  (Dw)
'Guardsman' (Dw) ESul
Guido = 'Kleugudo' (Z/d) LAst LRHS NBlu
'Gustav Emich' (Z/d) SKen
'Gwen' (Min/v) MWhe NFir
'H. Rigler' (Z) SKen
'Hadleigh' (Min) ESul
'Halo' (R) **new** ESul
§ 'Hannaford Star' (Z/St) ESul NFir WFib
'Hansen's Pinkie' (R) EWoo LDea
'Hansen's Wild Spice' (Sc) EWoo MBPg
'Happy Appleblossom' NFir SKen SSea
  (Z/v/d)
'Happy Birthday' (Z/T) LVER
Happy Face Amethyst = LAst
  'Penrad'[PBR] (I) **new**
Happy Face Mex = LAst LSou LVER
  'Pacvet'
Happy Face Scarlet = LAst
  'Penhap'[PBR] (I) **new**
Happy Face White **new** LAst
§ 'Happy Thought' (Z/v) CHal ESul LAst LVER MBri MOak
  ♡H1+3 MWhe NFir NVic SCoo SKen SSea
  WFib
'Happy Valley' (R) ESul
'Harbour Lights' (R) ESul LDea WFib WHPP
'Harewood Slam' (R) ESul EWoo LDea MSte WFib
'Harkstead' (Dw) ESul
'Harlequin' (Dw) ESul
'Harlequin Alpine Glow' MWhe
  (I/d)
'Harlequin Mahogany' (I/d) LDea LVER MWhe SKen
§ 'Harlequin Miss Liver Bird' SKen
  (I)
'Harlequin Picotee' (I/d) LDea SKen
'Harlequin Pretty Girl' LVER MWhe WFib
  (I x Z/d)
'Harlequin Rosie O'Day' (I) LDea MWhe SKen WFib
'Harlequin Ted Day' (I/d) LDea
Harmony (Z/Dw) LVER
'Harriet Le Hair' (Z) SKen
'Harvard' (I/d) WFib
'Harvey' (Z) MWhe
'Havenstreet' (Dw/St) ESul
'Hayley Charlotte' (Z/v) MWhe
'Hazel' (R) WFib
'Hazel Anson' (R) LDea
'Hazel Barolo' (R) LDea
'Hazel Birkby' (R) LDea
'Hazel Burtoff' (R) ESul LDea
'Hazel Candy' (R) **new** ESul
'Hazel Carey' (R) LDea
'Hazel Cerise' (R) LDea
'Hazel Cherry' (R) ESul LDea MSte WFib
'Hazel Chick' (R) ESul
'Hazel Choice' (R) ESul LDea NFir
'Hazel Dean' (R) NFir

'Hazel Glory' (R) LDea
'Hazel Gypsy' (R) ESul LDea
'Hazel Harmony' (R) ESul LDea
'Hazel Henderson' (R) LDea
'Hazel Herald' (R) ESul LDea
'Hazel Orchid' (R) **new** ESul
'Hazel Perfection' (R) NFir
'Hazel Ripple' (R) **new** ESul
'Hazel Rose' (R) LDea
'Hazel Saga' (R) ESul
'Hazel Satin' (R) LDea
'Hazel Star' (R) ESul
'Hazel Stardust' (R) ESul LDea NFir WHPP
'Hazel Wright' (R) LDea
§ 'Hederinum' (I) LSou
§ 'Hederinum Variegatum' CHal SPet SSea WFib
  (I/v)
'Heidi' (Min/d) ESul
'Helen Christine' (Z/St) ESul LVER MWhe NFir WFib
'Helena' (I/d) LDea MWhe
'Hemingstone' (A) LDea
'Hemley' (Sc) EWoo LDea MBPg
'Henhurst Gleam' (Dw/d) ESul
'Henley' (Min/d) ESul
'Henry Weller' (A) ESul MBPg MWhe NFir
'Hermanus Show' (Sc) MBPg
'Hermione' (Z/d) CHal MWhe WFib
'High Fidelity' (R) **new** ESul
'High Tor' (Dw/C/d) SKen
'Highfields Always' (Z/d) LVER
'Highfields Appleblossom' LVER SKen
  (Z)
'Highfields Attracta' (Z/d) LVER SKen WFib
'Highfields Ballerina' (Z/d) LVER
'Highfields Candy Floss' LVER NFir
  (Z/d)
'Highfields Charisma' (Z/d) LVER
'Highfields Choice' (Z) LVER SKen
'Highfields Comet' (Z) SKen
'Highfields Contessa' (Z/d) SKen WFib
'Highfields Dazzler' (Z) LVER
'Highfields Fancy' (Z/d) LVER NFir SKen
'Highfields Festival' (Z/d) LVER MWhe NFir SKen WFib
'Highfields Flair' (Z/d) LVER
'Highfields Joy' (Z/d) SKen
'Highfields Melody' (Z/d) WFib
'Highfields Orange' (Z) MWhe
'Highfields Paramount' (Z) SKen
'Highfields Pride' (Z) SKen WFib
'Highfields Prima Donna' LVER MWhe SKen
  (Z/d)
'Highfields Promise' (Z) SKen
'Highfields Snowdrift' (Z) LVER SKen
'Highfields Sugar Candy' SKen WFib
  (Z/d)
'Highfields Symphony' (Z) LVER
'Highfields Vogue' (Z) LVER
'Hilbre Island' (Z/C/d) NFir
'Hildegard' (Z/d) CHal SKen
'Hills of Snow' (Z/v) CHal MBri MHer SKen SSea WFib
'Hillscheider Amethyst'[PBR] see *P.* Amethyst = 'Fisdel'
'Hindoo' (RxU) CSpe EWoo LVER NFir SSea WFib
'Hindoo Rose' (U) NFir
'Hintlesham' (Min) ESul
hispidum MBPg MHer
'Hitcham' (Min/d) ESul WFib
'Holbrook' (Dw/C/d) ESul NFir WFib
'Honeywood Lindy' (R) ESul LDea
'Honeywood Margaret' (R) ESul
'Honeywood Suzanne' ESul LVER NFir SKen
  (Min/Fr)
'Honne Frühling' (Z) SKen
'Honneas' (Dw) ESul
'Honnestolz' (Dw) ESul SKen
'Hope Valley' (Dw/C/d) ESul MWhe NFir SKen
  ♡H1+3

'Horace Parsons' (R) ESul WFib
'Horace Read' (Dw) ESul
'Horning Ferry' (Dw) ESul
'House and Garden' (R) NFir
'Hula' (U x R) EWoo MHer
'Hulda Conn' (Z/Ca/d) WFib
'Hulverstone' (Dw/St) ESul
'Hunter's Moon' (Z/C) NFir
'Hurdy-gurdy' (Z/d/v) ESul MWhe
'Ian Read' (Min/d) ESul LVER
'Icecrystal'PBR (Sweetheart LAst
  Series) (Z/d)
'Icing Sugar' (I/d) ESul LDea SSea WFib
ignescens MBPg
'Immaculatum' (Z) WFib
'Imperial'PBR EWoo LAst
'Imperial Butterfly' (A/Sc) CRHN ESul GGar LDea LVER MBPg
  MSte MWhe NFir SKen SSea WFib
'Improved Rubin' (Z/d) SSea
  new
'Inca' (R) ESul
incrassatum NBur
Ingres = 'Guicerdan'PBR LAst LSou
  (I/d) ♀H1+3
'Inspiration' (R) **new** ESul
ionidiflorum CSpe EShb EWoo MBPg MHer
  XPep
'Ipswich Town' (Dw/d) ESul
'Irene' (Z/d) ♀H1+3 SKen WFib
'Irene Cal' (Z/d) ♀H1+3 SKen
'Irene Collet' (R) LDea
'Irene Picardy' (Z/d) SKen
'Irene Toyon' (Z) ♀H1+3 SKen WFib
§ 'Isabell' (Quality Series) LAst LSou NBlu
  (Z/d)
'Isidel' (I/d) ♀H1+3 SKen WFib
'Islington Peppermint' (Sc) MBPg SSea WFib
'Isobel Eden' (Sc) LDea MBPg
'Italian Gem' (I) SKen
'Ivalo' (Z/d) MWhe SKen WFib
'Ivory Snow' (Z/d/v) ESul LVER MWhe NFir SKen SSea
  WFib
'Jacey' (Z/d) SKen
'Jack of Hearts' (I x Z/d) WFib
'Jack Wood' (Z/d) NFir WFib
§ 'Jackie' (I/d) EShb EWoo LVER MBri WFib
'Jackie Gall' see *P.* 'Jackie'
'Jackie's Gem' (I/d) MWhe
'Jacko' (I/d) EWoo
'Jackpot Wild Rose' (Z/d) WFib
'Jacqueline' (Z/d) SKen
'Jane Biggin' (Dw/C/d) ESul MWhe SKen
'Janet Dean' (R) LDea
'Janet Hofman' (Z/d) WFib
'Janet Kerrigan' (Min/d) ESul MWhe WEas
'Jasmin' (R) ESul LDea SKen
'Jaunty' (Min/d) ESul
'Jayne' (Min/d) ESul
'Jayne Eyre' (Min/d) CHal ESul MWhe NFir WFib
'Jazzy' (Min/St) **new** ESul
'Jean Bart' (I) LVER
'Jean Beatty' (Dw/d) LVER
'Jean Oberle' (Z/d) SKen
'Jeanetta' (R) LDea
§ 'Jeanne d'Arc' (I/d) SKen WFib
'Jenifer Read' (Dw) ESul
'Jennifer' (Min) ESul
'Jennifer Strange' (R) **new** ESul
'Jericho' (Z/St/v) **new** LVER
'Jer'Ray' (A) ESul EWoo LDea MBPg MWhe NFir
  SSea WFib
'Jessel's Unique' (U) LDea MHer MSte SPet SSea
'Jewel' (Z/d) LAst
'Jewel' (R) ESul LAst
'Jimbar' (R) **new** ESul
'Jinny Reeves' (R) ESul LDea

'Joan Cashmere' (Z/d) ESul
'Joan Fontaine' (Z) WFib
'Joan Hayward' (Min) ESul
'Joan Morf' (R) ESul EWoo LDea NFir SSea WFib
'Joan of Arc' see *P.* 'Jeanne d'Arc'
'Joan Sharman' (Min) ESul
'Joanna Pearce' (R) LDea SKen
'John Thorp' (R) LDea
'John's Angela' LVER
'John's Pride' MBri NFir SSea
'Joseph Haydn' (R) ESul LDea MSte
'Joseph Paul' (R) SSea
'Joseph Wheeler' (A) ESul LDea MWhe
'Joy' (R) ♀H1+3 ESul EWoo LDea LRHS LSou NFir
  WFib
'Joy' (I) SPet
I 'Joy' (Z/d) LAst LVER SKen SSea WHPP
'Joy Lucille' (Sc) CSev ESul EWoo LDea MBPg MHer
'Joyful' (Min) ESul
'Jubilant' (R) **new** ESul
'Judy Read' (Dw) ESul
'Julia' (R) ♀H1+3 LDea
'Juliana' (R) LAst LDea
'Julie Bannister' (R) ESul
'Julie Smith' (R) ESul LDea WFib
'June Filbey' (R) LDea
'Jungle Night' (R) ESul EWoo
'Juniper' (Sc) EWoo MBPg MHer WFib
'Jupiter' (Min/d) SKen
'Jupiter' (R) ESul NFir
'Just Rita' (A) SSea
'Just William' (Min/C/d) ESul WFib
'Kamahl' (R) ESul WFib
§ 'Kardinal' (Z/d) SPet
'Karl Hagele' (Z/d) SKen SYvo WFib
'Karl Offenstein' (R) **new** ESul
'Karmin Ball' WFib
karrooense Knuth MHer
'Karrooense' see *P. quercifolium*
'Kathleen' (Min) ESul
'Kathleen Gamble' (Z) SKen WFib
'Kathryn' (Min) ESul
'Kathryn Portas' (Z/v) ESul SKen
'Kathy Kirby' (R) **new** ESul
'Katie' (R) EWoo LDea
'Katie Hillier' (R) **new** LDea
'Katrine' **new** LSou WGor
'Kayleigh Aitken' (R) NFir
'Kayleigh West' (Min) ESul SSea
'Keepsake' (Min/d) ESul WFib
'Keith Vernon' (Z) NFir SSea
'Kelly Brougham' (St/dw) ESul
'Kelvedon Beauty' (Min) WEas
'Ken Salmon' (Dw/d) ESul
'Kenny's Double' (Z/d) WFib
'Kensington' (A) LDea
'Kerensa' (Min/d) ESul SKen WFib
'Kershy' (Min) ESul
'Kesgrave' (Min/d) ESul LVER WFib
'Kettlebaston' (A) ♀H1+3 LDea WFib
'Kewense' (Z) EShb
'Key's Unique' (U) EWoo
'Kimono' (R) ESul NFir
'Kinder Gaisha' (R) NFir
'King Edmund' (R) ESul LDea
'King of Balcon' see *P.* 'Hederinum'
'King of Denmark' (Z/d) LVER WFib
'King Solomon' (R) LDea
'Kirton' (Min/d) ESul
§ 'Kleine Liebling' (Min) ESul MWhe WFib
'Knaves Bonfire' (R) **new** ESul
'Korcicum' (Sc) MBPg
'Krista' (Min/d) ESul WBrk WFib
'Kyoto' (R) NFir
'Kyra' (Min/d) ESul WFib
'La France' (I/d) ♀H1+3 LDea MWhe WFib

'La Paloma' (R)	ESul WFib
'Laced Mini Rose Cascade' (I)	NFir
Laced Red Mini Cascade = 'Achspen' (I)	NFir SKen
§ 'Lachskönigin' (I/d)	LVER SPet WFib
'Lady Cullum' (Z/C/v)	MWhe
'Lady Ilchester' (Z/d)	SKen WFib
'Lady Love Song' (R)	ESul LSou NFir SSea
'Lady Mary' (Sc)	ESul EWoo MBPg MHer
'Lady Mavis Pilkington' (Z/d)	WFib
'Lady Plymouth' (Sc/v) ♀H1+3	CHal CHrt CRHN CSpe CStu EPfP ESul GBar GGar LDea LRHS LVER MBPg MHer MNHC MSte MWhe NFir NHHG SKen SPet SSea WBrk WFib WHPP
Lady Ramona = 'Klep01007'PBR (Z/d)	LAst
§ 'Lady Scarborough' (Sc)	ESul EWoo LDea MBPg WFib
'Lady Scott' (Sc)	MBPg
'Lady Woods' (Z)	SSea
'Lakeland' (I)	ESul SKen SSea
'Lakis' (R)	LDea SSea
'Lamorna' (R)	ESul LDea SKen
'Land of Song' (A)	SSea
'Langley' (R)	ESul LDea
'Lanham Lane' (I)	LDea
'Lanham Royal' (Dw/d)	ESul
'Lara Aladin' (A)	LDea MBPg
'Lara Ballerina'	NFir
'Lara Candy Dancer' (Sc) ♀H1+3	CRHN ESul LDea MBPg MHer WBrk WFib
'Lara Jester' (Sc)	EWoo MBPg MHer WFib
'Lara Maid' (A) ♀H1+3	CHrt MWhe WFib
'Lara Nomad' (Sc)	EWoo LDea MBPg
'Lara Starshine' (Sc) ♀H1+3	CHal EAro ESul EWoo MBPg MHer NFir SSea WBrk WFib WHPP
'Lara Susan' (Dec)	EWoo
'Lara Waltz' (R/d)	WFib
'Lark' (Min/d)	ESul
'Larkfield' (Z/v)	SSea
N 'Lass o' Gowrie' (Z/v)	ESul LRHS MSte MWhe NFir SKen
'Lateripes' (I)	SKen
'Latte Coffee' (R) new	ESul
'Laura Parmer' (Dw/St)	ESul
'Laura Wheeler' (A)	ESul LDea MWhe
'Laurel Hayward' (R)	WFib
Lauretta = 'Pacamla'PBR (Quality Series) (Z/d)	LAst LSou
Lavenda = 'Penlava'PBR (Dark Line Series) (Z/d)	LAst LSou
'Lavender Grand Slam' (R) ♀H1+3	ESul LDea LVER NFir
'Lavender Harewood Slam' (R)	ESul LDea
'Lavender Mini Cascade'PBR	see *P.* Lilac Mini Cascade = 'Lilamica'
'Lavender Sensation' (R)	WFib
'Lavender Wings' (I)	LDea
'Lawrenceanum'	ESul EWoo WFib
'Layham' (Dw/d)	ESul
'L'Elégante' (I/v) ♀H1+3	CHal EWoo LAst LDea LVER MWhe SKen SSea WEas WFib
'Lemon Air' (Sc)	ESul EWoo MBPg
'Lemon Crisp'	see *P. crispum*
'Lemon Fancy' (Sc)	EWoo LDea LVER MBPg MHer MWhe NFir WFib
'Lemon Kiss' (Sc)	EWoo MBPg
'Lemon Meringue' (Sc)	MBPg
'Lemon Toby' (Sc)	MBPg
'Len Chandler' (Min)	ESul
'Lenore' (Min/d)	ESul
'Leo' (Min)	ESul
'Leonie Holbrow' (Min)	ESul
'Lesley Judd' (R) new	ESul

'Leslie Salmon' (Dw/C)	MWhe
'Leslie William Burrows' new	EWoo
'Lesmona'	LAst LSou
'Lessland'	LVER
Lila Compakt-Cascade	see *P.* 'Decora Lilas'
Lilac Cascade	see *P.* 'Roi des Balcons Lilas'
'Lilac Domaine de Courson' (Sc)	MBPg
'Lilac Domino'	see *P.* 'Telston's Prima'
'Lilac Elaine' (R)	LDea
'Lilac Gem' (Min/I/d)	LDea MWhe SKen
'Lilac Gemma' (R) new	ESul
'Lilac Jewel' (R)	ESul
'Lilac Joy' (R)	LVER
§ Lilac Mini Cascade = 'Lilamica'PBR (I)	ESul LAst LDea LVER NFir
'Lili Marlene' (I)	SKen SPet
'Lilian' (Min)	ESul LAst LSou
'Lilian Pottinger' (Sc)	CArn CHal CRHN ESul EWoo GBar LDea MBPg MHer MWhe NFir SKen SSea
'Lilo Cascade'	MBPg
'Limelight' (Z/v)	SSea
'Limoneum' (Sc)	CSev LDea MBPg MHer NBur
'Linda' (R)	ESul
'Lindsey' (Min)	ESul
'Lindy Portas' (I/d)	SKen
'Lipstick' (St)	WFib
'Lisa' (Min/C)	ESul WFib
'Lisa Jo' (St/v/Dw/d)	WFib
'Little Alice' (Dw/d) ♀H1+3	ESul MWhe NFir WFib
'Little Blakenham' (A)	ESul LDea SSea
'Little Fi-fine' (Dw/C)	ESul NFir
'Little Gem' (Sc)	EWoo LDea MBPg MHer MWhe SSea WFib WHPP
'Little Jim' (Min)	NFir
'Little Jip' (Z/d/v)	LVER NFir WFib
'Little Margaret' (Min/v)	ESul
'Little Primular' (Min)	ESul
'Little Rascal' (A)	LDea WHPP
'Little Spikey' (St/Min/d) new	ESul
'Lively Lady' (Dw/C)	ESul SSea
'Liverbird'	see *P.* 'Harlequin Miss Liver Bird'
'Lollipop' (Z/d)	LAst
longicaule	MBPg
'Lord Baden-Powell'	see *P.* 'Colonel Baden-Powell'
'Lord Bute' (R) ♀H1+3	CBos CSpe ECtt EShb ESul EWoo GGar LAst LDea LIck LRHS LVER MHer MSte NCiC NFir NPer SAga SDnm SIde SKen SMer SMrm SPet SSea SUsu WEas WFib WHPP
'Lord Constantine' (R)	LDea
'Lord de Ramsey'	see *P.* 'Tip Top Duet'
'Lord Roberts' (Z)	WFib
Lorena = 'Pacdala'PBR (Dark Line Series) (Z/d)	LAst WGor
'Loretta' (Dw)	ESul
'Lorna' (Dw/d)	ESul
'Lorraine' (Dw)	ESul
'Lotusland' (Dw/St/C)	ESul LAst LSou LVER NFir WFib
'Louise' (Min)	ESul
I 'Louise' (R)	ESul NFir
'Louise Waddington' (Min/St) new	ESul
'Love Song' (R/v)	ESul LDea LSou LVER NFir SSea WFib
'Love Story' (Z/v)	ESul
'Loveliness' (Z)	WFib
* 'Loverly' (Min/d)	ESul
'Lovesdown' (Dw/St)	ESul
'Lowood' (R)	ESul
'Lucie Caws' (St/d) new	ESul
'Lucilla' (Min)	ESul
'Lucinda' (Min)	ESul

'Lucy' (Min)   ESul
'Lucy Gunnett' (Z/d/v)   ESul MWhe NFir
'Lucy Jane' (R)   ESul LDea
'Lulu' (I/d)   NPri
Luna = 'Fisuna' (I/d)   NPri
'Lustre' (R)   ESul
'Lyewood Bonanza' (R)   ESul LDea
'Lynne Valerie' (A)   LDea
'Lyric' (Min/d)   ESul WFib
'Mabel Grey' (Sc) ♀H1+3   CHal CRHN CSev CSpe EShb ESul
                                          EWoo LIck MBPg MHer MSte
                                          MWhe NBur NFir NHHG NPer
                                          SBch SIde SKen SSea WFib WHPP
§ 'Madame Auguste Nonin'   CHal CHrt ESul EWoo MBPg MHer
   (U/Sc)   NFir SKen WFib
'Madame Butterfly' (Z/d/v) ESul MWhe NFir SKen
'Madame Crousse' (I/d)   WFib
   ♀H1+3
'Madame Fournier' (Dw/C) ESul
'Madame Hibbault' (Z)   SKen
'Madame Layal' (A)   EWoo LIck MHer MSte NFir WFib
'Madame Margot'   see *P.* 'Hederinum Variegatum'
'Madame Salleron' (Min/v) LDea LRHS LVER MSte
   ♀H1+3   SKen
'Madame Thibaut' (R)   LDea MSte
'Madge Taylor' (R)   NFir
'Magaluf' (I/C/d)   SSea
'Magda' (Z/d)   ESul LVER
magenteum   EWoo
'Magic Lantern' (Z/C)   NFir
'Magic Moments' (R)   ESul
'Magnum' (R)   WFib
'Maid of Honour' (Min)   ESul
'Maiden Petticoat'   LAst SAga
'Maiden Rosepink' (R)   LAst WGor
'Maiden Sunrise'   LAst
'Mairi' (A)   EWoo LDea WFib
'Majesta' (Z/d) **new**   SKen
'Mamie' (Z/d)   SKen
'Mandarin' (R)   ESul
'Mangles'Variegated' (Z/v)   SSea WFib
'Mantilla' (Min)   ESul
'Manx Maid' (A)   ESul LDea NFir
'Maple Leaf' (Sc)   EWoo MBPg
'Marble Sunset'   see *P.* 'Wood's Surprise'
'Marchioness of Bute' (R)   EMan LDea LVER MSte NFir NPer
                                          SSea WFib
'Maréchal MacMahon'   SKen SSea
   (Z/C)
'Margaret Parmenter' (I/C) ESul
'Margaret Pearce' (R)   LDea
'Margaret Salvidge' (R)   LDea
'Margaret Soley' (R) ♀H1+3   LDea
'Margaret Thorp'   LVER
'Margaret Waite' (R)   ESul WFib
'Margery Stimpson'   ESul WFib
   (Min/d)
'Maria Wilkes' (Z/d)   WFib
'Marie Rober' (R)   ESul
'Marie Rudlin' (R)   LVER SSea
'Marie Thomas' (Sc)   LDea MBPg MHer SBch SSea
§ 'Marie Vogel' (R)   ESul MSte
'Marilyn' (Dw/d)   ESul
Marimba = 'Fisrimba'[PBR]   NPri SCoo
'Marion' (Min)   ESul
'Mariquita' (R)   WFib
'Marja' (R)   LDea
'Marmalade' (Min/d)   ESul MWhe WFib
'Marquis of Bute' (R/v)   ESul LVER NFir
'Marquita' (R) **new**   ESul
'Martha Parmer' (Min)   ESul
'Martin Parrett' (Min/d)   WFib
'Martin's Splendour' (Min)   ESul
'Martlesham' (Dw)   ESul
'Mary' (R) **new**   ESul
'Mary Caws' (Dw/Z/d) **new**   ESul

'Mary Ellen Tanner' (Min/d) ESul
'Mary Read' (Min)   ESul
'Mary Webster' (Min)   ESul
'Masquerade' (R)   ESul SPet
'Masquerade' (Min)   ESul
'Master Paul' (Z/v)   ESul
'Matthew Salvidge' (R)   ESul
'Maureen' (Min)   ESul LVER NFir
'Mauve Beauty' (I/d)   SKen WFib
Maxime = 'Fismaxi' (I/d)   NPri
   new
'Maxime Kovalevski' (Z)   WFib
'Maxine' (Z/C)   NFir
'Maxine Colley' (Z/d/v)   LVER
'May Day' (R)   LDea
'May Magic' (R)   ESul NFir WFib
'Mayfield County Girl' (R)   ESul
   new
'Mayor of Seville' (Z/d)   WFib
'Meadowside Dark and   WFib
   Dainty' (St)
'Meadowside Fancy'   LVER
   (Z/d/C)
'Meadowside Harvest'   NFir WFib
   (Z/St/C)
'Meadowside Julie Colley'   NFir
   (Dw)
'Meadowside Mahogany'   LVER
   (Z/C)
'Meadowside Mardi Gras'   NFir
   (Dw/d)
'Meadowside Midnight'   MHer MWhe SHFr WFib
   (St/C)
'Meadowside Orange'   LVER
   (Z/d)
'Medallion' (Z/C)   MHer SSea
'Meditation' (Min)   ESul
'Medley' (Min/d)   MWhe WFib
'Meike' (R) **new**   ESul
'Melanie' (R)   ESul LDea
'Melanie' (Min)   ESul
'Melissa' (R) **new**   ESul
* 'Melissa' (Min)   ESul
Meloblue = 'Penblue'   NBlu
'Melody'[PBR] (Tempo Series) LAst
   (Z/d)
Melosilver = 'Penber'   LAst SPoG
   (Tempo Series) (Z/d/v)
'Memento' (Min/d)   ESul WFib
'Mendip' (R)   WFib
'Mendip Anne' (R)   NFir
'Mendip Barbie' (R)   NFir
'Mendip Blanche' (R)   NFir
'Mendip Candy Floss' (R)   ESul
'Mendip Lorraine' (R) **new** ESul
'Mendip Sentire' (R)   NFir
'Meon Maid' (R)   ESul LDea WFib WHPP
'Mere Casino' (Z)   WFib
'Mere Greeting' (Z/d)   MWhe WFib
'Mere Sunglow' (R)   LDea
'Merle Seville' (Z/d)   SKen
'Merlin' (Sc)   MBPg
'Merry-go-round' (Z/C/v)   MWhe SSea
'Mexica Katrine'   LAst
Mexica Tomcat (I/d)   LAst LSou WGor
'Mexically Rose' (R)   ESul
'Mexican Beauty' (I)   CHal WFib
'Mexicana'   see *P.* 'Rouletta'
'Mexicanerin'   see *P.* 'Rouletta'
'Michael' (A)   ESul LDea MHer NFir
'Michelle' (Min/C)   LDea
'Michelle West' (Min)   ESul WFib
'Midas Touch' (Dw/C/d)   ESul
'Mikado' (R) **new**   ESul
'Milden' (Dw/Z/C)   ESul NFir
'Millbern Choice' (Z)   MWhe

'Millbern Clover' (Min/d)	ESul MWhe
'Millbern Engagement' (Min/d)	MWhe
'Millbern Peach' (Z)	MWhe
'Millbern Serenade'	MWhe
'Millbern Sharna' (Min/d)	ESul MWhe
'Millbern Skye' (A)	MWhe
Millennium Dawn (Dw)	LVER
'Millfield Gem' (I/d)	LVER SKen WFib
'Millfield Rose' (I/d)	EWoo LVER MWhe
'Mimi' (Dw/C/d)	ESul SSea
'Mina Lorenzen' (R) **new**	ESul
'Mini-Czech' (Min/St)	ESul LVER
'Minnie' (Z/d/St)	ESul LVER WBrk
'Minstrel Boy' (R)	CSpe ESul EWoo LDea NFir SSea WFib
'Minuet' (Z/d)	SSea
'Minx' (Min/d)	WFib
'Miranda' (Dw)	ESul
'Miss Australia' (R/v)	LDea MBPg
'Miss Burdett Coutts' (Z/v)	ESul LVER MWhe SKen SSea WFib
'Miss Flora' (I)	MWhe
'Miss Liverbird' (I/d)	ECtt
'Miss McKinsey' (Z/St/d)	LVER NFir
§ 'Miss Stapleton'	EWoo MHer SSea WFib WHPP
'Miss Wackles' (Min/d)	ESul
'Mistress' (Z/C)	NFir
'Misty' (Z)	ESul
'Misty Morning' (R) **new**	EWoo
'Modesty' (Z/d)	SKen WFib
'Mohawk' (R)	ESul LDea LVER NFir WFib
Molina = 'Fismoli'[PBR] (I/d)	NPri
'Mollie' (R)	CSpe
'Molly' (A)	NFir WHPP
'Mona Lisa'[PBR]	ESul
'Monarch' (Dw/v)	ESul
'Monica Bennett' (Dw)	ESul SKen WEas
'Monkwood Charm' (R)	ESul
'Monkwood Rhapsody' (R)	ESul
'Monkwood Rose' (A)	LDea NFir
'Monkwood Sprite' (R)	ESul LDea SMrm
'Monsal Dale' (Dw/C/d)	ESul SKen
'Monsieur Ninon' misapplied	see *P.* 'Madame Auguste Nonin'
§ 'Monsieur Ninon' (U)	CRHN EWoo MSte WFib
'Mont Blanc' (Z/v)	ESul LVER MWhe SKen WFib
'Montague Garabaldi Smith' (R)	WFib
'Moon Maiden' (A)	CSpe ESul EWoo LDea WFib
'Moor' (Min/d)	ESul
'Moppet' (Min/d)	ESul
'Morello'[PBR] (R)	ESul
'More's Victory' (U/Sc)	SSea
'Morning Cloud' (Min/d)	ESul
'Morse' (Z)	SKen
'Morval' (Dw/C/d) ♀H1+3	ESul LVER MWhe SKen WFib
'Morwenna' (R)	ESul EWoo LDea LVER MSte NFir SKen WFib
'Mosaic Gay Baby' (I/v/d)	WFib
'Mosaic Silky' (Z/C/d/v)	LVER
'Mountie' (Dw)	ESul
'Mozart' (R) **new**	ESul
'Mr Everaarts' (Dw/d)	ESul MWhe
'Mr Henry Apps' (Dw/C/d)	MWhe
'Mr Henry Cox' (Z/v) ♀H1+3	ESul LVER MHer MWhe NFir SKen WFib
'Mr Wren' (Z)	CHal LVER MWhe SKen WFib
'Mrs Cannell' (Z)	WFib
'Mrs Dumbrill' (A)	ESul LDea LIck
'Mrs Farren' (Z/v)	MWhe SKen SSea
'Mrs G.H. Smith' (A)	ESul LDea MBPg MSte MWhe NFir SSea WFib WHPP
'Mrs G. Morf' (R)	ESul SSea
'Mrs Innes Rogers' (R) **new**	ESul
'Mrs J.C. Mappin' (Z/v) ♀H1+3	SKen SSea
'Mrs Kingsbury' (U)	WEas WFib
'Mrs Langtry' (R)	LDea
'Mrs Lawrence' (Z/d)	SKen
'Mrs Martin' (I/d)	WFib
'Mrs McKenzie' (Z/St)	WFib
'Mrs Morf' (R)	LDea NFir
'Mrs Parker' (Z/d/v)	ESul LRHS LVER MWhe NFir SKen WFib
'Mrs Pat' (Dw/St/C)	MWhe NFir
'Mrs Pollock' (Z/v)	LAst LRHS LVER MWhe NEgg NVic SCoo SKen SSea WBrk WFib WHPP
'Mrs Quilter' (Z/C) ♀H1+3	LVER MBri MHer MWhe NVic SKen SSea WFib
'Mrs Salter Bevis' (Z/Ca/d)	ESul LVER WFib
'Mrs Strang' (Z/d/v)	LVER MWhe SKen SSea
'Mrs Tarrant' (Z/d)	CHal
'Mrs Taylor' (Sc)	MBPg
'Mrs W.A.R. Clifton' (I/d)	LDea WFib
multicaule	EWoo
- subsp. *multicaule*	EShb
mutans	EWoo WFib WHPP
§ 'Mutzel' (I/v)	LVER NFir
'My Chance'	EWoo NFir SSea
'My Choice' (R)	LDea
§ *myrrhifolium* var. *c oriandrifolium*	CSpe
'Mysterioso' **new**	EWoo
'Mystery' (U) ♀H1+3	EWoo LVER MBPg NFir SAga SSea WFib
'Müttertag' (R)	MSte
'Nacton' (Min)	ESul
'Nancy Grey' (Min)	ESul NFir
'Nancy Mac' (St)	ESul
'Narina' (I)	NPri SCoo
'Natalie' (Dw)	ESul
'Naughton' (Min)	ESul
'Needham Market' (A)	ESul LDea MSte WFib
'Neene' (Dw)	ESul
'Neil Clemenson' (Sc)	MBPg WFib
'Neil Jameson' (Z/v)	SKen SSea
'Nell Smith' (Z/d)	WFib
'Nellie' (R)	ESul LDea
'Nellie Green' (R) **new**	LDea
'Nellie Nuttall' (Z)	WFib
'Nervosum' (Sc)	ESul MBPg MOak
'Nervous Mabel' (Sc) ♀H1+3	ESul EWoo LDea MBPg MHer NFir WBrk WFib
'Nettlecombe' (Min/St)	ESul
'Nettlestead' (Dw/d)	ESul LVER
'Nettlestone' (Dw/d) **new**	ESul
'Nettlestone Star' (Min/St) **new**	ESul
'Neville West' (Z)	SSea
'New Day' (A)	LDea
'New Life' (Z)	ESul MWhe
'Newbridge' (St/Min/d) **new**	ESul
'Newton Rigg' (Sc)	MBPg
'Newtown' (Min/St) **new**	ESul
'Nicola Buck' (R)	LDea NFir
'Nicor Star' (Min)	ESul WFib
'Nikki' (A)	LDea
'Nimrod' (R)	LDea
'Noche' (R)	ESul LDea SKen
'Noel' (Z/Ca/d)	WFib
'Noele Gordon' (Z/d)	LVER WFib
'Nomad' (R)	EWoo
'Nono' (I)	WFib
'Norrland' (Z/d)	LVER
'Nostra'	LAst LSou
'Notting Hill Beauty' (Z)	SKen
oblongatum	CMon NFir
'Occold Embers' (Dw/C/d)	ESul NFir
'Occold Lagoon' (Dw/d)	ESul
'Occold Orange Tip' (Min/d)	ESul

'Occold Profusion' (Dw/d)	ESul NFir
'Occold Shield' (Dw/C/d)	ESul LAst LRHS NFir SDnm WBrk WFib
'Occold Tangerine' (Z)	WFib
'Occold Volcano' (Dw/C/d)	WFib
odoratissimum (Sc)	CHal ESul EWoo GBar GPoy LDea MBPg MHer NFir NHHG SKen SSea WFib
'Offton' (Dw)	ESul
'Old Orchard' (A)	LDea SSea
'Old Rose' (Z/d)	WFib
'Old Spice' (Sc/v)	ESul GBar MBPg MHer NFir SSea SWal WFib
'Oldbury Duet' (A/v)	ESul LAst LDea LSou LVER MBPg MWhe NFir SSea
'Olga Shipstone' (Sc)	EWoo MBPg WHPP
'Olivia' (R)	WHPP
'Onalee' (Dw)	ESul WFib
'Opera House' (R)	WFib
'Orange' (Z/St)	MBPg
'Orange Fizz' (Sc)	ESul EWoo GGar MNHC SDnm WBrk WHPP
'Orange Fizz' (Z/d)	LDea
'Orange Imp' (Dw/d)	ESul
'Orange Parfait' (R)	WFib
'Orange Princeanum' (Sc)	MBPg
'Orange Ricard' (Z/d)	MWhe SKen
'Orange Ruffy' (Min)	ESul
'Orange Splash' (Z)	LVER SKen
'Orangeade' (Dw/d)	LVER WFib
'Orchid Clorinda' (Sc)	MBPg WBrk WFib
'Orchid Paloma' (Dw/d)	ESul SKen
'Oregon Hostess' (Dw)	ESul
'Orion' (Min/d)	ESul MWhe SKen SSea WFib
'Orsett' (Sc) ♀H1+3	EWoo LDea LVER MBPg
'Osna' (Z)	LAst SKen
'Otto's Red' (R)	EWoo NFir
'Our Gynette' (Dec)	EWoo NFir SSea
ovale subsp. *ovale*	EShb
'Oyster' (Dw)	ESul
PAC cultivars	see under cultivar name
'Pacdy' **new**	LAst
'Paclai' **new**	LAst
'Paddie' (Min)	ESul
'Pagoda' (Z/St/d)	ESul LVER MSte MWhe SKen WFib WHPP
'Paisley Red' (Z/d)	NFir WFib
'Palais' (Z/d)	LRHS SKen
'Pam Craigie' (R)	LDea
'Pamela' (R) **new**	ESul
'Pampered Lady' (A)	LDea NFir
panduriforme	EWoo MBPg WFib
papilionaceum	CHEx CRHN EWoo MHer MOak WEas WFib
'Parisienne' (R)	ESul EWoo LDea WFib
'Parmenter Pink' (Min)	ESul
'Party Dress' (Z/d)	MWhe SKen WFib
'Pascal' (Z)	SKen
'Pat Hannam' (St)	WFib
'Paton's Unique' (U/Sc) ♀H1+3	CHal CRHN CTbh EShb EWoo LIck LVER MBPg MHer MSte NFir SPet WFib WHPP
'Patricia Andrea' (T)	ESul LVER NFir NPer WFib
'Patricia Read' (Min)	ESul
'Patsy 'Q'' (Z/C)	SKen
'Paul Crampel' (Z)	CHal MHer WFib
'Paul Gotz' (Z)	SKen
'Paul Gunnett' (Min)	MWhe
'Paul West' (Min/d)	ESul
'Paula Scott' (R)	EWoo
'Pauline' (Min/d)	ESul MWhe SSea
'Pauline Harris' (R)	LDea
'Pax' (R)	LDea
'Pazzaz'	LVER
'Peace' (Min/C)	ESul WFib
'Peace Palace' (Dw)	ESul

'Peach Princess' (R)	ESul NFir SSea
'Peaches' (Z)	LAst LSou
'Peaches and Cream' (R)	MBPg
'Peacock'	LDea
'Pearly Queen' (Min/d)	ESul
'Pebbles' (Z/Min)	LVER
'Peggy Clare' (Dw/St)	ESul
'Peggy Sue' (R)	ESul LDea LVER
'Peggy West' (Min/C/d)	SSea
PELFI cultivars	see under cultivar name
peltatum	LPhx WFib
'Penny' (Z/d)	MWhe SKen WFib
'Penny Dixon' (R)	NFir
'Penny Lane' (Z)	WFib
'Penny Serenade' (Dw/C)	ESul SKen
'Pensby' (Dw)	ESul
'Penve' **new**	LAst
'Peppermint Lace' (Sc)	EWoo LDea MBPg
'Peppermint Scented Rose' (Sc)	MBPg
'Peppermint Star' (Z/St)	ESul
'Perchance' (R)	SSea
'Percival' (Dw/d)	MWhe
'Perfect' (Z)	WFib
§ Perlenkette Orange = 'Orangepen'PBR (Quality Series) (Z/d)	LAst LSou WGor
'Perlenkette Sabine' (Quality Series) (Z/d)	LAst
'Pershore Princess'	WBrk
'Persian King' (R)	LDea
'Persian Ruler' (Min)	ESul
'Persimmon' (Z/St)	WFib
'Petals' (Z/v)	MSte SKen
'Peter Beard' (Dw/d) **new**	ESul
'Peter Godwin' (R)	ESul LDea WFib
'Peter Read' (Dw/d)	ESul
'Peter's Choice' (R)	ESul LDea WFib
'Peter's Luck' (Sc) ♀H1+3	ESul MBPg WHPP
'Petit Pierre'	see P. 'Kleine Liebling'
'Petite Blanche' (Dw/d)	SSea WFib
'Philomel' (I/d)	SPet
'Phlox New Life' (Z)	ESul
'Phyllis' (Z)	LDea SSea
'Phyllis' (U/v)	ESul EWoo LVER MBPg NFir SSea WHPP
'Phyllis Brooks' (R)	ESul
'Phyllis Read' (Min)	ESul
'Phyllis Richardson' (R/d)	ESul LDea LVER
'Picotee' **new**	SSea
'Pin Mill' (Min/d)	ESul
'Pink Aura' (Min/St)	ESul SSea
'Pink Aurore' (U)	MHer MSte WFib
'Pink Bonanza' (R)	ESul LDea WFib
'Pink Bouquet' (R)	ESul
'Pink Capitatum'	see P. 'Pink Capricorn'
§ 'Pink Capricorn' (Sc)	CRHN ESul EWoo MBPg MHer MWhe SDnm WBrk WFib
'Pink Carnation' (I/d)	LDea
'Pink Cascade'	see P. 'Hederinum'
'Pink Champagne' (Sc)	CRHN ESul EWoo MBPg MHer
'Pink Countess Mariza' (Z)	SKen
'Pink Dolly Varden' (Z/v)	SSea WFib
'Pink Domaine de Courson' (Sc)	MBPg
'Pink Flamingo' (R)	LDea
'Pink Fondant' (Min/d)	ESul WFib
'Pink Fringed Aztec' (R) **new**	ESul
'Pink Gay Baby'	see P. 'Sugar Baby'
'Pink Golden Ears' (Dw/St/C)	ESul
'Pink Golden Harry Hieover' (Z/C)	ESul
'Pink Happy Thought' (Z/v)	LAst LRHS MWhe SDnm SSea WFib WHPP

'Pink Hindoo' (Dec)	EWoo
'Pink Ice' (Min/d)	ESul NFir
'Pink Margaret Pearce' (R)	ESul
'Pink Mini Cascade'	see *P.* 'Rosa Mini-cascade'
'Pink Needles' (Min/St)	ESul
'Pink Paradox'	LDea MBPg
'Pink Rambler' (Z/d)	MWhe SKen WFib
'Pink Raspail' (Z/d)	CTbh
'Pink Rosebud' (Z/d)	WFib
'Pink Snow' (Min/d)	ESul
'Pink Splash' (Min/d)	ESul
'Pink Tiny Tim' (Min)	ESul
Pink-Blizzard =	NPri
'Fispink' (I)	
'Pippa' (Min/Dw)	ESul
'Pixie' (Min)	ESul
'Playmate' (Min/St)	ESul SKen WFib
'Plum Rambler' (Z/d)	EShb SKen SSea WFib
'Poetesse' (A)	LDea
'Polestar' (Min/St) **new**	ESul
'Polka' (U)	ESul EWoo LVER MBPg MHer NFir
	SSea WBrk WFib WHPP
'Pompeii' (R)	ESul LDea NFir WFib WHPP
'Poquita' (Sc)	MBPg
'Porchfield' (Min/St)	ESul
'Portsmouth' (R)	ESul
'Potpourri' (Min)	SKen
'Potter Heigham' (Dw)	ESul
'Powder Puff' (Dw/d)	WFib
'Presto' (Dw/St)	ESul MWhe
'Preston Park' (Z/C)	SKen SPet WFib
'Pretty Girl' (I)	LDea
'Pretty Petticoat' (Z/d)	WFib
'Pretty Polly' (Sc)	LDea MBPg WFib
'Pride of Exmouth'	CStu
'Prim' (Dw/St/d)	ESul WFib
'Prince Consort' (R)	LDea
'Prince of Orange' (Sc)	CArn CRHN CSev CTbh EOHP
	ESul EWoo GBar GPoy LDea Llck
	LVER MBPg MHer MSte MWhe
	NFir NHHG Slde SSea WFib WHPP
'Princeanum' (Sc) ♀H1+3	MBPg MHer WFib
'Princess Alexandra' (R)	SSea
'Princess Alexandra'	ESul MWhe NFir
(Z/d/v)	
'Princess Anne' (Z)	MSte
'Princess Josephine' (R)	LDea WFib WHPP
'Princess of Balcon'	see *P.* 'Roi des Balcons Lilas'
'Princess of Wales' (R)	ESul LDea SSea WFib
'Princess Virginia' (R/v)	ESul Llck LVER WFib
'Priory Salmon' (St/d)	ESul
'Priory Star' (St/Min/d)	ESul
new	
'Prospect' (Z/d)	MWhe
'Prosperity'	LDea MBPg
pseudoglutinosum	EWoo WFib
'Pungent Peppermint' (Sc)	MBPg
'Purple Ball'	see *P.* Purpurball, *P.* Purpurball 2
'Purple Emperor' (R)	ESul LDea WFib
'Purple Flare' (St) **new**	ESul
'Purple Heart' (Dw/St/C)	ESul NFir
'Purple Muttertag' (R)	ESul
I 'Purple Radula Rosea' (Sc)	MBPg
'Purple Rambler' (Z/d)	ESul MWhe
'Purple Unique' (U/Sc)	CSpe EShb ESul EWoo LDea MHer
	MOak MSte NFir SKen SSea WFib
§ Purpurball (Z/d)	LAst SKen
§ Purpurball 2 =	LAst LSou
'Penbalu'PBR (Quality	
Series) (Z/d)	
'Pygmalion' (Z/d/v)	SSea WFib
'Quakeress' (R)	ESul
'Quakermaid' (Min)	ESul
'Quantock' (R)	ESul WFib
'Quantock Beauty' (A)	ESul LDea MWhe NFir
'Quantock Blonde' (A)	LDea NFir

'Quantock Butterfly' (A)	NFir
'Quantock Candy' (A)	EWoo NFir
'Quantock Chloe' (A)	NFir
'Quantock Cobwebs' (A)	NFir
new	
'Quantock Darren' (A) **new**	NFir
'Quantock Dragonfly' (A)	NFir
'Quantock Flamenco' (A)	NFir
new	
'Quantock Jayne' (A) **new**	ESul
'Quantock Kendy' (A)	ESul LDea NFir
'Quantock Kirsty' (A)	LDea NFir
'Quantock Marjorie' (A)	ESul LDea MBPg MWhe NFir
'Quantock Matty' (A)	ESul EWoo LDea MWhe NFir
'Quantock Maureen Ward'	NFir
(A)	
'Quantock May' (A)	EWoo LDea NFir SSea
'Quantock Medoc' (A)	ESul LDea MBPg NFir
'Quantock Millennium' (A)	ESul LDea MBPg NFir
'Quantock Mr Nunn' (A)	NFir
'Quantock Philip' (A)	ESul MBPg
'Quantock Picotee' (A)	NFir
new	
'Quantock Piksi' (A)	NFir
'Quantock Plume' (A)	MBPg NFir
'Quantock Rita' (A)	MWhe
'Quantock Rory' (A)	LDea
'Quantock Rose' (A)	ESul EWoo LDea MBPg NFir
'Quantock Sapphire' (A)	LDea NFir
'Quantock Sarah' (A)	ESul NFir
'Quantock Shirley' (A)	ESul LDea NFir
'Quantock Star' (A)	LDea MBPg MWhe NFir
'Quantock Star Gazer' (A)	NFir
'Quantock Starlet' (A) **new**	NFir
'Quantock Ultimate' (A)	ESul MBPg NFir
'Quantock Victoria' (A)	ESul MBPg NFir
'Queen of Denmark' (Z/d)	WFib
'Queen of Hearts' (I x Z/d)	LVER WFib
'Queen of Sheba' (R)	LDea
'Queen of the Lemons'	CTbh EWoo
N *quercifolium* (Sc)	CHal CRHN CSev EWoo GPoy
	MBPg MHer NFir NHHG SKen
	SYvo WFib WHPP
– variegated (v)	MBPg MHer
quinquelobatum	CSpe
'R.A. Turner' (Z/d)	WFib
'Rachel' (Min)	ESul
radens (Sc)	EPfP WFib
'Rads Star' (Z/St)	ESul NFir SSea WFib
'Radula' (Sc) ♀H1+3	CSev ESul EWoo GBar LDea Llck
	MBPg MHer MNHC MOak MWhe
	SSea WFib WHPP
'Radula Roseum' (Sc)	EWoo MBPg SSea WFib
radulifolium	CMon
'Ragamuffin' (Dw/d)	ESul MWhe
'Rager's Pink' (Dw/d)	ESul
'Rager's Star' (Dw)	ESul
'Rager's Veri-Star' (Min/C)	ESul
'Ragtime' (St)	NPri
'Rakastani' (Z)	SKen
'Raphael' (A)	LDea
'Raspberry Parfait' (R)	LDea
'Raspberry Ripple' (A)	ESul LDea MWhe NFir SSea WFib
	WHPP
'Raspberry Surprise' (R)	ESul LVER SSea
'Raspberry Yhu' (R) **new**	ESul
'Ray Bidwell' (Min)	ESul LVER MWhe NFir
'Raydon' (Min)	ESul
I 'Rebecca' (Sc) **new**	MBPg
'Rebecca' (Min/d)	ESul WFib
'Red Admiral' (Min/d/v)	ESul SKen
§ 'Red Black Vesuvius'	CHal ESul MWhe SKen SSea WEas
(Min/C)	WFib
'Red Cactus' (St)	NFir
'Red Capri' (Sc)	MBPg
§ 'Red Cascade' (I) ♀H1+3	MWhe WFib

'Red Gables'	WHPP
'Red Galilee' (I/d)	MWhe
'Red Glow' (Min)	ESul
'Red Ice' (Min/d)	ESul MWhe NFir
'Red Magic Lantern' (Z/C)	SKen
'Red Pandora' (T)	LVER NFir WFib
'Red Pimpernella' **new**	LVER
'Red Rambler' (Z/d)	CHal ESul LVER MWhe SKen WBrk
	WFib
Red Satisfaction =	LAst
'Usredsat'PBR (Z/d)	
'Red Silver Cascade'	see *P.* 'Mutzel'
'Red Spider' (Dw/Ca)	ESul WFib
'Red Startel' (Z/St/d)	MWhe SKen WFib
'Red Susan Pearce' (R)	ESul WFib
'Red Sybil Holmes' (I)	LSou WFib
Red Sybil = 'Pensyb'PBR	LAst LSou
(I/d)	
'Red Unique' (U)	CTbh
'Red Witch' (Dw/St/d)	ESul LVER WFib
Red-Blizzard =	NPri SCoo
'Fizzard'PBR (I)	
§ Red-Mini-Cascade =	ESul LAst LDea LVER MWhe SKen
'Rotemica' (I)	WFib
'Redondo' (Dw/d)	ESul LVER MWhe
'Reflections' (Z/d)	WFib
'Reg 'Q'' (Z/C)	NFir
'Regina' (Z/d)	LVER NFir SKen WFib
'Rembrandt' (R)	LDea LVER SSea WFib
'Renate Parsley'	EShb ESul MBPg NFir WFib
'Rene Roué' (Dw/d/v)	ESul NFir
reniforme	EWoo GBar MBPg MHer SSea SUsu
	WFib
'Retah's Crystal' (Z/v)	ESul LRHS LVER MWhe
'Rhian Harris' (A)	LDea
Rhodonit = 'Paccherry'PBR	LAst
(I/d)	
'Richard Gibbs' (Sc)	EWoo GGar LDea MBPg MHer
'Richard Key' (Z/d/C)	WFib
'Ricky Promise' (A)	LDea
'Ricky Ruby' (A)	LDea
'Rietje van der Lee' (A)	ESul WFib
'Rigel' (Min/d)	ESul LVER MWhe NFir SKen
'Rigi' (I/d)	MBri SKen
'Rigoletto' (I)	LDea NFir
'Rimey' (St)	NFir
'Rimfire' (R)	ESul EWoo LDea LVER NFir WFib
'Rio Grande' (I/d)	LDea LVER MWhe NFir SKen SPet
	WFib
'Rising Sun'	NFir
'Rita Scheen' (A/v)	ESul LDea MWhe SSea
'Ritchie' (R)	ESul
'Robbie Hare' (R)	ESul
'Robe'PBR (Quality Series)	LAst LRHS LVER
(Z/d)	
'Rober's Lemon Rose' (Sc)	CRHN ESul EWoo GBar LDea
	MBPg MHer SIde SKen SSea
	WBrk
'Rober's Salmon Coral'	ESul
(Dw/d)	
'Robert Fish' (Z/C)	ESul LRHS SCoo
'Robert McElwain'	WFib
'Robin' (Sc)	LDea LVER MBPg
'Robin' (R)	LDea
'Robin's Unique' (U)	EWoo NFir SSea WFib
'Robyn Hannah' (St) **new**	NFir
'Roger's Delight' (R/Sc)	EWoo MBPg
'Rogue' (R)	ESul EWoo MSte WFib
'Roi des Balcons'	see *P.* 'Hederinum'
§ 'Roi des Balcons Impérial'	MWhe
(I) ♀H1+3	
§ 'Roi des Balcons Lilas' (I)	LSou MWhe SKen WFib
♀H1+3	
'Roi des Balcons Rose'	see *P.* 'Hederinum'
'Roller's Echo' (A)	ESul LDea LIck MWhe WFib
'Roller's Pathfinder' (I/d/v)	LDea LVER

'Roller's Pioneer' (I/v)	EWoo LDea LVER SKen SSea
'Roller's Satinique' (U)	EWoo LIck MBPg MHer SSea
♀H1+3	WHPP
'Roller's Shadow' (A)	ESul EWoo LDea
'Rollisson's Unique' (U)	MBPg MHer MSte NBur SSea WFib
'Romeo' (R)	CSpe EWoo LVER WHPP
§ 'Romy' (I)	LDea
'Rookley' (St/d) **new**	ESul
§ 'Rosa Mini-cascade' (I)	ESul LAst LVER MWhe NFir
'Rosaleen' (Min)	ESul
'Rosalie' (R)	ESul
'Rose Bengal' (A)	CRHN ESul LDea MWhe WFib
Rose Evka = 'Penevro'PBR	(Dw/I/v) LAst NFir
'Rose Irene' (Z/d)	MWhe
'Rose Jewel' (R)	ESul
'Rose of Amsterdam'	ESul
(Min/d)	
'Rose Paton's Unique'	LDea
(U/Sc)	
'Rose Silver Cascade' (I)	LDea LVER
'Rosebud Supreme' (Z/d)	ESul WFib
'Rosecrystal'PBR	LVER
(Sweetheart Series) (Z/d)	
'Rosemarie' (Z/d)	MWhe
'Rosemary Reville' (R)	EWoo
'Rosina Read' (Dw/d)	ESul
'Rosmaroy' (R)	ESul LDea NFir WFib
§ 'Rospen' (Z/d)	SKen
'Rosy Dawn' (Min/d)	WFib
'Rosy Morn' (R)	NFir
'Rote Mini-cascade'	see *P.* Red-Mini-Cascade =
	'Rotemica'
§ 'Rouletta' (I/d)	ECtt LAst LDea LVER MWhe NBlu
	NPri SKen WFib
'Round Leaf Rose' (U)	MBPg
'Rousillon' (R)	LDea
'Royal Ascot' (R)	CHal ESul EWoo LDea MSte NFir
	SPet SSea WHPP
'Royal Carpet' (Min/d)	ESul
'Royal Court' (R)	LDea
'Royal Decree' (R)	LDea
'Royal Guernsey' (R)	EWoo
'Royal Magic' (R) **new**	LDea
'Royal Norfolk' (Min/d)	ESul LVER MWhe NFir SKen
'Royal Oak' (Sc) ♀H1+3	CRHN CSev CTbh EAro ESul EWoo
	GBar LDea MBPg MHer MNHC
	MWhe NBur SGar SPet SSea WFib
	WRha
'Royal Opera' (R)	LDea
'Royal Pride' (R)	LDea
* 'Royal Princess' (R) ♀H1+3	LDea
§ 'Royal Purple' (Z/d)	CHal LVER SKen WFib
'Royal Sovereign' (Z/C/d)	LDea
'Royal Star' (R)	LDea
'Royal Surprise' (R)	ESul EWoo LDea NFir
'Royal Wedding' (R)	ESul
'Royal Winner' (R)	EWoo LDea
'Rubi Lee' (A)	MWhe
'Rubin Improved' (Z/d)	SKen
'Ruby' (Min/d)	ESul WFib
Ruby Dream = 'Fisruby'	NPri
(I) **new**	
'Ruby Orchid' (A)	LDea NFir WHPP
'Ruby Wedding' (Z)	ESul
'Ruffled Velvet' (R)	EWoo SSea
'Rushmere' (Dw/d)	ESul WFib
'Rusty' (Dw/C/d)	ESul
'Sabine'PBR (Z/d)	LVER
'Saint Elmo's Fire'	WFib
(St/Min/d)	
'Saint Helen's Favourite'	ESul SSea
(Min)	
Saint Malo = 'Guisaint'PBR (I)	LAst
'Sally Munro' (R)	LDea SSea
'Sally Read' (Dw/d)	ESul
'Salmon Beauty' (Dw/d)	WFib

'Salmon Black Vesuvius' (Min/C)	ESul
§ 'Salmon Irene' (Z/d)	WFib
'Salmon Queen'	see *P.* 'Lachskönigin'
'Salmon Startel' (Z/St/d)	MWhe
salmoneum	SSea
'Saltford' (R)	ESul
'Samantha' (R)	ESul WFib
'Samantha Stamp' (Dw/d/C)	WFib
Samelia = 'Pensam'[PBR] (Dark Line Series) (Z/d)	LAst LSou
'Sammi Brougham' (Dw/Z) **new**	ESul
'Sammi Caws' (St) **new**	ESul
'Sancho Panza' (Dec) ♥H1+3	CSpe ESul EWoo LDea LVER MBPg MHer MSte SKen SSea WFib WHPP
'Sandford' (Dw/St)	ESul
'Sandown' (Dw/d)	ESul
'Sandra Lorraine' (I/d)	WFib
'Sanguineum'	CSpe WHPP
'Santa Maria' (Z/d)	SKen
'Santa Marie' (R)	LDea
'Santa Paula' (I/d)	ECtt LDea SKen
'Sarah Don'[PBR] (A/v)	WFib
'Sarah Hunt' (Min) **new**	NFir
'Sarah Jane' (Sc)	MBPg
'Sassa'[PBR] (Quality Series) (Z/d)	LAst LSou WGor
'Satsuki' (R)	ESul LDea NFir
§ *scabrum*	EWoo MBPg
'Scarlet Gem' (Z/St)	WFib
* 'Scarlet Kewense' (Dw)	ESul
'Scarlet Nosegay'	CHal
I 'Scarlet O'Hara' (Z)	LVER
'Scarlet Pet' (U)	CRHN ESul MBPg NFir
'Scarlet Pimpernel' (Z/C/d)	ESul
'Scarlet Rambler' (Z/d)	EShb EWoo SSea WFib
'Scarlet Unique' (U)	CHrt CRHN CTbh EWoo LDea MHer MSte NFir SKen SSea WFib
schizopetalum	WFib
§ 'Schneekönigin' (I/d)	ECtt LDea LVER MSte SKen
x *schottii*	see *P.* 'Schottii'
§ 'Schottii'	NFir WFib
'Secret Love' (Sc)	EWoo LDea MBPg
'Seeley's Pansy' (A)	EWoo LDea MHer SAga WFib WHPP
'Sefton' (R) ♥H1+3	ESul LDea WFib WHPP
'Selecta Royal Amethyst' **new**	NBlu
'Selecta Royal Blue' (I)	LSou
'Selena' (Min)	LDea
'Semer' (Min)	ESul SKen
* 'Serre de la Madone' (Sc)	WEas
'Shalfleet' (Min/St) **new**	ESul
'Shalimar' (St)	MSte NFir WHPP
'Shanks' (Z)	NFir
'Shannon'	WFib
'Sharon' (Min/d)	ESul
'Sheila' (Dw)	ESul
'Shelley' (Dw)	ESul SKen
'Sheraton' (Min/d)	MWhe
'Shimmer' (Z/d)	LVER MWhe
'Shirley Ash' (A)	LDea WFib
'Shirley Gillam' (Z/St/v) **new**	LVER
Shocking Pink = 'Pensho'[PBR] (Quality Series) (Z/d)	LAst
Shocking Violet = 'Pacshovi'[PBR] (Quality Series) (Z/d)	LAst LSou WGor
'Shogan' (R)	NFir
'Shorwell' (Dw/C/d) **new**	ESul
'Shottesham Pet' (Sc)	ESul EWoo MBPg MHer
'Show Off' (Z)	LVER
'Shrubland Pet' (U/Sc)	EWoo MHer SSea
'Shrubland Rose' (Sc)	SSea WHPP
'Sid' (R)	LDea
sidoides	CSpe EBee EPyc ERea EShb ESul EWoo IFro LPhx MBPg MHer MWea NFir SMrm SSea WCot WEas WFib
- black	CSpe SUsu
- 'Sloe Gin Fizz'	CSpe
Sidonia = 'Pensid'[PBR] (Dark Line Series) (Z/d) **new**	LAst LSou WGor
'Sienna' (R)	ESul LDea NFir
'Sil Frauke' **new**	LAst
'Sil Friesia'[PBR] (Z) **new**	LAst
'Sil Gesa' **new**	LAst
'Sil Pia'[PBR] (I) **new**	LAst
'Sil Raiko'[PBR] **new**	LAst
'Sil Rumika'[PBR] **new**	LAst
'Sil Sören' **new**	LAst LSou
'Sil Tedo' **new**	LAst LSou
'Sil Teske'[PBR] (I) **new**	LAst
'Silver Anne' (R/v)	ESul NFir
'Silver Delight' (v/d)	WFib
'Silver Kewense' (Dw/v)	ESul WFib
'Silver Leaf Rose' (Sc)	MBPg
'Silver Rimfire' (R) **new**	ESul
'Silver Wings' (Z/v)	ESul LRHS LVER MWhe SSea
'Silvia' (R)	ESul
'Simon Read' (Dw)	ESul
'Sir Colin' (Z)	SSea
'Skelly's Pride' (Z)	LVER SKen WEas WFib
'Skies of Italy' (Z/C/d)	CHal MBri MHer SKen SSea WFib
'Small Fortune' (Min/d)	ESul SKen
'Smuggler' (R)	LDea
'Snape' (Min)	ESul
'Sneezy' (Min)	ESul NFir
'Snow Cap' (MinI)	NFir
'Snow Flurry' (Sc)	MBPg WBrk
Snow Queen	see *P.* 'Schneekönigin'
'Snow White' (Min)	ESul
'Snowbaby' (Min/d)	ESul
'Snowberry' (R)	ESul
'Snowbright' (St/d) **new**	ESul
'Snowdrift' (I/d)	LVER WFib
'Snowflake' (Min)	see *P.* 'Atomic Snowflake'
'Snowmass' (Z/d)	MWhe
'Snowstorm' (Z)	SKen WFib
'Snowy Baby' (Min/d)	WFib
'Sofie'	see *P.* 'Decora Rose'
'Solent Waves' (R)	ESul LDea
'Solferino' (A)	ESul LDea
§ Solidor (I/d) ♥H1+3	LDea NFir
Solo = 'Guillio' (Z/I)	LVER
'Somersham' (Min)	ESul WFib
'Something Else' (Z/St/d) **new**	LVER
'Something Special' (Z/d)	LVER MWhe NFir WFib
'Sonata' (Dw/d)	ESul
'Sophie' (R) **new**	ESul
Sophie Casade	see *P.* 'Decora Rose'
'Sophie Caws' (St) **new**	ESul
'Sophie Dumaresque' (Z/v)	MBri MWhe NFir SKen SSea WFib
'Sorcery' (Dw/C)	ESul MWhe SKen
'Sound Appeal' (A)	ESul LDea MBPg
'South African Sun' (Z/d)	LVER
'South American Bronze' (R) ♥H1+3	ESul LDea SKen WFib WHPP
'South American Pink' (R) **new**	ESul
'South Walsham Broad' (Dw)	ESul
'Southern Belle' (A)	LDea SSea
'Southern Belle' (Z/d)	WFib
'Southern Cherub' (A)	LDea
'Southern Gem' (Min/d)	ESul

'Southern Peach' (Min/d) ESul
'Souvenir' (R) CHal ESul LDea SSea
'Souvenir de Prue' **new** EWoo
'Sowoma Lavender' (Sc) MBPg
'Spanish Angel' (A) ♀H1+3 ESul LDea NFir SSea WFib
'Spanish Banks' (Z/St/v) LVER
  new
'Sparkler' (Z) LVER
'Spellbound' (R) WFib
'Spital Dam' (Dw/d) ESul
'Spitfire' (Z/Ca/d/v) ESul LVER WFib WHPP
'Spithead Cherry' (R) LDea
'Splash Down' SSea
§ 'Splendide' CRHN CSpe EShb ESul MBPg
    MHer NFir SSea SWvt WCot WEas
    WFib WHPP
'Splendide' white-flowered MBPg
'Spotlite Hotline' (I) LDea
'Spotlite Winner' (I) LDea
'Spot-on-bonanza' (R) ESul LDea NFir WFib
'Spring Bride' (R) LDea
'Spring Park' (A) ESul LVER WFib
I 'Springfield Alba' (R) **new** ESul
'Springfield Ann' (R) ESul
'Springfield Black' (R) ESul EWoo LDea LVER SSea
'Springfield Charm' (R) ESul
'Springfield Joy' (R) **new** ESul
'Springfield Pearl' (R) ESul LDea
'Springfield Purple' (R) ESul
'Springfield Unique' (R) ESul LDea
'Springtime' (Z/d) MWhe SKen WFib
I 'Springtime' (R) **new** ESul
'Sprite' (Min/v) MWhe
'Sproughton' (Dw) ESul
'Stacey' (R) ESul LDea
'Stadt Bern' (Z/C) LAst LRHS LSou LVER MBri MSte
    MWhe NFir SKen
'Staplegrove Fancy' (Z) SKen
x *stapletoniae* see *P.* 'Miss Stapleton'
'Star Flair' (St/Min/d) **new** ESul
'Star Flecks' NFir
'Star of Persia' (Z/Ca/d) WFib WHPP
'Star Storm' (St/d) **new** ESul
'Starflecks' (St) LVER
'Starlet' (Ca) WFib
'Starlight' (R) WFib
'Starlight Magic' (A) ♀H1+3 ESul LDea
'Starry Eyes' (Dw) ESul
'Stella Read' (Dw/d) ESul
'Stellar Arctic Star' see *P.* 'Arctic Star'
'Stellar Cathay' (Z/St/d) LRHS
'Stellar Hannaford Star' see *P.* 'Hannaford Star'
'Stephen Read' (Min) ESul
'Stewart Meehan' (R) LDea
'Strawberries and Cream' NFir
  (Z/St)
'Strawberry Fayre' (Dw/St) LVER
'Strawberry Sundae' (R) ESul LDea MSte WFib WHPP
'Stringer's Delight' (Dw/v) ESul LVER
'Stringer's Souvenir' SSea
  (Dw/d/v)
'Stuart Mark' (R) LDea
'Stutton' (Min) ESul
'Suffolk Agate' (R) ESul
'Suffolk Amethyst' (A) ESul
'Suffolk Coral' (R) ESul
'Suffolk Emerald' (A) ESul
'Suffolk Garnet' (Dec) ESul MWhe
'Suffolk Jade' (Min) ESul
'Suffolk Jet' (Min) ESul
§ 'Sugar Baby' (DwI) ECtt ESul LDea MBri SKen
    WFib
'Summer Cloud' (Z/d) WFib
'Summer Rose Lilac' (I) NPri
'Summertime' (Z/d) see *P.* 'Deacon Summertime'
'Sun Rocket' (Dw/d) MWhe WFib

'Sundridge Moonlight' WFib
  (Z/C)
'Sunraysia' (Z/St) WFib
'Sunridge Moonlight' (Dw) NFir
'Sunset Snow' (R) ESul LVER NFir WFib
'Sunspot' (Min/C) NFir
'Sunspot Kleine Liebling' WFib
  (Min)
'Sunspot Petit Pierre' WFib
  (Min/v)
'Sunstar' (Min/d) ESul WFib
'Super Rose' (I) SKen SPet
'Super Rupert' (Sc) MBPg
'Supernova' (Z/St/d) ESul MWhe SKen WFib
'Surcouf' (I) EWoo WFib
'Susan Hillier' (R) LDea
'Susan Payne' (Dw/d) ESul LVER MHer
'Susan Pearce' (R) ESul LDea LVER SKen
'Susan Read' (Dw) ESul
'Susie "Q" (Z/C) LVER MWhe SKen SSea
'Sussex Delight' (Min) SPet
'Sussex Gem' (Min/d) ESul SKen WFib
'Sussex Lace' see *P.* 'White Mesh'
'Swainham Mellow Yellow' LVER
  (Z)
'Swan Lake' (Min) ESul
'Swanland Lace' (I/d/v) WFib
'Swedish Angel' (A) ESul EWoo LDea MWhe NFir SSea
    WFib
'Sweet Lady Mary' (Sc) LDea MBPg
'Sweet Mimosa' (Sc) CHal CRHN ESul EWoo LIck LVER
  ♀H1+3 MBPg MHer MSte NFir SDnm SKen
    SSea WBrk WFib
'Sweet Miriam' (Sc) LDea MBPg WHPP
'Sweet Olivia' (Dec) **new** EWoo
'Sweet Rosina' (Sc) MBPg
'Sweet Sixteen' WFib
'Sweet Sue' (Min) ESul
'Swilland' (A) LDea MWhe WFib WHPP
'Sybil Bradshaw' (R) LDea
'Sybil Holmes' (I/d) ECtt LAst LVER MBri MWhe NBlu
    SKen SPet WFib
'Sylbar' (R) **new** ESul
'Sylvia' (R) ESul
'Sylvia Gale' (R) ESul
'Sylvia Marie' (Dw/d) MWhe NFir SKen
'Taffety' (Min) ESul WFib
'Tamie' (Dw/d) ESul MWhe NFir
'Tammy' (Dw/d) ESul MWhe
'Tangerine' (Min/Ca/d) ESul LVER SSea WFib WHPP
'Tangerine Elf' (St) WFib
§ 'Tango' (Z/d) WHPP
Tango Pink = 'Fisgopi'PBR LAst
'Tanzy' (Min) ESul
'Tapestry' (R) WEas
'Tapriz' (R) **new** ESul
'Taspo' (R) ESul
'Tattingstone' (Min) ESul
'Tattoo' (Min) ESul
'Tavira' (I/d) LVER SPet
'Tazi' (Dw) ESul
'Ted Dutton' (R) ESul
'Telstar' (Min/d) ESul SKen
§ 'Telston's Prima' (R) ESul LDea WHPP
'Tenderly' (Dw/d) ESul
'Tenerife Magic' (MinI/d) ESul
tetragonum CRHN EShb EWoo MBPg MHer
    SHFr SSea WFib
'The Alde' **new** EWoo
'The Axe' (A) LDea MWhe
'The Barle' (A) ♀H1+3 LDea MWhe WFib
'The Boar' (Fr) ♀H1+3 EShb EWoo LDea MSte SRms WFib
    WHPP
'The Bray' (A) LDea
'The Creedy' (A) LDea
'The Culm' (A) ESul EWoo LDea MSte WFib

'The Czar'	see *P.* 'Czar'
'The Dart' (A)	LDea
'The Heddon' (A)	LDea
'The Joker' (I/d)	WFib
'The Kenn-Lad' (A)	LDea NFir
'The Lowman' (A)	LDea
'The Lyn' (A)	ESul EWoo LDea MWhe
'The Mole' (A)	ESul LDea LVER MBPg MHer MSte WFib WHPP
'The Okement' (A)	EWoo LDea MSte MWhe NFir
'The Otter' (A)	ESul LDea MWhe
'The Speaker' (Z/d)	SKen
'The Tamar' (A)	CFee EWoo LDea
'The Tone' (A) ♀H1+3	EWoo LDea MWhe
'Thomas' (Sc) **new**	MBPg
'Thomas Gerald' (Dw/C)	ESul SKen
'Tilly' (Min)	CHal NFir
'Tim' (Min)	ESul
'Timothy Clifford' (Min/d)	ESul MWhe
'Tinkerbell' (A)	LDea
§ 'Tip Top Duet' (A) ♀H1+3	CHal ESul EWoo LAst LDea LIck LRHS LSou MHer MWhe NFir SKen SSea WFib
'Tom Portas' (Dw/d)	ESul
'Tomcat' PBR (I/d)	LAst LSou LVER SSea
tomentosum (Sc) ♀H1+3	CArn CHEx CHal CRHN CSev CSpe CTbh EAro EShb ESul EWoo GBar GPoy IFro LDea LVER MBPg MHer MNHC MOak MWhe NFir NHHG SSea WFib WHPP
- 'Chocolate'	see *P.* 'Chocolate Peppermint'
'Tomgirl' (A) **new**	LSou
Tomgirl = 'Pactomgi' PBR (IxZ/d)	LAst LSou LVER
'Tommay's Delight' (R)	LDea
'Tony' (Min)	ESul
'Topan' (R)	ESul
'Topcliffe' (Dw/St)	ESul
'Topscore' (Z/d)	SKen WFib
'Tornado' (R)	ESul NFir SAga WFib WHPP
'Torrento' (Sc)	ESul EWoo LDea MBPg MHer SKen WFib
'Tortoiseshell' (R)	WFib
'Tracy' (Min/d)	ESul NFir
transvaalense	EWoo NFir
tricolor misapplied	see *P.* 'Splendide'
tricuspidatum **new**	EWoo
trifidum	EWoo MBPg SSea WFib WHPP
'Trimley' (Dw/d)	ESul
'Trinket' (Min/d)	WFib
'Triomphe de Nancy' (Z/d)	WFib
triste	CMon EBee EWoo WFib
'Trixie' (R)	LDea
'Trudie' (Dw/Fr)	ESul LVER MHer SHFr SKen WBrk WFib
'Trulls Hatch' (Z/d)	MWhe SKen
'Tu Tone' (Dw/d)	ESul
'Tuddenham' (Min/d)	ESul
'Tuesday's Child' (Dw/C)	ESul SKen
'Tunias Perfecta' (R)	ESul
'Turkish Coffee' (R)	ESul LVER NFir WFib
'Turkish Delight' (Dw/C)	ESul MWhe NFir SSea WFib
'Turtle's Surprise' (Z/d/v)	SKen
'Tuyo' (R)	WFib
'Tweedle-Dum' (Dw)	ESul MWhe
'Twinkle' (Min/d)	ESul WFib
'Tyabb Princess' (R)	EWoo
'Ullswater' (Dw/C)	ESul
§ 'Unique Aurore' (U)	LVER MBPg MHer MSte SKen
'Unique Mons Ninon'	see *P.* 'Monsieur Ninon'
'Unity' (Dw)	LVER
urbanum	EShb
'Urchin' (Min)	ESul MWhe NFir SHFr WFib
'Ursula Key' (Z/c)	SKen WFib
'Valencia' (R)	ESul
'Valentina' (Min/d)	ESul
'Valentine'	ESul WFib
'Valentine' (R)	ESul
'Vancouver Centennial' (Dw/St/C) ♀H1+3	CSpe ESul LAst LRHS LVER MBri MHer MWhe NFir SCoo SDnm SHFr SKen SPoG SSea WFib WHPP
'Vandersea'	EWoo
'Variegated Attar of Roses' (Sc/v)	MBPg
§ 'Variegated Clorinda' (Sc/v)	EWoo WFib
'Variegated Fragrans'	see *P.* (Fragrans Group) 'Fragrans Variegatum'
'Variegated Joy Lucille' (Sc/v)	MBPg
§ 'Variegated Kleine Liebling' (Min/v)	ESul SSea WFib
'Variegated Madame Layal' (A/v) ♀H1+3	WFib
'Variegated Petit Pierre' (Min/v)	MWhe WFib
'Vasco da Gama' (Dw/d)	ESul
'Vectis Allure' (Z/St)	LVER
'Vectis Blaze' (I)	EWoo
'Vectis Cascade'	EWoo
'Vectis Dream' (St) **new**	ESul
'Vectis Fanfare' (St/d) **new**	ESul
'Vectis Finery' (St/d) **new**	ESul
'Vectis Glitter' (Z/St)	CSpe ESul LVER MWhe NFir SSea WFib
'Vectis Sparkler' (Dw/St)	ESul
'Vectis Spider' (St/dw)	ESul
'Velvet' (Z)	LVER
'Velvet Duet' (A) ♀H1+3	CHal EWoo LAst LDea LIck LRHS LVER MBPg MWhe NFir SKen SSea
'Venus' (Min/d)	ESul LRHS
'Vera Dillon' (Z)	SKen
'Vera Vernon' (Z/v)	SSea
'Verdale' (A)	GGar LDea WFib
'Verity Palace' (R)	ESul EWoo LDea WFib
'Verona' (Z/C)	CHal MBri SKen SSea
'Verona Contreras' (A)	ESul LDea MWhe NFir WFib
'Veronica' (Z/d)	MWhe SKen
'Vicki Town' (R)	WFib
'Vicky' **new**	WGor
'Vicky Claire' (R)	CSpe ESul LDea NFir SKen WFib
'Vickybar' (R) **new**	ESul
Victor = 'Pacvi' PBR (Quality Series) (Z/d)	LAst
'Victoria' (Z/d)	LAst LSou SKen
'Victoria Regina' (R)	ESul LDea
'Viking' (Min/d)	SKen
'Viking Red' (Z)	MWhe
'Village Hill Oak' (Sc)	ESul LDea MBPg MHer
Ville de Dresden = 'Pendresd' PBR (I)	LAst LSou
'Ville de Paris'	see *P.* 'Hederinum'
'Vina' (Dw/C/d)	ESul MWhe SKen WFib
'Vincent Gerris' (A)	ESul LDea MWhe
Vinco = 'Guivin' PBR (I/d)	LSou WGor WHPP
violareum misapplied	see *P.* 'Splendide'
'Violet Lambton' (Z/v)	WFib
'Violet Unique' (U)	MHer
I 'Violetta' (R)	EWoo LDea WFib
'Virginia' (R)	LDea SPet
'Viscossisimum' (Sc)	MHer SKen
viscosum	see *P. glutinosum*
§ *vitifolium*	MBPg
'Viva' (R)	ESul
'Vivat Regina' (Z/d)	WFib
'Voo Doo' (Dec)	ESul
'Voodoo' (U) ♀H1+3	CBrm CSpe EShb EWoo LAst LSou MBPg MHer MSte NCiC NFir SSea SUsu WCot WFib WHPP
'Wallace Fairman' (R)	LDea
'Wallis Friesdorf' (Dw/C/d)	ESul MWhe

'Wantirna' (Z/v)	ECtt LIck LVER MHer NFir SSea
'Warrenorth Coral' (Z/C/d)	LVER NFir SSea WFib
'Warrion' (Z/d)	LVER SSea
'Washbrook' (Min/d)	ESul NFir
'Watersmeet' (R)	LDea
'Wattisham' (Dec)	LDea
'Waveney' (Min)	ESul
'Wayward Angel' (A)	ESul LDea LVER MWhe SSea WFib
♀H1+3	
'Wedding Royale' (Dw/d)	ESul WFib
'Welcome' (Z/d)	WFib
'Welling' (Sc)	ESul GBar LDea LVER MBPg NFir
'Wendy' (Min)	LAst
'Wendy Anne'	SKen
'Wendy Jane' (Dw/d)	WFib
'Wendy Read' (Dw/d)	ESul MWhe WFib
'Wendy-O' (R)	LDea
'Wensum' (Min/d)	ESul
'Westdale Appleblossom'	ESul LVER SSea WBrk WFib
(Z/d/C)	
'Westerfield' (Min) **new**	ESul
'Wherstead' (Min)	ESul
'Whisper' (R)	WFib
'White Bird's Egg' (Z)	WFib
'White Boar' (Fr)	EShb EWoo MSte WFib
'White Bonanza' (R)	ESul WFib
'White Charm' (R)	ESul LDea
'White Chiffon' (R)	ESul LVER
'White Duet' (A)	LDea MWhe
'White Eggshell' (Min)	ESul LVER WFib
'White Feather' (Z/St)	MHer
'White Glory' (R) ♀H1+3	ESul NFir
'White Lively Lady' (Dw/C)	ESul
§ 'White Mesh' (I/v)	ECtt MBri SKen
'White Prince of Orange'	MBPg
(Sc)	
'White Roc' (Min/d)	ESul
'White Truffle'	LAst
'White Unique' (U)	CHal EWoo LDea MBPg MHer
	MSte SPet SSea WFib WHPP
'White Velvet Duet' (A)	ESul
White-Blizzard =	NPri SCoo
'Fisbliz'PBR	
'Wickham Lad' (R)	LDea
Wico = 'Guimongol'PBR	LAst LSou WGor
(I/d)	
'Wild Spice' (Sc)	LDea LVER
'Wildmalva' (Sc)	MBPg
'Wilf Vernon' (Min/d)	ESul
'Wilhelm Kolle' (Z)	WFib
'Wilhelm Langath'	SCoo SDnm WHPP
'Winford Festival'	LVER
'Winnie Read' (Dw/d)	ESul
'Wirral Look Alike' (Z/d/C)	SSea
'Wirral Target' (Z/d/v)	ESul MWhe
'Wispy' (Dw/St/C)	ESul
'Witnesham' (Min/d)	ESul
§ 'Wood's Surprise'	EShb ESul LDea MWhe SKen SWal
(MinI/d/v)	
'Wookey' (R)	GGar
'Wooton's Unique'	CSpe
'Wordsworth'	MBPg
'Wroxham' (Dw)	ESul
'Wychwood' (A/Sc)	EWoo LDea MBPg
'Wyck Beacon' (I/d)	SKen
'Yale' (I/d) ♀H1+3	LDea MBri MSte MWhe SKen WFib
'Yhu' (R)	ESul LDea NFir SMrm WFib
'Yolanda' (Dw/C)	ESul
'York Florist' (Z/d/v)	LVER
'York Minster' (Dw/v)	SKen
'Yvonne' (Z)	WFib
'Zama' (R)	ESul NFir
'Zena' (Dw)	ESul
'Zinc' (Z/d)	WFib
'Zoe' (A)	LDea WHPP
zonale	EWoo SSea WFib

'Zulu King' (R)	WFib
'Zulu Warrior' (R)	WFib

Peliosanthes (Convallariaceae)

monticola B&SWJ 5183	WCru

Pellaea (Adiantaceae)

atropurpurea	CLAP WFib
falcata	CLAP MBri SEND
rotundifolia ♀H2	CHal CLAP LTwo MBri NMyG
	SMur SNut STre

Pellionia see *Elatostema*

Peltandra (Araceae)

alba	see *P. sagittifolia*
§ sagittifolia	CRow WDyG
undulata	see *P. virginica*
§ virginica	CDWL CRow EMFW LPBA NPer
	SWat
- 'Snow Splash' (v)	CRow

Peltaria (Brassicaceae)

alliacea	CSpe EBee ECha EPPr GBin LEdu
	SAga

Peltiphyllum see *Darmera*

Peltoboykinia (Saxifragaceae)

§ tellimoides	CCol CLAP EBee GCal GEdr GKev
	MGol NBir NHol SMac WBVN
	WFar WMoo
watanabei	CAby CDes CLAP CSec EBee EPPr
	GEdr LEdu SMac WCru WFar
	WMoo WPGP

Pennantia (Icacinaceae)

baylisiana	ECou
corymbosa	ECou
- 'Akoroa'	ECou
- 'Woodside'	ECou

Pennellianthus see *Penstemon*

Pennisetum ✿ (Poaceae)

§ alopecuroides	More than 30 suppliers
- Autumn Wizard	see *P. alopecuroides*
	'Herbstzauber'
- black	WSHC
- 'Black Beauty' **new**	SMHy
- 'Bruno Ears'	EHoe
- 'Cassian's Choice'	CBig CBrm CKno EHoe MWea
	NCGa SMrm SUsu
- 'Caudatum'	CBig CKno CPen EBee
- f. *erythrochaetum*	WCru
'Ferris'	
- 'Hameln'	More than 30 suppliers
§ - 'Herbstzauber'	CFir CMdw CPen CPrp EBee EGle
	EHoe EPfP GCal LHop SPoG WPnP
- 'Little Bunny'	CKno COIW CPen EBee EBrs
	EChP EHoe EMan EPfP GCal LAst
	LEdu LRHS NGdn SWvt WDin
- 'Little Honey' (v)	CKno EBee EMan EPPr MAvo NLar
	SPla WCot
- 'Magic'	CFwr
- 'Moudry'	CBig CBrm CKno CPen EHoe EPPr
	WFar
- 'National Arboretum'	CFwr CPen EHoe IPot
- var. *purpurascens*	CAby CBig CWCL
- f. *viridescens*	CKno EBee ECha EGle EHoe ELan
	EMan EPfP LEdu LRHS MLLN
	MMoz MWgw SMHy SWal
- 'Weserbergland'	CBig CKno CSam EBee EHoe EPPr
- 'Woodside'	CBig CBrm CKno CPen CSam
	CWCL EBrs EHoe EMan EPPr LBBr
	MBNS SMad SPla WHal

compressum	see *P. alopecuroides*
flaccidum	CSam EHul EPPr
glaucum 'Purple Majesty'	CKno CSpe CWCL EBee IPot MAvo MNrw NPri SCoo SMad SUsu SWal WPrP WRos
incomptum	EHoe LRHS NDov XPep
- purple	CBig CBrm CKno EBee MMoz
longistylum hort.	see *P. villosum*
macrostachyum	CBig CKno CPen MDKP SMad
'Burgundy Giant'	
macrourum	CBrm CElw CEnt CFwr CHrt CKno CMea CSam CWCL EBee ECha EGle EHoe EPGN EWsh LEdu LHop MWhi NDov SMHy SMad SMrm SUsu SWal WGwG WPGP
massaicum 'Red Buttons'	see *P. thunbergii* 'Red Buttons'
orientale ♀H3	More than 30 suppliers
- 'Karley Rose'PBR	CBig CKno CPen CRez EBee EHrv IPot LPhx LRHS MAvo MBNS MWgw SUsu
I - 'Robustum'	CDes
* - 'Shogun'	CPen MAvo WCot
- 'Tall Tails'	CBig CFwr CKno COlW CPen EBee EHoe EPPr IPot LBMP MAvo NBHF NDov NSti WCot
'Paul's Giant'	CKno
rueppellii	see *P. setaceum*
§ *setaceum* ♀H3	CBig CKno CPen LBMP MNrw SIde SMar SWal XPep
- 'Eaton Canyon'	CKno CPen
- 'Rubrum'	CAbb CBcs CBct CBig CKno CPen CSpe CTbh CWCL EBee ENot EWin LAst LEdu LHop LSRN MWgw NOrc SAga SCoo SDix SMad SPoG SUsu SWal SWvt WCot
§ *thunbergii* 'Red Buttons'	CBig CKno CPen CRez IPot MDKP
§ *villosum* ♀H3	More than 30 suppliers

pennyroyal see *Mentha pulegium*

Penstemon ✿ (Scrophulariaceae)

P&C 150	CFee
PC&H 148	EAro
RCB/Arg V-1	WCot
RCB/MO A-7	WCot
'Abberley'	WPer
'Abbotsmerry'	MBNS SAga SGar WSPU
'Agnes Laing'	LPen LRHS MBNS SPlb
alamosensis	GKev
albertinus	see *P. humilis*
§ 'Alice Hindley' ♀H3	More than 30 suppliers
alpinus	CNic CSec EAro NEgg NLAp NOak
ambiguus	EBee
§ 'Andenken an Friedrich Hahn' ♀H4	More than 30 suppliers
§ *angustifolius*	EBee MNrw SRms
- var. *caudatus*	NWCA
NNS 99-281	
'Apple Blossom' misapplied	see *P.* 'Thorn'
'Apple Blossom' ♀H3-4	More than 30 suppliers
aridus	CPBP
arizonicus	see *P. whippleanus*
'Ashton'	CElw EBee LPen SAga SLon WSPU
attenuatus	WLin
'Audrey Cooper'	EBee
'Axe Valley Pixie' **new**	CEnt
azureus	CFir CPBP GKev NWCA WLin
- subsp. *azureus*	GKev
'Baby Lips' **new**	LTwo
'Barbara Barker'	see *P.* 'Beech Park'
§ *barbatus*	CAby CFee ECha EHrv ELan ELau EPfP LPhx MLan SECG SPer SRms XPep
§ - 'Blue Spring'	ECtt
§ - 'Cambridge Mixed'	LRHS LRav NBlu

- subsp. *coccineus*	CBgR CMea EAro EBee ENot LPen LPhx LRHS MBNS MBri MWat NBPC NChi NDlv NLar WMow
- 'Jingle Bells'	EPfP LPen MWgw SMar SPav
- 'Navigator'	SECG
- orange-flowered	SMrm SPlb
- 'Peter Catt'	LSou SMrm
- var. *praecox*	CBgR MBNS NJOw WBrE WPer
- - f. *nanus*	LRHS MSte SRms
- - - 'Rondo'	MNFA NLar NWCA WBrE WWeb
'Beckford'	CPrp EBee EShb MBNS WCFE WSPU
§ 'Beech Park' ♀H3	ECtt ELan EWes IGor LPen LRHS MBNS NBir SAga WHCG WSPU
§ *berryi*	WLin
'Bisham Seedling'	see *P.* 'White Bedder'
'Blackbird'	More than 30 suppliers
'Bodnant'	LSou MBNS WHoo WPer
bradburii	see *P. grandiflorus*
'Bredon'	CElw CHea EBee MBNS NChi SAga WBrk WSPU
bridgesii	see *P. rostriflorus*
'Burford Purple'	see *P.* 'Burgundy'
'Burford Seedling'	see *P.* 'Burgundy'
'Burford White'	see *P.* 'White Bedder'
§ 'Burgundy'	CHrt CSam CWCL ECtt ENot GMaP GMac LLWP LPen LRHS MWgw MWhi NBir NPer SAga SGar SWal WFar WHCG WHil WPer WSHC
caeruleus	see *P. angustifolius*
caespitosus	CSec
- 'Claude Barr' misapplied (purple-flowered)	see *P. procumbens* 'Claude Barr'
- subsp. *suffruticosus*	see *P. tusharensis*
§ *californicus*	CPBP WAbe
calycosus	EBee
§ *campanulatus*	EAro ECtt EHyt EPfP EPot EWes GBBs GEdr MLLN NMen NRnb SPoG SRms WPer WSPU
- PC&H 148	EMan GBri NOak SGar SHFr
- *pulchellus*	see *P. campanulatus*
- *roseus* misapplied	see *P. kunthii*
'Candy Pink'	see *P.* 'Old Candy Pink'
cardwellii	EAro EWes ITim MDKP SRms
cardwellii x *davidsonii*	WAbe
'Carolyn Orr' (v)	CBow ECtt EMan LHop LSou WCot
'Castle Forbes'	EPyc GMac LPen MBNS MLLN NBur WHCG WPer
'Cathedral Rose' **new**	NPri
'Catherine de la Mare'	see *P. heterophyllus* 'Catherine de la Mare'
* - 'Centra'	MBNS MLLN MWgw
'Charles Rudd'	CWCL EBee ECtt ERou GMac LLWP LPen LRHS MBNS MLLN SBai SPav SRGP SWal SWvt SYvo WCot WHCG WLin
§ 'Cherry' ♀H3	GMac LPen MBNS MHer NBur SGar SHar SPla SPlb WHCG WHil WPer WSPU
'Cherry Ripe' misapplied	see *P.* 'Cherry'
§ 'Chester Scarlet' ♀H3	CMCo CWCL GBri GMac LPen MNrw MOak MRav MSte SDix SGar SLon WHCG WPer WSPU
cinicola **new**	LTwo
cobaea	CSec EBee GKev SUsu WPer
comarrhenus cyaneus	see *P. cyaneus*
'Comberton'	CHea EBee MBNS WSPU
confertus	CSec CTri EAro EBee ECho EGra EHyt EPot EWTr LPen MBNS NChi NLAp NMen NWCA SGar SRms WBVN WGwG WLin WPer
'Connie's Pink' ♀H3	ENot LPen MBNS MSte NBur WHCG WSPU
* 'Coral Pink'	SLon
'Cottage Garden Red'	see *P.* 'Windsor Red'

§ 'Countess of Dalkeith'   CBcs CHea COIW EBee ECtt EGra
ELan ERou EWes LLWP LPen LRHS
MLLN MNrw MOak MRav SBai
SGar SPer SPlb SUsu SWvt WCAu
WCot WFar WHCG WSPU
crandallii   CPBP
- subsp. *atratus* new   WLin
- subsp. *glabrescens*   WLin
§ - subsp. *taosensis*   NWCA SMrm
cristatus   see *P. eriantherus*
§ *cyaneus*   GAbr NWCA WLin
davidsonii   ECho EWes NLAp SRms WAbe
WFar
- var. *davidsonii*   CPBP SBla WLin
§ - var. *menziesii* ♀H4   MDun NWCA SRms
- - 'Broken Top Mountain'   CLyd
- - 'Microphyllus'   EHyt LTwo WAbe WLin
- var. *praeteritus*   CPBP EPot MDKP
'Dazzler'   CMMP CWCL ERou LPen NChi
SAga SWvt WPer WSPU
§ *deaveri*   NLAp
'Devonshire Cream'   CElw CWCL LPen LRHS MBNS
WHCG
diffusus   see *P. serrulatus*
digitalis   CRWN ECha EMan LPen LPhx
MBNS NLAp NWCA SHar WFar
WHCG WMow WPer
§ - 'Husker Red'   More than 30 suppliers
- 'Purpureus'   see *P. digitalis* 'Husker Red'
- 'Ruby Tuesday'   CDes EBee EWes WPGP
- white-flowered   LPhx SRms SWal
discolor pale lavender-   NBir WFar
flowered
dissectus   SGar
§ 'Drinkstone'   EGoo EHol LPen LRHS NChi SDix
WHCG WPer WSPU
'Drinkwater Red'   see *P.* 'Drinkstone'
'Editha'   LPen SRms WEas WIvy WKif WLin
ellipticus new   WLin
'Elmley'   MBNS MLLN NChi SAga WSPU
§ *eriantherus*   CGra EBee GKev
'Etna'   CWCL EBee ECtt ENot LRHS MBri
NEgg
euglaucus   EBee EHyt LTwo SGar
§ 'Evelyn' ♀H4   EBee ECha EDAr ELan EPfP EPot
ERou LAst LRHS MAsh MBNS
MRav NBPC NBir NWCA SPer SPet
SPla SPlb SPoG SRGP SRms SWvt
WFar WHCG WKif WLin WPtf
WSHC WSPU
'Evelyn' x 'Papal Purple'   LPen SBch
'Fanny's Blush'   SAga
'Firebird'   see *P.* 'Schoenholzeri'
'Flame'   LHop LPen LRHS MBNS NBur
SLon WHCG WPer WSPU
'Flamingo'   CWCL EBee EChP ECtt EPfP ERou
EWes LAst LPen LRHS MBNS MSte
NBir NEgg SBai SPoG SWal SWvt
WCFE WFar WHil WSPU
fruticosus   CSec EAro EBee MNrw NWCA
WAbe WFar
§ - var. *scouleri* ♀H4   MOne NLAp SRms WBVN WLin
§ - - f. *albus* ♀H4   CSpe NWCA WAbe WIvy WKif
- - 'Amethyst'   WAbe WLin
- - f. *ruber*   NWCA
- var. *serratus*   SBla WLin
- - 'Holly'   NMen SBla SHGN
Fujiyama = 'Yayama'PBR   ECtt LRHS LSou MBri NEgg SGar
WFar WRHF
'Garden Red'   see *P.* 'Windsor Red'
'Garnet'   see *P.* 'Andenken an Friedrich
Hahn'
gentianoides   MNrw NBro
'Geoff Hamilton'   CElw CFwr CWoW LHop LPen
MBNS SAga
'George Elrick'   LPen MBNS

§ 'George Home' ♀H3   CWCL ECGP ECtt EWes LPen
LRHS MBNS MLLN MSte NBur
SMrm WBVN WHCG
'Ghent Purple'   CFee
'Gilchrist'   LPhx LRHS SGar SLon WLin WWeb
glaber   CMea EAro GMac LHop LLWP
LPen LRHS LSRN MBNS MEHN
NGdn NLAp SBai SHFr SMrm SPlb
WKif WPer
- 'Roundway Snowflake'   LPhx SHar
- white-flowered   SGar
'Gloire des Quatre Rues'   CWCL
gormanii   CSec EAro EBee SGar
gracilis   WPer
§ *grandiflorus*   CAby CSec EAro EBee EDAr EShb
NLAp
- 'Prairie Snow'   EBee
hallii   CGra EAro EHyt EPot EWes LRHS
hartwegii ♀H3-4   EPyc GMac LPen WHCG WPer
WSPU
- 'Albus'   LHop LPen LRHS MSte MWat SGar
WHCG WSPU
- 'Tubular Bells Rose'   MWhi SPet
heterodoxus   EHyt NWCA SGar WLin
- NNS 93-564   NWCA
§ *heterophyllus*   GAbr LPen MNrw NBir NGdn SGar
SRkn SRms WAbe WEas WHCG
WHal WPer
- 'Blue Eye'   WBrk
- 'Blue Fountain'   CHar LPen MBNS
- 'Blue Gem'   CElw CTri ECtt LRHS NChi SIng
SPla
- 'Blue Spring'   CBrm ECtt LPen LRHS MSte NBir
NLAp SAga SBla SPoG WAbe
§ - 'Catherine de la Mare'   CHar ELan LHop LPen LRHS LSRN
♀H4   MBri MHer MWat NBir NBro NLAp
SAga SBch SMrm SPer SPla SRGP
SWal SWvt WBVN WEas WFar WHlf
WKif WSPU
- 'Electric Blue'   LPhx MCCP NBlu NPri SGar
- 'Heavenly Blue'   CSBt CWCL EBee ECtt EPfP ERou
EShb LAst LPen LRHS MBNS MBnl
MDun MLHP NLAp SPav SPoG
SWal SWat SWvt WBrk WFar WHil
WMnd WWhi
- 'Hergest Croft'   CElw
- 'Jeanette'   WCot WHoo
- subsp. *purdyi*   EPyc WHCG
- 'Roehrslev'   LPen
- 'True Blue'   see *P. heterophyllus*
- 'Züriblau'   CMdw CSam LPen WWFP
§ 'Hewell Pink Bedder' ♀H3   CBcs COIW EBee ECtt ENot EPfP
ERou GBri LPen LRHS MBNS
MOak MSte NBPC NBlu NEgg SBai
SWvt WCra WFar WHCG WHil
WHoo WMnd WPer WSPU
WWeb
'Hewitt's Pink'   ECtt MBNS NEgg
§ 'Hidcote Pink' ♀H3-4   More than 30 suppliers
- 'Hidcote Purple'   CElw CMMP NGdn SHar
* 'Hidcote White'   CMMP GBri MHer SWvt
'Hillview Pink'   WHil
'Hillview Red'   WHil
§ *hirsutus*   CNic CSec MNrw SGar WBVN
WFar WPer WSan
- f. *albiflorus*   CSec ECtt NWCA
- var. *minimus*   NLAp
- var. *pygmaeus*   CLyd CMea EAro ECho EDAr EShb
MHer NJOw NMen NWCA SBla
SGar SIng SPlb SRms SRot SWal
WHoo WLin WPer
- - f. *albus*   EHyt NWCA SHGN WPer
'Hopleys Variegated' (v)   CBow EBee EMan EWin MHer
NBir SAga SPav SWvt WCot WSPU
WWeb
'Hower Park'   MBNS

§ *humilis*	CNic EBee LEdu MLLN NLAp SRms WLin
- 'Pulchellus'	NLAp NWCA
idahoensis	NWCA
- NNS 01-337	NWCA
isophyllus ♀H3-4	CTri EChP EPfP LPen LRHS MAsh SWal WFar WHCG WPer WSPU
'James Bowden' **new**	MBNS
jamesii	CSec EBee EChP EHyt WHrl
janishiae	CGra NWCA
Jean Grace = 'Penbow'	CHar LRHS
'John Booth'	MSte WEas
'John Nash' misapplied	see *P.* 'Alice Hindley'
'John Nash'	CFwr MBNS MHer SRkn
'John Spedan Lewis'	SLon
'Joy'	EPyc LPen MLLN MSte WPer
'June'	see *P.* 'Pennington Gem'
Kilimanjaro = 'Yajaro'	LSou
'King George V'	More than 30 suppliers
'Knight's Purple'	LPen MBNS WHCG
'Knightwick' ambig.	LPen SGar WPer WSPU
'Knightwick'	MBNS
§ *kunthii*	EAro EBee EPPr GEdr LLWP LPen MDKP MWea NBur NLAp SAga WHrl WOut WPer WSPU
- upright	SGar WLin
§ *laetus* subsp. *roezlii*	EAEE ECho EHyt EPot GCrs GGar LHop LRHS MAsh MBar MDun NLAp NSla SRms
§ 'Le Phare'	LPen LRHS MBNS MHar SAga WHCG WPer WSPU
leiophyllus	EHyt WLin
leonensis	CSec EAro WLin
'Lilac and Burgundy'	EBee EChP ERou EWTr EWin LPen LRHS MBNS SAga SBai SWvt WFar
'Lilliput' **new**	CHVG LRHS
linarioides	LPen NLAp WLin WPat
- 'Fred Case' **new**	GKev
'Little Witley'	LPen MBNS WHCG WPer
'Lord Home'	see *P.* 'George Home'
lyallii	EAro EHrv ELan GKev LPen LSou MCCP MLLN MNrw NJOw SRms WPer WPtf WSan
'Lynette'	LPen LRHS MBNS SBch SPlb WHCG WPer
'Macpenny's Pink'	EBee EPyc LPen MBNS SAga
§ 'Madame Golding'	CWCL GMac LPen LRHS MBNS MNrw SGar SRkn WHCG WPer
'Malvern Springs'	MBNS
'Margery Fish' ♀H3	CElw EPyc ERou EWes LPen LRHS MNrw MSte SBai WPer WSPU
'Marilyn Ross' **new**	WSPU
'Maurice Gibbs' ♀H3	CBcs CMMP COIW EBee ECtt EPfP EPyc ERou EWTr EWes GAbr LPen LRHS LSRN MBNS MLLN NBPC NGdn SAga SBai SGar SPav SRGP WHCG WHil WMnd WSPU
mensarum	EBee
menziesii	see *P.davidsonii* var. *menziesii*
'Mesa' **new**	CPBP
Mexicali hybrids	CPBP EBee LPen MLLN WLin
'Midnight'	EBee EChP ELan EPfP GBri LLWP LPen MOak MRav MSte SAga SGar SWvt WBVN WCFE WCot WHCG WMnd WPer WSPU WWeb
'Mint Pink'	SGar
'Modesty'	EGra LPen LRHS MBNS NBur SMar WHCG WPer WSPU
montanus	NJOw NLAp
'Mother of Pearl'	More than 30 suppliers
'Mrs Miller'	LPen MBNS NBur
'Mrs Morse'	see *P.* 'Chester Scarlet'
multiflorus	LPen
§ 'Myddelton Gem'	LPen LRHS MBNS MNrw MWat WCot WFoF WHCG WSPU
'Myddelton Red'	see *P.* 'Myddelton Gem'

nanus	CGra
nemorosus NNS 00-572	EPPr
neotericus	NWCA
newberryi ♀H4	CMea CNic CSec MAsh NRnb SAga SBla WBVN WKif WLin
- subsp. *berryi*	see *P.berryi*
- f. *humilior*	EPot
§ - subsp. *sonomensis*	EPot WAbe WFar WLin
* 'Newbury Gem'	EBee EWin MBNS MLLN NBur SBai SRGP SWvt WFar
§ *nitidus*	MNrw WLin
'Oaklea Red'	ECtt EPyc ERou SWat
§ 'Old Candy Pink'	CFee LPen MBNS MSte SBai SWvt WPer WSPU
oliganthus	LRav
'Osprey' ♀H3	More than 30 suppliers
ovatus	CSec EBee GBBs LPen LPhx MBow MLLN NDlv NLAp SBla SGar SRms WKif WLin WSan WWeb
'Overbury'	EBee LPen MBNS WSPU
pallidus	EBee
palmeri	CBow EAro EBee EMan
'Papal Purple'	CMea ERou LLWP LPen LRHS MBNS MSte NBir NChi SLon SRms SWal WFar WHCG WSPU WWhi
parvulus	EBee
'Patio Bells Pink'	LPen MLHP MLLN SWal
'Patio Bells Shell'	LRHS
'Patio Coral'	WLin
'Patio Wine'	SAga
'Peace'	LPen LRHS MBNS SLon WHCG WSPU
'Pearl'	EPyc
§ 'Pennington Gem' ♀H3	CElw ECtt EGra ELan GBri GMac LLWP LPen LRHS MHer MNrw MSte NBir NGdn SBai SWvt WHCG WPer WSPU WWlt
'Pensham Amelia Jane' **new**	MBnl SRGP WHlf
'Pensham Aran Belle' **new**	MWea
'Pensham Arctic Fox'	EBee LHop SAga
'Pensham Arctic Sunset'	WHrl
'Pensham Avonbelle'	MBnl
'Pensham Bilberry Ice'	EBee EPyc MLLN SPav WMnd
'Pensham Blackberry Ice'	CFir EPyc MWea SPav WMnd
'Pensham Blueberry Ice'	CWoW EBee EPyc MBnl MBri MLLN SAga SPav WCra WFar WMnd WWlt
'Pensham Capricorn Moon'	SAga SRGP WLin
'Pensham Cassis Royale'	MLLN
'Pensham Czar' **new**	MBnl WHlf
'Pensham Dorothy Wilson'	EBee EPyc SRGP
'Pensham Edith Biggs'	CWCL WFar
'Pensham Eleanor Young' **new**	MBnl SRGP WHlf
'Pensham Freshwater Pearl'	CElw CHVG SAga
'Pensham Great Expectations'	MLLN SAga SPoG
'Pensham Just Jayne'	CElw CWoW EBee EPyc MBnl MLLN NPro SLon SRGP WMnd
'Pensham Kay Burton'	EPyc SRGP WMnd
'Pensham Laura' **new**	MBnl SRGP WHlf
'Pensham Loganberry Ice' **new**	MBnl WHlf
'Pensham Marjorie Lewis'	EPyc WMnd
'Pensham Petticoat'	MBnl MBri MWea WWlt
'Pensham Plum Jerkum'	EPyc MBri MLLN MWea WCra WMnd
'Pensham Raspberry Ice'	MBnl MLLN MWea SPav WMnd
'Pensham Tayberry Ice'	EBee EPyc MBnl MLLN SAga SGar WMnd
'Pensham The Dean's Damson'	CHVG
'Pensham Tiger Belle Coral'	MBnl MWea NChi WLin

'Pensham Tiger Belle Rose' SAga
'Pensham Victoria Plum' CWoW SHar
'Pensham Wedding Bells' EBee MBri MWgw SPoG WFar
'Pensham Wedding Day' MBnl SRGP WHlf
new
perfoliatus EBee
'Perrins Red' **new** MBNS
'Pershore Anniversary' WSPU
new
'Pershore Carnival' NPro WSPU
'Pershore Fanfare' LPen SAga WHrl WSPU
'Pershore Festival' **new** WSPU
'Pershore Pink Necklace' LPen LRHS MLLN SBai SMrm SWvt
WCot WHCG WSPU WWeb
'Phare' see *P.* 'Le Phare'
'Phyllis' see *P.* 'Evelyn'
pinifolius ♀H4 CBrm CDMG CMea ECho ECtt
EDAr EHyt EPot GAbr GCrs GMaP
LRHS NEgg NFor NJOw NLAp
SAga SBla SPoG SRms WBVN WFar
WHoo WLin WPat WSPU
- 'Mersea Yellow' CMea EBee ECho ECtt EDAr EHyt
EPfP EPot GAbr GCrs GEdr LHop
LRHS NDlv NJOw NLAp NWCA
SAga SBla SPlb SPoG SWal WBVN
WFar WLin WPat WPer
- 'Wisley Flame' ♀H4 ECho EPfP EPot EWes GEdr NJOw
NRya NWCA
'Pink Bedder' see *P.* 'Hewell Pink Bedder',
'Sutton's Pink Bedder'
'Pink Endurance' EBee ERou LPen MBNS MSte SRkn
WHCG WHal WPer WSPU
'Pink Ice' WHil
'Pink Profusion' MRav
'Pixie' CPen
'Port Wine' ♀H3 CSam CTri CWCL CWoW EBee
EPfP GAbr GMaP ISea LPen LRHS
MBow MLLN MWat NBir NChi
SAga SBai SPla SPoG SWal WBrE
WCot WHCG WHoo WMnd WPer
WSPU
'Powis Castle' ECtt EWes MHar WPer WWlt
'Prairie Dusk' LPen
'Prairie Fire' EBee ERou LPen
* 'Prairie Pride' LPen
'Priory Purple' MBNS WHCG WPer
procerus EChP ECho GBri GCal LPhx MLLN
NEgg SRms WLin WPer
- var. *brachyanthus* CNic NLAp
§ - var. *formosus* EHyt EPot NMen WAbe WFar WLin
- - NNS 01-345 NWCA
- 'Hawkeye' **new** CGra
- var. *procerus* EHyt
§ - 'Roy Davidson' ♀H4 CAby CMea EHyt EPot LBee LRHS
NLAp SBla WAbe WFar WLin
- var. *tolmiei* EPot GCal GEdr WLin
- - white-flowered WLin
§ *procumbens* 'Claude Barr' CPBP
pruinosus WLin
pubescens see *P. hirsutus*
pulchellus Greene see *P. procerus* var. *formosus*
pulchellus Lindl. see *P. campanulatus*
* *pulcherrimus* NBro
pumilus SRms
'Purple and White' see *P.* 'Countess of Dalkeith'
'Purple Bedder' More than 30 suppliers
'Purple Passion' CElw EBee EBrs EChP EHrv EPfP
EWes GBBs LPen LRHS
'Purpureus Albus' see *P.* 'Countess of Dalkeith'
purpusii LTwo NWCA WCot WLin
'Rajah' LPen
'Raven' ♀H3 More than 30 suppliers
'Razzle Dazzle' LPen LRHS MBNS SPlb WCot WPer
'Red Ace' MNrw
'Red Emperor' ECtt LPen MBNS MHar SPlb
WHCG WPer WSPU

'Red Knight' CWCL LPen LRHS MBNS
'Red Scarlet' **new** ISea
'Rich Purple' EPyc LRHS MBNS SPlb
'Rich Ruby' COlW CWCL EBee EBrs EChP ECtt
EGra EHrv ELan EPfP EWes GBBs
LHop LLWP LPen LRHS MNrw
MTis NBir SBai SMer SPlb SRGP
SUsu SWvt WCot WHCG WLin
WPer WSPU
richardsonii CStu EBee EHyt EShb MDKP
MNrw NWCA SRms WPer
'Ridgeway Red' MBNS WSPU
roezlii Regel see *P. laetus* subsp. *roezlii*
'Ron Sidwell' **new** MBNS
§ *rostriflorus* CPBP
- NNS 95-407 WCot
'Rosy Blush' LPen LRHS MBNS SAga SPlb
WHCG
'Roundhay' CFee NChi
'Roy Davidson' see *P. procerus* 'Roy Davidson'
'Royal White' see *P.* 'White Bedder'
'Rubicundus' ♀H3 CWCL EBee EBrs ECtt EHrv ELan
EPfP ERou LHop LPen LRHS MAsh
MBNS SAga SBai SMrm SPla SPoG
SWvt WCot WFar WHCG WMnd
WSPU WWeb
'Ruby' see *P.* 'Schoenholzeri'
'Ruby Field' EPyc WCFE WHCG
'Ruby Gem' LPen LRHS MBNS
rupicola ♀H4 EAEE EHyt GCrs LHop LRHS NSla
WAbe WLin
- 'Albus' LTwo NSla WAbe
- 'Conwy Lilac' WAbe
- 'Conwy Rose' WAbe
- 'Diamond Lake' CMea
'Russian River' EBee ECtt EPfP EPyc EWes EWin
LHop LPen LRHS SBch SGar SPlb
SWal WHCG WPer WSPU
rydbergii CSec NLAp
* Saskatoon hybrids EBee
Saskatoon hybrids blue CFwr
new
Saskatoon hybrids rose CFwr
new
Saskatoon hybrids violet CFwr
new
§ 'Schoenholzeri' ♀H4 More than 30 suppliers
scouleri see *P. fruticosus* var. *scouleri*
§ *serrulatus* CNic CSec EWes MSte SGar SHFr
SMad WBVN WHrl WKif WLin
- 'Albus' CAby
'Shell Pink' LPen NChi WPer
* 'Sherbourne Blue' GBuc MBNS SAga SLon WCot
WPer
'Shock Wave' MCCP MSte SAga
'Shot Silk' **new** WSPU
* 'Shrawley' WPer
'Sissinghurst Pink' see *P.* 'Evelyn'
'Six Hills' SRms WAbe WLin WPat
'Skyline' EAro EPfP
smallii CDes CMHG CWoW EAro EBee
EDAr EMan EPyc EShb EWTr EWes
LPen LPhx LSRN MCCP NBPC
NWCA SGar SIng SMac SMrm
SPoG WPGP
'Snow Storm' see *P.* 'White Bedder'
'Snowflake' see *P.* 'White Bedder'
'Son of Raven' CHVG
sonomensis see *P. newberryi* subsp.
sonomensis
'Sour Grapes' misapplied see *P.* 'Stapleford Gem'
§ 'Sour Grapes' M. Fish More than 30 suppliers
♀H3-4
'Southcombe Pink' LPen MLLN WHCG
'Southgate Gem' LPen LRHS MNrw MWat SWvt
WHCG

'Souvenir d'Adrian Regnier'	LPen MBNS
'Souvenir d'André Torres' misapplied	see *P.* 'Chester Scarlet'
'Souvenir d'André Torres'	LLWP LPen
spatulatus	WLin
§ 'Stapleford Gem' ♀H3	More than 30 suppliers
'Strawberry Fizz'	MBNS
strictus	CSec EAro EBee EGoo EMan EPPr LBBr LPen LRHS MBNS MCCP MHar MLLN MNFA NLAp SGar SRms WPer WWeb
Stromboli = 'Yaboli'	CElw MBri
subserratus	EBee
§ 'Sutton's Pink Bedder'	LRHS MBNS SPlb WSPU
'Sylvia Buss'	LPen MBNS
tall pink	see *P.* 'Welsh Dawn'
N 'Taoensis'	EWes MBNS SGar
taosensis	see *P. crandallii* subsp. *taosensis*
teucrioides	GEdr NLAp NWCA
- JCA 1717050	CPBP
'The Juggler'PBR	EBee EPfP EWin LPen LRHS MBNS MLLN SPav WCra WFar
§ 'Thorn'	CBcs CSpe EBee ECtt EGra ELan ERou EShb GBBs LPen LRHS MBow MLLN MNrw MSte MTis MWat NBir SAga SBai SMrm SPer SPla SWal SWvt WHCG WLin WSPU WWeb
'Threave Pink'	CPrp CWCL ERou LBBr LLWP MRav SEND SMrm SPer SPoG SWvt WLin WMoo
'Thundercloud' **new**	WSPU
'Torquay Gem'	GBuc LPen SDys WCot WHCG WPer
'True Sour Grapes'	see *P.* 'Sour Grapes'
§ *tusharensis*	SBla
utahensis	GBri SAga
venustus	EBee GBuc MHar MNrw NCob SGar SRms SRot WRos
'Vera' **new**	WSPU
Vesuvius = 'Yasius'	EBee ENot EPyc LSou MBri NEgg SGar SWal WFar WRHF
'Violet Dusk'	WPtf
virens	CNic CPBP EBee GAbr WPer
virgatus subsp. *arizonicus*	see *P. deaveri*
- 'Blue Buckle'	CBrm CPBP EBee EShb EWTr MBri NBir NMyG
watsonii	CSec EBee ELan EMan MLLN SRms WHoo
§ 'Welsh Dawn'	CEnt LPen MBNS WSPU
§ *whippleanus*	EAro GEdr LPhx LRav NRnb WAbb WLin
- 'Chocolate Drop'	EBee LSou SMar WOut WPtf WRos
§ 'White Bedder' ♀H3	More than 30 suppliers
'Whitethroat' Sidwell	LPen LRHS MBNS SAga SLon WHCG WSPU
I 'Whitethroat' purple-flowered	WPer
wilcoxii	EBee NEgg
'Willy's Purple'	MBNS SLon
§ 'Windsor Red'	COIW CTri EBee ECtt EPfP ERou LPen LRHS MAsh MBNS MSte SAga SBai SGar SPoG SUsu SWal SWvt WCot WGor WHCG WHil WSPU
wislizeni	CSec EPfP MLan MNrw SRms
'Woodpecker'	EBee WHil

Pentachondra (*Epacridaceae*)

pumila	IBlr

Pentaglottis (*Boraginaceae*)

§ *sempervirens*	CArn EPfP MBow MHer MSal WHen WHil WWye

Pentapanax (*Araliaceae*)

leschenaultii HWJK 2385	WCru

Pentapterygium see *Agapetes*

Pentas (*Rubiaceae*)

lanceolata	CCCN CHal ELan EShb LRHS MBri

Penthorum (*Penthoraceae*)

chinense **new**	EBee

Peperomia (*Piperaceae*)

§ *argyreia* ♀H1	MBri
arifolia	CHal
caperata	LRHS MBri
clusiifolia	CHal
- 'Variegata' (v)	CHal
glabella	CHal
- 'Variegata' (v)	CHal
obtusifolia 'Jamaica'	MBri
- (Magnoliifolia Group) 'Golden Gate' (v)	MBri
- - 'Greengold'	CHal MBri
- - 'USA' ♀H1	MBri
- 'Tricolor' (v)	MBri
orba 'Pixie'	MBri
I - 'Pixie Variegata' (v)	MBri
pulchella	see *P. verticillata*
sandersii	see *P. argyreia*
scandens ♀H1	MBri
- 'Variegata' (v)	CHal MBri
§ *verticillata*	CHal

pepino see *Solanum muricatum*

peppermint see *Mentha* x *piperita*

Perezia (*Asteraceae*)

linearis	GBuc MAvo NLar
recurvata	NWCA

Pericallis (*Asteraceae*)

§ *lanata* (L'Hér.) B. Nord.	CHll ELan EShb MBlu SAga SBch WDyG WPic
- Kew form	CRHN CSpe SAga
multiflora	LHop SAga

Perilla (*Lamiaceae*)

§ *frutescens* var. *crispa* ♀H2	CArn WJek
- green-leaved	EOHP MNHC
- var. *nankinensis*	see *P. frutescens* var. *crispa*
- var. *purpurascens*	CArn CSpe EOHP EUnu MNHC WJek

Periploca (*Asclepiadaceae*)

graeca	CArn CBcs CMac CPlN CRHN EBee EDsa ITer SLon SPoG SYvo WSHC
purpurea B&SWJ 7235	WCru
sepium	CPLG

Peristrophe (*Acanthaceae*)

speciosa	ECre ERea

Pernettya see *Gaultheria*

Perovskia (*Lamiaceae*)

abrotanoides	XPep
atriplicifolia	CArn CMea MHer MNHC WHCG WPer
- 'Little Spire'PBR	CSpe SPer WCMO WSHC
'Blue Haze'	SMHy
'Blue Spire' ♀H4	More than 30 suppliers

'Filigran' | EAEE EBee EMil EWin GBuc LAst LRHS MAsh NFla NSti SPet SPoG WPat XPep
'Hybrida' | EBee
'Longin' | XPep

Persea (Lauraceae)

ichangensis | CPLG
indica | CPLG WPGP
lingue | LEdu
thunbergii | CHEx WPGP

Persicaria (Polygonaceae)

§ *affinis* | CBcs CSBt EBee GAbr MBar MTho MWhi NBro NVic SWat WBVN WBor WBrE WBrk WCFE WFar WMoo
- CC 4423 | MGol
- 'Darjeeling Red' ♀H4 | More than 30 suppliers
- 'Dimity' | see *P. affinis* 'Superba'
- 'Donald Lowndes' ♀H4 | More than 30 suppliers
- 'Kabouter' | GBin LBuc
- Kew form | ECho
- 'Ron McBeath' | CRow
§ - 'Superba' ♀H4 | More than 30 suppliers
alata | see *P. nepalensis*
alpina | CRow SBch
amphibia | CRow NSco SWat WWpP
§ *amplexicaulis* | CBre COld CPrp CRow ELan EMar EWTr EWes GMaP MHer MSte NChi NFor NOrc SEND WBor WFar WMoo WRHF WTel WTin WWpP
- 'Alba' | CElw CHar CRow EBee ECha EMan EPPr EPla ERou GMaP LHop LPhx MLLN NDov SMrm SWat WCAu WCot WFar WGHP WMnd WMoo WPnP WTin WWhi
- 'Atrosanguinea' | CNic CRow CTri EBee EBrs ECha EGra ELan EMFW EMan EPla ERou GGar LRHS MNFA MRav MWgw NBir NDov NEgg NVic SPer SRms SWat SWvt WCAu WFar WOld WWpP
- 'Baron' | CRow
- 'Blush Clent' | EBee WSPU WTin
- 'Border Beauty' | EBee
- 'Clent Charm' | WCMO WSPU
- 'Cottesbrooke Gold' | CRow EMan EMar LSou
- 'Dikke Floskes' | CRow
- 'Firedance' | LPhx NDov SMHy SUsu SWat WCMO WCot
- 'Firetail' ♀H4 | More than 30 suppliers
- 'High Society' | EBee
- 'Inverleith' | CBre CHar CKno CRow EBee ECha ECtt EPla WMoo WPGP
I - 'Jo and Guido's Form' **new** | EBee SUsu
* - var. *pendula* | CRow NBir SBla WFar WMoo
- 'Pink Lady' | CRow NLar
- 'Rosea' | CElw CRow CSam EBee ECha ELan EMan EPPr EPla EWTr LPhx MRav MSte NBro NDov NSti SDys SMeo SWat WCAu WDyG WFar WGHP WMoo WPGP
- 'Rosy Clent' **new** | WSPU
- 'Rowden Gem' | CRow EPla WMoo
- 'Rowden Jewel' | CRow EPla
- 'Rowden Rose Quartz' | CRow
- 'Summer Dance' | EBee EMon NBre
- Taurus = 'Blotau' | CElw CKno CRow EBee EBrs EGle EPla ERou LBBr MBri MLLN NLar SMHy WCAu WFar WPGP WTin
§ *bistorta* | CArn CRow ELau GBar GPoy LAst MHer MSal MWhi NBir NGHP NSco SRms SWat WCra WDyG WGwG WSel WWpP WWye

- subsp. *carnea* | CRow EAEE EBee EBla EBrs ECha EWsh GGar LRHS MNFA NBir NDov WFar WMoo
- 'Hohe Tatra' | CKno CRow EBee EBrs EMan NDov WFar WTMC
- 'Superba' ♀H4 | More than 30 suppliers
bistortoides | MSal
campanulata | CElw CRow EChP ECha ECtt EShb GAbr GBuc GCal GGar GMaP NBid NBro NFor SPer WFar WMoo WOld WWpP WWye
- Alba Group | CElw CRow EBee GCal GGar NBro WHer WMoo WWye
- var. *lichiangense* **new** | GBin
- 'Madame Jigard' | CRow
- 'Rosenrot' | CBre CKno CRow EMan EPPr GBuc GCal NBir NHol NLar NSti SWat WFar WWpP
- 'Southcombe White' | CRow EPPr EPla GBri
§ *capitata* | CHal CPLG CRow EMan MWhi SHFr SIng SRms WEas WMoo XPep
- 'Pink Bubbles' | ECtt SPet SWvt
conspicua | EBee NBre
* *coriacea* | CRow
* *elata* | EMan EMar GBuc GGar NBur
* *emodi* | CRow NBre
hydropiper **new** | WJek
§ *longiseta* | MSal
* *macrophylla* | CRow LDai NLar WFar WGHP
microcephala | CRow EWes MHer SMac
- 'Red Dragon' PBR | More than 30 suppliers
- var. *wallichii* | CRow
* *milletii* | CDes CRow EBrs EWes GAbr GBuc MTho NLar WCAu WCru WFar
§ *mollis* | CRow WDyG WPGP
§ - var. *frondosa* | EBee
§ *nakaii* | EBee
§ *nepalensis* | CRow EPPr SMad
§ *odorata* | CArn ELau EOHP EUnu GPoy ILis LRav MHer MNHC MSal NGHP SHDw SIde WJek
orientalis | MSal
* *polymorpha* | CBct CDes CFwr CKno CRow EBee EBrs ECha EGle EHrv ELan EMan EMon EPPr GMaP LPhx MRav NCGa NDov SMad SWat WCot WFar WMoo WTin WWhi WWpP
polystachya | see *P. wallichii*
* *regeliana* | LRHS
§ *runcinata* | CPLG CRow EBee ECtt EMar GGar NBid NBir NCob NLar WFar WHer WMoo WPer WPtf
- Needham's form | CRow NBid
scoparia | see *Polygonum scoparium*
sphaerostachya Meisn. | see *P. macrophylla*
* *tenuicaulis* | CBre CPLG CRow EBee ECho EHrv EMon EPPr EPla GGar WCot WCru WFar WMoo WWpP
§ *tinctoria* | EOHP
vacciniifolia ♀H4 | More than 30 suppliers
- 'Ron McBeath' | CRow
§ *virginiana* | CRow EBrs ECtt EMan MSal NLar WMoo WTMC
- Compton's form | CBct CRow EBee EBrs ECha EMan EMar EPPr EWin LDai NCob WAul WCMO WCot WTMC WWpP
- 'Filiformis' | EBee ECtt EWin MAvo MHar WCMO WCot WDyG WRos
- 'Lance Corporal' | CRow EBee EPla NBre NCob WMnd WMoo
- 'Moorland Moss' **new** | WMoo
- Variegata Group | CMMP CRow EBee EChP ECha EMan EShb GCal MBNS NLar WCot WMoo WOld

§ - - 'Painter's Palette' (v)	More than 30 suppliers
- white-flowered	EPPr GCal NCob
vivipara	CRow NLar
§ *wallichii*	CRow GBri NBre NLar NSti SDix
	WCot WMoo WWpP
§ *weyrichii*	EBee EMon EPPr GCal NBir NBro
	NLar WCot WFar WMoo

persimmon see *Diospyros virginiana*

persimmon, Japanese see *Diospyros kaki*

Petalostemon see *Dalea*

Petamenes see *Gladiolus*

Petasites (Asteraceae)

albus	EBee EMon GPoy GSki NBre
	NLar
formosanus	LEdu
- B&SWJ 3025	WCru
fragrans	CNat ELan EMon MHer NLar SWat
	WFar WHer
§ *frigidus* var. *palmatus*	CRow EBee EPla LEdu MWgw
	NBre NLar NSti WCru WPGP
- - JLS 86317CLOR	SMad WCot
- var. *palmatus* 'Golden	EHrv NBre NSti SPur
Palms'	
hybridus	EMFW LEdu NSco SMad SWat
	WHer WMAq
japonicus	CBcs
- var. *giganteus*	CArn CHEx CRow ECha ELan
	EMon EPfP LEdu NVic SWat WCru
	WMoo WTMC
- - 'Nishiki-buki' (v)	CHEx CMCo CRow EBee EMag
	EMan EMon EPPr EPla ITer MFOX
	NSti SMad WBor WCHb WCru
	WFar WPGP WPnP WTMC
- - 'Variegatus'	see *P.japonicus* var. *giganteus*
	'Nishiki-buki'
- f. *purpureus*	CDes EBee EMan EPPr EWes
	WCMO WCru WPGP
palmatus	see *P.frigidus* var. *palmatus*
paradoxus	CDes CLAP EBee EPPr LEdu MRav
	NLar SMad WCMO WCot

Petrea (Verbenaceae)

volubilis	CCCN CHll CPIN SOWG

Petrocallis (Brassicaceae)

lagascae	see *P.pyrenaica*
§ *pyrenaica*	GKev NWCA WAbe
- *alba*	WAbe

Petrocoptis (Caryophyllaceae)

pyrenaica	EBur SBla SRms
§ - subsp. *glaucifolia*	NBir NJOw NLar

Petrocosmea (Gesneriaceae)

B&SWJ 7249 from Thailand	WCru
kerrii	WAbe
- B&SWJ 6634	WCru

Petrophytum (Rosaceae)

cinerascens	NWCA SIng
§ *hendersonii*	NHol NWCA WAbe

Petrorhagia (Caryophyllaceae)

'Pink Starlets'	EBee LHop LRav SHGN
§ *saxifraga* ♀H4	CDMG EBur ECho EShb NPri SRms
	SWal WMoo WPer WPnn WPtf
§ - 'Rosette'	MTho

Petroselinum (Apiaceae)

§ *crispum*	CArn CHrt CSev EDAr GPoy
	GWCH ILis LRHS MBar MDun

	MNHC MWat NBlu NGHP SECG
	SIde SWal WPer WSel WWye
- 'Bravour' ♀H4	ELau MBow MHer
- 'Darki'	CSev NGHP NPri
- French	CArn EDAr ELau MBow MHer
	MNHC NBlu NPri NVic WJek WWye
- 'Italian'	see *P.crispum* var. *neapolitanum*
§ - var. *neapolitanum*	ELau GWCH MHer SIde
- 'Super Moss Curled'	NVic
§ - var. *tuberosum*	MHer MNHC SIde WHer
- variegated (v) **new**	CNat
hortense	see *P.crispum*
tuberosum	see *P.crispum* var. *tuberosum*

Petteria (Papilionaceae)

ramentacea	EPfP NLar SLPl WBVN

Petunia (Solanaceae)

* 'Angels Blue'	LAst
Blue Spark =	LAst
'Dancasblue'PBR	
(Cascadias Series)	
Candyfloss = 'Kercan'PBR	LAst NPri
(Tumbelina Series)	
Carillon Series	see *Calibrachoa* Carillon Series
(Cascadias Series)	LAst
Cascadias Pink Spark	
= 'Dancaspink'PBR	
- Cascadias Yellow Eye	LAst
= 'Dancasye'PBR ♀H3	
* (Charlie's Angel Series)	LAst
'Charlie's Angels Pink'	
- 'Charlie's Angels	LAst
White' **new**	
'Chilli Red' **new**	SVil
(Conchita Series) Conchita	LSou
Blossom White =	
'Conbloss'PBR	
- Conchita Blueberry	LSou
Frost = 'Conblue'PBR	
♀H3	
- Conchita Pink Kiss =	LSou
'Mediopimo'PBR **new**	
- Conchita Strawberry	LSou
Frost = 'Constraw'PBR	
♀H3	
- Conchita Twilight Blue	LSou
= 'Ustuni' **new**	
(Conchita Doble Series)	LAst
Conchita Doble Dark	
Blue = 'Conblue'PBR (d)	
- Conchita Doble	LAst
Lavender =	
'Condolavender'	
- Conchita Doble Orchid	LAst
Lace = 'Ustni131' (d)	
- Conchita Doble Pink =	LAst
'Condopink'PBR	
- Conchita Doble Velvet	LAst
= 'Ustuni140'PBR	
- Conchita Doble White	LAst
= 'Condowhite'PBR	
(Doubloon Series) Doubloon	LAst
Blue Star = 'Dandbblst'	
(d)	
- Doubloon Pink Star =	LAst
'Dandpkst' (d)	
Julia = 'Kerjul'PBR	LAst NPri
(Tumbelina Series)	
Katrina (Tumbelina Series)	LAst
new	
Margarita = 'Kermar'PBR	LAst
(Tumbelina Series)	
patagonica	CPBP WAbe
Priscilla = 'Kerpril'PBR	LAst LSou NPri
(Tumbelina Series)	

*	'Purple Surprise'	LAst
	Queen (Tumbelina Series) **new**	LAst
	'Ramblin' Red' **new**	LAst
	Rosella Improved LAst = 'Kerrosim'^{PBR} (Tumbelina Series)	
	Rosella = 'Kerros' (Tumbelina Series)	LAst
	(Supertunia Series)	LAst
	Supertunia Blushing Princess = 'Kakegawa S38'	
-	Supertunia Lavender Morn = 'Kakegawa S29'	LAst
-	Supertunia Lavender Pink = 'Kakegawa S37'	LAst
-	Supertunia Mystic Pink = 'KakeS29'	LAst
-	Supertunia Royal Magenta = 'KakeS36'	LAst
-	Supertunia Royal Velvet = 'Kakegawa S28'	LAst
-	Supertunia White = 'Kakegawa S30'	LAst
	(Surfinia Series) Surfinia Apricot **new**	LSou
-	Surfinia Baby Pinkmorn = 'Sunpimo'	LAst
-	Surfinia Blue = 'Sunblu'	LAst LSou NBlu NPri
-	Surfinia Blue Vein = 'Sunsolos'^{PBR}	LAst NPri
-	Surfinia Burgundy **new**	LAst LSou
-	Surfinia Crazy Pink = 'Sunrovein'	NPri
-	Surfinia Double Purple = 'Keidopuel'^{PBR} (d)	LAst
-	Surfinia Hot Pink = 'Marrose'^{PBR}	LAst LSou NBlu
-	Surfinia Lime = 'Keiyeul'^{PBR}	LAst NBlu NPri
-	Surfinia Pastel 2000 = 'Sunpapi'^{PBR}	NPri
-	Surfinia Patio Blue = 'Keipabukas'^{PBR}	LAst
-	Surfinia Pink Ice = 'Hakice'^{PBR} (v)	LAst NPri
-	Surfinia Pink Mini 2000 = 'Sunmipi'^{PBR}	NBlu
-	Surfinia Pink Vein = 'Suntosol'^{PBR} ♀H3	NBlu
-	Surfinia Purple = 'Shihi Brilliant' ♀H3	LSou NBlu NPri
*	Surfinia Purple Sunrise	LAst
-	Surfinia Red = 'Keirekul'^{PBR}	LAst LSou NPri
-	Surfinia Rose Vein = 'Sunrove'^{PBR}	LAst NPri
-	Surfinia Sky Blue = 'Keilavbu'^{PBR} ♀H3	LAst LSou NBlu NPri
-	Surfinia Vanilla = 'Sunvanilla'	LSou
-	Surfinia Victorian Apricot = 'Sunapri' **new**	LAst
-	Surfinia Victorian Yellow **new**	LAst LSou
-	Surfinia White = 'Kesupite'	LAst NBlu

Peucedanum (Apiaceae)

japonicum	CSpe
ostruthium	EDAr GPoy
- 'Daphnis' (v)	CDes CElw CSpe EBee EGle EMan EMar EMon EPPr LEdu NChi NGby NLar NMRc NPro WCot WEas WHrl

---

	siamicum B&SWJ 264	WCru
	verticillare	CArn CSec CSpe EBee EBrs EDAr EMan ITer LPhx MDun MNFA MWgw NBid NChi NDov NLar SDix SMad WWye

Phacelia (Hydrophyllaceae)

bolanderi	LDai
grandiflora new	CSpe

Phaedranassa (Amaryllidaceae)

	carmiolii	CMon WCMO WCot
	cinerea new	WCMO
	cloracra	CMon WCot
	dubia	CMon ECho WCMO WCot
*	**haurii**	CMon
*	**montana**	ECho LRHS
	tunguraguae	ECho WCMO
	viridiflora	CMon ECho WCMO WCot WHil

Phaedranthus see *Distictis*

Phaenocoma (Asteraceae)

prolifera	SPlb

Phaenosperma (Poaceae)

globosa	CFwr CHrt CSam CSec EBee EGle EHoe EPPr EPla EShb EWes EWsh LEdu LRHS MAvo WBor WDyG WPGP WPrP

Phaiophleps see *Olsynium*

nigricans	see *Sisyrinchium striatum*

Phalaris (Poaceae)

§	**aquatica**	MGol MRav
	arundinacea	CWCL EGra EMFW EPla MBNS MGol MLan NNor SPlb SWat WTin
	- 'Elegantissima'	see *P. arundinacea* var. *picta* 'Picta'
	- var. **picta**	CBen CDul CHEx CHrt CWCL CWib EMFW LRHS NBid NBur NPer SPoG SYvo WDin WFar
	- - 'Aureovariegata' (v)	CBcs CSWP MRav NGdn NPer SWat WMoo
	- - 'Feesey' (v)	More than 30 suppliers
	- - 'Luteopicta' (v)	EBee EHoe EMan EPPr EPfP EPla MMoz WLeb WTin WWpP
	- - 'Luteovariegata' (v)	EShb NGdn
§	- - 'Picta' (v) ♀H4	COIW CPLG EBee EHon ELan EPfP EPla GWCH IHMH LEdu LPBA LRHS MBar MWgw NFor NHol SPer SWal SWat WMoo WWpP WWye
	- - 'Streamlined' (v)	EPPr EPla EWsh SLPl WFar WMoo
	- - 'Tricolor' (v)	CPen EHoe EPla MBar
	tuberosa var. **stenoptera**	see *P. aquatica*

Phanerophlebia (Dryopteridaceae)

caryotidea	see *Cyrtomium caryotideum*
falcata	see *Cyrtomium falcatum*
fortunei	see *Cyrtomium fortunei*

Pharbitis see *Ipomoea*

Phaseolus (Papilionaceae)

adenanthus new	CPIN
caracalla	see *Vigna caracalla*
vulgaris 'Yin Yang' **new**	LSou

Phegopteris (Thelypteridaceae)

§	**connectilis**	EFer EFtx EMon NVic SRms
	decursive-pinnata	CFwr CLAP CRez EFtx EMon GBri MAsh NHol NLar SPoG WOut

Phellodendron (Rutaceae)

amurense	CBcs CCCN CDul CMCN ELan EPfP GIBF LEdu NLar SBLw SBrw WBor WDin WNor WPGP
- var. **sachalinense**	GIBF LRHS
chinense	CMCN
lavalleei	EPfP

Phenakospermum (Strelitziaceae)

guianense	XBlo

Philadelphus ✿ (Hydrangeaceae)

'Albâtre' (d)	MBri
'Avalanche'	CMHG CPLG EBee LRHS NLar NPro SRms WDin WFar WHCG
'Beauclerk' ♀H4	CDoC CDul CMHG CSBt CTri EBee ECrN EPfP EWTr GQui LRHS MBri MGos MRav NEgg NHol NWea SPer SPoG SReu SRms SWvt WDin WHCG WKif
'Belle Etoile' ♀H4	More than 30 suppliers
'Bicolore'	MWya
'Boule d'Argent' (d)	CMHG
'Bouquet Blanc'	GQui MRav NLar SPer SPoG SRms WPat
brachybotrys	EPfP MRav NHol WHCG
'Buckley's Quill' (d)	EBee EPfP MRav MWya
'Burfordensis'	EBee EPfP LAst WPGP
'Burkwoodii'	LRHS
aff. **calvescens** BWJ 8005	WCru
caucasicus	WPGP
coronarius	CDul EPfP LBuc MWhi NFor SGar SHBN SMer SPer WBVN WDin XPep
- 'Aureus' ♀H4	More than 30 suppliers
- 'Bowles' Variety'	see *P. coronarius* 'Variegatus'
§ - 'Variegatus' (v) ♀H4	More than 30 suppliers
'Coupe d'Argent'	CPLG MRav
'Dame Blanche' (d)	EBee EWTr LRHS MAsh MRav EPfP NWea SGar SSpi WCru WCwm WHCG WPGP
delavayi	
- EDHCH 97170	EPPr
- var. **calvescens**	see *P. purpurascens*
- var. **melanocalyx** new	WPGP
'Enchantement' (d)	MRav SDix
§ 'Erectus'	CSBt CWib EBee EHol ENot EPfP ISea MAsh MRav SPer SPla SPoG WDin WHCG WPat WTel
fragrans	WPGP
'Frosty Morn' (d)	CBcs MBri MGos MRav NEgg SPer SPla SPoG WGwG
incanus B&SWJ 8616	WCru
§ 'Innocence' (v)	More than 30 suppliers
'Innocence Variegatus'	see *P.* 'Innocence'
§ **insignis**	MRav
x **lemoinei**	CDul CTri EWTr MGos MWat NFor SHBN SMer WDin WFar
- 'Erectus'	see *P.* 'Erectus'
- 'Lemoinei'	NWea
'Lemon Hill'	NEgg
lewisii L 1896	WPGP
- 'Waterton'	LBuc
maculatus new	CPlN
- 'Mexican Jewel' new	WPGP
madrensis	LHop
'Manteau d'Hermine' (d) ♀H4	More than 30 suppliers
mexicanus	GCal
- 'Rose Syringa'	WPGP
microphyllus	CDul CMHG CPSs EBee ELan EPfP LAst LRHS MGos MRav MWhi NHol SLon SPer SReu SSpi WBVN WHCG WPat WSHC
- var. **occidentalis**	NLar
'Miniature Snowflake' (d)	MAsh WPat
'Minnesota Snowflake' (d)	CBcs CMac EBee ECtt EWes LBuc LRHS MRav NHol NLar NPro SPur WDin WFar
'Mont Blanc'	CBcs WFar
'Mrs E.L. Robinson' (d)	CMac EBee ECtt LAst LRHS
'Natchez' (d)	CMac ECtt WDin WTel
'Oeil de Pourpre'	MRav
palmeri	WPGP
pekinensis	CPLG
'Perryhill'	MRav
§ **purpurascens**	EWes GIBF GQui MAsh MRav MTis NEgg SLon WCwm WPGP WPat
- BWJ 7540	WCru
x **purpureomaculatus**	MAsh WPat
'Russalka'	MWya
schrenkii	NLar WPGP
- B&SWJ 8465	WCru
§ 'Silberregen'	CDul CMac EBee ECtt EPfP LAst MAsh MBar MBri MGos MMuc MRav NCGa NPro SHBN SPoG SRms SWvt WFar WPat
Silver Showers	see *P.* 'Silberregen'
'Snow Velvet'	EPfP LRHS
'Snowbelle' (d)	EBee MAsh MBri
'Snowflake'	CWSG NMoo
'Souvenir de Billiard'	see *P. insignis*
subcanus	CPLG MRav
'Sybille' ♀H4	CMHG ECrN EPfP LRHS MAsh MBri MRav SDix SPer SPoG SRms SSpi WHCG WKif WPat WSHC
tenuifolius	CMCN GIBF NLar
tomentosus	CPLG WHCG WPGP
- B&SWJ 2707	WCru
- GWJ 9215	WCru
'Virginal' (d)	More than 30 suppliers
'Voie Lactée'	MRav
White Rock = 'Pekphil'	CDoC CMac CPLG CWSG EBee LAst LRHS LTwo NMoo SLim SPer SPoG WPat
'Yellow Cab'	NLar SPoG WPat
'Yellow Hill' new	NLar

Philesia (Philesiaceae)

buxifolia	see *P. magellanica*
§ **magellanica**	GGGa GSki ITim SOkd SSpi WCru WSHC

Philibertia (Asclepiadaceae)

gracilis new	EShb

Phillyrea (Oleaceae)

angustifolia	CBcs CDul CMCN EBee EHol ELan EPfP ERom MGos SBig SEND SLPl SPer SSpi WBVN WDin WFar WSHC XPep
- f. **rosmarinifolia**	CPLG EPfP LAst NLar SBrw WFar WPGP XPep
decora	see *Osmanthus decorus*
§ **latifolia**	CHEx CPLG EBee ELan EPfP LRHS NLar SAPC SArc SLPl SSpi WDin WFar XPep
I - 'Rodrigueziensis'	WCFE
media	see *P. latifolia*

Philodendron (Araceae)

epipremnum	see *Epipremnum pinnatum*
erubescens 'Burgundy' ♀H1	LRHS
- 'Red Emerald'	CHal
- **scandens** ♀H1	CHal
- 'Mica' new	XBlo
selloum	EAmu MOak WMul XBlo
xanadu	XBlo

Philotheca (Rutaceae)

buxifolia 'Cascade of Stars'	SOWG

Phlebodium (*Polypodiaceae*)

§ *aureum* ♀H1 **new**   CSpe

Phleum (*Poaceae*)

bertolonii   CRWN
pratense   CBig EHoe WOut WSFF

Phlomis ✿ (*Lamiaceae*)

* *anatolica*	NLar XPep
* - 'Lloyd's Variety'	CAbP CSam ELan GCal LRHS MBri
	MSte SPer SSvw WCot
atropurpurea	EBee
betonicoides B&L 12600	EPPr
bovei subsp. *maroccana*	GCal IFro SEND WHal XPep
bracteosa	MGol
cashmeriana	CBcs CBgR EBee EBrs ECha EDAr
	GAbr LDai MGol MNFA NDov
	NLar SMad SMar WCFE WLin
chrysophylla ♀H3	CAbP EBee ECha ELan EMan EPfP
	LRHS NLar SBla SDix SPer SPoG
	WCFE WCot XPep
cypria	XPep
'Edward Bowles'	EWTr NBid SLPl SLon SWvt WCot
	XPep
* 'Elliot's Variety'	CPLG
fruticosa ♀H4	More than 30 suppliers
- 'Butterfly'	XPep
- white-flowered **new**	EBee
grandiflora	SEND XPep
herba-venti	XPep
italica	More than 30 suppliers
lanata ♀H3-4	CAbP CBgR ELan EMan EPfP LRHS
	MSte NCGa NPro SBla SPer SPoG
	WEas WKif WWye XPep
- 'Pygmy'	MGos NPro SLon XPep
'Le Sud'	XPep
leucophracta	XPep
- 'Golden Janissary'	WPGP XPep
longifolia	CBgR CHad EPfP LHop LRHS LSou
	MGos NLar SPer WGer XPep
- var. *bailanica*	LRHS WFar WSPU
lunariifolia	XPep
lychnitis	MWrn XPep
lycia	LRHS XPep
monocephala	XPep
pratensis **new**	EBee
purpurea	CAbP CPLG CSam EBee ELan EPfP
	LRHS MAsh MGol NBir SBrw SPoG
	WCot WOVN WSHC XPep
- *alba*	EPfP EWTr LHop WSHC XPep
- subsp. *almeriensis*	CPom XPep
- subsp. *caballeroi*	XPep
§ *russeliana* ♀H4	More than 30 suppliers
samia Boiss.	see *P. russeliana*
samia L.	CPom EBee EWTr LDai LHop
	MGol NChi NGdn NLar SMar
	WCot WFar WHal XPep
- JMT 285	LRHS
tatsienensis var.	GAbr
tatsienensis	
taurica **new**	NChi
tuberosa	CBcs CFir CMil CPou EBee EMar
	EPPr EPfP ERou EWTr LAst LEdu
	LLWP MGol MHer MWgw MWrn
	NEgg NLar SMrm SPet WBVN
	WCAu WCot WGwG WHoo WOVN
	WPGP WSHC XPep
- 'Amazone'	CElw CFir CKno EBee EChP ECha
	EHrv EMan EPfP LAst LHop MBri
	MTis NBid NCGa NEgg NOrc
	NSti SAga SBla SMad SMrm SUsu
	WCAu WCot WFar WGHP WMnd
	WTMC
- 'Bronze Flamingo'	EBee EPfP EWin LAst NBHF NDov
	NFla NOrc WMnd WPer

viscosa misapplied   see *P. russeliana*
viscosa Poiret   XPep

Phlox ✿ (*Polemoniaceae*)

adsurgens ♀H4	ITim NCob WAbe
- 'Alba'	NSla SBla WAbe
- 'Oregon Blush' **new**	NHar
- 'Red Buttes'	CLyd ECho EPot SBla
- 'Wagon Wheel'	CWCL EAEE EBee ECho ECtt EHyt
	EPPr EPot EWes GBBs GGar GKev
	ITim LAst LRHS NLAp NRya NSla
	SIng SMrm SPlb SRms SRot WAbe
	WCFE WFar WPat WSHC
alyssifolia	CPBP
'Amazone' **new**	IPot
amplifolia	EBee NBre WFar
x *arendsii* 'Anja'	CPrp WCot
- 'Early Star'	EBee
- 'Eyecatcher'	CMMP NBro NCGa NGdn
- 'Lilac Girl' **new**	NBre
- 'Lilac Star'	CFir LAst
- 'Lisbeth'	SUsu WCot
§ - 'Luc's Lilac'	CBos CMHG CPrp EMar GBin
	LPhx LRHS LTwo NBro NCGa
	NDov NFla NGdn NVic SMeo STes
	WWlt
§ - (Spring Pearl Series)	CHea CMMP EBee EChP EGle
'Miss Jill'	NCob NHol SBla WTin
§ - - 'Miss Jo-Ellen'	EGle GBin
§ - - 'Miss Karen'	EChP EGle ERou NBro
§ - - 'Miss Margie'	EChP EGle ERou GBri GMaP LAst
	NBir
§ - - 'Miss Mary'	EChP EGle GBri GMaP LAst MDKP
	NCGa NHol NPro STes WWye
§ - - 'Miss Wilma'	CBos GMaP WWye
- 'Ping Pong'	CPrp EBee LDai MBnl NBPC NBre
	NBro NPro STes WSan
- 'Pink Attraction'	CFwr MNrw NBro NCGa
- 'Purple Star'	CPrp EBee MBnl
- 'Rosa Star'	CFir EBee LAst NBre
- 'Sabine'	CFir EBee
- 'Suzanne'	EBee
austromontana	EPot NWCA WLin
bifida	ECho
- 'Alba'	ECho EHyt LSou LTwo WAbe WFar
	WLin
- blue-flowered	ECho LRHS LSou SBla SUsu
- 'Colvin's White'	EDAr SBla
- 'Minima Colvin'	ECho ECtt EPot GKev NLAp
- 'Petticoat'	CLyd CMea CPBP EPot LRHS
	MDKP SBla SUsu WFar WLin
- 'Ralph Haywood'	CLyd CPBP EPot GBuc ITim NLAp
	WAbe
- 'Starbrite'	CLyd GBBs LRHS NLar WFar
- 'Thefi'	EWes LTwo MNrw
borealis	see *P. sibirica* subsp. *borealis*
* - *arctica*	EPot
bryoides	see *P. hoodii* subsp. *muscoides*
caespitosa	ECho EWes NDlv NWCA
- subsp. *condensata*	see *P. condensata*
- subsp. *pulvinata*	see *P. pulvinata*
canadensis	see *P. divaricata*
carolina subsp. *angusta*	NBre
- 'Bill Baker' ♀H4	More than 30 suppliers
- 'Magnificence'	CBos COIW CPrp EBee EChP EGle
	EWes GBuc GMac LAst MDKP MSte
	STes WCMO WCot WSHC WTin
- 'Miss Lingard' ♀H4	More than 30 suppliers
'Charles Ricardo'	CElw ETow EWes GBuc LSou
	SMrm SUsu WHoo
'Chattahoochee'	see *P. divaricata* subsp. *laphamii*
	'Chattahoochee'
§ *condensata*	ECho WPat
covillei	see *P. condensata*
'Daniel's Cushion'	see *P. subulata* 'McDaniel's
	Cushion'

§ *divaricata* ♀H4 — EHol MRav MSte SBod SHBN SPlb WPer
- f. *albiflora* — ELan
- 'Blue Dreams' — CFir CHea CMHG CPrp EBee EChP EHrv GBuc LRHS MNrw MSte NCob SPla SUsu WFar WHal WPGP WWlt
- 'Blue Perfume' — CMHG CMMP EBee EChP LSou MTis NBid NBro NCGa NLar NSti SHGN
- 'Clouds of Perfume' — CHea CMMP CPrp EBee EChP ENor GBri GMaP LAst LRHS LSRN MWgw NCGa NCob NMyG NSti SBla SBod SMer SMrm STes SWat WFar WLin
- 'Dirigo Ice' — EAEE EBee EHrv GBri LHop NLar SBla SIng WFar WRHF WSHC
- 'Eco Texas Purple' — EChP NCGa NCob NPro SAga SMrm WFar WPGP WWlt
- 'Fuller's White' — CWCL
§ - subsp. *laphamii* — EGle EWes NSti SUsu WFar WFoF
§ - - 'Chattahoochee' ♀H4 — More than 30 suppliers
§ - - 'Chattahoochee Variegated' (v) — LRHS
§ - 'Louisiana Purple' — WSHC
- 'May Breeze' — EAEE EBee ECho EGle EHrv GMaP LAst LHop LRHS MNrw MSte MWgw NCGa NCob SIng SPla WFar WPGP WSHC WWlt
- 'Plum Perfect' — EBee NBhm NBro NLar SHar WPtf
* - 'White Perfume' — CMHG CMMP CPrp EBee EChP EMil EWes GBri LAst LSou MBrN MDKP MTis NBid NBro NCGa NCob NLar NSti SHGN SMrm STes WLin

douglasii — ECho NPol NWCA SRms
- 'Apollo' — CTri ECho LRHS LTwo NHol NMen SBla
- 'Boothman's Variety' ♀H4 — CLyd ECha ECho EDAr ELan EPfP EPot LRHS MLHP MWat NMen SPoG SRms WEas WLin
- 'Crackerjack' ♀H4 — CLyd CMea EAEE ECho ECtt EDAr ELan ENot EPfP EPot GAbr GKev GMaP ITim LRHS MHer MLHP NBir NEgg NMen SIng SPoG SRGP WAbe WFar WLin
- 'Eva' — CLyd CMMP CPBP EAEE ECho EDAr ELan EPot GAbr GKev GMaP ITim LRHS NBir NHol NMen NWCA SPoG WLin
- 'Galaxy' — ECho EWes
- 'Ice Mountain' — ECho EDAr ELan EPot ITim NEgg NWCA SPoG SRot
- 'Iceberg' ♀H4 — ECho NMen WLin
- 'Lilac Cloud' — NPro SHGN SIng
- Lilac Queen — see *P. douglasii* 'Lilakönigin'
§ - 'Lilakönigin' — ECho WRHF
- 'Napoleon' — CPBP ECho EPot ITim LTwo NMen
- 'Ochsenblut' — ECho EHyt EPot GEdr LTwo MHer MLHP SIng
- 'Red Admiral' ♀H4 — ECho EWes GMaP LRHS NHol NMen WCFE WFar WGwG
- 'Rose Cushion' — ECho EDAr EWes ITim LRHS MHer NMen
- 'Rose Queen' — CLyd ECho
- 'Rosea' — ECho EDAr ELan GMaP LRHS NMen NPol WBVN WFar WRHF
- 'Silver Rose' — ECho EPot NWCA
- 'Sprite' — SRms
- 'Tycoon' — see *P. subulata* 'Tamaongalei'
- 'Violet Queen' — ECho EWes WFar
- 'Waterloo' — CMea ECho EPot LRHS NMen
I - 'White Admiral' — ECho EPot LSRN NPro SIng
'Fancy Feelings' — NBro NCob SPoG WHil
glaberrima 'Morris Berd' — EBee WPGP
hendersonii — CGra

hoodii — CPBP ECho
§ - subsp. *muscoides* — ECho
idahoensis — SOkd
(Intensia Series) Intensia Lavender Glow = 'Usphlo1' **new** — SVil
- Intensia Lilac Rose = 'Usphlo2' **new** — SVil
- Intensia Neon Pink = 'Usphlo3' **new** — SVil
'Junior Dance' — WWeb
'Junior Dream' — WWeb
'Junior Surprise' — WWeb
'Kelly's Eye' ♀H4 — CLyd CMMP CPBP ECho ELan EPot LRHS NBir NHar NHol NMen SPoG WBVN WFar WLin
kelseyi — ECho NWCA WAbe
- 'Lemhi Purple' — WLin
- 'Rosette' — CLyd ECho EPot LRHS MDKP NHol NMen WFar WLin WPer
Light Pink Flame = 'Bareleven'PBR — CPen
longifolia subsp. *brevifolia* — CPBP WAbe
'Louisiana' — see *P. divaricata* 'Louisiana Purple'
maculata — NOrc WBVN WPer
- 'Alpha' ♀H4 — More than 30 suppliers
- Avalanche — see *P. maculata* 'Schneelawine'
- 'Delta' — CHea CWCL EBee EBrs EChP EPfP GBuc LRHS LSou NEgg NHol NSti SMad SPer STes SWvt WBor WCAu WFar
- 'Natascha' — More than 30 suppliers
- 'Omega' ♀H4 — CHea CMHG CPLG EBee EPfP GBuc GGar GMaP LRHS MRav MSte MWgw NBid NCGa NEgg NGdn NHol NLar SMad SPer SPla SWvt WCAu WFar WSHC
- 'Princess Sturdza' ♀H4 — SDix
- 'Reine du Jour' — CBos GMac LPhx LSou MSte NDov SAga SMrm SUsu WHil WSHC
- 'Rosalinde' — COIW CPrp CWoW EBee EChP EMar GBuc LRHS MRav MSte NBPC NCGa NCob NEgg NHol NLar SBla SPla SPoG SRGP STes SWvt WCAu WFar WHil WSHC
§ - 'Schneelawine' — NCob
'Matineus' — LPhx
'Millstream' — see *P. x procumbens* 'Millstream'
'Millstream Jupiter' — ECho
muscoides — see *P. hoodii* subsp. *muscoides*
nivalis — CPBP NLAp
- 'Jill Alexander' — CMea SAga
- 'Nivea' — ETow LRHS LSou WAbe WLin
paniculata — CHad LPhx NBid NDov NFor SDix SMeo WCot WOld WTin
- 'A.E.Amos' — ERou
- 'Aida' — CFwr
- var. *alba* — CBos GCal NDov SDix WCot WTin
- 'Alba Grandiflora' ♀H4 — EHrv GMaP NCob SBla WEas WHoo
- 'Amethyst' misapplied — see *P. paniculata* 'Lilac Time'
- 'Amethyst' Foerster — CFir CFwr CSam EBee EGle EHrv EPfP ERou MTis NBir NBlu NEgg NOrc NPri SMer WCAu WFar WLin WWye
- 'Ann' — CFwr
- 'Antoinette Six' — CFwr
I - 'Aureovariegata Undulata' (v) — WCot
- 'Babyface' — CFwr
- 'Balmoral' — CFwr EBee ECtt EPfP LRHS MLHP MRav MSte NCob NSti SMer SWat SWvt
- 'Becky Towe'PBR (v) — CBow CFwr EBee EGle EKen EMan LHop LRHS LTwo SPoG

- 'Betty Symons-Jeune'	CFwr
- 'Bill Green'	LRHS
- 'Blue Boy'	CFwr EGle ERou EWTr GMaP LAst LRHS MDKP NBir NBro NChi NGby NLar NRnb STes WBrE WFar WHil WViv
- 'Blue Evening'	LSou NCob
- 'Blue Ice' ♀H4	EBee ELan EMar LPhx LRHS MMHG MRav NBro NCob NEgg SPla
- 'Blue Paradise'	More than 30 suppliers
- 'Blushing Bride'	SRms
- 'Border Gem'	CBcs CFwr EBee ECtt ERou MSte MWgw NChi NCob NEgg NLRH NLar SDix SMer SPur SWat SWvt WBrk WCot
- 'Branklyn'	LRHS WFar
- 'Brigadier' ♀H4	CSam EBee ECtt ELan GMaP LRHS MDKP NCob NEgg NVic SPer SPla SRms WCAu WFar
- 'Bright Eyes' ♀H4	CBcs CFwr COlW CSBt EBee EBrs ECtt ERou LRHS LSRN MArl MDKP NCGa NCob NEgg NHol NPri SMer SPoG STes SUsu SWvt WCAu WFar WHlf WTel
- 'Burgi'	CBos SDix
- 'Caroline van den Berg'	SRms
- 'Cecil Hanbury'	ERou NBlu NLar SRms
- 'Chintz'	MRav SRms
- 'Cinderella'	CFwr CSBt EBee ERou EWTr
§ - 'Cool of the Evening'	CFwr LPhx WKif WWlt
- Count Zeppelin	see *P. paniculata* 'Graf Zeppelin'
- 'Daisy Field'	NCob
- 'Danielle'	CFwr
- 'Darwin's Choice'	see *P. paniculata* 'Norah Leigh'
- 'David'	CBos CFwr EBee EBrs EChP ECha EGle ERou EShb IPot LAst LPhx LRHS NBid NBro NChi NCob NGby NHol NMoo NOrc NRnb SRGP STes SUsu WBor WCAu WCMO WCot WHil
- 'Delilah'	NCob
- 'Discovery'	EBee ECGP EMar EWes IPot NCob SPla STes SWat WCAu
- 'Dodo Hanbury-Forbes' ♀H4	EHol
- 'Doghouse Pink'	NCob
- 'Dresden China'	SWat
§ - 'Düsterlohe'	CBrm CSam EGle ERou GAbr GBuc GMac LSou NBPC NBir NLar NRnb NSti SMrm STes WFar WHil WHoo
- 'Eclaireur' misapplied	see *P. paniculata* 'Duesterlohe'
- 'Eclaireur' Lemoine	NCob SWat
- 'Eden's Crush'	CMMP EChP NBre NRnb NVic
- 'Eden's Flash'	EGle ERou NRnb
- 'Eden's Glory'	EChP EGle NCGa NRnb
- 'Eden's Glow'	EChP NRnb
- 'Eden's Smile'	EBee EChP ERou NRnb
- 'Elizabeth' (v)	CFwr EBee ENot LAst NRnb SRGP STes
- 'Elizabeth Arden'	CFwr ERou MSte NLar SWat
- 'Empty Feelings'PBR	EBee EChP EGle GBin NBro NCob WHil
- 'Ending Blue'	CFwr NRnb
- 'Etoile de Paris'	see *P. paniculata* 'Toits de Paris' Symons-Jeune
- 'Europa'	EBee ELan EPfP ERou LRHS MBri NBir NCob NEgg NGdn NHol NLar SPer SPla WCAu WFar
- 'Eva Cullum'	CFwr EAEE EBee ECtt EGle LRHS MArl MRav MTis NBPC NFla NHol NMoo SHop SMer SPer SPet SRGP SWat WCMO WCot WRHF
- 'Eventide' ♀H4	CFwr CWCL EBee ECtt EPfP LRHS MArl MWgw NCob SMer SPer SPet SPur SWat WCAu WCot
- 'Excelsior'	MRav
- 'Fairy's Petticoat'	MWat
- 'Flamingo'	CFwr EBrs ERou LRHS MBrN NGby NLar SWvt
- 'Franz Schubert'	CFwr CHrt EBee EBrs ECtt EGle LRHS MLHP MRav NBir NChi NFla NLar NSti STes SUsu SWat SWvt WCMO WCot WKif WTel
§ - 'Frau Alfred von Mauthner'	CFwr COlW MBri
- 'Frosted Elegance' (v)	EChP EMan EPPr LSou SHop
- 'Fujiyama'	see *P. paniculata* 'Mount Fuji'
- 'Glamis'	MWat
- 'Gnoom'	CFwr
- 'Goldmine'PBR (v)	CBow CWCL IBal MBnl MCCP NBro NCob SPoG
§ - 'Graf Zeppelin'	CFwr ELan LBMP LRHS NGby SRms
- 'Harlequin' (v)	More than 30 suppliers
I - 'Hesperis'	CMdw EBee GBin LPhx NDov SMeo SMrm SUsu WHil
- 'Hogg Rose'	NCob
- 'Iceberg'	NCob
- 'Iris'	CDes GBuc SRms
- 'Jubilee'	CFwr CMMP NRnb WHil
- 'Judy'	CFwr NBro
- 'Jules Sandeau'	CFwr LRHS MBri NCob
§ - 'Juliglut'	EChP ERou MWea NCGa SWat WCot
- July Glow	see *P. paniculata* 'Juliglut'
- 'Katarina'	CElw CHea EChP ECtt EMar EPfP NLar SUsu WBor
- 'Katherine'	CFwr
- 'Kelway's Cherub'	NCob
- 'Kirchenfürst'	MBri NBir SMrm SPoG
- 'Kirmesländler'	CFwr EBee ERou LRHS MBow MLLN NCob NLar SVil
- 'Lady Clare'	SRms
- 'Landhochzeit'	EBee LRHS NCob
* - 'Laura'	CMMP EBee EGle ERou IPot NBro NRnb NVic SMrm SPoG SRGP STes WFar WHoo WWeb
§ - 'Lavendelwolke'	CSam EBee GCal NBir NCob NLar SWat
- Lavender Cloud	see *P. paniculata* 'Lavendelwolke'
- Le Mahdi' ♀H4	CFwr ELan MBrN MRav MWat SMeo SRms
- 'Lichtspel'	LPhx NDov SAga SMeo
§ - 'Lilac Time'	CFwr CSBt EBee EHrv EWll MDKP MSte MWat NCob NMoo SMer SRGP SWvt WCMO
- 'Little Boy'	CElw EChP ECtt EGle ERou LRHS LSou MDKP NLar SPoG STes WFar WHil WWeb
- 'Little Laura'	CElw CHea CMHG MAvo MCCP MWea NLar SHop
- 'Little Princess'	CFwr EGle NLar SPoG SRGP
- 'Lizzy'PBR	CFwr ERou MBri MWea NLar
- 'Look Again'	CFwr
- 'Manoir d'Hézèques'	WCot
- 'Mary Christine' (v)	EBee
- 'Mary Fox'	CSam
- 'Mia Ruys'	ERou GMac MArl MBri MLHP MLLN SMrm
- 'Midnight Feelings'	LTwo NBro NCob NLar WCot
- 'Mies Copijn'	CFwr GMaP WFar
- 'Milly van Hoboken'	CBos WKif
- 'Miss Elie'	CMMP EGle ERou LAst SPoG WFar WHoo
- 'Miss Holland'	CHea EChP EGle NCGa NRnb WHoo
- 'Miss Jessica'	ERou LAst
- 'Miss Jill'	see *P. x arendsii* 'Miss Jill'

- 'Miss Jo-Ellen'	see *P.* x *arendsii* 'Miss Jo-Ellen'
- 'Miss Karen'	see *P.* x *arendsii* 'Miss Karen'
- 'Miss Kelly'	CFwr CMMP CMdw MWea SRGP WHoo
- 'Miss Margie'	see *P.* x *arendsii* 'Miss Margie'
- 'Miss Mary'	see *P.* x *arendsii* 'Miss Mary'
- 'Miss Pepper'	CWCL EMil ERou NLar SMrm SRGP WBor WFar WHil
- 'Miss Universe'	CMMP EGle MCCP NRnb SPoG WHoo WWye
- 'Miss Wilma'	see *P.* x *arendsii* 'Miss Wilma'
- 'Monica Lynden-Bell'	More than 30 suppliers
- 'Mother of Pearl' ♀H4	CFwr EAEE EBee ELan EMar LRHS MWat NCob NFla NHol NVic SBla SPer SPet WCMO
§ - 'Mount Fuji' ♀H4	More than 30 suppliers
- 'Mount Fujiyama'	see *P. paniculata* 'Mount Fuji'
- 'Mrs A.E. Jeans'	SRms
- 'Natural Feelings'PBR	CSpe EBee GBin MCCP NBPC NBro NCob NLar SPoG WCot WSan WTMC
- 'Newbird'	SRms WCMO
- 'Nicky'	see *P. paniculata* 'Duesterlohe'
§ - 'Norah Leigh' (v)	More than 30 suppliers
- 'Orange Perfection'	see *P. paniculata* 'Prince of Orange'
- 'Othello'	EBee EBrs EKen EMar EWll LRHS NChi NCob NSti SUsu
- 'Otley Choice'	CFwr EAEE EBee LAst LRHS MHer MRav MSte MWat NCob NHol NLar NSti SCoo SPoG
- 'Otley Purple' **new**	CFwr
- 'P.D. Williams'	WCot
- 'Pastorale'	WCot WTel
- 'Pax'	EBee EMon ERou LPhx SMeo
- 'Pink Posie'PBR (v)	MBri WFar
- 'Pinky Hill'	CFwr
- 'Pleasant Feelings' **new**	NBro
- 'Popeye'	CFwr ECtt MBri NLar
§ - 'Prince of Orange' ♀H4	CBcs CFwr CSam EBee EChP ECtt ELan EPfP ERou EWTr LAst LRHS LSRN MRav MWat MWgw NBlu NCob NPri NRnb SAga SPer SPet SPoG SWvt WCMO WCot WHil WViv
- 'Prospero' ♀H4	CHar CSam EBee ECGP EHrv LBMP MWgw NBid NEgg SMer SPer SUsu WTel
- 'Rainbow'	CFwr EGle
- 'Red Feelings'PBR	NBro NCob SPoG WHil WSan
- 'Red Indian'	MWat SMer
- 'Red Riding Hood'	CFwr CWCL LAst WRHF
- 'Rembrandt'	CFwr CPLG ERou GBri LRHS NBlu SBla
- 'Rijnstroom'	CBcs CFwr EBee ECot ERou LRHS MBow NBPC SMer WFar WHil WTel
- 'Robert Poore'	CFwr NCob
- 'Rosa Pastell'	CBos CDes CFwr EGle EHrv EMon GBri IPot LPhx LSou NCob SUsu
- 'Rosa Spier'	CFwr
- 'Rosy Veil'	CFwr
- 'Rowie'	NBid NCob WBor
- 'Rubymine'PBR (v)	EChP EMan ERou NCob
- 'San Antonio'	CFwr WFar
- 'Sandringham'	CFwr EBee EHrv EPfP LRHS MArl MNrw MRav MSte NBir NHol SBla SMer SPer SPoG SWvt WCAu
§ - 'Schneerausch'	LPhx
- 'Septemberglut'	CFwr NLar
- 'Silvermine' (v)	CBow EChP EMan LSou MCCP NBro NLar SDnm
- 'Sir Malcolm Campbell'	CFwr
- 'Skylight'	EBee LRHS LSRN NBre NBro NVic SDix SPer WLin
- 'Snow White'	NBre NVic
- Snowdrift	see *P. paniculata* 'Schneerausch'
- 'Speed Limit'	CFwr
- 'Speed Limit 45'	CBos WCot
- 'Spitfire'	see *P. paniculata* 'Frau Alfred von Mauthner'
- 'Starburst'	NBPC NGdn WHil
- 'Starfire' ♀H4	More than 30 suppliers
- 'Steeple Bumpstead'	EBee EGle LSou MBnl NCGa NCob SPoG WCot WTMC WWlt
- 'Tenor'	CDes CFir CWCL EAEE EBee EChP ERou LRHS MDKP MSte NCob NGdn NHol NPri NRnb SBla SMer SPet SPla SPoG SWvt WBor WBrE WCAu WCMO WCot WFar
- 'The King'	EBee EChP EGle GBri LRHS MAvo MDKP MSte NBro NGby SUsu SWat WBor WHil WMow WTel
- 'Toits de Paris' misapplied	see *P. paniculata* 'Cool of the Evening'
- 'Toits de Paris' ambig.	CBos SMHy
§ - 'Toits de Paris' Symons-Jeune	LPhx WSHC
- 'Uspekh'	CFwr CSam EAEE EBee ECGP EMar EPPr EShb EWes MDKP MSte MTis NBro NCGa NCob NOrc SAga SPer SUsu SVil WPat
- 'Utopia'	CDes EBee LPhx NRnb SUsu
- 'Van Gogh'	CMdw EHrv
- 'Victorian Lilac'	NCob
- 'Vintage Wine'	MSte
- 'Violetta Gloriosa'	LPhx
- 'Wenn Schon Denn Schon'	GBin
- 'White Admiral' ♀H4	CBcs CHrt CSBt EBee ECtt EGle EHrv ELan EPfP ERou GAbr GKev GMaP LRHS MHer MRav MWgw NPri NVic SMer SPer SPla SPoG SRms SWat SWvt WBVN WTel WViv
- 'White Sparr'	CFwr
- 'Wilhelm Kesselring'	CHrt NBre SRGP WBor
- 'Windsor' ♀H4	CFwr EBee EBrs ECtt EPfP ERou GBBs GBri LRHS MLLN MTis NEgg NHol NLar SCoo SMer SPoG SRms SWvt WCAu WFar
pilosa	ECha NPro WFar
Pink Flame = 'Bartwelve'PBR	CPen
§ x *procumbens* 'Millstream' ♀H4	GAbr SBla
- 'Variegata' (v)	CBrm ECha ECho EDAr LRHS MDKP SBla SPlb SRot SUsu WFar WLin WPat
§ *pulvinata*	NWCA
Purple Flame = 'Barfourteen'PBR	CPen
'Sandra'	LRHS
'Scented Pillow'	LRHS
§ *sibirica* subsp. *borealis*	EDAr GKev
'Sileniflora'	EPot
stolonifera	CBcs MNrw
I - 'Alba'	EBee EWin
- 'Ariane'	CWCL EBrs ECha EPPr EWTr LSou MBri MNrw SBch SBla WCFE WFar
I - 'Atropurpurea'	CBcs
- 'Blue Ridge' ♀H4	CFir CPLG CWCL EBee EBrs ECha ENot EPfP EShb GBuc LAst MBri MRav SMer SRms WFar WSan
- 'Bob's Motley' (v)	ECtt EMan LSou WCot
- compact	EPot
- 'Compact Pink'	WFar
- 'Fran's Purple'	CDes CLyd EBee MWhi NBro WCFE WFar WPGP WSPU WViv
- 'Home Fires'	CFwr EBee EPfP EWin EWll GAbr MNrw NBro NLar SAga SBla SMrm SPlb WFar

- 'Mary Belle Frey'	CEnt EBee MSte WFar
- 'Montrose Tricolor' (v)	EBee EPPr LHop NBro
- 'Pink Ridge'	EBrs EWll MBri MNrw NBir WDyG WRos
- 'Purpurea'	EBee EPPr EWin LSou
- variegated (v)	WCot
- 'Violet Vere'	GBuc MNrw WFar
subulata	CBrm NWCA
- 'Alexander's Surprise'	CMea EAEE ECho ECtt EDAr EPfP EPot LBee LRHS MDKP NBir SPlb SPoG SRGP
- 'Amazing Grace'	CWCL EAEE ECho EDAr ELan EPfP EWes LHop LRHS MHer NHol NLar SIng SPoG WBVN
- 'Apple Blossom'	EDAr NEgg NPro SPoG SRms WFar
- 'Atropurpurea'	LRHS NBlu NFor NJOw NPro
- Beauty of Ronsdorf	see *P. subulata* 'Ronsdorfer Schöne'
- 'Betty'	ECtt NJOw
- 'Blue Eyes'	see *P. subulata* 'Oakington Blue Eyes'
- 'Bonita'	CPBP EAEE ECho EHyt EPot EWin LBee LRHS WBor WBrE
- 'Bressingham Blue Eyes'	see *P. subulata* 'Oakington Blue Eyes'
- 'Brightness'	CNic ECho LRHS NHol
- 'Brilliant' **new**	ECho
- subsp. *brittonii* 'Rosea'	GEdr
- 'Candy Stripe'	see *P. subulata* 'Tamaongalei'
- 'Cavaldes White'	MDKP
- 'Christine Bishop'	LRHS
- 'Coral Eye'	EPfP
- 'Daisy Hill'	CPBP
- 'Drumm'	see *P. subulata* 'Tamaongalei'
- 'Emerald Cushion'	COfd CSam CTri CWCL ECho ECtt EDAr GKev MDKP MHer NFor WBVN WCFE WRHF
- 'Emerald Cushion Blue'	CBrm ECho EPfP NBir NMen NPri NPro SBla SGar SPlb WBrE WFar WLin WPer
- 'Fairy'	WPer
- 'Fort Hill'	NHar
- 'G.F.Wilson'	see *P. subulata* 'Lilacina'
* - 'Holly'	EPot ITim NMen
- 'Jupiter'	ECho
- 'Kimono'	see *P. subulata* 'Tamaongalei'
§ - 'Lilacina'	CLyd CMea ECha ECho ELan GMaP LRHS NFor NHol NJOw NLar SBla SPoG SRGP
§ - 'Maischnee'	CLyd CMea ECho ECtt EPfP GAbr LRHS MHer MWat NFor NHol SIng SPlb WEas WFar
- 'Marjorie'	CLyd ECho ECtt LBee MDKP MHer NBir NPri NWCA SMer SPoG
- May Snow	see *P. subulata* 'Maischnee'
§ - 'McDaniel's Cushion'	CLyd CNic COfd ECha ECho EDAr ELan EPfP EPot GAbr GKev GMaP ITim LAst LBee LRHS MLHP NFor NHar NHol NJOw NMen NWCA SPlb SPoG WCFE WFar WRHF WTel ♀H4
- 'Mikado'	see *P. subulata* 'Tamaongalei'
- 'Moonlight'	ECtt
- 'Nettleton Variation' (v)	EAEE ECho EPPr EPot EWes GKev LBee LHop LRHS MDKP MHer NPri NPro SPlb SPoG WBrE
§ - 'Oakington Blue Eyes'	LRHS SRms
- 'Pink Pearl'	EWes
- 'Purple Beauty'	CWCL NHar SBla WLin WSHC
- 'Red Wings' ♀H4	EAEE ECho ECtt EHyt EPfP LRHS NMen SPoG SRms
§ - 'Ronsdorfer Schöne'	EPot LBee LRHS NBir NJOw
- 'Samson'	LRHS SMer
- 'Scarlet Flame'	CMea CSam ECho ECtt EDAr ELan EPfP EPot MHer MWat NEgg NHol NPri SRGP WFar
- 'Schneewittchen'	CLyd

- 'Sensation'	SBla
- 'Snow Queen'	see *P. subulata* 'Maischnee'
§ - 'Tamaongalei'	CLyd CMea COfd CPBP EAEE EBrs ECho EDAr EHyt EPfP EPot EWes GKev LRHS MHer MMuc NEgg SBla SCoo SIng SPet SPoG SRGP SRms STes SWal WBor WCFE
- 'Temiskaming'	EAEE ECGP ECho EDAr ELan EWes GEdr LBee LRHS MLHP NMen SBla SPoG SRms WSHC
- 'Tschernobyl' **new**	EPot
- violet seedling	CLyd
- 'White Delight'	ECho ECtt ELan LAst LBee NMen SPoG WBor WFar
- 'Woodside'	CNic
'Sweet William'	LRHS SRGP
'Tiny Bugles'	CStu SBla
'Unique' **new**	CGra
'Vivid'	EDAr

Phoebe (Lauraceae)

sheareri	WPGP

Phoenix (Arecaceae)

canariensis ♀H1+3	More than 30 suppliers
§ *dactylifera* (F)	CRoM EAmu LPal MPRe SBig WMul
reclinata	CKob CRoM EAmu LPJP NPal SAin WMul
roebelenii ♀H1+3	CBrP CDoC CRoM EPfP LPal MBri NPal SAin SBig WMul
rupicola	CRoM LPal
sylvestris	EAmu LPal SAin WMul
theophrasti	CPHo EAmu EZes LEdu LPJP LPal WMul

Phormium ✿ (Phormiaceae)

'Alison Blackman'	CBcs CDoC CPen CSBt CTrC CWil EBee ENot IBal IBlr ISea LHop LSRN MPRe NScw SCoo SPoG SSto WViv
'Amazing Red'	CWil IBal IBlr
'Apricot Queen' (v)	CAbb CBcs CBrm CCCN CDoC CSBt CTrC CWil EBee EPfP GQui IBal IBlr LRHS MBri MCCP MDun MGos NMoo NPal NPri SHBN SLim SPer SPoG SRkn SSto WFar WGwG WPat
Ballyrogan variegated (v)	IBlr
* 'Black Edge'	CWil IBlr MRav NPri
'Bronze Baby'	More than 30 suppliers
'Buckland Ruby'	CDoC CWil MAsh
'Carousel' **new**	IBal
colensoi	see *P. cookianum*
§ *cookianum*	CTrC CWil ECre EPfP GKev IBlr MGos SAPC SArc SCoo SEND WFar WMul
- 'Alpinum Purpureum'	see *P. tenax* 'Nanum Purpureum'
- dwarf	IBlr SLPl
- 'Flamingo'	CHen CTrC CWil ECre EPfP MBri SLim SSto WCMO
- 'Golden Wonder'	IBlr
- subsp. *hookeri*	More than 30 suppliers
'Cream Delight' (v) ♀H3-4	
- - 'Tricolor' ♀H3-4	More than 30 suppliers
* 'Copper Beauty'	COtt CWil NMoo SMer WDyG
'Crimson Devil'	CBcs CBrm CPen EBee NScw
'Dark Delight'	CBcs EBee IBlr
'Dazzler' (v)	EWsh IBlr LAst MGos SHBN WCot
'Duet' (v) ♀H3	CBcs CCCN CDoC CSBt CWil EBee EHoe EPfP IBal IBlr LRHS MPRe NLar SPla SWvt WFar
'Dusky Chief'	CPen CSBt CWil IBal LRHS MAsh WPat
'Emerald Isle'	CDoC CWil

'Evening Glow' (v)	CBcs CCCN CPen CTrC CWil EBee ELan EPfP IBal IBlr LRHS MBri MGos MPRe MWat MWgw NBlu SPla SPoG SWvt WCot WGer WLeb WPat
'Firebird'	CBcs IBlr LSRN SAga SCoo SLon SWvt
'Flamingo' (v)	CBcs CCCN CSBt CWil IBal LRHS LSou MGos MJnS NBlu NScw SHBN SPer SPoG SSto WCot WPat
'Fortescue's Bronze'	CWil
'Glowing Embers'	CBrm CPen CTrC EBee IBal WLeb
'Gold Ray'	CBcs CTrC IBal IBlr
'Gold Sword' (v)	CBcs CCCN CMHG CSBt CTrC CWil EBee IBal IBlr LRHS MAsh MBri MGos SSto
'Green Sword' **new**	CCCN
'Guardsman' (v)	IBlr
'Jack Spratt' (v)	CBcs CBrm COtt CPen CWil ECou EHoe IBal IBlr LRHS MSwo SAga SPoG SWvt WCMO WLeb WPrP
'Jester' (v)	More than 30 suppliers
'Limelight'	CBcs CWil EBee SWvt
'Mahogany'	CWil
§ 'Maori Chief'	CSBt CWil EBee EPfP IBal IBlr LRHS NMoo SHBN SWvt WLeb WPat
'Maori Eclipse'	CPen CWil
'Maori Elegance'	CWil
§ 'Maori Maiden' (v)	CBcs CBrm CCCN CDoC CDul CSBt CTrC CTri EBee ECre EHoe EPfP IBal LAst LRHS MAsh MBri MGos MRav SSto SWvt WFar
§ 'Maori Queen' (v)	CBcs CCCN CDoC CHen CSBt CTrC CWil EPfP IBal IBlr LRHS MAsh MBri MGos MRav MSwo MWgw NBlu NMoo SCoo SPer SSto SWvt WFar
§ 'Maori Sunrise' (v)	More than 30 suppliers
'Margaret Jones'	CBcs CCCN CWil EBee SLim WViv
'Merlot'	CBcs CPen CWil EBee EKen NLar WCMO WGer
'Pink Panther' (v)	More than 30 suppliers
'Pink Stripe' (v)	CSBt CWil ECrN ENot IBal IBlr LRHS MBri NPal SPoG SWvt WCot WGer
'Platt's Black'	More than 30 suppliers
'Rainbow Chief'	see *P.* 'Maori Chief'
'Rainbow Maiden'	see *P.* 'Maori Maiden'
'Rainbow Queen'	see *P.* 'Maori Queen'
'Rainbow Sunrise'	see *P.* 'Maori Sunrise'
'Red Sensation'	CPen
I 'Rubrum'	CWil IBal NBlu
'Sea Jade'	CWil IBlr
'Stormy Dawn'	WCot
'Sundowner' (v) ♀H3	More than 30 suppliers
'Sunset' (v)	CBcs CCCN CSBt IBlr IFoB SWvt
'Surfer' (v)	CBcs COtt CTrC CWil EHoe IBlr LHop MCCP WCMO WLeb WPat WWhi
'Surfer Boy'	CSBt CWil LAst SMer
'Surfer Bronze'	CCCN CPen CSBt CWil IBal LSou MGos SHGC SSto WGer
'Surfer Green'	CCCN CDoC IBal MGos WHer
tenax ♀H4	More than 30 suppliers
- 'Atropurpureum'	CHEx IBal
- 'Bronze'	CHEx CWil SWal SWvt
- 'Co-ordination'	CCCN CWil EPfP IBal IBlr ISea LRHS
- 'Deep Purple' **new**	CHEx
* - dwarf	IBlr SLPl
I - 'Giganteum'	CHEx
* - *lineatum*	SEND WMul
§ - 'Nanum Purpureum'	IBlr MSte SEND
- Purpureum Group ♀H3-4	More than 30 suppliers
- 'Radiance' (v)	CWil IBlr
- 'Rainbow Queen'	see *P.* 'Maori Queen'
- 'Rainbow Sunrise'	see *P.* 'Maori Sunrise'
- 'Variegatum' (v) ♀H3-4	CBrm CHen CSBt EPfP IBal IBlr LPal LRHS MGos NBlu NMoo SAPC SArc SEND SPer SRms WBrE WFar WMul
- 'Veitchianum' (v)	CWil IBlr LRHS
'Thumbelina'	CBcs CCCN CTri EHoe IBal IFoB MSte SSto WPat
'Tom Thumb'	CBrm CWil GGar WDin WDyG WPrP
'Wings of Gold'	IBal
'Yellow Wave' (v) ♀H3	More than 30 suppliers

Photinia ✿ (*Rosaceae*)

arbutifolia	see *Heteromeles salicifolia*
beauverdiana	CSam CTho SRms WFar
- var. *notabilis*	EPfP NLar
§ 'Branpara'PBR	LBuc
§ *davidiana*	CDul CSam EBee ELan EPfP GIBF ISea MBar MRav NLar SPer SRms WDin WFar WNor
- 'Palette' (v)	More than 30 suppliers
- var. *undulata*	CMHG LRHS
- - 'Fructu Luteo'	CAbP CMHG CSam CTrG EPfP EPla LRHS MBri MRav NLar SPoG WFar
- - 'Prostrata'	ELan EPfP MBar MRav WDin WFar
x *fraseri*	CMCN
- 'Allyn Sprite'PBR	EBee
- 'Birmingham'	EBee EHoe EWes LRHS MAsh SRGP SRms WDin WWeb
- 'Canivily'	EMil MAsh MGos NLar SPoG
- 'Purple Peter'	LRHS
- 'Red Robin' ♀H4	More than 30 suppliers
- 'Red Select'	WWeb
- 'Robusta'	EPfP LRHS MAsh SLim SWvt
I - 'Robusta Compacta' **new**	MWea
glabra	SArc
- B&SWJ 8903	WCru
§ - 'Parfait' (v)	CAbP ELan LRHS MAsh MRav SHBN SPla SPoG WFar
- 'Pink Lady'	see *P. glabra* 'Parfait'
- 'Rubens'	ELan EPfP LRHS SPer SPla SSta WPat
- 'Variegata'	see *P. glabra* 'Parfait'
glomerata misapplied	see *P. prionophylla*
lasiogyna	CMCN
microphylla HWJ 564	WCru
nussia	CDoC
parvifolia	EPfP
§ *prionophylla*	CHEx
§ 'Redstart'	CAbP CBrm CSam EBee EPfP LRHS MGos NEgg NPro SLon SPer SSta SWvt WMoo
§ *serratifolia*	CBcs CDul CHEx CMHG EBee EPfP LRHS SAPC SArc SPer SPoG SSta WFar WPGP WSHC XPep
serrulata	see *P. serratifolia*
'Super Hedge'PBR	see *P.* 'Branpara'
villosa ♀H4	CAbP CTho GIBF MBar NPal
- B&SWJ 8877	WCru
- var. *laevis*	CPLG EPfP
- f. *maximowicziana*	EPfP GIBF

Phragmites (*Poaceae*)

from Sichuan, China	EPPr
§ *australis*	CBen CDWL CRWN EMFW LPBA MGol NMir SWat WFar WMAq XPep
- subsp. *australis* var. *striatopictus*	EMon EPPr
- - 'Variegatus' (v)	More than 30 suppliers
- subsp. *pseudodonax*	EMon EPPr
communis	see *P. australis*

karka	EPPr
- 'Candy Stripe' (v)	CBen CDWL EPPr
- 'Variegatus' (v)	LRav NLar

Phryganocydia (Bignoniaceae)
corymbosa new	CPlN

Phrynium (Marantaceae)
pubinerve	CKob

Phuopsis (Rubiaceae)
§ **stylosa**	More than 30 suppliers
- 'Purpurea'	CElw ELan MNrw MRav NChi

Phygelius ✿ (Scrophulariaceae)
aequalis	CFee CSev MNrw SPla WMoo WPer WSan
- **albus**	see *P. aequalis* 'Yellow Trumpet'
- 'Aureus'	see *P. aequalis* 'Yellow Trumpet'
- Cedric Morris form	SHom
- 'Cream Trumpet'	see *P. aequalis* 'Yellow Trumpet'
- 'Indian Chief'	see *P.* x *rectus* 'African Queen'
* - 'Pink Trumpet'	CDoC CHEx CWCL EAro GCal LRHS SCoo SMrm
- Sensation = 'Sani Pass'PBR	CDoC CPom EBee EChP ECtt EGra EPfP GBri GCal LAst LRHS LSRN MBri MDun MOak NBPC NCGa NPri SCoo SLim SPet SPoG SWal SWvt
- 'Trewidden Pink' ♀H4	CMMP CWCL CWib EBee EChP EPfP ERou LAst LHop MAsh MBow MHer MOak MTis NCiC NGdn NJOw SHFr SHom SLim SWal SWvt SYvo WBVN WGwG WHoo WMnd WMoo WPGP WSan
§ - 'Yellow Trumpet' ♀H3-4	More than 30 suppliers
aequalis x **capensis**	see *P.* x *rectus*
§ **capensis** ♀H3-4	CDul CPLG CWib EChP ELan EPfP MBNS MHer NLar SBch SGar SHom SPet SRms WFar WMnd WMoo WPer WWye
- CD&R	EWes
- **coccineus**	see *P. capensis*
- orange-flowered	LHop SHom
'Golden Gate'	see *P. aequalis* 'Yellow Trumpet'
Logan form	MCCP
New Sensation = 'Blaphy'PBR	COtt MAsh SBla SPer
§ x **rectus**	MDKP SYvo
- 'African Queen' ♀H3-4	More than 30 suppliers
- 'Aylesham's Pride'	SHom
- 'Devil's Tears' ♀H4	CBcs CDoC CFee EBee EChP ECrN ELan EMil EPfP ERou GKev LAst LRHS MBNS MDun MNHC MWgw NEgg NHol SHom SLim SRot SWvt WGwG WHoo WMnd WMoo WPGP WPer
- 'Ivory Twist'PBR	LRHS SHom
- 'Jodie Southon'	LSou SHom
* - 'Logan's Pink'	LSRN
- 'Moonraker'	More than 30 suppliers
- 'Pink Elf'	ELan SHom SLon
- 'Raspberry Swirl'PBR	EPfP MAsh SHom SSta
- 'Salmon Leap' ♀H4	CBcs CDoC CHrt CMMP CTri CWCL EBee ELan ENot EPfP ERou LAst LRHS LSRN MBNS NEgg SHFr SHom SLim SPlb SRot SWvt WFar WHoo WMnd WMoo WPer WWeb
- 'Sunshine'	COtt EBee EGra EHoe ELan EMan EWes LAst LHop LRHS MAsh MDKP NCiC SPoG SWal
- 'Sweet Dreams'	LRHS SHom
§ - 'Winchester Fanfare'	More than 30 suppliers
- 'Winton Fanfare'	see *P.* x *rectus* 'Winchester Fanfare'
Somerford Funfair Apricot = 'Yapapr' new	MAsh
Somerford Funfair Coral = 'Yapcor'	CDoC EBee GKev LHop LRHS LSou MAsh MBri NBPC NLar SIng SPav SPoG SRkn
Somerford Funfair Cream = 'Yapcre'	EBee EPfP LHop LRHS LSou MAsh MBri NLar SIng SPav SRkn
Somerford Funfair Orange = 'Yapor'	CBcs EBee LHop LRHS MAsh MBri SPav SPoG
Somerford Funfair Wine = 'Yapwin'	CBcs EBee ELan EShb LHop LSou MAsh MBri NBPC SGar SPav SPoG SRkn
Somerford Funfair Yellow = 'Yapyel'	EBee LHop LRHS MAsh NBPC SPoG

Phyla (Verbenaceae)
§ **nodiflora**	CNic CStu ECha EEls EWin NWCA SBch SBla SEND SIng WPer XPep
- 'Alba'	CNic
§ - var. **canescens**	GMac WCru WHal

Phylica (Rhamnaceae)
arborea 'Superba'	CBcs CPLG
ericoides	CPLG

x *Phylliopsis* (Ericaceae)
'Coppelia' ♀H4	EPot GCrs GEdr GGGa GKev ITim LTwo NLAp SBrw SReu SSta WPat
hillieri 'Askival'	GCrs GGGa LSou WAbe
- 'Pinocchio'	EPot GCrs ITim LRHS MDun NLAp NLar WAbe WPat
'Hobgoblin'	WAbe WPat
'Mermaid'	GGGa ITim WAbe
'Puck'	WAbe
'Sprite'	GCrs NLAp WPat
'Sugar Plum'	CCCN CWSG IDee ITim MDun NLAp NLar SBrw SSta SWvt WAbe WPat
'Swanhilde'	WAbe

Phyllitis see *Asplenium*

Phyllocladus (Phyllocladaceae)
trichomanoides var. **alpinus**	CDoC CDul CTrC GTSp LCon LLin NLar

Phyllodoce (Ericaceae)
aleutica	ECho GCrs MBar NDlv NMen SRms
aleutica x **caerulea**	GCrs
breweri	GIBF
caerulea ♀H4	ECho NDlv
- **japonica**	see *P. nipponica*
* - var. **japonica**	WThu
- 'Viking'	GCrs
empetriformis	ECho GCrs MBar SRms
§ **nipponica** ♀H4	GCrs NMen WAbe
- var. **oblongo-ovata**	GCrs NMen
tsugifolia	GCrs

Phyllostachys ✿ (Poaceae)
angusta	EPla SBig WJun
arcana	ENBC EPla WJun
- 'Luteosulcata'	EPla LPal MMoz MWht NLar NPal WJun WNor WPGP
§ **atrovaginata**	EPla ERod WJun
aurea ♀H4	More than 30 suppliers
- 'Albovariegata' (v)	EBee EFul MPRe
- 'Flavescens Inversa'	EPla ERod WJun
- 'Holochrysa'	CBrP CDul EFul EPla ERod MWht WJun WPGP
- 'Koi'	EFul EPla ERod LPal MMoz MWht NMoo NPal SBig WPGP
aureocaulis	see *P. aureosulcata* f. *aureocaulis*, *P. vivax* f. *aureocaulis*
aureosulcata	CWib EFul EMui EPfP EPla ERod LEdu LRHS MAsh MMoz MWht NMoo SBLw WBVN WJun WMoo

- f. *alata*	see *P. aureosulcata* f. *pekinensis*
- 'Argus'	EPla
§ - f. *aureocaulis* ♀H4	More than 30 suppliers
- 'Harbin'	EPla ERod
- 'Harbin Inversa'	EPla ERod
- 'Lama Temple'	EPla WPGP
§ - f. *pekinensis*	EPla NLar SBig WPGP
- f. *spectabilis* ♀H4	More than 30 suppliers
bambusoides	CBcs EPla MLan SBig SDix WJun
- 'Allgold'	see *P. bambusoides* 'Holochrysa'
- 'Castillonii'	CAbb CBcs EAmu EFul ENBC EPla ERod EWes LEdu LPal MMoz MWht NBea NMoo NPal SBLw SBig SDix SEND WJun WMul WPGP
- 'Castilloni Inversa'	ENBC EPla ERod LEdu LPal MMoz MWht WJun WMul WPGP
§ - 'Holochrysa'	CDoC CPen EPla ERod MBri MGos MMoz MWht NMoo NPal SEND WJun WMul WPGP
- 'Katashibo'	EPla
- 'Kawadana'	EPla ERod
- f. *lacrima-deae*	CTrC EBee EPfP EPla WMul
- 'Marliacea'	EPla ERod LPJP SBig WJun
- 'Subvariegata'	EPla WPGP
- 'Sulphurea'	see *P. bambusoides* 'Holochrysa'
- 'Tanakae'	ENBC MMoz MSwo NLar NMoo SBig WPGP
- 'Violascens'	NMoo SBig
bissetii	More than 30 suppliers
circumpilis	EPla
congesta misapplied	see *P. atrovaginata*
decora	CAbb EAmu EPla ERod MBri MMoz MWht NLar NMoo NPal SEND WJun WPGP
dulcis	EPfP EPla ERod LEdu LPJP MWht SBig WJun WPGP
§ *edulis*	CBcs CTrC EFul EHoe EPla ERod IFro LRav MGol MMoz MWht SBig WJun WMul WPGP
- 'Bicolor'	WMul
§ - 'Heterocycla'	XBlo
- f. *pubescens*	see *P. edulis*
flexuosa	CBcs CEnt CPen EFul EPfP EPla IMGH MWht SEND WJun WMul WPGP
glauca	CAbb EPla ERod MMoz MWht NLar NMoo NPal SBig WMul
- f. *yunzhu*	EPla ERod MWht WJun
heteroclada	NMoo WJun
- 'Solid Stem' misapplied	see *P. purpurata* 'Straight Stem'
heterocycla	see *P. edulis* 'Heterocycla'
- f. *pubescens*	see *P. edulis*
humilis	CBcs CDul ENBC EPla ERod MCCP MGos MMoz MWhi MWht NLar NMoo NPal SBig SEND WJun
iridescens	EPla MSwo NLar SBig WJun
lithophila	EPla
lofushanensis	EPla
makinoi	ERod
mannii	CPen EPla MWht
meyeri	CPen EPla
nidularia	EPla ERod MMoz SBig WJun
- f. *farcta*	EPla
§ - f. *glabrovagina*	EPla
- smooth-sheathed	see *P. nidularia* f. *glabrovagina*
nigella	EPla
nigra ♀H4	More than 30 suppliers
- 'Boryana'	CAbb CBig CBrm CDoC EAmu EBee EFul ENBC EPfP EPla MAsh MGos MLan MMoz MWht NMoo SArc SBig SWvt WFar WJun WMoo WMul WPGP
- 'Fulva'	EPla
- 'Hale'	EPla
- f. *henonis* ♀H4	CAbb CBcs EAmu EFul EMil ENBC EPla ERod LPal MJnS MLan MMoz MWht NBea NLar NMoo SBig WDyG WJun WMul WPGP
* - 'Lactae Deae' **new**	NScw
- 'Megurochiku'	EPla ERod WJun
- f. *nigra*	EPla MLan SPer
- f. *punctata*	CBrm CDoC ENBC EPfP EPla ERod MAvo MLan MWht NGdn SEND WDyG WJun WMoo WPGP
- 'Tosaensis'	EPla
- 'Wisley'	EPla
nuda	EAmu ENBC EPla ERod MMoz MWht NLar NPal WJun
- f. *localis*	MWht
parvifolia	EPla ERod MWht WJun WPGP
platyglossa	EPla ERod WPGP
praecox	EPla NMoo WJun
- f. *viridisulcata* **new**	EAmu
propinqua	CBig CDoC CDul ENBC EPla ERod LEdu MMoz MWht NMoo WJun WMul
* - 'Bicolor'	WJun
- 'Li Yu Gan'	EPla
§ *purpurata* 'Straight Stem'	EPla MWht
rubicunda	EPla WJun
rubromarginata	CPen EPla ERod MWht NLar WJun WPGP
stimulosa	EPla ERod LPan WJun
§ *sulphurea*	NMoo
- 'Houzeau'	EPla ERod
- 'Robert Young'	EPla
- 'Sulphurea'	see *P. sulphurea*
- f. *viridis*	EPla ERod LPal MAsh MWht NMoo SBig
violascens	CBcs EFul EPla ERod LPal MMoz SBig WJun WPGP
virella	EPla
viridiglaucescens	CAbb CBcs CHEx CHen EAmu EFul EPfP EPla LPan MBrN MMoz MWht SArc SBig SEND SPla WJun WMul
viridis	see *P. sulphurea* f. *viridis*
vivax	EFul EPfP EPla ERod GQui LEdu MMoz MPRe MWht NLar SBig WJun WMul WNor
§ - f. *aureocaulis* ♀H4	More than 30 suppliers
* - f. *huanvenzhu*	CTrC EBee EFul ENBC EPla ERod MMoz MWht NMoo WJun WMul
* - 'Inversa' **new**	MGos NScw
- 'Katrin'	LEdu

x *Phyllothamnus* (Ericaceae)

erectus	GCrs GGGa SSta WAbe WPat

Phymatosorus (Polypodiaceae)

§ *diversifolius*	WPGP

Phymosia (Malvaceae)

§ *umbellata*	CPLG CRHN ERea SOWG

Phyodina see *Callisia*

Physalis (Solanaceae)

alkekengi ♀H4	CAgr EBee EPfP MLan MNHC MWat NBir NLRH NLar SWvt WFar
- var. *franchetii*	More than 30 suppliers
- - dwarf	EBrs NLar NRnb SPoG
- - 'Gigantea'	ECGP GBuc NLar NRnb SPlb WHil
- - 'Gnome'	EBee NEgg
- - 'Variegata' (v)	ECtt EMan EPla EWes MAvo NPro WOld
angulata B&SWJ 7016	WCru
edulis (F)	see *P. peruviana*
§ *peruviana* (F)	CCCN LRav SHDw

Physaria (Brassicaceae)
didymocarpa	NJOw

Physocarpus (Rosaceae)
malvaceus	EWes
monogynus	NLar
opulifolius	CDul GIBF IFro MSal
- 'Dart's Gold' ♀H4	More than 30 suppliers
- 'Diabolo'PBR ♀H4	More than 30 suppliers
§ - 'Luteus'	CDoC CMHG CSam CWib EBee EPfP IMGH ISea MBar MDun MRav MWhi NEgg SPer SRms WDin WFar WMoo WPat
- 'Tilden Park' **new**	EBee
ribesifolius 'Aureus'	see *P. opulifolius* 'Luteus'

Physochlaina (Solanaceae)
orientalis	CAby CPom EDAr EMan MSal WAul

Physoplexis (Campanulaceae)
§ *comosa* ♀H2-3	ECho EWes ITim LRHS NSla SBla WHoo

Physostegia (Lamiaceae)
angustifolia	CSam NBre
§ *virginiana*	CHrt CSBt EBee EGra GBar GMaP LAst MBNS SGar SWat WBrk WFar WRHF
- 'Alba'	CEnt CoIW CSBt EBee EChP EGra EHrv EPfP EShb GBar GBri GMaP LRHS MSte MTis NLar NOrc NRnb SPet SPlb WEas WHrl WRha
§ - 'Crown of Snow'	CDWL CFir CMMP ECtt ERou MBNS MBow MHer MRav MWat MWhi STes SWal SWvt WFar WHil WPer WWpP
- 'Grandiflora'	CFir
- 'Miss Manners'	EAEE EBee MSte MWgw NFla SPer SRGP SUsu WCot WHil
- 'Olympic Gold' (v)	EBee EMan ENot MDKP SPoG WRHF
- pale pink-flowered	SWat
- 'Red Beauty'	CFir EBee ERou LRHS MDKP NLRH SPla
- 'Rose Queen'	CoIW MFOX MWat NBre NLRH SMar WTin
- 'Rosea'	CBcs CBrm EBee EChP ERou IFoB MBow MDKP NBPC NBre NPri NRnb SWal SWvt WFar WGHP WHrl WPer
- Schneekrone	see *P. virginiana* 'Crown of Snow'
- 'Snow Queen'	see *P. virginiana* 'Summer Snow'
- var. *speciosa*	WFar
§ - - 'Bouquet Rose'	CDWL CPrp EAEE EBee EBrs ECha EPfP LRHS MHer MNFA MRav MSte NBir NHol NOak SMac SPer SWvt WAul WCAu WFar WGwG WMoo WRos WSan WTel WWeb
- - Rose Bouquet	see *P. virginiana* var. *speciosa* 'Bouquet Rose'
- - 'Variegata' (v)	More than 30 suppliers
§ - 'Summer Snow' ♀H4	CBcs CPrp ECha ELan ENot EPfP IBal LHop LRHS MBri MNFA NCGa NHol SMer SPla SRms WBrk WCAu WCot WFar WHoo WMnd
- 'Summer Spire'	EBrs EHrv ELan EMan LSou MSte NHol SMer WFar
- 'Vivid' ♀H4	More than 30 suppliers
- 'Wassenhove'	EMon

Phyteuma (Campanulaceae)
comosum	see *Physoplexis comosa*
hemisphaericum	ECho
humile	EDAr

nigrum	EBee ECho GCal LRHS MNrw NBid NChi WCMO WCot WLin WPGP
scheuchzeri	CEnt CNic EBee ECho EPfP GBBs GEdr LPhx MHer NChi NEgg NJOw NOrc NPri NWCA SBch SBla SGar SMad SPet SRms SRot WCMO WHoo
sieberi	CPBP NBir WAbe
spicatum	NBro

Phytolacca (Phytolaccaceae)
acinosa	GPoy MGol MSal NLar SWat WHil
- HWJ 647	WCru
§ *americana*	CAgr CArn CBgR CHEx COld CSev EBee ECha ELan ELau EMar EPfP GPoy MBNS MHer MSal NEgg NJOw NLar SIde SMad SRms SWat WCru WEas WFar WHil WMnd WMoo WSHC
- 'Silberstein' (v)	EBee ITer LBuc LDai MBNS MDKP NEgg NLar SPoG WCot WGwG
- 'Variegata'	WHil
clavigera	see *P. polyandra*
decandra	see *P. americana*
dioica	CHEx CPLG
esculenta	EBee LEdu LHop
icosandra B&SWJ 8988	WCru
japonica B&SWJ 4897	WCru
octandra	CPLG
- B&SWJ 9514	WCru
§ *polyandra*	CPLG ECha NBid NBro NLar SRms WBor WWye

Picea ✿ (Pinaceae)
§ *abies*	CCVT CDul CLnd CSBt CTri CWib EHul ENot EPfP LAst LBuc LRHS MBar MBri MGos NBlu NWea SCoo SLim SPer SPoG WBVN WDin WEve WMou
- 'Acrocona'	ECho EHul EOrn LCon LLin MAsh MBar MBlu MBri MGos SCoo WEve WWes
- 'Archer'	CKen
- 'Argenteospica' (v)	ECho NHol WEve
- 'Aurea'	ECho EOrn GBin IMGH LLin WEve
- 'Capitata'	CKen GTSp MAsh MBar NLar
- 'Cee Jays Gem' **new**	CDHC
- 'Cinderella'	MBri
- 'Clanbrassiliana'	CDoC CKen ECho IMGH LCon MAsh MBar MGos NLar WEve
- Compacta Group	ECho LBee LRHS NEgg
I - 'Congesta'	CKen
- 'Crippsii'	CKen
I - 'Cruenta'	CKen
- 'Cupressina'	CKen
- 'Diffusa'	CKen LCon MBar
- 'Dumpy'	CKen LCon NLar
- 'Elegans'	MBar
- 'Ellwangeriana'	NLar
- 'Excelsa'	see *P. abies*
- 'Fahndrich'	CKen
- 'Finedonensis'	LCon NLar WEve
- 'Formanek'	CDoC CKen CMen ECho LCon LLin NLar
- 'Four Winds'	CAbP CKen
- 'Frohburg'	CDoC CKen COtt ECho MBar MGos
- 'Globosa'	ECho MBar
- 'Globosa Nana'	ECho LAst MGos
- 'Goblin'	NLar
- 'Goldstart' **new**	MGos
- 'Gregoryana'	CKen CMac ECho IMGH MBar NDlv
- 'Hasin' **new**	NLar
- 'Heartland Gem'	CKen

- 'Himfa'	NLar	
- 'Horace Wilson'	CKen	
- 'Humilis'	CKen	
- 'Hystrix'	CRob LCon NLar	
- 'Inversa'	CKen EBrs ECho EHul EOrn LCon LLin MBar MBlu MBri MGos SLim WEve	
- 'J.W. Daisy's White'	see *P. glauca* 'J.W. Daisy's White'	
- 'Jana'	CKen	
- 'Kral'	CKen	
- 'Little Gem' ♀H4	CDoC CFee CKen CMac CMen CRob ECho EHul EOrn GBin GEdr IMGH LBee LCon LLin LRHS MAsh MBar SLim SPer SPoG WEve	
- 'Maxwellii'	EHul MBar	
- 'Mikulasovice'	NLar	
- 'Nana'	MBar NEgg	
- 'Nana Compacta'	CKen CRob EHul IMGH LAst LBee MBar WFar	
- 'Nidiformis' ♀H4	CDoC CKen CMac CRob CSBt CTri ECho EHul ENot EOrn LAst LCon LLin MBar NBlu NHol NWea SLim SPer SPoG SRms WDin WEve WFar	
- 'Norrkoping'	CKen	
- 'Ohlendorffii'	CKen ECho EHul LCon MBar MGos NLar	
- 'Pachyphylla'	CKen	
- 'Pendula Major'	SHBN	
- 'Procumbens'	MBar	
- 'Pumila'	EOrn	
- 'Pumila Nigra'	ECho EHul LCon LLin MBar MGos SCoo SLim SPoG	
- 'Pusch'	CKen NLar	
- 'Pygmaea'	CKen ECho GTSp MBar MGos NLar	
- 'Reflexa'	ECho EHul GBin IMGH LCon WEve	
- 'Repens'	ECho LRHS MBar MBlu	
- 'Rydal'	CDul LCon MAsh NLar WEve	
- 'Saint James'	CKen	
- 'Tabuliformis'	MBar	
- 'Tufty'	EOrn	
- 'Vermont Gold'	CKen NLar SLim	
- 'Waldbrunn'	ECho LCon LLin MAsh WEve	
- 'Walter Bron'	CKen	
- 'Waugh'	MBar	
- 'Wichtel' **new**	NLar	
- Will's Dwarf	see *P. abies* 'Wills Zwerg'	
§ - 'Wills Zwerg'	LRHS MAsh MBri	
ajanensis	GIBF	
I *alcoquiana* 'Prostrata'	LCon MBar	
- var. *reflexa*	MPkF	
breweriana ♀H4	More than 30 suppliers	
engelmanii 'Compact'	EBrs	
engelmannii	CDul GTSp NWea	
glauca	CDul CTri NWea WEve	
- Alberta Blue = 'Haal'PBR	CDoC CKen CRob ECho EOrn LCon LLin LRHS MAsh SCoo SLim WEve WFar	
- var. *albertiana* 'Alberta Globe'	CDoC CRob CSBt ECho EHul EOrn IMGH LBee LCon LLin MAsh MBar MBri MGos NDlv NEgg NHol SAga SCoo SLim SPoG WEve WFar	
- - 'Conica'	More than 30 suppliers	
- - 'Gnome'	CKen WEve	
- - 'Laurin'	CDoC CKen CRob ECho EOrn LBee LCon LLin MAsh MBar MGos SCoo SLim WEve	
- - 'Tiny'	CKen EOrn LCon LLin MBar	
- 'Arneson's Blue Variegated' (v)	CDoC CKen LLin MAsh MBri SLim WEve WFar WGor	
- 'Blue Planet'	CKen LCon MGos NLar	
- 'Blue Wonder' **new**	MBri	
- 'Coerulea'	CDul ECho LCon MBar	
I - 'Coerulea Nana'	ECho NLar	
- 'Cy's Wonder'	CKen	
- 'Echiniformis' ♀H4	CKen ECho LBee LRHS MBar MBri	
- var. *glauca*	GIBF	
- 'Goldilocks'	CKen	
§ - 'J.W. Daisy's White'	CKen CRob EBrs ECho EOrn LCon LLin LRHS MAsh MGos SCoo SLim SMur SPer SPoG WEve WFar WGor	
- 'Lilliput'	CKen ECho EHul EOrn LCon MBar MGos NLar WEve	
- 'Nana'	CKen	
- 'Piccolo'	CKen ECho LRHS MAsh SLim	
- 'Pixie'	CKen	
- 'Rainbow's End' (v)	CKen ECho NLar SCoo SLim WFar	
- 'Sander's Blue'	CKen CRob ECho EOrn LBee MBri SCoo SLim SPoG WEve	
- 'Zuckerhut'	MBar MBri	
glehnii	GTSp LCon	
- 'Sasanosei'	CKen	
- 'Shimezusei'	CKen	
jezoensis	CMen MGos NWea	
- subsp. *hondoensis*	WNor	
- 'Yatsabusa'	CKen CMen	
koraiensis	CDul NWea	
kosteri 'Glauca'	see *P. pungens* 'Koster'	
likiangensis	CMCN EPfP GTSp ISea LCon	
- var. *balfouriana*	see *P. likiangensis* var. *rubescens*	
- var. *purpurea*	see *P. purpurea*	
§ - var. *rubescens*	CDoC LCon MBri NHol WOrn	
mariana	LCon NWea WEve	
- 'Aureovariegata' (v)	ECho LCon WFar	
- 'Austria Broom'	CKen	
- 'Doumetii'	EOrn	
- 'Fastigiata'	CKen EOrn	
- 'Nana' ♀H4	CDoC CKen CMac CMen CRob ECho EHul EPfP GEdr IMGH LCon LLin LRHS MAsh MBar MNrw MWat NBlu NDlv NWea SAga SCoo SEND SLim SPer SPoG WBrE WDin WEve WFar	
I - 'Pygmaea'	CKen	
x *mariorika*	MBar	
§ - 'Gnom'	MGos	
- 'Machala'	ECho	
obovata	GIBF LCon	
- var. *coerulea*	GIBF NLar NWea	
omorika ♀H4	CBcs CDul CMCN LBuc LCon LRav MBar MGos NWea SPer SPoG WCFE WDin WEve WFar WMou WRHF WWes	
I - 'Aurea'	ECho	
- 'Frohnleiten'	CKen	
- 'Frondenberg'	CKen ECho	
- 'Karel'	CKen NLar	
- 'Minimax'	CKen ECho	
- 'Nana' ♀H4	ECho EHul LBee LCon MAsh MBar SCoo SLim WEve	
- 'Pendula' ♀H4	CDoC ECho LCon LRHS MBar MBlu NLar SCoo SHBN SLim SPoG SSta	
- 'Peve Tijn' **new**	NLar	
- 'Pimoko'	CKen LCon LLin MAsh MGos NLar	
- 'Pygmy'	CKen	
- 'Schneverdingen'	CKen	
- 'Tijn'	CKen LCon SLim	
- 'Treblitsch'	CDoC CKen NLar	
orientalis ♀H4	CDul LCon LRav NWea WMou	
§ - 'Aurea' (v) ♀H4	CMac ECho EHul ElAn LCon LLin LPan MBar MBri MLan NHol NPri SCoo SHBN SLim WDin	
- 'Aureospicata'	CDoC CTho ECho MAsh MBlu WEve	
- 'Bergman's Gem'	CKen	
- 'Golden Start'	NLar	
- 'Gowdy'	MBar NLar	
- 'Jewel'	CKen NLar	
- 'Kenwith'	CKen ECho	
- 'Mount Vernon'	CKen	

- Pendula Group	MGos
- 'Professor Langner'	CKen LCon SLim
- 'Skylands'	CDoC CKen ECho ELan LCon LLin MAsh MBri MGos NHol NLar SLim SPoG WEve
- 'Tom Thumb'	CKen LCon SLim
* - 'Wittbold Compact'	LBee
- 'Wittboldt' **new**	MAsh
pungens	MBar WDin WNor
- 'Baby Blueeyes'	ECho MPkF
- 'Blaukissen'	CKen
- 'Blue Mountain'	ECho MPkF
- 'Blue Pearl' **new**	NLar
- 'Dans Dwarf' **new**	NLar
- 'Drayer'	ECho MPkF
- 'Edith'	EBrs MPkF NLar SLim WFar
- 'Endtz'	EBrs ECho MPkF
- 'Erich Frahm'	CTri ECho LCon LRHS MAsh MBar MBri MGos MPkF MWya SCoo SLim WFar
- 'Fat Albert'	CDul CRob CWib ECho MGos NLar SLim WFar
- 'Frieda'	NLar SLim
- Glauca Group	CDul CLnd GWCH LBee LCon MBar NWea SCoo SPoG WBVN WDin WEve WFar WMou WOrn
- - 'Glauca Procumbens'	CMen NLar
§ - - 'Glauca Prostrata'	ECho EHul MBar WEve
- 'Globe'	CKen CMen
I - 'Globosa' ♀H4	CBcs CDoC CKen CRob ECho EHul EOrn LBee LCon LLin MAsh MBar MBri MGos NPri SCoo SHBN SLim SPer SPoG SRms WEve WFar
I - 'Globosa Viridis'	ECho
- 'Gloria'	CKen
- 'Hoopsii' ♀H4	CBcs CDoC CDul CMac CRob CSBt ECho EHul ENot EPfP LAst LCon LRHS MAsh MBar MGos MWya NBlu NWea SCoo SHBN SLim SWvt WDin WEve WFar
- 'Hoto'	EHul EOrn LCon MBar
- 'Hunnewelliana'	EOrn
- 'Iseli Fastigiate'	CDoC CRob ECho LCon LLin MAsh MBri MGos SCoo SLim WEve
§ - 'Koster' ♀H4	CDoC CMac CRob CSBt ECho EHul EPfP LCon LLin MBar MGos NWea SCoo SLim SPoG SRms WDin WEve WFar
- 'Lucky Strike'	CDoC CKen ECho LCon LLin MGos NLar
- 'Maigold' (v)	CKen EBrs ECho LCon MAsh NLar SLim
- 'Moerheimii'	ECho EHul LCon MBar NLar WEve
- 'Montgomery'	CKen ECho LCon LLin MBar NLar WEve
- 'Mrs Cesarini'	CKen
- 'Nimety'	CKen NLar
- 'Oldenburg'	MBar NLar NWea
- 'Procumbens'	CKen LCon
- 'Prostrata'	see *P. pungens* 'Glauca Prostrata'
- 'Prostrate Blue Mist'	WEve
- 'Rovelli's Monument'	NLar
- 'Saint Mary's Broom'	CKen
- 'Schovenhorst'	ECho EHul WFar
- 'Snowkiss'	ECho MPkF WFar
- 'Spek'	ECho MPkF
- 'Thomsen'	ECho EHul LCon MAsh
- 'Thuem'	ECho EHul LLin MGos NDlv NLar WEve WFar
- 'Wendy'	CKen
§ *purpurea*	LCon WEve
retroflexa	GIBF NWea
rubens	LCon NLar NWea WEve
schrenkiana	LCon
sitchensis	CDul LCon LRav NWea WMou
- 'Nana'	CDoC ECho LLin NHol NLar

- 'Papoose'	see *P. sitchensis* 'Tenas'
- 'Silberzwerg'	CKen ECho SLim
- 'Strypemonde'	CKen
§ - 'Tenas'	CDoC CKen CRob EBrs ECho EOrn LCon MAsh NHol NLar SLim WEve
- 'Trinket'	NLar
smithiana	CDoC CDul CTho EPfP ISea LCon NLar NWea WMou
I - 'Aurea'	MGos
- 'Sunray'	LCon SIFN
wilsonii	GIBF LCon NLar

Picrasma (Simaroubaceae)

ailanthoides	see *P. quassioides*
§ *quassioides*	CMCN EPfP WPGP

Picris (Asteraceae)

echioides	CArn WHer

Picrorhiza (Scrophulariaceae)

kurrooa	GPoy

Pieris ✿ (Ericaceae)

'Bert Chandler'	LRHS SPer SSpi
'Brouwer's Beauty'	MGos MWea SLim
'Firecrest' ♀H4	CMHG CTrG CTrh SBrw SSpi
'Flaming Silver' (v) ♀H4	More than 30 suppliers
floribunda	MBar
'Forest Flame' ♀H4	More than 30 suppliers
formosa B&SWJ 2257	WCru
- var. *forrestii*	CDoC CTrw CWib ISea NWea
- - 'Ball of Fire'	SSpi
- - 'Fota Pink'	WHar
- - 'Jermyns'	SBrw SHBN
- - 'Wakehurst' ♀H3	CAbP CDul CSBt CTrG CWSG ENot EPfP LHyd LRHS MAsh MRav NHol NPen NWea SBrw SPer SPoG SSpi SSta WFar
Havila = 'Mouwsvila' (v)	MAsh MGos NLar SBrw WFar
japonica	CBcs CTrw GIBF MBar MGos NHol NWea SArc SReu WDin
- 'Bisbee Dwarf'	MBar NHol
- 'Blush' ♀H4	LRHS MAsh MBri MGos NHol SBrw SHBN
- 'Bonfire'	CEnd EBee EMil LBuc LRHS MBri MGos NLar SPoG
- 'Brookside Miniature'	NHol
- 'Carnaval' (v)	CDoC CEnd CSBt CWib EBee EGra ELan EMil ENot EPfP LBuc LRHS LSRN MAsh MGos NLar NPri SCoo SPer SPoG SWvt WFar
- 'Cavatine' ♀H4	CMHG LRHS
§ - 'Christmas Cheer'	MAsh MGos NHol NLar SSto WMoo
- 'Compacta'	NHol
- 'Cupido'	CDoC EMil LRHS MAsh MBar MBri MGos NHol SPoG WFar
- 'Daisen'	CTrw
- 'Debutante' ♀H4	CBcs CWSG CWib EBee ELan ENot EPfP LRHS MAsh MBri MDun MGos NHol NLar SBrw SCoo SPoG SSpi SWvt WFar
- 'Don'	see *P. japonica* 'Pygmaea'
- 'Dorothy Wyckoff'	CBcs CMHG CSBt CTrG CWSG LRHS MAsh MDun NDlv NHol SBrw SHBN SPer SSta
- 'Flaming Star'	ECot SWvt WBrE
- 'Flamingo'	CTrw GKev LRHS MBar MGos NDlv NHol
- 'Geisha'	NHol
- 'Grayswood' ♀H4	EPfP LRHS NHol SBrw WFar
- 'Katsura'	CBcs EPfP LAst LBuc LRHS MAsh MBlu MBri NLar SCoo SPer SPoG SRkn SSpi SSta WGer WPat
- 'Little Heath' (v) ♀H4	More than 30 suppliers

- 'Little Heath Green' ♀H4 — CDoC CMHG CSBt CTrG LHyd LRHS MAsh MBar MGos MMuc NDlv NEgg NHol SPer SPoG SSta SSto SWvt WFar WMoo WPic
- 'Minor' — MBar NHol WThu
- 'Mountain Fire' ♀H4 — More than 30 suppliers
- 'Pink Delight' ♀H4 — CAbP CBcs CDoC LRHS LSRN MAsh MBar MRav NEgg NHol SBrw SHBN SPoG SRms SSto WGwG WPat
- 'Prelude' ♀H4 — CSBt CTrG CWSG GKev LRHS MAsh MBri NHol NLar NPen SPoG WAbe WFar WPat
- 'Purity' ♀H4 — CBcs CDoC CMHG CWSG EPfP LRHS MAsh MBar MGos MLan NHol SBrw SMer SPer SPoG SReu SSta SSto SWvt WDin WFar
§ - 'Pygmaea' — CMHG NHol SPoG SSta
- 'Red Mill' — CEnd CWSG ENot EPfP LRHS MAsh NEgg NHol SPer SSpi WFar
- 'Rosalinda' — NLar WFar
- 'Rosea' — LHyd
- 'Sarabande' ♀H4 — COtt LRHS MAsh MBar MBri NHol NLar SBrw SPoG SSta WPat
- 'Scarlett O'Hara' — CSBt MGos NLar
- 'Select' — MGos
- 'Silver Mills' — MGos
- 'Snowdrift' — LRHS
- 'Spring Snow' — LRHS
- Taiwanensis Group — CMHG EPfP LRHS MAsh MBar MDun NWea SRms SSta WFar
- 'Temple Bells' — CSBt MGos SMer
- 'Tickled Pink' — NHol
- 'Valley Rose' — COtt CSBt ELan EPfP MAsh MGos NLar SPoG SSpi WFar
- 'Valley Valentine' ♀H4 — CBcs CBrm CDoC CDul CEnd COtt CSBt CTrh CWSG CWib ENot EPfP LRHS LSRN MAsh MBri MGos NDlv SBrw SCoo SLim SPer SPoG SReu SSta SSto SWvt WFar WPat
- 'Variegata' misapplied — see *P. japonica* 'White Rim'
§ - 'Variegata' (Carrière) — CMHG EPfP EPot LHyd MAsh Bean (v) MBar MGos NDlv NHol SBrw SHBN SPer SPoG SReu SSta WDin WFar WHar WPat
- 'Wada's Pink' — see *P. japonica* 'Christmas Cheer'
- 'White Cascade' — SBrw
- 'White Pearl' — CAbP CBcs MGos SBrw
§ - 'White Rim' (v) ♀H4 — CDul EPfP MAsh NEgg SBrw SPlb WFar
- 'William Buchanan' — GCrs MBar NHol
koidzumiana — SSta
nana — MBar
'Tilford' — LRHS NHol

Pilea (Urticaceae)

* 'Anette' — MBri
cadierei ♀H1 — CHal MBri
depressa — CHal
involucrata 'Norfolk' ♀H1 — CHal
§ *microphylla* — CHal EBak EShb
muscosa — see *P. microphylla*
nummulariifolia — CHal
peperomioides ♀H1 — CHal CSev EPem
repens — MBri

Pileostegia (Hydrangeaceae)
viburnoides ♀H4 — More than 30 suppliers
- B&SWJ 3565 — WCru

Pilosella (Asteraceae)
§ *aurantiaca* — CArn CHrt CMCo CNic CRWN ELan MBow MHer MWgw NBid NBlu NOrc NPri NSti SECG SIde SIng SPet WCAu WFar WHer WMoo WWye
§ - subsp. *carpathicola* — GGar
§ *officinarum* — NBlu NRya

Pilularia (Marsileaceae)
globulifera — CBgR EFer

Pimelea (Thymelaeaceae)
coarctata — see *P. prostrata*
drupacea — ECou
ferruginea — ECou
- 'Magenta Mist' — SOWG
filiformis — ECou
ligustrina — GGar
§ *prostrata* — CBcs CTri ECho ECou EPot MBar SRot WPat WPer
- f. *parvifolia* — ECou
- Tennyson's form — EHyt ETow SBla
tomentosa — ECou

Pimpinella (Apiaceae)
anisum — CArn MSal SIde WSel
bicknellii — CDes LPhx WCot WPGP
major 'Rosea' — CAby CBos CDes CElw CHad CMea CPLG CSpe EBee GMac GQue IFro LDai LHop LPhx LSou MLLN NCGa NChi NDov SBla SMrm SUsu WBor WCot WEas WFar WHal WPGP WTMC
niitakayamensis — WCru
B&SWJ 6942
saxifraga — CAgr NBre NDov

pineapple guava see *Acca sellowiana*

pineapple see *Ananas comosus*

Pinellia (Araceae)
cordata — CPom EMan LEdu MDKP MSte NMen SBla SOkd WCMO WCot WCru
pedatisecta — CDes CPom EBee EMan ERos LEdu MDKP WCMO WCot WPnP
pinnatisecta — see *P. tripartita*
ternata — CStu ERos MSal NMen WCMO WCot WWst WWye
- B&SWJ 3532 — WCru
§ *tripartita* — CPLG CPom CStu ECho MDKP WAbe WBVN WCMO WCot WCru WPnP WPrP
- B&SWJ 1102 — WCru
- 'Purple Face' — ITer WCru

Pinguicula (Lentibulariaceae)
acuminata — SHmp
crassifolia — CHew
crassifolia x *emarginata* — SHmp
cyclosecta — CHew SHmp
ehlersiae — EFEx
esseriana — EFEx
gracilis — CHew
grandiflora — CSWC EFEx GCrs GEdr IFro LRHS MCCP NMen NRya NWCA WAbe WPGP
hemiepiphytica — CHew
heterophylla — SHmp
jaumavensis — CHew
lauana — CHew
leptoceras — CFir
longifolia subsp. *longifolia* — EFEx WPGP
macrophylla — CHew SHmp
macrophylla x *zecheri* — SHmp
moctezumae — SHmp

moranensis var. *caudata*	EFEx	
– *moreana*	EFEx	
– *superba*	EFEx	
* *pilosa*	SHmp	
primuliflora	CSWC	
rotundiflora	CHew SHmp	
'Sethos'	SIng	
vallisneriifolia small	CHew	
vulgaris	EFEx	
'Weser'	CSWC SIng	

pinkcurrant see *Ribes rubrum* (P)

Pinus ✿ (*Pinaceae*)

albicaulis	WNor	
– 'Flinck'	CKen	
– 'Nana'	see *P. albicaulis* 'Noble's Dwarf'	
§ – 'Noble's Dwarf'	CKen	
aristata	CDul CLnd CMCN EHul EOrn LCon LLin MAsh MBar MBlu MBri MGos STre WDin WEve WWes	
– 'Cecilia'	CKen	
– 'Kohout's Mini' **new**	CKen	
– 'Sherwood Compact'	CKen LCon	
– 'So Tight' **new**	CKen	
armandii	CDoC CDul CTrC GTSp LCon WEve	
– 'Gold Tip'	CKen	
attenuata	LCon	
austriaca	see *P. nigra* subsp. *nigra*	
N *ayacahuite*	LCon	
balfouriana 'Dwarf Form'	CKen	
banksiana	CDul CLnd GTSp LCon	
– 'Arctis'	NLar	
– 'Chippewa'	CKen ECho LLin	
I – 'Compacta'	CKen	
– 'H.J. Welch'	CKen	
– 'Manomet'	CKen	
– 'Neponset'	CKen	
– 'Schneverdingen'	CKen NLar	
– 'Schoodic'	ECho LLin NLar SLim	
– 'Uncle Fogy'	ECho MGos NLar WEve	
– 'Wisconsin'	CKen	
bungeana	CDoC CDul CLnd CMCN CTho EPfP LCon LLin MBlu SLPl WEve WNor	
– 'Diamant'	CKen	
canariensis	EHul IDee LCon	
cembra	CDul CLnd EHul GIBF LCon MBar NLar NWea STre WEve	
– 'Aurea'	see *P. cembra* 'Aureovariegata'	
§ – 'Aureovariegata' (v)	CKen EBrs ECho LLin LRHS SPoG WEve	
– 'Barnhourie'	CKen	
– 'Blue Mound'	CKen	
– 'Chalet'	CKen	
– 'Compacta Glauca'	CDoC ECho MBri	
* – 'Griffithii'	WDin	
– 'Inverleith'	CKen	
– 'Jermyns'	CKen	
– 'King's Dwarf'	CKen	
– 'Ortler' **new**	CKen	
– 'Roughills'	CKen	
– 'Stricta'	CKen ECho	
– witches' broom	CKen	
cembroides **new**	LCon	
contorta	CBcs CDoC CDul LCon MBar MGos NWea WDin WMou	
– 'Asher'	CKen ECho	
– 'Frisian Gold'	CKen LLin SLim	
– var. *latifolia*	CDul CLnd LCon LRav WDin	
– 'Spaan's Dwarf'	CDoC CKen ECho LCon LLin MBar MGos NLar SCoo SLim SPoG WEve	
coulteri ♀H4	CDul CMCN CTho ECho EPfP GTSp LCon LLin SBig WNor WThu	

densiflora	CDul CMCN GTSp LEdu WNor	
– SF 99088	ISea	
– 'Alice Verkade'	CDoC CRob ECho EHul LBee LCon LLin LRHS MAsh MBri NDlv SCoo SLim WEve WFar	
– 'Aurea'	MBar MGos NLar SLim	
– 'Jane Kluis'	CKen ECho EHul LBee LCon LLin LRHS MBri NDlv NLar SCoo SLim WEve	
– 'Jim Cross'	CKen	
– 'Low Glow'	CKen ECho LCon NLar SLim	
– 'Oculus-draconis' (v)	ECho LCon LLin MBar MGos NLar SCoo SLim WEve	
– 'Pendula'	CKen ECho EOrn LLin MBri NEgg SLim WEve WFar	
– 'Pygmy'	LCon	
* – 'Pyramidalis'	ECho	
– 'Umbraculifera'	CDoC ECho IMGH LCon LLin MAsh MBar MGos NLar SCoo SSta WEve WFar	
I – 'Umbraculifera Nana'	ECho LLin	
§ *devoniana*	CBrP LCon LRHS SLim	
edulis	CAgr STre	
– 'Juno'	CKen	
elliottii	SBig	
engelmannii 'Glauca' **new**	EBrs	
flexilis	CDul GTSp LCon	
– 'Firmament'	ECho LCon LLin SLim	
– 'Glenmore Dwarf'	CKen	
– 'Nana'	CKen	
– 'Pendula'	LLin	
– 'Vanderwolf's Pyramid'	CRob MAsh NLar	
– WB No 1	CKen	
– WB No 2	CKen	
greggii	CTho EPfP	
griffithii	see *P. wallichiana*	
halepensis	ECrN	
§ *hartwegii*	CDul	
§ *heldreichii* ♀H4	CDoC CDul ECho LCon LPan LRav MBar MGos SCoo WNor	
– 'Aureospicata'	LCon LLin MBar NLar WEve	
– 'Dolce Dorme'	CKen NLar	
– 'Groen'	CKen	
– 'Kalous' **new**	NLar	
– var. *leucodermis*	see *P. heldreichii*	
– – 'Compact Gem'	CDoC CKen EBrs ECho LBee LCon LLin LRHS MBar MBri MGos NLar SCoo SLim SSta WEve	
– 'Malink'	CKen ECho	
– 'Ottocek'	CKen	
– 'Pygmy'	CKen ECho	
– 'Satellit'	CDoC CTri ECho EHul EMil EOrn LCon LLin LRHS MAsh NLar SCoo SLim SPoG WEve	
§ – 'Smidtii' ♀H4	CDoC CKen CRob ECho LCon LLin MAsh MBar MGos NLar SLim	
– 'Zwerg Schneverdingen'	CKen NLar	
jeffreyi ♀H4	CLnd CMCN CTho GTSp ISea LCon LRav MBar WEve	
– 'Joppi'	CKen CRob LCon NLar	
koraiensis	GTSp SLim WNor	
– 'Bergman'	CKen	
– 'Dragon Eye'	CKen	
– 'Jack Corbit'	CKen	
– 'Shibamichi' (v)	CKen	
– 'Silver Lining'	MAsh WWes	
– 'Silveray'	MAsh	
– 'Silvergrey'	CKen	
– 'Winton'	CKen NLar	
leucodermis	see *P. heldreichii*	
longaeva	EPfP	
magnifica	see *P. devoniana*	
'Marie Bregeon' PBR **new**	SPoG	
massoniana	WNor	
monophylla	ECho LLin	
montezumae misapplied	see *P. hartwegii*	

Name	Codes
- ambig.	SAPC SArc WNor
- Lamb.	SBig
monticola	CDul
- 'Pendula'	CKen MBar
- 'Pygmy'	see *P. monticola* 'Raraflora'
§ - 'Raraflora'	CKen
- 'Skyline'	MBar NLar WEve
- 'Strobicola'	LCon
- 'Windsor Dwarf'	CKen
mugo	CBcs CDul CSBt CTri EHul MBar MGos NWea WBor WBrE WDin WEve WFar
- 'Allgau'	CKen
- 'Benjamin'	CKen ECho NLar
- 'Bisley Green'	ECho LLin WEve
- 'Brownie'	CKen
- 'Carsten'	CKen ECho LLin SLim WEve
- 'Carsten's Wintergold'	LCon MAsh MBri NLar SCoo SPoG WEve
- 'Chameleon' **new**	NLar
- 'Corley's Mat'	CKen ECho LLin NHol NLar SCoo SLim WEve
- 'Devon Gem'	ECho SPoG
- 'Dezember Gold'	NLar SLim
- 'Flanders Belle'	ECho SLim
- 'Frohlings Gold'	NLar
- 'Gnom'	CDoC CMac ECho EHul EOrn IMGH LCon LLin LRHS MBar MBri MGos SCoo WDin WEve WFar
- 'Golden Glow'	CKen ECho LLin MBri NLar SLim
- 'Hesse' **new**	ECho
- 'Hoersholm'	CKen ECho
- 'Humpy'	CDoC CKen CMen CRob ECho EOrn IMGH LBee LCon LLin LRHS MAsh MBar MBri MGos SCoo SLim WEve WFar
- 'Jacobsen'	CKen NLar
- 'Janovsky'	CKen ECho
- 'Kissen'	CKen ECho LCon LLin MGos NLar WEve
- 'Klosterkotter'	ECho MGos NLar
- 'Kobold'	ECho NDlv NHol WFar
- 'Krauskopf'	CKen
- 'Laarheide'	CRob ECho NLar WEve
- 'Laurin'	CKen ECho
- 'Marand'	ECho LLin
- 'March'	CKen ECho EHul LLin
- 'Mini Mops'	CKen CMen ECho NLar
- 'Minikin'	CKen MAsh
- 'Mops' ♀H4	CDoC CRob ECho EHul EPfP LBee LCon LLin LRHS MAsh MBar MBlu MGos NHol NPri SCoo SLim SPer SPoG SSta WDin WEve WFar
- 'Mops Midget'	CRob ECho LBee LCon LLin MAsh MBri WEve
- var. *mughus*	see *P. mugo* subsp. *mugo*
§ - subsp. *mugo*	EOrn LBuc LPan MBar NBlu NWea WEve WFar
- 'Mumpitz'	CKen
- 'Ophir'	CDoC CDul CKen CRob ECho EHul EOrn EPfP IMGH LAst LBee LCon LLin LRHS MBar MBri MGos SCoo SLim SPer SPla SSta WDin WEve WFar
- 'Orange Sun' **new**	MBri
- 'Pal Maleter' (v)	CRob ECho LCon LLin MAsh NLar SCoo SLim SPoG WEve
- 'Paradekissen' **new**	NLar
- 'Paul's Dwarf'	CKen
- 'Picobello' **new**	NLar SLim
- 'Piggelmee'	CKen ECho NLar
- 'Pumilio Group' ♀H4	CDoC CLnd CMac ECho EHul ENot EOrn GBin LCon LLin MBar MGos MLan NBlu NWea SCoo SHBN STre WBVN WDin WFar WMoo WNor
- 'Pygmy'	ECho NDlv
- var. *rostrata*	see *P. mugo* subsp. *uncinata*
- 'Rushmore'	CKen
- 'Spaan'	CKen WEve
- 'Sunshine' (v)	CKen NLar
- 'Suzi'	CKen
- 'Tuffet'	ECho LLin MGos NLar
§ - subsp. *uncinata*	GIBF LCon NWea SLim WFar
- - 'Grüne Welle'	CKen ECho NLar SLim
- - 'Paradekissen'	CKen NLar
- 'Varella'	CKen NLar SLim
- 'White Tip'	CKen ECho
- 'Winter Gold'	CKen EBrs ECho EHul EOrn EPfP LAst LCon LLin LPan MAsh MGos NLar SCoo SPoG SSta WEve WFar
- 'Winter Sun'	CRob ECho MAsh
- 'Winzig'	CKen
- 'Zundert'	CDoC CKen ECho EHul LLin MBar MBri MGos NLar WEve
- 'Zwergkugel'	CKen
muricata ♀H4	CDoC CDul CLnd GTSp LCon LRav MGos NWea
nigra ♀H4	CBcs CDul CLnd CSBt CTri ECrN LCon MBar MGos SAPC SArc SHBN WBrE WDin WEve WMou
- var. *austriaca*	see *P. nigra* subsp. *nigra*
- 'Bambino'	CKen
- 'Black Prince'	CKen EBrs ECho EOrn IMGH LBee LCon LLin LRHS MAsh MGos NLar SCoo SLim SPoG WEve WGor
- var. *calabrica*	see *P. nigra* subsp. *laricio*
- var. *caramanica*	see *P. nigra* subsp. *pallasiana*
- var. *cebennensis*	see *P. nigra* subsp. *salzmannii*
N - 'Cebennensis Nana'	CKen
- var. *corsicana*	see *P. nigra* subsp. *laricio*
- 'Frank'	CKen ECho NLar
- 'Globosa' **new**	ECho
- 'Hornibrookiana'	CKen ECho GBin LLin NLar SCoo
- 'Komet' **new**	NLar
§ - subsp. *laricio* ♀H4	CAgr CDoC CDul CKen CSBt ECrN GWCH LAst LBuc LCon LRav MBar MGos NWea SBLw WMou
- - 'Bobby McGregor'	CKen ECho LLin SLim
- - 'Globosa Viridis'	ECho IMGH LLin NHol SLim WEve
- - 'Goldfingers'	CKen ECho LLin NLar WEve
§ - - 'Moseri'	CKen ECho EOrn LLin SLim SSta
- - 'Pygmaea'	CKen ECho EOrn NDlv WEve WFar
- - 'Spingarn'	CKen ECho
- - 'Talland Bay'	CKen ECho
- - 'Wurstle'	CKen
- subsp. *maritima*	see *P. nigra* subsp. *laricio*
- 'Nana'	CDoC LBee MBri
§ - subsp. *nigra*	CAgr CCVT CDoC CLnd CTho EWTr LBuc LPan MGos NLar NWea SPer WEve WFar
- - 'Birte'	CKen
- - 'Bright Eyes'	CKen CRob ECho EOrn IMGH LBee LCon LLin LRHS MAsh SCoo SLim SPoG WEve
- - 'Helga'	CKen
- - 'Schovenhorst'	CKen ECho
- - 'Strypemonde'	CKen
- - 'Yaffle Hill'	CKen ECho
§ - 'Obelisk'	CKen NLar
§ - subsp. *pallasiana*	CDul LCon NLar WPGP
- 'Richard'	CKen NLar
§ - subsp. *salzmannii*	GIBF
- 'Spielberg' **new**	NLar
- 'Uelzen'	CKen
palustris	CDoC CLnd CTho LCon LLin LRHS MAsh SBig SLim
parviflora	CDul CTri STre WDin WNor WThu
- 'Adcock's Dwarf' ♀H4	CDoC CKen ECho LCon LLin MBar MGos NLar SLim SPoG
- 'Aito-goyo' **new**	CKen

	– Aizu-goyo Group	ECho LLin
	– 'Al Fordham'	CKen
	– 'Aoi'	CKen CMen
	– 'Ara-kawa'	CKen CMen
	– Azuma-goyo Group	CKen
I	– 'Baasch's Form'	CKen MGos
	– 'Bergman'	ECho LCon MAsh MBar NLar
	– 'Blauer Engel'	CDoC ECho MGos
	– 'Blue Giant'	ECho NLar
	– 'Bonnie Bergman'	CKen ECho LLin WEve
	– 'Dai-ho'	CKen
	– 'Daisetsusan'	CKen
	– 'Doctor Landis Gold'	CKen ECho
	– 'Fatsumo'	CKen
	– 'Fukai' (v)	CKen MGos NLar
	– 'Fukiju'	CKen
	– Fukushima-goyo Group	CKen CMen WEve
	– 'Fuku-zu-mi'	CKen ECho LLin WEve
	– 'Fu-shiro'	CKen
	– 'Gin-sho-chuba'	CKen
	– Glauca Group	CDoC CMac CRob ECho EHul
		LCon LLin MBar MBlu MBri MGos
		NPal SPoG WEve WFar
I	– 'Glauca Nana'	CKen
	– 'Goldilocks'	CKen ECho NLar
	– 'Gyok-ke-sen'	CKen
	– 'Gyo-ko-haku'	CKen
	– 'Gyokuei'	CKen
	– 'Gyokusen Sämling'	CKen NLar
	– 'Gyo-ku-sui'	CKen ECho LLin
	– 'Hagaromo Seedling'	CKen ECho LLin MAsh NLar
	– 'Hakko'	CKen
	– 'Hatchichi'	CKen
	– 'Ibo-can'	CKen CMen
	– 'Ichi-no-se'	CKen
	– 'Iri-fune'	CKen
	– Ishizuchi-goyo Group	CKen
	– 'Ka-ho'	CKen ECho LLin
	– 'Kanrico' **new**	CKen
	– 'Kanzan'	CKen
	– 'Kiyomatsu'	CKen
	– 'Kobe'	CKen ECho LLin WEve
	– 'Kokonoe'	CKen CMen LLin
	– 'Kokuho'	CKen
	– 'Koraku'	CKen
	– 'Kusu-dama'	CKen
	– 'Meiko'	CKen ECho
	– 'Michinoku'	CKen
	– 'Momo-yama'	CKen
	– 'Myo-jo'	CKen
	– Nasu-goyo Group	CKen
	– 'Negishi'	CDoC CKen CMen CRob LCon
		LLin LPan LRHS MAsh MBri NLar
		SLim WEve
	– 'Ogon-janome'	CKen
	– 'Ossorio Dwarf'	CKen
	– 'Regenhold'	CKen
	– 'Richard Lee'	CKen
	– 'Ryo-ku-ho'	CKen
	– 'Ryu-ju'	CKen
	– 'Sa-dai-jin'	CKen
	– 'San-bo'	CKen ECho MBar MGos
§	– 'Saphir'	CKen ECho
	– 'Setsugekka'	CKen
	– 'Shika-shima'	CDoC CKen
	– Shiobara-goyo Group	CKen
	– 'Shirobana' **new**	NLar
	– 'Shizukagoten'	CKen
	– 'Shu-re'	CKen
	– 'Sieryoden'	CKen
	– 'Tani-mano-uki'	CKen
	– 'Tempelhof'	COtt CTho LRHS MAsh MBar NBlu
		NLar
	– 'Templeflora'	MLan
	– 'Tenysu-kazu'	CKen
	– 'Tokyo Dwarf' **new**	CKen

I	– 'Torulosa'	LLin
	– 'Tribune'	CDoC NLar
	– 'Watnong'	CKen
	– 'Zelkova'	CMen ECho LLin
	– 'Zui-sho'	CKen
	patula $\heartsuit^{H2-3}$	CAbb CBcs CBgR CDoC CDul
		CFwr CLnd CTrC EGra LAst LCon
		SAPC SArc SBig SBir SCoo SIFN
		SLim SPlb SPoG WEve
	peuce	CDoC CDul EHoe GIBF GTSp
		LCon LRav MBar NLar NWea
	– 'Arnold Dwarf'	CKen
	– 'Cesarini'	CKen
	– 'Thessaloniki Broom' **new**	CKen
	pinaster $\heartsuit^{H4}$	CAgr CBcs CDoC CDul CLnd EHul
		GTSp LCon WBVN
	pinea $\heartsuit^{H4}$	CAgr CArn CDoC CKen CLnd
		CMac CTho ECrN ELau EPfP GIBF
		LCon LEdu LPan LRHS LRav MGos
		SAPC SArc SBLw SCoo SEND WEve
		WNor WPGP
	– 'Queensway'	CKen
	ponderosa $\heartsuit^{H4}$	CDul CLnd CMCN GTSp LCon
		LRav NWea WEve WPGP
	– var. *scopulorum*	NWea
	pumila	CRob NEgg
	– from Kamchatka	GIBF
	– 'Buchanan'	CKen ECho
	– 'Draijer's Dwarf'	CDoC ECho EOrn LLin SCoo SLim
	– 'Dwarf Blue'	CRob ECho MAsh NDlv
§	– 'Glauca' $\heartsuit^{H4}$	CKen LLin LRHS MBar
	– 'Globe'	ECho LCon LLin MAsh MBri
	– 'Jeddeloh'	CKen
	– 'Knightshayes'	CKen
	– 'Säntis'	CKen ECho
	– 'Saphir'	see *P. parviflora* 'Saphir'
	radiata $\heartsuit^{H3-4}$	CAgr CBcs CDoC CDul CLnd CSBt
		CTri CTrw ECrN ELan ENot LCon
		LRHS LRav MNHC NWea SAPC
		SArc SHBN SPer WDin WEve
		WWes
	– Aurea Group	CDoC CKen CTho ECho EOrn
		LBee LCon LLin LRHS LRav MAsh
		SBir SCoo SLim SMur WEve WFar
	– 'Bodnant'	CKen
	– 'Isca'	CKen ECho
	– 'Marshwood' (v)	CKen ECho LCon MGos SLim
	resinosa	GIBF
	– 'Don Smith'	CKen
	– 'Joel's Broom'	CKen
	– 'Quinobequin'	CKen
	rigida	LCon
	roxburghii	IDee ISea LCon WPGP
	x *schwerinii*	CDoC ECho LCon LRHS MAsh
	– 'Wiethorst'	CKen NLar SLim
	sibirica	GIBF
	– 'Mariko' **new**	CKen
	strobiformis	ISea LCon
	– 'Coronado' **new**	CKen
	– 'Loma Linda' **new**	CKen
	strobus	CDul CMen ISea LCon LPan MBar
		NWea SLim WDin WEve WNor
§	– 'Alba'	MGos SLim
	– 'Amelia's Dwarf'	CKen
	– 'Anna Fiele'	CKen
	– 'Bergman's Mini'	CKen NLar
	– 'Bergman's Pendula Broom'	CKen
I	– 'Bergman's Sport of Prostrata'	CKen
	– 'Bloomer's Dark Globe'	CKen
	– 'Blue Shag'	CKen ECho EOrn LLin MGos NLar
		SLim SPoG WEve
	– 'Cesarini'	CKen
	– 'Densa'	CKen ECho LCon MAsh

- 'Dove's Dwarf'	CKen
- 'Ed's Broom'	CKen
- 'Elkins Dwarf'	CKen
- 'Fastigiata'	CKen ECho GBin IMGH LLin MBri SPoG
- 'Greg'	CKen ECho
- 'Hershey'	CKen
- 'Hillside Gem'	CKen
- 'Himmelblau'	LCon NLar SLim
- 'Horsford'	CKen ECho LLin NLar
- 'Jericho'	CKen EOrn
- 'Julian Pott' **new**	CKen
- 'Krügers Lilliput'	LCon LLin LRHS MBri NLar SLim
- 'Louie'	CKen NLar SLim
- 'Macopin'	ECho NLar
- 'Mary Butler'	CKen
- 'Merrimack'	CKen ECho NLar
- 'Minima'	CKen ECho EOrn LBee LCon LLin LRHS MAsh MBar MBlu MBri MGos SLim SPoG WEve WGor
- 'Minuta'	CKen
- 'Nana'	see *P. strobus* Nana Group
§ - Nana Group	LLin NPri
- 'Nivea'	see *P. strobus* 'Alba'
- 'Northway Broom'	CKen ECho LCon LLin SLim
- 'Ontario'	MBlu
- 'Pendula'	CKen WWes
I - 'Pendula Broom'	CKen
§ - 'Radiata'	CTri EHul EPla LCon MBar SPoG
I - 'Radiata Aurea'	WEve
- 'Reinshaus'	CKen ECho LLin
- 'Sayville'	CKen
- 'Sea Urchin'	CKen ECho SLim
- 'Uncatena'	CKen
- 'Verkade's Broom'	CKen
sylvestris ♀H4	More than 30 suppliers
- 'Abergeldie'	CKen
- 'Alderly Edge'	CMen WEve WFar
- 'Andorra'	CKen MAsh
§ - 'Argentea'	ECho SLim
§ - Aurea Group ♀H4	CDul CKen CMac CMen EBrs ECho EHul EPfP GBin IMGH LBee LCon LLin LRHS MAsh MBar MBri NPri SCoo SHBN SLim SPer SSta WEve
- 'Aurea'	see *P. sylvestris* Aurea Group
- 'Avondene'	CKen ECho
- 'Bergfield'	ECho NLar WEve
- 'Beuvronensis' ♀H4	CKen CLnd CMac CMen ECho EOrn IMGH LBee LLin LRHS MGos NHol SCoo SLim WEve
- 'Bonna'	CLnd LCon SCoo SIFN SLim
- 'Brevifolia'	MBar
- 'Buchanan's Gold'	CKen
- 'Burghfield'	CKen ECho LLin WEve
- 'Chantry Blue'	CDoC CMen CRob ECho EHul EMil EOrn IMGH LBee LCon LLin LRHS MAsh MBar MBri MGos NHol NLar SCoo SLim WEve WFar
- 'Clumber Blue'	CKen
- 'Compressa'	LLin SLim
- 'Corley'	ECho LLin
- 'Dereham'	CKen ECho LLin
- 'Doone Valley'	CKen ECho LLin MGos WEve
- 'Edwin Hillier'	see *P. sylvestris* 'Argentea'
- Fastigiata Group	CDoC CDul CEnd CKen CMen CRob ECho EOrn IMGH LBee LCon LLin LRHS MAsh MBar MGos SCoo SLim SPoG WEve WFar WWes
- 'Frensham'	CDoC CKen ECho EOrn IMGH LCon LLin MAsh MGos WEve WFar
- 'Globosa'	ECho LRHS WEve
- 'Gold Coin'	CDoC CDul CKen ECho EOrn EPfP LBee LCon LLin MAsh MGos

	NHol NLar SCoo SLim SPoG WEve WFar
- 'Gold Medal'	CKen ECho LLin SIFN SLim WEve
- 'Grand Rapids'	CKen
- 'Gwydyr Castle'	CKen
- 'Hibernia'	CRob
- 'Hillside Creeper'	CKen EBrs ECho LCon LLin NLar SCoo SLim WEve
- 'Humble Pie' **new**	CKen
- 'Inverleith' (v)	ECho EHul LBuc LCon LLin MBar MGos NHol SCoo SLim SPoG WEve
- 'Jeremy'	CKen ECho LCon LLin NHol SCoo SLim SPoG WEve
- 'John Boy'	CMen ECho LLin NLar
- 'Kelpie'	ECho LLin SLim
- 'Kenwith'	CKen ECho
- 'Lakeside Dwarf'	ECho LLin WEve
- 'Lodge Hill'	CMen CRob ECho EOrn IMGH LCon LLin LRHS MAsh SCoo SLim WEve
- 'Longmoor'	CKen ECho NLar
- 'Martham'	CKen ECho LLin WEve
- var. ***mongolica***	GIBF
* - 'Moseri'	ECho LBee LRHS MAsh SPoG WEve
- 'Munches Blue'	CKen
- L. 'Nana' misapplied	see *P. sylvestris* 'Watereri'
- 'Nana Compacta'	CMen LLin
§ - 'Nisbet's Gem'	CKen ECho LLin
- 'Padworth'	CMen LLin NLar
- 'Peve Miba' **new**	NLar
- 'Pixie'	CKen ECho LLin MGos NLar
I - 'Prostrata'	SCoo
- 'Pulham'	ECho LLin WEve
- 'Pygmaea'	SCoo SLim
- 'Reedham'	ECho LLin WEve
- 'Repens'	CKen
- 'Saint George'	CKen
- 'Sandringham'	ECho LLin WEve
- 'Saxatilis'	CKen ECho EOrn LBee LCon LLin MAsh WEve
- subsp. ***scotica***	GIBF
- 'Scott's Dwarf'	see *P. sylvestris* 'Nisbet's Gem'
- 'Scrubby'	ECho LLin NLar
- 'Sentinel'	CKen ECho SLim
- 'Skjak I'	CKen NLar
- 'Skjak II'	CKen ECho LLin
- 'Spaan's Slow Column'	CKen ECho SLim
- 'Tabuliformis'	ECho LLin
- 'Tage'	CKen ECho LLin WEve
- 'Tanya'	CKen MAsh
- 'Tilhead'	CKen ECho
- 'Treasure'	CKen ECho LLin
- 'Trefrew Quarry' **new**	CKen
§ - 'Variegata' (v)	WEve
§ - 'Watereri'	CMac ECho EHul IMGH LAst LBee LCon LLin LPan LRHS MAsh MBar MBri NHol NPri SCoo SLim SPer WDin WEve WFar
- 'Westonbirt'	CKen CMen ECho EHul LLin WEve
- 'Wishmoor'	ECho LLin WEve
- 'Wolf Gold'	CKen ECho
- 'Xawrey 1' **new**	NLar
* - 'Yaff Hill'	ECho
tabuliformis	CDul CMCN GIBF ISea LCon WWes
thunbergii	CDul CLnd EHul GTSp LCon LLin MGos STre WNor
- 'Akame'	CKen CMen
- 'Akame Yatsubusa'	CMen
- 'Aocha-matsu' (v)	CKen CMen NLar
- 'Arakawa-sho'	CKen CMen
- 'Banshosho'	CKen CMen ECho MGos NLar
- 'Beni-kujaku'	CKen CMen
- 'Compacta'	CKen CMen NLar

- 'Dainagon'   CKen CMen
- 'Eechee-nee' **new**   CKen
- 'Iwai'   CMen
- 'Janome' **new**   CMen
- 'Katsuga'   CMen
- 'Kotobuki'   CKen CMen CRob LCon NLar
- 'Koyosho'   CMen
- 'Kujaku'   CKen CMen
- 'Kyokko' **new**   CKen
- 'Kyushu'   CKen CMen
- 'Miyajuna'   CKen CMen
- 'Nishiki-ne'   CKen CMen
- 'Nishiki-tsusaka'   CMen ECho
- 'Oculus-draconis' (v)   CMen ECho LLin
- 'Ogon'   CKen CMen LCon NLar SLim
- 'Porky'   CKen CMen
§ - 'Sayonara'   CKen CMen ECho LLin MAsh
                            NHol NLar SLim
- 'Senryu'   CKen CMen
- 'Shinsho'   CKen CMen
- 'Shio-guro'   CKen CMen MAsh
- 'Suchiro Yatabusa'   CKen CMen ECho
- 'Sunsho'   CKen CMen ECho
- 'Taihei'   CKen CMen
I - 'Thunderhead'   CKen CMen EBrs LCon MAsh NLar
                            SLim
- 'Yatsubusa'   see *P. thunbergii* 'Sayonara'
- 'Ye-i-kan'   CKen
- 'Yoshimura' **new**   CMen
- 'Yumaki'   CKen CMen ECho
uncinata   see *P. mugo* subsp. *uncinata*
- 'Etschtal' **new**   CKen
- 'Jezek'   CKen NLar SLim
- 'Kostelnicek'   NLar
- 'Leuco-like'   CKen
- 'Litomysl' **new**   NLar
- 'Offenpass'   CKen
- 'Susse Perle'   CKen
virginiana 'Wate's   CKen
  Golden'
§ **wallichiana** ♀H4   CDoC CDul CKen CMCN CRob
                            CTho ECho ECrN EHul EPfP LCon
                            LLin MAsh MBar MBlu MGos MLan
                            NEgg NHol NWea SBir SLim STre
                            WDin WEve WFar WGer WNor
                            WOrn WPGP
- SF 00001   ISea
- 'Densa'   LPan
- 'Nana'   CKen EHul LCon LLin MBar NLar
                            SCoo SLim WEve
- 'Umbraculifera'   LRHS
- 'Zebrina' (v)   LBee LCon MAsh MBar MGos NLar
                            SMad WEve
yunnanensis   CTho GIBF WBor WEve WNor

Piper (Piperaceae)
auritum   GPoy
betle   MSal
excelsum   see *Macropiper excelsum*
nigrum   MSal

Piptanthus (Papilionaceae)
forrestii   see *P. nepalensis*
laburnifolius   see *P. nepalensis*
§ **nepalensis**   CBcs CDul CMac CSBt CSpe EBee
                            ECrN EGra ELan EMil EPfP EWTr
                            IDee ISea LRHS MGos MWhi NBid
                            SBrw SEND SGar SHBN SLon
                            SOWG SPer SPoG SRms WBVN
- B&SWJ 2241   WCru
tomentosus   MMHG WPGP

Pistacia (Anacardiaceae)
atlantica   EGFP
chinensis   CBcs CMCN CPMA EPfP WPic
                            XPep

lentiscus   CArn CBcs EAro MGos SEND XPep
terebinthus   XPep

Pistia (Araceae)
stratiotes   LPBA NPer SCoo

Pitcairnia (Bromeliaceae)
bergii **new**   CHll
heterophylla   WCot

Pithecoctenium (Bignoniaceae)
crucigerum **new**   CPIN
cynanchiodes   CPIN

Pittosporum ❀ (Pittosporaceae)
anomalum   ECou
- (f)   ECou
- (m)   ECou
- 'Falcon'   ECou
- 'Raven' (f)   ECou
- 'Starling' (m)   ECou
'Arundel Green'   CDoC CWSG EBee EJRN EPfP
                            LRHS MAsh SLim SPoG SWvt
bicolor   ECou EShb GQui SAPC SArc WBor
                            WPGP
- 'Cradle' (f)   ECou
- 'Mount Field' (f)   ECou
buchananii   SGar WCwm
colensoi   ECou
- 'Cobb' (f)   ECou
- 'Wanaka' (m)   ECou
crassifolium   CCCN CHEx ECou ERea IDee
                            WBrE WPGP XPep
- 'Compactum'   XPep
- 'Havering Dwarf' (f)   ECou
- 'Napier' (f)   ECou
- 'Variegatum' (v)   CPne EShb WSPU
crassifolium x   CWib ECou SWvt
  tenuifolium
'Craxten' (f)   ECou EJRN
'Crinkles' (f)   ECou
daphniphylloides   WCru
  B&SWJ 6789
'Dark Delight' (m)   ECou
divaricatum   ECou
'Essex' (f/v)   ECou EJRN
eugenioides   CBcs CHEx CMHG CPen CTrC
                            CTrG EDsa GGar IDee
- 'Mini Green'   CPen LSou NLar WBrE
- 'Platinum' (v)   CBcs CCCN MGos
- 'Variegatum' (v) ♀H3   CAbb CBcs CBrm CCCN CDoC
                            CDul CHEx CPLG EBee EJRN EMil
                            EPfP GGar GQui IArd ISea LRHS
                            MBri MGos MPRe SHBN SLim SPer
                            SPoG SSto WPGP WSHC WSPU
eugenoides 'Tens Gold' CPen
'Garnettii' (v) ♀H3   More than 30 suppliers
heterophyllum   CPen ECou EDsa SHBN XPep
- 'Ga Blanca'   CPen
- variegated (v)   ECou WSHC
'Holbrook' (v) **new**   CSam
'Humpty Dumpty'   ECou EJRN
illicioides var.   WCru
  angustifolium
  B&SWJ 6771 **new**
- var. **illicioides**   WCru
  B&SWJ 6712
'Limelight' (v)   CBcs CPen CSBt CSPN LRHS
                            SPoG
lineare   ECou
§ 'Margaret Turnbull' (v)   CBcs CPen CTrC ECou EJRN EWes
                            IArd LSRN MBri MGos MPRe
michiei   ECou
- (f)   ECou
- (m)   ECou
- 'Jack' (m)   ECou

- 'Jill' (f) — ECou
'Nanum Variegatum' — see *P. tobira* 'Variegatum'
obcordatum — ECou
- var. ***kaitaiaense*** — ECou
omeiense — ECou ECre EWes
'Peter Pan' **new** — EJRN
phillyreoides — XPep
pimeleoides var. — ECou
   reflexum (m)
'Purple Princess' — ECou EJRN
ralphii — CCCN ECou WBVN WPic
- 'Green Globe' — ECou XPep
- 'Variegatum' (v) — SSpi WPGP
* ***robustum*** — EWes
'Saundersii' (v) — CBcs
tenuifolium 'Croxton' — CCCN
   new
tenuifolium ♀H3 — More than 30 suppliers
- 'Abbotsbury Gold' (f/v) — CAbb CBcs CDoC CMac
   CSam CTri EBee ECou ELan EMil
   EWes GBri LRHS MPRe SAga SEND
   SHBN SLim SPer SPla SSto WSHC
- 'Atropurpureum' — CBcs
- 'County Park' **new** — CCCN
- 'County Park Dwarf' — CPen EBee ECou EJRN MAsh
   MPRe WCru
- 'Deborah' (v) — ECou EHol EJRN LSou SSto
- 'Dixie' — CPen ECou
§ - 'Eila Keightley' (v) — CMHG EJRN SAga
- 'Elizabeth' (m/v) — CBcs CDoC CMac CPen CTrC
   EBee ECou EJRN IArd ISea LRHS
   MBri MPRe
- 'French Lace' — CBcs CCCN CPen EBee ECou
   EJRN NLar WBrE WFar WWeb
- 'Gold Star' — CBcs CDoC CPen ECou ENot
   LRHS MGos NHol NPal SCoo SLim
   SPoG
- 'Golden Cut' — NLar
- 'Golden King' — CCCN CDoC CMHG CMac CSBt
   EBee EJRN LRHS LSou MPRe
   NScw SLim SPoG SRms SSto
   WWeb
- 'Golden Princess' (f) — ECou EJRN
- 'Green Elf' — ECou EJRN
- 'Green Thumb' — CWSG EBee LRHS MPRe
- 'Irene Paterson' (m/v) — More than 30 suppliers
   ♀H3
- 'James Stirling' — CCCN CPMA ECou EPfP LRHS
   SSto
- 'John Flanagan' — see *P.* 'Margaret Turnbull'
- 'Loxhill Gold' — CCCN CPen EBee EKen IArd LRHS
   LSou MGos NScw SSto
- 'Marjory Channon' (v) — CBcs LRHS
- 'Mellow Yellow' — CAbP LRHS
- 'Moonlight' (v) — CBcs CTrC EBee WDin
- 'Mountain Green' — LSou
- 'Nutty's Leprechaun' — CCCN
- 'Pompom' — SPoG
- 'Purpureum' (m) — CBrm CCCN CMac CSBt CSam
   CTri CTrw EBee ECou EPfP ISea
   LAst LRHS LSRN MBri MPRe
   MWgw SAga SCoo SHBN SPer SPla
   SPoG SRms SSto WGer WSHC
- 'Silver Haze' **new** — ISea
- 'Silver Magic' (v) — CBcs CPen CSBt EBee EJRN
   MGos
- 'Silver 'n' Gold' — LRHS
- 'Silver Princess' (f) — ECou EJRN
- 'Silver Queen' (f/v) ♀H3 — More than 30 suppliers
- 'Silver Sheen' (m) — CBcs CPen EBee ECou LRHS
- 'Stirling Gold' (f/v) — ECou EPfP EWes
- 'Sunburst' — see *P. tenuifolium* 'Eila Keightley'
- 'Tandara Gold' (v) — CBrm CCCN CDoC CDul CTrC
   ECou EJRN ENot EPfP LRHS LSRN
   MPRe SLim SPla SPoG WBrE WFar
   WGer WWeb

- 'Tiki' (m) — CBcs CCCN CTrC ECou
- 'Tom Thumb' ♀H3 — More than 30 suppliers
- 'Tresederi' (f/m) — CBrm CCCN CMac CTrC CTrw
   EBee ECou LRHS
- 'Variegatum' (m/v) — CBcs CDoC CSBt ECou GBri LAst
   LRHS MGos SPoG SWvt
- 'Victoria' (v) — CDoC CPen CTrC EBee EMil SPoG
- 'Warnham Gold' (m) — CMac COtt CSBt CTrw CWib EBee
   ♀H3 — ECou EJRN ELan EPfP GBri LRHS
   MCCP MGos MPRe SCoo SLim
   SPer SPoG SSpi SSto WAbe
- 'Wendle Channon' (m/v) — CCCN CMac CSBt CSam CTrC
   EBee ECot ECou EPfP LRHS NCGa
   NHol SLim SPer SSto WSHC
- 'Winter Sunshine' — SSta
- 'Wrinkled Blue' **new** — CFwr
tobira ♀H3 — More than 30 suppliers
- B&SWJ 4362 — WCru
* - 'Cuneatum' — LHop SAga
* - 'Nanum' — CBcs CCCN CDoC EBee ECou
   ELan EPfP ERea ERom LPan MGos
   MPRe MWya SAPC SArc SLim SPla
   SPoG WDin WGer XPep
§ - 'Variegatum' (v) ♀H2-3 — More than 30 suppliers
truncatum — ECre EWes XPep
* - 'Variegatum' — MPRe XPep
undulatum — CHEx CPen ECou
viridiflorum — ECou EShb

Plagianthus (Malvaceae)
betulinus — see *P. regius*
divaricatus — CBcs CTrC ECou ECre WPGP
lyallii — see *Hoheria lyallii*
§ ***regius*** — CBcs CTrC ECou GQui LRHS SBig

Plagiorhegma see *Jeffersonia*

Plantago (Plantaginaceae)
asiatica — MSal
- 'Ki Fu' (v) — ITer
- 'Variegata' (v) — EMan GBuc MBNS NBro NLar
   WGwG
cynops — MTho XPep
lanceolata — NMir WSFF
- 'Ballydowling Variegated' — EBee EChP
   (v)
- 'Blond Bomi-noka' — CNat
- 'Bomi-noka' — CNat
- 'Burren Rose' — CBgR CRow
- 'Dent's Downs Link' (v) — WCot
- 'Golden Spears' — CBgR CBre EBee EChP NSti
- 'Keer's Pride' (v) — WCot
- 'Pink Bomi-noka' — CNat
- 'Streaker' (v) — CRow EBee ITer WCot
major — WHbs
- 'Atropurpurea' — see *P. major* 'Rubrifolia'
- 'Bowles' Variety' — see *P. major* 'Rosularis'
- 'Frills' — CBre CNat CRow EBee
* - 'Karmozijn' — EMan
- 'Rosenstolz' **new** — CRow
§ - 'Rosularis' — CArn CNat CRow CSpe EBee
   EChP EDAr EShb ILis ITer LEdu
   MHer MTho MWgw NBid NBro
   NChi NEgg SPav WCAu WEas
   WHer WHer WWye
§ - 'Rubrifolia' — CArn CRow CSpe EBee EChP
   EMag EShb IHMH LDai MHer
   MWgw NBid NBro NChi NEgg
   NSti WCAu WHer WMoo WPer
   WWye
- 'Tony Lewis' — CNat
maritima — WHer
media — MHer
nivalis — EHyt ETow
psyllium L. — CArn MSal
rosea — see *P. major* 'Rosularis'

uniflora Hook. f.   WCot

Platanthera (*Orchidaceae*)
bifolia new	MDun NLAp
hologlottis	EFEx
metabifolia	EFEx

Platanus ✿ (*Platanaceae*)
x **acerifolia**	see *P.* x *hispanica*
§ x **hispanica** ♀H4	CBcs CCVT CDul CLnd CMCN
	CTho EBee ECrN EPfP EWTr LAst
	LBuc LPan MGos NWea SBLw
	SEND SHBN SPer WDin WFar
	WMou
- 'Bloodgood'	SBLw
- 'Dakvorm'	SBLw
- 'Dortmund'	SBLw
- 'Pyramidalis'	CTho SBLw WOrn
- 'Suttneri' (v)	CEnd CTho SMad WMou
occidentalis	NEgg
orientalis ♀H4	CCVT CDul CLnd CMCN CTho
	EBee EPfP LEdu NLar SBLw SDix
	SLPl WDin WMou
- MSF 0028 from Sfendili,	WPGP
Crete	
§ - f. **digitata** ♀H4	CDoC CDul CLnd CMCN CTho
	EPfP ERod MBlu SBLw SLPl SMad
	WMou
- var. **insularis**	CEnd WPGP
- 'Laciniata'	see *P. orientalis* f. *digitata*
- 'Minaret'	EMil WMou
- 'Mirkovec'	CDoC SMad SPer WMou

Platycarya (*Juglandaceae*)
strobilacea	CBcs EPfP

Platycerium (*Polypodiaceae*)
alcicorne misapplied	see *P. bifurcatum*
§ **bifurcatum** ♀H1	LRHS MBri

Platycladus (*Cupressaceae*)
§ **orientalis**	CDul
- 'Aurea Nana' ♀H4	CDoC CKen CMac CSBt CWib
	ECho EHul EPfP IMGH ISea LBee
	LCon LLin LPan LRHS MAsh MBar
	MBri NBlu NWea SLim SMer SPla
	SPoG WCFE WDin WEas WEve
	WFar WTel
- 'Autumn Glow'	CKen CRob LRHS MAsh SCoo
	SPoG WGor
- 'Beverleyensis'	LLin NLar WEve
- 'Blue Cone'	MBar WEve
- 'Caribbean Holiday'	MAsh
- 'Collen's Gold'	CTri EHul EOrn MBar
- 'Conspicua'	CKen CWib ECho EHul LBee
	MAsh MBar
- 'Elegantissima' ♀H4	CMac ECho EHul EOrn LBee LPan
	MBar SCoo
- 'Franky Boy' new	CDHC LCon MGos NLar SLim
- 'Golden Pillar'	EOrn
- 'Golden Pygmy'	CKen EOrn MAsh
- 'Golden Wonder'	ECho
- 'Juniperoides'	ECho EHul MBar
- 'Kenwith'	CKen ECho
- 'Lemon 'n Lime'	ECho SPoG WEve
- 'Little Susie'	CRob
- 'Madurodam'	LLin MBar
- 'Magnifica'	ECho EHul
- 'Meldensis'	CDoC CTri ECho EHul MBar WTel
- 'Minima'	CRob ECho EHul WGor
- 'Minima Glauca'	CKen ECho MBar
- 'Mint Chocolate'	ECho LLin
- 'Purple King'	LCon LRHS SCoo SLim SPoG
I - 'Pyramidalis Aurea'	LBee LCon LRHS NBlu WEve
- 'Rosedalis'	CKen CMac CSBt ECho EHul ENot
	EPfP LBee LCon LLin LRHS MAsh

	MBar MBri SCoo SLim SMer SPla
	SPoG WEve WFar WTel
- 'Sanderi'	ECho MBar WCFE
§ - 'Semperaurea'	CMac IMGH
- 'Shirley Chilcott'	LBee LCon MAsh
- 'Sieboldii'	EHul
- 'Southport'	LBee LCon LLin LRHS MAsh
- 'Summer Cream'	CKen EHul MBar
- 'Westmont' (v)	CKen CSBt EOrn

Platycodon ✿ (*Campanulaceae*)
grandiflorus ♀H4	CArn CMea COlW CTri EBrs ECha
	ELau EPot GKev LEdu LHop MHer
	MNrw MSal NEgg SGar SRms
	WGwG WHoo WWye
- 'Albus'	CBro CSec EAEE EBee EChP ECho
	EPfP LHop MBri MNFA SPer SPla
	SWvt WHoo WPer
- 'Apoyama' ♀H4	CLyd CStu ECho GKev LBee LRHS
	NMen WHoo WPer
- **apoyama albus**	CStu ECho WEas
- (Astra Series) 'Astra Blue'	ECho NEgg Nsfd WHoo
- - 'Astra Double Blue' (d)	CSpe NEgg Nsfd
- - 'Astra Pink'	Nsfd WHoo
- - 'Astra White'	Nsfd WHoo
- 'Blaue Glocke' new	NBre
- 'Blue Haze'	EBee
- 'Blue Pearl'	WHoo
- 'Fairy Snow'	CBgR EBee ELan EShb LBMP
	MBNS NBre WHoo WSel
- 'Florist Rose'	MHar WOut WWye
- 'Florist Snow'	WWye
- 'Fuji Blue'	LIck NLar SPet SPur WSel
- 'Fuji Pink'	CBrm CBro EAEE EBee ECho ELan
	EMar EPfP ERou LAst LHop MRav
	MTis NEgg NLar SMrm SPet SPoG
	SPur SWvt WCAu WLin WSel
- 'Fuji White'	ECho ELan ERou LAst NLar SMar
	SMrm SPet SPur WCAu WSel
- 'Hakone'	EBee LAst LHop MRav SMrm
	WHoo
- 'Hakone Blue'	CBgR ECho NBre NLar SMar WLin
* - 'Hakone Double Blue' (d)	CPrp EAEE EBee ECGP ELan EMar
	LRHS MBNS MTis SBch SPoG SRms
	WCAu
- 'Hakone White'	CBgR CBrm CMdw CPBP EAEE
	EBee ECGP ECho EPfP LAst NGby
	NLar NMen SBch SMad SMar SPet
	SPoG WHoo WLin
- 'Mariesii' ♀H4	CBgR CBro CPLG CSBt EAEE EBee
	EChP ECho ECtt EMar EPfP ERou
	LRHS MNFA MRav MWgw NBir
	NEgg NMen SMrm SPer SPet SPla
	SRms SWvt WEas WHoo WPer
- **mariesii albus**	WHoo
- 'Misato Purple'	WSel
- Mother of Pearl	see *P. grandiflorus*
	'Perlmutterschale'
- 'Park's Double Blue' (d)	WHoo
§ - 'Perlmutterschale'	CBgR CBrm CMMP EAEE EBee
	EChP ECho EMar EPPr EPfP EWTr
	IPot MBNS MNFA NEgg SPet
	WHoo
- **pumilus**	CStu EBee NChi NWCA WHoo
- **roseus**	MNrw NEgg
- 'Sentimental Blue'	CWib EBee ECho EWin NJOw
	NLar
- 'Shell Pink'	see *P. grandiflorus*
	'Perlmutterschale'
- white-flowered, double	CBro
- 'Zwerg'	CPBP EBee ECho GMac LBMP
	NBre WRHF

Platycrater (*Hydrangeaceae*)
arguta	NLar WCru
- B&SWJ 6266	WCru

Plecostachys (Asteraceae)

§ *serpyllifolia*	CHal MOak

Plectranthus (Lamiaceae)

from Puerto Rico	CArn
ambiguus	EOHP
- 'Manguzuku'	EOHP
- 'Umigoye'	EOHP
amboinicus	CArn CHal EOHP MOak NHor NTHB WDyG
* - 'Variegatus' (v)	EOHP EUnu
- 'Well Sweep Wedgewood'	EOHP EUnu
argentatus ♀H2	CBcs CDMG CDoC CHad CHal CHrt CMdw CPLG CSev CSpe EMan EOHP EShb MOak MSte MTis SBch SDix SEND SGar SHFr SUsu WDyG WKif WWlt
- 'Hill House' (v)	CHll CHrt CPne EMan EOHP EShb LDai MOak WCot
australis misapplied	see *P. verticillatus*
behrii	see *P. fruticosus*
Blue Angel = 'Edelblau'	EOHP
Blue Spire = 'Limplep1' (v) **new**	SVil
caninus **new**	NHor
ciliatus	CPne EOHP LPhx MOak SGar WWlt
- 'All Gold'	CPne
- 'Easy Gold'	EOHP MOak
- 'Sasha'	CDoC CHal CHll ECtt EOHP EShb LAst LSou SAga
coleoides 'Marginatus'	see *P. forsteri* 'Marginatus'
- 'Variegatus'	see *P. madagascariensis* 'Variegated Mintleaf'
Cuban oregano	EOHP EWll WJek
dolichopodus	EOHP
ecklonii	EOHP WDyG
- NJM 02.010	WPGP
- 'Medley-Wood'	EOHP
ernstii	EOHP MOak
§ *forsteri* 'Marginatus'	CHal ERea MOak SGar
frederici	see *P. welwitschii*
§ *fruticosus*	CHal CPne GBri MOak
- 'Frills'	CPne EOHP
- 'James'	CPne EOHP
hadiensis var. *tomentosus*	MOak
- - 'Carnegie'	EOHP
- green-leaved	EOHP
I - 'Variegata'	CPne
hilliardiae	CPne
hirtellus gold	MOak
- variegated (v)	MOak
'Lavender Moment'	CCtw
madagascariensis	CPne EOHP
- gold-leaved	EOHP
§ - 'Variegated Mintleaf' (v) ♀H1	CHal EOHP SHFr SPet SRms
menthol-scented, large-leaved	EOHP
menthol-scented, small-leaved	CStu EOHP MNHC
montanus	EOHP LToo
neochilus	LPhx
'Nico'	CSpe EOHP
§ *oertendahlii* ♀H1	CHal CPne EBak EOHP MOak SMur
- silver-leaved	EOHP
- 'Uvongo'	CPne
ornatus	EOHP MCCP MOak NHor NScw
- 'Pee Off'	EOHP
purpuratus	EOHP
rehmannii	EOHP
saccatus	CPne GFai
spicatus	EOHP
- 'Nelspruit'	EOHP
Swedish ivy	see *P. verticillatus, P. oertendahlii*

§ *thyrsoideus*	CHal ECre EOHP SBch
§ *verticillatus*	CHal EOHP SWal
Vick's plant	EOHP EUnu LSou
§ *welwitschii*	NHor
zatarhendii	CPne EOHP
zuluensis	CDoC CFee CHal CPne CSpe EOHP EShb MOak SUsu
- dark-leaved	EOHP
- 'Symphony'	CFee

Pleioblastus ✿ (Poaceae)

argenteostriatus	CTrC
§ - f. *glaber* (v)	MAsh MNHC
§ - 'Okinadake' (v)	EPla WViv
§ - f. *pumilus*	CDoC CSam EHoe ENot EPfP LPan LRHS MBlu MMoz MWgw MWht NHol SPla SPlb WFar WJun WNor WPat WPer WViv
auricomus	see *P. viridistriatus*
- 'Vagans'	see *Sasaella ramosa*
§ *chino*	EPla
- var. *argenteostriatus*	see *P. argenteostriatus* 'Okinadake'
- f. *aureostriatus* (v)	EPla LEdu MGos MMoz
- f. *elegantissimus*	CDoC CEnd CFir EBee ENBC EPla ERod MGos MMoz MWhi NMoo SBig SEND SPoG WJun WMoo WPGP WPnP
- var. *hisauchii*	EPla
'Gauntlettii'	see *P. argenteostriatus* f. *pumilus*
glaber 'Albostriatus'	see *Sasaella masamuneana* 'Albostriata'
gramineus	EPla WJun
§ *hindsii*	EPla ERod LPan MMoz NMoo SEND
§ *humilis*	ELan ENBC LPan SSto
- var. *pumilus*	see *P. argenteostriatus* f. *pumilus*
kongosanensis	EPla
'Aureostriatus' (v)	
linearis	CAbb CBcs CMCo EAmu EFul EPla ERod EShb LAst LPal MMoz MWht NMoo SBig WJun WMoo WPGP
longifimbriatus	see *Sinobambusa intermedia*
oleosus	EPla WJun
§ *pygmaeus*	More than 30 suppliers
§ - 'Distichus'	EFul EHul ENBC EPPr EPla LRHS MGos MMoz MMuc MWgw MWht NDlv NGdn NLar NMoo SSto WJun WMoo
§ - 'Mirrezuzume'	CPLG WFar
§ *simonii*	EBee EFul GBin LRHS MBNS MMoz MWhi MWht SPoG
§ - 'Variegatus' (v)	EPla MBar NGdn SPer WJun WPGP
variegatus (v) ♀H4	More than 30 suppliers
- 'Tsuboii' (v)	CAbb CBig CDoC CHen CKno CSBt ENBC EPPr EPla ERod GQui LAst LPJP LPal LRHS MBNS MBrN MBri MMoz MWhi MWht NMoo WFar WJun WMoo WMul WPGP WPnP
- var. *viridis*	see *P. argenteostriatus* f. *glaber*
§ *viridistriatus* ♀H4	More than 30 suppliers
- 'Chrysophyllus'	EPla MMoz WJun
- f. *variegatus* (v)	CHEx SAga SWvt WMoo

Pleione ✿ (Orchidaceae)

albiflora	CHdy
Alishan g.	CHdy CNic GCrs
- 'Merlin'	LBut NSpr
- 'Mount Fuji'	EPot LBut
- 'Soldier Blue'	LBut
Asama g.	CHdy
- 'Bittern'	LBut
- 'Red Grouse'	LBut
Askia g. **new**	LBut
aurita	EPot LBut NSpr
Bandai-san g.	EPot LBut

- 'Sand Grouse'	LBut
x *barbarae*	LBut NSpr
Barcena g.	CHdy LBut
Berapi g.	CHdy
- 'Purple Sandpiper'	LBut
Brigadoon g.	CHdy GCrs LBut NSpr NWCA
- 'Stonechat'	LBut
- 'Woodcock' **new**	LBut
Britannia g.	CHdy LBut
- 'Doreen'	EPot LBut NSpr
§ *bulbocodioides*	EPot ERos LBut NSpr
- Limprichtii Group	see *P. limprichtii*
- Pricei Group	see *P. formosana* Pricei Group
§ - 'Yunnan'	EPot NSpr
Burnsall g.	NSpr
Captain Hook g.	LBut
§ *chunii*	EFEx
x *confusa*	CHdy EPot LBut
Danan g.	LBut
Deriba g.	EPot LBut
Egmont g. 'Jay' **new**	LBut
Eiger g.	CHdy ERos LBut
- cream	ERos LBut
- 'Pinchbeck Diamond'	GCrs
El Pico g.	GCrs
- 'Goldcrest'	NSpr
- 'Pheasant'	LBut NSpr
Erebus g.	CHdy
- 'Quail'	LBut
Erh Hai g.	NSpr
Etna g.	CHdy GCrs LBut
Follifoot g. 'Princess Tiger'	NSpr
formosana ♀H2	CKob CStu ECho EFEx EPot ETow
	GBuc GCrs LEdu NCGa SIng WFar
	WPGP WPnP
- 'Achievement'	LBut
- Alba Group	CHdy ECho GCrs SIng WFar
- - 'Claire'	CHdy EPot ERos GCrs LBut NSpr
- - 'Snow Bunting'	LBut
- 'Avalanche'	LBut NSpr
- 'Blush of Dawn'	CHdy GCrs LBut NWCA
- 'Cairngorm'	NSpr
- 'Chen'	CHdy
- 'Christine Anne'	CHdy NSpr
- 'Eugenie'	CHdy
- 'Greenhill'	LBut
- 'Iris'	CHdy EPot
- 'Lilac Jubilee'	CHdy
- 'Lucy Diamond'	NSpr
- 'Lulu'	CHdy
- 'Pitlochry'	LBut
- 'Polar Sun'	CHdy
§ - Pricei Group	EPot ERos ETow
- - 'Oriental Grace'	CHdy LBut
- - 'Oriental Splendour'	CHdy LBut
- 'Red Spot'	EPot
- 'Snow White'	EPot GCrs LBut
forrestii	EFEx EPot
Fu Manchu g.	NSpr
Fuego g.	CHdy NSpr
Gerry Mundey g.	LBut NSpr
Giacomo Leopardi g.	NSpr
§ *grandiflora*	EPot LBut
Heathfield g.	NSpr
Hekla g.	CHdy ERos GCrs NSpr
- 'Partridge'	LBut
hookeriana	GCrs
humilis	LBut NSpr
Irazu g.	GCrs
- 'Wood Warbler' **new**	LBut
Jorullo g.	CHdy NSpr
- 'Long-tailed Tit'	LBut
Katla g.	CHdy
Katmai g.	LBut
Keith Rattray g. 'Kelty'	LBut
Kenya g.	LBut
Kilauea g.	EPot LBut
- 'Curlew'	LBut
Kohala g.	LBut
x *kohlsii*	NSpr
Krakatoa g.	NSpr
Kublai Khan g.	NSpr
§ *limprichtii* ♀H2	EFEx EPot ETow LBut
maculata	EFEx
Marco Polo g.	LBut NSpr
Marion Johnson g.	LBut
Masaya g.	LBut
Matupi g.	NSpr
Mawenzi g.	LBut
Mazama g.	LBut
Myojin g.	CHdy LBut NSpr
Novarupta g.	LBut
Orinoco g.	CHdy LBut
- 'Gemini'	LBut
Orizaba g.	LBut
Paricutin g.	LBut NSpr
Pavlof g.	LBut
pinkepankii	see *P. grandiflora*
Piton g.	CHdy EPot LBut
§ *pleionoides*	EPot LBut
- 'Blakeway-Phillips'	CHdy EPot
pogonioides misapplied	see *P. pleionoides*
pogonioides (Rolfe) Rolfe	see *P. bulbocodioides*
Quizapu g. 'Peregrine'	LBut
Rainier g.	LBut
Rakata g.	CHdy EPot
- 'Blackbird'	LBut
- 'Redwing'	LBut
- 'Shot Silk'	GCrs LBut NSpr
- 'Skylark'	LBut
Ruby Wedding g.	LBut
San Salvador g.	LBut
Sangay g.	LBut
Santorini g.	LBut
scopulorum	EFEx
Shantung g.	CFir EPot GCrs LBut NSpr
- 'Candyfloss'	NSpr
- 'Christine'	NSpr
- 'Ducat'	EPot LBut NSpr
- 'Gerry Mundey'	LBut NSpr
- 'Golden Jubilee'	NSpr
- 'Golden Plover'	LBut
- 'Gwen'	EPot
- 'Mikki'	NSpr
- 'Muriel Harberd' ♀H2	NSpr
- 'Pixie'	NSpr
- R6.48	NSpr
- R6.7	NSpr
- 'Ridgeway'	CHdy EPot LBut NSpr
- 'Silver Anniversary'	LBut
Shepherd's Warning g.	NSpr
'Gillian Clare'	
- 'Mary Buchanan'	NSpr
Sorea g.	LBut
Soufrière g.	LBut NSpr
- 'Sunrise'	NSpr
speciosa Ames & Schltr.	see *P. pleionoides*
Starbotton g.	NSpr
Stromboli g.	CHdy GCrs NSpr
- 'Fireball'	EPot GCrs LBut NSpr
- 'Robin'	LBut
Surtsey g.	EPot
- 'Stephanie Rose'	NSpr
Swaledale g.	NSpr
x *taliensis*	LBut
Tarawera g.	LBut
Tolima g.	CHdy CNic LBut NSpr
- 'Moorhen'	LBut
Tongariro g.	CHdy CPBP EPot ERos GCrs LBut
	NSpr
- 'Jackdaw'	CHdy EPot LBut NSpr
Versailles g.	CHdy EPot ERos NWCA

- 'Bucklebury' ♀H2	CNic EPot LBut
- 'Heron'	CHdy LBut
- 'Muriel Turner'	EPot
Vesuvius g.	CHdy EPot LBut
- 'Aphrodite'	EPot
- 'Grey Wagtail'	LBut
- 'Leopard'	LBut NSpr
- 'Phoenix'	EPot LBut NSpr
- 'Tawny Owl'	LBut
Vicky g.	NSpr
Volcanello g.	CHdy EPot GCrs LBut NSpr
- 'Honey Buzzard'	LBut
- 'Song Thrush'	LBut
'Wharfedale Pine Warbler'	LBut
new	
yunnanensis misapplied	see *P. bulbocodioides* 'Yunnan'
yunnanensis (Rolfe) Rolfe	CHdy EPot LBut
Zeus Weinstein g.	EPot LBut
- 'Desert Sands'	LBut

Pleomele see *Dracaena*

Pleurospermum (Apiaceae)

from Nepal HWJK 2329	WCru
aff. *amabile* BWJ 7886	WCru
benthamii B&SWJ 2988	WCru
brunonis	NChi
calcareum B&SWJ 8008	WCru

plum see *Prunus domestica*

Plumbago (Plumbaginaceae)

§ *auriculata* ♀H1-2	CBcs CCCN CHEx CRHN CSBt
	CTri CWSG EBak EBee ELan EPfP
	ERea EShb ISea MBri MLan MOak
	MRav NPal SDEP SOWG SPer SRms
	SYvo XPep
- var. *alba* ♀H1-2	CBcs CHEx CHal CRHN CSev EBak
	EBee EMil EPfP ERea EShb LRHS
	MLan MOak SOWG SYvo XPep
* - *aurea*	LIck
- 'Crystal Waters'	CDoC ELan
- dark blue-flowered	CSpe MJnS XPep
- 'Escapade Blue'	EShb
(Escapade Series)	
- 'Tobago Blue'	CPIN
capensis	see *P. auriculata*
§ *indica* ♀H1	CHal LRHS MJnS SOWG
- *rosea*	see *P. indica*
larpentiae	see *Ceratostigma*
	plumbaginoides

Plumeria (Apocynaceae)

sp.	ERea MJnS
§ *obtusa*	SDEP
rubra ♀H1	CCCN SDEP SOWG
- f. *acutifolia*	SOWG
'Siam Pink' **new**	SDEP
'Siam Rainbow' **new**	SDEP
'Singapore'	see *P. obtusa*

Poa (Poaceae)

alpina	CBig LAst NBre NGdn NJOw NLar
I - *nodosa*	CBig
chaixii	CBig EBee EHoe EPPr EPla NLar
	NNor SLPl SWal WFoF
cita	CBig LRav WPnP
colensoi	CBrm CKno CRez EBee EHoe EPPr
	MAvo NFor WPnP
eminens from Magadan,	EMan EPPr
Siberia	
x *jemtlandica*	EHoe EPPr
labillardierei	CBrm CKno CMea CWCL EBee
	EBrs ECha EGle EHoe EPPr GGar
	MAvo NBid SPer SPoG SUsu WDyG
	WMoo WPrP XPep

rodwayi	CBig
trivialis	CRWN

Podalyria (Papilionaceae)

calyptrata	SPlb
sericea	SPlb

Podocarpus (Podocarpaceae)

acutifolius	CBcs CDoC ECou EPla GGar MBar
	STre
- (f)	ECou
- (m)	ECou
alpinus R. Br. ex Hook. f.	NHol
new	
andinus	see *Prumnopitys andina*
'Autumn Shades' (m)	ECou
'Blaze' (f)	CBcs CDoC CRob ECho ECou
	LBuc LCon LLin NHol NLar SCoo
	SLim SPoG WEve
chilinus	see *P. salignus*
'Chocolate Box' (f)	ECou
'County Park Fire'PBR (f)	CBcs CDoC CKen CRob CWSG
	ECho ECou ENot EOrn EPfP LCon
	LLin MAsh MGos SCoo SLim SPoG
	SWvt WEve WFar WGor
'County Park Treasure' **new**	ECou
cunninghamii	CBcs ECou WCwm
- 'Kiwi' (f)	CBcs ECou
- 'Roro' (m)	CBcs CDoC ECou LLin
cunninghamii x *nivalis*	ECou
(f)	
dacrydioides	see *Dacrycarpus dacrydioides*
elongatus	CTrC IDee
'Flame'	CDoC ECho ECou EPla NEgg WEve
'Havering' (f)	CDoC ECou
henkelii	CTrC EShb GGar
'Jill' (f)	ECou
latifolius	ECou EShb IDee
lawrencei	ECho EHul GGar
- (f)	ECou MBar
- 'Alpine Lass' (f)	ECou
- 'Blue Gem' (f)	CDoC CRob ECho ECou EOrn EPla
	IArd LCon LLin LRHS MAsh MBar
	MGos NHol SCoo SLim SPoG WFar
- 'Kiandra'	ECou
- 'Red Tip'	CDoC ECho GBin LLin MAsh SCoo
	SLim STre
'Macho' (m)	ECou
macrophyllus	CHEx EOrn NLar SAPC SArc SMad
	STre WFar
- (m)	ECou
- 'Aureus'	CBcs
'Maori Prince' (m)	CDoC ECou EPla LLin
nivalis	CBcs CDul CMac CTrC ECho ECou
	EOrn EPla GGar LLin MBar SCoo
	SRms
- 'Arthur' (m)	ECou
- 'Bronze'	CDoC EPla WEve
- 'Christmas Lights' (f)	CKen ECou
- 'Clarence' (m)	ECou LLin
- 'Cover Girl'	CRob
- 'Green Queen' (f)	ECou
- 'Hikurangi'	CDoC
- 'Jack's Pass' (m)	ECho ECou
- 'Kaweka' (m)	ECou
- 'Kilworth Cream' (v)	CBcs CDoC CRob ECho ECou EPla
	GTSp LBuc LCon LLin MAsh MGos
	NHol NLar SCoo SLim SWvt WEve
- 'Little Lady' (f)	ECou
- 'Livingstone' (f)	ECou
- 'Lodestone' (m)	ECou
- 'Moffat' (f)	CBcs CDoC ECou LLin
- 'Otari' (m)	CBcs ECho ECou LLin NLar WEve
- 'Park Cover'	ECou
- 'Princess' (f)	ECou
- 'Ruapehu' (m)	CDoC ECou EPla

	- 'Trompenburg'	NLar
	nubigenus	CBcs
	'Orangeade' (f)	CBcs ECho MGos NLar
	'Red Embers'	ECho NEgg
*	'Redtip'	ECho SLim
	'Rough Creek'	LLin
§	*salignus* ♀H3	CAbb CBcs CBrd CDoC CDul
		CHEx CPLG EPfP EPla IDee ISea
		SAPC SArc SLim WFar WPic WSHC
	- (f)	ECou
	- (m)	ECou
	spicatus	see *Prumnopitys taxifolia*
	'Spring Sunshine' (f)	CBcs CDoC ECou EPla LLin NLar
		WEve
	totara	CBcs CTrC ECho ECou GGar LEdu
		STre WFar
	- 'Albany Gold'	CTrC IDee
	- 'Aureus'	CBcs CDoC ECho ECou EPla MBar
		SCoo SHBN WEve WFar
	- 'Pendulus'	CDoC ECou
	'Young Rusty' (f)	CBcs CDoC ECou EPla GTSp LLin
		MAsh MGos WEve

Podophyllum (Berberidaceae)

	aurantiocaule	WCot
§	*delavayi*	CBct CFir CLAP EBla ECho GEdr
		MDun NLar WCot WCru
	difforme	CLAP GEdr MGol WCot WCru
	emodi	see *P. hexandrum*
	- var. *chinense*	see *P. hexandrum* 'Chinense'
§	*hexandrum*	More than 30 suppliers
	- BWJ 7908	WCru
	- SDR 2948	GKev
§	- 'Chinense'	CBro CLAP CRow EBee EBla EHyt
		EMan GBuc GEdr GKev IBlr LEdu
		SMad WCru
	- 'Chinese White'	CFwr WCot
	- 'Majus'	CFir CLAP WCot WHal
	'Kaleidoscope' (v) **new**	NBhm
	peltatum	CArn CBct CBro CLAP COld CRow
		EBee EBla ECho GBBs GEdr GPoy
		IBlr LEdu LPhx MLul NMyG NSti
		WCru WFar WPGP WPnP
	pleianthum	CBct CDes CLAP GEdr WCot
		WCru
	- short	WCru
	veitchii	see *P. delavayi*
	versipelle	CLAP WCot WCru

Podranea (Bignoniaceae)

	brycei	CRHN EShb
§	*ricasoliana*	CHEx CPIN CRHN ERea EShb
		MJnS SOWG XPep
	- 'Comtesse Sarah'	XPep

Pogonarthria (Gramineae)

	squarrosa **new**	CBig

Pogonatherum (Poaceae)

§	*paniceum*	LRHS MBri
	saccharoideum	see *P. paniceum*

Pogostemon (Lamiaceae)

	from An Veleniki Herb Farm, Pennsylvania	CArn
§	*cablin*	GPoy MGol MSal
	patchouly	see *P. cablin*

Polemonium ✿ (Polemoniaceae)

	acutiflorum	see *P. caeruleum* subsp. *villosum*
	acutifolium var. *nipponicum*	see *P. caeruleum* var. *nipponicum*
	ambervicsii	see *P. pauciflorum* subsp. *binckleyi*
	'Apricot Beauty'	see *P. carneum* 'Apricot Delight'
N	*archibaldiae* ♀H4	NBir SRms

§	*boreale*	EBee ECho MBow NLRH NPol
		SBch SBla SPet SWvt WFar WMoo
	- 'Heavenly Habit'	EBee LSou NPro NRnb NVic SHGN
		SMar WWeb
§	*brandegeei* Greene	SAga SHGN SHop WPer
	- subsp. *mellitum*	see *P. brandegeei* Greene
	Bressingham Purple = 'Polbress'	CBow EBrs MMHG WFar
	caeruleum misapplied Himalayan	see *P. cashmerianum*
§	*caeruleum*	More than 30 suppliers
	- 'Bambino Blue'	LRHS NBre SWvt WPer
	- 'Blue Bell'	ELau
	- Brise d'Anjou = 'Blanjou'PBR (v)	More than 30 suppliers
	- subsp. *caeruleum* f. *album*	More than 30 suppliers
I	- f. *dissectum*	EBee NPol
	- 'Golden Showers' (v)	NPro
	- var. *grandiflorum*	see *P. caeruleum* subsp. *himalayanum*
§	- subsp. *himalayanum*	WMoo WPer
	- 'Humile'	see *P.* 'Northern Lights'
	- 'Idylle'	EMan EMon MAvo NCot
	- 'Larch Cottage' (v)	NLar
§	- var. *nipponicum*	EBee GBin GIBF NPol WPer
	- 'Sky Blue'	NRnb
	- 'Snow and Sapphires' (v)	CBct EBee LAst LRHS MBNS MBri
		MCCP MSte NLar NPer NPri NTHB
		SPav SPoG SRkn STes SVil WWeb
§	- subsp. *villosum*	NPol
	- subsp. *vulgare*	NPol
	californicum	NPol
	carneum	CTri CWan ECha EGle EMan GMaP
		LAst MCCP MNFA MNrw MTho
		NJOw NPol SECG STes WAul
		WCAu WFar WMoo WPer
§	- 'Apricot Delight'	EBee ECho EGle EMag GBri GMac
		LAst LRHS MCCP MNrw MTis
		NBPC NBir NDov NGHP NGdn
		NJOw NPol NPri SGar SIde SPoG
		STes WBVN WHer WPer WPnP
		WWeb
I	*cashmerianum*	EPPr GAbr LRHS NBur WFar WHen
		WOut
I	- *album*	WBor
	chartaceum	CGra LTwo
	'Churchills'	CBre EBee EChP WPGP WPrP
§	'Dawn Flight'	WFar
	delicatum	see *P. pulcherrimum* Hook. subsp. *delicatum*
	'Eastbury Purple'	CElw MAvo
	'Elworthy Amethyst'	CElw EBee EMan MAvo NPol SBch
		WPGP
	eximium	NBre
	flavum	see *P. foliosissimum* var. *flavum*
	foliosissimum misapplied	see *P. archibaldiae*
	foliosissimum A. Gray	CSec EBee IGor MNrw WPer
	- var. *albiflorum*	see *P. foliosissimum* var. *alpinum*
§	- var. *alpinum*	NBir NPol
	- 'Cottage Cream'	CBre EBee NPol
§	- var. *flavum*	NPol
	- var. *foliosissimum*	EWes NPol
	- 'White Spirit'	NPol
	'Glebe Cottage Lilac'	CCge CElw CHar CMil EBee MAvo
		NBir SBch WPGP
	grandiflorum	NPol
	'Hannah Billcliffe'	CDes CElw EBee EWes MBrN
		NCot NPol WPGP
	'Heavenly Blue'	ECtt
§	'Hopleys'	EChP EMan GBar GBri GCal IFro
		NCot NGdn WFar
	x *jacobaea*	CDes EBee EMan WCot WPGP
		WTin
	'Katie Daley'	see *P.* 'Hopleys'
	kiushianum	EBee

'Lace Towers' — NSti
§ 'Lambrook Mauve' ♀H4 — More than 30 suppliers
liniflorum — NBre
'Mary Mottram' — NPol
mellitum — see *P. brandegeei* Greene
'North Tyne' — EBee NBid NChi NPol
§ 'Northern Lights' — CDes CSev EBee EGle EMan EMon EPPr EWes GBri GMac MAvo MBnl MBri MNFA MNrw NCot NDov NPol NSti SBch STes SUsu WFar WMoo WPGP
'Norwell Mauve' — MNrw
occidentale subsp. *occidentale* — NPol
'Pam' (v) — CBow EBee NPol WSPU
§ *pauciflorum* — CEnt CHrt CStu EBee ECtt EHrv EShb IFro LAst LRHS MNFA MNrw MTho NBid NBir SHFr SYvo WCAu WFar WMoo WPer WWeb WWhi WWlt
§ – subsp. *hinckleyi* — NChi NCot NPol SBch SGar
§ – subsp. *pauciflorum* — LRHS NPol SGar SPav WSan
– silver-leaved — see *P. pauciflorum* subsp. *pauciflorum*
– 'Sulphur Trumpets' — ECtt LSou MAvo SPav SWvt WGwG
– subsp. *typicum* — see *P. pauciflorum* subsp. *pauciflorum*
§ 'Pink Beauty' — CBre ELan EPPr EPfP LRHS NBre NCot NPol SUsu WWhi
pulchellum Salisb. — see *P. reptans*
pulchellum Turcz. — see *P. caeruleum*
pulcherrimum misapplied — see *P. boreale*
– 'Tricolor' — see *P. boreale*
pulcherrimum Hook. — NBro SPoG WLin WPer WWeb
I – *album* — GKev
§ – subsp. *delicatum* — MTho NPol
§ – subsp. *pulcherrimum* — GKev LTwo NPol
§ *reptans* — CAgr CArn CHea EMag GBar GBri GPoy MHer MSal NBro NPol SIng WAul WFar WMoo WOut WPer WPtf WWeb WWye
– 'Album' — see *P. reptans* 'Virginia White'
– 'Blue Ice' — NPol
– 'Blue Pearl' — CElw CMea EBee EChP ELan EMan EPfP EShb LHop LRHS MBri MLLN MNrw NBro NCob NFor NGdn NHol NPol NPri SGar SPer SPla SWal WFar WHen WSan WWeb
– 'Firmament' — EBee WPGP
– 'Pink Dawn' — EBee EChP ELan EPfP MLLN MNFA MWgw NCob NGdn SPla SPoG STes
* – 'Sky Blue' — NBro
– 'Stairway to Heaven' new — CAbP CBow CSpe EBee ENot EPPr EWes LSou LTwo MBNS MBnl MLLN MNrw MTis NBro NCot NPol NSti SPoG STes WBor WCMO WCot WLin
§ – 'Virginia White' — CBre CDes CElw CMea CSev EBee LRHS MBnl NChi NPol SUsu WFar
– 'White Pearl' — EShb NPri WBVN
'Ribby' — NPol
richardsonii misapplied — see *P.* 'Northern Lights'
richardsonii Graham — see *P. boreale*
'Sapphire' — CBre EBrs ELan EMan EMon MBrN NPol WOut
scopulinum — see *P. pulcherrimum* Hook. subsp. *delicatum*
'Sonia's Bluebell' — CDes CElw CMil EBee ECGP EMan EPPr EWes MAvo MBnl MDKP MNrw MSte NCot NDov NPol NSti SBch SUsu WPGP
'Theddingworth' — MAvo NPol WFar
vanbruntiae — EBee NPol
viscosum — GBuc GKev LBMP NPol SGar SYvo WHen

– 'Blue Whirl' — MGol
– f. *leucanthum* — NPol
yezoense — CBre GBri MNrw NBre NPol WFar WPnP
– var. *hidakanum* — EBee EShb GIBF NPol
– 'Midnight Rain' new — CSpe
– 'Purple Rain' — CFwr CHar CSpe EBee EBrs EHrv EMan ENor EPfP EShb EWes GBuc GMaP LSRN MCCP MLLN MNrw MTis NPol SPoG STes WFar WMoo WWhi

Polianthes (Agavaceae)
nelsonii — CFir
tuberosa ♀H1-2 — CBcs CSpe CStu ECho LRHS
– 'The Pearl' (d) — CDes WHil WPGP

Poliomintha (Lamiaceae)
bustamanta — NBir
incana — EBee

Poliothyrsis (Flacourtiaceae)
sinensis ♀H4 — CAbP CPne CTho EPfP GIBF LAst LRHS MBri NLar WPGP

Pollia (Commelinaceae)
japonica — CMCN EMan

Polygala (Polygalaceae)
alpina — WLin
calcarea — ECho LTwo WAbe
– Bulley's form — LRHS
– 'Lillet' ♀H4 — EAEE ECho EHyt EWes LHop LRHS LTwo NLAp NLar NMen NSla WFar WPat
– 'Susan's Blush' — NLAp
chamaebuxus ♀H4 — CBcs EBee ECho GCrs LSou MDKP MGos NDlv NLAp NLar NSla SRms WBVN WSHC
I – *alba* — LBee LRHS LSou NLar SMur WAbe
§ – var. *grandiflora* ♀H4 — CBcs CFir CMea CWCL ECho EPfP EPot GEdr GGar GKev LBee MAsh MBar MDun MGos NHol NLAp NMen NSla SBla SMur SPoG WAbe WBVN WFar WPat WSHC
– 'Kamniski' — ECho LBuc NLar WLin
– 'Loibl' — EPot WLin
– 'Purpurea' — see *P. chamaebuxus* var. *grandiflora*
– var. *rhodoptera* — SBla
– 'Rhodoptera' — see *P. chamaebuxus* var. *grandiflora*
§ × *dalmaisiana* ♀H1 — CAbb CCCN CHEx CHll CRHN CSpe EBee SBla SBrw SGar SMur WAbe WBor WCFE
'Domino' — NLAp
myrtifolia — CPLG CSec EMil GFai MPRe SGar SHFr SMrm SPlb WWye XPep
– 'Grandiflora' — see *P.* × *dalmaisiana*
'Rosengarten' — SBla
tenuifolia — CArn
vayredae — NLar
virgata — CSec ERea EShb

Polygonatum ✿ (Convallariaceae)
ACE 1753 — EPot
acuminatifolium — EBla
altelobatum — EBla
– B&SWJ 286 — WCru
§ *biflorum* — More than 30 suppliers
– dwarf — EBla EPla IBlr WCMO
canaliculatum — see *P. biflorum*
cirrhifolium — CDes CFir CLAP CMdw CPom EBee EBla ELan GBin MDun WCMO WCot WCru WHil WPGP
commutatum — see *P. biflorum*

'Corsley'	CPou
cryptanthum	EBla WCru
curvistylum	CAvo CBct CLAP CPom CStu EBla ECha EGle EHrv EPPr GEdr IBlr LPhx NLar NRya WAbe WCru WFar WViv
- CLD 761	GEdr
cyrtonema misapplied	see *Disporopsis pernyi*
cyrtonema Hua	CLAP LEdu
- B&SWJ 271	WCru
falcatum misapplied	see *P. humile*
§ *falcatum* A. Gray	CLyd EBee EBla EGle EPot IBlr NOak WHer
- B&SWJ 1077	WCru
- silver-striped	EBee
- 'Variegatum'	see *P. odoratum* var. *pluriflorum* 'Variegatum'
'Falcon'	see *P. humile*
filipes	WCMO WCru
fuscum	WCMO WCru
geminiflorum	CLAP EBla IBlr SOkd WFar
- McB 2448	GEdr
giganteum	see *P. biflorum*
glaberrimum	EBla WCot
'Golden Gift'	SBla
§ *graminifolium*	CBct CLAP CPom EBee EBla ECho EPot ERos GEdr MSte NMen SCnR WCMO WCot WCru
- G-W&P 803	IPot
§ *hirtum*	CBct CLAP CPom EBla ECho EMon EPla IBlr WCru WFar
- BM 7012	EBee
- dwarf	WCMO WCot
hookeri	More than 30 suppliers
- McB 1413	GEdr
§ *humile*	CBct CLAP EBee EBla ECho EHrv EHyt ELan EMan EPfP ERos GBri GCal GGar IBlr LAst NJOw NMen SMac SMad SUsu WAul WCot WCru WFar WHil WWye
§ x *hybridum* ♀H4	More than 30 suppliers
- 'Betberg'	CBct CLAP CRow EBla ECha EHrv NBPC NBir WCot
- 'Flore Pleno' (d)	EBla WHer
- 'Nanum'	EBla
§ - 'Striatum' (v)	More than 30 suppliers
- 'Variegatum'	see *P. x hybridum* 'Striatum'
- 'Wakehurst'	EBla EHrv
inflatum	EBla ECho WCru
- B&SWJ 922	WCru
involucratum	ECho WCru
japonicum	see *P. odoratum*
kingianum	WCMO
- yellow-flowered B&SWJ 6562	WCru
'Langthorns Variegated' (v)	ELan
lasianthum	WCru
latifolium	see *P. hirtum*
leptophyllum KEKE 844 new	GEdr
maximowiczii	GCal GIBF
multiflorum misapplied	see *P. x hybridum*
multiflorum L.	CBcs CDes CElw CRow CSBt CWCL EBee ECha EPla EWsh GAbr LRHS MAvo NEgg NVic SAga SBig SEND SMer SPlb SPoG SRms SWal WBor WCAu
- *giganteum* hort.	see *P. biflorum*
* *nanum* 'Variegatum' (v)	CBcs ECho
nodosum	EBla WCru
* 'Nymans Variety'	WHil
obtusifolium	EBee EBla
§ *odoratum* ♀H4	CAby CAvo CBct CBro CPom CRow CSWP EBee EBla EBrs ECho EHrv ELau EPfP EPla GIBF GMaP

	IBlr MSal NBid NLar NRya WCru WFar WHil WPnP
§ - dwarf	ECho IBlr LEdu
- 'Flore Pleno' (d) ♀H4	CDes CLAP CRow EBee EBla ECha ECho EHrv EPla EPot ERou IBlr SBla SCnR SMHy WCMO WCot WHil WHoo WPGP WPnP
- 'Grace Barker'	see *P. x hybridum* 'Striatum'
- var. *pluriflorum*	GBuc IBlr
§ - - 'Variegatum' (v) ♀H4	More than 30 suppliers
- 'Red Stem'	WCru
- 'Silver Wings' (v)	CLAP EBla ECha EHrv ERou NBid NBir
officinale	see *P. odoratum*
oppositifolium	EBla WFar
- B&SWJ 2537	WCru
§ *orientale*	CLAP EBla ECho GEdr WCMO WCot
pluriflorum	see *P. graminifolium*
polyanthemum	see *P. orientale*
prattii	EBla SOkd
- CLD 325	GEdr
pubescens	WCru
pumilum	see *P. odoratum* dwarf
punctatum	EBee LEdu WFar
- B&SWJ 2395	CBct EBla WCru
aff. *punctatum* B&SWJ 6599 new	WCru
roseum	CDes EBee GEdr WHer WHil WPGP
* *rubrum* new	IPot
sewerzowii	EBla EPla
sibiricum	CAvo EBla GEdr IBlr WCot WCru
- DJHC 600	CDes
stenophyllum	EBla WCru
stewartianum	CLAP EBee EPPr IBlr
tonkinense HWJ 551	WCru
verticillatum	CAvo CBct CBro CFwr CRow EBla EBrs ECha EPfP EPla IBlr LEdu MNrw MTho NMyG NWCA SMad WCMO WCot WCru WFar WPGP
- 'Himalayan Giant'	EBee EBla ECho IPot WCMO
* - *rubrum*	CArn CBct CLAP CRow EBla EGle EHrv EPPr EPla GEdr IBlr IPot LEdu LPhx MAvo MSte MTho NBid NGby WGCot WHil WPrP
- 'Serbian Dwarf'	EBee EBla ECho IPot WCMO
aff. *verticillatum*	EMon
zanlanscianense	CBct EBla WCMO WCru

Polygonum ✿ (*Polygonaceae*)

affine	see *Persicaria affinis*
amplexicaule	see *Persicaria amplexicaulis*
aubertii	see *Fallopia baldschuanica*
aviculare	CArn
baldschuanicum	see *Fallopia baldschuanica*
bistorta	see *Persicaria bistorta*
capitatum	see *Persicaria capitata*
compactum	see *Fallopia japonica* var. *compacta*
equisetiforme hort.	see *P. scoparium*
filiforme	see *Persicaria virginiana*
forrestii	EBee
hydropiper 'Fastigiatum'	CArn EUnu
longisetum	see *Persicaria longiseta*
molle	see *Persicaria mollis*
multiflorum	see *Fallopia multiflora*
odoratum	see *Persicaria odorata*
polystachyum	see *Persicaria wallichii*
runciforme	see *Persicaria runcinata*
§ *scoparium*	CBcs CBrm CRow EMan EPPr EPla SDys SIng WCot WDyG WFar WTin
tinctorium	see *Persicaria tinctoria*
weyrichii	see *Persicaria weyrichii*

Polylepis (Rosaceae)

australis	LEdu LRav MBri SMad WCot WCru WPGP
pauta	WPGP

Polymnia (Asteraceae)

sonchifolia	EUnu LEdu
uvedalia	see *Smallanthus uvedalius*

Polypodium ✿ (Polypodiaceae)

aureum 'Glaucum' **new**	WCot
australe	see *P. cambricum*
§ **cambricum**	EFer WCot WFib WTin
§ - 'Barrowii'	CLAP WAbe WFib
- 'Cambricum' ♀H4	CBgR CLAP WAbe WWye
- 'Cristatum'	CLAP NBid WFib
- (Cristatum Group) 'Grandiceps Forster'	CLAP
- - 'Grandiceps Fox' ♀H4	WFib
- 'Hornet'	WFib
- 'Macrostachyon'	CLAP EFer WFib
- 'Oakleyae'	SMHy
- 'Omnilacerum Oxford'	CLAP WWye
- 'Prestonii'	WAbe WCot WFib
- Pulcherrimum Group	CLAP WAbe
- - 'Pulchritudine'	CLAP WAbe
- - 'Pulcherrimum Addison'	WAbe WWye
- 'Richard Kayse'	CDes CLAP EBee WAbe WCot WFib WPGP WWye
- (Semilacerum Group) 'Carew Lane'	WFib
- - 'Robustum'	WFib
- 'Whilharris' ♀H4	CLAP WAbe
I x **coughlinii** bifid	WFib
glycyrrhiza	CLAP GPoy WFib
- bifid	see *Polypodium* x *coughlinii* bifid
- 'Longicaudatum' ♀H4	CLAP EBee EMon WAbe WCot WFib WSPU WWye
- 'Malahatense'	CLAP
- 'Malahatense' (sterile)	WAbe
interjectum	CBgR CLAP CWCL EFer MAsh MMoz NVic WAbe WPnP
- 'Cornubiense' ♀H4	CLAP EFer EMon GCal GEdr MMoz NBir NHol NVic WAbe WTin WWye
- 'Glomeratum Mullins'	WFib
x **mantoniae**	WFib WIvy
- 'Bifidograndiceps'	NBid WFib
scouleri	CLAP NBro
vulgare	More than 30 suppliers
- 'Bifidocristatum'	see *P. vulgare* 'Bifidomultifidum'
§ - 'Bifidomultifidum'	CLAP CRez CWCL EMon GBin GEdr LLWP MAsh MCCP NHol NLar SPla WCot WOut
* - 'Congestum Cristatum'	SRms
- 'Cornubiense Grandiceps'	SRms WIvy
* - 'Cornubiense Multifidum'	EBee WCot
- 'Elegantissimum'	WFib
- 'Ramosum Hillman'	WFib
- 'Trichomanoides Backhouse'	CLAP GCal WAbe WFib

Polypompholyx see *Utricularia*

Polyscias (Araliaceae)

'Elegans'	MBri
fruticosa	MBri
scutellaria 'Pennockii' (v)	MBri

Polystichum ✿ (Dryopteridaceae)

BWJ 8182 from China	WCru
acrostichoides	CFwr CLAP CMHG CPrp CRez EBee ECGR EFtx EPPr ERod GCal GEdr GQui IBal NLar NMyG SNut

aculeatum ♀H4	More than 30 suppliers
I - Densum Group	EFer
- Grandiceps Group	EFer
- 'Portia'	WFib
andersonii	CLAP CWCL NHol
braunii	CBcs CBgR CMHG CWCL EFtx EGol GBin GMaP MLan MMoz NLar NOGN WFib WPnP
caryotideum	see *Cyrtomium caryotideum*
falcatum	see *Cyrtomium falcatum*
fortunei	see *Cyrtomium fortunei*
imbricans	CLAP SArc
makinoi	CLAP CRez NHol WFib
mohrioides	CLAP
munitum ♀H4	More than 30 suppliers
- 'Incisum'	GCal
neolobatum	NVic WFib
polyblepharum ♀H4	More than 30 suppliers
proliferum (R. Br.) C. Presl	CLAP EAmu EFtx GCal LAst SBig WFib
* - **plumosum**	CFwr NEgg NOak
richardii	SBig
rigens	CBgR CElw CFwr CLAP CPrp EBee EFer GCal LSou MAsh NDlv NHol NLar NOGN SNut SRms SRot WCru WFib
§ **setiferum** ♀H4	More than 30 suppliers
§ - Acutilobum Group	CBcs CFwr CLAP CMHG CPrp CWCL ECha EFtx GMaP NHol SDix SMad SPer STes WCru WMoo WPGP WPnP WPrP
- Congestum Group	CBgR CPrp GBin MMoz NCGa NHol SRms WFib
- 'Congestum'	CFwr CLAP EBee EFtx ELan EPfP ERod GCal LRHS MAsh MDun NBir NFor NMyG NSti SMac SNut SPla SPoG SSto WGor WMoo WPrP
- 'Cristatopinnulum'	CFwr CLAP WPGP
- Cristatum Group	CLAP EHrv SRms
- Cruciatum Group	CLAP
- - 'Cruciatum Kaye'	CLAP
- Divisilobum Group	CBcs CElw CFee CLAP CMHG CRow EFer ELan EMon LPBA MGos MMoz NHol NVic SBla SPla SRms STre WAbe WAul WFar WFib WHoo WIvy WPGP WTin WWhi WWye
- - 'Dahlem'	CDoC CFwr CLAP EBee ECha EFer EFtx ELan EMon GMaP MDun MMoz MSte NFor NHol NMoo SNut SPoG SSto WAbe WFib WMoo WPnP
- - 'Divisilobum Densum' ♀H4	CBgR CLAP EHrv EPfP NBir NOrc SNut
- - 'Divisilobum Iveryanum' ♀H4	CLAP NHol SRms WFib
- - 'Divisilobum Laxum'	CLAP
- - 'Herrenhausen'	More than 30 suppliers
- - 'Mrs Goffey'	WFib
- Foliosum Group	EFer
- 'Foliosum'	CLAP
- 'Gracile'	NBir
- 'Grandiceps'	CLAP EFer ELan
- Green Lace = 'Gracillimum'	GBin
- 'Hamlet'	WFib
- 'Helena'	WFib
- 'Hirondelle'	SRms
- Lineare Group	CLAP NEgg NHol WFib
- Multilobum Group	CLAP SRms WFib
- 'Othello'	WFib
- Perserratum Group	NBid WFib
- 'Plumo-Densum'	see *P. setiferum* 'Plumosomultilobum'
- 'Plumosodensum'	see *P. setiferum* 'Plumosomultilobum'

- Plumosodivisilobum Group	CLAP CMil CRow ECha EGol EHyt LSou NBid SPla WAbe WCru WFib
- - 'Baldwinii'	CLAP WFib
- - 'Bland'	WFib
§ - 'Plumosomultilobum'	CFwr CLAP CPrp CWCL EBee EFtx EPPr EPfP GBin LAst LRHS MAsh MBnl MMoz MWgw NBir NCGa NEgg NSti SMac SMer SNut SPla WBVN WBor WCot WFib WMoo WPnP WPrP
- Plumosum Group	CBgR CLAP CMHG CSpe EChP EFer EFtx NEgg NOrc SAPC SArc SRot
- - dwarf	CSBt
* - *plumosum grande* 'Moly'	CLAP SRms
- 'Proliferum Group	see *P. setiferum* Acutilobum Group
* - 'Proliferum Wollaston'	CBcs CFwr CPrp MMoz NRib SNut SSto WWeb
- 'Pulcherrimum Bevis' ♀H4	CLAP GBin NBid SHFr WFib WPGP
* - 'Ramopinnatum'	CLAP
- 'Revolvens Lowe'	CLAP
- Rotundatum Group	CLAP
- - 'Cristatum'	CLAP
- - 'Rotundatum Ramosum'	CLAP
- 'Smith's Cruciate'	CFwr CLAP GBin MWat WFib
- 'Wakeleyanum'	SRms
N - 'Wollaston'	CFwr CLAP GBin MAsh NEgg NHol NLar SMac WAbe
tsussimense ♀H4	More than 30 suppliers
vestitum	CLAP CTrC SBig

Polyxena (Hyacinthaceae)

corymbosa	CStu LBow WCot
§ *ensifolia*	CMon ECho ERos LBow
longituba **new**	EDif
odorata	CLyd CStu ECho WCot
pygmaea	see *P. ensifolia*

Pomaderris (Rhamnaceae)

apetala	CPLG
elliptica	CPLG ECou

pomegranate see *Punica granatum*

Poncirus (Rutaceae)

§ *trifoliata*	CAgr CArn CBcs CDoC EBee ELan EPfP EZes IDee IMGH LRHS MAsh MBlu MJnn MRav NEgg SBrw SPer SPoG WBVN WDin WFar WPGP WPat WSHC WTel
- 'Flying Dragon'	EZes SMad
- 'Frost' **new**	EZes
- 'Leatherhead' **new**	EZes

Ponerorchis (Orchidaceae)

graminifolia **new**	WWst

Pontederia (Pontederiaceae)

cordata ♀H4	CBen CDWL CHEx CRow CWat EHon ELan EMFW EPfP LNCo LPBA MCCP NPer SCoo SPlb SWat WFar WMAq WPnP WWpP
- f. *albiflora*	CDWL CRow CWat EMFW EPfP LPBA MCCP NLar WMAq WWpP
- 'Blue Spires'	CDWL
§ - var. *lancifolia*	CRow EMFW EPfP LPBA MCCP NPer SWat WTin WWpP
- 'Pink Pons'	CRow NLar
lanceolata	see *P. cordata* var. *lancifolia*

Populus ✿ (Salicaceae)

x *acuminata*	WMou

alba	CCVT CDoC CDul CLnd CSBt CTho CTri CWib ECrN LBuc MBar NBee NWea SBLw SHBN SPer WDin WMou WOrn
- 'Bolleana'	see *P. alba* f. *pyramidalis*
- 'Nivea'	SBLw
§ - f. *pyramidalis*	CBcs SRms WMou
§ - 'Raket'	CCVT CLnd CTho ECrN ELan NWea SBLw SPer
- 'Richardii'	CDul CLnd EBee ECtt MAsh MBar SPer WCot WFar WMou
- Rocket	see *P. alba* 'Raket'
alba x *grandidentata*	WMou
§ 'Balsam Spire' (f) ♀H4	CDoC CDul CLnd CTho NWea WDin WMou
§ *balsamifera*	CCVT CDoC CTho CTri ECrN MGos NWea SBLw SHBN SPer SRms WCot WDin WFar WWll
- 'Vita Sackville West' **new**	MBlu
x *berolinensis*	CDoC
x *canadensis*	ECrN SBLw
- 'Aurea' ♀H4	CDoC CDul CLnd CTho CWib ENot LRHS MDun MGos MRav SPer WDin WFar WMou
- 'Eugenei' (m)	CTho
- 'Robusta' (m)	CDoC CDul CLnd CTri EMil LBuc NWea WDin WMou
- 'Serotina' (m)	CDoC CDul ECrN WDin WMou
x *canadensis* 'Aurea' x *jackii* 'Aurora'	MRav WMou
x *candicans* misapplied	see *P.* x *jackii*
x *canescens*	CDoC CLnd ECrN SBLw WDin WMou
- 'De Moffart' (m)	SBLw
- 'Tower'	WMou
x *generosa* 'Beaupré'	CTho LBuc WDin WMou
§ x *jackii* (f)	NEgg WDin
- 'Aurora' (f/v)	CBcs CBrm CCVT CDul CLnd CSBt CTrG CTrw ELan LBuc MBar MBri MGos MMuc MNHC MRav MWat NBee NBlu NWea SBLw SHBN SPer SPoG SRms WDin WFar WHar WJas
lasiocarpa ♀H4	CDoC CDul CEnd CPLG CSdC CTho ELan EPfP EPla IDee MBlu MRav SBLw SLPl WMou WPGP
* - var. *tibetica*	WMou
maximowiczii	WMou
nigra	CDul CLnd EPfP NWea WDin
- (f)	ECrN SLPl
- (m)	SLPl
- subsp. *betulifolia*	CCVT CDul CTho CWan LBuc MDun NWea WDin WMou
- - (f)	WMou
- - (m)	WMou
N - 'Italica' (m) ♀H4	CCVT CDoC CDul CLnd CSBt CTho CTri CWib ECrN ELan LBuc MGos NBee NWea SBLw SHBN SPer SRms WDin WOrn
- 'Italica Aurea'	see *P. nigra* 'Lombardy Gold'
§ - 'Lombardy Gold' (m)	CEnd MBlu
- 'Pyramidalis'	see *P. nigra* 'Italica'
simonii 'Fastigiata'	WMou
- 'Obtusata'	WMou
szechuanica	WMou
tacamahaca	see *P. balsamifera*
'Tacatricho 32'	see *P.* 'Balsam Spire'
tomentosa	WMou
tremula ♀H4	CCVT CDoC CDul CLnd CRWN CSBt CTho CWib ECrN ELan LBuc LRHS NBee NWea SBLw SHBN SKee SPer SPoG WDin WMou WOrn
§ - 'Erecta'	CDul CEnd CLnd CTho EBee MBlu MBri SMad WFar WMou

- 'Fastigiata'	see *P. tremula* 'Erecta'
- 'Pendula' (m)	CEnd CLnd CTho ECrN SBLw WCFE WDin WMou
trichocarpa	CDul CTho ECrN SPer
- 'Fritz Pauley' (f)	CDul CTho WMou
violascens	see *P. lasiocarpa* var. *tibetica*
yunnanensis	CLnd WMou

Porana (Convolvulaceae)

volubillis new	CPIN

Porophyllum (Asteraceae)

coloratum	EUnu
ruderale	EUnu MSal

Portulaca (Portulacaceae)

grandiflora	MBri
oleracea	CArn MHer MNHC SIde WJek
- var. *aurea*	MNHC WJek

Potamogeton (Potamogetonaceae)

crispus	EHon EMFW NSco WMAq
natans new	NSco

Potentilla ✿ (Rosaceae)

CC 4195	MGol
alba	CPLG CSev CTri ECha ECho ELan GBuc GGar MLHP MNFA MWat NChi NSti SPer SUsu WAul WPer
alchemilloides	MNrw SMer WPer
alpicola	WPer
ambigua	see *P. cuneata*
andicola	EBee NBre
anserina	CArn GBar MHer WHbs WHer XPep
- 'Golden Treasure' (v)	EBee EMar ITer MLLN NBre NEgg WHer
anserinoides	EBee EGoo EMan GCal WCot WDyG WMoo WPer
arbuscula misapplied	see *P. fruticosa* 'Elizabeth'
'Arc-en-ciel'	CFwr CKno CRez EBee EChP EMan EMar ERou GSki LAst LSRN MBNS MBri MLHP NLar NPro SHar SUsu WBor WCAu WFar WMoo WPnP WSan WWye
argentea	CRWN CSev LIck MBNS SPlb WFar WPer
arguta	EBee NBre
argyrophylla	see *P. atrosanguinea* var. *argyrophylla*
* - *insignis rubra*	NChi NRnb NWCA
astracanica	NBre
atrosanguinea	More than 30 suppliers
§ - var. *argyrophylla*	COIW CSam EBee EChP ECha ELan EPfP GCal LHop LRHS MNFA MRav MWat MWgw NBir NBro NCGa NCot NJOw NMir NOak SBri SRms WFar WHil WMoo WPer WWhi
- - SS&W 7768	MSte
- - 'Alfred Star' new	EBrs
- var. *leucochroa*	see *P. atrosanguinea* var. *argyrophylla*
aucheriana	EHyt
aurea	EBee ECho ECtt EPfP GAbr MTho NBlu NEgg NLAp NMir NNor NWCA SIng WBrk WPat
- 'Aurantiaca'	EWes NLar SRot
§ - subsp. *chrysocraspeda*	GCrs NMen
§ - 'Goldklumpen'	ECtt MNFA MRav NPro
- 'Plena' (d)	SRot
'Blazeaway'	EBee ECGP EChP EMan LRHS LSou MBNS MWgw NGdn NHol WCAu WFar
* *boraea*	CSec

burmiensis	EBee
calabra	EBee ECha EMan EWes SHGN SMer SSvw WHer
§ *cinerea*	CTri ECho LBee
clusiana	WLin
collina	EBee SBri
§ *crantzii*	CMea EBee GCrs MBar MSte NBre SRms
- 'Nana'	see *P. crantzii* 'Pygmaea'
§ - 'Pygmaea'	ECho ECtt EPfP NBir NJOw NMen
§ *cuneata* ♀H4	CLyd CNic ECho GAbr IHMH MTho NWCA SIng WPer
aff. *cuneata*	MDun
'Custard and Cream'	EChP
delavayi	GIBF MNrw
detommasii	MHar WPer
- MESE 400	EBee
dickinsii	CNic CSec NMen
divina new	GKev
'Emilie'	CBgR CMea CSpe EChP EGle EMar ERou GCal MAvo MBNS NLar NMRc NPro NRnb SUsu SWvt WBor WFar WHal WHil
§ *erecta*	CArn CRWN CWan GBar GPoy GWCH MHer MSal WBri WHbs WWye
eriocarpa	CLyd EBee ECho ECtt EHol EHyt GEdr MWat NJOw NLAp NMen SBri WAbe WPat
'Esta Ann' new	EBee NCGa SRGP
'Etna'	CElw CHar CKno EBee EChP ECtt EDAr ELan EWsh GCal GMac MNFA MNrw MTis MWrn NBir NFor SBri SWal WCAu WHen WHil WLin WMoo WPGP WPer WWhi
'Everest'	see *P. fruticosa* 'Mount Everest'
'Fireflame'	ECha NBre NLar WMoo
fissa	CSec EBee EMag LPhx MNrw MSte NBir NBre
'Flambeau' (d)	CBos CFwr CHad EBee EChP EMan EPPr LHop MNFA MRav NBre NCob NGdn NHol NLar WCra
'Flamenco'	CBgR CSam CTri EBee EChP ECtt ERou GMac MArl MBri MLHP MNrw MRav NBir NFor SAga SUsu WAbb WFar
fragariiformis	see *P. megalantha*
fruticosa	LBuc MGan NWea
- CC 3929	CPLG
- 'Abbotswood' ♀H4	More than 30 suppliers
- 'Abbotswood Silver' (v)	ECtt LAst MSwo SLim SPoG WFar WMoo
- 'Alice'	WWeb
- 'Annette'	LRHS NPro WWeb
- 'Apple Blossom'	CWib
- var. *arbuscula* misapplied	see *P. fruticosa* 'Elizabeth'
- 'Argenta Nana'	see *P. fruticosa* 'Beesii'
- 'Barnbarroch'	WWeb
§ - 'Beesii'	ELan EPfP LRHS MBar SPla SPoG WPat WTel
- 'Bewerley Surprise'	NBir WHCG WWeb
- 'Cascade'	LHop
* - 'Chelsea Star' ♀H4	WWeb
- 'Chilo' (v)	MGos NEgg WMoo WWeb
- 'Clotted Cream'	MBar
- var. *dahurica* W 1213	WPGP
- - 'Farrer's White'	WFar
- - 'Hersii'	see *P. fruticosa* 'Snowflake'
- - 'Rhodocalyx'	CPle WFar
- 'Dart's Cream'	CPLG LRHS MGan
- 'Dart's Golddigger'	CTri ECtt SEND
- 'Daydawn'	More than 30 suppliers
§ - 'Elizabeth'	More than 30 suppliers
- 'Farreri'	see *P. fruticosa* 'Gold Drop'

- 'Floppy Disc'   EPfP LRHS MAsh MGos NHol SHBN SPla
- 'Frances, Lady Daresbury'   WWeb
- 'Glenroy Pinkie'   CSam EPfP LRHS SCoo SLon WWeb
§ - 'Gold Drop'   MAsh NHol WHCG WTel
- 'Gold Parade'   WWeb
- 'Golden Dwarf'   LRHS MGos
- 'Golden Spreader'   WWeb
- 'Goldfinger'   CDoC CDul CSBt EBee ELan EPfP LHop LRHS MAsh MGos MRav MSwo MWat NEgg NHol SCoo SLim SMer SPer SPlb SPoG WDin WHar WTel WWeb
- Goldkugel   see *P. fruticosa* 'Gold Drop'
- Goldstar'   CDul IArd LRHS MBri MGos NHol SCoo SLon SPoG WFar WHCG WWeb
- 'Goldteppich'   LBuc MBar NCGa SHBN
- 'Goscote'   MGos
- 'Grace Darling'   CAbP ELan EPfP EWes GGar MAsh NBir NEgg SPoG SWvt WBVN WHCG WMoo
- 'Groneland' ♀H4   WWeb
- 'Haytor's Orange'   CWib
- 'Honey'   WWeb
- 'Hopleys Orange' ♀H4   CEnt CHar ENot EPfP EWes LHop LRHS MWat NCGa NEgg NPri SCoo WBrE WFar WGor WHCG WMoo WWeb
- 'Hopleys Pink'   WWeb
- 'Hunter's Moon'   WWeb
- 'Hurstbourne'   NPro
- 'Jackman's Variety' ♀H4 CSam CWib ECtt SPer SRms WWeb
- 'Janet'   WWeb
- 'Jolina'   WWeb
- 'Katherine Dykes'   CDoC CDul CSBt CWib EBee EPfP LRHS LSRN MBar MDun MRav MWgw NWea SCoo SLim SLon SPer SRms WBVN WDin WFar WHar WMoo WTel WWeb
* - 'King Cup' ♀H4   WWeb
- 'Klondike'   CBcs CSBt EPfP MGan NWea
- 'Knap Hill Buttercup' WWeb
- 'Kobold'   MBar
* - 'Lemon and Lime'   MBlu NBir NPro WWeb
- 'Limelight' ♀H4   CSBt EBee ELan EPfP LRHS LSou MAsh MBri MRav MSwo NPri SPla SPoG WFar WHCG WWeb
- 'Longacre Variety'   CTri MBar MSwo NWea WFar WTel
- 'Lovely Pink'PBR   see *P. fruticosa* 'Pink Beauty'
§ - 'Maanelys'   CTrw ECtt ELan MGan MWat NWea SPer SRms WDin WFar WHCG WMoo
§ - 'Manchu'   CDoC CTri MBar MRav MWat NPro SHBN SPer SRms WCFE WTel
- Mango Tango = 'Uman' **new**   CDoC
- Marian Red Robin = 'Marrob'PBR ♀H4   CDoC CDul CSBt CWib EBee ELan ENot EPfP LAst LRHS MAsh MBri MRav MSwo MWat NCGa NWea SCoo SLim SLon SPer SPoG SWvt WDin
- 'Maybe'   WWeb
- 'McKay's White'   WWeb
- 'Medicine Wheel Mountain' ♀H4 ELan ENot EWes LRHS MAsh MGos MRav NHol NLar NPro SCoo SLim SPer WHCG WWeb
- Moonlight   see *P. fruticosa* 'Maanelys'
§ - 'Mount Everest'   EHol NHol NWea SLon SRms WWeb
- 'Nana Argentea'   see *P. fruticosa* 'Beesii'
- 'New Dawn'   CDoC LRHS MBri NCGa WFar WWeb
- 'Orange Star'   NHol WHCG WWeb
- 'Orangeade'   LRHS MAsh SMur WWeb

- 'Peaches and Cream'   WEas WWeb
* - 'Peachy Proud'   NPro
§ - 'Pink Beauty'PBR ♀H4   CBcs CDoC COtt CSBt EBee ELan ENot EPfP LRHS LSRN MAsh MRav NBlu NCGa NEgg NPri SCoo SPer SPoG SWvt WMoo WWeb
- 'Pink Pearl'   WMoo
- 'Pink Whisper'   WWeb
- 'Pretty Polly'   CSBt CTri CWSG ELan EPfP LAst LRHS MAsh MBar MGos MSwo NBlu NHol SHBN SPla SSta WBor WDin WFar WHCG WHar WMoo WWeb
- 'Primrose Beauty' ♀H4   CDoC CDul EBee EGra ELan ENot EPfP EWTr LAst LRHS MAsh MBar MRav MSwo MWgw NCGa NHol NJOw SCoo SLim SMer SPlb WBrE WDin WFar WHar WMoo WWeb
- Princess = 'Blink'PBR   CDul CSBt CTri CWSG ELan LRHS MAsh MBar MRav MSwo NEgg SCoo SLim SPer SReu SRms WDin WFar WHar WWeb
- 'Prostrate Copper'   NJOw
- 'Red Ace'   More than 30 suppliers
- var. *rigida*   CPLG
- - CC 3685   WRos
- 'Royal Flush'   MBar NHol
- 'Snowbird'   EBee EPfP LRHS MGos NPro SLim WFar WWeb
§ - 'Snowflake'   CBcs WGwG WMoo
- 'Sommerflor' ♀H4   EPfP MRav NCGa
- 'Sophie's Blush'   MRav NHol NWea WDin WHCG WSHC WWeb
- 'Sunset'   CBcs CSBt CSam CWSG CWib EBee ELan EPfP LRHS MBar MGos MRav NBir NEgg NHol NWea SCoo SLim SPer SReu SRms SSta WBVN WFar WMoo WWeb
- 'Super Ace' **new**   MGos
- 'Tangerine'   More than 30 suppliers
- 'Tilford Cream'   More than 30 suppliers
- 'Tom Conway'   WHCG
§ - var. *veitchii*   CSBt SHBN SSto
- 'Vilmoriniana'   CTri ELan EPfP LRHS MAsh MLHP MRav SLon SPer SPoG SSpi WAbe WCFE WHCG WSHC WTel WWeb
- 'Wessex Silver'   CHar WHCG
- 'Whirligig'   WHCG
- 'White Rain'   WWeb
- 'Wickwar Beauty'   CWib
- 'Wickwar Trailer'   CLyd
- 'William Purdom'   WHCG
- 'Wychbold White'   WWeb
- 'Yellow Bird' ♀H4   LRHS MGos
- 'Yellow Carpet'   WWeb
- 'Yellow Giant'   WWeb
- 'Gibson's Scarlet' ♀H4   More than 30 suppliers
glandulosa   GAbr MNrw NBre NOak SMad WBrk WHil
'Gloire de Nancy' (d)   CHad CKno EBee GCal IGor LBMP LHop LRHS MRav NBir NChi WPrP WWhi
'Gold Clogs'   see *P. aurea* 'Goldklumpen'
gracilis   CSec EBee NEgg SBri
grandiflora   CSec
'Harlow Cream'   NBid
'Helen Jane'   GBuc LRHS MHer NBir NGdn NLar NPro SAga STes WFar WMnd WPer
heptaphylla   GSki NBre
'Herzblut'   EBee EPfP GBuc MNrw NLar
x *hopwoodiana*   More than 30 suppliers
* x *hybrida* 'Jean Jabber' EBee EWll GBuc GMac MRav NBur NLar
hyparctica   MDKP
- *nana*   LBee LRHS NHol WPat
'Jack Elliot'   WWeb

'Light My Fire' new	EBee LTwo MBNS NMoo
'Mandshurica'	see *P. fruticosa* 'Manchu'
'Maynard's' new	NDov
§ **megalantha** ♀H4	More than 30 suppliers
- 'Gold Sovereign'	ENot EPfP NPro SPoG
'Melton'	EBee EMag MNrw NBir NOak WHen
* 'Melton Fire'	CEnt CWan ECtt EGra EShb LAst LEdu MBri MWrn NBir NBur NJOw SBri SGar SUsu WMnd WMoo WPnP
'Monarch's Velvet'	see *P. thurberi* 'Monarch's Velvet'
'Monsieur Rouillard' (d)	CSam EBrs EMar EPPr EShb MNrw MRav MWat NFor NGdn SHop WHoo WMnd WSan WWhi
'Mont d'Or'	MRav
montana	NHol WHer WPer
nepalensis	CEnt CSec EBrs EPPr LAst MLHP NBro NChi NFor NPro SBri SHFr WBrk WGwG
- 'Flammenspiel'	WFar
- 'Master Floris'	SAga WFar
§ - 'Miss Willmott' ♀H4	More than 30 suppliers
- 'Ron McBeath'	More than 30 suppliers
- 'Roxana'	EBee EBrs ECGP ElAn ERou GBuc GSki MBNS MRav NBro WAbb WFar WHoo WMoo WPer WRos
- 'Shogran'	CBgR EBee EChP GAbr GBuc GMac LAst MWrn NCGa NGby NLar NVic SMar WHil WRHF WWeb
§ **neumanniana**	NBir NPri XPep
- 'Goldrausch'	LEdu MRav SBla
§ - 'Nana'	ECho EPot LBee LRHS MHer NEgg NJOw NLAp NLar NMen NRya SPlb SPoG SRms WEas WFar WMoo
nevadensis	CLyd CTri ECho GEdr SRms WPer
nitida	GEdr GKev NMen SRms WAbe
- 'Alba'	ECho EPot NLAp NMen WAbe WLin
- 'Rubra'	CFir CMea ECho EDAr EPot GCrs NBir NHol NLAp NWCA SAga SBla SRms WAbe WPat
nivalis new	ECho
* 'Olympic Mountains'	WPer
ovina	WPer
palustris	MBow NLar WMoo WWye
pamiroalaica	EHyt WLin
pedata	LLWP
pensylvanica	NEgg
'Pink Orleans'	WWeb
recta	EBee ELau EMan ERou EWin NPri SMar WRos
- 'Alba'	EGoo GMaP LAst NBre NBur NEgg WPer
- 'Citrina'	see *P. recta* var. *sulphurea*
- 'Macrantha'	see *P. recta* 'Warrenii'
§ - var. **sulphurea**	CHad CMea CSam EBee EChP EGoo EWTr GCal GSki IGor LPhx MNrw MTis NBir NBre SIng SUsu WCAu WFar WHal WHoo WLin WMnd WMoo WPer WPtf WTin WWhi
§ - 'Warrenii'	CHea CSBt EBee EChP EPla GMaP LAst LRHS MBNS MRav MTis MWat NBir NEgg NJOw SPer SRms WCAu WFar WHal WMoo WPer
reptans	CRWN XPep
'Roxanne' (d)	MHer
rupestris	EBee EChP ECha EPPr LAst MLLN MNrw NDlv NEgg NSti SBri SGar WCAu WFar WHal WMoo WPer WWye
simplex new	NBre
speciosa	EHyt EWes IGor SMar WMoo
sterilis	IHMH WSFF

'Strawberry Temptation' new	NBre
* **sudermanii** new	MTis
'Sungold'	ECho WHCG
tabernaemontani	see *P. neumanniana*
ternata	see *P. aurea* subsp. *chrysocraspeda*
thurberi	CAby CBgR EBee EGle EGra EMan GMac LPhx MMHG MNFA MNrw NBHF NLar NMoo SHGN WMoo WSHC
§ - 'Monarch's Velvet'	More than 30 suppliers
- 'Pirate's Gold' new	NPro
tommasiniana	see *P. cinerea*
x **tonguei** ♀H4	More than 30 suppliers
tormentilla	see *P. erecta*
tridentata	see *Sibbaldiopsis tridentata*
'Twinkling Star' new	EBee NCGa
uniflora	GCrs
verna	see *P. neumanniana*
- 'Pygmaea'	see *P. neumanniana* 'Nana'
'Versicolor Plena' (d)	CMea
villosa	see *P. crantzii*
'Volcan'	CBos CKno CMea CMil EBee EWes GCal LPhx MBNS MBri NChi NDov NPro SAga SMHy SUsu WAbb WCra WFar WHal WPGP
§ 'White Queen'	EWll LAst MNrw NBur NCob NJOw SHar SPoG SRot SWal
'William Rollison' ♀H4	More than 30 suppliers
willmottiae	see *P. nepalensis* 'Miss Willmott'
'Yellow Queen'	CBcs CTri EBrs EMil EPfP ERou GMaP GSki LHop MBNS MNrw MRav NHol SPer SWat WCAu WFar

Poterium see *Sanguisorba*

sanguisorba	see *Sanguisorba minor*

Prasium (*Lamiaceae*)

majus	XPep

Pratia (*Campanulaceae*)

§ **angulata**	CPLG EWll GGar
- 'Jack's Pass'	ECho
- 'Tim Rees'	EDAr IHMH
§ - 'Treadwellii'	ECha ECho EDAr EMan EWin GEdr GGar GMac LBee LRHS MBNS SPlb WHal WHen
- 'Woodside'	ECho ECou EDAr NSfd
'Celestial Spice'	ECou EDAr NSfd
angulata x **pedunculata**	GGar
irrigua new	NSfd
§ **pedunculata**	More than 30 suppliers
- 'Blue Stars'	EDAr NSfd
- 'County Park'	CElw CEnt CMea CSpe CTri ECha ECho ECou EDAr ELan EPfP EPot GAbr GGar IHMH ITim MBar NJOw SAga SBla SIng SPlb SPoG SRms WHoo WMoo WPat WPer WWhi
- 'Kiandra'	ECou
- 'Tom Stone'	MBNS MWgw
§ **perpusilla**	ECou EDAr
- 'Fragrant Carpet'	ECou EDAr NSfd
- 'Summer Meadows'	ECou WPer

Prenanthes (*Asteraceae*)

§ **alba**	EBee

Preslia see *Mentha*

Primula ✿ (*Primulaceae*)

CC 4070	CPLG
Lismore 79-26	EHyt NHol
acaulis	see *P. vulgaris*
'Adrian Jones' (Au)	ITim NHol WAbe

'Alan Robb' (Pr/dPrim)	CWCL EPfP NCGa NGHP NHol SRGP WFar	
albenensis (Au) **new**	GFle	
'Alexina' (*allionii* hybrid) (Au)	ITim MFie NHar	
algida (Al)	ECho GKev	
§ ***allionii*** (Au) ♀H2	EHyt ITim MFie NWCA WAbe	
- GFS 1984	CGra	
- Hartside 14	EHyt	
- Hartside 383/3	NHol	
- HNG 12	ITim	
- JCA 4161-14	EHyt	
- KRW 75/504	CNic	
- Lismore 85-15-2	EHyt	
- 'A.K. Wells' (Au)	WAbe	
- 'Agnes' (Au)	EHyt ITim	
- 'Aire Waves'	see *P.* x *loiseleurii* 'Aire Waves'	
- var. ***alba*** (Au)	EHyt	
* - 'Alexander' (Au)	CGra EHyt	
- 'Andrew' (Au)	CGra EHyt	
- 'Anna Griffith' (Au)	EHyt ITim LRHS MFie NRya NWCA WAbe WLin	
- 'Anne' (Au)	EHyt ITim NDlv	
§ - 'Apple Blossom' (Au)	GAbr GKev	
- 'Archer' (Au)	EHyt ITim NDlv NHol WLin	
- 'Ares' (Au)	NHar	
- 'Austen' (Au)	ITim NDlv	
- 'Avalanche' (Au)	EHyt ITim WAbe	
- 'Biddy' (Au) **new**	EHyt	
- 'Bill Martin' (Au)	EPot ITim	
- 'Blood Flake' **new**	ITim	
- 'Brilliant' (Au)	WAbe	
- 'Chivalry' (Au)	CGra	
- 'Claude Flight' (Au)	EHyt WLin	
- 'Crowsley Variety' (Au)	LRHS NWCA WAbe	
- 'Crusader' (Au)	EHyt ITim WThu	
- 'Crystal' (Au)	EHyt	
- 'Duncan' (Au)	CNic ITim	
§ - 'Edinburgh' (Au)	CNic GKev ITim MFie NHol NJOw	
- 'Edrom' (Au)	ITim	
- 'Elizabeth Baker' (Au)	EHyt GNor ITim MFie WAbe	
- 'Elizabeth Burrow' (Au)	EHyt	
- 'Elizabeth Earle' (Au)	ITim WAbe	
- 'Elliott's Large'	see *P. allionii* 'Edinburgh'	
- 'Elliott's Variety'	see *P. allionii* 'Edinburgh'	
- 'Emily Jane' (Au) **new**	EHyt	
- 'Eureka' (Au)	CGra WLin	
- 'Fanfare' (Au)	ITim LRHS NHar WGwG WLin	
- 'Flute' (Au)	EHyt	
- 'Frank Barker' (Au)	NHol	
§ - 'Gilderdale Glow' (Au)	CGra EHyt GKev NRya	
- 'Giuseppi's Form'	see *P. allionii* 'Mrs Dyas'	
- 'Grandiflora' (Au)	ITim	
- 'Hemswell' (Au)	NHol	
- 'Hocker Edge' (Au)	ITim NHol	
- 'Huntsman' (Au)	MFie	
- 'Imp' (Au)	EHyt	
- 'James' (Au)	EHyt	
- 'Jan' (Au)	EHyt	
- 'Jenny' (Au)	CGra EHyt	
- 'Joseph Collins' (Au)	CGra	
- K R W	see *P. allionii* 'Ken's Seedling'	
§ - 'Kath Dryden' (Au)	EHyt GCrs	
- 'Ken's Seedling' (Au)	CNic NJOw	
- 'Little O' (Au)	WAbe	
- 'Malcolm' (Au)	EHyt	
- 'Margaret Earle' (Au)	WAbe	
- 'Marion' (Au)	GNor	
- 'Marjorie Wooster' (Au)	EHyt ITim MFie NWCA SBla WAbe	
- 'Martin' (Au)	ITim	
- 'Mary Anne' (Au)	EHyt	
- 'Mary Berry' (Au)	EHyt MFie NRya WAbe	
- 'Maurice Dryden' (Au)	EHyt	
- 'Minuet' **new**	WLin	
§ - 'Mrs Dyas' (Au)	EHyt NHol WAbe	
- 'Neptunes Wave' (Au)	NHar	
- 'New Dawn' (Au)	EHyt	
I - 'Norma' (Au)	EHyt WAbe	
- 'Peggy Wilson' (Au)	GKev	
- 'Pennine Pink' (Au)	MFie	
- 'Pennine Pink' x ***allionii*** 'Stephen' (Au)	EHyt	
- 'Perkie' (Au)	EHyt	
- 'Picton's Variety' (Au)	NDlv	
- 'Pink Ice' (Au)	GCai GCrs NHol	
- 'Pinkie' (Au)	CGra WLin	
- 'Pippa' (Au)	EHyt	
- 'Praecox' (Au)	CGra	
- 'Quip' (Au) **new**	EHyt	
- 'Raymond Wooster' (Au)	GKev ITim LRHS NHol	
- 'Robert' (Au)	CGra	
- 'Scimitar' (Au)	MFie NHol	
- 'Snowflake' (Au)	CGra GKev ITim LRHS NWCA WAbe	
- 'Stanton House' (Au)	MFie NDlv	
- 'Stephen' (Au)	EHyt ITim	
- 'Sue' (Au)	EHyt	
- 'Superba' (Au)	EHyt	
- 'Tranquillity' (Au)	EHyt ITim MFie NHol NJOw WAbe	
§ - 'Travellers' (Au)	EHyt	
- 'Val' (Au)	EHyt	
- 'William Earle' (Au)	EHyt GCrs GKev ITim LRHS MFie NDlv NHol NWCA WAbe	
allionii x ***auricula*** 'Blairside Yellow' (Au)	CPBP CStu ECho GNor ITim	
allionii x ***auricula*** 'Old Red Dusty Miller' (Au)	CStu ECho GCrs MFie NJOw	
allionii x ***clusiana*** (Au)	ECho	
allionii x ***hirsuta*** (Au)	ITim MFie NHol NLAp	
allionii x 'Lismore Jewel' (Au) **new**	NWCA	
allionii x 'Lismore Treasure' (Au)	CPBP NWCA	
allionii x ***pedemontana***	see *P.* x *sendtneri*	
allionii x ***pubescens*** (Au)	ECho	
allionii x ***pubescens*** 'Harlow Car' (Au)	CLyd GMac	
allionii x 'Snow Ruffles' (Au)	ITim	
allionii x 'White Linda Pope' (Au)	ITim MFie NHar	
alpicola (Si) ♀H4	CFee CRow CSWP CWCL EBee EPfP GAbr GCrs GEdr GFle GGar GIBF GKev LPBA LRHS MFOX MFie NBHF NBid NBro NDlv NHol NLAp NPen NRnb NWCA SPoG WAbe WBVN WLin	
- var. ***alba*** (Si)	CRow CSWP EBee GBuc GEdr GGar GKev MNrw NBid NPen SWat	
§ - var. ***alpicola*** (Si)	CLAP CSWP EBee GBBs GBuc GEdr GFle GKev MNrw WAbe WLin	
- hybrids (Si)	GMac NEgg NRnb WLin	
- 'Kevock Sky' (Si) **new**	EBee	
- var. ***luna*** (Si)	see *P. alpicola* var. *alpicola*	
- var. ***violacea*** (Si)	CAby CDWL CLAP CRow CSWP EBee GBBs GGar GKev LRHS MFie MNrw NBid NPen SWat WAbe WWhi	
'Altaica'	see *P. elatior* subsp. *meyeri*	
altaica grandiflora	see *P. elatior* subsp. *meyeri*	
'Amanda Gabrielle'	CGra	
'Amethyst' (Pr/Poly) **new**	WSHC	
amethystina SDR 2589 (Am)	GKev	
amoena	see *P. elatior* subsp. *meyeri*	
angustifolia (Pa)	GKev	
anisodora	see *P. wilsonii* var. *anisodora*	
'Annemijne'	EMon	

'April Rose' (Pr/dPrim) — ENot MRav
x *arctotis* — see *P.* x *pubescens*
atrodentata (De) — LHop
aurantiaca (Pf) — CFir EBee GBar GBuc GCai GEdr GFle GIBF GKev SRms
aureata (Pe) — GGGa WAbe
 - subsp. *fimbriata* (Pe) — ITim
§ *auricula* L. (Au) ♀H4 — EDAr ELan LRHS MFie MHer NBro NJOw NSla SPer SPet SPlb SPoG WAbe
 - var. *albocincta* (Au) — EBee NWCA
 - subsp. *balbisii* — see *P. auricula* subsp. *ciliata*
 - subsp. *bauhinii* var. *albocincta* (Au) — EBee
§ - subsp. *ciliata* (Au) — GFle
 auricula ambig. (Au) — MFie
 auricula misapplied '2nd Vic' (Au) — SPop WHil
 - A74 (Au) — NCob
 - 'Abrigde' (d) **new** — MAln
 - 'Achates' (A) — MAln
 - 'Admiral' (Au/A) — MAln WCre
 - 'Adrian' (Au/A) — GAbr MFie NBro SPop WHil WLin
 - 'Adrienne Ruan' (A) — MAln MOne
 - 'Aga Khan' (Au/A) — MAln
 - 'Agamemnon' (Au/A) — MAln WCre
 - 'Alamo' (Au/A) — MFie SPop WCre
 - 'Alan Ball' (Au) **new** — WCre
 - 'Alan Ravenscroft' (Au/A) — MAln MFie
 - 'Alansford' (Au/A) — MAln
 - 'Albert Bailey' (Au/d) — EWoo GAbr GCai GNor ITim MAln MFie SPop WCre
 - 'Alexandra Georgina' (Au/A) — MAln
 - 'Alf' (Au/A) — EWoo MAln
 - 'Alfred Charles' (Au/A) — MAln
 - 'Alice Haysom' (Au/S) — CNic CWCL ELan EWoo GCai MFie MOne NJOw SDnm SPav SPop WCre WHil WLin WOFF
 - 'Alicia' (Au/A) — MFie SDnm SPop WCre
 - 'Alison Jane' (Au/A) — MFie NOak SUsu WCre
 - 'Alison Telford' (Au/A) — WHil
 - 'Allensford' (Au/A) — WCre
 - 'Alloway' (Au/d) **new** — MAln
 - 'Almand' (d) **new** — MAln
 - alpine mixed (Au/A) — CNic EPfP SRms
 - 'Amber Light' (S) — MAln
 - 'Amicable' (Au/A) — MFie NHol SPop WCre WHil
 - 'Ancient Order' (A) — MAln
 - 'Ancient Society' (Au/A) — EWoo GAbr SPop
 - 'Andrea Julie' (Au/A) — ITim MFie MOne NRya SPop WCre WHil
 - 'Andrew Hunter' (Au/A) — MAln MFie SPop
 - 'Andy Cole' (A) — EWoo MAln
 - 'Angelo' (A) — MAln
 - 'Angie' (d) — MAln
 - 'Ann Taylor' (Au/A) — MAln
 - 'Anne Hyatt' (d) — GAbr MAln
 - 'Anne Swithinbank' (d) — MAln
 - 'Antoc' (Au/S) — SPop
 - 'Anwar Sadat' (Au/A) — GAbr MFie SPop WCre
 - 'Applecross' (Au/A) — CWCL MFie SPop WCre WHil WLin
 - 'April Moon' (S) — MAln SPop
 - 'April Tiger' (Au/St) — MAln
 - 'Arabian Night' (A) — MAln
 - 'Arapaho' (A) — MAln
 - 'Arctic Fox' — MAln SPop
 - 'Argus' (Au/A) — GAbr MFie NBir SPop SUsu WCre WHil WOFF
 - 'Arlene' (Au/A) — MAln
 - 'Arthur Delbridge' (Au/A) — MFie
 - 'Arundell' (Au/S/St) — EWoo GAbr GCai ITim MFie MOne NJOw NLAp SPop WCre WHil WLin
 - 'Ashcliffe Gem' (Au/A) — MAln
 - 'Ashcliffe Gold' (Au/A) — MAln

 - 'Astolat' (Au/S) — CWCL EWoo GAbr ITim NJOw NOak NRya SDnm SPav SPop SUsu WCre WHil WLin
 - 'Athene' (S) — MAln MOne
 - 'Audacity' (Au/d) — MAln
 - 'Aurora' (Au/A) — MFie
 - 'Austin' (Au/A) — MAln WCre
 - 'Avon Citronella' (Au) **new** — SPop
 - 'Avril' (Au/A) — MAln SPop
 - 'Avril Hunter' (Au/A) — EWoo MFie SPop WCre
 - 'Aztec' (Au/d) — MAln
 - 'Bacchante' (Au/d) — MAln
 - 'Bacchus' (Au/A) — MFie
 - 'Baggage' (Au) **new** — SPop
 - 'Balbithan' (Au/B) — GAbr
 - 'Baltic Amber' (Au) **new** — SPop
 - 'Barbara Mason' — MAln
 - 'Barbarella' (Au/S) — MFie SPop WCre
 - Barnhaven doubles (Au/d) — CSWP GAbr
 - 'Basilio' (Au/S) — MAln
 - 'Basuto' (Au/A) — MFie SPop WCre WHil
 - 'Beatrice' (Au/A) — EShb GAbr GCai GNor ITim MFie SPop WCre WHil
 - 'Beauty of Bath' (Au/S) — MAln
 - 'Beckminster' (Au/A) — MAln WCre
 - 'Beechen Green' (Au/S) — EWoo GAbr GCai NJOw SPop WCre WLin WOFF
 - 'Behold' (Au) **new** — WCre
 - 'Bellamy's Pride' (Au/B) — GAbr SPop WAbe WCre
 - 'Belle Zana' (Au/S) — EWoo MAln SPop
 - 'Bellezana' — MFie
 - 'Ben Lawers' (Au/S) — SPop WLin
 - 'Ben Wyves' (Au/S) — WCre
 - 'Bendigo' (Au/S) — MAln
 - 'Bewitched' (A) — MAln
 - 'Big Ben' (Au/S) **new** — ECho
 - 'Bilbao' (A) — MAln
 - 'Bilbo Baggins' (Au/A) — MAln
 - 'Bill Bailey' (Au) — MOne WCre
 - 'Bizarre' (Au) **new** — WCre
 - 'Black Ice' (Au/S) — ITim MAln
 - 'Black Jack'[PBR] (d) — COtt CStu MAln
 - 'Black Knight' (Au/d) — MAln
 - 'Blackhill' (Au/S) — MFie
 - 'Blackpool Rock' (Au/St) — MAln
 - 'Blairside Yellow' (Au/B) — ECho EHyt EWes NLAp NSla
 - 'Blakeney' (Au/d) — GCai MAln MFie
 - 'Blossom' (Au/A) — GAbr MFie
 - 'Blue Bonnet' (A/d) — MAln
 - 'Blue Bonnet' (Au/A/d) — EWoo GAbr GNor ITim MFie SPop WCre
 - 'Blue Chips' (Au/S) — MAln
 - 'Blue Cliffs' (Au/S) — MAln
 - 'Blue Denim' (S) — MAln
 - 'Blue Frills' (Au) — MAln
 - 'Blue Heaven' — MOne WCre
 - 'Blue Jean' (Au/S) — GAbr GNor MFie SPop
 - 'Blue Lagoon' (Au/S) **new** — EBrs
 - 'Blue Mist' (Au/B) — GAbr GNor
 - 'Blue Moon' (Au/A) — MAln
 - 'Blue Nile' (Au/S) — SPop WCre
 - 'Blue Velvet' (Au/B) — GAbr MFie NBro SPop WHil
 - 'Bob Dingley' (Au/A) — WCre
 - 'Bob Lancashire' (Au/S) — GNor ITim MFie MOne SPop SUsu WCMO WCot WCre WHil
 - 'Bokay' (d) **new** — MAln
 - 'Bold Tartan' (Au/St) — MAln
 - 'Bolero' (Au/A) — SPop
 - 'Bollin Tiger' (Au/St) — MAln
 - 'Bonafide' (d) **new** — MAln
 - 'Bonanza' (S) — MAln
 - 'Bookham Firefly' (Au/A) — GNor MFie NHol NRya SPop WCre WHil
 - 'Boromir' (Au/A) — MAln
 - 'Boy Blue' (S) — MAln

- 'Bradford City' (Au/A)   SDnm SPav
- 'Branno' (Au/S)   MAln
- 'Brasso' (Au)   MAln
- 'Brazen Hussy' (Au/d)   MAln
  new
- 'Brazil' (Au/S)   EWoo GAbr ITim LRHS MFie MOne
  NLAp NOak SPav SPop WCre WHil
- 'Brazos River' (A)   MAln
- 'Brenda's Choice' (Au/A)   MFie WCre
- 'Brentford Bees' (Au/St)   MAln
- 'Bright Eyes' (Au/A)   MFie WCre
- 'Broad Gold' (Au/A)   MAln MOne SPop WCre
- 'Broadwell Gold' (Au/B)   GAbr SPop
- 'Brompton' (Au/S)   MAln
- 'Brookfield' (Au/S)   GNor MFie SPop WCre
- 'Brookgood' (Au)   ITim
- 'Broughton' (Au/S)   MFie WLin
- 'Brown Ben' (Au)   MFie
- 'Brown Bess' (Au/A)   GAbr GCai GNor ITim MFie MOne
  SPop WCre WLin
- 'Brownie' (Au/B)   NBir SDnm SPav
- 'Buccaneer'   ECho MAln
- 'Bucks Green' (Au/S)   GAbr SPop
- 'Bunty' (Au/A)   MFie
- 'Butterwick' (Au/A)   EWoo GAbr LRHS MBNS MFie
  SPav SPop
- 'C.G. Haysom' (Au/S)   GAbr GNor MFie SPop WCre
  WOFF
- 'C.W. Needham' (Au/A)   CWCL NLAp SPop WCre
- 'Calypso' (Au/d)   MAln
- 'Cambodunum' (Au/A)   MFie SPop WCre
- 'Camelot' (Au/d)   ECho ELan GCai GNor MFie MOne
  NBro SPop SUsu WCre WFar WHil
- 'Cameo' (Au/A)   WCre
- 'Cameo Beauty' (d) **new**   SPop
- 'Camilla' (Au/A)   MAln
- 'Candida' (Au/d)   MAln SPop WCre
- 'Caramel' (Au/A)   MAln
- 'Carioca' (A)   MAln
- 'Carole' (Au/A)   MFie
- 'Catherine Redding' (d)   MAln
- 'Catherine Wheel' (Au/St)   MAln
- 'Chaffinch' (Au/S)   EWoo GAbr GNor MOne SPop
- 'Chamois' (Au/B)   GAbr WHil
- 'Channel' (S)   MAln
- 'Chantilly Cream' (Au/d)   MAln WCre
- 'Charles Bronson' (d)   MAln
- 'Charles Rennie' (Au/B)   MAln
- 'Charlie's Aunt' (A)   MAln
- 'Checkmate' (Au)   MAln SPop
- 'Chelsea Bridge' (Au/A)   MFie MOne SPop WCre
- 'Chelsea Girl' (Au/d)   MOne
- 'Cheops'   EWoo WHil
- 'Cherry' (Au/S)   EWoo ITim MFie WCre
- 'Cherry Picker' (Au/S)   MFie WCre
- 'Cheyenne' (Au/S)   GAbr MFie WCre
- 'Chiffon' (S)   EWoo MAln SPop
- 'Chirichua' (Au/S)   MAln
- 'Chloë' (Au/S)   MOne
- 'Chloris' (Au/S)   MAln NBir
- 'Chorister' (Au/S)   ECho ELan EWoo GAbr GCai GNor
  ITim MFie MOne NBir NLAp NOak
  NPri SUsu WCre WHil WLin
- 'Chyne' (Au) **new**   EWoo
- 'Cicero' (Au/A)   MAln
- 'Cindy' (Au/B)   ECho
- 'Cinnamon' (Au/d)   ITim MFie SPop WCMO WCre
  WLin
- 'Ciribiribin' (A)   MAln
- 'Clare' (Au/S)   GAbr MFie NRya SPop
- 'Clatter-Ha' (Au/d)   GCrs
- 'Claudia Taylor' (Au)   WLin
- 'Clouded Yellow' (S)   MAln
- 'Cloudy Bay' (Au)   WCot
- 'Cloverdale' (d) **new**   MAln
- 'Clunie' (Au/S)   EWoo GNor ITim WCre

- 'Clunie II' (Au/S)   ITim NLAp WLin
- 'Cobden Meadows'   MAln WCre
  (Au/A)
- 'Coffee' (Au/S)   CWCL MFie NRya SUsu WCre
- 'Colbury' (Au/S)   SPop WCre
- 'Colonel Champney'   EWoo GNor ITim MFie NJOw
  (Au/S)   NLAp SPop WCre WLin
- 'Comet' (Au/S)   WHil
- 'Confederate' (Au/S)   MAln
- 'Connaught Court' (Au/A) EWoo MAln
- 'Conservative' (Au/S)   GAbr SUsu WLin
- 'Consett' (Au/S)   EWoo MFie NLAp WHil
- 'Coppi' (Au/A)   EWoo MAln SPop
- 'Coral' (Au/S)   EWoo MFie WCre WHil
- 'Coral Sea' (S)   MAln
- 'Cornmeal' (Au/S)   MAln MFie
- 'Corntime' (Au/S)   MAln
- 'Corporal Kate' (Au/St)   MAln
- 'Corrie Files' (Au/d)   MAln
- 'Cortez Silver' (Au/S)   MAln
- 'Cortina' (Au/S)   ECho EWoo GAbr GCai GNor ITim
  MOne NLAp NOak NRya SDnm
  SPav SPop SUsu WCre WHil
- 'County Park Red' (Au/B) ECou
- 'Crackley Tagetes' (Au/d) ECho
  new
- 'Craig Vaughan' (Au/A)   MFie WLin
- 'Cranbourne' (Au/A)   MAln
- 'Crecy' (Au/A)   MAln
- 'Crimson Glow' (Au/d)   MAln NLAp SPop WOFF
- 'Cuckoo Fair'   GAbr SPop WCre
- 'Cuckoo Fare' (S)   MAln
- 'Cuddles' (A)   MAln
- 'Curry Blend' (Au/B)   GAbr
- 'D.S.J.' (Au/S)   WLin
- 'Daftie Green' (Au/S)   GAbr ITim MOne NLAp WCre
  WHil
- 'Dales Red' (Au/B)   GAbr ITim MAln MFie SDnm SPop
  WHil
- 'Dan Tiger' (Au/St)   ITim MAln MFie
- 'Daniel' (Au/A)   MAln
- 'Daphnis' (Au/S)   MAln WCre
- 'Dark Eyes' (d)   MAln NLAp WLin
- 'Dark Lady' (A)   MAln
- 'David Beckham' (Au/d)   MAln
- 'Decaff' (Au/St)   MAln
- 'Deckchair' (Au) **new**   SPop
- 'Dedham' (d) **new**   MAln
- 'Delilah' (Au/d)   GAbr GNor MFie MOne WCre
  WLin
- 'Denise' (Au/S)   MAln
- 'Denna Snuffer' (Au/d)   GAbr GNor ITim NLAp
- 'Devon Cream' (Au/d)   ECho GNor ITim MFie SPop WFar
- 'Diamond' (Au/d)   MAln
- 'Diane' (Au/A)   MFie MOne
- 'Digby' (Au/d)   MAln
- 'Digit' (Au/d)   MAln
- * 'Dill' (Au/A)   MAln
- 'Dilly Dilly' (Au/A)   MAln SPop
- 'Divint Dunch' (Au/A)   MFie SPop WCre
- 'Doctor Duthie' (Au/S)   MAln
- 'Doctor Jones' (Au/d)   MAln
- 'Doctor Lennons'(Au)   GAbr
  new
- 'Doctor Lennon's White'   MFie SPop
  (Au/A)
- 'Dolly Viney' (d)   MAln
- 'Donhead' (Au/A)   MFie SPop WCre
- 'Donna Clancy' (Ua/S)   EWoo SPop
- 'Dorado' (Au/d)   MAln
- 'Doreen Stephens' (Au/A) MAln
- 'Doris Jean' (Au/A)   MFie
- 'Dorothy' (Au/S)   MAln
- 'Doublet' (Au/d)   ECho GAbr GCai GNor MFie NOak
  SPop WCre WHil WLin
- 'Doubloon' (Au/d)   ECho

- 'Doublure' (Au/d) — GAbr GNor
- 'Douglas Bader' (Au/A) — MFie WCre
- 'Douglas Black' (Au/S) — EWoo GAbr NLAp SPop WCre WLin
- 'Douglas Blue' (Au/S) — MAln
- 'Douglas Green' (Au/S) — MFie SPop WCre
- 'Douglas Red' (Au/A) — WLin
- 'Douglas White' (Au/S) — MFie SPop
- 'Dovedale' (Au/S) — MAln
- 'Doyen' (Au/d) — ITim MAln MFie WOFF
- 'Drax' (Au/A) — MAln
- 'Dubarii' (Au/A) — MAln
- 'Duchess of Malfi' (Au/S) — SPop
- 'Duchess of York' (Au) — GBuc
* - 'Dusky' (Au) — WLin
- 'Dusky Girl' (Au/A) — MAln
- 'Dusky Maiden' (Au/A) — GAbr GCai GNor MFie SPop WCre WHil WLin
- 'Dusky Yellow' (Au/B) — ECho
- 'Dusty Miller' (Au/B) — ECho MRav NBid NBir
- 'Eastern Promise' (A) — GCai MFie SPop
- 'Ed Spivey' (Au/A) — WCre
- 'Eddy Gordon' (Au/A) — MAln
- 'Eden Carmine' (Au/B) — MFie
- 'Eden David' (Au/B) — MFie SPop WLin
- 'Edith Allen' (Au/A) — MAln
- 'Edith Major' (Au/D) — MFie
- 'Edward Sweeney' (Au/S) — MAln
- 'Eglinton' — WCre
- 'Eli Jenkins' (Au) — MAln
- 'Elizabeth Ann' (Au/A) — GAbr
- 'Ellen Thompson' (Au/A) — EWoo GAbr MFie WCre WLin
- 'Elsie' (Au/A) — GNor WCre
- 'Elsie May' (Au/A) — GNor ITim MFie MOne SPop WCre
- 'Elsinore' (Au/S) — WCre
- 'Emberglow' (Au/d) — MAln
- 'Embley' (Au/S) — GNor ITim SPop
- 'Emery Down' (Au/S) — NLAp SPop
- 'Emmett Smith' (A) — MAln
- 'Enigma' (S) — MAln
- 'Envy' (Au/S) — MAln
- 'Erica' (Au/A) — ITim MFie SPop SUsu WCre WLin
- 'Erjon' (Au/S) — MAln MFie
- 'Error' (Au/S) — MAln
- 'Ethel' (Au) — WHil
- 'Etna' (Au/S) — MAln
- 'Ettrick' (Au/S) — MAln
- 'Eventide' (Au/S) — EWoo NLAp SPop
- 'Everest Blue' (Au/S) — GAbr SPop SUsu WCre WOFF
- 'Excalibur' (d) — MAln WLin
- (Exhibition Series) — MFie
  'Exhibition Blau' (Au/B)
- - 'Exhibition Gelb' (Au/B) — MFie
- - 'Exhibition Rot' (Au/B) — MFie
- 'Eyeopener' (Au/A) — MAln SPop WCre
- 'Fairy' (Au/A) — MAln
- 'Fairy Moon' (Au/S) — MAln
- 'Falaraki' (Au/A) — MAln
- 'Faliraki Fanciful' (Au) **new** — EWoo
- 'Falstaff' (d) — MAln
- 'Fanciful' (Au/S) — MFie WLin
- 'Fancy Free' (Au) **new** — SPop
- 'Fandancer' (Au/A) — MAln
- 'Fanfare' (S) — MAln SPop
- 'Fanny Meerbeck' (Au/S) — GAbr GCai GNor MFie MOne NOak SPop WLin WOFF
- 'Faro' (Au/S) — MAln
- 'Favourite' (S) — EWoo GAbr ITim MFie MOne NJOw SPop WCre WHil WLin
- 'Fen Tiger' (Au/St) — MAln
- 'Fennay' (Au/S) — MAln
- 'Fiddler's Green' (Au) **new** — SPop

- 'Figaro' (Au/S) — MAln MFie SPop WCre
- 'Finchfield' (Au/A) — SUsu
- 'Firecracker' (Au) — MAln
- 'Firenze' (Au/A) — MFie SPop
- 'Firsby' (Au/d) — MAln SPop WCre
- 'First Lady' (Au/A) — MAln
- 'Fishtoft' (Au/d) — MAln
- 'Fleminghouse' (Au/S) — SPop
- 'Florence Brown' (Au/S) — ITim
- 'Forest Pines' (Au/S) — MAln
- 'Fradley' (Au/A) — MAln
- 'Frank Bailey' (Au/d) — MAln SPop
- 'Frank Crosland' (Au/A) — CStu MFie WCre WHil
- 'Frank Faulkner' (Au/A) — MAln
- 'Frank Jenning' (A) — MAln
- 'Frank Taylor' (Au/S) — EWoo
- 'Fred Booley' (Au/B) — GAbr ITim SPop WCre WHil WLin
- 'Fred Livesley' (Au/A) — MAln
- 'Friskney' (d) — MAln
- 'Frittenden Yellow' (Au/B) — GAbr WLin
- 'Fuller's Red' (Au/S) — SPop
- 'Fuzzy' (Au/St) — MAln
- 'Gaia' (Au/d) — MAln MFie SPop
- 'Galatea' (Au/S) — MAln
- 'Galen' (Au/A) — MFie WCre
- 'Ganymede' (Au/d) — MAln
- 'Gary Pallister' (A) — MAln
- 'Gavin Ward' (Au/S) — MAln
- 'Gay Crusader' (Au/A) — GAbr GNor MFie SPop WCre
- 'Gazza' (Au/A) — MAln
- 'Gee Cross' (Au/A) — GNor SPop WCre
§ - 'Geldersome Green' (Au/S) — GCai GNor MFie NWCA SPop WCre WLin
- 'Generosity' (Au/A) — SPop WCre
- 'Geordie' (Au/A) — MAln
- 'George Harrison' (Au/B) — GAbr
- 'George Jennings' (A) — MAln MFie
- 'George Stephens' (A) — MAln
- 'Geronimo' (Au/S) — GNor MFie SPop
- 'Ghost Grey' (Au) **new** — WCre
- 'Girl Guide' (Au/S) — MAln
- 'Gizabroon' (Au/S) — CWCL GCai MFie NLAp SDnm SPav SPop WCre WLin
- 'Glasnost' (Au/S) — MAln
- 'Gleam' (Au/S) — CWCL ECho EWoo GCai GNor ITim LTwo MFie NJOw NLAp SPop WCre WHil WLin
- 'Glencoe' (Au/S) — ECho
- 'Gleneagles' (Au/S) — EShb EWoo GCai MAln NLAp SPop WCre
- 'Glenelg' (Au/S) — EWoo GAbr GCrs MFie SPop WCre WHil WLin
- 'Glenna Goodwin' (Au/d) — MAln
- 'Gold Seam' (A) — MAln
- 'Golden Boy' (Au/A) — MAln
- 'Golden Eye' (Au/S) — MAln
- 'Golden Fleece' (Au/S) — EWoo GAbr GCai GNor MFie SPop
- 'Golden Glory' (A) — MAln
- 'Golden Hill' (Au/S) — SPop
- 'Golden Hind' (Au/d) — EWoo SPop WLin
- 'Golden Splendour' (Au/d) — EWoo MFie NLAp SPop WCre
- 'Golden Wedding' (Au/A) — MAln SPop
- 'Goldthorn' (Au/A) — WCre
- 'Goldwin' (Au/A) — MAln
- 'Gollum' (Au/A) — MAln
- 'Good Report' (Au/A) — EWoo MFie SPop
- 'Gorey' (Au/A) — WCre
- 'Grabley' (Au/S) — MAln
- 'Grandad's Favourite' (Au/B) — SPop
- 'Green Finger' (Au/S) — SPop
- 'Green Frill' (Au) — ITim
- 'Green Goddess' (Au/St) — MAln

- 'Green Isle' (Au/S) — GAbr MFie MOne NBir SPop WCre WLin
- 'Green Jacket' (Au/S) — GNor WCre
- 'Green Magic' (Au/S) — MAln
- 'Green Meadows' (Au/S) — MAln SPop
- 'Green Parrot' (Au/S) — SPop WCre
- 'Green Shank' (Au/S) — EWoo GNor ITim MFie SPop WHil WLin
- 'Greenfield' (Au) **new** — EWoo
- 'Greenfield's Fancy' (Au) **new** — CStu
- 'Greenfinger' (Au/S) — MAln MOne
- 'Greenheart' (Au/S) — CWCL GNor
- 'Greenpeace' (Au/S) — LRHS SPop
- 'Greensleeves' (Au/S) — GNor SPop
- 'Greenways' (Au/S) — MAln
- 'Greta' (Au/S) — ECho ELan EWoo GAbr GNor ITim NLAp NOak SPop WCot WCre WHil WLin
- 'Gretna Green' (Au/S) — SPop
- 'Grey Dawn' (Au/S) — MAln
- 'Grey Edge' — ECho ITim SUsu
- 'Grey Friar' (Au/S) — MAln
- 'Grey Hawk' (Au/S) — MFie
- 'Grey Lady' (Au/S) — MAln
- 'Grey Lag' (Au/S) — GNor MFie WHil
- 'Grey Monarch' (Au/S) — GCai GNor ITim MFie SPop WCre WLin WOFF
- 'Grey Owl' (Au/S) — MAln
- 'Grey Shrike' (Au/S) — MAln
- 'Grizedale' (Au/S) — MAln
- 'Guildersome Green' — see *P. auricula* misapplied 'Geldersome Green'
- 'Guinea' (Au/S) — EWoo GAbr SPop WLin
- 'Gwen' (Au/A) — MAln MFie MOne SPop WCre
- 'Gwen Baker' (Au/d) — GAbr WCre
- 'Gwen Gaulthiers' (Au/S) — MAln
- 'Gwenda' (Au/A) — MAln WHil
- 'Gypsy Rose Lee' (Au/A) — MAln
- 'Habanera' (Au/A) — EWoo MFie SPop WCre
- 'Hadrian's Shooting Star' (Au/d) — MAln
- 'Haffner' (Au/S) — MAln SPop
- 'Hallmark' (Au/A) — MAln
- 'Hardley' (Au/S) — MAln
- 'Harmony' (Au/B) — MFie NBro
- 'Harry Hotspur' (Au/A) — EWoo MFie SPop
- 'Harry "O"' (Au/S) — EWoo NLAp SPop WCre
- 'Harvest Glow' (Au/S) — WHil
- 'Hawkwood' (Au/S) — CWCL GNor ITim NJOw NLAp SDnm SPav SPop SUsu WHil WOFF
- 'Hawkwood Fancy' (Au/S) — MFie WLin
* - 'Hazel' (Au/A) — MFie MOne SPop WCre
- 'Headdress' (Au/S) — CStu GAbr ITim MFie SPop WCre WHil
- 'Heady' (Au/A) — EWoo MFie SPop
- 'Heart of Gold' (Au/A) — MAln MFie SPop
- 'Hebers' (Au) — MAln
- 'Helen' (Au/S) — EWoo GAbr ITim MFie SPop WHil
- 'Helen Barter' (Au/S) — MFie SPop
- 'Helen Ruane' (Au/d) — MAln SPop WLin
- 'Helena' (Au/S) — ITim MFie NOak
- 'Helena Dean' (Au/d) — MAln
- 'Hetty Woolf' (Au/S) — ECho GAbr GNor ITim WCre
- 'High Hopes' (Au) — MAln
- 'Hinton Admiral' (Au/S) — EWoo ITim MAln NLAp SPop
- 'Hinton Fields' (Au/S) — CStu CWCL EBee EShb EWoo GAbr GCai GNor MFie MOne NLAp SDnm SPav SPop WCre WHil
- 'Hobby Horse' (Au) — WLin
- 'Hoghton Gem' (Au/d) — MAln
- 'Holyrood' (Au/S) — GAbr SPop
- 'Honey' (Au/d) — MAln SPop
- 'Honeymoon' (Au/S) — MAln
- 'Hopleys Coffee' (Au/d) — GAbr GCai GNor MAln SPop WCre

- 'Hurstwood Midnight' (Au) — MFie
* - 'Hyacinth' (Au/S) — LRHS
- 'Iago' (Au/S) — MAln
- 'Ian Greville' (Au/A) — MAln
- 'Ibis' (Au/S) — MAln WCre
- 'Ice Maiden' (Au) — EWoo MAln MOne SPop
- 'Idmiston' (Au/S) — ECho SPop WCre
- 'Immaculate' (Au/A) — MAln SPop WHil
- 'Impassioned' (Au/A) — MAln MFie SPop
- 'Impeccable' (Au/A) — MAln
- 'Imperturbable' (Au/A) — MAln MFie
- 'Indian Love Call' (Au/A) — EWoo MFie SPop WCre WHil
- 'Isabel' (Au/S) — MAln
- 'Isabella' (Au) — MAln
- 'Jack Dean' (Au/A) — MAln MFie SPop WCre WHil
- 'James Arnot' (Au/S) — GAbr GNor MFie NOak NRya SPop
- 'Jane' (Au/S) — MAln
- 'Jane Myers' (Au/d) — MAln WHil
- 'Janet' (Au) — ECho GEdr
- 'Janie Hill' (Au/A) — MFie MOne WCre
- 'Jean Fielder' (Au/A) — MAln
- 'Jean Jacques' (Au/A) — MAln
- 'Jeanne' (Au/A) — MFie
- 'Jeannie Telford' (Au/A) — MFie SPop WCre
- 'Jenny' (Au/A) — EBee ECho GEdr ITim LHop MBNS MFie SPop WCre WHil
- 'Jersey Bounce' (Au/A) — MAln
- 'Jesmond' (Au/S) — MAln
- 'Jessie' (Au/d) — MAln
- 'Joan Elliott' (Au/A) — GAbr
- 'Joanne' (Au/A) — MFie WCre
- 'Joe Perks' (Au/A) — EWoo MAln MFie WHil
- 'Joel' (Au/S) — EWoo MAln MFie NLAp SPop WCre
- 'John Stewart' (Au/A) — MFie WCre
- 'John Wayne' (Au/A) — GAbr MFie WCre
- 'John Woolf' (Au/S) — ECho
- 'Jonathon' (Au/A) — MAln
- 'Joy' (Au/A) — CWCL ECho GNor LTwo MFie NLAp SPop WCre WHil
- 'Joyce' (Au/A) — GAbr MFie NBir SPop WCre
- 'Julia' (Au/S) — MAln
- 'June' (Au/A) — MAln MFie
- 'Jungfrau' (Au/d) — MAln
- 'Jupiter' (Au/S) — MAln
- 'Jura' (Au/A) — MAln
- 'Just Steven' (Au/A) — MAln
- 'Karen Cordrey' (Au/S) — ECho EWoo GAbr GKev GNor ITim MFie SDnm SPav SPop WCre WHil
- 'Karen McDonald' (Au/A) — SPop
- 'Kath Dryden' — see *P. allionii* 'Kath Dryden'
- 'Kelso' (Au/A) — MFie
- 'Ken Chilton' (Au/A) — EWoo MAln MFie WHil
- 'Kentucky Blues' (Au/d) **new** — SPop
- 'Kercup' (Au/A) — MFie SPop
- 'Kevin Keegan' (Au/A) — SPop WHil
- 'Key West' (Au/A) — MAln
- 'Khachaturian' (Au/A) — MAln
- 'Kim' (Au/A) — MFie MOne WCre
- 'Kingcup' (Au/A) — MFie SPop WCre
- 'Kingfisher' (Au/A) — SPop WHil
- 'Kiowa' (Au/S) — SPop
- 'Kirklands' (Au/d) — MFie SPop WHil
- 'Klondyke' (Au/A) — MAln
- 'Kohinoor' (Au) **new** — MFie
- 'Königin der Nacht' (Au/St) — MAln WHil
- 'Lady Daresbury' (Au/A) — MFie SPop
- 'Lady Diana' (Au/S) — MAln
- 'Lady Emma Monson' (Au/S) — CHad
- 'Lady Joyful' (Au/S) — WCre
- 'Lady of the Vale' (Au/A) — MAln

- 'Lady Penelope' (Au/S)	MAln
- 'Lady Zoë' (Au/S)	MAln MFie NHol SPop WCre
- 'Lambert's Gold' (Au) **new**	SPop
- 'Lamplugh' (d)	MOne WHil
- 'Lancelot' (Au/d)	MAln SPop WHil
- 'Landy' (Au/A)	GCrs MFie SPop WCre WHil
- 'Langley Park' (Au/A)	EShb MFie SPop WCre WHil
- 'Lara' (Au/A)	MAln MFie
- 'Laredo' (Au/A)	MAln
- 'Larry' (Au/A)	MAln MFie SPop WCre
- 'Lavender Lady' (Au/B)	SPav
- 'Lavenham' (Au/S)	MAln
- 'Laverock' (Au/S)	NBir NBro WCre WHil
- 'Laverock Fancy' (S)	GCai GNor MFie SUsu WLin
- 'Lazy River' (Au/A)	MAln
- 'Leather Jacket' (Au)	GAbr
- 'Lechistan' (Au/S)	ECho ITim MFie SPop WCre WHil
- 'Lee' (Au/A)	MAln WCre
- 'Lee Clark' (Au/A)	MAln WCre
- 'Lee Paul' (Au/A)	CStu EWoo GAbr GCai GNor MFie
	MOne SPop WCre WHil WLin
- 'Lee Sharpe' (Au/A)	MAln SPop
- 'Lemmy Getatem' (d) **new**	SPop
- 'Lemon Drop' (Au/S)	EWoo NBro SPop WCre
- 'Lemon Sherbet' (Au/B)	MFie
- 'Lemon Sorbet' (Au)	NRya
- 'Lepton Jubilee' (Au/S)	GAbr MAln
- 'Leroy Brown' (Au/A)	MAln
- 'Letty' (Au/S)	MAln
- 'Leverton' (Au/d)	MAln
- 'Lichfield' (A/d)	MAln SPop WCre
- 'Light Hearted' (Au)	MFie
- 'Light Music' (d) **new**	MAln
- 'Lila' (Au/S)	EWoo MAln
- 'Lilac Domino' (Au/S)	EWoo GAbr MFie SPop WCre WHil
	WLin
- 'Lilac Domino' (Au/S)	ITim MAln SPop
- 'Lillian Hill' (Au/A)	MAln
- 'Lima' (Au/d)	MAln
- 'Limelight' (Au/A)	MAln SPop
- 'Limelight' (Au/S)	MAln
- 'Lincoln Charm' (Au) **new**	GAbr
- 'Lincoln Fair' (Au) **new**	GAbr
- 'Lincoln Imp' (Au/d) **new**	SPop
- 'Lindsey Moreno' (Au/S)	MAln
- 'Ling' (Au/A)	ITim MFie SPop WCre
- 'Lisa' (Au/A)	ITim MFie SPop WCre WLin
- 'Lisa Clara' (Au/S)	EWoo GCai GNor ITim MFie WLin
- 'Lisa's Smile' (Au/S)	EWoo GCai MFie MOne WHil
- 'Little Rosetta' (Au/d)	MAln MFie NJOw WHil
- 'Lochlands' (Au/S) **new**	ITim
- 'Lord Saye and Sele'	EWoo GAbr GCai GNor ITim MFie
(Au/St)	NLAp SPop WCre WLin
- 'Lothlorien' (Au/A)	MAln
- 'Louisa Woolhead' (Au/d)	SPop
- 'Lovebird' (Au/S)	GAbr GNor ITim MFie SPop SUsu
	WCre WHil WOFF
- 'Lucky Strike' (Au)	MAln
- 'Lucy Locket' (Au/B)	CWCL MOne NBir NHol
- 'Ludlow' (Au/S)	GAbr MAln
- 'Lupy Minstrel' (Au/S)	MAln
- 'Lynn' (A)	MAln
- 'Lynn Cooper' (Au)	WLin
- 'Maggie' (Au/A)	GAbr GNor ITim WCre WLin
- 'Magnolia' (Au/B)	WCre
- 'Maid Marion' (Au/d)	WCre
- 'Maizie' (Au/S)	MAln
- 'Mandarin' (Au/A)	EWoo MFie SPop WCre
- 'Mansell's Green' (Au/S)	MAln NJOw WHil
- 'Mara Cordrey' (Au)	MOne
- 'Margaret Dee' (Au/d)	MAln
- 'Margaret Faulkner'	GAbr GCai GNor MFie WCre
(Au/A)	
- 'Margaret Irene' (A)	MAln SPop WCre WHil
- 'Margaret Martin' (Au/S)	GAbr MAln SPop

- 'Margot Fonteyn' (Au/A)	GAbr MAln SPop WHil
- 'Marie Crousse' (Au/d)	CMea CPBP MFie SPop WCre WLin
- 'Marigold' (Au/d)	WFar
- 'Marion Howard Spring'	MAln MFie WCre
(Au/A)	
- 'Marion Tiger' (Au/St)	MAln
- 'Mark' (Au/A)	GNor MFie NBro SPop WCre
- 'Marmion' (Au/S)	EWoo MAln MFie SPop WHil WLin
- 'Martha Livesley' (A)	MAln
- 'Martha's Choice' (Au/A)	MAln
- 'Martin Fish' (Au) **new**	WCre
- 'Martin Luther King'	CWCL
(Au/S)	
- 'Mary' (Au/d)	GAbr GNor SPop WCre
- 'Mary Taylor' (Au/S)	MAln
- 'Mary Zach' (Au/S)	EWoo WHil
- 'Matthew Yates' (Au/d)	CHad CWCL EWoo GAbr GCai
	ITim LHop MFie MOne NPri SDnm
	SPav SPop SUsu WCMO WCot
	WCre WHil WRha
- 'Maureen Millward'	MFie SPop WCre WHil
(Au/A)	
- 'May' (Au/A)	MAln WCre
- 'Mazetta Stripe' (Au/S/St)	EWoo GAbr ITim NLAp NLar SPop
- 'McWatt's Blue' (Au/B)	GNor IGor MOne SPop WCre WLin
- 'Meadowlark' (Au/A)	MAln MFie WCre
- 'Mease Tiger' (Au/St)	GAbr MAln
- 'Megan' (d)	MAln
- 'Mellifluous' (Au)	MAln MFie WCre
- 'Melody' **new**	SPop
- 'Mere Green' (S)	MAln
- 'Merlin' (Au/A)	EWoo WLin
- 'Merlin' (S)	MAln NLAp
- 'Merlin Stripe' (Au/St)	GNor ITim MFie MOne SPop WCre
	WHil
- 'Mermaid' (Au/d)	GAbr GNor WCre
- 'Merridale' (Au/A)	MFie WCre WHil
- 'Mersey Tiger' (Au/S)	GAbr ITim MFie NLAp SPop
- 'Metha' (A)	MAln MFie
- 'Mexicano' (A)	MAln
- 'Michael' (Au/S)	MAln
- 'Michael Watham' (Au/S)	MAln
- 'Michael Wattam' (Au/S)	MAln
- 'Mick' (Au/A)	MAln
- 'Midnight' (Au/A)	MAln
- 'Mikado' (Au/S)	MFie SPop WOFF
- 'Milkmaid' (Au/A)	WMAq
- 'Millicent' (Au/A)	MAln MFie
- 'Mink' (Au/A)	ITim MFie WHil
- 'Minley' (Au/S)	GCai GNor MFie NBir NBro NHol
	SPop WCre WHil
- 'Mirabella Bay' (A)	MAln
- 'Mirandinha' (Au/A)	MAln MFie WCre
- 'Miriam' (Au/A)	MAln
- 'Mish Mish' (Au/d)	WHil
- 'Miss Bluey' (Au/d)	MAln SPop
- 'Miss Newman' (Au/A)	MAln SPop
- 'Miss Pinky' (Au) **new**	SPop
- 'Mojave' (Au/S)	CWCL EWoo GNor MFie NHol
	NLAp NRya SPop WCre WHil WLin
- 'Mollie Langford' (Au/A)	MAln MFie SPop WHil
- 'Monet' (Au/S)	MAln
- 'Moneymoon' (Au/S)	EWoo MFie WHil
- 'Monica' (Au/A)	MFie
- 'Monk' (Au/S)	ITim MFie WCre WHil
- 'Monk's Eleigh' (Au/A)	MAln
- 'Moonglow' (Au/S)	MFie
- 'Moonlight' (Au/S)	GAbr MAln
- 'Moonriver' (Au/A)	EWoo MAln MFie SPop WCre WHil
- 'Moonshadow' (d)	MAln
- 'Moonstone' (Au/d)	MFie
- 'Moselle' (Au/S)	MAln
- 'Mr A' (Au/S)	SPop WHil WLin
- 'Mr Greenfingers' (Au) **new**	WCre
- 'Mrs A. Bolton' (Au/A)	MFie

- 'Mrs L. Hearn' (Au/A) GNor ITim MFie SPop WHil
- 'Mrs R. Bolton' (Au/A) WCre
- 'Murray Lanes' (A) MAln
- 'My Fair Lady' (A) MAln MFie
- 'Myrtle Park' (A) MAln
- 'Nankenan' (Au/S) MAln MFie WHil
- 'Neat and Tidy' (Au/S) ECho LRHS MFie NLAp NOak NRya SPop WCre WFar WHil WLin
- 'Nefertiti' (A) MAln SPop WHil
- 'Nessun Dorma' (Au) **new** MAln MFie
- 'Neville Telford' (Au/S) GNor ITim MFie WCre WLin
- 'Nickity' (Au/A) GAbr ITim MFie SPop WCre WLin
- 'Nicola Jane' (Au/A) MAln
- 'Nigel' (Au/d) GAbr ITim
- 'Nightwink' (Au/S) MAln
- 'Nina' (Au/A) MAln
- 'Nita' (Au/d) MAln
- 'Nitelford' (Au) MOne
- 'Nocturne' (Au/S) GNor NBro NHol NLAp SPop WLin
- 'Noelle' (Au/S) ITim
- 'Nona' (Au/d) SPop
- 'Nonchalance' (Au/A) MFie
- 'Norma' (Au/A) MFie WLin
- 'Notability' (Au/A) MAln
- 'Notable' (Au/A) MAln
- 'Nureyev' (Au/A) MAln
- 'Nymph' (d) **new** CStu EWoo SPop WHil
- 'Oakie' (Au/S) MAln
- 'Ol' Blue Eyes' (Au/St) MAln
- 'Old Clove' MOne
- 'Old Clove Red' (Au/B) WLin
- 'Old England' (Au/S) MFie SPop WCre
- 'Old Gold' (Au/S) GAbr SUsu WLin
- 'Old Irish Blue' (Au/B) ECho IGor
- 'Old Irish Scented' (Au/B) IGor ITim NBro WHil WLin
- 'Old Mustard' (Au/B) SMHy WLin
- 'Old Pink Dusty Miller' (Au/B) GAbr
- 'Old Red Dusty Miller' (Au/B) ECha LTwo NBir NLAp WHil
- 'Old Red Elvet' (Au/S) GNor MAln SPop
- 'Old Smokey' (Au/A) MAln MFie SPop
- 'Old Suffolk Bronze' (Au/B) GAbr
- 'Old Yellow Dusty Miller' (Au/B) EWes GAbr GCai MFie MSte NBro NHol NLAp NRya WHil
- 'Olton' (Au/A) MFie WCre
- 'Opus One' (Au/A) MAln
- 'Orb' (Au/S) GAbr ITim MFie SPop WCre
- 'Ordvic' (Au/S) MAln WLin
- 'Orlando' (S) MAln
- 'Orwell Tiger' (Au/St) EWoo SPop
- 'Osbourne Green' (Au/B) EWoo GAbr GCai GNor MFie NJOw NLAp SPop SUsu WCre WHil WOFF
- 'Otto Dix' (Au/A) MAln
- 'Overdale' (Au/A) MAln WCre
- 'Paddlin Madeleine' (A) MAln
- 'Pagoda Belle' (Au/A) MAln
- 'Paleface' (Au/A) EWoo ITim MAln MFie WCre WHil
- 'Pam Tiger' (Au/St) MAln
- 'Panache' (Au/S) MAln
- 'Papageno' (Au/St) MAln
- 'Paphos' (d) **new** SPop
- 'Paradise Yellow' (Au/B) GEdr GNor SPop
- 'Paragon' (Au/A) MAln WHil
- 'Paris' (Au/S) MAln
- 'Party Time' (Au/S) MAln
- 'Pastiche' (Au/A) WCre
- 'Pat' (Au/S) MFie NLAp SPop
- 'Pat Barnard' (Au) NJOw
- 'Patience' (Au/S) NJOw SPop WHil
- 'Patricia Barras' (Au/S) MAln
- 'Pauline' (Au/A) MFie
- 'Pauline Taylor' (d) MAln
- 'Pear Drops' (Au) GAbr

- 'Pegasus' (Au/d) MAln SPop
- 'Peggy' (Au/A) WHil WLin
- 'Peggy's Lad' (A) MAln
- 'Pequod' (A) MAln
- 'Peter Beardsley' (Au/A) MAln
- 'Peter Hall' (d) MAln
- 'Phantom' (Au) MAln
- 'Pharaoh' (A) EShb MAln MFie SPop
- 'Phyllis Douglas' (Au/A) ITim MFie NLAp SPop WCre
- 'Pierot' (Au/A) MFie SPop WCre WHil
- 'Piers Telford' (Au) CWCL GAbr GCai GNor MFie SBch SDnm SPav SPop WCre WHil WLin
- 'Piglet' (Au) **new** GAbr
- 'Pink Fondant' (d) GAbr MAln
- 'Pink Lady' (Au/A) MFie NBro SPop
- 'Pink Lilac' (A/S) GNor
- 'Pink Panther' (Au/S) MAln
- 'Pinkie' (Au/A) MAln WHil
- 'Pinstripe' MOne SPop WHil
- 'Pioneer Stripe' (Au/S) NJOw WHil
- 'Pippin' (Au/A) GAbr MFie NBro SPop WCre WHil WLin
- 'Pixie' (Au/A) EWoo MAln
- 'Playboy' (Au/A) MAln
- 'Plush Royal' (Au/S) MAln
- 'Polestar' (Au/A) EWoo MFie SPop WCre WLin
- 'Pop's Blue' (Au/S/d) SPop
- 'Portree' (Au/S) GAbr
- 'Pot o' Gold' (Au/S) ECho EWoo GNor ITim MFie NLAp NOak SPop WCre WHil
- 'Prague' (Au/S) GAbr MFie NBir SPop SUsu WCre WLin
- 'Pretender' (Au/A) MAln SPop
- 'Prince Bishop' (S) MAln
- 'Prince Charming' (Au/S) ITim MFie MOne SPop SUsu WLin
- 'Prince Igor' (A) MAln
- 'Prince John' (Au/A) CWCL ITim MFie NBro SPop WCre WHil WLin WOFF
- 'Prince Regent' (Au/B) NBro
- 'Prometheus' (Au/d) MAln NRya WCre
- 'Purple Emperor' (Au/A) MFie WCre
- 'Purple Glow' (d) MAln WLin
- 'Purple Sage' (Au/S) GCai GNor
- 'Purple Velvet' (Au/S) CWCL SPop
- 'Quality Chase' (A) WCre
- 'Quatro' (Au/d) MAln SPop
- 'Queen Alexandra' (Au/B) GAbr
- 'Queen Bee' (Au/S) GAbr GNor ITim MFie WHil
- 'Queen of Sheba' (Au/S) MAln
- 'Queen's Bower' (Au/S) SPop
- 'Quintessence' (A) MAln MFie WCre
- 'Rab C. Nesbitt' (Au/A) MAln
- 'Rabley Heath' (Au/A) GCai MFie SPop WCre
- 'Rachel' (A) GAbr MAln
- 'Rajah' (Au/S) CWCL ECho ELan GAbr GNor ITim MFie MOne SPop WCMO WCre WHil
- 'Raleigh Stripe' (Au/St) MAln SPop
- 'Ralenzano' (A) MAln
- 'Rameses' (A) MAln WCre
- 'Rebecca Hyatt' (Au/d) MAln
- 'Red Admiral' (Au) MAln
- 'Red Arrows' (Au) MAln
- 'Red Embers' (S) MAln
- 'Red Gauntlet' (Au/S) EDAr GCai ITim LBBr MFie MRav MSte SPop WHil WLin
- 'Red Mark' (Au/A) MFie WCre
- 'Red Rum' (S) MFie
- 'Red Vulcan' (Au) **new** WCre
- 'Redcar' (Au/A) MAln
- 'Redstart' (Au/B) ITim
- 'Regency' (A) MAln
- 'Remus' (Au/S) CWCL ECho ELan EWoo GAbr GCai GNor ITim LTwo MFie SPop SUsu WCre WHil WLin

- 'Rene' (Au/A)	GAbr MFie WCre
- 'Respectable' (Au/A)	MAln
- 'Reverie' (d)	MAln
- 'Riatty' (Au/d)	GAbr MAln MFie
- 'Richard Shaw' (Au/A)	MFie MOne WLin
- 'Ring of Bells' (S)	MAln
- 'Rita' (Au/S)	MAln
- 'Robert Lee' (Au/A)	MAln
- 'Roberto' (Au/S)	MAln
- 'Robin Hood' (Au/A)	MAln
- 'Rock Sand' (Au/S)	ECho GCai GNor MFie WHil WLin
- 'Rodeo' (Au/A)	GAbr NLAp WCre WPat
- 'Rolts' (Au/S)	CWCL ECho ELan EShb EWoo
	GAbr GNor ITim MFie NBir NBro
	NHol NLAp NOak SDnm SPav
	SPop WCre WHil WOFF
- 'Rondy' (Au/S)	MAln NLAp
- 'Ronnie Johnson' (Au)	MAln
- 'Ronny Simpson'	WCre
- 'Rosalie' (Au)	SPop
- 'Rosalie Edwards' (Au/S)	GNor MFie
- 'Rose Conjou' (d)	GAbr MAln
- 'Rose Kaye' (Au/A)	MAln SPop WCre
- 'Rose Three' (Au) new	WCre
- 'Rosebud' (Au/S)	GAbr GNor
- 'Rosemary' (Au/S)	EWoo ITim MFie SUsu WCre WHil
- 'Rothesay Robin' (A)	MAln
- 'Rowena' (Au/A)	GCai MFie NBro SDnm SPav SPop
	WCre WHil
- 'Roxborough' (Au/A)	CWCL MAln
- 'Roxburgh' (Au/A)	MFie SPop WCre
- 'Roy Keane' (Au/A)	MFie SPop
- 'Royal Mail' (Au/S)	MAln
- 'Royal Marine' (Au/S)	MAln
- 'Royal Purple' (Au/S)	NBir
- 'Royal Velvet' (Au/S)	GAbr WHil
- 'Ruby Hyde' (Au/B)	GAbr
- 'Rusty Dusty' (Au)	IGor
- 'Ryecroft' (Au/A)	MAln
- 'Sabrina' (Au/A)	MAln
- 'Saginaw' (A)	MAln
- 'Sailor Boy' (Au/S)	MFie
- 'Saint Boswells' (Au/S)	GAbr GNor MAln NRya SPop
- 'Saint Quentin' (Au/S)	MAln
- 'Salad' (Au/S)	GAbr GCrs
- 'Sale Green' (Au/S)	MFie
- 'Sally' (A)	MAln
- 'Sam Gamgee' (A)	MAln
- 'Sam Hunter' (Au/A)	MAln SPop
- 'Samantha' (Au/A)	MAln
- 'San Antonio' (A)	MAln
- 'Sandhills' (Au/A)	MAln MFie
- 'Sandmartin' (Au/S)	MFie
- 'Sandra' (Au/A)	ECho ELan GAbr MFie SPop WCre
- 'Sandra's Lass' (A)	MAln
- 'Sandwood Bay' (Au/A)	EShb GAbr GCai GNor LRHS MFie
	MOne NBro SPop WCre
- 'Sarah Humphries' (d)	MAln
- 'Sarah Lodge' (Au/d)	CWCL GAbr MFie SPop WLin
- 'Scipio' (Au/S)	MAln
- 'Scorcher' (Au/S)	MAln SPop
- 'Sea Mist' (d)	MAln
- 'Second Victory' (Au) new	WCre
- 'Serenity' (Au/S)	GNor MFie WCre WHil WOFF
- 'Sergeant Wilson' (Au)	MAln
- 'Shalford' (Au/d)	MFie SPop WLin
- 'Sharman's Cross' (Au/S)	MAln MFie
- 'Sharon Louise' (Au/S)	WCre WLin
- 'Sheila' (Au/S)	ECho ITim MFie NJOw SPop WCre
	WHil WLin
- 'Shere' (Au/S)	EWoo MFie SPop WCre WLin
- 'Shergold' (Au/A)	MFie WCre
- 'Sherwood' (Au/S)	GCai ITim MFie SPop WHil WLin
- 'Shirley' (Au/S)	MAln
- 'Showman' (Au/S)	MAln
- 'Sibsey' (Au/d)	MAln SPop
- 'Sidney' (A)	MAln
- 'Silas' (Au/B)	SPav
- 'Silmaril' (Au)	MAln SPop
- 'Silverway' (Au/S)	EWoo ITim SPop WCre WHil WLin
- 'Simply Red' (Au)	MAln
- 'Sir John' (A)	MFie
- 'Sir Robert' (Au/d)	MAln
- 'Sirbol' (Au/A)	EWoo MFie WCre
- 'Sirius' (Au/A)	CWCL EWoo GAbr GNor LRHS
	MFie MOne NRya SPop WCot
	WCre WHil
- 'Skipper' (Au/d)	SPop
- 'Skylark' (Au/A)	GAbr MAln SPop WCre WHil
- 'Slioch' (Au/S)	ECho EWoo GAbr GNor ITim MFie
	SPop WCre
- 'Slip Anchor' (A)	MAln
- 'Smart Tar' (Au/S)	MAln
- 'Snooty Fox' (Au/A)	GAbr MFie MOne NJOw
- 'Snooty Fox II' (Au/A)	GNor SPop WCre
- 'Snowy Owl' (Au/S)	GNor MFie SPop WCre
- 'Somersby' (d)	MAln SPop
- 'Soncy Face' (A)	MAln
- 'Sonny Boy' (Au/A)	MAln
- 'Sonya' (Au/A)	ITim WLin
- 'Sophie' (Au/d)	MAln
- 'South Barrow' (Au/d)	GAbr ITim SPop SUsu WCre
- 'Sparky' (A)	MAln
- 'Spartan' (Au)	MAln
- 'Spring Meadows' (Au/S)	CWCL EWoo GAbr GNor MFie
	MOne SPop SUsu
- 'Springtime' (Au/A)	MAln SPop
- 'Stant's Blue' (Au/S)	EShb GCai GNor ITim MFie NBro
	WCre
- 'Star Wars' (Au/S)	GAbr MAln MFie SPop WLin
- 'Starburst' (S)	MAln
- 'Starling' (Au/B)	GAbr SPop
- 'Starry' (Au/S)	MOne WCre
- 'Stella Coop' (Au/d)	MAln
- 'Stetson' (A)	MAln
- 'Stoke Poges' (Au/A)	MAln
- 'Stoney Cross' (Au/S)	SPop
- 'Stonnal' (Au/A)	MFie SPop WCre
- 'Stormin Norman' (Au)	MAln MFie
- 'Stripey' (Au/d)	MAln WCre
- 'Stuart West' (Au/A)	WCre
- 'Stubb's Tartan' (Au/S)	WLin
- 'Subliminal' (Au/A)	MAln
- 'Sue' (Au/A)	MFie WCre
- 'Sugar Plum Fairy' (Au/S)	GAbr WHil
- 'Sultan' (Au/A)	MAln
- 'Summer Sky' (Au/A)	SPop WCre
- 'Summer Wine' (A)	MFie
- 'Sumo' (Au/A)	GAbr MAln MFie SPop WCre WHil
	WLin
- 'Sunflower' (A/S)	EShb EWoo GAbr ITim MFie NLAp
	SPop WCre WLin
- 'Super Para' (Au/S)	EWoo GAbr GKev GNor MFie
	SPop
- 'Superb' (Au/S)	MAln
- 'Susan' (Au/A)	MFie WCre
- 'Susannah' (Au/d)	CWCL EWoo GAbr GCai GNor
	ITim LRHS MFie MOne NPri SDnm
	SPav SPop WHil
* - 'Sweet Chestnut' (Au/S)	MAln
- 'Sweet Georgia Brown' (A)	MAln
- 'Sweet Pastures' (Au/S)	ECho GAbr GNor ITim MFie NLAp
	SPop WCre
- 'Sword' (Au/d)	CStu ECho GAbr GCrs GNor MAln
	MFie MOne SPop WCre WHil WLin
	WOFF
- 'Symphony' (Au/A)	EWoo MFie MOne SUsu WCre
	WHil
- 'T.A. Hadfield' (Au/A)	EWoo MFie WHil
- 'Taffeta' (S)	CWCL MAln SDnm SPav

- 'Tall Purple Dusty Miller' (Au/B)	SPop
- 'Tally-ho' (Au/A)	MAln
- 'Tamino' (Au/S)	MAln
- 'Tandem' (Au/St)	MAln
- 'Tarantella' (Au/A)	GAbr GNor MFie WCre WLin
- 'Tawny Owl' (Au/B)	GAbr NBro
- 'Tay Tiger' (Au/St)	SPop
- 'Teawell Pride' (Au/d)	WHil
- 'Ted Gibbs' (Au/A)	EWoo ITim MAln MFie MOne
- 'Ted Roberts' (Au/A)	EShb MFie SPop SUsu WCre WHil WLin
- 'Teem' (Au/S)	GAbr GNor NRya SPop WCre WOFF
- 'Temeraire' (A)	MAln
- 'Tenby Grey' (Au/S)	WCre WLin
- 'Tender Trap' (A)	MAln
- 'Terpo' (A)	MAln MFie
- 'Tess' (Au/A)	MAln
- 'The Baron' (Au/S)	EWoo GCai GNor ITim MFie MOne SPop WCre WHil WLin
- 'The Bishop' (Au/S)	ITim MFie SPop WHil
- 'The Bride' (Au/S)	WCre
- 'The Cardinal' (Au/d)	MAln SUsu
- 'The Czar' (Au/A)	MFie
- 'The Egyptian' (A)	ITim MAln SPop WHil
- 'The Hobbit' (Au/A)	MAln
- 'The Raven' (Au/S)	EWoo GAbr ITim MFie SPop WOFF
- 'The Sneep' (Au/A)	SPop WCre WHil
- 'The Snods' (Au/S)	EWoo GNor MFie
- 'The Wrekin' (Au/S)	MAln
- 'Thebes' (A)	MAln
- 'Thetis' (Au/A)	MFie SPop WCre
- 'Thirlmere' (Au/d)	MAln
- 'Three Way Stripe' (St)	WCre WHil
- 'Thutmoses' (Au/A)	MAln
- 'Tiger Tim' (Au/St)	MAln
- 'Tinker' (S)	MAln
- 'Tinkerbell' (Au/S)	MFie SPop WCre WOFF
- 'Titania' (Au) **new**	SPop
- 'Toddington Green' (Au/S)	MAln
- 'Toffee Crisp' (Au/A) **new**	WCre
- 'Tom Farmer' (Au) **new**	WCre
* - 'Tomato' (Au)	WLin
- 'Tomboy' (Au/S)	MFie SDnm SPop
- 'Toolyn' (Au/S)	MAln
- 'Top Affair' (d)	MAln
- 'Tosca' (Au/S)	EWoo GCai GCrs GNor ITim NRya SPop WCre WHil WLin
- 'Trish'	GAbr
- 'Trojan' (Au/S)	WOFF
- 'Trouble' (Au/d)	CStu EBee GAbr LHop LRHS MBNS MFie MOne SPop WCre WLin
- 'Troy Aykman' (A)	MAln
- 'Trudy' (Au/S)	EWoo GAbr GCai GNor ITim MFie MOne SPop WCre WHil
- 'True Briton' (Au/S)	MFie SPop WCre
- 'Trumpet Blue' (Au/S)	MFie
- 'Tumbledown' (Au/A)	MFie
- 'Tummel'	EWoo MAln MFie SPop WHil
- 'Tuthmoses'	MFie
- 'Twiggy' (Au/S)	GCai MAln NRya
- 'Tye Lea' (Au/S)	MAln
- 'Typhoon' (Au/A)	EWoo MFie SPop WCre
- 'Uncle Arthur' (Au/A)	MAln
- 'Unforgettable' (A)	MAln MFie
- 'Upton Belle' (Au/S)	MAln MFie
- 'Valerie' (Au/A)	ITim SPop WCre WHil
- 'Valerie Clare'	MAln
- 'Vee Too' (Au/A)	GAbr MFie SPop WCre
- 'Vega' (A)	MAln SPop
- 'Vein' (Au/St)	MAln
- 'Velvet Moon' (A)	MAln MFie
- 'Venetian' (A)	MAln MFie SPop

- 'Venus' (A)	MAln
- 'Vera Hill' (Au/A)	MAln
- 'Verdi' (Au/A)	ITim MAln
- 'Victoria' (Au/S)	MAln
- 'Victoria de Wemyss' (Au/A)	MFie WCre
- 'Victoria Park' (Au/A)	MAln
- 'Virginia Belle' (Au/St)	ITim MAln
- 'Vivian' (Au/S)	MAln
- 'Vulcan' (Au/A)	ECho MFie NBro SPop
- 'Walhampton' (Au/S)	WHil
- 'Walter Lomas' (Au/S)	MAln
- 'Walton' (Au/A)	CWCL MFie SPop WCre WHil
- 'Walton Heath' (Au/d)	ECho MFie SPop WCre WLin
- 'Wanda's Moonlight' (d) **new**	MAln
- 'Watchett' (A)	MAln
- 'Wayward' (S)	MAln WCre
- 'Wedding Day' (Au/S)	MAln MFie
- 'Wentworth' (Au/A)	MAln
- 'Whistle Jacket' (S)	MAln SPop
- 'White Ensign' (Au/S)	ECho EWoo GAbr GNor ITim MFie NOak SPop WCre WHil WLin WOFF
- 'White Water' (A)	MAln SPop
- 'White Wings' (Au/S)	EWoo GCai GNor MFie SPop
- 'Whitecap' (Au/S)	MAln
- 'Whoopee' (A)	EWoo MAln
- 'Wichita Falls' (A)	MAln
- 'Wilf Booth' (Au/A)	MAln MFie SPop
- 'William Telford' (Au)	MOne
- 'Wincha' (Au/S)	EShb EWoo GCai MFie SPop WCre
- 'Windways Pisces' (d)	MAln
- 'Winifrid' (Au/A)	EShb GAbr GNor LRHS MFie SPop WCre WHil
- 'Witchcraft' (Au) **new**	SPop
- 'Woodmill' (Au/A)	EWoo MAln SPop
- 'Wycliffe Midnight' (Au)	GAbr GNor
- 'Wye Hen' (Au/St)	MAln
- 'Y.I. Hinney' (Au/A)	WCre
- 'Yellow Hammer' (Au/S)	MAln
- 'Yellow Isle' (Au/S)	MAln
- 'Yitzhak Rabin' (A)	MAln WHil
- 'Yorkshire Grey' (Au/S)	MFie NBro
- 'Zambia' (Au/d)	ECho GAbr ITim MFie SPop SUsu WCre WHil
- 'Zircon' (S)	MAln
- 'Zodiac' (Au/S)	MAln
- 'Zoe' (A)	MAln
- 'Zoe Ann' (Au/S)	MAln
- 'Zorro' (Au/St)	MAln
auriculata (Or)	GKev NLAp SBla
- subsp. *tournefortii*	GFle
'Barbara Barker' (Au)	GEdr
'Barbara Midwinter' (Pr)	CDes CMea WAbe
Barnhaven Blues Group (Pr/Prim) ♀H4	CSWP GAbr
Barnhaven doubles (Pr/dPrim)	CSWP
Barnhaven Gold-laced Group	see *P.* Gold-laced Group Barnhaven
Barnhaven Traditional Group (Pr)	CSWP
'Beatrice Wooster' (Au)	CLyd CNic EAEE GKev ITim LRHS MFie NDlv NJOw NLAp NWCA WAbe
'Bee' x 'Jo-Jo'	EHyt GCrs
'Beeches' Pink'	GAbr
beesiana (Pf)	More than 30 suppliers
'Belinda'	ITim
bella (Mi) SDR 3236	GKev
bellidifolia (Mu)	CSec EBee GEdr GFle GIBF
§ - subsp. *hyacinthina* (Mu)	WAbe
aff. *bellidifolia* (Mu)	GKev

beluensis	see *P.* x *pubescens* 'Freedom'
Bergfrühling Julianas Group (Pr/Prim)	MFie
§ x *berninae* 'Windrush' (Au)	WAbe
'Bewerley White'	see *P.* x *pubescens* 'Bewerley White'
bhutanica	see *P. whitei* 'Sherriff's Variety'
'Big Red Giant' (Pr/dPrim)	CWCL NGHP
bileckii	see *P.* x *forsteri* 'Bileckii'
'Blue Riband' (Pr/Prim)	CDes EBee EPfP SBla WFar
'Blue Sapphire' (Pr/dPrim)	CWCL EPfP GAbr LRHS MBNS MBow MFie NCGa NGHP NWCA WGwG
'Blutenkissen' (Pr/Prim)	GAbr
'Bon Accord Cerise' (Pr/dPoly)	GAbr
'Bon Accord Purple' (dPoly)	WFar
boothii (Pe) EN 382	WThu
I - *alba* (Pe)	GCrs GFle GGGa LTwo
- subsp. *autumnalis* (Pe)	GGGa
- subsp. *repens* (Pe)	MNrw
'Boothman's Ruby'	see *P.* x *pubescens* 'Boothman's Variety'
§ *bracteosa* (Pe)	GCrs GFle ITim
Bressingham (Pf)	WFar
brevicula SDR 2769	GKev
brevicula x *chionantha* subsp. *sinopurpurea* (Cy)	NEgg
brigantia	GIBF
'Broadwell Chameleon'	EHyt
'Broadwell Milkmaid' **new**	WAbe WLin
'Broadwell Pink' (Au)	EHyt ITim WAbe
'Broadwell Ruby' (Au)	EHyt WAbe WLin
'Bronwyn' (Pr/Prim)	NBir WCot
'Broxbourne'	ITim NHol NLAp
'Buckland Wine' (Pr/Prim)	CElw
x *bulleesiana* (Pf)	CMMP EBee EChP EMFW EMar LRHS MTis NBro NHol NLar NRnb NScw SMrm SPer SPet SRms SWat WBrE WFar WHil WLin WMnd WMoo WPer
- Moerheim hybrids (Pf)	WFar
bulleyana (Pf) ♀H4	More than 30 suppliers
- ACE 2484	WAbe
burmanica (Pf)	EBee GAbr GBuc GEdr GGar GIBF GKev MDun MMuc NEgg NLAp SIng SRms SWat WBVN WFar WMoo
'Butter Yellow' (Belarina Series) (d) **new**	CHVG CWCL SVil WCMO
'Butter's Bronze' (Pr/Prim)	WOut
'Butterscotch' (Pr/Prim)	CSWP NDov
'Caerulea Plena' (Pr/Prim)	GCal
calderiana (Pe)	GFle NLAp
Candelabra hybrids (Pf)	CBre CBro CHar COIW CTbh CWCL EChP ECho EPot GAbr GGar ITim LSou MAvo MDun MNHC NBir NCob NGdn NRnb SPet SWal SWat WCra WRos
Candy Pinks Group (Pr/Prim)	CSWP
capitata (Ca)	CMMP CSWP EBee ECho EDAr GCrs GFle GIBF GKev IFro MFie NLAp NRya NWCA SPoG WAbe WFar WGwG
- CC 4399	GKev
- subsp. *mooreana* (Ca)	CFir CPBP CSec EChP EPot GFle GIBF NDlv NGdn SPlb SRot WBVN WHil WPtf
- subsp. *sphaerocephala* (Ca)	GKev
- - SDR 3225	GKev
'Captain Blood' (Pr/dPrim)	EPfP MBNS MBow MFie MSte NLar NWCA WFar WRha
Carnation Victorians Group (Pr/Poly)	MFie
carniolica (Au)	GFle MFie
Casquet mixture (Pr/Prim)	CSWP
cernua (Mu)	GIBF GKev WLin
Chartreuse Group (Pr/Poly)	CSWP MFie WRha
'Cherry' (Pr/Prim)	WHil
§ *chionantha* (Cy) ♀H4	CLAP CWCL EBee EPfP GAbr GBBs GCrs GFle GGar GKev LRHS MDun MFie MNrw NBir NCob NEgg NLAp NMyG NVic SBch SPer SWat WAbe WBVN WFar WGwG
- subsp. *chionantha* (Cy)	EBee GIBF GKev
- - SDR 1865	GKev
§ - subsp. *melanops* (Cy)	EBee GFle GIBF GMac LRHS
§ - subsp. *sinopurpurea* (Cy)	CLAP CWCL EBee EChP GFle GGar GIBF GKev ITim NCGa NLar NSti SPer SWat WAbe WFar WHil WPer
chungensis (Pf)	CBcs CLAP CWCL EBee EDAr EWTr GBuc GEdr GFle GGar GIBF GKev ITim MLLN NDlv NEgg NRnb NSti SRms SWat SWvt WMoo
§ *chungensis* x *pulverulenta* (Pf)	CLAP EChP GBuc GCai GEdr MFie NEgg NGdn NLar NRnb SMrm WAbe WFar WMnd
x *chunglenta*	see *P. chungensis* x *pulverulenta*
§ 'Clarence Elliott' (Au)	CDes CGra CLyd CPBP EHyt GCrs GKev GNor ITim MFie NHar SBch WAbe WLin
clarkei (Or)	CLyd GEdr GFle WAbe
clusiana (Au)	GFle GKev MFie
- 'Murray-Lyon' (Au)	GCrs NMen NSla
cockburniana (Pf) ♀H4	CBcs CRow CSec EBee EChP EDAr GBBs GEdr GFle GGar GIBF GKev GQui MDKP MFie NEgg NGdn NSti SPoG SRms SWat WAbe WFar WHil
- SDR 1967	GKev
- hybrids (Pf)	SWat
- yellow-flowered (Pf)	EBee GEdr GKev
concholoba (Mu)	GFle GKev MFie NLAp
'Corporal Baxter' (Pr/dPrim)	CBgR ENot EPfP MBNS MNrw NGHP SPer SRGP WRha
cortusoides (Co)	CLAP CMil CSec EBee GFle GIBF GKev LSou NLar NRnb SRms
Cowichan Amethyst Group (Pr/Poly)	CDes CSWP EBee
Cowichan Blue Group (Pr/Poly)	CSWP
Cowichan Garnet Group (Pr/Poly)	CDes CSWP EWoo GBuc MFie NDov WPGP
Cowichan Red Group (Pr/Poly)	WFar
Cowichan Venetian Group (Pr/Poly)	CDes CSWP WFar
Cowichan Yellow Group (Pr/Poly)	CDes WCot
'Coy'	CGra EHyt WAbe WLin
'Craven Gem' (Pr/Poly)	GBuc
'Cream' (Belarina Series) (d) **new**	CWCL SVil WCMO
Crescendo Series (Pr/Poly)	GAbr
'Crimson Velvet' (Au)	GAbr GNor ITim NLAp
crispa	see *P. glomerata*
cuneifolia (Cu)	CSec GFle GKev
cusictiana subsp. *nevadensis* (Pa)	GFle
daonensis (Au)	GFle GKev
darialica (Al)	CNic GKev

'Dark Rosaleen' (Pr/Poly)	GAbr	
'David Valentine' (Pr)	GAbr GBuc WAbe	
'Dawn Ansell' (Pr/dPrim)	CDes CHad CHrt CRow CWCL	
	ENot EPfP GAbr ITer LRHS MBNS	
	MFie MSte NBir NDov NGHP	
	NLRH NSti SIng SRGP SUsu	
	WCMO WCot WHer	
Daybreak Group (Pr/Poly)	CSWP MFie	
decipiens (Pax) Stein	see *P. hirsuta*	
deflexa (Mu)	GCrs GFle LRHS WLin	
– BWJ 7877	WCru	
denticulata (De) ♀H4	More than 30 suppliers	
– var. *alba* (De)	More than 30 suppliers	
– blue (De)	ECho GAbr NLar	
– 'Bressingham Beauty' (De)	EBrs	
– 'Glenroy Crimson' (De)	CLAP EBee SRms SWvt	
– 'Karryann' (De/v)	CBow EBee EMon MBNS NEgg	
	WCot WHrl	
– lilac (De)	ECho EHon MFie NCob NCot	
	NLAp NPri WWeb	
– 'Prichard's Ruby' (De)	NCob	
– purple (De)	ECho WMoo	
– red (De)	ECho EPfP GGar MWgw NLAp	
	NOrc WMoo	
– 'Robinson's Red' (De)	GBuc	
– 'Ronsdorf' (De)	LRHS	
– 'Rubin' (De)	CSam ECho EHon GAbr IHMH	
	MBrN MBri MFie MBro NChi NCob	
	NOak SPoG SRms WHen WHil	
	WPer WWpP	
– 'Rubinball' (De)	EBee GCrs NHol WCot	
– 'Snowball' (De)	NOak WHen	
deorum (De)	GKev	
x *deschmannii*	see *P. x vochinensis*	
'Desert Sunset' (Pr/Poly)	CSWP MFie	
'Devon Cream' (Pr/Prim)	GBuc WFar	
'Dianne'	see *P. x forsteri* 'Dianne'	
'Discovering Stripes' (Poly) **new**	WHil	
'Dorothy' (Pr/Poly)	MRav	
'Double Lilac'	see *P. vulgaris* 'Lilacina Plena'	
'Duckyls Red' (Pr/Prim)	GBuc WHal	
'Dusky Lady'	MBri WFar	
'Early Bird' (*allionii* hybrid) (Au) **new**	MFie	
'Easter Bonnet' (Pr/Prim)	ENot LRHS NBid	
edelbergii (Sp)	MMHG	
edgeworthii	see *P. nana*	
§ *elatior* (Pr) ♀H4	More than 30 suppliers	
– hose-in-hose (Pr/d)	NBid	
– subsp. *intricata* (Pr)	GFle GKev NWCA	
I – 'Jessica'	WHil	
– subsp. *leucophylla* (Pr)	EBee ECho SBch	
§ – subsp. *meyeri* (Pr)	GFle GKev NEgg	
– subsp. *pallasii* (Pr)	GFle	
'Elizabeth Killelay'PBR (Pr/dPoly)	More than 30 suppliers	
'Ellen Page' (Au)	EHyt MFie	
'Ethel Barker' (Au)	CGra ITim LRHS NDlv NHol	
'Eugénie' (Pr/dPrim)	MBNS MDun NGHP SRGP	
'Fairy Rose' KRW 180/48 (Au)	ITim NHol WAbe	
farinosa (Al)	CLyd CWCL EBee GFle GKev MFie	
	NEgg NRya SPoG WAbe	
fasciculata (Ar)	EHyt GCai GEdr GFle GKev NLAp	
	NWCA SBla	
– CLD 345	WAbe	
'Fife Yellow' (Pr/dPrim)	GBuc	
'Fire Opal' **new**	EBrs	
§ *firmipes* (Si)	EWes GCrs GIBF	
§ *flaccida* (Mu)	GFle GGGa GIBF GKev NLAp	
	WAbe	
Flamingo Group (Pr/Poly)	CSWP MFie	
§ x *floerkeana* (Au)	GCrs	
– f. *biflora* 'Alba' (Au)	SBla	

florida (Y)	NCob	
florindae (Si) ♀H4	More than 30 suppliers	
– bronze (Si)	GQui NBir SWat WWhi	
I – 'Butterscotch' (Si)	WHrl	
– hybrids (Si)	CDWL EChP EHrv GAbr GEdr	
	GGar ITim MFie NCob NEgg NHol	
	WHil	
– Keillour hybrids (Si)	LBMP NChi WPtf	
– magenta (Si)	MDKP	
– orange (Si)	CSam GMac ITim MDKP MNrw	
	NRnb WCru WFar WMoo WWpP	
– peach (Si)	MDKP	
– 'Ray's Ruby' (Si)	CHar CLAP CWoW EBee GBBs	
	GBuc GMac MDKP MFOX MNrw	
	NBir SWat WRos WWFP WWhi	
	WWpP	
– red (Si)	CDes GBuc GCal GGar GKev	
	MFie NBid NEgg NLar NRnb	
	WFar	
– terracotta (Si)	CSWP	
Footlight Parade Group (Pr/Prim)	CSWP	
forbesii (Mo) CC 4084	CPLG	
forrestii (Bu)	CWCL EBee EHyt GGGa GIBF	
	GKev MFie NLAp NPen	
– ACE 2474	GFle	
– DJH 138	LPhx	
– SDR 3304	GKev	
§ x *forsteri* (Au)	GFle MFie	
§ – 'Bileckii' (Au)	CStu EHyt GCrs GFle LRHS NBir	
	NLAp NWCA SRms WAbe	
– 'Bileckii' white-flowered (Au)	GCrs	
§ – 'Dianne' (Au)	GAbr GBuc GCrs NBro NHol	
	NJOw NRya WAbe	
– 'Dianne' hybrids (Au)	MFie	
'Francisca' (Pr/Poly)	CBos CSpe EBee MBNS NGdn	
	WCMO WCot	
'Freckles' (Pr/dPrim)	CWCL ENot MBNS MDun SPer	
	SWat	
'Freedom'	see *P. x pubescens* 'Freedom'	
frondosa (Al) ♀H4	CLyd CWCL ECho GFle GIBF LRHS	
	MDKP MFie NLAp NMen NWCA	
	SOkd SPoG WAbe WBVN	
Fuchsia Victorians Group (Pr/Poly)	MFie	
'Garnet' (*allionii* hybrid) (Au)	MFie WLin	
'Garryard Guinevere'	see *P.* 'Guinevere'	
gaubana (Sp)	GKev	
gemmifera (Ar)	GFle	
– var. *zambalensis*	see *P. zambalensis*	
geraniifolia (Co)	GKev	
§ 'Gigha' (Pr/Prim)	CSWP EBee GCrs	
I *glabra* (G)	WAbe	
glaucescens (Au)	CLyd GCrs GFle GKev MFie NSla	
§ *glomerata* (Ca)	ECho GBuc	
– GWJ 9213	WCru	
– GWJ 9280	WCru	
'Glowing Embers' (Pf)	LRHS MFie NBir	
glutinosa All.	see *P. allionii*	
Gold-laced Group (Pr/Poly)	CBre CMMP CMea CSWP CWCL	
	EBee EChP EPfP EWoo IHMH ITer	
	MBri MHer NGdn NHol NJOw	
	NPri NRya NWCA SPer SPet SUsu	
	WBor WFar WHer WHil WWeb	
	WWhi	
§ – Barnhaven (Pr/Poly)	CDes GAbr MFie NBir NCGa NEgg	
§ – Beeches strain (Pr/Poly)	NCob SSth	
– red (Pr/Poly)	MAvo	
'Gordon'	MOne	
gracilipes (Pe)	CDes CLAP GCrs GFle GGGa	
	SRms WAbe	
– L&S 1166	WAbe	
– early-flowering (Pe)	WAbe	
– 'Major'	see *P. bracteosa*	

- 'Minor'	see *P. petiolaris*
graminifolia	see *P. chionantha*
Grand Canyon Group (Pr/Poly)	MFie
grandis (Sr)	GFle GKev
'Green Lace' (Poly) **new**	NBhm WCot
griffithii (Pe)	GGGa
'Groenekan's Glorie' (Pr/Prim)	GAbr GEdr LRHS MBri MRav NBir NBro WFar WViv
§ 'Guinevere' (Pr/Poly) ♀H4	CSam EBee EBrs EPfP GAbr GEdr GMaP LRHS MBri NBid NBir NBro NDov NSla NSti NVic SIng SPer SPlb WCot WEas WFar WHil WHoo WLin WPat WViv WWeb WWhi
'Hall Barn Blue'	CBgR GAbr GEdr NHol NMyG
§ *halleri* (Al)	EBee GKev MFie NDlv NRnb WAbe WLin
- DJHC 0083	WCru
- 'Longiflora'	see *P. halleri*
Harbinger Group (Pr/Prim)	CSWP
Harbour Lights mixture (Pr/Poly)	CSWP MFie
Harlow Carr hybrids (Pf)	CSWP GCai GQui LRHS MLLN NDlv NEgg NSla WEas WMoo
Harvest Yellows Group (Pr/Poly)	MFie NDov WCot
'Helen Evans'	EHyt
'Helmswell Abbey'	GKev
helodoxa	see *P. prolifera*
§ 'Hemswell Blush' (Au)	GCai GKev GNor ITim MOne NLAp NLar
§ 'Hemswell Ember' (Au)	CNic CPBP GCai GCrs MOne NDlv NLAp NRya
heucherifolia (Co)	GFle GKev
hidakana (R)	EHyt GEdr
'High Point' (Au)	CGra
§ *hirsuta* (Au)	CNic EHyt GCrs GEdr GFle GIBF GKev ITim MFie
- var. *exscapa* (Au)	GFle
- 'Lismore Snow' (Au)	SOkd WAbe
- *nivea* (Au)	GKev
- red-flowered (Au)	GKev
hirsuta x *minima* (Au)	see *P. x forsteri*
hongshanensis (Cy)	GKev
hose-in-hose (Pr/dPoly)	CSWP ITer MHer MNrw
- Barnhaven (Pr/Poly) **new**	MFie
§ 'Hyacinthia' (Au)	CLyd GIBF MFie NLar
hyacinthia	see *P. bellidifolia* subsp. *hyacinthia*
ianthina	see *P. prolifera*
incana (Al)	GFle NEgg
Indian Reds Group (Pr/Poly)	CSWP MFie
'Ingram's Blue' (Pr/Poly)	CBgR LRHS
Inshriach hybrids (Pf)	CMHG CSWP NLar WFar
integrifolia (Au)	GBuc GEdr GFle WAbe
integrifolia x *minima* (Cu x Au) **new**	CStu
integrifolia x *minima* 'Kilchuimin' (Au)	CStu GCrs GEdr
§ 'Inverewe' (Pf) ♀H4	CRow GBin GCal GKev GQui NBir NBre NPen SUsu
involucrata	see *P. munroi*
ioessa (Si)	EWes GFle GQui NGdn WAbe
- hybrids (Si)	NLAp
'Iris Mainwaring' (Pr/Prim)	GAbr GEdr NHol NWCA WCot
irregularis (Pe)	GGGa WAbe
issiori	GIBF
Jack in the Green Group (Pr/Poly)	CDMG CSWP GWWP ITer MNrw MRav MWgw WBor WFar WRha
- Barnhaven (Pr/Poly) **new**	MFie
'Jackie Richards' (Au)	EHyt GCrs GKev MFie WLin
jaffreyana (Pu) **new**	GKev
japonica (Pf)	More than 30 suppliers
- 'Alba' (Pf)	CPrp EBee ECho EHrv EPfP GIBF MAvo NDlv NGdn NMyG NPri

	NRnb SPer SPoG WAbe WCAu WFar WHil WMnd
- 'Apple Blossom' (Pf)	CAby CFir EBee GBri GCai GCal GKev NBHF NGdn NHol SWvt WHil
* - 'Carminea' (Pf)	CMil CWCL EBee GBuc GKev MFie NBro NGdn NLar NMyG WFar
- 'Cherry Red' (Pf) **new**	WHil
- 'Fuji' (Pf)	CSWP NBro
- 'Fuji' hybrids (Pf)	NLar
- 'Merve's Red' (Pf)	CDes EBee WPGP
- 'Miller's Crimson' (Pf) ♀H4	More than 30 suppliers
- 'Oriental Sunrise' (Pf)	CMil CSWP GKev MFie NEgg
- pale pink (Pf) **new**	WHil
- 'Postford White' (Pf) ♀H4	More than 30 suppliers
- red (Pf)	MBow WAbe
- 'Valley Red' (Pf)	GBuc GCai
jesoana (Co)	EHyt GGar GKev LTwo
- B&SWJ 618	WCru
'Joan Hughes' (*allionii* hybrid) (Au)	CLyd EHyt SBla WAbe WLin
'Joanna'	ECou GCrs
'Johanna' (Pu)	GAbr GBuc GEdr GFle GKev NGdn NHar NHol NSla NWCA SIng SOkd WAbe
'John Fielding' (Sr x Pr)	CBgR CBro CElw GAbr GEdr
'Jo-Jo' (Au)	CLyd MFie WAbe WLin
juliae (Pr)	EAEE ECho EHyt ETow GIBF LRHS NBid NWCA SPlb WAbe WEas
I - 'Millicent' (Pr)	WCot
'Kate Haywood'	CLyd WLin
'Ken Dearman' (Pr/dPrim)	CWCL ENot EPfP MBNS MBow MFie MRav MSte NBir NGHP NWCA SIng SPer SRGP WFar WGwG
kewensis (Sp) ♀H2	EShb GGar GKev
'Kinlough Beauty' (Pr/Poly)	EMon GAbr GEdr GFle LRHS NRya NSti NWCA WEas WThu
§ *kisoana* (Co)	CLAP GCai GKev NLAp SBla WCru
- var. *alba* (Co)	CLAP GGGa
- var. *shikokiana*	see *P. kisoana*
kitaibeliana (Au)	GKev WLin
knuthiana	see *P. jaffreyana*
'Lady Greer' (Pr/Poly) ♀H4	CBgR CSam CStu EBee EPfP ETow GAbr GBuc GKev LLWP MRav NBir NChi NGdn NLAp NRya NSti NWCA SAga SIng SMac SUsu WHil WOFF WViv
§ *latifolia* (Au)	GFle GIBF
latisecta (Co)	GFle
§ *laurentiana* (Al)	CSec EBee GFle GIBF NMen WAbe
'Lea Gardens' (*allionii* hybrid) (Au)	EHyt ITim MFie NHol
'Lee Myers' (*allionii* hybrid) (Au)	GNor ITim MFie NDlv
leucophylla	see *P. elatior*
'Lilian Harvey' (Pr/dPrim)	CElw CHrt EPfP LRHS MRav NBir WRHF
'Lindum Finale' (Au) **new**	EHyt
'Lindum Moonlight'	EHyt
'Lindum Rapture' (Au) **new**	EHyt
'Lindum Serenade' (Au) **new**	EHyt
'Lindum Snowdrift' (Au) **new**	EHyt
'Lindum Wedgwood' (Au) **new**	EHyt
'Lingwood Beauty' (Pr/Prim)	CAby GAbr
'Linnet' (Pe)	ITim
'Lismore' (Au)	EHyt
'Lismore Jewel' (Au)	GCrs WAbe
'Lismore Treasure' (Au)	MFie WAbe
'Lismore Yellow' (Au)	GKev WAbe WLin

Lissadel hybrids (Pf) — GFle
littoniana — see *P. vialii*
x *loiseleurii* 'Aire Mist' (Au) — CGra CPBP CStu GCai GNor ITer ITim MFie MOne NHol NLAp NRya WAbe WHil WLin
§ – 'Aire Waves' (Au) — EHyt GCai GNor ITim NHol NLAp WLin
longiflora — see *P. halleri*
luteola (Or) — ECho GFle GGar LTwo NEgg NLar WFar WPer
macrophylla (Cy) — EBee GFle GKev NEgg
magellanica (Al) — EBee GKev WAbe
– subsp. *magellanica* (Al) J&JA 2.749.900 — NWCA
malacoides (Mo) — MBri
mandarin red (Pf) — CSWP CWCL
marginata (Au) ♀H4 — CPne EAEE ECho EPot GCrs GEdr GFle LFox LHop LRHS NDlv NHol NJOw NLAp SBch SIng WAbe WFar
– from the Dolomites (Au) — NHol NLAp
– 'Adrian Evans' (Au) — EHyt ITim WLin
I – *alba* (Au) — LRHS NBro NDlv NLAp
– 'Barbara Clough' (Au) — CLyd GEdr ITim
– 'Beamish' (Au) ♀H4 — CLyd NBro NHol NRya SOkd
– 'Beatrice Lascaris' (Au) — CPBP GCrs MFie MOne WAbe
– 'Beverley Reid' (Au) — ITim NRya
– 'Boothman's Variety' (Au) — CTri ECho GCrs ITim NLAp
– 'Caerulea' (Au) — CLyd GKev MOne NLAp WAbe
– 'Casterino' (Au) — GCrs
– 'Clear's Variety' (Au) — ITim NJOw
– 'Correvon's Variety' (Au) — CLyd WAbe
– cut-leaved (Au) — ITim NHol
– 'Doctor Jenkins' (Au) — ITim NHol NLar NRya
– 'Drake's Form' (Au) — ITim NLAp NLar NRya SOkd
– dwarf (Au) — EAEE LRHS MFie
I – 'Earl L. Bolton' — see *P. marginata* 'El Bolton'
§ – 'El Bolton' (Au) — NHol WAbe
– 'Elizabeth Fry' (Au) — CLyd LFox
– 'F.W. Millard' (Au) — NRya
– 'Grandiflora' (Au) — NHol
– 'Highland Twilight' (Au) — NSla
– 'Holden Clough' (Au) — ITim NJOw NRya
– 'Holden Variety' (Au) — CStu ITim NDlv NHol WAbe
– 'Ivy Agee' (Au) — CLyd GCrs ITim NLAp NRya
– 'Janet' (Au) — CLyd NLAp
– 'Jenkins Variety' (Au) — CLyd ECho
– 'Kesselring's Variety' (Au) — CLyd CMMP CMea CStu ECho GCai GEdr GNor MOne NDlv NJOw NLAp WAbe WTin
– 'Laciniata' (Au) — EAEE ITim SBla
– lilac-flowered (Au) — LFox
– 'Linda Pope' (Au) ♀H4 — CLyd GCai GKev ITim NBir NDlv NHar NHol NSla SUsu WAbe
– 'Manfield' — WThu
– maritime form (Au) — NJOw
– 'Millard's Variety' (Au) — CLyd
– 'Miss Savory' (Au) — ITim
– 'Mrs Gatenby' (Au) **new** — NWCA
– 'Nancy Lucy' (Au) — WAbe
– 'Napoleon' (Au) — EHyt GEdr ITim NLAp
– 'Prichard's Variety' (Au) ♀H4 — CLyd ECho ELan GEdr ITim LFox MFie NCob NDlv NJOw NLAp NMyG NRya NWCA SBla WAbe WFar
– 'Sheila Denby' (Au) — ITim NLAp
– 'The President' (Au) — ITim
– violet-flowered (Au) — ECho
– 'Waithman's Variety' (Au) — GCrs ITim NLAp NRya
– wild-collected (Au) — ITim MFie
'Maria Talbot' (*allionii* hybrid) (Au) — EHyt NJOw
'Marianne Davey' (Pr/dPrim) — MRav NBir
'Marie Crousse' (Pr/dPrim) — CBgR CWCL ENot EPfP GAbr LRHS MBNS MDun MWgw NWCA SRGP WCot WFar WHal WRha

Marine Blues Group (Pr/Poly) — CSWP MFie NDov
'Maris Tabbard' — EHyt MFie WAbe
'Marlene' — NBir
'Mars' (*allionii* hybrid) (Au) — GNor NDlv NHol NRya WLin
'Marven' (Au) — CLyd GCai GEdr NJOw
'Mary Anne' — GAbr
Mauve Victorians Group (Pr/Poly) — CSWP MFie
maximowiczii (Cy) — GBuc GFle GKev
'McWatt's Claret' (Pr/Poly) — GAbr LLWP
'McWatt's Cream' (Pr/Poly) — CSWP EBee EBla EWTr GAbr GCrs GEdr GFle LHop NChi NHol SIng WCMO WCot
megalocarpa (Cy) — GKev
megaseifolia (Pr) — GCrs GKev
melanops — see *P. chionantha* subsp. *melanops*
x *meridiana* (Au) — MFie NHol
§ – 'Miniera' (Au) — CLyd ITim WAbe WLin WThu
'Mexico' — MFie WCot
Midnight Group — CSWP GWWP MFie
'Miniera' — see *P. x meridiana* 'Miniera'
minima (Au) — CLyd GFle GKev NBro NLar NSla WAbe
– var. *alba* (Au) — CStu GCrs GFle GGGa MFie NRya
minima x *wulfeniana* — see *P. x vochinensis*
minor (Cy) — GCrs GKev
'Miss Indigo' (Pr/dPrim) — CDes CWCL ENot EPfP LRHS MBNS MDun MFie MRav MSte MWgw NGHP NWCA SGar SPer WCAu WCot WFar
mistassinica f. *leucantha* (Al) — NEgg
– var. *macropoda* — see *P. laurentiana*
miyabeana (Pf) — GFle
– B&SWJ 3407 — WCru
modesta (Al) — CWCL
I – *alba* ambig. (Al) — GFle
– var. *faurieae* (Al) — GKev MFie NWCA
– var. *matsumurae* (Al) — GFle
– var. *samanimontana* (Al) — GKev
mollis (Co) — GIBF GKev
montana Opiz — see *P. elatior*
montana Reuter ex Nyman — see *P. veris*
moupinensis — CDes CLAP CStu EBee GCrs GGGa ITim WCot
– C&H 7038 — GFle
* 'Mrs Eagland' — GAbr
'Mrs McGillivray' (Pr/Prim) — GAbr
§ *munroi* (Ar) — CDes EBee GFle SWat WAbe
§ – subsp. *yargongensis* (Ar) — GAbr GCrs GFle GGar GKev LRHS NLAp NPen SWat WAbe WFar
– – SDR 3096 — GKev
muscarioides (Mu) — EBee GFle GKev
Muted Victorians Group (Pr/Poly) — CSWP MFie
§ *nana* (Pe) — GKev ITim
– 'Alba' (Pe) — WAbe
– blue-flowered (Pe) — ITim
'Nectarine' (Belarina Series) (d) **new** — CWCL LAst SVil WCMO
New Pinks Group (Pr/Poly) — CSWP MFie
'Nightingale' — ITim NHol
nivalis Pallas — see *P. chionantha*
§ *nivalis* (Fed.) Halda subsp. *xanthobasis* (Cy) — EBee GIBF GKev
nutans Delavay ex Franch. — see *P. flaccida*
§ *nutans* Georgi (Ar) — NEgg
obconica (Ob) — LRHS MBri WGwG
obtusifolia (Cy) **new** — GKev
'Old Port' (Pr/Poly) — CBgR CElw EBee GKev LLWP NHol WCot WPat
Old Rose Victorians Group (Pr/Poly) — CSWP MFie

'Olive Wyatt' (Pr/dPrim) — NBir
orbicularis (Cy) — GKev WAbe
'Oriental Sunset' — MDKP
Osiered Amber Group — CSWP
  (Pr/Prim)
'Our Pat' (Pr/dPoly) — GAbr
Pagoda hybrids (Pf) — NEgg
palinuri (Au) — GIBF
palmata (Co) — GCrs GEdr GFle GGGa WAbe
pamirica (Ar) **new** — GFle
'Paris '90' (Pr/Poly) — CSWP MFie NDov
parryi (Pa) — CGra EBee GCrs GFle GIBF WFar
'Pat Cottle' (Pr/dPoly) — CBos
'Peardrop' (Au) — CGra GAbr NHol NLAp
pedemontana (Au) — GFle GKev MSte NWCA WAbe
 - 'Alba' (Au) — EHyt
'Perle von Bottrop' — GAbr
  (Pr/Prim)
'Peter Klein' (Or) — CBos CElw GBuc GEdr GFle LTwo
    NLAp WAbe WTin
petiolaris misapplied — see *P.* 'Redpoll'
§ *petiolaris* (Pe) — EHyt GCrs GFle GGGa GKev GNor
    ITim MDun NWCA WAbe
 - L&S 19856 — GFle
 - Sherriff's form — see *P.* 'Redpoll'
'Petticoat' — NCGa NLar SPer
§ 'Pink Aire' (Au) — EHyt GNor ITim MFie
'Pink Fairy' — ITim
'Pink Ice' (*allionii* hybrid) — CGra CLyd CPBP GCrs GKev ITim
  (Au) — MFie NHol NRya WLin
'Pink Ice' (Belarina Series) — CWCL SVil
  (d) **new**
poissonii (Pf) — CDWL CTri EBee EChP ELan GFle
    GGar GIBF GMac GQui IBal IFro
    LPBA MDun MFie MNrw NEgg
    NGby NGdn NPen NRnb SWat
    WAbe WBVN WGwG WHil WShi
 - ACE 1946 — NWCA
 - ACE 2030 — EPot
 - B&SWJ 7525 — WCru
 - SDR 3216 — GKev
* - f. *alba* (Pf) — GIBF
polyanthus (Pr) — WFar
polyneura (Co) — CAby EBee ECha GFle GGar GIBF
    GKev IGor MFie NBid NEgg NPen
    NVic SPoG SRms WAbe WCot
'Port Wine' (Pr) — GAbr
'Powdery Pink' **new** — EBrs
prenantha (Pf) — EBee GGGa GKev WAbe
'Prince Silverwings' — WEas
  (Pr/dPoly)
§ *prolifera* (Pf) ♀H4 — More than 30 suppliers
 - double-flowered (Pf/d) — CFir
§ x *pubescens* (Au) ♀H4 — EWTr LFox NEgg NJOw NLAp
    WPer
 - 'Alba' (Au) — WAbe
 - 'Alison Gibbs' (Au) — MOne
 - 'Apple Blossom' (Au) — CLyd ITim MFie
 - 'Balfouriana' (Au) — CNic LFox NHol
§ - 'Bewerley White' (Au) — CStu EBee ECho MOne NDlv
    NJOw NLAp NMyG WHoo
 - 'Blue Wave' (Au) — NJOw
§ - 'Boothman's Variety' (Au) — CLyd CStu ECho EPfP GKev ITim
    LRHS MFie MSte NDlv NLAp
    NMyG NRnb NWCA WFar WHoo
    WTin
 - 'Carmen' — see *P.* x *pubescens* 'Boothman's
    Variety'
 - 'Christine' (Au) — CLyd CMea GKev ITim MFie NBir
    NDlv NLAp WCot
 - 'Cream Viscosa' (Au) — MFie NDlv NLAp
 - 'Deep Mrs Wilson' (Au) — MFie
 - 'Faldonside' (Au) — CLyd CNic NDlv WHoo
§ - 'Freedom' (Au) — CLyd CTri EAEE ECho GAbr GKev
    ITim LRHS MFie NBir NDlv NHol
    NJOw NLAp NLar SRms WEas

 - 'Harlow Car' (Au) — CLyd CMea CPBP GMac GQui
    MFie NDlv NWCA WFar WTin
 - 'Henry Hall' (Au) — CLyd EWes MOne
 - 'Herbert Beresford' (Au) — GCrs
 - 'Joan Danger' (Au) — CLyd CNic ITim
 - 'Joan Gibbs' (Au) — CLyd ECho GCai ITim MFie MOne
    NLAp
 - 'Lilac Fairy' (Au) — CNic ITim NDlv NHol NJOw WLin
 - mixed (Au) — ITim
 - 'Mrs J.H. Wilson' (Au) — CGra CLyd EHyt GEdr LRHS MFie
    NDlv NHol NRya
 - 'Pat Barwick' (Au) — CNic GCrs ITim LFox NDlv NLAp
 - 'Peggy' (Au) — MFie
 - 'Peggy Fell' (Au) — WHil
 - 'Rufus' (Au) — CLyd CWCL ECho ETow EWes
    GAbr GCrs WTin
 - 'S.E. Matthews' (Au) — NHol
 - 'Snowcap' (Au) — EHyt GCrs
 - 'Sonya' (Au) — ITim
 - 'The General' (Au) — CLyd GNor ITim MOne SPop
 - 'Verity's Violet' (Au) **new** — WOFF
§ - 'Wedgwood' (Au) — GCai GNor ITim NRya
 - 'Winifred' (Au) — EWoo MFie SPop
x *pubescens* x 'White — ITim
  Linda Pope' (Au)
pulchra (Pe) — GCrs GEdr
pulverulenta (Pf) ♀H4 — More than 30 suppliers
 - 'Bartley' — SWat
 - Bartley hybrids (Pf) ♀H4 — CAby CDWL CDes CWCL GBuc
    GGar LSou NBre NHol SMur
 - 'Bartley Pink' (Pf) — CHar CRow GBuc WEas
 'Quaker's Bonnet' — see *P. vulgaris* 'Lilacina Plena'
 'Rachel Kinnen' (Au) — EHyt ITim MFie SIng SOkd WLin
 'Ramona' (Pr/Poly) — MFie
 'Ravenglass Vermilion' — see *P.* 'Inverewe'
 'Red Velvet' (Pr/dPrim) — CWCL ENot MDun MSte NGHP
§ - 'Redpoll' (Pe) — CDes CLAP WAbe
 - LS&H 19856 — NHar
reidii (So) — GCrs GEdr GFle
 - var. *williamsii* (So) — GGGa GNor
* - - *alba* (So) — GFle WAbe
 'Reverie' (Pr/Poly) — CSWP MFie
 'Rheniana' (Au) — ITim
 'Rose O'Day' (dPrim) — MNrw NBir
rosea (Or) ♀H4 — CAby CRow CWCL EBee ECho
    EDAr EMFW EPfP GEdr MFie
    NBid NBir NLAp NRya NSti NVic
    SWal WFar
 - 'Delight' — see *P. rosea* 'Micia Visser-de Geer'
 - 'Gigas' (Or) — CRez NHol
 - 'Grandiflora' (Or) — CPrp CWCL ECho EHon EPfP
    EWTr GBar GFle GGar GKev
    IHMH LPBA MBow MBri MRav
    NDlv NEgg NWCA SIng SPoG
    SRms SWat WFar WHil WPer
    WWpP
§ - 'Micia Visser-de Geer' — LRHS
  (Or)
§ *rotundifolia* — GKev
 'Rowallane Rose' (Pf) — CBro GBuc IGor WWFP
I 'Rowena' — GCrs WCot
roxburghii — see *P. rotundifolia*
 'Roy Cope' (Pr/dPrim) — CWCL GAbr MFie NBir NWCA
    SRGP WFar
 'Roydon Ruby' — WCot WLin WViv
rubra — see *P. firmipes*
rupicola SDR 3030 (Y) — GKev
  new
rusbyi (Pa) — EBee GFle GIBF GKev NWCA
    WLin
 - subsp. *ellisiae* (Pa) — CGra GFle
 'Sapphire' — MFie
saxatilis (Co) — GCrs GKev MFie
scandinavica (Al) — GCrs GIBF GKev WAbe
x *scapeosa* (Pe) — GGGa GKev
scapigera (Pe) — GGGa

§	'Schneekissen' (Pr/Prim)	CBre GAbr MBri MHer NBir NBro NChi NGHP NMyG NPro SBla WHil WViv
	scotica (Al)	CSec EBee GCrs GIBF GKev GPoy LFox NLap NSla NWCA WAbe WGwG
	secundiflora (Pf)	More than 30 suppliers
	- B&SWJ 7547	WCru
§	x *sendtneri* (Au)	MFie
	septemloba (Co)	GFle
	x *serrata*	see *P.* x *vochinensis*
	serratifolia (Pf)	GGGa GIBF
	sibthorpii	see *P. vulgaris* subsp. *sibthorpii*
	sieboldii (Co) ♀H4	CRow ECho EHyt GCai GFle ITim LFox MLHP MNrw NEgg NMen NRya NWCA SMac SRms SUsu WAbe WFar
	- 'Bide-a-Wee Blue' (Co) new	NBid
I	- 'Blue Lagoon' (Co) new	EBrs
	- blue-flowered (Co)	CLAP CWCL ECho GCrs NMen
	- 'Blush' (Co)	CLAP
	- 'Carefree' (Co)	CLAP LTwo NBro NLar NMen
	- 'Cherubim' (Co)	EBee EBrs WCra
	- 'Dancing Ladies' (Co)	CAby CLAP CMil CSWP MFie NBro
	- 'Duane's Choice' (Co) new	CDes
	- 'Frilly Blue' (Co) new	EBrs
	- 'Galaxy' (Co)	NBro NRya
	- 'Geisha Girl' (Co)	CFir CLAP EBrs MRav NLar WAbe WFar
	- f. *lactiflora* (Co)	CDes CLAP EBee GMac NBro NDov NMen SMHy SRot WCru WFar WPGP WTin
	- 'Lilac Sunbonnet' (Co)	ENot EPfP LRHS LTwo
	- 'Manakoora' (Co)	CLAP CSWP MFie NBro
	- 'Mikado' (Co)	CLAP EBee EBrs MRav
	- 'Pago-Pago' (Co)	CAby CDes CLAP MFie NBro
	- 'Purple Back' (Co)	EBee
	- 'Seraphim' (Co)	CLAP EBee EBrs WCra
	- 'Snowflake' (Co)	CAby CLAP EBrs NLar NSla SBla WAbe WCra
	- 'Tah-ni' (Co)	NBro
	- 'Winter Dreams' (Co)	CLAP CSWP MFie NBid NBro
§	*sikkimensis* (Si) ♀H4	CMil CRow CWCL EBrs ECho EPot EWTr GBBs GCrs GEdr GFle GGGa GGar GIBF GKev LPBA MNrw NGdn NPen SPoG WAbe WBVN WHil WPnP
	- ACE 1422	GBuc
	- B&SWJ 4808	WCru
	- CC 3409	WRos
	- CC&McK 1022	GQui
	- DJHC 01051	WCru
	- SDR 1717	GKev
	- var. *pudibunda* (Si)	GEdr GKev
	- 'Tilman Number 2' (Si)	CWCL GAbr GFle
	aff. *sikkimensis* (Si)	ITim NEgg
	- ACE 2176	GBuc
	Silver-laced Group (Pr/Poly)	SWvt WCot
	- 'Silver Lining' (Pr/Poly)	LRHS
	'Silverwells' (Pf)	GEdr
	sinopurpurea	see *P. chionantha* subsp. *sinopurpurea*
	'Sir Bedivere' (Pr/Prim)	CDes GAbr GBuc NLar
	smithiana	see *P. prolifera*
	'Snow Carpet'	see *P.* 'Schneekissen'
	'Snow Cushion'	see *P.* 'Schneekissen'
	'Snow White' (Pr/Poly)	EHyt GEdr MRav
	Snowcushion	see *P.* 'Schneekissen'
	'Snowruffles'	ITim
	sonchifolia (Pe)	CFir CLAP GGGa GKev ITim MDun
	- from Tibet (Pe)	MDun
	sorachiana	see *P. yuparensis*
	souliei (Yu)	GKev
	- SDR 1855	GKev
	spathulifolia (Mi)	WAbe
	spectabilis (Au)	EBee GEdr GFle GKev WLin
	specuicola (Al)	GIBF GKev
	Spice Shades Group (Pr/Poly)	CSWP GWWP MFie NDov WCot
	'Split Pink' new	CSpe
	x *steinii* (Au)	see *P.* x *forsteri*
	stenocalyx (Pu)	GCrs WAbe
	'Stradbrook Charm' (Au)	CPBP EHyt EPot NHol WLin
	'Stradbrook Dainty' (Au)	MFie
	'Stradbrook Dream' (Au)	CNic EHyt EPot ITim MFie NLAp
	'Stradbrook Gem' (Au)	WAbe WLin
	'Stradbrook Lilac Lustre' (Au)	EHyt MFie
	'Stradbrook Lucy' (Au)	EHyt EPot ITim NHol NLAp WAbe WLin
	'Stradbrook Mauve Magic' (Au)	MFie
	stricta (Al)	GFle
	Striped Victorians Group (Pr/Poly)	CSWP MFie NDov
	'Sue Jervis' (Pr/dPrim)	CWCL MBow NBir NCGa NGHP NLar NSti SPer SRGP WGwG WHal WRha
	suffrutescens (Su)	WAbe
	'Sunshine Susie' (Pr/dPrim)	CWCL ENot EPfP LRHS MBNS MFie MRav MSte NCGa NGHP SIng SRGP WCot
	tanneri (Pe)	GFle
	'Tantallon' (Pe)	GGGa GGar GKev ITim NLAp
§	Tartan Reds Group (Pr/Prim)	CSWP
	'Tawny Port' (Pr/Poly)	GAbr GBuc NBro SRms
	tibetica (Ar)	GFle GGGa GKev ITim
	'Tie Dye' (Pr/Prim)	CDes ENot GBri ITer LRHS NBhm NLar WCot
	'Tipperary Purple' (Pr/Prim)	GAbr GEdr
	'Tomato Red' (Pr/Prim)	CBgR WCot
	'Tony' (Au)	CPBP EHyt WAbe WLin
	tosaensis var. *brachycarpa* (R)	GFle
	'Tournaig Pink' (Pf)	GGar
	tournefortii	see *P. auriculata* subsp. *tournefortii*
	uniflora Gmelin	see *P. vulgaris*
*	*urumiensis*	GKev
	vaginata (Co)	WAbe
	'Val Horncastle' (Pr/dPrim)	CWCL GAbr LRHS MBNS MDKP MNrw MSte MWgw NCGa NGHP NLar NSti NWCA SPer SRGP WCot WLin
	Valentine Victorians Group (Pr/Poly)	MFie
§	*veris* (Pr) ♀H4	More than 30 suppliers
	- subsp. *columnae* (Pr)	EBee
I	- 'Coronation Cowslips' (Pr) new	NDov
	- feather-petalled (Pr) new	WCot
	- hybrids (Pr)	NEgg SGar
	- 'Katy McSparron' (Pr/d)	EBee WCMO WCot
§	- subsp. *macrocalyx* (Pr)	EBee GKev NWCA
	- orange-flowered (Pr)	WMoo
	- red-flowered (Pr)	CMMP NBid NGdn WMoo
	- 'Sunset Shades' (Pr)	NChi NEgg NGHP NJOw NLar
	vernalis	see *P. vulgaris*
	verticillata (Sp)	GKev
§	*vialii* (So) ♀H4	More than 30 suppliers
§	*villosa* (Au)	GFle
	- var. *cottia*	see *P. villosa*
	Violet Victorians Group (Pr/Poly)	CSWP MFie
	viscosa All.	see *P. latifolia*
§	x *vochinensis* (Au)	CFee CLyd CStu NWCA
§	*vulgaris* (Pr/Prim) ♀H4	More than 30 suppliers

- var. **alba** (Pr/Prim) | CRow NSla WBrk
- 'Alba Plena' (Pr/Prim) | CRow GBuc GGar IGor ITer NSti
- 'Alex Brenton' (Pr/d) | LHop
- green-flowered | see *P. vulgaris* 'Viridis'
- 'Greyshot' | NBir
§ - 'Lilacina Plena' | CWCL ENot EPfP MBNS MBow
(Pr/dPrim) | MRav NCGa NCot NGHP SPer
| WCot
§ - subsp. **sibthorpii** | CMHG CSam EBee EBrs ECho
(Pr/Prim) ♀H4 | ETow GAbr GBuc ITim LFox LLWP
| LRHS MHer MLHP MRav MWgw
| NBro NChi NGHP NMyG SBla
| SRms WEas WHil WOut
- – HH&K 337 | GFle
§ - 'Viridis' (Pr/dPrim) | CDes CRow
walshii (Mi) | WLin
waltonii (Si) | CMil EBee GBuc GCai GCrs GEdr
| GFle GKev MDKP MNrw
- hybrids (Si) | NEgg
'Wanda' (Pr/Prim) ♀H4 | CBcs CStu CTri ECho ENot GAbr
| LBMP LLWP LRHS NBid NSti NVic
| SBla SRGP SRms WBrk WCFE
| WCMO WCot WEas WFar WHil
| WTin
Wanda Group (Pr/Prim) | CBcs CNic ECho NEgg
'Wanda Hose-in-hose' | EMon GAbr MMHG NBir WCot
(Pr/dPrim) | WHer WHil
'Wanda Jack in the Green' | CBgR CRow MLLN WCot WFar
(Pr/Prim) |
wardii | see *P. munroi*
warshenewskiana (Or) | CNic GEdr GFle GKev MNrw
| NCob NLAp NMen NRya NWCA
| WAbe WFar WGwG WPat
watsonii (Mu) | EBee GAbr GCrs GGGa GKev
| NLAp SWat
'Wedgwood' | see *P.* x *pubescens* 'Wedgwood'
wessa var. **hopeana** (Si) | GCrs GFle
'Wharfedale Ballerina' (Au) | EHyt ITim
'Wharfedale Bluebell' (Au) | CLyd EHyt ITim NBir WAbe
'Wharfedale Buttercup' | ITim NHar NLAp
(Au) |
'Wharfedale Butterfly' | EHyt ITim NHol
(Au) |
'Wharfedale Crusader' | ITim
(Au) |
'Wharfedale Gem' | GCai GNor ITim MFie NLAp NRya
(*allionii* hybrid) (Au) | WAbe
'Wharfedale Ling' | CGra CPBP CStu EHyt GCai GCrs
(*allionii* hybrid) (Au) | MFie NLAp NRya
'Wharfedale Sunshine' | EHyt ITim MFie NLAp
(Au) |
'Wharfedale Superb' | EHyt ITim MFie NLAp
(*allionii* hybrid) (Au) |
'Wharfedale Village' (Au) | CLyd EHyt GKev GNor ITim NLAp
| WAbe WGwG WLin
'White Linda Pope' (Au) | CLyd
'White Wanda' (Pr/Prim) | GAbr NCGa NDov WHil
'White Waves' (*allionii* | EHyt ITim
hybrid) (Au) |
whitei (Pe) | MDun
§ - 'Sherriff's Variety' (Pe) | CLAP GCrs GKev
wigramiana (So) | WAbe
'William Genders' (Pr/Poly) | GAbr
wilsonii (Pf) | CDWL CTri EChP EPot GBBs GBuc
| GGar GKev GMac LDai MOne
| NDlv NEgg NPen NRnb NWCA
| SEND SWat WBVN WFar WGwG
| WLin
§ - var. **anisodora** (Pf) | CLAP CMil EBee EPot GCrs GFle
| GGar GKev GQui MFie NEgg
| NLAp
'Windrush' | see *P.* x *berninae* 'Windrush'
'Windward Blue' | SBla
'Winter White' | see *P.* 'Gigha'
'Wisley Crimson' | see *P.* 'Wisley Red'
§ 'Wisley Red' (Pr/Prim) | CElw

wollastonii (So) | GCrs
wulfeniana (Au) | CGra GCrs GEdr GFle GKev MFie
| WAbe
- subsp. **baumgarteniana** | WLin
(Au) |
xanthobasis | see *P. nivalis* subsp. *xanthobasis*
yargongensis | see *P. munroi* subsp. *yargongensis*
aff. **yunnanensis** (Y) | GIBF
§ **yuparensis** (Al) | CSec EBee GFle GKev NEgg WAbe
- white-flowered (Al) **new** | GKev
§ **zambalensis** (Ar) | GCrs GFle GKev WAbe

Prinsepia (Rosaceae)

sinensis | CArn CBcs CFee CMCN MBlu NLar
| SLon WSHC
utilis | CTrG

Pritzelago (Brassicaceae)

alpina | CNic NJOw

Prostanthera (Lamiaceae)

aspalathoides | EBee ECou EWes SOWG WCot
'Badja Peak' | WAbe
baxteri | ECou
chlorantha | SOWG
cuneata ♀H4 | More than 30 suppliers
- 'Alpine Gold' | CMHG CWSG WFar
- Kew form | CPLG WPGP
* **digitiformis** **new** | ECou SOWG
§ **incisa** | CPLG CTrw EBee SHDw SPla
- 'Rosea' | SBod SBrw
lasianthos | CBcs CDoC CHll EBee ECou EShb
| EWes SBrw SHDw SOWG
- 'Kallista Pink' **new** | SOWG
- var. **subcoriacea** | CPLG CRHN
magnifica | SOWG
'Mauve Mantle' | ECou SOWG
melissifolia | CArn CPLG ECre EShb LHop SBrw
| WSel
§ - var. **parvifolia** | CTrw EBee ECre WAbe
nivea | ECou
ovalifolia ♀H2 | CPle EBee ECou SOWG
I - 'Variegata' **new** | ECou SOWG
phylicifolia **new** | EBee
'Poorinda Ballerina' | CDoC CPLG CWSG EBee ECou
| EMan EShb LHop MCCP MDun
| MGos MNHC SBrw SMur SOWG
| SPer SPoG WFar WLeb
rotundifolia ♀H2 | CBcs CBrm CDul CFwr CHEx CSBt
| CSev CTrG CTri CWSG EBee ECho
| EOHP ERea MNHC MTis MWgw
| NGHP SBrw SEND SMad SOWG
| SPer WLeb
- 'Chelsea Girl' | see *P. rotundifolia* 'Rosea'
§ - 'Rosea' ♀H2 | CSBt CTbh CTrC CTrG EBee ECou
| GGar NGHP SPoG
* **scheelii** | SOWG
scutellarioides | ECou
'Lavender Lady' |
sieberi misapplied | see *P. melissifolia* var. *parvifolia*
walteri | CBrm CDoC ECou SBrw

Protea ✿ (Proteaceae)

aurea | EShb SPlb
burchellii | SPlb
coronata | SPlb
cynaroides | CBcs CCtw CHEx CTbh CTrC
| IDee SBig SOWG SPlb WSAf
dracomontana | SPlb
effusa | SPlb
eximia | CBcs EShb WSAf
grandiceps | SPlb WSAf
lacticolor | SPlb
laurifolia | SPlb
magnifica | WSAf
mundii | WSAf

neriifolia	EShb WSAf
obtusifolia	SPlb
subvestita	SPlb
susannae	CBcs SPlb

Prumnopitys (Podocarpaceae)

§ *andina*	WFar
elegans	see *P. andina*
§ *taxifolia*	CTrC ECou

Prunella (Lamiaceae)

§ *grandiflora*	CArn CHby CPrp ECha GBar MWat
	SMac SWat WCHb WFar WMoo
	WMow WPGP WWye
- 'Alba'	CSBt EBee ECha EPfP EPyc GMaP
	MFOX MRav MWgw NBid NGHP
	NGdn NLar SPer SPla SPoG WCAu
	WCHb WFar WMnd
- 'Blue Loveliness'	EMan WCHb
- 'Carminea'	EBee MNrw NGby SPer
- light blue-flowered	CSim NLar WMoo
- 'Little Red Riding Hood'	see *P. grandiflora* 'Rotkäppchen'
- 'Loveliness' ♀H4	CDoC EBee ECha ECtt GMaP
	MFOX MRav MWgw NBro NGdn
	NSti NVic SPer SPla SPlb SPoG
	SRGP WCAu WFar WMnd WTin
- 'Pagoda'	CEnt CSpe LIck NBre NLar WCHb
- 'Pink Loveliness'	CPrp CSBt ENot LRHS SRms
	WCHb WFar
- 'Rosea'	CSBt EBee EPfP WOut
§ - 'Rotkäppchen'	ECtt MNrw
- 'Rubra'	CSim EBee GAbr NGHP NLar SBch
	WMoo WPer
- 'White Loveliness'	CElw CPrp CTri LRHS WFar
	WMow WPer WWye
hyssopifolia	XPep
incisa	see *P. vulgaris*
* 'Inshriach Ruby'	NBir
laciniata	CMCo EPPr EShb WCHb WMoo
§ *vulgaris*	CAgr CArn CRWN GBar GPoy
	MBow MHer MNHC MSal NLan
	NMir NPri NSco SECG WCHb
	WHbs WHer WWye
- 'Gleam' (v)	EBee
- var. *leucantha*	GBar WHer
- var. *rubrifolia*	WRha
- 'Ruth Wainwright' (v)	WCHb
- 'Voile'	LAst
x *webbiana*	see *P. grandiflora*

Prunus ✿ (Rosaceae)

'Accolade' ♀H4	CAbP CDul CEnd CLnd COtt CSBt
	CTho EBee ECrN ELan EPfP EWTr
	LAst LPan LRHS MAsh MBri MRav
	NBea NWea SCrf SEND SHBN SLim
	SPer SPoG WDin WFar WJas WOrn
§ 'Amanogawa' ♀H4	More than 30 suppliers
americana new	EMui
x *amygdalopersica*	MCoo SCoo
'Ingrid' (F)	
- 'Pollardii'	MAsh WJas
- 'Robijn' (F)	LBuc
- 'Spring Glow'	CDoC MBri NWea WJas
amygdalus	see *P. dulcis*
armeniaca 'Alfred' (F)	CTho EMui ERea GTwe SDea SKee
- var. *ansu* 'Flore Pleno'	NEgg
(d)	
- 'Blenheim' (F)	ERea
- 'Bredase' (F)	CWib SDea
- 'Early Moorpark' (F)	CAgr CTri CWib EPfP ERea GTwe
	LAst MBri SDea WOrn
- 'Farmingdale' (F)	ERea SDea
- Flavorcot = 'Bayoto'PBR	SPer
new	
- 'Garden Aprigold' (F)	EMui ENot NPri
- 'Goldcot' (F)	EPfP ERea LRHS MCoo SDea

- 'Golden Glow' (F)	CTri ERea GTwe LRHS MCoo SKee
- 'Goldrich' (F)	CAgr
- 'Harglow' (F)	ERea
- 'Hargrand' (F)	CAgr
- 'Harogem' (F)	CAgr
- 'Hemskirke' (F)	ERea SKee
- 'Hongaarse' (F)	SDea
- 'Isabella' (F)	ERea LRHS MBri MCoo MGan
	MNHC SPoG
- 'Moorpark' (F) ♀H3	CEnd CSBt CWib EMui ENot ERea
	GTwe LAst LBuc MGos SDea
	SHBN SKee SPer
- 'New Large Early' (F)	ERea GTwe SDea SEND SKee
- 'Tom Cott' (F)	LRHS MCoo SFam
- 'Tomcot' (F)	MBri SKee SPoG
- 'Tross Orange' (F)	CWib SDea
avium ♀H4	CBcs CCVT CDul CLnd CRWN
	CSBt CWib ECrN EPfP EWTr GIBF
	LBuc MBar MGos MNHC MRav
	MSwo NBee NWea SFam SHBN
	SKee SPer WDin WHar WMoo
	WMou WOrn
- 'Amber Heart' (F)	SKee
- 'August Heart' (F)	SKee
- 'Bigarreau Gaucher' (F)	SHBN SKee
§ - 'Bigarreau Napoléon' (F)	GTwe SHBN SKee
- 'Birchenhayes'	see *P. avium* 'Early Birchenhayes'
- 'Black Eagle' (F)	CTho SKee
- 'Black Elton' (F)	SKee
- 'Black Glory' (F)	SKee
- 'Black Heart' (F)	CWib
- 'Black Tartarian' (F)	SKee
- 'Bottlers'	see *P. avium* 'Preserving'
- 'Bradbourne Black' (F)	ECrN MGan SCrf SKee
- 'Bullion' (F)	CEnd CTho
- 'Burcombe' (F)	CEnd CTho
- Celeste = 'Sumpaca'PBR	EMil EMui GTwe MBri MNHC
(D)	SDea SFam SKee SPoG WOrn
- 'Cherokee'	see *P. avium* 'Lapins'
- 'Colney' (F) ♀H4	GTwe SFam SKee WJas
- 'Dun' (F)	CTho
§ - 'Early Birchenhayes' (F)	CEnd CTho
- 'Early Rivers' (F)	CSBt CWib ECrN ENot GTwe SDea
	SHBN SKee
- 'Elton Heart' (F)	CTho SKee
- 'Emperor Francis' (F)	ECrN SKee
- 'Fice' (F)	CEnd CTho
- 'Florence' (F)	SKee
- 'Governor Wood' (F)	CWib GTwe SKee
- 'Grandiflora'	see *P. avium* 'Plena'
- 'Greenstem Black' (F)	CTho
- 'Hannaford' (D/C)	CTho
- 'Hertford' (F) ♀H4	SFam SKee
- 'Inga' (F)	SFam SKee
- 'Kassins Frühe Herz' (F)	SKee
- 'Kentish Red' (F)	CTho SKee
§ - 'Lapins' (F)	CAgr CDul CLnd CTho ECrN EMui
	GTwe LAst LRHS SDea SFam SKee
	SPoG WHar WJas WOrn
- 'May Duke'	see *P.* x *gondouinii* 'May Duke'
- 'Merchant' (F) ♀H4	ECrN GTwe SKee
- 'Merton Crane' (F)	SKee
- 'Merton Favourite' (F)	SKee
- 'Merton Glory' (F)	CSBt ECrN EMui ENot GTwe
	MGan MGos SCrf SFam SKee
	WOrn
- 'Merton Late' (F)	SKee
- 'Merton Marvel' (F)	SKee
- 'Merton Premier' (F)	SKee
- 'Nabella' (F)	WJas
- 'Napoléon'	see *P. avium* 'Bigarreau Napoléon'
- 'Newstar' (F)	EMui
- 'Noble' (F)	SKee
- 'Noir de Guben' (F)	ECrN GTwe SKee
- 'Nutberry Black' (F)	SKee
- 'Old Black Heart' (F)	SKee

- 'Penny' **new**	EMui SKee
§ - 'Plena' (d) ♀H4	CBcs CCVT CDul CLnd CSBt CTho CWSG EBee ECrN ELan EPfP LBuc LRHS MGos MRav MSwo NWea SCrf SFam SPer WDin WFar WHar WJas WOrn
§ - 'Preserving' (F)	CTho
- 'Regina' **new**	SKee
- 'Ronald's Heart' (F)	SKee
- 'Roundel Heart' (F)	SKee
- 'Sasha' (F)	GTwe
- 'Small Black' (F)	CTho
- 'Starkrimson' (F)	ECrN GTwe
- 'Stella' (F) ♀H4	CAgr CEnd CLnd CMac CTri CWSG CWib ECrN EMui EPfP ERea GTwe LAst LBuc LRHS MBri MGos MRav SCoo SCrf SDea SFam SHBN SKee SPer SPoG WBVN WHar WJas WOrn
- 'Stella Compact' (F)	CWib ECrN ENot LAst MBri SDea WHar
- 'Summer Sun' (D) ♀H4	CTho CTri EMui GTwe LRHS MBri MCoo SCoo SDea SFam SKee SPoG
- 'Summit' (F)	SHBN SKee
- 'Sunburst' (F)	CAgr CCVT CEnd CTho CTri CWib ECrN EMui GTwe LAst LBuc LRHS MBri SCoo SDea SFam SKee SPer SPoG WJas WOrn
- 'Sweetheart' (F)	EMui GTwe MBri SPoG
- 'Sylvia' (F)	SFam
- 'Turkish Black' (F)	SKee
- 'Upright' (F)	CTho
- 'Van' (F)	CLnd ECrN ENot GTwe SKee
- 'Vega' (F)	CAgr CLnd GTwe SFam SKee WJas
- 'Waterloo' (F)	CTho SKee
- 'White Heart' (F)	CTho CWib ECrN SKee
- 'Wildstar'	CEnd
* 'Beni-no-dora'	SMur
* 'Beni-yutaka'	CEnd CTho LBuc LRHS MAsh SCoo SLim
besseyi	CAgr NLar
'Blaze'	see *P. cerasifera* 'Nigra'
x *blireana* (d) ♀H4	CDoC CDul CEnd CTri EBee ENot EPfP LAst LRHS MBar MBri MDun MGan MGos MRav MWat SBLw SCoo SPer SPoG WFar WHar
- 'Moseri' (d)	SBLw
'Blushing Bride'	see *P.* 'Shôgetsu'
cerasifera	CAgr CDul CRWN CTri ECrN LBuc NWea SEND SKee SPer WDin
- 'Cherry Plum' (F)	CTri SDea SKee
- 'Crimson Dwarf'	SCoo
- 'First' (F)	CAgr
- 'Golden Sphere' (F) **new**	CAgr EMui SCoo
- 'Gypsy' (F) **new**	CAgr EMui SCoo
- 'Hessei' (v)	CBow CEnd LRHS MBlu MBri MDun MGos MRav SCoo SLim SPoG
§ - Myrobalan Group (F)	ECrN EMui MRav SDea SKee
§ - 'Nigra' ♀H4	More than 30 suppliers
- 'Pendula'	CTho ECrN
§ - 'Pissardii'	CWib ECrN LAst MAsh MBar MRav NBea NEgg NFor NWea SCoo SFam SLim SPer WFar WGwG WJas
* - 'Princess'	CEnd CWSG EMui
- 'Rosea'	LRHS
- 'Spring Glow'	CEnd EBee EGra EPfP LRHS MAsh SCoo SLim SPoG WOrn
§ - 'Woodii'	SBLw
cerasus 'Montmorency' (F)	SKee
- 'Morello' (C) ♀H4	CAgr CCVT CDul CMac CSBt CTho CTri CWSG CWib EMui ENot EPfP GTwe LAst LBuc LRHS
	MBri MGan MGos MNHC NPri SCrf SDea SFam SHBN SKee SPer SPoG WJas WOrn
- 'Nabella' (F)	SKee
- 'Rhexii' (d)	CDul ECrN MAsh MGos SPer
'Champagne Dream'	SCoo
'Cheal's Weeping'	see *P.* 'Kiku-shidare-zakura'
'Chocolate Ice'	MAsh
§ 'Chôshû-hizakura'	MGan
§ x *cistena* ♀H4	CBcs CCVT CDul CSBt CWSG EBee ELan EPfP LAst MAsh MDun MGan MGos MWat NBlu SBLw SCoo SHBN SLim SPer SPla SPlb SPoG WCFE WDin
- 'Crimson Dwarf'	see *P.* x *cistena*
'Collingwood Ingram'	MGos
conradinae	see *P. hirtipes*
'Daikoku'	MBri
davidiana	CTho SPlb
domestica 'Allgroves Superb' (D)	ERea
- 'Angelina Burdett' (D)	ERea GTwe SDea SKee
- 'Anna Späth' (C/D)	SKee
- 'Ariel' (C/D)	SDea SKee
- 'Autumn Compote' (C)	SKee
- 'Avalon' (D)	CAgr CCVT ECrN GTwe SDea SKee
- 'Bavay Ringloja' (D) **new**	SKee
- 'Belgian Purple' (C)	SKee
- 'Belle de Louvain' (C)	CDul CTho CTri ECrN ERea GTwe SDea SKee
- 'Birchenhayes' (F)	CEnd
- 'Black Diamond'	see *P. salicina* 'Black Diamond'
- 'Blaisdon Red' (C)	CTho
- 'Blue Imperatrice' (C/D)	SKee
- 'Blue Rock' (C/D) ♀H4 **new**	SKee
- 'Blue Tit' (C/D) ♀H4	CAgr CTho EMui ERea GTwe LAst SDea SKee
- 'Bonne de Bry' (D)	SKee
§ - 'Bountiful' (C)	ERea
- 'Brandy Gage' (C/D)	SKee
- 'Bryanston Gage' (D)	CTho SKee
- 'Burbank's Giant'	see *P. domestica* 'Giant Prune'
- 'Burcombe'	CEnd
- 'Bush' (C)	LAst
- 'Cambridge Gage' (D) ♀H4	CAgr CDoC CDul CTho CTri CWib ECrN EMui EPfP ERea GTwe LAst LRHS MBri MGan MWat SCoo SCrf SDea SFam SHBN SKee SPer SPoG WJas WOrn
- 'Chrislin' (F)	CAgr CTho
- 'Coe's Golden Drop' (D)	CDoC ECrN EMui ERea GTwe LAst LRHS MGan MGos MRav SCoo SDea SFam SKee SPer
- 'Count Althann's Gage' (D)	ERea GTwe SDea SFam SKee
- 'Cox's Emperor' (C)	SKee
- 'Crimson Drop' (D)	ERea SKee
- 'Cropper'	see *P. domestica* 'Laxton's Cropper'
- 'Csucsos Szilva' (D) **new**	SDea SKee
- 'Curlew' (C)	SDea SKee
- 'Czar' (C) ♀H4	CAgr CDoC CDul CSBt CTri CWib ECrN EMui EPfP GBut GTwe LAst LBuc LRHS MGos NPri NWea SDea SFam SKee SPer SPoG WOrn
- 'De Montfort' (D) **new**	SKee
- 'Delicious'	see *P. domestica* 'Laxton's Delicious'
- 'Denniston's Superb'	see *P. domestica* 'Imperial Gage'
- 'Des Bejonnieres' (D) **new**	SKee
- 'Diamond' (C)	SKee
- 'Dittisham Black' (C)	CAgr CTho

- 'Dittisham Ploughman' (C) — CTho SKee
- 'Drap d'Or d'Esperen' (D) **new** — SKee
- 'Dunster Plum' (F) — CAgr CTho CTri CWib
- 'Early Favourite' (D/C) **new** — SKee
- 'Early GreenGage' (D) **new** — SKee
- 'Early Laxton' (C/D) ⁴ ♀ᴴSKee — ECrN ERea GTwe LAst SDea SFam
- 'Early Prolific' — see *P. domestica* 'Rivers's Early Prolific'
- 'Early Rivers' — see *P. domestica* 'Rivers's Early Prolific'
- 'Early Transparent Gage' (C/D) — CSBt CTho CTri ECrN EMui ERea GTwe LAst LBuc MCoo SDea SFam SKee
- 'Early Victoria' (C/D) — SDea
- 'Edda' (D) **new** — SKee
- 'Edwards' (C/D) ♀ᴴ⁴ — CTri CWib ECrN GTwe SDea SKee
- 'Excalibur' (D) — ECrN GTwe SDea
§ - German Prune Group (C) — CTho SKee
§ - 'Giant Prune' (C) — CWib ECrN GTwe SDea SKee
I - 'Godshill Big Sloe' (F) — SDea
  - 'Godshill Blue' (C) — SDea
  - 'Godshill Minigage' (F) — SDea
  - 'Gold Dust' **new** — ENot
  - 'Golden Transparent' (D) — CTho ERea GTwe MCoo SFam SKee
  - 'Goldfinch' (D) — GTwe MCoo SKee
  - 'Gordon Castle' **new** — SKee
  - Green Gage Group — see *P. domestica* Reine-Claude Group
  - - 'Old Green Gage' — see *P. domestica* (Reine-Claude Group) 'Reine-Claude Vraie'
  - 'Grey Plum' (F) — CAgr CTho
  - 'Grove's Late Victoria' (C/D) — SKee
  - 'Guthrie's Late Green' (D) — SKee
  - 'Herman' (C/D) — CAgr ECrN GTwe LAst LRHS MBri SDea SKee SPoG
  - 'Heron' (F) — ECrN GTwe SKee
  - 'Impérial Epineuse' (D) — SKee
§ - 'Imperial Gage' (C/D) ♀ᴴ⁴ — CAgr CTho CTri CWib ECrN EMui ERea GTwe LAst NLar SDea SFam SKee SPoG WOrn
  - subsp. *italica* **new** — EMui
  - 'Jan James' (F) — CEnd
  - 'Jefferson' (D) ♀ᴴ⁴ — CAgr ECrN EMui ERea GTwe NLar SDea SFam SKee
* - 'Jubilaeum' (D) — EMui GTwe SKee
  - 'Kea' (C) — CAgr CTho SKee
  - 'Kirke's' (D) — CTho CTri ECrN ERea GTwe SDea SFam SKee WOrn
  - 'Landkey Yellow' (F) — CAgr CTho
  - 'Langley Gage' — CAgr SDea
  - 'Late Muscatelle' (C) — ERea SKee
  - 'Laxton's Bountiful' — see *P. domestica* 'Bountiful'
§ - 'Laxton's Cropper' (C) — CTri GTwe MCoo SKee
§ - 'Laxton's Delicious' (D) — GTwe SKee
§ - 'Laxton's Delight' (D) ♀ᴴ⁴ — GTwe
  - 'Laxton's Early Gage' (D/C) **new** — SKee
  - 'Laxton's Gage' (D) — SDea SKee
  - 'Laxton's Ideal' **new** — SKee
  - 'Laxton's Supreme' (C/D) — SKee
  - 'Liegel's Apricot' **new** — SKee
  - 'Mallard' (D) ♀ᴴ⁴ — SKee
  - 'Manaccan' (C) — CAgr CTho
  - 'Marjorie's Seedling' (C) ♀ᴴ⁴ — CAgr CDoC CDul CSBt CTho CTri CWib ECrN EMui ERea GTwe LAst LBuc LRHS MGan MWat NPri SCoo SDea SEND SFam SKee SPer SPoG WJas WOrn
  - 'McLaughlin' (D) — SKee
  - 'Merton Gage' **new** — SKee
  - 'Merton Gem' (C/D) — GTwe SFam SKee
  - 'Monarch' (C) — GTwe SKee
  - 'Olympia' (C/D) — SKee
  - 'Ontario' (C/D) — SKee
  - 'Opal' (D) ♀ᴴ⁴ — CAgr CDoC CWSG CWib ECrN EMui ERea GBut GTwe LAst LBuc MBri MGan MGos MLan MWat NWea SCrf SDea SEND SFam SKee SPoG WOrn
  - 'Orleans' (C) — SKee
  - 'Oullins Gage' (C/D) ♀ᴴ⁴ — CAgr CDoC CDul CSBt CTri CWib ECrN EMui ENot EPfP ERea GTwe LAst LBuc MBri MGan MRav SDea SFam SKee SPer SPoG WJas WOrn
  - 'Pershore' (C) ♀ᴴ⁴ — CDul CTho CWib ECrN ERea GTwe LAst MBri MNHC SDea SFam SKee WOrn
  - 'Pond's Seedling' (C) — CSBt SDea SKee
  - 'President' (C/D) — GTwe SDea SKee
  - 'Primate' (D/C) **new** — SKee
  - 'Priory Plum' (D) — SDea
  - 'Purple Pershore' (C) — CAgr CTri CWib ECrN ERea GTwe SDea SFam SKee WOrn
  - 'Quetsche d'Alsace' — see *P. domestica* German Prune Group
  - 'Reeves' (C) ♀ᴴ⁴ — GTwe MCoo SFam SKee
  - 'Reine-Claude Dorée' — see *P. domestica* Reine-Claude Group
§ - Reine-Claude Group (C/D) — ECrN EMui GTwe MGos SDea SFam SKee SPer
  - - 'Ingall's Grimoldby Green Gage' (D) **new** — SKee
  - - 'Reine Claude de Brahy' (D) — SKee
  - - 'Reine-Claude de Bavais' (D) — CTho CTri ERea GTwe SDea SFam SKee
  - - 'Reine-Claude de Moissac' (D) **new** — SKee
  - - 'Reine-Claude de Vars' (D) **new** — SKee
  - - 'Reine-Claude Precoce Leon Hisse' (D) **new** — SKee
  - - 'Reine-Claude Rosee' (D) **new** — SKee
  - - 'Reine-Claude Sagot' (D) **new** — SKee
  - - 'Reine-Claude Tardive de Chambourcy' (D) **new** — SKee
§ - - 'Reine-Claude Vraie' (C/D) — CCVT CWib EMui EPfP ERea LAst SCrf SKee SLon SPer SPoG WJas WOrn
  - - 'Uhinks Reine-Claude' **new** — SKee
§ - - 'Willingham Gage' (C/D) — ERea GTwe LRHS MLan
  - - 'Reine-Claude Violette' (D) — ERea SKee
§ - 'Rivers's Early Prolific' (C) — CSBt CTho CTri ECrN ENot EPfP ERea GBut GTwe MCoo NWea SCoo SDea SHBN SKee
  - 'Royale de Vilvoorde' (D) — ERea SKee
  - 'Sanctus Hubertus' (D) ♀ᴴ⁴ — CDoC ECrN EPfP GTwe SDea SKee
  - 'Severn Cross' (D) — GTwe SKee
  - 'Stella' — CCVT LAst MGan NPri
  - 'Stint' (C/D) — SKee
  - 'Swan' (C) — ECrN GTwe SKee
  - 'Syston' — CTho MGos
  - 'Teme Cross' (D/C) **new** — SKee
  - 'Thames Cross' (D) — SKee
  - 'Transparent Gage' (D) — ECrN ERea SKee

- 'Upright' (F)	CEnd
- 'Utility' (D)	SKee
- 'Valor' (C/D) ♀H4	ECrN MCoo
- 'Verity' (D/C) **new**	SKee
- 'Victoria' (C/D) ♀H4	More than 30 suppliers
- 'Violetta'PBR (C/D)	EMui GTwe SKee SPoG
- 'Warwickshire	CTho CWib ERea GTwe LAst SDea
Drooper' (C)	SFam SKee SPer SPoG WBVN
	WOrn
- 'Washington' (D)	SDea SKee
- 'White Magnum	CTho SDea
Bonum' (C)	
- 'Willingham'	see *P. domestica* (Reine-Claude
	Group) 'Willingham Gage'
- 'Woolston Black' **new**	SKee
- 'Wyedale' (C)	GTwe
§ *dulcis*	CDul CLnd CTri CWSG CWib
	ECrN EMui LAst LRHS MWat NBea
	NWea SBLw SBod SCoo SCrf SDea
	SFam WDin WOrn
- 'Ai' (F)	CAgr
- 'Ardechoise' (F)	CAgr
- 'Ferraduel' (F)	CAgr
- 'Ferragnes' (F)	CAgr
- 'Lauranne' (F)	CAgr
- 'Macrocarpa' (F)	ECrN
- 'Mandaline' (F)	CAgr
- 'Titan' (F)	ECrN
Easter Bonnet =	LRHS
'Comet'PBR	
x *eminens* 'Umbraculifera'	SBLw
Fragrant Cloud = 'Shizuka'	CEnd CWSG CWib LRHS MAsh
	MBri SCoo SLim SPer SPoG WOrn
fruticosa 'Globosa'	LPan MAsh NHol
'Fugenzō'	CSBt
'Fuki'	MBri
glandulosa 'Alba Plena'	CEnd CPLG CPle CSBt EBee ECrN
(d)	LRHS MBow MDun NBea SBLw
	SHBN SPer SPlb SPoG SRms SWvt
	WCFE WDin WSHC
- 'Rosea Plena'	see *P. glandulosa* 'Sinensis'
§ - 'Sinensis' (d)	CEnd CPLG CPle CSBt EBee LRHS
	SBLw SHBN SPer SPoG SRms
	WDin WSHC
§ x *gondouinii* 'May Duke'	CTho SKee
(F)	
- 'Schnee'	SBLw
'Gyoikō'	CEnd CTho
'Hally Jolivette'	CEnd ELan LRHS MAsh SBLw
	WDin
'Hanagasa'	EBee LRHS MAsh MBri NLar SCoo
'Hillieri'	ECrN MBar MGos
'Hillieri Spire'	see *P.* 'Spire'
'Hilling's Weeping'	LRHS
§ *hirtipes*	CTho SPoG
'Hisakura'	see *P.* 'Chôshû-hizakura'
Hollywood	see *P.* 'Trailblazer'
'Horinji'	MBri
'Ichiyo' (d) ♀H4	CLnd ECrN EPfP LAst MBri SCoo
	SCrf SPer SPoG SPur
incisa	CTri NBea SPer
- 'Beniomi'	MRav
- 'February Pink'	CAbP CPMA LRHS MRav SBLw
	WDin
- 'Fujima'	LAst SMur
- 'Kojo-no-mai'	More than 30 suppliers
- 'Mikinori'	MAsh NLar SCoo SPoG WFar
- 'Oshidori'	LRHS MBri MGos NLar SCoo SLim
	WFar
* - 'Otome'	WFar
- 'Pacan'	NLar WSPU
- 'Pendula'	CPMA LRHS SCoo
- 'Praecox' ♀H4	CTho CWSG EPfP LRHS SCoo
	SPoG
- 'The Bride'	CEnd CWSG LRHS MAsh MBri
	SCoo

§ - f. *yamadae*	CBcs CEnd CPMA NLar
§ *insititia* (F)	CRWN
- 'Black Bullace' (F) **new**	EMui
§ - 'Bradley's King Damson'	CWib ECrN GTwe SKee
(C)	
- bullace (C)	SDea
- 'Dittisham Damson' (C)	CTho
- 'Farleigh Damson' (C)	CAgr CWib ECrN ERea GBut
♀H4	GTwe LBuc SDea SEND SFam SKee
	SPer SPoG WJas
- 'Godshill Damson' (C)	SDea
- 'Golden Bullace'	see *P. insititia* 'White Bullace'
- 'King of Damsons'	see *P. insititia* 'Bradley's King
	Damson'
- 'Langley Bullace' (C)	CAgr CTho ECrN EMui ERea GTwe
	SKee
- 'Merryweather Damson'	CAgr CCAT CCVT CDoC CDul
(C)	CMac CSBt CTho CTri CWib ECrN
	EMui ERea GTwe LAst LBuc MBri
	MGan MGos NPri SDea SFam SKee
	SPoG WBVN WHar WJas WOrn
- 'Mirabelle de Nancy' (C)	CAgr CTho CTri GTwe LAst SDea
	SFam SKee
- 'Mirabelle de Nancy	SDea
(Red)' (C)	
§ - 'Prune Damson' (C) ♀H4	CDoC CTho CTri CWSG CWib
	ECrN EMui EPfP ERea GTwe LAst
	LBuc MBri MGan NLar SCrf SDea
	SFam SKee SPer WHar WJas WOrn
- 'Shepherd's Bullace' (C)	CTho ERea SKee
- 'Shropshire Damson'	see *P. insititia* 'Prune Damson'
- 'Small Bullace' (C)	CAgr SKee
§ - 'White Bullace' (C)	CAgr ERea SKee
- 'Yellow Apricot' (C)	ERea SKee
§ *jamasakura*	CTho
japonica	GIBF
'Jô-nioi'	CEnd CLnd CTho SBLw
§ 'Kanzan' ♀H4	More than 30 suppliers
§ 'Kiku-shidare-zakura' ♀H4	More than 30 suppliers
Korean hill cherry	see *P. verecunda*
kurilensis	see *P. nipponica* var. *kurilensis*
'Kursar' ♀H4	CDul CLnd CSBt CTho CTri EMui
	EPfP LRHS MAsh MBri NWea SCoo
	SCrf SLim SPoG WOrn
laurocerasus ♀H4	CBcs CBrm CCVT CDul CPMA
	CTrG CWSG EBee ECrN ELan EPfP
	LAst MRav MWat NBea NEgg NFor
	NWea SEND SPer SPoG SReu WFar
	WMoo WMou
- 'Angustifolia'	WDin
- 'Aureovariegata'	see *P. laurocerasus* 'Taff's Golden
	Gleam'
- 'Camelliifolia'	CTri EPla MBlu WCFE WDin
	WHCG
§ - 'Castlewellan' (v)	CDoC CDul CPLG CTri CTrw
	CWib EGra EPfP EPla ISea LAst
	LHop MBar MGos MSwo NBea
	NEgg NPro SDix SEND SLim SMad
	SPer SPoG SSta WDin WFar WHar
	WLeb WMoo
- 'Caucasica'	LPan MGos SMer
- 'Cherry Brandy'	MRav SPer WCot WDin
- Etna = 'Anbri'PBR	EBee ENot EPfP LPan LRHS MBri
	MGos MRav NPri SCoo
- 'Green Marble' (v)	CPMA CTri WSHC
- 'Herbergii'	NLar
§ - 'Latifolia'	CHEx EPla SLPl
§ - Low 'n' Green = 'Interlo'	MRav
- 'Magnoliifolia'	see *P. laurocerasus* 'Latifolia'
- 'Mano'	MGos NLar
- 'Marbled White'	see *P. laurocerasus* 'Castlewellan'
- 'Miky'	CPMA
- 'Mischeana'	SLPl
- 'Mount Vernon'	MBar MBlu MGos WDin
- 'Novita'	EMil
- 'Otinii'	CHEx

- 'Otto Luyken' ♀H4	More than 30 suppliers
- Renault Ace = 'Renlau'	MGos MRav
- 'Reynvaanii'	CPMA LRHS MBri
- 'Rotundifolia'	CDoC CSBt CTri CWib ELan EMil ENot LBuc LPan LRHS LSRN MBNS MBar MBri MGos MSwo NBea NBlu NEgg NWea SLim SPoG SRms STop SWvt WDin WHar WMoo WTel
- 'Schipkaensis'	SLPl SPer
§ - 'Taff's Golden Gleam' (v)	CBow CPMA
- 'Van Nes'	CPMA EMil NLar WDin
- 'Variegata' misapplied	see *P. laurocerasus* 'Castlewellan'
- 'Variegata' ambig. (v)	CPLG CWib EPla MBNS SRms
- 'Zabeliana'	CDul CTri EBee ECrN EPfP MBar MGos MSwo NHol NWea SHBN SPer SRms WDin WFar WTel
litigiosa	LRHS MBri NLar SCoo
'Little Pink Perfection' **new**	SPoG
lusitanica ♀H4	More than 30 suppliers
- subsp. *azorica*	CDoC CPLG MRav WFar WPGP
- 'Myrtifolia'	EBee EPfP EPla LRHS MBri MLLN MRav SLon SMad SWvt WCFE WDin WGer
- 'Variegata' (v)	More than 30 suppliers
maackii	CTho ECrN EPfP GIBF MDun SBLw SEND SSpi WDin
- 'Amber Beauty'	CDoC CDul CEnd EBee EPfP MRav SBLw WDin
mahaleb	CTho
mandshurica	GIBF
'Matsumae-beni-murasaki'	MAsh SCoo
'Matsumae-beni-tamanishiki'	MAsh
'Matsumae-hana-gasa'	MBri
maximowiczii	GIBF
'Mount Fuji'	see *P.* 'Shirotae'
mume	CMCN WDin WNor
§ - 'Beni-chidori'	CEnd CWib ECrN EPfP LBuc LRHS MAsh MBlu MBri MGos NBea NLar SHBN SLim SPoG WJas WOrn WPGP
I - 'Beni-shidori'	see *P. mume* 'Beni-chidori'
§ - 'Omoi-no-mama' (d)	CEnd WOrn
- 'Omoi-no-wac'	see *P. mume* 'Omoi-no-mama'
myrobalana	see *P. cerasifera* Myrobalan Group
§ *nipponica* var. *kurilensis*	CBcs MNHC
- var. *kurilensis* 'Brilliant'	CBcs CLan MAsh MBri MGos NLar SCrf SPer WFar
- - 'Ruby'	CBcs CDul CEnd LRHS MBri MGos NBlu NEgg SMur WFar
- - 'Spring Joy'	LRHS
'Okame' ♀H4	CDul CLnd CSam CTho EBee ECrN ENot EPfP LRHS MAsh MBri MGos MRav NBlu NEgg NWea SCoo SCrf SLim SPer SPoG WBVN WFar WOrn WWeb
* 'Okame Harlequin' (v)	SLim SPoG
'Okumiyako' misapplied	see *P.* 'Shôgetsu'
padus	CCVT CDul CLnd CRWN CSBt CTri ECrN EWTr GIBF LBuc MDun MGos MSwo NBea NBee NBlu NWea SBLw SHGC WBVN WDin WMou WOrn
- 'Albertii'	CTho MDun WJas
- 'Colorata' ♀H4	CDoC CDul CEnd CSam CTho ECrN ELan LBuc MAsh MDun MGos NBee SBLw SCoo SHBN SPer WDin WFar WJas
- 'Grandiflora'	see *P. padus* 'Watereri'
- 'Plena' (d)	CTho
- 'Purple Queen'	CEnd CTho ECrN
§ - 'Watereri' ♀H4	CBcs CCVT CDoC CDul CEnd CLnd CMCN CTho CWib EBee ECrN ELan EPfP EWTr MDun

	NWea SBLw SCoo SHBN SLim SPer WDin WJas WOrn
'Pandora' ♀H4	CBcs CLnd EBee ECrN EPfP LAst LRHS MAsh MBri MDun MGos MRav MSwo MWat NBea NBee NWea SBLw SCoo SCrf SEND SHBN SPer SPoG WFar WOrn
pendula	SCrf
§ - 'Pendula Rosea' ♀H4	CDoC CDul CEnd CSBt CTri CWib EPfP LAst LPan MAsh SBLw SCrf SPoG WFar WJas WOrn
§ - 'Pendula Rubra' ♀H4	CDoC CEnd CLnd CSBt CWib ECrN EPfP LAst LRHS MAsh MBri MGos MSwo SCoo SHBN SLim SPer SPoG WPat
§ - 'Stellata'	EBee LRHS SPer
persica 'Amsden June' (F)	CWib EREa GTwe LRHS SDea SFam SKee
- 'Bellegarde' (F)	EREa GTwe SDea SFam
- 'Bonanza' (F)	EMui
- 'Clara Meyer'	MDun
- 'Dixi Red' **new**	LPan
- 'Doctor Hogg' (F)	SDea
- 'Duke of York' (F) ♀H3	CTri EREa GTwe SDea SFam SKee WOrn
- 'Dymond' (F)	EREa
- 'Flat China' (F)	EREa
- 'Foliis Rubris' (F)	CDul WPGP
- 'Francis' (F)	SKee
- 'Garden Lady' (F)	EREa GTwe SKee SPoG
- 'Hale's Early' (F)	EREa GTwe LRHS SEND SFam SKee SPer SPoG WOrn
- 'Hylands' (F)	SDea
- 'Melred'	MGos
- 'Melred Weeping'	SBLw
- 'Natalia' (F)	SDea
- var. *nectarina* Crimson Gold (F)	SDea
- - 'Early Gem' (F)	EREa SDea
- - 'Early Rivers' (F) ♀H3	EREa GTwe SDea SPer
- - 'Elruge' (F)	EREa GTwe SDea SFam
- - 'Fantasia' (F)	EREa SDea
- - 'Fire Gold' (F)	SDea
- - 'Garden Beauty' (F/d)	EMui ENot SPer
- - 'Humboldt' (F)	EREa GTwe SDea SKee
- - 'John Rivers' (F)	GTwe SDea SFam
- - 'Lord Napier' (F) ♀H3	CAgr CDoC CSBt CWSG CWib EMui EPfP EREa LAst LBuc LRHS MGan MGos SDea SFam SKee SPer SPoG WOrn
- - 'Nectared' (F)	CWib
- - 'Nectarella' (F)	EMui EREa GTwe SKee
- - 'Pineapple' (F)	CTri EREa GTwe LRHS MGan SDea SFam SKee
- - 'Ruby Gold' (F)	SDea
- - 'Terrace Ruby' (F)	CDul ENot
- 'Peregrine' (F) ♀H3	CAgr CDul CMac CSBt CTri CWSG CWib EMui ENot EPfP EREa GTwe LAst LRHS MBri MGan MGos MLan SDea SFam SHBN SKee SPer WJas
- 'Pink Peachy' (F) **new**	NLar
- 'Red Haven' (F)	CAgr CWib GTwe SDea SKee
- 'Reliance' (F)	SDea
- 'Robin Redbreast' (F)	SDea
- 'Rochester' (F) ♀H3	CAgr CWSG CWib EMui ENot EREa GTwe LAst LRHS MBri SDea SFam SKee SPer SPoG WOrn
- 'Royal George' (F)	GTwe SFam
- 'Saturne' (F)	EMui SPoG
- 'Springtime' (F)	EREa SDea
- 'Terrace Amber'	EMui ENot SPer
- 'Terrace Diamond'	ENot
- 'Terrace Garnet'	ENot
- 'White Peachy' (F) **new**	NLar
'Petite Noir' **new**	MAsh

'Pink Perfection' ♀H4	CBcs CDul CLnd CSBt CWSG CWib EBee ECrN ENot EPfP LAst LRHS MBri NBee SCrf SHBN SPer WDin WFar WJas WOrn
'Pink Shell' ♀H4	CLnd CTho EPfP MBri SFam SPur WOrn
pissardii	see *P. cerasifera* 'Pissardii'
'Pissardii Nigra'	see *P. cerasifera* 'Nigra'
* *prostrata* 'Anita Kistler'	ECho
* - var. *discolor*	NLar WNor
pseudocerasus 'Cantabrigiensis'	ECrN
pumila var. *depressa*	EMil MBar MBlu MMHG MRav NLar NPro
'Rebecca'	SCoo
'Rosie's Dream'	SCoo
'Royal Burgundy'	CDul CEnd CWSG EBee ECrN EMil ENot LRHS LSRN MAsh MBri MDun MGos MWat NBee SCoo SKee SLim SPer SPoG SPur WGer WOrn
rufa	CLnd CPMA CTho MDun SSpi
sachalinensis	GIBF
salicina	GIBF
- 'Beauty'	ERea
§ - 'Black Diamond' (F)	SDea
- 'Methley' (D)	ECrN ERea
- 'Satsuma' (F)	ERea
- 'Shiro' (D)	ERea
sargentii ♀H4	More than 30 suppliers
- 'Rancho'	CLnd SPoG WOrn
x *schmittii*	CLnd ECrN SCoo SPer WJas
'Sekiyama'	see *P.* 'Kanzan'
serotina	CDul NLar SBLw
§ *serrula* ♀H4	More than 30 suppliers
- Dorothy Clive form	LRHS MDun
§ - 'Mahogany Lustre'	CLnd WPat
- var. *tibetica*	see *P. serrula*
serrula x *serrulata*	CBcs CTho
serrulata (d)	MGos
- 'Erecta'	see *P.* 'Amanogawa'
- 'Grandiflora'	see *P.* 'Ukon'
- 'Longipes'	see *P.* 'Shôgetsu'
- 'Miyako' misapplied	see *P.* 'Shôgetsu'
N - var. *pubescens*	see *P. verecunda*
- 'Rosea'	see *P.* 'Kiku-shidare-zakura'
- var. *spontanea*	see *P. jamasakura*
'Shidare-zakura'	see *P.* 'Kiku-shidare-zakura'
'Shimizu-zakura'	see *P.* 'Shôgetsu'
'Shirofugen' ♀H4	CBcs CDoC CDul CLnd CMCN CSBt CTho CWSG CWib EBee ECrN EMil ENot EPfP LBuc LRHS MAsh MBri MRav MWat NBee NEgg SCrf SEND SPer SPoG WDin WJas WOrn
§ 'Shirotae' ♀H4	More than 30 suppliers
§ 'Shôgetsu' ♀H4	CBcs CDul CEnd CLnd CSBt CTho CWSG ECrN ELan ENot EPfP LAst LRHS MBri NBlu SCrf SFam SHBN SLim SPer SPoG WDin
'Shosar'	CEnd CLnd CWib ECrN LAst LRHS SCoo SPer SPoG
'Snow Goose'	CDoC EBee LAst LRHS NEgg SCoo
'Snow Showers'	CEnd CWSG EMui LRHS MAsh MBri MDun MWat NWea SPer WGer
spinosa	CCVT CDoC CDul CRWN CTri ECrN EPfP LBuc LRHS MBar MBlu NWea SPer WDin WFar WMou WNor XPep
- 'Plena' (d)	CEnd CTho MBlu
- 'Purpurea'	MAsh MBlu NHol WDin WHCG WMou WPat
§ 'Spire' ♀H4	CCVT CDoC CDul CLnd CMCN CSBt CTho CWib EBee ECrN EPfP LAst LBuc LRHS MAsh MGos MRav

	MSwo NBlu NWea SCoo SHBN SPer SPoG WDin WFar WJas WOrn
ssiori	GIBF
x *subhirtella*	LAst WNor
- 'Autumnalis' ♀H4	More than 30 suppliers
- 'Autumnalis Rosea' ♀H4	More than 30 suppliers
- 'Fukubana'	CLnd CTho EBee EPfP SBLw
- 'Pendula'	see *P. pendula* 'Pendula Rosea', *P. pendula*
- 'Pendula Plena Rosea' (d)	LAst LPan SBLw
- 'Pendula Rubra'	see *P. pendula* 'Pendula Rubra'
N - 'Rosea'	CLnd MRav WBVN
- 'Stellata'	see *P. pendula* 'Stellata'
'Taihaku' ♀H4	More than 30 suppliers
'Taki-nioi'	ECrN
'Taoyame'	CLnd
tenella	CAgr CBcs ECrN ELan WCot
- 'Fire Hill'	CBcs CPMA CSBt CWib ECho EGra ELan ENot EPfP LRHS MGan MGos MWea NHol SBLw SCrf SHBN SPer SSpi WCot WDin WJas WOrn
tibetica	see *P. serrula*
tomentosa	ECrN MWea WBVN
§ 'Trailblazer' (C/D)	CEnd CLnd CSBt CTho ECrN LAst SBLw WOrn
triloba	CBcs CSBt CTri CWib ECrN ENot GIBF LBuc LRHS MDun NBee NBlu NHol NPri NWea SBLw SHBN SPoG WDin
- 'Multiplex' (d)	ECho ENot MGos MRav SPer SRms WJas WSPU
§ 'Ukon' ♀H4	CBcs CDoC CDul CLnd CMCN CTho CTri EBee ECrN EPfP EWTr LPan LRHS MAsh MBar MBri MGos MRav NBee NWea SCrf SHBN SPer WDin WFar WOrn
'Umineko'	CCVT CDoC CLnd CWib ECrN GQue LPan MGos SCoo SPer SPur WDin
§ *verecunda*	CDoC CLnd NWea SPur WJas
- 'Autumn Glory'	CTho NBea
virginiana	CAgr
- 'Schubert'	CDul CLnd EBee ECrN SBLw WFar WJas WOrn WPat
'White Cloud'	CTho
yamadae	see *P. incisa* f. *yamadae*
x *yedoensis* ♀H4	CCVT CDul CLnd CMCN CSBt CTho CTri CWSG ECrN EPfP LAst MAsh NWea SBLw SLim SPer WDin WJas WOrn
- 'Ivensii'	CBcs CDul CSBt CTri CWib EBee EGra EWTr LPan MDun NBee NEgg NWea SCoo SHBN SPer WDin
- 'Pendula'	see *P.* x *yedoensis* 'Shidare-yoshino'
- 'Perpendens'	see *P.* x *yedoensis* 'Shidare-yoshino'
§ - 'Shidare-yoshino'	CCVT CEnd CLnd EBee ECrN EPfP LPan LRHS MBar MBri MGos MRav MSwo NWea SBLw SLim δPer SPoG WOrn
'Yoshino'	see *P.* x *yedoensis*
'Yoshino Pendula'	see *P.* x *yedoensis* 'Shidare-yoshino'

Pseudocydonia (Rosaceae)

§ *sinensis*	CAgr CBcs GIBF NLar

Pseudofumaria see *Corydalis*

Pseudogynoxys (Asteraceae)

chenopodioides	CPlN ELan ERea SOWG

Pseudolarix (Pinaceae)

§ *amabilis* ♀H4	CDoC CEnd CMCN CTho ECrN EHul EPfP LCon MBar MBlu MBri NWea SCoo SLim SPoG WNor WPGP
kaempferi	see *P. amabilis*

Pseudomuscari see *Muscari*

Pseudopanax (*Araliaceae*)

(Adiantifolius Group)	CBcs CHEx CTrC GQui
'Adiantifolius'	
- 'Cyril Watson' ♀H1	CBcs CDoC CHEx SBig
	SBrw
arboreus	CAbb CBcs CDoC CHEx CTrC
	ECou LEdu SBig
chathamicus	CDoC CHEx SAPC SArc
colensoi **new**	SBrw
crassifolius	CAbb CBcs CBrP CTrC EAmu
	SAPC SArc SBig WCot
- var. *trifoliolatus*	CHEx
davidii	SLon
discolor	ECou LEdu
ferox	CAbb CBcs CBrP EAmu LEdu
	SAPC SArc SBig SMad
laetus	CAbb CBcs CHEx CTrC ECou LEdu
	SAPC SArc SBig
lessonii	CBcs CHEx ECou
- 'Gold Splash' (v) ♀H1	CBcs CHEx SBig SBrw SEND
	WCMO
- 'Rangitira'	CBcs SBig
'Lineariifolius'	CHEx CTrC IDee LEdu
'Purpureus' ♀H1	CHEx
'Sabre'	CHEx
'Trident'	CDoC CHEx CTrC LEdu

Pseudophegopteris (*Thelypteridaceae*)
levingei	EMon

Pseudophoenix (*Arecaceae*)
* *nativo*	MBri

Pseudosasa (*Poaceae*)
amabilis misapplied	see *Arundinaria gigantea*
§ *amabilis* (McClure)	LPal WFar
Keng f.	
§ *japonica* ♀H4	More than 30 suppliers
§ - 'Akebonosuji' (v)	EFul EPla MMoz MWht NMoo
	WJun WNor WPGP
I - var. *pleioblastoides*	EPla MWht
- 'Tsutsumiana'	CHEx CPen ENot EPla ERod
	MMoz MWht NLar NMoo SBig
	WJun
- 'Variegata'	see *P. japonica* 'Akebonosuji'
orthotropa	see *Sinobambusa orthotropa*
usawai	EPla WJun
viridula	NMoo

Pseudotsuga (*Pinaceae*)
§ *menziesii* ♀H4	CAgr CBcs CDoC CDul CLnd ECrN
	EPfP LCon LLin LRHS LRav MBar
	MBlu MMuc NWea SPoG WDin
	WFar WMou
- 'Bhiela Lhota'	CKen
- 'Blue Wonder'	CDoC CKen
- 'Densa'	CKen
- 'Fastigiata'	CKen
- 'Fletcheri'	CKen MBar
- var. *glauca*	LCon MBar
- 'Glauca Pendula'	LCon MBar MBlu MGos
I - 'Gotelli's Pendula'	CKen
- 'Graceful Grace'	CKen
- 'Idaho Gem'	CKen
- 'Julie'	CKen
- 'Knaphill'	NLar WEve
- 'Little Jamie'	CKen MBar
- 'Lohbrunner'	CKen
- 'McKenzie'	CKen
- 'Nana'	CKen
- Pendula Group	IDee
- 'Stairii'	CKen
taxifolia	see *P. menziesii*

Pseudowintera (*Winteraceae*)
§ *colorata*	CBcs CDoC CMac CPLG CTrw
	EBee EPla GCal GGar IDee IMGH
	ISea LBuc MAsh MDun NHol NRib
	SLon WCru WFar WFoF
- 'Mount Congreve'	LBuc MBri SSpi WGer

Psidium (*Myrtaceae*)
cattleyanum	see *P. littorale* var. *longipes*
guajava (F)	CArn SDEP XBlo
littorale (F)	ERea
§ - var. *longipes* (F)	XBlo

Psilotum (*Psilotaceae*)
nudum	ECou

Psophocarpus (*Papilionaceae*)
tetragonolobus	CPLG

Psoralea (*Papilionaceae*)
aphylla	EShb
bituminosa	WSHC XPep
glabra	SPlb
glandulosa	CArn LRav WSHC
oligophylla	SPlb
pinnata	CHEx CTrC CTrG GGar IDee

Psychotria (*Rubiaceae*)
capensis	CPLG EShb
carthagenensis	MGol
viridis	MGol

Ptelea (*Rutaceae*)
trifoliata	CBcs CDul CLnd CMCN CTho
	CWib EBee ECrN EPfP IMGH MBlu
	SBLw SPer SRms WDin WFar
	WHCG WNor WOrn WPGP
- 'Aurea' ♀H4	CAbP CBcs CEnd CLnd CMCN
	CPMA EBee ELan ENot EPfP EWTr
	GBin LRHS MAsh MBlu MBri MGos
	SBLw SBrw SHBN SMad SMur SPer
	SPoG SSpi WDin WHCG WPat
- 'Fastigiata' **new**	EPfP

Pteracanthus see *Strobilanthes*

Pteridophyllum (*Papaveraceae*)
racemosum	EFEx GCrs WCru

Pteris (*Pteridaceae*)
from Yunnan	CLAP
angustipinna B&SWJ 6738	WCru
argyraea	MBri
cretica ♀H1+3	CHEx MBri SAPC SArc
- var. *albolineata* ♀H1	GQui MBri SRms
- 'Cristata'	MBri
- 'Gautheri'	MBri
- 'Parkeri'	MBri
- 'Rivertoniana'	MBri
- 'Rowei'	MBri
- 'Wimsettii'	MBri
ensiformis	MBri
* - 'Arguta'	MBri
- 'Victoriae'	MBri
gallinopes	CLAP WAbe
tremula	CHEx GQui MBri SRms
umbrosa	MBri
vittata	SRms
wallichiana	CFir CHEx CLAP WPGP

Pterocarya (*Juglandaceae*)
fraxinifolia ♀H4	CBcs CDul CLnd CMCN CTrG
	ECrN EPfP EWTr MBlu NBee SBLw
	WDin
x *rehderiana*	CTho MBlu WMou

rhoifolia	MBri
stenoptera	CBcs CDul CLnd CMCN CTho SLPl
- 'Fern Leaf'	MBlu SMad WMou WPGP

Pteroceltis (Ulmaceae)

tatarinowii	CMCN

Pterocephalus (Dipsacaceae)

depressus	WPat
dumetorum	CSec
parnassi	see *P. perennis*
§ *perennis*	CBrm CMea ECho EDAr LRHS MHer NBir NJOw NLar NMen NRya NWCA SBla SMad SRms WAbe WEas WHoo XPep
- subsp. *perennis*	EGoo WHrl
pinardii	NWCA

Pterodiscus (Pedaliaceae)

ngamicus	LToo
speciosus	LToo

Pterostylis (Orchidaceae)

acuminata var. *ingens*	EPot
coccinea	GCrs
curta	CStu ECho GCrs SCnR
insignis **new**	EBee
Nodding Grace g.	CDes EBee
obtusa	GCrs
revoluta	EPot

Pterostyrax (Styracaceae)

corymbosa	CBcs CMCN CPMA IArd IDee MBlu NLar SSpi WFar
hispida ♀H4	CAbP CBcs CDul CEnd CHEx CLnd CMCN CPMA CPne CWib EBee EPfP EPla IArd IDee LAst LRHS MBlu MGos MRav NLar SSpi SSta WBVN WDin WFar WMul WPGP
psilophylla	CMCN

Ptilostemon (Asteraceae)

afer	CMdw EHrv EMan MWea MWgw
§ *diacantha*	CSam EBee EDAr LHop NLar NVic SRkn WMnd
echinocephalus	EBee GBri MDKP NBhm NBre

Ptilotrichum see *Alyssum*

Pueraria (Papilionaceae)

montana var. *lobata*	CAgr CArn CBcs ELau LRav MSal

Pulicaria (Asteraceae)

§ *dysenterica*	CAgr CArn IHMH MHer MSal NMir SIde WBri WCHb WDyG WSFF WWye

Pulmonaria ✿ (Boraginaceae)

'Abbey Dore Pink'	EBee WAbb
affinis	EMon LRHS
- 'Margaret'	NCob
angustifolia ♀H4	EBee EPfP GKev GMaP LRHS MDun MNHC MNrw MSal NOrc SRms WBVN WCru WEas WFar WTin
* - *alba*	IFoB
- 'Azurea'	More than 30 suppliers
- 'Blaues Meer'	CFir CSam EBee EPfP GBuc LBMP MBNS MNFA NFla WCru
- 'Munstead Blue'	CElw CHea CLAP EBee ECha EGle EHrv ENot IBlr LRHS MNFA MRav MTho MWgw NCob NHol NRya NSti SRms WCru
- 'Rubra'	see *P. rubra*
'Apple Frost'	CFwr EBee EBrs ECtt MBnl NBhm NLar NSti WCra WLin
'Barfield Regalia'	CMHG EBee EMon IGor NSti SDys WCru
'Benediction'	LPhx NSti
'Berries and Cream'	NSti
§ 'Beth's Blue'	EMon WCAu WCru
'Beth's Pink'	ECha GAbr WCru WFar
'Blauer Hügel'	CBct CElw EMon NSti
§ 'Blauhimmel'	EGle EMon
'Blue Buttons'	CFir CHea
'Blue Crown'	CElw CLAP CSev EHrv EWes LRHS SAga WCAu WCru WEas
'Blue Ensign'	More than 30 suppliers
'Blue Moon'	see *P. officinalis* 'Blue Mist'
'Blue Pearl'	NSti
'Blueberry Muffin'	CSpe
'Bonnie'	CMea SAga
'Botanic Hybrid'	WCru
'British Sterling'	EBee GBin
Cally hybrid	CElw EMon GBin GCal NBre WCru
'Cedric Morris'	CElw
'Chintz'	CLAP CSam EBee GBuc
'Cleeton Red'	NSti WCru
'Coral Springs'	EBrs MAvo NSti
'Corsage'	EBee ECtt
'Cotton Cool'	CElw CLAP CPrp EAEE EBee ECha ECtt EMon EPla EShb GBuc MAvo MBNS MBnl MMHG MNFA NCGa NEgg NOrc NSti SPer SUsu WCAu WCru WMoo WPGP
'Crawshay Chance'	WCru
'De Vroomen's Pride' (v)	CSam EBee EChP EGle LAst MSte NSti WMnd WSan
'Diana Clare'	More than 30 suppliers
'Elworthy Rubies'	CElw MAvo
'Emerald Isles'	NSti
'Esther'	GSki WCru
'Excalibur'	EBrs EHrv ENot EPPr GBuc MNFA NLar
'Fiona'	CBct MAvo WCAu
'Gavin Compton' (v)	EMon
'Glacier'	CBro CElw EMon LRHS MArl MSte NSti WWhi
'Hazel Kaye's Red'	CElw NSti WCru
'High Contrast'PBR	NSti
'Highdown'	see *P.* 'Lewis Palmer'
'Ice Ballet' (Classic Series)	EBee LRHS
'Joan's Red'	CElw WTin
§ 'Lewis Palmer' ♀H4	CBro CMHG CSam EChP ECtt EGle ELan EMar EPla EWTr GCal GMaP GSki IBlr LRHS MAvo MNFA MRav NBid NBir NHol SBla SRGP WBor WBrk WCFE WCot WCru WHoo WTin
'Lime Close'	SAga
'Linford Blue'	WCru
'Little Blue'	NSti
'Little Star'	EMon GBuc NBre NDov NSti SRGP SUsu WCru
longifolia	CArn CBro CFee CHar CPrp CSam EAEE EBee ECha ELan EMag EPfP GAbr GCal GSki LLWP LRHS MNFA MSal NBir NGdn NOrc NSti SPet WBrk WCru WEas WFar WSel
§ - 'Ankum'	CBct CElw CLAP CSam EBee EGle EPfP EPla GBuc ITer LRHS MBrN MRav MSte NBir NSti SAga SMrm SPoG SVil WCot WLin WMoo WWlt
- 'Ballyrogan Blue'	IBlr
- 'Bertram Anderson'	CBgR COIW EChP ECtt EGle GMaP LAst LRHS MBnl MBow MLLN NBid NBir NCGa NVic SBla SPer SRGP SWvt WBrk WCAu WCMO WCot WCru WFar WGHP WMnd

- subsp. *cevennensis*	CBgR CLAP CSam EBee EBrs EChP ENot EPfP LAst MBNS MBnl MLLN MSte NCGa NSti WCAu WCMO
- 'Coen Jansen'	see *P. longifolia* 'Ankum'
- 'Coral Spring'	MBNS NBre SHGN WCAu
- 'Dordogne'	CLAP EBee EBrs GBuc MLLN MRav NBir NEgg NLar SBla WCAu WCru
- 'Howard Eggins'	WSPU
'Lovell Blue'	CElw NCot
'Majesté'	More than 30 suppliers
§ 'Margery Fish' ♀H4	CBro CHar CLAP CSam EBee EChP EGle EMar EPfP EPla IBlr LAst LRHS MBri MLLN MNFA NHol NPri NSti SAga SPer WCru WMnd WTel
'Mary Mottram'	CElw CMea EChP ECtt ELan LAst MLLN MNFA NBir NPol NSti SAga SBla SMrm WCru WMnd WMoo WWhi
'Matese Blue'	SBla
'Mawson's Blue'	CLAP ECha EMon LRHS MRav MWat MWea NBir SWvt WBrk WCru WEas WMoo WRHF WSHC WWhi WWye
'May Bouquet'PBR	NRnb NSti
'Melancholia'	IBlr
'Merlin'	EBee EMon LRHS NSti
'Middleton Red'	CElw
§ 'Milchstrasse'	CLAP
Milky Way	see *P.* 'Milchstrasse'
mollis	CLAP CSWP EBee ECGP EGoo EMon GCal IBlr LRHS MNrw NSti SBch WCru
- WM 9206	SBla
- 'Royal Blue'	EBee MRav
'Monksilver'	EMon
'Moonshine'	NSti
'Moonstone'	CElw CLAP CPom LAst WCru
'Mountain Magic'	CHVG EWll
'Mournful Purple'	CElw EHrv EMag SWat WCru
'Mrs Kittle'	CBct CElw CMMP EBee EChP EPPr GBri IFoB MLLN MNFA MRav NBir NSti SDys WBrk WCru WFar WLin WMnd
'Netta Statham'	ECha
'Northern Lights'PBR	SHar
'Nürnberg'	EMon MAvo
officinalis	CAgr CArn CBro CHby EHon GBar GPoy IFoB LLWP MDun MHer MLHP MWat NVic SIde WBrk WCru WFar WWye
- 'Alba'	EBee ELan WBrk WCru
§ - 'Blue Mist'	CBro CElw CLAP EBee ECha ELan GBri GBuc NBir WAbb WBrk WCot WCru WHoo WMnd WMoo WTin
- 'Bowles' Blue'	see *P. officinalis* 'Blue Mist'
- Cambridge Blue Group	CPrp EBee ECGP EChP EMar EMon GMaP LAst LRHS MBNS MNFA MRav MWat NBir NFla NLar WCAu WCot WCru WEas WPtf
- 'Plas Merdyn'	IBlr
- *rubra*	see *P. rubra*
- 'Stillingfleet Gran'	NSti
- 'White Wings'	CElw CHea CLAP EBrs EPla LRHS MBNS NLar NPri NSti SIde SPoG WEas WFar WMoo
'Oliver Wyatt's White'	CLAP EBee
Opal = 'Ocupol'	More than 30 suppliers
'Pewter'	WCru
'Pippa's Pink'	SBla
'Polar Splash'	CBct EBee GBin MBnl SIde SPoG SRot WCra WFar
'Purple Haze'	NSti
'Raspberry Splash'PBR	CBct CLAP CPom CRez EBee GKev LHop NEgg NLar NSti SHar SIde SPoG

'Richard Nutt' **new**	EMon
'Roy Davidson'	CBgR CElw CLAP COlW CSam EBee EChP ECtt EGle EHrv EMon EPPr LHop LRHS MBow MNFA NBir NCGa NChi NDov NSti SAga SBla SRGP WCot WCra WCru WLin WPnP
§ *rubra* ♀H4	CBcs CElw CPom CSWP ECha ELan EMar EShb EWTr GAbr IBlr LLWP NBid NCob NOrc NSti SBla SRms WCAu WFar WTin
- var. *alba*	see *P. rubra* var. *albocorollata*
§ - var. *albocorollata*	CBct CBgR CBre CElw CMHG EBee ECha EGle EHrv EMon GAbr GMac LRHS MNFA MSte SHar WCru WFar
- 'Ann'	CBct CElw CLAP EBee EChP IBlr LRHS MBNS NMoo WCru WFar WTin
- 'Barfield Pink'	CBgR CBro EBee EChP ECtt ELan EWTr GBar GCal LAst LRHS MLLN NBir NLar SHGN WBrk
- 'Barfield Ruby'	EMon GBuc LRHS MAvo
- 'Bowles' Red'	EBee ECtt EHrv EPfP IFoB LAst LRHS MRav MWat MWgw NBir NCGa NGdn SBch SIde SPer STes WFar WMnd
- 'David Ward' (v)	More than 30 suppliers
- 'Prestbury Pink'	LRHS
- 'Rachel Vernie' (v)	CLAP CPom CPou EBee EMon WCot
- 'Redstart'	More than 30 suppliers
§ *saccharata*	ECha EHrv ELan GMaP IHMH NEgg SIde SPet SRms WCAu WCru WFar
- 'Alba'	CBro CElw ECha GBuc SRms
- Argentea Group ♀H4	CBro CSev EBee ELan EMag EPfP GMaP LAst LRHS MRav MTho NGdn SBla SPer SPet SWvt WCAu WCot
- blue-flowered	WCru
- 'Brentor'	EBee WCru
- 'Clent Skysilver'	EBee WSPU
- 'Dora Bielefeld'	More than 30 suppliers
- 'Frühlingshimmel'	CBro CElw CMea CSam EBee EBrs ECtt MBNS MRav WCAu WFar
- 'Glebe Cottage Blue'	CElw ECGP WCru
- 'Jill Richardson'	ELan
- 'Lady Lou's Pink'	WCru
- 'Leopard'	CBct CElw CEnt CLAP CMea COlW CSam EBee EChP ECtt EMil GBuc GMaP GSki LAst LRHS MLLN NBir NBre SBla SRGP SUsu WBrk WCot WCru WFar WGHP WHoo WMnd
- 'Mrs Moon'	CSam CWib EBee ECho ECtt ENot EPfP GMaP LRHS MBNS MHer MWgw NBlu NOrc NPri SMer SPer SRGP SWvt WHen WMnd WPnP
- 'Old Rectory Silver'	CLAP NBir
- 'Picta'	see *P. saccharata*
- 'Pink Dawn'	CMHG EBee LRHS WCru WMnd
- pink-flowered	WCru
- 'Reginald Kaye'	CElw ECha EWes MNrw SHBN
- 'Silverado'PBR	EBee EBrs ENot MBNS NLar NOrc NSti
- 'Stanhoe'	EBee EWes
- 'White Barn'	see *P.* 'Beth's Blue'
'Saint Ann's'	CBct CElw EMon NBre NSti WCru
'Samurai'	EBee MBNS NSti
'Silver Lance' **new**	EBrs
'Silver Maid'	WCAu
'Silver Mist'	MAvo
'Silver Sabre'	IBlr
'Silver Shimmers'	SHar
'Silver Surprise'	WCot

'Sissinghurst White' ♀H4   More than 30 suppliers
'Skylight'   CElw
'Smoky Blue'   CLAP CRez EBee ECtt EMon EPfP
  LBMP MRav MWgw NBPC NMoo
  SMar SWat WCru WFar WMnd
'Spilled Milk'   EBee NBre NLar
'Sterling Silver' **new**   EBee
'Stillingfleet Meg'   CSam EAEE EBee ECGP EPPr LRHS
  MAvo MBNS MLLN NCob NSti SPla
  SRGP WCra
'Trevi Fountain'   CBct CLAP COfd CRez EBee EShb
  GKev LHop NBre NEgg SMac
  SPoG SRot WCot
'Ultramarine'   EBee
'Vera May'   EBee
'Victorian Brooch'PBR   CBct CLAP COIW CSam EBee
  GAbr GCai GKev LRHS LSou NEgg
  NLar NSti SIde SPoG WFar WPtf
'Weetwood Blue'   CBgR CBre CLAP EPfP EPla MNrw
  MSte WCru
'Wendy Perry'   CElw
'Wisley White'   CElw

Pulsatilla (*Ranunculaceae*)

alba   CBro NSla NWCA WCra
albana   CBro EAEE LHop LRHS SBla
- 'Lutea'   EBee GKev
alpina   EChP ECho SRms WPat
§ - subsp. *apiifolia* ♀H4   EBee ELan GKev MFOX NRya NSla
- subsp. *sulphurea*   see *P. alpina* subsp. *apiifolia*
bungeana   EHyt
campanella   GAbr
caucasica   LRHS
cernua   CBro EAEE EBrs GBuc LHop LRHS
dahurica   CSec
x *gayeri*   ECho NBir
georgica   EHyt NSla
halleri ♀H4   CSec EBee ECho GKev LBMP
- subsp. *slavica* ♀H4   CLyd GCrs LRHS NWCA
- subsp. *taurica*   MSte
lutea   see *P. alpina* subsp. *apiifolia*
montana   GBuc GKev NMen SPlb
multifida   GBuc GlBF
§ *patens*   NBHF
pratensis   GPoy SRms
- subsp. *nigricans*   CBro CSec EAEE EHyt LHop LRHS
  SMHy
rubra   EBee ECho NEgg NGHP
turczaninovii   GBuc
§ *vernalis* ♀H2   CSec ECho EPot GBuc GCrs GKev
  NJOw NSla NWCA SBla WLin
§ *vulgaris* ♀H4   More than 30 suppliers
- 'Alba' ♀H4   More than 30 suppliers
- 'Barton's Pink'   CBro EAEE EWes LHop LRHS SBla
  SIng
- 'Blaue Glocke'   CBgR CBrm EWll GEdr GSki MHer
  NJOw NLar SWvt WHil WWeb
- Czech fringed hybrids   WLin
- 'Eva Constance'   CBro EAEE EHyt ENot LHop LRHS
  NBir SIng
- 'Gotlandica'   CLyd
- subsp. *grandis*   EPot NMen
- - 'Budapest Seedling'   GCrs
- - 'Papageno'   CBgR CBrm CPBP CSpe EAEE
  EBee EChP ECho GKev GMaP
  LHop LRHS MAvo NHol NLar
  NWCA SMrm SPoG WFar WHil
- Heiler hybrids   EAEE EBee MWgw NChi NEgg
  NGdn WHal
- Red Clock   see *P. vulgaris* 'Röde Klokke'
§ - 'Röde Klokke'   CBgR CBrm EBee EChP ENot GEdr
  GKev IBal LRHS MAvo NBPC NChi
  NHol NJOw NLar NPri NWCA
  SWvt WHil WSel WWeb
I - *rosea*   EHyt GAbr WBrE
- Rote Glocke   see *P. vulgaris* 'Röde Klokke'

- var. *rubra*   More than 30 suppliers
- violet blue-flowered   ITim
§ - 'Weisse Schwan'   ECho GEdr GMaP NJOw NMen
- White Swan   see *P. vulgaris* 'Weisse Schwan'
zimmermannii **new**   NWCA

pummelo see *Citrus maxima*

Punica (*Lythraceae*)

granatum   CBcs CHEx CMen EPfP ERea
  ERom LPan MGos MPRe SBLw
  SDnm SLim SOWG STre WBVN
  WSHC XPep
- 'Chico'   CBcs XPep
- 'Fina Tendral'   ERea
- 'Fruits Violets'   XPep
- 'Legrelleae' (d)   SBrw XPep
- 'Maxima Rubra'   XPep
- 'Mollar de Elche'   XPep
- var. *nana* ♀H3   CArn CCCN CMen CPle EPfP EShb
  LPan MPRe SBrw SDEP SMrm
  SPoG SRms WPat
- f. *plena* (d)   CBcs MRav SBrw WCFE
- - 'Flore Pleno Luteo' (d)   XPep
- 'Provence'   XPep
* - 'Striata'   SOWG

Purshia (*Rosaceae*)
aff. *mexicana* B&SWJ 9040   WCru

Puschkinia (*Hyacinthaceae*)
scilloides   EBrs ECho LRHS NBir
§ - var. *libanotica*   CBro ECho EPfP EPot GAbr LHop
  LPhx LRHS SPer WHoo WPer
  WShi
- - 'Alba'   ECho EPot LPhx LRHS SPer

Putoria (*Rubiaceae*)
calabrica   CLyd NWCA

Puya (*Bromeliaceae*)
RCB/Arg L-3   WCot
RCB/Arg L-5   WCot
RCB/Arg S-2   WCot
alpestris   CBrP CCCN CHEx CTrC EOas
  EShb SAPC SBig SSpi WMul
berteroana   EAmu SPlb WMul
castellanosii CDPR 3109   WPGP
new
chilensis   CAbb CBcs CBrd CCCN CCtw
  CDoC CHEx CKob CPne EBee
  EOas SAPC SArc SChr SPlb WMul
coerulea   CFir EAmu EBee EOas LEdu MGol
  SMad WMul
§ - var. *violacea*   EPyc
ferruginea   EOas
gilmartiniae   IDee WCot
laxa   SChr
mirabilis   CAbb CHEx CKob CTrC EBee
  EOas MFOX WMul
venusta   WMul
violacea   see *P. coerulea* var. *violacea*
weberbaueri   CHEx

Pycnanthemum (*Lamiaceae*)
pilosum   CAgr CArn EBee ELau EMan EUnu
  GPoy MHer MSal NLar NPri SBch
  SIde WBri WPer WPic WSHC
  WWye
tenuifolium   NBre NLar

Pycnostachys (*Lamiaceae*)
reticulata   EShb
urticifolia   ECre EOHP EWes

Pygmea see *Chionohebe*

Pyracantha ✿ (*Rosaceae*)

Alexander Pendula = 'Renolex'	EHol LHop MRav MSwo SRms WFar WHar
angustifolia	WCFE
§ *atalantioides*	CMac SPlb WCFE
'Brilliant'	EPfP
'Buttercup'	EPla SPoG
§ *coccinea* 'Lalandei'	LAst SMer XPep
- 'Red Column'	More than 30 suppliers
- 'Red Cushion'	LRHS MGos MRav SPoG SRms
crenulata	WCFE
Dart's Red = 'Interrada'	CSBt LRHS SMac SPoG
'Fiery Cascade'	SPoG
gibbsii	see *P. atalantioides*
'Golden Charmer' ♀H4	EBee ECtt EPfP LRHS MAsh MGan MGos MRav MSwo NBlu NEgg NWea SHBN SPer SPoG SRms SWvt WDin WFar WHar
'Golden Dome'	LRHS
'Golden Glow'	LRHS
'Golden Sun'	see *P.* 'Soleil d'Or'
'Harlequin' (v)	ECtt EHoe EHol SHBN
'John Stedman'	see *P.* 'Stedman's'
'Knap Hill Lemon'	MBlu
koidzumii 'Victory' **new**	MGos
'Mohave'	CBrm CMac EBee ECrN ELan LRHS MAsh MBar MGan MNHC MWat NEgg NWea SHBN SMac SMer SPer SRms SWvt WDin
'Mohave Silver' (v)	CCVT CWSG EBee EHoe LAst LRHS MBNS
'Monrovia'	see *P. coccinea* 'Lalandei'
'Mozart'	EBee WWeb
'Navaho'	EPfP SPoG
'Orange Charmer'	CBrm CTri EBee ELan EPfP EWTr LHop MGan MGos MRav MWat NBlu NEgg NWea SHBN SMer SPer SPlb WFar WTel
'Orange Glow' ♀H4	CBcs CMac CSBt CSam CTri EBee ECrN ECtt EPfP IBal LAst LBuc LRHS MAsh MBar MGos MRav MSwo NBlu NFor NWea SPoG SRms SWvt WBrE WDin WFar WHar WWeb
'Renault d'Or'	SLPl
rogersiana ♀H4	EBee ECrN EPfP MRav WFar WTel
- 'Flava' ♀H4	CSBt CTri EBee ECrN EHol EPfP LAst MBar MRav MWhi NWea SMer SPoG WTel
'Rosedale'	WSPU
Saphyr Jaune = 'Cadaune'PBR	CBcs CDoC CEnd CSBt CWSG EBee ENot EPfP MBNS MGos MRav NPri SBra SMer SPer SPoG WWeb
Saphyr Orange = 'Cadange'PBR ♀H4	CBcs CDoC CEnd COtt CSBt CWSG EBee EMil ENot EPfP EPla LRHS MBri MGos MRav NCGa NPri SBra SMac SPer WWeb
Saphyr Panache = 'Cadvar' (v)	EBee SPoG
Saphyr Rouge = 'Cadrou'PBR ♀H4	CBcs CCVT CDoC CEnd COtt CSBt CWSG EBee ENot EPfP LRHS MBri MGos MRav NCGa NPri SBra SPer SPoG WWeb
'Shawnee'	CMac CSBt ECot EPfP MSwo MWat WWeb
§ 'Soleil d'Or'	More than 30 suppliers
'Sparkler' (v)	CMac EBee EHoe LAst LPan LRHS MAsh MGos WFar WHar
§ 'Stedman's'	NLar
'Teton' ♀H4	CMac CWSG EBee ECrN ELan EPfP EPla LAst LHop LPan LRHS MAsh MBar MBri MRav MSwo NBlu SMac SPoG SRms WDin WFar WWeb

'Watereri'	SLPl SPer WTel
'Yellow Sun'	see *P.* 'Soleil d'Or'

Pyrenaria (*Theaceae*)

spectabilis	see *Tutcheria spectabilis*

Pyrethropsis see *Rhodanthemum*

Pyrethrum see *Tanacetum*

Pyrola (*Ericaceae*)

minor	NMen
picta **new**	EBee
rotundifolia	WHer

Pyrostegia (*Bignoniaceae*)

venusta	CPIN SOWG

Pyrrocoma (*Asteraceae*)

clementis	EBee
§ *lanceolata*	EBee

Pyrus ✿ (*Rosaceae*)

amygdaliformis	CTho
- var. *cuneifolia*	CLnd
betulifolia	WJas
calleryana 'Bradford'	CLnd
- 'Chanticleer' ♀H4	More than 30 suppliers
- 'Chanticleer' variegated	CDul CLnd
x *canescens*	CTho
communis (F)	CCVT CDul CTri LBuc SBLw SKee SPer WMou
- 'Abbé Fétel' (D)	SKee
- 'Barnet' (Perry)	CTho
- 'Baronne de Mello' (D)	CTho SFam SKee
- 'Beech Hill' (F)	CDul CLnd EBee ECrN EMil EPfP SBLw SPer
- 'Belle Guérandaise' (D)	SKee
- 'Belle Julie' (D)	SKee
- 'Bergamotte Esperen' (D)	SKee
- 'Beth' (D) ♀H4	CAgr CDoC CSBt CTri CWib ECrN EMil EMui EPfP GTwe LAst LBuc MBri MGan NPri SDea SFam SKee SPer SPoG WHar WOrn
- 'Beurré Alexandre Lucas' (D)	SKee
- 'Beurré Bedford' (D)	SKee
- 'Beurré Clairgeau' (C/D)	SKee
- 'Beurré d'Amanlis' (D)	SKee
- 'Beurré d'Avalon' (D)	SKee
- 'Beurre de l'Assumption' **new**	SKee
- 'Beurré de Naghin' (C/D)	SKee
- 'Beurré Diel' (D)	SKee
- 'Beurré Dumont' (D)	SFam
- 'Beurré Giffard' (D) **new**	CAgr
- 'Beurré Gris d'Hiver' (D)	SKee
- 'Beurré Hardy' (D) ♀H4	CAgr CCAT CDoC CDul CSBt CTho CTri CWib ECrN EMui ENot ERea GTwe LAst LPan LRHS MBri MGan MRav MWat SDea SFam SKee WOrn
- 'Beurré Mortillet' (D)	SKee
- 'Beurré Six' (D)	SKee
- 'Beurré Superfin' (D)	ECrN GTwe MCoo SFam SKee
- 'Bianchettone' (D)	SKee
- 'Bishop's Thumb' (D)	SDea
- 'Black Worcester' (C)	GTwe SDea SFam SKee WJas WOrn WSPU
- 'Blakeney Red' (Perry)	CTho SDea
- 'Blickling' (D)	SKee
- 'Brandy' (Perry)	CTho SDea SKee
- 'Bristol Cross' (D)	CAgr GTwe SKee
§ - 'Butirra Precoce Morettini' (D)	SDea
- 'Catillac' (C) ♀H4	CAgr CTho GTwe SFam SKee

- 'Chalk'	see *P. communis* 'Crawford'
- 'Chaumontel' (D)	SKee
- 'Clapp's Favourite' (D)	CTho ECrN GTwe SKee
- 'Colmar d'Eté' (D)	CTho
- 'Comte de Lamy' (D)	SKee
- 'Concorde'^{PBR} (D) ♀H4	More than 30 suppliers
- 'Conference' (D) ♀H4	More than 30 suppliers
- 'Crassane'	CTho
§ - 'Crawford' (D)	SKee
- 'Deacon's Pear' (D)	SDea
- 'Devoe' (D)	SDea
- 'Docteur Jules Guyot' (D)	CAgr ECrN SDea SKee
- 'Double de Guerre' (C/D)	SKee
- 'Doyenné Blanc' (F)	SKee
- 'Doyenné Boussoch' (D)	SKee
- 'Doyenné d'Eté' (D)	ERea SFam
- 'Doyenné du Comice' (D) ♀H4	More than 30 suppliers
- 'Duchesse d'Angoulême' (D)	SKee
- 'Durondeau' (D)	CTho GTwe SDea SFam SKee
- 'Emile d'Heyst' (D)	CTho GTwe MCoo
- 'Eva Baltet' (D)	SKee
- 'Fertility' (D)	CLnd SKee
- 'Fertility Improved'	see *P. communis* 'Improved Fertility'
- 'Fondante d'Automne' (D)	CAgr CTho SKee
- 'Forelle' (D)	SKee
- 'Gin' (Perry)	CTho
- 'Glou Morceau' (D)	CAgr CTho ECrN EMui GTwe MCoo MGan MWat SDea SFam SKee
- 'Glow Red Williams' (D)	SFam
- 'Gorham' (D)	CAgr CTho ECrN GTwe MCoo SFam SKee
- 'Gratiole de Jersey' (D)	CTho
- 'Green Horse' (Perry)	CTho
- 'Green Pear of Yair' (D)	SKee
- 'Hacon's Imcomparable' (D)	SKee
- 'Harrow Delight' (D)	SDea
- 'Harvest Queen' (D/C)	SDea
§ - 'Hellen's Early' (Perry)	SKee
- 'Hessle' (D)	CAgr GTwe MCoo SDea SFam SKee
- 'Highland' (D)	SKee
§ - 'Improved Fertility' (D)	CAgr CDoC GTwe SDea SKee SPoG
- Invincible 'Delwinor' (D/C) **new**	CDul EMui LBuc LRHS SPoG
- 'Jargonelle' (D)	CAgr CTho ECrN GTwe SDea SFam SKee
- 'Joséphine de Malines' (D) ♀H4	CTho GTwe SDea SFam SKee WOrn
- 'Kieffer' (C) **new**	CAgr
- 'Laxton's Foremost' (D)	CAgr SKee
- 'Laxton's Satisfaction' (D)	SFam
- 'Louise Bonne of Jersey' (D) ♀H4	CAgr CDoC CTho CTri ECrN EMui GTwe LAst MGan MGos SDea SFam SKee
- 'Marguérite Marillat' (D)	SDea
- 'Max Red Bartlett'	MCoo
- 'Merton Pride' (D)	CTho ECrN GTwe MWat SDea SFam SKee
- 'Moonglow' (D/C)	CAgr MCoo SDea SKee
- 'Morettini'	see *P. communis* 'Butirra Precoce Morettini'
- 'Nouveau Poiteau' (C/D)	CAgr CTho ECrN GTwe SKee
- 'Onward' (D) ♀H4	CAgr CCAT CLnd CTri CWib ECrN EMui GTwe MBri NWea SDea SFam SKee WHar WOrn
- 'Ovid' (D)	CAgr
§ - 'Packham's Triumph' (D)	CAgr CDoC CTri CWib ECrN GTwe LAst MGan SDea SKee

- 'Passe Colmar' (D)	CTho
- 'Passe Crassane' (D)	SKee
- 'Pear Apple' (D)	SDea
- 'Pero Nobile'	SKee
- 'Pitmaston Duchess' (C/D) ♀H4	ECrN GTwe SDea SKee
- 'Red Comice' (D/C)	GTwe SKee
- 'Red Sensation Bartlett' (D/C)	EMui GTwe LRHS SKee
- 'Robin' (C/D)	ERea SDea SKee
- 'Roosevelt' (D)	SKee
- 'Santa Claus' (D)	SDea SFam SKee
- 'Seckel' (D)	SFam SKee
- 'Sierra' (D) **new**	CAgr
- 'Soleil d'Automne' (F)	SKee
- 'Souvenir du Congrès' (D)	CAgr
- 'Swan's Egg' (D)	CTho SKee
- 'Terrace Pearl'	EMui ENot
- 'Thompson's' (D)	GTwe SFam
- 'Thorn' (Perry)	CTho SKee
- 'Triomphe de Vienne' (D)	SFam
- 'Triumph'	see *P. communis* 'Packham's Triumph'
- 'Uvedale's St Germain' (C)	CTho SKee
- 'Verbelu'	SKee
- 'Vicar of Winkfield' (C/D)	GTwe SDea SKee
- 'Williams' Bon Chrétien' (D/C) ♀H4	CAgr CCVT CDul CMac CSBt CTri CWSG CWib ECrN EMui ENot EPfP ERea LBuc LPan LRHS MBri MGan MGos MWat NPri SCrf SDea SFam SKee SPer SPoG WHar WJas WOrn
- 'Williams Red' (D/C)	EMui GTwe SKee
- 'Winnal's Longdon' (Perry)	CTho
- 'Winter Nelis' (D)	CTri CWib ECrN GTwe LRHS MBri SDea SFam SKee
cordata	CDul CTho
elaeagnifolia	CWSG LRHS
- var. *kotschyana*	CDul CEnd GIBF SLim WOrn
- 'Silver Sails'	CLnd LRHS MAsh MBlu MBri MGos NLar SCoo SPoG SPur
korshinskyi	GIBF
nivalis	CDul CLnd CTho EBee ECrN EPfP GIBF SBLw SCoo SPer
- 'Catalia'	LRHS MBri NLar SCoo SPoG
pashia	NLar
- CC 3609	WRos
pyraster	CDul
pyrifolia '20th Century'	see *P. pyrifolia* 'Nijisseiki'
- 'Chojuro' (F)	ERea
- 'Kumoi' (F)	SDea
§ - 'Nijisseiki' (F)	ERea
- 'Shinseiki' (F)	CLnd EMui ERea LRHS SDea SKee
- 'Shinsui' (F)	SDea SKee
* *salicifolia* var. *orientalis* **new**	CTho
- 'Pendula' ♀H4	More than 30 suppliers
ussuriensis	CTho GIBF GKev

Q

Qiongzhuea see *Chimonobambusa*

Quercus ✿ (*Fagaceae*)

acerifolia **new**	EPfP
§ *acuta*	CBcs
acutifolia × *mexicana* **new**	SBir
§ *acutissima*	CBcs CDul CLnd CMCN EPfP MBlu SBir WNor

aegilops	see *Q. ithaburensis* subsp. *macrolepis*	*gilva*	CDul
		glandulifera	see *Q. serrata*
affinis	CMCN SBir	§ *glauca*	CDul CMCN EPfP SAPC SArc SBir
agrifolia	CAgr CDul CMCN SBir WPGP		SLon WNor
alba	CMCN CTho SBir WDin	*grisea*	CDul CMCN SBir
- f. *elongata*	EPfP	x *hastingsii*	CMCN EPfP
aliena	CDul CMCN	*hemisphaerica*	CDul CMCN EPfP SBir
- var. *acutiserrata*	CMCN	x *heterophylla*	CMCN EPfP SBir
alnifolia	CDul	x *hickelii*	CMCN CTho SBir
arkansana	CMCN SBir	- 'Gieszelhorst'	MBlu
austrina	CMCN SBir	*hinckleyi*	WDin
x *beadlei*	see *Q.* x *saulii*	§ x *hispanica*	CLnd WPic
bicolor	CDul CMCN EPfP IArd SBir WDin	- 'Ambrozyana'	CDul CMCN EPfP SMad WDin
	WNor	- 'Diversifolia'	CMCN EPfP MBlu
borealis	see *Q. rubra*	- 'Fulhamensis'	CMCN MBlu SEND
breweri	see *Q. garryana* var. *breweri*	§ - 'Lucombeana' ♀H4	CBcs CDul CMCN CSBt CTho EPfP
x *bushii*	CMCN EPfP MBlu SBir		IArd IDee MBlu SBir SPer
canariensis ♀H4	CLnd CMCN CTho CTrG EPfP	§ - 'Pseudoturneri'	CBcs CDul EBee EPfP IArd LPan
canariensis x *faginea*	WPGP		MBlu SIFN
NJM 03.001 **new**		- 'Suberosa'	CTho
castaneifolia	CDul CMCN EPfP SBLw WDin	- 'Waasland' **new**	SBir
- 'Green Spire' ♀H4	CDoC CMCN CTho EPfP IArd	- 'Wageningen'	CMCN EPfP SBir
	MAsh MBlu SMad SPer	*hypoleucoides* **new**	EPfP
cerris	CBcs CCVT CDoC CDul CLnd	*ilex* ♀H4	More than 30 suppliers
	CMCN ECrn EMil EPfP IArd LAst	*ilicifolia*	CMCN SBir WNor
	LPan MGos MLan NWea SBLw SBir	*imbricaria*	CDul CMCN MBlu SBir WDin
	SEND SPer SPoG WDin WMou	§ *incana* Bartram	CMCN SBir
§ - 'Argenteovariegata' (v)	CDul CMCN CMCN CTho EBee	*incana* Roxb.	see *Q. leucotrichophora*
	ELan EPfP MAsh MBlu MGos SBir	x *introgressa* **new**	SBir
	SIFN SMad SPoG WOrn WPGP	*ithaburensis*	CMCN EPfP
	WPat	- subsp. *macrolepis*	CMCN LEdu SBir
* - 'Marmorata'	SBir	x *jackiana* **new**	EPfP
- 'Variegata'	see *Q. cerris* 'Argenteovariegata'	*kelloggii*	CBcs CDul CMCN
- 'Wodan'	CMCN EPfP MBlu	x *kewensis*	CMCN
chapmanii	CMCN	*laevigata*	see *Q. acuta*
chrysolepis	CMCN	*laevis*	CDul CMCN EPfP SBir
coccifera	CDul CMCN SSpi WDin WPGP	§ *laurifolia*	CDul CMCN
- subsp. *calliprinos*	CMCN WPGP	*laurina*	SBir
coccinea	CBcs CDul CLnd CMCN CWSG	§ *leucotrichophora*	CDul CMCN
	ECrn EPfP GIBF NBea NWea SBLw	*liaotungensis*	see *Q. wutaishanica*
	SBir SPer SPoG STre WDin WNor	x *libanerris*	CDul SBir
- 'Splendens' ♀H4	CDoC CDul CEnd CMCN CTho	- 'Rotterdam'	CMCN
	CTri ELan EPfP EWTr MAsh MBlu	*libani*	CDul CMCN EPfP WDin
	MBri NEgg SBLw SHBN SMad SPer	*lobata*	CMCN LEdu
	SPoG WDin WOrn WPat	x *lucombeana*	see *Q.* x *hispanica*
conspersa **new**	SBir	- 'William Lucombe'	see *Q.* x *hispanica* 'Lucombeana'
x *deamii* **new**	SBir	x *ludoviciana*	CMCN EPfP SBir
dentata	CMCN EPfP WDin	§ *lusitanica* Lamarck	CMCN
- 'Carl Ferris Miller'	CBcs CMCN EPfP IArd MBlu MBri	*lyrata*	CMCN
	WPat	'Macon'	LPan
- 'Pinnatifida'	CMCN EPfP IArd IDee MBlu MBri	*macranthera*	CLnd CMCN EPfP SBir
	SMad	*macrocarpa*	CDul CLnd CMCN EPfP SBir WDin
- subsp. *yunnanensis*	CMCN		WNor
douglasii	CMCN	*macrocarpa* x	CMCN
dumosa	CMCN SBir WNor	*turbinella*	
ellipsoidalis	CDul CMCN SBir WNor	*macrolepis*	see *Q. ithaburensis* subsp.
- 'Hemelrijk'	CDoC EPfP MBlu		*macrolepis*
emoryi	CDul SBir	*margarettiae*	CMCN
fabrei	SBir	*marilandica*	CBcs CDul CEnd CMCN EPfP IDee
faginea	CBcs CMCN		SBir WPGP
falcata	CDul CMCN EPfP	*mexicana*	CMCN SBir
- var. *pagodifolia*	see *Q. pagoda*	*michauxii*	CDul CMCN SBir
x *fernaldii*	CMCN	*mongolica* subsp.	CMCN
frainetto	CCVT CDoC CDul CLnd CMCN	*crispula* var.	
	CTho ECrn EPfP EWTr ISea LPan	*grosseserrata*	
	MLan NWea SBLw SEND SPer	§ *montana*	CMCN EPfP
	WDin WMou WNor	*muehlenbergii*	CDul CMCN CTho EPfP MBlu SBir
- 'Hungarian Crown' ♀H4	CMCN EPfP MBlu SBir SMad	*myrsinifolia*	see *Q. glauca*
- 'Trotworth'	SMad	*myrtifolia*	CMCN EPfP
- 'Trump'	CMCN MBlu	*nigra*	CMCN SBir WNor
fruticosa	see *Q. lusitanica* Lamarck	*nuttallii*	see *Q. texana*
gambelii	CMCN	*obtusa*	see *Q. laurifolia*
garryana	CDul CMCN	*oglethorpensis*	SBir
§ - var. *breweri*	SBir	§ *pagoda*	CMCN MBlu SBir
- var. *fruticosa*	see *Q. garryana* var. *breweri*	*palustris* ♀H4	CCVT CDoC CDul CLnd CMCN
georgiana	CMCN SBir		CSam CTho ECrn EPfP EWTr LPan

	MAsh MBlu MBri MLan NEgg NWea SBLw SBir SPer WDin WNor WOrn
* - 'Compacta'	EPfP
- 'Green Dwarf'	CMCN MBlu
- 'Pendula'	CEnd CMCN
- 'Swamp Pygmy'	CMCN MBlu
parusca **new**	SBir
pedunculata	see *Q. robur*
pedunculiflora	see *Q. robur* subsp. *pedunculiflora*
§ *petraea* ♀H4	CDoC CDul CLnd CSBt ECrN EPfP IMGH LBuc MBlu NBee NWea SBLw SPer WDin WMou
§ - 'Insecata'	CDoC CDul CEnd CMCN
- 'Laciniata'	see *Q. petraea* 'Insecata'
- 'Mespilifolia'	CTho
§ - 'Purpurea'	CDul CLnd CMCN MBlu
- 'Rubicunda'	see *Q. petraea* 'Purpurea'
§ *phellos*	CDul CLnd CMCN CTho ECrN EPfP MBlu SLPl SPoG WDin WNor
- var. *latifolia*	see *Q. incana* Bartram
phillyreoides	CBcs CDul CMCN EPfP IDee SBir SLPl WDin WNor
polymorpha	CDul CMCN
'Pondaim'	CMCN SBir
pontica	CDul CMCN EPfP MBlu NWea
prinoides	CMCN
§ *prinus* L.	CMCN SBir
prinus Engelm.	see *Q. montana*
pubescens	CMCN SBir
pumila Michx.	see *Q. montana*
pumila Walt.	see *Q. phellos*
pumila ambig.	SBir
pyrenaica	CDul CMCN CTho
- 'Pendula'	CMCN EPfP WDin
rhysophylla	EPfP MBlu SBir
x *riparia* **new**	SBir
§ *robur* ♀H4	More than 30 suppliers
- 'Alkarp' **new**	IArd
- 'Argenteomarginata' (v)	CDul CMCN MBlu SSta
- 'Atropurpurea'	CDul EBee GTSp MGos SIFN WDin
* - 'Compacta'	MBlu
- 'Concordia'	CDoC CEnd CLnd CMCN EBee EPfP LRHS MBlu NLar SIFN WDin
- 'Contorta'	CMCN
- 'Cristata'	CDul CMCN
- 'Cucullata'	CMCN
* - *dissecta*	CMCN
- 'Facrist'	CDul
- f. *fastigiata*	CDoC CDul CLnd CTho EBee ECrN ENot EPfP IMGH LRHS MBar MGos NBee NWea SBLw SCoo SLPl SLim SPer WDin WFar WOrn
- 'Fennesseyi'	CMCN
- 'Filicifolia' misapplied	see *Q. robur* 'Pectinata'
- 'Filicifolia'	see *Q.* x *rosacea* 'Filicifolia'
- var. *haas* **new**	CDul
- 'Hentzei'	CMCN
- 'Irtha'	EPfP
§ - 'Pectinata'	CTho EPfP MBlu WDin
§ - subsp. *pedunculiflora*	CDul CMCN
- 'Pendula'	CDul CEnd CMCN CTho MBlu MGos SMad
- 'Purpurascens'	CEnd CMCN MBlu
- 'Raba'	CMCN
- 'Salicifolia'	MBlu
- 'Strypemonde'	CMCN
- 'Totem'	SMad
- f. *variegata* (v)	MGos
- - 'Fürst Schwarzenburg' (v)	CMCN
robur x *turbinella*	CMCN
robusta f. *fastigiata* 'Koster' ♀H4	CDoC CDul CMCN EPfP LPan MBlu SIFN SPoG SSta
§ x *rosacea* 'Filicifolia'	CEnd CLnd NBea NEgg NLar WPat
rotundifolia NJM 03.009 **new**	WPGP
§ *rubra* ♀H4	More than 30 suppliers
- 'Aurea'	CEnd CMCN CPMA EPfP MBlu SPer WPGP
- 'Boltes Gold'	MBlu
- 'Magic Fire'	EPfP MBlu SMad
* - 'Sunshine'	CDul CMCN MBlu
rugosa	CDul CMCN SBir
x *runcinata*	SBir
sadleriana	CDul CMCN
salicina **new**	WPGP
sartorii	SBir
§ x *saulii*	CMCN SBir
x *schochiana*	EPfP
x *schuettei*	SBir
- *serrata*	CDoC CMCN SBir
sessiliflora	see *Q. petraea*
shumardii	CDul CMCN EPfP MBlu SBir WDin WNor
stellata	CMCN EPfP SBir
suber	CBcs CDoC CDul CLnd CMCN CTho EPfP IArd ISea LEdu LPan MGos SAPC SArc SEND WDin WPGP
- 'Cambridge'	EPfP
§ *texana*	CMCN EPfP SBir
trojana	CMCN SBir
turbinella	CMCN
x *turneri*	CDoC CLnd CMCN CTho EPfP SBLw WDin WMou
- 'Pseudoturneri'	see *Q.* x *hispanica* 'Pseudoturneri'
vacciniifolia	CMCN
variabilis	CMCN EPfP SBir
velutina	CDul CLnd CMCN CPMA CTho EPfP SBir
- 'Albertsii'	MBlu
- 'Rubrifolia'	CMCN EPfP
- 'Vilmoriana'	CMCN
virginiana	CMCN
'Warburgii'	EPfP
wislizeni	CDul CMCN SBir
§ *wutaishanica*	CDul CMCN

Quillaja (Rosaceae)

saponaria	CCCN CPle CTrG

quince see *Cydonia oblonga*

Quisqualis (Combretaceae)

indica	CCCN CPlN SOWG
- double-flowered (d)	CPlN

R

Rabdosia (Lamiaceae)

calycina	SPlb

Racosperma see *Acacia*

Ramonda (Gesneriaceae)

§ *myconi* ♀H4	CBrm CLAP CPBP CStu ECho EHyt GKev ITim LSou LTwo NLAp NLar NMen NSla NWCA SBla SIng SRms WAbe
- var. *alba*	CLAP ECho MTho NLAp WKif
- 'Jim's Shadow'	WAbe
- 'Rosea'	CLAP SBla
nathaliae ♀H4	CLAP CPBP NWCA WAbe WThu
- JCA 686	SOkd
- 'Alba'	CLAP NSla SBla
pyrenaica	see *R. myconi*
serbica	ECho SBla WThu

Ranunculus ✿ (*Ranunculaceae*)

abnormis	NRya
aconitifolius	EChP ECha NEgg NGby NLar SHar SWat WCMO WMnd
- 'Flore Pleno' (d) ♀H4	More than 30 suppliers
acris	EWTr NBir NLan NPer
* - *citrinus*	CElw CEnt EChP ECtt EGle EMag EWoo LRHS MFOX MSte MTis NCGa NRya WMoo WRha
- 'Farrer's Yellow'	CRow
- 'Flore Pleno' (d) ♀H4	CDes CElw CFee CFir CRow EBee EChP ECha ECho EGle EHrv ELan EPPr GBuc MSte NBid NBro NCGa NDov NPri NRya NSti SPoG SRms STes WCAu WHil WMoo
- 'Hedgehog'	EBee ECho EPPr LSou NDov WPrP
- 'Stevenii'	CAby CFee CRow EBee EPPr IGor SDix WHal
- 'Sulphureus'	CBre ECha WEas WFar WHal
alpestris	ECho GEdr NMen NRya
amplexicaulis	EBee ERos GCrs MRav NHar NLar NMen NSla SBla WAbe
aquatilis	EHon EMFW NSco SWat WPnP
x *arendsii* 'Moonlight'	SBla SRot
asiaticus var. *albus*	SBla
- var. *flavus*	SBla
bilobus	NMen
bulbosus	NMir NSco
§ - 'F.M. Burton'	CBos EBee ECtt EGle EHrv NRya WTMC
- *farreri*	see *R. bulbosus* 'F.M. Burton'
- 'Speciosus Plenus'	see *R. constantinopolitanus* 'Plenus'
calandrinioides ♀H2-3	ECho EHyt EWes GIBF NBir SBla WAbe WCot
- SF 137	WCot
§ *constantinopolitanus* 'Plenus' (d)	CElw CRow EBee ECha GCal GMac MBri MLLN MRav NBid NBro NRya WCot WEas WFar WMoo
cortusifolius	CMHG SBla SWat WCru
crenatus	EBee ECho GCrs GEdr GIBF NMen NRya WAbe WHal
creticus	SPoG
ficaria	CArn CNat CRow GBar MBow MHer MSal NMir NSco WFar WHbs WHer WShi WWye
- var. *albus*	CRow EMon ERos LRHS NRya SIng SPoG WOut
- anemone-centred	see *R. ficaria* 'Collarette'
- 'Ashen Primrose'	CRow EBee
§ - var. *aurantiacus*	CBgR CNic CRow CStu ECha EMon ERos LPhx LRHS MRav NJOw NLar NRya SIng SRms WAbe WFar
- 'Bantam Egg'	CRow
- 'Blackadder'	CRow
- 'Bowles' Double'	see *R. ficaria* 'Double Bronze', 'Picton's Double'
- 'Brambling'	CBre CHea CLAP CNic CRow ECGP ECho EMon LRHS MRav NLar SBch SIng SSvw
- 'Brazen Child'	CRow EBee MDKP
- 'Brazen Daughter'	CRow
- 'Brazen Hussy'	More than 30 suppliers
- 'Bregover White'	CRow
- 'Broadleas Black'	CNat
- 'Budgerigar'	CRow
- subsp. *bulbilifer* 'Chedglow'	CRow MDKP
- 'Bunch' (d)	CRow
- 'Cartwheel' (d)	CRow
- 'Champernowne Giant'	CRow
- 'Chocolate Cream'	CRow

§ - subsp. *chrysocephalus*	CRow ECha EMon NRya SBch SIng WCot WFar
- 'Clouded Yellow' (v)	CRow
- 'Coffee Cream'	CRow EBee
- 'Coker Cream'	CRow
§ - 'Collarette' (d)	CRow CStu ECho EHyt EMon ERos GBar GBuc LRHS MAvo MRav MTho NBir NJOw NMen NRya SBla SIng SMac SPoG WAbe WCMO WFar
- 'Coppernob'	CBre CElw CRow ECGP ECha ECho GAbr MAvo MDKP SBch SBla WCMO WCot WFar WPnP
- 'Corinne Tremaine'	WHer
- 'Coy Hussy' (v)	CNat
- 'Crawshay Cream'	CDes CElw CRow EBee
- 'Cupreus'	see *R. ficaria* var. *aurantiacus*
- 'Damerham' (d)	CRow EMon LRHS
- 'Deborah Jope'	CRow SUsu
- 'Diane Rowe'	EMon
- 'Dimpsey'	CRow
§ - 'Double Bronze' (d)	CRow CStu ECGP ECho EMon ERos LEdu LRHS MDKP MTho NBir NLar NRya SIng
- double cream (d)	see *R. ficaria* 'Double Mud'
- double green eye (d)	CRow
§ - 'Double Mud' (d)	CBow CLAP CRow CSpe CStu ECGP EMon ERos EWsh GBuc LRHS MTho NJOw NRya SBla SIng SPoG WAbe WCMO WFar WHal WSHC
- double yellow (d)	see *R. ficaria* flore-pleno
- 'Dusky Maiden'	CRow EMon LRHS NLar SBch SIng WFar
- 'E.A. Bowles'	see *R. ficaria* 'Collarette'
- 'Elan' (d)	CDes CRow EBee
- subsp. *ficariiformis*	EMon
§ - *flore-pleno* (d)	CBgR CFee CRow CStu ECha ECho ELan EMar EMon EPPr EPfP ERos LRHS NJOw NRya NSti SBch SIng SRms WAbe WCot WFar
- 'Fried Egg'	CRow
- 'Granby Cream'	EMon
- 'Green Petal'	CAby CRow CStu ECho EMon LPhx MDKP MRav MTho NBir NJOw NLar NRya SIng WHal WHer WOut
- 'Greencourt Gold' (d)	CRow
- 'Holly'	see *R. ficaria* 'Holly Green'
- 'Holly Bronze'	CRow
§ - 'Holly Green'	CRow ECho
- 'Hoskin's Miniature'	CRow
- 'Hoskin's Variegated' (v)	CRow
- 'Hyde Hall'	EMon LRHS NLar SBch SIng WFar
- 'Jake Perry'	CDes EBee
- 'Jane's Dress'	CRow
- 'Ken Aslet Double' (d)	CDes CRow CSpe EBee EMon LRHS WHal WOut
- 'Lambrook Black'	WHer
- 'Laysh On' (d)	CRow
- 'Leo'	EMon MDKP
- 'Limelight'	CRow
- 'Little Southey'	CRow
- subsp. *major*	see *R. ficaria* subsp. *chrysocephalus*
- 'Mimsey' (d)	CRow
- 'Mobled Jade'	CNat CRow EBee
- 'Mud' **new**	MDKP
- 'Newton Abbot'	CBre CRow
I - 'Nigrifolia'	MDKP
- 'Oakenden Cream'	CRow
- 'Old Master'	CBow EBee MAvo WCMO WCot
- 'Orange Sorbet'	CRow EMon NLar
§ - 'Picton's Double' (d)	CRow CStu ECGP GBar MTho NJOw NRya WAbe

- 'Primrose' CRow EMon LRHS MRav MTho NLar NRya SIng WCot
- 'Primrose Brassy' **new** EMon
- 'Primrose Elf' CRow
- 'Quantock Brown' CBgR
- 'Quillet' (d) CRow EMon
- 'Ragamuffin' (d) CDes CRow EBee EMon
- 'Randall's White' CRow CSWP CStu LPhx MRav MTho SHar WCMO WCot WFar WSHC
- 'Rowden Magna' CRow
- 'Salad Bowl' (d) CRow
- 'Salmon's White' CBre CFee CRow ECho ELan EMar EPPr LPhx MRav NBir NCGa NJOw NRya SIng SSvw WAbe WFar WHal WHer WHrl
- 'Samidor' CRow
- 'Sheldon' CRow
- 'Sheldon Silver' CRow
- 'Silver Collar' EMon
- single cream EMon
- 'Suffusion' CNat CRow
- 'Sutherland's Double' (d) CRow
- 'Sweet Chocolate' CRow
- 'Torquay Elf' CRow
- 'Tortoiseshell' CRow EBee MAvo MDKP MRav WFar
- 'Trenwheal' (d) CRow
- 'Winkworth' EMon
- 'Wisley White' NSti
- 'Witchampton' **new** CDes
- 'Yaffle' CBre CRow EBee EChP EMon LRHS MDKP MRav SIng

flammula CDWL CRow EHon EMFW LNCo LPBA SWat WPnP WWpP
- subsp. *minimus* CRow WWpP
gouanii NRya
gramineus ♀H4 CGra CMea EAEE EBee ECho EHyt EPot ERos EShb GBuc GCrs LBee LPhx LRHS MNrw MRav MTho NMen NRya SMad SPoG SRms WCAu WFar WHil WPer
- 'Pardal' SBla WFar
* *guttatus* NMen
illyricus CDes EBee ECha NRya WHal
insignis EBee GKev
lanuginosus EPPr SUsu
lapponicus GIBF
lingua CFir COld EMFW EMag MCCP NSco SPlb WSFF
- 'Grandiflorus' CBen CRow EHon LNCo LPBA NPer SWat WHal WMAq WWpP WWye
lyallii CBos CFis SBla WAbe
macauleyi GCrs
millefoliatus EBee ECho EHyt ERos GBuc MTho NMen NRya WPGP
montanus double (d) EBee EBrs SBla WCot
- 'Molten Gold' ♀H4 CStu ECho ECtt GAbr GCrs MRav MTho NRya SBla WAbe
muelleri var. *brevicaulis* SBla
nivicola NWCA
parnassiifolius EBee GAbr GCrs GKev NMen NSla SBla WAbe
platanifolius EBrs LPhx SMHy
pyrenaeus NMen
repens 'Boraston O.S.' (v) WCHb
* - 'Buttered Popcorn' CBow CRow EBee NLar WMoo
- 'Cat's Eyes' (v) CBow CDes EBee EMan WCot
- 'Gloria Spale' CBre CRow
- 'Joe's Golden' EHoe
- var. *pleniflorus* (d) CBre CRow EBee EChP GAbr GGar NSti WEas WFar

- 'Snowdrift' (v) WCot
- 'Timothy Clark' (d) CBre EMon WSHC
rhomboideus **new** EBee
sceleratus WHer
seguieri WAbe
serbicus EBee EPPr GCal
speciosus 'Flore Pleno' see *R. constantinopolitanus* 'Plenus'

Ranzania (Berberidaceae)
japonica WCru

Raoulia (Asteraceae)
australis misapplied see *R. hookeri*
australis Hook. EDAr GAbr GEdr GGar ITim MBar MWat NRya NWCA SIng WHoo
§ - Lutescens Group ECha ECho EPot ITim
haastii ECho ECou
§ *hookeri* ECha ECho ECou EDAr GEdr ITim NWCA SIng SPlb SRms WAbe WFar WLin WPat WThu
- var. *apice-nigra* WAbe
- var. *laxa* EPot EWes
x *loganii* see x *Leucoraoulia loganii*
lutescens see *R. australis* Lutescens Group
petriensis ECho
x *petrimia* 'Margaret Pringle' EHyt WAbe
subsericea ECho ECou EWes NMen NWCA
tenuicaulis ECha ECou SPlb

Raoulia x *Leucogenes* see x *Leucoraoulia*

raspberry see *Rubus idaeus*

Ratibida (Asteraceae)
columnifera CMea CRWN EBee EBrs EMan EPfP LRHS LSou MGol NBre SPav SPet
- 'Cheyenne Yellow' **new** SPoG
- f. *pulcherrima* CMea CSpe EBee EGoo LHop LPhx LSou MNFA NBre NJOw SMad SPav SPet WBVN WCAu WCMO WMnd
- red LRav SPav
- 'Red Midget' SPav SPoG
pinnata CEnt CFwr CMea CRWN CSam EBee EBrs LPhx LRHS MWgw NBre SMad SPav SPet WCAu WHal WMnd
tagetes EBee SPav

Rauvolfia (Apocynaceae)
serpentina MGol

Ravenala (Strelitziaceae)
madagascariensis EAmu LPal WMul XBlo

Ravenea (Arecaceae)
rivularis CCCN EAmu LPal WMul

Rechsteineria see *Sinningia*

redcurrant see *Ribes rubrum* (R)

Rehderodendron (Styracaceae)
macrocarpum CBcs

Rehmannia (Scrophulariaceae)
angulata misapplied see *R. elata*
§ *elata* ♀H2 More than 30 suppliers
- 'White Dragon' CSpe
glutinosa ♀H3 CStu EWTr GKev WWye

Reichardia (Asteraceae)
picroides CAgr

Reineckea (Convallariaceae)

§ *carnea*	CDes CFee CPLG CPom CStu EBee EChP ECha EGra ELan EMar EPla ERos EWTr GCal GEdr LEdu LRHS MHar MRav NJOw NSti SDys SPlb SUsu WCot WCru WPGP WPtf WTin
- B&SWJ 4808	WCru
- SDR 330	GKev
- 'Variegata' (v)	WCot WCru

Reinwardtia (Linaceae)

elata	SMrm
§ *indica*	CHll CPLG EShb
trigyna	see *R. indica*

Remusatia (Araceae)

hookeriana	CKob EAmu MOak
pumila	CKob EAmu MOak
vivipara	CKob MJnS MOak WMul

Reseda (Resedaceae)

alba	MHer
lutea	MBow MSal SECG SIde
luteola	CHby GBar GPoy MHer MSal NSco SECG WBri WCHb WHer WWye

Restio (Restionaceae)

bifarius	CTrC
brunneus	CBig EBee WPGP
festuciformis	EAmu
quadratus	WMul WNor WPGP
subverticillatus	see *Ischyrolepis subverticillata*
tetraphyllus	CAbb CBct CBig CBod CBrm CFir CPen CTrC EBee EMan EPPr GCal GGar IDee LAst LHop MBNS NVic SMad WCot WDyG WPGP WPrP

Retama (Papilionaceae)

§ *monosperma*	CBcs EShb XPep
raetam	XPep

Reynoutria see *Fallopia*

Rhagodia (Chenopodiaceae)

triandra	ECou

Rhamnus (Rhamnaceae)

alaternus	XPep
- var. *angustifolia*	WFar WPGP
§ - 'Argenteovariegata' (v) ♀H4	More than 30 suppliers
- 'Variegata'	see *R. alaternus* 'Argenteovariegata'
californica **new**	NLar
cathartica	CCVT CDul CLnd CTri ECrN LBuc NWea WDin WMou WSFF WTel
imeretina	WPGP WPat
pallasii	NLar
pumila	NLar
purshiana	MSal
taquetii **new**	NLar

Rhaphiolepis (Rosaceae)

x *delacourii*	CMHG CWSG CWib ELan EPfP LRHS MWea SBrw SMur WHCG
- 'Coates' Crimson'	CDoC EBee ELan EMil EPfP IArd LHop SBra SBrw SHBN SLon SOWG WPat WSHC
- Enchantress = 'Moness'	CMHG EBee ELan EPfP LRHS SBrw SMur SPoG
- 'Spring Song'	EBee SLon
indica	ERom
- B&SWJ 8405	WCru
- 'Coppertone'	LRHS SBra SBrw

- Springtime = 'Monme'	SPer WDin XPep
umbellata ♀H2-3	CBcs CBrm CHEx CPLG CTri CWib EBee ELan EPfP IDee LAst LHop LRHS MRav SBra SBrw SEND SLon SOWG WFar WHCG WSHC
- f. *ovata*	CRez
- - B&SWJ 4706	WCru

Rhaphithamnus (Verbenaceae)

cyanocarpus	see *R. spinosus*
§ *spinosus*	EBee EDsa EPfP ERea

Rhapidophyllum (Arecaceae)

hystrix	CBrP LPal NPal SAin

Rhapis ✿ (Arecaceae)

§ *excelsa* ♀H1	CBrP CRoM CTrC EAmu LPal NPal WMul
multifida	LPal

Rhazya (Apocynaceae)

orientalis	see *Amsonia orientalis*

Rheum ✿ (Polygonaceae)

CC 4612	WCot
CC 4613	MGol WCot
CC 4768	CPLG MGol WCot
CC 4845	WCot
GWJ 9329 from Sikkim	WCru
§ 'Ace of Hearts'	More than 30 suppliers
'Ace of Spades'	see *R.* 'Ace of Hearts'
acuminatum	EBee GBin GIBF SBla WPGP
- HWJCM 252	WCru
alexandrae	CAgr CBos CFir EBee GCal GIBF NChi WCot
- BWJ 7670	WCru
'Andrew's Red'	GTwe
§ *australe*	CAgr CArn CFir CRow EBee GCal GIBF LEdu LPBA LRHS MLLN NBro NLar SMad WCot WFar WHoo WMnd
delavayi	EBee GIBF
- BWJ 7592	WCru
emodi	see *R. australe*
forrestii	CAgr GIBF
x *hybridum* 'Appleton's Forcing'	GTwe
- 'Baker's All Season'	GTwe
- 'Brandy Carr Scarlet'	NGHP
- 'Canada Red'	GTwe
- 'Cawood Delight'	GTwe LRHS SEND
- 'Champagne'	CAgr GTwe
- 'Daw's Champion'	GTwe
- 'Early Cherry'	GTwe
- 'Fenton's Special'	GTwe MCoo NGHP
- 'Glaskin's Perpetual'	CWib LBuc MAsh
- 'Goliath'	GTwe
- 'Greengage'	GTwe
- 'Hadspen Crimson'	CBct CDes CHad WCot
- 'Hammond's Early'	GTwe SEND
- 'Harbinger'	GTwe
- 'Hawke's Champagne' ♀H4	GTwe
- 'Holsteiner Blut'	EBee
- 'Livingstone' PBR (F)	ENot EPfP LRHS
- 'Mac Red' ♀H4	GTwe
- - 'Prince Albert'	GTwe NGHP
- 'Red Champagne'	CFwr IPot NGHP
- 'Red Prolific'	GTwe
- 'Reed's Early Superb' ♀H4	GTwe
- 'Stein's Champagne' ♀H4	GTwe
- 'Stockbridge Arrow'	CSut GTwe NGHP
- 'Stockbridge Bingo'	GTwe
- 'Stockbridge Emerald'	GTwe
- 'Stockbridge Guardsman'	GTwe

- 'Strawberry' — EMui GTwe MAsh
- 'Strawberry Red' **new** — LRHS
- 'Strawberry Surprise' — GTwe
- 'Sutton's Cherry Red' — GTwe
- 'The Sutton' — CWib GTwe
- 'Timperley Early' ♀H4 — CDoC CMac CTri CWib EMui ENot EPfP GTwe LRHS MAsh NBlu NGHP NPri SCoo SDea SKee SPer
- 'Tingley Cherry' — GTwe
- 'Victoria' — CWib ELau GTwe LBuc LRHS MAsh MCoo MHer MNHC NGHP WTel
- 'Zwolle Seedling' — GTwe

kialense — CBct CDes EGle GCal NBid NSti WPnP

moorcroftianum — CSec GCal GKev

nobile — EBee
- HWJK 2290 — WCru
- SDR 2783 — GKev

officinale — CAgr CArn CBct CHEx GCal LRHS MBri SIde SWat

palmatum — CArn CBcs CDWL COlW EAEE EBee ECha ELan ELau EMFW ENot EPfP GIBF GMaP LAst LPBA LRHS MNHC MRav MSal MWat NEgg NGdn SPer SWat WCAu WFar WMul WWeb
- 'Atropurpureum' — see *R. palmatum* 'Atrosanguineum'
§ - 'Atrosanguineum' ♀H4 — CBct CMea CRow EAEE EChP ECha ELan EPla EShb GBuc IFro LPBA LRHS LRav MRav MWgw NBid NBro NFor SMad SPer SPlb SPoG SWat WCot WCru
- 'Bowles' Crimson' — CBct CHad MBri
- 'Red Herald' — CBct SBla WCot
- *rubrum* — COtt LRHS MCCP NBir WFar
- 'Saville' — LRHS MBri MRav
- var. *tanguticum* — CAgr CHar CRow EBee ECha EPfP GIBF LHop LPBA MBow MCCP MDun MWhi NBid NCGa NEgg NGdn NSti SMad SMer SPoG SRms SWat SWvt WFar WHil WHoo WMnd WPnP
- - 'Rosa Auslese' — WHil

rhaponticum — NLar

ribes — EBee GBin WCot

subacaule — EBee NLar

tataricum — LEdu

Rhigozum (Bignoniaceae)
obovatum — CSec

Rhinanthus (Scrophulariaceae)
minor — NSco

Rhodanthe (Asteraceae)
§ *anthemoides* — ECou
§ - 'Paper Cascade'PBR — LRHS

Rhodanthemum (Asteraceae)
from High Atlas, Morocco — SIng
'African Eyes' — EBee ECho EPfP EWin GGar LRHS NBhm SRot
§ *atlanticum* — ECho EWes NSla
§ *catananche* — EBee ECho ETow EWes LSou MBNS SRot XPep
§ - 'Tizi-n-Test' — ECho LRHS SBla WKif
- 'Tizi-n-Tichka' — CPBP EAEE ECho EWes LRHS NBir SBla SUsu WCMO WLin
§ *gayanum* — EBee ECho ECtt EShb EWes LRHS WCot WHen XPep
- 'Flamingo' — see *R. gayanum*
§ *hosmariense* ♀H4 — CHrt CMHG CMea EAEE EBee ECha ECho EDAr ELan EPfP GGar LAst LHop LRHS NPri SBla SCoo SEND SPer SPoG SRms SRot WAbe WCMO WCot WEas WPat XPep

Rhodiola (Crassulaceae)
atuntsuensis — EHyt
bupleuroides CLD 1196 — EMon
crassipes — see *R. wallichiana*
cretinii HWJK 2283 — WCru
§ *fastigiata* — EMon NMen NWCA
§ *heterodonta* — ECha EGle ELan EMon MRav WCot
himalensis (D. Don) Fu — EMon
- HWJK 2258 — WCru
§ *ishidae* — CTri
§ *kirilovii* — EBrs EMon GBin
- var. *rubra* — WFar
linearifolia — EMon
§ *pachyclados* — CNic EBur ECho EDAr EHoe EPot LBee LRHS MBar MHer MOne NBir NJOw NRya SIng SPlb SPoG SRot WAbe WEas WFar WHoo WPer
aff. *purpureoviridis* BWJ 7544 — WCru
§ *rosea* — More than 30 suppliers
semenovii — EBee MHar NLar
sinuata HWJK 2318 — WCru
- HWJK 2326 — WCru
§ *trollii* — CNic CStu GCrs
§ *wallichiana* — GCrs MLHP NBid WCot WDyG
- GWJ 9263 — WCru
- HWJK 2352 — WCru

Rhodochiton (Scrophulariaceae)
§ *atrosanguineus* ♀H1-2 — CArn CBcs CCCN CEnd CHEx CRHN CSec CSpe CTbh ELan EPfP EShb GGar IDee LRHS MAsh NEgg SGar SHFr SOWG SPer SPoG WBVN WBor WGwG
volubilis — see *R. atrosanguineus*

Rhodocoma (Restionaceae)
arida — CBct CCCN CCtw WMul WPGP
capensis — CAbb CBct CBig CCCN CCtw CFir CPen CSpe CTrC IDee WMul WPGP
foliosa — WMul
fruticosa — CTrC
gigantea — CAbb CBig CCtw CFwr CPen CTrC EBee ITer WMul WNor WPGP
* *ovida* — CBig

Rhododendron ✿ (Ericaceae)
'A.J. Ivens' — see *R.* 'Arthur J. Ivens'
'Abegail' — MGos SLdr
aberconwayi — CWri LMil SLdr SReu
- 'His Lordship' — GGGa LHyd NPen
acrophilum (V) — GGGa
Argent 2768
'Actress' — WCwm
'Ada Brunieres' (K) — CSdC
'Addy Wery' (EA) ♀H3-4 — CDoC ECho LKna MBar MGos NPen SBrw SCam SLdr SPoG
adenogynum — CDoC GGGa LMil NPen SLdr
- Cox 6502 — GGGa
§ - Adenophorum Group — EMui
- - F 20444 — SLdr
- - R 11471 — NPen
adenophorum — see *R. adenogynum* Adenophorum Group
adenopodum — GGGa LMil SLdr
adenosum — NHol
- R 18228 — GGGa
'Admiral Piet Hein' — SReu
'Adonis' (EA/d) — CMac LMil MBar NEgg NLar SBrw SCam SLdr
'Adriaan Koster' (M) — SLdr
'Advance' (O) — SLdr

aeruginosum — see *R. campanulatum* subsp. *aeruginosum*
aganniphum — GGGa ISea LMil NPen
- EGM 284 — LMil
§ - var. *aganniphum* — GGGa
  Doshongense Group
- - KR 4979 — LMil
- - Glaucopeplum Group — GGGa
- - Schizopeplum Group — GGGa
- var. *flavorufum* — GGGa MDun NPen
- - EGM 160 — LMil
- pink, KR 3528 from Pe, — LMil
  Doshang La
- 'Rusty' — NPen
x *agastum* PW 98 — LMil
'Ahren's Favourite' — MAsh
'Aida' (R/d) — CSBt SReu
'Aksel Olsen' — CTri ECho GEdr MAsh MBar MDun NHol
'Aladdin' (EA) — CDoC ECho SLdr WFar
Aladdin Group — SReu
'Aladdin' (*auriculatum* hybrid) — GGGa
Albatross Group — IDee LKna LMil SLdr SReu
'Albatross Townhill Pink' — LMil
'Albert Schweitzer' ♀H4 — CWri GGGa LMil MBar MDun SLdr SPoG WFar
albrechtii (A) — GGGa LMil SReu
- Whitney form (A) — LMil
'Album Elegans' **new** — NPen
'Alena' — GGGa
'Alexander' (EA) ♀H4 — CDoC LMil MGos SHBN SReu
'Alfred' — CWri LMil LRHS MAsh
'Alice' (EA) — LHyd LKna NPen SLdr
'Alice' (hybrid) ♀H4 — CSBt LHyd LKna LMil SBrw SLdr SReu
'Alice de Stuers' (M) — SLdr
'Alisa Nicole' (V) — SFai
Alison Johnstone Group — CBcs GGGa ISea MDun NPen SLdr SReu WPic
'Alix' — LHyd
'Aloha' — MBar NDlv SHBN
Alpine Gem Group — GQui NHol SLdr
'Alpine Gem' — LHyd
alutaceum var. *alutaceum* — GGGa LMil
§ - var. *alutaceum* — LMil
  Globigerum Group
- - - R 11100 — GGGa NPen
§ - var. *iodes* — GGGa LMil NPen
§ - var. *russotinctum* — GGGa MDun
- - R 158 — SLdr
§ - - Triplonaevium Group — GGGa
  USDAPI 59442/
  R10923
amagianum (A) — GGGa GIBF LMil
Amaura Group — WCwm
ambiguum — CTbh LMil NPen SLdr SReu
* - KR 185 select — GGGa
I - 'Crosswater' — LMil
- 'Jane Banks' — LMil
'Ambrosia' (EA) — CSBt
'America' — CBcs MBar MDun SLdr WFar
amesiae — GGGa
§ 'Amethystinum' (EA) — LKna
'Amity' — CWri ECho ISea LMil MAsh MBri MLea NPen SLdr WFar
§ 'Amoenum' (EA/d) — CBcs CDoC CMac CSBt CTrG CTrw ECho LHyd LKna MBar MGos NPen SBrw SCam SLdr SPer WFar WPic
'Amoenum Coccineum' (EA/d) — GKev SCam SReu WPat
Amor Group — LHyd
'Anah Kruschke' — ENot MAsh SLdr SPoG
'Analin' — see *R.* 'Anuschka'

'Anchorite' (EA) — LMil SLdr
* 'Andrae' — SReu
'Angelo' — LHyd LMil NPen
Angelo Group — CWri LHyd LMil SLdr SReu
'Ann Callingham' (K) — CSdC
'Ann Cooper' (A) **new** — LMil
'Ann Lindsay' — SReu
'Anna Baldsiefen' — ECho LMil MAsh NHol SPoG SReu WBVN
'Anna H. Hall' — MAsh
'Anna Rose Whitney' — CBcs CWri GGGa LHyd LKna LPan LRHS MBar MDun MGos NPen NPri SHBN WMoo
'Annabella' (K) ♀H4 — CSdC SLdr
sikkimensis — GGGa LMil NPen
aff. *sikkimensis* — LMil
  C&H 7185
'Anne Frank' (EA) — MGos SReu WFar
'Anne George' — LHyd
'Anne Teese' — IDee LMil
'Annegret Hansmann' — GGGa
'Anneke' (A) — ENot LMil MBar MDun NDlv SLdr SReu SSta WFar
'Anny' (EA) — LKna
anthopogon — GIBF LMil
- from Marpha Meadow, — WAbe
  Nepal
- 'Betty Graham' — GGGa
I - 'Crosswater' — LMil
- subsp. *hypenanthum* — GCrs LMil MDun
- - 'Annapurna' — GGGa NHol WAbe
§ *anthosphaerum* — GGGa SLdr SReu
'Antilope' (Vs) — CWri ECho ISea LMil MDun MLea NHol SLdr SPer SReu SSta WBVN
'Antje' — MAsh
'Antonio' — LMil WGer
Antonio Group — ELan
§ 'Anuschka' — MAsh
§ *anwheiense* — CWri LHyd LMil
aperantum F 27022 — GGGa
apodectum — see *R. dichroanthum* subsp. *apodectum*
'Apotrophia' — SLdr
'Apple Blossom' ambig. — CMac
'Apple Blossom' Wezelenburg (M) — SLdr
N 'Appleblossom' (EA) — see *R.* 'Ho-o'
'Apricot Blaze' (A) **new** — MDun NHol
'Apricot Fantasy' — LMil
'Apricot Surprise' — LRHS MAsh NPri
'Apricot Top Garden' — SLdr
'April Dawn' — GGGa
'April Glow' — LHyd
'April Mist' — MBri
'April Rose' — MBri
'April Showers' (A) — LMil
I 'Arabella' — MAsh
'Arabesk' (EA) — MAsh MBri SLdr WFar
araiophyllum — GGGa
  BASEX 9698
- KR 4029 — LMil
arborescens (A) — GGGa LHyd LKna LMil SLdr
- pink-flowered (A) — LMil
arboreum — CBcs CDoC CHEx CTbh GGGa IDee ISea LMil MDun NPen SLdr SReu WPic
- B&SWJ 2244 — WCru
- 'Blood Red' — NPen SLdr
- subsp. *cinnamomeum* — CDoC GGGa LMil NPen SLdr SReu WGer
- - var. *album* — LHyd SLdr SReu
- - var. *cinnamomeum* Campbelliae Group — NLar SLdr
- - var. *roseum* — GGGa
* - - - *crispum* — SLdr
- - - 'Tony Schilling' — CDoC IDee LHyd LMil SLdr SReu

- subsp. *delavayi*	GGGa ISea LMil NPen SLdr
- - C&H 7178	GGGa
- EGM 360	LMil
- 'Heligan'	CWri SReu
- mid-pink-flowered	CDoC SLdr
§ - subsp. *nilagiricum*	GGGa SLdr
- var. *roseum*	SLdr
§ - subsp. *zeylanicum*	SLdr
'Arcadia' (EA)	LKna
'Arctic Fox' (EA)	GGGa
'Arctic Regent' (K)	CSdC GQui SLdr
'Arctic Tern'	see x *Ledodendron* 'Arctic Tern'
argipeplum	GGGa SLdr
'Argosy' ♀H4	LMil SLdr SReu
argyrophyllum	CWri NPen SLdr
- subsp. *argyrophyllum*	SLdr
- - W/A 1210	SLdr
§ - subsp. *hypoglaucum*	NPen
§ - - 'Heane Wood'	GGGa
- subsp. *nankingense*	GGGa LMil
- - 'Chinese Silver' ♀H4	CDoC IDee LHyd LMil LRHS
	MDun NPen SReu WGer
§ *arizelum*	CDoC GGGa GTSp LMil LRHS
	MDun NPen SLdr
- BASEX 9580	GGGa
- R 25	GGGa
- subsp. *arizelum*	LMil LRHS MDun
Rubicosum Group	
'Armantine'	LKna
armitii (V) Woods 2518	GGGa
'Arneson Gem' (M)	CDoC CSam GGGa ISea LMil MAsh
	NDlv NLar SLdr
'Arneson Pink' **new**	ISea
'Arpege' (Vs)	ECho LMil MDun NLar SReu
'Arthur Bedford'	CBcs CSBt LKna SLdr SReu
§ 'Arthur J. Ivens'	SLdr
'Arthur Osborn'	GGGa
'Arthur Stevens'	SLdr
'Arthur Warren'	LKna
'Arthur's Choice' (V)	SFai
'Asa-gasumi' (EA)	LHyd SCam SLdr
'Ascot Brilliant'	SBrw SLdr
asterochnoum	LMil
- C&H 7051	GGGa
- EGM 314	LMil
Asteroid Group	SLdr
'Astrid'	ENot
atlanticum (A)	CSec GGGa GKev LMil
- 'Seaboard' (A)	IDee LMil SLdr
'Audrey Wynniatt' (EA)	MAsh
Augfast Group	CTrw ISea SLdr
'August Lamken'	MDun
augustinii	CBcs CTrG CTrw CWri GGGa ISea
	LHyd LMil LRHS MLea NLar NPen
	SLdr SPer SSpi SSta
- subsp. *augustinii*	GGGa
C&H 7048	
§ - subsp. *chasmanthum*	GGGa LMil MDun SLdr
- - white-flowered	GGGa
C&Cu 9407	
- compact EGM 293	LMil
§ - Electra Group	CDoC GGGa IDee LHyd LMil
	MDun SLdr
- Exbury best form	LHyd LMil MDun SReu
§ - subsp. *hardyi*	GGGa SLdr
- pale lilac-flwoered	SLdr
§ - subsp. *rubrum*	GGGa
* - 'Trewithen'	LMil
I - 'Werrington'	SLdr SReu
§ *aureum*	GGGa LMil SLdr
- from Kamchatka	GIBF
auriculatum	GGGa IDee LHyd LMil LRHS
	MDun NLar NPen SLdr SReu SSpi
	SSta WBVN WGer
- PW 50	GGGa
- Reuthe's form	SReu
auriculatum x	GGGa
hemsleyanum	
auritum	GGGa NPen SLdr WPic
'Aurora' (K)	SLdr WPic
'Aurore de Rooighem' (A)	SLdr
§ *austrinum* (A)	IDee LMil SPoG
- yellow-flowered (A)	LMil
'Autumn Gold'	SBrw SLdr
'Avalanche' ♀H4	LMil SLdr SReu
Avocet Group	LMil SLdr
'Award'	LMil
'Ayah'	SBrw
'Aya-kammuri' (EA)	LHyd SLdr
Azamia Group	LHyd
Azor Group	LHyd NPen SBrw SReu
Azrie Group	SLdr
§ 'Azuma-kagami' (EA)	CDoC LHyd LKna LMil MGan SLdr
'Azurika'	NHol
'Azurro'	GGGa
'Azurwolke'	LMil
'Babette'	see *R.* (Volker Group) 'Babette'
'Babuschka'	LMil
'Bad Eilsen'	MAsh
'Baden-Baden'	CDoC ECho ENot GCrs GEdr LHyd
	LKna MAsh MBar MDun MGos
	NEgg NHol NPen NWea SHBN
	SLdr WFar
'Bagshot Ruby'	LKna SBrw SLdr SReu
baileyi	GGGa NPen SLdr WAbe
bainbridgeanum	LMil
'Balalaika'	MDun
balangense EN 3530	GGGa
balfourianum	GGGa LMil SLdr
'Balsaminiflorum'	see *R. indicum* 'Balsaminiflorum'
'Baltic Amber' (A)	GGGa
'Balzac' (K)	ECho LHyd LMil MGos MLea NEgg
	SLdr SPer SPur WBVN
'Bambi'	SLdr SReu
'Bandoola'	SReu
'Barbara Coates' (EA)	SLdr
barbatum	CDoC GGGa GGar IDee LHyd LMil
	MDun NPen SLdr WGer
- B&SWJ 2237	WCru
'Barbecue' (K)	LMil
Barclayi Group	LHyd SLdr
'Bariton'	CDoC LMil
barkamense	LMil
'Barmstedt'	CWri MAsh
'Barnaby Sunset'	GGGa LMil LRHS MAsh NHol
'Bashful' ♀H4	CSBt ECho EMui ENot EPfP LHyd
	LRHS MGos NPen SLdr SReu
§ *basilicum*	GGGa GTSp IDee LMil LRHS SLdr
- AC 3009	WCwm
- AC 616	NPen
x *bathyphyllum* Cox 6542	GGGa
bauhiniiflorum	see *R. triflorum* var.
	baubiniiflorum
beanianum	GGGa
- KC 122	GGGa
- KW 6805	NPen
- compact	see *R. piercei*
'Beatrice Keir'	LMil SReu
Beau Brummel Group	CDoC ELan LMil SPoG
'Beaulieu Manor'	GQui
'Beauty of Littleworth'	LHyd LKna NPen SReu
'Beefeater' **new**	SLdr
'Beefeater' x	SLdr
yakushimanum **new**	
beesianum	GGGa LMil SLdr
- CN&W 1316	ISea
- JN 300	GGGa
- KR 4150	LMil
'Beethoven' (EA) ♀H3-4	CTrG LHyd NPen SBrw SCam SLdr
	SMer SReu WPic
'Belkanto'	EMil MDun NBlu SPoG
'Belle Heller'	SBrw SLdr

'Ben Morrison' (EA) — SReu
'Bengal' — ECho GEdr MAsh MBar MDun NDlv NHol SReu
'Bengal Beauty' (EA) — GQui SLdr
'Bengal Fire' (EA) — CMac SLdr
§ 'Benifude' (EA) — LHyd
'Bergie Larson' — CBcs CDoC ECho LMil MAsh MBri MDun MLea NPen SLdr
bergii — see *R. augustinii* subsp. *rubrum*
'Berg's Yellow' — CWri ECho LMil MDun MLea NPen WBVN WFar
'Bernard Shaw' — SReu
'Bernstein' — MAsh NBlu SPoG WFar
'Berryrose' (K) ♀H4 — CBcs CSBt CWri ECho ENot EPfP LHyd LKna LMil MAsh MBar MLea SLdr SPer WBVN WFar
Berryrose Group — CDoC MDun
'Bert's Own' — SLdr
'Beryl Taylor' — GGGa
'Betty' (EA) — CTrG LHyd
'Betty Anne Voss' (EA) — ECho ENot LHyd LMil LRHS MAsh NPri SCam SCoo SLdr SReu
* 'Betty Robinson' — ISea
'Betty Wormald' — CSBt ECho LHyd LMil MBri MGos MLea NPen SHBN SLdr SPer WBVN
bhutanense — LMil
– CH&M — GGGa
Bibiani Group — SLdr
'Big Punkin' — LMil
'Bijinsui' (EA) — LHyd
'Billy Budd' — SLdr
'Birthday Girl' — CBcs ECho ENot LMil MDun MLea SPoG
Biskra Group — GGGa LMil
'Blaauw's Pink' (EA) ♀H3-4 — CDoC CDul CMac CSBt CTrh ECho EGra ENot EPfP GQui LHyd LKna LMil LRHS MAsh MBar MBri MGos NPen SBrw SCam SLdr SPer SPlb SPoG SReu SRms WFar
'Black Hawk' (EA) — CBcs CTrG
'Black Knight' (A) — SLdr
'Black Magic' — CWri LMil
'Black Sport' — MLea
Blaue Donau — see *R.* 'Blue Danube'
'Blazecheck' — MGos SCoo
'Blewbury' ♀H4 — LHyd LMil MDun SLdr SPoG SReu SSta
'Blue Beard' — SLdr
'Blue Bell' — LKna SBrw
'Blue Boy' — ENot LMil
'Blue Chip' — LHyd SLdr
§ 'Blue Danube' (EA) ♀H3-4 — More than 30 suppliers
Blue Diamond Group — CBcs CMHG CTrh ECho ENot EPfP LKna LRHS MAsh MBar MDun MGos NHol NPen SHBN SLdr SReu SRms WPic
'Blue Diamond' — CSBt ECho MLea SPer SPoG
'Blue Moon' — MBar
'Blue Peter' ♀H4 — CDoC CSBt CWri ECho ENot EPfP GGGa LHyd LKna LMil MAsh MBar MBri MDun MGos SBrw SHBN SLdr SPer SPoG SReu SSta
'Blue Pool' — LMil MBar
Blue Ribbon Group — CMHG CTrw ISea SLdr
'Blue Silver' — GGGa LMil MAsh SPoG
'Blue Star' — ECho GGar LHyd LRHS MDun MLea NLAp NMen
'Blue Steel' — see *R. fastigiatum* 'Blue Steel'
Blue Tit Group — CBcs CSBt CTrG ECho EPfP LHyd LKna LRHS MAsh MBar MDun NEgg NPen SHBN SLdr SReu SSta WPic
Bluebird Group — CSBt ECho MAsh MBar MDun MGos NDlv NWCA SLdr SPoG SRms
'Bluette' — ECho MDun MLea NDlv

'Blurettia' — CWri LMil NLar
'Blutopia' — LMil
'Bob Bovee' — NLar
'Bobbie' — SReu
'Bob's Blue' — MDun
'Boddaertianum' — LHyd SLdr SReu
'Bodnant Yellow' — LMil
'Bold Janus' (V) — SFai
'Bonfire' — SLdr SReu
boothii — GGGa
'Bo-peep' — GQui LMil LRHS SReu
Bo-peep Group — CBcs LMil NPen SLdr
'Boskoop Ostara' — CDoC LMil MGos
'Boule de Neige' — MDun
'Bouquet de Flore' (G) — CDoC CSdC LMil MBar SLdr SReu ♀H4
Bow Bells Group — CSam ISea LHyd LKna LMil MAsh MBar MDun MGos MLea SHBN
'Bow Bells' ♀H4 — ECho EPfP GEdr LMil LRHS NBlu NLar NPri SLdr WFar
'Bow Street' — LHyd
brachyanthum — GGGa
– subsp. *hypolepidotum* — GGGa LMil
brachycarpum — GGGa GIBF NPen SLdr
– subsp. *brachycarpum* — LMil SReu
   Tigerstedtii Group
– 'Roseum Dwarf' — GGGa
brachysiphon — see *R. maddenii* subsp. *maddenii*
'Brambling' — GGGa
'Brazier' (EA) — CTrh LHyd NPen SCam SLdr SPoG
'Brazil' (K) — CSBt LKna SBrw SReu
'Bremen' — ECho LMil
Bric-à-brac Group — CBcs CTrw SLdr
'Bric-à-brac' — ENot EPfP SLdr SPoG
'Bride's Bouquet' (EA/d) — SReu
'Bridesmaid' (O) — ENot EPfP SLdr SPoG
'Brigadoon' — LMil MBri
'Bright Forecast' (K) — CWri ECho MAsh NLar SLdr WBVN
'Brigitte' — CDoC CWri GGGa LMil LRHS MAsh SLdr
'Brilliant' (EA) — MGos
'Brilliant' (hybrid) — MGos NHol WFar
'Brilliant Blue' — MAsh
'Brilliant Crimson' (EA) — SLdr
'Britannia' — CBcs CSBt CSam CWri ENot EPfP LHyd LKna MBar NPen NWea SHBN SLdr SPer SReu WFar
'Britannia' x — SLdr
   griersonianum
'Brocade' — CSam LKna LMil MDun NPen SLdr
'Bronze Fire' (A) — NHol SLdr SReu
'Brown Eyes' — ECho MAsh MDun MLea SLdr WFar
'Bruce Brechtbill' ♀H4 — CDoC CWri ECho GGGa LMil MAsh MBri MDun MGos NHol NLar SLdr SReu SSta
'Bruce Hancock' (Ad) — ECho WBVN
§ 'Bruns Elfenbein' — NLar
§ 'Bruns Gloria' — LMil
'Bruns Schneewitchen' — SReu
   new
'Buccaneer' (EA) — LHyd
'Bud Flanagan' — ENot LMil MDun SBrw
'Buketta' — GGGa MDun
bullatum — see *R. edgeworthii*
bulu C&V 9503 — GGGa
'Bungo-nishiki' (EA/d) — CMac
bureavii ♀H4 — CDoC GGGa IDee LHyd LMil MDun NPen SLdr SReu SSta
– SEH 211 — LMil
– SF 517 — ISea
– 'Ardrishaig' — GGGa
* – *cruentum* — LMil
I – 'Lem's Variety' — NLar
bureavii x Elizabeth — SReu
   Group

bureavii x NPen SReu
  yakushimanum
bureavioides LMil MDun NPen SReu
- Cox 5076 GGGa
'Burletta' GGGa
burmanicum GGGa LMil MDun
'Burning Love' NLar
'Butter Brickle' ECho LMil MDun MLea WBVN
'Butter Yellow' ECho MDun
'Buttercup' (K) MBar
'Butterfly' LKna MDun SLdr
'Buttermint' ECho GQui MAsh MBri MDun
   MGos MLea NPen SBod SHBN
   WBVN WGwG
'Buttons and Bows' (K) GGGa MBri
'Buzzard' (K) CSdC LKna LMil
'Byron' (A/d) SLdr
'Caerhays Lavender' CBcs
caesium SLdr
calendulaceum (A) GKev LMil SReu
- red-flowered (A) CSec LMil
- yellow-flowered (A) IDee LMil
Calfort Group SLdr
'Calico' (K) CSdC
caliginis (V) GGGa
callimorphum GGGa LMil
- var. *myiagrum* SLdr
   F 21821a
calophytum ♀H4 CWri GGGa GTSp IDee LMil LRHS
   NPen SLdr
- EGM 343 LMil
- var. *openshawianum* GGGa
   C&H 7055
- EGM 318 LMil
calophytum x WCwm
  praevernum
calostrotum CWri WAbe
- SF 357 ISea
- 'Gigha' ♀H4 CDoC ECho GGGa LMil LRHS
   LTwo MAsh MDun NPen SLdr
   WAbe WGer
§ - subsp. *keleticum* ♀H4 CDoC CTrG GEdr GKev MBar
   MDun MGos NHol WAbe
- - F 19915 NHol
- - R 58 LMil
§ - - Radicans Group GCrs GEdr MBar MDun MLea
   NHol WAbe WPat
- - USDAPI 59182/R11188 MLea
- - Radicans Group NHol
   mound form
- subsp. *riparium* ISea
   SF 95089
- - Calciphilum Group GGGa MDun
§ - - Nitens Group CDoC GGGa IDee MAsh NDlv
   NMen WAbe
§ - - Rock's form R178 GGGa NHol WAbe
caloxanthum see *R. campylocarpum* subsp.
   caloxanthum
'Calsap' GGGa
Calstocker Group LMil
camelliiflorum GGGa MDun
'Cameronian' (Ad) LKna
campanulatum LHyd LKna LMil MDun NPen SLdr
   SReu WAbe
- HWJCM 195 WCru
§ - subsp. *aeruginosum* GGGa LMil MDun NLar NPen SLdr
   SReu
- - Airth 10 GGGa
- *album* SLdr
- subsp. *campanulatum* NPen
   'Roland Cooper'
- - 'Knap Hill' NPen
§ 'Campfire' (EA) SLdr
Campirr Group LHyd
campylocarpum GGGa LHyd LMil MDun NPen SLdr
   SReu

§ - subsp. *caloxanthum* GGGa GTSp LMil MDun NPen
   SLdr
- - KR 3516 from Pe, LMil
   Doshang La
- - KR 6152 LMil
- East Nepal MDun
campylogynum ♀H4 GCrs LMil MLea NMen SSpi WAbe
- SF 95181 ISea
- 'Album' see *R.* 'Leucanthum'
- 'Bramble' GGGa
- Charopoeum Group ECho GCrs GGGa MBar MDun
   NHol
- - 'Patricia' ECho GCrs MDun
- claret-flowered ECho GGGa MDun
§ - Cremastum Group CTrG GGGa LHyd NHol
- - 'Bodnant Red' GGGa LHyd MDun NPen
- var. *leucanthum* see *R.* 'Leucanthum'
- var. *leucanthum* x NHol
  keiskei var. *ozawae*
   'Yaku Fairy'
- Myrtilloides Group CDoC CTrw ECho GGGa GQui
   IDee LHyd LMil LRHS MDun NLAp
   NMen NPen SLdr SReu WAbe
- - Farrer 1046 GGGa
- pink-flowered MBar WAbe
- salmon pink-flowered ECho GCrs GEdr MDun NLAp
camtschaticum GGGa GIBF LMil WAbe
- from Hokkaido, Japan GCrs NMen
- var. *albiflorum* GGGa GIBF NMen
- red-flwoered GGGa GIBF
canadense (A) GGGa NHol SLdr SReu
- f. *albiflorum* (A) GGGa LMil
- dark-flowered (A) LMil
- 'Deer Lake' (A) SReu
'Canary' LKna SReu
canescens (A) LMil
'Cannon's Double' (K/d) CWri ECho GGGa LHyd LMil
   ♀H4 MAsh MBri MDun MGos MLea
   NLar NPen SLdr SPer
'Canzonetta' (EA) ♀H4 ECho GGGa LMil MAsh MGos
'Capistrano' GGGa
capitatum GGGa
'Caprice' (EA) SReu
'Captain Jack' GGGa SLdr
'Caractacus' MBar WFar
'Carat' SLdr SReu
cardiobasis see *R. orbiculare* subsp.
   cardiobasis
Carita Group LKna SReu
'Carita Charm' SLdr
'Carita Golden Dream' LKna LMil
'Carita Inchmery' LHyd LKna SLdr
'Carmen' CWri ECho GCrs GGGa ISea LHyd
   LKna LMil LRHS MAsh MBar
   MDun MGos MLea NHol NMen
   NPen NWea SHBN SLdr SReu
   SRms WBVN
carneum GGGa LMil
'Carnival' (EA) **new** CBcs
'Caroline' **new** EMui
'Caroline Allbrook' ♀H4 CDoC CWri EBee ECho ENot EPfP
   GGGa LHyd LMil MAsh MBri
   MDun MGos MLea NDlv NHol
   NPen SLdr SPoG WBVN
'Caroline de Zoete' LHyd
carolinianum see *R. minus* var. *minus*
   Carolinianum Group
'Cary Ann' CBcs CWri ENot LRHS MAsh SLdr
   SPoG SReu WFar
'Casablanca' (EA) SLdr
'Cassley' (Vs) LMil SLdr
'Castle of Mey' SLdr
catacosmum GGGa
§ 'Catalode' GGGa
catawbiense CSec GGGa GIBF LHyd NPen SLdr
- SDR 2219 GKev

'Catawbiense Album'	CWri GGGa LRHS MAsh WFar
'Catawbiense Boursault'	CWri SLdr WFar
'Catawbiense Grandiflorum'	LMil LRHS MAsh WFar
'Catherine Hopwood'	SLdr
§ *caucasicum*	MDun
'Cunningham's Sulphur'	
'Caucasicum Pictum'	GGGa LHyd LMil MBar SLdr
Cavalier Group **new**	MDun
'Cecile' (K) ♀H4	CBcs CSam CWri ECho LHyd LKna LMil MAsh MBar MBri MDun MGos MLea NPen SBod SLdr SPer SReu WBVN
'Celestial' (EA)	CMac
'Centennial'	see *R.* 'Washington State Centennial'
cephalanthum	GGGa LMil
- subsp. *cephalanthum* SBEC 0751	WAbe
- - Crebreflorum Group	GGGa LMil LRHS WAbe
- - Nmaiense Group C&V 9513	GGGa
- subsp. *platyphyllum*	GGGa LMil
cerasinum	GGGa ISea LMil NPen
- C&V 9504	GGGa
- KR 3460	LMil
- KR 3490 from Pe, Doshang La	LMil
- 'Cherry Brandy'	LHyd NPen
'Cetewayo' ♀H4	CWri SReu
chaetomallum	see *R. haematodes* subsp. *chaetomallum*
'Chaffinch' (K)	LKna
chamaethomsonii	GGGa LMil
- CCH&H 8195	GGGa
- SF 95084	ISea
- var. *chamaethauma* KR 3506 from Pe, Doshang La	LMil
- - KW 5847	LMil
chameunum	see *R. saluenense* subsp. *chameunum*
§ 'Champagne' ♀H3-4	CSBt EPfP LHyd LKna LMil MAsh MDun MLea NPen SLdr SReu
championiae	GGGa
'Chanel' (Vs)	MDun SReu SSta
'Chanticleer' (EA)	CTrh SCam SLdr SReu
chapaense	see *R. maddenii* subsp. *crassum*
'Chapeau'	LMil
charitopes	GGGa LMil
- subsp. *charitopes* F 25570	SReu
§ - subsp. *tsangpoense*	GGGa GQui LMil NHol WPic
'Charlemagne' (G)	SLdr
* 'Charles Puddle'	WPic
Charmaine Group	GGGa NHol SReu
'Charme La'	GGGa
'Charming Valentino' (V)	SFai
chasmanthum	see *R. augustinii* subsp. *chasmanthum*
'Cheer'	CWri ENot MAsh MBar SLdr SReu WFar WMoo
'Cheerful Giant' (K)	LMil MGos
'Chelsea Reach' (K/d)	CSdC LKna
'Chelsea Seventy'	LRHS MAsh NLar NPen SLdr
'Chenille' (K/d)	LKna
'Cherokee'	SCam SLdr
'Cherries and Cream'	LMil
'Cherry Drop' (EA)	MAsh
'Chetco' (K)	LMil SLdr
'Chevalier Félix de Sauvage' ♀H4	LMil SReu
'Cheyenne' (M)	SLdr
'Chicago' (M)	LKna

'Chiffchaff'	LHyd NMen WAbe
'Chikor'	CSBt CTrG ECho GGGa ISea LKna MAsh MBar MBri MDun MGos MLea NHol NPen SLdr SReu WFar
China Group	LKna SBrw SReu
'China A'	LKna SBrw SLdr
'Chinchilla' (EA)	GQui
'Chink'	CBcs MAsh MBar MDun SLdr
'Chionoides'	GGGa LKna NBlu SLdr
'Chipmunk' (EA/d)	LMil
'Chippewa' (EA)	GGGa LMil
'Chocolate Ice' (K/d)	LKna SLdr
'Choremia' ♀H3	LHyd LMil SLdr SReu
'Chris' (EA)	SLdr
'Chris Bagley'	SBrw
christi (V)	GGGa
'Christina' (EA/d)	CMac NHol SLdr SReu
'Christmas Cheer' (EA/d)	see *R.* 'Ima-shojo'
'Christmas Cheer' (hybrid)	CBcs CMac CSBt CWri GGGa ISea LHyd LKna LMil MAsh MGos MLea NBlu NLar NPen SHBN SLdr SPer SPoG SReu WPic
'Chromatella' **new**	SLdr
chrysanthum	see *R. aureum*
chryseum	see *R. rupicola* var. *chryseum*
chrysodoron	GGGa LMil
ciliatum	CBcs CTrG GGGa LHyd SLdr
ciliicalyx subsp. *lyi*	see *R. lyi*
Cilpinense Group	CBcs LKna LMil MAsh MBar MDun NPen SLdr SPer WPic
'Cilpinense' ♀H3-4	CSBt CTbh CWri ECho EPfP GGGa LHyd LMil LRHS NPri SPoG SReu WBVN WBrE WPic
cinnabarinum	LMil MDun NPen SLdr
- 'Caerhays Lawrence'	SLdr
- subsp. *cinnabarinum*	MDun SLdr
- - BL&M 234	LMil
- - from Ghunsa, Nepal	MDun
- - 'Aestivale'	LMil
- - Blandfordiiflorum Group	GGGa LMil NPen SLdr
§ - - 'Conroy'	CDoC GGGa LMil LRHS MDun MLea SReu
- - 'Nepal'	LHyd LMil
- - Roylei Group	GGGa LMil MDun MLea NPen SReu WPic
- - - 'Magnificum'	MDun
- - - 'Vin Rosé'	LMil MDun
§ - subsp. *tamaense*	GGGa
- - KW 21021	GGGa
§ - subsp. *xanthocodon*	IDee LMil MDun MLea NPen SLdr
§ - - Concatenans Group	GGGa LMil MDun MLea NPen SLdr WPic
- - - C&V 9523	GGGa
- - - KW 5874	LMil
- - - 'Amber'	LMil MDun MLea
- - - 'Copper'	SLdr
- - - 'Daffodilly'	LHyd
- - Purpurellum Group	GGGa MDun NPen SLdr
Cinnkeys Group	GGGa MDun
Cinzan Group	LMil SReu
citriniflorum	LMil
- R 108	GGGa LMil
- Brodick form	LMil
- var. *citriniflorum*	LMil
- var. *horaeum*	SLdr
* - - F 21850	GGGa
'Citronella'	SLdr
'Claret Bumble' **new**	NPen
'Claydian Variegated' (v)	SLdr
clementinae	GGGa LMil MDun NPen SReu
- F 25705	LMil
- JN 729	GGGa
'Cliff Garland'	GQui LMil

'Coccineum Speciosum' (G) 🏆H4	CSBt CSdC GGGa IDee LMil MBar SReu
'Cockade' (EA)	LKna
'Cockatoo' (K)	LKna
§ *coelicum* F 25625	GGGa
coeloneuron	GGGa LMil MDun
– EGM 334	LMil
'Colin Kenrick' (K/d)	LKna SLdr
collettianum H&W 8975	GGGa
'Colonel Coen'	CDoC CWri ECho GGGa LMil LRHS MBri MGos MLea NPen SHBN WBVN
Colonel Rogers Group	LHyd SLdr SReu
x *columbianum*	see *Ledum* x *columbianum*
(Comely Group) 'Golden Orfe'	SLdr
complexum F 15392	GGGa
'Comte de Gomer' (hybrid)	CBcs
concatenans	see *R. cinnabarinum* subsp. *xanthocodon* Concatenans Group
concinnum	CTrw CWri LHyd MDun MLea SLdr
– Pseudoyanthinum Group	GGGa GQui LMil MDun SLdr SReu WPic
'Concorde'	NBlu
'Conroy'	see *R. cinnabarinum* subsp. *cinnabarinum* 'Conroy'
'Constable'	LHyd
'Constant Nymph'	LKna
'Contina'	GGGa
* *continentalis* new	GIBF
cookeanum	see *R. sikangense* var. *sikangense* Cookeanum Group
'Coral Flare' (V)	SFai
'Coral Mist'	CDoC GGGa LMil MDun
'Coral Reef'	SLdr SReu
'Coral Sea' (EA)	MDun SLdr SReu
'Coral Seas' (V)	SFai
'Corany' (A)	SLdr
'Cordial Orange' (V)	SFai
coriaceum	GGGa LMil LRHS NPen WCwm
– R 120	NPen
'Corneille' (G/d) 🏆H4	CSBt LMil SLdr SReu
'Cornish Cracker'	SLdr
Cornish Cross Group	LHyd NPen SLdr SReu
Cornish Early Red Group	see *R.* Smithii Group
'Cornish Red'	see *R.* Smithii Group
Cornubia Group	SLdr
'Corona'	LKna
'Coronation Day'	LMil SLdr SReu
'Coronation Lady' (K)	ENot LKna
'Corry Koster'	LKna
coryanum	GGGa
– KR 5775	LMil
– KR 6315	LMil
– 'Chelsea Chimes'	LMil NPen SLdr
'Cosmopolitan'	CWri ENot GGGa LMil MAsh MBar MDun MGos SLdr SPoG SReu WFar
'Costa del Sol'	NPen
Cote Group (A)	SLdr
'Countess of Athlone'	LKna SBrw SLdr
'Countess of Derby'	MDun SReu
'Countess of Haddington' 🏆H2	CBcs ISea LMil MDun SLdr
'Countess of Stair'	WFar WPic
'County of York'	see *R.* 'Catalode'
cowanianum	GGGa
Cowslip Group	CSam CTri CWri LHyd LKna LMil LRHS MBar MDun MGos MLea NPen NPri SHBN SLdr SReu
coxianum C&H 475B	GGGa
'Craig Faragher' (V)	SFai
'Cranbourne'	LHyd SReu
'Crane' 🏆H4	EPfP GGGa GQui LMil LRHS MAsh MDun NPri WGer
crassum	see *R. maddenii* subsp. *crassum*
'Cream Crest'	GQui MDun SHBN WFar
'Cream Glory'	LHyd SReu
'Cream Serene' (V)	SFai
'Cream Supreme' (V)	SFai
'Creamy Chiffon'	CWri GGGa MBri MDun MGos MLea
§ 'Creeping Jenny'	ECho GGGa GGar LHyd MBar MDun NHol SLdr
cremastum	see *R. campylogynum* Cremastum Group
'Crest' 🏆H3-4	CWri GGGa LHyd LKna LMil MDun MGos SHBN SLdr SPer
'Crete'	LMil MDun SReu
'Crimson Pippin'	LMil
crinigerum	GGGa LHyd LMil MDun NPen
– JN 756	GGGa
'Crinoline' (K)	LRHS SBrw SLdr SReu
'Crinoline' (EA)	SCam
'Croceum Tricolor' (G)	CSdC
Crossbill Group	WPic
* *crossium*	SReu
'Crosswater Belle'	LMil
'Crosswater Red' (K)	LMil
cubittii	see *R. veitchianum* Cubittii Group
cucullatum	see *R. roxieanum* var. *cucullatum*
cumberlandense (A)	GGGa IDee LMil LRHS
– 'Sunlight' (A)	LMil LRHS
cuneatum	GGGa
'Cunningham's Blush'	GGGa LRHS SHBN
'Cunningham's Sulphur'	see *R. caucasicum* 'Cunningham's Sulphur'
'Cunningham's White'	CBcs CSBt CSam CTbh CWri EBee ELan ENot EPfP GGGa LKna LMil LRHS MAsh MBar MDun MGos NPen NWea SLdr SPer SPoG SReu WFar
'Cupcake'	see *R.* 'Delp's Cupcake'
'Cupreum Ardens'	CSdC
'Curlew' 🏆H4	CDoC CSBt ECho EPfP GEdr GGGa ISea LMil LRHS MAsh MBar MBri MDun MGos NHol NMen NPen SHBN SLdr SPoG SReu SSpi WBVN WFar
cyanocarpum	GGGa LMil NPen
– Bu 294	GGGa
'Cynthia' 🏆H4	CDoC CSBt CWri ECho EPfP GGGa LHyd LKna LMil MBar MBri MDun MGos NPen SBrw SHBN SLdr SPer SReu SSta WBVN WFar
'Daimio' (EA)	LHyd
'Dairymaid'	LKna SReu
dalhousieae	GGGa SLdr
§ – var. *rhabdotum*	GGGa SLdr
Damaris Group	NPen SLdr
'Damaris Logan'	see *R.* 'Logan Damaris'
'Damozel'	SLdr
'Dandy' (hybrid)	LKna
'Daphne Millais' new	SLdr
'Dartmoor Blush'	SReu
'Dartmoor Pixie'	SReu
* 'Dartmoor Rose'	SReu
dasycladum	see *R. selense* subsp. *dasycladum*
dasypetalum	ECho MBar MDun NDlv
dauricum	GIBF SLdr
– 'Arctic Pearl'	GGGa SLdr
– 'Hokkaido' x *leucaspis*	GGGa
– 'Midwinter' 🏆H4	GGGa LHyd LMil SLdr
– 'David' 🏆H4	LHyd SLdr SReu
davidii AC 4100	LMil
davidsonianum 🏆H3-4	CTrw GGGa LHyd LMil NPen SLdr SSpi WPic
– EGM 351	LMil
– Bodnant form	LMil MDun
– 'Caerhays Blotched'	SLdr
– 'Caerhays Pink'	GGGa SLdr
– 'Ruth Lyons'	LMil

'Daviesii' (G) ♡H4	CBcs CDoC CSBt CSam CSdC CTri CWri ECho ENot EPfP GGGa GQui IDee LHyd LKna LMil MBri MDun MLea SBod SLdr SPer SPoG SReu SSpi WBVN WBrE WCFE WFar
'Dawn's Delight'	SLdr
* 'Day Dawn'	SReu
'Day Dream'	SReu
Day Dream Group	LKna
'Daybreak' (K)	GQui
N 'Daybreak' (EA/d)	see *R.* 'Kirin'
'Dear Grandad' (EA)	CTri LMil LRHS NPri SCoo
'Dearest' (EA) **new**	NPri
N 'Debutante'	NHol SPoG
decorum ♡H4	CDoC CSec GGGa GKev IDee LHyd LMil LRHS MDun NPen SLdr SReu WGer WPic
– Bu 286	NHol
– C&H 7023	GGGa
– SF 252	ISea
– 'Cox's Uranium Green'	SReu
§ – subsp. *diaprepes*	LMil
– – 'Gargantua'	LMil SReu
– late-flowering **new**	LMil
– pink-flowered	SLdr
decorum x *yakushimanum*	SLdr SReu
degronianum	GGGa
§ – subsp. *degronianum*	LMil SLdr
– – 'Gerald Loder'	LHyd
§ – subsp. *heptamerum*	GGGa MDun NPen
– – 'Ho Emma'	LMil MDun
– – var. *kyomaruense*	LMil
– – 'Oki Island'	LMil
– 'Rae's Delight'	LMil
dekatanum	GGGa
deleiense	see *R. tephropeplum*
'Delicatissimum' (O)	CBcs CWri ECho GGGa GQui MAsh MLea NLar SLdr SPer WBVN
§ 'Delp's Cupcake'	NLar
'Delta'	MAsh NBlu
dendricola	SLdr
– KW 20981	GGGa
dendrocharis	GGGa
– CC&H 4012	GGGa
– Cox 5016	GGGa NHol WAbe
– 'Glendoick Gem'	GGGa
– 'Glendoick Jewel'	GGGa
* 'Denny's Rose' (A)	LMil MDun SReu
'Denny's Scarlet'	MDun SReu
'Denny's White'	LMil MDun NHol SLdr SReu
denudatum C&H 70102	GGGa
– C&H 7118	GGGa
– EGM 294	LMil
– SEH 334	LMil
'Desert Orchid'	LHyd
'Desert Pink' (K)	LKna
desquamatum	see *R. rubiginosum* Desquamatum Group
x *detonsum* F13784	SLdr
'Devisiperbile' (EA)	SLdr
'Diabolo' (K)	LKna
(Diamant Group) 'Diamant Enzianblau' (EA)	LMil
– lilac (EA)	ECho LMil MLea
– pink (EA)	ECho GCrs LMil MDun MGos MLea SLdr SReu
§ – purple (EA)	ECho GCrs LMil MDun MGos MLea NEgg SLdr
§ – red (EA)	ECho GCrs LMil MDun MLea SLdr
– rosy red (EA)	ECho
– salmon pink (EA)	LMil
– white (EA)	ECho GCrs LRHS MDun MLea SLdr
'Diamant Purpur'	see *R.* Diamant Group purple
'Diamant Rot'	see *R.* Diamant Group red
'Diana Pearson'	LHyd

'Diane'	LKna
diaprepes	see *R. decorum* subsp. *diaprepes*
dichroanthum	GGGa LHyd LMil MDun SLdr SReu
– CCH&H 8198	GGGa
§ – subsp. *apodectum*	GGGa LMil
– subsp. *dichroanthum*	LMil
– – SBEC 545	GGGa
§ – subsp. *scyphocalyx*	GGGa LMil SLdr
– – F 24546	GGGa
– – Farrer 1024	GGGa
– subsp. *septentronale*	GGGa
– – JN 575	GGGa
didymum	see *R. sanguineum* subsp. *didymum*
'Dietrich'	WFar
dignabile C&V 9569	GGGa
– KR 5385	LMil
dilatatum	LMil
– 'Satsumense'	NPen
dimitrum	MDun
'Diny Dee'	MGos
'Diorama' (Vs)	SReu SSta WFar
§ 'Directeur Moerlands' (M)	SLdr
discolor	see *R. fortunei* subsp. *discolor*
'Doc'	ENot EPfP LRHS MAsh MBar MDun MGos NBlu NDlv SLdr SReu WFar
'Doctor A. Blok'	SLdr
'Doctor Chas Baumann' (G)	SLdr
'Doctor Ernst Schäle'	GGGa
'Doctor H.C. Dresselhuys'	MBar SHBN
'Doctor Herman Sleumer' (V)	
'Doctor M. Oosthoek' (M) ♡H4	CSBt SLdr SReu
'Doctor Stocker'	NPen
'Doctor V.H. Rutgers'	MBar MDun WFar
'Don Giovanni'	NLar
'Don Quixote' (K)	CSdC MAsh
'Doncaster'	ENot LKna MBar MGos NWea SHBN SPoG WFar
'Dopey' ♡H4	CBcs CDoC CSBt CWri ECho EMui ENot EPfP GGGa LHyd LMil LRHS MAsh MBar MBri MDun MGos MLea NDlv NHol NPen SHBN SLdr SPoG SReu WBVN
'Dora Amateis' ♡H4	CBcs COtt ECho GGGa ISea LHyd LMil LRHS MAsh MBar MBri MGos NHol NPen NPri SLdr SPer SReu WPic
Dormouse Group	ECho GGGa LMil SLdr SReu WBVN
'Dorothea'	SLdr
'Dorothy Corston' (K)	LKna
'Dorset Sandy' (EA)	LMil
'Dörte Reich'	GGGa
doshongense	see *R. aganniphum* var. *aganniphum* Doshongense Group
'Double Beauty' (EA/d)	LKna SPoG SReu SSta
'Double Damask' (K/d) ♡H4	LKna SBrw SLdr
'Double Date' (d)	CDoC SLdr
double yellow **new**	SLdr
'Douglas McEwan'	MDun SLdr
'Dracula' (K)	GGGa
Dragonfly Group	SReu
Dragonfly Group x *serotinum*	SLdr
'Drake's Mountain'	ECho MBar MDun MLea
'Drapa' (EA) **new**	GGGa
'Dreamland' ♡H4	COtt CSBt CWri ECho ENot LMil MAsh MDun MGos MLea NPen SLdr SReu WFar
'Driven Snow' (EA)	SLdr
drumonium	see *R. telmateium*
'Drury Lane' (K)	GQui LMil

dryophyllum misapplied see *R. phaeochrysum* var. *levistratum*
'Duchess of Teck' SBrw SReu
'Dusky Dawn' SLdr
'Dusky Orange' MDun SReu
'Dusty' MDun
'Dusty Miller' ECho ENot ISea LRHS MAsh MBar MDun MGos NDlv NPen SHBN SLdr
'Earl of Athlone' SReu
'Earl of Donoughmore' LHyd LKna MDun SReu SSta
'Early Beni' (EA) LHyd
Early Brilliant Group LKna
'Ebony Pearl' CBcs CWri ECho GGGa ISea MGos MLea WBVN
eclecteum LMil MDun SLdr
 – Cox 6054 GGGa
 – 'Rowallane Yellow' SLdr
 – 'Eddy' (EA) LKna
§ *edgeworthii* ♀H2-3 CTbh GGGa ISea SLdr WAbe
 – KC 0106 GGGa
edgeworthii × *leucaspis* CBcs
'Edith Bosley' GGGa
'Edith Mackworth Praed' SReu
Edmondii Group LHyd
'Edna Bee' (EA) LMil
'Effner' LMil MAsh
'Egret' ♀H4 CDoC ECho GEdr GGGa GGar LMil MAsh MBar MDun MGos MLea NHol NLar SLdr WAbe WThu
'Ehrengold' LMil SPoG
'Eider' GGGa ISea MAsh SLdr SReu WFar
'Eileen' LMil SBrw SReu
'El Camino' CWri ECho ISea LMil MBri NPen SHBN SLdr
'El Greco' SLdr
Eldorado Group GQui
Electra Group see *R. augustinii* Electra Group
elegantulum GGGa GTSp LMil MDun NPen
'Elfenbein' see *R.* 'Bruns Elfenbein'
'Elfin Gold' SReu
'Elisabeth Hobbie' ♀H4 ECho GGGa LKna LMil MAsh MBar MDun WMoo
Elizabeth Group CBcs CDoC CTrw CWri GGGa LHyd LKna LMil LRHS MAsh MBar NHol NWea SHBN SLdr SPer SReu WFar
N 'Elizabeth' (EA) CSBt EPfP MGos NWCA SBrw SLdr
'Elizabeth' ECho MGos NHol NPri
'Elizabeth de Rothschild' MDun SLdr
'Elizabeth Jenny' see *R.* 'Creeping Jenny'
'Elizabeth Lockhart' ECho GEdr GGGa GQui MBar MDun MGos
'Elizabeth of Glamis' GGGa
'Elizabeth Red Foliage' CDoC CTri GGGa LHyd LMil LRHS MAsh MDun SPer SReu
'Elizabeth' × *yakushimanum* GGGa
elliottii GGGa SReu
Elsae Group SLdr SReu
'Else Frye' GGGa
'Elsie Lee' (EA/d) ♀H3-4 CTrh ECho GGGa LMil MAsh SBrw SLdr
'Elsie Pratt' (A) MBar NHol
'Elsie Straver' MDun NHol SHBN SLdr SReu
'Elsie Watson' GGGa LMil
'Elspeth' LHyd LKna
§ 'Emasculum' LKna SLdr SReu
Emerald Isle Group SReu
'Emma Williams' CBcs
'Empire Day' LKna
'Endsleigh Pink' LMil
'English Roseum' SLdr
'Erato' GGGa

eriocarpum 'Jitsugetsuse' LHyd
eriogynum see *R. facetum*
eritimum see *R. anthosphaerum*
'Ernest Inman' LHyd SLdr
erosum GGGa SLdr
N 'Esmeralda' CMac CTrG
'Esther May' (A) **new** MDun
Ethel Group SLdr
'Etna' (EA) SCam SLdr
'Etta Burrows' CWri GGGa MDun
'Euan Cox' GGGa NHol NMen
euchroum NPen
eudoxum GGGa NPen
'Eunice Updike' (EA) LHyd
'Europa' SReu
eurysiphon NPen
 – Arduaine form GGGa
'Eva Goude' (K) LKna
'Evening Fragrance' (A) SReu
'Evensong' (EA) LKna
'Ever Red' GGGa
'Everbloom' (EA) SLdr
'Everest' (EA) ENot LHyd LMil MAsh SLdr SPoG
'Everestianum' GGGa LKna MBar SLdr
'Everitt Hershey' (A) SLdr
§ 'Everlasting' SReu
'Evita' (EA) **new** GGGa
exasperatum KC 0116 GGGa
 – KC 0126 GGGa
 – KW 8250 GGGa
'Exbury Albatross' LKna
'Exbury Calstocker' LMil
'Exbury Naomi' LHyd LKna LMil NPen SLdr
'Exbury White' (K) EPfP GQui
'Excalibur' GGGa
excellens LMil WCwm
 – AC 146 GGGa
 – SF 92074 ISea
 – SF 92079 ISea
 – SF 92303 ISea
eximium see *R. falconeri* subsp. *eximium*
'Exquisitum' (O) ♀H4 CDoC CWri ECho EPfP GGGa LMil MBri MLea NLar SLdr SSpi WBVN
exquisitum see *R. oreotrephes* Exquisitum Group
§ *faberi* GGGa LMil SLdr
 – subsp. *prattii* see *R. prattii*
'Fabia' ♀H3 CDoC GGGa LHyd LMil MDun WPic
Fabia Group LKna MDun NPen SLdr
'Fabia Roman Pottery' CWri MDun
§ 'Fabia Tangerine' LHyd MDun MLea SReu
'Fabia Waterer' CDoC LMil SLdr
§ *facetum* GGGa LMil MDun
 – AC 3049 LMil
'Faggetter's Favourite' ♀H4 LKna LMil MDun SPoG SReu SSta
Fairy Light Group LMil SLdr
'Falcon' see *R.* (Hawk Group) 'Hawk Falcon'
falconeri ♀H3-4 CHEx GGGa IDee ISea LMil LRHS MDun NPen SLdr SPer WGer
 – from East Nepal MDun
§ – subsp. *eximium* GGGa LMil MDun
'Fanny' see *R.* 'Pucella'
'Fantastica' ♀H4 CDoC ELan EPfP GGGa LHyd LMil LRHS MBri MDun NLar NPen SPoG SReu
fargesii see *R. oreodoxa* var. *fargesii*
'Fashion' CTrG SLdr
fastigiatum ECho GCrs GEdr ISea LMil MBar MLea NLAp NPen
 – C&H 7159 GGGa
 – SBEC 804/4869 GGGa MDun NHol
§ – 'Blue Steel' ♀H4 CBcs CDoC CWri LMil LRHS MAsh MDun MGos NHol SPlb SPoG SReu WPat

'Fastuosum Flore Pleno' (d) ♀H4 — CBcs CSBt CWri ENot GBin GGGa ISea LHyd LKna LMil MBar MDun MGos MLea NPen SLdr SPer SPoG SReu SSta WFar

§ *faucium* — GGGa LMil
- C&V 9508 — GGGa
- KR 3465 from Pe, Doshang La — LMil
- KR 3771 — LMil
- KR 5024 — GGGa
- KR 5040 — LMil
- KR 6229 — LMil
- SF 95098 — ISea

'Favorite' (EA) — CTrw LHyd LKna LRHS NPen SCam SLdr
'Fedora' (EA) — CBcs LKna SLdr
'Fénelon' (G) **new** — SLdr
'Fernanda Sarmento' (A) — SReu
ferrugineum — GGGa LHyd LKna LMil MBar MGos SReu
* - *compactum* — ECho
- 'Plenum' (d) — MDun
'Festive' — LHyd
'Feuerwerk' (K) — NEgg SLdr
FH134 — SLdr
fictolacteum — see *R. rex* subsp. *fictolacteum*
Fire Bird Group — SLdr
'Fire Rim' — GGGa
'Fireball' (K) ♀H4 — CBcs CDoC CTri CWri ECho GGGa ISea LHyd LMil LRHS MAsh MLea NDlv SBrw SLdr SPer WMoo
'Fireball' (hybrid) — LRHS SLdr
Firedrake Group — SReu
'Fireglow' — CSBt CSdC SLdr WFar
I 'Firelight' (hybrid) **new** — LMil
'First Light' (V) — SFai
'Flamenco Dancer' (V) — SFai
'Flaming Bronze' — SReu
'Flaming June' (K) — LKna
Flamingo Group — SLdr
§ *flammeum* (A) — LMil
'Flanagan's Daughter' — LMil LRHS MAsh
I Flava Group — see *R.* Volker Group
flavidum — CBcs GGGa LMil SLdr
- Cox 6143 — GGGa
- 'Album' — LMil LRHS SLdr WThu
§ 'Flavour' — LKna
fletcherianum — LHyd
- 'Yellow Bunting' — GGGa
fleuryi KR 3286 — GGGa
§ *flinckii* — GGGa LHyd LMil LRHS MDun
- CH&M 3080 — GGGa
floccigerum — GGGa LMil SLdr
'Floradora' (M) — SReu
'Floriade' — LKna
'Floriade' x *yakushimanum* — SLdr
floribundum — LMil LRHS NPen SLdr WCwm
- EGM 294 — LMil
- 'Swinhoe' — SLdr
'Florida' (EA/d) ♀H3-4 — CMac LKna LMil MAsh SBrw SLdr SReu WFar WMoo
'Flower Arranger' (EA) — LMil NPri SCoo
formosanum — GGGa
formosum — CBcs GGGa GQui SLdr
§ - var. *formosum* — GGGa
  Iteaphyllum Group
- - 'Khasia' C&H 320 — GGGa
- var. *inaequale* C&H 301 — GGGa
forrestii — GGGa NPen
- KR 6113 — LMil
- subsp. *forrestii* — LMil
- - Repens Group — GGGa LMil SLdr
- - - 'Seinghku' — GGGa
- Tumescens Group — GGGa NHol
- - C&V 9517 — GGGa

Fortune Group — SLdr
fortunei — GGGa LHyd LKna LMil MDun SLdr SReu
§ - subsp. *discolor* ♀H4 — GGGa LMil MDun NPen SLdr WGer
- - PW 34 — GGGa
§ - - Houlstonii Group — LMil SLdr
- - - 'John R. Elcock' — CDoC LMil
- subsp. *discolor* x 'Lodauric Iceberg' — SLdr
- 'Foxy' — SLdr
- 'Lu-Shan' — MDun
- 'Mrs Butler' — see *R. fortunei* 'Sir Charles Butler'
§ - 'Sir Charles Butler' — CDoC LMil LRHS MDun SLdr
'Fox Hunter' — LKna SLdr
fragariiflorum — ISea
- C&V 9519 — GGGa
- LS&E 15828 — GGGa
'Fragrans' — SLdr
'Fragrant Star' (A) — GGGa SLdr
'Fragrantissimum' ♀H2-3 — CBcs CDoC CTbh CTrG CTrw CWri GGGa GGar ISea LHyd LMil MDun MRav NLar NPen SLdr WPic
'Francesca' — GGGa
Francis Hanger (Reuthe's) Group — SLdr SReu
'Frank Baum' — SReu
'Frank Galsworthy' ♀H4 — LKna LMil NLar SReu
'Frans van der Bom' (M) — SLdr
'Fraseri' (M) — GGGa SLdr
'Fred Hamilton' — CWri
'Fred Nutbeam' (EA) — LMil
'Fred Peste' — CDoC ECho LMil MAsh MDun MGos MLea NPen SReu
'Fred Wynniatt' — LHyd SLdr
'Fred Wynniatt Stanway' — see *R.* 'Stanway'
'Frere Organ' (G) — SLdr
'Freya' (R/d) — LMil SLdr
'Fridoline' (EA) — GGGa
'Frieda' (EA) — SLdr
'Frigata' (EA) **new** — SLdr
'Frilled Petticoats' — SReu
'Frilly Lemon' (K/d) — CDoC MDun NLar SLdr
'Frome' (K) — LKna
'Frosted Orange' (EA) — LMil MAsh SLdr
'Frosthexe' — GGGa WAbe
§ 'Frühlingstraum' — LHyd
'Fulbrook' — LHyd
fulgens — GGGa LHyd LMil MDun NPen
fulvum ♀H4 — CDoC GGGa IDee LHyd LMil LRHS MDun NPen SLdr SReu SSta
- AC 3083 — LMil
- subsp. *fulvoides* — LMil
- - Cox 6532 — GGGa
'Furnivall's Daughter' ♀H4 — CSBt CWri ECho ENot EPfP GGGa LHyd LMil LRHS MBar MDun MGos NLar NPen SLdr SPer SReu SSta WFar
'Fusilier' — SReu
'Gabrielle Hill' (EA) — CDoC COtt ENot SLdr
'Gaiety' (EA) — LMil SBrw SReu
'Galactic' — SLdr
galactinum — LMil MDun
- EN 3537 — GGGa
'Galathea' (EA) — CDoC
'Gandy Dancer' — CWri MBri MDun NPen SLdr
'Garden State Glow' (EA/d) — SLdr
'Gartendirektor Glocker' — CWri ECho GGGa MAsh MDun MLea NPen SLdr
'Gartendirektor Rieger' ♀H4 — CWri GGGa LMil MDun NHol SReu
'Gauche' (A) — GQui SLdr
'Gaugin' — GQui
Gaul Group — SLdr
'Gauntlettii' x *thomsonii* — SLdr
'Gay Lady' — SLdr

	'Geisha' (EA)	MBar
	'Geisha Lilac' (EA)	COtt ECho LMil LRHS MBar MDun MGos MLea NDlv
§	'Geisha Orange' (EA) ♀H4	CBcs COtt CSBt CTrh ECho EGra EPfP GGGa LMil LRHS MAsh MBar MDun MGos MLea NDlv NPri SLdr SMer WAbe
	'Geisha Purple' (EA)	COtt CSBt ECho ENot LMil MAsh MBar MDun MLea SBrw WFar
	'Geisha Red' (EA)	COtt ECho ENot EPfP LMil MAsh MBar MDun MGos MLea NDlv WAbe WFar
	Geisha White = 'Hisako' (EA)	ECho MDun MLea NDlv
	'Gekkeikan' (EA)	CBcs
	'Gena Mae' (A/d)	GGGa SLdr
	'General Eisenhower'	CSBt SReu
	'General Eric Harrison'	LHyd SLdr
	'General Practitioner'	NPen SLdr
	'General Wavell' (EA)	CMac LKna SLdr
	'Gene's Favourite'	SReu
	genestierianum CC&H 8080	GGGa
	'Genoveva'	LMil MAsh
	'Geoffroy Millais'	LMil
	'Georg Arends' (Ad)	NPri SLdr
	'George Haslam'	SLdr
	'George Hyde' (EA)	ENot LMil SCoo
	'George Reynolds' (K)	ECho LHyd MLea SLdr
	'George's Delight'	GGGa MAsh MLea WMoo
	'Georgette'	LHyd SLdr
§	x *geraldii*	SLdr
	'Germania'	CDoC LMil MAsh MBar SPoG SReu
	Gertrud Schäle Group	CTri ECho GEdr MBar MDun NHol SReu
	Gibraltar Group	CTri
	'Gibraltar' (K) ♀H4	CBcs CDoC CSBt CWri ENot EPfP GGGa LKna LMil LRHS MAsh MBar MBri MDun MGos MLea NBlu NPri SBrw SLdr SPer SReu SSta WFar WMoo
	giganteum	see *R. protistum* var. *giganteum*
	'Gilbert Mullie' (EA)	MBri NBlu
I	'Gill's Arboreum'	SLdr
	'Gill's Crimson'	SLdr
	'Ginger' (K)	CSBt EPfP LMil LRHS SLdr
	'Ginny Gee' ♀H4	CDoC COtt CSBt CTrh CWri ECho ENot EPfP GCrs GEdr GGGa GGar LHyd LMil LRHS MAsh MBar MBri MDun MGos MLea NHol NMen NPen SLdr SPoG SReu SSta WFar
§	'Girard's Hot Shot' (EA)	CTrh ECho ENot GQui MGos SBrw SLdr SReu WFar
	'Girard's Hot Shot' variegated (EA/v)	GGGa MAsh
	'Glacier' (EA)	MGos SLdr
	glanduliferum C&H 7131	GGGa
	- EGM 347	LMil
	- PW 044 from Miao Miao Shan	LMil
	glaucophyllum	GGGa LHyd LMil MDun NPen SLdr WAbe
	- B&SWJ 2638	WCru
	- var. *album*	GGGa
	- Borde Hill form	LMil
	'Glendoick Butterscotch'	GGGa
	'Glendoick Crimson' (EA)	GGGa
	'Glendoick Dream' (EA)	GGGa
	'Glendoick Ermine' (EA)	GGGa
	'Glendoick Frolic' **new**	GGGa
	'Glendoick Garnet' (EA)	GGGa
	'Glendoick Glacier'	GGGa
	'Glendoick Goblin' (EA)	GGGa
	'Glendoick Gold'	GGGa
	'Glendoick Honeydew'	GGGa
	'Glendoick Mystique'	GGGa

	'Glendoick Petticoats' **new**	GGGa
	'Glendoick Ruby'	GGGa
	'Glendoick Vanilla'	GGGa
	'Glendoick Velvet'	GGGa
	'Gletschernacht'	CWri LMil
	glischrum	GGGa NPen
	- subsp. *glischroides*	GGGa LMil
	- subsp. *glischrum*	GGGa LMil
§	- subsp. *rude*	GGGa NPen
	- - C&V 9524	GGGa
	globigerum	see *R. alutaceum* var. *alutaceum*
		Globigerum Group
	'Glockenspiel' (K/d)	LKna
	'Glomerulatum'	see *R. yungningense*
		Glomerulatum Group
	'Gloria'	see *R.* 'Bruns Gloria'
	'Gloria Mundi' (G)	WFar
	'Glory of Littleworth' (Ad)	LMil
	'Glory of Penjerrick'	CTbh
	'Glowing Embers' (K)	CDoC CSam CTri CWri ECho ENot ISea LMil LRHS MAsh MBri MDun MLea NHol NPri SLdr SPur SReu WBVN WFar
	Goblin Group	SLdr
	'Gog' (K)	CSBt LKna
	'Gold Crest' (K)	LKna
	'Gold Dust' (K)	SBrw
	'Gold Mohur'	SLdr SReu
	'Gold Tee'	LHyd
§	'Goldbukett'	GGGa LHyd
	'Golden Bee'	GGGa NHol
	'Golden Belle'	CWri
	Golden Bouquet	see *R.* 'Goldbukett'
	'Golden Charm' (V)	SFai
	'Golden Clipper'	LHyd
	'Golden Coach'	CWri ECho ISea MDun MGos MLea SLdr WBVN
	'Golden Eagle' (K)	CDoC COtt ECho LHyd LMil MDun MGos NEgg SBrw SLdr WBVN
	'Golden Flare' (K)	CBcs CDoC ECho MAsh MBri MLea SLdr WBrE WMoo
	'Golden Fleece'	CSec GKev LKna SReu
	'Golden Gate'	CDoC ECho ISea LMil MDun NPen SReu
	'Golden Horn' (K)	GQui
	'Golden Horn Persimmon'	see *R.* 'Persimmon'
	'Golden Lights' (A)	CDoC CWri ECho LMil LRHS MBri MDun SBod SLdr WBVN
	'Golden Orfe'	LHyd
	Golden Oriole Group	NHol
	'Golden Oriole'	LKna
	'Golden Princess'	LMil MDun NHol
	'Golden Splendour'	LMil
	'Golden Sunlight'	see *R.* 'Directeur Moerlands'
	'Golden Sunset' (K)	CSdC ECho LHyd LMil MAsh MBar MBri MDun MLea NEgg NHol NLar SBrw SLdr SPur WFar
	'Golden Torch' ♀H4	CAbP CBcs CMHG COtt CSBt CWri ECho ENot EPfP LHyd LMil LRHS MBri MDun MGos MLea NDlv NPen SHBN SLdr SPer SPoG SReu SSta
	'Golden Wedding'	CBcs CDoC CSBt CWri EBee ECho ENot LHyd LMil MAsh MBri MDun MGos MLea NLar SLdr WBVN
	'Golden Wit'	ECho MDun
	'Goldeneye' (K)	LKna
	'Goldfinch' (K)	LKna
	'Goldfinger'	MDun
	'Goldflamme'	SLdr
	'Goldflimmer' (v)	CDoC EMil ENot GGGa LMil LRHS MAsh MGos MLan MLea NBlu NPri SLdr SPoG SReu WFar
	'Goldfort'	CWri LKna SBrw SReu
	'Goldika'	LMil

Name	Codes
'Goldkrone' ♀H4	CDoC CWri ECho ENot EPfP GGGa ISea LHyd LMil MAsh MDun MGos MLea NLar NPen SBod SLdr SPer SPoG SReu
Goldschatz = 'Goldprinz'	GGGa
'Goldstrike'	LMil SLdr
'Goldsworth Crimson'	LHyd
'Goldsworth Orange'	CSBt CWri GGGa LKna MGos NPen SBrw SLdr SReu
'Goldsworth Pink'	LKna SReu
'Goldsworth Yellow'	CSBt LKna MGos SBrw SLdr SReu
'Golfer'	GGGa LMil
'Gomer Waterer' ♀H4	CDoC CSBt CSam CWri ECho ENot EPfP GGGa ISea LHyd LMil MBar MBri MDun MGos MLea NBlu NPen NWea SLdr SPer SPoG SReu SSta WBVN WFar
'Gorbella'	WFar
'Gordon Jones'	GGGa
'Govenianum' (Ad)	LKna SLdr
'Grace Seabrook'	CDoC COtt CSam CTri CWri ECho ENot GGGa LHyd LRHS MDun MGos NPri SLdr SPer SReu WBVN
gracilentum (V)	GGGa
'Graciosum' (O)	LKna SReu
'Graf Lennart'	LMil
'Graham Thomas'	LMil SReu
'Grand Slam'	ECho GQui LMil MDun MLea NPen WBVN
grande	GGGa NPen SLdr
– KC 0105	GGGa
– pink-flowered	NPen
'Grandeur Triomphante' (G)	CSdC SReu
gratum	see *R. basilicum*
'Graziella'	GGGa
'Greensleeves'	CDoC LKna LMil
'Greenway' (EA)	CBcs SLdr
'Greta' (EA)	LHyd
'Gretzel'	NLar SReu
griersonianum	GGGa LHyd LMil MDun WGer WPic
griersonianum x *yakushimanum*	SLdr
griffithianum	CWri GGGa SLdr
'Gristede' ♀H4	CDoC ECho GGGa LMil MAsh MDun NHol GGGa SReu WBVN
groenlandicum	see *Ledum groenlandicum*
'Grosclaude'	NPen
'Grouse' x *keiskei* var. *ozawae* 'Yaku Fairy'	ECho
'Grumpy'	CBcs CBrm CDoC CSBt CWri ECho EMui ENot GGGa LHyd LMil LRHS MAsh MBar MGos NDlv NPen SHBN SLdr SPoG SReu
'Guelder Rose'	SLdr
§ 'Gumpo' (EA)	CBcs CMac SBrw SLdr
'Gumpo Pink' (EA)	SLdr
'Gumpo White' (EA)	ENot MAsh
'Gwenda' (EA)	LHyd SLdr
'Gwenevere' (V)	SFai
'Gwillt-king'	CWri WCwm
'H.H. Hume' (EA)	SLdr
habrotrichum	GGGa LMil
'Hachmann's Brasilia'	LMil
'Hachmann's Charmant'	GGGa LMil MBri
'Hachmann's Constanze'	LMil
'Hachmann's Diadem'	LMil
'Hachmann's Eskimo' **new**	LMil
'Hachmann's Feuerschein'	LMil NBlu
'Hachmann's Kabarett'	LMil MDun
'Hachmann's Marlis' ♀H4	ENot LHyd LMil SPoG SReu
§ 'Hachmann's Polaris' ♀H4	LHyd LMil MBri MDun SPoG
'Hachmann's Porzellan'	EMil LMil
§ 'Hachmann's Rokoko' (EA)	ECho GGGa LMil
haematodes	GGGa LHyd LMil MDun NPen SRms
– CLD 1283	LMil
– 'Blood Red'	SLdr
§ – subsp. *chaetomallum*	GGGa LMil NPen SLdr
– – JN 493	GGGa
– subsp. *haemotodes*	LMil
– – SBEC 585	GGGa
'Haida Gold'	SLdr SReu
'Halfdan Lem'	CBcs CDoC CDul ECho GGGa ISea LHyd MBri MDun MGos MLea NPen SHBN SLdr SPer SReu SSta WBVN
'Hallelujah'	MAsh
'Halopeanum'	SLdr
'Hamlet' (M)	LMil
'Hammondii' (Ad)	LKna
'Hana-asobi' (EA)	LHyd LRHS SCam SLdr
hanceanum	SLdr
– 'Canton Consul'	GGGa LHyd
– Nanum Group	GGGa
'Hansel'	CDoC ECho GQui LMil MAsh MDun NLar SLdr
§ *haofui* Guiz 75	GGGa
Happy Group	ECho SHBN
§ 'Hardijzer Beauty' (Ad)	LKna SLdr SReu
'Hardy Gardenia' (EA/d)	SBrw
hardyi	see *R. augustinii* subsp. *hardyi*
'Harkwood Premiere'	
'Harkwood Red' (EA)	LHyd SCam SLdr
Harmony Group	SLdr
'Harry Tagg'	CTrG SLdr WAbe WPic
'Harumiji' (EA)	SLdr
'Harvest Moon' (K)	MDun SCoo SLdr SReu
'Harvest Moon' (hybrid)	MBar SBrw SReu
'Hatsugiri' (EA)	CMac ENot EPfP LHyd LKna LMil MBar SBrw SCam SLdr SReu
(Hawk Group) 'Hawk Buzzard'	SLdr
§ – 'Hawk Falcon'	SReu
'Heather Macleod' (EA)	LHyd SLdr
heatheriae KR 6150	GGGa
– KR 6158	GGGa
– SF 99068	ISea
heftii	NPen SLdr
'Helen Close' (EA)	CTrh SCam SLdr
'Helen Curtis' (EA)	SReu
'Helen Martin'	NLar
'Helena Pratt' (Vs)	LMil
'Helene Schiffner' ♀H4	GGGa LMil SReu
heliolepis	GGGa LMil
– SF 489	ISea
– SF 516	ISea
– var. *fumidum*	see *R. heliolepis* var. *heliolepis*
§ – var. *heliolepis*	LMil
– – CN&W 1038	ISea
x *hemigynum*	NPen
hemsleyanum	GGGa LMil MDun NPen SLdr
heptamerum	see *R. degronianum* subsp. *heptamerum*
'Herbert' (EA)	CMac
'Heureuse Surprise' (G)	SLdr
'High Summer'	CDoC LMil WGer
'Hilda Margaret'	SReu
'Hilda Niblett' (EA)	ENot
'Hille'PBR	LMil
'Hino-crimson' (EA) ♀H3-4	CBcs CDoC CMac CSBt CTrG CTrh CTri ENot LKna LMil LRHS MBar MBri MGos NHol SBrw SCam SLdr SPer SReu SSta WFar
'Hinode-giri' (EA)	CBcs CMac CSBt CTrw LHyd LKna SBrw SCam SLdr SReu WFar WPic
'Hinode-no-taka' (EA)	LHyd
N 'Hinomayo' (EA) ♀H3-4	CMac CSBt CTrG EPfP GQui LHyd LKna LMil LRHS MBar NPen SBrw SCam SLdr SReu SSta WPic

'Hino-scarlet'	see *R.* 'Campfire'
'Hino-tsukasa' (EA)	SLdr
hippophaeoides	CDoC EPfP LMil MDun NMen
	NPen SLdr WAbe WFar
- F 22197a	SLdr
- Yu 13845	GGGa LMil MDun
- 'Bei-ma-shan'	see *R. hippophaeoides* 'Haba Shan'
- 'Glendoick Iceberg'	GGGa
§ - 'Haba Shan' ♀H4	ECho GGGa LMil MDun
§ - var. *hippophaeoides*	WThu
Fimbriatum Group	
hirsutum	GGGa GIBF LHyd LMil SReu
- f. *albiflorum*	GGGa SReu
- 'Flore Pleno' (d)	ECho GCrs GGGa MBar MDun
	MLea
hirtipes	GGGa LMil
- C&V 9546	GGGa
- KR 5059	LMil
- KR 5219	LMil
hodgsonii	CDoC GGGa IDee LHyd LMil LRHS
	MDun NHol SLdr SReu WGer
- B&SWJ 2656	WCru
- TSS 42A	SLdr
- TSS 9	SLdr
'Holden'	WFar
'Hollandia' (hybrid)	SHBN
'Homebush' (K/d) ♀H4	CBcs CDoC CTri CWri ECho ENot
	EPfP GGGa LHyd LKna LMil MAsh
	MBar MBri MDun MGos MLea
	SBrw SLdr SPer SPoG SReu SSta
	WBVN
'Honey'	LKna SBrw
'Honey Star' (V)	SFai
'Honeysuckle' (K)	MBar NHol SLdr SReu
hongkongense	GGGa
§ 'Ho-o' (EA)	CBcs NEgg NLar SLdr
hookeri	CTrG LHyd LMil SReu
- Tigh-na-Rudha form	GGGa
'Hope Findlay'	LHyd
'Hoppy'	CBcs CDoC CSBt CWri ENot
	GWCH LMil LRHS MAsh MDun
	MGos MLea NBlu NPen SLdr SPoG
	SReu WBVN
'Horizon Lakeside'	GGGa LMil
'Horizon Monarch' ♀H3-4	CDoC CWri GGGa LMil MDun
horlickianum	GGGa
'Hortulanus H. Witte' (M)	CSBt SLdr SReu WFar
'Hot Shot'	see *R.* 'Girard's Hot Shot'
'Hot Shot Variegated'	CDoC
(EA/V) **new**	
'Hotei' ♀H4	CBcs CDoC CSBt CTri CWri ECho
	EPfP GEdr GGGa LHyd LMil LRHS
	MBar MDun MGos MPen NPri
	SHBN SReu WBVN WFar
Hotspur Group (K)	GGGa LHyd SCoo
'Hotspur' (K)	CSBt CTri CWri ECho ISea MGos
	NLar SLdr SPer WBVN
'Hotspur Red' (K) ♀H4	CDoC CDul LKna LMil SBrw SReu
'Hotspur Yellow' (K)	SReu
houlstonii	see *R. fortunei* subsp. *discolor*
	Houlstonii Group
huanum	LMil
- C&H 7073	GGGa
- EGM 316	LMil
'Hugh Koster'	CSBt LKna MGos SLdr
'Hullaballoo' **new**	LMil
'Humboldt'	LMil WFar
Humming Bird Group	CMHG ECho GGGa ISea LHyd
	LKna MBar MDun MLea NHol
	SHBN SLdr SReu SRms
hunnewellianum	NPen
'Hurricane'	MDun
'Hussar'	CWri
'Hyde and Seek'	GQui
'Hydie' (EA/d)	ENot LMil MGos SCoo
'Hydon Amethyst'	LHyd

'Hydon Ball'	LHyd
'Hydon Ben'	LHyd
'Hydon Comet'	LHyd
'Hydon Dawn' ♀H4	CDoC CWri ECho GGGa LHyd
	LMil LRHS MAsh MDun MGos
	MLea NDlv NLar NPen SLdr SReu
	SSta
'Hydon Glow'	LHyd
'Hydon Gold'	LHyd
'Hydon Haley'	LHyd
'Hydon Hunter' ♀H4	ECho LHyd LMil MLea NDlv NPen
	SLdr SPer SReu SSta
'Hydon Juliet'	LHyd
'Hydon Mist'	LHyd
'Hydon Pearl'	LHyd
'Hydon Primrose'	LHyd
'Hydon Rodney'	LHyd
'Hydon Salmon'	LHyd
'Hydon Velvet'	LHyd SReu
hylaeum	NPen
- BASEX 9659	GGGa
Hyperion Group	LKna LMil SReu SSta WFar
hyperythrum	GGGa LHyd LMil MDun NHol SLdr
	SSpi
- ETOT 196	MDun
hypoglaucum	see *R. argyrophyllum* subsp.
	hypoglaucum
- 'Heane Wood'	see *R. argyrophyllum* subsp.
	hypoglaucum 'Heane Wood'
'Ice Cream'	LKna
'Ice Cube'	ECho ISea LMil MDun NLar WBVN
'Ice Maiden'	SReu
'Iceberg'	see *R.* 'Lodauric Iceberg'
'Icecream Flavour'	see *R.* 'Flavour'
'Icecream Vanilla'	see *R.* 'Vanilla'
'Idealist'	SReu
'Idealist' x 'Victory'	SLdr
'Ightham Gold'	SReu
'Ightham Peach'	SReu
'Ightham Purple'	SReu
'Ightham Yellow'	MDun NPen SLdr SReu
'Igneum Novum' (G)	SReu
'Il Tasso' (R/d)	SLdr
§ 'Ilam Melford Lemon' (A)	LMil
§ 'Ilam Ming' (A)	LMil
'Ilam Violet'	LHyd LKna LMil
'Imago' (K/d)	CSdC LKna MBri SLdr
§ 'Ima-shojo' (EA/d)	CSBt LHyd LMil MAsh SBrw SCam
	SLdr
'Impala' (K)	LKna
impeditum	CBcs CDoC CSBt CWib ECho ENot
	GGGa GQui LHyd MAsh MBar
	MDun MGos MLea NHol NLAp
	NMen NPen SLdr SPer SPoG SReu
	SSta WBVN WBrE WFar
- F 29268	GGGa
- 'Blue Steel'	see *R. fastigiatum* 'Blue Steel'
- dark, compact	LKna
- 'Indigo'	CMHG MAsh MDun WAbe
- 'Johnston's Impeditum'	LKna
- 'Pygmaeum'	WAbe
- Reuthe's form	SReu
- 'Williams'	SLdr
imperator	see *R. uniflorum* var. *imperator*
'Impi'	NPen SReu
Impi Group	LKna MDun NLar
'Inamorata'	SLdr
§ ***indicum*** (EA)	GIBF WBVN
§ - 'Balsaminiflorum' (EA/d)	CMac SLdr
§ - 'Macranthum' (EA)	LHyd SLdr
x ***inopinum***	GGGa
insigne ♀H4	CDoC GGGa IDee LHyd LMil
	MDun NPen WGer
- Reuthe's form	SReu
insigne x	SReu
yakushimanum	

- CER 9906	GGGa
- EGM 064	LMil
- KC 0112	GGGa
- KC 0115	GGGa
'Kilimanjaro'	GGGa LHyd LMil SReu
Kilimanjaro Group	LMil
'Kimberly'	GGGa
'Kimbeth'	GGGa
'Kimigayo' (EA)	LHyd
'King George' Loder	see *R.* 'Loderi King George'
'King George' van Nes	SReu
'King of Shrubs'	NLar
kingianum	see *R. arboreum* subsp. zeylanicum
'Kings Ride'	LHyd
'Kingston'	MDun
§ 'Kirin' (EA/d)	CBcs CMac CSBt CTrw LHyd LRHS SLdr WPat
'Kirishima' (EA)	LKna SRms
'Kiritsubo' (EA)	LHyd
'Kisses' (V)	SFai
'Kitty Cole'	SLdr
kiusianum (EA) ♀H4	GGGa GIBF LHyd NPen SReu SRms
- 'Album' (EA)	LHyd LMil SReu WAbe
- 'Hillier's Pink' (EA)	LMil
'Kiwi Majic'	LMil MBri MDun
'Klondyke' (K) ♀H4	CBcs CSBt CTri ENot EPfP GGGa LMil LRHS MAsh MBri MDun MGos NPri SBrw SLdr SReu
'Kluis Sensation' ♀H4	CSBt LKna MDun NHol NPen SHBN SLdr SPoG SReu
'Kluis Triumph'	LKna SLdr SReu
'Knap Hill Apricot' (K)	LKna LMil
'Knap Hill Red' (K)	CDoC LKna LMil WMoo
'Knap Hill White' (K)	CSdC
'Kobold' (EA)	SLdr
'Koichiro Wada'	see *R. yakushimanum* 'Koichiro Wada'
'Kokardia'	EMil LMil
kongboense	GGGa LMil
- C&V 9540	GGGa
- KR 5689	LMil
'Königstein' (EA)	LMil
§ 'Koningin Emma' (M)	LMil NLar SLdr
§ 'Koningin Wilhelmina' (M)	SLdr
konori var. *phaeopeplum* (V)	GGGa
'Koster's Brilliant Red' (M)	CSBt ENot EPfP LMil MGos SReu
kotschyi	see *R. myrtifolium*
'Kralingen'	NLar
'Kupferberg'	GGGa
§ 'Kure-no-yuki' (EA/d)	CSBt CTrG EPfP LHyd LKna LMil SCam SLdr
'Lackblatt'	see *R.* (Volker Group) 'Lackblatt'
lacteum	LMil MDun NPen SLdr
- CN&W 936	LMil
- EGM 356 from Wumenshan	LMil
- KR 2760	GGGa
- SBEC 345	GGGa
- SF 374	ISea
'Lady Adam Gordon'	SLdr
'Lady Alice Fitzwilliam' ♀H2-3	CBcs CEnd CMHG CTbh CTrG GGGa IDee ISea LHyd LMil WGer
'Lady Annette de Trafford'	LKna
'Lady Armstrong'	CSBt
Lady Bessborough Group	SLdr
'Lady Bowes Lyon'	LHyd LMil SLdr
Lady Chamberlain Group	GGGa NPen SLdr
'Lady Chamberlain Salmon Trout'	see *R.* 'Salmon Trout'
'Lady Clementine Mitford' ♀H4	CDoC CSBt CWri ECho ENot EPfP GGGa GQui LHyd LKna LMil MAsh MBri MDun MGos MLea NLar NPen NWea SHBN SLdr SPer SPoG SReu
'Lady Decies'	SReu
'Lady Digby'	CWri
'Lady Eleanor Cathcart'	EPfP LKna NPen SLdr
'Lady Grey Egerton'	LKna
'Lady Longman'	LHyd
'Lady Louise' (EA)	SLdr
'Lady Primrose'	SReu
'Lady Robin' (EA)	SLdr
'Lady Romsey'	LMil NPen SLdr
'Lady Rosebery' (K)	CSdC MDun
Lady Rosebery Group	MLea
Ladybird Group	LMil SReu
laetum (V)	GGGa
Lamellen Group	LHyd SLdr
'Lampion'	GGGa
'Lamplighter'	SLdr SReu
lanatoides	LMil
- C&C 7548	GGGa
- C&C 7574	GGGa
- C&C 7577	GGGa
- KR 6385	LMil
lanatum	GIBF LMil
- dwarf, cream-flowered	GGGa
- Flinckii Group	see *R. flinckii*
lanatum x *yakushimanum*	GGGa
'Langmans' (EA)	LKna
'Langworth'	CWri ECho GQui LKna LMil MAsh MDun MLea NPen SLdr SReu
lanigerum	LMil MDun NPen SReu
- C&V 9530	GGGa
- KW 8251	GGGa
lapidosum	GGGa
lapponicum Confertissimum Group	GGGa
- Parviflorum Group	GIBF
- - from Kamchatka	GIBF
- - from Siberia	GGGa WAbe
'Lapwing' (K)	LKna SLdr
'Lascaux'	SReu
'Late Inverue' (EA) **new**	MAsh
'Late Love' (EA)	CDoC MGos
late pink, from Inverewe	WBVN WMoo
* *laterifolium*	GGGa
§ *latoucheae* (EA) PW 86	GGGa
laudandum var. *temoense*	GGGa
Laura Aberconway Group	SLdr
'Laura Morland' (EA)	LHyd
'Lava Flow'	LHyd NHol
'Lavender Girl' ♀H4	GGGa LHyd LKna LMil NLar NPen SLdr SPoG SReu SSta
'Lavender Lady' (EA)	CTrG
'Lavender Queen'	CWri ENot
'Lavendula'	GGGa
'Le Progrès'	LMil MAsh SReu
'Lea Rainbow'	MLea
'Ledifolium'	see *R.* x *mucronatum*
'Ledifolium Album'	see *R.* x *mucronatum*
'Lee's Dark Purple'	CDoC CSBt CWri LMil MBar MDun NWea WFar
'Lee's Scarlet'	LKna LMil SLdr
'Lem' **new**	SReu
'Lemon Dream' **new**	LMil
* 'Lemon Drop' (A)	GGGa
'Lemonora' (M)	SLdr
'Lem's 45'	CWri MDun NPen SLdr
'Lem's Cameo' ♀H3	GGGa LHyd LMil MDun SPoG SReu SSta
'Lem's Monarch' ♀H4	CBcs CDoC CDul CWri ECho GGGa LHyd LMil MBri MDun MGos MLea NPen SReu SSta WBVN
'Lem's Tangerine'	CDoC LMil SPoG
'Lemur' (EA)	ECho GEdr GGGa MAsh MDun MLea NHol NLar SReu WPat

'Leni'	LRHS MAsh
'Leny' (EA)	NHol
'Leo' (EA)	GQui LHyd LKna LRHS NPen
	SCam SLdr
'Leo' (hybrid)	EPfP
'Leonardslee Giles'	SLdr
'Leonardslee Primrose'	SLdr
Leonore Group	SReu
lepidostylum	CBcs CDoC CWri GGGa LHyd
	LMil MBar MDun NHol NLAp
	NPen SLdr SReu WFar
lepidotum	GGGa MDun WAbe
- Elaeagnoides Group	GGGa
- purple-flowered EN 6280	LMil
- yellow-flowered	ITim
- - McB 110	WThu
§ *leptocarpum*	GGGa LMil
leptothrium	CBcs GGGa WAbe
Letty Edwards Group	CSBt LKna SLdr SReu
§ 'Leucanthum'	GGGa
leucaspis	GGGa LHyd MDun SLdr SReu
'Leverett Richards'	SReu
levinei	GGGa
'Lewis Monarch'	GQui
'Lila Pedigo'	COtt CWri ECho ISea MAsh MBri
	MDun MLea NPen SPer WBVN
	WFar
'Lilac Time' (EA)	MBar SLdr
'Lilacinum' (EA)	WPic
liliiflorum Guiz 163	GGGa
'Lilofee' **new**	LMil
'Lily Marleen' (EA)	CTri SCoo SReu
'Linda' ♀H4	CDoC CSam CTri ECho GGGa LMil
	LRHS MAsh MBar MDun MGos
	NBlu SLdr
'Linda Lee'	SLdr
lindleyi	GQui LHyd
- L&S	GGGa
- 'Dame Edith Sitwell'	LMil
'Linearifolium'	see *R. stenopetalum*
	'Linearifolium'
'Linnet' (K/d)	LKna
Lionel's Triumph Group	LMil NPen SLdr
'Little Beauty' (EA)	SCam SLdr
'Little Ben'	ECho MBar MDun NDlv
'Littlest Angel' (V)	SFai
'Loch Awe' **new**	GGGa
'Loch Earn'	GGGa
'Loch Leven'	GGGa
'Loch Lomond'	GGGa
'Loch o' the Lowes'	ECho GGGa LHyd LMil MAsh
	MDun MGos MLea
'Loch Rannoch'	CDoC ECho GGGa LMil MGos
	NPri
'Loch Tummel'	GGGa
lochiae (V)	GGGa
'Lochinch Spinbur'	GQui
x *lochmium*	GGGa
Lodauric Group	SLdr SReu
§ 'Lodauric Iceberg' ♀H3-4	CDoC LKna LMil SLdr SReu
'Lodbrit'	SReu
§ Loderi Group	SLdr
'Loderi Fairy Queen'	SLdr
'Loderi Fairyland'	LHyd
§ 'Loderi Game Chick' ♀H3-4	LHyd MDun MLea SLdr SReu
'Loderi Georgette'	SLdr
'Loderi Helen'	SLdr
§ 'Loderi King George' ♀H3-4	CBcs CDoC CDul CTbh CWri
	ECho GGGa IDee ISea LHyd LKna
	LMil MDun MGos MLea NPen
	SHBN SLdr SReu SSta WBVN
'Loderi Patience'	SLdr
'Loderi Pink Coral'	LMil SLdr
'Loderi Pink Diamond'	CWri LMil MDun SLdr
♀H3-4	
'Loderi Pink Topaz' ♀H3-4	LHyd LMil SLdr

'Loderi Pretty Polly'	CWri
'Loderi Princess Marina'	SLdr
'Loderi Sir Edmund'	LHyd SLdr
'Loderi Sir Joseph Hooker'	LHyd SLdr
'Loderi Titan'	SLdr SReu
§ 'Loderi Venus' ♀H3-4	CDoC CWri GGGa LHyd LMil
	MDun MLea SHBN SLdr SReu SSta
	WBVN
'Loderi White Diamond'	LHyd SLdr
'Loder's White' ♀H3-4	CWri GGGa LHyd LKna LMil
	MDun SLdr SReu SSta
§ 'Logan Damaris'	LHyd SLdr SReu
longesquamatum	GGGa LMil NPen SLdr
longipes	SLdr
- EGM 336	LMil
- EGM 337	LMil
- var. *chienianum*	LMil
- var. *longipes* C&H 7072	GGGa
- - C&H 7113	GGGa
longistylum	GGGa
'Looking Glass'	MDun SHBN
'Lord Roberts' ♀H4	CBcs CTri CWri ECho ENot EPfP
	GGGa LKna LMil MAsh MBar
	MGos MLea NEgg NPen SHBN
	SLdr SPer SReu WBVN WFar WMoo
'Lord Swaythling'	LHyd SLdr
'Lori Eichelser'	ECho MDun MLea NDlv
'Lorna' (EA)	GQui LMil
'Louis Aimée van Houtte'	SLdr
(G)	
'Louis Hellebuyck' (G)	SLdr
'Louis Pasteur'	SReu
'Louisa' (EA)	SBrw
'Louisa Hill' (EA)	ENot
'Louise' (EA)	SLdr
'Louise Dowdle' (EA)	LMil SCam SLdr
'Lovely William'	NPen SLdr
lowndesii	WAbe
luciferum CER 9935	GGGa
'Lucy Lou'	GGGa
ludlowii	GGGa
ludlowii x *viridescens*	NHol
ludwigianum	GGGa
'Lullaby' (EA)	LKna SLdr
'Lunar Queen'	LHyd SLdr
Luscombei Group	LHyd SLdr
luteiflorum	LMil NPen
- KW 21556	GGGa
lutescens	CBcs CWri ISea LMil MDun NPen
	SLdr SLon SReu SSta WAbe
- C&H 7124	GGGa
- Cox 5092	NHol
- Cox 5100	NHol
- 'Bagshot Sands' ♀H3-4	GGGa LHyd LMil LRHS SReu
§ *luteum* (A) ♀H4	More than 30 suppliers
§ *lyi* KR 2962	GGGa
maccabeanum ♀H3-4	CBcs CDoC CTbh EPfP GGGa
	GTSp IDee LHyd LMil LRHS MBri
	MDun NPen SLdr SReu SSpi SSta
	WFar WHer
- deep cream-flowered	SLdr
- Embley form **new**	SLdr
- Reuthe's form	SReu
maccabeanum x	SReu
sinogrande	
- Towercourt form **new**	SLdr
macgregoriae (V)	GGGa
Woods 2646	
macranthum	see *R. indicum* 'Macranthum'
'Macranthum Roseum' (EA)	MMHG SBrw SReu
macrophyllum	GGGa
macrosmithii	see *R. argipeplum*
maculiferum	GGGa SLdr
- subsp. *anwheiense*	see *R. anwheiense*
'Madame Albert Moser'	LKna
'Madame de Bruin'	LKna NWea

'Madame Galle'	NBlu SBrw
'Madame Knutz' (A)	SLdr
'Madame Masson'	CDoC CTri CWri ECho GGGa
	GWCH ISea LMil LRHS MAsh MBri
	MDun MGos MLea NBlu NPen
	NPri SHBN SLdr SPer SPoG SReu
	SSta WBVN WFar
'Madame van Hecke' (EA)	COtt CTri EPfP LMil MBri SBrw
	SLdr SReu WFar
maddenii	IDee LMil SLdr WPic
§ - subsp. *crassum*	CTrw GGGa LMil SLdr WPic
§ - subsp. *maddenii*	LMil
KR 2978	
§ - - Polyandrum Group	CBcs GQui ISea SLdr
'Madeline's Yellow'	SLdr
'Mademoiselle Masson'	ENot WFar
'Magic Flute' (EA)	ENot
I 'Magic Flute' (V)	LMil NPri SCoo
'Magnificum' (O)	SLdr
magnificum	SReu
'Maharani'	GGGa LRHS MAsh NPri SBrw
'Maja' (G)	SLdr
§ *makinoi* ♥H4	CDoC GGGa LHyd LMil LRHS
	MDun NLar NMen SLdr SReu SSpi
	SSta
- 'Fuju-kaku-no-matsu'	MGos NLar
'Malahat' **new**	NPen
mallotum	CWri GGGa IDee LHyd LMil
	MDun NPen SLdr SReu
- BASEX 9672	GGGa
- Farrer 815	GGGa
Mandalay Group	LHyd
'Mandarin Lights' (A)	LMil LRHS MBri
maoerense	GGGa
'Marcel Ménard'	LMil NBlu NLar SReu WFar
'Marchioness of	CSBt
Lansdowne'	
'Marcia'	SLdr
'Mardi Gras'	GGGa LMil
Margaret Dunn Group	CWri
'Margaret Falmouth'	SReu
'Margaret George' (EA)	LHyd
'Maria Derby' (EA)	ENot
'Maricee'	GGGa
'Marie Curie'	LMil SReu
'Marie Verschaffelt' (G)	SLdr
'Marietta'	LHyd
'Marilee' (EA)	CDoC ECho LRHS MGos NLar
	SLdr
Mariloo Group	SLdr
'Marinus Koster'	LKna MDun SLdr
'Marion Merriman' (K)	LKna
'Marion Street' ♥H4	LHyd LMil SLdr SReu
'Mark Turner'	SReu
'Markeeta's Flame'	MDun
'Markeeta's Prize' ♥H4	CDoC CWri ECho GGGa LMil
	LRHS MAsh MBri MDun MGos
	MLea SBod SLdr SPoG WBVN
'Marley Hedges'	CDoC GGGa LMil
'Marlies' (A)	SLdr
'Marmot' (EA)	ECho MBar MDun MLea
'Mars'	GGGa SLdr SReu
'Martha Hitchcock' (EA)	LKna SRms
'Martha Isaacson' (Ad)	MGos SReu WCwm
♥H4	
'Martine' (Ad)	LKna MGos
martinianum	LMil SLdr
aff. *martinianum*	GGGa
KW 21557	
'Maruschka' (EA)	LMil
'Mary Drennen'	LMil SPoG
'Mary Fleming'	MAsh MDun SLdr
'Mary Helen' (EA)	LHyd LRHS MAsh NPri SCoo SReu
	WPat
'Mary Hoffman' (EA)	SPoG
'Mary Meredith' (EA)	LHyd

'Mary Poppins' (K)	ENot LMil LRHS MAsh MBri SCoo
	SPoG
'Maryke'	CDoC LMil
'Master of Elphinstone'	SLdr
(EA)	
Matador Group	SLdr SReu
'Mauna Loa' (K)	LKna
maximum	GGGa SLdr
'Maxine Childers'	LMil
§ 'Maxwellii' (EA)	CMac SBrw SLdr
'May Day' ♥H3-4	CDoC MAsh
May Day Group	CBcs CTrw CWri ISea LKna MDun
	MGos NPen SHBN SLdr
'May Glow'	MGos
May Morn Group	SReu
'Mayor Johnstone'	CTri LRHS MAsh NPri
'Mazurka' (K)	LKna
meddianum	GGGa
- var. *atrokermesinum*	GGGa
KW 2100a	
Medea Group	SLdr
Medusa Group	GGGa SLdr SReu
megacalyx	CBcs GGGa ISea
'Megan' (EA)	ECho GGGa MAsh NLar WGwG
megaphyllum	see *R. basilicum*
megeratum	GGGa SLdr SReu
- 'Bodnant'	WAbe
mekongense	GGGa
- KR 5044	LMil
- var. *mekongense*	SReu
- - Rubroluteum Group	see *R. viridescens* Rubroluteum
	Group
- - Viridescens Group	see *R. viridescens*
§ - var. *melinanthum*	SReu
- var. *rubrolineatum*	LMil
'Melford Lemon'	see *R.* 'Ilam Melford Lemon'
'Melidioso'	LMil
'Melina' (EA/d)	GGGa LMil
melinanthum	see *R. mekongense* var.
	melinanthum
mengtszense **new**	NPen
'Merganser' ♥H4	ECho GCrs GEdr GGGa LMil
	MDun MLea NDlv NHol SReu
	WAbe
'Merlin' (EA)	SLdr
metternichii	see *R. degronianum* subsp.
	heptamerum
- var. *pentamerum*	see *R. degronianum* subsp.
	degronianum
'Mi Amor'	LMil
'Miami' (A)	SLdr
'Michael Hill' (EA)	CBcs CDoC COtt LHyd MAsh
'Michael Waterer'	MDun NPen SLdr
'Michael's Pride'	CBcs GQui
micranthum	GGGa GIBF MDun SLdr
microgynum F 14242	GGGa
microleucum	see *R. orthocladum* var.
	microleucum
micromeres	see *R. leptocarpum*
microphyton	ISea
'Midnight Mystique'	GGGa
'Midsummer'	CWri SLdr
'Mikado' (EA)	see *R. kaempferi* 'Mikado'
'Mikado' (hybrid)	SLdr
'Milton' (R)	LMil SLdr
mimetes	NPen
§ - var. *simulans* F 20428	GGGa
'Mimi' (EA)	CMac LHyd
'Mimra'	SLdr
'Mina van Houtte' (G)	SLdr
'Mindy's Love'	LMil
'Ming'	see *R.* 'Ilam Ming'
'Minterne Cinnkeys'	MDun
minus	CSec GQui
- SDR 2228	GKev
§ - var. *minus*	SLdr

Name	Suppliers
§ - - Carolinianum Group	LMil
- - - 'Epoch'	LMil
§ - - Punctatum Group	MBar
'Miss Muffet' (EA)	SLdr
§ 'Moerheim' ♀H4	CWri ECho EMil LRHS MAsh MBar MGos NHol NPri SReu WBVN
§ 'Moerheim's Pink'	CDoC LHyd LKna LMil MDun NHol SLdr
'Moerheim's Scarlet'	LKna
'Moffat'	SReu
'Moidart' (Vs)	LMil
'Moira Salmon' (EA)	LHyd
§ *molle* subsp. *japonicum* (A)	GGGa SLdr
- - JR 871	GGGa
- subsp. *molle* (A) C&H 7181	GGGa
mollicomum F 30940	SLdr
'Mollie Coker'	CWri SLdr
Mollis orange (M)	MBar SRms
Mollis pink (M)	GGGa MBar NBlu SRms
Mollis red (M)	MBar NBlu SRms
Mollis salmon (M)	GGGa GQui
Mollis yellow (M)	GQui MBar NBlu SRms
'Molly Ann'	ECho GGGa LRHS MDun NPen SLdr SReu
'Molten Gold' (v)	ENot LRHS MAsh
monanthum CCH&H 8133	GGGa
monosematum	see R. *pachytrichum* var. *monosematum*
montiganum AC 2060	LMil
montroseanum	CDoC GTSp ISea LMil LRHS MDun SLdr WCru
* - 'Baravalla'	GGGa
'Moon Maiden' (EA)	ECho GQui NLar SLdr
Moonbeam Group	LKna
Moonshine Group	SLdr
'Moonshine'	SReu
'Moonshine Bright'	LHyd MDun
'Moonshine Supreme'	LKna
Moonstone Group	ECho MBar MDun MLea SLdr
- pink-tipped	GEdr NHol
'Moonstone Yellow'	GGGa
'Moonwax'	CWri SLdr
§ 'Morgenrot'	EMui GGGa LMil MAsh MGos NBlu SReu WFar
morii	GGGa LHyd LMil MDun
'Morning Cloud' ♀H4	CAbP ECho EPfP LHyd LMil MBar MLea NDlv NHol SReu
'Morning Magic'	CWri LHyd SLdr
Morning Red	see R. 'Morgenrot'
'Moser's Maroon'	CDoC CWri ENot LKna MGos MLea NLar NPen SLdr SPoG WBVN
'Moser's Strawberry'	LKna
'Motet' (K/d)	CSdC LKna SLdr
'Moth'	NHol
'Mother Greer'	GGGa
'Mother of Pearl'	LKna SLdr SReu
'Mother Theresa'	LKna
'Mother's Day' (EA) ♀H4	More than 30 suppliers
Moulten Gold = 'Blattgold'	GGGa
'Mount Everest'	CDoC GGGa LHyd LMil SReu SSta
'Mount Rainier' (K)	SLdr SReu
'Mount Saint Helens'	GGGa LMil SLdr
'Mount Seven Star'	see R. *nakaharae* 'Mount Seven Star'
'Mountain Star'	SLdr
moupinense	CBcs CTbh GGGa IDee LHyd LMil NPen SLdr SReu
'Mrs A.C. Kenrick'	SLdr
'Mrs A.T. de la Mare' ♀H4	CSBt CWri GGGa LHyd LKna LMil MDun NHol NPen SLdr SReu SSta
'Mrs Anthony Waterer' (O)	LKna
'Mrs Anthony Waterer' (hybrid)	LKna
'Mrs Betty Robertson'	ECho GWCH LMil MAsh MBri MDun MGos MLea SLdr SReu
'Mrs C.B. van Nes'	SReu
Mrs C. Whitner Group	SLdr
'Mrs C. Whitner' x 'Tally Ho' **new**	SLdr
'Mrs Charles E. Pearson' ♀H4	CSBt ENot LHyd LKna LMil NPen SHBN SLdr SReu
'Mrs Davies Evans' ♀H4	CWri LHyd LKna MBar SReu SSta
'Mrs Dick Thompson'	SReu
'Mrs Donald Graham'	SBrw SReu
'Mrs E.C. Stirling'	LHyd LKna SRms
'Mrs Emil Hager' (EA)	LHyd
'Mrs Furnivall' ♀H4	CBcs CWri ECho EPfP GGGa LHyd LKna LMil MAsh MDun MGos MLea SLdr SReu
'Mrs G.W. Leak'	CDoC CSBt CSam CWri EPfP GGGa ISea LHyd LKna LMil MDun SHBN SLdr SPoG SReu
'Mrs Helen Koster'	LKna
'Mrs J.C. Williams' ♀H4	LKna LMil
'Mrs J.G. Millais'	LKna LMil MDun
'Mrs John Kelk'	LMil
'Mrs Kingsmill'	SLdr
'Mrs Lindsay Smith'	LKna
'Mrs Lionel de Rothschild' ♀H4	MDun SReu
Mrs Lionel de Rothschild Group	CWri
'Mrs P.D. Williams'	LKna SReu
'Mrs Peter Koster' (M)	SLdr WFar
'Mrs Philip Martineau'	LKna
'Mrs R.S. Holford' ♀H4	LKna SLdr
'Mrs T.H. Lowinsky' ♀H4	CSBt ECho EPfP GGGa LKna LMil MAsh MDun MGos MLea NPen SLdr SPer SReu SSta WBVN
'Mrs W.C. Slocock'	LHyd LKna MDun SLdr SReu
'Mrs William Agnew'	LKna
'Mucronatum'	see R. x *mucronatum*
§ x *mucronatum* (EA)	CBcs GIBF LHyd SBrw SRms WPic
'Mucronatum Amethystinum'	see R. 'Amethystinum'
mucronulatum	CBcs GGGa NPen
- pink-flowered	WPGP
- var. *chejuense*	see R. *mucronulatum* var. *taquetii*
- 'Cornell Pink' ♀H4	GGGa LHyd LMil WFar
§ - var. *taquetii*	GGGa
§ 'Multiflorum'	SReu
'Muncaster Mist'	LHyd
§ *myrtifolium*	GIBF LMil
nakaharae (EA)	NPen SLdr SReu
§ - 'Mariko' (EA)	EPot GGGa LHyd MBar NHol NLAp SLdr WPat
§ - 'Mount Seven Star' (EA) ♀H4	ECho GGGa LHyd LMil NHol NLAp SLdr SReu WAbe WBVN WPat
§ - orange-flowered (EA)	ECho LMil LRHS MGos NPen NPri SBrw SHBN SReu
- pink-flowered (EA)	ECho LMil LRHS MGos NPen NPri SLdr SPer SReu SSta
- red-flowered (EA)	ECho MGos
- 'Scree' (EA)	SReu
'Nakahari Orange'	see R. *nakaharae* orange-flowered
'Nakahari-mariko'	see R. *nakaharae* 'Mariko'
'Nancy Buchanan' (K)	SLdr
'Nancy Evans' ♀H3-4	CDoC COtt CSBt CWri ECho EPfP GGGa LHyd LMil LRHS MAsh MBri MDun MLea NPri SLdr SPoG SReu SSpi WFar WGer
'Nancy Waterer' (G) ♀H4	EPfP NLar SBrw SReu
'Nanki Poo' (EA)	LHyd SLdr
Naomi Group	CWri LHyd LKna NPen SLdr
'Naomi' (EA)	GQui LKna NPen SCam SHBN SLdr WPic
'Naomi Astarte'	LKna MDun SLdr

'Naomi Hope'   SLdr
'Naomi Nautilus'   LMil
'Naomi Stella Maris'   LHyd SLdr
'Narcissiflorum' (G/d) ♀H4   CDoC CSBt ENot EPfP IDee LHyd
                              LKna LMil NLar SPoG SReu
'Naselle'   GGGa LMil SReu
'Ne Plus Ultra' (V)   SFai
neriiflorum   GGGa LMil MDun NPen SReu
- Bu 287   GGGa
- subsp. *neriiflorum*   GGGa
  L&S 1352
§ - subsp. *phaedropum*   MDun
- - CCH&H 8125   GGGa
- - KR 5593   LMil
nervulosum Sleumer (V)   GGGa
'Nestor'   SReu
'Netty Koster'   SLdr
'New Comet'   LHyd NPen SLdr
'New Moon'   SReu
'Newcomb's Sweetheart'   LMil MDun
'Niagara' (EA) ♀H3-4   CTrh ENot EPfP GQui LHyd LMil
                              NMen SLdr
'Nichola' (EA)   SBrw SReu
'Nico' (EA)   CMac LRHS WPat
'Nicoletta'   ENot LMil MBri
'Night Sky'   CDoC ECho GGGa LHyd LMil
                              LRHS MAsh MDun MGos MLea
                              NHol NLar NPen SLdr WBVN
'Nightingale'   SBrw SReu
nigroglandulosum   GGGa
nilagiricum   see *R. arboreum* subsp.
                              nilagiricum
'Nimbus'   LKna LMil SLdr
Nimrod Group   SLdr
'Nippon'   SLdr
nipponicum   SReu
'Nishiki' (EA)   CMac
nitens   see *R. calostrotum* subsp.
                              riparium Nitens Group
nitidulum var. *omeiense* NPen
- - KR 185   GGGa NHol
nivale   GIBF
- subsp. *boreale*   GIBF WPic
- - Ramosissimum Group   GGGa
§ - - Stictophyllum Group   GGGa WAbe
§ - subsp. *nivale*   CSec GKev
niveum ♀H4   CDoC GGGa IDee LMil LRHS
                              MDun NPen SLdr SReu WGer
- B&SWJ 2675   WCru
- 'Nepal'   LHyd
§ Nobleanum Group   GGGa LHyd LKna LMil NPen SLdr
                              SSta
'Nobleanum Album'   GGGa LHyd LKna LMil SReu SSta
'Nobleanum Coccineum'   ISea SLdr SReu
'Nobleanum Lamellen'   SLdr
'Nobleanum Venustum'   CSBt CWri IDee LHyd LKna LMil
                              SReu SSta
'Nofretete'   GGGa
'Nora'   WPic
'Nordlicht' (EA)   SLdr
N 'Norma' (R/d) ♀H4   LMil SReu
Norman Shaw Group   LHyd
'Northern Hi-Lights' (A)   LMil LRHS SLdr
'Northern Star'   LHyd
'Northern Starburst'   LMil
'Nova Zembla'   CDoC ECho EPfP GGGa ISea LMil
                              MAsh MBar MGos NPri SBrw
                              SHBN SLdr SPer SPoG SReu SSta
                              WBVN
nudiflorum   see *R. periclymenoides*
nudipes   LMil
nuttallii   CBrd GGGa LMil SLdr
'Oban'   ECho GGGa LMil MDun NHol
                              NLAp NMen WAbe
Obtusum Group (EA)   LHyd SLdr
obtusum f. *amoenum*   see *R.* 'Amoenum'

occidentale (A) ♀H4   GGGa IDee LMil LRHS MDun SLdr
                              SSpi
- 'Crescent City Double'   GGGa
  SM 28-2
ochraceum   LMil
- C&H 7052   GGGa
- EGM 312   LMil
'Odee Wright'   CDoC CTri CWri GGGa LRHS
                              MAsh MLea NLar SLdr SPer SReu
'Odoratum' (Ad)   MLea
'Oi-no-mezame' (EA)   LHyd SLdr
'Old Copper'   CWri SLdr
'Old Gold' (K)   ECho MLea SLdr SReu
'Old Port' ♀H4   CWri LHyd LMil SHBN SReu
oldhamii (EA)   CPLG
- B&SWJ 3742   WCru
- ETOT 601   GGGa
'Olga' ♀H4   LHyd LKna LMil SLdr SPoG SReu
                              SSta
'Olga Mezitt'   LHyd NHol
'Olga Niblett' (EA)   ENot LMil
oligocarpum   GGGa
- Guiz 148*   GGGa
'Olive'   LHyd LKna LMil
'Oliver Cromwell'   SReu
Olympic Lady Group   MLea SLdr
Omar Group   MBar
§ 'One Thousand Butterflies' GGGa MDun MLea NPen SLdr
N 'Ophelia'   SCam SLdr
'Oporto'   SLdr
'Orange Beauty' (EA)   CBcs CDoC CMac CSBt CTrh ECho
  ♀H3-4   GGGa LHyd LKna LMil MAsh MBar
                              MGos NPen SCam SLdr SReu
                              WBVN WFar WPic
'Orange King' (EA)   ENot
I 'Orange Queen' (V)   SFai
'Orange Scout'   SLdr WMoo
'Orange Splendour' (A)   LRHS MBri
'Orange Sunset'   MDun
'Orangengold'   MDun
orbiculare ♀H3-4   GGGa LHyd LMil MDun NPen SLdr
- C&K 230   GGGa
§ - subsp. *cardiobasis*   LMil MDun SLdr
- Sandling Park form   SReu
'Orchid Lights'   LRHS MAsh
'Oregon' (EA)   SLdr
oreodoxa   LMil NPen WPic
- var. *fargesii* ♀H4   GGGa LHyd LMil SLdr
- var. *oreodoxa*   LMil
- - EN 4212   GGGa
- var. *shensiense*   GGGa
oreotrephes   CBcs LMil LRHS MDun MLea NPen
                              SLdr SReu
- 'Bluecalyptus'   GGGa
§ - Exquisitum Group   CBcs SLdr SReu
- 'Pentland'   LMil
- Timeteum Group   SReu
Orestes Group   SLdr
orthocladum   LMil MDun
§ - var. *microleucum*   GGGa NHol
- var. *orthocladum*   GGGa NHol
  F 20488
- - JN 819   GGGa
'Oryx' (O)   CSdC LKna
'Osaraku Seedling' (EA)   EPfP ISea
  new
'Osmar' ♀H4   CBcs GGGa MGos NPen SReu
'Ostara'   COtt MDun MGos
'Ostergold' **new**   LMil
'Ouchiyama'   LKna
'Oudijk's Sensation'   CBcs CWri ECho GQui LKna
                              MDun MGos NBlu SLdr WBVN
ovatum (EA)   CBcs NPen
- CN&W 548   ISea
'Oxydol' (K)   MBri SLdr
§ *pachypodum*   GGGa

	– KR 4053	LMil
	pachysanthum ♀H4	CDoC CWri IDee LHyd LMil MDun NPen SLdr SReu SSpi
	– RV 72/001	GGGa SLdr
	– 'Crosswater'	LMil LRHS MDun
	pachysanthum x **yakushimanum**	GGGa SReu
	pachytrichum	GGGa SLdr
	– W 1435	SLdr
§	– var. **monosematum**	SLdr SReu
	– – CN&W 953	LMil
	– var. **pachytrichum** 'Sesame'	LMil
	'Palestrina' (EA) ♀H3-4	CBcs CMac CSBt CTrh ECho EPfP LHyd LKna LMil MGos NHol NPen SBrw SCam SLdr SMer SPer SReu SSta WFar WMoo
	'Pallas' (G)	SReu
	paludosum	see *R. nivale* subsp. *nivale*
	'Pamela Miles' (EA)	LHyd
	'Pamela Robinson'	LHyd
	'Pamela-Louise'	LHyd
	'Pancake'	CMac
	'Panda' (EA) ♀H4	CDoC CSBt CTri ECho GGGa LHyd LMil LRHS MBar MDun MLea NDlv NPri SPoG SReu
	'Papaya Punch'	CDoC LMil MDun
	'Paprika Spiced'	CDoC COtt CWri ECho ISea LMil MAsh MBri MDun MGos MLea NLar SBod WBVN
	'Paradise Pink' (EA)	LMil
	paradoxum	GGGa
	'Paramount' (K/d)	LKna
	'Paris'	LHyd
	'Parkfeuer' (A)	LMil SLdr
	parmulatum	LMil MDun NPen
	– C&C 7538	GGGa
	– 'Ocelot'	GGGa LHyd MDun NPen
	– pink-flowered	GGGa
	parryae	GGGa
	'Party Pink'	CWri
	'Patty Bee' ♀H4	CBcs CDoC CSBt CSam CWri ECho EPfP GCrs GEdr GGGa GGar IDee LHyd LMil MAsh MBar MDun MGos MLea NBlu NHol NLAp NMen SPoG SReu SSpi SSta WFar
	patulum	see *R. pemakoense* Patulum Group
	'Pavane' (K)	LKna
	'Peace'	GGGa
	'Peach Blossom'	see *R.* 'Saotome'
	'Peach Lady'	SLdr
	'Peep-bo' (EA)	LHyd SLdr
	'Peeping Tom'	CDoC MBri MDun SHBN SReu
	pemakoense	CDoC CSBt CTrG GGGa IDee MAsh MBar MDun NHol NPen SLdr SReu WAbe
	– Patulum Group	ECho MBar NHol SLdr
	'Pemakofairy'	WAbe
	pendulum LS&T 6660	GGGa
	Penelope Group	SReu
	'Penheale Blue' ♀H4	CBrm CDoC CTrh GGGa LMil MAsh MDun NDlv NHol
	'Penjerrick Cream'	NPen SLdr
	'Penjerrick Pink'	LHyd NPen
	pennivenium	see *R. tanastylum* var. *pennivenium*
	pentaphyllum (A)	LMil
	'Peppina' **new**	GGGa
	'Percy Wiseman' ♀H4	More than 30 suppliers
	'Perfect Lady'	LMil
§	**periclymenoides** (A)	CSec GGGa GIBF GKev LMil SLdr
	'Persil' (K) ♀H4	CBcs CSBt CWri ECho ENot EPfP GGGa LHyd LKna LMil MAsh MBar MBri MDun MGos MLea SCoo SLdr SPer SReu WBVN WBrE

§	'Persimmon'	LKna
	'Peter Bee' **new**	GGGa
	'Peter Berg'	MGos
	'Peter John Mezitt'	see *R.* (PJM Group) 'Peter John Mezitt'
	'Peter Koster' (hybrid)	CWri SHBN SLdr WFar
	petrocharis Guiz 120	GGGa
	'Petrouchka' (K)	LKna MBri MDun
	phaedropum	see *R. neriiflorum* subsp. *phaedropum*
	phaeochrysum	GGGa GIBF LMil NPen SLdr
	– var. **agglutinatum**	GGGa LMil
§	– var. **levistratum**	LMil SLdr SReu
	– – AC 1757	WCwm
	'Phalarope'	ECho GEdr GGGa MBar NHol SReu
	'Phoebe' (R/d)	SLdr SReu
	'Phyllis Korn'	CDoC CDul CWri LHyd MBri MDun NLar SLdr SPer
	'Piccolo' (K/d)	CSdC LKna
§	**piercei**	LMil MDun NPen
	– KW 11040	GGGa
	Pilgrim Group	LKna LMil
	pingianum	SLdr
	– EGM 304	LMil
	– KR 184	GGGa
	'Pink and Sweet' (A)	LMil
	'Pink Bountiful'	LKna
	'Pink Bride'	SLdr
	'Pink Cameo'	CWri
	'Pink Cherub' ♀H4	CDoC ECho EMui ENot LRHS MBar MBri MDun NBlu SBod SLdr SReu
	'Pink Delight'	GQui LKna NLar
	'Pink Delight' (V)	SFai
I	'Pink Delight' (A)	ECho MAsh MGos MLea SLdr
	'Pink Drift'	CSBt ECho LKna LMil MBar MDun MGos NHol SHBN SLdr SPer
	'Pink Gin'	LMil MDun
	'Pink Glory'	SLdr
	'Pink Lady' (A)	SReu
	'Pink Leopard'	LMil MLea SLdr
	'Pink Mimosa' (Vs)	SLdr
	'Pink Pancake' (EA) ♀H4	CBcs ECho EPfP GQui LMil LRHS MGos NLar SLdr SSpi WGer
	'Pink Pearl' (EA)	see *R.* 'Azuma-kagami'
	'Pink Pearl' (hybrid)	CBcs CSBt CTri CWri ECho ENot EPfP GGGa LMil LRHS MAsh MBar MBri MDun MGos NPen NPri NWea SLdr SPer SPoG SReu SSta WBVN WFar
	'Pink Pebble' ♀H3-4	CTrw ECho LHyd MAsh MDun MLea
	'Pink Perfection'	MBar MGos NPen SLdr SReu WFar
	'Pink Photo'	SLdr
	'Pink Polar Bear'	LMil
	'Pink Rosette'	LKna
N	'Pink Ruffles'	SLdr
	'Pink Sensation'	MDun
	'Pinkerton'	LKna
	'Pintail'	GGGa IDee LMil WAbe
	'Pipit'	GGGa WAbe
	'Pippa' (EA)	CMac CTrG
	PJM Group	MDun
§	– 'Peter John Mezitt' ♀H4	LHyd LMil MAsh SLdr SReu
	'PJM Elite'	GGGa LHyd
	planetum	LMil
	'Pleasant White' (EA)	SBrw
	pocophorum	GGGa NPen SLdr
	– 'Cecil Nice'	LHyd
	– var. **hemidartum**	GGGa NPen
	– var. **pocophorum**	SLdr
	'Point Defiance'	CWri ECho GGGa ISea LMil MDun NLar NPen SLdr SPer WBVN
	'Polar Bear' (EA)	MBar MDun SLdr

'Polar Bear' ♥H3-4 | IDee LHyd LMil LRHS MGos MLan SReu WBVN
Polar Bear Group | CWri ECho GGGa LMil MLea NPen SLdr
'Polar Haven' (EA) | LKna
'Polaris' | see *R.* 'Hachmann's Polaris'
'Polaris' (EA) | ENot SReu
§ *poluninii* | GGGa
polyandrum | see *R. maddenii* subsp. *maddenii* Polyandrum Group
§ *polycladum* | LMil
§ - Scintillans Group | ECho LHyd MBar MDun MLea NHol SLdr WPic
- - 'Policy' ♥H4 | GGGa SReu
polylepis | GGGa LMil NPen
- C&K 284 | GGGa
§ *ponticum* | CBcs CDul CSBt CTri ENot IDee MBar MGos NScw NWea SPer WFar
- AC&H 205 | GGGa
- 'Foliis Purpureis' | SReu
§ - 'Silver Edge' (v) | CSBt LMil SLdr SMur
- 'Variegatum' (v) | CBcs CTri ENot EPfP GGGa LRHS MAsh MBar MDun MGos MLea NBlu NPen NPri SPer SPoG SReu SRms SSta WFar
'Pooh-Bah' (EA) | LHyd
'Pook' | LHyd
'Popcorn' (V) | GGGa SFai
'Popocatapetl' | SReu
'Port Knap' (EA) | LKna
'Port Wine' (EA) | LKna
'Potlatch' | GGGa
poukhanense | see *R. yedoense* var. *poukhanense*
§ 'Praecox' ♥H4 | CBcs CDoC CDul CSBt CTrw ECho ENot EPfP GGGa ISea LHyd LKna LMil LRHS MAsh MDun MGos NBlu NHol NPri SBrw SHBN SLdr SPer SPoG SReu SSta WFar WPic
praestans | GGGa GTSp LMil MDun NPen SLdr
praevernum | GGGa LMil
§ *prattii* | NPen SLdr
- 'Perry Wood' | LMil
'Prawn' | LKna SReu
Prelude Group | SLdr
preptum | GGGa SLdr
'President Roosevelt' (v) | CSBt LKna LMil LRHS MAsh MDun MGos MLea NPen NPri SHBN SPer SPoG SReu WFar
'Pretty Girl' | LKna
'Pretty Woman' | GGGa LMil
'Pride of Leonardslee' | SLdr
'Pridenjoy' | LMil
'Prima Donna' | ENot LMil
primuliflorum | GGGa WAbe
- CN&W 1237 | ISea
- 'Doker-La' | LMil WAbe
- white-flowered | WAbe
'Prince Camille de Rohan' | LMil
'Prince Henri de Pays Bas' (G) | CSdC SLdr
'Princess Alexandra' (V) | SFai
'Princess Alice' | CBcs LHyd WGer WPic
'Princess Anne' ♥H4 | CDoC CMHG CSam ECho EPfP GGGa LHyd LMil LRHS MAsh MBar MDun MGos MLea NPen SHBN SLdr SPer SReu SSta WMoo
'Princess Galadriel' | SLdr
'Princess Ida' (EA) | LHyd
'Princess Juliana' | ECho ISea LMil MLea WMoo
'Princess Margaret of Windsor' (K) | GQui LMil
'Princess Margaret Toth' | CSdC
principis | LMil SLdr

- C&V 9547 | GGGa
- KR 3844 from Pasum Tzo | LMil
- SF 95085 | ISea
- 'Lost Horizon' | CDoC LMil MDun
§ - Vellereum Group | SLdr
§ *prinophyllum* (A) | IDee LMil WGer
'Prins Bernhard' (EA) | LKna SCam SLdr
'Prinses Juliana' (EA) | SLdr SReu WFar
'Professor Hugo de Vries' ♥H4 | SLdr SReu
'Professor J.H. Zaayer' | MGos
pronum | GGGa
- R.B. Cooke form | GGGa
- Towercourt form | GGGa
§ 'Prostigiatum' | SLdr
prostratum | see *R. saluenense* subsp. *chameunum* Prostratum Group
proteoides | GGGa
* - 'Ascreavie' | GGGa
proteoides x *tsariense* | GGGa
proteoides x *yakushimanum* | GGGa
protistum | SLdr
- KR 1986 | GGGa
§ - var. *giganteum* | SReu
pruniflorum | GGGa GIBF
prunifolium (A) | GGGa GKev LMil SLdr SSpi
przewalskii | GGGa LHyd
- subsp. *dabanshanense* | GGGa
pseudochrysanthum ♥H4 | CDoC CStu GGGa LHyd LMil LRHS NLar NPen SLdr SReu SSta
pseudociliipes | GGGa
Psyche Group | see *R.* Wega Group
'Psyche' (EA) | MDun
'Ptarmigan' ♥H3-4 | CBcs CDoC ECho EPfP GEdr GGGa IDee LHyd LMil MAsh MBar MGos MLea NEgg NHol NLap NMen NPen SLdr SReu SSta WFar
pubescens KW 3953 | GGGa
pubicostatum | LMil
- AC 2051 | LMil
- CN&W 906 | ISea
§ 'Pucella' (G) ♥H4 | CWri NLar SLdr SReu
pudorosum L&S 2752 | GGGa
'Pulchrum Maxwellii' | see *R.* 'Maxwellii'
pumilum | GGGa MDun WAbe
'Puncta' | GGGa NHol
punctatum | see *R. minus* var. *minus* Punctatum Group
purdomii | GGGa
'Purple Diamond' | see *R.* Diamant Group purple
'Purple Emperor' | LKna
'Purple Gem' | NHol SPoG
purple Glenn Dale (EA) | SLdr
'Purple Heart' | ENot LMil
'Purple Lace' | CDoC
'Purple Splendor' (EA) | CMac SCam SLdr SPoG
'Purple Splendour' ♥H4 | CBcs CDoC CSBt CWri ECho ENot EPfP IDee ISea LHyd LKna LMil LRHS MAsh MBar MBri MDun MGos MLea NEgg NPen SHBN SPer SReu SSta WBVN WFar WMoo
'Purple Triumph' (EA) ♥H3 | LKna LMil SCam SLdr SReu SSta
'Purpurkissen' (EA) | LMil
'Purpurtraum' (EA) ♥H4 | GGGa
'Quail' | GGGa
Quaver Group | SRms
'Queen Alice' | LRHS MAsh MDun
'Queen Elizabeth II' ♥H4 | LHyd
Queen Emma | see *R.* 'Koningin Emma'
'Queen Mary' | MBar MDun
'Queen Mother' | see *R.* 'The Queen Mother'
'Queen of England' (G) | CSdC
Queen of Hearts Group | CWri
'Queen of Hearts' | LHyd SLdr SReu
'Queen Souriya' | SLdr SReu

- var. ***oreonastes*** ♀H4	CDoC GGGa LHyd LMil LRHS MDun NPen SSta
- - USDAPI 59222/R11312	GGGa
- - Nymans form	SReu
- var. ***parvum***	GGGa
- var. ***recurvum***	LMil
'Royal Blood'	LHyd SLdr
'Royal Command' (K)	COtt CWri MAsh MBar MDun NEgg SBrw SLdr
Royal Flush Group	CBcs ISea
'Royal Lodge' (K)	SLdr
'Royal Ruby' (K)	CWri ECho MBri MGos MLea SLdr
'Roza Stevenson'	LHyd NPen SLdr
'Rozanne Waterer' (K/d)	LKna
'Rubicon'	CDoC CWri ECho GQui MAsh MDun MLea SLdr
rubiginosum	CBcs GGGa GTSp LHyd LMil NPen
- SF 368	ISea
§ - Desquamatum Group	CBcs LHyd SLdr
- pink-flowered	LMil
- white-flowered	LMil
rubineiflorum	GGGa
'Rubinetta' (EA)	LMil LRHS WFar
rubroluteum	see *R. viridescens* Rubroluteum Group
'Ruby F. Bowman'	CBcs SReu
'Ruby Hart'	GGGa MAsh MDun NHol SReu
Ruddigore Group	LHyd
rude	see *R. glischrum* subsp. *rude*
'Ruffles and Frills'	ECho MDun
rufum	CDoC GGGa SLdr
- AC 4110	LMil
'Rumba' (K)	LKna
rupicola	LMil NMen SLdr
§ - var. ***chryseum***	GGGa LHyd
- var. ***muliense*** Yu 14042	GGGa
russatum ♀H4	EPfP GGGa LHyd LMil MDun NPen SLdr SPoG WAbe WFar WPic
- blue-black-flowered	LMil LRHS
- 'Purple Pillow'	CSBt
russotinctum	see *R. alutaceum* var. *russotinctum*
'Sacko'	CWri ECho GGGa LMil LTwo MAsh MDun NHol NLar WBVN
'Saffrano'	NLar
'Saffron Queen'	CBcs CTrG CTrw ISea LMil WPic
'Sahara' (K)	CSdC LKna LMil SLdr
'Saint Breward'	CTrG GGGa GQui LHyd MDun MLea NHol SLdr
'Saint Kew'	SLdr
'Saint Merryn' ♀H4	CDoC CTrG ECho GGGa LHyd MDun NHol NLAp SLdr SPoG
'Saint Michael'	SReu
'Saint Minver'	LHyd SLdr
'Saint Tudy'	EPfP LHyd LKna MDun SLdr WAbe
'Saint Valentine' (V)	SFai
'Salmon Bedspread'	SReu
'Salmon Queen' (M)	WFar
'Salmon Sander' (EA)	SLdr
§ 'Salmon Trout'	LMil SPoG
'Salmon's Leap' (EA/v)	CBcs COtt CSBt ENot GQui LMil LRHS NPri SBrw SHBN SLdr SReu WAbe WFar
saluenense	GGGa LHyd LMil NPen SLdr
- JN 260	GGGa
§ - subsp. ***chameunum***	GGGa LMil SLdr
- - ACE 2143	WAbe
§ - - Prostratum Group	GGGa WAbe
- subsp. ***riparioides***	see *R. calostrotum* subsp. *riparium* Rock's form
'Sammetglut'	CWri SReu
'Samuel Taylor Coleridge' (M)	NLar
'Sang de Gentbrugge' (G)	CSdC SReu
sanguineum	GGGa LMil MDun NPen SLdr
§ - subsp. ***didymum***	GGGa MDun
§ - subsp. ***sanguineum*** var. ***didymoides*** Roseotinctum Group USDAPI 59038/R10903	GGGa
- - var. ***haemaleum***	CWri GGGa LMil
- - var. ***sanguineum*** F 25521	LMil
'Santa Maria'	COtt ECho SBrw SLdr SReu SSta
§ 'Saotome' (EA)	LHyd SLdr
'Sapphire'	CSBt CTrG ECho GEdr MAsh MBar MDun NDlv SLdr SRms
'Sappho'	CBcs CDul CSBt CWri ECho EPfP GBin GGGa ISea LHyd LKna LMil MBar MBri MDun MGos MLea NPen SBrw SHBN SLdr SPer SReu SSta WBVN WFar WGer
'Sapporo'	GGGa LMil MBri
'Sarah Boscawen'	SReu
sargentianum	GGGa LMil MLea NMen WAbe
- 'Whitebait'	GGGa WAbe
'Sarita Loder'	LHyd
'Sarled' ♀H4	GGGa LMil NMen SReu
Sarled Group	SRms WAbe
'Sarsen' (K)	CSdC
'Saskia' (K)	LKna
'Satan' (K) ♀H4	CSBt SReu
'Satschiko'	see *R.* 'Geisha Orange'
'Satsop Surprise'	GGGa
'Satsuki' (EA)	ECho
'Saturne' (G)	SLdr
'Saxon Bonnie Belle' (V)	SFai
'Saxon Dwarf' (V)	SFai
scabrifolium	CTrG
§ - var. ***spiciferum***	GGGa SLdr WAbe
- - SF 502	ISea
'Scandinavia'	LHyd
'Scarlet Romance'	MBri
'Scarlet Wonder' ♀H4	CBcs CDoC CMHG CSBt CTrh CWri ECho EPfP GGGa IDee ISea LKna LMil LRHS MAsh MBar MBri MDun MGos NBlu NHol NPen NPri NWea SLdr SPer SPoG SReu WFar WMoo
schistocalyx F 17637	NPen
'Schlaraffia'	NLar
schlippenbachii (A)	CTrG GGGa GIBF LMil NPen SLdr SSpi
- 'Sid's Royal Pink' (A)	LMil MDun
'Schneeflöckchen'	GGGa
'Schneekrone'	GGGa LMil MBri MDun NBlu NHol
'Schneeperle' (EA)	LMil
'Schneewolke'	LMil
'Schubert' (EA)	MBar SBrw
scintillans	see *R. polycladum* Scintillans Group
'Scintillation'	CWri GGGa ISea LMil MBar MDun MLea NPen SBrw SHBN SLdr
scopulorum	SLdr
- C&C 7571	GGGa
- KR 5770	LMil
- KW 6354	GGGa
'Scotian Bells' **new**	GGGa
scottianum	see *R. pachypodum*
'Scout' (EA)	SLdr
scyphocalyx	see *R. dichroanthum* subsp. *scyphocalyx*
scyphocalyx x 'Tally Ho' **new**	SLdr
Seagull Group	SLdr
searsiae	LMil SLdr
'Sea-Tac'	MLea
'Seb'	SLdr
'Second Honeymoon'	CBcs CDoC CWri ECho ISea LMil MAsh MLea NLar NPen SReu
seinghkuense	LMil
- CCH&H 8106	GGGa

'Souvenir of Anthony Waterer' ♀H4   LKna MDun SReu

'Souvenir of W.C. Slocock'   LKna SHBN SLdr SReu

'Sparkler' (Vs)   GGGa

'Sparkler' (hybrid)   LRHS

speciosum   see *R. flammeum*

'Spek's Orange' (M) ♀H4   MGos

sperabile var. *weihsiense*   GGGa LMil SLdr

- - AC 1915   LMil

sperabiloides   GGGa

sphaeranthum   see *R. trichostomum*

sphaeroblastum   GGGa SLdr

- var. *wumengense*   CDoC MDun

- - CN&W 510   ISea

- - CN&W 962   LMil

- - CN&W 968   GGGa

- - CN&W 1051   LMil

- - EGM 350   LMil

- - EGM 359   LMil

spiciferum   see *R. scabrifolium* var. *spiciferum*

spilotum   GGGa LMil SLdr

spinuliferum   GGGa

- SF 247   ISea

'Spitfire'   MDun SBrw SReu

'Splendens' (G)   CSdC

'Spoonbill' (K)   LKna

'Spring Beauty' (EA)   CMac SCam SLdr SReu

'Spring Magic'   LMil NPen SLdr

'Spring Pearl'   see *R.* 'Moerheim's Pink'

'Spring Rose'   SLdr

'Spring Sunshine'   LMil

'Springbok'   LHyd

'Squirrel' (EA) ♀H4   CDoC ECho GEdr GGGa LHyd LMil LRHS MAsh MDun MGos MLea NDlv NHol NPen SLdr SReu WGer

'Squirrel' tall (EA)   SLdr

Stadt Essen Group   LMil SLdr

stamineum   GGGa LMil NPen

- SF 417   ISea

'Standishii'   SLdr

'Stanley Rivlin'   LHyd

§ 'Stanway'   SLdr

'Star of Woking'   LKna

'Starbright Champagne'   LMil

'Starcross'   LHyd

'Starfish'   SReu

§ *stenopetalum*   CMac ISea LHyd LMil SLdr WAbe
  'Linearifolium' (A)

stenophyllum   see *R. makinoi*

stewartianum   GGGa LMil MDun SLdr

- SF 370   ISea

'Stewartstonian' (EA)   CMac ENot LHyd MBar NBlu NHol SBrw SReu SSta WFar WPic

stictophyllum   see *R. nivale* subsp. *boreale* Stictophyllum Group

'Stoat' (EA)   GQui MDun

'Stopham Girl' (A)   LMil

'Stopham Lad' (A)   LMil

'Stranraer'   MDun

'Strategist'   SLdr

'Strawberry Cream'   GGGa NHol

'Strawberry Ice' (K) ♀H4   CBcs CDoC CSBt CTri CWri ECho EPfP GGGa ISea LKna LMil LRHS MAsh MBar MBri MDun MGos MLea MMHG SLdr SPer SReu WMoo

strigillosum   GGGa MDun NPen SLdr

- C&H 7035   GGGa

- EGM 305   LMil

- EGM 338   LMil

- Reuthe's form   SReu

subansiriense C&H 418   GGGa

suberosum   see *R. yunnanense* Suberosum Group

succothii   LHyd MDun SLdr

- EGM 086   LMil

- LS&H 21295   SLdr

'Suede'   MDun

'Sugared Almond' (K)   LMil

'Sui-yohi' (EA)   LHyd

sulfureum SBEC 249   GGGa

'Sulphamer'   SLdr

'Summer Blaze' (A)   SReu

'Summer Flame'   SReu

'Summer Fragrance' (O) ♀H4   LMil MDun SReu SSta

'Sun Chariot' (K)   CBcs CSam ECho LKna LMil MLea MMHG NEgg SLdr SReu

'Sunbeam' (EA)   see *R.* 'Benifude'

'Sunbeam' (hybrid)   LKna SReu

'Sunny' (V)   GGGa

(Sunrise Group) 'Sunrise'   NPen SLdr

'Sunset Pink' (K)   SLdr

'Sunspray'   NPen

'Sunte Nectarine' (K) ♀H4   ECho GQui LHyd LMil MBri MDun SLdr

superbum (V)   GGGa

'Superbum' (O)   SBrw SLdr

'Surprise' (EA)   CDoC CTrh CTri EPfP LRHS SCam SLdr SPoG

'Surrey Heath'   CBcs CDoC COtt CWri ECho ENot EPfP ISea LMil LRHS MAsh MBar MBri MDun MGos NDlv NPen NPri SLdr SReu

'Susan' ♀H4   CDoC CSBt CWri GGGa LHyd LKna LMil MBri MDun NHol SLdr SPoG SReu

'Susannah Hill' (EA)   CBcs CDoC ENot MGos SLdr

'Sussex Bonfire'   SLdr

sutchuenense   CDoC GGGa IDee LMil MDun NPen SLdr WCwm WGer

- var. *geraldii*   see *R.* x *geraldii*

'Swamp Beauty'   CWri ECho LMil MAsh MDun NLar NPen WBVN

'Swansong' (EA)   CMac

'Sweet Simplicity'   CSBt CWri LKna

'Sweet Sue'   NPen SLdr SReu

'Swift'   CDoC ECho GGGa GQui LMil LRHS LTwo MAsh NHol NPri SReu WGer

'Sylphides' (K)   LKna MDun

'Sylvester'   MGos NMen SBrw SReu

'T.S. Black' (EA)   SLdr

taggianum 'Cliff Hanger'   LMil

'Taka-no-tsukasa' (EA)   SLdr

'Takasago' (EA/d)   CBcs LHyd

taliense   GGGa LHyd LMil MDun

- KR 4056 from Cangshan   LMil

'Tally Ho'   SLdr

Tally Ho Group   SLdr

tamaense   see *R. cinnabarinum* subsp. *tamaense*

'Tama-no-utena' (EA)   SLdr

'Tamarindos'   LMil SPoG

'Tan Crossing'   SBrw

'Tanager' (EA)   CTrh LKna SLdr

§ *tanastylum* var. *pennivenium* SF 593   ISea

'Tangerine'   see *R.* 'Fabia Tangerine'

tapetiforme   GGGa

'Tarantella'   LMil NBlu NEgg

tashiroi (EA)   GIBF SLdr

'Tatjana' ♀H4   LRHS

tatsienense   GGGa

'Taurus' ♀H4   CDoC COtt CWri ECho GGGa LMil MAsh MDun MLea NPen SBod WBVN

taxifolium (v)   GGGa

'Tay' (K)   SLdr

'Teal'   ECho GEdr MBar MDun MGos MLea NHol

'Teddy Bear' CWri GGGa LMil LRHS MDun SLdr
§ **telmateium** SLdr
temenium MDun
- var. **dealbatum** LMil
- var. **gilvum** 'Cruachan' GGGa LMil
-- R 22272 LMil
Temple Belle' CWri ECho MDun
Temple Belle Group CSam LHyd LKna MLea NDlv SLdr
'Tender Heart' (K) SLdr
§ **tephropeplum** GGGa LHyd MDun
- SF 92069 ISea
- USDAPQ 3914/R18408 GGGa
- Deleiense Group see *R. tephropeplum*
Tequila Sunrise' LHyd LMil
'Terra-cotta' CDoC LKna LMil
'Terra-cotta Beauty' (EA) CTrG WPat
'Tessa' CBcs ECho MAsh
Tessa Group ECho LKna LMil LRHS MGos
'Tessa Bianca' GGGa
'Tessa Roza' ♀H4 GGGa GQui NBlu
'Thai Gold' (V) SFai
thayerianum GGGa LMil
'The Dowager' SLdr
'The Freak' SLdr
§ 'The Hon. Jean Marie CAbP CDoC CWri ECho EPfP
   de Montague' ♀H4 LKna LMil MBri MDun MGos MLea
   NPen SLdr SPoG SReu WBVN
'The Master' ♀H4 LHyd LKna LMil SLdr SReu WGer
§ 'The Queen Mother' LHyd
thomsonii GGGa IDee LHyd LMil LRHS
   MDun NHol SLdr SReu
- B&SWJ 2638 WCru
- subsp. **lopsangianum** GGGa
- subsp. **thomsonii** GGGa
   L&S 2847
Thor Group GGGa SBrw SReu
'Thousand Butterflies' see *R.* 'One Thousand Butterflies'
'Thunderstorm' LHyd LKna SReu
thymifolium GGGa
'Tibet' ♀H3-4 GQui LMil MBar MDun SHBN SLdr
'Tidbit' ♀H4 CDoC GGGa LMil MGos NPen
   SLdr
'Tilford Seedling' LKna
'Timothy James' ENot LRHS MAsh
'Tinkerbird' GGGa
'Tinsmith' (K) SLdr
'Tit Willow' (EA) LHyd LMil LRHS NPri SCoo SLdr
'Titian Beauty' CBcs CDoC COtt CSBt CWri ECho
   ENot EPfP GGGa ISea LHyd LMil
   LRHS MAsh NBlu NDlv NPen NPri SBod SLdr
   SPer WBVN WBrE WFar
'Titipu' (EA) LHyd SLdr
'Titness Delight' **new** SLdr
'Titness Park' LHyd
'Tolkien' SReu
'Tom Hyde' (EA) LMil
'Too Bee' NHol
'Top Banana' MDun SLdr
'Topsvoort Pearl' SReu
'Torch' LKna
'Toreador' (EA) CTrG SBrw SCam SLdr
'Torero' GGGa LMil
'Torridon' (Vs) LMil
'Tortoiseshell Champagne' see *R.* 'Champagne'
'Tortoiseshell Orange' CDoC CSBt EMil LHyd LKna LMil
   ♀H3-4 MBri MDun NBlu SHBN SLdr SPoG
   SReu SSta
'Tortoiseshell Salome' LKna SReu
'Tortoiseshell Scarlet' MDun SReu
'Tortoiseshell Wonder' LKna LMil MAsh NPri SLdr SReu
   ♀H3-4
'Totally Awesome' (K) MBri SLdr
'Toucan' (K) CSBt MDun SLdr
'Tower Beauty' (A) LHyd
'Tower Dainty' (A) LHyd

'Tower Daring' (A) LHyd SLdr
'Tower Dexter' (A) LHyd
'Tower Dragon' (A) LHyd LMil SLdr
'Trail Blazer' GGGa
traillianum GGGa LMil NPen SLdr
- CN&W 746 ISea
Treasure Group LHyd SLdr
'Trebah Gem' CTbh
'Treecreeper' GGGa
'Tregedna Red' SReu
'Trelawny' SLdr
'Trewithen Orange' MBar MDun SHBN SLdr
'Trewithen Purple' CTbh CTrw
trichanthum CPne GGGa LMil
- 'Honey Wood' LHyd LMil SLdr
- white-flowered LMil
trichocladum NPen
- CN&W 880 ISea
- SF 661 ISea
- SF 96179 ISea
§ **trichostomum** GGGa LRHS WAbe
- Ledoides Group LMil MLea SReu
-- 'Collingwood Ingram' LMil SLdr SReu
   ♀H4
triflorum GGGa ISea LMil MDun NPen
- C&V 9573 GGGa
- SF 95149 ISea
§ - var. **bauhiniiflorum** CBcs NPen
'Trilby' SReu
trilectorum GGGa
'Trill' (EA) SLdr
'Trinidad' MDun
triplonaevium see *R. alutaceum* var.
   russotinctum Triplonaevium
   Group
'Troll' (EA) SLdr
'Tromba' GGGa LMil
'Troupial' (K) LKna
'Trude Webster' GGGa SReu
tsangpoense see *R. charitopes* subsp.
   tsangpoense
tsariense GGGa LMil NHol NPen SOkd
- Poluninii Group see *R. poluninii*
- var. **trimoense** CDoC GGGa LMil MDun NPen
-- KW 8288 LMil
- 'Yum Yum' GGGa SLdr
tsariense x GGGa
   yakushimanum
tschonoskii **new** GIBF
§ **tsusiophyllum** GGGa GIBF
'Tsuta-momiji' (EA) LHyd SLdr
'Tuffet' SLdr SReu
'Tulyar' LKna
'Tunis' (K) ECho
'Turacao' GGGa
'Twilight Pink' SLdr
'Twilight Sky' (A) SBrw SLdr
'Ukamuse' (EA/d) LHyd SLdr
'Umpqua Queen' (K) MBri
ungernii GGGa LMil NPen SLdr
uniflorum NHol
§ - var. **imperator** LMil
-- KW 6884 GGGa
'Unique' (G) ECho EPfP ISea LKna LRHS NEgg
   SLdr SPer
'Unique' (*campylocarpum* CBcs CDoC CSam GGGa LHyd
   hybrid) ♀H4 LKna LMil LRHS MAsh MBri MDun
   NPen NPri SHBN SLdr SReu SSta
   WMoo
'Unique Marmalade' ECho LMil MBri NPen SLdr WBVN
uvariifolium GGGa SLdr
- CN&W 127 ISea
- CN&W 1275 ISea
- Cox 6519 GGGa
- KR 4158 from Zhongdian, LMil
   Napa Hai

- var. **griseum**	IDee SLdr
- - C&C 7506	GGGa
- - KR 3423	LMil
- - KR 3428	LMil
- - KR 3774	LMil
- - KR 3782	LMil
- - SF 95184	ISea
- 'Reginald Childs'	LMil SLdr
- 'Yangtze Bend'	GGGa
vaccinioides (V)	GGGa
CCH&H 8051	
'Valentine' (EA)	GGGa
valentinianum	GGGa NPen SLdr
- F 24347	NPen
- var. **oblongilobatum**	LMil
C&H 7186	
'Van'	LMil
'Van Houttei Flore Pleno'	SLdr
'Van Nes Sensation'	LMil
Vanessa Group	LMil SReu
'Vanessa Pastel' ♀H3-4	CDoC GGGa LHyd LMil MDun
	SReu
§ 'Vanilla'	LKna
vaseyi (A) ♀H3-4	GGGa GIBF GKev LMil SLdr
- 'White Find'	GGGa
- white-flowered (A)	LMil
'Vayo' (A)	SLdr
veitchianum	GGGa
§ - Cubittii Group	GGGa SLdr
- - 'Ashcombe'	LHyd
- KNE Cox 9001	GGGa
'Veldtstar'	LHyd
vellereum	see *R. principis* Vellereum Group
'Velvet Gown' (EA)	ENot
venator	GGGa MDun WPic
'Venetian Chimes'	ECho ENot ISea MDun NLar NPen
	SLdr SReu
vernicosum	GGGa LMil NPen
- JN 180	GGGa
- SF 416	ISea
'Veryan Bay'	CBcs
vialii (A)	GGGa
'Victoria Hallett'	SLdr SReu
'Vida Brown' (EA/d)	CMac LKna SBrw SLdr SReu WPat
'Viennese Waltz'	GGGa
'Viking' (EA)	LHyd
'Viking Silver'	GGGa
'Vincent van Gogh'	NPen
'Vinecourt Duke' (R/d)	CWri ECho MDun SLdr
'Vinecourt Troubador'	CDoC CWri ECho MDun MLea
(K/d)	SBod
'Vineland Dream' (K/d)	CWri ECho MAsh SLdr
'Vineland Fragrance'	MDun SLdr
'Vintage Rosé' ♀H4	ENot LMil MLea SLdr SPoG SReu
'Violet Longhurst' (EA)	LHyd
'Violetta' (EA)	NMen SLdr
Virginia Richards Group	CDoC CWri LRHS MGos SLdr
	SReu
§ **viridescens**	NPen
- 'Doshong La'	GGGa LMil
§ - Rubroluteum Group	LMil
viscidifolium	GGGa
'Viscosepalum' (G)	CSdC
viscosum (A) ♀H4	GGGa GIBF GQui IDee LHyd LKna
	LMil LRHS MDun SLdr SPer SReu
	SSpi WBVN WBrE WMoo WPic
- SDR 2312	GKev
- 'Grey Leaf' (Vs)	LMil
- var. **montanum** (A)	ENot IBlr
- f. **rhodanthum** (A)	LMil
- 'Roseum' (Vs)	LMil
'Viscount Powerscourt'	ENot LMil
'Viscy' ♀H4	CDoC CDul CWri ECho EPfP
	GGGa GQui LHyd LMil MBri
	MDun MGos MLea NLar NPen
	WBVN

§ Volker Group	CWri ECho LMil MAsh MBar
	MDun SReu SSta WFar
§ - 'Babette'	ENot LMil
§ - 'Lackblatt'	CDoC LMil MBri MLea SLdr
'Vulcan' ♀H4	CDoC EPfP GGGa LMil MLea
	SHBN
'Vulcan' x **yakushimanum**	SReu
'Vuyk's Rosyred' (EA) ♀H4	CBcs CDoC CMac CSBt CTri ENot
	GQui LHyd LKna LMil LRHS MAsh
	MBar MGos NHol NPri SBrw SCam
	SLdr SPer SReu WFar
'Vuyk's Scarlet' (EA) ♀H4	More than 30 suppliers
'W.E. Gumbleton' (M)	SReu
'W.F.H.' ♀H4	CWri LMil SLdr WGer
wadanum var.	LMil
leucanthum	
'Wagtail'	NHol
wallichii	GGGa LHyd MDun SLdr
- B&SWJ 2633	WCru
- DM 21	LMil
Walloper Group	NPen SReu
'Wallowa Red' (K)	ECho MLea SLdr
'Wally Miller'	ECho ISea LMil MAsh MBri MDun
	SReu WBVN
aff. **walongense** C&H 373	GGGa
wardii	CDoC GGGa IDee ISea LHyd LMil
	LRHS MDun NPen SLdr
- KR 3684	LMil
- KR 4913	LMil
- KR 5268	LMil
- L&S	SReu
- var. **puralbum**	GGGa NPen
- var. **wardii**	LMil
- - LS&T 5679	NPen
- - Litiense Group	SLdr
- - CN&W 1079	ISea
'Ward's Ruby' (EA)	CTrw
§ 'Washington State	GGGa MBri
Centennial' (A)	
wasonii	CDoC GGGa LHyd LMil NPen
- f. **rhododactylum**	GGGa
KW 1876	
- var. **wenchuanense**	NHol
- - C 5046	GGGa
watsonii	GGGa
- Cox 5075	GGGa
'Waxbill'	GGGa
'Waxwing'	LKna MBri
websterianum	SLdr
- Cox 5123	GGGa
'Wee Bee' ♀H4	CDoC ECho GCrs GEdr GGGa
	GGar LMil LTwo MDun MLea NDlv
	NHol SPoG SReu WAbe
§ Wega Group	LHyd
'Wendy' **new**	MAsh
'Western Lights' (A)	LMil MAsh
'Westminster' (O)	LKna LMil
'Weston's Pink	GGGa LMil NHol
Diamond' (d)	
'Weybridge'	SLdr
weyrichii (A)	GGGa LMil
'Wheatear'	GGGa
'Whidbey Island'	LMil
'Whisperingrose'	ECho LMil MDun NDlv
'White Frills' (EA)	SLdr
White Glory Group	SLdr
'White Gold'	GGGa MDun
'White Grandeur' (EA)	CTrh
'White Jade' (EA)	SLdr
'White Lady' (EA)	LKna MBar SBrw SCam SLdr
'White Lights' (A) ♀H4	EPfP LMil LRHS MAsh MBri NPri
	SLdr
'White Olympic Lady'	LKna
'White Perfume'	MDun SReu
'White Rosebud' (EA)	SReu WFar
'White Swan' (K)	MLea

'White Swan' (hybrid)	LKna SBrw SReu
'White Wings'	GQui LHyd SLdr WPic
'Whitethroat' (K/d) ♀H4	CSdC CWri ECho EPfP GQui ISea LKna LMil MAsh MDun MLea MMHG SLdr SPer WBVN WMoo
'Whitney's Dwarf Red'	SLdr
'Wigeon'	GGGa LMil LRHS NHol
wightii	GGGa MDun NPen SLdr
'Wild Affair'	MDun
'Wilgen's Ruby'	CDoC CSBt LKna LMil MBar MGos NBlu NHol NPen NWea SHBN SLdr SPoG WFar
'Will Silent' (V)	SFai
'Willbrit'	CDoC CWri ECho LHyd MAsh MGos SLdr WBrE
'William III' (G)	SLdr
williamsianum ♀H4	CBcs CDoC CTrG CWri ECho GBin ISea LHyd LMil LRHS MAsh MBar MDun MLea SLdr SReu SRms SSpi WFar WPic
- Caerhays form	LMil MDun
- 'Special'	GGGa
'Willy' (EA)	SCam SLdr
wilsoniae	see *R. latoucheae*
Wilsonii Group	CTrG LKna
wiltonii ♀H4	GGGa LHyd LMil MDun SLdr
- CC&H 3906	GGGa
'Windlesham Scarlet'	LHyd SLdr
'Windsor Lad'	LKna SBrw SReu
'Windsor Peach Glow' (K)	LMil
'Windsor Sunbeam' (K)	CWri
'Winsome' (hybrid) ♀H3	CBcs CDoC GGGa LHyd LMil NPri SReu
Winsome Group	CTrw CWri LKna LRHS MAsh MBar MDun NPen SLdr SSta
'Winston Churchill' (M)	MBar NHol SReu
'Wintergreen' (EA)	COtt
'Wishmoor'	SLdr SReu
'Wisley Blush'	CDoC LMil MAsh
'Witch Doctor'	ECho LMil MDun
'Witchery'	GGGa
'Wombat' (EA) ♀H4	COtt CTri GGGa LHyd LMil LRHS MGos NHol NPri SLdr SReu
'Wonderland'	LKna
wongii	GGGa GQui NPen SLdr
'Woodcock'	LHyd
* 'Woodstock'	SLdr
'Wren'	ECho GCrs GEdr GGGa LMil LRHS MAsh MBar MDun MLea NHol NLAp SLdr SReu WBVN
'Wryneck' (K)	CSdC LHyd LMil SLdr SReu
'Wye' (K)	SLdr
x *xanthanthum*	MLea
xanthocodon	see *R. cinnabarinum* subsp. *xanthocodon*
xanthostephanum CCH&H 8070	GGGa
- KR 3095	LMil
- KR 4462	LMil
'Yaku Angel'	MDun
'Yaku Incense'	ECho MAsh MBri MDun NPen
'Yaku Prince'	ECho MAsh MBri MDun MGos SLdr
yakushimanum	CDoC CMHG CSam CWri ECho ENot EPfP GGGa GIBF IDee LHyd LKna LMil LRHS MAsh MBar MBri MDun MGos MLea NHol NPen NWea SLdr SPer SReu SSta WGer
- 'Berg'	MDun
- 'Edelweiss'	ENot
- Exbury form	SReu
- Exbury form x *roxieanum* var. *oreonastes*	SReu
- FCC form	see *R. yakushimanum* 'Koichiro Wada'

§ - 'Koichiro Wada' ♀H4	EPfP GGGa GGar LHyd LMil LRHS MAsh MDun MGos SLdr SPoG SReu WGer
- subsp. *makinoi*	see *R. makinoi*
- 'Snow Mountain'	SReu
I - 'Torch'	WBrE
* 'Yaya'	SLdr
'Yaye' (EA)	CDoC
'Yaye-hiryu' (EA)	LHyd
§ *yedoense* var. *poukhanense*	GIBF SLdr SReu
'Yellow Cloud' (K)	ECho LMil MBri MDun
'Yellow Hammer' ♀H4	CBcs CTrG ECho EMil EPfP ISea LHyd MDun NWea WBVN WBrE WFar WPic
Yellow Hammer Group	CBcs CWri GGGa LKna LMil MBar MGos NPen SHBN SLdr SPer SReu SSta
'Yellow Rolls Royce'	MDun
'Yoga' (K)	LKna
'Yol'	SLdr
I 'Yolanta'	WAbe
'Youthful Sin'	ISea
yuefengense	GGGa
yungningense	MDun
§ - Glomerulatum Group	SLdr
yunnanense	CDoC GGGa GIBF ISea LHyd LMil MDun NPen SLdr SSpi WPic
- AC 751	MDun NPen
- C&H 7145	GGGa
- KGB 551	SReu
- KGB 559	SReu
- SF 379	ISea
- SF 400	ISea
- SF 96102	ISea
- 'Openwood' ♀H3-4	GGGa LMil
- pink-flowered	GGGa
- 'Red Throat'	SLdr
- red-blotched	LMil
§ - Suberosum Group	SLdr
- white-flowered	GGGa LMil
zaleucum	LMil MDun
- AC 685	MDun
- F 15688	GGGa
- KR 2687	GGGa
- KR 3979	LMil
- SF 347	ISea
- SF 578	ISea
Zelia Plumecocq Group	SLdr SReu
zeylanicum	see *R. arboreum* subsp. *zeylanicum*
Zuiderzee Group	SLdr
'Zuiderzee' **new**	NPen

Rhodohypoxis (Hypoxidaceae)

'Albrighton'	ECho ERos EWes GEdr IBal ITim NHol NMen SAga SBla SIng WAbe WPat
'Andromeda'	EWes
'Appleblossom'	CWrd ECho EPot ERos EWes GKev IBal ITim LBee MSte NMen SCnR SIng WAbe
baurii ♀H4	CElw CMea CNic CPBP ECho GCrs GEdr IBal ITim LRHS MTho NMen NSla SAga SPoG SRms WAbe WFar
- 'Alba'	CMea ECho EDAr IBal ITim NMen
- var. *baurii*	CWrd EWes LBee NJOw SIng
- 'Bridal Bouquet' (d)	EWes WFar
- 'Coconut Ice'	EPot EWes IBal
- var. *confecta*	EWes ITim SAga SBla SIng
- 'Daphne Mary'	EWes
- 'David Scott' **new**	EWes
- 'Dulcie'	ECho EWes GBin ITim SCnR SIng SUsu WAbe

- 'Lily Jean' (d)	CFwr CStu CWrd ECho ENot EPfP EWes GEdr IBal LRHS NCGa SIng SRGP
- 'Mars'	EWes
- 'Pearl'	ECho ITim
- 'Perle'	ECho ERos EWes GEdr NJOw NMen SCnR SIng WAbe
- 'Pictus'	ECho IBal ITim
- 'Pink Pearl'	EPot EWes IBal ITim NHol
- pink-flowered	ITim NLAp WCru
- var. *platypetala*	CFwr CStu CWrd ECho ENot EPfP EPot EWes IBal ITim LRHS NHol NMen WAbe
- - Burtt 6981	EWes
- var. *platypetala* x *milloides*	IBal LTwo WAbe
- 'Rebecca'	EWes
- 'Red King'	EWes IBal
- red-flowered	NLAp SPlb
- 'Susan Garnett-Botfield'	CWrd EPot EWes GEdr IBal ITim NMen SIng WAbe
- white-flowered	EPot ITim NLAp NMen WCru
'Betsy Carmine'	GEdr IBal
'Bright Eyes' (d) **new**	EWes
'Burgundy'	SIng
'Candy Stripe'	ECho EWes GEdr SIng
'Carina'	EWes
'Confusion'	CWrd EWes WAbe WFar
'Dainty Dee' (d) **new**	EWes
'Dawn'	CWrd ECho EPot EWes IBal ITim NHol NMen SAga SBla SIng WAbe
deflexa	CGra CLyd CWrd ECho EWes GCrs GEdr IBal ITim MSte NHol SAga SBla SCnR SIng WAbe WFar
'Donald Mann'	ECho EWes ITim NMen
double, red-flowered (d)	CStu
'Douglas'	CWrd ECho ENot EPfP EPot EWes GEdr IBal ITim LRHS NHol NMen SAga SBla SIng SRGP WAbe WSPU
'Dusky'	CWrd EWes
'E.A. Bowles'	ECho EWes IBal ITim NMen SIng WAbe
'Ellicks'	IBal
'Emily Peel'	CWrd EWes WAbe
'Eva-Kate'	CWrd ECho ERos EWes ITim NHol SAga SBla SIng WAbe WPat
'Fred Broome'	CNic CWrd ECho EWes ITim NHol NMen SAga SBla SIng SRGP WAbe WPat
'Garnett'	CWrd ECho EDAr EWes IBal ITim NMen SBla WAbe
'Great Scot'	CWrd ECho ERos EWes GEdr IBal ITim
'Harlequin'	CWrd ECho EPot EWes IBal ITim NHol NMen SIng WAbe
'Hebron Farm Biscuit'	see *Hypoxis parvula* var. *albiflora* 'Hebron Farm Biscuit'
'Hebron Farm Cerise'	see x *Rhodoxis* 'Hebron Farm Cerise'
'Hebron Farm Pink'	see x *Rhodoxis hybrida* 'Hebron Farm Pink'
§ 'Helen'	ECho EPot EWes GEdr IBal ITim NHol SBla SIng WAbe
'Hinky Pinky'	CFwr
'Holden Rose' **new**	NHol
hybrids	CAvo ELan
'Kiwi Joy' (d)	CStu
'Knockdolian Red'	NHol
'Margaret Rose'	CWrd ECho EWes IBal NMen SIng WAbe
'Midori' **new**	EWes GEdr
milloides	CNic ECho EPot EWes GEdr GGar IBal ITim LBee LRHS NHol NLAp NMen NWCA SAga SBla SCnR SIng WAbe WFar
- 'Claret'	CNic CSam CStu CWrd ECho EWes IBal LTwo SAga SBla SIng SUsu WAbe WFar WPat
- 'Damask'	CNic CStu EWes SAga SBla
- 'Drakensberg Snow'	EWes
- giant	ECho GEdr
'Monty'	ECho EWes GEdr SIng WAbe
'Mystery'	EWes WAbe
'Naomi'	EWes
'New Look'	ECho ERos EWes GEdr IBal ITim LTwo NMen SIng WAbe WFar
'Pearl White'	IBal
'Picta' (v)	CWrd ECho EPot EWes GEdr IBal NHol SAga SBla WAbe
'Pink Ice'	GEdr IBal
'Pinkeen'	ECho EPot EWes GEdr IBal ITim LTwo SIng WAbe WFar
'Pinkie'	IBal
'Pintado'	EWes SBla
'Rosie Lee'	EWes
'Ruth'	ECho EWes IBal MSte NHol SBla SIng SRGP WAbe WFar
'Shell Pink'	EWes IBal ITim WAbe
'Snow' **new**	EWes
'Snow White'	EWes
'Starlett'	EWes
'Starry Eyes' (d)	CStu EWes SAga
'Stella'	ECho EPot ERos EWes GEdr GKev IBal ITim MSte NHol NMen SAga SBla SIng SRGP WAbe
tetra	ITim
'Tetra Pink'	ECho EWes IBal NHol SIng WAbe
'Tetra Red'	CFwr CWrd ECho EPot EWes IBal ITim NHol NMen SIng WAbe WFar
'Tetra Rose' **new**	GEdr
'Tetra White'	see *R.* 'Helen'
thodiana	CStu CWrd ECho ERos EWes GEdr IBal NMen SBla SCnR SIng WAbe WFar
'Two Tone' **new**	EWes
'Venetia'	CMea ECho IBal SIng WAbe
'Westacre Picotee'	EWes
'White Prince'	IBal
'Wild Cherry Blossom'	CFwr EWes SIng

Rhodohypoxis x *Hypoxis* see x *Rhodoxis*
R. baurii x *H. parvula*   see x *Rhodoxis hybrida*

Rhodophiala (Amaryllidaceae)
§ *advena*	WCot
andicola	WCot
bagnoldii F&W 8695	WCot
§ *bifida*	CMon SCnR WCot
- *spathacea*	CMon
chilensis	WCot
elwesii	WCot
fulgens	WCot
mendocina BC&W 5028	CStu
pratensis	EBee
rhodolirion	WCot

Rhodora see *Rhododendron*

Rhodothamnus (Ericaceae)
chamaecistus   GCrs GIBF WAbe

Rhodotypos (Rosaceae)
kerrioides	see *R. scandens*
§ *scandens*	CBcs CPLG CPle CTri EBee EPfP EWTr GIBF IMGH MMHG MWea NLar SLon SSpi WCru WSHC WSPU

x *Rhodoxis* (Hypoxidaceae)
'Aurora'	EWes
'Bloodstone' **new**	EWes

'Hebron Farm Biscuit' — see *Hypoxis parvula* var. *albiflora* 'Hebron Farm Biscuit'
§ 'Hebron Farm Cerise' — CWrd ERos EWes GEdr NMen SIng SUsu
§ *hybrida* — CPne ECho EWes IBal NMen SIng WAbe
 - 'Aya San' — EWes SIng
§ - 'Hebron Farm Pink' — CBro CNic CWrd ECho ERos EWes GEdr IBal NMen SAga SBla SCnR SIng WAbe WFar
 - 'Hebron Farm Red Eye' — CWrd EWes GEdr SBla SCnR SIng WAbe WFar
 'Little Pink Pet' **new** — EWes

Rhoeo see *Tradescantia*

Rhopalostylis (Arecaceae)
baueri — CBrP LPal WMul
sapida — CBrP CKob CTrC LPal MPRe WMul
 - 'Chatham Island' — CBrP
 - 'East Cape' — SBig

rhubarb see *Rheum* x *hybridum*

Rhus (Anacardiaceae)
ambigua — CPIN EPfP
 - B&SWJ 3656 — WCru
§ *aromatica* — CAgr CArn EPfP NEgg NLar
chinensis — CDoC CMCN EPfP
copallina — ELan EPfP GIBF LRHS
coriaria — CArn EPfP NLar
cotinus — see *Cotinus coggygria*
glabra — CAgr CArn CBcs CDoC EPfP MGos SPer WDin
 - 'Laciniata' misapplied — see *R.* x *pulvinata* Autumn Lace Group
 - 'Laciniata' Carrière — NLar
glauca — EShb
N *hirta* — see *R. typhina*
incisa — SPlb
integrifolia — CArn LRav
magalismontana — EShb
potaninii — EPfP LRHS
§ x *pulvinata* Autumn Lace Group — CDoC EPfP MGos SDix SHBN WPat
 - - 'Red Autumn Lace' ♀H4 — LRHS MBlu MBri SPer
punjabensis — CBcs
§ *radicans* — CArn COld GPoy
toxicodendron — see *R. radicans*
trichocarpa — EPfP SSpi
trilobata — see *R. aromatica*
N *typhina* ♀H4 — CAgr CBcs CDoC CDul CHEx CLnd CTrG ECrN ELan ENot EPfP LRHS MAsh MBar MGos NBea NBlu NFor NWea SHBN SPer SPoG SSta WBrE WDin WFar WTel
§ - 'Dissecta' ♀H4 — CBcs CDoC CDul CLnd CSBt EBee ECrN ELan ENot EPfP LPan MAsh MBar MBri MGan MGos MWat MWgw NBea NBlu NEgg SEND SPer SPoG WDin WFar WMul WOrn WTel
 - 'Laciniata' hort. — see *R. typhina* 'Dissecta'
 - Tiger Eyes = 'Bailtiger' — ENot LBuc LRHS MAsh MGos NSti
 new — SCoo SPoG
§ *verniciflua* — CLnd CMCN NLar SSpi

Rhynchelytrum see *Melinis*

Rhynchospora (Cyperaceae)
§ *colorata* — CRow CStu NOak NPer SHom WHal
latifolia — CKno

Ribes ✿ (Grossulariaceae)
alpinum — CAgr CPLG LBuc MRav MWht NSti NWea SPer SRms WDin WGwG
 - 'Aureum' — CMHG EHoe NFor WCot WDin WSHC
 - 'Schmidt' — LBuc MBar
americanum 'Variegatum' (v) — EHoe ELan EPla MAsh MRav NHol SPer WPat
aureum misapplied — see *R. odoratum*
* - 'Roxby Red' — MCoo
 'Ben Hope' PBR (B) — CAgr EMui MAsh
 'Black Velvet' (D) — CAgr MCoo MGan
§ x *culverwellii* jostaberry (F) — CAgr CWib EMui GTwe LBuc LEdu MAsh SDea SPoG
§ *divaricatum* — CAgr LEdu
 - 'Worcesterberry' — see *R.* 'Worcesterberry'
gayanum — CBcs CPMA NLar SLPl
x *gordonianum* — More than 30 suppliers
himalense GWJ 9331 **new** — WCru
jostaberry — see *R.* x *culverwellii* jostaberry
latifolium — CPLG
laurifolium — CBcs CDul CPLG ELan NLar SBrw SPer WBor WCru WDin WHCG WSHC
 - (f) — CPMA EPfP
 - (m) — CHar CPMA EPfP WPat
 - 'Mrs Amy Doncaster' — EPla
 - Rosemoor form — CSam EPfP SBrw SPoG SSpi WCot WHCG WPGP
lobbii — EWes
menziesii **new** — CHll
nigrum **new** — SEND
 - 'Baldwin' (B) — CDoC CMac CTri CWSG EPfP LRHS SDea SKee SPoG
 - 'Barchatnaja' (B) — CAgr
 - 'Ben Alder' PBR (B) — CAgr CWib LRHS MAsh SDea
 - 'Ben Connan' PBR (B) ♀H4 — CAgr CCVT CDoC COtt CWib EMui EPfP ERea GTwe LRHS MAsh MBri MGos SCoo SDea SKee SPer SPoG
 - 'Ben Gairn' PBR (B) **new** — CAgr
 - 'Ben Lomond' PBR (B) ♀H4 — CAgr CSBt CTri CWib EMui ENot GTwe LAst LBuc LRHS MAsh MGos MRav SDea SKee SPer
 - 'Ben Loyal' (B) — GTwe
 - 'Ben More' (B) — CAgr CSBt CWib GTwe MBri MGan SDea
 - 'Ben Nevis' (B) — CAgr CSBt CTri CWib GTwe MAsh SDea SKee
 - 'Ben Sarek' PBR (B) ♀H4 — CAgr CDoC CSBt CSut CTri CWSG CWib EMui ENot GTwe LBuc LRHS MAsh MGos MNHC MRav SDea SKee SPer SPoG WOrn
 - 'Ben Tirran' PBR (B) — CAgr CDoC CWib ERea LBuc LRHS MAsh MBri MGos SKee SPoG WOrn
 - 'Black Reward' (B) — CAgr MCoo
 - 'Boskoop Giant' (B) — CAgr GTwe MGan SPer
* - 'Byelorussian Sweet' (B) — CAgr
 - 'Consort' (B) — CAgr
 - 'Daniel's September' (B) — GTwe
 - 'Goliath' **new** — MCoo
* - 'Hystawneznaya' (B) — CAgr
 - 'Jet' (B) — CAgr ENot GTwe SPer
* - 'Kosmicheskaya' (B) — CAgr
 - 'Laxton's Giant' (B) — GTwe
 - 'Mendip Cross' (B) — GTwe MGan
 - 'Pilot Alexander Mamkin' (B) — CAgr
 - 'Seabrook's' (B) — CAgr MGan
 - 'Titania' (B) **new** — EMui LRHS
 - 'Tsema' (B) **new** — MCoo
 - 'Wellington XXX' (B) — CAgr CSBt CTri GTwe LBuc MGan NBlu SPer
 - 'Westwick Choice' (B) — GTwe

§ **odoratum** — More than 30 suppliers
- 'Crandall' — CAgr LEdu
praecox — CBcs SEND
rubrum 'Bar-le-Duc' **new** — MCoo
- 'Blanka' (W) — CSut
- 'Cascade' (R) — CAgr
- 'Cherry' (R) — CAgr MCoo
- 'Fay' **new** — MCoo
- 'Fay's New Prolific' (R) — GTwe
- 'Hollande Rose' (P) — GTwe
- 'Jonkheer van Tets' (R) — CAgr CSBt CWSG CWib EMui EPfP
    ♀H4 — GTwe IArd LRHS MAsh MCoo
    NLar SDea SKee SPer
- 'Junifer' (R) — CAgr EMui GTwe LRHS SKee
- 'Laxton's Number One' — CAgr CTri EMui ENot GTwe MGan
    (R) — MRav SDea SPer
- 'Laxton's Perfection' (R) — MCoo
- 'October Currant' (P) — GTwe
- 'Raby Castle' (R) — GTwe
- 'Red Lake' (R) ♀H4 — CAgr CMac CWSG CWib EPfP
    ERea GTwe LBuc LRHS MGan
    MGos MNHC NBlu SDea SKee
    SPoG WOrn
- 'Redpoll' **new** — SKee
- 'Redstart'PBR (R) — CAgr COtt CSBt CWib GTwe LBuc
    MAsh MBri SDea SKee SPoG
- 'Rondom' (R) — CAgr SDea
- 'Rovada' (R) — CAgr CSut CWib EMui ERea GTwe
    MAsh SKee
- 'Stanza' (R) ♀H4 — CAgr GTwe SDea
- 'Transparent' (W) — GTwe
§ - 'Versailles Blanche' (W) — CAgr CMac CSBt CTri CWib EMui
    ENot EPfP GTwe LBuc MAsh MBri
    MGan MGos SDea SKee SPer SPoG
    WOrn
- 'White Dutch' (W) — MCoo
- 'White Grape' (W) ♀H4 — GTwe
- 'White Pearl' (W) — CBcs MCoo SDea
- White Versailles — see *R. rubrum* 'Versailles Blanche'
- 'Wilson's Long Bunch' (R) — GTwe
sanguineum — CDul MBar NEgg WFar WMoo
I - 'Atrorubens Select' — MBri
- 'Brocklebankii' — CAbP CPLG ELan EPfP EPla LRHS
    MAsh MGos MRav NPri NSti SHBN
    SLim SLon SPer SPla WEas WSHC
- 'Elkington's White' — SLon
- 'Jooii' **new** — MAsh
- 'King Edward VII' — More than 30 suppliers
- 'Koja' — GBin LRHS MAsh MBri MGos SPoG
- 'Lombartsii' — MRav
- 'Poky's Pink' — GSki MGos MRav SPoG WOVN
- 'Pulborough Scarlet' ♀H4 — More than 30 suppliers
- 'Red Pimpernel' — CDoC CSBt EBee LSRN MAsh
    MBNS NCGa SCoo SWvt WFar
- 'Taff's Kim' (v) — EPla SLon SMad
- 'Tydeman's White' — CDul CPLG CSBt ELan EPfP MBar
    NLar NPri SDnm SSpi WPat
- var. **variegata** — WFar
- White Icicle = 'Ubric' — More than 30 suppliers
    ♀H4
speciosum ♀H3 — More than 30 suppliers
trilobum — LEdu
uva-crispa 'Achilles' — GTwe
    (C/D)
- 'Admiral Beattie' (F) — GTwe
- 'Annelii' — CAgr SDea
- 'Bedford Red' (D) — GTwe
- 'Bedford Yellow' (D) — GTwe
- 'Beech Tree Nestling' (F) — GTwe
- 'Blucher' (D) — GTwe
- 'Bright Venus' (D) — GTwe
- 'Broom Girl' (D) — GTwe
- 'Captivator' (F) — GTwe SDea
- 'Careless' (C) ♀H4 — CMac CSBt EMui ENot GTwe LRHS
    MAsh MBri MGan MGos MRav
    SDea SKee SPer SPoG

- 'Catherine' — SDea
- 'Champagne Red' (F) — GTwe
- 'Cook's Eagle' (C) — GTwe
- 'Cousen's Seedling' (F) — GTwe
- 'Criterion' (C) — GTwe
- 'Crown Bob' (C/D) — GTwe MGan
- 'Dan's Mistake' (C) — GTwe
- 'Drill' (F) — GTwe
- 'Early Sulphur' (D/C) — GTwe SDea
- 'Firbob' (D) — GTwe
- 'Forester' (D) — GTwe
- 'Freedom' (C) — GTwe
- 'Gipsey Queen' (F) — GTwe
- 'Glenton Green' (D) — GTwe
- 'Golden Ball' (D) — SDea
- 'Golden Drop' (D) — GTwe
- 'Green Gem' (C/D) — GTwe
- 'Green Ocean' (F) — GTwe
- 'Greenfinch'PBR (F) ♀H4 — CAgr EMui GTwe SDea
- 'Gretna Green' (F) — GTwe
- 'Guido' (F) — GTwe
- 'Gunner' (D) — GTwe
- 'Heart of Oak' (F) — GTwe
- 'Hebburn Prolific' (D) — GTwe
- 'Hedgehog' (D) — GTwe
- 'Hero of the Nile' (C) — GTwe
- 'High Sheriff' (D) — GTwe
- 'Hinnonmäki' (C) — CAgr
- 'Hinnonmäki Gul' — CAgr ENot SDea
- 'Hinnonmäki Röd' (F) — CAgr ENot GTwe MCoo SDea
    SPoG
- 'Howard's Lancer' (C/D) — GTwe SDea
- 'Invicta'PBR (C) ♀H4 — CAgr CDoC CMac CSBt CSut CTri
    CWSG EMui ENot EPfP LBuc LRHS
    MAsh MBri MGan MGos MNHC
    SCoo SDea SKee SPer SPoG WBVN
    WOrn
- 'Ironmonger' (D) — GTwe
- 'Jubilee' (C/D) — COtt LBuc MBri MGos
- 'Keen's Seedling' (C) — GTwe
- 'Keepsake' (C/D) — GTwe MRav SDea WBVN
- 'King of Trumps' (F) — GTwe
- 'Lancashire Lad' (C/D) — GTwe MGan
- 'Langley Gage' (F) — GTwe MCoo
- 'Laxton's Amber' (D) — GTwe
- 'Leveller' (D) ♀H4 — CMac CSBt CSut CTri EMui ENot
    GTwe LAst LBuc LRHS MAsh
    MGan MGos MRav SDea SKee SPer
- 'London' (C/D) — GTwe
- 'Lord Derby' (C/D) — GTwe
- 'Martlet' (F) — CAgr GTwe
- 'May Duke' (C/D) — SDea
- 'Mitre' (C) — GTwe
- 'Pax'PBR (F) — CAgr CDoC CSBt EMui EPfP GTwe
    LBuc LRHS MAsh MBri SDea SKee
    SPoG WOrn
- 'Peru' (F) — GTwe
- 'Pitmaston Green Gage' — GTwe
    (D)
- 'Plunder' (F) — GTwe
- 'Prince Charles' (F) — GTwe
- 'Queen of Trumps' (D) — GTwe
- var. **reclinatum** — see *R. uva-crispa* 'Warrington'
    'Aston Red'
- 'Rifleman' (D) — GTwe
- 'Rokula'PBR (D) — CDoC EMui GTwe SDea SKee
- 'Rosebery' (D) — GTwe
- 'Scotch Red Rough' — GTwe
- 'Scottish Chieftan' (D) — GTwe
- 'Snow' (F) **new** — EPfP SCoo SLim
- 'Snowdrop' (D) — GTwe
- 'Spinefree' (F) — GTwe
- 'Surprise' (C) — GTwe
- 'Telegraph' (C) — GTwe
- 'Tom Joiner' (F) — GTwe
- 'Victoria' (C/D) — GTwe

§ - 'Warrington' (D) — GTwe
- 'Whinham's Industry' (C/D) ♀H4 — CMac CSBt CSut CTri EMui ENot GTwe LAst LBuc LRHS MAsh MBri MGos MRav SDea SPer SPoG WBVN
- 'White Lion' (C/D) — GTwe
- 'White Transparent' (C) — GTwe
- 'Whitesmith' (C/D) — GTwe MGan NBlu SDea
- 'Woodpecker' (D) — GTwe
- 'Yellow Champagne' (D) — GTwe
viburnifolium — CBcs CSam LEdu NLar
§ 'Worcesterberry' (F) — EMui MGos SDea SPer

Richea (*Epacridaceae*)
dracophylla — GGar SAPC

Ricinocarpos (*Euphorbiaceae*)
pinifolius — ECou

Ricinus (*Euphorbiaceae*)
communis — SWal SYvo
- 'Carmencita' ♀H3 — CHEx LRav SGar
- 'Carmencita Pink' **new** — CHen
- 'Carmencita Red' **new** — CHen
- 'Gibsonii' — WMul
- 'Impala' — CSpe SYvo
- 'Zanzibariensis' — CHen EShb WMul

Riocreuxia (*Asclepiadaceae*)
torulosa — CPLG EShb SPlb

Robinia (*Papilionaceae*)
x *ambigua* — SSpi
fertilis — EBee
§ *hispida* — CDul CEnd CLnd CWib ECrN ELan EPfP EWTr MAsh MBlu SBLw SBrw SHBN SPer SPoG SSpi WDin WJas WOrn WSHC WSPU
- 'Macrophylla' — CEnd
- 'Rosea' misapplied — see *R. hispida*
- 'Rosea' ambig. — CBcs EBee LPan SBLw
kelseyi — CDul SPer
x *margaretta* Casque Rouge — see *R.* x *margaretta* 'Pink Cascade'
- 'Pink Cascade' — CDoC CDul CEnd CLnd EBee ECrN EPfP LAst LPan LRHS MAsh MBlu MBri MGos SBLw SBod SCoo SCrf SHBN SLim SLon SPer WDin WFoF WPGP
neomexicana — CLnd
pseudoacacia — CAgr CCVT CDul CLnd EBee ECrN ELan EPfP LBuc LPan LRav MCoo SBLw SPlb WBVN WDin WFar WNor
- 'Bessoniana' — EBee ECrN LAst SBLw
- 'Fastigiata' — see *R. pseudoacacia* 'Pyramidalis'
- 'Frisia' ♀H4 — More than 30 suppliers
- 'Inermis' hort. — see *R. pseudoacacia* 'Umbraculifera'
§ - 'Lace Lady'PBR — CWSG ELan ENot EPfP LPan LRHS MAsh MBri MGos MRav NLar SCoo SLim SPoG
- 'Myrtifolia' — SBLw
§ - 'Pyramidalis' — SBLw
- 'Rozynskiana' — CDul MAsh SFam
- 'Tortuosa' — CDul CEnd CLnd EBee ECrN ELan EMil EPfP LAst LPan LRHS MBlu MGos SBLw SPer WPGP
- 'Twisty Baby'PBR — see *R. pseudoacacia* 'Lace Lady'
§ - 'Umbraculifera' — CDul CLnd ECrN EMil LPan MBri MGos SBLw SFam
- 'Unifoliola' — SBLw
x *slavinii* 'Hillieri' ♀H4 — CDoC CDul CEnd CLnd EBee ECrN ELan EPfP EWTr LRHS LSRN MBlu MBri MGos MWat SCoo SCrf SPer SPoG WOrn WPGP

Rochea see *Crassula*

Rodgersia ✿ (*Saxifragaceae*)
ACE 2303 — GBuc
CLD 1329 — NHol
CLD 1432 — NHol
aesculifolia ♀H4 — More than 30 suppliers
- green bud — IBlr
- pink-flowered — IBlr SSpi
- 'Red Dawn' — IBlr
aff. *aesculifolia* petaloid — IBlr
'Blickfang' — IBlr
'Die Anmutige' — CRow
'Die Schöne' — CLAP EBee MSte NLar
'Elfenbeinturm' — IBlr
'Fireworks' — CFir EBee SPer
henrici — CBct CLAP CRow IBlr MBri NBro NMyG SWat WMoo WTin
- 'Buckshaw White' — IBlr
- 'Castlewellan' — IBlr
- hybrid — CAby EBee EWTr GBuc ITim NHol NLar WAul WHil
'Herkules' — CBct EBee GCal MBNS NBPC NBhm NLar SSpi WMul
'Ideal' — WCot
'Irish Bronze' ♀H4 — CLAP EBrs IBlr LRHS SSpi WCAu WFar WMoo WPnP
'Koriata' — IBlr
'Kupfermond' — CRow IBlr
'Maigrün' — IBlr
nepalensis — CLAP IBlr MDun
'Panache' — IBlr
'Parasol' — CBct CHad CLAP GBuc IBlr NHol SSpi WPGP WPnP
pinnata — More than 30 suppliers
- B&SWJ 7741A — WCru
- L 1670 — CLAP SSpi
- SDR 3301 — GKev
- from SW China — GIBF
- 'Alba' — EBee IBlr MLLN NHol WMAq WPnP
- 'Buckland Beauty' — CLAP IBlr SBla SSpi
- 'Cally Salmon' — EGle EWes GCal IBlr
- 'Chocolate Wing' **new** — IBal IPot MBNS NBhm NMoo
- 'Crûg Cardinal' — WCru
- 'Elegans' — CBct CHad EBee EBrs EChP ELan ENot EPfP EPla IBlr LAst LRHS MRav NEgg NHol NMyG NOrc SMad SPer SWvt WAul WCot WHil WPnP
- 'Jade Dragon Mountain' **new** — IBlr
- 'Maurice Mason' — EBee IBlr SDix SMHy
- 'Mont Blanc' — IBlr
- Mount Stewart form — IBlr
- 'Perthshire Bronze' — IBlr
- 'Rosea' — IBlr
- 'Superba' ♀H4 — More than 30 suppliers
- white-flowered — GAbr GCal
pinnata x *sambucifolia* — IBlr
podophylla ♀H4 — More than 30 suppliers
- 'Braunlaub' — EBee NBro WMoo WPnP
- 'Bronceblad' — IBlr
- Donard form — IBlr MBri WPGP
- 'Pagode' **new** — GBin
- 'Rotlaub' — CDes CLAP CRow EBee EGle IBlr LRHS WCot WMoo WPGP
- 'Smaragd' — CDes CLAP CRow EGle GCal IBlr LRHS NLar
purdomii hort. — CDes CLAP EBee GCal LRHS WCot WPGP
§ 'Reinecke Fuchs' — IBlr
'Rosenlicht' — CRow
'Rosenzipfel' — IBlr

sambucifolia	CBcs CDWL CLAP CRow EBee
	EBrs GBBs GKev GSki ITim LEdu
	MLHP NEgg NLar NSti SMac SPer
	WCAu WCru WFar WMoo WPnP
	WTin
- B&SWJ 7899	WCru
- dwarf pink-flowered	IBlr
- dwarf white-flowered	IBlr
- 'Mountain Select'	WFar
- white-flowered	ITim
tabularis	see *Astilboides tabularis*

Rohdea (Convallariaceae)

japonica	CHEx WCot WPGP
- B&SWJ 4853	WCru
- 'Godaishu' (v)	WCot
- 'Gunjaku' (v)	EMon WCot
- 'Lance Leaf'	EPla
- long-leaved	WCru WFar
- 'Miyakonojo' (v)	EBee WCot
- 'Talbot Manor' (v)	EBee EBla EPla WCot
- 'Tama-jishi' (v)	WCot
- 'Tuneshige Rokujo' (v)	WCot
watanabei	EBee
- B&SWJ 1911	WCru

Romanzoffia (Hydrophyllaceae)

§ ***californica***	NJOw
§ ***sitchensis***	CTri EBee MAvo NJOw
§ ***suksdorfii*** E. Greene	see *R. sitchensis*
tracyi	CDes CLAP EBee GGar NRya WBor
	WPrP
unalaschcensis	CLAP GKev NJOw NWCA SGar
	SRms WBVN WPer

Romneya (Papaveraceae)

coulteri ♀H4	More than 30 suppliers
§ - var. ***trichocalyx***	CFir CPLG SBrw WPGP
§ - 'White Cloud' ♀H4	EHol ENot SBrw SMad WPGP
x ***hybrida***	see *R. coulteri* 'White Cloud'
trichocalyx	see *R. coulteri* var. *trichocalyx*

Romulea (Iridaceae)

amoena 'Niewoodlville'	ECho
atrandra	CStu
autumnalis	CStu ECho
barkerae 'Paternoster'	ECho
battandieri	ECho
- AB&S 4659 from Morocco	CMon
bifrons AB&S 4359 from	CMon
Morocco	
bulbocodium	CBro CNic ECho
- var. ***clusiana***	CNic ECho
- - MS 239	EHyt
- - from Morocco	CMon
* - 'Knightshayes'	EHyt SCnR
- var. ***leichtliniana*** from	CMon
Crete	
camerooniana	CStu
campanuloides	EDif
columnae	ECho
- var. ***melitensis*** from	CMon
Malta	
dichotoma	ECho
engleri	CStu
- SF 3 from Morocco	CMon
gigantea	CDes CStu LBow
hirta	CMon
kamisensis	ECho
leipoldtii	ECho
ligustica var. ***rouyana***	CMon
SF 360 from Morocco	
linaresii	CNic EHyt
- CE&H 620 from Greece	CMon
* ***luteoflora*** var. ***sanguinea***	GCrs NMen
macowanii var. ***alticola***	WAbe
- var. ***macowanii***	CStu
monticola	CMon
namaquensis	ECho
nivalis	ECho EHyt
obscura var. ***blanda***	ECho
- var. ***obscura***	ECho
- var. ***subtestacea***	ECho
pearsonii	EHyt
ramiflora	CPBP CPLG ECho
- subsp. ***gaditana***	EHyt
requienii	CNic NMen
- L 65	EHyt
saldanhensis	CStu LBow
tortuosa	CPLG
* ***zahnii***	CNic

Rondeletia (Rubiaceae)

amoena	SOWG

Rorippa (Brassicaceae)

nasturtium-aquaticum	EMFW WMAq WWpP

Rosa ✿ (Rosaceae)

ACE 241	CFee
A Shropshire Lad =	CSam ESty LRHS LStr MAsh MAus
'Ausled'PBR (S)	MJon NEgg NSRo SPoc SWCr
Abbeyfield Rose =	ENot GCoc GGre MGan MRav SPer
'Cocbrose'PBR (HT)	
♀H4	
§ 'Abbotswood' (*canina*	MAus
hybrid)	
Abigaile =	MJon
'Tanelaigib'PBR (F)	
Abraham Darby =	CGro CTri EBee EPfP ESty EWTr
'Auscot'PBR (S)	LAst LRHS LStr MAsh MAus MFry
	MJon MRav MWgw NEgg SPer
	SPoc SSea SWCr WHCG
achburensis new	GIBF
acicularis	GIBF
'Adam Messerich' (Bb)	MAus SWCr WHCG
'Adélaïde d'Orléans' (Ra)	CRHN EBee EWTr LRHS MAus
♀H4	MRMR MRav NSRo SFam SPer
	SPoc SWCr WAct WHCG
Admirable = 'Searodney'	MJon
(Min)	
'Admiral Rodney' (HT)	MGan MJon
Adriana = 'Frydesire'	MBri MFry
(HT)	
Agatha Christie =	ENot MRav SPoc SWCr
'Kormeita'PBR (ClF)	
'Aglaia' (Ra)	MAus WHCG
'Agnes' (Ru) ♀H4	ECnt EPfP EWTr GCoc IArd LRHS
	MAsh MAus MGan MRav NLar SPer
	SPoc SSea SWCr WAct WHCG
	WOVN
'Aimée Vibert' (Ra)	CSam EBee MAus MRav NLar SPer
	SPoc SWCr WAct WHCG
'Alain Blanchard' (G)	MAus WHCG
§ x ***alba*** 'Alba Maxima' (A)	CBgR GCoc GGre LRHS MAsh
	MAus MRMR MRav NBPC NEgg
	NLar SFam SPer SSea SWCr WAct
	WHCG
§ - 'Alba Semiplena' (A) ♀H4	CHad LRHS MAus SPer SWCr WAct
	WHCG
- Celestial	see *R.* 'Céleste'
- 'Maxima'	see *R.* x *alba* 'Alba Maxima'
Alba Meidiland =	WOVN
'Meiflopan'PBR (S/GC)	
'Albéric Barbier' (Ra) ♀H4	More than 30 suppliers
'Albertine' (Ra) ♀H4	More than 30 suppliers
'Alchymist' (S/Cl)	CHad CPou EBee ENot EPfP LRHS
	MAsh MAus MBNS MGan MJon
	MRav SPer SPoc SWCr WAct
	WHCG WKif
Alec's Red = 'Cored' (HT)	CBcs CGro CSBt CTri CWSG ENot
	GCoc GGre LAst LRHS LStr MAsh

	MAus MGan MJon MRav NPri SPer SPoG SWCr
Alexander = 'Harlex' (HT) $\widetilde{Y}$H4	CGro CSBt ENot GCoc LGod LStr MAus MFry MGan MJon MRav SPer SPoc SSea SWCr
'Alexander von Humboldt' (Cl)	MGan
'Alexandre Girault' (Ra)	CRHN EBee EMFP LRHS MAsh MAus SPer SWCr WHCG
'Alfred de Dalmas' misapplied	see *R.* 'Mousseline'
'Alfresco'PBR (ClHT)	CSBt LGod MJon SPoc SSea SWCr
'Alida Lovett' (Ra)	MAus
Alison = 'Coclibee'PBR (F)	GCoc SPoc SWCr
§ 'Alister Stella Gray' (N)	EBee LRHS MAus MGan MRav NEgg SPer SSea SWCr WAct WHCG
'Allen Chandler' (ClHT)	MAus
'Allgold' (F)	CBcs CGro MGan
Alnwick Castle = 'Ausgrab'PBR (S)	MAus
alpina	see *R. pendulina*
'Alpine Sunset' (HT)	CTri ESty GGre MAsh MRav SPer SPoG SWCr
altaica misapplied	see *R. spinosissima* 'Grandiflora'
altaica Willd.	see *R. spinosissima*
Altissimo = 'Delmur' (Cl)	CHad EBee LRHS MAus MGan SPer SSea SWCr WAct
'Amadis' (Bs)	MAus MRMR WHCG
Amanda = 'Beesian' (F)	ESty MBri
'Amazing Grace' (HT)	GGre SWCr
Amber Abundance = 'Harfizz'PBR (S)	ESty LRHS MAsh SPoc SWCr
Amber Cover = 'Poulbambe'PBR (GC)	ECnt ESty MAsh SWCr
Amber Hit = 'Poultrav'PBR (Patio)	SPoc
Amber Nectar = 'Mehamber'PBR (F)	MAsh MJon SWCr
Amber Queen = 'Harroony'PBR (F) $\widetilde{Y}$H4	CGro CSBt CTri EPfP ESty GCoc GGre IArd LAst LGod LStr MAsh MAus MBri MFry MGan MJon MRav NPri SPer SPoG SPoc SWCr
Amber Star = 'Manstar' (Min)	MJon
Amber Sunset = 'Manamsun' (Min)	MJon
amblyotis	GIBF
Ambridge Rose = 'Auswonder' (S)	LRHS MAus MJon NEgg SPer
'Amélia'	see *R.* 'Celsiana'
Amelia = 'Poulen011'PBR (S)	ECnt MAsh SWCr
'American Pillar' (Ra)	CGro CRHN CSBt CSam CTri CWSG EBee ECnt ELan ENot LRHS LStr MAsh MAus MGan MRav SPer SPoG SPoc SSea SWCr WHCG
'Amy Robsart' (RH)	MAus
'Anaïs Ségalas' (G)	MAus
§ 'Andersonii' (*canina* hybrid)	ISea MAus WAct
'Andrea' (ClMin)	MJon
§ *anemoniflora*	MAus
anemoniflora	see *R. x beanii*
anemonoides	see *R.* 'Anemone'
'Angel Gates'	WAct
Angela Rippon = 'Ocaru' (Min)	CSBt MFry MJon SPer SWCr
'Angela's Choice' (F)	MGan SWCr
Anisley Dickson = 'Dickimono'PBR (F) $\widetilde{Y}$H4	IDic LGod MGan SPer
'Ann Aberconway' (F)	MJon
Ann = 'Ausfete'PBR	LRHS MAus

Ann Henderson = 'Fryhoncho' (F)	MFry
Anna Ford = 'Harpiccolo'PBR (Min/Patio) $\widetilde{Y}$H4	CWSG LStr MAus MGan SPer SWCr
Anna Livia = 'Kormetter'PBR (F) $\widetilde{Y}$H4	ECnt ENot GGre MBri MGan MJon MRav
Anne Boleyn = 'Ausecret'PBR (S)	LRHS MAus MJon NEgg SPoc SWCr
'Anne Cocker' (F)	GCoc
'Anne Dakin' (ClHT)	MAus
Anne Harkness = 'Harkaramel' (F)	MAus MGan SPer
'Anne of Geierstein' (RH)	MAus MGan
Annick = 'Fryfrenzy' (F)	MFry
Antique '89 = 'Kordalen'PBR (ClF)	ENot MJon MRav WGer
Aperitif = 'Macwaira'PBR (HT)	ECnt GCoc MJon
apothecary's rose	see *R. gallica* var. *officinalis*
'Apple Blossom' (Ra)	SSea WHCG
Apricot Ice = 'Diceyti'PBR (Poly/F)	IDic
'Apricot Nectar' (F)	MAus MGan SPer
'Apricot Silk' (HT)	CBcs CTri LAst MAus MGan MRav SPer SWCr
Apricot Summer = 'Korpapiro'PBR (Patio)	ENot MBri MJon
Apricot Sunblaze = 'Savamark' (Min)	CSBt
Arc Angel = 'Fryorst' (HT)	MFry
'Archiduc Joseph' misapplied	see *R.* 'Général Schablikine'
Ards Beauty = 'Dicjoy' (F)	SPer
'Arethusa' (Ch)	EBee SPla
'Arizona Sunset' (Min)	MJon
§ *arkansana* var. *suffulta*	GIBF WHCG
Armada = 'Haruseful' (S)	SSea
'Arrillaga' (HP)	MAus
'Arthur Bell' (F) $\widetilde{Y}$H4	CGro CSBt CWSG ENot EPfP ESty GGre IArd LAst LRHS LStr MAsh MAus MGan MRav NPri SPer SPoG SPoc SSea SWCr WBVN
'Arthur de Sansal' (DPo)	MAus MGan WHCG
arvensis	CCVT CRWN LBuc MAus NHaw NWea WAct
'Assemblage des Beautés' (G)	MAus
'Astra Desmond' (Ra)	WTin
Atco Royale = 'Frywinner'PBR (F)	MFry
Atlantic Star = 'Fryworld'PBR (F)	MFry
Audrey Wilcox = 'Frywilrey' (HT)	CSBt MFry
'Auguste Gervais' (Ra)	LRHS MAus SPer WHCG
Austrian copper rose	see *R. foetida* 'Bicolor'
Austrian yellow	see *R. foetida*
'Autumn Delight' (HM)	MAus WHCG
Autumn Fire	see *R.* 'Herbstfeuer'
'Autumn Sunlight' (ClF)	MGan SPer SPoc
'Autumn Sunset' (S)	MJon
'Autumnalis'	see *R.* 'Princesse de Nassau'
'Aviateur Blériot' (Ra)	MAus
'Avignon' (F)	ECnt
Avon = 'Poulmulti'PBR (GC) $\widetilde{Y}$H4	EBee ECnt ELan GCoc LGod MGan MJon MRav NPri SPer SSea SWCr WHCG
Awakening = 'Probuzeni' (Cl)	EBee SWCr WHCG
Awareness = 'Frybingo'PBR (HT)	MFry
'Ayrshire Splendens'	see *R.* 'Splendens'
'Baby Bio' (F/Patio)	CBcs ESty SWCr
'Baby Darling' (Min)	MGan SWCr

'Baby Faurax' (Poly) — MAus
Baby Gold Star (Min) — see R. 'Estrellita de Oro'
Baby Love = 'Scrivluv'^{PBR} (yellow) (Min/Patio) ♀H4 — MAus MJon
Baby Masquerade = 'Tanba' (Min) — MGan MJon SPer SWCr
Babyface = 'Rawril'^{PBR} (Min) — ESty
'Bad Neuenahr' (Cl) — MGan
'Ballerina' (HM/Poly) ♀H4 — More than 30 suppliers
Ballindalloch Castle = 'Cocneel'^{PBR} (F) — GCoc
'Baltimore Belle' (Ra) — CRHN MAus WHCG
banksiae (Ra) — CPIN CPou GQui SRms
- SF 96051 — ISea
- *alba* — see R. banksiae var. banksiae
§ - var. *banksiae* (Ra/d) — CPou CSBt CTri EBee ELan EPfP ERea LPan LStr MAus MRMR SBra WGer XPep
- 'Lutea' (Ra/d) ♀H3 — More than 30 suppliers
- 'Lutescens' (Ra) — MRMR XPep
- var. *normalis* (Ra) — CSBt LRHS MAus NSti SLon SWCr WCot WHer WOut XPep
I - 'Rosea' **new** — NLar
'Bantry Bay' (ClHT) — CSBt EBee ELan ENot LStr MGan MRav NBlu SPer SPla SPoc SSea SWCr
Barbara Austin = 'Austop'^{PBR} (S) — LRHS MAus
Barkarole = 'Tanelorak'^{PBR} (HT) — CSBt LStr
'Baron de Wassenaer' (CeMo) — MGan
'Baron Girod de l'Ain' (HP) — EBee MAus MRav NBPC NEgg NHaw SPla SPoG SPoc SWCr WAct WGer WHCG
'Baroness Rothschild' (HP) — see R. 'Baronne Adolph de Rothschild'
§ 'Baronne Adolph de Rothschild' (HP) — EBee MGan MRav NBPC SPoc SWCr WHCG
Baronne Edmond de Rothschild = 'Meigriso' (HT) — MAus MGan WAct
Baronne Edmond de Rothschild, Climbing = 'Meigrisosar' (Cl/HT) — CSBt
'Baronne Prévost' (HP) — MAus SFam WHCG
§ x *beanii* (Ra) — EPla
'Beau Narcisse' (G) — MAus
'Beauté' (HT) — MGan
Beautiful Britain = 'Dicfire'^{PBR} (F) — CWSG IDic LStr MGan MRav SWCr
Beautiful Sunrise = 'Bostimebide'^{PBR} (Cl/Patio) — ESty MBri MJon SPoc SWCr
Beauty Star^{PBR} — see R. Liverpool Remembers
Behold = 'Savahold' (Min) — MJon
'Bel Ange' (HT) — MGan SWCr
bella — LRHS
Bella = 'Pouljill'^{PBR} (S) — CPou EPfP MAsh SPoG SWCr
'Belle Amour' (AxD) — MAus WAct WHCG
'Belle Blonde' (HT) — MGan SPer
'Belle de Crécy' (G) ♀H4 — CPou CSam LRHS LStr MAsh MAus NPri SFam SPer SPoG SWCr WAct WHCG
'Belle des Jardins' misapplied — see Rosa x centifolia 'Unique Panachée'
Belle Epoque = 'Fryyaboo'^{PBR} (HT) — GCoc LStr MFry MGan MJon SPoc SWCr
'Belle Isis' (G) — MAus MRav SPer
'Belle Poitevine' (Ru) — MAus
'Belle Portugaise' (ClT) — EHol MAus
§ 'Belvedere' (Ra) — MAus MBri SPer WHCG
Benita = 'Dicquarrel'^{PBR} (HT) — IDic

Benjamin Britten = 'Ausencart'^{PBR} (S) — CSBt ECnt EPfP MAsh MAus MJon NEgg SWCr
§ 'Bennett's Seedling' (Ra) — SSea
Benson and Hedges Gold = 'Macgem' (HT) — CWSG
Benson and Hedges Special = 'Macshana'^{PBR} (Min) — ELan ESty GGre MJon
Berkshire = 'Korpinka'^{PBR} (GC) ♀H4 — ENot LStr MGan MJon MRav SSea SWCr
Best of Friends = 'Pouldunk'^{PBR} (HT) — ECnt
Best Wishes = 'Chessnut'^{PBR} (Cl/v) — COtt SPoG SPoc SWCr
Bettina = 'Mepal' (HT) — MGan
Betty Boop = 'Wekplapic'^{PBR} (F) — GCoc MJon SPoc SWCr
Betty Driver = 'Gandri'^{PBR} (F) — MGan SPer
Betty Harkness = 'Harette'^{PBR} (F) — GCoc GGre LStr MJon
'Betty Prior' (F) — GCoc MGan
§ Bewitched = 'Poulbella'^{PBR} (F) — ECnt EPfP MAsh SPoc SWCr
Bianco = 'Cocblanco'^{PBR} (Patio/Min) — GCoc GGre MAus SPoG SWCr
Biddulph Grange = 'Frydarkeye' (S) — MFry
'Big Chief' (HT) — MJon
Big Purple = 'Stebigpu'^{PBR} (HT) — ECnt MJon
Birthday Girl = 'Meilasso'^{PBR} (F) — ESty LAst MJon MRav SPoc SSea SWCr
Birthday Wishes = 'Guesdelay' (HT) — LRHS MAsh SPoG SWCr
Bishop Elphinstone = 'Cocjolly' (F) — GCoc
'Black Beauty' (HT) — MAus MJon
'Black Ice' (F) — CGro MGan SWCr
'Black Jack' (Ce) — see R. 'Tour de Malakoff'
Black Jade = 'Benblack' (Min/Patio) — MJon
'Blairii Number Two' (ClBb) ♀H4 — LRHS MAus MRav NBPC NEgg SFam SPer SPoc SWCr WAct WHCG
'Blanche de Vibert' (DPo) — EBee MAus
'Blanche Double de Coubert' (Ru) ♀H4 — CDul CSam EBee ECnt ELan EPfP GCoc LBuc LSRN LStr MAus MFry MGan MJon MWgw SFam SPer SSea SWCr WAct WEas WHCG WOVN
'Blanche Moreau' (CeMo) — EWTr MAus MGan NHaw NLar SPer WAct
'Blanchefleur' (CexG) — MAus MRav WAct
'Blessings' (HT) ♀H4 — CBcs CGro CSBt ENot GGre LAst LStr MAsh MAus MFry MGan MJon MRav NBlu SPer SPoc SWCr
'Bleu Magenta' (Ra) ♀H4 — EWTr IArd MAus MRMR MRav NBPC SPoc SWCr WAct WHCG WKif
'Blonde Bombshell' (F) — ESty
'Bloomfield Abundance' (Poly) — CPou MAus MGan MRav SPer SWCr WAct WHCG WHer
Blooming Marvellous (Patio) — GGre
'Blossomtime' (Cl) — SMad SPer
'Blue Diamond' (HT) — MGan SWCr
Blue Moon = 'Tannacht' (HT) — CGro CTri ELan EPfP GCoc GGre LAst LGod LRHS MAsh MGan MJon NPri SPer SPoG SSea SWCr
Blue Peter = 'Ruiblun'^{PBR} (Min) — ESty MFry MJon
'Blush Damask' (D) — WHCG
'Blush Hip' (A) — MAus
'Blush Noisette' — see R. 'Noisette Carnée'

'Blush Rambler' (Ra) — CSBt MAus SPer SPla SSea SWCr WHCG

'Blushing Lucy' (Ra) — MTPN SMrm WAct WHCG

Blythe Spirit = 'Auschool'PBR (S) — LRHS LStr MAus MBNS NEgg

Bob Greaves = 'Fryzippy' (F) — MFry

'Bobbie James' (Ra) ♀H4 — CHad CPLG EBee EWTr LRHS LStr MAus MFry MGan MJon MRav NEgg NLar NSRo SPer SPoc SSea SWCr WAct WBVN WHCG

'Bobby Charlton' (HT) — MFry SSea

'Bobolink' (Min) — SWCr

Bonbon Hit = 'Poulbon'PBR (Patio) — SPoc

Bonica = 'Meidomonac'PBR (GC) ♀H4 — CBrm CSam CTri EBee ECnt ELan EPfP ESty GCoc LGod LRHS LStr MAsh MAus MFry MGan MJon MRMR MRav MWgw NPri NSRo SPer SPoG SSea SWCr WAct WBor WHCG WOVN

Bonita = 'Poulen009'PBR (S) — ECnt MAsh SWCr

'Bonn' (HM/S) — CBcs

'Bonnie Scotland' (HT) — MGan SWCr

Boogie-Woogie = 'Poulyc006' (Cl) — ECnt LRHS MAsh SPoG SWCr

'Bottanix' (F) — MGan

'Botzaris' (D) — SFam

'Boule de Neige' (Bb) — CBcs CGro EBee ECnt ELan ENot EPfP GCoc LRHS LStr MAsh MAus MRMR MRav SFam SPer SPla SWCr WAct WHCG WOVN

'Bouquet d'Or' (N) — MAus MRMR SWCr

'Bouquet Tout Fait' misapplied — see R. 'Nastarana'

'Bouquet Tout Fait' (N) — WHCG

'Bourbon Queen' (Bb) — MAus SWCr WHCG

Bow Bells = 'Ausbells' (S) — MAus

Bowled Over = 'Tandolgnil'PBR (F) — ESty SCoo SPoc SWCr

Boy O Boy = 'Dicuniform'PBR (GC) — IDic

Boys' Brigade = 'Cocdinkum' (Patio) — GCoc

§ **bracteata** — CHll CRHN EHol GQui MAus WHCG

Brass RingPBR — see R. Peek-a-boo

Brave Heart = 'Horbondsmile' (F) — GGre LRHS MAsh MAus MBri MRav SCoo SPoG SWCr

Breath of Life = 'Harquanne'PBR (ClHT) — CGro CSBt CTri CWSG ELan EPfP GGre LGod LRHS LStr MAus MBri MFry MGan MJon MRav NBPC SPer SPoG SPoc SSea SWCr

Breathtaking = 'Hargalore'PBR (HT) — ESty SPoc SWCr

Bredon = 'Ausbred' (S) — MAus MBri

'Brenda Colvin' (Ra) — ISea MAus

Bride = 'Fryyearn'PBR (HT) — ESty GCoc LStr MFry SWCr

Bridge of Sighs = 'Harglowing'PBR (Cl) — EBee ECnt GGre LStr MBri MJon SPoG SPoc SWCr

Bright Cover = 'Poultw003' — ECnt

Bright Day = 'Chewvermillion' (Min) (Cl) — ESty SPoc SWCr

Bright Fire = 'Peaxi'PBR (Cl) — MJon SSea SWCr

Bright Smile = 'Dicdance'PBR (F/Patio) — IDic MAus MFry MGan MRav SPer SSea

Brilliant Pink Iceberg = 'Probril' (F) — ECnt LStr MFry SWCr

'Brindis' (ClF) — MGan SWCr

Britannia = 'Frycalm'PBR (HT) — ECnt ESty LRHS MAsh MFry MJon SPoc SWCr

Broadlands = 'Tanmirsch'PBR (GC) — CTri LGod MGan MRav NLar SPoc SWCr

Brother Cadfael = 'Ausglobe'PBR (S) — EBee LRHS LStr MAus MBri MJon SPer SSea SWCr

Brown Velvet = 'Maccultra'PBR (F) — ESty MJon SPoc SWCr

§ **brunonii** (Ra) — CDoC CPLG CPlN EWes MAus WCot

- 'Betty Sherriff' (Ra) — CDoC GGar

§ - 'La Mortola' (Ra) — EBee MAus MRav SPer SPoc SWCr

Bubbles = 'Frybubbly'PBR (GC) — MFry

Buck's Fizz = 'Poulgav'PBR (F) — MGan SWCr

'Buff Beauty' (HM) ♀H4 — CHad CSBt CSam CWSG EBee ECnt ENot EPfP EWTr GCoc LRHS LStr MAsh MAus MFry MGan MJon MRav MWgw NEgg NPri SFam SMad SPer SSea SWCr WAct WHCG WOVN XPep

'Bullata' — see R. x centifolia 'Bullata'

§ 'Burgundiaca' (G) — LRHS MAus SSea WAct

Burgundian rose — see R. 'Burgundiaca'

Burgundy Ice = 'Prose' (F) **new** — ESty MFry

'Burma Star' (F) — MGan

burnet, double pink — see R. spinosissima double pink

burnet, double white — see R. spinosissima double white

Bush Baby = 'Peanob'PBR (Min) — LGod LStr SPer SPoc SWCr

Buttercup = 'Ausband'PBR (S) — LRHS MAsh MAus

Buxom Beauty = 'Korbilant'PBR (HT) — EBee ECnt ENot ESty GCoc LRHS MAsh MJon NPri SCoo SPoG SWCr

'C.F. Meyer' — see R. 'Conrad Ferdinand Meyer'

§ **caesia** subsp. **glauca** — SPoc

californica (S) — GIBF MAus

- 'Plena' — see R. nutkana 'Plena'

Calliope = 'Harfracas'PBR (F) — SWCr

'Callisto' (HM) — MAus SWCr WHCG

CalypsoPBR — see Rosa Concert

'Camayeux' (G) — CPou EWTr MAus SPer WAct WHCG

Cambridgeshire = 'Korhaugen'PBR (GC) — LAst LGod LStr MAus MRav NPri SPer SSea SWCr

'Camélia Rose' (Ch) — WHCG

'Cameo' (Poly) — MAus MGan

Camille Pisarro = 'Destricol' (F) — CBgR SPoc SWCr

'Canary Bird' — see R. xanthina 'Canary Bird'

Candle in the Wind = 'Mackincat'PBR (S) — MJon

'Candy Stripe' (HT) **new** — NBlu

canina (S) — CArn CCVT CDul CGro CLnd CRWN CTri EPfP LBuc MAus MRav NPri NWea WMou XPep

- 'Abbotswood' — see R. 'Abbotswood'

- 'Andersonii' — see R. 'Andersonii'

'Cantabrigiensis' (S) ♀H4 — CSam EBee EWTr MAus SFam SPer SPoc SSea SWCr WAct WFar WHCG

Canterbury = 'Ausbury' (S) — MAus

'Capitaine Basroger' (CeMo) — MAus

'Capitaine John Ingram' (CeMo) ♀H4 — EWTr MAus SPer SSea WHCG

'Captain Christy' (ClHT) — see R. 'Climbing Captain Christy'

Caramella = 'Korkinteral'PBR **new** — ENot

'Cardinal de Richelieu' (G) ♀H4 — CPou CSam EBee EPfP EWTr GCoc LAst LRHS LStr MAsh MAus MDun MGan MRMR MRav NEgg SFam SPer SPoG SPoc SWCr WAct WHCG

Cardinal Hume = 'Harregale' (S) — MGan SPer SWCr

Carefree Days = 'Meirivouri' (Patio) — ENot GGre MAsh SPoG SWCr

§ Carefree Wonder = 'Meipitac' (S) — LAst

Caribbean Dawn = 'Korfeining'[PBR] (Patio) — ENot

Caring for You = 'Coclust'[PBR] (HT) — GCoc GGre SWCr

§ 'Carmenetta' (S) — MAus NHaw WAct

'Carol' (Gn) — see R. 'Carol Amling'

'Carol Amling' (Gn) — MJon

carolina — GIBF LHop NHaw SLPl WHCG

Caroline de Monaco = 'Meipierar' (HT) — MJon

'Caroline Testout' — see R. 'Madame Caroline Testout'

Cascade = 'Poulskab'[PBR] (Min/Cl) — ECnt

Casino = 'Macca' (ClHT) — CTri EWTr GCoc GGre MAsh MFry MGan MJon MRav SPer SPoG SWCr

'Castle Apricot'[PBR] — see R. Lazy Days

'Castle Cream' — see R. Perfect Day

'Castle Fuchsia Pink'[PBR] — see R. Bewitched = 'Poulbella'

'Castle Lilac'[PBR] — see R. Lambert Castle

Castle of Mey = 'Coclucid' (F) — GCoc

'Castle Peach'[PBR] — see R. Imagination = 'Pouldron'

'Castle Red'[PBR] — see R. Krönberg

'Castle Shrimp Pink'[PBR] — see R. Fascination = 'Poulmax'

'Castle White'[PBR] — see R. Ledreborg

'Castle Yellow'[PBR] — see R. Summer Gold

Catherine Cookson = 'Noscook' (HT) — MJon

§ 'Catherine Mermet' (T) — MAus

§ 'Cécile Brünner' (Poly) ♀H4 — CTri EBee ECnt ELan ENot GCoc LStr MAus MGan MRav NLar SMad SPer SPla SPoc SSea SWCr WAct WHCG

'Cécile Brünner, White' — see R. 'White Cécile Brünner'

Cecily Gibson = 'Evebright' (F) — MJon

Celebration 2000 = 'Horcoffitup'[PBR] (S) — MAus

§ 'Céleste' (A) ♀H4 — EWTr GCoc LGod LStr MAsh MFry MRav SFam SPer SSea SWCr WAct WHCG WOVN

'Célina' (CeMo) — MGan

'Céline Forestier' (N) ♀H3 — CPou EWTr MAus MRav SFam SPer SWCr WHCG

§ 'Celsiana' (D) — CSam LRHS MAus MRMR NEgg SFam SPer SSea SWCr WAct WHCG

Centenaire de Lourdes = 'Delge' (F) — SPoc SWCr

Centenary = 'Koreledas'[PBR] (F) ♀H4 — ENot SPer

§ x *centifolia* (Ce) — MAus MRav SSea SWCr WAct WHCG

§ - 'Bullata' (Ce) — MAus

§ - 'Cristata' (Ce) ♀H4 — CSam ECnt EPfP EWTr LStr MRav SFam SPer SSea SWCr WAct WHCG

§ - 'De Meaux' (Ce) — MAus MRav SPer SPla SPoc SSea WAct WHCG

§ - 'Muscosa' (CeMo) — GCoc LStr MAus MGan MRMR MRav MWgw NEgg SFam SPoG SPoc SSea WAct

- 'Muscosa Alba' — SSea

- 'Parvifolia' — see R. 'Burgundiaca'

§ - 'Shailer's White Moss' (CeMo) — LRHS MAus MGan SFam SSea WHCG

- 'Spong' (Ce) — EBee MAus WAct

§ - 'Unique' (Ce) — EWTr MAus SSea

§ - 'Unique Panachée' (Ce) — MAus MGan

'Centifolia Variegata' — see R. x *centifolia* 'Unique Panachée'

Centre Stage = 'Chewcreepy' (S/GC) — MJon

Century Sunset = 'Tansaras'[PBR] (HT) — SPoc

'Cerise Bouquet' (S) ♀H4 — LRHS MAus MRav SPer WAct WHCG

Champagne Cocktail = 'Horflash'[PBR] (F) ♀H4 — GGre MJon SPer SPoG SWCr

'Champagne Dream' (Patio) — MAsh SWCr

Champagne = 'Korampa' (F) — MJon

Champagne Moments = 'Korvanaber'[PBR] (F) **new** — CSBt ECnt ENot ESty

'Champneys' Pink Cluster' (China hybrid) — MAus SFam

Champs Elysées = 'Meicarl' (HT) — MGan

'Chanelle' (F) — MGan SPer

Chapeau de Napoléon — see R. x *centifolia* 'Cristata'

'Chaplin's Pink Climber' (Cl) — MGan MRMR SWCr

Charity = 'Auschar' (S) — LRHS MAus

Charles Austin = 'Ausles' (S) — CGro MAus MRav WAct WHCG

Charles Darwin = 'Auspeet' (S) — MAsh MAus SWCr

'Charles de Mills' (G) ♀H4 — CHad CSam EBee ECnt ELan EPfP EWTr LRHS LStr MAsh MAus MDun MFry MRav NEgg NSRo SFam SPer SPoc SSea SWCr WAct WHCG

Charles Notcutt = 'Korhassi' (S) — ENot

Charles Rennie Mackintosh = 'Ausren' (S) — CSBt CSam LRHS LStr MAus MBNS NEgg SPoc

Charlie's Rose = 'Tanellepa' (HT) — ESty MBri SPoc SWCr

Charlotte = 'Auspoly'[PBR] (S) ♀H4 — CAbP EPfP ESty LRHS LStr MAus MJon SPer SPoc SSea SWCr

Charmant = 'Korpeligo'[PBR] (F) — ENot

Charmian = 'Ausmian' (S) — MAus

Charming Cover = 'Poulharmu'[PBR] (GC/S) — ECnt MAsh SWCr

'Charter 700' (F) — MFry

Chartreuse de Parme = 'Delviola' (S) — SPoc SWCr

'Château de Clos-Vougeot' (HT) — IArd

Chatsworth = 'Tanotax'[PBR] (Patio/F) — MJon MRav SPer SPoc SSea SWCr

§ Chaucer = 'Auscer' (S) — MAus

Cheerful Charlie = 'Cocquimmer' (F) — GCoc

Chelsea Belle = 'Talchelsea' (Min) — MJon

§ Cherry Brandy '85 = 'Tanryrandy'[PBR] (HT) — CSBt MGan

Cheshire = 'Fryelise'[PBR] (HT) — GCoc MFry MJon SPoc SWCr

Cheshire = 'Korkonopi'[PBR] (County Rose Series) (S) — ENot MAus

'Cheshire Life' (HT) — GGre MAus MFry MGan MJon MRav NPri SWCr

Chester Cathedral = 'Franshine' (HT) — MJon

'Chevy Chase' (Ra) — WAct

Chianti = 'Auswine' (S) — MAus NLar WAct WHCG

Chicago Peace = 'Johnago' (HT) — MGan MJon SWCr WBVN

Childhood Memories = 'Ferho' (HM/Cl) — SPla

Chilterns = 'Kortemma'[PBR] (GC) — ENot MRav SPoc SWCr

'Chinatown' (F/S) ♀H4 — CBcs CGro CSBt CTri ENot EPfP GGre LStr MAsh MAus MGan MJon MRMR MRav NBlu SPer SPoG SWCr

chinensis misapplied — see R. x *odorata*

I **chinensis** 'Angel Rose' NJOw
(Min)
- 'Old Blush' see *R.* x *odorata* 'Pallida'
Chivalry = 'Macpow' (HT) SWCr
Chloe = 'Poulen003'PBR CHad CPou ECnt SPoc SWCr
(S)
'Chloris' (A) CPou
Chris = 'Kirsan'PBR (Cl) EBee ECnt ESty LStr MJon SPoc
SWCr WGor
Christian Dior = 'Meilie' SWCr
(HT)
'Christine Gandy' (F) MGan
Christopher = 'Cocopher' GCoc
(HT)
Christopher Columbus = IArd
'Meinronsse' (HT)
Christopher Marlowe = MAus SWCr
'Ausjump'PBR (S)
Cider Cup = 'Dicladida'PBR EPfP ESty GGre IDic
(Min/Patio) ♥H4 LStr MAus MFry SWCr
'Cinderella' (Min) CSBt MGan SWCr
cinnamomea see *R. majalis*
Citron-Fraise = 'Delcifra' SPoc SWCr
(S)
City Lights = 'Poulgan'PBR CSBt
(Patio)
'City of Leeds' (F) CWSG GGre MAsh MGan
City of London = CSBt LStr MJon SPer SWCr
'Harukfore'PBR (F)
'City of Portsmouth' (F) CBcs
Clair Matin = 'Meimont' MAus SPer SWCr WAct
(ClS)
'Claire Jacquier' (N) EBee MAus SFam SPer WHCG
Claire Rayner = MJon
'Macpandem' (F/Patio)
Claire Rose = 'Auslight'PBR ESty LRHS MAus MJon MRav SPer
(S) SWCr
Clara = 'Poulen004' (S) SPoc
Clarinda = GCoc SWCr
'Cocsummery'PBR (F)
Claude Monet = 'Jacdesa' SPoc
(HT)
Cleo = 'Beebop' (HT) MJon
§ Cleopatra = 'Korverpea'PBR ENot
(HT)
'Cliff Richard' (F) ESty
'Climbing Alec's Red' SPer SWCr
(ClHT)
'Climbing Allgold' (ClF) MRMR
'Climbing Arthur Bell' CSBt CTri ESty GGre LAst LGod
(ClF) ♥H4 MAsh SPer SPoG SPoc SSea SWCr
'Climbing Ballerina' (Ra) CSBt MGan SPoc SWCr
'Climbing Blue Moon' LAst MGan SWCr
(ClHT)
§ 'Climbing Captain Christy' MAus
(ClHT)
'Climbing Cécile Brünner' CSBt EBee ECnt EPfP LRHS LStr
(ClPoly) ♥H4 MAus MGan MRav MWgw SPer
SPoc SSea SWCr WAct WHCG
'Climbing Château de MAus
Clos-Vougeot' (ClHT)
'Climbing Christine' MAus
(ClHT)
§ 'Climbing Columbia' ERea SPer WHCG
(ClHT)
'Climbing Crimson Glory' CPou MAsh MAus MGan SWCr
(ClHT) WAct
§ 'Climbing Devoniensis' CPou
(ClT)
'Climbing Ena Harkness' CBcs CSam GCoc GGre LRHS
(ClHT) MAus MGan MRav SEND SPer SPla
SPoG SWCr
'Climbing Etoile de CSBt CSam CTri CWSG EPfP GCoc
Hollande' (ClHT) ♥H4 GGre LRHS LStr MAus MGan MJon
MRav MWgw SFam SMad SPer
SPoG SPoc SSea SWCr

Climbing Fragrant Cloud CBcs ELan MGan
= 'Colfragrasar' (ClHT)
§ Climbing Gold Bunny = MJon
'Meigro-Nurisar' (ClF)
'Climbing Iceberg' (ClF) CGro CSBt EBee ELan ENot EPfP
♥H4 ESty GGre IArd LRHS LStr MAsh
MAus MGan MJon MRav SPer SPla
SPoG SPoc SSea SWCr WAct
WHCG
'Climbing Josephine Bruce' LRHS MGan
(ClHT)
'Climbing la France' MAus MRav
(ClHT)
§ 'Climbing Lady Hillingdon' EPfP EWTr LRHS MAus MGan
(ClT) ♥H3 MRav MWgw NBPC NEgg SFam
SPer SPoG SPoc SSea SWCr WAct
WHCG
'Climbing Lady Sylvia' CSBt EBee EPfP LRHS MAsh MAus
(ClHT) MGan SPer SWCr
'Climbing Little White Pet' see *R.* 'Félicité Perpétue'
'Climbing Madame Abel MAus
Chatenay' (ClHT)
'Climbing Madame LRHS MAus MGan SPer SWCr
Butterfly' (ClHT)
'Climbing Madame CPou MAsh MAus NBPC NPri SPer
Caroline Testout' SWCr
(ClHT)
§ 'Climbing Madame MAus MGan SWCr
Edouard Herriot'
(ClHT)
'Climbing Madame Henri MAus
Guillot' (ClHT)
'Climbing Maman Cochet' MAus
(ClT)
'Climbing Masquerade' MAus MGan MJon MRav SPer SPoc
(ClF) SSea SWCr
§ 'Climbing Mevrouw G.A. MAus
van Rossem' (ClHT)
'Climbing Mrs Aaron Ward' MAus
(ClHT)
'Climbing Mrs G.A. van see *R.* 'Climbing Mevrouw G.A. van
Rossem' Rossem'
'Climbing Mrs Herbert EBee LRHS MAus MRMR MRav
Stevens' (ClHT) SPer SWCr WHCG
'Climbing Mrs Sam CGro CSBt CSam MAus MGan
McGredy' (ClHT) ♥H4 SWCr
'Climbing Niphetos' (ClT) MAus SWCr
'Climbing Ophelia' (ClHT) CPou MAus SPer
Climbing Orange MJon SPer
Sunblaze = 'Meiji
Katarsar'PBR (ClMin)
'Climbing Pascali' (ClHT) MGan
§ 'Climbing Paul Lédé' (ClT) EBee LRHS MAus NEgg SPoc
SWCr
'Climbing Peace' (ClHT) CSBt
'Climbing Picture' (ClHT) MAus
§ 'Climbing Pompon de CTri EMFP LHop LRHS MAus
Paris' (ClMinCh) MGan MRav SPer WHCG
'Climbing Ruby Wedding' GGre SPoG
'Climbing Shot Silk' CSBt EBee MGan SPer SWCr
(ClHT) ♥H4
§ 'Climbing Souvenir de CPou EBee MAus SPer SPoc SWCr
la Malmaison' (ClBb) WAct WHCG
'Climbing Sterling Silver' MGan
(ClHT) **new**
Climbing Super Star = MAus
'Tangostar' (ClHT)
'Climbing Sutter's Gold' MGan
(ClHT)
'Climbing The Queen SWCr
Elizabeth' (ClF)
Clodagh McGredy = ESty MJon
'Macswanle'PBR (F)
Cloud Nine = 'Fryextra' EBee ECnt ESty LGod MFry MJon
(HT) SWCr
Cocktail = 'Meimick' (S) MGan

Colchester Beauty = 'Cansend' (F) — ECnt

Colchester Castle = 'Poulcs008'[PBR] **new** — ECnt

§ 'Colibri' = 'Meimal' (Min) — SPer

§ 'Colonel Fabvier' — MAus XPep

colonial white — see *R.* 'Sombreuil'

'Columbian' (ClHT) — see *R.* 'Climbing Columbia'

'Commandant Beaurepaire' (Bb) — EBee LRHS MAus SWCr

common moss — see *R.* x *centifolia* 'Muscosa'

Commonwealth Glory = 'Harclue'[PBR] (HT) — ESty SPoc SWCr

'Compassion' (ClHT) ♀[H4] — More than 30 suppliers

§ 'Complicata' (G) ♀[H4] — CAbP EPfP LRHS LStr MAsh MAus MGan MRMR MRav SFam SPer SPoc SSea SWCr WAct WHCG WOVN

N 'Comte de Chambord' misapplied — see *R.* 'Madame Knorr'

Comtes de Champagne = 'Ausufo'[PBR] (S) — MAus SCoo

'Comtesse Cécile de Chabrillant' (HP) — MAus

'Comtesse de Lacépède' misapplied — see *R.* 'Du Maître d'Ecole'

§ 'Comtesse de Murinais' (DMo) — MAus SFam

Comtesse de Ségur = 'Deltendre' (S) — SPoc SWCr

§ 'Comtesse du Caÿla' (Ch) — MAus SSea

§ Concert = 'Poulclimb'[PBR] (Cl) — ECnt MBri SPoc SSea SWCr

§ 'Conditorum' (G) — SFam WAct

Congratulations = 'Korlift'[PBR] (HT) — CSBt CTri ECnt ENot GCoc IArd LGod LStr MAus MFry MGan MJon MRav NBPC NPri SPer SPoG SPoc SSea SWCr

Connie = 'Boselftay'[PBR] (F) — SWCr

Conquest = 'Harbrill'[PBR] (F) — MRav

§ 'Conrad Ferdinand Meyer' (Ru) — CSBt MAus MDun MGan NHaw SPer

Conservation = 'Cocdimple'[PBR] (Min/Patio) — GCoc GGre LAst MBri SWCr

Constance Finn = 'Hareden'[PBR] (F) — GGre SPoG SWCr

'Constance Spry' (Cl/S) ♀[H4] — EBee ECnt ELan ENot EPfP LRHS LStr MAsh MAus MGan MJon MRav NEgg NPri SFam SPer SPoc SSea SWCr WAct WGer WHCG

§ 'Cooperi' (Ra) — CAbP MAus MRMR SLon SPer SPoc SSea SWCr WAct WHCG WPGP

Cooper's Burmese — see *R.* 'Cooperi'

'Copenhagen' (ClHT) — LRHS MAus

Copper Pot = 'Dicpe' (F) — MGan SPer

'Coral Cluster' (Poly) — MAus MGan

'Coral Dawn' (ClHT) — MFry

Coral Palace[PBR] — see *R.* Imagination = 'Pouldron'

Coral Reef = 'Cocdarlee'[PBR] (Min/Patio) — ESty GGre SWCr

'Coral Satin' (Cl) — MGan

Cordelia = 'Ausbottle'[PBR] (S) — LRHS MAus MBri

'Cornelia' (HM) ♀[H4] — CBcs CSBt CSam EBee ECnt ENot EPfP EWTr GCoc IArd LAst LRHS LStr MAsh MAus MFry MGan MJon MRMR MRav SFam SPer SPoc SSea SWCr WAct WHCG WOVN

'Coronet' (F) — WHCG

Corvedale = 'Ausnetting'[PBR] (S) — MAus

cottage maid — see *Rosa* x *centifolia* 'Unique Panachée'

Cottage Rose = 'Ausglisten'[PBR] (S) — MAus MJon MRav NEgg SPoc SWCr

Countess Celeste[PBR] — see *R.* Imagination = 'Pouldron'

'Coupe d'Hébé' (Bb) — MAus

§ Courage = 'Poulduf'[PBR] (HT) — ECnt

Courvoisier = 'Macsee' — CSBt

'Cramoisi Picotée' (G) — MAus

'Cramoisi Supérieur' (Ch) — MAus WHCG

Crathes Castle = 'Cocathes' — GCoc

Crazy for You = 'Wekroalt'[PBR] (F) — ESty LGod MJon SPoc SSea SWCr

Cream Abundance = 'Harflax'[PBR] (F) — ESty LStr MAsh SPoc SWCr

'Crème Anglaise'[PBR] (Cl) — CGro EBee ECnt MGan

'Creme Brulee'[PBR] (Cl) — MGan

Crème de la Crème = 'Gancre'[PBR] (Cl) — CGro CSBt ECnt ESty GCoc MBri MGan MJon SPoc SSea SWCr

'Crépuscule' (N) — SWCr WHCG

crested moss — see *R.* x *centifolia* 'Cristata'

Cricri = 'Meicri' (Min) — MAus MGan

Crimson Cascade = 'Fryclimbdown'[PBR] (Cl) — CSam ESty LRHS MAsh MAus MBri MFry MRav SPoc SPoc SSea SWCr WHCG

crimson damask — see *R. gallica* var. *officinalis*

'Crimson Descant' (Cl) — ECnt

Crimson Floorshow = 'Harglamour'[PBR] (GC) — MBri

'Crimson Globe' (Mo) — MGan

'Crimson Glory' (HT) — EBee MGan SWCr

'Crimson Shower' (Ra) ♀[H4] — CSam EMFP LRHS MAus MGan MJon MRMR MRav NEgg NSRo SPer SWCr WAct WGer WHCG WHer

'Cristata' — see *R.* x *centifolia* 'Cristata'

Crocus Rose = 'Ausquest'[PBR] (S) — EPfP LRHS MAus NEgg SWCr

Crown Princess Margareta = 'Auswinter'[PBR] (S) — ECnt LRHS MAus MBNS MFry MJon NEgg SCoo SPer SPoc SWCr

Crystal Palace = 'Poulrek'[PBR] (F/Patio) — SPoc

cuisse de nymphe — see *R.* 'Great Maiden's Blush'

'Cupid' (ClHT) — MAus SPer SPoc

§ Cymbeline = 'Auslean' (S) — SPer

Dacapo = 'Poulcy012' (Cl/Patio) **new** — ECnt

'D'Aguesseau' (G) — EBee MAus

'Daily Mail' — see *R.* 'Climbing Madame Edouard Herriot'

'Dainty Bess' (HT) — EWTr MAus SSea

'Dainty Maid' (F) — MAus

'Daisy Hill' ('Macrantha' hybrid) — MJon

x *damascena* var. *bifera* — see *R.* x *damascena* var. *semperflorens*

§ - var. *semperflorens* (D) — CBgR EWTr MAus MRMR MRav NLar SPoc SSea SWCr WAct WHCG

N - 'Trigintipetala' misapplied — see *R.* 'Professor Emile Perrot'

§ - var. *versicolor* (D) — CGro MGan SFam SPer SSea WAct

§ 'Dame de Coeur' (HT) — NBlu SWCr

Dame Wendy = 'Canson' (F) — MAus MGan

Dames de Chenonceau = 'Delpabra' (S) — CBgR SPoc SWCr

'Danaë' (HM) — CHad EBee MAus WHCG

Dancing Pink = 'Hendan' (F) — MJon

'Dancing Queen' (Cl) **new** — MFry

Danny Boy = 'Dicxcon'[PBR] (Patio) — IDic MJon WGor

'Danse du Feu' (Cl) — CBcs CGro CSBt CTri CWSG EBee ELan EGre LGod LRHS LStr MAsh MAus MGan MJon MRav NPri SPer SPoG SPoc SWCr WBVN

'Daphne Gandy' (F) — MGan
Dapple Dawn = 'Ausapple' (S) — MAus SPer
Darling Flame = 'Meilucca' (Min) — MGan MRav
'Dart's Defender' — SLPl
David Whitfield = 'Gana'PBR (F) — MGan
davidii — MAus
Dawn Chorus = 'Dicquasar'PBR (HT) ♥H4 — CGro CSBt CWSG ECnt ENot EPfP ESty GCoc GGre IDic LGod LRHS LStr MAsh MAus MBri MGan MRav SPer SPoG SPoc SSea SWCr
'Daybreak' (HM) — MAus WAct WHCG
Dazzling Delight = 'Cocuseful' (F) — GCoc
'De Meaux' (Ce) — see *R.* x *centifolia* 'De Meaux'
'De Meaux, White' — see *R.* 'White de Meaux'
§ 'De Rescht' (DPo) ♥H4 — CBgR CPou EBee EPfP EWTr LRHS MAsh MAus MGan MJon MRav MWgw NBPC SPer SPla SPoG SPoc SSea SWCr WAct WGer WHCG
'Dearest' (F) — CBcs CSBt MGan MRav SPer SWCr
'Debbie Thomas' (HT) — MJon
Deb's Delight = 'Legsweet'PBR (F) — ELan MJon
'Debutante' (Ra) — CHad CSam EBee LRHS MAus SWCr WHCG
'Deep Secret' (HT) ♥H4 — CGro CTri CWSG EBee ECnt EPfP ESty GCoc GGre LRHS LStr MAsh MFry MGan MJon MRav SPer SPoG SPoc SSea SWCr
'Delambre' (DPo) — MAus MRav
'Delicata' (Ru) — MAus
Della Balfour = 'Harblend'PBR (Cl) — SWCr
'Dentelle de Malines' (S) — LRHS MAus WAct
Desert Island = 'Dicfizz' (F) new — GCoc IDic
'Desprez à Fleurs Jaunes' (N) — EBee EWTr IArd LRHS MAus MRav NBPC NEgg SFam SPer SPoc SWCr WHCG
'Devon Maid' (Cl) — SWCr
'Devoniensis' (ClT) — see *R.* 'Climbing Devoniensis'
Devotion = 'Interfluco'PBR (HT) — IDic
Diamond Border = 'Pouldiram'PBR (S) — ECnt
'Diamond Jubilee' (HT) — MGan NBlu SWCr
Diamond = 'Korgazell'PBR (Patio) — ENot ESty GCoc MJon
'Diamond Wishes' (HT) new — LRHS MAsh
Dick's Delight = 'Dicwhistle'PBR (GC) — ESty IDic SPoc SWCr
Die Welt = 'Diekor' (HT) — MBri MJon
'Directeur Alphand' (HP) — WHCG
Dixieland Linda = 'Beadix' (ClHT) — MJon SSea
Dizzy Heights = 'Fryblissful'PBR (Cl) — ECnt ESty GCoc MAsh MFry MGan MJon SPoG SPoc SWCr
'Docteur Grill' (T) — MAus
'Doctor A.J. Verhage' (HT) — MGan
Doctor Dick = 'Cocbaden' (HT) — MBri
§ Doctor Goldberg = 'Gandol' (HT) — MGan
Doctor Jackson = 'Ausdoctor' (S) — MAus
§ Doctor Jo = 'Fryatlanta'PBR (F) — MFry SPoc SWCr
'Doctor John Snow' (HT) — MGan
Doctor McAlpine = 'Peafirst' (F/Patio) — MBri
'Doctor W. Van Fleet' (Ra/Cl) — MAus

'Doktor Eckener' (Ru) — MGan
'Don Juan' (Cl) — MGan SWCr
'Doris Tysterman' (HT) — CGro CTri GGre LStr MAus MGan MJon SPer SSea SWCr
Dorothy = 'Cocrocket' (F) — GCoc
'Dorothy Perkins' (Ra) — CGro CSBt CTri EWTr GCoc GGre LRHS MAus MGan MJon MRMR MRav NPer SPer SSea SWCr WHCG
'Dorothy Wheatcroft' (F) — MGan
'Dortmund' (ClHScB) ♥H4 — CPLG EBee LGod LRHS MAus MGan NHaw SPer SWCr WAct WHCG
Double Delight = 'Andeli' (HT) — CGro ESty GCoc GGre MGan MJon MRav SPer SPoG SPoc SSea SWCr
'Dream Girl' (Cl) — MAus SFam
Dream Lover = 'Peayetti'PBR (Patio) — MJon MRav SPoc SWCr
'Dreaming Spires' (Cl) — CSBt ENot MRMR SPer SSea SWCr
Dreamland = 'Träumland' (F) — MGan
Drummer Boy = 'Harvacity'PBR (F/Patio) — GGre MGan SWCr
§ 'Du Maître d'Ecole' (G) — MAus MRav WHCG WHer
Dublin Bay = 'Macdub' (Cl) ♥H4 — CSBt CSam CTri ECnt ELan ENot EPfP ESty GGre IArd LAst LGod LRHS LStr MAsh MFry MGan MJon MRav SPer SPoG SPoc SSea SWCr WGer
'Duc de Guiche' (G) ♥H4 — CSam MAus MRMR SFam SPer WAct WHCG WHer
'Duchess of Portland' — see *R.* 'Portlandica'
'Duchesse d'Angoulême' (G) — MAus SFam
'Duchesse de Buccleugh' (G) — CBgR MAus MRav NBPC WAct
§ 'Duchesse de Montebello' (G) ♥H4 — EWTr LRHS MAus SFam SPer WAct WHCG
'Duchesse de Verneuil' (CeMo) — MAus SFam
'Duke of Edinburgh' (HP) — MAus
'Duke of Wellington' (HP) — SWCr WHCG
'Duke of Windsor' (HT) — MGan SPer SWCr
dumalis new — GIBF
'Dundee Rambler' (Ra) — MAus
§ 'Duplex' (S) — MAus MRav WAct
'Dupontii' (S) — LRHS MAus MRav NBPC NLar SFam SPer WAct WOVN XPep
'Dupuy Jamain' (HP) — WHCG
'Dusky Maiden' (F) — CBos CHad MAus SWCr WHCG
Dusty Springfield = 'Horluvdust' (F) new — MGan
'Dutch Gold' (HT) — CGro CWSG GGre MAus MGan MRav SPer SSea SWCr
'E.H. Morse' — see *R.* 'Ernest H. Morse'
'Easlea's Golden Rambler' (Ra) ♥H4 — CSBt EBee LRHS MAus MRav SWCr WAct WHCG
Easy Cover = 'Pouleas'PBR (GC) — MAsh SWCr
Easy Going = 'Harflow'PBR (F) — GGre IArd LRHS MAsh MJon SWCr
'Eblouissant' (Poly) — MGan
ecae — MAus
'Eddie's Jewel' (*moyesii* hybrid) — MAus MGan
'Eden Rose' (HT) — MGan
Eden Rose '88 = 'Meiviolin'PBR (ClHT) — MJon SPer SPoc SWCr
Edith Holden = 'Chewlegacy'PBR (F) — MJon
'Edward Hyams' — MAus
eglanteria — see *R. rubiginosa*
Eglantyne = 'Ausmak'PBR (S) ♥H4 — CSBt EPfP GCoc LRHS LStr MAus MBri MFry MJon MRav SEND SPer SPoc SSea SWCr
'Eleanor' (Min) new — SBra

§ marks appear before certain entries.

Eleanor Annelise = 'Cocslightly' (HT)	GCoc
Eleanor = 'Poulberin'^{PBR} (S)	ECnt SWCr
'Elegance' (ClHT)	MAus
§ *elegantula* 'Persetosa' (S)	MAus NLar SPer SPoc WAct WHCG
Elfe = 'Tanelfe' (HT) **new**	NHaw
§ Elina = 'Dicjana'^{PBR} (HT) ♀^{H4}	CSBt EBee ECnt ENot ESty GGre IDic LGod LStr MAus MFry MGan MJon MRav NBlu SPer SPoG SPoc SWCr
'Eliza Boëlle' (HP)	WHCG
Elizabeth = 'Coctail' (F)	GCoc
'Elizabeth Harkness' (HT)	CWSG MAus MGan SPer SWCr
Elizabeth of Glamis = 'Macel' (F)	CGro CTri CWSG GCoc MGan SPer SWCr
Elle = 'Meibderos'^{PBR} (HT)	ESty SPoc SWCr
Ellen = 'Auscup' (S)	MAus
'Ellen Poulsen' (Poly)	MGan
'Ellen Willmott' (HT)	MAus SWCr
'Elmshorn' (S)	CBcs MGan WHCG
'Else Poulsen' (Poly)	WHCG
Emanuel = 'Ausuel' (S)	MAus
'Emily Gray' (Ra)	CGro CSBt EBee ECnt ENot ESty LRHS LStr MAsh MAus MGan MRav NPri SMad SPer SSea SWCr WAct WHCG
'Emma Wright' (HT)	MAus
'Emotion' (F)	SWCr
'Empereur du Maroc' (HP)	EBee MAus MRav WHCG
Empress Michiko = 'Dicnifty'^{PBR} (HT)	ESty IDic
'Ena Harkness' (HT)	CTri ElAn GGre MGan SWCr
§ England's Rose = 'Ausrace'^{PBR} (S)	CSam MAsh MAus SCoo SWCr
English Elegance = 'Ausleaf' (S)	MAus
English Garden = 'Ausbuff'^{PBR} (S)	CGro EBee ENot EPfP LRHS LStr MAus MRav SPer SWCr
'English Miss' (F) ♀^{H4}	CSBt CTri ECnt EPfP ESty LAst LStr MAsh MAus MGan MJon MRav SPer SPoG SPoc SWCr
'Erfurt' (HM)	MAus MGan SPer SWCr WHCG
§ 'Erinnerung an Brod' (S)	WHCG
§ 'Ernest H. Morse' (HT)	CSBt CTri CWSG GCoc GGre LAst MGan MJon MRav SPer SSea SWCr
'Ernest May' (HT)	SSea
'Escapade = 'Harpade' (F)	MAus MGan SWCr
Especially for You = 'Fryworthy'^{PBR} (HT)	CSBt CTri ESty GCoc LGod LRHS LStr MAsh MFry NPri SCoo SPoG SPoc SSea SWCr
Essex = 'Poulnoz'^{PBR} (GC)	MRav SPer SWCr WHCG
§ 'Estrellita de Oro' (Min)	SPer
§ 'Etain' (Ra)	EBee ECnt
§ 'Etendard'	MRMR SPla SPoc WAct
Eternal Flame = 'Korassenet'^{PBR} (F)	ENot ESty SPoc SWCr
§ Eternally Yours = 'Macspeego'^{PBR} (HT)	MJon
'Ethel' (Ra)	CPou EBee EMFP SWCr
'Etoile de Hollande' (HT)	CHad CSBt EBee ElAn ENot NEgg NPri
'Etude' (Cl)	WBVN
'Eugénie Guinoisseau' (Mo)	WHCG
Euphoria = 'Intereup'^{PBR} (GC/S)	GCoc IDic SPoc SWCr
'Euphrates = 'Harunique' (*persica* hybrid)	MAus WAct
'Europeana' (F)	MGan
'Evangeline' (Ra)	MAus
Evelyn = 'Aussaucer'^{PBR} (S) ♀^{H4}	CSBt CSam EPfP ESty GCoc LRHS LStr MAsh MAus MFry MJon MRMR MRav NEgg SPer SPla SPoc SWCr
§ Evelyn Fison = 'Macev' (F)	CSBt ElAn MAus MGan MJon MRav SPer SPoc SWCr
Evening Light = 'Chewpechette' (ClMin)	MJon
Evening Light = 'Tarde Gris' (Min) (Cl)	ESty SWCr
'Excelsa' (Ra)	CSBt CTri EPfP IArd LGod MAsh MGan MRav NWea SSea SWCr
§ Eye Paint = 'Maceye' (F)	MAus SMrm
'Eyecatcher' (F)	EBee ECnt
Eyeopener = 'Interop'^{PBR} (S/GC)	CGro MGan SWCr
'F.E. Lester'	see *R.* 'Francis E. Lester'
§ 'F.J. Grootendorst' (Ru)	LRHS MAus MGan SSea WAct
Fab = 'Bosconpea'^{PBR} (F)	GGre SWCr
'Fabvier'	see *R.* 'Colonel Fabvier'
Fairhope = 'Talfairhope' (Min)	MJon
§ Fairy Prince = 'Harnougette' (GC)	ESty
Fairy Queen = 'Sperien' (Poly/GC)	IDic MAsh SWCr
'Fairy Rose'	see *R.* 'The Fairy'
§ Fairy Snow = 'Holfairy' (S)	SPoc
§ Fairygold = 'Frygoldie'^{PBR} (Patio)	MFry
Faithful = 'Haressay'^{PBR} (F)	GGre SPoG SWCr
Falstaff = 'Ausverse'^{PBR} (S)	CSBt ECnt EPfP LRHS LStr MAsh MAus MBNS MJon NEgg NSRo SPoc SWCr
'Fantin-Latour' (*centifolia* hybrid) ♀^{H4}	CTri EBee ECnt ElAn EPfP GCoc LAst LGod LRHS LStr MAus MDun MGan MRav NBPC NEgg SFam SMad SPer SPoc SSea SWCr WAct WHCG WKif
farreri var. *persetosa*	see *R. elegantula* 'Persetosa'
Fascination = 'Jacoyel' (HT)	LStr MBri SCoo
§ Fascination = 'Poulmax'^{PBR} (F) ♀^{H4}	CSBt ECnt ENot EPfP ESty GCoc LGod MAsh MGan MRav SPer SPoG SPoc SWCr
Favourite Hit = 'Poululv'^{PBR} (Patio)	ECnt
fedtschenkoana misapplied	MAus SPer WAct WHCG
fedtschenkoana Regel	MRMR SLPl
'Felicia' (HM) ♀^{H4}	CHad CSBt CSam EBee ECnt ElAn ENot EPfP EWTr GCoc LGod LRHS LStr MAsh MAus MDun MFry MGan MJon MRav NBPC SFam SPer SPoG SPoc SWCr WAct WHCG WKif WOVN
'Félicité Parmentier' (AxD) ♀^{H4}	EBee LRHS MAsh MAus MRMR MRav NEgg SFam SPer SWCr WAct WHCG
§ 'Félicité Perpétue' (Ra) ♀^{H4}	More than 30 suppliers
Felicity Kendal = 'Lanken' (HT)	MJon
'Fellemberg' (ClCh)	MAus WHCG XPep
Fellowship = 'Harwelcome'^{PBR} (F) ♀^{H4}	ECnt ENot ESty GCoc GGre LGod LStr MAus MFry MGan MJon MRav SCoo SPoc SSea SWCr
'Femina' (HT)	MGan
'Ferdinand Pichard' (Bb) ♀^{H4}	CPou CSBt ECnt EPfP ESty EWTr LAst LRHS MAus MBri MDun MGan MJon MRav MWgw NEgg SPer SPoG SPoc SSea SWCr WAct WFoF WGer WHCG WKif WOVN
§ Ferdy = 'Keitoli'^{PBR} (GC)	MRav SPer SWCr
Fergie = 'Ganfer'^{PBR} (F/Patio)	MGan SWCr
Festival = 'Kordialo'^{PBR} (Patio)	ENot ESty LStr MRav SPer SPoG SWCr

Fiery Hit = 'Poulfiry'^{PBR} (Min) — ECnt

Fiery Sunblaze = 'Meineyta'^{PBR} (Min) — SPoc SWCr

Fiesta = 'Macfirinlin' (Patio) — MBri MJon

§ *filipes* — GIBF

§ - 'Kiftsgate' (Ra) ♀^{H4} — More than 30 suppliers

§ 'Fimbriata' (Ru) — CPou EWTr MAus MBri NLar SPer SSea SWCr WAct WHCG

Financial Times Centenary = 'Ausfin' (S) — MAus

Fiona = 'Meibeluxen'^{PBR} (S/GC) — GGre SWCr

Firestorm = 'Peazoe' (Patio) — SPoc

'First Class' (HT) — GGre SWCr

'First Love' (HT) — MGan

'Fisher and Holmes' (HP) — MAus WAct WHCG

Fisherman's Friend = 'Auschild'^{PBR} (F) — MAus SPer

Flamenco = 'Poultika'^{PBR} (Cl) — ECnt SSea

Flashdance = 'Poulyc004' (ClMin) — ECnt MAsh SWCr

Flirt = 'Korkopapp'^{PBR} — ENot

'Flora McIvor' (RH) — MAus MGan

'Flore' (Ra) — CRHN MAus SFam

'Florence Mary Morse' (S) — SDix

Florence Nightingale = 'Ganflor'^{PBR} (F) — MGan

'Flower Carpet Coral'^{PBR} (GC) — CGro ENot GCoc LRHS MAsh SCoo SPoG SWCr

Flower Carpet Pink^{PBR} — see *R*. Pink Flower Carpet

Flower Carpet Red Velvet = 'Noare'^{PBR} (GC) — CGro ELan ENot GCoc GGre MAsh MGan MRav SCoo SPoG

§ Flower Carpet Sunshine = 'Noason'^{PBR} (GC) — CGro ELan ENot EPfP GCoc GGre LRHS LStr MAsh MRav SCoo SPoG SWCr

§ Flower Carpet Twilight = 'Noatwi'^{PBR} (GC) — GGre LRHS

Flower Carpet Velvet (GC/S) — EPfP GGre LRHS SWCr

Flower Carpet White = 'Noaschnee'^{PBR} (GC) ♀^{H4} — CGro CTri ELan ENot EPfP GCoc GGre LRHS LStr MAsh MFry MGan MRav SCoo SPer SPoG SWCr

Flower Power = 'Frycassia'^{PBR} (Patio) — CSBt ECnt ESty GCoc GGre LStr MAsh MAus MFry MJon MRav SPoG SPoc SWCr

§ *foetida* (S) — MAus NHaw

§ - 'Bicolor' (S) — EBee LRHS MAus MRMR NHaw SPer WAct

§ - 'Persiana' (S) — MAus MGan NHaw

foliolosa — SLPl WHCG

Fond Memories = 'Kirfelix'^{PBR} (Patio) — GCoc LStr MJon SPoc SWCr

Forever Royal = 'Franmite' (F) — ESty

Forever Young = 'Jacimgol'^{PBR} (F) — IDic MJon

forrestiana — EWTr MAus WHCG

x *fortuneana* (Ra) — WFar

Fortune's double yellow — see *R*. x *odorata* 'Pseudindica'

'Fountain' (HT/S) — MAus MGan SPer SWCr

Fragrant Cloud = 'Tanellis' (HT) — CGro CTri CWSG EBee ECnt ENot EPfP ESty GCoc GGre LAst LRHS LStr MAsh MAus MBri MGan MJon MRav SPer SPoG SPoc SSea SWCr

'Fragrant Delight' (F) ♀^{H4} — CSBt GCoc GGre LAst LStr MAus MGan MJon MRav SPer SWCr WBVN

Fragrant Dream = 'Dicodour'^{PBR} (HT) — CGro ESty IDic LStr MGan SPoG SWCr

Fragrant Memories = 'Korpastato'^{PBR} (HT/S) — ENot ESty GCoc LRHS MAsh NPri SCoo SPoG SPoc SWCr WOVN

France Info = 'Delcril' (S) — SPoc

Frances Perry = 'Bosrexcity'^{PBR} (F) — SWCr

'Francesca' (HM) — CPou EWTr LRHS MAus MGan MRMR SFam SPer SWCr WAct WHCG

Francine Austin = 'Ausram'^{PBR} (S/GC) — LRHS MAsh MAus MJon NEgg SPer SWCr WAct

§ 'Francis E. Lester' (HM/Ra) ♀^{H4} — CHad CRHN CSam EBee LRHS MAus MBri MJon NSRo SPer SPoc SSea SWCr WAct WHCG

x *francofurtana* misapplied — see *R*. 'Impératrice Joséphine'

- 'Empress Josephine' — see *R*. 'Impératrice Joséphine'

'François Juranville' (Ra) ♀^{H4} — CHad CPou CRHN CSBt EBee LAst LRHS LStr MAsh MAus MBri MGan MRMR MRav NLar SPer SPoc SWCr WAct

§ 'Frau Karl Druschki' (HP) — MAus WAct

'Fred Loads' (F/S) ♀^{H4} — MAus MGan MJon MRav

Freddie Mercury = 'Batmercury' (HT) — MJon

Free as Air = 'Mehbronze' (Patio) — MBri

Freedom = 'Dicjem'^{PBR} (HT) ♀^{H4} — ECnt ENot GCoc GGre IDic LGod LStr MAus MFry MGan MRav NPri SPer SPoc SWCr

'Frensham' (F) — CBcs LStr MGan SSea SWCr WBVN

Fresh Pink (Min/Poly) — MGan

Friend for Life = 'Cocnanne'^{PBR} (F) ♀^{H4} — GCoc GGre MJon MRav SWCr

'Friendship' (Patio) — GGre SWCr

'Fritz Nobis' (S) ♀^{H4} — CAbP CHad LRHS LStr MAus MGan MRav NLar SPer SPoc SWCr WAct

Frothy = 'Macfrothy'^{PBR} (Patio) — ECnt MAus MJon

'Fru Dagmar Hastrup' (Ru) ♀^{H4} — CDul CSBt EBee ECnt ELan EPfP EWTr GCoc LBuc LStr MAus MDun MFry MGan MJon MWgw SPer SPoc SWCr WAct WHCG WOVN

'Frühlingsanfang' (PiH) — MAus SWCr WAct

'Frühlingsduft' (PiH) — SWCr

'Frühlingsgold' (PiH) ♀^{H4} — CBcs ELan EPfP GCoc LRHS LStr MAus MDun MFry MGan MRav NLar NWea SPer SWCr WAct WHCG WOVN

'Frühlingsmorgen' (PiH) — GCoc LStr MAus MGan MRav NPri SPer SSea SWCr WHCG WOVN

* *fuchianus* — GIBF

Fulton Mackay = 'Cocdana'^{PBR} (HT) — GCoc GGre MGan

Fyvie Castle = 'Cocbamber' (HT) — GCoc

'Gail Borden' (HT) — MGan SWCr

§ *gallica* (G) — WAct

§ - var. *officinalis* (G) ♀^{H4} — CAbP CBgR CSam GCoc GPoy LRHS MAsh MAus MGan MJon MNHC MRav SFam SPer SPoc SSea SWCr WAct WHCG

- 'Velutiniflora' (G) — SSea

§ - 'Versicolor' (G) ♀^{H4} — More than 30 suppliers

Galway Bay = 'Macba' (ClHT) — EBee EWTr GGre LRHS MAsh MGan MRav SPer SWCr

§ Garden News = 'Poulrim'^{PBR} (HT) — EBee ECnt ESty MAsh SCoo SWCr

'Gardenia' (Ra) — CPou EBee EWTr MAus SPoc SWCr WHCG

'Gardiner's Pink' (Ra) — WHCG

'Garnette Carol' — see *R*. 'Carol Amling'

'Garnette Pink' — see *R*. 'Carol Amling'

'Gavotte' (HT) — MJon

'Général Jacqueminot' (HP) — MAus

'Général Kléber' (CeMo) — MAus MRav SFam SSea WAct WHCG

§ 'Général Schablikine' (T) — EBee MAus MRMR SWCr

N **gentiliana** H. Lév. & Variot | see *R. multiflora* var. *cathayensis*

Gentle Touch = | CSBt CWSG IDic LAst MFry MRav
'Diclulu'[PBR] (Min/Patio) | SPer SPla SWCr

Geoff Hamilton = | CSBt ESty LRHS LStr MAsh MAus
'Ausham'[PBR] (S) | MBNS MJon NEgg SCoo SPer SPoG
 | SPoc SWCr

'Georg Arends' (HP) | MAus

'George Dickson' (HT) | MAus

'Georges Vibert' (G) | EBee MAus WHCG

Geraldine = 'Peahaze' (F) | SWCr

§ 'Geranium' (*moyesii* | CBcs CHad CSam EBee ELan ENot
hybrid) ♥[H4] | EPfP GCoc IArd LGod LRHS LStr
 | MAsh MAus MBri MGan MJon
 | MRav NBlu NEgg NPri NScw
 | SEND SPer SPoc SSea SWCr WAct
 | WHCG WOVN

'Gerbe Rose' (Ra) | MAus

Gertrude Jekyll = | More than 30 suppliers
'Ausbord'[PBR] ♥[H4]

'Ghislaine de Féligonde' | CHad CPou EBee EWTr LStr NLar
(Ra/S) | SPer SPoG SSea SWCr WHCG

Ghita = 'Poulren013' | ECnt
(S) **new**

gigantea | ISea
- 'Cooperi' | see *R.* 'Cooperi'

Giggles = 'Kingig' (Min) | MJon

Ginger Syllabub = | ESty GCoc GGre LStr MJon SPoc
'Harjolly' (Cl) | SWCr

§ Gingernut = 'Coccrazy'[PBR] | SWCr
(Patio)

Gipsy Boy | see *R.* 'Zigeunerknabe'

Glad Tidings = | CSBt CWSG LAst MBri MGan MRav
'Tantide'[PBR] (F) | SPer SWCr

Glamis Castle = | CBcs CSam CTri ESty LRHS LStr
'Auslevel'[PBR] (S) | MAus MBNS MBri NEgg SPer SPoc
 | SWCr

§ **glauca** Pourr. (S) ♥[H4] | More than 30 suppliers

'Glenfiddich' (F) | CGro CSBt CTri CWSG GCoc
 | GGre LStr MAus MBri MJon MRav
 | NPri NWea SPer SWCr

'Glenn Dale' (Cl) | EBee

Glenshane = | ESty IDic SPoc SWCr
'Dicvood'[PBR] (GC/S)

Global Beauty = | ESty SPoc SWCr
'Tan 94448' (HT)

'Gloire de Dijon' (ClT) | CGro CHad CSBt CWSG EBee
 | ECnt ELan ENot EPfP LAst LGod
 | LRHS LStr MAsh MAus MBri MGan
 | MJon MRMR MRav MWgw NEgg
 | NPri SMad SPer SPla SSea SWCr
 | WAct WHCG

'Gloire de Ducher' (HP) | MAus MGan MRav WAct WHCG

'Gloire de France' (G) | MAus MRav WHer

'Gloire de Guilan' (D) | MAus SPoc SWCr WAct

'Gloire des Mousseuses' | EBee EWTr SFam WHCG
(CeMo)

'Gloire du Midi' (Poly) | MAus

'Gloire Lyonnaise' (HP) | EBee EWTr WHCG

Gloriana = | CGro ESty LRHS MAsh MAus MBri
'Chewpope'[PBR] | MJon SCoo SPer SPoc SSea SWCr
(ClMin)

Glorious = 'Interictira'[PBR] | ESty GCoc IDic MBri MJon SPoc
(HT) | SWCr

Glowing Amber = | ESty MJon
'Manglow' (Min)

Gold Crown | see *R.* 'Goldkrone'

Gold Reef = 'Pouldom'[PBR] | ECnt

Gold Symphonie = | MAsh SPoc
'Macfraba' (Min)

'Goldbusch' (RH) | MGan WAct

'Golden Anniversary' | GGre LStr MAsh SPer SPoG SWCr
(Patio)

'Golden Anniversary' | CGro
(HT) **new**

Golden Beauty = | ENot ESty
'Korberbeni'[PBR] (F)

Golden Beryl = 'Manberyl' MJon
(Min)

Golden Celebration = | CGro CSBt CWSG ECnt EPfP ESty
'Ausgold'[PBR] (S) ♥[H4] | GCoc LAst LGod LRHS LStr MAsh
 | MAus MBri MFry MJon MRav NPri
 | SPer SPoG SPoc SWCr WGer

'Golden Chersonese' (S) | MAus

Golden Future = | GGre MJon SPoc SWCr
'Horanymoll'[PBR] (Cl)

Golden Gate = | ENot ESty
'Korgolgat' (Cl) **new**

§ Golden Jewel = | ESty MAsh SPoG SWCr
'Tanledolg'[PBR] (F/Patio)

Golden Jubilee = | CGro CTri GCoc GGre MRav
'Cocagold' (HT) | SWCr

Golden Kiss = | ECnt ESty GCoc IDic MJon SPoc
'Dicalways'[PBR] (HT) | SWCr

Golden Memories = | CGro CSBt EBee ECnt ENot ESty
'Korholesea'[PBR] (F) | GCoc GGre LGod LRHS LStr MAsh
 | MFry MJon MRMR NPri SCoo
 | SPoG SPoc SSea SWCr

Golden Moments = | MFry
'Frytranquil'[PBR] (HT)

Golden Oldie = | GCoc MFry
'Fryescape'[PBR] (HT)

§ Golden Penny = 'Rugul' | MFry MGan
(Min)

'Golden Rambler' | see *R.* 'Alister Stella Gray'

'Golden Salmon' (Poly) | MGan

'Golden Shot' (F) | MGan

'Golden Showers' (Cl) | More than 30 suppliers
♥[H4]

'Golden Slippers' (F) | CBcs MGan

'Golden Sunblaze' | see *R.* 'Rise 'n Shine'

§ Golden Symphonie = | SWCr
'Meitoleil' (Min/Patio)

Golden Tribute = | MGan
'Horannfree' (F)

Golden Trust = | GGre LStr SPoG
'Hardish'[PBR] (Patio)

Golden Wedding = | CGro CSBt CWSG EBee ECnt ELan
'Arokris'[PBR] (F/HT) | ENot EPfP ESty GCoc GGre IArd
 | LAst LGod LRHS LStr MAsh MAus
 | MFry MAsh MJon MRav NBPC
 | NPri NWea SPer SPoG SPoc SSea
 | SWCr

'Golden Wedding | ESty GGre
Celebration'

'Golden Wings' (S) ♥[H4] | CHad CTri ECnt ELan EPfP GCoc
 | LRHS LStr MAsh MAus MFry MAsh
 | MJon MRav SEND SPer SPoc SSea
 | SWCr WAct WHCG

'Goldfinch' (Ra) | CHad EBee ELan EMFP EWTr LRHS
 | LStr MAsh MAus MBri MRav NEgg
 | NSRo SPer SPoG SPoc SWCr WAct
 | WHCG

§ 'Goldkrone' (HT) | SWCr

§ Goldstar = 'Candide' (HT) | ECnt MGan

Good as Gold = | CSBt ECnt ESty LStr MBri MFry
'Chewsunbeam'[PBR] | MJon MRMR MWgw NPri SPer
(ClMin) | SPoG SPoc SSea SWCr WGer

Good Life = | GCoc GGre SCoo SPoG SWCr
'Cococircus'[PBR] (HT)

Good Luck = | GCoc
'Burspec'[PBR] (F/Patio)

Good News 95 = | GGre SWCr
'Chespink'[PBR]

§ Gordon Snell = | IDic
'Dicwriter' (F)

Gordon's College = | ESty GCoc MFry MJon
'Cocjabby'[PBR] (F) ♥[H4]

Grace Abounding' (F) | MJon

Grace = 'Auskeppy'[PBR] (S) | CSBt ECnt EPfP LGod MAsh MAus
 | MBri MJon NEgg SWCr

Grace de Monaco = | MGan
'Meimit' (HT)

'Grace Kimmins' (F) **new**	EBee
Gracious Queen =) 'Bedqueen' (HT	GCoc SWCr
Graham Thomas = 'Ausmas'^{PBR} (S) ♀H4	More than 30 suppliers
Grand Amore = 'Korliegra' (HT) **new**	ENot GCoc
Grand Hotel = 'Mactel' (ClHT)	SPer
Grand-mère Jenny = 'Grem' (HT)	MGan
'Grandpa Dickson' (HT)	CSBt CWSG GGre LAst LGod MAsh MAus MGan MJon MRav NPri SPer SWCr WBVN
Granny's Favourite (F)	GGre SWCr
Great Expectations = 'Jacdal' (F)	EBee ENot SPoG
Great Expectations = 'Lanican' (HT)	CBcs
Great Expectations = 'Mackalves'^{PBR} (F)	CSBt ECnt EPfP ESty GCoc IArd LGod LRHS LStr MAsh MFry MJon SCoo SPer SPoc SWCr
§ 'Great Maiden's Blush' (A)	GCoc MRMR MRav NBPC NLar SFam SPoc WAct
'Great News' (F)	MAus
'Green Diamond' (Min)	MJon
Greenall's Glory = 'Kirmac'^{PBR} (F/Patio)	MAus MJon SPoG
'Greenmantle' (RH)	MAus
Greensleeves = 'Harlenten' (F)	SPer SPoc SWCr
Greetings = 'Jacdreco'^{PBR} (F)	IDic MAsh MRav SWCr
Grenadine = 'Poulgrena'^{PBR} (HT)	EBee ECnt SPoc
Grimaldi = 'Delstror' (F)	SPoc SWCr
'Grootendorst'	see *R.* 'F.J. Grootendorst'
'Grootendorst Supreme' (Ru)	MAus SPer
N 'Gros Choux de Hollande' (Bb)	WHCG
§ Grouse 2000 = 'Korteilhab'^{PBR} (GC)	ENot
Grouse = 'Korimro'^{PBR} (S/GC) ♀H4	CTri GCoc MAus MJon MRav SPer SWCr WAct WOVN
'Gruss an Aachen' (Poly)	EPfP EWTr LStr MAus MGan SPer SWCr WAct WHCG
'Gruss an Teplitz' (China hybrid)	MAus SPer WHCG
'Guinée' (ClHT)	CHad CSBt EBee ECnt ELan ENot EPfP ESty EWTr LAst LRHS LStr MAus MGan MRav MWgw NPri SPer SPla SPoG SPoc SSea SWCr WHCG
'Gustav Grünerwald' (HT)	MAus
Guy Savoy = 'Delstrimen' (F)	SPoc
Gwen Mayor = 'Cocover'^{PBR} (HT)	GCoc GGre SWCr
Gwent = 'Poulurt'^{PBR} (GC)	CSBt ELan GCoc LSRN LStr MAus MRMR MRav SPer SSea SWCr WAct WOVN
§ *gymnocarpa* var. *willmottiae*	MGan SPer SSea WAct WHCG
Gypsy Boy	see *R.* 'Zigeunerknabe'
'Hakuun' (F/Patio) ♀H4	MAus MGan SWCr
Hallé = 'Fryelectric'^{PBR} (HT)	EBee MFry
'Hamburger Phönix' (Ra)	CGro MGan SPer WAct
Hampshire = 'Korhamp'^{PBR} (GC)	MAus MGan MRav
Hand in Hand = 'Haraztec'^{PBR} (Patio/Min)	GGre MAsh SPoG SPoc SWCr
Handel = 'Macha' (Cl) ♀H4	CGro CSBt CTri CWSG ELan ENot EPfP ESty GGre LAst LRHS LStr

	MAsh MBri MFry MGan MJon MRav SPer SPoG SPoc SSea SWCr WBVN
Hanky Panky = 'Wektorcent'^{PBR}	GCoc MJon
Hannah Gordon = 'Korweiso'^{PBR} (F)	ECnt ENot MGan SSea SWCr
'Hanne' (HT)	NBlu
'Hansa' (Ru)	EBee GCoc LBuc MAus MGan SPer SWCr WHCG WOVN
Happy Anniversary = 'Bedfranc'^{PBR}	ESty MJon NPri SWCr
Happy Anniversary = 'Delpre' (F)	CGro GGre LRHS LStr MAsh MRav SPoG SSea
'Happy Birthday' (Min/Patio)	CWSG ESty GGre LStr SPoG SWCr
Happy Child = 'Auscomp'^{PBR} (S)	CWSG LRHS MAus MJon SCoo SPer SPoc SWCr
Happy Ever After = 'Dicvanilla'^{PBR} (F)	IDic
Happy Retirement = 'Tantoras'^{PBR} (F)	ESty GCoc LRHS LStr MAsh NPri SCoo SPoG SPoc SSea SWCr
'Happy Thought' (Min)	CWSG
Happy Times = 'Bedone'^{PBR} (Patio/Min)	GGre LRHS MAsh SPoG SWCr
Harewood = 'Taninaso'^{PBR} (Patio/F)	MRav
§ x *harisonii* 'Harison's Yellow' (PiH)	MAus MRMR SPer
§ - 'Williams' Double Yellow' (PiH)	EWTr GCoc MAus WAct
Harlow Carr = 'Aushouse' **new**	MAus
Harper Adams = 'Fryflash'^{PBR} (F)	MFry
'Harry Edland' (F)	GGre SPoG SSea SWCr
'Harry Wheatcroft' (HT)	CBcs CGro MAus MGan SPer SWCr
Harvest Fayre = 'Dicnorth'^{PBR} (F)	CGro CTri GGre IDic MGan SPer
'Headleyensis'	MAus WHCG
Heart of Gold = 'Coctarlotte'^{PBR} (HT)	ECnt GCoc MFry
§ Heartbeat '97 = 'Cocorona'^{PBR} (F)	GCoc GGre SWCr
Heartbreaker = 'Weksibyl' (Min)	MJon
Heather Austin = 'Auscook'^{PBR} (S)	LRHS MAus
§ 'Heather Muir' (*sericea* hybrid) (S)	MAus
'Heaven Scent' (F)	MJon
Heavenly Rosalind = 'Ausmash'^{PBR} (S)	LRHS MAus
'Hebe's Lip' (DxSwB)	MAus WAct
§ 'Helen Knight' (*ecae* hybrid) (S)	MAsh MAus MBri SSea WHCG
Helena = 'Poulna'^{PBR} (S)	ECnt LRHS MAsh SPoc SWCr
helenae	CTri EBee GCal MAus MRMR SPer WHCG
- hybrid	WHCG
hemisphaerica (S)	MAus WAct
§ 'Henri Martin' (CeMo)	MAus NLar SPer SPoc SWCr WAct WHCG
Henri Matisse = 'Delstrobla' (HT)	SWCr
'Henry Nevard' (HP)	MAus
Her Majesty = 'Dicxotic'^{PBR} (F)	IDic
§ 'Herbstfeuer' (RH)	MAus SPer
Heritage = 'Ausblush'^{PBR} (S)	EBee ELan ENot EPfP EWTr GCoc LGod LRHS LStr MAus MFry MRMR MRav MWgw NEgg SPer SPla SPoG SPoc SWCr WHCG WOVN

'Hermosa' (Ch) — EBee LAst LRHS MAus MRav NBPC SPla SPoc SWCr WAct WHCG XPep

Hero = 'Aushero' (S) — MAus

Hertfordshire = 'Kortenay'PBR (GC) ♀H4 — ELan ENot MAus MRav NPri SPer SWCr

Hi Society = 'Cocquation'PBR (Patio) — GCoc

'Hidcote Gold' (S) — MAus

Hide and Seek = 'Diczodiac'PBR (F) — GCoc IDic

High Flier = 'Fryfandango' (Cl) — MFry

High Hopes = 'Haryup'PBR (Cl) ♀H4 — CSBt EBee ECnt GGre LGod LRHS LStr MAsh MAus MGan MJon SPer SPla SPoG SPoc SSea SWCr WHCG

§ 'Highdownensis' (*moyesii* hybrid) (S) — ELan MAus MRMR SPer

Highfield = 'Harcomp'PBR (Cl) — CSBt MAus MRav SPer SPoc SWCr

Hilda Murrell = 'Ausmurr' (S) — MAus

§ 'Hillieri' (S) — MAus

'Hippolyte' (G) — MAus

holy rose — see *R.* x *richardii*

Home of Time = 'Cocquamber'PBR (HT) — ESty GCoc

Home Sweet Home = 'Mailoeur' (Cl/G) — SPoc SSea SWCr

Homère (T) — MAus

Honey Bunch = 'Cocglen'PBR (F) — ESty GCoc GGre LStr SPer SWCr

Honeymoon — see *R.* 'Honigmond'

Honeywood = 'Fryfixit'PBR (F) — GCoc MFry

§ 'Honigmond' (F) — CWSG SWCr

'Honorine de Brabant' (Bb) — CHad CPou LRHS MAus SPer SPla SPoc SWCr WAct WHCG

Hospitality = 'Horcoff'PBR (F) — ESty MJon

Hot Chocolate = 'Wekpaltez' (F) **new** — ECnt ESty GCoc MFry

Hot Stuff = 'Maclarayspo' (Min) — MJon

Hot Tamale = 'Jacpoy' (Min) — MJon

House Beautiful = 'Harbingo'PBR (Patio) — MRav

'Hugh Dickson' (HP) — MAus SPoc

hugonis — see *R. xanthina* f. *hugonis*

- 'Plenissima' — see *R. xanthina* f. *hugonis*

'Hula Girl' (Min) — LGod

Humanity = 'Harcross'PBR — MRav

'Hunter' (Ru) — WAct

Hyde Hall = 'Ausbosky' — LRHS MAsh MAus SCoo SWCr

I Love You = 'Geelove' (HT) — ESty

Ice Cream = 'Korzuri'PBR (HT) ♀H4 — CWSG ENot ESty LStr MAus MGan MJon MRav NBpG SPoc SSea SWCr

§ Iceberg = 'Korbin' (F) ♀H4 — CBcs CGro CSBt CWSG EBee ECnt ENot EPfP ESty GCoc GGre LAst LGod LRHS LStr MAsh MAus MFry MGan MJon MRMR MRav NBlu SPer SPoG SPoc SSea SWCr WAct WBVN

'Iced Ginger' (F) — CGro MGan SPer SWCr

'Illusion' (Cl/F) — SPoc SWCr

§ Imagination = 'Pouldron'PBR (F) — MAsh

§ 'Impératrice Joséphine' ♀H4 — CSam MAsh MAus MRav NBPC NEgg SFam SWCr WAct WHCG

In the Pink = 'Peaverity' (F) — SPoc SWCr

Incognito = 'Briincog' (Min) — MJon

Indian Summer = 'Peaperfume'PBR (HT) ♀H4 — CSBt CWSG GCoc GGre LAst LGod MBri MFry MRav SPoc SWCr

'Indica Major' — XPep

'Indigo' (DPo) — CPou MAus SWCr WHCG

Ingrid Bergman = 'Poulman'PBR (HT) ♀H4 — ECnt ENot ESty GCoc GGre LGod LStr MAus MFry MGan MJon MRav SPoc SWCr

§ Innocence = 'Cocoray'PBR (Patio) — GCoc

Intense Cover = 'Poultw001'PBR (GC/S) — MAsh SWCr

§ Intrigue = 'Korlech'PBR (F) — CSBt ENot LStr MJon SSea SWCr

Invincible = 'Runatru'PBR (F) — EBee ECnt MFry MGan SWCr

'Ipsilanté' (G) — MAus WAct WHCG

'Irène Watts' (Ch) — CPou EBee ECre EPfP EWTr MAus SPla SPoc SSea SWCr WAct WHCG

Irish Eyes = 'Dicwitness'PBR (F) — CWSG ECnt EPfP ESty GCoc IArd IDic LGod LRHS LStr MAsh MBri MFry MGan MJon MRav MRMR NPri SCoo SPer SPoG SPoc SSea SWCr

Irish Hope = 'Harexclaim'PBR (F) — SCoo SPoG SPoc SWCr

Irresistible = 'Tinresist' (Min/Patio) — MJon

Isabella = 'Poulisab'PBR (S) — CPou CTri ECnt EPfP LRHS MAsh SPoG SWCr

Isobel Derby = 'Horethel' (HT) — MJon SPoc SWCr

'Ispahan' (D) ♀H4 — CFee CHad EPfP EWTr LRHS MAus NEgg NLar NSRo SFam SPer SPoc SWCr WAct WHCG

Jack Wood = 'Frydabble'PBR (F) — MFry

Jack's Wish = 'Kirsil' (HT) — MJon

§ x *jacksonii* 'Max Graf' (GC/Ru) — LRHS MAus MGan MRav WAct WFar

- White Max Graf = 'Korgram'PBR (GC/Ru) — MRav WAct

Jacobite rose — see *R.* x *alba* 'Alba Maxima'

'Jacpico'PBR — see *R.* 'Pristine'

Jacqueline du Pré = 'Harwanna'PBR (S) ♀H4 — CSBt EBee ECnt EPfP ESty GCoc LRHS MAus MGan MJon MRav SPer SPoc SWCr WAct WHCG

Jacquenetta = 'Ausjac' (S) — MAus

N 'Jacques Cartier' hort. — see *R.* 'Marchesa Boccella'

James Galway = 'Auscrystal'PBR (S) — CSBt CWSG LGod LRHS LStr MAus MJon NEgg SCoo SWCr

'James Mason' (G) — CSam MAus

'James Mitchell' (CeMo) — MAus SSea WHCG

'James Veitch' (DPoMo) — MAus WHCG

Jane Asher = 'Peapet'PBR (Min/Patio) — MJon SWCr

Jane Eyre = 'Mehpark'PBR (Cl) — COtt

Janet = 'Auspishus' (S) — CSBt LRHS MAus

'Janet's Pride' (RH) — MAus

§ 'Japonica' (CeMo) — MAus

§ Jardins de Bagatelle = 'Meimafris' (HT) — MJon

Jayne Austin = 'Ausbreak'PBR (S) — CSBt CWSG LRHS MAus SPer SWCr

Jazz PBR (Cl) — see *R.* That's Jazz

'Jazz' (F) **new** — MRMR

'Jean Armour' (F) — GGre

Jean = 'Coupland' (Patio) — GCoc

Jean Kenneally = 'Tineally' (Min) — MJon

'Jean Mermoz' (Poly) — MAus

'Jeanie Deans' (RH) — MAus

'Jeanne de Montfort' (CeMo)   MAus

'Jenny Duval' misapplied   see *R.* 'Président de Sèze'

'Jenny Wren' (F)   MAus

'Jenny's Dream' (HT)   LGod

Jenny's Rose = 'Cansit' (F)   EBee ECnt

'Jens Munk' (Ru)   NHaw WAct

Jillian McGredy = 'Macarnhe' (F)   MJon

Jill's Rose = 'Ganjil'^PBR (F)   MGan SPoc SWCr

'Jimmy Greaves' (HT)   MGan

Jive = 'Poulyc009' (Cl) **new**   ECnt

'Joanne' (HT)   MJon

'John Cabot' (S)   SSea

John Clare = 'Auscent'^PBR (S)   MAsh MAus SWCr

'John Hopper' (HP)   MAus SWCr

John Willan = 'Fryeager' (HT)   MFry

Johnnie Walker = 'Frygran'^PBR (HT)   ESty MFry

'Josephine Bruce' (HT)   CBcs CSBt LGod MGan MRav SWCr

'Joseph's Coat' (S/Cl)   IArd LGod LStr MFry MGan SSea SWCr

'Journey's End' (HT)   MGan

Jubilee Celebration' (F)   EPfP

Jubilee Celebration = 'Aushunter' (S)   CSBt EPfP LRHS MAus SWCr

Jude the Obscure = 'Ausjo'^PBR (S)   ESty LRHS MAus MJon NEgg SWCr

'Judy Fischer' (Min)   LGod

'Julia's Rose' (HT)   CGro LStr MAus MGan MJon SPer SPoc SSea SWCr

jundzillii   CFee

'Juno' (Ce)   MAus WAct WHCG

'Just for You' (F)   GGre SWCr

'Just Jenny' (Min)   MJon

'Just Joey' (HT) ♀H4   CGro CSBt CWSG ECnt ELan ENot EPfP GCoc GGre IArd LAst LGod LRHS LStr MAsh MAus MBri MFry MGan MJon MRav NPri SPer SPoG SPoc SSea SWCr

'Kanegem' (HT) **new**   NBlu

'Karl Foerster' (PiH)   MAus

'Katharina Zeimet' (Poly)   CPou MAus MGan NLar WAct WHCG

Katherine Mansfield = 'Meilanein' (HT)   CSBt

'Kathleen Ferrier' (F)   MGan

'Kathleen Harrop' (Bb)   EWTr LRHS LStr MAus SFam SPer SPoc SSea SWCr WAct WHCG

Kathleen's Rose = 'Kirkitt' (F)   MJon

Kathryn McGredy = 'Macauclad'^PBR (HT)   ESty MJon

§ Kathryn Morley = 'Ausclub'^PBR (F)   LRHS MAus

'Katie' (ClF)   MGan SWCr

'Kazanlik' misapplied   see *R.* 'Professeur Emile Perrot'

Keep in Touch = 'Hardrama'^PBR (F)   SPoc

Keep Smiling = 'Fryflorida' (HT)   ESty MFry

Keepsake = 'Kormalda' (HT)   MGan MJon

§ Kent = 'Poulcov'^PBR (S/GC) ♀H4   ECnt ELan ENot EPfP ESty EWTr GCoc LStr MAsh MFry MGan MJon MRMR MRav NPri SPer SPla SPoG SPoc SSea SWCr WAct WHCG

'Kew Rambler' (Ra)   CRHN CSam EBee EMFP EWTr MAus MRav SEND SFam SPer SPoc WHCG

'Kiese' (*canina* hybrid)   NHaw

'Kiftsgate'   see *R. filipes* 'Kiftsgate'

'Kilworth Gold' (HT)   MGan

Kind Regards = 'Peatiger' (F)   LAst

King's Macc = 'Frydisco' (HT)   ESty LGod MAus MFry SWCr

'King's Ransom' (HT)   CBcs CSBt MGan MJon MRav SPer SPoG SSea SWCr

Knock Out = 'Dadler' (F)   MJon

§ 'Königin von Dänemark' (A) ♀H4   CHad CSam EPfP GCoc MAus MJon MRav NEgg NSRo SPer SPoc SSea SWCr WAct WHCG

Korona = 'Kornita' (F)   MGan SPer

'Korresia' (F)   CSBt CTri ECnt ENot EPfP ESty GCoc GGre LAst LGod LStr MAsh MAus MBri MFry MGan MJon MRav SPer SPoG SPoc SWCr

§ Kristin = 'Benmagic' (Min)   MJon

§ Krönberg = 'Poultry'^PBR (F)   EPfP MAsh

'Kronprinzessin Viktoria' (Bb)   MAus WHCG

L.D. Braithwaite = 'Auscrim'^PBR (S) ♀H4   CGro CTri ELan EPfP ESty GCoc LAst LGod LRHS LStr MAus MFry MJon MRMR MRav NEgg NPri SPer SPoc SWCr WAct WHCG

La Bamba = 'Diczoom'^PBR (GC)   IDic

'La Belle Distinguée' (RH)   MAus WHCG

'La Belle Sultane'   see *R.* 'Violacea'

'La France' (HT)   MAus NBPC

'La Mortola'   see *R. brunonii* 'La Mortola'

'La Perle' (Ra)   CRHN MAus

'La Reine Victoria'   see *R.* 'Reine Victoria'

'La Rubanée'   see *R.* x *centifolia* 'Unique Panachée'

La Sévillana = 'Meigekanu'^PBR (F/GC)   SPer SWCr WAct WOVN

'La Ville de Bruxelles' (D) ♀H4   MAus MRav SFam SPer WAct WHCG

'Lady Curzon' (Ru)   MAus

'Lady Gay' (Ra)   EBee SWCr WHCG

'Lady Godiva' (Ra)   MAus

'Lady Hillingdon' (T)   MAus

'Lady Hillingdon' (ClT)   see *R.* 'Climbing Lady Hillingdon'

'Lady Iliffe' (HT)   MGan SWCr

Lady in Red = 'Sealady' (Min)   MJon

'Lady Love '95' (Patio)   MAsh SPoG SWCr

Lady MacRobert = 'Coclent' (F)   GCoc

Lady Penelope = 'Chewdor'^PBR (ClHT)   CSBt MAsh MFry MJon SSea SWCr

§ 'Lady Penzance' (RH) ♀H4   CBcs CGro MAus MGan SPer SPoc SWCr

§ Lady Rachel = 'Candoodle' (F)   EBee ECnt

Lady Rose = 'Korlady' (HT)   MAsh SWCr

'Lady Sylvia' (HT)   CSBt CTri MAus MGan MRMR NEgg SPer

'Lady Waterlow' (ClHT)   EBee MAus NLar SPer SWCr WHCG

laevigata (Ra)   CArn MAus NLar XPep

- 'Anemonoides'   see *R.* 'Anemone'

L'Aimant = 'Harzola'^PBR (F) ♀H4   CSBt ESty GCoc LGod LStr MAus MFry MGan SPoc SWCr

'Lamarque' (N)   CPou EBee MAus

§ Lambert Castle = 'Poulcs006'^PBR (F)   MAsh

'Laminuette' (F)   MJon

§ Lancashire = 'Korstesgli'^PBR (GC) ♀H4   ECnt ENot ESty GCoc LGod LSRN LStr MAus MRav SSea SWCr

Laura Anne = 'Cocclarion' (HT)   GCoc

§ Laura Ashley = 'Chewharla' (GC/ClMin) — MAus

Laura Ford = 'Chewvarvel'^PBR (ClMin) ♀H4 — CGro CSBt CTri ENot ESty GGre LRHS LStr MAsh MAus MBri MJon MRav NPri SPer SPoG SSea SWCr

§ 'Laura Jane' (HT) — MGan

'Laure Davoust' (Ra) — CPou

'Lavender Jewel' (Min) — MAus

'Lavender Lassie' (HM) ♀H4 — CSam MAus MGan SPer SPoc SSea SWCr WHCG

'Lavender Pinocchio' (F) — MAus

§ Lawinia = 'Tanklewi'^PBR (ClHT) ♀H4 — CSBt EPfP LRHS LStr MAsh MJon MRav NPri SPer SSea SWCr

'Lawrence Johnston' (Cl) — LRHS MAus MJon SPer

§ Lazy Days = 'Poulkalm'^PBR (F) — ECnt EPfP MAsh SPoG

'Le Rêve' (Cl) — MAus

'Le Vésuve' (Ch) — MAus

Leander = 'Auslea' (S) — MAus

Leaping Salmon = 'Peamight'^PBR (ClHT) — CGro CSBt EBee ELan GCoc LAst LGod LStr MAus MGan MRav SPer SPoc SSea SWCr

'Leda' (D) — LAst MAus SFam SPer SSea SWCr WAct

§ Ledreborg = 'Poulcs004'^PBR (F) — MAsh

'Lemon Pillar' — see *R*. 'Paul's Lemon Pillar'

Léonardo de Vinci = 'Meideauri'^PBR (F) — CSBt

'Léontine Gervais' (Ra) — CAbP CRHN LRHS MAus NLar SPoc SWCr WAct

Leslie's Dream = 'Dicjoon'^PBR (HT) — IDic MJon

'Leverkusen' (Cl) ♀H4 — CHad EBee LRHS MAus MGan MJon MRMR MRav NEgg SPer SPla SPoc SWCr WAct WHCG

x *Iheritieriana* (Bs) — SWCr

§ Lichtkönigin Lucia = 'Korlillub' (S) — SSea

Life Begins at 40! = 'Horhohoho' (F) — GGre SPoG SWCr

'Lilac Dream' (F) — GGre SPoG SWCr

§ Lilac Rose = 'Auslilac' (S) — MAus

Lilian Austin = 'Ausli' (S) — MAus MBri

Liliana = 'Poulsyng'^PBR (S) — ECnt LRHS MAsh SPla SPoG SWCr

§ Lilli Marlene = 'Korlima' (F) — CSBt CWSG GCoc GGre MGan SPer SWCr

Lincoln Cathedral = 'Glanlin'^PBR (HT) — MJon SPer

'Lionheart' (HT) — GGre SWCr

Lions International = 'Frycharm'^PBR (HT) — MFry

Lisa = 'Kirdisco' (F) **new** — MJon

Little Bo-peep = 'Poullen'^PBR (Min/Patio) ♀H4 — MJon

'Little Buckaroo' (Min) — LGod SPer SWCr

'Little Flirt' (Min) — MAus MGan SWCr

'Little Gem' (DPMo) — MAus MGan

Little Jackie = 'Savor' (Min) — MJon

Little Muff = 'Horluisbond' (Min) — MJon

Little Rambler = 'Chewramb'^PBR (MinRa) ♀H4 — CSBt ECnt ELan ENot LRHS LStr MAsh MAus MFry MJon SCoo SPer SPoG SPoc SSea SWCr WGer

'Little White Pet' — see *R*. 'White Pet'

Little Woman = 'Diclittle'^PBR (Patio) — IDic LStr

'Liverpool Echo' (F) — MJon

§ Liverpool Remembers = 'Frystar'^PBR (HT) — MFry

Lochinvar = 'Ausbilda' (S) — MAus

Lolita Lempicka = 'Meizincaro' (HT) — SPoc SWCr

§ Lolita = 'Litakor' (HT) **new** — SSea

'Long John Silver' (Cl) — MAus SSea

longicuspis misapplied — see *R. mulliganii*

longicuspis Bertoloni (Ra) — SPla
- AC 2097 — GGar

§ - var. *sinowilsonii* (Ra) — GCal MAus
aff. *longicuspis* AC 1808 — GGar

§ Lord Byron = 'Meitosier' (ClHT) — MBri MJon NBlu SSea SWCr

'Lord Penzance' (RH) — CBgR MGan MRav SPer SPoc

Lorna = 'Cocringer' (F) **new** — GCoc MJon

'L'Ouche' misapplied — see *R*. 'Louise Odier'

'Louis Gimard' (CeMo) — MAus SPer WAct

'Louis XIV' (Ch) — CHad WHCG

Louisa Stone = 'Harbadge' (S) — GGre

§ 'Louise Odier' (Bb) — EBee ECnt EPfP IArd LRHS LStr MAus MBri MJon MRMR MRav MWgw NBPC SFam SPer SPla SPoc SSea SWCr WAct WHCG WOVN

Love (F) **new** — COtt

Love & Peace = 'Baipeace'^PBR (HT) — ELan ESty SPoc SWCr

Love Knot = 'Chewglorious'^PBR (ClMin) — CSBt ECnt ESty MAsh MBri MJon SCoo SPoc SWCr WGor

Lovely Fairy = 'Spevu'^PBR (Poly/GC) — IDic MAsh SWCr WAct

Lovely Lady = 'Dicjubell'^PBR (HT) ♀H4 — CSBt CTri ECnt ESty IDic LStr MGan MJon MRav SPoc SSea SWCr

Lovely Meidiland = 'Meiratcan'^PBR (Patio) — MAsh SWCr

'Lovers' Meeting'^PBR (HT) — GGre MGan MRav SPer SSea SWCr

Loving Memory = 'Korgund'^PBR (HT) — CGro CSBt CWSG ECnt ENot ESty GCoc GGre IArd LStr MFry MGan MJon MRav NPri SPer SPoG SPoc SWCr

Lucetta = 'Ausemi' (S) — MAus SPer

luciae var. *onoei* — CLyd

'Lucy Ashton' (RH) — MAus

Lucy = 'Kirlis' (F) — MJon

Ludlow Castle^PBR — see *R*. England's Rose

'Lykkefund' (Ra) — MAus

'Mabel Morrison' (HP) — MAus

Macartney rose — see *R. bracteata*

Macmillan Nurse = 'Beamac' (S) — ESty

'Macrantha' (Gallica hybrid) — LRHS MAsh MAus WAct

macrophylla — MAus
- B&SWJ 2603 — WCru

§ - 'Master Hugh' ♀H4 — MAus

'Madame Abel Chatenay' (HT) — MAus

'Madame Alfred Carrière' (N) ♀H4 — More than 30 suppliers

'Madame Alice Garnier' (Ra) — CPou EBee SPer

Madame Bovary = 'Deljam' (S) — SPoc

'Madame Bravy' (T) — MAus

'Madame Butterfly' (HT) — MAus MGan SFam SSea SWCr

§ 'Madame Caroline Testout' (HT) — LRHS MRav SFam SPoG WAct

'Madame de Sancy de Parabère' (Bs) — IArd MAus SFam WHCG

'Madame Delaroche-Lambert' (DPMo) — CPou EBee MAus WAct WHCG

'Madame Driout' (ClT) — WHCG

'Madame Ernest Calvat' (Bb) — CPou EBee MAus SWCr

'Madame Eugène Résal' misapplied — see *R*. 'Comtesse du Caÿla'

Madame Figaro = 'Delrona' (S) — SPoc

'Madame Georges Bruant' (Ru) — MAus

§ 'Madame Grégoire Staechelin' (ClHT) ♀H4 — CWSG EBee ECnt ELan ENot EPfP EWTr LAst LRHS LStr MAus MBri MGan MJon MRav NEgg SFam SMad SPer SPoG SPoc SWCr WAct WHCG

'Madame Hardy' (ClD) ♀H4 — CBgR CPou CSBt EPfP EWTr EGoc LGod LRHS LStr MAus MGan MJon MRav NEgg SFam SPer SPoc SSea SWCr WAct WHCG WOVN

'Madame Isaac Pereire' (ClBb) ♀H4 — CHad CSBt CTri EBee ECnt ENot EPfP ESty EGoc LGod LRHS LStr MAsh MAus MDun MFry MGan MJon MRMR MRav NEgg SFam SMad SPer SPoc SSea SWCr WAct WHCG

'Madame Jules Gravereaux' (ClT) — MAus

'Madame Jules Thibaud' (Poly) — MAus

§ 'Madame Knorr' (DPo) ♀H4 — CBgR CPou EBee ECnt EPfP EWTr MAsh MWgw NBPC SPer SPoc SSea SWCr WAct WOVN

'Madame Laurette Messimy' (Ch) — EBee MAus WHCG

'Madame Lauriol de Barny' (Bb) — MAus MGan MRav NLar SFam SWCr WHCG

'Madame Legras de Saint Germain' (AxN) — CPou EBee MAus SFam SPer SWCr WAct WHCG

'Madame Louis Laperrière' (HT) — MAus

'Madame Louis Lévêque' (DPMo) — NLar SWCr WAct WHCG

'Madame Pierre Oger' (Bb) — EBee ECnt LRHS LStr MAus MRav SPer SPoc SWCr WAct

'Madame Plantier' (AxN) — CPou LRHS MAus MRav NHaw NLar SPer SWCr WHCG WOVN

'Madame Scipion Cochet' (T) — WHCG

'Madame Zöetmans' (D) — MAus

'Madeleine Selzer' (Ra) — MGan

'Madge' (HM) — SDix

Madrigal = 'Harextra'PBR (S/F) — SPoc SWCr

'Magenta' (S/HT) — MAus SPer

Magic Carpet = 'Jaclover'PBR (S/GC) ♀H4 — CWSG ECnt GCoc IDic MAus MFry MGan MRav NPri SPoc SSea SWCr

'Magic Fire' (Patio) — ESty

Magic Hit = 'Poulhit004'PBR (Min) — LRHS MAsh

'Magnifica' (RH) — MAus MGan

'Maid of Kent'PBR (Cl) — CSBt MGan MJon SBra SCoo SPer SWCr

'Maiden's Blush' hort. (A) ♀H4 — CTri ELan EWTr LRHS MAsh MAus MGan MRav SFam SPer SPoc SSea SWCr WHCG

'Maiden's Blush, Great' — see R. 'Great Maiden's Blush'

'Maigold' (ClPiH) ♀H4 — CBcs CGro CSam CWSG EBee ECnt ELan ENot EPfP GCoc GGre LGod LRHS LStr MAsh MAus MGan MJon MRav MWgw NEgg SMad SPer SPoG SPoc SSea SWCr WAct WHCG

§ *majalis* — GIBF

Majestic = 'Poulmp001'PBR (HT) — ECnt

Make a Wish = 'Mehpat'PBR (Min/Patio) — LStr

Maltese rose — see R. 'Cécile Brünner'

Malvern Hills = 'Auscanary'PBR (Ra) — CSBt LRHS MAus MJon

Mandarin = 'Korcelin'PBR (Min) — ENot ESty GGre LStr MJon

'Manning's Blush' (RH) — CBgR MAus MRav SSea WAct

Manou Meilland = 'Meitulimon' (HT) — SSea

'Manx Queen' (F) — MJon SWCr

Many Happy Returns = 'Harwanted'PBR (S/F) ♀H4 — CGro CSBt CWSG EBee ECnt ELan ENot EPfP GCoc GGre LAst LGod LRHS LStr MFry MGan MJon MRav SPer SPoG SPoc SSea SWCr

maracandica new — GIBF

'Marbrée' (DPo) — MAus

'Märchenland' (F/S) — MAus

§ 'Marchesa Boccella' (DPo) ♀H4 — CPou CSam CTri EBee ENot EPfP MAsh MAus MDun MGan MRMR NPri SPer SPla SPoc SSea SWCr WAct

'Marcie Gandy' (HT) — MGan

'Maréchal Davoust' (CeMo) — MAus MRav SFam WAct

'Maréchal Niel' (N) — ERea EShb MAus SPer WHCG

'Margaret' (HT) — MGan SWCr

Margaret Merril = 'Harkuly' (F/HT) ♀H4 — CSBt CWSG EBee ECnt ELan ENot EPfP ESty GCoc GGre IArd LGod LRHS LStr MAsh MAus MBri MFry MGan MJon MRMR MRav SPer SPoG SPoc SSea SWCr

Margaret's World = 'Kirbill' (F) — MJon

'Margo Koster' (Poly) — MAus

Marguerite Anne = 'Cocredward'PBR (F) — GCoc

'Marguerite Hilling' (S) ♀H4 — CAbP CTri EBee EPfP EWTr GCoc MAus MGan MRav SPer SSea WAct WHCG WOVN

Maria McGredy = 'Macturangu'PBR (HT) — MBri MJon

'Maria Theresa' (HT) — MJon

x *mariae-graebnerae* — MAus SLPl WHCG

'Marie Louise' (D) — MAus SFam WAct WHCG

'Marie Pavič' (Poly) — CHad MAus WHCG

'Marie van Houtte' (T) — MAus

'Marie-Jeanne' (Poly) — MAus

'Marijke Koopman' (HT) — MFry

Marinette = 'Auscam'PBR (S) — MAus MJon

Mario Lanza = 'Horaardvark' (HT) — MJon

Marjorie Fair = 'Harhero' (Poly/S) ♀H4 — ECnt ESty MAsh MAus MGan MRav SPoc SWCr

Marjorie Marshall = 'Hardenier'PBR — SPoc

'Marlena' (F/Patio) — GCoc MAus MGan

Marry Me = 'Dicwonder'PBR (Patio) ♀H4 — ESty IDic MJon

'Martha' (Bb) — MAus

'Martian Glow' (F/S) — MGan

'Martin Frobisher' (Ru) — MAus SSea

'Mary' (Poly) — LStr

§ Mary Gammon = 'Frysweetie' (Min/Patio) — MFry

Mary Magdalene = 'Ausjolly'PBR (S) — LRHS LStr MAus NEgg SWCr

'Mary Manners' (Ru) — SPer

Mary Rose = 'Ausmary'PBR (S) ♀H4 — CGro CHad CSBt CSam CTri CWSG EBee ELan ENot EPfP ESty GCoc LGod LRHS LStr MAsh MAus MBri MFry MJon MRav NPri SPer SPoG SPoc SSea SWCr WKif

'Mary Wallace' (Cl) — MAus

Mary Webb = 'Auswebb' (S) — MAus

'Masquerade' (F) — CBcs CGro CWSG ELan ENot LStr MGan MJon MRav SPer SSea SWCr

'Master Hugh' — see R. *macrophylla* 'Master Hugh'

Matangi = 'Macman' (F) ♀H4 — MGan SWCr

Matawhero Magic^{PBR} — see *R.* Simply the Best

'Max Graf' — see *R.* x *jacksonii* 'Max Graf'

'Maxima' — see *R.* x *alba* 'Alba Maxima'

maximowicziana — GIBF

'May Queen' (Ra) — CPou EBee EMFP LRHS MAus MRav NLar SFam SPer SPoc SWCr WHCG

Mayor of Casterbridge = 'Ausbrid'^{PBR} (S) — LRHS MAus MJon

'Meg' (ClHT) — EBee EWTr LRHS MAus MGan SPer SPoc SSea SWCr WAct WHCG

'Meg Merrilies' (RH) — MAus MGan SSea WAct

'Megiddo' (F) — MGan

'Meicobuis'^{PBR} — see *R.* Terracotta = 'Meicobuis'

Mellow Yellow = 'Wekosomit' (HT) — GCoc

Melody Maker = 'Dicqueen'^{PBR} (F) ♀H4 — CWSG IDic

Memento = 'Dicbar' (F) — MGan SWCr

'Memoriam' (HT) — MGan

Memory Lane = 'Peavoodoo'^{PBR} (HT) — SPoc SWCr

§ 'Mermaid' (Cl) ♀H3-4 — CBcs CBrm CGro CSBt CWSG EBee ECnt EPfP LHop LRHS LStr MAus MGan MJon MRav SBra SMad SPer SPla SPoG SSea SWCr WAct WBVN WHCG XPep

§ Message = 'Meban' (HT) — SWCr

'Meteor' (F/Patio) — MGan

§ 'Mevrouw Nathalie Nypels' (Poly) ♀H4 — EBee EWTr LRHS LStr MAus MRav NBPC SPer SPoc SWCr WKif WOVN

§ Michael Crawford = 'Poulvue'^{PBR} (HT) — ECnt

Michel Bras = 'Deltil' (F) — SPoc

'Michèle Meilland' (HT) — MAus MJon

x *micrugosa* — MAus

- 'Alba' — MAus

'Millennium Rose 2000'^{PBR} — see *R.* Rose 2000

'Mills and Boon' (F) — MGan

Mini Metro = 'Rufin' (Min) — MFry

'Minnehaha' (Ra) — EMFP LGod MAus SSea

Minnie Pearl = 'Savahowdy' (Min) — MJon

mirifica stellata — see *R. stellata* var. *mirifica*

Mischief = 'Macmi' (HT) — GGre MGan SPer SWCr

Miss Alice = 'Ausjake'^{PBR} (S) — LRHS MAsh MAus NSRo SWCr

'Miss Edith Cavell' (Poly) — MAus

Miss Flippins = 'Tuckflip' (Min) — MJon

Missing You = 'Horcakebread' (F) **new** — MGan

§ 'Mister Lincoln' (HT) — ESty LGod MGan SPer SSea SWCr

Mistress Quickly = 'Ausky'^{PBR} (S) — CTri LRHS MAus MJon NEgg

Misty Hit = 'Poulhi011'^{PBR} (Patio) — ECnt

§ 'Moersdag' (Poly/F) — GGre LStr MJon NPri SPoG SWCr

'Mojave' (HT) — MGan

Moje Hammarberg (Ru) — MJon WAct

§ Molineux = 'Ausmol'^{PBR} (S) ♀H4 — CSBt CTri ECnt EPfP ESty GCoc LRHS MAsh MAus MBri NEgg NPri SWCr

'Monique' (HT) — MGan

Moonbeam = 'Ausbeam' (S) — MAus

'Moonlight' (HM) — CHad CTri ECnt LRHS MAus MGan MRav SPer SPoc SWCr WAct WHCG

'Morgengruss' (Cl) — MGan SWCr

Moriah = 'Ganhol'^{PBR} (HT) — MGan

'Morlettii' (Bs) — EHol MRav SWCr WHCG

'Morning Jewel' (ClF) ♀H4 — GCoc MFry MGan SPer SPoc

Morning Mist = 'Ausfire' (S) — LRHS MAus

Mortimer Sackler = 'Ausorts' (S) — MAsh MAus MBri MJon SWCr

moschata (Ra) — MAus MRMR MRav SSea SWCr WAct

- 'Autumnalis' — see *R.* 'Princesse de Nassau'

- var. *nepalensis* — see *R. brunonii*

Mother's Day — see *R.* 'Moersdag'

Mother's Joy = 'Horsiltrop' (F) — GGre SWCr

Mountain Snow = 'Aussnow' (Ra) — LRHS MAus NSRo SWCr

Mountbatten = 'Harmantelle'^{PBR} (F) ♀H4 — CBcs CGro CWSG ELan EPfP GGre LGod LRHS LStr MAsh MAus MFry MGan MJon MRav NPri SPer SPoG SPoc SSea SWCr

§ 'Mousseline' (DPoMo) — CPou EBee EWTr MAus SPer SSea WAct WHCG

'Mousseuse du Japon' — see *R.* 'Japonica'

moyesii (S) — CTri ELan ISea MAus MDun MFry MGan MJon MRMR NWea SPer WAct WOVN

- 'Evesbatch' (S) — WAct

'Mozart' (HM) — WHCG

'Mr Bluebird' (MinCh) — MAus MGan SWCr

'Mrs Anthony Waterer' (Ru) — MAus SPer WAct WHCG

Mrs Doreen Pike = 'Ausdor'^{PBR} (Ru) — MAus WAct

'Mrs Eveline Gandy' (HT) — MGan

'Mrs Honey Dyson' (Ra) — CHad

'Mrs John Laing' (HP) — EBee EPfP MAus MRav SPoc SWCr

'Mrs Oakley Fisher' (HT) — CHad EWTr MAus MBri SPer SWCr WAct WCot

'Mrs Paul' (Bb) — MAus

'Mrs Sam McGredy' (HT) — CSBt MAus MGan SSea

'Mullard Jubilee' (HT) — MGan NBlu SWCr

§ *mulliganii* (Ra) ♀H4 — EPfP MAus SWCr WAct WHCG

multibracteata (S) — MAus WHCG

multiflora (Ra) — GIBF LBuc MAus NHaw NWea WAct WPic

§ - var. *cathayensis* (Ra) — MAus WBor WHCG XPep

§ - 'Grevillei' (Ra) — CPou EBee MAus SPer

- 'Platyphylla' — see *R. multiflora* 'Grevillei'

Mummy^{PBR} — see *R.* Newly Wed = 'Dicwhynot'

mundi — see *R. gallica* 'Versicolor'

- 'Versicolor' — see *R. gallica* 'Versicolor'

'Mutabilis' — see *R.* x *odorata* 'Mutabilis'

'My Choice' (HT) — MGan SWCr

My Love = 'Cogamo' (HT) — GGre MJon

My Mum = 'Webmorrow'^{PBR} — ESty SWCr

My Valentine = 'Mormyval' (Min) — ESty

Myriam = 'Cocgrand' (HT) — GCoc

Mystique = 'Kirmyst' (F) — MJon

'München' (HM) — MAus

Nahéma = 'Deléri' (Cl) — SPoc

'Nan of Painswick' — WAct

'Narrow Water' (Ra) — CPou EBee SPoc SWCr WAct WHCG

§ 'Nastarana' (N) — EBee

'Nathalie Nypels' — see *R.* 'Mevrouw Nathalie Nypels'

'National Trust' (HT) — ENot GGre IArd MAsh MGan MJon SPer SWCr

'Nestor' (G) — MAus

'Nevada' (S) ♀H4 — CSBt ECnt ELan ENot EPfP GCoc IArd LAst LGod LStr MAsh MAus MFry MGan MRav NWea SPer SSea SWCr WAct WHCG WOVN

New Age = 'Wekbipuhit'^{PBR} (F) — ESty GCoc MJon SPoc SWCr

'New Arrival' (Patio/Min) — GCoc GGre MGan SWCr

§ 'New Dawn' (Cl) ♀H4 — More than 30 suppliers

'New Look' (F) — MGan SWCr
'New Penny' (Min) — MRav
New Zealand = 'Macgenev'[PBR] (HT) — MJon SPoc SWCr
§ Newly Wed = 'Dicwhynot'[PBR] (Patio) — IDic MJon SSea
News = 'Legnews' (F) — MAus MGan
Nice Day = 'Chewsea'[PBR] (ClMin) ♥H4 — CGro CSBt CWSG ENot EPfP ESty GGre LGod LRHS LStr MAsh MFry MJon MRav SPer SPoG SPoc SSea SWCr
'Nice 'n' Easy' (Patio) — GGre SWCr
'Nicola' (F) — MGan SWCr
Nigel Hawthorne = 'Harquibbler' (S) — WAct
Night Light = 'Poullight'[PBR] (Cl) — EBee ECnt MFry MGan MJon SPoc SWCr
Night Sky = 'Dicetch'[PBR] (F) — IDic MJon SSea
Nina = 'Mehnina'[PBR] (S) — SPoc SWCr
Nina Nadine = 'Kirhand' (F) — MJon
'Nina Weibull' (F) — SWCr
nitida — LRHS MAus MRMR NHaw NWea SPer SSea SWCr WAct WHCG WHer WOVN
Noble Antony = 'Ausway'[PBR] (S) — LRHS LStr MAus MJon SPoc SWCr
§ 'Noisette Carnée' (N) — CHad CSam EBee EPfP LStr MAus MBNS MJon MRav NBPC NLar NSRo SLPl SPer SPoc SSea SWCr WAct WHCG
Norfolk = 'Poulfolk'[PBR] (GC) — EWTr MGan SPer SPla SWCr
'Norma Major' (HT) — MJon
Northamptonshire = 'Mattdor'[PBR] (GC) — MGan MRav
'Northern Lights' (HT) — GCoc
'Norwich Pink' (Cl) — MAus
'Norwich Salmon' (Cl) — MAus
'Norwich Union' (F) — MBri
Nostalgia = 'Savarita' (Min) — ESty
Nostalgie = 'Taneiglat'[PBR] (HT) — LStr MBri MFry MJon SCoo SPoG SPoc SSea SWCr
'Nottingham Millennium' (F) — MGan
'Nova Zembla' (Ru) — MAus
'Nozomi' (ClMin/GC) ♥H4 — CGro CLyd ELan ESty GCoc GGre MAus MGan MJon MRMR MRav MWgw NWCA SMad SPer SSea SWCr WAct WHCG WOVN
'Nuits de Young' (CeMo) ♥H4 — GCoc MAus MRMR SFam SPoc SSea SWCr WHCG
'Nur Mahal' (HM) — MAus WHCG
nutkana (S) — MAus
§ - 'Plena' (S) ♥H4 — EPfP MAus MRMR NLar SFam SWCr WAct WGer WHCG
'Nymphenburg' (HM) — EWTr MAus SPer SWCr
'Nypels' Perfection' (Poly) — MAus
'Nyveldt's White' (Ru) — MAus
Octavia Hill = 'Harzeal'[PBR] (F/S) — CSBt MRav NPri SPer SWCr
§ x *odorata* — GIBF XPep
* - 'Burmese Crimson' — SLon
- 'Fortune's Double Yellow' — see *R.* x *odorata* 'Pseudindica'
§ - 'Mutabilis' (Ch) ♥H3-4 — CBgR CHad CRHN ECre EHol ENot EPfP EWTr GCoc LRHS MAus MGan MRMR SMad SMrm SPer SPoc SSea SWCr WAct WBor WCFE WCot WHCG WKif WOVN XPep
§ - 'Pallida' (Ch) — CBgR EBee EPfP GCoc MAus MRMR MRav SPer SPla SPoc SWCr WAct WHCG
§ - 'Pseudindica' (ClCh) — MAus

§ - Sanguinea Group (Ch) — WHCG XPep
- - 'Bengal Crimson' (Ch) — LRHS WCot
§ - 'Viridiflora' (Ch) — LFol MAus SMad SPer SPoc SSea SWCr WHCG
Odyssey = 'Franski'[PBR] (F) — ESty
'Oeillet Flamand' — see *R.* 'Oeillet Parfait'
'Oeillet Panaché' (Mo) — WAct
§ 'Oeillet Parfait' (G) — MAus
officinalis — see *R. gallica* var. *officinalis*
'Oklahoma' (HT) — MGan NBlu SWCr
old blush China — see *R.* x *odorata* 'Pallida'
old cabbage — see *R.* x *centifolia*
Old John = 'Dicwillynilly'[PBR] (F) — IDic MJon
old pink moss rose — see *R.* x *centifolia* 'Muscosa'
Old Port = 'Mackati'[PBR] (F) — IArd MJon
old red moss — see *R.* 'Henri Martin'
old velvet moss — see *R.* 'William Lobb'
old yellow Scotch (PiH) — see *R.* x *harisonii* 'Williams' Double Yellow'
Oliver Roellinger = 'Delkal' (F) — SPoc
Olympic Palace = 'Poulymp'[PBR] (F) — ECnt
'Omar Khayyám' (D) — CBgR MAus MRav
omeiensis — see *R. sericea* subsp. *omeiensis*
Open Arms = 'Chewpixcel'[PBR] (ClMin) ♥H4 — ENot ESty MAsh MAus MFry MJon SPer SPoc SSea SWCr WGer
'Ophelia' (HT) — EBee MAus MGan NEgg SWCr
§ 'Orange Sensation' (F) — CTri CWSG MAus MGan
§ Orange Sunblaze = 'Meijikatar'[PBR] (Min) — CSBt MGan SPer
Orangeade (F) — MGan
§ Oranges and Lemons = 'Macoranlem'[PBR] (S/F) — CGro ECnt ELan ENot ESty GCoc LGod LStr MAus MFry MGan MJon SCoo SPoG SPoc SSea SWCr
'Oriana' (HT) — SWCr
'Orient Express' (HT) — CWSG
Othello = 'Auslo'[PBR] (S) — ESty MAus SPer WAct
Our George = 'Kirrush' (Patio) — MJon WGor
§ Our Jubilee = 'Coccages' (HT) — ESty
Our Love = 'Andour' (HT) — CWSG
Our Molly = 'Dicreason'[PBR] (GC/S) — IDic MGan MJon SWCr
Oxfordshire = 'Korfullwind'[PBR] (GC) ♥H4 — ENot LStr MRav SSea SWCr
oxycantha new — GIBF
Paddy McGredy = 'Macpa' (F) — CGro MGan
Paddy Stephens = 'Macclack'[PBR] (HT) — MFry MGan MJon SPoc SWCr
Painted Moon = 'Dicpaint'[PBR] (HT) — ESty
Panache = 'Poultop'[PBR] (Patio) — ECnt LRHS LStr MAsh
'Papa Gontier' (T) — MAus
Papa Meilland = 'Meisar' (HT) — CGro CSBt MAus MGan MJon SPer
Paper Anniversary (Patio) — SWCr
Papi Delbard = 'Delaby' (Cl) — SPoc
'Parade' (Cl) ♥H4 — MAus MFry MRav WHCG
'Paradise' (Patio) — GGre SPoG SWCr
Paradise = 'Weizeip' (HT) — MGan
'Parkdirektor Riggers' (Cl) — CHad CSam EWTr LStr MAus MBri MGan MRMR SPer SWCr WHCG
'Parkjuwel' (CeMo) new — MGan
Parson's pink China — see *R.* x *odorata* 'Pallida'
Partridge = 'Korweirim'[PBR] (GC) — ENot MAus MGan MJon SPer SWCr WAct WOVN

'Party Girl' (Min)   MJon

parvifolia =   see R. 'Burgundiaca'

Pas de Deux =   EBee LRHS MAsh SWCr
'Poulhult'PBR (Cl)

Pascali = 'Lenip' (HT)   CTri EPfP GCoc GGre MAus
MGan MJon MRav NBlu SPer
SSea SWCr

§ Pat Austin =   CSBt ECnt ESty LRHS LStr MAsh
'Ausmum'PBR (S) ♀H4   MAus MBNS MBri MJon NEgg SPoc
SWCr

Pathfinder =   MDun MJon
'Chewpobcy' (GC)

Paul Cézanne = 'Jacdeli'   SPoc
(S)

'Paul Crampel' (Poly)   MAus MGan NBir WAct

'Paul Lédé' (ClT)   see R. 'Climbing Paul Lédé'

'Paul Neyron' (HP)   EWTr MAus SPer WHCG

'Paul Ricault' (CexHP)   MAus

Paul Shirville =   ELan ESty MAus MGan MRav SPer
'Harqueterwife'PBR   SWCr
(HT) ♀H4

'Paul Transon' (Ra) ♀H4   CPou CRHN EBee EMFP LRHS
MAsh MAus MRMR NEgg SPer
SPoc SWCr WHer

§ 'Paulii' (Ru)   CArn MAus WAct WOVN

'Paulii Alba'   see R. 'Paulii'

'Paulii Rosea' (Ru/Cl)   MAus WAct

'Paul's Himalayan Musk'   More than 30 suppliers
(Ra) ♀H3-4

§ 'Paul's Lemon Pillar' (ClHT)   EWTr LRHS MAus MBNS SPer SSea
SWCr

'Paul's Perpetual White'   MRMR WHCG
(Ra)

'Paul's Scarlet Climber'   CGro CSBt ECnt ELan ENot EPfP
(Cl/Ra)   GGre LAst LGod LRHS LStr MAsh
MAus MGan MJon MRav NBlu
NEgg NPri SPer SWCr WBVN

'Pax' (HM)   CPou MAus MRMR WAct WHCG
WKif

Peace = 'Madame   CGro CSBt ECnt ELan ENot EPfP
A. Meilland' (HT) ♀H4   ESty GCoc GGre LAst LGod LRHS
LStr MAsh MAus MBri MFry MGan
MJon MRav NBlu SPer SPoG SPoc
SSea SWCr

'Peace Maker' (F) **new**   CSBt

Peacekeeper =   CSBt GGre MRav SWCr
'Harbella'PBR (F)

Peach Blossom =   MAus
'Ausblossom'PBR (S)

§ Peach Sunblaze =   SPoc
'Meixerul' (Min)

Peach Surprise =   EBee
'Poulrise'PBR (HT)

§ Pearl Abundance =   MAsh SCoo SWCr
'Harfrisky'PBR (F)

§ Pearl Anniversary =   CSBt ESty GCoc GGre LStr MRav
'Whitston'PBR   SSea SWCr
(Min/Patio)

Pearl Drift = 'Leggab' (S)   MAus MJon SPer SPoc SWCr
WHCG

Pearly King =   SWCr
'Gendee'PBR (S)

§ Peek-a-boo =   IDic MFry MGan SPer
'Dicgrow'PBR
(Min/Patio)

§ Peer Gynt = 'Korol' (HT)   GGre MGan NBlu SWCr

Pegasus = 'Ausmoon'PBR   LRHS LStr MAus MJon NEgg SPoc
(S)   SSea SWCr

§ *pendulina*   GIBF MAus NHaw WHCG
- 'Nana'   NHol

'Penelope' (HM) ♀H4   CHad CSBt CSam EBee ECnt ELan
ENot EPfP EWTr GCoc LRHS LStr
MAsh MAus MBri MFry MGan
MJon MRav MWgw SFam SPer
SPoc SSea SWCr WAct WHCG WKif
WOVN XPep

Penelope Keith =   MJon
'Macfreego'
(Min/Patio)

Penny Lane =   CGro CSBt ECnt ENot EPfP GCoc
'Hardwell'PBR (Cl) ♀H4   GGre LAst LGod LRHS LStr MAsh
MAus MBri MFry MGan MJon
MRav MWgw NPri SCoo SPer
SPoG SPoc SSea SWCr

Pensioner's Voice =   MFry MGan SWCr
'Fryrelax'PBR (F)

x *penzanceana*   see R. 'Lady Penzance'

Perception =   SPoc SWCr
'Harzippee'PBR (HT)

Perdita = 'Ausperd' (S)   CGro ESty LRHS MAus MJon MRav
SPer

Perennial Blue =   ECnt ESty SPoc SWCr
'Mehblue'

§ Perestroika =   ENot MJon
'Korhitom'PBR (F/Min)

§ Perfect Day =   ECnt
'Poulrem' (F)

§ Perfecta = 'Koralu' (HT)   MGan

'Perle des Jardins' (T)   MAus

§ 'Perle d'Or' (Poly) ♀H4   ECnt ENot EPfP LRHS MAus SPer
SWCr WAct WHCG

Perpetually Yours =   CGro GCoc GGre LStr MJon MRav
'Harfable'PBR (Cl)   SCoo SPoc SWCr

Persian yellow   see R. *foetida* 'Persiana'

'Peter Frankenfeld' (HT)   MJon

Peter Pan =   MAsh MAus MJon SWCr
'Chewpan'PBR (Min)

Peter Pan = 'Sunpete'   ENot LRHS NPri SPoG
(Patio)

'Petite de Hollande' (Ce)   MAus NLar WAct WHCG

'Petite Lisette' (CexD)   MAus NLar

Phab Gold =   ESty GCoc MFry
'Frybountiful'PBR (F)

§ Pheasant = 'Kordapt'PBR   GCoc MAus MGan MJon SPer
(GC)   SWCr WAct WHCG WOVN

Phillipa = 'Poulheart'PBR   ECnt
(S)

Phoebe (Ru)   see R. 'Fimbriata'

'Phyllis Bide' (Ra) ♀H4   CAbP EBee EMFP EPfP EWTr IArd
LRHS LStr MAus MGan MJon
MRMR NSRo SPer SPoc SSea SWCr
WAct WHCG

Picasso = 'Macpic' (F)   MGan SWCr

Piccadilly = 'Macar' (HT)   CGro CSBt CTri ENot GGre MGan
MJon MRav SPer SSea SWCr

Piccolo = 'Tanolokip'PBR   CGro ESty LStr MBri MFry MJon
(F/Patio)   SWCr

'Picture' (HT)   MGan SPer

Pierre Gagnaire =   SPoc
'Delroli' (F)

'Pilgrim'PBR   see R. The Pilgrim

Pimpernelle = 'Deldog' (S)   SPoc SWCr

pimpinellifolia   see R. *spinosissima*

Pink Abundance =   LStr MAsh SPoc SWCr
'Harfrothy'PBR (F)

Pink Bells = 'Poulbells'PBR   CGro GCoc MAus SPer WHCG
(GC)

'Pink Bouquet' (Ra)   CRHN

'Pink Favorite' (HT)   CSBt MGan SPer SWCr

Pink Fizz = 'Poulycool'   ECnt LRHS MAsh SWCr

§ Pink Flower Carpet =   CGro CSBt CTri ELan ENot EPfP
'Noatraum'PBR (GC)   GCoc GGre LRHS LStr MAsh MAus
♀H4   MFry MGan MRav SCoo SPer SPoG
SWCr

'Pink Garnette'   see R. 'Carol Amling'

'Pink Grootendorst' (Ru)   EBee EPfP MAus MGan NLar SPer
♀H4   SSea SWCr WAct WHCG

§ Pink Hit = 'Poultipe'PBR   ECnt
(Min/Patio)

Pink La Sevillana =   SWCr
'Meigeroka'PBR
(F/GC)

pink moss   see *R.* x *centifolia* 'Muscosa'
'Pink Parfait' (F)   MAus MGan SPer
'Pink Patio'^{PBR} (Patio)   GGre
Pink Peace = 'Meibil' (HT)   GGre MRav SPoG
'Pink Perpétué' (Cl)   CBcs CGro CSBt CTri ECnt
   ELan ENot EPfP GCoc GGre
   LAst LRHS LStr MAus MBri
   MGan MJon MRav SPer SPoG
   SSea SWCr WAct
'Pink Prosperity' (HM)   MAus
'Pink Showers' (ClHT)   WAct
Pink Skyliner =   MJon
   'Franwekpink' (ClS)
Pink Surprise = 'Lenbrac'   MAus
   (Ru)
Pirouette = 'Poulyc003'   ECnt LRHS MAsh MGan SWCr
   (Cl)
'Playtime' = 'Morplati' (F)   MAsh MAus
Pleine de Grâce =   LRHS MAus WAct
   'Lengra' (S)
'Plentiful' (F)   MBri
Poetry in Motion =   ESty GGre MJon SPoG SPoc SWCr
   'Harelan'^{PBR} (HT)
Polar Star =   CSBt ECnt GGre LGod LStr MFry
   'Tanlarpost'^{PBR} (HT)   MGan MRav SPer SPoG SWCr
x *polliniana*   SLPl
'Polly' (HT)   MGan SWCr
pomifera   see *R. villosa* L.
Pomona = 'Fryyeh'^{PBR} (F)   MFry
'Pompon Blanc Parfait' (A)   MAus
'Pompon de Bourgogne'   see *R.* 'Burgundiaca'
'Pompon de Paris'   see *R.* 'Climbing Pompon de Paris'
   (ClMinCh)
'Pompon Panaché' (G)   MAus
Portland rose   see *R.* 'Portlandica'
§   'Portlandica'   CGro LRHS MAsh MAus MRMR
   SPer SPoc WAct WHCG
Portmeirion =   MAus SCoo
   'Ausguard'^{PBR} (S)
Pot o' Gold =   IDic MFry MRav SPer
   'Dicdivine'^{PBR} (HT)
Pour Toi = 'Para Ti' (Min)   MAus MGan MJon NPri SWCr
prairie rose   see *R. setigera*
Precious Moments =   GGre SWCr
   'Lyopr'
'Precious Platinum' (HT)   LGod MJon MRav SPer SWCr
Preservation =   GGre SWCr
   'Bosiljurika'^{PBR} (S/F)
§   'Président de Sèze' (G)   MAus NLar SFam SPer SWCr WAct
   ♀^{H4}   WHCG
Pretty in Pink =   ECnt IDic MJon SPoc SWCr
   'Dicumpteen'^{PBR}
   (GC)
Pretty Jessica =   CGro CTri LRHS MAus MJon MRav
   'Ausjess' (S)   SPer
Pretty Lady = 'Scrivo'^{PBR}   LStr MAus MJon SPoc SSea SWCr
   (F) ♀^{H4}
Pretty Polly =   CGro CTri EPfP ESty GGre LAst
   'Meitonje'^{PBR} (Min)   LRHS LStr MAsh MBri MFry MGan
   ♀^{H4}   MJon MRav SPoG SPoc SWCr
Pride of England =   GCoc GGre MJon SPoG SWCr
   'Harencore'^{PBR} (HT)
Pride of Scotland =   GCoc MJon
   'Macwhitba' (HT)
'Prima Ballerina' (HT)   CGro CSBt CTri CWSG ENot GCoc
   GGre LAst LRHS LStr MAsh MGan
   MJon SPer SSea SWCr
primula (S) ♀^{H3-4}   EWTr MAus MGan MJon NLar
   SPoc SSea SWCr WAct WHCG
'Prince Camille de Rohan'   MAus WHCG
   (HP)
'Prince Charles' (Bb)   MAus SPoc WHCG WKif
Prince Palace =   ECnt
   'Poulzin'^{PBR} (F)
Prince Regent =   SSea
   'Genpen' (S)

Princess Alexandra =   CTri ECnt EPfP EWTr MAsh SPoc
   'Pouldra'^{PBR} (S)   SWCr
Princess Alice =   MGan MJon
   'Hartanna' (F)
Princess Nobuko =   GCoc
   'Coclistine'^{PBR} (HT)
'Princess of Wales' (HP)   EPfP MRMR
Princess of Wales =   CGro CSBt ECnt ENot GCoc GGre
   'Hardinkum'^{PBR} (F)   LRHS LStr MAsh MBri MFry MGan
   ♀^{H4}   MRav NPri SCoo SPer SPoc SWCr
Princess Royal =   GCoc IDic
   'Dicroyal'^{PBR} (HT)
§   'Princesse de Nassau'   MAus SWCr WAct WHCG
   (Ra)
'Princesse Louise' (Ra)   CRHN MAus SFam
'Princesse Marie'   see *R.* 'Belvedere'
   misapplied
§   'Pristine'^{PBR} (HT)   IDic MAus MJon SPer
N   'Professeur Emile   WAct
   Perrot' (D)
'Prolifera de Redouté'   see *R.* 'Duchesse de Montebello'
   misapplied
'Prosperity' (HM) ♀^{H4}   CBcs CTri EBee EPfP GCoc LRHS
   MAus MFry MGan MJon MRav
   MWgw SPer SWCr WAct WHCG
   WOVN
Prospero = 'Auspero' (S)   MAus MBri
Pur Caprice = 'Deljavert'   SWCr
   (S)
Pure Bliss = 'Dictator'^{PBR}   EBee ECnt GCoc IDic MGan
   (HT)
§   'Purezza' (Ra)   NLar
'Purity' (Cl)   EBee EWTr SWCr
'Purple Beauty' (HT)   MGan
Purple Skyliner =   MJon
   'Franwekpurp' (ClS)
Purple Tiger =   ESty IDic MJon SPoc SSea SWCr
   'Jacpurr'^{PBR} (F)
'Purpurtraum' (Ru)   WHCG
Quaker Star =   IDic
   'Dicperhaps' (F)
quatre saisons   see *R.* x *damascena* var.
   semperflorens
'Quatre Saisons Blanche   WAct
   Mousseuse' (DMo)
Queen Elizabeth   see *R.* 'The Queen Elizabeth'
Queen Margarethe =   ECnt
   'Poulskov'^{PBR} (F)
Queen Mother =   CSBt ELan ENot EPfP GCoc GGre
   'Korquemu'^{PBR}   LGod LRHS LStr MAus MFry MGan
   (Patio) ♀^{H4}   MRav NPri SPer SPoG SPoc SWCr
Queen of Denmark   see *R.* 'Königin von Dänemark'
Queen of Sweden =   MAus
   'Austiger' **new**
Queen's Palace =   ECnt
   'Poulelap'^{PBR} (F)
'Rachel' ambig.   GCoc
Rachel = 'Tangust'^{PBR} (HT)   ESty MJon SPoc SWCr
Racy Lady =   IDic MJon
   'Dicwaffle'^{PBR} (HT)
Radio Times =   ESty MAus
   'Aussal'^{PBR} (S)
'Rainbow' (T)   MRMR
Rainbow Magic =   ESty IDic MJon SWCr
   'Dicxplosion'^{PBR}
   (Patio)
'Ralph Tizzard' (F)   SSea
'Rambling Rector' (Ra)   More than 30 suppliers
   ♀^{H4}
'Ramona' (Ra)   MAus SWCr
§   'Raubritter' ('Macrantha'   CAbP MAus SPer SPoc SSea SWCr
   hybrid)   WAct WHCG
Ray of Hope =   GCoc LGod SWCr
   'Cocnilly'^{PBR} (F)
Ray of Sunshine =   GCoc MFry
   'Cocclare'^{PBR} (Patio)

Name	Suppliers
'Raymond Chenault' (Cl)	MGan SWCr
Razzle Dazzle = 'Frybright'^PBR (F)	MFry
Rebecca (Patio)	ESty
'Rebecca Claire' (HT)	SPoc SWCr
Reconciliation = 'Hartillery'^PBR (HT)	ESty SPoc SWCr
Red Abundance	see R. Songs of Praise
Red Bells = 'Poulred'^PBR (Min/GC)	CGro MAus MRav SPer WHCG WOVN
Red Blanket = 'Intercell' (S/GC)	GCoc MAus MGan MRav SPer WAct WOVN
§ Red Coat = 'Auscoat' (F)	MAus
§ Red Devil = 'Dicam' (HT)	GGre MAsh MGan MJon MRav SCoo SWCr
Red Eden Rose = 'Meidrason' (Cl)	SPoc SSea SWCr
Red Finesse = 'Korvillade'^PBR	ENot MFry MJon
'Red Grootendorst'	see R. 'F.J. Grootendorst'
Red Meidiland = 'Meineble'^PBR (GC)	MDun
red moss	see R. 'Henri Martin'
Red New Dawn	see R. 'Etendard'
Red Rascal = 'Jacbed'^PBR (S/Patio)	CSBt IDic MFry
red rose of Lancaster	see R. gallica var. officinalis
§ Red Sunblaze = 'Meirutral' (Min)	MJon
Red Trail = 'Interim' (S/GC)	ESty MJon
§ 'Red Wing' (S)	MAus
§ Redgold = 'Dicor' (F)	SWCr
Redouté = 'Auspale'^PBR (S)	LRHS MAus SPer SWCr
Regensberg = 'Macyoumis'^PBR (F/Patio)	MAus MFry MGan MJon MRav SPer SSea SWCr
'Reine des Centifeuilles' (Ce)	SFam
'Reine des Violettes' (HP)	CGro CHad CPou EPfP IArd LRHS LStr MAsh MAus MGan MRav SPer SPoc SWCr WAct WHCG
§ 'Reine Victoria' (Bb)	EBee EPfP LRHS LStr MAsh MAus MGan MRav SPer SPla SPoc SWCr WAct
Remember Me = 'Cocdestin'^PBR (HT) ♀^H4	CGro CWSG ECnt ENot EPfP ESty GCoc GGre IArd LGod LStr MAus MBri MFry MGan MJon MRav NPri SPer SPoG SPoc SSea SWCr
Remembrance = 'Harxampton'^PBR (F) ♀^H4	CGro CTri ESty LGod LRHS LStr MAsh MFry MGan MJon MRav NPri SPer SPoG SWCr
Renaissance = 'Harzart'^PBR (HT)	CSBt ESty GCoc LStr MFry MRav SPoc SWCr
'René André' (Ra)	CPou CRHN EMFP MAus SWCr
'René d'Anjou' (CeMo)	MAus
'Rescht'	see R. 'De Rescht'
Rest in Peace = 'Bedswap' (Patio/F)	GGre SWCr
'Rêve d'Or' (N)	CSam MAus MRMR SPer
'Réveil Dijonnais' (ClHT)	MAus
Rhapsody in Blue = 'Frantasia'^PBR (S)	CGro CSBt CTri EBee ECnt ELan ENot ESty GGre LGod LRHS LStr MAsh MAus MBri MFry MGan MJon MRMR NPri SCoo SPer SPoG SPoc SSea SWCr
§ x *richardii*	MAus MRav WAct WHCG
Ring of Fire = 'Morfire' (Patio)	SPoG
§ 'Rise 'n' Shine' (Min)	LGod
'Rival de Paestum' (T)	MAus
'River Gardens'	NPer
Rob Roy = 'Cocrob' (F)	GCoc MGan SPer SWCr
Robbie Burns = 'Ausburn' (PiH)	MAus
'Robert Burns' (HT)	GGre
'Robert le Diable' (Ce)	CPou MAus SPer SWCr WAct WHCG
'Robin Hood' (HM)	EBee
§ Robusta = 'Korgosa' (Ru)	ECnt MAus SSea
Rockabye Baby = 'Dicdwarf' (Patio) **new**	GCoc IDic
'Roger Lambelin' (HP)	MAus
Romance = 'Tanezamor'^PBR (S)	MJon MRav
'Romantic Heritage' (F)	SWCr
Romantic Palace = 'Poulmanti'^PBR (F)	ECnt
'Rosa Mundi'	see R. gallica 'Versicolor'
§ Rosabell = 'Cocceleste'^PBR (F/Patio)	ESty GCoc MFry
Rosalie Coral = 'Chewallop'^PBR (ClMin)	ESty
Rosarium Uetersen = 'Kortersen' (ClHT)	MJon
§ Rose 2000 = 'Cocquetrum'^PBR (F)	SWCr
§ 'Rose d'Amour' (S) ♀^H4	CFee MAus
'Rose de Meaux'	see R. 'De Meaux'
'Rose de Meaux White'	see R. 'White de Meaux'
'Rose de Rescht'	see R. 'De Rescht'
'Rose du Maître d'Ecole'	see R. 'Du Maître d'Ecole'
'Rose du Roi' (HP/DPo)	EWTr MAus WAct WHCG
'Rose du Roi à Fleurs Pourpres' (HP)	MAus
§ Rose Gaujard = 'Gaumo' (HT)	GGre LGod MAsh MGan NBlu SPoG SWCr
Rose of Picardy = 'Ausfudge' **new**	MAus
'Rose of Yunnan'	WAct
Rose Pearl = 'Kortserschi'^PBR (S)	ENot MGan SWCr
Rose-Marie = 'Ausome' (S)	MAus
§ 'Rose-Marie Viaud' (Ra)	CFee CPou CSam EBee MAus SWCr WHCG
'Rosemary Gandy' (F)	MGan
Rosemary Harkness = 'Harrowbond'^PBR (HT)	ESty LStr MRav SPer SPoc
'Rosemary Rose' (F)	SPer
Rosemoor = 'Austough'	CSBt LRHS MAus
Rosendal = 'Pouldahle'^PBR (F) **new**	EBee ECnt
Rosenprofessor Sieber^PBR	see R. The Halcyon Days Rose
Roseraie de l'Haÿ (Ru) ♀^H4	More than 30 suppliers
Roses des Cistercians = 'Deltisse'	SPoc SWCr
'Rosy Cheeks' (HT)	MGan SWCr
Rosy Cushion = 'Interall' (S/GC) ♀^H4	CSam MAus MGan MRav SPer SWCr WAct WHCG WOVN
Rosy Future = 'Harwaderox'^PBR (F/Patio)	CSBt SPoc SWCr
'Rosy Mantle' (Cl)	CBcs CSBt MGan SPer SWCr
§ Rote Max Graf = 'Kormax'^PBR (GC/Ru)	MRav WAct
'Roundelay' (HT)	MAus
roxburghii (S)	CArn LEdu MRMR WAct WHCG
- var. *hirtula* (S)	CPLG
- f. *normalis* (S)	CFee GIBF
- 'Plena'	see R. roxburghii f. roxburghii
§ - f. *roxburghii* (d/S)	MAus
'Royal Albert Hall' (HT)	GCoc
Royal Celebration = 'Wekbiphitsou' (F) **new**	MJon
Royal Copenhagen = 'Poulht001'^PBR (HT)	ECnt
'Royal Gold' (ClHT)	LAst MBri MFry MGan SWCr

'Royal Occasion' (F) — MRav SPer SWCr

Royal Parks = 'Harlyric' (HT) **new** — GCoc

Royal Star and Garter = 'Frybizzy' (Cl) — MFry

Royal William = 'Korzaun'PBR (HT) ♀H4 — CSBt ECnt ELan ENot ESty GGre LGod LRHS LStr MAus MBri MGan MJon MRav NBlu NPri SPer SPoG SPoc SWCr

§ *rubiginosa* — CArn CCVT CGro CRWN EPfP EWTr GPoy IFro ILis LBuc MAus MHer MJon MRav NWea SFam SPer SWCr WAct WMou

rubra — see *R. gallica*

rubrifolia — see *R. glauca* Pourr.

'Rubrotincta' — see *R.* 'Hebe's Lip'

rubus (Ra) — GIBF MAus MBNS

- SF 96062 — ISea

- *velutescens* — WAct

Ruby Anniversary = 'Harbonny' (Patio) — CGro CSBt CWSG ESty GGre LStr MAsh MFry MRav SCoo SSea SWCr

Ruby Celebration = 'Peawinner'PBR (F) — CWSG ESty MJon SPoc SWCr

'Ruby Pendant' (Min) — MJon

'Ruby Wedding' (HT) — More than 30 suppliers

'Ruby Wedding Anniversary' (F) — GGre

rugosa (Ru) — CAgr CDul CLnd CTri EBee EPfP LBuc MAus MBri MHer MRav NBlu NWea SPlb SWCr WBVN

- 'Alba' (Ru) ♀H4 — CBcs CCVT CDul EBee ECnt ELan EPfP GBin LAst LBuc LRHS LStr MAus MGan MJon MRav NWea SPer SPoG SSea SWCr WHen WOVN

- 'Rubra' (Ru) ♀H4 — CBcs CCVT CTri CWib EBee EPfP LAst LBuc LStr MFry MGan MRMR SPer SPoG WAct WHen

- Sakhalin form — GIBF MCCP

- 'Scabrosa' — see *R.* 'Scabrosa'

'Rugspin' (Ru) — WAct

'Rumba' (F) — NBlu SWCr

Running Maid = 'Lenramp' (S/GC) — MAus

Rush = 'Lenmobri' (S) — MAus

Rushing Stream = 'Austream'PBR (GC) — MAus MBNS NSRo

'Ruskin' (HPxRu) — MAus

'Russelliana' (Ra) — EBee MAus SFam WAct WHCG WRha

Rutland = 'Poulshine'PBR (Min/GC) — MWgw

Safe Haven = 'Jacreraz' (F) **new** — ESty IDic

Saint Alban = 'Auschesnut' (S) — CSBt MAus

Saint Boniface = 'Kormatt' (F/Patio) — CSBt

'Saint Catherine' (Ra) — CFee

'Saint Cecilia' = 'Ausmit'PBR (S) — LRHS MAus MJon MWgw SWCr

Saint Dunstan's Rose = 'Kirshru' (S) — MJon

Saint John = 'Harbilbo'PBR (F) — CSBt MRav

Saint John's rose — see *R.* x *richardii*

Saint Mark's rose — see *R.* 'Rose d'Amour'

'Saint Nicholas' (D) — CAbP MAus

Saint Swithun = 'Auswith'PBR (S)SWCr — ECnt LRHS MAus MJon SPoc SSea

'Salet' (DPMo) — MAus WHCG

Salita = 'Kormorlet' (Cl) — MJon

'Sally Holmes'PBR (S) ♀H4 — CHad GCoc MAus MFry MGan MJon MRav MWgw SPer SPoc SSea SWCr WAct WHCG

Sally's Rose = 'Canrem' (HT) — EBee ECnt SPoc

Salmo = 'Poulnoev'PBR (Patio) — MJon

§ Samaritan = 'Harverag'PBR (HT) — CSBt ESty SPoc SWCr

sancta — see *R.* x *richardii*

'Sander's White Rambler' (Ra) ♀H4 — CRHN CSam CTri EBee EMFP EPfP LRHS LStr MAus MGan MJon MRav MWgw NEgg NPri SMad SPer SPoc SSea SWCr WAct WHCG

Sandra = 'Poulen055'PBR (Renaissance Series) **new** — SWCr

'Sanguinea' — see *R.* x *odorata* Sanguinea Group

'Sarah van Fleet' (Ru) — CTri EPfP EWTr GCoc IArd LRHS LStr MAus MDun MFry MGan MRav NBPC NLar SFam SMad SPer SPla SWCr WAct WOVN

Savoy Hotel = 'Harvintage'PBR (HT) ♀H4 — CGro CSBt ECnt EPfP GGre LGod LStr MAus MGan MRav SPer SPoG SWCr

§ 'Scabrosa' (Ru) ♀H4 — ECnt GCoc LAst LRHS MAus MGan MJon SPer SPoG SSea SWCr WAct WHCG WOVN

Scarborough Fair = 'Ausoran' (S) — MAus

Scarlet Fire — see *R.* 'Scharlachglut'

Scarlet Glow — see *R.* 'Scharlachglut'

Scarlet Hit = 'Poulmo'PBR (F) — ECnt LRHS MAsh SWCr

Scarlet Patio = 'Kortingle'PBR (Patio) — ENot ESty LRHS MAsh SPoG SWCr

Scarlet Queen Elizabeth = 'Dicel' (F) — CBcs GGre MRav

'Scented Air' (F) — MGan SPer

Scented Memory = 'Poulht002' (HT) **new** — ECnt

Scentimental = 'Wekplapep'PBR (F) — ESty MAsh MBri SCoo SPoG SPoc SWCr

§ Scent-sation = 'Fryromeo'PBR (HT) — CWSG ESty GCoc LGod LRHS MAsh MFry MRav NPri SCoo SPoG SPoc SWCr

Scepter'd Isle = 'Ausland'PBR (S) ♀H4 — CSBt CSam EBee ECnt LRHS LStr MAsh MAus MFry MJon NPri SCoo SPer SPoc SWCr

§ 'Scharlachglut' (ClS) ♀H4 — CPou LRHS MAus MGan MRMR MRav SPer SWCr WAct WHCG WOVN

* *schmidtiana* — CFee

'Schneelicht' (Ru) — MAus

§ 'Schneezwerg' (Ru) ♀H4 — GCoc MAus MGan MJon MRav NBPC SPer SPla SPoc SSea SWCr WAct WHCG WOVN

'Schoolgirl' (Cl) — CBcs CGro CSBt CTri EBee ELan ENot EPfP EWTr GGre LAst LStr MAsh MBri MFry MGan MJon MRav SPer SPoG SPoc SSea SWCr

'Scintillation' (S/GC) — MAus

Scotch pink (PiH) — WAct

Scotch rose — see *R. spinosissima*

Scotch yellow (PiH) — see *R.* x *harisonii* 'Williams' Double Yellow'

'Seagull' (Ra) ♀H4 — CGro CTri CWSG EBee ECnt EMFP EPfP ESty LAst LGod LRHS LStr MAsh MAus MGan MJon MRav NPri NWea SLon SPer SPla SPoG SPoc SSea SWCr WHCG WHer

'Seale Peach' (Patio) — SSea

§ 'Sealing Wax' (*moyesii* hybrid) — MBri MRMR WAct

Selfridges = 'Korpriwa' (HT) — MJon

'Semiplena' — see *R.* x *alba* 'Alba Semiplena'

sempervirens (Ra) — XPep

sericea (S) — CFee MAus WHCG

	- CC 3306	WRos
	- var. ***morrisonensis***	WCru
	B&SWJ 7139	
§	- subsp. ***omeiensis***	WCru
	BWJ 7550	
	- - f. ***pteracantha*** (S)	CBcs EBee ELan EPfP GGar MAus
		MGan MRav NWea NPer SSea WAct
		WOVN
	- - - 'Atrosanguinea' (S)	CArn
	sertata	GIBF
§	***setigera***	GIBF MAus
	setipoda	MAus MRMR WAct WFar WHCG
	seven sisters rose	see *R. multiflora* 'Grevillei'
	Seventh Heaven =	GCoc MFry
	'Fryfantasy' (HT)	
	Sexy Rexy = 'Macrexy'[PBR]	CGro CSBt EPfP ESty GCoc GGre
	(F) ♀[H4]	LAst LRHS LStr MAsh MAus MBri
		MFry MGan MJon MRav SPer SPoG
		SPoc SWCr
	'Shailer's White Moss'	see *R. x centifolia* 'Shailer's White
		Moss'
	Sharifa Asma =	CSBt EBee ELan ENot LRHS LStr
	'Ausreef'[PBR] (S)	MAus MBNS MJon MRav NEgg
		SPer SPoc SWCr WAct
	Sheila's Perfume =	CGro ECnt ESty GCoc GGre LStr
	'Harsherry'[PBR] (HT/F)	MGan MJon MRav SPer SPoG SPoc
		SSea SWCr
	Shine On = 'Dictalent'[PBR]	CSBt ECnt ESty IDic MAsh MFry
	(Patio) ♀[H4]	MJon MRav SPoG SPoc SWCr
	Shining Light =	GCoc MAsh SCoo SWCr
	'Cocshimmer'[PBR]	
	(Patio)	
	Shirley Spain =	GCoc
	'Cocharod' (F)	
	Shocking Blue =	CSBt ECnt ENot MAus MGan MJon
	'Korblue'[PBR] (F)	SPer SPoc SWCr
	Shona = 'Dicdrum' (F)	IDic
	'Shot Silk' (HT)	CSBt MGan SWCr
	Shrimp Hit =	ECnt
	'Poulshrimp'[PBR]	
	(Patio)	
	'Shropshire Lass' (S)	LRHS MAus SPer
	Sightsaver =	ESty MFry
	'Fryaffair'[PBR] (HT)	
§	Silver Anniversary =	CGro CSBt CTri EBee ECnt ELan
	'Poulari'[PBR] (HT) ♀[H4]	ENot GCoc GGre LAst LGod LRHS
		LStr MAsh MAus MFry MGan MJon
		MRav NPri SCoo SPer SPoG SPoc
		SSea SWCr
	Silver Ghost =	ENot
	'Kormifari' (S) **new**	
	'Silver Jubilee' (HT) ♀[H4]	CBcs CGro CSBt ECnt ENot EPfP
		ESty GCoc GGre IArd LGod LRHS
		LStr MAsh MAus MFry MGan MJon
		MRav SPer SPoG SPoc SWCr
	'Silver Lining' (HT)	SWCr
	'Silver Moon' (Cl)	CRHN
	'Silver Wedding' (HT)	CWSG ELan GCoc IArd LAst LRHS
		MAus MFry MRav NBir NWea SPer
		SPoc SWCr WBVN
	Silver Wedding	CTri ESty GGre SPoG SWCr
	Celebration (F)	
	Silver Wishes =	LRHS MAsh SWCr
	'Poulhipe'	
§	Simba = 'Korbelma'[PBR]	ENot MGan
	(HT)	
	Simply Heaven =	ESty GCoc IDic MJon SPoc SWCr
	'Diczombie'[PBR] (HT)	
§	Simply the Best =	CGro CSBt ECnt ELan ENot ESty
	'Macamster'[PBR] (HT)	GCoc GGre LGod LRHS LStr MAsh
		MAus MBri MFry MJon SCoo SPer
		SPoG SPoc SWCr
§	Singin' in the Rain =	MJon SPoc SWCr
	'Macivy' (F)	
	sinowilsonii	see *R. longicuspis* var. *sinowilsonii*
	'Sir Cedric Morris' (Ra)	SSea WAct

	Sir Clough = 'Ausclough'	MAus
	(S)	
	Sir Edward Elgar =	LStr MAus
	'Ausprima'[PBR] (S)	
	'Sir Joseph Paxton' (Bb)	CAbP MAus
§	Sir Walter Raleigh =	MAus MRav
	'Ausspry' (S)	
	Smarty = 'Intersmart'	CAbP MAus SPer SWCr WAct
	(S/GC)	
§	'Smooth Angel' (HT)	MGan
	Smooth Lady = 'Hadlady'	LGod MGan
	(HT)	
	Smooth Melody =	LAst
	'Hadmelody' (F)	
	Smooth Prince =	LAst LGod SPoc
	'Hadprince' (HT)	
§	'Smooth Velvet' (HT)	LAst MGan SPer
	Snow Carpet =	MAus MJon
	'Maccarpe'[PBR]	
	(Min/GC)	
	'Snow Dwarf'	see *R.* 'Schneezwerg'
	Snow Goose =	CSBt MAus MJon NSRo SWCr
	'Auspom'[PBR] (Cl/S)	
	Snow Hit =	ECnt MAsh NPri SPoc SWCr
	'Poulsnows'[PBR]	
	(Min/Patio)	
	'Snow Queen'	see *R.* 'Frau Karl Druschki'
§	Snow Sunblaze =	CSBt MRav SPer
	'Meigovin' (Min)	
	Snow White =	MJon
	'Landisney' (HT)	
	Snowball = 'Macangeli'	MJon
	(Min/GC)	
	Snowcap = 'Harfleet'[PBR]	ESty SPoG SSea
	(Patio)	
	'Snowdon' (Ru)	MAus SWCr
	'Snowdrift' (Ra)	WHCG
§	Snowdrop = 'Amoru'	MFry
	(Min/Patio)	
	'Snowflake' (Ra)	WHCG
	'Soldier Boy' (Cl)	WHCG
§	Solitaire =	MJon
	'Macyefre'[PBR] (HT)	
	Solo Mio =	CTri ECnt MAsh SPla SWCr
	'Poulen002'[PBR] (S)	
§	'Sombreuil' (ClT)	CHad EBee EPfP EWTr IArd LRHS
		MAus MRMR MRav NEgg NLar
		SFam SPer SPla SPoc SSea SWCr
		WAct WHCG
	Something Special	ECnt GCoc MAus MJon SWCr
	= 'Macwyo'[PBR]	
	(HT)	
§	Songs of Praise =	ESty MJon
	'Harkimono' **new**	
	'Sophie's Perpetual' (ClCh)	CPou ENot LRHS MAus MGan SPer
		SPoc SWCr WAct WHCG XPep
	Sophy's Rose =	ESty LRHS LStr MAsh MAus MJon
	'Auslot'[PBR] (S)	NEgg SPoc SWCr
	soulieana (Ra/S) ♀[H3-4]	MAus WAct WKif
	'Soupert et Notting'	LRHS MAus MRav NBPC SPer WAct
	(DPoMo)	
	'Southampton' (F) ♀[H4]	ENot GGre LStr MAus MGan MRav
		SPer SPoc SSea SWCr
	'Souvenir d'Alphonse	WHCG
	Lavallée' (ClHP)	
	'Souvenir de Brod'	see *R.* 'Erinnerung an Brod'
	'Souvenir de Claudius	EBee MAus SPer
	Denoyel' (ClHT)	
	'Souvenir de Jeanne	WHCG
	Balandreau' (HP)	
	'Souvenir de la	see *R.* 'Climbing Souvenir de la
	Malmaison' (ClBb)	Malmaison'
	'Souvenir de la	GCoc LRHS MAus MGan MRav
	Malmaison' (Bb)	NBPC SPer SWCr WAct
	Souvenir de Louis	SPoc SWCr
	Amade = 'Delalac' (S)	

'Souvenir de Madame Léonie Viennot' (ClT) — CPou MAus MRav

Souvenir de Marcel Proust = 'Delpapy' (S) — SPoc SWCr

'Souvenir de Saint Anne's' (Bb) — CHad EBee EWTr MAus MRMR SWCr WAct WHCG

'Souvenir di Castagneto' (HP) — MRav

'Souvenir du Docteur Jamain' (ClHP) — CHad CPou EBee EHol ELan ESty EWTr LRHS LStr MAus SFam SMrm SPer SPoc SSea SWCr WAct WHCG WKif

Spangles = 'Ganspa'[PBR] (F) — MGan SPoc

'Spanish Beauty' — see R. 'Madame Grégoire Staechelin'

Sparkling Scarlet = 'Meihati' (ClF) — ELan MAsh MGan

Sparkling Yellow = 'Poulgode'[PBR] (GC/S) — ECnt

'Special Anniversary' — ESty LRHS MAsh NPri SCoo SPoG SWCr

Special Child = 'Tanaripsa' — SPoc SWCr

Special Friend = 'Kirspec'[PBR] (Patio) — GCoc LStr MJon

Special Occasion = 'Fryyoung'[PBR] (HT) — ENot ESty GCoc MFry MRav NBPC SPoc SWCr

'Spectabilis' (Ra) — WHCG

Spek's Centennial (F) — see Rosa Singin' in the Rain

Spice of Life = 'Diccheeky'[PBR] (F/Patio) — GCoc IDic

spinosissima — CDul EBee LBuc MAus MGan NHaw NWea SPer SSea WAct WHCG WOVN

- 'Altaica' — see R. spinosissima 'Grandiflora'
§ - 'Andrewsii' ♀[H4] — MAus MRav WAct
§ - double pink — WBor
§ - double white — CNat ECha GCoc IGor MAus WAct
- double yellow — see R. x harisonii 'Williams' Double Yellow'
§ - 'Dunwich Rose' — EBee EPfP LRHS MAsh MAus MGan MJon NEgg SPer SWCr WAct WHCG
- 'Falkland' — ECha MAus
§ - 'Glory of Edzell' — MAus
§ - 'Grandiflora' — MAus MRMR
§ - 'Harisonii' — see R. x harisonii 'Harison's Yellow'
- 'Marbled Pink' — MAus
- 'Mary, Queen of Scots' — MAus SRms WAct
- 'Mrs Colville' — MAus
- 'Ormiston Roy' — MAus
§ - 'Robbie' — WAct
- 'Single Cherry' — MAus SSea
- 'Variegata' (v) — CArn
- 'William III' — EWes MAus SLPl

Spirit of Freedom = 'Ausbite' (S) — MAsh MAus NEgg SWCr

§ 'Splendens' (Ra) — CHad EBee SLPl SPoc SWCr WAct

St. Helena = 'Canlish' (F) — ECnt

§ St Tiggywinkle = 'Korbasren'[PBR] (GC) — ENot LGod

§ 'Stanwell Perpetual' (PiH) — CBgR CTri EWTr GCoc LStr MRav NBPC NLar SEND SPer SPoc SSea SWCr WAct WHCG WOVN

'Star of Waltham' (HP) — WHCG

'Star Performer'[PBR] (ClPatio) — CSBt ECnt ESty MAsh MBri MJon SPoc SWCr

Stardust = 'Peavandyke'[PBR] (Patio/F) — ESty MJon SPoG SWCr

Starina = 'Megabi' (Min) — MGan

Starlight Express = 'Trobstar'[PBR] (Cl) — MAsh SCoo SPer SPoG SPoc SWCr

Starry Eyed = 'Horcoexist' (Patio) — MGan SWCr

'Stars 'n' Stripes' (Min) — LGod MAus MFry

Stella (HT) — MGan

stellata — MAus
§ - var. *mirifica* — EBee MAus MGan SSea

'Stephanie Diane' (HT) — MJon

'Sterling Silver' (HT) — LStr MGan SPoG SWCr

Sting = 'Meimater'[PBR] — SWCr

Strawberries and Cream = 'Geestraw' (Min/Patio) — ELan ESty

Strawberry Fayre = 'Arowillip'[PBR] (Min/Patio) — CTri ESty LAst MFry MRav SPoG

Strawberry Fields = 'Rawbus' (GC) — SPoc

§ Sue Hipkin = 'Harzazz'[PBR] (HT) — ESty SPoG SPoc SWCr

Sue Lawley = 'Macspash' (F) — MGan

§ Suffolk = 'Kormixal'[PBR] (S/GC) — CBrm CGro CSBt ELan ENot GCoc LStr MAus MGan MRav SPer SSea SWCr WAct

suffulta — see R. arkansana var. suffulta

Sugar and Spice = 'Peaallure'[PBR] (Patio) — MBri SPoG SWCr

Sugar Baby = 'Tanabagus'[PBR] (Patio) — ESty MAsh SPoG SWCr

Sugar 'n' Spice = 'Tinspice' (Min) — MAsh MRav

Suma = 'Harsuma' (GC) — EPfP ESty MJon WAct

Summer Breeze = 'Korelasting'[PBR] (Cl) — ENot

Summer Dream = 'Frymaxicot'[PBR] (F) — CSBt LStr MFry

§ Summer Dream = 'Jacshe' (HT) — LAst

Summer Fragrance = 'Tanfudermos'[PBR] (HT) — CSBt ESty GCoc SWCr

§ Summer Gold = 'Poulreb'[PBR] (F) — ECnt ENot EPfP MAsh SPoG SPoc SWCr

'Summer Holiday' (HT) — SPer SWCr

Summer Love = 'Franluv' (F) — MJon

'Summer Magic' (Patio) — GGre

Summer Memories = 'Koruteli' (F) **new** — ENot

Summer Palace = 'Poulcape'[PBR] (F/Patio) — ECnt SPoc SWCr

Summer Snow = 'Weopop' (Patio) — MJon

Summer Wine = 'Korizont'[PBR] (Cl) ♀[H4] — CSBt EBee ECnt ENot ESty MAsh MGan MJon SCoo SPer SPoG SPoc SSea SWCr

Summertime = 'Chewlarmoll' (Patio/Cl) — CGro COtt CSBt EBee ECnt ELan ENot ESty GCoc GGre LGod LStr MAsh MBri MFry MJon NPri SCoo SPer SPoG SWCr

§ Sun Hit = 'Poulsun'[PBR] (Patio) — CSBt ECnt LRHS MAsh MRav SPoc SWCr

Sunblest = 'Landora' (HT) — GGre LRHS MAsh MFry MRav SPoG SWCr

Sunderland Supreme = 'Nossun' (HT) — MJon

'Sunny Abundance' — MAsh SPoG SWCr

Sunrise = 'Kormarter'[PBR] (Cl) — ENot ESty MFry SPoc SWCr WGer

§ Sunseeker = 'Dicracer'[PBR] (F/Patio) — EPfP ESty GGre IDic LRHS MAsh MRav SPoG SWCr

§	Sunset Boulevard = 'Harbabble'PBR (F) ♀H4	CSBt EBee ECnt ENot GGre LGod LStr MAsh MAus MGan MRav SCoo SPer SPoc SSea SWCr
	'Sunshine' (Poly)	MGan SPer
	'Sunsilk' (F)	SWCr
	Sunsplash = 'Cocweaver' (F)	GCoc GGre SPoG SWCr
	Super Dorothy = 'Heldoro' (Ra)	MAus MJon SPoc SWCr
	Super Elfin = 'Helkleger'PBR (Ra) ♀H4	ECnt LStr MFry MGan MJon MRav SPer SPoc SSea SWCr
	Super Excelsa = 'Helexa' (Ra)	ESty GGre LStr MAsh MAus MGan MJon MRav SPoG SSea SWCr
	Super Fairy = 'Helsufair'PBR (Ra)	EBee ECnt ESty LStr MAus MFry MGan MJon MRav SPer SPoc SSea SWCr
§	Super Sparkle = 'Helfels'PBR (Ra)	ECnt LStr MGan SSea SWCr
§	Super Star = 'Tanorstar' (HT)	CTri GGre LStr MGan MJon MRav SPoc SWCr
	'Surpasse Tout' (G)	MAus WHCG
§	'Surpassing Beauty of Woolverstone' (ClHP)	WHCG
§	Surrey = 'Korlanum'PBR (GC) ♀H4	CSBt CTri ECnt ELan ENot ESty EWTr LGod LStr MAus MFry MGan MRMR MRav NPri SPer SPla SPoc SSea SWCr WAct
	Susan = 'Poulsue' (S)	EBee ECnt MAsh SBra SPoc SWCr
	Sussex = 'Poulave'PBR (GC)	CSBt ECnt GCoc LStr MFry MGan MRav NPri SPer SPoc SSea SWCr
	'Sutter's Gold' (HT)	MAus MGan
	Swan = 'Auswhite' (S)	MAus
	Swan Lake = 'Macmed' (Cl)	ECnt ELan ENot EPfP ESty GGre LGod LStr MFry MGan MRav NPri SPer SWCr
	Swany = 'Meiburenac' (Min/GC) ♀H4	CGro ESty LSRN MAus MGan MRMR SPer SWCr WHCG
	Sweet Cover = 'Poulweeto'PBR	MAsh SWCr
	Sweet Dream = 'Fryminicot'PBR (Patio) ♀H4	CGro CSBt ECnt ELan ENot EPfP ESty GCoc GGre LAst LGod LRHS LStr MAsh MAus MBri MFry MGan MJon MRav NPri SPer SPla SPoG SPoc SSea SWCr
	'Sweet Fairy' (Min)	CSBt
	Sweet Juliet = 'Ausleap'PBR (S)	CAbP CHad CSBt CWSG ESty LGod LRHS MAus MJon NEgg NPri NSRo SPer SPoc SWCr
*	'Sweet Lemon Dream' (Patio)	MAsh SPoG SWCr
	Sweet Magic = 'Dicmagic'PBR (Min/Patio) ♀H4	CGro CSBt CTri ENot EPfP GGre IDic LRHS LStr MAsh MBri MFry MGan MJon MRav NPri SPla SPoG SWCr
	Sweet Memories = 'Whamemo' (Patio)	COtt CTri ECnt ENot EPfP ESty GCoc GGre LGod LRHS LStr MAsh MJon MRav NPri SCoo SPer SPla SPoG SPoc SWCr WGer
§	Sweet Promise = 'Meihelvet' (GC)	MGan
	'Sweet Remembrance' (HT)	LStr MJon
	'Sweet Repose' (F)	MGan
	'Sweet Revelation'PBR	see *R.* Sue Hipkin
§	Sweet Symphonie = 'Meibarke'PBR (Patio)	SWCr
	'Sweet Velvet' (F)	MGan
	'Sweet Wonder' (Patio)	EPfP GGre MAsh SPoG SWCr
N	Sweetheart = 'Cocapeer' (HT)	GCoc
	sweginzowii	GCal GIBF MAus
	'Sydonie' (HP)	WHCG
	'Sympathie' (ClHT)	MGan SPer SSea SWCr
	Tall Story = 'Dickooky'PBR (F) ♀H4	IDic MJon SPoc SWCr WHCG WOVN

	Tamora = 'Austamora' (S)	MAus
§	Tango = 'Macfirwal' (F)	MJon
	Tango = 'Poulyc005' (Patio/Cl)	ECnt
	Tapis Jaune	see *R.* Golden Penny = 'Rugul'
	Tatoo = 'Poulyc002'PBR (Patio/Cl)	ECnt MAsh SPoG SWCr
	Tatton = 'Fryentice'PBR (F)	ESty MAus MBri MFry MJon SWCr
	Tawny Tiger = 'Frygolly' (F)	ESty MFry
§	Tear Drop = 'Dicomo'PBR (Min/Patio)	IDic LStr MFry MGan SWCr
§	Teasing Georgia = 'Ausbaker'PBR (S)	ECnt EPfP ESty LRHS MAsh MAus MJon NEgg SPoc SWCr
	'Telstar' (F)	MGan
	Temptress = 'Korramal' (Cl)	ENot ESty MJon
	'Tenerife' (HT)	GGre
	Tequila Sunrise = 'Dicobey'PBR (HT) ♀H4	CTri ECnt ELan EPfP ESty GGre IDic LRHS LStr MAsh MAus MGan MJon MRav SMrm SPer SPoG SPoc SSea SWCr
§	Terracotta = 'Meicobuis'PBR (HT)	ESty MJon SWCr
	Tess of the D'Urbervilles = 'Ausmove'PBR (S)	CSam LStr MAus MBNS NEgg SWCr
	'Tessa' (F)	MGan SWCr
	Thank You = 'Chesdeep'PBR (Patio)	GCoc GGre LStr SPoG SWCr
§	That's Jazz = 'Poulnorm'PBR (ClF)	EBee ECnt LRHS MAsh MJon SWCr
	The Alexandra Rose = 'Ausday'PBR (S)	LRHS MAus SEND
	The Attenborough Rose = 'Dicelope'PBR (F)	ESty IDic MJon SWCr
	'The Bishop' (CexG)	MAus
	The Care Rose = 'Horapsunmolbabe' (Patio)	SWCr
	The Cheshire Regiment = 'Fryzebedee' (HT)	MFry
	The Compass Rose = 'Korwisco'PBR (S)	ENot SPer
	The Compassionate Friends = 'Harzodiac'PBR (F)	SWCr
§	The Countryman = 'Ausman' (S)	LRHS MAus MBri MFry SWCr
§	The Daily Telegraph = 'Peahigh' (F)	SPoc
	The Dark Lady = 'Ausbloom'PBR (S)	LRHS MAus MJon NEgg SPer SPoc SWCr
	'The Doctor' (HT)	MGan SSea SWCr
§	The Dove = 'Tanamola'PBR (F)	MGan SWCr
	'The Ednaston Rose' (Cl)	WHCG
§	'The Fairy' (Poly) ♀H4	More than 30 suppliers
	'The Garland' (Ra) ♀H4	CRHN EMFP LRHS MAus MRMR SFam SPer SPoc SWCr WAct WHCG XPep
	The Generous Gardener = 'Ausdrawn' (S)	LRHS MAus NEgg NSRo SCoo SWCr
	The Gold Award Rose = 'Poulac008'	ECnt
§	The Halcyon Days Rose = 'Korparesni'PBR (F)	ENot
	The Herbalist = 'Aussemi' (S)	LRHS MAus

The Ingenious Mr Fairchild = 'Austijus' (S)	MAsh MAus SCoo SWCr	
§ The Jubilee Rose = 'Poulbrido'^{PBR} (F)	EBee ECnt SCoo SWCr	
The Lady = 'Fryjingo'^{PBR} (S) ♀^{H4}	MFry MJon	
The Maidstone Rose = 'Kordauerpa'^{PBR}	SCoo	
The Mayflower = 'Austilly'^{PBR} (S)	CSBt MAsh MAus MBri MJon NSRo SSea SWCr	
§ The McCartney Rose = 'Meizeli'^{PBR} (HT)	GGre LStr MJon SPer SPoG SPoc SWCr	
'The New Dawn'	see *R.* 'New Dawn'	
The Nun = 'Ausnun' (S)	MAus	
The Painter = 'Mactemaik'^{PBR} (F)	LStr MJon SSea	
§ The Pilgrim = 'Auswalker'^{PBR} (S)	CAbP CSBt CSam ENot EPfP ESty LRHS LStr MAus MBri MJon NEgg SPer SPla SPoc SWCr WHCG	
The Prince = 'Ausvelvet'^{PBR} (S)	LRHS LStr MAus MBNS MBri MJon NEgg SPer SSea SWCr	
The Prince's Trust = 'Harholding'^{PBR} (CI)	LStr MJon SPoG SWCr	
'The Prioress' (S)	MAus	
§ 'The Queen Elizabeth' (F)	CBcs CGro CSBt CWSG ECnt ENot GCoc GGre LGod LStr MAsh MBri MFry MGan MJon MRav NBlu SEND SPer SPoG SPoc SSea SWCr	
The Reeve = 'Ausreeve' (S)	MAus	
The Rotarian = 'Fryglitzy' (HT)	MFry	
I 'The Royal Society of Organists' Rose' (HT)	SPoc	
I 'The Rugby Rose' (HT)	MGan	
The Scotsman = 'Poulscots'^{PBR} (HT)	EBee ECnt GCoc	
The Soham Rose^{PBR}	see *R.* Pearl Abundance	
The Soroptimist Rose = 'Benstar' (Patio)	MJon	
§ The Squire = 'Ausquire' (S)	MAus	
§ The Times Rose = 'Korpeahn'^{PBR} (F) ♀^{H4}	ECnt ENot LGod LStr MAus MGan MJon MRav SPer SPoc SWCr	
'Thelma' (Ra)	MAus	
Thelma Barlow = 'Fryforce' (HT)	MFry	
'Thérèse Bugnet' (Ru)	MAus NHaw	
Thinking of You = 'Frydandy'^{PBR} (HT)	ESty GCoc LGod LRHS LStr MAsh MFry MJon SPoc SWCr	
'Thisbe' (HM)	MAus SWCr WAct WHCG XPep	
§ Thomas Barton = 'Meihirvin' (HT)	ESty LStr SPoG	
'Thoresbyana'	see *R.* 'Bennett's Seedling'	
'Thoughts of You' (Patio)	SWCr	
'Thoughts of You' (HT)	GGre	
Three Cheers = 'Dicdomino' (F) **new**	IDic	
threepenny bit rose	see *R. elegantula* 'Persetosa'	
tibetica **new**	GIBF	
Tigris = 'Harprier' (*persica* hybrid) (S)	WAct	
Times Past = 'Harhilt'^{PBR} (CI)	ESty GCoc LStr MJon SPoc SWCr	
'Tina Turner' (HT)	MJon	
Tintinara = 'Dicuptight'^{PBR} (HT)	ECnt IDic MGan	
Tip Top = 'Tanope' (F/Patio)	CBcs MGan SPer	
'Tipo Ideale'	see *R.* x *odorata* 'Mutabilis'	
Titanic = 'Macdako'^{PBR} (F)	MJon SPoc SWCr	
Tivoli = 'Poulduce'^{PBR} (HT)	ECnt	
'Toby Tristam' (Ra)	CRHN	
'Tom Foster' (HT)	MJon	

Too Hot to Handle = 'Macloupri'^{PBR} (S/CI)	MJon SSea	
Top Marks = 'Fryministar'^{PBR} (Min/Patio)	CGro CSBt CTri EPfP GCoc LAst LGod LStr MBri MFry MGan MJon MRav NPri SCoo SPer SWCr	
'Top of the Bill' (Patio)	SCoo	
Topkapi Palace = 'Poulthe'^{PBR} (F)	ECnt	
§ Toprose = 'Cocgold'^{PBR} (F)	GCoc GGre	
'Topsi' (F/Patio)	SPer	
§ 'Tour de Malakoff' (Ce)	CPou CSBt EHol LRHS MAus MRav SFam SPer SWCr WAct WHCG	
Tournament of Roses = 'Jacient' (HT)	MJon	
Tower Bridge = 'Haravis' (HT)	GGre	
'Trade Winds' (HT)	MGan	
Tradescant = 'Ausdir'^{PBR} (S)	LRHS MAus MBNS SPoc SWCr	
§ Tradition '95 = 'Korkeltin'^{PBR} (CI) ♀^{H4}	ENot	
'Treasure Trove' (Ra)	CRHN EMFP LRHS MAus MJon SPoc SWCr WAct	
Trevor Griffiths = 'Ausold'^{PBR} (S)	MAus	
'Tricolore de Flandre' (G)	MAus	
'Trier' (Ra)	CPou EBee MAus MRMR SWCr WHCG	
'Trigintipetala' misapplied	see *R.* 'Professeur Emile Perrot'	
'Triomphe de l'Exposition' (HP)	MAus	
'Triomphe du Luxembourg' (T)	MAus	
triphylla	see *R.* x *beanii*	
Troika = 'Poumidor' (HT) ♀^{H4}	CSBt ENot GGre LStr MAsh MAus MFry MGan MJon MRav NBlu SPer SPoG SPoc SWCr	
Troilus = 'Ausoil' (S)	MAus	
Trumpeter = 'Mactru' (F) ♀^{H4}	CSBt EBee ECnt ENot ESty GGre IArd LRHS LStr MAsh MAus MFry MGan MJon MRav SPer SPoG SSea SWCr	
Tumbling Waters = 'Poultumb'^{PBR} (F/S)	MRav	
'Tuscany' (G)	GCoc MAus WAct WHCG	
'Tuscany Superb' (G) ♀^{H4}	CBgR CHad CPou CSam ENot EPfP EWTr ISea LAst LRHS MAus MGan MRav SPer SPoc SSea SWCr WAct WHCG WKif	
§ Twenty-one Again! = 'Meinimo'^{PBR} (HT)	SPoc SWCr	
Twice in a Blue Moon = 'Tan96138' (F)	ESty LGod LRHS MFry MJon SCoo SPoG SPoc SWCr	
Twist = 'Poulstri'^{PBR} (Patio/CI)	CGro ECnt ESty MAsh MGan SWCr	
Tynwald = 'Mattwyt'^{PBR} (HT)	ENot LStr MJon	
'Ulrich Brünner Fils' (HP)	MAus	
Uncle Walter = 'Macon' (HT)	SWCr	
UNICEF = 'Cocjojo'^{PBR} (F)	GCoc	
'Unique Blanche'	see *R.* x *centifolia* 'Unique'	
Valencia = 'Koreklia'^{PBR} (HT) ♀^{H4}	CSBt ECnt ENot ESty MAus MJon	
§ Valentine Heart = 'Dicogle'^{PBR} (F) ♀^{H4}	CSBt ESty IArd IDic LRHS MAsh MAus MFry MJon MRav SPoG SPoc SWCr	
Valiant Heart = 'Poulberg' (F)	EBee ECnt SPoG	
'Vanity' (HM)	MAus	
'Variegata di Bologna' (Bb)	EPfP LRHS MAus MRMR MRav SPoc SSea SWCr WAct	
Variety Club = 'Haredge'^{PBR} (Patio)	LGod	

'Veilchenblau' (Ra) ♀H4 — CHad CRHN CSBt EBee ECnt ELan EMFP EPfP EWTr LAst LGod LRHS LStr MAsh MAus MGan MRMR MRav NEgg NPri SPer SPoc SSea SWCr WAct WHCG

Velvet Fragrance = 'Fryperdee'PBR (HT) — CSBt ECnt ESty GCoc GGre LRHS LStr MAsh MAus MFry MJon MRav SPoG SWCr

'Venusta Pendula' (Ra) — MAus

Versailles Palace = 'Poulsail'PBR (F) — SPoc SWCr

'Verschuren' (HT/v) — MJon

versicolor — see *R. gallica* 'Versicolor'

'Vick's Caprice' (HP) — MAus

'Vicomtesse Pierre du Fou' (CIHT) — MAus

Vidal Sassoon = 'Macjuliat'PBR (HT) — MGan MJon SPoc SWCr

Viking PrincessPBR — see *R.* Imagination = 'Pouldron'

'Village Maid' — see *Rosa* x *centifolia* 'Unique Panachée'

§ *villosa* L. — CArn MAus WAct

§ 'Violacea' (G) — EBee LRHS MAus WHCG

'Violette' (Ra) — CPou CRHN MAus SWCr WAct WHCG

virginiana ♀H4 — CFee GCal GIBF MAus MGan MRMR MSte NHaw NWea SPer WAct WHCG WHen WOVN

- 'Harvest Song' — NHaw

- 'Plena' — see *R.* 'Rose d'Amour'

'Virgo' (HT) — NBlu

'Viridiflora' — see *R.* x *odorata* 'Viridiflora'

vosagiaca — see *R. caesia* subsp. *glauca*

Waltz = 'Poulkrid'PBR (Patio/CI) — ECnt LRHS MAsh SWCr

Wandering Minstrel = 'Harquince' (F) — SPoG SWCr

wardii var. *culta* — MAus

Warm Welcome = 'Chewizz'PBR (ClMin) ♀H4 — CGro ECnt ENot EPfP ESty GGre LGod LRHS LStr MAsh MAus MBri MFry MJon MRav MWgw NEgg SMad SPer SPoG SPoc SSea SWCr

§ Warm Wishes = 'Fryxotic'PBR (HT) ♀H4 — CSBt ECnt ENot ESty GCoc GGre LAst LGod LRHS LStr MAsh MAus MFry MGan MJon NBlu NPri SPoG SPoc SWCr

'Warrior' (F) — MGan SPer

Warwick Castle = 'Auslian'PBR (S) — MAus SPer

Warwickshire = 'Korkandel'PBR (GC) — MRav SPer SWCr WOVN

webbiana — MAus SPer SPoc WHCG

'Wedding Day' (Ra) — More than 30 suppliers

Wee Cracker = 'Cocmarris'PBR (Patio) — ESty GCoc GGre LGod SWCr

Wee Jock = 'Cocabest'PBR (F/Patio) — GCoc GGre SPoG SWCr

'Weetwood' (Ra) — CRHN SPer

'Weisse aus Sparrieshoop' (S) — MGan

Welcome Home = 'Koraubala'PBR (F) — ENot

'Well Done' (Patio) — GGre SPoG SWCr

Well-Being = 'Harjangle' (S) — ESty MJon SWCr

Welwyn Garden Glory = 'Harzumber'PBR (HT) — ESty SPoc

'Wendy Cussons' (HT) — CBcs CTri CWSG GCoc MGan MJon MRav SPer SSea SWCr

Wenlock = 'Auswen' (S) — ESty GGre MAus SPer

'West Country Millennium' (F) — MGan

§ Westerland = 'Korwest' (F/S) ♀H4 — MGan MJon SPoc SWCr

Westminster Pink = 'Fryamour'PBR (HT) — ECnt MFry

Where the Heart Is = 'Cocoplan'PBR (HT) — GCoc

'Whisky Gill' (HT) — MGan

Whisky Mac = 'Tanky' (HT) — CBcs CGro CSBt CTri CWSG ELan GCoc GGre MFry MGan MJon MRav NPri SPer

'White Bath' — see *Rosa* x *centifolia* 'Shailer's White Moss'

White Bells = 'Poulwhite'PBR (Min/GC) — MRav SPer WHCG WOVN

§ 'White Cécile Brünner' (Poly) — MAus WHCG

'White Christmas' (HT) — MGan

§ White Cloud = 'Korstacha'PBR (S/CIHT) ♀H4 — CSBt EBee ECnt ENot ESty LGod MJon SPoc SWCr WHCG

White Cloud = 'Savacloud' (Min) — MBri MFry

'White Cockade' (Cl) — EBee GCoc MGan SPer SPoG

White CoverPBR (GC) — see *R.* Kent

§ 'White de Meaux' (Ce) — MAus

White Diamond = 'Interamon'PBR (S) — IDic MJon

§ White Gold = 'Cocquiriam'PBR (F) — GCoc GGre SPoG SWCr

'White Grootendorst' (Ru) — MAus SSea WAct

White Knight (HT) — see *R.* Message = 'Meban'

White Knight = 'Poullaps' (CIHT/S) — SPoc SWCr

White Max GrafPBR — see *Rosa* x *jacksonii* White Max Graf = 'Korgram'

white moss — see *R.* 'Comtesse de Murinais', *R.* 'Shailer's White Moss'

§ 'White Pet' (Poly) ♀H4 — CHad CSBt ECnt EPfP ESty GCoc LGod LRHS LStr MAus MBri MGan MJon MRMR MRav NEgg SEND SPer SPla SPoc SWCr WAct

white Provence — see *R.* x *centifolia* 'Unique'

white rose of York — see *R.* x *alba* 'Alba Semiplena'

White Skyliner = 'Franwekwhit' (ClS) — MJon

'White Tausendschön' (Ra) — MAus

'White Wings' (HT) — CHad EWTr MAus MGan SPer SWCr WAct WHCG

N *wichurana* (Ra) — CBcs MAus SWCr WHCG XPep

- 'Variegata' (Ra/v) — CBow CSWP

* - 'Variegata Nana' (Ra/v) — MRav SMad

'Wickwar' (Ra) — CSWP EHol EPla GCal MSte SWCr WAct WHCG

§ Wife of Bath = 'Ausbath' (S) — MAus

Wildeve = 'Ausbonny' (S) — MAus NSRo SWCr

Wildfire = 'Fryessex' (Patio) — ECnt ESty MAus MFry

'Wilhelm' (HM) — MAus MRav SPer WHCG

'Will Scarlet' (HM) — MAus

'William Allen Richardson' (N) — MAus WHCG

'William Cobbett' (F) — SSea

§ 'William Lobb' (CeMo) ♀H4 — CBgR CHad CPou CRHN CSBt EPfP LGod LRHS LStr MAsh MAus MBri MGan MWgw NEgg SPer SPoc SSea SWCr WAct WHCG WKif

William Morris = 'Auswill'PBR (S) — CSBt ECnt MAus MJon NEgg SPoc SWCr

William Shakespeare 2000 = 'Ausromeo'PBR (S) — CSBt CSam ECnt EPfP ESty LGod MAsh MAus MJon SPoc SWCr

William Shakespeare = 'Ausroyal'PBR (S) — MBNS MFry NEgg NSRo SPer

'William Tyndale' (Ra) — MJon WHCG

'Williams' Double Yellow' — see *R.* x *harisonii* 'Williams' Double Yellow'

willmottiae	see *R. gymnocarpa* var. *willmottiae*
Wilton = 'Eurosa'	SPoc SWCr
Wiltshire = 'Kormuse'[PBR] (S/GC) ♥H4	CSBt ECnt ENot ESty LSRN LStr MFry MJon MRav NPri SPoc SSea SWCr WOVN
Winchester Cathedral = 'Auscat'[PBR] (S)	CGro CSBt CSam EBee ECnt EPfP ESty LAst LGod LRHS LStr MAsh MAus MBri MFry MJon MNHC MRMR MRav NEgg NPri NSRo SPer SPoG SPoc SWCr
Windflower = 'Auscross' (S)	LRHS MAus
Windrush = 'Ausrush' (S)	MAus MJon WAct WHCG
Wine and Dine = 'Dicuncle'[PBR] (GC)	IDic
x *wintoniensis*	WAct WHCG
Wise Portia = 'Ausport' (S)	MAus
Wishing = 'Dickerfuffle'[PBR] (F/Patio)	IDic MAus MGan
Wisley = 'Ausintense'	CSBt LRHS MAsh MAus SCoo SWCr
With Love = 'Andwit' (HT)	GGre MJon SPoG SWCr
With Thanks = 'Fransmoov'[PBR] (HT)	ESty MBri SWCr
'Woburn Abbey' (F)	CWSG SSea WBVN
Wolley-Dod'	see *R.* 'Duplex'
§ Woman o'th' North = 'Kirlon' (F/Patio)	MJon
Wonderful News = 'Jonone'[PBR] (Patio)	ESty GCoc MJon
§ *woodsii*	GIBF MAus MRMR WHCG
- var. *fendleri*	see *R. woodsii*
'Woolverstone Church Rose'	see *R.* 'Surpassing Beauty of Woolverstone'
Worcestershire = 'Korlalon'[PBR] (GC)	CSBt ENot GCoc MAus MRav SPer SPoc SWCr
World Peace 2000 = 'Peayellow' (HT)	SPoc SWCr
§ *xanthina* 'Canary Bird' (S) ♥H4	More than 30 suppliers
§ - f. *hugonis* ♥H4	MAus MGan NHaw SPer SPoc WAct
- f. *spontanea*	CArn
X-rated = 'Tinx' (Min)	MJon
Yellow Button = 'Auslow' (S)	WAct
'Yellow Cécile Brünner'	see *R.* 'Perle d'Or'
Yellow Charles Austin = 'Ausyel' (S)	MAus
§ Yellow Dagmar Hastrup = 'Moryelrug'[PBR] (Ru)	EBee EPfP MAus MGan MJon SPer SPla SWCr WAct WOVN
'Yellow Doll' (Min)	MAus SWCr
'Yellow Dream' (Patio)	GGre LRHS MAsh SPoG
Yellow Flower Carpet[PBR]	see *R.* Flower Carpet Sunshine
'Yellow Patio' (Min/Patio)	LRHS LStr MAsh SSea SWCr
yellow Scotch	see *R.* x *harisonii* 'Williams' Double Yellow'
Yellow Sunblaze = 'Meitrisical' (Min)	CSBt
'Yesterday' (Poly/F/S) ♥H4	EWTr MAsh MAus MGan MRav SPoG SWCr
York and Lancaster	see *R.* x *damascena* var. *versicolor*
Yorkshire Bank = 'Rutrulo'[PBR] (HT)	MFry
Yorkshire = 'Korbarkeit'[PBR] (GC)	ENot GCoc LStr MRav SSea
'Yorkshire Lady' (HT)	MJon
'Yvonne Rabier' (Poly) ♥H4	LStr MAus MRav SPer SWCr WAct WHCG
Zambra = 'Meicurbos' (F)	CBcs
'Zéphirine Drouhin' (Bb)	More than 30 suppliers
§ 'Zigeunerknabe' (S)	EBee ECnt MAus MRav NLar SPer SSea SWCr WAct WHCG

'Zitronenfalter' (S)	MGan
Zorba Poulyc008 (Patio/Cl)	ECnt
'Zweibrücken' (Cl)	MGan

Roscoea ✿ (*Zingiberaceae*)

ACE 2539	GEdr
alpina	CBct CBro CLAP CPLG EBee EBrs EChP ECho EHrv EHyt ERos GBuc GCrs GEdr GKev GSki IBlr ITim MTho MTis NGdn NLAp NMen NWCA SOkd SRms WCot WCru WLin
- CC 3667	GEdr GKev WRos
- pink-flowered	ITer
§ *auriculata*	More than 30 suppliers
- early-flowering	WCru
- 'Floriade'	CLAP GBuc IBlr
- late-flowering	WCru
- 'Special'	CLAP
australis	CFir GBuc GEdr IBlr MNrw SOkd WCru
'Beesiana'	More than 30 suppliers
'Beesiana' dark-flowered	ERos
'Beesiana' pale-flowered	ECho ERos IBlr LEdu WCru
'Beesiana' white-flowered	CBct CDes CFwr CLAP EBee EHrv EPfP EPot GEdr GSki IBlr LPhx MBNS MMHG NBir NGdn NMyG SMeo WAbe WPGP
blanda new	NLAp
brandisii	CBct ECho
capitata	SOkd
cautleyoides ♥H4	More than 30 suppliers
- CLD 687	GEdr
I - 'Alba'	NGdn NLAp
- Blackthorn strain	SBla
- var. *cautleyoides*	CDWL
- - red-flowered new	CFir
- - white-flowered new	CFir
- 'Early Purple'	CLAP EBee ECho GSki
- hybrid	ECho GSki MLLN
- 'Jeffrey Thomas'	CBct CFwr CLAP CSam ECho EPot GBuc GEdr GSki IBlr MLHP NMyG SMeo WCot
- 'Kew Beauty' ♥H4	CDes CFir CLAP EBee EBrs ETow GSki MTho SRms WCot WPGP
- 'Kew Beauty' seedlings	EGle GCal
- 'Purple Giant'	CLAP WCot
- purple-flowered	GBuc IBlr NHar
- 'Reinier'	CLAP GBuc WCot
cautleyoides x *humeana*	CLAP IBlr
forrestii new	IBlr
'Gestreept'	CLAP
'Himalaya'	CLAP
humeana ♥H4	CBct CBro CFee CLAP CSam EAEE EBrs ECho EHyt ERos GBin GCrs GEdr GKev GMac LRHS SBla WCFE WCot WCru WPrP WThu
- ACE 2539	IBlr
- Forrest's form new	IBlr
- lavender-flowered new	IBlr
- f. *lutea*	CLAP IBlr
- 'Purple Streaker'	CBct CDes CLAP EBee WPGP
- 'Rosemoor Plum'	CLAP
- 'Snowy Owl'	CLAP
- f. *tyria*	IBlr
kunmingensis var. *elongatobractea*	IBlr
- var. *kunmingensis*	IBlr
- 'Monique'	CDes CLAP IBlr
procera misapplied	see *R. auriculata*
procera Wall.	see *R. purpurea*
§ *purpurea*	More than 30 suppliers
- CC 3628	WCot
- HWJK 2400	WCru
- KW 13755	IBlr
- 'Brown Peacock'	CDes CLAP IBlr SBla WCot

- var. *gigantea*	CLAP IBlr
- - CC 1757	MNrw
- lilac-flowered	CDWL GSki SOkd
- 'Nico'	CBct CLAP ERou WCot WGwG
- 'Niedrig'	EBee
- pale-flowered	EBla
- 'Peacock'	CLAP IBlr SCnR WFar
- 'Peacock Eye'	CLAP IBlr WCot
- var. *procera*	see *R. purpurea*
- 'Red Gurkha'	SBla
- Rosemoor form **new**	WWst
- short	CLAP IBlr
- tall	CLAP NLAp
- 'Wisley Amethyst' **new**	CLAP SBla
schneideriana **new**	IBlr MLul NLAp
§ *scillifolia*	CBro CDes CFir CPBP EAEE EBrs
	ECho EPot ERos GBuc GCal GEdr
	GKev GSki IBlr LHop LRHS MAvo
	MTho NBir NGdn NMen SBla
	WCot WCru WLin WPrP
- dark-flowered	CPom CStu EBee EHrv WCru
	WPGP
- pink-flowered	CBct EChP ECho EHrv EMar ERos
	GEdr IBlr IFoB NMen NMyG WAbe
	WCot
tibetica	CFir CFwr CLAP EBee GEdr GKev
	IBlr NLAp SOkd WCot WCru
	WThu
- ACE 2538	IBlr
tumjensis	CLAP EBee EWes IBlr
'Vincent'	WCot
wardii	EHyt IBlr
'Yeti'	CLAP

rosemary see *Rosmarinus officinalis*

Rosmarinus ✿ (*Lamiaceae*)

* 'Compactus Albus' **new**	WGwG
corsicus 'Prostratus'	see *R. officinalis* Prostratus Group
§ *eriocalyx*	XPep
lavandulaceus misapplied	see *R. officinalis* Prostratus Group
lavandulaceus Noë	see *R. eriocalyx*
officinalis	More than 30 suppliers
- var. *albiflorus*	CArn CPbn CPrp CSev ELau EPfP
	GBar GPoy LRHS MBar MBow
	MHer MNHC MSwo NHHG SDow
	SHDw SLim SPer SPlb STre WCHb
	WGwG WWye XPep
- - 'Lady in White'	CSBt EBee EDsa ELan EPfP LAst
	LRHS NGHP SDow SPer WGwG
	WJek
- 'Alderney'	GBar MHer SDow
- var. *angustissimus*	XPep
§ - - 'Benenden Blue' ♀H4	CBcs CBgR CSBt CSev CWan CWib
	EBee EGoo ELau EShb GBar GPoy
	LHop LRHS MHer MNHC NHHG
	SDix SMHy SMer SPer SPlb STre
	WWye
§ - - 'Corsican Blue'	CArn EBee ELan EPfP GBar GPoy
	MHer MNHC NGHP SDow SHDw
	SIde SLon SMer WBrE WPer XPep
- - 'Corsicus Prostratus'	ELau
- arching **new**	MNHC
- 'Aureovariegatus'	see *R. officinalis* 'Aureus'
- 'Aureus' (v)	CBow GBar NBlu NHHG WCHb
	WEas
- 'Baie d'Audierne'	EBee XPep
- 'Baie de Douarnenez'	XPep
- 'Barbecue'PBR	ELau EWin MHer MNHC NGHP
	SIde
- 'Barcelona'	XPep
- 'Blue Boy'	MHer
- 'Blue Lagoon'	EBee ELau EOHP EWin MHer
	MNHC NGHP WCHb WGwG
	WJek
- 'Blue Rain'	CPbn EAro LAst MHer NGHP

- 'Boule'	CPbn CPrp EWin MHer WCHb
	XPep
- 'Bowles' **new**	ELau
- 'Cap Béar'	XPep
- 'Capercaillie'	SDow
- 'Cisampo'	XPep
- 'Collingwood Ingram'	see *R. officinalis* var.
	angustissimus 'Benenden Blue'
- 'Columbian' **new**	MNHC
- dwarf, blue-flowered	ELau GBar
- dwarf, white-flowered	WCHb
- 'Eve'	XPep
- 'Farinole'	CPrp ELau MNHC XPep
- 'Fastigiatus'	see *R. officinalis* 'Miss Jessopp's
	Upright'
- 'Fota Blue'	CArn CBgR CBod CBow CPrp
	CSev CWib EAro ELau EOHP GBar
	IArd MHer MNHC NGHP NHHG
	SAga SDow SHDw SIde WCHb
	WJek WWye
- 'Foxtail' **new**	EWin
- 'Golden Rain'	see *R. officinalis* 'Joyce DeBaggio'
- 'Gorizia'	GBar SDow XPep
- 'Green Ginger'	CBod CPrp CSpe EChP EOHP EPfP
	EUnu EWin GBin LHop MHer
	NGHP NPer SDow SPoG WCHb
	WGwG WMnd
- 'Guilded'	see *R. officinalis* 'Aureus'
- 'Gunnel's Upright'	GBar WRha
- 'Haifa'	CBod CPbn EBee ELau EWin GGar
	MNHC NGHP SIde WCHb
- 'Heavenly Blue'	GBar WGwG
- 'Henfield Blue'	SHDw
- 'Iden Blue'	SIde
- 'Iden Blue Boy'	SIde
- 'Iden Pillar'	SIde
§ - 'Joyce DeBaggio' (v)	LSou MHer SDow
- 'Lady in Blue'	WGwG
- *lavandulaceus*	see *R. officinalis* Prostratus Group
- 'Lérida'	XPep
- 'Lilies Blue'	GPoy
- 'Lockwood Variety'	see *R. officinalis* (Prostratus
	Group) 'Lockwood de Forest'
- 'Loupian'	XPep
- 'Majorca Pink'	CBgR CPbn CPrp CSBt CSam
	CWan EGoo ELau ENot GBar MHer
	MNHC MRav SDow SIde SLon SPer
	SRms SSto WCHb WGwG WWye
	XPep
- 'Marenca'	ELau MNHC WCHb XPep
- 'Marinka'	CWan
- 'Mason's Finest'	SDow
- 'McConnell's Blue' ♀H4	CArn CBgR CDoC CPbn CPrp
	EBee ELan ELau EShb GBar LHop
	LRHS MAsh MGos MNHC MRav
	SDow SHDw SPla WCHb WFar
	WHoo WPGP WTel WWye
- 'Minerve'	XPep
§ - 'Miss Jessopp's Upright'	More than 30 suppliers
♀H4	
- 'Montagnette'	XPep
- 'Mrs Harding'	CBod CPbn CPrp MHer
- 'Pointe du Raz'	EBee ELan EPfP MRav SPoG
§ - 'Primley Blue'	CArn CBcs CMea CPbn CPrp
	CSam CSev CWSG EBee ECtt ELau
	GBar LRHS MHer MNHC MRav
	NGHP NHHG NJOw SIde SMer
	WCHb WPer
§ - Prostratus Group	More than 30 suppliers
- - 'Capri'	CAbP CSBt ENot EOHP LRHS
	MBrN MHer MRav NGHP SDow
	SMer SPoG
- - 'Deben Blue'	ENot
- - 'Gethsemane'	SIde
- - 'Jackman's Prostrate'	CBcs ECtt
§ - - 'Lockwood de Forest'	GBar LSou

- 'Punta di Canelle'	XPep
- f. *pyramidalis*	see *R. officinalis* 'Miss Jessopp's Upright'
- 'Rampant Boule'	GBar SDow
- *repens*	see *R. officinalis* Prostratus Group
- 'Rex' **new**	ELau
- 'Roman Beauty'	LAst MAsh SVil
- 'Rosemarey'	XPep
- 'Roseus'	CArn CPrp CSBt CWib EBee EChP ELan ELau EMil EPfP GPoy LHop LRHS MHer MNHC NHHG SDow SLim SPoG WAbe WHer WMnd WPer WWeb WWye
- 'Russell's Blue'	WFar
- 'Saint Florent'	XPep
- 'Salem'	MHer
- 'Santa Barbara Blue'	XPep
- 'Sawyer's Select'	MHer
- 'Sea Level'	CBod CPbn ELau MBow MHer WCHb
- 'Severn Sea' ♀[H4]	CArn CBcs CBgR CPrp CSBt CSev CWSG ECtt ELan ELau EPfP GBar GPoy LHop LRHS MGos MHer MNHC MRav MSwo NFor SDow SIde SLon SMer WCFE WCHb WEas WPer WWeb
- 'Silver Sparkler'	CBow WPat
- Silver Spires = 'Wolros'	LRav MNHC
- 'Sissinghurst Blue' ♀[H4]	CArn CBcs CSev CWan EBee ECha ELan ELau EMil EPfP GBar LRHS MBow MHer MLHP MNHC MRav NGHP SDow SIde SLim SMer SPer SPlb SRms WCHb WGwG WSel WWye XPep
- 'Sissinghurst White'	WGwG
- 'South Downs Blue'	SHDw
- 'Sudbury Blue'	EBee ELau EPfP EWin GBar MHer MNHC NGHP NHHG SDow SHDw WEas WJek XPep
- 'Trusty'	CWan GBar LRHS XPep
- 'Tuscan Blue'	More than 30 suppliers
- 'Ulysse'	XPep
- 'Variegatus'	see *R. officinalis* 'Aureus'
- 'Vicomte de Noailles'	ERea XPep
repens	see *R. officinalis* Prostratus Group

Rostrinucula (Lamiaceae)

dependens	EMan NLar WSHC
sinensis	CPLG

Rosularia ✿ (Crassulaceae)

from Sandras Dag	CWil LBee LRHS
alba	see *R. sedoides* var. *alba*
alpestris from Rhotang Pass	WThu
§ *chrysantha*	EAEE EBur EPot MHer NJOw NMen SIng SPlb
- number 1	CWil LRHS
crassipes	see *Rhodiola wallichiana*
§ *muratdaghensis*	EBur SIng
pallida A. Berger	see *R. chrysantha*
platyphylla misapplied	see *R. muratdaghensis*
sedoides	CWil LRHS MBar SIng
§ - var. *alba*	ECho EDAr EHol EPot GGar MBar NLAp WFar WTin
sempervivum	CWil ECho EWes NMen
§ - subsp. *glaucophylla*	CWil WAbe
spatulata hort.	see *R. sempervivum* subsp. *glaucophylla*

Rothmannia (Rubiaceae)

capensis	EShb SOWG
§ *globosa*	ERea

Rubia (Rubiaceae)

peregrina	CArn GPoy MSal

tinctorum	CArn CHby EOHP EUnu GBar GPoy GWCH MSal SWat WCHb WWye

Rubus ✿ (Rosaceae)

RCB/Eq C-1	WCot
alceifolius Poir.	CFee SDys SMac
arcticus	EBee EPPr GGar GIBF MCCP NLAp NLar SHar SRms SRot WCru WGHP WPat
x *barkeri*	ECou
§ 'Benenden' ♀[H4]	More than 30 suppliers
'Betty Ashburner'	CAgr CBcs CDoC ECrN EPfP EWTr GQui LAst LBuc MGos MRav MWgw MWhi NHol SLPl SPer SPoG WBVN WDin WGHP WMoo WTin
biflorus ♀[H4]	CBcs EBee EPfP EWes LEdu LRHS MBlu SMac WPGP
'Black Butte'	LRHS SDea
'Boatsberry'	SDea
'Boysenberry, Thornless' (F)	EMui GTwe LBuc LRHS MGan SDea SPer
calophyllus	WBor WPGP
calycinoides Hayata	see *R. rolfei*
chamaemorus	GIBF GPoy
cissoides	WCot
cockburnianus (F)	CArn CBcs CTri EBee ELan EPfP EWTr IFoB LBuc LRHS MBlu MRav MSwo NBea NHol NLRH NSti NWea SPer SPlb SRms WDin WEas WFar
- 'Goldenvale' ♀[H4]	More than 30 suppliers
coreanus	EPla
crataegifolius	CBrd CWan SMac WPat
'Emerald Spreader'	SBod
flagelliflorus	MBar
fockeanus misapplied	see *R. rolfei*
formosensis B&SWJ 1798	WCru
N *fruticosus* agg.	WSFF
- 'Adrienne' (F)	CAgr EMui
- 'Ashton Cross' (F)	GTwe LBuc
- 'Bedford Giant' (F)	CSBt ENot GTwe LBuc MAsh MGan MGos MRav SPoG
- 'Black Satin' (F)	CAgr EMil LRHS NLar SDea
- 'Chester' (F) **new**	EMil SKee
- 'Fantasia'[PBR] (F) ♀[H4]	EMui
- 'Godshill Goliath' (F)	SDea
- 'Helen'	CAgr CSut EMui SDea
- 'Himalayan Giant' (F)	ENot GTwe MGan MRav NEgg SDea SPer
- 'Loch Ness'[PBR] (F) ♀[H4]	CAgr COtt CSBt CWib EMil EMui ENot ERea GTwe IArd LBuc LRHS MAsh NEgg SCoo SDea SKee SPer SPoG
- 'Merton Thornless' (F)	CSBt CWib ERea GTwe MAsh MGan MGos
- 'No Thorn' (F)	SDea
- 'Oregon Thornless' (F)	CAgr CCVT CSBt CWib EMui ENot GTwe LRHS MAsh MBri MRav NEgg SCoo SDea SKee SPer SPoG SRms WOrn
- 'Parsley Leaved' (F)	MRav SDea
* - 'Sylvan' (F)	EMil MCoo MGos SKee SPer
- 'Thornfree' (F)	CAgr SDea
- 'Variegatus' (v)	MBlu NHol SMad WPat
- 'Veronique' (F)	EMui
- 'Waldo'	CAgr COtt CSBt CWib EMui LBuc MAsh MGos SDea
'Gold Lace' **new**	WEas
'Golden Showers'	CWib
hakonensis B&SWJ 5555	WCru
henryi	CPIN EPla MRav NLar NSti SLon SMac SPoG WCot WFar
- var. *bambusarum*	CMCN CPIN EBee EMan EPfP EPla MCCP NVic WCru

hupehensis		SLPl
ichangensis		CBcs CPlN EPla LEdu
I	*idaeus* 'Allgold'	see *R. idaeus* 'Fallgold'
	- 'Aureus' (F)	ECha ELan EPla MRav NBid NBre SMac WCot WFar WMoo
	- 'Autumn Bliss'^{PBR} (F) ♀H4	CAgr CSBt CSut CTri CWSG CWib EMui ENot EPfP ERea GTwe LBuc LRHS MAsh MBri MGan MGos MNHC MRav NEgg SCoo SDea SKee SPer SPoG WOrn
§	- 'Fallgold' (F)	CAgr CWib EMui EPfP ERea LBuc LRHS MAsh MCoo SKee SPer SPoG WOrn
	- 'Galante'^{PBR} (F)	EMui
	- 'Glen Ample'^{PBR} (F) ♀H4	CAgr CSBt CSut CWSG CWib EMui EPfP GTwe LBuc LRHS MAsh MBri MCoo SCoo SDea SKee SPer SPoG
	- 'Glen Clova' (F)	CAgr CSBt CTri CWib ENot ERea GTwe LRHS MAsh MGan MNHC MRav NBlu NEgg SKee SPer SPoG WOrn
	- 'Glen Lyon'^{PBR} (F)	CWib EMui GTwe LBuc MAsh MBri SCoo
	- 'Glen Magna'^{PBR} (F)	CSBt CSut CWSG CWib EMil EMui GTwe LBuc LRHS MAsh MBri SCoo SDea SKee SPoG
	- 'Glen Moy'^{PBR} (F) ♀H4	CAgr CSBt CWib EMil EMui EPfP GTwe MAsh MGos MRav SCoo SDea SKee
	- 'Glen Prosen'^{PBR} (F) ♀H4	CAgr CSBt CWib EMui GTwe MAsh MBri MRav SCoo SDea SKee SPer
	- 'Glen Rosa' (F)	GTwe
	- 'Glen Shee' (F)	GTwe
	- 'Heritage' (F)	CWib ENot MAsh MRav SCoo
	- 'Joan J'^{PBR} new	EMil
	- 'Joan Squire'^{PBR} (F) new	SKee
	- 'Julia' (F)	CAgr GTwe MCoo
	- 'Leo'^{PBR} (F) ♀H4	CAgr CSBt CWib EMui ERea GTwe MAsh MGos NEgg SCoo SKee SPer
	- 'Malling Admiral' (F) ♀H4	CTri CWib EMui ENot GTwe MAsh SCoo SKee SPer
	- 'Malling Delight' (F)	CSBt CWib MAsh MRav SCoo
	- 'Malling Jewel' (F) ♀H4	COtt CSBt CTri CWib EMui ENot ERea GTwe LBuc MAsh MGan NEgg SDea SKee SPer
	- 'Malling Promise' (F)	CWib ERea
	- 'Octavia' (F) new	EMui
	- 'Polka' (F) new	SKee
	- 'Redsetter' (F)	EMui
	- 'Summer Gold' (F)	GTwe
	- 'Tulameen' (F)	CAgr CWib EMil EMui LBuc LRHS MAsh MBri SCoo SEND SKee SPoG
	- 'Zeva Herbsternte' (F)	CWib MAsh
	illecebrosus (F)	GIBF ITer NLar
	irenaeus	CPlN
	Japanese wineberry	see *R. phoenicolasius*
	'Kenneth Ashburner'	CDoC NLar SLPl WFar WTin
	'King's Acre Berry' (F)	EMui
	laciniatus	EHol EPla
	lambertianus	CPlN
	leucodermis NNS 00-663	EPPr
	lineatus	CDoC CMCo CPLG EPfP LRHS NSti SDix SMad WCru WDin WPGP WPat
	- HWJ 892 from Vietnam new	WCru
	- HWJK 2045	WCru
	x *loganobaccus* 'Brandywine'	SDea
	- 'LY 59' (F) ♀H4	EMui ENot EPfP GTwe MRav NEgg SDea SKee SRms
	- 'LY 654' (F) ♀H4	GTwe LBuc MBri MGos SDea SPer
	- thornless (F)	CAgr CTri CWSG CWib ECot ENot GTwe MAsh MGan SDea SPoG
	'Margaret Gordon'	MRav SBrw WHCG
	microphyllus 'Variegatus' (v)	EMan WPat
§	*nepalensis*	CAgr CDoC CEnd LEdu NLAp
	niveus	EPla
	nutans	see *R. nepalensis*
	odoratus	CPLG CPle CPom CTri ELan EPfP LEdu MRav NPal SPer WBor WCMO WCot WHCG WTin
	parviflorus	CArn
	- double (d)	WCru
	- 'Sunshine Spreader'	WPat
	parvus	ECou
	pectinellus var. *trilobus*	CFee LEdu NLar SMac
	- - B&SWJ 1669B	GSki NPro WCru WDyG
	peltatus	NLar WPGP
	pentalobus	see *R. rolfei*
§	*phoenicolasius*	CAgr EMui EPfP EWTr GTwe LEdu LHop MBlu MGan MRav MWhi NSti SDea SPer WAbb WCru WHCG
§	*rolfei*	CTri EPPr EPla MBar NFor NMyG SMac WFar
	- B&SWJ 3546	WCru
	- B&SWJ 3878	WCru
	- 'Emerald Carpet'	CAgr NLar SBod
	rosifolius	CBcs CSpe
	- 'Coronarius' (d)	CFee CHar CSpe ECrN ELan EMan GAbr LSou MRav MWhi NPro NSti WCMO WCot WFar WHil
	sachalinensis	GIBF
	sanctus new	CNat
	saxatilis	GIBF
	setchuenensis	CMCN CSWP
	'Silvan' (F) ♀H4	EMui GTwe
	'Sir Arthur Harris' new	CPlN
	spectabilis	CBcs CSev CWib ELan EPPr EPla EWTr LEdu MRav WFar WRha WSHC WWFP
	- 'Flore Pleno'	see *R. spectabilis* 'Olympic Double'
§	- 'Olympic Double' (d)	More than 30 suppliers
	splendidissimus B&SWJ 2361	WCru
	squarrosus	CPle ECou EHol
	'Sunberry' (F)	GTwe SDea
	swinhoei B&SWJ 1735	WCru
	taiwanicola	EDAr GEdr NLar WWhi
	- B&SWJ 317	GBin MHar NPro WCru WPrP
	Tayberry Group (F) ♀H4	CTri EMui ENot EPfP GTwe MAsh MGan MGos NLar SPer SRms
	- 'Buckingham' (F)	CSut EMil EMui GTwe LBuc
	- 'Medana Tayberry' (F)	CAgr EMui ERea LRHS SDea SKee SPoG
§	*thibetanus* ♀H4	More than 30 suppliers
	- 'Silver Fern'	see *R. thibetanus*
	tricolor	CAgr CBcs CDul CSBt CTri CWib EBee ECrN EPfP GBri GIBF MMuc MRav MSwo MTis MWhi NEgg NFor NHol SDix SHBN SLon SMac SPer WDin WGHP WHCG
	- 'Dart's Evergreen'	SLPl
	- 'Ness'	SLPl
	tridel 'Benenden'	see *R.* 'Benenden'
	trilobus	GAbr
	- B&SWJ 9096	WCru
§	- 'Tummelberry' (F)	GTwe
	ulmifolius 'Bellidiflorus' (d)	EBee MBlu MRav MSwo NFor NSti SDix SMac SPer WAbb WEas WHrl
	ursinus	LEdu
§	- 'Veitchberry' (F)	GTwe
	xanthocarpus	NLar
§	- 'Youngberry' (F)	SDea

Rudbeckia ✿ (Asteraceae)

Autumn Sun	see *R. laciniata* 'Herbstsonne'
californica	CSam EBee MNrw WCMO WPer

deamii	see *R. fulgida* var. *deamii*
echinacea purpurea	see *Echinacea purpurea*
fulgida **new**	NNor
§ – var. *deamii* ♀H4	More than 30 suppliers
– var. *fulgida*	MDKP NRnb WHil
§ – var. *speciosa* ♀H4	CKno CMMP CPLG CSam EBee
	ECha ECtt ELan EPfP ERou GAbr
	LAst LRHS MHar NGdn SBch SDix
	SMac SPlb SRms WEas WFar WMoo
	WPer WTel WTin WViv WWpP
– var. *sullivantii*	More than 30 suppliers
'Goldsturm' ♀H4	
– Viette's Little Suzy =	EBee EBrs LRHS WCra
'Blovi'	
gloriosa	see *R. hirta*
'Golden Jubilee'	LRHS WWeb
§ *hirta*	CHar CHrt EBrs NBir
– 'Chim Chiminee'	LBMP
– 'Goldilocks'	GWCH
– 'Indian Summer' ♀H3	SPav
– 'Irish Eyes'	LBMP LRHS LRav SPav
– 'Marmalade'	LBMP NEgg NJOw
– 'Prairie Sun' **new**	LBMP
– var. *pulcherrima*	EBee MGol SMHy
– 'Sonora'	COtt
– 'Toto' ♀H3	LBMP SPav SWvt WSan WWpP
– 'Toto Gold' **new**	LBMP
– 'Toto Rustic' **new**	LBMP
July Gold	see *R. laciniata* 'Juligold'
laciniata	CBrm CElw COIW EBee EBrs
	EChP ELan EMon EPPr EPfP GCal
	GQue LEdu MDKP MWrn NLar
	NOrc NRnb NSti SMHy SMar WCot
	WMoo WOld
– 'Golden Glow'	see *R. laciniata* 'Hortensia'
– 'Goldquelle' (d) ♀H4	More than 30 suppliers
§ – 'Herbstsonne' ♀H4	More than 30 suppliers
§ – 'Hortensia' (d)	EMon GQue MLLN WOld
§ – 'Juligold'	CPrp EBee ETow IPot LRHS MBNS
	MBnl MWgw NBre NEgg NGdn
	SMrm SPla SPoG WCAu WCMO
	WFar WWhi WWpP
maxima	More than 30 suppliers
missouriensis	NBre SUsu
mollis	EBee NBre
newmannii	see *R. fulgida* var. *speciosa*
nitida	EShb IHMH
occidentalis	EBrs MLLN NBre NRnb NVic WFar
	WPer
– 'Black Beauty'PBR	EBee EChP EHrv EPfP MBNS
	MMHG NBhm NBro NLar NMoo
	NSti SBig SHop WMnd
– 'Green Wizard'	More than 30 suppliers
* *paniculata*	NBre WCMO WCot
purpurea	see *Echinacea purpurea*
speciosa	see *R. fulgida* var. *speciosa*
subtomentosa	CSam EBee EBrs EMon GCal LRHS
	MAvo MDKP MNFA MWea NBre
	NSti SMHy WCAu WOld WWpP
'Takao'	CWCL EBee LSou MAvo MBNS
	MDKP MLLN MSph MWea NLar
	SPoG SUsu
triloba	CSam EBee EPPr EPfP EShb GBri
	LRHS MNrw NBPC NGdn NRnb
	SAga SMad SMar WCAu WFar
	WHoo WMoo WPGP WSan WTin

rue see *Ruta graveolens*

Ruellia (Acanthaceae)

amoena	see *R. graecizans*
ciliata f. *depressa* **new**	CPBP
§ *graecizans*	ECre
humilis	EBee EShb NLar WBVN WHil
macrantha	CCCN MJnS
makoyana ♀H1	CHal CSev MBri

'Mr Foster'	CHal
tweediana	MJnS

Rumex (Polygonaceae)

§ *acetosa*	CArn CHby CSev CWan ELau GBar
	GPoy GWCH IHMH LRHS MBow
	MHer MNHC NBir NGHP NPri
	NSco SEND SIde WHer WSFF WSel
	WWye
– 'Abundance'	ELau
– subsp. *acetosa* 'Saucy'	CBow WCot
(v)	
– 'De Belleville'	CPrp
– 'Profusion'	GPoy
– subsp. *vinealis*	EBee WCot
acetosella	CArn MNHC MSal NMir WSel
alpinus	LEdu WCot
flexuosus	EBee EHoe EShb EUnu MDKP
	NLar WJek
hydrolapathum	CArn CHEx EMFW LPBA SPlb
	WSFF WWpP
obtusifolius 'Golden	CNat
My Foot'	
patientia	CAgr
sanguineus	CAgr .CTri EMan EPfP EShb EUnu
	EWin IHMH LBMP LPBA MWgw
	NCob NLar SWal WBrk WFar
	WMAq WWeb WWpP
– var. *sanguineus*	CArn CBgR CElw CPrp CRow
	CSev EBee EHoe ELan EPla IFoB
	LRHS MHer MNrw MTho NBro
	NHol WHer WPer WSel WWye
* 'Schavel'	CAgr
scutatus	CAgr CArn CHby CSev ELau EUnu
	GPoy MHer MNHC SIde SPlb
	WGHP WHbs WHer WJek WWye
– 'Silver Shield'	CBod CRow ELau EMar SIde
	WCHb WJek
venosus	MSal

Rumohra (Davalliaceae)

adiantiformis ♀H1	EFtx SEND WFib
– RCB/Arg D-2	WCot

Rupicapnos (Papaveraceae)

africana	GKev

Ruschia (Aizoaceae)

uncinata	SChr

Ruscus ✿ (Ruscaceae)

aculeatus	CArn CBcs CDul CRWN EBee ELan
	ENot EPfP GPoy IDee LEdu MGos
	MRav MWat MWgw NWea SAPC
	SArc SCoo SPer SPlb SPoG SRms
	SSta WDin WHer WPGP WRHF
	WWye
– (f)	WFar WMou
– hermaphrodite	EPfP EPla EWes GCal SMad WGer
	WPGP
– (m)	WMou
– var. *aculeatus*	GCal
'Lanceolatus' (f)	
– var. *angustifolius* Boiss.	EPla
– – (f)	EPla
– 'Christmas Berry' **new**	EPfP
* – 'Wheeler's Variety' (f/m)	CPMA
hypoglossum	EPla SEND WRHF
'John Redmond' **new**	MWea WCot
x *microglossum* (f)	CDul
racemosus	see *Danae racemosa*

Russelia (Scrophulariaceae)

§ *equisetiformis* ♀H1	CHll EShb SOWG XPep
– yellow-flowered	EShb
juncea	see *R. equisetiformis*

Ruta (*Rutaceae*)

chalepensis	CArn XPep
corsica	CArn
graveolens	CArn CPLG CWan EChP EPfP
	EWin GBar GPoy GWCH MNHC
	NPri SIde WGHP WJek WPer
	WWye XPep
- 'Jackman's Blue'	CBcs CDul CSev CTri EBee ECrN
	EHoe ELan EPfP GMaP GPoy LAst
	MGos MHer MRav MSwo MWgw
	NFor SMer SPer SRms WEas WMnd
	WTel
- 'Variegata' (v)	CBow CWan ELan EMan EOHP
	GBar MFOX MNHC NFor NPer
	SPer WJek

Ruttya (*Acanthaceae*)

fruticosa 'Scholesii'	ERea

x *Ruttyruspolia* (*Acanthaceae*)

'Phyllis van Heerden'	GFai

Rytidosperma (*Poaceae*)

* **arundinaceum**	EShb
* **stricta** new	CBig

S

Sabal (*Arecaceae*)

§ **bermudana**	CRoM EAmu LPal WMul
domingensis	EAmu
etonia	LPal
mauritiiformis	WMul
§ **mexicana**	CRoM CTrC EAmu WMul
minor	CBrP CHEx CPho CRoM CTrC
	EAmu EZes LPal MPRe NPal SAin
	SBig WMul
palmetto	CArn CDoC CRoM CTrC EAmu
	LPal MPRe WMul WNor
princeps	see *S. bermudana*
rosei	LPal WMul
texana	see *S. mexicana*
uresana	LPal

Saccharum (*Poaceae*)

arundinaceum	EPPr
§ **baldwinii**	CBig
brevibarbe var.	CBig
contortum	
officinarum	MJnS
ravennae	CBig CPLG CPen EBee EHoe
	EMan LRav MSte NBid SMad SPlb
	WFar
strictum (Ell.) Ell.	see *S. baldwinii*
ex Nutt.	
strictum (Host) Spreng.	NBre

sage see *Salvia officinalis*

sage, annual clary see *Salvia viridis*

sage, biennial clary see *Salvia sclarea*

sage, pineapple see *Salvia elegans*

Sageretia (*Rhamnaceae*)

§ **thea**	STre
theezans	see *S. thea*

Sagina (*Caryophyllaceae*)

boydii	ECho EWes
subulata	ECho EDAr IHMH LAst

§ - var. **glabrata** 'Aurea'	CMea CTri ECha ECho ECtt EDAr
	MBNS MWhi SIng SPoG SRms
	WEas WHal WPer

Sagittaria (*Alismataceae*)

'Bloomin Babe'	CRow
graminea 'Crushed Ice'	CRow
(v)	
japonica	see *S. sagittifolia*
latifolia	COld LPBA NPer SMad
* **leucopetala** 'Flore Pleno'	NLar NPer
(d)	
§ **sagittifolia**	CBen CDWL CRow CWat EHon
	EMFW EPfP GAbr LNCo LPBA
	NSco SWat WFar WMAq WPnP
	WWpP
- 'Flore Pleno' (d)	CBen CDWL CRow CWat EMFW
	LPBA SWat WMAq WPnP WWpP
- var. **leucopetala**	WMAq

Saintpaulia (*Gesneriaceae*)

'Akira' new	EAVC
'Bangle Blue' new	WDib
'Beatrice Trail'	WDib
'Blue Dragon'	WDib
'Bob Serbin' (d)	WDib
'Bohemian Sunset'	WDib
'Bright Eyes' new	EAVC
'Buffalo Hunt'	WDib
'Candy Gem' new	EAVC
'Centenary'	WDib
'Chelsea Belle' new	EAVC
'Cherries 'n' Cream'	WDib
'Chiffon Fiesta'	WDib
'Chiffon Mist' (d)	WDib
'Chiffon Moonmoth'	WDib
'Chiffon Stardust'	WDib
'Chiffon Vesper'	WDib
'Chiko' new	EAVC
'Chloe' new	EAVC
'Cilla' new	EAVC
'Corolaire' new	EAVC
'Coroloir'	WDib
'Delft' (d)	WDib
'Dorothy' new	EAVC
'Electric Dreams' new	WDib
'Emi' new	EAVC
'Ena' new	EAVC
'Florence' new	EAVC
'Golden Glow' (d)	WDib
'Halo' (Ultra Violet Series)	WDib
'Halo's Aglitter'	WDib
'Hanna' new	EAVC
'Hisako' PBR new	EAVC
'Irish Flirt' (d)	WDib
'Juliana' new	EAVC
'Kumiko' new	EAVC
'Kuzuko' new	EAVC
'Lemon Drop' (d)	WDib
'Lemon Whip' (d)	WDib
'Love Spots'	WDib
'Lucky Lee Ann' (d)	WDib
'Marching Band'	WDib
'Mari' new	EAVC
'Mermaid' (d)	WDib
'Meteor Trail' new	EAVC
'Mia' new	EAVC
'Midget Lillian' (v)	WDib
'Midnight Flame'	WDib
'Midnight Magic' new	EAVC
'Midnight Waltz'	WDib
'Niki' new	EAVC
'Norfolk Beauty' new	EAVC
'Nubian Winter'	WDib
'One-O-One' new	EAVC
'Otoe'	WDib

'Patty' **new**	EAVC	
'Powder Keg' (d)	WDib	
'Powwow' (d/v)	WDib	
'Rachel' **new**	EAVC	
'Ramblin' Magic' (d)	WDib	
'Rapid Transit' (d)	WDib	
'Rebecca' **new**	EAVC	
'Rob's Bamboozle'	WDib	
'Rob's Dandy Lion' **new**	WDib	
'Rob's Denim Demon'	WDib	
'Rob's Dust Storm' (d)	WDib	
'Rob's Firebrand'	WDib	
'Rob's Gundaroo' (d)	WDib	
'Rob's Heat Wave' (d)	WDib	
'Rob's Hopscotch'	WDib	
'Rob's Ice Ripples' (d)	WDib	
'Rob's Loose Goose' **new**	WDib	
'Rob's Macho Devil' **new**	WDib	
'Rob's Mad Cat' (d)	WDib	
'Rob's Rinky Dink' (d)	WDib	
'Rob's Sarsparilla' (d)	WDib	
'Rob's Seduction'	WDib	
'Rob's Shadow Magic' (d)	WDib	
'Rob's Sticky Wicket'	WDib	
'Rob's Toorooka' (d)	WDib	
'Rob's Twinkle Pink' **new**	WDib	
'Rococo Pink' **new**	EAVC	
'Royal Pearl' **new**	EAVC	
'Royal Velvet' **new**	EAVC	
'Salmon' **new**	EAVC	
'Sami' **new**	EAVC	
'Shannon'^{PBR} **new**	EAVC	
shumensis	WDib	
'Sixty' **new**	EAVC	
'Sky Bandit' (d)	WDib	
'Starry Trail' **new**	EAVC	
'Tamiko' **new**	EAVC	
'The Madam' **new**	WDib	
§ 'Tippy Toe' (d)	WDib	
'Tippy Toes' (d)	see *S.* 'Tippy Toe'	
'Twinkle Trail' **new**	EAVC	

Salix ✿ (*Salicaceae*)

acutifolia	ELan GIBF SPla WDin	
- 'Blue Streak' (m) ♀^{H4}	CDul CEnd CWiW CWon EPfP	
	EPla EWes MAsh MBlu MRav NBir	
	SLon SMhy SWat WFar	
- 'Lady Aldenham No 2'	EPla	
- 'Pendulifolia' (m)	MAsh SBLw WPat	
aegyptiaca	CDoC CLnd ECrN MBlu NWea	
	WMou	
alaxensis **new**	WWll	
alba	CAgr CCVT CDul CLnd CWiW	
	ECrN LBuc NWea SBLw WDin	
	WMou WOrn	
- f. *argentea*	see *S. alba* var. *sericea*	
- 'Aurea'	CLnd CTho CWon MRav WIvy	
	WMou	
- 'Belders' (m)	SBLw	
- var. *caerulea*	CAgr CDul CLnd CWon MRav	
	NWea WMou	
- - 'Wantage Hall' (f)	CWiW	
- 'Cardinalis' (f)	CWiW CWon GQue SWat WWll	
- 'Chermesina' hort.	see *S. alba* var. *vitellina* 'Britzensis'	
- 'Dart's Snake'	CBgR CTho ELan EPfP MBrN MRav	
	NScw SCoo	
- 'Hutchinson's Yellow'	CDoC CTho CWon MGos NWea	
	WDin	
- 'Liempde' (m)	MRav SBLw	
- 'Raesfeld' (m)	CWiW CWon	
- 'Saint Oedendrode' **new**	CWon	
§ - var. *sericea* ♀^{H4}	CBcs CDoC CLnd CTho CWon	
	ECrN EPfP MBlu MRav NFor NWea	
	SBLw SHBN SPer WDin WGer	
	WIvy WMou	
- 'Splendens'	see *S. alba* var. *sericea*	

- 'Tristis' misapplied	see *S.* x *sepulcralis* var.	
	chrysocoma	
§ - 'Tristis' ambig.	CCVT CLnd CTri ECrN ELan LRHS	
	MBri MGos MSwo NLar NWea	
	SBLw SLim SRms SWat WDin WFar	
	WHar	
- 'Tristis' Gaud. **new**	MMuc	
- var. *vitellina* ♀^{H4}	CDul CWon EPfP GQue LBuc LPan	
	MBNS MBrN NWea SLon SWat	
	WDin WIvy WJas WMoo WWll	
§ - - 'Britzensis' (m) ♀^{H4}	More than 30 suppliers	
§ - - 'Yelverton'	MRav SWat WWll	
- 'Vitellina Pendula'	see *S. alba* 'Tristis' Gaud.	
- 'Vitellina Tristis'	see *S. alba* 'Tristis' Gaud.	
§ *alpina*	CLyd ECho EHyt GIBF NBir NHol	
'Americana'	CWiW	
amplexicaulis 'Pescara' (m)	CWiW WWll	
amygdaloides	CWiW	
'Aokautere'	see *S.* x *sepulcralis* 'Aokautere'	
apennina 'Cisa Pass' **new**	CWon	
apoda	CWon	
- (m)	ECho EWes GIBF NBir WPer	
§ *arbuscula*	CWon ECho GIBF NWCA WDin	
arctica var. *petraea*	NLAp WPat	
arenaria	see *S. repens* var. *argentea*	
aurita	LRav NLar NWea	
babylonica	CDul CEnd CTrG CWon LPan	
	SBLw SHBN WMou	
- 'Annularis'	see *S. babylonica* 'Crispa'	
§ - 'Crispa'	CDul CFwr CRez CWon ELan EPla	
	LHop MBri NPro SMad SPla SPoG	
	WFar	
§ - 'Lavalleei' (m) **new**	WWll	
- 'Pan Chih-kang'	CWiW	
- var. *pekinensis* 'Snake' **new**	CWon WWll	
§ - - 'Tortuosa' ♀^{H4}	More than 30 suppliers	
* - 'Tortuosa Aurea'	LPan MCCP SWvt	
x *balfourii* **new**	CWon	
x *basaltica* (m)	GIBF	
bebbiana **new**	CWon WWll	
bicolor (f)	GIBF	
- (m)	GIBF WWll	
'Blackskin' (f)	CWiW	
x *blanda* **new**	CWon	
bockii	LRHS LTwo MBar WCFE WFar	
'Bowles' Hybrid'	CAgr MRav WMou	
§ 'Boydii' (f) ♀^{H4}	CFee CWon ECho EPfP EPot GAbr	
	GCrs ITim MAsh MDun MGos	
	NBir NFor NHol NLAp NMen	
	NRya NSla SBla SIng SPoG SRms	
	WAbe WFar WPat	
§ 'Boyd's Pendulous' (m)	CLyd CWib EHyt MBar	
breviserrata	CLyd GIBF NWCA	
burjatica	CWon	
caesia	GIBF NWCA WIvy WWll	
x *calliantha* **new**	WWll	
candida	CWon GIBF WWll	
cantabrica **new**	CWon	
caprea	CAgr CBcs CCVT CDul CLnd CTri	
	CWon ECrN EPfP LBuc NWea	
	SBLw SPer WDin WMou WSFF	
- 'Black Stem'	CDul CNat	
- 'Curlilocks'	COtt MBar MSwo NEgg	
§ - 'Kilmarnock' (m)	More than 30 suppliers	
- var. *pendula* (m)	see *S. caprea* 'Kilmarnock' (m)	
- 'Silberglanz' **new**	WWll	
x *capreola* **new**	CWon	
cascadensis	GIBF	
cashmiriana	CLyd GEdr NHol NWCA WPat	
caspica **new**	WWll	
* - *rubra nana*	SWat	
x *cepusiensis* (f)	GIBF	
x *cernua*	NWCA	
chaenomeloides **new**	EBrs	

'Chrysocoma'	see *S.* x *sepulcralis* var. *chrysocoma*
cinerea	CAgr CBcs CDoC CWon ECrN LBuc NWea SBLw WDin
- 'Tricolor' (v)	CArn NPro SLim
commutata	GIBF
§ *cordata*	ECrN SLPl WDin
x *cottetii*	GIBF IArd MBar WDin
daphnoides	CCVT CDoC CDul CLnd EBee EPfP MBrN MSwo NWea SBLw SPer SPla SRms STre SWat WDin WFar WJas WMou WSFF
- 'Aglaia' (m)	CBcs CTri CWon ECrN MGos WIvy
- 'Continental Purple' **new**	CWon WWll
- 'Meikle' (f)	CAgr CWiW SWat
- 'Netta Statham' (m)	CWiW
- 'Ovaro Udine' (m)	CWiW
- 'Oxford Violet' (m)	CWon ECrN NWea WIvy WWll
- 'Sinker'	WIvy
- 'Stewartstown'	CWiW
x *dasyclados* **new**	CWon
- 'Grandis'	NWea
§ x *doniana* 'Kumeti'	CWiW
'E.A. Bowles'	see *S.* 'Bowles' Hybrid'
x *ehrhartiana*	CNat CWon
§ *elaeagnos*	CAgr CCVT CDoC CLnd CTho CTri ECrN EPfP LRHS MBlu MBrN MRav SLon SWat WDin WFar WMou
§ - subsp. *angustifolia* ♀H4	CDul ELan EMil GQue LRav MAsh MBar MRav MTis NLar NWea SRms STre WIvy
'Elegantissima'	see *S.* x *pendulina* var. *elegantissima*
eriocephala 'American Mackay' (m)	CWiW
- 'Green USA' **new**	CWon
- 'Kerksii' (m)	CWiW CWon
- 'Mawdesley' (m)	CWiW
- 'Russelliana' (f)	CWiW
§ 'Erythroflexuosa'	CBcs CBgR CDoC CEnd EBee ELan EPfP EPla LAst LHop LRHS MAsh MBar MGos MRav MWgw MWya NBlu NScw NWea SLim SPer SPla SPoG SWat WDin WFar WHer WPat
exigua	CBcs CDul CLnd CTho ECrN ELan EPfP EWes LBuc LRHS MBar MBlu MBrN MBri MCoo MGos MRav NBir NCGa NWea SLPl SLim SMad SMrm SPer WDin WMou WPat
fargesii	CDoC CEnd CFee EBee ELan EPfP GIBF LEdu LHop LRHS MAsh MBlu MDun MGos MRav NHol SBrw SDix SPoG SSpi WCru WFar WPGP WPat
§ x *finnmarchica*	CWon GEdr GIBF NWCA
foetida (f)	GIBF
formosa	see *S. arbuscula*
fragilis	CCVT CDul CLnd ECrN MRav NWea SBLw WDin WMou
- var. *bullata* **new**	WWll
- 'Legomey'	WIvy
x *friesiana* **new**	CWon
x *fruticosa* 'McElroy' (f)	CWiW
§ *fruticulosa*	CTri GKev NLap NWCA SBla WPat
'Fuiri-koriyanagi'	see *S. integra* 'Hakuro-nishiki'
furcata	see *S. fruticulosa*
geyeriana **new**	WWll
glauca	CNat
- subsp. *callicarpaea* (f)	GIBF
glaucophylloides **new**	CWon
'Golden Curls'	see *S.* 'Erythroflexuosa'
gracilistyla	CTho CWon ECrN SLPl WMou
§ - 'Melanostachys' (m)	More than 30 suppliers
x *grahamii* (f)	GIBF
x *greyi*	EPla NPro
hastata (f)	GIBF SWat
- 'Wehrhahnii' (m) ♀H4	CBcs CMea CWib CWon EBee ECho EHyt ELan EPfP LEdu LRHS MAsh MBNS MBar MRav MSwo MWgw MWhi NBir NEgg NFor NWea SHBN SPer SWat WDin WFar WPat WPer WTel
helvetica ♀H4	CBcs CBgR ECho ELan EPfP GAbr LRav MBar MBlu MBri MDun MRav MWgw NBir NEgg NFor NLAp NWCA NWea SHBN SPer WDin WFar WHar WPat
herbacea	ECho EPot GEdr GIBF NMen
hibernica	see *S. phylicifolia*
himalayas **new**	CWon
x *hirtei* 'Rosewarne' **new**	CWon
hookeriana	CLnd CTho CWon ELan EPla MBlu MBrN MRav SLPl SSpi WCFE WIvy WMou WPGP WTin
x *hungarica* **new**	CWon
incana	see *S. elaeagnos*
integra 'Albomaculata'	see *S. integra* 'Hakuro-nishiki'
- 'Flamingo' PBR	SPoG
§ - 'Hakuro-nishiki' (v)	More than 30 suppliers
- 'Pendula' (f)	CEnd MAsh MBri
irrorata	CDul CLnd CTho CWon ECrN MBlu SWat
'Jacquinii'	see *S. alpina*
japonica misapplied	see *S. babylonica* 'Lavalleei'
kinuyanagi (m)	CWon ELan EPla WIvy
§ *koriyanagi*	CWiW CWon
'Kumeti'	see *S.* x *doniana* 'Kumeti'
'Kuro-me'	see *S. gracilistyla* 'Melanostachys'
x *laestadiana*	GIBF
lanata ♀H4	More than 30 suppliers
- 'Drake's Hybrid'	NMen
- 'Mrs Mac' (m) **new**	CWon
lapponum	GEdr GIBF NWea SRms
- (m)	GIBF
- var. *daphneola* (f)	GIBF
- - (m)	GIBF
lasiolepis **new**	WWll
x *laurina* (f)	CWon
liliputa	see *S. turczaninowii*
§ *lindleyana*	NBir
lucida	CWon ECrN
mackenzieana **new**	CWon
'Maerd Brno' (f)	MBlu
magnifica ♀H4	CDul CEnd CLnd CMCN CTho EBee ELan EMil EPfP EPla GIBF IDee LEdu MSte NPen SBrw SMad SPoG SSpi SWat WCru WDin WFar WMou WPGP
§ 'Mark Postill' (f)	CBgR CDoC CWon EBee EMil GBin LRHS MBNS SBrw SPla SPoG SPur
matsudana 'Tortuosa'	see *S. babylonica* var. *pekinensis* 'Tortuosa'
- 'Tortuosa Aureopendula'	see *S.* 'Erythroflexuosa'
'Melanostachys'	see *S. gracilistyla* 'Melanostachys'
x *meyeriana*	WIvy
- 'Daza' **new**	WWll
- 'Lumley' (f)	CWiW
miyabeana **new**	WWll
x *mollissima* var. *hippophaifolia* **new**	WWll
- - 'Jefferies' (m)	CWiW
- - 'Notts Spaniard' (m)	CWiW
- - 'Stinchcombe'	WIvy
- - 'Trustworthy' (m)	CWiW
- var. *undulata*	CWiW
'Kottenheider Weide' (f)	
moupinensis	CWon EPfP MBri NLar
- EDHCH 97.319	WPGP

Name	Suppliers
§ *myrsinifolia*	EPla MBlu NSti WWll
- subsp. *alpicola* new	CWon
§ *myrsinites*	GIBF
- var. *jacquiniana*	see *S. alpina*
myrtilloides	CLyd
- 'Pink Tassels' (m)	CWon ECho EHyt MBrN NWCA SIng
myrtilloides x *repens*	see *S.* x *finnmarchica*
nakamurana var. *yezoalpina*	CEnd CFee CWon EMil EPot EWes GAbr GEdr GIBF MRav NHar NLAp NLRH NPro NWCA WFar WIvy WPat
nepalensis	see *S. lindleyana*
nigricans	see *S. myrsinifolia*
nivalis	see *S. reticulata* subsp. *nivalis*
x *obtusifolia*	GIBF
onychiophylla (f)	GIBF
x *ovata*	CLyd NMen
§ x *pendulina* var. *elegantissima*	CTho ECrN SWat
pentandra	CAgr CDul CLnd ECrN LRav NWea WDin WFar WMou WWll
- 'Patent Lumley'	CWiW
'Philip's Fancy'	NWCA
§ *phylicifolia*	ECrN WMou
- 'Malham' (m)	CWiW
polaris	CLyd GIBF
pseudopentandra new	WWll
x *punctata*	GIBF
§ *purpurea*	CCVT CDul GIBF MBrN NWea SRms WDin WGwG WMou
- 'Brittany Blue' new	WWll
- 'Brittany Green' (f)	CWiW WWll
- 'Carl Jensen' new	WWll
- 'Continental Reeks'	CWiW WIvy
- 'Dark Dicks' (f)	CWiW WIvy WWll
- 'Dicky Meadows' (m)	CAgr CWiW WIvy WWll
* - 'Elegantissima'	WWll
- 'Goldstones'	CAgr CWiW WIvy WWll
- f. *gracilis*	see *S. purpurea* 'Nana'
- 'Green Dicks'	CAgr CWiW WIvy
- 'Helix'	see *S. purpurea*
- 'Howki' (m)	CWon WMou
- 'Irette' (m)	CWiW WWll
- 'Jagiellonka' (f)	CWiW WIvy
- var. *japonica*	see *S. koriyanagi*
- subsp. *lambertiana*	CWiW WIvy
- 'Lancashire Dicks' (m)	CWiW
- 'Leicestershire Dicks' (m)	CWiW
- 'Light Dicks'	CWiW
- 'Lincolnshire Dutch' (f)	CWiW
§ - 'Nana'	CLyd EBee EPfP MMuc NLar SLPl SLon SPer SPur STre WFar WMoo
- 'Nancy Saunders' (f)	CHad CTho CWiW EHoe EPPr EPla GBuc MBNS MBlu MBrN MBri MRav MSte NPro NSti SCoo SMHy SUsu WCot WIvy WWll
I - 'Nicholsonii Purpurascens' new	CWon WWll
- 'Norbury' new	WWll
- 'Pendula' ♀H4	CEnd CWib CWon EBee ECrN LRHS MAsh MBar MBri MRav MSwo NHol NWea SPer SPoG WDin
- 'Procumbens' new	WWll
- 'Read' (f)	CWiW
- 'Reeks' (f)	CWiW
- 'Richartii' (f)	CWiW CWon
- 'Uralensis' (f)	CWiW
- 'Whipcord' new	WWll
pyrenaica	CLyd EHyt EWes GIBF NWCA
pyrenaica x *retusa*	ECho
pyrifolia new	CWon WWll
rehderiana new	CWon
repens	ECho ECrN GIBF LRav MBar NWea SRms STre SWat WDin WGwG
§ - var. *argentea*	CWon EPfP EWes GIBF MBar MRav MWhi NWCA NWea SBrw SLim SPer WDin WFar
- 'Armando' PBR	MGos
- 'Iona' (m)	CLyd MBar
- *pendula*	see *S.* 'Boyd's Pendulous' (m)
- 'Voorthuizen' (f)	CWib ECho EHol EHyt MBar MGos WDin WGer
reticulata ♀H4	ECho EPot GCrs GIBF NBir NLAp NMen NRya NSla
§ - subsp. *nivalis*	EPot GIBF NWCA
retusa	CTri ECho GIBF NBir NLAp
retusa x *serpyllifolia*	EPot NWCA
rosmarinifolia misapplied	see *S. elaeagnos* subsp. *angustifolia*
§ x *rubens* var. *basfordiana* new	WWll
- 'Basfordiana' (m)	CDoC CDul CLnd CTho CWiW EPla EWes MBNS MRav NEgg NWea SWat WMou
- 'Bouton Aigu'	CWiW
- 'Farndon'	CWiW
- 'Flanders Red' (f)	CWiW
- 'Fransgeel Rood' (m)	CWiW
- 'Glaucescens' (m)	CWiW
- 'Golden Willow'	CWiW CWon
- 'Hutchinson's Brown' new	CWon
- 'Jaune de Falaise'	CWiW
- 'Jaune Hâtive'	CWiW
- 'Laurina'	CWiW
- 'Natural Red' (f)	CWiW CWon
- 'Parsons'	CWiW
- 'Rouge Ardennais'	CWiW
- 'Rouge Folle'	CWiW
- 'Russet' (f)	CWiW
x *rubra*	CWiW
- 'Abbey's Harrison' (f)	CWiW
- 'Continental Osier' (f)	CWiW CWon
- 'Eugenei' (m)	CDul CTho ECrN EPla GQui MBlu SWat WIvy WMou
- 'Fidkin' (f)	CWiW
- 'Harrison's' (f)	CWiW
- 'Harrison's Seedling A' (f)	CWiW
- 'Mawdesley'	CWiW
- 'Mawdesley Seedling A' (f)	CWiW
- 'Pyramidalis'	CWiW
sachalinensis 'Kioryo' new	CWon WWll
x *sanguinea*	see *S.* x *rubens* var. *basfordiana*
Scarlet Curls = 'Scarcuzam'	WPat
schwerinii new	WWll
x *sepulcralis*	NWea
§ - 'Aokautere'	CWiW
- 'Caradoc'	CWiW NScw WWll
§ - var. *chrysocoma*	CDoC CDul CSBt CWib ECrN ENot EPfP EWTr LAst LBuc LPan LRHS MBar MGos MWat NBea NBee NBlu NEgg SBLw SCoo SHBN SLim SPer SPoG SWat WDin WOrn
x *sericans* new	CWon
serissima new	WWll
serpyllifolia	CLyd CTri EHyt GIBF NLAp NMen WPat
serpyllum	see *S. fruticulosa*
sessilifolia new	WWll
'Setsuka'	see *S. udensis* 'Sekka'
x *simulatrix*	CLyd CWon EHyt EPot GIBF MBar NWCA
sitchensis new	WWll
x *smithiana* new	NWea
x *sobrina*	GIBF
x *stipularis* (f)	CWon NWea

§ 'Stuartii' GAbr GIBF MBar NMen NWCA SRms
subfragilis **new** WWll
subopposita CDul EBee ELan EWes MBNS MBar NPro SLon STre WGwG
x *tetrapla* GIBF
thomasii GIBF
'Tora'^{PBR} (f) LRav
triandra CWon LRav WMou
- 'Belge' **new** WWll
- 'Black German' (m) CWiW
- 'Black Hollander' (m) CAgr CWiW WIvy
- 'Black Maul' CAgr CWiW WWll
- 'Faux Plant de Tourraine' WWll **new**
- 'Grisette de Falaise' CWiW
- 'Grisette Droda' (f) CWiW
- 'Grisette Noire' **new** WWll
- var. *hoffmanniana* **new** WWll
- 'Long Bud' CWiW
- 'Noir de Challans' CWiW WWll
- 'Noir de Touraine' CWiW
- 'Noir de Villaines' (m) CWiW CWon WIvy WWll
- 'Rouge d'Orléans' ECrN
- 'Sarda d'Anjou' CWiW
- 'Semperflorens' (m) CNat WWll
- 'Whissander' CAgr CWiW WIvy
x *tsugaluensis* 'Ginme' (f) MAsh SLPl WPat WWll
§ *turczaninowii* (m) GIBF
§ *udensis* WWll
§ - 'Sekka' (m) CTho CWon ECtt ELan LRav NBir NWea STre SWat WFar WIvy WMou WWll
'Ulbrichtweide' **new** WWll
uva-ursi CLyd GIBF
viminalis CCVT CDul CWon ECrN LBuc NWea WDin WMou
- 'Black Satin' **new** WWll
- 'Brown Merrin' CAgr WIvy
- 'Green Gotz' CWiW WIvy
- 'Mulattin' **new** CWon WWll
- 'Reader's Red' (m) CAgr WIvy WWll
- 'Riefenweide' WIvy
- 'Romanin' **new** CWon
- 'Stone Osier' **new** WWll
- 'Yellow Osier' CAgr CWon WIvy
vitellina 'Pendula' see *S. alba* 'Tristis' Gaud.
§ *waldsteiniana* GIBF MBar NWCA
x *wimmeriana* SRms
'Yelverton' see *S. alba* var. *vitellina* 'Yelverton'

Salsola (*Chenopodiaceae*)
soda CArn EUnu

Salvia ❀ (*Lamiaceae*)
ACE 2172 SPin
CD&R 1162 SPin
CD&R 1458 SPin
CD&R 1495 SHGN SPin
CD&R 3071 CStr SPin
DJH 93 T SPin
PC&H 226 SPin
acetabulosa see *S. multicaulis*
aerea **new** CPom
aethiopis CPle CSev CStr EAro EWes LPhx SDnm SPav SPin WWye XPep
§ *africana* CPle CStr GGar SPin WDyG WWye XPep
africana-caerulea see *S. africana*
africana-lutea see *S. aurea*
agnes CStr LIck SPin
albimaculata SBla SPin
alborosea **new** NBir
algeriensis CSpe LPhx SBch SPin
'Allen Chickering' XPep
amarissima CPle CStr SPin

'Amber' SPin SUsu
ambigens see *S. guaranitica* 'Blue Enigma'
§ *amplexicaulis* EAro EPPr LSou MGol MWea NLar SBch SPin WPer WWye XPep
angustifolia Cav. see *S. reptans*
angustifolia Mich. see *S. azurea*
'Anthony Parker' CPle CStr MAJR SAga SDys SPin
apiana CArn CStr EAro EOHP EPyc EUnu GPoy MDKP MGol MHer MSal SGar SPin WCMO XPep
argentea ♀H3 More than 30 suppliers
arizonica CBgR CPle CPom CStr CWCL EAro LIck MLLN SDys SPin XPep
atrocyanea CAby CPle CSpe CStr EDsa EPyc LIck MLLN SDys SGar SPin SUsu WCMO WDyG WHal WKif WWlt WWye
aucheri GBar GCal
§ *aurea* CHal CHll CPle CSev CStr EKen ELan EShb LHop MGol MOak MSte SGar SPin WDyG WPer XPep
- 'Kirstenbosch' CPle CSev CStr EAro EBee ECtt EMan EWin MLLN NCGa SDys SPin WCMO WGwG WHer WKif WOut WPer WRos WWye
aurita LIck SPin
- var. *galpinii* SPin
aurita x *aurita* var. *galpinii* **new** CStr
austriaca CPle CStr SHFr SPin
§ *azurea* CPle CRWN EUnu LPhx MSte SAga SBod SMrm SPin XPep
- var. *grandiflora* CStr LRav SPin
bacheriana see *S. buchananii*
§ *barrelieri* CPle SHFr SPin XPep
'Bee's Bliss' XPep
'Belhaven' WDyG WOut
bertolonii see *S. pratensis* Bertolonii Group
bicolor Des. see *S. barrelieri*
'Black Knight' CStr SPin
blancoana CArn CMea CPle CStr ECha ELau GBar LEdu MHer MLLN MOak MSte SAga SBch SDys SPin
blepharophylla CPle CSpe CStr EAro EBee ECtt EShb LAst LHop LIck MHar MHer MSte NCGa SAga SBch SDnm SPav SPin SRkn SRot WCMO WWye
- 'Diablo' CStr ECtt SDys SPin
- 'Painted Lady' CStr SDys SPin WOut
'Blue Chiquita' CStr LIck SDys SPin
'Blue Sky' CStr SDys
'Blue Vein' NPri
blue, B&SWJ 9032 from Guatemala SPin WCru
brandegeei **new** SPin
broussonetii SPin
§ *buchananii* ♀H1+3 CBrm CDoC CHal CHll CPle CPom CSWP CSam CSpe CStr EAro EBee ELan EPfP EShb GQui LHop LIck MHar MHer MLLN SAga SBch SGar SPav SPin SPoG SRkn SWal WFar
bulleyana misapplied see *S. flava* var. *megalantha*
bulleyana Diels CBgR CSev EChP EDAr EWes GBar GKev LEdu LIck MDKP MGol MHer MLLN MWgw NLar NSti SDnm SHFr SPav SWal WCru WFar WLin
cacaliifolia ♀H1+3 More than 30 suppliers
cadmica SPin
caerulea misapplied see *S. guaranitica* 'Black and Blue'
caerulea L. see *S. africana*
caespitosa EHyt SBla SPin
campanulata CPom EBee LPhx MGol SPin
- CC 4038 ITer
- CC 4193 MGol
- CC&McK 1071 CFir

– GWJ 9294	WCru	
canariensis	CPle CStr EAro EShb IGor MLLN SHFr SPin WWye XPep	
– f. *candidissima*	XPep	
candelabrum ♀H3-4	CAbP CArn CDes CMea CPle CSpe ECtt LPhx MHer MLLN MSte SHFr SPav SPin WCHb WCMO WCot WEas WKif WSHC WWlt WWye XPep	
candidissima	CStr SPin	
canescens	EAro XPep	
cardinalis	see *S. fulgens*	
carduacea	SPin	
castanea	CAby MHar	
cedrosensis	SDys	
§ *chamaedryoides*	CBgR CPle CSev CStr CWCL EPyc LPhx NGHP SBla SDnm SDys SGar SPin WSHC XPep	
– SF 69	CStr	
– var. *isochroma*	CStr EAro SDys SPin	
– 'Marine Blue'	CStr SDys SPin	
– silver-leaved	CBgR CStr LPhx MSte SAga SPin XPep	
chamaedryoides x *microphylla*	EAro XPep	
chamelaeagnea	CStr GFai LHop SDys SHar SPin WOut XPep	
chapalensis	CStr SAga SPin	
chiapensis	CPle CSpe CStr SDys SPin	
chinensis	see *S. japonica*	
'Christine Yeo'	CDes CDoC CPle EBee EChP ECtt EPPr EPyc GGar LIck MDKP MSte SBch SDys SGar SMeo SPav SPin SWal WCMO WDyG WHil WMnd WPGP WPtf WSHC WWye	
cleistogama misapplied	see *S. glutinosa*	
cleistogama DeBary & Paul	MHer	
clevelandii	CPle EAro MGol MHer SPav SPin WJek XPep	
– 'Winnifred Gilman'	EAro SDys	
clinopodioides	SPin	
coahuilensis ambig.	CMdw LIck LSou NDov SAga SGar SHFr SMeo SMrm SPin SUsu WSHC WWye	
coahuilensis Fernald new	EAro MGol	
coccinea	MGol MHer SHFr SPin WWye	
– 'Brenthurst'	CStr SDys SPin	
– (Nymph Series) 'Coral Nymph'	ECtt LDai LIck LRHS MGol SDnm SDys SMrm SPav SPin SUsu SWat	
– – 'Lady in Red' ♀H3	CStr ECtt LIck SDys SPav SWat	
* – – 'Snow Nymph'	LIck	
columbariae	SPin	
concolor misapplied	see *S. guaranitica*	
concolor Lamb.	CDes CPle CPne CStr GCal SPin WDyG WPGP WSHC WWye	
confertiflora	CBos CDMG CDes CDoC CHEx CHVG CPle CPom CSam CSpe CStr ECtt ELan EShb LIck MHar MHer MLLN MOak MSte SAga SDys SGar SPin SWal WCMO WDyG WPGP WWlt WWye	
corrugata	More than 30 suppliers	
'Crème Caramel'	SDys	
cyanescens	CPle CStr EPot SPin XPep	
cyanosa new	EBee	
daghestanica	CStr SDys SPin	
darcyi misapplied	see *S. roemeriana*	
darcyi J. Compton	CHen CHll CPle CPom CSpe CStr EChP EPyc LIck LPhx SAga SBch SDys SHFr SPin WCMO WEas WSHC XPep	
'Darky'	CStr SPin	
davidsonii	SPin	
dentata	CStr EUnu SDys SPin XPep	
desoleana	CStr EAro XPep	

digitaloides BWJ 7777	CStr SPin WCru	
discolor ♀H1	More than 30 suppliers	
* – *nigra*	CMdw WDin	
disermas	CPle EUnu SDys SPin SPlb WOut XPep	
– blue new	CStr	
disjuncta	CStr SPin	
divinorum	EOHP EWin GPoy MGol MSal WCMO WWye	
dolichantha	CDMG CSpe CStr EAro EBee EDsa EPyc EShb MDKP MGol MHar MWea MWrn SBch SBod SGar SPin WHil WWye	
– pale blue/white new	CStr	
dolomitica	CStr EDAr SPav SPin XPep	
dombeyi	CHll CPne CStr EAro SDys SPin	
dominica	CStr SPin XPep	
dorisiana	CFee CPle CPne CSpe CStr EAro ELan EOHP EUnu LPhx MLLN SDys SPin WWye	
dorrii	CStr SPin	
eigii	CStr SPin	
§ *elegans*	CPle CSev CStr ELau EWes LIck MNHC MSte WFar WOut WWye	
– 'Honey Melon'	CStr EOHP EUnu SDys	
§ – 'Scarlet Pineapple'	More than 30 suppliers	
– 'Sonoran Red'	CStr EAro SDys	
– 'Tangerine'	CArn CDoC CPrp CWan ELau EOHP GBar LAst LFol LSou MBow MGol MHer NGHP SBch SDnm SPet SPin SWal WGwG	
eremostachya	CStr	
evansiana	CPom	
– BWJ 8013	SPin WCru	
fallax	CStr MHar SPin	
farinacea	SPin	
– 'Rhea'	LIck LRHS	
– 'Strata'	ECtt LRHS SDys	
– 'Victoria' ♀H3	CStr ELau MHer MWat SDys WGwG	
§ *flava* var. *megalantha*	CPle CStr EBee EBla ELan LEdu LRHS LSRN NChi NGdn SPin WFar WPer WWye	
forreri	CBgR CDes EBee SAga SDys SPin WPGP WSPU	
– CD&R 1269	CStr	
§ *forsskaolii*	More than 30 suppliers	
– 'Frieda Dixon'	EOHP LSou	
frigida	CStr	
§ *fruticosa*	CArn CPle EAro ELau LRHS SIde SPin XPep	
§ *fulgens* ♀H3	CPle CPne CSec CStr GBar ILis SBch SGar SHFr SPin SRkn WFar WOut WRha WWeb WWlt WWye	
gesneriiflora	CPle CPne CStr ECtt MGol MHom MSte SDys SPin WWye	
– Huitzilac 506 new	CStr	
– 'Tequila'	SPin	
gilliesii	CStr SPin XPep	
glechomifolia	SPin WOut	
§ *glutinosa*	CArn CBgR CHad CPLG CPle EAro EBee ECtt EPPr EPyc EPyc GCal LDai MGol MNrw NBro SMar SPav SPin WCAu WCMO WGwG WOut WPer WWye	
gracilis	SPin	
grahamii	see *S. microphylla* var. *microphylla*	
greggii	CDMG CPle EBee ECtt EWes MHer MSte MWgw SBod SUsu WCMO WKif WPer XPep	
– CD&R 1148	EAro LIck LSou SDys WSPU	
– 'Alba'	CBgR CBrm CHal CPle CStr EBee ENot EOHP LIck MHer NBur NGHP SAga SDys XPep	
– 'Blush Pink'	see *S. microphylla* 'Pink Blush'	

- 'Caramba' (v) — CBgR CBow CBrm CStr EAro EOHP EPyc EShb EWin MLLN NGHP SAga SDnm SHGN SPav SPoG WCra
- 'Devon Cream' — see *S. greggii* 'Sungold'
- 'Furman's Red' — XPep
- 'Keter's Red' — CStr
- 'Magenta' — MDKP
* - 'Navajo Cream' — EAro EPyc WFar
* - 'Navajo Dark Purple' — CStr EAro EPyc LSou WFar
* - 'Navajo Rose' **new** — CStr
* - 'Navajo Salmon Red' — EPyc WFar
* - 'Navajo White' — EPyc WFar
- 'Peach' misapplied — see *S.* x *jamensis* 'Pat Vlasto'
- 'Peach' — CBgR CBrm CDes CDoC CHar CPle CSpe EBee ELau EPfP LHop LRHS MHer MLLN MSte NGHP SAga SDnm SGar SPav Spin SUsu SWal WMnd WPGP WWeb
- 'Sierra San Antonio' — see *S.* x *jamensis* 'Sierra San Antonio'
- 'Sparkler' (v) — CPle CStr SBch
- 'Stormy Pink' — CDes CHll CSpe CStr EBee EPyc WIvy WPGP WSHC
§ - 'Sungold' — CDes CPle CStr EAro EBee EPfP LHop LIck LRHS MLLN NGHP SAga SBch SDys SHGN SPin SWal WCMO WMnd WWeb
- variegated (v) — XPep
- 'Wild Thing' **new** — CStr
- yellow-flowered — LRHS XPep
greggii x *lycioides* — see *S. greggii* x *serpyllifolia*
§ *greggii* x *serpyllifolia* — CAbP CBgR CPle CSpe CStr EPyc SDys SGar SPin WPGP WWlt WWye XPep
§ *guaranitica* — CBcs CBgR CEnt CHEx CHrt CPle CPne CTbh EBrs ECtt EShb SAga SDnm SDys SPav SPer SPin SRkn WCHb WKif WPGP WWlt WWye
- 'Argentine Skies' — CPle CStr EPyc EWin LIck LPhx SAga SDys SMrm SPin WDyG WPGP WWlt WWye
§ - 'Black and Blue' — CBgR CPle CPne CPrp CRHN CSWP CSev CStr EBee EPPr LIck LPhx MAvo MSte NGHP SAga SBch SDnm SGar SPav SPin SUsu WCMO WPGP WPer WPrP WWye
§ - 'Blue Enigma' ♀H3-4 — More than 30 suppliers
- 'Indigo Blue' — EPfP MLLN NEgg SPin WWlt
- 'Purple Splendor' — CPne EShb
- purple-flowered — CSam
haematodes — see *S. pratensis* Haematodes Group
haenkei — CStr SPin SUsu
heldreichiana — CSec CSev CStr SPin
henryi — SPin
hians — CPle EAro EBee EWin GBBs GBar LAst MDKP MLLN MNrw SDnm SGar SPav SPin SRms WCot WHoo WPer WWye
- CC 1787 — MGol SPin
hirtella — CStr SPin
hispanica misapplied — see *S. lavandulifolia*
hispanica L. — CSam SPin
holwayi — CStr SPin
horminum — see *S. viridis* var. *comata*
huberi — CStr SPin
hypargeia — SPin
indica — SPin XPep
'Indigo Spires' — CHll CHrt CPle CSpe CStr EBee ECtt EPPr EShb GMaP LPhx MEHN MHar MHom MLLN SBch SDys SMrm SPin SUsu WDyG WOut WSHC WWlt WWye
interrupta — CPle CStr EHol EOHP EWes LIck SHFr SPin XPep

involucrata ♀H3 — CFir CPLG CPle CPom CSev CStr GCal GQui MHar NBro NBur SBch SDys SPet SPin WOut WSHC
- 'Bethellii' ♀H3-4 — More than 30 suppliers
- 'Boutin' ♀H3 — CPle CStr GBri MAJR MLLN SDys
- Dover form **new** — CStr
§ - 'Hadspen' — CHad CHll CRHN CSam CSpe CStr LIck MSte SPin WKif WWye
- 'Joan' **new** — CStr
- 'Mrs Pope' — see *S. involucrata* 'Hadspen'
* - var. *puberula* — CPle CStr SDys SPin
- - from Hidalgo — CStr
- - 'El Butano' — CStr
iodantha — CPle CStr LIck SAga SDys SPin WWye
x *jamensis* — CStr SDys XPep
- CPN 5096 — CStr
- 'Cherry Queen' — CBrm CPle CSpe CStr EAro EBee EPyc SDys SPin WFar WHil WWye
- 'Dark Dancer' — CPle CStr SDys WWlt
- 'Desert Blaze' (v) — CBgR CBow CDes CDoC CStr EAro EBee EChP ECtt EMil LHop LIck MHar NCGa NDov NGHP SDys SPer SPin WCot WHer WPGP WSPU WWeb
- 'Dyson's Orangy Pink' — CStr
- 'James Compton' — CStr EAro LIck MSte SDys SGar WHoo
- 'La Luna' — CBrm CEnt CPle CPom CPrp CSam CSev CTri EAro ECtt EPfP EShb GGar LHop MHar MHer MSte NDov SDys SGar SHGN SPin SWal WCMO WFar WMnd WPGP WSHC WWye
- 'La Siesta' — CPle CStr EAro EBee SDys WWeb
- 'La Tarde' — CEnt CPle CStr CTri MSte SBch SDys
- 'Lemon Sorbet' — CPle CStr EAro EBee SDys WWeb
- 'Los Lirios' ♀H3-4 — CBgR CPle CPom CStr CTri EAro LIck MSte SAga SDys SMrm SPin WSPU
- 'Maraschino' — CAbP CStr EAro EPfP EWin LRHS SDys SMrm SPin WCMO WCot WMnd
* - 'Mauve' — SDys
- 'Moonlight Over Ashwood' (v) — CPle CStr EAro EPyc SDys SPin SUsu
- 'Moonlight Serenade' — CPle CSev CStr EAro EBee EPyc EWin LPhx MWea SAga SBch SDys SHGN WHil WHoo WSPU WWeb
§ - 'Pat Vlasto' — CStr EAro EBee EPyc LIck MWea SDys SMrm SPin SWal WWye
- 'Pleasant Pink' — CPle CSev CStr EBee LIck SDys SPin
- 'Plum Wine' — CPle CStr
§ - 'Raspberry Royale' ♀H3-4 — More than 30 suppliers
- 'Red Velvet' — CPle CStr ECtt MHom SUsu WEas
- 'San Isidro Moon' — CPle CStr
- 'Señorita Leah' — SDys
§ - 'Sierra San Antonio' — CPle CSev CStr EAro ECtt SAga SDys SMrm SUsu
§ - 'Trebah' — CDes CPle CPom CStr ECre EPyc LSou MSte SDys SGar SPav SPin SRot WIvy WPGP WWye
- 'Trenance' — CPle CStr ECre EPyc LRHS LSou MSte SDys SGar SPav SPin SRot
- white-flowered — SPin
§ *japonica* — CArn CPle CStr SPin WWye
judaica — EBee EChP SPin XPep
jurisicii — CArn CFir CPle CStr CWib EAro EBee EPyc EShb LPhx MGol NLar SGar SPav SPin WJek WWye
- pink-flowered — CStr SPin
karwinskyi — CStr SPin
keerlii — SPin
koyamae — SPin

lanceolata	CStr EAro SPin XPep
lanigera	SPin
lasiantha **new**	CStr
§ *lavandulifolia*	More than 30 suppliers
lavanduloides	CStr
- B&SWJ 9053	WCru
lemmonii	see *S. microphylla* var. *wislizeni*
leptophylla	see *S. reptans*
leucantha ♀H1	More than 30 suppliers
- 'Eder'	CStr MAJR SDys SPin
- 'Midnight'	LIck
- 'Purple Velvet'	CPle CStr MAJR MHar NGHP SDys SPin WWlt
- 'San Marcos Lavender'	SPin
- 'Santa Barbara'	CStr SDys
leucophylla	CStr WCMO XPep
- NNS 01-375	SPin
- NNS 95-445	WCot
littae	SPin
longispicata	CStr SPin
longistyla	CStr SPin
lycioides misapplied	see *S. greggii* x *serpyllifolia*
lycioides A. Gray	CAbP CHll CPle CStr LPhx NDov SDys SPer SPin SRkn WDyG XPep
lyrata	CBgR CPle CStr EBee EOHP MDKP MGol MSal SGar SHFr SPin WWye
- 'Burgundy Bliss'	see *S. lyrata* 'Burgundy Bliss'
§ - 'Purple Knockout'	CBod CBow EAro EBee EChP EMag EMan EMil EPyc EShb GSki LAst LHop LPhx MBri MWhi NDov NGHP SBod SGar SHar SHGN SPav SPin SPoG WHrl WWeb
- 'Purple Vulcano'	see *S. lyrata* 'Burgundy Bliss'
macellaria misapplied	see *S. microphylla*
macellaria Epling	CSam
madrensis	CStr LIck MAJR MOak SPin
- 'Dunham'	SDys
melissodora	CStr SDys SPin
mellifera	CArn CPle CStr SPin XPep
merjamie	EBee SPin XPep
- 'Mint-sauce'	CSev CStr EAro ELan GBar SHFr WCMO WHer WPer
mexicana	CPle CSam CStr LIck SBch SPin WWye
- T&K 550	CArn
- 'Limelight'	CSev CStr
- var. *minor*	CPle CStr MAJR
- 'Snowflake'	MAJR
- 'Tula'	SDys
meyeri	CStr MAJR SPin SUsu
§ *microphylla*	CArn CHrt CMHG CPle CPom CPrp CWan EAro ELau EOHP EWes GBar GGar LFol LHop MBow MHer NSti SBri SHFr SPet SYvo WCru WHCG WPer XPep
- CD&R 1141	SPin
- CD&R 1958	CStr
- 'Cerro Potosi'	CBgR CMdw CPle CPom CSev CSpe CStr EBee MLLN MSte SAga SBch SDys SGar SHFr SMrm SPin SUsu WDyG WHil WWlt WWye
- 'Dieciocho de Marzo'	CStr SDys
- 'Hot Lips'	CStr SDys SPin SUsu
- 'Huntington'	CStr EOHP
- hybrid, purple-flowered	CPom GCal
- 'Kew Red' ♀H3-4	CDoC CFir CHVG CPle CSpe CStr EBee MNrw MWea SBch SPin SPoG WHoo WWeb
- 'La Trinidad'	CStr SDys
§ - var. *microphylla*	More than 30 suppliers
- - 'La Foux'	CHea CPle CStr ECtt LPhx LSou MWea SBch SDys SMeo SMrm SUsu WSPU
- - 'Newby Hall' ♀H3-4	CBrm CPle CStr EBee ECtt EPyc EWes LIck LPhx MSte MWea NGHP WPGP

- var. *neurepia*	see *S. microphylla* var. *microphylla*
- 'Orange Door'	SDys
- 'Oregon Peach'	LRHS
- 'Oxford'	CPle CStr SDys SPin
§ - 'Pink Blush' ♀H3-4	CPle CPne EAro EBee ECtt ELan ENot EPfP GBri LRHS MHer MLLN MSte NGHP SMrm SPin SWal WKif WPGP WSHC
- 'Pleasant View' ♀H3-4	CPle CStr EPyc EWin
§ - 'Ruth Stungo' (v)	ECre
- 'San Carlos Festival'	CDes CSev EAro EBee ECtt EWin SBch SDys SPin WPGP WWlt
- 'Trelawny Rose Pink'	see *S.* 'Trelawney'
- 'Trelissick Creamy Yellow'	see *S.* 'Trelissick'
- 'Trewithen Cerise'	see *S.* 'Trewithen'
- 'Variegata' splashed	see *S. microphylla* 'Ruth Stungo'
- 'Wild Watermelon'	CPle CStr EAro EBee SDys SPoG WWeb
§ - var. *wislizeni*	CPle CStr SDys SPin WPer
miltiorhiza	CArn MGol MSal SPin
miniata	CPle CSev CStr LIck MAJR SDys SPin
misella	CSpe SPin
mohavensis	CStr SPin
'Monrovia'	EWin
moorcroftiana	CStr MGol SDnm SPin
'Mrs Beard'	XPep
muelleri misapplied	see *S. greggii* x *serpyllifolia*
muelleri Epling **new**	EAro EPyc
muirii	CStr SHar SPin
'Mulberry Wine'	CDes CHll CPle CSev CStr EBee ECtt EWin MAJR SAga SDys SPin SUsu WKif WPGP WWeb
§ *multicaulis* ♀H4	CPle CStr ECha EMan EPyc ETow GBri MSte SHFr SPin WEas WSHC
munzii	CFir XPep
* *murrayi*	CAbP CStr SPin
namaensis	CSpe CStr EAro LIck SDys SPin XPep
napifolia	EBee EBrs EDsa EKen GSki LPhx MGol NBHF SAga SBod SDnm SPav SPin WGwG WPer WSPU
'Nazareth' **new**	EAro
nemorosa	SHFr SPin SRms XPep
- 'Amethyst' ♀H4	More than 30 suppliers
- 'Blue Mound'	ENot
- 'Brightness'	CStr
- 'Caradonna'	More than 30 suppliers
- East Friesland	see *S. nemorosa* 'Ostfriesland'
- 'Lubecca' ♀H4	CPrp EBee EBrs ECGP ECtt EGle EHrv EPfP EPla EPug LRHS MLLN MWgw NCGa NDov NLar SPer WCAu WMnd
- Marcus = 'Haeumanarc'PBR	CElw CFir CSpe EBee EBrs EGle ELan EMan ENot EPfP EPyc LAst LHop LRHS LSRN MBNS MBri MLLN NLar SDys SMer SPla SPoG SUsu WCMO WCot
- 'Midsummer'	MGol
§ - 'Ostfriesland' ♀H4	More than 30 suppliers
- 'Phoenix Pink'	LPhx
- 'Plumosa'	see *S. nemorosa* 'Pusztaflamme'
- 'Porzellan' ♀H4	ECtt WCMO
§ - 'Pusztaflamme' ♀H4	CPrp EBee EChP ECha ECtt EMan EPfP LRHS LSou MMHG NOrc NPro NSti SBla SUsu WCAu
- 'Rose Queen'	CBgR CStr ECtt EPPr GSki LAst MWat NBir NDlv SDys SPer SPla SWat WFar
- 'Rosenwein'	CSam EBee GBuc LBMP LDai LPhx MDKP NBPC NGdn SMrm SPoG WHil
- 'Royal Distinction'	EBee ECtt EMan ERou LSou MSph

- 'Schwellenburg'	EBee EGle EMan EPfP ERou IPot LBuc LHop LSou MAvo MBNS MSph NBPC NMoo SMrm SPoG SUsu
§ - subsp. *tesquicola*	EBee ECha EGle EPyc LPhx MNFA NGdn NLar SMrm WGHP WOut
- 'Wesuwe'	CPle EBee EGle NDov NGby
neurepia	see *S. microphylla* var. *microphylla*
nilotica	CArn CStr EAro EBee EKen MGol SHFr SPin WHer WLin XPep
nipponica	CPle
- B&SWJ 5829	SPin WCru
- 'Fuji Snow' (v)	CBow ECtt EMan EPyc EWes LSou MLLN
nubicola	CBgR CPLG CPle CStr EBee EPPr GPoy LDai MGol MHer SPin WWye XPep
-- CC 4607	MGol
officinalis	More than 30 suppliers
- 'Alba'	see *S. officinalis* 'Albiflora'
§ - 'Albiflora'	CBod CMea CStr ECtt EGoo EOHP GBar NGHP SBch SPin WCHb WJek WPer XPep
I - 'Albiflora Nana' **new**	LRav
N - 'Aurea' ambig.	CWib ECho GPoy MBar NPri
- 'Berggarten'	CArn EBee ECha ELau EMan EOHP EPfP EUnu GBar GCal LHop LPhx MHer MRav NSti SDix SPin SSvw WCFE WHer WMnd XPep
- 'Blackcurrant'	CHal EUnu LSou WGwG
§ - broad-leaved	CSWP CWan ELau MHer SBch SWat WGHP WJek WWye
- 'Crispa'	CStr SPin WCHb XPep
- 'Extrakta'	EOHP EUnu NGHP
- 'Grandiflora'	EAro
- 'Grete Stolze'	EBee
- 'Growers Friend' **new**	EWin
- 'Herrenhausen'	MSte
§ - 'Icterina' (v) ♀H4	More than 30 suppliers
- 'Kew Gold'	ELau MRav WJek
- *latifolia*	see *S. officinalis* broad-leaved
- 'Minor'	EGoo
- narrow-leaved	see *S. lavandulifolia*
- 'Nazareth'PBR **new**	EBee EWin
* - 'Pink Splash' (v)	CBow WCHb
- *prostrata*	see *S. lavandulifolia*
- 'Purpurascens' ♀H4	More than 30 suppliers
- 'Purpurascens Variegata' (v)	CStr GBar WEas
- 'Robin Hill'	GBar
- 'Rosea'	EOHP SECG WCHb
- Tomentosa Group	CArn
- 'Tricolor' (v)	More than 30 suppliers
- 'Variegata'	see *S. officinalis* 'Icterina'
- variegated (v)	ECho
- 'Würzburg'	CSam
omeiana BWJ 8062 **new**	WCru
oppositiflora misapplied	see *S. tubiflora*
oppositiflora ambig.	CBgR CPle CStr LIck SDys SPin
orbignaei **new**	CStr
oxyphora **new**	CStr
pachyphylla	SPin WCMO XPep
pachystachya	SPin
palaestina	XPep
pale blue, BWJ 9062 from Guatemala	WCru
§ *patens* ♀H3	More than 30 suppliers
- 'Alba' misapplied	see *S. patens* 'White Trophy'
- 'Blue Angel' **new**	EAro NJOw
* - 'Blue Trophy'	LIck
- 'Cambridge Blue' ♀H3	More than 30 suppliers
- 'Chilcombe'	CBgR CMdw CPle CSam CStr ECtt EPyc ERou EWin LIck LSou MBow MHar MLLN SAga SDys SHFr SPin

	WCMO WHil WOut WSHC WWlt WWye
- 'Guanajuato'	CBcs CDoC CFwr CPle CPom CSam CSpe CStr EBee EChP EShb EUnu EWes LAst MHar MHer MSte MWrn SDnm SDys SMad SPin SRkn SRot SUsu WCMO WSHC
- 'Guanajuato Lavender' **new**	CStr
- 'Oxford Blue'	see *S. patens*
- 'Royal Blue'	see *S. patens*
§ - 'White Trophy'	CHal CPle CStr CWCL EBee EChP ECtt ELan ERou EShb LDai LHop LIck LRHS MHer MSte NGHP NPri SDnm SDys SGar SPer SPin SWal WCMO WFar WSHC WWeb WWye
pauciserrata	SPin
penstemonoides	CStr SDys SPin XPep
'Peru Blue' **new**	CStr SDys
phlomoides	MGol
pinguifolia	CStr SPin
'Pink Ice' **new**	CPom
pisidica	SPin
plectranthoides	SPin
pogonochila **new**	CPom
polystachya	CPle CStr EBee SPin WWye
pratensis	CArn CBgR CPle CWib EBee ELan MNHC MSal MWgw NChi SECG SGar SMar SPin SWat WGHP WOut WPer WWye XPep
- 'Albiflora'	CDes LRHS NVic SWat
§ - Bertolonii Group	EPyc
§ - Haematodes Group ♀H4	CBgR CPle EBee EChP ECha ELan EPyc LDai MGol MNrw NLar SBch SBla SDnm SPav SPin SRms SWat WPer WWye XPep
- 'Indigo' ♀H4	CDes CPrp CStr EBee ECtt EPPr EPfP EWll LBMP LPhx LRHS MRav MWgw NDov NLar SPin WMnd WPGP
- 'Lapis Lazuli'	CDes CElw CStr EBee EMon EPyc LPhx MWea NBre SPin
* - 'Pink Delight'	EBee ERou
- 'Rosea'	CBgR EBee ECha LPhx LRHS SPin WWye
- 'Swan Lake' **new**	CBod LPhx NBHF NChi WPer
- 'White Swan' **new**	WOut
prunelloides	CStr SPin
przewalskii	CDes CFwr CPle CPom CStr EBrs EWsh GIBF GSki IFro LPhx MCCP MGol MSal MWgw NBid NEgg SBch SDnm SGar SHFr SPin WBVN WLin WPer WWye
- ACE 1157	EBee WCru
- BWJ 7920	SPin WCru
- DJH 210524	EPPr
'Purple Majesty'	CHea CHll CPle CPne CSev CSpe CStr EBee LHop LIck LPhx MLLN MSte NCGa SAga SDys SMrm SPin SRkn SUsu WKif WWeb WWlt WWye
'Purple Queen'	CPle MBri
purpurea	CMMP CStr LAst LSRN SPin
recognita	CPle CPom CStr NBHF SPin WKif WSHC XPep
§ *reflexa*	CStr SPin
regeliana misapplied	see *S. virgata* Jacq.
regeliana Trautv.	EBee MGol MLLN NBir SPin
regla	CPle CStr SDys SPin XPep
- CD&R 1174	CStr
- 'Jame'	SPin WCMO
- 'Mount Emory'	SPin
repens	CDMG CPle CSec CStr EAro EBee EPyc IGor LSou SDys SPin WDyG WLin WWye
- var. *repens*	SGar XPep

§	*reptans*	CPle CSam CStr CWCL LHop LIck SPin WDyG WOut WPer XPep
	- from Mexico	SDys
	- from Western Texas	SDys
	ringens	CPom EAro NBHF SDys SPin XPep
	riparia misapplied	see *S. rypara*
	roborowskii	SPin
§	*roemeriana* ♀H3	CPle CSpe CStr EPyc LIck MHom NWCA SDnm SDys SPin WCMO WGwG WPGP XPep
	rubescens	CStr LIck SDys SPin
	rubiginosa	CStr SDys SPin
	runcinata	EAro LPhx SPin XPep
	rutilans	see *S. elegans* 'Scarlet Pineapple'
§	*rypara*	CPle CPom CStr EAro SDys SPin
	sagittata	CStr SDys SPin WIvy WWlt
*	*sauntia*	SPin
	scabiosifolia	CPom SPin
	scabra	CFir CPle CStr EBee EChP MGol MSte SDys SPin WOut WWye XPep
	sclarea	CArn CHby CPle CWan EBee ECtt ELau GPoy LRHS MHer MNHC NChi NGHP NGdn SECG SIde SPin WCHb WHoo WPer WSel WWye XPep
§	- var. *sclarea*	CKno EBee EBla NSti
	- var. *turkestanica* hort.	More than 30 suppliers
§	- 'Vatican White'	CBcs CBod EAro EBrs EMar LDai MCCP NCGa NChi NGdn NLar SBch SDnm SPav WHil WPer WWeb
	- white-bracted	CBod CWib EMag EOHP NDlv NGHP NLar SBod SPin SWvt WGwG XPep
*	*scordifolia*	SPin
	scutellarioides	CStr SPin
	semiatrata misapplied	see *S. chamaedryoides*
	semiatrata Zucc.	CDes CPle CPom CSpe EBee LIck LSou SAga SDys SPin SRkn SUsu WWye
	serpyllifolia	SDys SPin
	sessei	CStr SPin
	'Shirley's Creeper'	XPep
	'Silas Dyson' **new**	SDys
	'Silke's Dream'	CPle CStr EAro ECtt EPyc SDys SPin SUsu WWlt
	sinaloensis	CBgR CPle CStr EBee EMan EPyc EShb LSou SBch SDys SPin WCMO WFar
	- 'Aztec Blue' **new**	ENot
	somalensis	CDoC CPle CStr SDys SHar SPin XPep
	sonomensis	XPep
	spathacea ♀H3-4	CDes CPle CStr EMan EShb LPhx SDys SPin WSHC WWye XPep
	splendens	CStr SPin
	- 'Dancing Flame' (v) **new**	EWin
	- 'Peach'	CStr SPin
§	- 'Van-Houttei' ♀H3	CDoC CPle CSpe CStr ECre EPyc LIck MLLN SDys SPin WWlt WWye
	sprucei	CStr SPin
	squalens	SPin
§	*staminea*	CPle CStr EBee MGol SDys SHFr SPin WWye XPep
	stenophylla	CPle CSec CStr EChP MGol SPin WOut WPer
	stepposa	CStr SPin XPep
	x *superba* ♀H4	CPrp CSBt EBee ECtt ELan EPfP EShb LAst LEdu LRHS MBri MHer MWat NEgg SDix SHBN SPer SRms SSvw WHoo WMnd WOut WWhi WWye
	- 'Adrian'	ECtt SPoG
	- 'Dear Anja'	EGle LHop LPhx NDov
	- 'Forncett Dawn'	EBee EGle
	- 'Merleau'	EBee EPyc
	- 'Merleau Rose' **new**	NBlu
*	- 'Rosea'	NEgg
	- 'Rubin' ♀H4	EBee ECtt NBre NDov SMrm
	- 'Superba'	CSev ECha ECtt EHrv LPhx MRav WCAu
§	x *sylvestris*	LAst SPin XPep
	- 'Blauhügel' ♀H4	CSev EBee EChP ECha ECtt ELan EPfP EShb LPhx LRHS MArl MLLN MSte MWgw NDov NPri SBch SBla SMrm WCAu WGwG WPer WPtf
§	- 'Blaukönigin'	EBee EPfP ERou GMaP IBal IHMH LPhx LRHS MNHC MWat NDlv NEgg NJOw NLar NMir NVic SPet SPlb SPoG SWvt WBrk WFar WHil WPer WWeb
	- Blue Queen	see *S.* x *sylvestris* 'Blaukönigin'
	- 'Lye End'	ECtt ERou MRav NCGa NDov
§	- 'Mainacht' ♀H4	More than 30 suppliers
	- May Night	see *S.* x *sylvestris* 'Mainacht'
	- 'Negrito'	EBee EGle NDov
	- 'Rhapsody in Blue'	EAro EBee LRHS NLar WCMO WCot
	- 'Rose Queen'	EBee EChP ECha ECtt ELan EMag EPfP ERou GMaP IBal LHop LRHS MSte MWgw NDov NJOw NOrc SCoo SHBN SPer SPet SPoG SWvt WGwG WMnd WPer WWeb
	- 'Rügen'	CBgR EBee EChP EGle EPyc IBal LBBr LRHS MBri NDov
	- 'Schneehügel'	EBee EChP ECha EGle ELan EPPr EPfP GMaP LAst LRHS MBNS MBri MWgw NBre NCob NMoo NPri NPro SBla SPer WCAu WGHP WMnd
	- 'Tänzerin' ♀H4	EBee EGle EPyc NDov SDys WCMO WCot
	- 'Viola Klose'	CStr EBee EBrs ECGP ECha EGle EShb LRHS LSRN MTis NCGa NFla NLar SMrm SSvw WCAu
	tachiei hort.	see *S. forsskaolii*
	'Tammy'	CStr SPin
	taraxacifolia	CStr SDys SPin
	tesquicola	see *S. nemorosa* subsp. *tesquicola*
	tiliifolia	CArn EAro EUnu MGol SHFr SPav SPin SRms
	tingitana	SDys SPin
	tomentosa	CPle EMag EUnu MGol SPin
	transcaucasica	see *S. staminea*
	transsylvanica	CArn CBgR CHea CPle CStr EChP EPPr LRHS MGol MWgw SDnm SPav SPin SWat WCAu WPer WPep
	- 'Blue Spire'	CPrp EBee ECtt EMil MBri MWhi MWrn SPav SPur SSvw
	'Trebah Lilac White'	see *S.* x *jamensis* 'Trebah'
§	'Trelawney'	EPyc LRHS MHar MSte SDys SPav SPin SRot
§	'Trelissick'	CStr ECre ECtt EPyc LAst LRHS MSte SDys SPav SPin SRot WWlt
§	'Trewithen'	CPom CStr ECre ECtt EPyc LAst LRHS MSte SPav SPin SRot
	trijuga	SPin
	triloba	see *S. fruticosa*
	tubifera	SPin
§	*tubiflora* ♀H1+3 **new**	CStr EPyc SPin
	uliginosa ♀H3-4	More than 30 suppliers
	- 'African Skies'	MNrw SPin WDyG
	urica	CSpe CStr MAJR SDys SPav SPin
	- short	CSpe CStr SDys
	'Valle de Bravo' **new**	CStr
	'Van-Houttei'	see *S. splendens* 'Van-Houttei'
	'Vatican City'	see *S. sclarea* 'Vatican White'
	verbenaca	CArn MBow MHer MSal NMir NSco SPin WHil WOut WPer WWye XPep

verticillata	CArn CPle CStr EBee ECha EGoo EHrv ITim LRHS MGol MWgw NSti SDys SEND SPin WCAu WGwG WOut WPer WWye XPep
§ - 'Alba'	CAbP CBgR CPle CSec EAEE EBee EChP ECtt EPPr EPfP ERou EShb LRHS MRav NGdn NSti SBla SMer SPer SPet SPin WCAu WHer WMnd WPer XPep
- subsp. *amasiaca*	SGar
- 'Purple Rain'	More than 30 suppliers
- 'Smouldering Torches'	LPhx NDov SMHy
- 'White Rain'	see *S. verticillata* 'Alba'
villicaulis	see *S. amplexicaulis*
villosa	SPin
§ *virgata* Jacq.	CPle EBee SGar SPin WWye
viridis	EWsh LPhx MGol MNHC NDov SPin
§ - var. *comata*	CArn GSki NGHP SECG SIde WJek
- var. *viridis*	SBod WHrl
viscosa Jacq.	CPle CStr MGol SPin WWye XPep
wagneriana	CStr MHar SPin
'Waverly'	CDes CPle CStr MAJR SDys WOut WWlt
xalapensis	CStr SPin
yunnanensis	EBee
- BWJ 7874	WCru
aff. *yunnanensis* **new**	SPin

Salvinia (*Salviniaceae*)

sp.	LPBA
auriculata	WDyG
natans	EFtx

Sambucus ✿ (*Caprifoliaceae*)

adnata	EBee WFar
- B&SWJ 2252	WCru
caerulea	see *S. nigra* subsp. *cerulea*
callicarpa	NLar
chinensis	EBee
- B&SWJ 6542	WCru
coraensis	see *S. williamsii* subsp. *coreana*
ebulus	EBee LEdu NLar NSti SMad WDyG
- DJHC 0107	WCru
formosana	LEdu
- B&SWJ 1543	WCru
* *himalayensis*	EWes
§ *javanica* B&SWJ 4047	WCru
miquelii	GIBF SPoG
nigra	CArn CBcs CCVT CDul CRWN GPoy GWCH IHMH LBuc MHer MSwo NWea SHFr SIde WDin WMou XPep
- 'Albomarginata'	see *S. nigra* 'Marginata'
- 'Albovariegata' (v)	CDoC LSou WMoo
* - 'Ardwall'	GCal
N - 'Aurea' ♀H4	CBcs CCVT CDul CLnd CSBt CWan ECrN ELan EPfP MBar MRav NWea SPer WDin WFar WMoo WSHC
- 'Aureomarginata' (v)	CBgR ECrN ELan ENot EPfP ISea MRav NFor NLar NPen NSti SHBN WCFE WFar
- 'Bradet'	CAgr
- 'Cae Rhos Lligwy'	WHer
- subsp. *canadensis*	NWea
- - 'Aurea'	CWib MBar MBlu NWea WHar
- - 'Goldfinch' **new**	MAsh NHol
- - 'John's'	CAgr
- - 'Maxima'	EPfP SMad WCot
- - 'York' (F)	CAgr
§ - subsp. *cerulea*	CAgr EPfP NLar SMad
§ - 'Eva'PBR	More than 30 suppliers
- 'Frances' (v)	EPPr WCot

§ - 'Gerda'PBR ♀H4	More than 30 suppliers
- 'Godshill' (F)	CAgr SDea
- 'Golden Locks'	MWgw
- 'Heterophylla'	see *S. nigra* 'Linearis'
- 'Ina'	CAgr
- f. *laciniata* ♀H4	CBcs CBgR CPLG ELan EPPr EPfP EPla MBlu MLLN MRav NBea NEgg NFor NGHP NSti NWea SDix SLon SPer SSta WCFE WCot WDin WFar WPGP
§ - 'Linearis'	CPMA ELan EPla MRav NLar
- 'Long Tooth'	CDul CNat
- 'Madonna' (v)	CBcs CBgR EBee EPla LSou MAsh MGos MLLN MRav NLar SPer SPla SPoG SPur WCMO WCot
§ - 'Marginata' (v)	CBow CDul CPLG CWan CWib EHoe GAbr ISea MBar MHer MLLN MRav SDix SLon SPer SPoG WCot WDin WFar WHar
- 'Marion Bull' (v)	CDul CNat
I - 'Monstrosa'	SMad
- 'Nana'	EMon
- 'Plaque' (v)	CNat
- 'Plena' (d)	EPla WCot
- f. *porphyrophylla* 'Black Beauty'PBR	see *S. nigra* 'Gerda'
- - 'Black Lace'PBR	see *S. nigra* 'Eva'
§ - - 'Guincho Purple'	CBcs CBow CDoC CDul CWib EBee ECrN EHoe ELan EPPr EPfP EWTr GAbr GCal IHMH ISea MBar MBlu MCCP MDun MHer MRav NFor WBor WCMO WCot WDin WFar WMoo
- - 'Purple Pete'	CDul CNat
- - 'Thundercloud'	CElw CMHG EWTr MAsh MBri MTis NChi NPro WCMO WCot WFar WPat
- 'Pulverulenta' (v)	CBgR CBow CDoC EPfP EPla GCal LHop MLLN MRav SPer WCMO WCot
- 'Purpurea'	see *S. nigra* f. *porphyrophylla* 'Guincho Purple'
- 'Pyramidalis'	CPMA EPla MBlu NLar SMad
- 'Sambu' (F)	CAgr
- 'Samdal' (F)	CAgr
- 'Samidan' (F)	CAgr
- 'Samnor' (F)	CAgr
- 'Sampo' (F)	CAgr
- 'Samyl' (F)	CAgr
* - 'Tenuifolia'	MRav
- 'Variegata'	see *S. nigra* 'Marginata'
- f. *viridis*	CAgr CBgR CNat EMon
racemosa	CAgr EPfP GWCH NWea WRha
- 'Aurea'	EHoe NEgg
- 'Chedglow'	CNat
- 'Crûg Lace'	EDsa WCru WSHC
- 'Goldenlocks'	CRez EWes MAsh MGos MSwo NLar SPer
- 'Plumosa Aurea'	More than 30 suppliers
- 'Sutherland Gold' ♀H4	More than 30 suppliers
- 'Tenuifolia'	CPMA CSWP ELan EPfP LRHS NLar WPGP
wightiana	see *S. javanica*
§ *williamsii* subsp. *coreana*	CBcs CMCN WFar

Samolus (*Primulaceae*)

repens	CPBP ECou

Sanchezia (*Acanthaceae*)

nobilis misapplied	see *S. speciosa*
§ *speciosa*	CHal

Sandersonia (*Colchicaceae*)

aurantiaca	CKob CPne ECho EPot LRHS WViv
- 'Phoenix'	WViv

Sanguinaria (Papaveraceae)

canadensis	More than 30 suppliers
- f. **multiplex** (d)	CDes CLAP ECho EMan EMon EPot ERos GEdr IFro IPot LRHS SOkd
- - 'Plena' (d) ♀H4	More than 30 suppliers
- 'Peter Harrison'	LPhx

Sanguisorba (Rosaceae)

DJHC 535 from Korea	SMHy
§ **albiflora**	CCVN CDes CFwr CKno CRow EBee EBla EBrs EGle ELan EMon EPPr ERou GBuc MRav NDov NGdn NLar NPro SHop WCAu WFar WPGP
armena	EBee EBla EPPr EWes MNrw MSph SSvw WTin WWye
benthamiana	CHEx EBla
canadensis	More than 30 suppliers
* **caucasica**	CAby EWes LPhx NBre SMeo WGHP
'Chocolate Tip' new	EBee IPot NBro
hakusanensis	CDes CHar CKno EBee EBla EPPr IFro LEdu MNrw NBir NBre NBro NDov NPro WCMO WCot WFar WPGP
- B&SWJ 8709	WCru
'John Coke' new	NLar
magnifica	CDes CFir EWes
- alba	see *S. albiflora*
menziesii	More than 30 suppliers
§ **minor**	More than 30 suppliers
- subsp. **muricata**	GWCH
obtusa	More than 30 suppliers
- var. **albiflora**	see *S. albiflora*
I - 'Nana' new	LBmB
officinalis	CArn CKno COIW CSam CWan EBee EBla EDAr EHrv EPfP GBar IHMH MBow MHer NEgg NMir NPro SWat WCAu WGHP WMoo WWye
- CDC 262	NDov
- CDC 282	LPhx
- 'Arnhem'	CKno CMdw EBee EBla EGle EPPr LPhx NDov SMHy SUsu
- 'False Tanna'	CWib
- late-flowering	NDov
- 'Lemon Splash' (v)	CBow WCot
- 'Martin's Mulberry'	EBee EWes
- 'Pink Tanna'	CFwr CKno EBee EBla EMan EMar EMon EPPr LPhx MAvo MBri MDKP NBhm NBid NBre NBro NDov NSti SMHy SPoG SUsu WCMO WCot
- 'Red Thunder'	IPot
- 'Shiro-fukurin' (v)	EMon WCot
parviflora	see *S. tenuifolia* var. *parviflora*
pimpinella	see *S. minor*
'Pink Brushes'	EBla LHop LPhx NDov
sitchensis	see *S. stipulata*
§ **stipulata**	EBee EBrs GCal IBlr MNrw NDov NGby
'Tanna'	More than 30 suppliers
'Tanna' seedling	EPPr
tenuifolia	CBrm CKno EBla LPhx LRHS MGol MSph NDov NLar NPro WMoo
- 'Alba'	CDes CKno EBee EBla GBuc LPhx MDun NDov NPro SAga SBla SMHy SMad WCot WFar
- - CDC	LPhx NDov
- 'Big Pink' new	GCal
§ - var. **parviflora**	EBee MNrw NLar SMHy
- - white-flowered	EBla WTin
- 'Pink Elephant'	CDes CFwr CKno EBee EBla GBin NLar WPGP WTin

- 'Purpurea'	CDes CKno EBee EBla EPPr NLar WFar WPGP
- 'Stand Up Comedian'	EBee NLar

Sanicula (Apiaceae)

coerulescens new	NBhm WCot
europaea	EBee GBar GPoy NSco WHer WTin WWye

Saniella (Hypoxidaceae)

verna	GCrs

Sansevieria (Dracaenaceae)

trifasciata 'Golden Hahnii' (v) ♀H1	MBri
- var. **laurentii** (v) ♀H1	MBri

Santolina (Asteraceae)

benthamiana	EAro XPep
§ **chamaecyparissus** ♀H4	More than 30 suppliers
- var. **corsica**	see *S. chamaecyparissus* var. *nana*
- 'Double Lemon'	EPfP EWin SPla SPoG WCot
- 'Lambrook Silver'	CDoC CHar EBee EGoo EPfP LRHS MAsh SCoo SLim SPla SPoG
- 'Lemon Queen'	CArn CDoC EBee EGoo ELau EPfP GBar LRHS MAsh MBow MGos MHer MNHC MSwo NBir NPri SIde SPla SWat WCHb WFar WGwG WPer XPep
§ - var. **nana** ♀H4	EBee ECha ECho ENot EPfP LRHS MAsh MBar MDun MHer MRav MSwo NFor SPoG SRms SWat WPer XPep
- - 'Weston'	ECho
- 'Pretty Carol'	CAbP EBee ELan EMil EPfP EWTr GBar GGar LRHS MAsh MBri NGHP NLRH SCoo SIde SLim SMeo SPla WPla WPep XPep
- 'Small-Ness'	CDoC EBee ECho EGoo ELan EPfP EWes GBar GEdr LRHS MAsh MHer MSte NLAp SBla SIng SLim SPer STre SWvt WCot WFar WPat
- subsp. **squarrosa**	XPep
elegans	WAbe
incana	see *S. chamaecyparissus*
* **lindavica**	XPep
'Oldfield Hybrid'	EChP EWin MLan WCot XPep
pectinata	see *S. rosmarinifolia* subsp. *canescens*
§ **pinnata**	CArn CSev CTri MHer WPer
§ - subsp. **neapolitana** ♀H4	CArn CSBt CSev EBee ECha ECho ECrN ELan ENot EPfP GBar LRHS MBri MNHC NCob NFor NPri SDix SIde WEas WHCG WMnd WSel WTin WWye XPep
- - cream	see *S. pinnata* subsp. *neapolitana* 'Edward Bowles'
§ - - 'Edward Bowles'	More than 30 suppliers
- - 'Sulphurea'	CArn CMea ECrN EGoo EPfP EWin LPhx LRHS MAsh NCob NGHP SAga SPer WKif WPer WWhi XPep
rosmarinifolia	CArn CBrm CDoC CDul CWan EBee ECrN ELau GWCH MNHC MRav MWhi NGHP SLon SPlb SRms WCHb WSel WWye XPep
I - 'Caerulea'	XPep
§ - subsp. **canescens**	EPfP EWin MBri WPer WWye
§ - subsp. **rosmarinifolia**	More than 30 suppliers
- - 'Primrose Gem' ♀H4	CBcs CDoC CEnt CSBt CTri EBee EChP ECha ECho ECrN ELau EMil ENor EPfP GBar LHop LRHS MAsh MSwo MWat NCob NPri SBod SPer SPla SWvt WCot WPer WWye XPep
- - white-flowered	SSvw
tomentosa	see *S. pinnata* subsp. *neapolitana*

virens	see *S. rosmarinifolia* subsp. *rosmarinifolia*
viridis	see *S. rosmarinifolia* subsp. *rosmarinifolia*

Sanvitalia (*Asteraceae*)

sp.	LAst
'Aztekengold'	EWin
'Cuzco Compact' **new**	WGor
'Little Sun'	LRHS SPet
procumbens 'Aztec Gold' **new**	NBlu
'Sunbini'^{PBR}	CSpe NPri SPoG SVil WGor

Sapindus (*Sapindaceae*)

mukorossi	CBcs
saponaria var. *drummondii*	EGFP

Sapium (*Euphorbiaceae*)

japonicum	CMCN WPGP
- B&SWJ 8744	WCru

Saponaria (*Caryophyllaceae*)

'Bressingham' ♀^{H4}	CBow ECho ECtt EDAr EPfP LBee LRHS NHol NLAp NMen SBla SBod SIng SPoG WAbe WPat
caespitosa	ECho EWes NJOw WAbe
x *lempergii* 'Max Frei'	CAbP CSam EBee EMan EPPr GBuc LPhx LRHS LSou MSte NCob NDov SAga SBla SDix SHar WCot WGHP WOVN WSHC XPep
lutea	GEdr NWCA
ocymoides ♀^{H4}	More than 30 suppliers
- 'Alba'	ECha ECho GAbr WFar
- 'Rubra Compacta' ♀^{H4}	LRHS NSla
- 'Snow Tip'	CBrm ECho EPfP EShb NGdn NLar SBch SMar WGor
- 'Splendens'	ECho XPep
officinalis	CAgr CArn CBre CHby CPbn CWan ELau EUnu GBar GPoy LEdu MHer MLHP MSal NGHP NPri SECG SIde SPlb SWal WBrk WFar WHer WMoo WPer WWye
- 'Alba Plena' (d)	CBre EBee ECha EMag GBar NLar NSti WCHb WFar WHer WPer WPtf WRha WTin
- 'Betty Arnold' (d)	CDes EBee GMac WCMO WCot WFar WTin
§ - 'Dazzler' (v)	EMan EPPr EUnu GBar NBir WCHb WHer
- 'Rosea Plena' (d)	More than 30 suppliers
- 'Rubra Plena' (d)	CBre CHad EBee ELan MEHN MWhi NBre NGHP NSti SHar WCHb WHer WRha WTin
- 'Variegata'	see *S. officinalis* 'Dazzler'
x *olivana* ♀^{H4}	CNic CPBP ECho EDAr EPot GAbr MTho NLAp NMen SBla SPoG WAbe WPat
pamphylica	MNrw
pulvinaris	see *S. pumilio*
§ *pumilio*	GEdr NGdn SPlb
'Rosenteppich'	SBla WLin
zawadskii	see *Silene zawadskii*

Saposhnikovia (*Apiaceae*)

divaricata	CArn MSal

Sarcocapnos (*Papaveraceae*)

enneaphylla	GKev LSRN

Sarcococca ✿ (*Buxaceae*)

confusa ♀^{H4}	More than 30 suppliers
hookeriana ♀^{H4}	CTrG ECot EPfP GSki IFoB LAst LSRN MDun WFar WPGP
- B&SWJ 2585	WCru

- HWJK 2393	WCru
- Sch 2396	EPla
- var. *digyna* ♀^{H4}	More than 30 suppliers
- - 'Purple Stem'	CBrm CHar CTri EBee EHol EPfP EPla MGos MRav NLar SCoo SPoG WCru WDin
I - - 'Schillingii'	MAsh
- var. *hookeriana*	CPMA
- - GWJ 9369	WCru
- var. *humilis*	More than 30 suppliers
orientalis	CAbP CMCN CPMA ELan EPfP EPla LBuc LRHS MAsh MGos SLon SPla SPoG SSpi WFar WPGP
'Roy Lancaster'	see *S. ruscifolia* 'Dragon Gate'
ruscifolia	CBcs CBgR CDul CMCN CPMA CSBt EBee ECrN ELan ENot EPfP EPla LRHS MAsh MGos MRav SLim SLon SMac SPer SPoG SRms SSpi WCru WFar
- var. *chinensis* ♀^{H4}	CPMA CSam EPfP EPla MRav SLon WCru WFar WGwG WPGP
- - L 713	EPla
§ - 'Dragon Gate'	CDoC CPMA ELan EPfP EPla LRHS LTwo MAsh SReu SSta WPGP WPat
saligna	CBcs CPMA EPfP NLar WCru
vagans B&SWJ 7285	WCru
wallichii	WPGP
- B&SWJ 2291	WCru
- GWJ 9427	WCru

Sarcopoterium (*Rosaceae*)

spinosum	XPep

Sarcostemma (*Asclepiadaceae*)

viminale	EShb

Saritaea (*Bignoniaceae*)

magnifica **new**	CPlN

Sarmienta (*Gesneriaceae*)

repens ♀^{H2}	WAbe WCru

Sarothamnus see *Cytisus*

Sarracenia ✿ (*Sarraceniaceae*)

alata	CFwr CSWC MCCP SHmp WSSs
- 'Black Tube'	WSSs
- heavily-veined	SHmp WSSs
- pubescent	CSWC WSSs
- 'Red Lid'	CSWC WSSs
- wavy lid	SHmp WSSs
- white-flowered	WSSs
alata x *flava* var. *maxima*	CSWC
x *areolata*	CSWC WSSs
x *catesbyi* ♀^{H1}	CSWC WSSs
'Dixie Lace'	CSWC
x *excellens* ♀^{H1}	CSWC WSSs
x *exornata*	CSWC
flava ♀^{H1}	CFwr CSWC EBla MCCP WSSs
- all green giant	see *S. flava* var. *maxima*
- var. *atropurpurea*	WSSs
- 'Burgundy'	WSSs
- var. *cuprea*	WSSs
- var. *flava*	WSSs
§ - var. *maxima*	CSWC WNor WSSs
- var. *ornata*	CSWC SHmp WSSs
- var. *rubricorpora*	WSSs
- var. *rugelii*	MYeo SHmp WSSs
- veinless	CSWC
x *harperi*	CSWC
'Ladies in Waiting'	CSWC
leucophylla ♀^{H1}	CFwr CSWC EBla SHmp WSSs
- green **new**	WSSs
- pubescent	WSSs
- 'Schnell's Ghost'	WSSs

– 'Yellow Flower' **new**   NBir
leucophylla x *oreophila*   CSWC
'Lynda Butt'   SHmp WSSs
'Marston Mill' **new**   NBir
x *miniata*   SHmp
minor   CSWC SHmp WSSs
§ – 'Okee Giant'   CSWC EBla CHew MYeo WSSs
– 'Okefenokee Giant'   see *S. minor* 'Okee Giant'
minor x *oreophila*   CSWC
x *mitchelliana* ♀H1   CFwr WSSs
x *moorei*   WSSs
– 'Brook's Hybrid'   CHew CSWC WSSs
oreophila   CSWC MYeo SHmp WSSs
oreophila x *purpurea*   CSWC
  subsp. *venosa*
x *popei*   CSWC
psittacina   CSWC SHmp WSSs
– f. *heterophylla* **new**   CSWC
purpurea   EBla NWCA
– subsp. *purpurea*   CFwr CSWC MCCP WSSs
– – f. *heterophylla*   CSWC WSSs
– subsp. *venosa*   CSWC SHmp WSSs
– – var. *burkii*   CSWC WSSs
x *readii*   SHmp WSSs
– 'Farnhamii'   CSWC
x *rehderi*   SHmp
rubra   CSWC WSSs
– subsp. *alabamensis*   CSWC WSSs
– subsp. *gulfensis*   CSWC SHmp WSSs
* – – f. *heterophylla*   CSWC WSSs
– subsp. *jonesii*   CSWC WSSs
* – – f. *heterophylla*   CSWC WSSs
– subsp. *rubra*   CSWC WSSs
– subsp. *wherryi*   CSWC WSSs
– – giant   WSSs
– – yellow-flowered   CSWC WSSs

Saruma (Aristolochiaceae)
henryi   CAby CLAP SBla WCMO WCot
  WPGP WSHC

Sasa ❀ (Poaceae)
chrysantha misapplied   see *Pleioblastus chino*
disticha 'Mirrezuzume'   see *Pleioblastus pygmaeus* 'Mirrezuzume'
glabra f. *albostriata*   see *Sasaella masamuneana* 'Albostriata'
kagamiana   NLar
kurilensis   EPla LPal MWht NMoo WFar WJun
§ – 'Shima-shimofuri' (v)   EPPr EPfP EBla ERod MWht WJun
– 'Shimofuri'   see *S. kurilensis* 'Shima-shimofuri'
– short   EPla
nana   see *S. veitchii* f. *minor*
nipponica   WJun
oshidensis   EPla
§ *palmata*   CAbb CBcs CDul COld CTrG CWib
  EBee EHoe ENot MCCP MMuc
  MWhi SEND WDin WFar WHer
  WPnP
– f. *nebulosa*   CBcs CBct CDoC CFir CHEx EFul
  EHul ENBC ENot EPfP EPla EWes
  MBrN MMoz MWht NMoo SAPC
  SArc SSto WDyG WFar WJun
  WMoo WMul WPnP
quelpaertensis   EPla
tessellata   see *Indocalamus tessellatus*
tsuboiana   CBcs CDoC ENBC EPla GQui LPal
  MMoz MNHC MWgw MWht NGdn
  NLar SBig WDyG WFar WMoo
§ *veitchii*   CAbb CBcs CKno CPLG CTrC
  CTrG EBrs ECha EHoe ENBC ENot
  EPfP EPla LEdu MDun MMoz
  MPRe MWgw NMoo SPer SPla
  WBor WDin WFar WJun WMoo
  WMul WViv WWye
§ – f. *minor*   MCCP MMoz WMoo

Sasaella (Poaceae)
glabra   see *S. masamuneana*
§ *masamuneana*   CDul ENBC EPla
§ – 'Albostriata' (v)   CDoC CMCo COtt CWib EBee
  ENBC EPPr EPla ERod GAbr LEdu
  LPal MBar MCCP MMoz MWgw
  MWht NGdn NMoo SBig SSto
  WDyG WFar WJun WMoo WMul
  WPGP WPnP WViv
– f. *aureostriata* (v)   COtt EPla GCal MMoz NPal
§ *ramosa*   CFwr CHEx ENot EPla LEdu MCCP
  MMoz MWht NMoo NRya WDin
  WMul

Sassafras (Lauraceae)
albidum   CArn CBcs CCCN CTho EPfP LEdu
  LRHS WPGP
tzumu   EBee WPGP

satsuma see *Citrus unshiu*

Satureja ❀ (Lamiaceae)
amani   XPep
§ *coerulea* ♀H4   CWan ECho EWes NBir NLAp
douglasii   CArn EOHP GBar SHDw WGHP
  WJek
– 'Indian Mint' PBR   CFwr EDAr MNHC NGHP
hortensis   CBod GPoy ILis MHer MLan
  MNHC SIde WJek WSel
– 'Selektion' **new**   LLWP
montana   CArn CHby CWan ECho ELau
  EUnu GPoy ILis ITim LLWP MBri
  MHer MNHC NMen SDix SHGN
  SIde SRms WCHb WGHP WHer
  WPer XPep
* – *citriodora*   GPoy MHer WJek XPep
– 'Coerulea'   see *S. coerulea*
§ – subsp. *illyrica*   GEdr WJek
– 'Purple Mountain'   GPoy LLWP MHer
– *subspicata*   see *S. montana* subsp. *illyrica*
parnassica   LLWP WPer
repanda   see *S. spicigera*
§ *spicigera*   CArn CBod CLyd CNic CPBP EBee
  ECho ELau EPot GBar GEdr LEdu
  LFol LLWP MHer NBir NMen
  SHGN SIde WCHb WJek WSel
  WWye
thymbra   CArn EOHP SHDw XPep
§ *viminea*   EOHP

Saurauia (Actinidiaceae)
subspinosa   CHEx

Sauromatum (Araceae)
guttatum   see *S. venosum*
§ *venosum*   CHEx CKob CMea EAmu EBee
  EBrs ECho EMan EShb ITer LEdu
  LRHS MOak MSph SBig WCMO
  WCot WCru WRos

Saururus (Saururaceae)
cernuus   CBen CHEx CRow CWat EHon
  ELan EMFW EPfP LNCo LPBA
  SRms SWat WMAq WPnP
  WWpP
chinensis   CRow

Saussurea (Asteraceae)
CC 3385 **new**   GEdr
albescens   EBee EMan WCot
auriculata HWJCM 490   WCru
obvallata HWJK 2272   WCru
uniflora GWJ 9269   WCru

savory, summer see *Satureja hortensis*

Saxegothaea (*Podocarpaceae*)
conspicua   CDoC CMCN ECou EPla WCwm

Saxifraga ✿ (*Saxifragaceae*)
McB 1377   CLyd
McB 1397 from Nepal   CLyd
SEP 22   CLyd EHyt
SEP 45   CLyd
'Ada' (x *petraschii*) (7)   NMen
'Aemula' (x *borisii*) (7)   NMen
§ 'Afrodite' (*sempervivum*) CLyd
   (7)
aizoides (9)   ECho GKev WAbe
- var. *atrorubens* (9) ECho NHol
aizoon   see *S. paniculata*
'Aladdin' (x *borisii*) (7) NMen
'Alan Hayhurst' (8)   WAbe WFar
'Alan Martin'   CLyd ECho EPot ITim NMen
   (x *boydilacina*) (7)
'Alba' (x *apiculata*) (7) ECho ELan EPot LFox LRHS MHer
                         NHol NLAp NMen NRya SBla SPlb
                         WAbe WPat
'Alba' (x *arco-valleyi*) see *Saxifraga* 'Ophelia'
'Alba' (*oppositifolia*) (7) CLyd EHyt ELan EWes ITim NDlv
                         NLAp NWCA WAbe
'Albert Einstein'   NMen
   (x *apiculata*) (7)
'Albertii' (*callosa*) (8) see *S.* 'Albida'
§ 'Albida' (*callosa*) (8) ECho LRHS NLar WAbe
'Aldebaran' (x *borisii*) (7) NMen
'Aldo Bacci' (Milford   NMen
   Group) (7)
'Alfons Mucha' (7)   CLyd EPot NMen WAbe
'Allendale Acclaim'   NDlv NMen
   (x *lismorensis*) (7)
'Allendale Accord'   NDlv NMen
   (*diapensioides* x
   lilacina) (7)
'Allendale Allure' (7)   NMen
'Allendale Amber' (7)   NMen
'Allendale Andante'   CLyd NMen
   (x *arco-valleyi*) (7)
'Allendale Angel'   NMen
   (x *kepleri*) (7)
'Allendale Argonaut' (7) NDlv NMen
'Allendale Ballad' (7)   NMen
'Allendale Ballet' (7)   CLyd EHyt NMen
'Allendale Bamby'   NMen
   (x *lismorensis*) (7)
'Allendale Banshee' (7) NMen
'Allendale Beau'   NMen
   (x *lismorensis*) (7)
'Allendale Beauty' (7)   CPBP NMen
'Allendale Betty'   CLyd EHyt NMen
   (x *lismorensis*) (7)
'Allendale Billows' (7) NMen
'Allendale Blossom'   CLyd
   (x *limorensis*) (7) **new**
'Allendale Bonny' (7)   GCrs NMen
'Allendale Bounty' (7)   NMen
'Allendale Bravo'   CLyd EHyt NMen WAbe
   (x *lismorensis*) (7)
'Allendale Cabal' (7)   CLyd NMen
'Allendale Celt' (7)   CLyd EHyt NMen
   (x *novacastelensis*) (7)
'Allendale Charm'   CLyd EHyt NMen WAbe
   (Swing Group) (7)
'Allendale Chick' (7)   EHyt GCrs NMen
'Allendale Comet' (7)   GCrs NMen
'Allendale Dance' (7)   NMen
'Allendale Dream' (7)   EHyt EPot NMen
'Allendale Duo' (7)   NMen
'Allendale Elegance' (7) NMen
'Allendale Elf' (7)   CLyd NMen
'Allendale Elite' (7)   CLyd NMen

'Allendale Enchantment' NMen
   (7)
'Allendale Envoy' (7)   NMen
'Allendale Epic' (7)   NMen
'Allendale Fairy' (7)   NMen
'Allendale Fame' (7)   NMen
'Allendale Frost' (7)   NMen
'Allendale Garnet' (7)   CLyd NDlv NMen
'Allendale Ghost' (7)   EHyt NMen
'Allendale Goblin' (7)   NMen
'Allendale Grace' (7)   CLyd NMen
'Allendale Gremlin' (7) NMen
'Allendale Harvest' (7) **new** NMen
'Allendale Hobbit' (7) **new** NMen
'Allendale Host' (7) **new** NMen
'Allendale Joy'   NMen
   (x *wendelacina*) (7)
'Allendale Pearl'   CLyd EHyt NMen
   (x *novacastelensis*) (7)
'Allendale Ruby' (7)   CLyd CPBP EHyt NMen
'Allendale Snow'   NMen
   (x *rayei*) (7)
'Alpenglow' (7)   NMen
alpigena (7)   CLyd WAbe
'Amitie' (x *gloriana*) (7) CFee NMen
andersonii (7)   CLyd NDlv NMen NRya
- McB 1475   NHol
x *andrewsii* (8x11)   MTho
angustifolia Haw.   see *S. hypnoides*
'Anna' (x *fontanae*) (7) NMen
'Anne Beddall'   CLyd NMen WAbe
   (x *goringiana*) (7)
'Antonio Vivaldi' (7)   WAbe
'Aphrodite' (*sempervivum*) see *S.* 'Afrodite'
   (7)
x *apiculata sensu stricto* see *S.* 'Gregor Mendel'
   hort.
'Apple Blossom' (15)   ECtt NRya SPoG WGor WHoo
'Archdale' (*paniculata*) WRHF
   (8) **new**
'Archfield White' (*callosa*) CStu
   (8)
§ 'Arco' (x *arco-valleyi*) (7) NJOw
x *arco-valleyi sensu*   see *S.* 'Arco'
   stricto hort.
x *arendsii* (15)   WEas
- pink (15)   NBlu
- purple (15)   NBlu NNor
§ 'Aretiastrum' (x *boydii*) (7) CLyd LFox NDlv NMen
aretioides (7)   NMen
'Ariel' (x *bornibrookii*) (7) CLyd LFox NMen
'Arthur' (x *anglica*) (7) NMen
'Assimilis' (x *petraschii*) (7) CLyd NMen WAbe
'August Hayek' (x *leyboldii*) NMen
   (7)
'Aurea Maculata'   see *S.* 'Aureopunctata'
   (*cuneifolia*)
§ 'Aureopunctata'   ECha ECho EMan GAbr GBuc GCal
   (x *urbium*) (11/v)   MHer MWgw NHol SPer SPlb
                         SPoG SRms WHen WMoo WPtf
'Autumn Tribute' (*fortunei*) WAbe
   (5)
'Balcana' (*paniculata*) (8) EPot
'Baldensis'   see *S. paniculata* var. *minutifolia*
'Ballawley Guardsman' (15) LFox SIng
§ 'Beatrix Stanley' (x *anglica*) CLyd LFox MHer NDlv NHol NLAp
   (7)   NMen NRya WGor
'Becky Foster' (x *borisii*) NMen
   (7)
'Beechcroft White' (15) LRHS
'Bellisant' (x *bornibrookii*) CLyd NMen
   (7)
'Benimizu' **new**   IPot
'Berenika' (x *bertolonii*) (7) NMen
'Beryl' (x *anglica*) (7) NMen
'Bettina' (x *paulinae*) (7) NMen

Name	Suppliers
× *biasolettoi sensu stricto* hort.	see S. 'Phoenix'
× *bilekii* (7)	CLyd ECho
'Birch Baby' (15)	SIng
'Birch Yellow'	see S. 'Pseudoborisii'
'Black Beauty' (15)	LRHS MHer NHol NLRH SIng
'Black Ruby' (*fortunei*) (5)	More than 30 suppliers
'Blackberry and Apple Pie' (*fortunei*) (5)	CBct CBod CElw CLAP EBee EChP ECtt EMar GEdr IBal MBrN MNrw MSte MWgw NBro NEgg NHol NMen NMyG NPri SWvt WAul WBor WCot WFar WOld WWeb WWhi
'Blaník' (× *borisii*) (7)	CLyd NMen
'Blanka' (× *borisii*) (7)	NMen
'Blütenteppich' (15)	WPer
'Bob Hawkins' (15/v)	CLyd LFox LRHS NHol
§ 'Bodensee' (× *hofmannii*) (7)	NDlv WPat
'Bohdalec' (× *megaseiflora*) (7)	NMen
'Bohemia' (7)	CLyd CStu ECho EPot ITim NMen NSla SBla WAbe
× *borisii sensu stricto* hort.	see S. 'Sofia'
'Bornmuelleri' (7)	NMen
'Boston Spa' (× *elisabethae*) (7)	CLyd EAEE ECho LRHS MHer NDlv NHol NJOw NLAp NMen SPlb WPat
'Brailes' (× *poluanglica*) (7)	CLyd NMen
'Bridget' (× *edithae*) (7)	CLyd CMea EAEE ECho LFox LRHS NDlv NHol NMen SIng
'Brno' (× *elisabethae*) (7)	EPot NHol NMen
bronchialis (10)	CLyd CNic
'Brookside' (*burseriana*) (7)	EPot NMen
brunoniana	see S. brunonis
§ *brunonis* (1)	LFox WCru
– CC&McK 108	NWCA
bryoides (10)	CLyd ECho GCrs NRya NWCA
× *burnatii* (8)	CLyd LFox LRHS NDlv NLar NMen NPro WGor
burseriana (7)	ECho NLAp WAbe WGor
'Buster' (× *hardingii*) (7)	NMen
'Buttercup' (× *kayei*) (7)	CLyd NHol NJOw NLAp NMen NWCA WHoo
× *byam-groundsii* (7)	CLyd
caesia L. (8)	SRms
caesia hort. (× *fritschiana*)	see S. 'Krain'
§ *callosa* (8) ♀H4	ECho GEdr MLHP MWat NHol NLAp SBla WEas WFar WPat WTin
– subsp. *callosa* (8)	ECho
§ – – var. *australis* (8)	EPot GCrs NBro NHol NMen WAbe
– var. *lantoscana*	see S. callosa subsp. callosa var. australis
– *lingulata*	see S. callosa
– 'Wartosque' **new**	EPot
callosa × *cochlearis* (8)	see S. Silver Farreri Group
'Cambridge Seedling' (7)	NDlv NMen
'Camyra' (7)	WAbe
× *canis-dalmatica*	see S. 'Canis-dalmatica' (× *gaudinii*)
§ 'Canis-dalmatica' (× *gaudinii*) (8) ♀H4	CLyd EAEE ECho ECtt EGoo EPot GGar LRHS NDlv NHol NMen NWCA SPoG WGor WPer
§ 'Carmen' (× *elisabethae*) (7)	LRHS NDlv NLAp NMen WAbe
§ 'Carniolica' (*paniculata*) (8)	CLyd EPot LFox LRHS MBar NBro NHol NMen NWCA SBla
'Carniolica' (× *pectinata*) (8)	WAbe
carolinica	see S. 'Carniolica'
'Castor' (× *bilekii*) (7)	NMen
'Caterhamensis' (*cotyledon*) (8)	NHar
'Cathy Reed' (× *polulacina*) (7)	NMen
§ *caucasica* (7)	ECho
– var. *desoulavyi*	see S. desoulavyi
cebennensis (15) ♀H2	CLyd EPot LFox NMen NRya
– dwarf (15)	WAbe
cespitosa (15)	WAbe
'Chambers' Pink Pride'	see S. 'Miss Chambers'
'Charlecote' (× *poluanglica*) (7)	CLyd CStu ITim
'Charles Chaplin' (7)	CLyd CPBP ECho NHar WAbe
'Cheap Confections' (*fortunei*) (4)	CBct CBod CElw CHEx CLAP CMMP CSpe EBee EChP ECtt EMar EWll GAbr GEdr LTwo MSte NEgg NHol NMen SPer SPla SPoG WBor WCot WFar WOld WPGP
'Cherry Pie' (*fortunei*) (5)	CBct CHea CLAP EBee GAbr LHop LTwo MBNS MNrw NBir NCGa NEgg NHar NMyG WBor WCot
'Cherrytrees' (× *boydii*) (7)	NMen
'Chetwynd' (*marginata*) (7)	CLyd NMen WAbe
'Chez Nous' (× *gloriana*) (7/v)	CLyd NJOw NMen
'Chodov' (7)	NMen
'Christine' (× *anglica*) (7)	CLyd ECho LFox NDlv NHol NLAp NMen
cinerea (7)	GCrs NMen SIng WAbe
'Cio-Cio-San' (Vanessa Group) (7)	NMen
'Citronella' (7)	ECho WAbe
'Claire Felstead' (*cinerea* × *poluniniana*) (7)	GCrs NMen
'Clare' (× *anglica*) (7)	NMen
'Clare Island' (15)	SIng
§ 'Clarence Elliott' (*umbrosa*) (11) ♀H4	CLyd CMea CTri ECho EHyt EWes GCal GKev LRHS MDKP MHar MHer NHol NRya NVic WAbe WHoo WPat
'Claudia' (× *borisii*) (7)	NMen
'Cleo' (× *boydii*) (7)	NMen
§ × *clibranii* (7)	SIng
§ 'Cloth of Gold' (*exarata* subsp. *moschata*) (15)	CLyd CWCL ECha ECho ECtt ELan LAst LRHS MBar MHer NHol NJOw NMen NRya SIng SPlb SPoG SRms WAbe WBVN WFar
cochlearis (8)	CTri EAEE EHyt GEdr LBee LRHS MWat NBro NDlv NMen WAbe WPer
'Cockscomb' (*paniculata*) (8)	EPot NHol NJOw NMen NRya WAbe
columnaris (7)	EHyt NMen WAbe
columnaris × *dinnikii*	NSla
'Combrook' (× *poluanglica*) (7)	CLyd
continentalis (15)	NWCA
'Conwy Snow' (*fortunei*) (5)	WAbe
'Conwy Star' (*fortunei*) (5)	WAbe
'Coolock Gem' (7)	EHyt NMen
'Coolock Kate' (7)	CGra CStu EHyt NMen WAbe
'Cordata' (*burseriana*) (7)	NMen
'Corona' (× *boydii*) (7)	LFox NHol NMen
'Corrennie Claret' (15)	EWes
§ 'Corrie Fee' (*oppositifolia*) (7)	CGra GCrs
§ *cortusifolia* (5)	CLAP EBrs ECho
– B&SWJ 5879	WCru
– var. *fortunei*	see S. fortunei
– var. *stolonifera* (5)	ECho
– – B&SWJ 6205	WCru
'Cotton Crochet' (*fortunei*) (5/d)	CBct EBee EChP EMan GEdr GSki LAst MBNS MLLN NMyG WCot WFar WOld
cotyledon (8)	ECho GCrs LBee LRHS NFor NHol WEas WPer
– 'Lutea' (*paniculata*) **new**	EPot

§ 'Cranbourne' (x *anglica*) (7) ♀H4 — CLyd CStú EAEE ECho EPot GCrs LFox LRHS NHol NLAp NMen SBla WPat

'Cream' (*paniculata*) (8) — ECho

'Cream Seedling' (x *elisabethae*) (7) — NDlv NJOw NLAp NMen

'Crenata' (*burseriana*) (7) — CLyd EPot GCrs LFox LRHS NDlv NMen WAbe WHoo

'Crimson Rose' (8) — see *S.* 'Rosea' (*paniculata*)

§ *crustata* (8) — ECho EHyt MDKP NMen WAbe

- var. *vochinensis* — see *S. crustata*

'Crystal Pink' (*fortunei*) (5/v) — CBct CMil EBee EChP EHrv GAbr GEdr LAst LHop MNrw NBro NHar NMen NMyG WBor WCot WFar WGor WOld

'Crystalie' (x *biasolettoi*) (7) — EPot LRHS NRya WPat

'Cultrata' (*paniculata*) (8) — NBro

'Cumulus' (*iranica* hybrid) (7) ♀H4 — CLyd CPBP EHyt GCrs ITim NMen SBla WAbe

§ *cuneifolia* (11) — CNic ECho GGar IHMH LBee LRHS MHer MWat NDlv NSti NWCA NPer WRos

- var. *capillipes* — see *S. cuneifolia* subsp. *cuneifolia*

§ - subsp. *cuneifolia* (11) — ECtt

* - var. *subintegra* (11) — ECho

§ 'Cuscutiformis' (*stolonifera*) (5) — CAby CElw CPLG EBee EBla ETow GCal SBch SBla SRms WAbe WCru WPGP

cymbalaria (2) — EBur SIng

- var. *huetiana* (2) — CNic

'Cyril Mortimor Pritchard' (x *hardingii*) (7) — CLyd

dahurica — see *S. cuneifolia*

'Dainty Dame' (x *arco-valleyi*) (7) — CLyd LFox LRHS NDlv NMen WAbe

'Dana' (x *megaseiflora*) (7) — CLyd NHol NMen

'Dartington Double' (15/d) — EWes LRHS NHol NLAp

'Dartington Double White' (15/d) — NHol NJOw

'David' (7) **new** — EPot

'Dawn Frost' (7) — CLyd EPot NDlv NLAp NMen SBla WAbe

'Delia' (x *bornibrookii*) (7) — CLyd EPot ITim NMen

§ 'Denisa' (x *pseudokotschyi*) (7) — NMen

densa — see *S. cherlerioides*

'Dentata' (x *geum*) — see *S.* 'Dentata' (x *polita*)

§ 'Dentata' (x *polita*) (11) — CMea CNic CSpe ECha GGar NVic SUsu WMoo

'Dentata' (x *urbium*) — see *S.* 'Dentata' (x *polita*)

§ *desoulavyi* (7) — GCrs NMen

diapensioides (7) — CLyd WAbe

dinnikii — WAbe

'Dobruska' (x *irvingii*) (7) **new** — NMen

'Doctor Clay' (*paniculata*) (8) — EPot GKev LBee NHar NMen NRya WAbe

'Doctor Ramsey' (8) — EAEE EHyt EWes GEdr LBee LRHS NBro NDlv NHol NJOw NLar NMen WAbe WGor WPnn

'Don Giovanni' (7) — WAbe

'Donald Mann' (15) — EWes

'Dorothy Milne' (7) — NMen

aff. *doyalana* (7) — NDlv

- SEP 45 — EHyt

'Drakula' (*ferdinandi-coburgi*) (7) — CLyd LRHS NDlv NMen SIng

'Dubarry' (15) — EWes NRya WPnn

'Dulcimer' (x *petraschii*) (7) — NMen

'Duncan Lowe' (*andersonii*) (7) ♀H4 — CLyd GCrs

'Dwight Ripley' (7) — LFox NMen

'Edgar Irmscher' (7) — CLyd LFox NMen NWCA

'Edith' (x *edithae*) (7) — EAEE ECho LRHS NJOw SIng

'Edward Elgar' (x *megaseiflora*) (7) — NHol

x *elegantissima* (15) — see *S.* x *clibranii*

'Elf' (7) — see *S.* 'Beatrix Stanley'

'Elf' (15) — ECtt EPfP LRHS NHol NMen SIng SPoG SRms WGor

'Eliot Hodgkin' (x *millstreamiana*) (7) — LFox

x *elisabethae sensu stricto* hort. — see *S.* 'Carmen'

'Elizabeth Sinclair' (x *elisabethae*) (7) — CLyd EPot GKev ITim NJOw NMen

'Ellie Brinckerhoff' (x *bornibrookii*) (7) — NMen

x *engleri* (8) — CLyd

epiphylla BWJ 7750 — WCru

§ 'Ernst Heinrich' (x *heinrichii*) (7) — CLyd NMen

'Esther' (x *burnatii*) (8) — CMea EAEE EHyt EPot GCrs GEdr GKev LBee LRHS NHol NMen NWCA SBla SMer WAbe WHoo WPnn

§ 'Eulenspiegel' (x *geuderi*) (7) — CLyd EPot NMen

'Eva Hanzlíková' (x *izari*) (7) — CLyd CPBP WAbe

exarata (15) — LFox LRHS NMen

- subsp. *moschata* (15) — MWgw

fair maids of France — see *S.* 'Flore Pleno'

'Fairy' (*exarata* subsp. *moschata*) (15) — ECtt ELan EPot

'Faldonside' (x *boydii*) (7) ♀H4 — CLyd CPBP LFox NDlv NHol NLAp NMen NRya WAbe WHoo WPat

'Falstaff' (*burseriana*) (7) — CLyd LFox NDlv NRya

x *farreri* (15) **new** — GEdr

§ 'Faust' (x *borisii*) (7) — NMen WAbe

§ *federici-augusti* (7) — GCrs

§ - subsp. *grisebachii* (7) ♀H2-3 — CLyd ECho NSla WAbe WLin

'Ferdinand' (x *hofmannii*) (7) — NMen

ferdinandi-coburgi (7) ♀H4 — CLyd ECtt EPot LFox LRHS NDlv NRya NWCA WAbe WBrE

§ - var. *rhodopea* (7) — CLyd EPot GCrs LRHS NDlv NMen SBla SIng

'Findling' (15) — EPot IHMH LRHS NHol NJOw NMen SPoG WAbe

'Firebrand' (7) **new** — WAbe

'Five Color' (*fortunei*) (5) — see *S.* 'Go-nishiki'

§ *flagellaris* (1) — GKev NMen WAbe

'Flavescens' misapplied — see *S.* 'Lutea' (*paniculata*)

x *fleischeri* (7) — NMen

'Flore Pleno' (*granulata*) (15/d) — CFir EBee EWes LFox MAvo NBir SIng WFar

'Florissa' (*oppositifolia*) (7) — CLyd

'Flowers of Sulphur' — see *S.* 'Schwefelblüte'

§ *fortunei* (5) ♀H4 — CHEx ECho GKev GMaP IFro MRav NBir NHol NLAp SRms WAbe WCru WMoo

- B&SWJ 6346 — WCru

- f. *alpina* (5) — CLAP

- - from Hokkaido (5) — CLAP WCru

- 'Daniela' **new** — EMil

- var. *koraiensis* (5) B&SWJ 8688 — WCru

- var. *obtusocuneata* (5) — CLAP EBee ECho EHyt LTwo NMen WAbe

- f. *partita* — CLAP WCru

- var. *pilosissima* (5) B&SWJ 8557 — WCru

- pink (5) — CLAP WAbe WFar WTMC

- 'Silver Velvet' **new** — WCot

- var. *suwoensis* (5) — CLAP

'Foster's Gold' (x *elisabethae*) (7) — CLyd NMen

'Four Winds' (15) — EWes LRHS NHol SIng

'Francesco Redi' (7) — NMen WAbe
'Francis Cade' (8) — CStu GAbr WAbe
'Frank Sinatra' — CLyd NMen
  (x *poluanglica*) (7)
'Franz Liszt' (7) — WAbe
'Franzii' (x *paulinae*) (7) — NMen
'Frederik Chopin' (7) — WAbe
'Friar Tuck' (x *boydii*) (7) — NMen WAbe
'Friesei' (x *salmonica*) (7) — CLyd EPot NMen
x *fritschiana* **new** — GEdr
'Frosty' (8) **new** — EPot
'Fumiko' (*fortunei*) (5) — WAbe WCru
'Funkii' (x *petraschii*) (7) — NMen
'Gaertneri' (*mariae-* — NMen
  theresiae) (7)
'Gaiety' (15) — CWCL EAEE SPoG WFar
'Galaxie' (x *megaseiflora*) — CLyd EPot LFox NDlv NHol NMen
  (7)
'Ganymede' (*burseriana*) — NJOw NMen WAbe
  (7)
'Gelber Findling' (7) — EPot LRHS WAbe
'Gem' (x *irvingii*) (7) — CLyd NDlv NMen WAbe
'General Joffre' (15) — see *S*. 'Maréchal Joffre'
'Geoff Wilson' — EPot
  (x *biasolettoi*)
georgei (7) — CLyd GCrs NDlv NMen WAbe
  - McB 1379 — NHol
georgei x 'Winifred' — CLyd
'Gertie Pritchard' — see *S*. 'Mrs Gertie Prichard'
  (x *megaseiflora*)
x *geuderi* sensu stricto — see *S*. 'Eulenspiegel'
  hort.
§ x *geum* (11) — MLHP MRav WFar WMoo
  - Dixter form (11) — ECha SMHy
'Gleborg' (15) — EWes SPoG
'Gloria' (*burseriana*) (7) — CLyd EAEE EHyt LFox LRHS NHol
  ♀H4 — NMen NSla SIng WPat
x *gloriana* (7) — see *S*. 'Godiva'
'Gloriana' — see *S*. 'Godiva'
'Gloriosa' (x *gloriana*) (7) — see *S*. 'Godiva'
§ 'Godiva' (x *gloriana*) (7) — CLyd NMen WAbe
'Goeblii' (7) — NDlv
'Gold Dust' (x *eudoxiana*) — CLyd CStu ECho GCrs LFox NJOw
  (7) — NLAp NMen NRya
'Golden Falls' (15/v) — EWes LAst LRHS NEgg NHol SPlb
   — SPoG
Golden Prague — see *S*. 'Zlatá Praha'
  (x *pragensis*)
§ 'Go-nishiki' (*fortunei*) (5) — EBee LTwo WGor
'Goring White' (7) — NMen
'Gothenburg' (7) — CLyd EPot NMen WAbe
'Grace' (x *arendsii*) (15/v) — see *S*. 'Seaspray'
'Grace Farwell' (x *anglica*) — EAEE ECho EPot LRHS MBar NDlv
  (7) — NHol NMen NRya NWCA SBla
   — WHoo
'Grandiflora' (*burseriana*) — NHol
  (7)
granulata (15) — CNic CRWN ECho EDAr MBow
   — NSco WAbe
'Gratoides' (x *grata*) (7) — NMen
§ 'Gregor Mendel' — CLyd CMea CSam CStu EAEE ECho
  (x *apiculata*) (7) ♀H4 — EPot LRHS NDlv NHol NMen NLAp
   — NMen SBla SRms WAbe WHoo WTel
grisebachii — see *S*. *federici-augusti* subsp.
   — *grisebachii*
  - subsp. *montenegrina* — see *S*. *federici-augusti*
'Haagii' (x *eudoxiana*) (7) — CStu ECho ELan NDlv NMen WTel
'Harbinger' (7) — CLyd WAbe WGor
'Hare Knoll Beauty' (8) — ECho EPot GCrs GKev NHar NLAp
   — NMen NRya WAbe
'Harlow Car' (7) — CLyd LFox NMen NSla
'Harry Marshall' (x *irvingii*) — CLyd NDlv NMen
  (7)
'Hartside Pink' (*umbrosa*) — CLyd
  (11)
'Hartswood White' (15) — MWat

'Harvest Moon' (*stolonifera*) — CBct CBow CHEx EBee
  (5) — ECtt EMan LHop NCGa
'Hedwig' (x *malbyana*) (7) — NHol NMen
x *heinreichii* sensu stricto — see *S*. 'Ernst Heinrich'
  hort.
'Hi-Ace' (15/v) — CLyd ECtt LFox MHer NLAp SPlb
   — SPoG
'Highdownensis' (8) — NDlv
'Hime' (*stolonifera*) (5) — WCru
'Hindhead Seedling' — CLyd EAEE LRHS NDlv NJOw
  (x *boydii*) (7) — NMen SIng WAbe
hirsuta (11) — EBla EBrs GGar IFro WCru
'Hirsuta' (x *geum*) — see *S*. x *geum*
'Hirtella' Ingwersen — EPot
  (*paniculata*) (8)
'His Majesty' (x *irvingii*) (7) — LFox NMen WAbe
'Hocker Edge' (x *arco-* — CLyd ITim LFox NDlv NMen WAbe
  valleyi) (7)
'Holden Seedling' (15) — ECtt EWes
x *hornibrookii* (7) — WPat
hostii (8) — CLyd ECho LBee LRHS NHol
   — NJOw WTin
§ - subsp. *hostii* (8) — GEdr
  - - var. *altissima* (8) — STre
  - subsp. *rhaetica* (8) — NBro NDlv NMen WAbe
'Hradcany' **new** — NMen
'Hsitou Silver' (*stolonifera*) — CFee EBee EPPr GCal MDKP WCru
  (5)
'Hunscote' (x *poluanglica*) — NMen
  (7)
hybrid JB 11 — NMen
§ *hypnoides* (15) — WAbe
hypostoma (7) — CLyd
'Icicle' (x *elisabethae*) (7) — NMen WAbe
'Ignaz Dörfler' (x *doerfleri*) — WAbe
  (7)
imparilis — CLAP WCru
'Ingeborg' (15) — ECha LRHS SIng
iranica (7) — CLyd CStu EHyt ITim NLAp NMen
   — NSla
  - pink (7) — EHyt
'Irene Bacci' (x *baccii*) (7) — CLyd NMen
'Iris Prichard' (x *bardingii*) — CLyd EPot ITim WAbe
x *irvingii* sensu stricto — see *S*. 'Walter Irving'
  hort.
x *irvingii* (7) — NDlv
'Isobel Young' (7) **new** — WAbe
'Ivana' (x *caroliquarti*) (7) — WAbe
jacquemontiana (1) — WAbe
'James Bremner' (15) — LRHS NBur SIng
'Jan Neruda' — NMen
  (x *megaseiflora*)
  (7) **new**
'Jan Palach' (x *krausii*) (7) — EPot NMen
'Jason' (x *elisabethae*) (7) — NMen
'Jenkinsiae' (x *irvingii*) (7) — CFee CLyd CStu EAEE ECho EPot
  ♀H4 — LRHS NDlv NHol NLAp NMen
   — NRya NWCA SIng SMer WAbe
   — WHoo WPat
§ 'Johann Kellerer' — CFee EPot LFox NDlv SBla WAbe
  (x *kellereri*) (7)
'John Tomlinson' — CLyd NMen
  (*burseriana*) (7)
'Jorg' (x *biasolettoi*) — EPot
'Josef Čapek' — CLyd EPot NMen
  (x *megaseiflora*) (7)
'Josef Mánes' (x *borisii*) (7) — NMen
'Joy' — see *S*. 'Kaspar Maria Sternberg'
'Joy Bishop' (7) — WAbe
'Judith Shackleton' — CLyd CStu EPot GCrs NDlv NMen
  (x *abingdonensis*) (7) — WAbe
'Juliet' — see *S*. 'Riverslea'
§ *juniperifolia* (7) — CMea EAEE ECho GAbr LRHS
   — MHer NDlv NJOw NLAp NWCA
   — SMer SRms

- subsp. **sancta** — see *S. sancta*
'Jupiter' (x *megaseiflora*) (7) — CLyd LRHS NDlv NHol NLAp NMen WAbe
'Kampa' (7) — CLyd NMen
§ **karadzicensis** (7) — NMen
'Karasin' (7) — CLyd NMen
'Karel Čapek' (x *megaseiflora*) (7) — CLyd EPot NDlv NHol NJOw NLar NRya NSla WAbe
'Karel Stivín' (x *edithae*) (7) — CLyd NMen
'Karlstejn' (x *borisii*) (7) — NDlv WAbe
§ 'Kaspar Maria Sternberg' (x *petraschii*) (7) — CLyd LFox NHol NJOw NMen WPat
'Kath Dryden' (x *anglica*) (7) — ECho GKev ITim NHol WAbe
'Kathleen Pinsent' (8) ♀H4 — CLyd ECho NDlv NWCA WAbe
'Kathleen' (x *polulacina*) (7) — CLyd NHol NLAp
'Katrin' (x *borisii*) (7) — WAbe
x **kellereri** *sensu stricto* hort. — see *S.* 'Johann Kellerer'
'Kew Gem' (x *petraschii*) (7) — NMen
'Kewensis' (x *kellereri*) (7) — NDlv NMen WAbe
'Kineton' (x *poluanglica*) (7) — NMen
'King Lear' (x *bursiculata*) (7) — CLyd EAEE EPot LFox LRHS NMen SBla
'Kingscote White' (15) — SIng
'Kinki Purple' (*stolonifera*) (5) — EBee GCal GGar WCru
'Klondike' (x *boydii*) (7) — WAbe
'Knapton Pink' (15) — EPfP NHol NRya SIng WAbe WFar
'Knapton White' (15) — SIng
'Knebworth' (8) **new** — ECho
§ x **kochii** (7) — EHyt
§ 'Kolbiana' (x *paulinae*) (7) — CLyd
§ 'Krain' (x *fritschiana*) (8) — ECho EPot
'Krákatit' (x *megaseiflora*) (7) — NMen WAbe
'Krasava' (x *megaseiflora*) (7) — CLyd CPBP EPot ITim NHol NMen
'Kyrillii' (x *borisii*) (7) — CLyd NMen
'Labe' (x *arco-valleyi*) (7) — CLyd CNic EAEE EPot LRHS NMen SBla WAbe
'Ladislav Celakovsky' (7) **new** — NMen
'Lady Beatrix Stanley' — see *S.* 'Beatrix Stanley'
§ 'Lagraveana' (*paniculata*) (8) ♀H4 — ECtt EHyt EPot LRHS MHer MOne NDlv NJOw NRya WGor
x **landaueri** *sensu stricto* hort. — see *S.* 'Leonore'
'Lantoscana Superba' (*callosa*) **new** — EPot
'Latonica' (*callosa*) (8) — EPot
'Lemon Hybrid' (x *boydii*) (7) — NMen
'Lemon Spires' (7) — NMen
'Lenka' (x *byam-groundsii*) (7) — NJOw NMen NSla WAbe
'Leo Gordon Godseff' (x *elisabethae*) (7) — CStu LRHS NMen
§ 'Leonore' (x *landaueri*) (7) — LRHS WAbe
'Letchworth Gem' (x *urbium*) (11) — ECho GCal NWCA
'Lidice' (7) — CLyd NDlv NLAp NMen WAbe WHoo
'Lilac Time' (x *youngiana*) (7) — NMen
lilacina (7) — CLyd CStu NMen WAbe WPat
'Limelight' (*callosa* subsp. *callosa* var. *australis*) (8) — WAbe
'Lindau' (7) — NMen
lingulata — see *S. callosa*
'Lismore Carmine' (x *lismorensis*) (7) — CLyd GCrs NDlv NLAp NMen NWCA
'Lismore Cherry' (7) — CLyd

'Lismore Gem' (x *lismorensis*) (7) — GCrs NMen
'Lismore Mist' (x *lismorensis*) (7) — CLyd CPBP EHyt NMen
'Lismore Pink' (x *lismorensis*) (7) — CLyd EPot GCrs NDlv NMen NWCA
* 'Little Piggy' (*epiphylla*) (5) — WCru
'Lohengrin' (x *boerhammeri*) (7) — EPot
longifolia (8) — ECho EPyc GKev NSla WAbe WGor
Love Me — see *S.* 'Miluj Mne'
'Louis Armstrong' (Blues Group) (7) — EPot WAbe
lowndesii (7) — EHyt
'Loxley' (x *poluanglica*) (7) **new** — GEdr
'Ludmila Šubrová' (x *bertolonii*) (7) — CLyd NMen
'Lusanna' (x *irvingii*) (7) — CLyd NHol
'Lutea' (*diapensioides*) — see *S.* 'Wilhelm Tell', *S.* 'Primulina'
'Lutea' (*marginata*) — see *S.* 'Faust'
§ 'Lutea' (*paniculata*) (8) ♀H4 — ECho EPot GEdr LRHS NBro NDlv NHol NJOw
'Lužníce' (x *poluluteopurpurea*) (7) — NMen
macedonica — see *S. juniperifolia*
'Magdalena' (x *thomasiana*) (7) — NMen
'Major' (*cochlearis*) (8) ♀H4 — LRHS WGor
§ 'Maréchal Joffre' (15) — LAst NEgg NPri
'Margaret Webster' (*trifurcata*) (15/v) — MAvo
'Margarete' (x *borisii*) (7) — CLyd NMen
marginata (7) — CLyd LFox WAbe
- var. **balcanica** — see *S. marginata* var. *rocheliana*
- var. **boryi** (7) — CLyd EPot LRHS NMen
- var. **coriophylla** (7) — EPot NMen NWCA WAbe
- var. **karadzicensis** — see *S. karadzicensis*
§ - var. **rocheliana** (7) — CLyd EPot LRHS NMen SAga
- - 'Balkan' (7) — CLyd
'Maria Callas' (x *poluanglica*) (7) — CLyd WGor
'Maria Luisa' (x *salmonica*) (7) — GCrs LFox NDlv NMen NWCA WAbe
'Marianna' (x *borisii*) (7) — CLyd CStu NDlv NMen NRya
'Marie Louise' — CFee
'Maroon Beauty' (*stolonifera*) (5) — EBee ECtt EMan EMar MDKP NBre WCot
'Mars' (x *elisabethae*) (7) — NMen
'Marshal Joffre' (15) — see *S.* 'Maréchal Joffre' (15)
§ 'Martha' (x *semmleri*) (7) — CLyd NMen
'Mary Golds' (Swing Group) (7) — CLyd WGor
matta-florida (7) — NMen
'May Queen' (7) — NMen
x **megaseiflora** *sensu stricto* hort. — see *S.* 'Robin Hood'
'Melrose' (x *salmonica*) (7) — NMen
mertensiana (6) — CLyd NBir WCru
'Meteor' (7) — CStu NDlv NJOw NRya
micranthidifolia (4) — CLAP EBee WPGP
'Millstream' (8) **new** — NWCA
'Millstream Cream' (x *elisabethae*) (7) — CLyd NJOw NMen
§ 'Miluj Mne' (x *poluanglica*) (7) — CStu ECho EHyt LFox NDlv NLAp WAbe
'Minnehaha' (x *elisabethae*) (7) — WAbe
'Minor' (*cochlearis*) (8) ♀H4 — EAEE EHyt EPot LFox LRHS NHol NMen NWCA SIng WGor WPat
§ 'Miss Chambers' (x *urbium*) (11) — EMan MWgw SUsu WCot WMoo WSHC
'Mona Lisa' (x *borisii*) (7) — CLyd NMen WAbe WPat
'Monarch' (8) ♀H4 — GCrs WAbe

§ 'Mondscheinsonate' (x *boydii*) (7) — NHol

'Moonlight' — see S. 'Sulphurea'

'Moonlight Sonata' (x *boydii*) — see S. 'Mondscheinsonate'

moorcroftiana (1) **new** CC 4630 — GKev

'Morava' (7) **new** — NMen

moschata — see S. *exarata* subsp. *moschata*

'Mossy Pink' **new** — NBlu

'Mossy Triumph' — GAbr NEgg

'Mother of Pearl' (x *irvingii*) (7) — CLyd ECho NDlv NLAp NMen

'Mother Queen' (x *irvingii*) (7) — CLyd NHol NLAp NMen WPat

'Mount Nachi' (*fortunei*) (5) — CBct CDes CLyd CWCL EBee EBrs EMar EPfP EWes GAbr GEdr GMaP IBal LRHS MSte NBhm NBro NMen NMyG SPla SPoG WAbe WCot WFar WOld WPGP WPer

§ 'Mrs Gertie Prichard' (x *megaseiflora*) (7) — LFox NHol NMen WAbe

'Mrs Helen Terry' (x *salmonica*) (7) — CLyd EPot LRHS NDlv NMen

'Mrs Leng' (x *elisabethae*) (7) — MDKP NMen

'Multipunctata' (*paniculata*) (8) **new** — CStu

mutata (9) — CLyd

'Myra' (x *anglica*) (7) — CLyd LFox LRHS NHol NMen NWCA WHoo WPat

'Myra Cambria' (x *anglica*) (7) — NDlv NHol NMen WAbe

'Myriad' (7) — CLyd NMen

'Nancye' (x *goringiana*) (7) — CLyd EHyt EPot ITim NDlv NLAp NMen WAbe

§ ***nelsoniana*** (4) — NHol NJOw

'Nimbus' (*iranica*) (7) — CLyd NMen WAbe

'Niobe' (x *pulvilacina*) (7) — CLyd EHyt NMen

'Notata' (*paniculata*) (8) — NLAp

'Nottingham Gold' (x *boydii*) (7) — CLyd EPot ITim NHol NJOw NMen

'Obristii' (x *salmonica*) (7) — NDlv NHol NMen NRya

§ ***obtusa*** (7) — EPot NMen

'Ochroleuca' (x *elisabethae*) — NMen WAbe

'Odysseus' (*sancta*) (7) — NMen

'Olymp' (*scardica*) (7) — NMen

'Opalescent' (7) — CLyd LFox NJOw NMen

§ 'Ophelia' (x *arco-valleyi*) (7) — NHol NMen

oppositifolia (7) — ECho MBNS MHer MOne NLAp NSla SPlb SPoG SRms WAbe

I - 'Holden Variety' **new** — NHol

- 'Iceland' (7) — EHyt WAbe

- 'Le Bourg d'Oisans' — EHyt EPot

* - subsp. ***oppositifolia*** var. *latina* (7) — CLyd ECho EPot GCrs NLAp

oppositifolia x ***biflora*** — see S. x *kochii*

'Oriole' (x *boydii*) (7) — NMen

'Orjen' (*paniculata* var. *orientalis*) (8) — GEdr

'Oxhill' (7) — ITim NMen

§ ***paniculata*** (8) — CNic ECho EPot EPyc GGar GKev LRHS MDKP MHer MWat NDlv NLAp NSla SPlb SRms WAbe WFar WHoo

§ - subsp. ***cartilaginea*** (8) — NHol SBla WAbe

- subsp. ***kolenatiana*** — see S. *paniculata* subsp. *cartilaginea*

§ - var. ***minutifolia*** — CLyd CPBP CTri EHyt LFox LRHS MBar MWat NBro NDlv NHol NLAp NMen NRya NWCA SBla SPlb SPoG

paradoxa (15) — EPot GEdr LRHS NHol SBla WGor

'Parcevalis' (x *finnisiae*) (7x9) — CLyd WAbe

'Parsee' (x *margoxiana*) (7) — CStu NDlv NJOw NMen

x ***patens*** (8x9) — NJOw

§ 'Paula' (x *paulinae*) (7) — NMen

'Peach Blossom' (7) — CLyd EPot GCrs LRHS NDlv NMen NRya

'Peach Melba' (7) — CLyd CPBP CStu EPot NMen WAbe

'Pearl Rose' (x *anglica*) (7) — LFox

'Pearly Gates' (x *irvingii*) (7) — CLyd NDlv NMen

'Pearly Gold' (15) — CMea LRHS NRya

'Pearly King' (15) — GKev LRHS MHer WAbe WFar

'Pearly King' variegated (v) (15) — NHol

x ***pectinata*** Schott, Nyman & Kotschy (8) — see S. 'Krain'

pedemontana subsp. ***cymosa*** (15) **new** — NWCA

* - from Mount Kasbak (15) — CLyd

'Penelope' (x *boydilacina*) (7) — CLyd CMea CStu EAEE ECho EPot LRHS NHol NMen WAbe WHoo WPat

pensylvanica (4) — GCal

'Perikles' (7) — NMen

'Peter Burrow' (x *poluanglica*) (7) — CLyd CPBP ECho EHyt NLAp NMen NWCA ♀H4

'Peter Pan' (15) — CWCL EPfP EPot LFox MHer NHol NMen NPro NRya SIng SPoG WFar WPat WPnn

'Petra' (7) — CLyd EPot NHol NJOw NMen WAbe

x ***petraschii*** (7) — CLyd

§ 'Phoenix' (x *biasolettoi*) (7) — EAEE EHyt LRHS WAbe

'Pilatus' (x *boydii*) (7) — NMen

'Pink Cloud' (*fortunei*) (5) — WAbe

'Pink Haze' (*fortunei*) (5) — WAbe

'Pink Mist' (*fortunei*) (5) — WAbe

'Pink Pagoda' (*nipponica*) (5) — CLAP GEdr WCru

'Pink Pearl' (7) — CMea NMen

'Pixie' (15) — CTri ECtt LRHS NHol NMen SIng SPoG SRms

'Pixie Alba' — see S. 'White Pixie'

'Plena' (*granulata*) — see S. 'Flore Pleno'

'Pollux' (x *boydii*) (7) — EPot NHol NMen

poluniniana (7) — CLyd GCrs LFox NHol WAbe

poluniniana x 'Winifred' — CLyd ECho EPot

'Pompadour' (15) — LRHS

'Popelka' (*marginata*) (7) — CLyd

porophylla (7) — GCrs GKev NMen

- var. ***thessalica*** — see S. *sempervivum* f. *stenophylla*

aff. ***porophylla*** (7) — NWCA

'Portae' (x *fritschiana*) (8) — NJOw

'Primrose Bee' (x *apiculata*) (7) — EPot ITim

'Primrose Dame' (x *elisabethae*) (7) — ITim MDKP NHol NMen WAbe

'Primulaize' (9x11) — CLyd EWin MHer NMen

'Primulaize Salmon' (9x11) — MWgw NDlv NHol WHoo WPer

§ 'Primulina' (x *malbyana*) (7) — LFox NMen

primuloides — see S. 'Primuloides'

§ 'Primuloides' (*umbrosa*) (11) ♀H4 — ECho LFox NPri SPoG SRms SWvt WEas

'Prince Hal' (*burseriana*) (7) — CLyd EAEE ECho EPot LRHS NDlv NJOw NLAp NMen

'Princess' (*burseriana*) (7) — CLyd EAEE EHyt LRHS NJOw NMen

'Probynii' (*cochlearis*) (8) — EPot MWat NDlv NMen WAbe

'Prometheus' (x *prossenii*) (7) — CLyd

'Prospero' (x *petraschii*) (7) — NMen

x ***prossenii*** sensu stricto hort. — see S. 'Regina'

x *proximae* 'Slzy Coventry' **new** — CPBP

§ 'Pseudoborisii' (x *borisii*) (7) — EPot

'Pseudofranzii' (x *paulinae*) (7) — NWCA

x *pseudokotschyi* *sensu stricto* hort. — see S. 'Denisa'

'Pseudopungens' (x *apiculata*) (7) — EPot

'Pseudoscardica' (x *wehrhahnii*) (7) — NMen

'Pseudovaldensis' (*cochlearis*) (8) — CNic NHar WAbe

pubescens (15) — WAbe
- subsp. *iratiana* (15) — EPot NLAp

punctata (4) — see S. *nelsoniana*

'Pungens' (x *apiculata*) (7) — NDlv NHol NJOw NMen
'Purple Piggy' (*epiphylla*) (5) — CFee CLAP WCru

'Purpurea' (*fortunei*) — see S. 'Rubrifolia'
'Purpurteppich' (15) — WPer

§ 'Pygmalion' (x *wehrii*) (7) — CLyd NHol WAbe WGor
'Pyramidalis' (*cotyledon*) (8) — EPfP EWTr SRms
'Pyrenaica' (*oppositifolia*) (7) — ECho NMen

'Quarry Wood' (x *anglica*) (7) — CLyd NHol NMen

'Rainsley Seedling' (8) — EPot GKev NBro NMen
ramulosa (7) — NMen
'Red Poll' (x *poluanglica*) (7) — CLyd CPBP EHyt EPot NDlv NMen NRya NWCA WAbe

§ 'Regina' (x *prossenii*) (7) — CLyd MHer NMen
retusa (7) — CLyd NMen NSla WAbe
'Rex' (*paniculata*) (8) — EHyt EPot NHol

§ 'Riverslea' (x *hornibrookii*) (7) — LFox LRHS NHol NMen WAbe

§ 'Robin Hood' (x *megaseiflora*) (7) — CFee CLyd CPBP EPot LFox LRHS NHol NMen SBla WAbe WHoo WPat

'Rokujō' (*fortunei*) (5) — CLAP EBee NLar NPro WFar WTMC

'Romeo' (x *hornibrookii*) (7) — CLyd NMen

'Rosea' (*cortusifolia*) (5) — CLAP

§ 'Rosea' (*paniculata*) (8) — LBMP LBee NBro NDlv NHol NSla ♀H4 — SBla SRms WTel
'Rosea' (x *stuartii*) (7) — NDlv NMen
'Rosemarie' (x *anglica*) (7) — CLyd ECho NHol NMen
'Rosenzwerg' (15) — LRHS NMen
'Rosina Sündermann' (x *rosinae*) (7) — EPot NDlv

rotundifolia (12) — CLyd EBee MDKP NHol
- subsp. *chrysospleniifolia* var. *rhodopea* (12) — WCru

'Roy Clutterbuck' (7) — NMen
'Rubella' (x *irvingii*) (7) — CLyd

§ 'Rubrifolia' (*fortunei*) (5) — More than 30 suppliers
* 'Ruby Red' — NPro
'Ruby Wedding' (*cortusifolia*) (5) — WCru

rufescens (5) — GEdr
- BWJ 7510 — WCru
- BWJ 7684 — WCru
'Rusalka' (x *borisii*) (7) — CLyd NMen
'Russell Vincent Prichard' (x *irvingii*) (7) — NMen
'Ruth Draper' (*oppositifolia*) (7) — WAbe
'Ruth McConnell' (15) — CMea LRHS
'Sabrina' (x *fallsvillagensis*) (7) — CLyd
'Saint John's' (8) — EBur ECho GEdr NJOw WAbe
'Saint Kilda' (*oppositifolia*) (7) — GCrs ITim

x *salmonica* *sensu stricto* hort. — see S. 'Salomonii'

§ 'Salomonii' (x *salmonica*) (7) — CLyd GKev NDlv NMen SRms

'Samo' (x *bertolonii*) (7) — CLyd NMen

§ *sancta* (7) — CLyd ECho EPot LFox LRHS NMen SRms
- subsp. *pseudosancta* (7) — see S. *juniperifolia*
- - var. *macedonica* — see S. *juniperifolia*
'Sandpiper' (7) — NMen
'Sanguinea Superba' (x *arendsii*) (15) ♀H4 — SIng

'Sara Sinclair' (x *arco-valleyi*) (7) — CMea
'Šárka' (7) **new** — NMen

sarmentosa — see S. *stolonifera*
'Sartorii' — see S. 'Pygmalion'
'Saturn' (x *megaseiflora*) (7) — NHol NMen WAbe
'Sázava' (x *poluluteopurpurea*) (7) — CLyd NMen WAbe

scardica (7) — NBro NMen
- var. *dalmatica* — see S. *obtusa*
- f. *erythrantha* (7) — CLyd
- subsp. *korabensis* (7) — GCrs
- var. *obtusa* — see S. *obtusa*

§ 'Schelleri' (x *petraschii*) (7) — EHyt NJOw NMen
'Schneeteppich' (15) — WPer

§ 'Schwefelblüte' (15) — EAEE LRHS NJOw NPri NWCA SPoG WPat

scleropoda (7) — EPot NMen

§ 'Seaspray' (x *arendsii*) (15/v) — EWes
'Seissera' (*burseriana*) (7) — EPot NMen
'Semafor' (x *megaseiflora*) (7) **new** — NMen

x *semmleri* *sensu stricto* hort. — see S. 'Martha'

sempervivum (7) — CLyd LFox NGdn NMen NSla NWCA WTin

§ - f. *stenophylla* (7) — ECho MHer
sendaica (5) — CLAP WCru
- B&SWJ 7448 — GEdr
'Sendtneri' (8) — WAbe

§ 'Silver Cushion' (15/v) — CMea CTri EAEE ELan EPfP LAst LRHS MBar NBlu NHol NJOw SMer SPlb SPoG WAbe

'Silver Edge' (x *arco-valleyi*) (7) — NMen WAbe

§ (Silver Farreri Group) 'Snowflake' (8) ♀H4 — CNic NDlv

'Silver Maid' (x *engleri*) (7) — NMen SOkd WAbe
'Silver Mound' — see S. 'Silver Cushion'
'Sir Douglas Haig' (15) — SIng
'Slack's Ruby Southside' ♀H4 **new** — NSla WAbe WFar
'Snowcap' (*pubescens*) (15) — EHyt NDlv NWCA
'Snowdon' (*burseriana*) (7) — NMen
'Snowflake' — see S. (Silver Farreri Group) 'Snowflake'

§ 'Sofia' (x *borisii*) (7) — EPot LFox
'Sorrento' (*marginata*) (7) — NMen

§ 'Southside Seedling' (8) ♀H4 — CLyd ECho EPfP GAbr GCrs GEdr GGar GKev GMaP IHMH LHop LRHS MAvo MBar NBro NHol NJOw NMen NPri NRya NWCA SIng SPet SPoG SRms WHoo WLin WPat WTin

'Southside Star' ♀H4 **new** — WAbe WFar
'Spartakus' (x *apiculata*) — NDlv

spathularis (11) — CEnt EBee MHar WCot WEas
'Speciosa' (*burseriana*) (7) — NDlv

'Splendens' (*oppositifolia*) (7) ♀H4 — ECho EHyt ELan EPfP LFox NDlv NHol NLAp SBla SRms WAbe WPat

* 'Spotted Dog' — GEdr NHar

'Sprite' (15) — LRHS NPri SPoG

spruneri (7) — LRHS NMen SIng

- var. *deorum* (7) — NMen

'Stansfieldii' (*rosacea*) (15) — LRHS NHol NJOw NMen SPlb WFar

§ 'Stella' (x *stormonthii*) (7) — SBla

stenophylla subsp. *stenophylla* — see *S. flagellaris*

stolitzkae (7) — EPot ITim NMen NWCA WAbe

§ *stolonifera* (5) ♀H2 — CArn CCVN CEnt CHEx CHal CSpe EBee ECho EWTr GBin LDai MHar NBro SDix SIng SWvt WEas WFar WMoo WPnn

'Stormonth's Variety' — see *S.* 'Stella'

stribrnyi (7) — NMen

- JCA 861-400 — NWCA

'Sturmiana' (*paniculata*) (8) — NMen SRms

'Suendermannii' (x *kellereri*) (7) — EAEE NDlv SIng

'Suendermannii Major' (x *kellereri*) (7) — CLyd LRHS NRya

'Sugar Plum Fairy' (*fortunei*) (5) — CBcs CBct CLAP EBee EChP EHrv EMil GSki LAst MBNS NBro NCGa SPoG WCot WTMC

§ 'Sulphurea' (x *boydii*) (7) — CNic CStu EAEE LFox LRHS NHol NMen SIng WAbe WHoo WPat

'Sun Dance' (x *boydii*) (7) — NHol

'Sunset' (*anglica*) (7) — WThu

'Superba' (*callosa* subsp. *callosa* var. *australis*) (8) ♀H4 — GCrs

'Swan' (x *fallsvillagensis*) (7) — NMen

'Sylva' (x *elisabethae*) (7) — NMen

'Symons-Jeunei' (8) — WAbe

'Tábor' (x *schottii*) (7) — NMen

'Tamayura' (*fortunei*) (5) — CBct EBee LSou MBNS NCGa

'Theoden' (*oppositifolia*) (7) ♀H4 — CLyd CMea ECho EHyt EWes GCrs NJOw NLAp NWCA SBla WAbe

'Theresia' (x *mariae-theresiae*) (7) — NDlv NMen

'Thorpei' (7) — NMen

'Timmy Foster' (x *irvingii*) (7) — CLyd NHol NMen

tombeanensis (7) — CLyd NMen

'Tricolor' (*stolonifera*) (5) ♀H2 — CBow EBak LRHS WFar

trifurcata (15) — GGar

'Triumph' (x *arendsii*) (15) — ECtt LRHS NEgg NPri SBla WBVN

'Tully' (x *elisabethae*) (7) — NHol WGor WPat

'Tumbling Waters' (8) ♀H4 — EAEE EBee ECho EPot GAbr LHop LRHS NHol NLAp NMen NSla SIng WAbe WGor WPat

§ 'Tvůj Den' (x *poluanglica*) (7) — NDlv NMen WAbe

§ 'Tvůj Píseň' (x *poluanglica*) (7) — CLyd GKev NDlv NLAp

§ 'Tvůj Polibek' (x *poluanglica*) (7) — ECho EHyt MDKP NDlv NLAp NMen SBla WAbe

§ 'Tvůj Přítel' (x *poluanglica*) (7) — ECho NDlv NLAp

§ 'Tvůj Úspěch' (x *poluanglica*) (7) — CLyd ECho EHyt NDlv NLAp NMen SBla WAbe

§ 'Tvůj Úsmev' (x *poluanglica*) (7) — CLyd CPBP NDlv NLAp NMen

'Tycho Brahe' (x *doerfleri*) (7) — CLyd NDlv NMen WAbe

'Tysoe' (7) — CLyd ITim NMen

umbrosa (11) — CBrm EBee ECho ENot LRHS MRav SPer SPlb SRms SWvt WCAu WHen WMoo

- 'Aurea' — see *S.* 'Aureopunctata'

- var. *primuloides* — see *S.* 'Primuloides'

'Unique' — see *S.* 'Bodensee'

x *urbium* (11) ♀H4 — CHEx EAEE EBee ECho ELan EPfP LAst LEdu MWgw NSti SPet SRms WBrk WCFE WFar WPer

- *primuloides* 'Elliott's Variety' — see *S.* 'Clarence Elliott'

'Vaccariana' (*oppositifolia*) (7) — ECho NHol

'Václav Hollar' (x *gusmusii*) — NMen

'Vahlii' (x *smithii*) (7) — NMen

'Valborg' — see *S.* 'Cranbourne'

'Valentine' — see *S.* 'Cranbourne'

'Valerie Finnis' — see *S.* 'Aretiastrum'

I 'Variegata' (*cuneifolia*) (11/v) — ECho ECtt EPfP GGar IHMH MBar NBlu NEgg NVic SHFr SPet SPlb SPoG WFar WMoo WPer WTel

'Variegata' (*umbrosa*) — see *S.* 'Aureopunctata'

I 'Variegata' (x *urbium*) (11/v) — EAEE EBee ECho EPfP GGar LAst LRHS MRav NFor NLar NSti NVic SRms SSto WBrk WEas WFar

vayredana (15) — GCrs NWCA WAbe

veitchiana (5) — GEdr NBro WCru

'Vesna' (x *borisii*) (7) — CLyd NHol NJOw NMen WAbe

'Vincent van Gogh' (x *borisii*) — CLyd NHol NMen

'Vladana' (x *megaseiflora*) (7) — CLyd CPBP EPot NHol NJOw NMen SIng WAbe

'Vlasta' (7) — CLyd NMen

'Vltava' (7) — CLyd EPot NMen

'Volgeri' (x *hofmannii*) (7) — CLyd

'Vreny' (8) — GKev

'W.A. Clark' (*oppositifolia*) (7) — WAbe

'Wada' (*fortunei*) (5) — CAbP CBcs CBct CDes CHar CLAP EBee EChP ECtt GEdr GKev LAst MBri MDun MSte NBir NMyG NPri SPer SPoG WBor WCot WFar WOld WPGP WTMC WWeb

§ 'Wallacei' (15) — NMen

§ 'Walpole's Variety' (8) — CBrm WAbe WPer

§ 'Walter Ingwersen' (*umbrosa*) (11) — SIng SRms

§ 'Walter Irving' (x *irvingii*) (7) — CLyd EPot ITim LRHS NHol NMen

'Weisser Zwerg' (15) — WAbe

'Wellesbourne' (x *abingdonensis*) (7) — CLyd

'Welsh Dragon' (15) — WAbe

'Welsh Red' (15) — WAbe

'Welsh Rose' (15) — WAbe

wendelboi (7) — CLyd EHyt LFox NMen

'Wendrush' (x *wendelacina*) (7) — CLyd NMen WAbe

'Wendy' (x *wendelacina*) (7) — NMen WAbe

'Wetterhorn' (*oppositifolia*) (7) — CLyd

'Wheatley Lion' (x *borisii*) — NMen

'Wheatley Rose' (7) — CLyd EAEE ITim LRHS NHol NHol NMen

'White Cap' (x *boydii*) (7) — NHol NMen

§ 'White Pixie' (15) — CLyd ECtt EPfP LFox LRHS MHer NHol NJOw NPri NPro NRya SBla SIng SPlb SPoG SRms WFar

'White Star' (x *petraschii*) — see *S.* 'Schelleri'

'Whitehill' (8) ♀H4 — CLyd CMea ECho ELan GEdr GMaP LBee LFox LRHS MWgw NBro NHol NLAp NMen SPet WFar WHoo WPat WPer WTin

§ 'Wilhelm Tell' (x *malbyana*) (7) — NMen

'William Boyd' (x *boydii*) (7) — NSla WAbe

'Winifred' (x *anglica*) (7) — CLyd ECho EPot GCrs LFox NLAp NMen WAbe

'Winifred Bevington' CLyd ECho EPot GKev LBee LRHS
  (8x11) ♀H4 MMuc NBro NDlv NHol NJOw
  NLAp NMen NPri NRya SAga
  WAbe WFar WHoo WLin WPer
  WPnn
'Winston Churchill' (15) EPfP LRHS NHol NPri SIng
I 'Winston Churchill Alba' NPri
'Winton' (x *paulinae*) (7) CLyd NMen
'Wisley' (*federici-augusti* CNic NLAp NMen SIng WPat
  subsp. *grisebachii*)
  (7) ♀H2-3
'Wisley Primrose' see *S.* 'Kolbiana'
'Yellow Rock' (7) NDlv NRya
Your Day see *S.* 'Tvůj Den'
Your Friend see *S.* 'Tvůj Přítel'
Your Good Fortune see *S.* 'Tvůj Úspěch'
Your Kiss see *S.* 'Tvůj Políbek'
Your Smile see *S.* 'Tvůj Úsmev'
Your Song see *S.* 'Tvůj Píseň'
Your Success see *S.* 'Tvůj Úspěch'
x *zimmeteri* (8x11) CLyd ECho NMen
§ 'Zlatá Praha' (x *pragensis*) CLyd EPot NDlv NMen NRya WAbe
  (7)
'Zlin' (x *leyboldii*) (7) NMen

Scabiosa (Dipsacaceae)

africana CElw EWes LSou
'Agnes Whitfield' EBee EChP EWin
alpina L. see *Cephalaria alpina*
argentea CKno EWes SMHy SUsu WPGP
atropurpurea CEnt CHrt EGoo GKev LEdu
  SPav
- 'Ace of Spades' CDes CHad CSpe CWCL EBee
  EChP LRHS MBri MDun SMad SPav
  SPoG WPGP
§ - 'Chile Black' More than 30 suppliers
§ - 'Chilli Pepper'PBR CWCL EMan ENot EPfP LBmB
  LHop LIck NLar NPri SAga SPoG
  SRGP SUsu
§ - 'Chilli Red' SAga
§ - 'Chilli Sauce'PBR CBcs CHar CWCL EBee EMan
  ENot EPfP LBmB LHop LIck NLar
  NPri SUsu WCMO
- dark-flowered SPav
§ - subsp. *maritima* EBee
- 'Mixed Chile' SUsu
- 'Nona' **new** LTwo
- 'Peter Ray' CElw ECtt MSph SPav WWlt
- 'Salmon Queen' **new** NBre
banatica see *S. columbaria*
'Burgundy Bonnets' LRHS
§ 'Butterfly Blue' EBee EPfP IHMH LRHS LSRN MBri
  NLar NMoo NRnb SCoo SHBN
  SMrm SPer SPla SPoG SWvt WAul
  WCAu WFar WWhi
caucasica CWCL EPfP GKev LAst LEdu NBlu
  WFar WHoo
- var. *alba* CKno EHrv EPfP WFar WHal
  WHoo
- 'Blausiegel' CSam EBee EChP LAst LBMP LRHS
  MTis NBre NCGa NFla NGdn SPet
  SPla SPoG WFWP
- 'Clive Greaves' ♀H4 CBcs CHar CWCL EBee ECha EHrv
  ELan EPfP ERou LHop LRHS MBri
  MWat MWgw NCob NFor SGar
  SPer SPet SPla SRGP SRms SWvt
  WAul WCMO WCot WEas WFar
  WMnd WWeb
- 'Fama' CMdw CSim CSpe CWCL CWib
  EKen EMan EShb LPhx MBNS
  MWrn NBPC NBir NLar SPlb SPoG
  SRms WFar WHil WPtf
- 'Goldingensis' CWCL GMac GWCH MBNS MHer
  NBPC NBre NGdn NPri WBVN
  WPer
- House's hybrids CSBt NGdn NVic SRms

- 'Isaac House' NEgg NLar
- 'Kompliment' CSim ENot LRHS MWgw NBre
  NChi NEgg NLar WHil WHoo
- 'Lavender Blue' WFar WGwG
- 'Miss Willmott' ♀H4 CHad CMMP CSam EBee EChP
  ECha ELan EPfP ERou LAst LHop
  LRHS MBri MHer MLHP MWat
  MWgw NCGa NCob SPer SPet SPla
  SPoG SWvt WAul WCAu WFar
  WMnd
- 'Moerheim Blue' ERou NGby
- 'Nachtfalter' EBee
- Perfecta Series CSpe CWib EBee EChP LAst LRHS
  MMHG MWgw NGdn NLar SMrm
  SWat
- - 'Perfecta Alba' COlW CSpe CWib EBee EChP
  EMan GMaP GMac LAst MWat
  NChi NLar NOrc NPri NRnb SHGN
  SMrm STes SWat WHil WPtf
- - 'Perfecta Lilac Blue' CWib GMaP GMac NRnb STes
  WCot
- 'Stäfa' CKno CMMP EBee ERou EShb
  LRHS MBri MMHG NCGa NLar
  SBla SPet SPla SUsu WAul WFar
  WMnd
'Chile Black' see *S. atropurpurea* 'Chile Black'
'Chile Pepper'PBR see *S. atropurpurea* 'Chilli Pepper'
'Chile Red' see *S. atropurpurea* 'Chilli Red'
'Chile Sauce'PBR see *S. atropurpurea* 'Chilli Sauce'
'Chile Spice' **new** CHar SRGP WHlf
cinerea CSec LPhx
§ *columbaria* CBgR EBee ECGP MLLN MWgw
  NBre NLan NMir NSco NWCA
  SMrm SWal WHer WJek WSFF
* - *alpina* CSec
- 'Flower Power' EBee
- 'Misty Butterflies' CSam ENot EShb GBri GSki
  MWgw NBHF NGdn NJOw NLar
  NMoo NVic SHBN SPoG
- 'Nana' CBrm CMdw CWCL EBee EGoo
  EShb GEdr GSki IBal NBir NCGa
  NGdn NLar NMen NPri SMar
  WCFE WGwG WHil WMow
§ - subsp. *ochroleuca* More than 30 suppliers
- - MESE 344 EBee
- - var. *webbiana* SUsu
- 'Pincushion Pink' **new** NBHF NGdn NPri WHil
cretica XPep
drakensbergensis CDMG CFis EBee EKen EMan
  LPhx LSou MTPN SHar SPav STes
  WCMO WHrl WLin
farinosa CDes EBee LSou MHar SGar WFar
  WPer
gigantea see *Cephalaria gigantea*
graminifolia ECho EDAr EGoo EHol GBuc LPhx
  LRHS MDKP NBir NMen NRnb
  NWCA SBch SRms
- *rosea* EWes
'Helen Dillon' CBgR CFir CSam EBee EMan EWes
  EWin LSou SHBN WWhi
hymnettia XPep
incisa EShb
'Irish Perpetual Flowering' EMan NDov WCot
japonica MGol NEgg WPer
- var. *acutiloba* NDov
- var. *alpina* CPrp CSec EBee EChP EMag GAbr
  GBuc GKev GSki IBal MLLN NGdn
  SHGN SPet WHoo WTin
- 'Blue Diamonds' IBal WHil
lucida EAEE EBee EBrs EChP ECho EPfP
  EShb LRHS MRav NHol NJOw
  NLAp NPri SBla SPet WCAu WMnd
  WPGP WPat WPer
maritima see *S. atropurpurea* subsp.
  maritima
'Midnight' CMea CSpe

'Miss Havisham' — EBee ECtt EMan EWes LEdu LSou WPGP
montana Mill. — see *Knautia arvensis*
montana (Bieb.) DC. — see *Knautia tatarica*
ochroleuca — see *S. columbaria* subsp. *ochroleuca*
parnassi — see *Pterocephalus perennis*
'Peggotty' — EBee EChP EWin
'Pink Buttons' — CFir CKno EAEE EBee LRHS MBNS NEgg NFla SPet SPla
'Pink Mist'[PBR] — EBee EPfP LRHS MBri NBir NEgg NLar SCoo SHBN SPer SPoG SRms WCAu
prolifera — LPhx
pterocephala — see *Pterocephalus perennis*
'Rosie's Pink' — ECtt EGra EMan SMrm
rumelica — see *Knautia macedonica*
'Satchmo' — see *S. atropurpurea* 'Chile Black'
songarica JJ&JH 90/216 — EBee
succisa — see *Succisa pratensis*
tatarica — see *Cephalaria gigantea*
tenuis — CSpe LPhx NDov SHar
triandra — EBee LEdu SUsu
ucranica — EShb LEdu WOut XPep

Scadoxus ✿ (*Amaryllidaceae*)
multiflorus — LRHS MBri MOak WCot
§ - subsp. *katherinae* ♀H1 — ECho ERea
natalensis — see *S. puniceus*
§ *puniceus* — CDes ERea SYvo

Scaevola (*Goodeniaceae*)
aemula 'Blue Fan'[PBR] — see *S. aemula* 'Blue Wonder'
§ - 'Blue Wonder'[PBR] — LAst LSou MOak NPer SWvt
- 'New Wonder' — LAst
- 'Petite' — CHal
- 'Zig Zag'[PBR] — CCCN LAst LSou
Blauer Facher = 'Saphira'[PBR] — CCCN EWin NBlu
'Blue Yonder' **new** — LSou SVil
crassifolia — SPlb
'Diamond' — LSou SPoG
'My Blue' **new** — SVil
saligna Blue Ice = 'Danscaice'[PBR] — LAst

Scandix (*Apiaceae*)
pecten-veneris — MSal

Sceletium (*Aizoaceae*)
tortuosum — MGol

Schefflera (*Araliaceae*)
actinophylla ♀H1 — EBak SRms WMul
arboricola ♀H1 — CHEx SEND WMul XBlo
- B&SWJ 7040 — WCru
- 'Compacta' — MBri WMul
- 'Gold Capella' ♀H1 — LRHS MBri SEND XBlo
- 'Trinetta' — MBri
delavayi — CHEx WMul
digitata — CHEx
elegantissima ♀H1 — EShb SEND
gracilis HWJ 622 — WCru
hoi var. *fantsipanensis* B&SWJ 8228 — WCru
impressa — CHEx
- GWJ 9375 — WCru
microphylla B&SWJ 3872 — WCru
pueckleri — WMul
taiwaniana — CHEx
- B&SWJ 7096 — WCru

Schima (*Theaceae*)
argentea — see *S. wallichii* subsp. *noronhae* var. *superba*

§ *wallichii* subsp. *noronhae* var. *superba* — CBcs CCCN CPLG EPfP
- subsp. *wallichii* var. *khasiana* — ISea
* *yunnanensis* — GGGa

Schinus (*Anacardiaceae*)
molle — IDee XPep
polygamus — CBcs

Schisandra (*Schisandraceae*)
TH **new** — CHEx
arisanensis — NLar
- B&SWJ 3050 — WCru
aff. *bicolor* BWJ 8151 — WCru
chinensis — CAgr CArn CPIN EBee GPoy LEdu MSwo WBVN WNor WSHC
- B&SWJ 4204 — WCru
grandiflora — CDoC CPIN ECot ELan EPfP LRHS MBlu MWgw NLar SBrw SCoo
- B&SWJ 2245 — WCru
grandiflora x *rubriflora* — CPIN WCru
henryi subsp. *yunnanensis* B&SWJ 6546 — WCru
aff. *neglecta* BWJ 7739 **new** — WCru
nigra B&SWJ 5897 — WCru
propinqua var. *sinensis* — CPIN CSPN LEdu MBlu NLar SBrw WSHC
- - BWJ 8148 — WCru
rubriflora — CBrm CHEx CPIN CSPN CTri CWSG EPfP LRHS MAsh MBlu MDun MGos MWgw NRib NSti SBrw SHBN SSpi
- (m) — NHol
- (f) — CBcs ELan MGos SBra WSHC
- BWJ 7898 — WCru
sphenanthera — EBee ELan EMil EPfP IMGH LRHS MDun NLar WSHC
verrucosa HWJ 664 — WCru

Schivereckia (*Brassicaceae*)
doerfleri — CNic CSec

Schizachyrium (*Poaceae*)
§ *scoparium* — CBig CBrm CKno CSpe EBee EBrs EHoe EPPr GSki LRHS LRav MWhi NSti SUsu WDyG WGHP WMnd WWeb
- blue — LRav
- 'The Blues' — CBig

Schizanthus (*Solanaceae*)
porrigens **new** — CSpe

Schizocodon see *Shortia*

Schizolobium (*Caesalpiniaceae*)
excelsum — SBig

Schizophragma (*Hydrangeaceae*)
corylifolium — CBcs CPIN NLar
hydrangeoides — CBcs CDoC CPIN EBee ELan EPfP EWTr LRHS MBlu MDun MGos NPal SBra SBrw SHBN SLim SLon SMur SPer SPoG SSpi SSta SWvt WDin
- B&SWJ 5954 — WCru
- B&SWJ 6119 from Yakushima, Japan — WCru
- B&SWJ 8505 from Korea — WCru
- from Korea — NLar SBrw

- 'Brookside Littleleaf'	see *Hydrangea anomala* subsp. *petiolaris* var. *cordifolia* 'Brookside Littleleaf'
- 'Iwa Garami'	CBcs NLar
- 'Moonlight' (v)	More than 30 suppliers
* - f. *quelpartensis*	WCru
B&SWJ 1160	
- 'Roseum' ♀H4	More than 30 suppliers
integrifolium ♀H4	CBcs CMac CPlN EBee ELan EPfP LRHS NEgg NLar SBrw SDix SHBN SPer SSpi WPGP WSHC
- var. *fauriei*	CBcs NLar WSHC
- - B&SWJ 1701	WCru
- var. *molle*	CPlN
aff. *megalocarpum*	WCru
BWJ 8150	

Schizostachyum (Poaceae)
§ *funghomii*	EPla MMoz WJun WPGP

Schizostylis ✿ (Iridaceae)
§ *coccinea*	More than 30 suppliers
- f. *alba*	More than 30 suppliers
- 'Anne'	WHoo
- 'Ballyrogan Giant'	CFir CKno EBee ECho GBuc IBlr MAvo WPGP
- 'Cardinal'	MAvo WFar
- 'Cindy Towe'	EBee GBuc
- 'Countesse de Vere'	EBee
- 'Elburton Glow'	WFar WHoo
- 'Fenland Daybreak'	CBgR CHar CKno CPrp EAEE EBee EBrs EChP ECho ELan GMac IBal LIck LRHS MAvo MBnl MLan NCGa NCot NHol NLar SGar SPet SPla WFar WHil WHoo
- 'Gigantea'	see *S. coccinea* 'Major'
- 'Good White' **new**	MAvo
- 'Grandiflora'	see *S. coccinea* 'Major'
- 'Hilary Gould'	EBee EPPr GBuc MAvo NCGa SChr WFar WHal
- 'Hint of Pink'	MAvo MDKP WOut
- 'Jack Frost'	EBee WMoo
- 'Jennifer' ♀H4	More than 30 suppliers
- late-flowering	NBPC
- 'Maiden's Blush'	EBee EBrs ECGP EChP ECtt EGle EHrv GBuc LRHS MAvo MBnl MDKP MSte NCot NFla NLar WFar WMnd
§ - 'Major' ♀H4	More than 30 suppliers
* - 'Marietta'	MAvo
- 'Mollie Gould'	CStu EAEE EBee EHrv EKen EMar EShb LAst MAvo MBNS MMHG NBre NCGa NHol NLar SCoo SRGP WOut WPrP WTin
- 'Mrs Hegarty'	More than 30 suppliers
- 'November Cheer'	EBrs ECot IBlr LRHS MAvo MSte NBir NLar WFar
- 'Oregon Sunset'	EBee GBuc
- 'Pallida'	CAby CMil CPom CSam ECha EGra EHrv ELan GBuc MLHP MRav NBir NCot NLar WFar
- 'Professor Barnard'	CCCN CFee CFwr CHar CSpe ECho EShb GCal IBlr LAst MSte NBir SPla WFar WHil WOld WPnn
- 'Red Dragon'	EBee GBuc MAvo WFar
- 'Salmon Charm'	EBrs GBuc LRHS MAvo WFar
- 'Silver Pink'	IBlr
- 'Snow Maiden'	CAbP CElw GBuc GMac IBal LRHS MBNS SPav
- 'Strawberry'	SPav
- 'Strawberry Fair'	SMrm
§ - 'Sunrise' ♀H4	More than 30 suppliers
- 'Sunset'	see *S. coccinea* 'Sunrise'
- 'Tambara'	CMHG CMdw CPou CSam EHrv GBuc NLar WFar
- 'Viscountess Byng'	CBro CFwr CHea CTri CWCL EBee ECho EGle ERou GAbr GCal IBlr

	IGor LAst NLar SPav WFar WPer WWye
- 'Wilfred H. Bryant'	CBro CKno CPen CPrp CSpe EAEE EBee EKen EShb LAst LBMP MBnl MDKP NCGa NSti SCoo SPoG SUsu WHlf
- 'Zeal Salmon'	CAby CBro CFee CFir CPou EBee ECha EGle GAbr LHop MAvo NBir NHol SMHy WFar WMoo

Schoenoplectus (Cyperaceae)
§ *lacustris*	EMFW IHMH
§ - subsp. *tabernaemontani*	LNCo
- - 'Albescens' (v)	CDWL CKno CWat EBee EHon EMFW LNCo LPBA SWal SWat WCot WDyG WHal WPrP WWpP
- - 'Zebrinus' (v)	CBen CDWL CKno CWat EHon ELan EMFW EPfP LPBA NScw SPlb SWal SWat WCot WDyG WFar WHal WMAq WPnP WPrP WWpP
pungens	NBre

Schoenus (Cyperaceae)
pauciflorus	CBow CWCL EBee ECou EHoe EMan EPPr EWes MAvo NBro NOak SPoG WDyG WMoo WPGP WPrP

Schotia (Caesalpiniaceae)
afra	CKob
brachypetala	CKob

Schrebera (Oleaceae)
alata	CKob

Sciadopitys (Sciadopityaceae)
verticillata ♀H4	CBcs CDoC CDul CKen CTho EHul IDee LBee LCon LLin LPan LRHS MAsh MBar MBlu MBri MDun MGos SCoo SLim SPoG SWvt WDin WEve WFar WNor WOrn
- 'Firework'	CKen
- 'Globe'	CKen
- 'Gold Star'	CKen
- 'Goldammer' **new**	NLar
- 'Golden Pendula' **new**	WEve
- 'Golden Rush'	CKen ECho LCon LLin MAsh MGos NLar WEve
- 'Goldmahne'	CKen
- 'Grüne Kugel'	CKen ECho NLar SLim
- 'Jeddeloh Compact'	CKen
- 'Kugelblitz' **new**	WEve
- 'Kupferschirm'	CKen ECho
- 'Mecki'	CKen ECho LCon LLin WEve
- 'Megaschirm'	CKen
- 'Ossorio Gold'	CKen ECho WEve
- 'Picola'	CKen ECho NLar
- 'Pygmy'	CKen
- 'Richie's Cushion'	CKen ECho WEve
- 'Shorty'	CKen
- 'Speerspitze'	CKen
- 'Starburst'	CKen
- 'Sternschnuppe'	CDoC CKen ECho LCon LLin NLar SLim WEve

Scilla (Hyacinthaceae)
adlamii	see *Ledebouria cooperi*
x *allenii*	see x *Chionoscilla allenii*
amethystina	see *S. litardierei*
amoena	ECho WCot WShi
aristidis from Algeria	ECho
autumnalis	CAvo CNic CPom CStu ECho EPot ERos LRHS WShi
- AB&S 4305 from Morocco	CMon

- from Crete	ECho
- MS 771 from Crete	CMon
- subsp. *fallax*	ECho
bifolia ♀H4	CAvo CBgR CBro CFFs CPom CStu ECho EPot LLWP LPhx LRHS WRHF WShi
- 'Alba'	ECho LPhx LRHS
- 'Norman Stevens' **new**	SCnR
- 'Rosea'	ECho EPot LLWP LRHS
bithynica ♀H4	WShi
campanulata	see *Hyacinthoides hispanica*
chinensis	see *S. scilloides*
cilicica	CMon CStu
greilhuberi	CStu ECho ERos WAbe WCot
haemorrhoidalis	CMon
MS 923 from Tenerife	
hohenackeri	ERos WThu
- BSBE 811	CMon WCot
hyacinthoides	CMon ECho ERos WBVN WCot
ingridiae	ECho WWst
italica	see *Hyacinthoides italica*
japonica	see *S. scilloides*
kraussii	GIBF
latifolia from Morocco	ECho
- SF 25 from Morocco	CMon
libanotica	see *Puschkinia scilloides* var. *libanotica*
liliohyacinthus	CAvo CBro CRow EHyt IBlr MMHG SBch SSvw WWst
- 'Alba'	ERos
lingulata	CStu ECho ERos
- var. *ciliolata*	CBro ECho EPot ERos
- - SF 288 from Morocco	CMon
§ **litardierei** ♀H4	CAvo CFFs CPom CStu ECho EPPr EPot ERos GIBF LPhx LRHS MBri NMen WCot
- from Yugoslavia	CMon
madeirensis from Madeira	CMon
* **mauritanica alba**	CMon
- SF 65 from Morocco	CMon
melaina	WCot
messeniaca	CPom GIBF
- MS 38 from Greece	CMon WCot
§ **mischtschenkoana** ♀H4	CAvo CBro CFFs ECho EHyt EPot LRHS MBri SPer WBVN WDav
- 'Tubergeniana' ♀H4	CBgR CMea ECho GKev LPhx WCot
§ - 'Zwanenburg'	ECho
monophyllos	ECho
- S&B 184 from Portugal	CMon
- var. *tingitana*	ERos
morrisii	ERos
natalensis	CMon WCot WHil
non-scripta	see *Hyacinthoides non-scripta*
numidica	ECho
nutans	see *Hyacinthoides non-scripta*
obtusifolia	ECho
- AB&S 4410 from Morocco	CMon
persica ♀H4	CPom ECho ERos WCot
- BSBE 1054 from Iran	CMon
- JCA 0.876.501	WCot
peruviana	More than 30 suppliers
- S&L 285	WCot
- SB&L 20/1	WCot
- 'Alba'	CBcs CBro CFwr CMon CSWP CSpe CStu EBrs ECho MTho SMrm WCot
- var. *elegans* from Morocco	CMon
- from Spain	CMon
- var. *gattefossei* from Morocco	CMon

- 'Grand Bleu'	CFwr
* - var. *ifniensis*	WCot
- - from Morocco	CMon
- var. *venusta* S&L 311/2	WCot
- - from Morocco	CMon
pratensis	see *S. litardierei*
puschkinioides	ECho
ramburei	ECho
reverchonii	ERos WWst
- MS 418 from Spain	CMon
rosenii	ECho EHyt
§ **scilloides**	CBro ECho ERos GIBF SCnR SRot WCot
siberica ♀H4	CAvo CFFs EBrs ECho EPfP LRHS NBlu NJOw SBch SPer WPer WShi
- 'Alba'	CBro ECho EPfP EPot LHop LRHS SBch WShi
- subsp. *armena*	CHEx ECho
- 'Spring Beauty'	CBro CMdw CMea ECho EPot GKev IPot LHop LPhx LRHS MBri SRms
- var. *taurica*	ECho ERos
'Tubergeniana'	see *S. mischtschenkoana*
verna	CDes CNic ERos WHer WShi
vicentina	see *Hyacinthoides vicentina*
violacea	see *Ledebouria socialis*

Scindapsus (Araceae)

aureus	see *Epipremnum aureum*
pictus (v)	LRHS MBri

Scirpoides (Cyperaceae)

§ **holoschoenus**	CBig CRWN EBee

Scirpus (Cyperaceae)

angustifolius	LNCo
cernuus	see *Isolepis cernua*
cyperinus	WWpP
holoschoenus	see *Scirpoides holoschoenus*
lacustris	see *Schoenoplectus lacustris*
- 'Spiralis'	see *Juncus effusus* f. *spiralis*
maritimus	see *Bolboschoenus maritimus*
tabernaemontani	see *Schoenoplectus lacustris* subsp. *tabernaemontani*

Scleranthus (Illecebraceae)

biflorus	CTrC CWil ECho EDAr EWes NDlv NWCA SPlb WPer
perennis	ECho
singuliflorus	NHol
uniflorus	CLyd CTrC ECho EShb GAbr GEdr NHol NWCA SMad SPlb WPrP

Scoliopus (Trilliaceae)

bigelowii	CStu SCnR SOkd WFar WHal
hallii	EBee GCrs GEdr NMen SCnR SOkd WCru WWst

Scolopendrium see *Asplenium*

Scopola (Solanaceae)

anomala	CArn CPLG
carniolica	CArn CFir COld EBee EChP EGle ELan EMon GCal GPoy IBlr LEdu LPhx MAvo MBlu MPhe MSal MSte NChi NLar NSti SPlb WCru WPGP
§ - var. *brevifolia*	CAvo EBrs EHrv EPPr SDys WTin
- - WM 9811	MPhe
- subsp. *hladnikiana*	see *S. carniolica* var. *brevifolia*
- *podolica*	CAvo
- 'Zwanenburg'	CAvo EBee EHrv EPPr LPhx
lurida	see *Anisodus luridus*
physaloides	MSal
sinensis	see *Atropanthe sinensis*
stramoniifolia	CElw

Scorzonera (*Asteraceae*)

radiata	EBee
suberosa subsp. *cariensis*	EBee EHyt

Scrophularia (*Scrophulariaceae*)

aquatica	see *S. auriculata*
§ *auriculata*	ELau EPfP LPBA MHer MSal NMir NPer WHer WWpP WWye
§ - 'Variegata' (v)	CArn CBcs CBgR EAEE EBee EChP ECha ECtt EHoe ELan ENot EPfP ERou EWTr GCal LPBA LRHS MBri MDun MHer MRav MWgw NEgg NSti SDnm SPer SPlb SPoG SRms WFar
buergeriana	MSal
- 'Lemon and Lime' misapplied	see *Teucrium viscidum* 'Lemon and Lime'
californica **new**	EBee
calliantha	MDKP NJOw
chrysantha	NJOw
grandiflora	NBre WDyG WFar
marilandica	EBee
nodosa	CArn CRWN EBee ELau GPoy MSal NMir NSco WBri WHbs WHer WSel
- *tracheliodes*	CNat
- *variegata*	see *S. auriculata* 'Variegata'
scopolii	EBee

Scutellaria ✿ (*Lamiaceae*)

albida	EBee EPPr EWin
§ *alpina*	CPBP ECho EDAr EMan GCrs GEdr GKev LAst LBee LRHS NJOw SBla SMar SPlb SRms SRot WGor WPer
- 'Arcobaleno'	NLar SMar SPet
- 'Greencourt'	EBee
- 'Moonbeam'	EBrs GEdr SHGN
altissima	CArn CBgR CDMG EBee ECha EDAr ELan EMan EMar GBuc GKev MSal NBro NCGa NJOw NWCA SBod SPlb STes SYvo WCHb WPer WPtf
'Amazing Grace'	EChP EWes
baicalensis	CArn GPoy IBlr MSal NJOw SBla SPet SSvw WPer WPtf
barbata	MSal
brevibracteata subsp. *subvelutina* **new**	EBee
californica NNS 98-511	WCot
canescens	see *S. incana*
columnae	EBee IFro
diffusa	ECtt GKev WPer
formosana 'China Blue'	CAbP EPfP
galericulata	GPoy GWCH MHer MNHC MSal NVic WCHb WHer WJek WWye
hastata	see *S. hastifolia*
§ *hastifolia*	CTri ECho ECot ECtt EDAr EHyt NFor NSti WPer
§ *incana*	CPom CSam EBee ECGP EHrv ELan EMon LHop LPhx LRHS NDov NSti SMrm SSvw SUsu WCot WWye
indica	MSph WCFE
- var. *japonica*	see *S. indica* var. *parvifolia*
§ - var. *parvifolia*	CPBP CStu EBee EBur ECho EHyt EMan EWes LBee LRHS NWCA SBla SRot
- - 'Alba'	CPBP ECho EHyt ETow LBee LRHS LTwo SBla
lateriflora	CArn CBod CSec EBee ELau EOHP GBar GPoy LPhx MGol MSal NCGa WCHb WHbs WHer WJek WPer WSel WWye
maekawae	WPGP

- B&SWJ 557a	WCru
minor	WWye
nana var. *sapphirina*	GKev NWCA
novae-zelandiae	ECou EHyt LRHS NWCA
orientalis	CFis CMdw CPBP ECtt GEdr LRHS NLAp SBch SBla WLin WOut WPat
- subsp. *bicolor*	ECtt NWCA
- subsp. *carica*	WWye
- 'Eastern Star'	SPet
- 'Eastern Sun'	EBee
- subsp. *pectinata* **new**	ITim
- subsp. *pinnatifida*	EHyt GEdr LPhx NLar NWCA
pontica	CPBP CSec MAvo NJOw NLar SBch
prostrata	EMan LTwo NLAp
scordiifolia	CEnt CLyd CMea CMil CSam EBee ECha ECho IHMH NRya NWCA SBla SRms SUsu WFar WHal WHoo WTin WWye
- 'Seoul Sapphire'	EMan GBin GCrs LSou WBVN WCot WPtf
suffrutescens	XPep
- 'Texas Rose' **new**	SIng SRot
supina	see *S. alpina*
tournefortii	EChP ECtt LLWP
* *zhongdianensis* **new**	CEnt

seakale see *Crambe maritima*

Sebaea (*Gentianaceae*)

thomasii	GCrs WAbe

Securigera see *Coronilla*

Securinega (*Euphorbiaceae*)

suffruticosa	CBcs

Sedastrum see *Sedum*

Sedum ✿ (*Crassulaceae*)

B&SWJ 737	EGoo
NS 622	NWCA
§ 'Abbeydore'	CKno EBee EBrs ECGP EChP EGle EGoo EMan EMon EWsh NGby NSti WAbb WPGP WWeb
acre	CTri ECho ECot GPoy LAst LEdu MBar MHer MNHC NBlu SPlb XPep
- 'Aureum'	ECho EDAr EPfP IHMH LAst MBar MOne NBlu NLar SPer SPoG WFar WPat
- 'Elegans'	ECtt NJOw
§ - var. *majus*	CNic
- 'Minus'	ECho EDAr
adolphi	EPfP
'African Pearl' **new**	NBPC
'African Sunset' **new**	CElw EBee EPfP NCGa
§ *aizoon*	EAro EBee ECho LAst NBre SIde SPlb WBVN
- 'Aurantiacum'	see *S. aizoon* 'Euphorbioides'
§ - 'Euphorbioides'	CMea CWCL EAEE EBee ECha ECtt EGoo ELan LDai LRHS MBNS MHer MRav MWgw NLar SAga SGar SPer SPlb WFar WTin
albescens	see *S. rupestre* f. *purpureum*
alboroseum	see *S. erythrostictum*
§ *album*	CHal IHMH MBNS NBro WPer
- 'Coral Carpet'	CBrm CNic ECho EDAr EPfP EPot EWTr GAbr IHMH MBar MWat NHol NJOw NPri NRya SPoG WFar XPep
§ - subsp. *teretifolium* 'Murale'	CTri MBar
altissimum	see *S. sediforme*

altum	EMon LPhx NBre WCot WFar WMoo	
amplexicaule	see *S. tenuifolium*	
§ *anacampseros*	CNic EGoo NHol SUsu WPer	
– B&SWJ 723	WCru	
anglicum	MBow SChr	
athoum	see *S. album*	
atlanticum	see *S. dasyphyllum* subsp. *dasyphyllum* var. *mesatlanticum*	
Autumn Joy	see *S.* 'Herbstfreude'	
'Bertram Anderson' ♀H4	More than 30 suppliers	
beyrichianum misapplied	see *S. glaucophyllum*	
bithynicum 'Aureum'	see *S. hispanicum* var. *minus* 'Aureum'	
'Black Emperor'	EBee	
brevifolium	GGar IHMH	
caeruleum	LPhx WGwG	
'Carl'	More than 30 suppliers	
caucasicum	WAbb WEas	
cauticola ♀H4	CLyd CNic COIW CSpe ECho EDAr EMan GCal MBrN MHer MRav NBre SMrm SPoG SRms SRot WAbe	
– from Lida	ECho	
– 'Coca-Cola'	CBct CCVN EPPr EWin LAst NPri	
§ – 'Lidakense'	CHEx CMea CStu CTri ECho ECtt EGle EMan EPfP LRHS MBar MBri MLHP NSla SBch SBla SIng SRot WFar	
– 'Purpurine'	ECho GCal	
– 'Robustum'	EBee EWll	
cauticola x *tatarinowii*	EWes	
'Citrus Twist'	CPrp EBee EMan LSou MBNS NBhm NMRc NPro	
compressum new	SEND	
confusum	SChr SEND WFar	
crassipes	see *Rhodiola wallichiana*	
crassularia	see *Crassula setulosa* 'Milfordiae'	
'Crazy Ruffles' new	WCot	
cryptomerioides B&SWJ 054	WCru	
cyaneum Rudolph	EPot WAbe	
dasyphyllum	CNic ECho EDAr MBar MHer MOne MWat NHol NRya NWCA SRms XPep	
– subsp. *dasyphyllum* var. *glanduliferum*	CHal	
§ – – var. *mesatlanticum*	CNic GKev NBir	
– *mucronatis*	see *S. dasyphyllum* subsp. *dasyphyllum* var. *mesatlanticum*	
divergens	XPep	
douglasii	see *S. stenopetalum* 'Douglasii'	
drymarioides	NBre	
'Dudley Field'	MHer SBch	
'Eleanor Fisher'	see *S. telephium* subsp. *ruprechtii*	
ellacombeanum	see *S. kamtschaticum* var. *ellacombeanum*	
§ *erythrostictum*	MTho WAbb	
– 'Frosty Morn' (v)	More than 30 suppliers	
§ – 'Mediovariegatum' (v)	COIW EAEE EBee EBrs EChP EGle EGoo ELan EMon EPfP ERou EShb IFro LRHS MHer MNrw MRav NBPC NEgg SHBN SWvt WBrE WFar WMnd WMoo WPer	
'Evening Cloud' new	EBee	
§ *ewersii*	CHEx EBee ECho EDAr GMaP LRHS NBro NLar SPlb WAbe	
§ – var. *homophyllum*	IHMH	
§ *fabaria*	EChP EMan EWsh WAbb WCot WFar	
fastigiatum	see *Rhodiola fastigiata*	
floriferum	see *S. kamtschaticum*	
forsterianum subsp. *elegans*	SPlb	
frutescens	STre	
furfuraceum	NMen WAbe	

'Garnet Brocade' new	CCVN SVil	
§ *glaucophyllum* new	WPer	
'Gold Mound'	CStu CTbh LAst MGos NLar SVil	
'Great Expectations' new	LRHS	
* 'Green Expectations'	EBee EChP EGle EShb MSph MSte MWat NBre SHop SUsu	
greggii new	EShb	
gypsicola	EBee WPer	
'Harvest Moon'	EBur	
§ 'Herbstfreude' ♀H4	More than 30 suppliers	
heterodontum	see *Rhodiola heterodonta*	
hidakanum	CAby CLyd ECtt EPot GGar GMaP NBro NHol NMen SUsu WGHP WHoo WPat WTin	
§ *hispanicum*	ECho EDAr IHMH NBre SPlb	
– 'Albescens'	CNic	
– *glaucum*	see *S. hispanicum* var. *minus*	
§ – var. *minus*	ECho ECtt MBNS MBar NPri SIng SPlb SPoG	
§ – – 'Aureum'	ECha ECho EDAr MBar NHol NJOw SPoG	
– 'Pewter' new	ECho	
humifusum	CPBP EBur EHyt EPot ETow NHol NWCA SIng	
§ *hybridum*	WEas	
ishidae	see *Rhodiola ishidae*	
'Jaws' new	EBee WCot	
'Joyce Henderson'	COIW CPrp EBee EBrs EChP ECtt EGle EMan GQue LHop MRav NCGa NCob NEgg NLar SPer SRGP SUsu WBrk WCMO WCot WEas WMoo WTin	
§ *kamtschaticum* ♀H4	ECho MBar NJOw WFar	
§ – var. *ellacombeanum* ♀H4	CNic EDAr EGoo NMen WCot	
– – B&SWJ 8853	WCru	
§ – var. *floriferum* 'Weihenstephaner Gold'	CMea CNic CTri ECho ECtt EDAr EGoo EPfP GAbr GMaP IHMH LRHS MBar MHer MRav MWat NBir NFor NJOw NMen NPri NVic SIng SPlb SPoG SRms WFar WPat XPep	
– var. *kamtschaticum* 'Variegatum' (v) ♀H4	CBrm CLyd CMea EBee ECho ECtt EDAr EPPr EPfP LAst LBMP LBee MHer MWat SBla SIng SPoG SRms SRot SWvt WEas	
– var. *middendorffianum*	see *S. middendorffianum*	
'Karfunkelstein'	GBin LPhx	
kirilovii	see *Rhodiola kirilovii*	
lanceolatum	WPer	
lineare	CHEx LAst SSto	
'Little Gem'	CStu	
§ *lydium*	ECho MBar MHer MOne SPlb	
– 'Aureum'	see *S. hispanicum* var. *minus* 'Aureum'	
– 'Bronze Queen'	see *S. lydium*	
'Lynda Windsor'PBR	CBct CHVG CWCL EBee EChP EHrv EMan EPfP LAst MBNS MCCP NBPC NBhm NBro NLar NMoo	
makinoi 'Ogon'	CStu EBee	
I 'Marchant's Best Red' new	SMHy	
maweanum	see *S. acre* var. *majus*	
maximowiczii	see *S. aizoon*	
§ *middendorffianum*	CLyd ECho EDAr EGoo EPPr MBrN MHer MWat NMen SRms SRot WHoo	
'Moonglow'	ECtt NMen	
moranense	CHal CNic ETow	
morganianum ♀H1	CHal EBak EShb	
murale	see *S. album* subsp. *teretifolium* 'Murale'	
N *nevii* hort.	EGle SPlb	
nicaeense	see *S. sediforme*	
obcordatum	NMen	
§ *obtusatum*	ECtt EDAr GGar GKev NBro NJOw NSla	

§	*ochroleucum*	XPep
	oppositifolium	see *S. spurium* var. *album*
§	*oreganum*	ECha ECho EDAr EWin GAbr GMaP IHMH MBar MHer MWat NMen SPlb SRms SRot WPer
	- 'Procumbens'	see *S. oreganum* subsp. *tenue*
§	- subsp. *tenue*	NHol NRya WPat
§	*oregonense*	EBur NJOw NMen
	oryzifolium 'Minor'	EBur
	oxypetalum	STre
	pachyclados	see *Rhodiola pachyclados*
	pachyphyllum	EPfP
	palmeri	CHEx CNic CSpe EMan ETow LSou NBir SChr SDix XPep
	pilosum	NMen
	'Pink Chablis'PBR	EChP EMan MLLN NBhm NLar WCot
§	*pluricaule*	CStu ECho EHyt SPlb SRms
	populifolium	ECha GCal MHer STre WPer
	praealtum	GGar SChr STre
	pulchellum	EWTr
§	'Purple Emperor'	More than 30 suppliers
	'Red Cauli'	EBee EGle IPot MBNS SMHy SUsu
	'Red Rum'	LRHS
	reflexum L.	see *S. rupestre* L.
	reptans	ECho
	rhodiola	see *Rhodiola rosea*
	'Ringmore Ruby'	WCMO WCot
	'Rose Carpet'	MBrN SWvt WWeb
	rosea	see *Rhodiola rosea*
	rubroglaucum misapplied	see *S. oregonense*
	rubroglaucum Praeger	see *S. obtusatum*
	x *rubrotinctum*	CHEx CHal SChr XPep
	- 'Aurora'	SChr
§	'Ruby Glow' ♀H4	More than 30 suppliers
	'Ruby Port'	CSpe
§	*rupestre* L.	CNic ECho GGar MBNS MBar MWhi NBlu NJOw SIng SPlb SPoG WFar WHer XPep
	- 'Angelina'	EBee ENot EPPr EWes EWin MAvo MGos NBir NJOw SIng SUsu WCMO WCot
	- 'Minus'	CNic
	- 'Monstrosum Cristatum'	ITer NBir SMad
§	- f. *purpureum*	NRya
	ruprechtii	see *S. telephium* subsp. *ruprechtii*
	sarcocaule hort.	see *Crassula sarcocaulis*
	sarmentosum	ECho
§	*sediforme*	CArn EDAr XPep
	- *nicaeense*	see *S. sediforme*
	selskianum	EBee EWin GGar IHMH MOne NBre
	sempervivoides	ECho
	sexangulare	ECho EDAr GAbr GGar IHMH MBar MHer MOne NRya SEND SPlb SRms WPer XPep
	sibiricum	see *S. hybridum*
§	*sieboldii*	ECho SIng
	- 'Mediovariegatum' (v) ♀H2-3	CHEx COlW ECho EMan LAst SIng SPlb WFar WPer
	'Silver Moon'	EBur
	spathulifolium	ECha ECho EPot MDKP MOne WEas
	- 'Aureum'	EBur ECho ECtt MBar NRya WAbe
	- 'Cape Blanco' ♀H4	More than 30 suppliers
	- 'Purpureum' ♀H4	More than 30 suppliers
§	*spectabile* ♀H4	CArn CHEx CHrt CPrp EBee ELan EPfP EWTr GMaP LRHS MHer MRav SGar SHFr SPlb SRms SWal WBVN WBor WBrk WCAu WFar WSFF WTel WTin XPep
	- 'Abendrot'	EMon
	- 'Album'	CHEx
	- 'Brilliant' ♀H4	More than 30 suppliers
	- 'Carmen'	EBee NEgg WMoo
	'Iceberg'	More than 30 suppliers
	- 'Indian Chief'	CMMP COIW CPrp EBee EBrs EChP EGle GMaP LAst LRHS MBrN MSte NFla SPoG WFar WMnd WMoo
	- 'Jaws' **new**	LSou SPoG
	- 'Lisa'	EMon MTPN NLar
	- 'Meteor'	EBee MBNS MLLN MSte MWat NLar WAbe WCAu WPer
*	- 'Mini'	ELan MRav
	- 'Neon'	EBee LRHS
	- 'Rosenteller'	EBee EGle EMon NBre
	- September Glow	see *S. spectabile* 'Septemberglut'
§	- 'Septemberglut'	EBee EGoo EMan EMon NBre NSti WCot
	- 'Stardust'	COIW CPrp EAEE EBee EBrs EGle EMil ENot EPfP ERou GKev GMaP LRHS MBNS MHer NCGa NOrc SPer SPet SPoG WAbe WCAu WFar WGor WViv WWeb
	- 'Steve Ward'	EBee EWes
	- 'Variegatum'	see *S. erythrostictum* 'Mediovariegatum'
	spinosum	see *Orostachys spinosa*
	spurium	CHEx ECho EGoo MBNS SEND SGar SRms
§	- var. *album*	EGoo NRya
*	- 'Atropurpureum'	ECha NFor WMoo
	- 'Coccineum'	ECho MBar MNHC NBlu SSto WBVN WRHF
	- Dragon's Blood	see *S. spurium* 'Schorbuser Blut'
	- 'Erdblut'	LRHS NJOw NMen
	- 'Fuldaglut'	CHal CNic EAEE EBee ECho EDAr EHoe EMan EWin GBuc GMaP IHMH MBNS NRya SIng SMrm WFar WMoo WPer
	- 'Green Mantle'	EBee ECha ECho EPfP EWin MWgw SMer SSto
	- Purple Carpet	see *S. spurium* 'Purpurteppich'
	- 'Purpureum'	EGoo MWgw SRms
§	- 'Purpurteppich'	EBee ECho LRHS MRav NBro NHol NLar SRms
	- 'Roseum'	EWll SRms
	- 'Ruby Mantle'	EWll GKev WBVN
§	- 'Schorbuser Blut' ♀H4	CMea EBee ECho ECtt EPfP IHMH MBNS MLHP MWat NBir NJOw NRya NVic SMar SPlb SRms WEas WHoo WPat WTin WWeb
	- 'Summer Glory'	NLar
	- 'Tricolor'	see *S. spurium* 'Variegatum'
I	- 'Variegatum' (v)	CBrm CHEx CNic CTri EBee ECha ECho EDAr EGoo EHoe GGar LAst MBar MHer MLHP MNHC MRav NJOw NPri NRya SBod SIng SPlb SPoG WEas WFar WMoo WPat
	- 'Voodoo' **new**	GWWP
	stenopetalum	IHMH SPlb
§	- 'Douglasii'	CNic MOne SRms
	'Stewed Rhubarb Mountain'	CBgR CFwr CPrp EAEE EBee EChP ECtt EGle EMan LDai LHop MBNS MRav MSte MWgw NBro NDov WCot WHil WMoo WPGP
	stoloniferum	ECho
	- 'Variegatum'	WWeb
	'Strawberries and Cream'	More than 30 suppliers
	'Sunset Cloud'	CHEx CMHG CSam EBee ECtt EGle EWes GCal LRHS MRav NBre NCob
	surculosum var. *luteum* **new**	NJOw
	takesimense B&SWJ 8518	WCru
§	*tatarinowii*	EDAr
§	*telephium*	CAgr CArn CHrt CMea MBNS NBir SRms WGwG WWye
	- 'Abbeydore'	see *S.* 'Abbeydore'

- 'Arthur Branch' — EPPr GBuc MNrw MSte MTho
- 'Bon Bon' **new** — EBee MBNS
- var. **borderei** — CElw EGle EMan EMon LHop LRHS SBch SUsu
- 'El Cid' — EBee EGle EWes
- subsp. **fabaria** — see *S. fabaria*
* - 'Hester' — EBee EChP
- 'Jennifer' — EMan WCot
- 'Leonore Zuuntz' — EBee NBre
- 'Matrona' — More than 30 suppliers
- subsp. **maximum** — CHad CMea COlW EBee EGle ELan
  'Atropurpureum' ♀H4 — EMag EMan EPfP MRav SWvt WCot WEas WHal
- - 'Bressingham Purple' **new** — EBrs
- - 'Gooseberry Fool' — CBgR CFwr CKno EBee ECGP ECtt EGle EGoo EMan EMon ERou GMaP LPhx MBri NSti SBch WCot WFar WWeb
- 'Mohrchen' — CPrp EBee EChP EGle EHrv EWTr GMaP LRHS MLLN MRav NGdn SBla SMrm SPla SPoG WCAu WFar WMnd WMoo
- 'Munstead Red' — More than 30 suppliers
§ - subsp. **ruprechtii** — More than 30 suppliers
- - 'Hab Gray' — CBgR CSpe EBee EChP EGle EWes GBin LAst MSte WCot WWhi
- 'Samuel Oliphant' (v) **new** — WCot
- subsp. **telephium** — CKno EGle EGoo EMan EMon
  'Lynda et Rodney' — MSph MSte WCot
- 'Variegatum' (v) — COtt EMag LRHS MDKP WHal
§ **tenuifolium** — EBur
- subsp. **tenuifolium** — EBur
trollii — see *Rhodiola trollii*
ussuriense — EMon SUsu WOut
§ 'Vera Jameson' ♀H4 — CMea CPrp EAEE EBee EChP ECha EGle EHoe EPfP LRHS LSRN MBrN MRav MTis MWat MWgw NHol NSti SBch SBla SHBN SPer SPla WEas WFar WMoo WWhi
viviparum B&SWJ 8662 — WCru
'Washfield Purple' — see *Sedum* 'Purple Emperor'
'Weihenstephaner Gold' — see *S. kamtschaticum* var. *floriferum* 'Weihenstephaner Gold'
weinbergii — see *Graptopetalum paraguayense*
yezoense — see *S. pluricaule*

Seemannia see *Gloxinia*

Selaginella ❀ (*Selaginellaceae*)
apoda — MBri
braunii — WCot
helvetica — CStu
kraussiana ♀H1 — CHal CLAP MBri NRya
- 'Aurea' — CCCN CHal CLAP GGar SMad
- 'Brownii' ♀H1 — CLAP
- 'Gold Tips' — CLAP
sanguinolenta — CStu SIng

Selago (*Scrophulariaceae*)
myrtifolia **new** — GFai

Selinum (*Apiaceae*)
carvifolium — EBee LDai MWgw NLar
tenuifolium — see *S. wallichianum*
§ **wallichianum** — CHad CRow CSec EBrs EChP EGoo EWTr GBuc GIBF IFro ITer NBid NCGa SMHy SMeo WPGP WPrP WWhi
- EMAK 886 — EBee GPoy MBri NSti SDix

- HWJK 2224 — WCru
- HWJK 2347 — WCru

Selliera (*Goodeniaceae*)
radicans — ECou GGar

Semele (*Ruscaceae*)
androgyna — CHEx CRHN EShb

Semiaquilegia (*Ranunculaceae*)
§ **adoxoides** — CPom EBee SHar
- B&SWJ 1190 — WCru
'Early Dwarf' — EDif NLar
§ **ecalcarata** — CPom CSec CSpe EBee ECho GGar LDai NLar SBch SRms WCru WFar WPGP WPer WSan WWFP
* - f. **bicolor** — CPom WCru
- 'Flore Pleno' (d) — EChP
simulatrix — see *S. ecalcarata*

Semiarundinaria (*Poaceae*)
from Korea — EPla
§ **fastuosa** ♀H4 — CAbb CBig CDoC CHEx EAmu EBee EFul ENBC EPfP EPla ERod LPal MBri MMoz MWht NMoo NVic SAPC SArc SDix SPlb WJun WMul
- var. **viridis** — EPla ERod LPJP SBig WCru WJun
kagamiana — CDoC CPen ENBC EPla MMoz MMuc MWht NMoo SBig SEND WJun
makinoi — EPla MWht WJun WPGP
nitida — see *Fargesia nitida*
§ **okuboi** — ENBC EPla ERod LPal MMoz MWht WJun
villosa — see *S. okuboi*
yamadorii — EPla ERod MMoz MWht WJun
- 'Brimscombe' — EPla
yashadake — EPla ERod WJun
- f. **kimmei** — CAbb CDoC CDul CPen EBee ENBC EPla ERod MAsh MMoz MPRe MWht NMoo SBLw SBig SEND WDyG WFar WJun WMoo WMul WPGP

Sempervivella see *Rosularia*

Sempervivum ❀ (*Crassulaceae*)
EKB 1727 **new** — MOne
from Andorra ambig. — NHol
from Sierra Nova — NDlv
'Abba' — MOne WHal WPer
acuminatum — see *S. tectorum* var. *glaucum*
'Adelaar' — CWil NMen
'Adelmoed' — CWil
'Adeltruid' — NHol
'Adlerhorst' — NHol
'Aglow' — MHom MOne NMen
'Aladdin' — CWil MOne NMen SRms
'Albernelli' — NHol
'Alchimist' — MOne
'Alcithoë' — MOne
'Aldo Moro' — CWil EDAr GAbr LBee LRHS MHom MOne NMen WIvy
'Alidae' — MOne
allionii — see *Jovibarba allionii*
'Alluring' — GAbr MOne
'Alpha' — LBee LRHS MOne NHol NMen SIng SRms STre WHal WPer WTin
altum — CWil EAEE MHom NMen
'Amanda' — CWil MOne NMen SIng SRms WHoo WPer WTin
'Ambergreen' — NMen
andreanum — see *S. tectorum* var.*andreanum*
'Apache' — MOne NMen
'Apollo' — NHol

'Apple Blossom'	CMea GCrs MOne NMen
arachnoideum ♀H4	More than 30 suppliers
- from Cascade Piste 7	MOne
- from Gorges du Valais	EPem
- from the Abruzzi, Italy	GCrs SIng
- 'Ararat'	SDys
- 'Boria'	MOne
- var. *bryoides*	CWil MBrN NJOw NMen WAbe
	WIvy WPer
- 'Clärchen'	NHol NJOw NMen NSla
- cristate	CWil
* - *densum*	EHyt MBrN NRya WAbe
- subsp. *doellianum*	see *S. arachnoideum* var.
	glabrescens
- form No 1	ECho
§ - var. *glabrescens*	EHyt NMen SDys
- 'Laggeri'	see *S. arachnoideum* L. subsp.
	tomentosum (C.B. Lehm. &
	Schnittsp.) Schinz & Thell.
- 'Mole Harbord'	LRHS
- 'Peña Prieta'	NHol
- red	NMen
- 'Rubrum'	CHEx EAAE EDAr LRHS MCCP
	MOne NEgg WHoo
- 'Sultan'	MOne
- subsp. *tomentosum*	see *S. x barbulatum* 'Hookeri'
misapplied	
§ - subsp. *tomentosum*	CHEx CHal CWil EPot GKev LRHS
Schinz & Thell. ♀H4	MHer NHol NMen NPer NRya SIng
	SRms WAbe WBrE WPer
- - GDJ 92.04	CWil
- - 'Minus'	NHol NJOw NMen SIng
§ - - 'Stansfieldii'	EAAE GAbr NMen SDys SIng STre
	WHal
§ - 'White Christmas'	CWil
arachnoideum x	CWil NHol NMen WIvy WTin
calcareum	
arachnoideum x	CWil SDys
nevadense	
arachnoideum x	GAbr
pumilum	
arachnoideum x	CWil NHol NJOw NMen WAbe
pittonii	
arenarium	see *Jovibarba arenaria*
armenum	MOne NMen
- var. *insigne* new	MOne
'Arondina'	CWil
'Aross'	CMea GAbr NMen
'Arrowheads Red'	MOne
'Artist'	CWil MOne NMen
arvernense	see *S. tectorum*
'Ashes of Roses'	EGoo EPot ITim MHom MOne
	NMen WAbe WGor WPer
'Asteroid'	CWil MOne NMen
'Astrid'	CWil
atlanticum	GEdr MHom NDlv NJOw NMen
	NSla SRot WOut
- from Atlas Mountains,	CWil MOne
Morocco	
- from Oukaïmeden,	CWil GAbr MOne NHol NMen
Morocco	WTin
- 'Edward Balls'	CWil EPem MOne SDys
'Atlantis'	NHol
'Atropurpureum'	CHEx CWil GAbr MBrN MOne
	NMen SRms WGor WIvy WPer
'Averil'	CWil
'Averley' new	MOne
§ 'Aymon Correvon'	MOne
balcanicum	CWil EDAr MOne NMen WIvy
ballsii	NMen
- from Kambeecho,	MHom
Greece	
- from Smólikas, Greece	CWil MHom MOne NMen
- from Tschumba Petzi,	CWil MHom MOne SDys SIng
Greece	
'Banderi'	CWil MOne

'Banjo'	MOne
'Banyan'	MTPN
'Barbarosa'	CWil MOne
§ x *barbulatum*	NMen SDys WPer
- 'Hookeri'	CWil MOne NLar NMen SIng
	WAbe WPer
'Bascour Zilver'	CWil MOne
'Beaute'	CWil MOne
'Bedivere'	CPBP CWil LBee LRHS MOne
	NMen SRms
'Bedivere Crested'	CWil
'Bedley Hi'	MHom MOne
'Bella Donna'	MHom MOne NHol NMen
	WPer
'Bella Meade'	CWil EPem MOne NMen SRms
	WPer
'Bellotts Pourpre'	CWil NHol
'Bennerbroek'	MOne
'Benny Hill'	CWil MOne
'Bernstein'	CWil MHer MOne WHal
'Beta'	MHom MOne NHol NMen WAbe
	WPer WTin
'Bethany'	CWil MOne NHol NMen WHal
'Bicolor'	EPfP
'Big Mal'	NHol
'Big Slipper'	EPem MOne NHol
'Binstead'	MOne NHol
'Birchmaier'	NMen
'Black Cap'	MOne
'Black Claret'	NHol WGwG
'Black Knight'	CStu EAAE EDAr LBee LRHS SBla
	SRms WHal
'Black Mini'	CWil GAbr MDKP NBir NMen
	SRms
'Black Mountain'	CHEx CWil LBee LRHS MOne
'Black Prince'	EDAr
'Black Velvet'	WIvy WPer
'Bladon'	WPer
'Blari'	MOne
'Blood Sucker' new	WGor
'Blood Tip'	CHEx CHal CWil EAAE EBee EHyt
	GAbr LBee LRHS MHer NHol
	NJOw NMen SBch SPoG SRms
	WFar WGor WHal
'Blue Boy'	CWil EAAE GAbr LBee LRHS MOne
	MSte NHol NMen SRms WHoo
	WLin WPer
'Blue Moon'	MOne NMen
'Blue Time'	CWil MOne WTin
'Blush'	MOne
'Boissieri'	see *S. tectorum* subsp. *tectorum*
	'Boissieri'
'Bold Chick'	MOne
'Booth's Red'	CHEx EPem MOne NMen SIng
	WGor
'Boreale'	see *Jovibarba hirta* subsp. *borealis*
borisii	see *S. ciliosum* var. *borisii*
borissovae	CWil EDAr MHom NMen SDys
'Boromir'	CWil MOne
'Boule de Neige'	NMen
'Bowles's Variety'	WPer
brevipilum from Turkey	MOne
new	
'Bright Eyes' new	MOne
'Britta'	MOne SDys
'Brock'	CWil EAAE MHer MHom NHol
	WPer
'Bronco'	CWil EBee ECho LBee MHom
	MOne NMen SRms SUsu WFar
'Bronze Pastel'	CNic CWil MHom MOne NMen
	NSla SRms SRot WTin
'Bronze Tower'	NHol
'Brown Owl'	CWil ECho MOne NHol SRms
	WFar
'Brownii'	GAbr MOne NMen SBla WPer
	WTin

'Brunette'	ECho GAbr
'Burgundy'	MOne
'Burgundy Velvet'	MOne
'Burnatii'	CWil MOne NMen
'Burning Desire' **new**	WGor
'Butterbur'	CWil
'Butterfly'	MOne
'Café'	CWil EGoo NHol NMen SRms WIvy WPer
× *calcaratum*	EDAr SIng SRms
calcareum	CNic CSam CWil EHyt EPot MOne NBro NEgg NMen SPlb SRms SRot WBVN WFar WHoo WLin WPer
- from Alps, France	CWil MOne
- from Calde la Vanoise, France	CWil MOne NMen
- from Ceüze, France	CWil MOne WIvy
- from Cherion **new**	MOne
- from Col Bayard, France	CWil GAbr MOne NMen
- from Colle St Michel	CWil MOne NMen
- from Gleize	see *S. calcareum* 'Limelight'
- from Gorges supérieures du Cians, France	CWil MOne NMen
- from Guillaumes, Mont Ventoux, France	CWil MOne NMen SRot WHoo
- from La Mata de la Riba **new**	MOne
- from Mont Ventoux, France	CWil MOne
- from La Petite Ceüse, France	SRot
- - GDJ 92.15	CWil
- - GDJ 92.16	CWil
- from Queyras, France	CWil MOne NMen
- from Route d'Annôt	CWil MOne NMen
- from Triora, Italy	CWil MOne NHol NMen
- 'Benz'	SDys
- 'Cristatum' **new**	CStu
- 'Extra'	CHEx CWil GAbr SRot
- 'Greenii'	CWil EAEE MOne NDlv NHol NMen SPlb
§ - 'Grigg's Surprise'	CWil MHer MOne NMen
§ - 'Limelight'	CMea CWil MOne NHol NMen WHal WIvy WTin
- 'Monstrosum'	see *S. calcareum* 'Grigg's Surprise'
- 'Mrs Giuseppi'	CWil ECho GAbr LBee LRHS MOne MSte NMen NOak SBla SRms STre WAbe WFar WPer
- 'Pink Pearl'	CWil EGoo MOne NMen SDys WIvy WTin
- 'Sir William Lawrence'	CMea CPBP CWil ECho EPem NMen WAbe WHal WHoo WIvy WPer WThu WTin
'Caldera'	NHol
* *callosum barnesii*	GAbr
* *calopticum* × *nevadense*	WTin
'Cameo'	see *Jovibarba heuffelii* var. *glabra* 'Cameo'
'Canada Kate'	CWil NHol WPer
'Cancer'	MOne
'Candy Floss'	CWil MOne NMen WGor
cantabricum	CWil NMen
- from Cuevas del Sil	CWil MOne
- from Cuengas Piedras **new**	MOne
- from Navafria, Spain	CWil MOne NHol WTin
- from Peña Prieta, Spain	MOne NMen
- from Piedrafita, Spain	MOne
- from Riaño, Spain	CWil GAbr
- from San Glorio, Spain	CWil GAbr MOne NMen
- from Santander, Spain	NHol
- from Ticeros	EPem MOne NMen
- from Tizneros, Spain	CWil
- from Valvanera, Spain	MOne NMen
- subsp. *cantabricum* from Leitariegos, Spain	CWil ETow GAbr MHom MOne NMen
- - from Peña de Llesba, Spain GDJ 93.13	CWil
- - from Pico del Lobo, Spain	CWil
- subsp. *guadarramense*	see *S. vicentei* subsp. *paui*
- - from Pico del Lobo, Spain, No 1	MOne SRot
- - from Pico del Lobo, Spain, No 2	EPem MOne
- - from Valvanera, Spain No 1	CWil NMen
- subsp. *urbionense*	CWil
- - from El Gatón	CWil
- - from Picos de Urbión, Spain	CWil MOne NMen
- - from Sierra de la Demanda GDJ 94.09	CWil
- - from Sierra de Pineda GDJ 95.01	CWil
- - from Sierra de Urbión GDJ 94.12	CWil
- - GDJ 94.10	CWil
cantabricum × *montanum* subsp. *stiriacum*	WEas WTin
cantabricum × *giuseppii* from Picos de Europa GDJ 93.10	CWil
cantabricum × *montanum* subsp. *stiriacum* 'Lloyd Praeger'	CWil
'Canth'	NHol
'Caramel'	MOne
* 'Carinal'	NBir
* × *carlsii*	MOne
'Carluke'	MOne
'Carmen'	CHal GAbr MOne
'Carneum'	MOne NHol
'Carnival'	CHal MOne NMen WPer
caucasicum	CWil EHol MHom MOne NMen
'Cauticola'	MOne
'Cavo Doro'	CWil MOne
'Celon'	MOne
'Centennial'	MOne
'Chalon'	MOne
charadzeae	CWil LBee LRHS MOne NHol
'Cherry Frost'	ECho MOne NJOw NMen
'Cherry Glow'	see *Jovibarba heuffelii* 'Cherry Glow'
'Chivalry' **new**	MOne
'Chocolate'	MOne NHol WPer
§ × *christii*	MOne NHol NMen
'Christmas Time'	MOne NHol
ciliosum ♀H4	CMea CPBP CWil ECho NMen NRya SIng
§ - var. *borisii*	CWil EPfP GCal GKev NDlv NMen NRya WAbe WHal
- from Alí Butús, Bulgaria	GCrs SDys
- var. *galicicum* from Mali Hat, Albania	GCrs NMen
ciliosum × *ciliosum* var. *borisii*	CHal GEdr NMen
ciliosum × *grandiflorum*	CWil MOne NMen
ciliosum × *marmoreum*	NMen
ciliosum × *tectorum*	WTin
'Cindy'	MOne SRms
'Circlet'	CWil MOne NMen
* *cistaceum*	WEas
'Clara Noyes'	MOne SMer WFar WPer
'Clare'	EPem MHer MOne
'Claudine' **new**	MOne
'Clemanum'	MOne

'Cleveland Morgan' EPem LRHS MHom MOne NBro NMen
'Climax' EBee ECho EPem MHom MOne NMen SMer SSto WFar
'Clipper' CWil
'Cobweb Capers' MHom MOne
'Cobweb Centres' MOne NMen
'Cochise' **new** MOne
'Collage' MOne NHol
'Collecteur Anchisi' MOne NHol SDys
'Commander Hay' ♀H4 CHEx CMea COlW CWil EAEE EBee EPfP EWes GKev MBNS MHom MOne MWgw NMen NPer SBch SRGP SRms WEas WHal WIvy WPer
'Comte de Congae' MOne NMen
'Congo' MOne NMen
'Conran' NHol
'Corio' MOne
'Cornstone' NHol
'Corona' CWil GKev MOne NHol SRms WPer
'Corsair' CWil GKev MBrN MOne NMen WGor WIvy WPer WTin
'Cranberry' MOne
'Cresta' MOne
'Crimson Velvet' CHEx CMea EBee EDAr GKev LBee LRHS MOne NHol WPer
§ 'Crispyn' CBrm CWil EHyt EPot LBee MHom MOne NHol NMen WEas WPer
'Croky' MOne
'Croton' SIng WPer
'Cupream' CWil NDlv SRms WPer
'Czakor' NHol
'Dakota' CWil MOne NHol NMen
'Dallas' CWil MOne NHol NMen SRms
'Damask' CWil LBee MOne NMen WPer
'Dame Arsac' MOne
'Dancer's Veil' MOne
'Darjeeling' CWil
'Dark Beauty' CMea CWil EHyt MOne NMen WAbe WGor WHal WPer
'Dark Cloud' CWil GAbr LBee LRHS MOne WHoo WIvy WPer
'Dark Point' CWil MHom MOne NMen
'Darkie' CWil WPer
'Deebra' CWil
'Deep Fire' CWil MOne NHol NMen SRms WIvy WTin
x *degenianum* GAbr MOne NMen WPer
'Delta' NMen WHoo WTin
densum see *S. tectorum*
'Devon Jewel' **new** WGor
'Diamant' MOne
'Diane' CWil
'Director Jacobs' CWil EDAr GAbr MOne NHol NMen WEas WPer WTin
'Doctor Roberts' NHol
dolomiticum NMen
– from Rif Sennes, Italy MOne
dolomiticum x CWil MOne NBro NMen WTin
  montanum
'Donarrose' NHol
'Downland Queen' CWil MOne NHol
'Dragoness' MOne
'Duke of Windsor' MOne NMen
'Dusky' MOne
'Dyke' CTri CWil GAbr MOne NHol NMen WHal
dzhavachischvilii MOne NMen
'Edge of Night' CWil NHol SRms
'Eefje' CWil
'El Greco' MOne
'El Toro' MHom
'Elene' MOne

'Elgar' MOne WIvy WPer
'Elizabeth' WPer
'Elvis' CWil GAbr NMen
'Emerald Giant' CWil MOne NHol SRms WPer WTin
'Emerson's Giant' CWil MOne NMen
'Emma Jane' MOne
'Emmchen' CWil
'Engle's' EAEE EBee EWin GKev LRHS MHer MOne NMen SRms WHal WPer
'Engle's 13-2' MOne NBro NHol NMen
'Engle's Rubrum' CPBP GAbr LBee NHol NMen
erythraeum MHom NHol NMen WAbe WHal
– from Pirin, Bulgaria MOne NMen
– from Rila, Bulgaria NMen
– 'Red Velvet' MOne
'Excalibur' MOne NMen WIvy
'Exhibita' CWil MOne SDys SRms
'Exorna' CWil MHom MOne NMen SIng WEas WIvy WPer
'Fabienne' **new** CWil
'Fair Lady' CWil MHom MOne NMen
'Fame' EPem MOne NHol
'Fat Jack' CWil
x *fauconnettii* CWil EDAr NHol NMen SIng
– 'Thompsonii' CWil MOne NHol NMen SIng
'Feldmaier' MOne WFar WGwG
'Festival' MOne NMen
'Feu de Printemps' MOne
'Fiery Furness' MOne
'Fiesta' WHal
fimbriatum see *S.* x *barbulatum*
'Finerpointe' MOne
'Fire Glint' CWil MOne NHol SRms WIvy
'Firebird' MOne NMen
'Firefly' MOne
'First Try' MOne
'Flaming Heart' CWil MBrN MOne NMen WGor WPer
'Flamingo' MOne NMen
'Flamme' MOne
'Flanders Passion' EPot ITim LBee LRHS NMen SRms WPer
'Flasher' WEas WPer
'Flavipiluns' **new** WFar
'Fluweel' MOne
'Fontanae' MOne
'Forden' CHEx MOne WGor
'Ford's Amiability' SDys
'Ford's Shadows' SDys
'Ford's Spring' CWil MOne NHol NJOw NMen WIvy WPer
'Freckles' MOne
'Freeland' WPer
'Frigidum' NDlv
'Frolic' MOne SIng
'Fronika' CWil
'Frost and Flame' NHol
'Frosty' CWil MOne SRms
'Fuego' CWil MHom MOne
x *funckii* CHEx CWil EDAr IHMH MBrN MOne NHol NJOw NMen SDys SIng WOut WPer WTin
– var. *aqualiense* CWil
'Furryness' MOne
'Fuzzy Wuzzy' MOne NJOw
'Galahad' GAbr
'Gallivarda' CWil
'Gambol' NHol
'Gamma' CHEx CWil LBee LRHS NHol NMen SDys SIng SRms WEas WTin
'Garnet' ECho WIvy WPer
'Gay Jester' CTri CWil MOne WHoo WTin
'Gazelle' WIvy WPer

'Genevione'   CWil
'Georgette'   CWil NMen WPer
'Ginger'   MOne
'Ginnie's Delight'   CWil NMen
'Gipsy'   CWil MOne
giuseppii   MHer NHol NMen SIng WPer
  - from Coriscao, Spain   CWil
    GDJ 93.17
  - from Cumbre de   CWil
    Cebolleda GDJ 93.04
  - from Peña Espigüete, CWil GAbr MOne NMen SDys
    Spain
  - from Peña Prieta,   CWil MOne NMen
    Spain
  - from Vega de Liordes-W CWil
'Gizmo'   CWil
'Glaucum'   see *S. tectorum* var. *glaucum*
'Gleam'   MOne
'Gloriosum'   GAbr WPer
'Glowing Embers'   CWil MHom MOne NMen WHal
       WPer
'Goldie'   MOne
'Gollum'   MOne
'Graceum'   CWil
'Granada'   GAbr NMen
'Granat'   CWil MHer MOne NMen SRms
       WIvy WPer
'Granby'   CWil ECho LBee MOne NMen
       SDys
grandiflorum   CBrm CWil NMen SIng WBrE WPer
  - from Valpine   MOne NMen
  - 'Fasciatum'   CWil MOne NMen
  - 'Keston'   MOne
grandiflorum x   see *S.* x *christii*
  montanum
grandiflorum x   MOne
  tectorum
grandiflorum x   CWil
  tectorum from
  Valtournenche
  GDJ 96B.11
'Grannie's Favourite'   MOne
'Grape Idol'   CWil
'Grapetone'   MHom NMen SDys WHal
'Graupurpur'   CWil
'Gray Dawn'   EAEE MHom
'Green Apple'   CWil GAbr MHom NMen SDys
'Green Dragon'   CWil EAEE
'Green Gables'   WPer
'Green Giant'   MTPN
'Greenwich Time'   NMen
* *greigii*   GEdr NJOw
'Grenadier'   MOne
'Grey Ghost'   NMen WIvy WPer
'Grey Green'   CWil NHol
'Grey Lady'   CMea CWil
'Grey Owl'   EAEE LRHS
'Grey Velvet' **new**   CWil
'Greyfriars'   CMea EPot EWll LBee LRHS NMen
       WGor WOut WPer
'Greyolla'   CWil WPer
'Gruaud Larose'   NHol
'Grünrand'   MOne
'Grünschnabel'   MOne
'Grünspecht'   MOne
'Gulle Dame'   CWil
'Halemaumau'   CWil MOne
'Hall's Hybrid'   CWil GAbr NBro SRms
'Happy'   CWil MOne NMen SRms WGor
       WIvy WPer WThu
'Hart'   CWil EPem NHol SRms WTin
'Hartside'   MOne
'Haullauer's Seedling'   MOne
I 'Hausmanni'   see *S.* x *barbulatum*
       'Hausmannii'
'Havana'   NMen

'Hayling'   EAEE EDAr LRHS MOne NHol
       NMen SIng SRms WPer
'Heavenly Joy'   NHol
'Heigham Red'   CWil GCrs LBee LRHS MOne NHol
       NMen WPer
'Heliotroop'   MOne SDys SRot
helveticum   see *S. montanum*
'Hester'   CHEx CWil EBee ECho EPyc GAbr
       MBrN NBro NMen SIng SRms WFar
'Hey-hey'   EAEE EDAr EPot GCrs LBee LRHS
       MBrN NMen SPlb SRms WAbe
       WPer
'Hidde'   CWil WIvy WPer
'Hidde's Roosje'   MOne NMen
hirtum   see *Jovibarba hirta*
'Hispidulum'   MOne
'Hookeri'   see *S.* x *barbulatum* 'Hookeri'
'Hopi'   CWil MOne NHol SRms
'Hortulanus Smit'   NMen
'Hullabaloo'   MOne
'Hurricane'   CWil MOne WIvy WPer
'Icicle'   CHEx CMea EAEE LRHS NBro
       NHol NMen SIng SRms WAbe
       WGor
imbricatum   see *S.* x *barbulatum*
'Imperial'   CWil MHom
ingwersenii   MHom MOne SIng
ingwersenii x *pumilum*   CWil
'Interlace'   MOne
'Iophon'   LBee MOne
'Irazu'   CWil EAEE GAbr MOne NMen
       SDys SRms WPer
'Isaac Dyson'   SDys SRot
ispartae   CWil
italicum   MHom NMen
'Itchen'   MOne NMen
'IWO'   CHEx NMen WIvy
'Jack Frost'   CWil MOne NBro NMen
'Jacquette' **new**   CWil
'Jade' ambig.   MOne
'Jane'   MOne
'Jelly Bean'   CWil MOne NMen
'Jet Stream'   CWil NMen SDys WGor
'Jewel Case'   CWil EAEE LRHS MOne NMen
       SIng SRms
'John T.'   MOne WEas
'Jolly Green Giant'   MHom MOne
'Jo's Spark'   NSla
'Jubilee'   CMea CWil ECho EHyt ELan EPem
       GKev NHol NMen SRms WGor
       WPer
'Jubilee Tricolor'   NHol NMen
'Jungle Fires'   CWil EPot ITim NHol SDys SRms
       WHoo
'Jupiter'   GKev
'Jurato'   NHol
'Justine's Choice'   CWil SRms
'Kalinda'   CWil MHom NMen
§ 'Kappa'   CTri MOne NBro NHol NMen
       SDys SRot WPer
'Katmai'   CWil NHol
'Kelly Jo'   CWil EBee EWin EWll ITim NBro
       NMen WTin
'Kelut'   MOne
'Kermit'   MHom NMen
'Kerneri'   NHol
'Kibo'   MOne WIvy
'Kimble'   WPer
kindingeri   CWil MHom NMen NWCA
'King George'   CHal CTri CWil EPem GAbr ITim
       LBee LRHS MOne NMen SIng
       SRms WGor WHal WHoo WPer
       WTin
'Kip'   CMea NMen WGor WIvy
       WPer
'Kismet'   NMen

'Koko Flanel'	CWil
'Kolagas Mayfair'	MOne
'Korspel Glory 4'	CWil
'Korspelsegietje'	CWil
kosaninii	LRHS MOne NHol NMen SIng WPer WTin
- from Koprivnik	MOne NMen SDys WAbe
* - from Visitor	CWil MOne
- 'Hepworth'	NHol
'Krakeling'	MOne
'Kramers Purpur'	NMen
'Kramers Spinrad'	CHEx CMea CWil GAbr LBee LEdu LRHS MOne NMen SDys SIng WEas WHoo WIvy WTin
'La Serenissima'	MOne
'Lady Kelly'	CMea CNic MOne NMen WIvy
'Launcelot'	WPer
'Lavender and Old Lace'	CHEx CWil EAEE GAbr GCrs LRHS NMen WPer
'Laysan'	CWil NHol
Le Clair's hybrid No 4	NMen
'Lennik's Glory'	see *S.* 'Crispyn'
'Leocadia's Nephew'	MOne NMen
'Leocadia's Niece' **new**	MOne
'Leon Smits'	CWil
'Les Yielding'	MOne
'Lilac Time'	CWil EAEE GAbr GEdr LRHS MHer MOne NMen SRms WHal WIvy WPer
'Limbo'	CWil
'Linaria'	MTPN
'Lipari'	NMen SRms
'Lipstick'	NMen
'Lively Bug'	CWil LBee LRHS SDys WGor WPer
'Lloyd Praeger'	see *S. montanum* subsp. *stiriacum* 'Lloyd Praeger'
'Lonzo'	CWil SRms
'Lustrous'	MOne
'Lynne's Choice'	CWil GAbr MOne SIng WHal WIvy
macedonicum	EDAr NDlv NMen WTin
- from Ljuboten	CWil MOne NMen
'Madeleine'	CWil
'Magic Spell'	CWil MOne NMen
'Magical'	CWil
'Magnificum'	CWil NMen WGor
'Mahogany'	CHEx CTri CWil ECho EWll LBee LRHS MOne NBlu NHol NMen NWCA SBla SRms SWal WEas WGor WGwG WHal WIvy
'Maigret'	CWil SIng WPer
'Majestic'	CWil LBee NMen
'Major Desmert' **new**	EDAr
'Major White'	CHEx
'Malby's Hybrid'	see *S.* 'Reginald Malby'
'Marella'	WPer
'Maria Laach'	CWil
'Marijntje'	CWil NHol NMen
'Marjorie Newton'	CWil
§ *marmoreum*	EAEE ECho EPot GKev LBee LRHS NMen SRms STre WHal WPer
- from Kanzas Gorge	EPot MOne NHol NMen
- from Monte Tirone	CWil SDys
- from Okol	MOne NMen
- 'Brunneifolium'	CWil EGoo GAbr LBee LRHS MOne NHol NMen SIng WIvy WPer
- subsp. *marmoreum* var. *dinaricum*	CWil EDAr NMen
§ - 'Ornatum'	SRms
'Matador'	MOne
'Mate'	NMen
'Maubi'	CHEx CWil
'Mauvine'	MOne NHol
'Mayfair Imp'	MOne

'Medallion'	MOne
'Meisse'	ECho MOne
'Melanie'	CWil MBrN NMen WIvy
'Mercury'	CWil EAEE GAbr LRHS NBro NHol NMen SIng SRms
'Merkur'	MOne
'Midas'	CWil EAEE
'Mila'	CWil
'Minaret'	MOne
'Mini Frost'	CWil GAbr NMen SIng WPer
'Missouri Rose'	NHol
'Mixed Spice'	CMea CWil
'Moerkerk's Merit'	CWil GAbr NHol NMen
'Mondstein'	CWil MOne SRms WIvy
'Montage'	CWil
§ *montanum*	GCrs LEdu LRHS NMen WPer
- from Arbizion	CWil MOne
- from Windachtal	CWil NMen
- from Monte Tonale, Italy	CWil
- subsp. *burnatii*	CWil MHom SIng WIvy
- subsp. *carpaticum*	CWil
- - 'Cmiral's Yellow'	EPot NMen WIvy
* - Fragell form	SChr
- subsp. *montanum*	CWil
- - var. *braunii*	NLAp
- 'Rubrum'	see *S.* 'Red Mountain'
§ - subsp. *stiriacum*	CWil MOne NMen SIng
§ - - 'Lloyd Praeger'	CWil LBee LRHS MOne NMen SDys WIvy
montanum x *tectorum* var. *boutignyanum*	CWil
	GDJ 94.15
'Moondrops' **new**	CWil
'More Honey'	CWil NMen SRms
'Morning Glow'	WGor WHal
'Mount Hood'	EAEE LRHS SIng SRms WHal
'Mrs Elliott'	MOne
'Mulberry Wine'	CWil EBee LBee LRHS NHol
'Mystic'	CWil MBrN NMen WPer
'Neon' **new**	CWil
nevadense	CWil EPot MOne NMen SRms
- GDJ 96A-07 from Calar de Santa Barbara, Spain	CWil
- from Puerto de San Francisco	CWil MOne
- var. *hirtellum*	CWil NMen SIng
'Nico'	CWil SRms
'Night Raven'	CMea WIvy
'Nigrum'	see *S. tectorum* 'Nigrum'
'Niobe'	MOne WHal
'Noir'	CWil EDAr IHMH NBro NMen WAbe
'Norbert'	CWil EDAr SRms WIvy
'Norne'	MOne
'Nörtofts Beauty'	MOne
'Nouveau Pastel'	CMea CWil MOne NMen WHal
'Novak'	CWil
'Octet'	CWil EPem MOne NMen SIng
octopodes	NBir SIde
- var. *apetalum*	CWil GAbr GKev MOne NMen SIng SRms WIvy
'Oddity'	CPBP CWil MBrN MHer NMen WCot WHal WPer
'Ohio Burgundy'	MOne NDlv NMen WAbe WPer WTin
'Old Rose'	.MOne
'Olivette'	NMen WPer WTin
'Omega'	MOne WPer
'Opitz'	WPer
'Ornatum'	EPot MHer MOne NMen WAbe WEas WHal WIvy
ossetiense	CWil GAbr MOne NMen
'Othello'	CHEx CHal CTri EPfP EWin GAbr GKev MBNS NBir STre WCot WTin
'Pacific Blue Ice' **new**	EDAr

'Pacific Feather Power'   NMen
'Pacific Hep' **new**   CWil
'Pacific Purple Shadows'   CWil
  new
'Packardian'   CWil MOne NHol NMen
   WIvy
'Painted Lady'   CWil
'Palissander'   EDAr GAbr MOne NMen
'Pam Wain'   MHom NMen
'Panola Fire' **new**   WFar
'Parade'   MOne
'Paricutin'   SDys
'Passionata'   CWil
'Pastel'   CWil NMen SIng
patens   see *Jovibarba heuffelii*
'Patrician'   CWil LBee LRHS SRms
'Pekinese'   CWil EAEE EPem EPot GEdr ITim
   MSte NBro NHol NMen SIng SRms
   WCot WEas WGor WPer
'Peterson's Ornatum'   MOne SDys
'Petsy'   CWil SRms
'Pilatus'   EAEE EBee EWes MBNS MWgw
   SRms
§ x *piliferum*   MOne
  'Hausmannii'
'Pink Astrid'   CWil
'Pink Cloud'   CWil NMen SBla SRms
'Pink Dawn'   MOne
'Pink Delight'   MOne
'Pink Flamingoes'   MOne SRot
'Pink Lemonade'   CWil MHom
'Pink Mist'   WPer
'Pink Puff'   CWil MHom MOne NMen SRms
'Pippin'   CWil GAbr SRms WPer
'Piran'   CWil MOne
pittonii   CHal CMea CWil EPot GAbr GCrs
   NMen SIng WHal
'Pixie'   CNic CWil GCrs MOne NDlv
   NMen WIvy
'Plum Frosting' **new**   WGor
'Plum Mist'   NHol
'Plumb Rose'   CWil MOne NMen WIvy
'Pluto'   CWil LBee NHol
'Polaris'   CWil MHom
'Poldark'   MOne
x *pomelii* **new**   WAul
'Pompeon'   MOne
'Ponderosa'   CWil
'Pottsii'   CWil GAbr MHer MOne
I 'Powellii'   MOne
'Prairie Sunset'   GCrs
'Procton'   MOne
'Proud Zelda'   GAbr MOne NMen
'Pruhonice'   CWil MOne SRms
'Pseudo-ornatum'   EPfP LBee LRHS SRms
'Pumaros'   NMen SDys
pumilum   CWil MBar NMen
 – from Adyl Su No 1   CWil
 – from Armchi   SDys
 – from El'brus No 1   CWil
 – from Techensis   CWil NMen
pumilum x *ingwersenii*   MOne NMen
   from Armchi
'Purdy'   MHom WAbe
'Purdy's 50-6'   CWil GAbr
'Purdy's 70-40'   MOne
'Purple Beauty'   EPot GKev MOne
'Purple King'   CMea MHom SDys
'Purple Queen'   CWil EAEE SIng
'Pygmalion'   CWil SIng
'Queen Amalia'   see *S. reginae-amaliae*
'Queen Amealia'   CWil
'Quintessence'   CWil NHol SRms
'Racy'   CWil
'Ragtime'   MOne
'Ramses'   MOne SDys

'Raspberry Ice'   CMea ITim LBee NBro NHol NMen
   WPer
'Rauer Kulm'   CWil
* 'Rauheit'   MOne
'Rauhreif'   WFar
'Red Ace'   CWil NBro NMen SRms WFar
'Red Beam'   CWil MOne
'Red Bug' **new**   SIng
'Red Chips'   MHom
'Red Cross'   MOne
'Red Delta'   CWil MOne NBir NMen
'Red Devil'   CWil EHyt MOne NHol NMen
   WHoo WLin WMow WTin
'Red King'   MOne
'Red Lion'   CWil
'Red Lynn'   CWil
§ 'Red Mountain'   CHal CWil LBee LRHS MOne
   NJOw SRms
'Red Pink'   CWil MOne
'Red Robin'   EAEE EBee MOne SIng
'Red Rum'   WPer
'Red Shadows'   LBee WPer WTin
'Red Spider'   CWil MHom NBro NMen
'Red Summer'   MOne
'Red Wings'   MOne NMen SRms
'Regal'   MOne NMen
'Reggy'   CWil WGor
'Regina'   NMen
reginae   see *S. reginae-amaliae*
§ *reginae-amaliae*   NHol NMen
 – from Kambeecho,   NMen SDys
   Greece No 2
 – from Mavri Petri   CWil MOne SDys
 – from Sarpun, Turkey   CWil NMen SDys WTin
 – from Vardusa, Serbia   CWil SDys
§ 'Reginald Malby'   CTri EAEE ECho LRHS NMen SRms
   WIvy
* *regis-fernandii*   ECho
'Reinhard'   CBrm CMea CWil EAEE EDAr
   EPot GEdr MBrN MHer MOne
   NJOw NMen SRms WFar
   WGwG WHal WHoo WIvy
   WLin WPer
'Remus'   CWil MOne NMen SDys SIng SRms
   WGor
'Rex'   NMen
'Rhône'   CWil LBee MOne
* *richardii*   MBar
'Risque'   CWil LBee WPer
'Rita Jane'   CWil MHom MOne NMen WTin
'Robin'   ITim LBee LRHS NBro NHol NLar
   SRms WTin
'Ronny'   CWil
'Rose Splendour'   NHol
x *roseum*   MOne
 – 'Fimbriatum'   CWil GAbr LBee LRHS NDlv NHol
   WEas
'Rosie'   CMea CNic CPBP CWil EAEE EPot
   GAbr ITim LBee LRHS MOne NHol
   NMen SIng SPoG SRms WHal
   WHoo WLin WPer WTin
'Rotkopf'   CWil MOne NHol NMen SRms
'Rotmantel'   SDys WTin
'Rotsandsteinriese'   MOne
'Rotund'   CWil
'Rouge'   NMen
'Royal Mail'   MOne
'Royal Opera'   CWil MOne NMen
'Royal Ruby'   GAbr LBee LRHS MBrN NMen
   SRms WIvy
'Rubellum'   CWil MOne
'Rubikon Improved'   MOne
'Rubin'   CTri CWCL ECGP EGoo EPPr EPfP
   GAbr GEdr IHMH MSte NBir NEgg
   NLAp NMen SPoG SRms WAbe
   WEas WPer

Name	Codes
'Rubrum Ash'	CWil EHyt EPem GAbr MOne NMen WAbe WTin
'Rubrum Ornatum'	MHom
'Rubrum Ray'	CWil MOne SRms
'Russian River'	WHoo WTin
'Rusty'	CWil
ruthenicum	EAEE LRHS MHom
'Safara'	CWil
'Saffron'	MOne NMen
'Saga'	EPem MHom MOne
'Sanford's Hybrid'	MOne
'Sarah'	MOne NMen
'Sarotte' **new**	CWil
'Sassy Frass'	NMen
'Saturn'	MOne NMen
schlehanii	see *S. marmoreum*
schnittspahnii	MOne
x *schottii*	MOne
'Seminole'	CWil MOne
'Serena'	MOne
'Sha-Na' **new**	CWil
'Sharon's Pencil'	CWil
'Sheila'	GAbr
'Shirley Moore'	CWil MOne WTin
'Shirley's Joy'	CHal GAbr NMen WGwG WTin
'Sideshow'	CWil MOne
'Sigma'	MOne
'Silberkarneol' misapplied	see *S.* 'Silver Jubilee'
'Silberspitz'	CWil MHer MHom NBro NMen WPer
'Silver Cup'	CWil WIvy
§ 'Silver Jubilee'	CMea CWil EAEE EDAr GAbr NBro NDlv SPlb SRms WGor WGwG
'Silver Queen'	CWil
'Silver Shadow' **new**	WGor
'Silver Thaw'	CWil EAEE NMen SIng
'Silverine'	CWil
'Silvertone'	CWil
'Simonkaianum'	see *Jovibarba hirta*
'Sioux'	CPBP CWil GAbr LBee LRHS MBrN NMen SIng WFar WHal WIvy WOut WPer WTin
'Skrocki's Bronze'	GAbr WPer
'Slabber's Seedling'	CWil
'Small Wonder'	CWil
'Smaragd'	CWil LBee WFar
'Sněhová Koule'	SIng
'Snowberger'	CMea CWil EPem EPot LRHS MOne NMen SRms WHal WPer
'Soarte'	MOne
soboliferum	see *Jovibarba sobolifera*
'Soothsayer'	CWil MOne NMen
'Sopa'	CWil MOne NMen
sosnowskyi	CWil MOne NMen
'Spanish Dancer'	NMen
'Speciosum'	MOne
'Spherette'	CWil MBrN NMen WPer
'Spice'	MOne
'Spider's Lair'	SIng
'Spinnelli'	MOne WTin
'Spiver's Velvet'	MOne
'Sponnier'	MOne
'Spring Mist'	CMea CWil EAEE MBrN MOne NLar SPoG SRms WGor WPer WTin
'Sprite'	CWil MOne NMen SDys WIvy WTin
stansfieldii	see *S. arachnoideum* subsp. *tomentosum* 'Stansfieldii'
'Starion'	CWil MOne
'Starshine'	MHer NHol NMen
'State Fair'	CWil NHol NMen SIng WIvy WPer
* *stoloniferum*	GAbr
'Strawberry Fields'	MOne
'Strider'	CWil GAbr WTin
'Stuffed Olive'	CWil MOne SDys SRot
I 'Subanum'	MOne
'Sun Waves'	CWil MOne NHol SDys
'Sunray Magic' **new**	WGor
'Sunrise'	GAbr MOne
'Super Dome'	CWil
'Supernova'	MOne
'Syston Flame'	CWil NMen
'Tambimuttu'	MOne
'Tarita'	CWil
'Tarn Hows'	MOne
'Teck'	CWil
§ *tectorum* ♀H4	CArn CHby CPrp CSam CWil EBee ECho ELan EPfP GKev GPoy LBee LRHS MBar MHer MNHC MWgw NMen SIde SIng SPlb STre WFar WJek WWye
- from Eporn	CWil MOne NMen
§ - var. *alpinum*	CWil MHom MOne NBro NHol NMen SIng
- - from Sierra del Cadi, Spain	MOne NHol
- var. *andreanum*	CWil
- 'Atropurpureum'	ECho ELan NHol NMen WTin
- 'Atrorubens'	EPem NHol
- 'Atroviolaceum'	EDAr GCal NHol NLar NMen WFar WIvy WTin
- var. *boutignyanum*	CWil
GDJ 94.04 from Route de Tuixèn	
- - GDJ 94.02 from Sant Joan de Caselles	CWil
- - GDJ 94.03	CWil
- var. *calcareum*	ECho MOne
- subsp. *cantalicum*	SRms
§ - var. *glaucum*	MOne NDlv
§ - 'Nigrum'	EHyt LBee LRHS MHer MOne NBro NHol NMen SDys SRms WGor WTin
- 'Red Flush'	CWil MBrN NMen SDys SPoG WFar
- 'Royanum'	GAbr
* - subsp. *sanguineum*	EDAr
- 'Sunset'	CWil NMen SDys WHal
- subsp. *tectorum*	MOne
§ - - 'Boissieri'	CWil NMen SRms WIvy
- - 'Triste'	CHEx CWil EBee LBee LRHS MOne NMen SRms WFar
- 'Violaceum'	MHom SRms STre WAbe WGor
tectorum x *zeleborii*	WTin
'Tederheid'	EAEE EBee MBNS MOne MWgw
'Telfan'	MOne NMen
'Tenburg'	MOne
'Terracotta Baby'	CWil
'Thayne'	NMen
'The Platters'	CWil
'The Rocket'	CWil
thompsonianum	CWil NDlv NHol NMen
'Thunder'	CWil
'Tiffany'	CBrm NHol WPer
'Tiger Bay'	NHol
'Tina'	WPer
'Tip Top'	CNic CWil
'Titania'	CWil EPem NBro NMen WHal WTin
'Tombago'	MOne
'Topaz'	CWil EBee LBee LRHS MOne NMen SBla SRms
'Tordeur's Memory'	CWil LBee LRHS MOne NMen
'Trail Walker'	CWil LBee LRHS MOne SRms
transcaucasicum	CWil
'Tree Beard'	CWil
'Tristesse'	CWil MOne NMen WGor WGwG
'Truva'	CWil MOne NMen
'Tumpty' **new**	WGor
'Twilight Blues'	CWil
'Undine'	CWil

x *vaccarii* — CWil NMen
'Vanbaelen' — CWil GAbr NMen SDys
'Vanessa' — CWil
* *verschaffii* — EPem
x *versicolor* — NHol
'Veuchelen' — CWil MOne
vicentei — MHom NDlv NMen WTin
− from Gaton — LBee LRHS MOne NMen WFar
§ − subsp. *paui* — NSla
'Victorian' — MOne
'Video' — CWil MHom NMen
'Virgil' — CWil GAbr MBrN NMen SDys SIng WGor WPer WTin
'Virginus' — CWil GAbr
'Warners Pink' — MDKP
'Watermelon Rind' — MOne
webbianum — see *S. arachnoideum* L. subsp. *tomentosum* (C.B. Lehm. & Schnittsp.) Schinz & Thell.

'Webby Flame' — CWil
'Webby Ola' — NMen
'Wega' — NMen
'Weirdo' — CWil
'Wendy' — MOne NMen
'Westerlin' — CWil MOne NMen
'White Christmas' — see *S. arachnoideum* 'White Christmas'
'White Eyes' — NMen
'Whitening' — GAbr NMen
'Wollcott's Variety' — CWil EBee ECho EPem EWin GAbr LRHS MDKP MOne NBir NMen WPer WTin
wulfenii — CWil NMen
* − *roseum* — EDAr
'Xaviera' — CWil
zeleborii — CHal SDys WHal
'Zenith' — CWil GAbr SRms
'Zenobia' — MHom
'Zenocrate' — WHal
'Zepherin' — CWil
'Zilver Moon' — CWil NMen
'Zilver Suzanna' new — CWil
'Zircon' — NMen
'Zone' — CHEx NMen
'Zorba' — NMen

Senecio (Asteraceae)

B&SWJ 9115 from Guatemala — WCru
HWJK 2118 from Nepal — WCru
§ *articulatus* — CHal EShb
aureus — see *Packera aurea*
bicolor subsp. *cineraria* — see *S. cineraria*
buchananii — see *Brachyglottis buchananii*
candicans — see *S. cineraria*
cannabifolius — GCal
chrysanthemoides — see *Euryops chrysanthemoides*
chrysocoma — CSec
§ *cineraria* — NBlu XPep
− 'Silver Dust' ♀H3 — EPfP LRHS
− 'White Diamond' — ECha SBch
* *coccinilifera* — SBch
compactus — see *Brachyglottis compacta*
crassissimus new — EShb
doria — LRHS WCot WFar WHrl
fistulosus — LEdu
glastifolius — ERea
gnaphaloides new — CBcs
'Goldplate' — NLar
'Gregynog Gold' — see *Ligularia* 'Gregynog Gold'
greyi Hook. — see *Brachyglottis greyi* (Hook. f.) B. Nord.
greyi misapplied — see *Brachyglottis* (Dunedin Group) 'Sunshine'

heritieri DC. — see *Pericallis lanata* (L'Hér.) B. Nord.
hoffmannii — CPIN EShb
integrifolius subsp. *capitatus* — EBee
kleiniiformis — CSec EShb
laxifolius hort. — see *Brachyglottis* (Dunedin Group) 'Sunshine'
leucophyllus — WAbe
leucostachys — see *S. viravira*
macroglossus — CHll EShb
− 'Variegatus' (v) ♀H1 — CHal ERea EShb LAst SMur
maritimus — see *S. cineraria*
monroi — see *Brachyglottis monroi*
nemorensis — NBre
ovatus — NBre
petasitis — CHEx
polyodon — CSpe EBla EShb GBri MNrw NCGa NLar SUsu WPGP
− S&SH 29 — CFir SAga
− subsp. *subglaber* — EMan EMon
przewalskii — see *Ligularia przewalskii*
pulcher — CDes CFwr CSam EBee ETow GBri LEdu LSou MNrw MTho SMrm SUsu WCot WPGP
reinholdii — see *Brachyglottis rotundifolia*
rowleyanus — EBak EShb
scandens — CMac ELan ERea EShb MNrw WCwm WPGP
scaposus new — WCot
seminiveus — EBee
§ *serpens* — CHal CStu CTbh EShb
§ *smithii* — CRow EBee ELan EMan NBid WCot WCru WFar
speciosus — NBir
spedenii — see *Brachyglottis spedenii*
squalidus — WHer
'Sunshine' — see *Brachyglottis* (Dunedin Group) 'Sunshine'
tamoides — CPIN
− 'Variegatus' (v) — ERea
tanguticus — see *Sinacalia tangutica*
§ *viravira* ♀H3-4 — EDsa EGoo EHol EPfP ERea EShb EWin LIck MWgw SMad SMrm SPer WCot WEas WGHP WSHC XPep

Senna (Caesalpiniaceae)

alata new B&SWJ 9772 — WCru
alexandrina — WPGP
artemisioides ♀H1 — CTrC SOWG XPep
§ *corymbosa* — CBcs CCCN CDul CHEx CPIN CRHN ERea LRHS LRav SDEP SOWG SYvo XPep
didymobotrya — LRav SOWG
x *floribunda* — XPep
hebecarpa — EMan
§ *marilandica* — CArn EBee ELan ELau GCal WHil
§ *obtusifolia* — MSal
retusa — CHEx
roemeriana — EBee
septemtrionalis — WPGP
spectabilis — CSec

Sequoia (Cupressaceae)

sempervirens ♀H4 — CBcs CDoC CDul CLnd CMCN CTho CTrG ECrN EHul EPfP ERom ISea LCon MBar MLan SBLw SLon SPoG WDin WEve WMou WNor WWes
− 'Adpressa' — CDoC CDul CMac CRob CSli CTho EHul EOrn EPla IDee LCon LLin MAsh MBar MGos NHol SCoo SLim SPoG WEve WFar
− 'Cantab' — CDul SLim
− 'Prostrata' — CDoC CSli EOrn GBin LLin MAsh MBar SLim WFar

Sequoiadendron (Cupressaceae)
giganteum ♀H4	More than 30 suppliers
- 'Argentea Spicata'	NLar
- 'Bajojeka' **new**	NLar
- 'Barabits Requiem'	MBlu NLar SLim SMad
- 'Blauer Eichzwerg'	NLar SLim
- 'Blue Iceberg'	CKen
- 'Bultinck Yellow'	NLar SMad
- 'Cannibal'	MBri
- 'French Beauty'	NLar
- 'Glaucum'	CDoC CTho EMil LCon LPan MAsh
	MBlu MBri NLar SLim SMad SPoG
	WEve
- 'Greenpeace'	NLar
- 'Hazel Smith'	WWes
- 'Little Stan'	NLar
- 'Pendulum'	CDoC CKen ERod LCon LPan
	MBlu MGos NLar SLim SWvt
	WEve
- 'Peve Bonsai'	NLar
- 'Philip Curtis' **new**	NLar
- 'Powdered Blue' **new**	NLar
- 'Variegatum' (v)	MAsh MGos WEve
- 'Von Martin'	NLar

Serapias (Orchidaceae)
lingua	EHyt SBla SCnR WHil
parviflora	WHer

Serenoa (Arecaceae)
repens	CBrP LPal

Seriphidium (Asteraceae)
caerulescens var. **gallicum**	EEls XPep
§ **canum**	EEls MHer
§ **ferganense**	EEls
§ **fragrans**	EEls
§ **maritimum**	CArn GGar ILis MHer NSti XPep
- var. **maritimum**	EEls
§ **nutans**	EBee EEls MWgw
§ **tridentatum**	CArn EBee
- subsp. **tridentatum**	EEls
- subsp. **wyomingense**	EEls
tripartitum var. **rupicola**	EEls
§ **vallesiacum** ♀H4	EBee ECGP EEls MWgw WEas XPep
vaseyanaum	EEls

Serissa (Rubiaceae)
foetida	see *S. japonica*
§ **japonica**	STre
- **rosea**	STre
- 'Variegata' (v)	CHal STre

Serratula (Asteraceae)
coronata	EBrs
§ **seoanei**	CMea CPom CStu CTri EBee
	ECha EDAr EMan EMon LHop
	MHer MLHP NJOw SAga SBch
	SDix SIng SRms WCot WEas
	WFar WMoo WPGP WPat WPrP
	WTin WWhi
shawii	see *S. seoanei*
tinctoria	CArn CBgR EBee EMan GBar MSal
	NDov NLar NMir
- subsp. **macrocephala**	EBrs LRHS SHGN
wolffii	EBee

Serruria (Proteaceae)
florida **new**	WSAf

Sesamum (Pedaliaceae)
indicum	CArn

Sesbania (Papilionaceae)
punicea	SOWG XPep

Seseli (Apiaceae)
elatum	CSpe
- subsp. **osseum**	EBee
gummiferum	CArn CSpe EBee EMan EMar EWin
	LEdu LPhx MCCP MNFA NLar NSti
	SBla WRHF
hippomarathrum	LPhx SMHy WCot WHoo WPGP
libanotis	CAby CSpe EBee LEdu LPhx MLLN
	NDov NLar SAga SBch
montanum	CDes EBee WPGP
rigidum	EBee

Sesleria (Poaceae)
§ **argentea**	GIBF
autumnalis	EMon EPPr LBBr LPhx WGHP
caerulea	CAby CSam EChP EHoe ELan LAst
	LBuc LPhx MBar MLLN MMoz
	MWhi SWal WGHP WPtf XPep
- 'Malvern Mop'	CBrm EBee WPGP
* **candida**	EPPr
cylindrica	see *S. argentea*
glauca	CRez EHoe MNHC NLar NOak
	NPro WPer
heufleriana	CElw EChP EHoe EMan EPPr EPla
	NLar SLPl SPlb WCot WGHP
insularis	CSWP EMon EPPr EShb LRHS
	SUsu
'Morning Dew'	EBee GCal
nitida	CBig CKno EBee EHoe EMan
	EMon LPhx LRHS MMoz WGHP
	WPGP
rigida	EHoe
sadleriana	CBig EBee EPPr EWes WPrP

Setaria (Poaceae)
RCB/Arg BB-2	WCot
macrostachya ♀H3	CHrt CKno LLWP LPhx SBch
palmifolia	CAby CHEx CHll CKno CKob EPPr
	WCot WDyG WHal WPrP
viridis	CHrt CSpe NChi NSti WCot
	WTin

Setcreasea see *Tradescantia*

shaddock see *Citrus maxima*

Sharon fruit see *Diospyros kaki*

Shepherdia (Elaeagnaceae)
argentea	CAgr CPle NLar

Sherardia (Rubiaceae)
arvensis	MSal

Shibataea (Poaceae)
kumasaca	CAbb CBcs CBig CBrm CDoC
	CHEx EBee EHoe ENBC EPfP EPla
	ERod GCal IBal LEdu LPal MBrN
	MCCP MMoz MWhi MWht NMoo
	NVic SBig SLPl WJun WMul WNor
	WPGP
- 'Aureostriata'	EPla
lancifolia	EPla WJun

Shortia (Diapensiaceae)
galacifolia	IBlr
- var. **brevistyla**	IBlr
soldanelloides	IBlr
- var. **ilicifolia**	IBlr
- var. **magna**	IBlr
uniflora	IBlr
* - var. **kamtchatica**	WCru

* - var. **nana**	WCru
- var. **orbicularis**	CMac GCrs IBlr
'Grandiflora'	

Sibbaldia (Rosaceae)

procumbens	EBee

Sibbaldiopsis (Rosaceae)

§ **tridentata**	EMar GMac
- 'Lemon Mac'	MAsh SIng SMac
- 'Nuuk'	CNic CStu GSki LRHS MBar NHol SMac

Sibthorpia (Scrophulariaceae)

europaea	CHEx CPLG

Sida (Malvaceae)

acuta	MGol
hermaphrodita	EBee EMan WCot

Sidalcea (Malvaceae)

'Brilliant'	CBcs EBee EChP EPfP LRHS MBnl MDKP NBPC NMRc NPri NRnb NSti SPer SRkn WFar WMoo WViv
candida	More than 30 suppliers
- 'Bianca'	CMdw EBee EHrv ERou EShb MFOX MSte NLar NPri SMar WFar WHal WMoo WMow WPer WWhi
- 'Shining Heart'	CFwr
'Crimson King'	WFar
'Croftway Red'	CFir EBee ELan EMan EPfP GGar LRHS MRav MWgw NBro NCob NEgg NHol NRnb SAga SPet SPoG SWvt WAul WCAu WMoo WSan WOut
cusickii	WOut
'Elsie Heugh' ♀H4	More than 30 suppliers
* **grandiflora**	EBee WMow
hendersonii	EBee WMow
hickmanii subsp. **anomala**	EBee
hirtipes	EBee
'Little Princess' PBR	CFir EBee GBri MBri NLar SPoG
'Loveliness'	CMMP EBee EChP ECtt ELan EMan EShb LSou MRav NBro NChi NCob NGdn NLar SAga SRGP WViv
malviflora	MGol NBre NSti SEND SRms SYvo WBVN
- 'Alba'	WFar
- dark-flowered	WMow
'Mary Martin'	SMrm
'Monarch'	MDKP WFar WHil WPnP
'Moorland Rose Coronet'	WMoo
'Mr Lindbergh'	EBee EPfP ERou LBmB LRHS NHol SAga WFar
'Mrs Borrodaile'	CMMP EBee ECtt EMan GBuc GMac LAst LRHS MBNS MBnl MRav MTis MWgw NBro NCob NEgg NGdn NHol NPro SPoG WCAu WFar WMoo WMow
'Mrs Galloway'	WFar
'Mrs T. Alderson'	WFar WMoo WMow
'My Love'	ECha NDov SMrm
neomexicana	EMan GCal
'Oberon'	EBrs GBuc WFar
oregana	NBid NGdn
- subsp. **spicata**	WFar WMoo
'Party Girl'	More than 30 suppliers
'Präriebrand'	LSou SAga SMrm
'Purpetta'	CBrm EChP LBMP MDKP MFOX NLar NPro NRnb STes
'Reverend Page Roberts'	MRav WCot WFar WMow
'Rosaly'	CMdw CMea EBee EChP IFoB LBMP MWrn NLar NVic SMar WGor WHal WLin
'Rosanna'	CBrm EBee EChP GMaP LPhx LRHS MDKP NLar WHil WWeb
'Rose Queen'	CKno EBee ECha EPPr LHop LRHS MBNS MFOX MRav MTis NBro NCob NFla SPer SRms WCAu WFar
'Rosy Gem'	ECtt LRHS MBNS NBre WFar
Stark's hybrids	LRHS SRms
'Sussex Beauty'	CMCo CSam EBee EMan LRHS MArl MAvo MLLN MRav MSte NCiC NDov NEgg NGdn WAul WCMO WCot WFar WMoo WMow WWeb
'Sweet Joy'	SMrm
'The Duchess'	WFar
'William Smith' ♀H4	COtt CSam CWCL EBee ECtt EGra EPfP EWTr EWes LAst LRHS MLLN MRav NChi NCiC NCob NGdn NOrc SGar SPer SPla SRGP WBVN WCAu WFar
'Wine Red'	CFir CKno CMMP EBee EMan ERou EShb IPot MBnl MDKP MSph MSte NCob SPet SWvt WCAu WCra WHil WWhi

Sideritis (Lamiaceae)

cypria	XPep
hyssopifolia	EBee
scordioides	EBee XPep
syriaca	CArn EBee EMan EOHP IFro SGar SSvw

Sieversia (Rosaceae)

pentapetala	see *Geum pentapetalum*
§ **reptans**	GBin NCob

Silaum (Apiaceae)

silaus	NMir

Silene (Caryophyllaceae)

acaulis	ECho EDAr LBee LRHS MTho NLAp NLar NMen SBla SRms WAbe
§ - subsp. **acaulis**	CGra ECho SPlb SRms
- 'Alba'	CMea ECho EPot EWes LRHS NLan NMen WAbe WPat
- 'Blush'	NMen WAbe WLin
§ - subsp. **bryoides**	NWCA
- subsp. **elongata**	see *S. acaulis* subsp. *acaulis*
- subsp. **exscapa**	see *S. acaulis* subsp. *bryoides*
- 'Frances'	EPot GCrs GEdr GMaP NHar NLAp NMen NRya NSla NWCA WAbe
- 'Francis Copeland'	ECho NMen
- 'Helen's Double' (d)	ECho
- 'Mount Snowdon'	ECho EDAr ELan EPfP EWes GMaP LBee LRHS NEgg NHol NLar NMen NRya NWCA SPoG SRms WPat
- 'Pedunculata'	see *S. acaulis* subsp. *acaulis*
alba	see *S. latifolia*
alpestris	CSec EBee EPfP MBar MHer MTho SRms SRot WMoo
- 'Flore Pleno' (d) ♀H4	EWes LBee LRHS NFor NSla
argaea	EHyt
x **arkwrightii**	see *Lychnis* x *arkwrightii*
armeria	EBee WHer
- 'Electra' **new**	CSpe
asterias	GBuc GCal IFro IGor MBNS MHar MNrw NBid NBre NSti WPer
- MESE 429	EBee GBin
atropurpurea	see *Lychnis viscaria* subsp. *atropurpurea*
bellidioides	WPGP
brahuica	CSec
californica	EHyt NWCA
caroliniana	CHrt
- subsp. **wherryi**	NGdn
chungtiensis	EBee GKev

§	*compacta*	CSec EShb NLar WOut
	dinarica	WAbe
§	*dioica*	CArn CHrt CRWN EGoo EPfP MBow MHer NLan NLar NMir NVic SECG SGar SWat WHen WMoo WRos WSFF WShi
	- 'Clifford Moor'^{PBR} (v)	ECtt EHoe LRHS NSti SCoo
	- 'Compacta'	see *S. dioica* 'Minikin'
§	- 'Flore Pleno' (d)	EBee GMac MNrw MRav MTho NBid NBro NGdn SBch SMrm WEas WFar WHoo WPer WTin
§	- 'Graham's Delight' (v)	EMag ITer WCHb WMoo
	- 'Inane'	CBgR MAvo SBch SHar
	- f. *lactea*	MHer
§	- 'Minikin'	CBgR ECha EMon LRHS MAvo WTin
	- 'Pat Clissold' (v)	WCHb
	- 'Pembrokeshire Pastel' (v)	MAvo
§	- 'Richmond' (d)	EBee GBuc NBre SBch SHar
§	- 'Rosea Plena' (d)	CBre EMan MTho NCob WPer WWFP
	- 'Rubra Plena'	see *S. dioica* 'Flore Pleno'
	- 'Thelma Kay' (d/v)	CDes CFee CMil CSev EBee ECtt EWes GBuc MDun NBid NBre NLar WMoo WPGP
	- 'Underdine'	EBee EWes
	- 'Variegata'	see *S. dioica* 'Graham's Delight'
	elisabethae	NEgg
	- 'Alba'	GKev
§	*fimbriata*	More than 30 suppliers
	- 'Marianne'	MNrw
	gallica var. *quinquevulnera*	CSec NLar
	hookeri	WLin
	- Ingramii Group	CGra CPBP
	'Ice Clips'	WPtf
	inflata	see *S. vulgaris*
	italica	NCGa WCot
	keiskei	EMag
	- var. *minor*	EAEE EWes LRHS MTho
	laciniata	EShb
	- 'Jack Flash'	EMag LDai WHrl WSan
§	*latifolia*	CArn MBow NMir NSco WHen
	- subsp. *alba*	CHrt GWCH SECG
	maritima	see *S. uniflora*
	maroccana	CRWN
	morrisonmontana B&SWJ 3149	WCru
	multifida	see *S. fimbriata*
	nigrescens	GKev NWCA
	- HWJK 2287	WCru
	nutans	MNrw SMar SRms SSth WHer WSFF
	orientalis	see *S. compacta*
	petersonii	NWCA
	pusilla	CHal NLar
	regia	CDes EDif LRav MNrw NBre WPGP
	rubra	see *S. dioica*
	saxifraga	XPep
	schafta ♀^{H4}	CHal CHrt ECha ECho ECtt EDAr EPfP GKev LRHS NBid NBlu NCob NJOw NWCA SHGN SPet SRms WAbe WFar WHoo WPer
	- 'Abbotswood'	see *Lychnis* x *walkeri* 'Abbotswood Rose'
	- 'Robusta'	LRHS SBla
§	- 'Shell Pink'	ECha EWes LBee LRHS LSou NBid NCob NWCA WHoo
	sieboldii	see *Lychnis coronata* var. *sieboldii*
	suksdorfii	CSec EPot
*	*tenuis*	GBuc
	- ACE 2429	GBuc
§	*uniflora*	CHrt ECho ECtt EMar EPfP GGar GKev IHMH MWat NBid NBlu

		NBro NJOw SPlb SRms SWal WFar WHen WHer WMoo
	- 'Alba Plena'	see *S. uniflora* 'Robin Whitebreast'
I	- 'Compacta'	ECho EDAr EPPr NDlv SHGN WMoo WPtf
§	- 'Druett's Variegated' (v)	More than 30 suppliers
	- 'Flore Pleno'	see *S. uniflora* 'Robin Whitebreast'
	- pink-flowered	LBee
§	- 'Robin Whitebreast' (d)	CHar CNic EBee ECha ECho ECtt EPfP GCal GMaP MBar MNHC MTho MWat NBid NBro NOak SRms SRot WMoo WPer
	- 'Rosea'	CNic EBee ECtt EMar GGar GKev IHMH LRHS MRav NFor NJOw SPlb SRot SUsu WPer
	- 'Silver Lining' (v)	GBuc
	- 'Swan Lake' (d)	IHMH
	- 'Variegata'	see *S. uniflora* 'Druett's Variegated'
	- Weisskehlchen	see *S. uniflora* 'Robin Whitebreast'
	- 'White Bells'	CTri ECtt EPfP SPet WHoo WKif WSHC
	vallesia	WPer
	virginica	CDes GIBF
§	*vulgaris*	CRWN MHer NLan NMir NSco SECG
	- subsp. *maritima*	see *S. uniflora*
	wallichiana	see *S. vulgaris*
	- 'Wisley Pink'	CHal ECtt
	yunnanensis	LPhx WSHC
§	*zawadskii*	GBuc GKev MDKP NJOw SWal WPer WTin

Silphium (Asteraceae)

	integrifolium	EBee NBre NDov SAga SMad WCot
	laciniatum	CArn EBee EMan LPhx NBre NDov SMad SMrm WCot
	perfoliatum ♀^{H4}	CArn COld EBee GPoy LPhx NBre NDov NLar NRnb NSti SMad SMrm WCot WFar WWpP
	terebinthinaceum	EBee LPhx NDov SMad WCot

Silybum (Asteraceae)

	marianum	CArn CMea CSec CSpe EBee ELan EMag EMan EPfP GAbr GPoy MNHC MSal MWgw NGHP SECG SIde SPav WFar WHer WWye
	- 'Adriana'	EMag EUnu SPav

Simmondsia (Simmondsiaceae)

	chinensis	MSal

Sinacalia (Asteraceae)

§	*tangutica*	CPLG CRow CSam ECha EPPr GGar MBNS MFOX NBid NBro NSti SDix SUsu WAbb WCru WDyG WFar

Sinarundinaria (Poaceae)

	anceps	see *Yushania anceps*
	jaunsarensis	see *Yushania anceps*
	maling	see *Yushania maling*
	murielae	see *Fargesia murielae*
	nitida	see *Fargesia nitida*

Sinningia (Gesneriaceae)

	'Blue Wonder'	MBri
*	*caerulea*	WDib
	canescens ♀^{H1}	CHal ERea WDib
§	*cardinalis*	CHal CSpe EBak WDib
	- 'Innocent'	WDib
§	x *cardosa*	MBri
	'Diego Rose'	MBri
	'Duchess of York'	CSut

'Duke of York'   CSut
'Kaiser Wilhelm'   MBri
nivalis   WDib
speciosa 'Etoile de Feu'   MBri
- 'Kaiser Friedrich'   MBri
- 'Mont Blanc'   MBri
- 'Violacea'   MBri
tubiflora   CMon

Sinobambusa (*Poaceae*)

§ *intermedia*   EPla WJun
* *orthotropa*   EPla WPGP
  rubroligula   EPla NMoo WPGP
  tootsik   EPla WJun
§ - 'Albostriata' (v)   LPJP
  - 'Variegata'   see *S. tootsik* 'Albostriata'

x *Sinocalycalycanthus* (*Calycanthaceae*)

raulstonii 'Hartlage Wine' EPfP
  new

Sinocalycanthus (*Calycanthaceae*)

chinensis   CBcs CMCN CPMA CPle EBee
                     EPfP IDee IMGH MBlu MWea NLar
                     SBrw SPoG SSpi WBVN WFar
                     WPGP

Sinofranchetia (*Lardizabalaceae*)

sp.   CBcs CPIN GCal NLar WCru

Sinojackia (*Styracaceae*)

rehderiana **new**   CBcs CPle
xylocarpa   CBcs EPfP MBlu NLar SSpi
                       WFar

Sinowilsonia (*Hamamelidaceae*)

henryi   CBcs NLar SBrw

Siphocampylus (*Campanulaceae*)

foliosus   EBee
- CDPR 3240   WPGP

Siphocranion (*Labiatae*)

§ *macranthum*   CDes CPne CPom EBee WPGP

Sisymbrium (*Brassicaceae*)

§ *luteum*   WHer

Sisyrinchium ✿ (*Iridaceae*)

from Andes Mountains   EWes
x *anceps*   see *S. angustifolium*
§ *angustifolium*   CMHG CNic EBur ECha ECho
                       LPBA MBNS MBar MNFA MSal
                       MWat NBir NLAp SPlb SRms WPer
- *album*   ECho NLar
§ *arenarium*   CMea CPBP EBur EPot NRya
atlanticum   NBro SUsu WPer
bellum hort.   see *S. idahoense* var. *bellum*
bermudianum   see *S. angustifolium*
- 'Album'   see *S. graminoides* 'Album'
'Biscutella'   CBod CHad CKno CLyd CPrp CTri
                       EBee EBur ECho ECtt EPfP GMaP
                       ITer ITim NEgg NMen NRya SIng
                       SPla SPlb SPoG SWal SWvt WFar
                       WHal WHoo WKif WTin
'Blue Ice'   CBrm CMea CPBP CWCL EBee
                       EBur EDAr MAvo NHol WAbe
                       WHoo WMoo WPat WPer
boreale   see *S. californicum*
brachypus   see *S. californicum* Brachypus
                       Group
'Californian Skies'   More than 30 suppliers
§ *californicum*   CBen EBur ECho EGra EHon
                       EMFW EPfP LPBA MBar MWat
                       NBid NBro WFar WMAq WPer
                       WWye

§ - Brachypus Group   ECho ECtt EDAr EPot IHMH MBNS
                        MWgw NBir NJOw NLAp NLar
                        NPri NVic SGar SPet SPlb SPoG
                        SWal SWat SWvt WMoo
* *capsicum*   CPLG
§ *chilense*   ERos
  coeleste   EBur
  coeruleum   see *Gelasine coerulea*
  commutatum   ECho EDAr GBuc MNrw SGar
  convolutum   EChP LRHS NDov
  cuspidatum   see *S. arenarium*
  'Deep Seas'   NLar SUsu
  demissum   CLyd EBur
  depauperatum   CLyd EBur MNrw MWea WHer
                        WPer
  'Devon Blue'   ECho
  'Devon Skies'   CMCo CMHG CRez CWCL EBur
                        ECho MDKP SBch SIng SWvt
                        WAbe
  douglasii   see *Olsynium douglasii*
  'Dragon's Eye'   CElw CMea CPBP EBur MAvo
                        MBrN MSph SIng SMHy SRot SSvw
                        SUsu WHal WKif
  'E.K. Balls'   More than 30 suppliers
  elmeri   EBur
  'Emmeline'   EBur
  filifolium   see *Olsynium filifolium*
  graminoides   EBur IFoB NBro SYvo WPer
§ - 'Album'   EBur GGar LRHS NBro WPer
  grandiflorum   see *Olsynium douglasii*
  'Hemswell Sky'   CLyd EBur ECho EHoe EPot LAst
                        NRya
  'Iceberg'   EAro EBur EShb MWgw SBch SUsu
                        WKif
  idahoense   ECha ECho EDAr GEdr LRHS
                        LSou MHer NJOw NRya SPlb
                        SRms
  - 'Album'   see *S. idahoense* var. *macounii*
                        'Album'
§ - var. *bellum*   CTri EBur ECho EPfP GGar IFro
                        IHMH LRHS MBNS MWhi NEgg
                        NMen NPri NWCA SGar SPet SRms
                        SSto WHen WMoo WPat WPer
                        XPep
  - - pale-flowered   CKno SMHy
  - - 'Rocky Point'   CElw CLyd CMCo CSpe EAro EBee
                        EBur MAvo NLAp SPoG SRot
                        WHoo WPat
  - blue   EGra
  - dwarf **new**   EBee
  - var. *macounii*   WFar
§ - - 'Album' ♀H4   CMea CTri EBur ECho EDAr EGra
                        EHyt EMFW ERos GAbr LRHS
                        MTho MWat NHol NJOw NLAp
                        SAga SUsu WAbe WPat WPer
                        WWye
  iridifolium   see *S. micranthum*
  junceum   see *Olsynium junceum*
  littorale   CPLG EBur NLar WPer
  macrocarpon ♀H2-3   CFee CLyd CPBP EBur ECho ERos
                        LBee LRHS MDKP NJOw NMen
                        SBla SBri SWal WPer
  'Marie'   EBur
  'Marion'   CMea CPBP MAvo NLar SBch SBla
                        SMHy SPet SRot SSvw SUsu WWye
  'May Snow'   see *S. idahoense* var. *macounii*
                        'Album'
  'Miami'   EBur
§ *micranthum*   CBro EBur ECho WRos
  montanum   ECho ERos IHMH
  'Mrs Spivey'   EBur ECho ECtt MBar MHer NBir
                        NOak
  'North Star'   see *S.* 'Pole Star'
  nudicaule x *montanum* CFee EBur ECho GAbr MNrw
                        NJOw NLAp NRya SRot
                        WPer

palmifolium	CDes EBee EDAr MAvo MDKP MHer SGar
- JCA 2.880.010	WPGP
patagonicum	CPLG EBur EDAr ERos GBuc WPer
'Pole Star'	CFee CLyd CNic CSpe EBur EChP EcHo LRHS LSou NHol WPer
'Quaint and Queer'	More than 30 suppliers
'Raspberry'	CMea EBur NJOw NLAp WAbe
'Sapphire' new	CHar NPri STes
scabrum	see *S. chilense*
'Sisland Blue'	EBur EWes
§ *striatum*	More than 30 suppliers
§ - 'Aunt May' (v)	More than 30 suppliers
- 'Variegatum'	see *S. striatum* 'Aunt May'

Sium (Apiaceae)

sisarum	ELau EOHP EUnu GBar GPoy MHer MSal

Skimmia ✿ (Rutaceae)

anquetilia	MBar
arborescens GWJ 9374	WCru
- subsp. *nitida* B&SWJ 8239	WCru
arisanensis B&SWJ 7114	WCru
x *confusa*	EHol WFar
- 'Kew Green' (m) ♀H4	More than 30 suppliers
§ *japonica*	CDul CMHG CMac CTrw CWib GQui MGan MGos NScw SReu SSta WDin WFar WHCG
- B&SWJ 5053	WCru
- (f)	CMac CTrG CTri ELan ENot EPfP SRms
- 'Alba'	see *S. japonica* 'Wakehurst White'
- 'Bowles' Dwarf Female' (f)	CMHG EPla MBar MBri MGos MRav MWht NHol SLon
- 'Bowles' Dwarf Male' (m)	CMHG EPla MBar
- 'Bronze Knight' (m)	CMac ENot MBar MBri MRav NHol SLim WFar
- 'Cecilia Brown' (f)	WFar
- 'Chameleon'	LAst
- 'Claries Repens'	EPla
- 'Emerald King' (m)	MBar MBri WFar
N - 'Foremanii'	see *S. japonica* 'Veitchii'
§ - 'Fragrans' (m) ♀H4	CDoC CMac CSBt CSam CTri CTrw CWib EBee ECrN ENot EPfP LRHS MBar MBri MGos MRav MWgw NCGa SHBN SLim SPoG SWvt WFar WGwG
- 'Fragrant Cloud'	see *S. japonica* 'Fragrans'
- 'Fragrantissima' (m)	WFar
- 'Fructu Albo'	see *S. japonica* 'Wakehurst White'
- 'Godrie's Dwarf' (m)	EBee EMil MAsh SPoG
- 'Highgrove Redbud' (f)	MBar MGos
- var. *intermedia* f. *repens*	WFar
- - B&SWJ 5560	WCru
- 'Keessen' (f)	EBee WFar
- 'Kew White' (f)	CAbP CDoC CWib EBee ECrN EPfP IArd LRHS MAsh MGos MLan NHol SLon SSta SWvt WCFE WDin WFar WHCG
- 'Luwian' = 'Wanto' PBR	NHol WFar
- 'Marlot' (m)	EPfP NLar SPoG
- 'Nymans' (f) ♀H4	CDoC CEnd CSam EBee ELan EPfP LRHS MAsh MBar MBri MRav MWht NDlv NHol SHBN SLim SMer SPer SPla SPoG SReu SSpi SSta WFar
- 'Oblata'	SMer
- 'Obovata' (f)	EPla
- 'Red Dragon'	CMac

- 'Red Princess' (f)	EPla LAst MAsh WFar
* - 'Red Riding Hood'	NHol SLon
- 'Redruth' (f)	CBcs CDoC CDul CMac CSBt CSam LAst LHop LRHS MAsh MBar MGos MWat MWht NHol SSta WFar
§ - subsp. *reevesiana*	More than 30 suppliers
- - B&SWJ 3763	WCru
- - 'Chilan Choice'	EPfP LRHS MAsh SLim SPla SPoG SSta
- - 'Fata Morgana' (m)	MGos
- - var. *reevesiana* B&SWJ 3544	WCru
- - 'Robert Fortune'	MBar
§ - Rogersii Group	CMac CTri MBar
- - 'Dunwood'	MBar
- - 'George Gardner'	MBar
- - 'Helen Goodall' (f)	MBar
§ - - 'Nana Mascula' (m)	CTri MGos
- - 'Rockyfield Green'	MBar
- - 'Snow Dwarf' (m)	LRHS MBar WFar
- 'Rubella' (m) ♀H4	More than 30 suppliers
- 'Rubinetta' (m)	EPfP IArd LSRN MAsh MBar MGos NCGa NHol SLim WFar
- 'Ruby Dome' (m)	LRHS MBar WFar
- 'Ruby King' (m)	CDoC CSBt ECrN IArd LRHS LSRN MBar NHol
- 'Scarlet Dwarf' (f)	MBar
- 'Scarlet Queen' (f)	CWib
- 'Stoneham Red'	EPla
- 'Tansley Gem' (f)	EPfP IArd LBuc LRHS MAsh MBar MBri MWht SPoG SSta WFar
- 'Thelma King'	WFar
§ - 'Veitchii' (f)	CBcs CDul CMac CSBt CTri ELan ENot EPfP IArd IMGH LRHS MAsh MBar MDun MGos MRav MSwo NHol SEND SHBN SLim SMer SPer SPoG SWvt WDin WTel
§ - 'Wakehurst White' (f)	CBcs CMHG CPle CSBt CTrw EPfP MBar MRav NLar SLim SLon SReu SSpi SSta WFar
- 'White Gerpa'	MGos
- 'Winifred Crook' (f)	EPla IArd LBuc MBar MBri WFar
- 'Winnie's Dwarf'	MGos
- 'Wisley Female' (f)	CTri ECtt EPla NHol WFar
laureola	CBcs CDoC CSam EBee ECot MRav NHol SRms WFar WSHC
- GWJ 9364	WCru
- 'Borde Hill' (f)	NPri
- subsp. *multinervia* B&SWJ 8259	WCru
* *mica* new	ISea
'Olympic Flame'	EBee EPfP LRHS MGos NHol WFar
reevesiana	see *S. japonica* subsp. *reevesiana*
rogersii	see *S. japonica* Rogersii Group

Smallanthus (Asteraceae)

§ *uvedalius*	MSal

Smilacina (Convallariaceae)

bicolor	CDes
racemosa	see *Maianthemum racemosum*

Smilax (Smilacaceae)

B&SWJ 6628 from Thailand	WCru
from Thailand	LEdu
asparagoides 'Nanus'	see *Asparagus asparagoides* 'Myrtifolius'
aspera	EPla EShb LEdu WCru WPGP
china B&SWJ 4427	WCru
discotis	CBcs SEND
glaucophylla B&SWJ 2971	WCru
nipponica B&SWJ 4331	WCru
rotundifolia	LEdu
sieboldii	LEdu MRav
- B&SWJ 744	WCru

Smithiantha (Gesneriaceae)
'Little One' — WDib

Smyrnium (Apiaceae)

olusatrum	CAgr CArn CHrt CSev CSpe EPyc GBar IHMH MHer MNHC MSal SIde SWat WHer WWye
perfoliatum	CPom CSpe EDAr EHrv ELan EMar EPyc EWes MNFA SDix WCot WEas WHal WSHC
rotundifolium	WCot

Socratea (Arecaceae)
montana — LPal

Solandra (Solanaceae)

grandiflora misapplied	see *S. maxima*
grandiflora Swartz	WMul
hartwegii	see *S. maxima*
longiflora	CPlN
§ maxima	CCCN CPlN ERea EShb

Solanum (Solanaceae)

aculeatissimum	EUnu
atropurpureum	CSpe
aviculare G.Forst.	EUnu XPep
bonariense	XPep
crispum	EHol SGar WDin
- 'Autumnale'	see *S. crispum* 'Glasnevin'
- 'Elizabeth Jane Dunn' (v)	WCot
§ - 'Glasnevin' ♀H3	More than 30 suppliers
- 'Variegatum' (v)	WGwG
dulcamara	CArn GPoy MGol
- 'Hullavington' (v)	CNat
- 'Variegatum' (v)	CBcs CFRD CMac CWan EBee ECrN EHoe EPfP EWin LRHS MAsh MBNS NSti SPet SPoG WFar WSHC
giganteum	EUnu
hispidum	CHEx
jasminoides	see *S. laxum*
laciniatum	CArn CBrm CHEx CPLG CSec CSev CSpe EAmu EMan EShb EWes GGar LHop SAPC SArc SBig SGar SHFr SNew SPav WWlt
§ laxum	CPlN EBee EPfP EShb LRHS MNHC MSwo NSti SPer SPet SPoG SRms SWvt WDin WFar WSHC XPep
- 'Album' ♀H3	More than 30 suppliers
- 'Album Variegatum' (v)	CWib EBee EPfP EShb EWin LRHS MGos NEgg SCoo SLim SPer SPla SPlb SPoG WRHF WWeb
* - 'Aureovariegatum' (v)	CBcs CSBt EBee EPfP EShb EWin LRHS MGos NEgg SCoo SLim SPer SPla SPlb SPoG WRHF WWeb
linearifolium	CHea EDsa WPGP WPat WSPU
muricatum (F)	EShb EUnu EWin
pseudocapsicum	EUnu MBri SWal
- 'Ballon'	MBri
- variegated (v)	EShb WCot
quitoense (F)	CHEx EUnu MGol SBig WMul
§ rantonnetii	CCCN CHll CSpe ELan ERea EShb IDee MOak SOWG SYvo XPep
- 'Royal Robe'	CBcs CRHN
* - 'Variegatum' (v)	CSpe ERea EShb MOak
salicifolium	EShb EWin
seaforthianum	CPlN SOWG
§ sessiliflorum (F)	EUnu
sinaicum 'Burbankii'	EUnu
sisymbriifolium	CSec EUnu WWlt
* spontaneum	EUnu
tomentosum	EUnu
topiro	see *S. sessiliflorum*

valdiviense 'Variegatum' (v)	WDin
vespertilio	CSec
wendlandii	CPlN

Solaria (Alliaceae)
sp. — GCal

Soldanella (Primulaceae)

	alpina	ECho GCrs GKev LBMP MTho MWea NMen SBla SIng SRms WAbe WBVN
I	- 'Alba'	ECho WAbe
	austriaca	WAbe
	carpatica	ECho EDAr EHyt ETow GKev LTwo NHol NRya SIng WAbe
	- 'Alba'	ECho MDKP NSla SBla WAbe
	carpatica x pusilla	CPBP ECho NRya NSla SBla
	carpatica x villosa	ECho MDKP
	cyanaster	EBee ECho EHyt GEdr GKev NRya NSla SBla WAbe
	dimoniei	CFee ECho GKev ITim NMen NSla NWCA SBla WAbe
§	hungarica	CLyd ECho ITim MTho WAbe WFar
	minima	CLyd ECho EHyt GCrs NDlv NMen NRya NSla NWCA SBla WAbe
	- 'Alba'	WAbe
	montana	CLAP CLyd ECho GCrs LTwo MTho NJOw NLar NMen SIng WAbe WRha
	- subsp. hungarica	see *S. hungarica*
	pindicola	EBee ECho EHyt EMan EWes GKev NDlv NJOw NMen NWCA WAbe WFar
	pusilla	EBee GKev ITim NSla WAbe
*	- alba	ECho
	villosa	CBgR CDes CLAP CWCL EBee ECho GCrs GGar GKev LRHS MTho NHol NJOw NRya NSla SBch SBla WAbe WFar WSHC

Soleirolia (Urticaceae)

soleirolii	CHEx CHal CTri EPot LPBA LRHS MBri MCCP MWhi SHFr SIng SPer STre WDyG WHer XPep
- 'Argentea'	see *S. soleirolii* 'Variegata'
§ - 'Aurea'	CHal CTri EDAr EPot EWin SIng STre
- 'Golden Queen'	see *S. soleirolii* 'Aurea'
- 'Silver Queen'	see *S. soleirolii* 'Variegata'
§ - 'Variegata' (v)	CHal LPBA WHer

Solenomelus (Iridaceae)

chilensis	see *S. pedunculatus*
§ pedunculatus	CFee WPGP
sisyrinchium	CPBP ERos

Solenopsis (Campanulaceae)
axillaris — see *Isotoma axillaris*

Solenostemon ✿ (Lamiaceae)

'Alice Horn' **new**	NHor
'Angel of the North'	NHor
'Anne Boleyn' (v)	CHal
'Autumn'	NHor
'Autumn Gold'	CHal NHor
'Autumn Rainbow'	WDib
'Beauty' (v)	CHal NHor WDib
'Beauty of Lyons'	CHal NHor
'Beckwith's Gem'	CHal NHor
'Billy Elliot'	NHor
'Bizarre Croton' (v)	CHal NHor
'Black Dragon'	CHal NHor
'Black Heart'	NHor WDib

'Black Prince'	CHal MOak NHor WDib
'Blackheart'	NHor
'Brightness' (v)	NHor
'Brilliant' (v)	NHor WDib
'Bronze Gloriosus' (v)	NHor
'Buttercup'	CHal NHor WDib
'Buttermilk' (v) ♀H1	CHal NHor
'Carnival' (v)	CHal NHor WDib
'Carousel' (v)	NHor
'Castle Eden' **new**	NHor
'Catherine Cookson'	NHor
'Chamaeleon' (v)	NHor WDib
'City of Durham' (v)	NHor
'City of Liverpool'	CHal NHor
'City of Middlesborough' **new**	NHor
'City of Newcastle'	NHor
'City of Sunderland'	NHor
'Combat' (v)	CHal LSou NHor SVil WDib
'Copper Sprite'	CHal
'Coppersmith'	NHor
'Crimson Ruffles' (v) ♀H1	CHal NHor WDib
'Crimson Velvet'	CHal MOak NHor SVil
'Crinkly Bottom'	NHor
'Crown of Bohemia'	NHor
'Dairy Maid' (v)	CHal NHor
'Dazzler' (v)	CHal MOak NHor
'Display'	CHal MOak NHor WDib
'Dolly' (v)	NHor
'Dracula'	CHal NHor
'Durham Gala'	NHor
'Ellas Fire'	NHor
'Emerald Forest'	NHor
'Etna' (v)	CHal NHor
'Fire Fingers'	MOak NHor
'Firebrand' (v) ♀H1	CHal NHor
'Firedance' (v)	NHor
'Firefly'	CHal NHor
'Flamenco Dancer'	NHor
'Flamestitch' **new**	CSpe
'Freckles' (v)	CHal NHor WDib
'Funfair' (v)	CHal NHor
'Gertrude Jekyll' **new**	NHor
'Gloriosus'	CHal NHor
'Glory of Luxembourg' (v) ♀H1	CHal NHor
'Goldie' (v)	CHal NHor
'Grace Darling'	NHor
'Green Mars' (v)	NHor
'Hanna Hauxwell'	NHor
'Hannay Harding'	NHor
'Harvest Time' (v)	NHor
'Holly' (v)	NHor
'Inky Fingers' (v)	CHal NHor WDib
'Jean' (v)	NHor
'Joseph's Coat' (v)	NHor
'Juliet Quartermain'	CHal MOak NHor SVil WDib
'Jupiter'	CHal MOak NHor
'Kate Adie' **new**	NHor
'Kentish Fire' (v)	CHal NHor
'Kiwi Fern' (v)	CHal MOak NHor WDib
'Klondike'	CHal NHor
Kong Series **new**	LRHS
- 'Kong Rose' **new**	NPri
'Laing's Croton' (v)	CHal NHor WDib
'Lemon Dash'	NHor
'Lemondrop'	CHal NHor
'Leopard' (v)	NHor
'Lord Falmouth' ♀H1	CHal NHor WDib
'Luminous'	NHor
'Melody' (v)	CHal NHor WDib
'Midas'	CHal NHor
'Midnight'	MOak NHor
'Mission Gem' (v)	CHal NBlu NHor SVil
'Molten Lava' (v)	NHor
'Mrs Pilkington' (v)	NHor
'Muriel Pedley' (v)	CHal NHor
'Nettie' (v)	NHor
'Ottoman'	CHal NHor
'Paisley Shawl' (v) ♀H1	CHal NHor WDib
'Palisandra'	CSpe
pentheri	CHal NHor
'Percy Roots'	NHor
'Peter Wonder' (v)	CHal NBlu NHor SVil WDib
'Phantom'	NHor
'Pheasant's Eye' (v)	NHor
'Picturatus' (v) ♀H1	CHal NHor WDib
'Pineapple Beauty' (v) ♀H1	CHal MOak NHor WDib
'Pineapplette' ♀H1	CHal MOak NHor WDib
'Pink Devil' (v)	NHor
'Pink Shawl'	NHor
'Primrose Cloud' (v)	NHor
'Primrose Spire' (v)	NHor
'Purple Oak'	CHal NHor
'Raspberry Ripple'	CHal
'Red Croton' (v)	NHor WDib
'Red Mars'	NHor WDib
'Red Nettie' (v)	CHal NHor WDib
'Red Paisley Shawl' (v)	NHor
'Red Rosie'	CHal NHor WDib
'Red Stinger'	CHal
'Red Velvet'	CHal NHor
'Rob Roy'	MOak
'Rose Blush' (v)	CHal MOak NHor WDib
'Rosie'	NHor
'Roy Pedley'	CHal NHor
'Royal Scot' (v) ♀H1	CHal NHor WDib
'Salmon Plumes' (v)	CHal NHor
'Saturn'	NHor
'Scarlet Poncho'	NHor
'Scarlet Ribbons'	CHal MOak NHor
'Speckles' (v)	CHal NHor
'Spire' (v)	NHor
'Strawberry Jam'	CHal NHor
'Sunbeam' (v)	NHor
'The Durham Angel' **new**	NHor
thyrsoideus	see *Plectranthus thyrsoideus*
'Timotei'	NHor
'Tom Cooke'	NHor
'Treales' (v)	CHal NHor WDib
'Vesuvius'	CHal NHor
'Volcano' **new**	NHor
'Walter Turner' (v) ♀H1	CHal MOak NHor WDib
'White Gem' (v)	CHal NHor
'White Pheasant' (v)	CHal NHor
'Winsome' (v)	CHal NHor WDib
'Winter Sun' (v)	CHal NHor
'Wisley Flame'	NHor WDib
'Wisley Tapestry' (v) ♀H1	CHal LAst MOak NHor WDib
'Yellow Croton' (v)	NHor

Solidago (Asteraceae)

Babygold	see *S.* 'Goldkind'
brachystachys	see *S. cutleri*
caesia	EBee ECha EMon ERou EShb EWes MFOX MSte NBir WFar WMoo WOld WTin
canadensis	CAgr CTri ELan NBre SEND SPlb WFar WHoo
§ - var. *scabra*	WOld WTin
'Citronella'	NFla
'Cloth of Gold'	CBcs COtt EBee EBrs ECho LRHS NPro SWvt WMnd WOld
§ 'Crown of Rays'	CPrp EBee ECtt ERou LRHS MRav MWgw WFar WLin WMnd
§ *cutleri*	EBee ECho ELan EWsh MBar MTho MWat NJOw NLar SBla SPlb SRms WFar WPer
I - *nana*	ECho EWes WBor

'Dzintra' — EBee
'Early Bird' — WFar
'Featherbush' — EBrs LRHS
§ *flexicaulis* — GMaP
§ - 'Variegata' (v) — CWan EChP ELan EMag EMan EMar EMon EPfP GMaP LRHS MHar NLar NSti WFar WHer WOld WPer
'Gardone' ♀H4 — WFar
gigantea — EMon NBid WPer
glomerata — EMon EShb NBre NLar NNor WPer
Golden Baby — see *S.* 'Goldkind'
'Golden Crown' — WViv
§ 'Golden Dwarf' — LRHS
'Golden Falls' — EBrs
'Golden Fleece' — see *S. sphacelata* 'Golden Fleece'
Golden Gate = 'Dansolgold' — WViv
'Golden Shower' — CSam CWCL MWat
'Golden Thumb' — see *S.* 'Queenie'
'Golden Wings' — CBre ERou MWat
'Goldenmosa' ♀H4 — CSBt EMan EPfP ERou GMaP LRHS MRav MWat SPoG WCot WFar WOld
'Goldilocks' — NPri SRms
§ 'Goldkind' — CHrt CMMP COIW CSBt CWib EBee ECho ECtt EPfP ERou EShb GAbr IHMH MBow MNHC NBPC NEgg NNor NOrc SPet SPoG SWal SWvt WBrk WFar WMoo WWeb
'Goldwedel' **new** — EBee
Goldzwerg — see *S.* 'Golden Dwarf'
graminifolia — see *Euthamia gymnospermoides*
'Harvest Gold' — CElw ERou
hispida — EMon
hybrida — see x *Solidaster luteus*
latifolia — see *S. flexicaulis*
'Laurin' — EBrs EMil EPfP NLar WTin
'Ledsham' — EBee LRHS NBre SPoG WMnd
'Lemore' — see x *Solidaster luteus* 'Lemore'
'Linner Gold' — NBre
Monte d'Oro = 'Dansolmonte'PBR — WViv
Monte Solo = 'Dansosolo' — WViv
odora — MGol MSal
ohioensis — EBee
* 'Peter Pan' — ERou LHop WFar
§ 'Queenie' — EBee ECha ECho MHer MLHP NBre NPro NVic SRms
rigida — MRav NBre WCot WPer WWpP
- JLS 88002WI — EMon
roanensis — NBre
rugosa — ECha MWgw NBre WCot
- subsp. *aspera* — EMon
- 'Fireworks' — CBgR CBre CMHG CPrp CSam EBee EBrs EChP EMan EPPr ERou GQue MAvo MBNS MHar MNFA NBPC NDov SUsu WCot WHil WHoo WOld WTin
sciaphila — EBee NBre
sempervirens — WCot
simplex subsp. *simplex* — NWCA WLin WPer
  var. *nana*
'Sonnenschein' **new** — NBre
'Spätgold' — EBee
speciosa — EBrs EUnu NBre WPer
spectabilis var. — EBee
  confinis **new**
§ *sphacelata* 'Golden Fleece' — EAEE EBee LHop LRHS NBre SPoG WHoo WMnd
spiraeifolia — NBre
Strahlenkrone — see *S.* 'Crown of Rays'
'Summer Sunshine' — ERou
Sweety = 'Barseven'PBR — MBri

'Tom Thumb' — MRav SRms WEas
uliginosa — EShb NBre
ulmifolia — EBee LRHS NBre
virgaurea — CArn CSam EBee GPoy GWCH MHer MNHC NBre NLar NSco WHer WPer WSel
- subsp. *alpestris* var. — CLyd CStu NBre
  minutissima
- var. *cambrica* — see *S. virgaurea* subsp. *minuta*
§ - subsp. *minuta* — CSam
§ - 'Variegata' (v) — EHoe NPro
vulgaris 'Variegata' — see *S. virgaurea* 'Variegata'

x *Solidaster* (Asteraceae)

hybridus — see x *S. luteus*
§ *luteus* — CBgR CTri EBee EWTr GBri MBri MHar SRms WEas WFar WHil
§ - 'Lemore' ♀H4 — CElw CHea CHrt CMea COIW CPrp EBee ELan EMan ENot EPfP ERou EWsh GMac LRHS MWat NCGa NPri NVic SPer WFar
'Super' — WCot WFar

Sollya (Pittosporaceae)

fusiformis — see *S. heterophylla*
heterophylla ♀H1 — More than 30 suppliers
- 'Alba' — CBcs CCCN CRez EBee ELan LBuc LRHS SPoG SWvt WCMO
- mauve-flowered — ECou
- pink-flowered — CCCN CRez CSPN EPfP SAdn SWvt
- 'Pink Charmer' — EBee ELan ERea LRHS MWgw SBrw SMur SPer SPoG WSHC

Sonchus (Asteraceae)

fruticosus — CHEx CSec
giganteus **new** — CHll
palustris — EMon

Sophora (Papilionaceae)

§ *davidii* — CPle CWib ECou EPfP EWTr IDee MBlu MGos MWea SBrw SOWG WPGP WSHC
flavescens — NLar
japonica ♀H4 — CAbP CBcs CDul CLnd CTho CWib EBee EPfP EWTr LBuc LRHS MDun MGos MNHC MWhi SBLw SBrw SHBN SMHT SPlb WBVN WDin WNor WOrn
- 'Pendula' — LRHS MBlu MGos SBLw
- 'Red Dragon' — SBrw
§ 'Little Baby' — CWib EBee EPfP ERea LAst MCCP MGos MWea SBrw SHFr SMur SPoG SWvt WPGP WPat
macrocarpa — GQui
microphylla — CBcs CHEx CPle CWCL EBee ECou EPfP IFro LHop SEND WHer WPGP
- 'Dragon's Gold' — CBcs EBee ECou ELan EPfP ERea LRHS MAsh SBrw SPoG SSta WDin
- 'Early Gold' — ERea GQui SPoG
- var. *fulvida* — ECou
- var. *longicarinata* — ECou
mollis — CPLG
- CC 4540 — MGol
prostrata misapplied — see *S.* 'Little Baby'
prostrata Buch. — CBcs ECou
- Pukaki form — ECou
Sun King = 'Hilsop'PBR ♀H4 — EBee EPfP EWes LRHS LSRN MBlu MGos NLar SCoo SPoG
tetraptera ♀H3 — CAbP CBcs CDul CMac EBee ECou EPfP GQui ISea MLan SBrw SEND SPer SRms WBVN WPGP
- 'Grandiflora' — CBrm
viciifolia — see *S. davidii*

Sorbaria (Rosaceae)

SF 95205	ISea
aitchisonii	see *S. tomentosa* var. *angustifolia*
arborea	see *S. kirilowii*
aff. **assurgens**	WCru
BWJ 8185	
§ **kirilowii**	CPLG GIBF IFro NLar SLon WDyG WOut
lindleyana	see *S. tomentosa*
rhoifolia	EPfP
sorbifolia	CAbP CBcs CMCo EBee ECrN EMil EWTr GIBF LRHS MBar MDun MLHP MTis MWgw MWhi NPro SEND SLPl SPer SPoG WCot WDin WFar WHil
- 'Sem'PBR **new**	CBgR GBin MAsh NLar WBor WMoo
- var. **stellipila**	SLPl
- - B&SWJ 776	WCru
§ **tomentosa**	CAbP SHBN WHCG
§ - var. **angustifolia** ♀H4	CBcs CDul CTri CWan EBee ELan EPfP IMGH LRHS MDun MRav NPro SEND SLon SPer SPoG WCru WEas WFar WHer

x Sorbopyrus (Rosaceae)

auricularis **new**	CTho

Sorbus ✿ (Rosaceae)

Harry Smith 12732	LRHS MDun
Harry Smith 12799	GIBF
§ **alnifolia**	CLnd CMCN CTho EPfP GIBF MBlu SLPl
amabilis	NLar
americana	CLnd GIBF NWea
- 'Belmonte'	SBLw
- *erecta*	see *S. decora* (Sarg.) C.K. Schneid.
aff. **amurensis**	WCru
B&SWJ 8665	
anglica	CDul CNat
'Apricot'	CEnd
'Apricot Lady'	MAsh WJas
'Apricot Queen'	CLnd ECrN EMil LAst MDun NEgg SBLw
aria	CCVT CDul CLnd CSBt CTri ECrN EPfP LBuc MBar MGan MGos NBee NEgg NWea WDin WMou WOrn
- 'Aurea'	CLnd MBlu MGos WFar
- 'Chrysophylla'	CDul CSBt EBee ECrN IMGH LRHS MBri MGos NWea SLim SPer SPoG
- 'Decaisneana'	see *S. aria* 'Majestica'
- 'Gigantea'	EWTr
- 'Lutescens' ♀H4	More than 30 suppliers
- 'Magnifica'	CDoC CDul CTho ECrN ELan EWTr LPan NEgg SBLw WDin WJas
§ - 'Majestica' ♀H4	CCVT CDoC CDul CLnd CTho EBee ECrN GIBF LPan NWea SBLw SPer SPoG WJas WOrn
- 'Mitchellii'	see *S. thibetica* 'John Mitchell'
- 'Orange Parade'	SBLw
- var. **salicifolia**	see *S. rupicola*
arnoldiana 'Golden Wonder'	see *S.* 'Lombarts Golden Wonder'
aronioides misapplied	see *S. caloneura*
arranensis	CDul CNat GIBF
§ **aucuparia**	More than 30 suppliers
- 'Aspleniifolia'	CBcs CCVT CDul CLnd CMCN CSBt CTho CWSG EBee ECrN LAst LPan LRHS MBri MDun MGos NWea SBLw SLim SPer SPoG WDin WFar WJas WOrn
I - 'Aurea'	SBLw
§ - 'Beissneri'	CDul CLnd MBri MGos NLar SCoo
- Cardinal Royal = 'Michred'	CDoC ECrN GQui LRHS NEgg SCoo WJas
- 'Crème Lace'	CDul GTSp SCoo
- 'Dirkenii'	CDul CWSG MAsh MDun SPoG WDin WJas
§ - var. **edulis** (F)	CDul CLnd CTho LBuc LPan MGos SBLw SCoo WDin
§ - - 'Rossica Major'	CDul CTho ECrN GQui SBLw SCoo WFar
§ - 'Fastigiata'	CEnd CLnd CSBt CTri ECrN EPfP LAst MGos NBee SBLw SHBN WDin WFar
- 'Hilling's Spire'	CTho MAsh MLan SLPl
- 'Pendula'	EBee SBLw
- **pluripinnata**	see *S. scalaris* Koehne
- var. **rossica** Koehne	see *S. aucuparia* var. *edulis*
- 'Rossica Major'	see *S. aucuparia* var. *edulis* 'Rossica Major'
- 'Sheerwater Seedling' ♀H4	CCVT CDoC CDul CLnd CMCN CTho EBee ECrN ELan EPfP EWTr LAst LRHS MGos MLan MRav MSwo NBee NBlu NEgg SCrf SLim SPer SSta WDin WFar WOrn
- 'Wettra'	SBLw
- 'Winterdown'	CNat
- 'Xanthocarpa'	see *S. aucuparia* var. *xanthocarpa*
§ - var. **xanthocarpa** ♀H4	CLnd EPfP SBLw WDin
Autumn Spire = 'Flanrock'	CDoC CWSG LRHS MAsh MBri MGos MLan SCoo
'Bellona'	WPat
'Burka'	see *Aronia* x *Sorbus* 'Burka'
§ **caloneura**	EPfP EPla SSpi WPGP
'Carpet of Gold'	CLnd
cashmiriana Hedl. ♀H4	More than 30 suppliers
cashmiriana misapplied pink-fruited	EMui LRHS
- 'Rosiness'	CLnd MAsh MBri MDun SCoo SLim
chamaemespilus	GIBF WPat
'Chamois Glow'	WJas
'Chinese Lace'	More than 30 suppliers
§ **commixta**	CBcs CDul CEnd CLnd CMCN CTho EBee ECrN EGra EPfP EPla GIBF LAst LRHS MBar MBlu MBri MGos MLan MRav MSwo NBea NBee SBLw SLim SPer WDin WJas WOrn
- 'Embley' ♀H4	CBcs CCVT CDul CMCN CSBt CSam CTho CTri ECrN ELan ENot EPfP EWTr GQue MBar MDun MGos MRav SLim SPoG SSta WDin WOrn
- var. **rufoferruginea**	GQui
- - B&SWJ 6078	WCru
conradinae Koehne	see *S. esserteauana*
'Copper Kettle'	MAsh MBri SCoo
'Coral Beauty'	CDul CLnd
'Covert Gold'	CEnd CLnd
croceocarpa	CDul CNat
cuspidata	see *S. vestita*
§ **decora** (Sarg.) C.K. Schneid.	CTho GIBF NBlu SBLw
* - 'Grootendorst'	CDul
- var. **nana**	see *S. aucuparia* 'Fastigiata'
devoniensis	CAgr CDul CNat CTho
- 'Devon Beauty' **new**	CAgr
discolor misapplied	see *S. commixta*
discolor ambig. **new**	SEND
discolor (Maxim.) Maxim.	CLnd CMCN EBee MAsh MBlu NLar NWea WJas
domestica	CDul CMCN EPfP WDin
'Eastern Promise'	CSam CWSG ECrN LRHS MAsh MBlu MBri MDun MLan MWat

		NLar SCoo SLim SMHT SPoG SSta WDin WJas WOrn
	eminens	CDul CNat
§	*esserteauana*	CDoC CLnd CTho EPfP
	'Fastigiata'	see *S. aucuparia* 'Fastigiata', *S.* x *thuringiaca* 'Fastigiata'
	folgneri	CDoC CEnd
	- 'Emiel'	EPfP MBlu
	- 'Lemon Drop'	CDul CEnd CLnd CWSG EPfP MAsh MBlu MDun NLar SCoo SMad SSpi
§	*foliolosa*	CDul EPfP NWea WKif
	- 'Lowndes'	CLnd
	forrestii	CBcs EPfP NBea NLar SLPl SMHT
*	*fortunei*	CLnd
I	*fruticosa* McAllister	CEnd CLnd EBee EPfP GIBF NWea SSta WJas
	- 'Koehneana'	see *S. koehneana* C.K. Schneid.
	'Ghose'	CEnd CLnd MBlu SCoo SPer SSpi
	'Golden Wonder'	see *S.* 'Lombarts Golden Wonder'
N	*gonggashanica*	CLnd EGFP
*	*gorrodini*	CLnd
§	*graeca*	CMCN GIBF SEND
	harrowiana	WPat
	'Harvest Moon'	GQui
	hedlundii	GTSp NLar WOrn
	hemsleyi	CDul CLnd GIBF MBri MDun WPGP
	x *hostii*	MRav SPer
§	*hupehensis* C.K. Schneid. ♀H4	More than 30 suppliers
	- SF 96268	ISea
	- 'November Pink'	see *S. hupehensis* 'Pink Pagoda'
§	- var. *obtusa* ♀H4	CCVT CDul CLnd CMCN EPfP GIBF MDun SSpi SSta WDin
§	- 'Pink Pagoda'	CDoC CDul CLnd CWSG CWib EBee EGra EMui EPfP IArd IMGH LAst LRHS LSRN MAsh MBlu MDun MGos MLan MWat NWea SCoo SLim SLon SPoG WDin
	- 'Rosea'	see *S. hupehensis* var. *obtusa*
	hybrida misapplied	see *S.* x *thuringiaca*
	hybrida L.	ECrN
	- 'Gibbsii' ♀H4	CDoC CLnd EBee ELan EPfP MAsh MBri SPur
	insignis	CDoC EPfP GIBF WPat
	intermedia	CBcs CCVT CDul CLnd CSBt CTho CTri CWib ECrN GIBF LRHS MGos NBee NBlu NWea SBLw WDin WMou
	- 'Brouwers'	ELan LPan SBLw WMoo
	'Joseph Rock'	More than 30 suppliers
§	x *kewensis*	CDul CLnd NWea SMHT SPer SPlb
	'Kirsten Pink'	CDul CLnd CWib EBee ECrN MDun MMuc SMHT SPer WFar
§	*koehneana* C.K. Schneid. ♀H4	CBcs CLnd CMCN ECrN EGra GCrs GGGa GQui MDun NBlu NLAp NMen NWea WPat WTin
	aff. *koehneana*	WCwm
	- Harry Smith 12799	GQui
	'Kukula'	MDun
	kurzii	GIBF
	lanata misapplied	see *S. vestita*
	lancastriensis	CDul CNat GIBF
	latifolia	CLnd ECrN GIBF NWea SBLw WDin
	'Leonard Messel'	MAsh MBri NBea
	'Leonard Springer'	ECrN EPfP GQui SSta
	leptophylla	CDul
	leyana	WMou
§	'Lombarts Golden Wonder'	CBcs CDoC CDul CLnd MAsh MBlu MDun NWea SBLw WJas
	'Maidenblush'	SBLw
	matsumurana misapplied see *S. commixta*	

	megalocarpa	CDoC CPMA EPfP SSpi WCwm WNor WPGP WPat
	microphylla GWJ 9252	WCru
	'Molly Sanderson'	SSta
	monbeigii (Card.) Yü	CLnd GIBF
	moravica 'Laciniata'	see *S. aucuparia* 'Beissneri'
	mougeotii	GIBF
	multijuga	GIBF
§	*munda*	CMCN GBin SCoo
N	*parva*	GIBF
	'Peachi-Ness'	CLnd
	'Pearly King'	CSam CTho MAsh NBea WJas
	pekinensis	see *S. reticulata* subsp. *pekinensis*
§	'Pink Pearl'	CDul MDun
	'Pink-Ness'	EBee MDun SCoo SLim SPoG
	pogonopetala Koehne	GIBF
	pohuashanensis misapplied	see *S.* x *kewensis*
	porrigentiformis	CDul CNat
	poteriifolia	GCrs NLar
	prattii misapplied	see *S. munda*
	prattii Koehne	CLnd WCwm
	- var. *subarachnoidea*	see *S. munda*
	pseudofennica	GIBF
N	*pseudovilmorinii*	GBin GIBF MBri NLar
	- MF 93044	SSpi
	randaiensis	GIBF GQui SPlb
	- B&SWJ 3202	SSpi WCru
	'Ravensbill'	CTho
	'Red Tip'	CDul CLnd MBar
	reducta ♀H4	CBcs CEnd CMCN CSWP CSec EPfP EPot GBin GCrs GIBF GKev GQui LRHS MBlu NBlu NHar NHol NLAp NWea SBrw SCoo SPer SPoG SSpi WDin WFar WNor
	reflexipetala misapplied	see *S. commixta*
	rehderiana misapplied	see *S. aucuparia*
	rehderiana Koehne	CLnd GIBF WNor
§	*reticulata* subsp. *pekinensis*	GIBF
	rhamnoides GWJ 9363	WCru
	'Rowancroft Coral Pink'	CTho EWTr MBar MGos
	rufopilosa	WPat
§	*rupicola*	GIBF
	'Salmon Queen'	CLnd
	sambucifolia	GIBF
	sargentiana ♀H4	CDul CEnd CLnd CMCN CTho CTri EBee ECrN EGra ELan EPfP IMGH LAst LBuc LRHS MBlu MBri MGos MRav MSwo NWea SLim SMad SPer SSpi WDin WJas WOrn
§	*scalaris* Koehne	CBcs CEnd CTho CTri EBee EPfP LRHS MBlu MBri MGos SCoo SPer SPoG SSpi WDin WJas WOrn
	'Schouten'	ECrN SBLw
	scopulina misapplied	see *S. aucuparia* 'Fastigiata'
	setschwanensis	GGGa
	sibirica	GIBF
	'Sunshine'	CDoC CDul MAsh MGos NBlu WJas
	thibetica	WPGP
§	- 'John Mitchell' ♀H4	CAgr CDul CEnd CLnd CMCN CWib ECrN EPfP GQui LRHS MAsh MBlu MBri MGos MRav MWya NBea NWea SBir SLim SPer WJas WOrn
	aff. *thibetica* BWJ 7757a	WCru
	x *thuringiaca*	NBea WMou
§	- 'Fastigiata'	CBcs CDul CLnd CSBt EPfP GIBF LPan MAsh MGos NBee SBLw WDin WJas
	torminalis	CCVT CDul CLnd CTho CTri EBee ECrN EPfP LBuc LRHS MBri MRav MWya NWea SBLw SCoo SPer WDin WFar WMou WOrn

umbellata	CMCN
- var. *cretica*	see *S. graeca*
ursina	see *S. foliolosa*
x *vagensis*	CLnd GIBF WMou
verrucosa var. *subulata* HWJ 579	WCru
§ *vestita*	CLnd CMCN CTho MBlu
vexans	CDul CNat GBin GIBF
thibetica ♀H4	More than 30 suppliers
- 'Robusta'	see *S.* 'Pink Pearl'
aff. *thibetica*	GIBF LAst
wardii	CBcs CTho EPfP MBlu
'White Swan'	NBlu
'White Wax'	CDul CWSG EPfP GQue LAst MAsh MDun MGos MLan SBLw SPer WDin WPat
'Wilfrid Fox'	CLnd SHBN SLPl
wilmottiana	CDul
wilsoniana	CLnd GQui
'Wisley Gold'	CWSG LRHS MBri MGos NLar SCoo WHCr

Sorghastrum (Poaceae)

avenaceum	see *S. nutans*
§ *nutans*	CBig CKno CRWN ECha LRav NBre
- 'Indian Steel'	CBig CBrm CPen CSam EBee EChP EPPr EWin LBBr MSte MWhi NBre NDov SMar WMnd

Sorghum (Poaceae)

halepense	MSte

sorrel, common see *Rumex acetosa*

sorrel, French see *Rumex scutatus*

Souliea see *Actaea*

Sparaxis (Iridaceae)

bulbifera	ECho LBow
'Colour Mill' **new**	WHil
elegans	EPot
- 'Coccinea'	LBow
grandiflora subsp. *acutiloba*	LBow
- subsp. *fimbriata*	LBow
- subsp. *grandiflora*	CGrW ECho WCMO WCot
parviflora	ECho LBow
tricolor	ECho MDun
§ *variegata* (v)	LBow
- subsp. *metelerkampiae* (v) **new**	CDes
villosa	ECho

Sparganium (Sparganiaceae)

§ *erectum*	CRow EHon EMFW EMag LNCo LPBA NPer NSco SWat WFar WMAq WSFF WWpP
ramosum	see *S. erectum*

Sparrmannia (Tiliaceae)

africana ♀H1	CBcs CHEx CHll CKob CPLG CPle CTrG EAmu ERea EShb MBri SDnm SMur SPav SYvo
- 'Variegata' (v)	ERea
palmata	see *S. ricinocarpa*
§ *ricinocarpa*	CKob

Spathipappus see *Tanacetum*

Spartina (Poaceae)

patens	EHoe EPPr
pectinata	CHEx EChP GBin NNor WFar
- 'Aureomarginata' (v)	More than 30 suppliers

Spartium (Papilionaceae)

junceum ♀H4	More than 30 suppliers
- 'Brockhill Compact'	CDul LRHS SBra SPoG

Spartocytisus see *Cytisus*

Spathantheum (Araceae)

orbignyanum	EBee ITer WCot

Spathiphyllum (Araceae)

'Viscount'	MBri
wallisii	CHal EOHP LRHS MBri

spearmint see *Mentha spicata*

Speirantha (Convallariaceae)

§ *convallarioides*	CDes CLAP CPom CStu EBee ECho EHrv ERos LEdu SOkd WCot WCru WPGP
gardenii	see *S. convallarioides*

Spergularia (Caryophyllaceae)

purpurea	ECho
rupicola	ECho SECG

Sphacele see *Lepechinia*

Sphaeralcea (Malvaceae)

ambigua	ELan XPep
'Childerley'	CSpe LHop SAga
coccinea	SPlb
fendleri	CBcs CHll CSam WWye
- subsp. *venusta*	CPom XPep
grossulariifolia	LRav
'Hopleys Lavender'	EBee EChP EMan EWin LHop NLar SAga SWvt
'Hyde Hall'	EBee EChP EPPr EWin WBor
incana	SAga
malviflora	WPer
miniata	CHll ELan MOak SAga
munroana	CDMG CPom CSev CWCL EBee ELan EPPr EWin LHop MOak WCFE WSHC XPep
- 'Dixieland Pink'	EBee
- 'Manor Nursery' (v)	EMan EWes LHop
- pale pink	ECtt EMan EWin
* - 'Shell Pink'	CSpe ECGP
'Newleaze Coral'	CSpe EBee EMan EPPr LHop NLar SAga SPoG SWvt
'Newleaze Pink'	LHop SAga
obtusiloba **new**	CSpe
parvifolia	EBee
remota	CPLG EMan EShb MGol SPlb
rivularis	EMan MGol
umbellata	see *Phymosia umbellata*

Sphaeromeria (Asteraceae)

§ *capitata*	EPot NWCA

Spigelia (Loganiaceae)

marilandica 'Wisley Jester'	LRHS MBri SCoo

Spilanthes (Asteraceae)

acmella	see *Acmella oleracea*
oleracea	see *Acmella oleracea*

Spiraea ❀ (Rosaceae)

'Abigail'	CDoC
albiflora	see *S. japonica* var. *albiflora*
arborea	see *Sorbaria kirilowii*
§ 'Arguta' ♀H4	More than 30 suppliers
x *arguta* 'Bridal Wreath'	see *S.* 'Arguta'
- 'Compacta'	see *S.* x *cinerea*

– 'Nana'	see *S.* x *cinerea*
bella	SLon WHCG WTin
betulifolia	MRav NHol SMac WDin WHCG
– var. ***aemiliana***	CWSG EBee ECtt MAsh MGos
	NHol SLPl WFar
x ***billardii*** 'Triumphans'	see *S.* x *pseudosalicifolia*
	'Triumphans'
x ***bumalda***	see *S. japonica* 'Bumalda'
– 'Wulfenii'	see *S. japonica* 'Walluf'
callosa 'Alba'	see *S. japonica* var. *albiflora*
canescens	CPLG
– AC 1354	NPen
– CC 4545	MGol
§ ***cantoniensis*** 'Flore Pleno'	SLon
(d)	
– 'Lanceata'	see *S. cantoniensis* 'Flore Pleno'
§ x ***cinerea***	SSta
– 'Grefsheim' ♀H4	CDoC COtt CSBt EBee ECtt ENot
	MBri MMuc NEgg SLim SPer SSta
	WCFE WDin WFar WRHF
crispifolia	see *S. japonica* 'Bullata'
decumbens	CPle
douglasii	MBar
formosana B&SWJ 1597	CPLG
– RWJ 10003	WCru
§ x ***foxii***	SLPl
fritschiana	SLPl SLon
hayatana	SLon
– RWJ 10014	WCru
hendersonii	see *Petrophytum hendersonii*
§ ***japonica***	SBod SMer WFar
– 'Alba'	see *S. japonica* var. *albiflora*
§ – var. ***albiflora***	CBcs CEnd CMac CSBt CWib ELan
	EPfP LAst LRHS MAsh MBar MGos
	MRav MSwo MWat MWhi NEgg
	NHol SEND SHBN SLim SPla SRms
	SWvt WDin WFar WHCG WMoo
	WTel WWeb
– 'Allgold'	CBcs
– 'Alpina'	see *S. japonica* 'Nana'
– 'Alpine Gold'	GBin NPro WWeb
– 'Anthony Waterer' (v)	More than 30 suppliers
– 'Barkby Gold'	MGos
– 'Blenheim'	SRms
§ – 'Bullata'	CFee CMac EPfP GEdr MBar
	NWCA SRms WAbe
§ – 'Bumalda'	WFar
– 'Candlelight' ♀H4	CAbP CBcs CSBt CWSG EBee
	EGra EPfP LAst LRHS MAsh
	MBri MGos NEgg NHol SCoo
	SHBN SLim SPer SPla SPoG
	SWvt WMoo
§ – 'Crispa'	CRez EPfP LRHS MBar NPro WFar
	WLeb WMoo WWeb
– 'Dart's Red' ♀H4	SSta WFar
– 'Firelight'	CAbP CBcs CSBt EBee ECrN EGra
	ELan ENot EPfP LHop LRHS MAsh
	MBri MGos MSwo MTis NHol
	SCoo SLim SPer SPla SPoG SSta
	SWvt WBrE WDin
§ – 'Genpei' **new**	MAsh NBlu SPer
– 'Glenroy Gold'	SLon WHen
– 'Gold Mound'	CMac CPLG CWSG CWib EBee
	ECrN ELan ENot EPfP LRHS
	MAsh MBar MRav MSwo MWgw
	MWhi NFor NHol SCoo SHFr
	SPer SPlb SRms WDin WFar
	WHar WWeb
– Golden Princess =	CMac CTri CWSG EPfP LAst LBuc
'Lisp'PBR ♀H4	LRHS MAsh MBar MGos NHol
	SCoo SMer SReu SRms SSta WCFE
	WDin WFar WWeb
– 'Goldflame'	More than 30 suppliers
– 'Little Princess'	CBcs CBrm CMac CWSG CWib
	EBee ECrN EMil ENot LRHS MAsh
	MBar MRav MSwo MWat MWhi
	NEgg NHol SCoo SLim SPer SRms
	SSta SWvt WBVN WDin WFar
	WHar
– Magic Carpet =	EBrs LRHS MAsh SCoo SPoG
'Walbuma'PBR ♀H4	
– 'Magnifica'	WHCG WPat
§ – 'Nana' ♀H4	CMac CSBt ECho EHyt MBar MRav
	SRms WEas WPer
– 'Nyewoods'	see *S. japonica* 'Nana'
– 'Shirobana' misapplied	see *S. japonica* 'Genpei'
– 'Shirobana'	see *S. japonica* var. *albiflora*
– 'Snow Cap'	CWib
§ – 'Walluf'	CPLG CTri CWib NFor WHCG
– 'White Cloud'	ELan
– 'White Gold'PBR	CAbP CSBt EBee ELan EPfP LAst
	LBuc LRHS MAsh MBri MMHG
	NPro SCoo SPer SPoG SWvt WMoo
	WOVN WRHF
'Margaritae'	SPer SWvt
micrantha	CPLG
nipponica	CBcs MBar
– 'Halward's Silver'	LBuc MGos MRav NHol NPro SLPl
	SPoG
– 'June Bride'	NBlu
§ – 'Snowmound' ♀H4	More than 30 suppliers
– var. ***tosaensis***	see *S. nipponica* 'Snowmound'
misapplied	
– var. ***tosaensis*** (Yatabe)	LHop SReu
Makino	
palmata 'Elegans'	see *Filipendula purpurea*
	'Elegans'
§ ***prunifolia*** (d)	CMac ECrN ELan MBlu MRav SLon
	SPer SPoG WDin WHCG WTel
– 'Plena'	see *S. prunifolia*
§ x ***pseudosalicifolia***	SHFr
'Triumphans'	
salicifolia	WFar
stevenii	SPer
'Summersnow'	SLPl
'Superba'	see *S.* x *foxii*
tarokoensis ETE 212	GIBF
thunbergii ♀H4	CDul CSBt CTri CWib EBee EPfP
	MRav NWea SCoo SLim SMer
	SRms WDin WGwG WHCG
– 'Fujino Pink'	WDin
– 'Mellow Yellow'	see *S. thunbergii* 'Ōgon'
– 'Mount Fuji'	CAbP CMac CWib EHoe GSki
	MGos NPro WFar
§ – 'Ōgon'	WFar
ulmaria	see *Filipendula ulmaria*
x ***vanhouttei***	CBcs CSBt CTri EBee EPfP MBar
	MRav MSwo NEgg NLRH SHBN
	SHFr SPer SPla SRms WDin WFar
	WTel
– 'Gold Fountain'	NHol WFar
– 'Pink Ice' (v)	CAbP CBcs CDoC CMHG COtt
	CPMA CWib EHoe EPfP LAst LHop
	LRHS MAsh MGos NHol SHBN
	SPer SPlb SPoG SWvt WDin WFar
	WHar WTel
veitchii	MRav
venusta 'Magnifica'	see *Filipendula rubra* 'Venusta'

Spiranthes (Orchidaceae)

aestivalis	CHdy
cernua	CHdy MSSP
– var. ***odorata***	CPom LSou
– – 'Chadd's Ford'	More than 30 suppliers

Spirodela (Lemnaceae)

§ ***polyrhiza***	EMFW

Spodiopogon (Poaceae)

sibiricus	CBig CBrm CKno EBee EChP
	EHoe EMon EPPr LBBr LEdu MSte
	MWhi NFor SMad

Sporobolus (Poaceae)

airoides	CBig CBrm EBee EPPr
cryptandrus	EBee
heterolepis	CBig EHoe EShb NDov WPrP
wrightii	EBee WGHP WSPU

Spraguea (Portulacaceae)

'Powder Puff'	LRHS
umbellata var.	WLin
caudicifera	

Sprekelia (Amaryllidaceae)

formosissima	CSpe CStu EBrs ECho LRHS SPav

Staberoha (Restionaceae)

aemula	CBig
remota new	CBig

Stachys ❀ (Lamiaceae)

aethiopica 'Danielle'	see *S. thunbergii* 'Danielle'
§ *affinis*	CAgr CArn CFir ELau GPoy LEdu
albens	IFro
§ *albotomentosa*	EBee EMan EShb EWTr GBri LHop
	LPhx LSou MBNS MDKP MSph
	NBir WCHb WCot WOut
alpina	CNat EBee
x *ambigua*	NSti
bacanica	EBee
– MESE	WPGP
balansae	NSti
betonica	see *S. officinalis*
§ *byzantina*	More than 30 suppliers
§ – 'Big Ears'	CAby CBow EBee ECha EMan
	ENot EWTr GMaP LAst LHop
	MBri MWat NDov SBch SEND
	SMrm SPoG WBor WCAu
	WCMO WCot WFar WHoo
	WMnd WMoo
§ – 'Cotton Boll'	COIW EBee ECha GCal GMac
	MHar SBch SPer WCot WFar
– 'Countess Helen	see *S. byzantina* 'Big Ears'
von Stein'	
– gold-leaved	see *S. byzantina* 'Primrose Heron'
– large-leaved	see *S. byzantina* 'Big Ears'
– 'Limelight'	WCMO WCot
§ – 'Primrose Heron'	EBee ECha ECot EMan EPfP GKev
	LRHS MWgw NLar NOrc SMer
	SPoG SWvt
– 'Sheila McQueen'	see *S. byzantina* 'Cotton Boll'
– 'Silver Carpet'	CBcs COIW EBee ECha EHoe EPfP
	EWTr GMaP LAst LRHS MRav
	MWat MWgw NBlu NOrc
	NSti SPer SPla SRms SWvt WCAu
	WCot WFar WGHP WHoo WMnd
	WMoo WTel WWeb
§ – 'Striped Phantom' (v)	CBow EBla EMan WCAu WCHb
	WCMO WCot WEas
– 'Variegata'	see *S. byzantina* 'Striped Phantom'
candida	EHyt
chamissonis var.	EBee
cooleyae new	
chrysantha	EHyt LPhx
citrina	CMea EBla GCal LRHS SBla SPoG
coccinea	CPom EBee EChP ECtt EHrv EMan
	EShb GBBs LRHS MHer NBir SBch
	SDnm SHFr SPav SPet SRkn WCHb
	WMoo WPat WRos
– 'Burning Embers' new	LAst
corsica	EBee WPGP
cretica	EMan WWlt XPep
– subsp. *salviifolia*	XPep
densiflora	see *S. monieri*
§ *discolor*	CMea EBee EChP GBri IFro MDKP
	MLLN NChi NLar WAbe WCot
	WOut WPer WViv
germanica	CPom EMan NBre NLar WBri
– subsp. *bithynica*	EBee
glutinosa	MDKP XPep
grandiflora	see *S. macrantha*
heraclea	EBee XPep
'Hidalgo'	CSpe SAga
iva	LPhx
lanata	see *S. byzantina*
lavandulifolia	EHyt
§ *macrantha*	More than 30 suppliers
* – 'Alba'	ECha WMoo
– 'Cally Splash' (v) new	GCal
– 'Hummelo'	see *S. officinalis* 'Hummelo'
* – 'Nivea'	EBee EHrv ELan GCal MMHG
	WPat
§ – 'Robusta' ♀H4	CDes EBee ELan NBro NGdn
	WCAu WCMO WCot WRHF
	WWye
– 'Rosea'	CElw CMHG EGra ELan GMaP
	LLWP MArl MLHP SPlb WEas WPer
	WRha WWye
– 'Superba'	CBgR CSpe EBee EBla EChP ECtt
	EGra EPfP GMaP IBal LAst LRHS
	MBri MDun MMHG MRav MTis
	NEgg NScw SBla SMrm SPer SWvt
	WBor WCHb WCMO WCot WFar
	WMoo
– 'Violacea'	EBee MAvo NChi WCot WPGP
mexicana misapplied	see *S. thunbergii*
monieri misapplied	see *S. officinalis*
§ *monieri* ambig.	CAbP CMMP EBee EChP EGle
	LRHS MAvo NLar WPer WViv
monieri (Gouan) P.W. Ball	GBin LBMP WOut
* – 'Rosea'	EBee GBin NBre SBla WOut
– 'Saharan Pink'	see *S. officinalis* 'Saharan Pink'
– 'Spitzweg'	SUsu
nivea	see *S. discolor*
obliqua	NBre WOut
§ *officinalis*	CArn CBgR CEnt CRWN CSev
	CWan EBee EUnu EWTr GBar
	GPoy IHMH ILad MBow MHer
	MNHC MSal NEgg NLan NMir NPri
	WGHP WGwG WHbs WHer WWye
– SDR 3554	GKev
– 'Alba'	CArn CBgR EBee NBro NRya STes
	WCAu WCHb WFar WHer WOut
	WRha WTin WWye
§ – 'Hummelo'	EBee EBrs EGle EPfP GAbr LHop
	LPhx LSou MDKP NDov NLar
	SAga SHop SUsu WCAu WFar
	WWeb
– mauve-flowered	WTin
– 'Powder Puff' new	EBee
– 'Rosea'	CMea NBPC NBro SHop STes
	WCot WFar WGHP WTin
– 'Rosea Superba'	CBgR EBee ECha MDKP NBre SIng
	WCAu WCot WFar WMoo
§ – 'Saharan Pink'	CBgR EBee EPfP EWll LSou MHer
	NJOw SSvw WOut
– 'Wisley White'	EBee WCot
olympica	see *S. byzantina*
ossetica	CDes EBee
palustris	LPBA NLan NMir NSco WFar
'Pinkie'	LRHS WWeb
plumosa	XPep
recta new	LPhx NBHF
saxicola	MDKP
scardica MESE 362 new	MDKP
setifera	EBee NBre
spicata	see *S. macrantha*
swainsonii	XPep
sylvatica	CArn NLan NMir NSco SECG WBri
	WHer WOut
– 'Hoskin's Variegated' (v)	WCHb
– 'Huskers' (v)	EBee EPPr ITer LSou NBre
thirkei	EBee SBch XPep

§ *thunbergii*	CDes EShb LLWP LPhx MAvo MDKP MSte SAga SMeo SSvw SUsu WOut WPGP WPrP
§ – 'Danielle'	EAro EBee ECtt LAst MHer NBre SPoG SRkn SVil WMoo WOVN
tuberifera	see *S. affinis*

Stachytarpheta (Verbenaceae)
mutabilis	SBig SOWG

Stachyurus (Stachyuraceae)
chinensis	CBcs CMCN CPMA CPle CWib IArd IDee IMGH LRHS MGos NLar SBrw SMad SPoG
– 'Celina'	CPMA EBee MBlu MGos NLar
– 'Goldbeater' **new**	NLar
– 'Joy Forever' (v)	CBcs CDul CEnd CMCN EBee EMil EPfP IArd LTwo MBlu MGos MWea NLar SBrw SPoG SSpi SSta SWvt
himalaicus	CBcs IDee NLar
– HWJCM 009	WCru
– HWJK 2035	WCru
leucotrichus	CPMA
'Magpie' (v)	CPMA EPfP MGos NLar SAga WCru
praecox ♀H4	More than 30 suppliers
– B&SWJ 8898	WCru
§ – var. *matsuzakii*	CPMA NBhm
– – B&SWJ 2817	WCru
– – 'Scherzo' (v)	WCru
* – 'Rubriflorus'	CPMA ELan EPfP LRHS MAsh NLar SMur WFar
salicifolius	CMCN CPMA IDee NLar WPGP
* *sigeyosii* B&SWJ 6915	WCru
aff. *szechuanensis* BWJ 8153	WCru
yunnanensis	CPMA WSHC

Staehelina (Asteraceae)
dubia	MAvo XPep

Stapelia (Asclepiadaceae)
grandiflora **new**	EShb

Staphylea (Staphyleaceae)
bolanderi	CBcs NLar
bumalda	CBcs CPMA EPfP NLar
colchica	CBcs CDul EBee ELan EPfP EWTr GIBF NPal SBrw SPer WDin WSHC
holocarpa	CBcs CDul CPMA EPfP LHop MRav WBVN WFar
– 'Innocence' **new**	NLar
N – var. *rosea*	CPMA EPfP MBri SMad
N – 'Rosea'	CBcs CMCN MBlu NLar SBrw SSpi
pinnata	CAgr CBcs CEnd CPMA EPfP GIBF LEdu NLar SBrw WHCr WNor
trifolia	CAgr CBcs

Statice see *Limonium*

Stauntonia (Lardizabalaceae)
hexaphylla	CBcs CDoC CHEx CPln CSam CTri EBee EHol EPfP GQui LRHS MAsh MBri MDun SAdn SBig SBra SBrw SPoG SReu SRkn SSpi SSta WBrE WCMO WCot WSHC
– B&SWJ 4858	WCru
purpurea	CPln EBee NLar
– B&SWJ 3690	WCru

Stegnogramma (Thelypteridaceae)
pozoi	EFer

Stellaria (Caryophyllaceae)
sp. **new**	GIBF

holostea	CRWN MBow NMir NSco WBri WShi

Stemmacantha (Asteraceae)
carthamoides	MSal NLar
§ *centaureoides*	EBee EBrs ECGP ECha EGle GBin GCal LPhx MAvo NBid NBre SAga SUsu WCAu WCot
§ *rhapontica*	NBre

Stenanthium (Melanthiaceae)
robustum	WPGP

Stenocarpus (Proteaceae)
sinuatus	EShb

Stenochlaena (Blechnaceae)
palustris	MBri

Stenomesson (Amaryllidaceae)
aurantiacum	CMon
coccineum	CMon
§ *miniatum*	CStu
pearcei	CMon
variegatum (v)	CMon

Stenotaphrum (Poaceae)
secundatum	EShb XPep
– 'Variegatum' (v) ♀H1	CHal EShb MAvo WDyG

Stephanandra (Rosaceae)
chinensis	SLon
incisa	CBcs CPLG WHCG
§ – 'Crispa'	CDoC CDul CPle CTri ECrN ELan EMil EPfP EWTr LAst LHop MBar MBlu MRav MWgw MWhi NEgg NFor NHol SHBN SPer SPla SPoG WCFE WDin WFar WHCG WMoo WTel
– 'Dart's Horizon'	SLPl
– 'Prostrata'	see *S. incisa* 'Crispa'
tanakae	CBcs CDoC CDul CPLG CPle CTri ELan EPfP EWTr IMGH LAst MBar MBlu MRav NEgg NFor SHBN SLPl SLon SPer SPla WDin WFar WHCG

Stephania (Menispermaceae)
japonica B&SWJ 2396	WCru

Stephanotis (Asclepiadaceae)
floribunda ♀H1	CBcs CCCN EBak GQui LRHS MBri NBlu SMur SOWG

Sterculia (Sterculiaceae)
rupestris	see *Brachychiton rupestris*

Sternbergia (Amaryllidaceae)
'Autumn Gold'	ECho
candida	CBro ECho EHyt
§ *clusiana*	WWst
colchiciflora	EHyt WWst
fischeriana	CBro
greuteriana	ECho EHyt SOkd
lutea	CAvo CBgR CBro CNic CStu EAEE ECho EHyt EPot EWes LRHS MRav NWCA SDix WEas WTin
– Angustifolia Group	CBro CDes CMea EBee EHyt EMon WCot WWst
– var. *lutea* B&S from Italy	CMon
– – MS 971	CMon
macrantha	see *S. clusiana*
sicula	CBro CStu EBrs ECho EHyt EPot WCot XPep
– MS 956 from Italy	CMon

- var. **graeca**	ECho EHyt WWst
- - from Crete	ECho
- - MS 802	CMon
- 'John Marr'	CDes

Stevia (Asteraceae)

rebaudiana	EBee EOHP EUnu EWin GPoy MSal WCot

Stewartia ✿ (Theaceae)

gemmata	see *S. sinensis*
'Korean Splendor'	see *S. pseudocamellia* Koreana Group
koreana	see *S. pseudocamellia* Koreana Group
malacodendron ♀H4	EPfP LRHS SBrw
monadelpha	CMen EPfP SSpi WNor
ovata	CMen SSpi
N - var. **grandiflora**	CMen LRHS SBrw
pseudocamellia ♀H4	More than 30 suppliers
- var. **koreana**	see *S. pseudocamellia* Koreana Group
§ - Koreana Group ♀H4	CBcs CDul CEnd CMCN CMen CTho ECrN EPfP LRHS MBri MDun NLar SBrw SSpi WDin WFar WNor WPGP
pteropetiolata	CBcs WPGP
rostrata	CBcs CMCN MBlu MBri NLar SSpi WNor
serrata	CMen SSpi
§ **sinensis** ♀H4	CBcs CMen CPMA EPfP LPan MBlu MDun NLar SBrw SSpi SSta WNor

Stictocardia (Convolvulaceae)

beraviensis	CPIN
tiliifolia <u>new</u>	CPIN

Stigmaphyllon (Malpighiaceae)

ciliatum	CPIN

Stipa (Poaceae)

arundinacea	see *Anemanthele lessoniana*
barbata	CBig CBrm CDes CKno CSpe CWCL EBee ECha EGle EHoe EPPr EWes LRHS MAvo MNHC NOGN SBla SMHy SPer SUsu WCMO WCot WPGP WRos XPep
- 'Silver Feather'	CBig LIck LRav MWhi
* **boysterica**	CFee
§ **brachytricha**	see *Calamagrostis brachytricha*
§ **calamagrostis**	More than 30 suppliers
- 'Lemperg'	EPPr
capillata	CKno EBee EChP EGle EHoe EPPr MNHC MWhi NCGa SPoG SWal SYvo WCot WOVN WPGP WPnP XPep
- 'Brautschleier'	CHrt CWib LIck NBre WPtf
* - 'Lace Veil'	CBig LRav
chrysophylla F&W 9321	WPGP
columbiana	MLLN
comata	EBee IFro LRav NFor
elegantissima	CKno CSam EHoe
extremiorientalis	CBig CKno ECha EPPr GSki LAst NOGN SLPl
gigantea ♀H4	More than 30 suppliers
- 'Gold Fontaene'	CBig CDes CFir CKno EBee ECha EPPr EWes LPhx MMoz MNrw NDov SBch SMad WPGP WPrP
- 'Pixie'	EWsh LPhx
grandis	CBig CKno ECha EPPr GBin WHal WMoo WPer
joannis	GCal
lasiagrostis	see *S. calamagrostis*
lessingiana	CHrt CMMP CPLG CSam EBee EHul GBin MAvo NLar WPGP WPnP

offneri	CKno EBee EPPr EWes SBla
pennata	CBcs CBig CKno EHoe GBin GCal LRav MNHC NCGa NOak WHal
pulcherrima	CKno GCal XPep
- 'Windfeder'	CFir LBBr LBMP SLPl SMad SMrm WPnP
ramosissima	CKno
robusta	EBee EPPr LRav XPep
splendens misapplied	see *S. calamagrostis*
§ **splendens** Trin.	CBig EHoe EMag EPPr LEdu WFoF
stenophylla	see *S. tirsa*
stipoides	GGar
tenacissima	ECha EHoe EHul GSki NCob WDin WMoo XPep
tenuifolia misapplied	see *S. tenuissima*
tenuifolia Steud.	CHar CMea CMil EBee EHul EPfP LRHS MBri MRav NBir NBro NHol NSti NVic SIng SPer WCAu WHal WMoo XPep
§ **tenuissima**	More than 30 suppliers
§ **tirsa**	EBrs GBin NDov
turkestanica	EBee GBin NDov SUsu SWat WHal
ucrainica	CAby CBig GAbr
verticillata	CKno CRez

Stokesia (Asteraceae)

cyanea	see *S. laevis*
§ **laevis**	CHea EBee ECGP ECha EGle EPfP GAbr LAst LRHS NBro NFor NLar NWCA SMer SMrm SPet WBrE WCAu WFar WMoo WPer WWeb
- 'Alba'	CHea CMMP COIW EBee ECha EGle EHrv ELan EMan EPfP ERou GMac LAst LPhx LRHS MRav NHol STes WCAu WMow
- 'Blue Star'	More than 30 suppliers
- 'Klaus Jelitto'	CFwr EBee ERou MBri SHBN SHar
- 'Mary Gregory'	More than 30 suppliers
- mixed	CPou MLan
- 'Omega Skyrocket'	CBgR CHea CMHG CPou EBee EChP EMar ERou EWTr LRHS MBri MLLN NBPC NHol NOak SMrm SPoG SUsu WBor WCAu WCot WFar WMnd
- 'Peach Melba'	EBee NCGa SPoG
- 'Purple Parasols'	More than 30 suppliers
- 'Silver Moon'	CMHG EAEE EBee EChP EGle EMan EMar EMil EPfP ERou EShb LAst MTPN NBir NEgg NPri SAga SHar SPoG WBor WCot WFar WTMC
- 'Träumerei'	EAEE EBee EChP EGle EMar LAst LRHS NHol SPet WMnd WMoo

Stranvaesia see *Photinia*

x *Stranvinia* see *Photinia*

Stratiotes (Hydrocharitaceae)

aloides	CDWL CWat EHon EMFW EMag LNCo LPBA NPer NSco SWat WMAq WPnP WWpP

strawberry see *Fragaria*

Strelitzia (Strelitziaceae)

alba	CCCN EAmu
juncea	ERea MJnS XBlo
nicolai	CAbb CHEx CKob CRoM EAmu EShb ITer LPal LPan MJnS NPer SBig SDEP WMul XBlo
reginae ♀H1	CAbb CBcs CBrP CKob CTbh ELan ERea EShb GQui LPal LPan LRHS MJnS MOak NPal NPer SAPC SArc

	SBig SChr SDEP SEND SPlb SRms WMul XBlo
- var. **citrina**	ERea
'Humilis'	XBlo
- 'Kirstenbosch Gold'	MJnS XBlo

Streptocarpella see *Streptocarpus*

Streptocarpus ✿ (*Gesneriaceae*)

'Albatross' ♀H1	SBrm SDnm SPav WDib
'Alice'	WDib
'Amanda' Dibley ♀H1	WDib
'Amanda'^{PBR} (Marleen Series) **new**	WDib
'Anne'	CSpe SBrm WDib
'Athena'	CSpe WDib
baudertii	WDib
'Beryl'	WDib
'Bethan' ♀H1	SAga SBrm WDib
'Beverley Ruth'	MOak
'Bicentenary' **new**	MOak
'Black Gardenia'	WDib
'Black Panther'	SAga SBrm WDib
'Blue Bird'	MOak
'Blue Gem'	WDib
'Blue Heaven'	SBrm WDib
'Blue Ice'	MOak
'Blue Moon'	CHal WDib
'Blue Nymph'	WDib
'Blue Pencil'	SBrm
§ 'Blue Upstart'	MOak
'Blushing Bride' (d)	SBrm SDnm SPav WDib
'Blushing Pink'	MOak SBrm
'Border Line'	MOak
* 'Boysenberry Delight'	WDib
'Branwen'	SBrm SDnm SPav WDib
'Brimstone'	MOak SBrm
'Bristol's Black Bird'	SBrm WDib
'Bristol's Ice Castle'	SBrm WDib
'Bristol's Very Best'	WDib
'Buttons'	SBrm
caeruleus	WDib
'Caitlin' **new**	WDib
candidus	WDib
'Carol'	WDib
'Carolyn Ann'	MOak
'Carys' ♀H1	WDib
'Catania' (Marleen Series) **new**	WDib
'Catrin' ♀H1	SBrm WDib
caulescens	CHal WDib
* - 'Compactus'	CHal
- var. **pallescens**	EOHP WDib
'Charlotte'	MOak SBrm WDib
'Chorus Line' ♀H1	SDnm SPav WDib
'Clare'	WDib
'Clouds'	CSpe
'Concord Blue'	WDib
'Constant Nymph'	SBrm WDib
'Copper Knob'	MOak
'Coral Flair' **new**	WDib
'Crystal Beauty'^{PBR}	WDib
'Crystal Blush'^{PBR}	WDib
'Crystal Charm'	WDib
'Crystal Dawn'	WDib
'Crystal Ice'^{PBR} ♀H1	WDib
'Crystal Snow'^{PBR}	WDib
'Crystal Wonder'	WDib
cyaneus	WDib
- subsp. **polackii**	WDib
'Cynthia' ♀H1	SBrm WDib
'Dainty Lady'	MOak
'Daphne' ♀H1	SAga WDib
'Dark Eyes Mary'	SBrm
'Dark Secret'	SBrm
'Demeter'	SBrm

'Diana'	SBrm WDib
dunnii	SGar WDib
'Eira'	WDib
'Elegance'	MOak SBrm
'Ella'	MOak SBrm
'Ella Mae' **new**	SBrm
'Elsi'	SBrm SDnm SPav WDib
'Emily'	WDib
'Emma'	SBrm WDib
'Falling Stars' ♀H1	CSpe ERea SAga SBrm WDib
'Festival Wales'	SBrm WDib
'Fiona'	SBrm WDib
floribundus	WDib
'Frances'	SBrm
gardenii	WDib
'Gillian'	MOak
glandulosissimus ♀H1	CHal EOHP WDib
'Gloria' ♀H1	CSpe SAga SBrm WDib
'Good Hope'	ERea
'Gower Daybreak'	SBrm
'Gower Garnet'	MOak
'Gower Midnight'	MOak SBrm
'Grape Slush'	WDib
'Gwen'	SBrm WDib
'Hannah Ellis'	MOak SBrm
'Happy Snappy' ♀H1	SBrm SDnm SPav WDib
'Heidi' ♀H1	SBrm SDnm SPav WDib
'Helen' ♀H1	SBrm WDib
'Huge White'	CSpe SAga
'Ida'	MOak SBrm
'Inky Fingers'	MOak SBrm
'Izzy'	MOak SBrm
'Jaco's Gem' **new**	WDib
'Jane Elizabeth'	MOak SBrm
'Jennifer' ♀H1	SBrm SDnm SPav WDib
'Joanna'	SBrm WDib
johannis	WDib
'Josie'	SBrm
'Judith'	MOak
'Julie'	WDib
'Karen'	SBrm SDnm SPav WDib
kentaniensis	WDib
'Kerry's Gold'	MOak
'Kim' ♀H1	CSpe EShb SBrm SDnm SPav WDib
kirkii	WDib
'Kisie'	MOak SBrm
'Largesse'	SBrm
'Laura' ♀H1	SAga SBrm WDib
'Lemon Ice'	SBrm
'Lisa' ♀H1	SBrm
'Little Gem'	CSpe SBrm
'Louise'	SBrm WDib
'Lynette'	SBrm
'Lynne'	SBrm WDib
'Maassen's White' ♀H1	ERea SBrm WDib
'Magpie'	MOak
'Mandy'	SDnm SPav WDib
'Margaret'	SBrm WDib
'Marie'	WDib
'Mary'	MOak SBrm
'Megan'	SBrm WDib
'Melanie' Dibley ♀H1	SBrm WDib
I 'Melanie' (Marleen Series) **new**	WDib
meyeri	WDib
'Midnight Flame'	ERea EShb SAga SBrm WDib
'Mini Nymph'	CSpe WDib
'Modbury Lady'	MOak
modestus	WDib
'Molly'	SBrm
'Moonlight'	SBrm WDib
'Muse'	MOak SBrm
'Neptune'	SBrm WDib
'Nerys'	WDib

'Nia'	CSpe WDib
'Nicola'	SBrm WDib
'Nita'	MOak
'Olga'	SBrm WDib
'Olwen'	WDib
'Pale Rider' **new**	MOak
'Party Doll'	SBrm WDib
'Passion Pink'	SBrm WDib
'Patricia'	MOak SBrm
'Paula' ♀H1	SBrm WDib
pentherianus	WDib
'Pink Fondant'	CSpe
'Pink Souffle'	SBrm SDnm SPav WDib
'Plum Crazy'	SBrm
polyanthus subsp. *dracomontanus*	WDib
primulifolius	WDib
- subsp. *formosus*	WDib
'Princesse' (Marleen Series) **new**	WDib
prolixus	WDib
'Purple Haze'	MOak
* 'Purple Passion'	SBrm
'Raspberry Dream'	MOak
rexii	WDib
'Rhiannon'	CSpe SAga SBrm SDnm SPav WDib
'Rose Gower'	MOak
'Rosebud'	SBrm WDib
'Rosemary' (d)	SPav WDib
'Ruby' ♀H1	EShb SBrm WDib
'Ruby Anniversary'	MOak
'Ruffled Lilac'	CSpe SBrm
'Ruffles'	SBrm
'Sally'	SBrm WDib
'Samantha'	MOak
'Sandra'	SBrm SDnm SPav WDib
'Sarah'	SBrm SPav WDib
saxorum ♀H1	CHal EMan EOHP EShb EWin LIck LSou MBri MOak SRms WDib WFar
- compact	EOHP WDib
'Sian'	SBrm SDnm SPav WDib
silvaticus	WDib
'Snow White' ♀H1	CSpe SDnm SPav WDib
'Something Special'	SAga SBrm SDnm WDib
'Sophie'	WDib
'Southshore'	WDib
'Spider'	MOak
'Stacey'	MOak SBrm
'Stella' ♀H1	SBrm WDib
'Stephanie'	CSpe WDib
stomandrus	WDib
'Strawberry Fondant'	MOak SBrm
'Sugar Almond'	CSpe SBrm
'Susan' ♀H1	SAga WDib
'Swaybelle'	SBrm
'Tanga'	SBrm
'Terracotta'	MOak SAga SBrm
'Texas Hot Chili'	SBrm WDib
'Texas Sunrise'	MOak SBrm
thompsonii	WDib
'Tina' ♀H1	SAga SBrm SDnm SPav WDib
'Tracey'	SBrm WDib
'Turbulent Tide'	SBrm
'Upstart'	see *S.* 'Blue Upstart'
variabilis	WDib
'Velvet Underground'	SBrm
'Vera'	SBrm
'Violet Lace'	CSpe SBrm
wendlandii	WDib
'Wendy'	SBrm SPav WDib
'White Wings'	MOak SBrm
'Wiesmoor Red'	SAga WDib
'Winifred'	SBrm WDib

Streptolirion (Commelinaceae)
volubile B&SWJ 8569	WCru

Streptopus (Convallariaceae)
amplexifolius	EBee ECho GBuc GIBF NMen WCru
- M&PS 98/022	GCrs NLar
roseus	GCrs SOkd

Streptosolen (Solanaceae)
jamesonii ♀H1	CHal CHll CPle CSev CSpe EBak ELan ERea EShb MOak SAga
- 'Fire Gold'	ERea

Strobilanthes (Acanthaceae)
§ CC 4071	CPLG
anisophylla	EShb WHlf
atropurpurea misapplied	see *S. attenuata*
atropurpurea Nees	see *S. wallichii*
§ *attenuata*	More than 30 suppliers
- subsp. *nepalensis*	CHll CLAP EBee EMar WOut WPrP WWye
- 'Out of the Ocean'	WOut
dyeriana (v) ♀H1	CHal EBak ECtt EMan EShb GBri LSou WCot WRha
flexicaulis	CDes EBee WPGP WPrP
- B&SWJ 354	WCru
- clone 2 **new**	LSou
glutinosa **new**	CPLG
nutans	CDes CLAP CPLG CPom CPou EBee LSou WPrP
rankanensis	CDes CLAP EBee WPrP
- B&SWJ 1771	CPom WCru
'Silver Star' **new**	EShb
violacea	CPrp CStu WPer
§ *wallichii*	CDes CLAP CPLG EBee EHol EPPr LRHS LSou WCru WFar WPrP WSHC

Stromanthe (Marantaceae)
amabilis	see *Ctenanthe amabilis*
sanguinea	CHal MBri
- 'Triostar'PBR (v)	XBlo
'Stripestar'	MBri

Strongylodon (Papilionaceae)
macrobotrys	CPIN SOWG

Strophanthus (Apocynaceae)
caudatus	CPIN
divaricatus	CPIN
gratus	CPIN
preussii	CPIN
speciosus	CPIN CSec EShb

Stuartia see *Stewartia*

Stylidium (Stylidiaceae)
affine	SPlb
graminifolium	GGar
- 'Little Sapphire' **new**	EPPr
- 'Tiny Trina' **new**	EPPr
soboliferum	ECou

Stylophorum (Papaveraceae)
diphyllum	CFwr CPBP CPou ECha EGle EMar GBri GEdr MRav MSal NMen SBch WCru WFar WPnP
lasiocarpum	CPBP CPLG CPom CSpe EMan EMar MGol NBid SGar WCru WPrP WRos

Styphelia (Epacridaceae)
colensoi	see *Leucopogon colensoi*

Styrax (*Styracaceae*)

americanus	CBcs NLar
confusus	CMCN
faberi	GIBF
formosanus	CTho
- var. *formosanus*	EPfP WPGP
- - B&SWJ 3803	WCru
- var. *hayatiana*	WCru
B&SWJ 6823 **new**	
hemsleyanus ♀H4	CAbP CBcs CEnd CTho EPfP IDee
	IMGH LRHS MBlu MDun NLar
	SBrw SPer SSpi WBor WFar WNor
	WPGP
hookeri **new**	CBcs
japonicus ♀H4	More than 30 suppliers
- B&SWJ 4405	WCru
§ - Benibana Group ♀H4	SReu SSta
- - 'Pink Chimes'	CAbP CBcs CMCN CPLG CPMA
	ELan EPfP IDee LRHS MAsh MBlu
	MBri MDun NLar SCoo SPer SSpi
	SSta
- 'Fargesii'	CBcs CDoC CPMA CTho EPfP
	IMGH LRHS MBri MDun SBrw
	SCoo SPoG SSpi WFar
- 'Purple Dress' **new**	NLar
- 'Roseus'	see *S. japonicus* Benibana Group
- 'Sohuksan'	WPGP
obassia ♀H4	CArn CBcs CMCN CPne CTho
	EPfP GIBF IMGH LRHS MBlu
	MDun MWya NLar SPer SSpi
	WNor
- B&SWJ 6023	WCru
odoratissimus	WPGP
wuyuanensis **new**	GIBF

Suaeda (*Chenopodiaceae*)

vera	XPep

Succisa (*Dipsacaceae*)

§ *pratensis*	CArn CBgR EBee EMag MBow
	MHer MSph NDov NLan NLar
	NMen NSco NWCA SBch SMHy
	WHer WPrP WSFF WTin
- *alba*	EBee EWes MDKP
- dwarf	NGby NRya
- 'Peddar's Pink'	EBee EWes

Succisella (*Dipsacaceae*)

inflexa **new**	EBee

sunberry see *Rubus* 'Sunberry'

Sutera (*Scrophulariaceae*)

Abunda Blue Improved =	NPri
'Balabimblu' (Abunda	
Series) **new**	
Cabana Trailing White	WGor
new	
Candy Floss = 'Yasflos'	EShb LAst LSou
'Copia Pink Touch' **new**	LAst
cordata	LHop
- 'Blizzard'	LAst LSou WGor
- Blue Showers =	LAst
'Bacoble'PBR	
- 'Bridal Showers'	NPri
- Lavender Showers =	NPri
'Sunlav'PBR	
- pale pink	LAst
- 'Pink Domino'	ECtt EWin LAst
§ - 'Snowflake'	CTbh ECtt EWin LAst MLan MOak
	NBlu NPer SCoo SPet SPoG
- 'Typhoon White P.'	LAst
'Giant Cloud'	EWin LAst
jurassica	see *Jamesbrittenia jurassica*
neglecta	WPGP

Olympic Gold = 'Prosutv'	ECtt EWin LAst NBlu SCoo SPoG
(v)	
Sea Mist = 'Yagemil'PBR	NPri
Suteranova Pink =	LAst
'Mogoto'PBR	

Sutherlandia (*Papilionaceae*)

frutescens	CArn GGar SPlb WOut XPep
- 'Prostrata'	EMan WPat
montana	CPLG WPic

Swainsona (*Papilionaceae*)

galegifolia	CHll
- 'Albiflora'	CSpe LPhx SBla SOWG WSHC

sweet cicely see *Myrrhis odorata*

Swertia (*Gentianaceae*)

from Tibet **new**	GIBF
tibetica **new**	GIBF

Syagrus (*Arecaceae*)

§ *romanzoffiana*	CBrP CRoM EAmu LPJP LPal

x *Sycoparrotia* (*Hamamelidaceae*)

semidecidua	CBcs CPMA MBlu NLar SBrw
	WPGP

Sycopsis (*Hamamelidaceae*)

sinensis	CAbP CMCN CWib EMil EPfP
	LRHS MBlu NLar SBrw SDnm SMur
	SSpi WCMO WDin WFar WPGP
	WSHC

Symphoricarpos (*Caprifoliaceae*)

albus	CDul ECrN MSwo NWea SPoG
	WDin
- 'Constance Spry'	SRms
§ - var. *laevigatus*	EPfP LBuc MBar
§ - 'Taff's White' (v)	WMoo
- 'Variegatus'	see *S. albus* 'Taff's White'
x *chenaultii* 'Hancock'	CSBt ECrN ELan EPfP MBar MGos
	MRav MSwo NPro SHBN WDin
	WFar
x *doorenbosii* 'Magic	EBee MBar MRav NWea
Berry'	
- 'Mother of Pearl'	EBee ELan EPfP MBar MGos MRav
	NBlu NWea SPoG
- 'White Hedge'	CSBt ELan LBuc MRav NWea SPer
	SPlb SPoG WTel
orbiculatus	CDul IMGH SLon
- 'Albovariegatus'	see *S. orbiculatus* 'Taff's Silver
	Edge'
- 'Argenteovariegatus'	see *S. orbiculatus* 'Taff's Silver
	Edge'
- 'Bowles' Golden	see *S. orbiculatus* 'Foliis Variegatis'
Variegated'	
§ - 'Foliis Variegatis' (v)	CTri ECrN EGra EHoe ELan
	EPfP MGos MRav NPro NSti
	SHBN SPer WDin WEas WFar
	WHCG WSHC
§ - 'Taff's Silver Edge' (v)	EBee EHoe MBar NSti
- 'Variegatus'	see *S. orbiculatus* 'Foliis Variegatis'
rivularis	see *S. albus* var. *laevigatus*

Symphyandra (*Campanulaceae*)

asiatica	see *Hanabusaya asiatica*
ossetica	see *Campanula ossetica*

Symphyotrichum see *Aster*

Symphytum (*Boraginaceae*)

asperum	CPom ECha ELan EMon MSal NLar
	WCHb WMoo WTMC
* *azureum*	MSte NLar WCAu WCHb WFar
	WMnd WTMC

'Belsay' — GBuc WHil
'Belsay Gold' — SDix
caucasicum ♀H4 — CBgR CElw CMHG ECha GBar GPoy IFro IHMH LEdu LRHS MBri MHar SBch SIde SSvw WCHb WHer WHil WMoo WRha WWye
- 'Eminence' — CMdw EGoo WCHb
- 'Norwich Sky' — CKno EBee EChP NMir WCHb
- pale blue **new** — SSvw
cordatum — EMon
'Denford Variegated' (v) — CBgR ITer
§ 'Goldsmith' (v) — More than 30 suppliers
grandiflorum — CArn CTri CWan GKev GPoy LEdu WGwG
* - 'Sky-blue-pink' — EBee NCot
'Hidcote Blue' — CBct CBre CPrp CTri EBee EChP ECha ECtt EPfP EPla GBar ILis LRHS MSte MWgw NBro NEgg NGHP NHol SLPl SPoG WCAu WCru WMnd WMoo WTMC
§ 'Hidcote Pink' — CBct CPrp EBee EChP ECha ENot EPla EWsh LRHS MBow MSte MWgw NBir NEgg SBch SLPl SPer SPoG WCAu WFar WMnd WMoo WPnP WTMC
'Hidcote Variegated' (v) — WCHb
ibericum — CAgr CArn CMHG CSam EBee ECha EHrv ELau EPfP EPla GBar GMaP GPoy IHMH LRHS MTis MWgw NBlu NSti SGar SRms WBor WCAu WCHb WMoo WTMC WWye
- 'All Gold' — CArn EBee EBrs ECha ECtt ELau EWsh GSki WCAu WMoo WTMC
- 'Blaueglocken' — CSev EChP ECha WMoo WPrP WSan
- dwarf — NPri WMoo
- 'Gold in Spring' — EGoo NLar WCHb WFar
- 'Jubilee' — see S. 'Goldsmith'
- 'Lilacinum' — WHer
- 'Pink Robins' — WCHb
- 'Variegatum' — see S. 'Goldsmith'
- 'Wisley Blue' — CBcs EPfP EWTr IHMH NLar WFar WMnd WMoo
'Lambrook Sunrise' — CFis CLAP EAEE EBee EPPr LAst LHop LRHS NBro NFla SPla WCMO WCot WMoo WTMC
'Langthorns Pink' — CPom ELan EMar GBar GBri GBuc WCHb
'Mereworth' — see S. x uplandicum 'Mereworth'
officinale — CAgr CArn COld CSev CWan EBee GBar GPoy MHer MNHC MNrw MSal NBlu NGHP NMir NPer NSco NSti SIde SRms WBrk WHer WWye
- 'Boraston White' — MHer WCHb
- var. *ochroleucum* — WHer WTMC
orientale — CAgr CPom EMon GCal STes WCHb
peregrinum — see S. x uplandicum
'Roseum' — see S. 'Hidcote Pink'
'Rubrum' — CDes CEnt CPrp EBee ECot EHrv ELan ELau EPPr EPfP EWes GSki LAst LRHS MHer NEgg NGHP NOrc WCAu WCot WFar WGwG WHil WPGP WSan WTMC
tuberosum — CArn CBre CElw CEnt COld CPom CSam EOHP EPPr GPoy IHMH MBow MDun MHer MSte NHol NSti WBor WCHb WFar WHer WRha WTMC WWye
§ x *uplandicum* — CSev CTri ELan ELau EMar EOHP GBar GPoy GWCH IHMH MHer MSal SIde WCHb WHbs WJek WWye

- 'Axminster Gold' (v) — CBct CBos CDes CEnt CLAP CMea EBee EMan IBlr ITer LHop LPhx NBid WPGP
- 'Bocking 14' — CAgr CBod CEnt CHby CPbn CPrp GAbr GBar IHMH SIde
- 'Droitwich' (v) — WCot
§ - 'Mereworth' (v) — CBct EBrs SMad SUsu WCHb
- 'Moorland Heather' — MAvo WMoo
- 'Variegatum' (v) ♀H4 — CLAP EBee ECtt ELan EMar EPfP EWes GCal GMaP GPoy ITer MTho MWgw NBir NGHP NGdn NSti SDix SMeo WCAu WCHb WCot WFar WMoo WTMC

Symplocarpus (Araceae)
foetidus — EBee ECho ITer WCot

Symplocos (Symplocaceae)
paniculata — see S. sawafutagi
§ *sawafutagi* — CBcs GIBF MBri NLar

Syncarpha (Asteraceae)
eximia — SPlb

Syneilesis (Asteraceae)
aconitifolia — CDes CFwr CLAP GEdr WCot
- B&SWJ 879 — WCru
palmata — CLAP GEdr LEdu WCot
- B&SWJ 1003 — WCru
subglabrata — CLAP LEdu
- B&SWJ 298 — WCru

Syngonium (Araceae)
'Maya Red' — MBri
podophyllum ♀H1 — XBlo
- 'Emerald Gem' — CHal
- 'Silver Knight' — MBri
- 'Variegatum' (v) — MBri
'White Butterfly' — CHal MBri

Synnotia see *Sparaxis*

Synthyris (Scrophulariaceae)
missurica — CDes CLAP EBrs ETow GBuc
- var. *stellata* — CLAP EBee EHrv EWsh NGby SBla WFar WHal WPGP
pinnatifida — GBuc NWCA
reniformis — CLAP GBuc IBlr

Syringa ✿ (Oleaceae)
afghanica misapplied — see S. protolaciniata
amurensis — see S. reticulata subsp. amurensis
x *chinensis* — CTho ECrN WDin WFar WGob
- 'Alba' — SLon
- 'Saugeana' — EBee IDee NLar SLPl SPer
emodi — WHCG
- 'Aurea' — IArd NLar
- 'Aureovariegata' (v) — CBcs CDoC CEnd EPfP LRHS MAsh MDun NEgg SSpi WDin
'Hagny' **new** — WGob
x *hyacinthiflora* — IArd IDee
'Clarke's Giant'
- 'Esther Staley' ♀H4 — ECrN ENot EPfP MRav SBLw
- 'Missimo' **new** — MAsh
- 'Sunset' (d) — MAsh
'Josee' — EMil EPfP MAsh SPoG SWvt WFar WGob WPat WWeb
x *josiflexa* — CPLG
- 'Anna Amhoff' — NLar
- 'Bellicent' ♀H4 — CEnd CLnd CTho EBee ELan ENot EPfP LAst MBar MRav NEgg NPri NSti SHBN SMur SPer SPlb SPoG SRms SSpi SWvt WDin WGob WHCG WPat WTel

- 'James MacFarlane'	LBuc NLar
- 'Lynette'	EPla NPro
§ - 'Royalty'	LBuc
josikaea	CSBt CTho GIBF MBar NLar WGob WHCG
komarovii	GIBF NLar
- L 490	GGGa
§ - subsp. *reflexa*	CDul CTho EPfP MBar MGos WDin WFar WGob
§ x *laciniata* Mill.	CPMA EBee EDsa EHol EHyt EPfP LRHS MGos MRav MWea NLar SCoo SEND SMur SPer SSpi WGor WHCG WKif WPGP
§ *meyeri* 'Palibin' ♀H4	More than 30 suppliers
microphylla	see *S. pubescens* subsp. *microphylla*
- 'Superba'	see *S. pubescens* subsp. *microphylla* 'Superba'
'Minuet'	MGos NBlu WGob
'Miss Canada'	MBri WGob
palibiniana	see *S. meyeri* 'Palibin'
patula misapplied	see *S. meyeri* 'Palibin'
patula (Palibin) Nakai	see *S. pubescens* subsp. *patula*
pekinensis	see *S. reticulata* subsp. *pekinensis*
x *persica* ♀H4	CDul CPLG CPMA CSam CTri EPfP EWTr MGos NLar NPal SLon SPer SPoG WTel XPep
- 'Alba' ♀H4	CPMA EQui SMad WFar WHCG WPat
- var. *laciniata*	see *S. x laciniata* Mill.
pinnatifolia	IArd IDee MBri MWea NLar WHCG
x *prestoniae* 'Agnes Smith'	NLar WGob
- 'Audrey'	WGob
- 'Coral'	WFar
- 'Desdemona'	SSta
- 'Donald Wyman'	MBri WGob
- 'Elinor' ♀H4	CMHG EPfP MRav NSti SPer
- 'Hiawatha'	MGos
- 'Isabella'	MGos SCoo
- 'Kim'	CTho NLar WRHF WWeb
- 'Nocturne'	MGos WFar WGob
- 'Redwine'	MGos NBlu
- 'Royalty'	see *S. x josiflexa* 'Royalty'
§ *protolaciniata*	CPle IDee MGos WAbe WFar
- 'Kabul'	EPfP NLar
§ *pubescens* subsp. *microphylla*	CBrm CFwr EWTr
§ - - 'Superba' ♀H4	More than 30 suppliers
§ - subsp. *patula*	CMac ECho EGra EPfP GIBF LAst MRav NEgg NWea SEND SLon SPla SPoG WFar
§ - - 'Miss Kim' ♀H4	CDoC CSBt CWSG EBee ENot IArd LAst LRHS LSRN MAsh MBri MGos MRav MSwo NBlu NEgg SCoo SHBN SLim SPoG SSta WDin WFar WGob WHCG WPat
'Red Pixie'	LRHS MBri SCoo
reflexa	see *S. komarovii* subsp. *reflexa*
reticulata	GIBF
§ - subsp. *amurensis*	GIBF
- 'City of Toronto'	EBee
- 'Ivory Silk'	CTho CWSG EPfP MBri NLar
- var. *mandschurica*	see *S. reticulata* subsp. *amurensis*
§ - subsp. *pekinensis*	CMCN CTho IDee
- - 'Pendula'	IArd IDee
x *swegiflexa*	CDul CPLG NLar SPoG
sweginzowii	CTho EWTr GIBF LBuc MTis NLar SPer WFar
- 'Lark Song'	NLar
- 'Superba' **new**	WMoo
tomentella	NWea SRms
velutina	see *S. pubescens* subsp. *patula*
villosa	MWhi SPlb WBVN WDin WGob

vulgaris	CDul CLnd ECrN GIBF LBuc MBar NWea WBVN XPep
- 'Agincourt Beauty'	MBri
- var. *alba*	MBar
§ - 'Andenken an Ludwig Späth' ♀H4	More than 30 suppliers
- 'Aurea'	CNat EPla MRav NPro WFar
- Beauty of Moscow	see *S. vulgaris* 'Krasavitsa Moskvy'
- 'Belle de Nancy' (d)	CDul EBee ELan LAst MRav SBLw SEND SHBN SWvt WDin
- Burgundy Queen 'Lecburg' **new**	WGob
- 'Charles Joly' (d) ♀H4	More than 30 suppliers
- 'Congo'	ENot MRav NMoo SEND SPer WGob
- 'Edward J. Gardner' (d)	ECrN EDsa SCoo SPer WGob
- 'Firmament' ♀H4	CTho ELan ENot EPfP MRav NEgg NLar SCoo SEND SHBN SPer WGob
- 'G. J. Baardse'	SBLw
- 'Général Pershing'	SBLw
- 'Katherine Havemeyer' (d) ♀H4	More than 30 suppliers
§ - 'Krasavitsa Moskvy'	MBri WGob
- 'La Tour d'Auvergne'	SBLw
- 'Lois Amee Utley' (d) **new**	WGob
- 'Lucie Baltet'	MBri
- 'Madame Antoine Buchner' (d)	MRav
- 'Madame Florent Stepman'	EBee
- 'Madame Lemoine' (d) ♀H4	More than 30 suppliers
- 'Masséna'	MRav WSPU
- 'Maud Notcutt'	ENot SPer
- 'Michel Buchner' (d)	CBcs CDul EBee ELan LAst MBar MGan MRav NBlu SBLw SCoo SLim SPer WGob
- 'Miss Ellen Willmott' (d)	MBri MRav SBLw
- 'Mont Blanc'	SBLw
- 'Mrs Edward Harding' (d) ♀H4	ECrN EPfP LAst LBuc MGos NPri NWea SCoo SPer SRGP WGob
- 'Olivier de Serres'	SBLw
- 'Paul Thirion' (d)	WGob
- 'Président Fallières' **new**	WSPU
- 'Président Grévy' (d)	CDoC CLnd CMac LAst NEgg SBLw SPer
- 'President Lincoln'	SBLw
- 'Primrose'	CBcs CDoC CDul CMac CSBt CTho ECrN ELan ENot EPfP GBin IArd LAst LRHS MBri MDun MGos MRav NEgg NPen NPri SCoo SEND SPer SPoG SSta WBVN WDin WFar WGob
- 'Prince Wolkonsky' **new**	EMil WGob
- 'Sarah Sands' **new**	WGob
- 'Sensation'	CBcs CDoC CSBt CWSG EBee ECrN ENot EPfP IArd IMGH LAst LBuc LRHS LSRN MBri MDun MGos MRav MSwo NEgg NWea SCoo SEND SHBN SLim SPer SPoG SSta WGob
- 'Souvenir d'Alice Harding' (d)	LRHS MBri
- 'Souvenir de Louis Spaeth'	see *S. vulgaris* 'Andenken an Ludwig Späth'
- 'Sweetheart'	WGob
- variegated (v)	MGos SPoG
- 'Vestale' ♀H4	ENot MRav NPri SCoo
- 'Viviand-Morel' **new**	WGob
- 'Znamya Lenina'	MBri
wolfii	CArn CTho EDsa GIBF WBVN

yunnanensis CPLG CTho GIBF LTwo
- 'Prophecy' **new** MHer WGob
- 'Rosea' WGob

Syzygium (*Myrtaceae*)
australe EShb
jambos EShb

T

Tabernaemontana (*Apocynaceae*)
coronaria see *T. divaricata*
§ *divaricata* CCCN SOWG

Tacca (*Taccaceae*)
chantrieri CCCN EAmu ECho
integrifolia EAmu ECho

Tacitus see *Graptopetalum*

Tagetes (*Asteraceae*)
lemmonii SHDw SMad XPep
lucida CArn EOHP MSal NBlu NTHB
 WJek
tenuifolia CArn

Talbotia (*Velloziaceae*)
§ *elegans* CSpe SOkd WCot WFar

Talinum (*Portulacaceae*)
caffrum LToo
calycinum CBrm EDAr EWin WDyG
'Kingwood Gold' CBow
okanoganense CGra EDAr

tamarillo see *Cyphomandra betacea*

tamarind see *Tamarindus indica*

Tamarindus (*Caesalpiniaceae*)
indica (F) SPlb

Tamarix (*Tamaricaceae*)
gallica CSBt LPan NWea SAPC SArc WSHC
 XPep
§ *parviflora* EMil LRHS MGos
pentandra see *T. ramosissima*
§ *ramosissima* CTri ELan EPfP MBar MBrN SEND
 SRms SSta WDin WSHC
- 'Pink Cascade' CBcs CSBt EBee EMil ENot EPfP
 LPan LRHS MBri MGos MRav NBlu
 SPer SPoG SWvt WDin XPep
- 'Rosea' CBcs MGan SLon
§ - 'Rubra' ♀H4 CDoC CWSG EBee EMil EPfP
 LRHS MBlu MGos NLar SLon SPer
 WDin
- 'Summer Glow' see *T. ramosissima* 'Rubra'
tetrandra ♀H4 More than 30 suppliers
- 'Africance' **new** ERom
- var. *purpurea* see *T. parviflora*

Tamus (*Dioscoreaceae*)
communis CArn MSal

Tanacetum ✿ (*Asteraceae*)
§ *argenteum* ECho MRav SIde
- subsp. *canum* ECho EWes LRHS
§ *balsamita* CAgr CArn CCge CHrt COld
 CPrp EAro EBee ELan ELau
 EOHP GPoy MBri MHer MNHC
 MSal NTHB SHGN SWal WGHP
 WJek WPer WSel WTin WWye
 XPep

§ - subsp. *balsamita* CBod CWan GPoy MSal SIde
§ - subsp. *balsamitoides* CBod CHby CPrp ELau GBar
 GWCH MHer NPri WJek
 WWye
- var. *tanacetoides* see *T. balsamita* subsp. *balsamita*
- *tomentosum* see *T. balsamita* subsp.
 balsamitoides
capitatum see *Sphaeromeria capitata*
§ *cinerariifolium* CArn CBod CPrp CWan EChP
 EOHP GBar GPoy MNHC WPer
 XPep
§ *coccineum* EWTr GPoy MSal NBPC SGar SRms
 WFar
- 'Aphrodite' (d) CPrp EBee ECtt LRHS MBNS NEgg
 WCAu WHil
- 'Beauty of Stapleford' CPrp EBee LRHS NEgg WCAu WHil
- 'Bees' Pink Delight' CPrp EBee LRHS MBNS NEgg
- 'Brenda' EBee EPfP LHop LRHS MBNS NEgg
 NFla
* - 'Duplex' (d) LAst
- 'Duro' CFir EChP GBuc WHrl
- 'Eileen May Robinson' CBcs CPrp EBee ECot EHol ENot
 ♀H4 EPfP EShb LHop LRHS LSRN
 MWgw NBre NEgg SUsu WCAu
 WHil
- 'Evenglow' CPrp EBee ECtt EPfP LRHS NEgg
 WCAu WHil
- 'H.M. Pike' CPrp EBee LRHS MBNS SUsu WHil
- 'James Kelway' ♀H4 CPrp EBee ECot ECtt EHol ELan
 EPfP EShb EWll LRHS MWgw NBir
 NEgg SRms WCAu WHer WHil
- 'King Size' SGar WFar
- 'Laurin' EBrs
- 'Madeleine' (d) CPrp EBee LBMP MWgw SRGP
 WHil
- 'Robinson's' ENot
- Robinson's giant-flowered SRms WMoo
- 'Robinson's Pink' CMdw CPrp EBee EChP ELan ENot
 EPfP GMaP LAst LRHS MWgw
 NBre NFla NOrc SMar SRGP SRms
 WHil
- 'Robinson's Red' CSBt EChP GMaP IHMH LAst LIck
 MBNS NOrc NPri NVic SPur SRms
 SWvt WBVN
- 'Robinson's Rose' MBNS
* - *rubrum* GWCH
- 'Snow Cloud' CPrp EBee ELan LRHS MBNS
 MWgw NBre WCAu WHil
- 'Vanessa' CPrp EBee MBNS NEgg NSti WHil
§ *corymbosum* EBee GMac
densum ECho EPot WCFE
- subsp. *amani* EBee ECha ECho GBar GMaP LRHS
 MHer MWat NWCA SEND SPoG
 SRms XPep
§ *haradjanii* CMea ECho ECtt ELan NFor NLAp
 SBch SBla WHer WSHC
herderi see *Hippolytia herderi*
huronense EBee
macrophyllum misapplied see *Achillea grandifolia* Friv.
§ *macrophyllum* (Waldst. EChP ECtt EMon EPPr GCal LPhx
 & Kit.) Sch.Bip. WCot WPer
niveum CArn EAro ECha EOHP MSal WBri
 WCot
- 'Jackpot' CWib EAro EBee EDAr EWes LRHS
 MBNS MBri SHar SSvw
§ *parthenium* CArn CBod CHby CPbn CWan
 ELau GBar GPoy IHMH MBow
 MHer MNHC NPer SECG SIde
 SRms SWal WBri WGwG WHer
 WWye
- 'Aureum' CBgR CEnt CPbn CRow ECha
 ELan ELau EWes EWin GBar
 GPoy IHMH MBow MBri MHer
 MNHC MWgw NGHP SECG SIng
 SPer SPlb SRms WCot WEas WHer
 WMoo WPer

- double white (d)	CSWP EUnu GBar MNHC NPer SEND SRms
- 'Golden Ball'	ETow MNHC
- 'Golden Moss'	NVic
- 'Malmesbury'	CNat
- 'Plenum' (d)	EHrv SIng
§ - 'Rowallane' (d)	CHea EBee EHol ELan ERou GBuc GMac MBri SUsu WCMO WCot
- 'Sissinghurst White'	see *T. parthenium* 'Rowallane'
- 'White Bonnet' (d)	EChP WEas
poteriifolium	EBee EBrs
§ *ptarmiciflorum* ♀H3-4	MNHC
- 'Silver Feather'	EChP WJek
tommansii **new**	EBrs
vulgare	CAgr CArn CBod CHby CSev ECtt ELau GPoy IHMH MBow MHar MHer MNHC MSal NSco SIde WMoo WSFF WWye
- 'All Gold'	EMar
- var. *crispum*	CBod CHby CPrp CWan EBee EHol ELau EOHP GBar GPoy MHer SIde SMad WCot WFar WHer WJek WRha WSel
- 'Isla Gold' (v)	CBow CElw EBee EGle EPPr EWes GBar GCal LHop MHar NBid NBre NSti WCHb WCMO WCot WFar WGHP WMoo WRha WWye
- 'Silver Lace' (v)	CBow CElw EBee GBar GBri ITer NGHP NSti SEND WCHb WFar WGwG WHer WMoo

Tanakaea (Saxifragaceae)

radicans	WCru

tangelo see *Citrus* x *tangelo*

tangerine see *Citrus reticulata*

tangor see *Citrus* x *nobilis* Tangor Group

Tapeinochilos (Costaceae)

ananassae	MOak

Taraxacum (Asteraceae)

albidum	CNat WCMO WCot
coreanum	CNat
faeroense	WCMO WCot
officinale agg.	CArn
- variegated agg. (v)	WCot
pamiricum	EHyt
pseudoroseum **new**	CNat
rubrifolium	CSpe WHrl

Tarchonanthus (Asteraceae)

camphoratus	CTrC

tarragon see *Artemisia dracunculus*

Tasmannia see *Drimys*

Taxodium (Cupressaceae)

§ *distichum* ♀H4	More than 30 suppliers
- 'Cascade Falls' PBR	CDul LCon MBlu MGos NLar SLim
- 'Hursley Park' **new**	SLim
§ - var. *imbricatum*	CMCN EPfP NLar WPGP
- - 'Nutans' ♀H4	CBcs CEnd CTho LCon LPan LRHS MAsh MBlu SCoo SLim SMad
- 'Minaret'	MBlu
- 'Peve Minaret'	CDoC LCon LRHS MAsh NLar SLim
- 'Peve Yellow'	NLar SLim
- 'Schloss Herten' **new**	NLar SLim
- 'Secrest'	CBcs LRHS MAsh MBlu MBri SLim

- Shawnee Brave = 'Mickelson'	MBlu NLar
mucronatum	CDoC

Taxus ✿ (Taxaceae)

baccata ♀H4	More than 30 suppliers
- 'Adpressa' (f)	ECho NEgg
- 'Adpressa Aurea' (v)	CKen ECho EPla
- 'Adpressa Variegata' (m/v) ♀H4	CDoC ECho EHul
- 'Aldenham Gold'	CKen ECho
- 'Amersfoort'	CDoC EOrn LCon MDun NLar SLim SPoG
- 'Argentea Minor'	see *T. baccata* 'Dwarf White'
- Aurea Group	NHol SRms
I - 'Aurea Pendula'	ECho EOrn
I - 'Aureomarginata' (v)	CBcs CBow CSBt ECho EOrn MAsh NEgg SWvt
- 'Autumn Shades'	CBcs ECho
- 'Cavendishii' (f)	ECho
- 'Compacta'	EOrn EPla
- 'Corleys Coppertip'	CBgR CKen CRob ECho EHul LCon MAsh MBar NEgg NLar SCoo SLim WEve WFar
- 'Cristata'	CKen NLar
- 'David'	CDoC IArd MBri NLar SPoG WEve
- 'Dovastoniana' (f) ♀H4	CMac ECho MBar NLar NWea WMou
- 'Dovastonii Aurea' (m/v) ♀H4	CMac ECho EHul EOrn EPfP EPla LBee LCon MAsh MBar MBlu MBri NEgg NLar NPri NWea SCoo SLim WCFE WDin WFar
- 'Drinkstone Gold' (v)	ECho EHul
§ - 'Dwarf White' (v)	ECho EOrn EPla SCoo SPoG WGor
- 'Elegantissima' (f/v)	ECho ECrN EHul EPfP MTis SPoG WEve WFar
- 'Erecta' (f)	ECho EHul SHBN
§ - 'Fastigiata' (f) ♀H4	More than 30 suppliers
- Fastigiata Aurea Group	CLnd CWib ECho EHul ENot EPfP GKev IArd LBuc LLin MAsh MGan MGos NGHP NHol NPri SRms WBrE WEve WFar WHar
- 'Fastigiata Aureomarginata' (m/v) ♀H4	More than 30 suppliers
- 'Fastigiata Robusta' (f)	CDoC CRob ECho EPfP EPla LCon MBar MBri NHol SLim SPoG WEve WFar WGer
- 'Goud Elsje'	CKen
- 'Gracilis Pendula' **new**	ECho
- 'Grayswood Hill' **new**	ECho
- 'Green Column'	CKen ECho
- 'Green Diamond'	CKen NLar
- 'Hibernica'	see *T. baccata* 'Fastigiata'
- 'Icicle'	CBcs ECho EPla LCon LLin MAsh MGos NLar WEve
- 'Itsy Bitsy'	CKen
- 'Ivory Tower'	CBcs CDoC CKen ECho ELan LBee LCon LLin LRHS MAsh MGos NLar SLim SPoG WEve WFar WGor
- 'Klitzeklein'	CKen
- 'Laurie'	SPoG
- 'Melfard'	CDoC EHul
- 'Nana' **new**	ECho
- 'Nutans'	CDoC CKen CNic CRob CSBt ECho EHul EOrn IMGH LLin MBar NDlv SCoo SPoG
- 'Overeynderi'	EHul
- 'Pendula'	ECho MRav
- 'Prostrata'	CMac WFar
- 'Pygmaea'	CKen
- 'Repandens' (f) ♀H4	CDoC EHul IArd LCon MBar SHBN WCFE WDin WFar

I – 'Repens Aurea' (v) ♀H4   CDoC CKen CRob ECho ECrN
                        EHul EOrn EPfP LCon LLin LRHS
                        MAsh MBar MGos NEgg NHol
                        SCoo WFar

  – 'Semperaurea' (m) ♀H4   CBcs CDoC CMac ECho
                        EHul EOrn LBuc LCon LRHS
                        MAsh MBar MGan MGos
                        NEgg NHol NWea SCoo SLim
                        SPla SPoG WCFE WDin
                        WFar

  – 'Silver Spire' (v)   CKen MDKP
  – 'Standishii' (f) ♀H4   More than 30 suppliers
  – 'Stove Pipe'   CKen
  – 'Summergold' (v)   CRob ECho EHul ELan EPfP
                        LCon LRHS MAsh MBar MGos
                        NBir NBlu NEgg NHol NLar
                        SCoo SLim SPoG WDin WEve
                        WFar

  – 'Washingtonii' (v)   IArd MBar SHBN
  – 'White Icicle'   ECho EOrn LBee MGos WGor
  brevifolia   EPla
  cuspidata   CMen ECho
  – 'Aurescens' (v)   CKen EPla SRms
  – var. *nana*   CNic EHul EOrn LCon MBar
  – 'Robusta'   EHul LLin
  – 'Straight Hedge'   CDoC ECho EHul IMGH LRHS
                        SLim WGor
  x *media* 'Brownii'   EHul LBuc
  – 'Hicksii' (f) ♀H4   CDul ECho EHul IMGH LBuc LRHS
                        MBar MGan MGos NBlu NWea
                        SLim WFar

  – 'Hillii'   MBar
  – 'Lodi'   LBee LRHS

Tayberry see *Rubus* Tayberry Group

Tecoma (*Bignoniaceae*)
x *alata*   SOWG
capensis ♀H1   CHEx CPLG CPIN CSec CSev EBak
                  LRHS SHFr SOWG SYvo
– 'Aurea'   CSev EShb SOWG
§ – 'Coccinea'   EShb
– 'Lutea'   EShb LRHS
garrocha   EShb
'Orange Glow'   SOWG
ricasoliana   see *Podranea ricasoliana*
stans   SOWG

Tecomanthe (*Bignoniaceae*)
dendrophila   CPIN
speciosa   CHEx CPIN ECou SOWG
venusta new   CPIN

Tecomaria see *Tecoma*

Tecophilaea (*Tecophilaeaceae*)
cyanocrocus ♀H2   CAvo CBro CFFs EBrs ECho EHyt
                  EPot GCrs LRHS SBla SOkd WCMO
                  WCot
– 'Leichtlinii' ♀H2   CBro ECho EHyt EPot LRHS SCnR
                  WCMO
– 'Purpurea'   see *T. cyanocrocus* 'Violacea'
– Storm Cloud Group   CBro GCrs WCMO
§ – 'Violacea'   CAvo CBro ECho GCrs LRHS
                  WCMO
violiflora   ECho

Tectaria (*Dryopteridaceae*)
gemmifera   GQui

Telanthophora (*Asteraceae*)
grandifolia   CHEx SAPC SArc

Telekia (*Asteraceae*)
§ *speciosa*   More than 30 suppliers
speciosissima new   EBee

Telesonix see *Boykinia*

Teline see *Genista*

Tellima (*Saxifragaceae*)
grandiflora   More than 30 suppliers
– 'Delphine' (v)   CBow EBee EMan EPPr SAga SUsu
                  WCMO WCot
– 'Forest Frost'   CBct CBow EBee EMan GCai
                  LAst LHop MDun NBre NGdn
                  NLar NSti SPoG WCMO WCot
                  WGor WMoo
– Odorata Group   CBre CPLG EBee EChP ECha
                  EGoo MRav NSti WHen WMoo
                  WWye
– 'Perky' new   ECho
– 'Purpurea'   see *T. grandiflora* Rubra Group
– 'Purpurteppich'   EBee EBrs ECha ECho EGoo EHrv
                  EMan EPPr GAbr LRHS MRav
                  NGdn WCot WMnd WMoo
                  WTMC
§ – Rubra Group   More than 30 suppliers
– 'Silver Select'   EPPr

Telopea (*Proteaceae*)
speciosissima   CTrC SOWG SPlb
– 'Red Embers' new   CTrC

Templetonia (*Papilionaceae*)
retusa   ECou

Temu see *Blepharocalyx*

Tephroseris (*Asteraceae*)
integrifolia   WHer

Tephrosia (*Papilionaceae*)
vogelii   CArn

Tetracentron (*Tetracentraceae*)
sinense   CBcs CMCN EPfP GQui IArd LRHS
          NLar

Tetradenia (*Lamiaceae*)
riparia   EOHP

Tetradium (*Rutaceae*)
§ *daniellii*   CBcs CMCN EPfP IArd IDee NLar
          SSpi WPGP WPat
– *henryi* new   NLar
§ – Hupehense Group   CMCN CPle MBri SSpi WDin
          WOrn
– 'Moonlight' new   NLar
glabrifolium   WPGP
– B&SWJ 3541   WCru
ruticarpum   WPGP
– B&SWJ 6882   WCru
* *velutinum*   CMCN NLar

Tetragonia (*Tetragoniaceae*)
tetragonoides   CArn

Tetragonolobus see *Lotus*

Tetraneuris (*Asteraceae*)
§ *acaulis* var. *caespitosa*   WLin
§ *grandiflora*   GAbr ITim NWCA
scaposa   EPot LRHS

Tetrapanax (*Araliaceae*)
§ *papyrifer* ♀H2-3   CBrP CHEx CHen SAPC SArc
                  SBig WCMO WMul
                  XBlo
– B&SWJ 7135   WCru
– 'Empress'   WCru

- 'Rex'	CHEx CPLG EAmu EGFP WCru WMul WPGP

Tetrapathaea see *Passiflora*

Tetrastigma (Vitaceae)

obtectum	CPIN ECre EWes
voinierianum ♀H1	CPIN MBri SAPC SArc WCot

Tetratheca (Tremandraceae)

ciliata var. *alba*	SOWG
thymifolia	ECou
- pink-flowered	SOWG

Teucrium (Lamiaceae)

* *ackermannii*	CLyd ECho EGoo LBee LRHS NMen SBla SMac WAbe WEas WHoo WPat WTin XPep
arduinoi	XPep
aroanium	CLyd CMea ECho EPot LBee LRHS MWat NMen NWCA SBla WAbe WLin
asiaticum	CPom EGoo XPep
bicolor	CPle
botrys	MHer MSal
brevifolium	XPep
canadense	MSal
chamaedrys misapplied	see *T.* x *lucidrys*
chamaedrys L.	CHal CPom CSam CWan CWib ECho EGoo GAbr GBar IHMH LEdu LRHS LSRN MSwo NGHP NJOw NWCA SLim SRms STre WBrk WHbs WJek WSel WTin WWeb XPep
- 'Nanum'	ECho NLAp WWye
- 'Rose'	WMoo
- 'Rose Carpet'	EChP ECrN EGoo
- 'Variegatum' (v)	CBow EMan GBar WCHb WPer WRha
aff. *chamaedrys* new	MNHC
§ *cossonii*	XPep
§ *creticum*	ECho WLin
divaricatum	NWCA XPep
- NS 614	NWCA
dunense	EAro XPep
flavum	EChP EDAr EGoo NBre SGar SHFr WCHb WJek WOut XPep
- subsp. *grandiflorum*	XPep
fruticans	More than 30 suppliers
- 'Azureum' ♀H3	CBcs CMMP CWSG EBee EChP EPfP EWin LRHS LSou SBra SRkn WEas XPep
- 'Compactum'	CDoC EBee EMan ENot EWin LRHS LSou MCCP SHGC SLon SPer SPla
- 'Drysdale'	CDoC LRHS
gnaphalodes	XPep
hircanicum	More than 30 suppliers
- 'Paradise Delight'	EBee MAvo MBri NBid NOrc SPoG WCra WSan
- 'Purple Tails'	CPrp CWib LBBr LSou NBir NCob SPoG
laciniatum	XPep
lamiifolium new	EBee
§ x *lucidrys*	More than 30 suppliers
lucidum	XPep
marum	CArn EOHP MSal NMen SBla WJek XPep
- 'Feuilles Vertes'	XPep
'Massif Central'	LRHS
massiliense misapplied	see *T.* x *lucidrys*
massiliense L.	EAro EBee EGoo WHer XPep
microphyllum	XPep
micropodioides	XPep
montanum	EGoo EShb GBar NJOw SHGN XPep

musimonum	EPot
orientale	XPep
polium	CArn CPLG ECho MWat NLAp WJek WPat XPep
- subsp. *aureum*	EHyt NWCA SBla XPep
- subsp. *capitatum*	XPep
pyrenaicum	CHal CMea CPBP CPom EBee ECho EHyt EMan EWes GCrs GEdr MHer NWCA SBch SBla SIng WPat WWye
rosmarinifolium	see *T. creticum*
scordium	CNat
scorodonia	CArn COld CRWN CSev EGoo ELau GBar GPoy MHer MNHC MSal NMir WHer WJek WSel XPep
- 'Binsted Gold'	EBee EGoo EMan EMon EPPr LDai LSou MHar WOut
- 'Crispum'	CBgR CHby CWan ELau EMar EUnu GBar MHar MHer MLLN MMuc MWgw NBid NBro NCob NJOw SPer WBrE WCHb WGwG WHoo WJek WKif WMoo WPer WSel
* - 'Crispum Aureomarginatum'	EChP
§ - 'Crispum Marginatum' (v)	EChP ECha EGoo EHoe EHrv EMag EMar EPPr EPfP GBar IBlr ILis LHop LRHS MDun MNrw MRav MTis NHol NOak NSti WCra WEas WFar WTin WWeb
- 'Spring Morn' new	EBee
- 'Winterdown' (v)	CBow CRez EBee EGoo EMan EPPr NPro SAga SBch WCHb WHoo WLin WWeb
subspinosum	CMea ECho LBee LRHS NLAp NMen SBch WHoo WPat XPep
thyranicum 'Crispum' new	EBrs
§ *viscidum* 'Lemon and Lime' (v)	EBee ECtt EMan LHop LSou NSti SDnm
webbianum	CSec ECho
'Winterdown'	GBri WDyG

Thalia (Marantaceae)

dealbata	CBen CDWL CHEx EAmu EMFW LPBA MJnS NLar SBig SDix WMAq WMul WWpP
geniculata	CDWL WMul

Thalictrum (Ranunculaceae)

CC 3691	ITer
CC 4051	WCot
CC 4575	CPLG MGol
CC 4576	CPLG GKev MGol WCot
CC 4577	CPLG MGol WCot
from Afghanistan	see *T. isopyroides*
actaeifolium	CLAP CWib
- B&SWJ 4664	WCru
- var. *brevistylum* B&SWJ 8819	WCru
adiantifolium	see *T. minus* 'Adiantifolium'
alpinum	EPPr NRya SBch
angustifolium	see *T. lucidum*
aquilegiifolium	More than 30 suppliers
- var. *album*	CFwr CMea CMil COIW EBee ECha EGle ELan EPfP LHop LPhx MDun MNFA MWgw NBid NChi SBla SPla WCAu WCru WMnd WPer WSHC
- dwarf	CMea
* - 'Hybridum'	CHad GBBs WFar WMoo WPer
- Purple Cloud	see *T. aquilegiifolium* 'Thundercloud'
- 'Purpureum'	CPom CSev EBee MDun NLar SPla WCAu WCru WHoo

- 'Sparkler'	GCai WCMO
§ - 'Thundercloud' ♀H4	CBct CCVN CFir CKno CWan EBee ECtt ENot EPfP GBBs GCal LHop LRHS MBri MDKP NBPC NLar NRnb NSti SMer WBrE WCMO WCra WHlf WWeb
baicalense	CPom EBee
'Black Stockings' **new**	CKno EWes MBnl WCMO
'Braveheart'	NRnb
§ *chelidonii*	GMaP MGol
- GWJ 9349	WCru
- HWJK 2216	WCru
clavatum	CAby CDes CLAP EBee WPGP
contortum	EBee SDys
coreanum	see *T. ichangense*
coriaceum	EBee
cultratum	CDes CWCL EChP NCGa NSti WPGP
- HWJCM 367	EBee NLar WCru
dasycarpum	EBee MLLN NLar WPnP
§ *delavayi* ♀H4	More than 30 suppliers
- BWJ 7903	WCru
- DJHC 473	WCru
- var. *acuminatum* BWJ 7535	WCru
- - BWJ 7971	WCru
- 'Album'	CFwr CLAP CPom CWCL EBee EBrs ECha EGle LPhx LRHS NCGa NLar NOak SPoG WCMO WHil WMoo WPrP
- 'Ankum' **new**	NCot
- var. *decorum*	CBos CFwr CLAP CWCL EDsa GBin GMac LPhx NCGa NCob NFla SBla SMHy WCot WCru WSHC
- - CD&R 2135	CAby
- 'Hewitt's Double' (d) ♀H4	More than 30 suppliers
- var. *mucronatum*	WCru
- purple-stemmed BWJ 7748	WCru
diffusiflorum	CDes CLAP GBri GBuc GEdr SBla SUsu WPrP WSHC
dioicum	WPnP
dipterocarpum misapplied	see *T. delavayi*
dipterocarpum Franch.	MDun WMnd
- ACE 4.878.280	CMil
elegans HWJK 2271	WCru
- from China	CFwr
'Elin'	CBos CFir CKno CLAP CSam CSpe EBee EPPr ERou EWes GBuc GMac IPot LHop MBri MLLN MNFA NBir NCGa NCob NCot NDov NEgg SBla SMHy SPoG SUsu WBor WCMO WKif
fendleri	GBin GBuc
- var. *polycarpum*	NHol
filamentosum B&SWJ 777	WCru
- var. *yakusimense* B&SWJ 6094	WCru
finetii	CLAP
aff. *finetii*	CLAP
- DJHC 473	CDes CPom
flavum	CHar CPLG EBee EBrs ECtt EDAr GBBs GBin LPhx MBow NBro SWat WBrE WShi
§ - subsp. *glaucum* ♀H4	More than 30 suppliers
- - 'True Blue' **new**	LRHS NDov
- 'Illuminator'	CHad CKno CPar EBee EGle EPPr EPfP GBri LRHS MArl MBow MHer MOne MRav NEgg NHol SPlb SPoG SUsu WCAu WCot WPnP WPrP
flexuosum	see *T. minus* subsp. *minus*
foetidum	EBee NBre
- BWJ 7558	WCru
aff. *foetidum* BWJ 7558	WCru
foliolosum B&SWJ 2705	WCru
- HWJK 2181	WCru
- S&SH 382	GBri
grandiflorum	EBee NCob WCot
honanense	CFwr WCot
§ *ichangense*	GBri
* - var. *minus*	WCru
§ *isopyroides*	CFir CPBP CPom CSev EAEE EBee EBrs EChP ELan EMar EPla GBin GBuc LAst LRHS MRav MWgw NChi NGdn NJOw NMen SRot WCot WDyG WTin
javanicum	LEdu
- B&SWJ 9506	WCru
- var. *puberulum*	GMac
- - B&SWJ 6770	WCru
johnstonii B&SWJ	WCru
kiusianum	More than 30 suppliers
- Kew form	SBla WSHC
koreanum	see *T. ichangense*
§ *lucidum*	CAby CKno CPou EBee ELan EShb IHMH LPhx MLLN MRav NBre NDov NLar NSti SBla SGar SHar SMHy WCot WFar WPrP
minus	CAgr CMHG EBee ECGP ELan EMon GBuc GIBF MLLN NBre NOak SECG SEND WWye
§ - 'Adiantifolium'	EBee MLLN MRav MWgw NBre NCob NGdn NLar NOak SHar SRms WCMO WFar WPer
- var. *hypoleucum* B&SWJ 8634	WCru
- subsp. *kemense* **new**	EBee
§ - subsp. *minus*	NBre
§ - subsp. *olympicum*	WPer
- subsp. *saxatile*	see *T. minus* subsp. *olympicum*
- var. *sipellatum* B&SWJ 5051	WCru
occidentale	EBee
- JLS 86255	MNrw
omeiense	CDes
- BWJ 8049	WCru
orientale	EWes SBla
osmundifolium **new**	CFwr
polygamum	see *T. pubescens*
przewalskii	WCru
§ *pubescens*	CAby ECha GBin GBri GIBF GMaP LPhx MSal NBre NDov SHar WPrP
punctatum	CBos CLAP MDun NEgg
- B&SWJ 1272	LPhx WCru
reniforme	CBos CFir GBuc GIBF
- B&SWJ 2610	WCru
- HWJK 2152	WCru
reticulatum	WCru
rochebruneanum	More than 30 suppliers
sachalinense	CDes EPPr GIBF ITer MCCP NCGa WCMO WCot
- AER 0279	EKen MGol
- RBS 0279	MHar
* *shenshianum* from China **new**	CFwr
simplex	MLLN NHol
- var. *brevipes* B&SWJ 4794	WCru
speciosissimum	see *T. flavum* subsp. *glaucum*
sphaerostachyum	CDes EBrs GMac IFro LRHS MBri MWhi SMrm WGer WHal
squarrosum	EBee EBrs LRHS
tenuisubulatum BWJ 7929	WCru

tuberosum	CDes CElw CMea EBee EHyt GBuc MLLN NDov NLAp SBla WAbe WCMO WPGP WPat
uchiyamae	CFwr CPom EBee EGle EPPr GBin GBri LBMP WSPU
virgatum B&SWJ 2964	WCru

Thamnocalamus (*Poaceae*)

aristatus	EPfP EPla WPGP
crassinodus	EPla SBig
- dwarf	EPla
- 'Gosainkund'	EPla
- 'Kew Beauty'	CAbb CDoC CPen EFul EPfP EPla ERod MBrN MBri MGos MMoz MWht NPal SBig WJun WMul WPGP
- 'Lang Tang'	EFul EPla ERod WJun WPGP
- 'Merlyn'	CDoC CPen EPfP EPla ERod MMoz MWht WJun WPGP
- 'Pitt White' **new**	MBri
falcatus	see *Drepanostachyum falcatum*
falconeri	see *Himalayacalamus falconeri*
funghomii	see *Schizostachyum funghomii*
khasianus	see *Drepanostachyum khasianum*
maling	see *Yushania maling*
spathaceus misapplied	see *Fargesia murielae*
§ *spathiflorus*	EFul EPla WJun
- subsp. *nepalensis*	EPla SBig
§ *tessellatus*	CAbb EFul EPla MMoz WDyG WJun

Thamnochortus (*Restionaceae*)

bachmannii	CBcs
cinereus	CBcs CBct CBig CCtw CTrC EAmu WPGP
insignis	CBcs CBig CCtw CHEx CTrC SPlb WMul WNor WPrP
rigidus	CCCN
spicigerus	CBig

Thapsia (*Apiaceae*)

decipiens	see *Melanoselinum decipiens*
garganica	CArn EMan

Thea see *Camellia*

Thelypteris (*Thelypteridaceae*)

limbosperma	see *Oreopteris limbosperma*
nevadensis NNS 00-725	WCot
palustris	CAby CRWN EBee EMon LPBA MAsh NHol NVic SRms WFib WPnP WWye
phegopteris	see *Phegopteris connectilis*

Themeda (*Poaceae*)

japonica	EHoe EPPr GIBF
triandra	GIBF SMad

Thermopsis (*Papilionaceae*)

barbata ACE 2298	EBee
caroliniana	see *T. villosa*
fabacea	see *T. lupinoides*
gracilis var. *gracilis* NNS 03-568 **new**	WCot
lanceolata	CHad CTri EBee ECGP EChP EDAr EMan GBin LRHS MBri MEHN MLLN MNFA MWgw NBPC NCGa NPri NSti SAga SPoG WAul WCAu WFar WHrl WPer WWye
§ *lupinoides*	ECha EHrv GIBF ITer MFOX MGol NBre NEgg SUsu WCot WFar WPer
- AER 0280	MGol
macrophylla **new**	EBee

mollis	CPLG NBid
montana	see *T. rhombifolia* var. *montana*
§ *rhombifolia* var. *montana*	CRez EBee EDAr ELan EPfP GGar GMaP LBMP LHop MNrw MSte MWgw MWhi NBre NCGa NEgg NOrc NPol NSti SBod SPer WAbb WBVN WPer
§ *villosa*	EMan GIBF IFro MGol MLLN MNFA MRav MSte MWrn NBre NDov NFla NGdn SBla SMar WCot WHoo WPGP

Therorhodion see *Rhododendron*

Thevetia (*Apocynaceae*)

neriifolia	CSec
peruviana	LRHS MSal

Thladiantha (*Cucurbitaceae*)

dubia	CPIN SDix

Thlaspi (*Brassicaceae*)

alpinum	NJOw
bellidifolium	NBir
biebersteinii	see *Pachyphragma macrophyllum*
§ *cepaeifolium* subsp. *rotundifolium*	WBri
diacicum	NJOw
fendleri	MNrw
praecox	NJOw
rotundifolium	see *T. cepaeifolium* subsp. *rotundifolium*

Thrinax (*Arecaceae*)

campestris **new**	SAin
radiata	EAmu

Thryptomene (*Myrtaceae*)

saxicola	ECou
- 'F.C. Payne'	CBcs

Thuja ✿ (*Cupressaceae*)

'Extra Gold'	see *T. plicata* 'Irish Gold'
'Gnome'	IBal
§ *koraiensis*	IDee LCon LRHS MBar SLim SPoG WCwm WThu
occidentalis	NWea
- 'Amber Glow'	CBrm CDoC CKen CRob ECho GBin LCon LLin LRHS MAsh MGos NHol NLar SCoo SLim SPoG WBor WEve
- Aurea Group	ECho MBar
- 'Aureospicata'	ECho EHul
- 'Bateman Broom'	CKen
- 'Beaufort' (v)	CKen ECho EHul MBar
- 'Brabant'	ECho LPan NLar SLim
- 'Brobecks Tower'	CKen NLar SLim
- 'Caespitosa'	CFee CKen ECho LLin NEgg NHol NLar SCoo SPoG WEve WGor
- 'Cloth of Gold' **new**	ECho
- 'Cristata Aurea'	CKen
- 'Cuprea' **new**	ECho
- 'Danica' ♀H4	CMac CRob ECho EHul ENot EOrn LCon LLin MAsh MBar NEgg NWea SBod SCoo SLim SMer SPoG SRms WCFE WEve WFar
- 'Dicksonii'	EHul
- 'Douglasii Aurea' (v)	CKen
- 'Ellwangeriana Aurea'	MGos
- Emerald	see *T. occidentalis* 'Smaragd'
- 'Ericoides'	CDoC CTri ECho EHul LRHS MBar MGos SRms
- 'Europa Gold'	CBrm CDoC ECho EHul LBee MBar MGos NLar SLim

	- 'Fastigiata'	ECho MBar
	- 'Filiformis'	CKen ECho EPla
	- 'Globosa'	CMac ECho MBar WRHF
I	- 'Globosa Compacta Nana' **new**	ECho
I	- 'Globosa Variegata' (v)	CKen MBar WEve
	- 'Gold Drop'	CKen
	- 'Golden Globe'	CDoC ECho EHul EOrn LLin LPan MBar MGos NEgg NHol SCoo SLim SPla SPoG WDin WRHF
	- 'Golden Minaret'	EHul
	- 'Golden Tuffet' **new**	LCon MGos SLim
	- 'Hetz Midget'	CKen ECho EHul IMGH LLin MBar NEgg NHol NLar SCoo SLim SMer SPlb SPoG WDin WFar
	- 'Holmstrup' ♀H4	CDoC CMac CRob CSBt CTri CWib ECho EHul EOrn LLin LRHS MAsh MBar NBlu SCoo SLim SPoG SRms WDin WEve WFar WTel
	- 'Holmstrup's Yellow'	ECho EGra EHul LCon NHol SCoo SLim SPoG WBVN
	- 'Hoveyi'	CMac CTri EHul WEve
	- 'Linesville'	CKen
	- 'Little Champion'	EHul NLar
	- 'Little Gem'	ECho EHul MGos NHol NLar SRms WDin
	- 'Lutea Nana' ♀H4	CMac ECho EHul EOrn MBar NDlv WCFE WRHF
	- 'Marrisen's Sulphur'	EHul LRHS NLar SCoo SLim SPla WEve
	- 'Meineke's Zwerg' (v)	CKen NLar
	- 'Miky'	CKen
	- 'Mr Bowling Ball' **new**	SLim
	- 'Ohlendorffii'	CDoC CKen ECho EHul EOrn LLin MBar NHol
	- 'Orientalis'	see *Platycladus orientalis* Semperaurescens 'Semperaurea'
I	- 'Pumila Sudworth'	NHol
I	- 'Pygmaea'	CKen ECho MBar SLon
	- 'Pyramidalis Aurea'	MGos NHol WEve
	- 'Pyramidalis Compacta'	EHul WGor
	- 'Recurva Nana'	EHul MBar NHol
	- 'Rheingold' ♀H4	More than 30 suppliers
	- 'Robusta' **new**	ECho
§	- 'Smaragd' ♀H4	More than 30 suppliers
*	- 'Smaragd Variegated' (v)	CKen
	- 'Southport'	CKen WEve
	- 'Spaethii'	EHul EOrn
	- 'Spiralis'	ECho EHul IMGH MBar NLar WCFE
§	- 'Stolwijk' (v)	ECho EHul EOrn LLin MBar MGos
	- 'Sunkist'	CKen CMac CRob CSBt CSli CTri CWib ECho EHul ENot EOrn LPan MAsh MBar MGos NEgg SBod SCoo SLim SMer SPla SPoG WEve WFar
	- 'Suzie'	LLin
	- 'Teddy'	CDoC CFee CRob ECho LBee LCon LLin LRHS MAsh NHol NLar SCoo SLim SPoG WEve WFar
	- 'Tiny Tim'	CDoC CMac CNic CRob CSBt CWib ECho EHul IMGH LCon LLin MBar MGos NHol SCoo WEve WFar WGor WRHF
	- 'Trompenburg'	CRob ECho EHul EOrn MAsh NLar SCoo
	- 'Wansdyke Silver' (v)	CKen ECho EHul EOrn LRHS MBar SCoo SLim SPoG WRHF
	- 'Wareana'	CMac
	- 'Wareana Aurea'	see *T. occidentalis* 'Wareana Lutescens'
§	- 'Wareana Lutescens'	CWib EHul EOrn MBar MGos NHol WEve
	- 'Woodwardii'	ECho EHul MBar SMer
	- 'Yellow Ribbon'	CKen CSBt ECho EHul LCon LRHS MBar NLar SCoo SLim SMer SPla SPoG WEve WFar
	plicata	CDul EHul EPfP MBar MGos NBlu NWea SLim SPer SPoG WDin WMou
	- 'Atrovirens' ♀H4	CDul CTho CTri ECho ECrN ENot LBee LBuc LCon LPan LRHS MAsh MBar MBri MGos SBLw SCoo SLim SMer SPoG SRms WDin WEve WHar
*	- 'Atrovirens Aurea'	SLim WEve
	- 'Aurea' ♀H4	ECho EHul LBee LRHS MAsh SLim SPoG SRms
	- 'Barabits'	ECho
	- 'Brooks Gold'	CKen
	- 'Can-can' (v)	CRob ECho NLar SCoo
I	- 'Cole's Variety'	CWib ECho MBar MGos SLim
	- 'Collyer's Gold'	CTri ECho EHul NHol NLar SRms WEve
	- 'Copper Kettle'	CKen ECho EHul LCon MAsh MBar NDlv NEgg NLar SCoo SLim WEve WGor WRHF
	- 'Cuprea'	CKen ECho EHul MBar
	- 'Doone Valley'	CKen CSli ECho EHul EOrn MBar NDlv NHol
	- 'Fastigiata' ♀H4	CDul CMac LRHS WTel
	- 'Gelderland'	ECho EHul NBlu NLar SCoo SLim WEve WFar
	- 'Gracilis Aurea'	ECho EHul
	- 'Grüne Kugel'	CDoC
	- 'Hillieri'	CDul MBar WRHF
§	- 'Irish Gold' (v) ♀H4	CAbP CMac LCon LLin LRHS NLar
	- 'Rogersii'	CDoC CKen CMac CTri ECho EHul EOrn EPfP LCon LLin MAsh MBar MGos NHol SCoo SPoG SRms WFar WRHF WTel
	- 'Stolwijk's Gold'	see *T. occidentalis* 'Stolwijk'
	- 'Stoneham Gold' ♀H4	CDoC CKen CMac ECho EHul EOrn LBee LCon MAsh MBar MGos NHol SBod SLim SMer SPoG SRms WCFE WEve WTel
	- 'Sunshine'	CKen
	- 'Whipcord' **new**	LCon SLim
*	- 'Windsor Gold'	ECho EHul
	- 'Winter Pink' (v)	CKen NLar
	- 'Zebrina' (v)	More than 30 suppliers
	standishii	GIBF

Thujopsis (Cupressaceae)

	dolabrata ♀H4	CBcs CDul CTho CTrG EHul LBee LRHS MBar MMHG NDlv NEgg NLar NWea SEND SHBN SPer WBrE WDin WFar WPGP
	- 'Aurea' (v)	CDoC CKen EHul EOrn LCon LRHS MBar MGos NLar SCoo SHBN SLim WEve
	- 'Laetevirens'	see *T. dolabrata* 'Nana'
§	- 'Nana'	CDoC CKen CMac EHul EOrn LBee LCon LLin MBar SCoo SLim SPoG SRms STre WEve WFar
	- 'Variegata' (v)	CDoC CDul CFee EHul EOrn LCon LLin LRHS MBar NDlv SCoo SHFr SLim SPoG WDin WEve WFar
	koraiensis	see *Thuja koraiensis*

Thunbergia (Acanthaceae)

	'Alamain Glory'	CPlN
	alata	CPlN MBri SYvo
	- 'African Sunset'	CSpe EShb
	battiscombeii	CCCN CPlN MJnS
	chinensis **new**	CPlN
	coccinea	CPlN EShb MJnS
I	- 'Lutea'	CPlN
	erecta	CCCN CPlN ELan ERea SOWG

fragrans	ERea EShb
- var. *rosea* **new**	CPlN
grandiflora ♀H1	CHll CPlN CTrG ELan EPfP ERea
	EShb MJnS SOWG WMul
- 'Alba'	CHll CPlN WMul
- 'Angkor Beauty' **new**	CPlN
gregorii ♀H1+3	CCCN CHll CPlN CSpe ERea
	SOWG
laevis	CPlN
'Molly'	CPlN
mysorensis ♀H1	CPlN ERea MJnS SOWG
natalensis	ERea EShb

Thylacospermum (Caryophyllaceae)

caespitosum **new**	GIBF

thyme, caraway see *Thymus herba-barona*

thyme, garden see *Thymus vulgaris*

thyme, lemon see *Thymus* x *citriodorus*

thyme, wild see *Thymus serpyllum* L.

Thymbra (Lamiaceae)

spicata	XPep

Thymus ✿ (Lamiaceae)

from Turkey	ECho EWes LLWP SHDw
§ 'Alan Bloom'	LLWP
'Anderson's Gold'	see *T. pulegioides* 'Bertram Anderson'
azoricus	see *T. caespititius*
'Blush'	SHDw
'Caborn Lilac Gem'	LLWP SHDw
'Caborn Purple Haze'	LLWP
'Caborn Rosanne' **new**	LLWP
§ *caespititius*	CArn ECho ELau EUnu GBar GMaP
	GPoy LLWP MHer NLRH NMen
	NRya SPlb SRot WCHb WJek
	WPer
caespitosus	CTri LLWP
camphoratus	CArn CBod ELau EOHP EUnu
	EWes GBar MHer MNHC MWea
	NGHP SHDw WJek XPep
- 'A Touch of Frost'	SHDw
- 'Derry'	CSpe
capitatus	CArn XPep
carnosus misapplied	see *T. vulgaris* 'Erectus'
carnosus Boiss.	GBar STre XPep
'Carol Ann' (v)	CBod ECho ELau EWes GBar LLWP
	MBNS MNHC
'Caroline'	SHDw
'Carshalton'	CWan
cephalotos	EHyt WAbe
ciliatus	CArn LLWP MWat WPer XPep
cilicicus ambig.	CPBP ETow GBar MNHC NMen
	SBla WAbe WCHb WWye
cilicicus Boiss. & Bail.	EHyt EWes
§ x *citriodorus*	CArn CHby CHrt CWan ECho
	EDAr ELau GAbr GBar GKev
	GPoy LLWP MBrN MHer MNHC
	MWat NGHP NNor SWal WBrE
	WGwG WHen WJek WPer WWye
	XPep
- 'Archer's Gold'	see *T. pulegioides* 'Archer's Gold'
- 'Aureus'	see *T. pulegioides* 'Aureus'
- 'Bertram Anderson'	see *T. pulegioides* 'Bertram Anderson'
- 'Golden King' (v)	EAEE ECha ECho EDAr ELan GBar
	LHop LLWP LRHS MBar MBri
	MHer NGHP NSti WCHb WHoo
	WPer WSel
- 'Golden Lemon' misapplied	see *T. pulegioides* 'Aureus'

§ - 'Golden Lemon' (v)	CArn GPoy LLWP WJek WWye
- 'Golden Queen' (v)	ECho EDAr GBar GKev MHer
	MWat NBlu NPri SHDw SPer SPet
	SRms WFar
- 'Lemon Supreme'	LLWP
- 'Lime'	LLWP
- 'Nyewoods' (v)	GAbr
- *repandus*	see *T.* 'Rosemary's Lemon Carpet'
- 'Silver King' (v)	ECho LLWP
- 'Silver Posie'	see *T. vulgaris* 'Silver Posie'
- 'Silver Queen' (v) ♀H4	CBcs COfd CSam EAro ECha
	ECho EDAr ELan ENot EOHP
	EPfP GBar GGar GKev LRHS
	MBar MHer MNHC NBlu NGHP
	SPlb WFar
- 'Variegatus' misapplied	see *T.* x *citriodorus* 'Golden King'
* - 'Variegatus' (v)	GBar LHop LSRN MBri MNHC
	NGHP
- 'Villa Nova' (v)	LLWP
'Coccineus'	see *T.* Coccineus Group
N Coccineus Group ♀H4	CArn CHby COfd CTri ECha ECho
	ECtt EDAr EHyt ELan ELau GMaP
	IHMH LLWP LRHS MBar MBri
	MHer MNHC NCGa NHol SBla
	SIng SRms SRot WHen WHoo WPat
	WTel
§ - 'Atropurpureus' misapplied	LLWP SHDw
- 'Bethany' **new**	LLWP SGar
- 'Coccineus Major'	CMea CWan ECho EDAr GAbr
	LRHS MHer MNHC SIde WAbe
	WJek XPep
§ - 'Hardstoft Red' (v)	GBar LLWP
- 'Kurt'	LLWP SHDw
§ - 'Purple Beauty'	LLWP MHer
§ - 'Purpurteppich'	LLWP
§ - 'Red Elf'	ECho GBar SHDw WJek
comosus	GBar MHer SHDw WEas WPer
'Cow Green'	LLWP SHDw
'Creeping Lemon'	ELau EUnu GBar LLWP MHer
	SHDw WGwG WJek
'Creeping Mauve'	LLWP
'Creeping Orange'	LLWP
'Dark Eyes'	SHDw
'Dartmoor'	GBar GCal LLWP SHDw
'Desboro'	GBar LLWP MBNS MHer
doerfleri	CLyd ECha LLWP WSel XPep
- 'Bressingham'	CArn CMea CWan EAEE ECho
	ECtt EDAr ELau GBar LBee
	LLWP LRHS MHer MNHC NGHP
	SBla SPlb SRms SWal WPat WPer
	WTel
'Doone Valley' (v)	More than 30 suppliers
drucei	see *T. polytrichus* subsp. *britannicus*
'E.B. Anderson'	see *T. pulegioides* 'Bertram Anderson'
'Eastgrove Pink'	LLWP SHDw
'Elf'	NWCA
'Emma's Pink'	LLWP
erectus	see *T. vulgaris* 'Erectus'
* *ericoides*	EPot MHer
'Fragrantissimus'	CArn CEnt CMea ELau EOHP
	EUnu GBar GPoy GWCH LLWP
	MHer MNHC MWat NGHP
	SIde SPlb WHen WJek WPer
	WWye
'Gibson's Cave'	LLWP
'Glenridding'	LLWP
'Goldie'	SHDw
'Gowbarrow'	LLWP
'Gratian'	LLWP SHDw
'Hans Stam'	LLWP
'Hardstoft Red'	see *T.* (Coccineus Group) 'Hardstoft Red'
§ 'Hartington Silver' (v)	More than 30 suppliers

§ **herba-barona** | CArn CHrt CMea CPrp CTri CWan ECha EDAr ELau EOHP EUnu GBar GPoy LEdu LLWP MBow MHer MNHC MWat NFor NGHP NHol NRya SIde SRms WGwG WPer WWye XPep
- 'Bob Flowerdew' | LLWP
- *citrata* | see *T. herba-barona* 'Lemon-scented'
§ - 'Lemon-scented' | CArn ECha ELau GBar GPoy LLWP MHer SHDw SIde WCHb
'Highdown' | ECtt SHDw
'Highdown Adus' | SHDw
'Highdown Lemon' | SHDw
'Highdown Red' | SHDw
'Highdown Stretham' | SHDw
'Highland Cream' | see *T.* 'Hartington Silver'
hirsutus | NBir XPep
integer | SBla
'Lake District' | LLWP
I 'Lantanii' | LLWP SHDw
lanuginosus misapplied | see *T. pseudolanuginosus*
§ 'Lavender Sea' | ELau EOHP EWes LLWP
'Lemon Caraway' | see *T. herba-barona* 'Lemon-scented'
'Lemon Sorbet' **new** | SHDw
* 'Lemon Variegated' (v) | EDAr ELau EPfP GBar
leucotrichus | WPat XPep
'Lilac Time' | EWes GBar LLWP MHer NTHB SHDw SIde SPlb WCHb WGwG WJek
longicaulis | CArn CLyd ECha ELau EOHP EWin GBar LLWP MBNS MHer WJek XPep
'Low Force' | LLWP
marschallianus | see *T. pannonicus*
mastichina | CArn GBar SBla WGwG WWye XPep
- 'Didi' | CArn LLWP MHer
membranaceus | CPBP WAbe
micans | see *T. caespititius*
minus | see *Calamintha nepeta*
montanus Waldst. & Kit. | see *T. pulegioides*
'Mountain Select' | LLWP SHDw
neiceffii | CLyd CMea ECha ELau GBar LLWP NWCA XPep
'New Hall' | SHDw
* **nummularius** | ELau
odoratissimus | see *T. pallasianus* subsp. *pallasianus*
'Orange Balsam' | LLWP
'Orange Spice' | LLWP SHDw
pallasianus | ELau LLWP SHDw
§ - subsp. *pallasianus* | GBar MHer
§ **pannonicus** | EOHP LLWP MHer WPer
parnassicus | XPep
'Peter Davis' | CArn CPBP EAEE EAro EDAr EOHP GBar LHop LLWP MBNS MBow MHer MNHC NBir NCGa NGHP SBla SIde WAbe WJek
§ 'Pink Ripple' | CBod CMea ELau EOHP EWes GBar LLWP MHer SHDw SIde SIng WCHb WGwG WHal WHoo WJek
polytrichus misapplied | see *T. praecox*
§ **polytrichus** A. Kern. ex Borbás | XPep
§ - subsp. *britannicus* | ECho GPoy LLWP LSou NSti SHDw SPlb WAbe WJek WPer
- - 'Minor' | ECho EPot LLWP WPer
§ - - 'Thomas's White' ♀H4 | ECho LLWP
'Porlock' | CMea CPrp CWan ECho ELau EPfP ETow GBar GPoy LLWP MHer NGHP NRya SECG SIde SRms STre WGHP WGwG WHoo WJek WPer

§ **praecox** | CPbn GBar LLWP MHer NLan NSco
- subsp. *arcticus* | see *T. polytrichus* subsp. *britannicus*
'Provence' | LLWP
§ **pseudolanuginosus** | CArn CMea ECha ECho ELau EPot GAbr GBar GGar GMaP LLWP LRHS MBNS MBar MBri MHer MNHC NBir NChi NGHP NSti NWCA SPlb SRms WGwG WHoo WPer XPep
- 'Hall's Variety' | ELau GBar
§ **pulegioides** | CArn CBod CHby CHrt ELau GBar GGar GPoy LLWP MBow MBri MHer MNHC NPri NRya SHDw SIde WGwG WJek WPer WWye
§ - 'Archer's Gold' | More than 30 suppliers
§ - 'Aureus' ♀H4 | GAbr GBar GMaP LLWP LRHS MBar MBri MWgw NBlu NWCA SBla SPer SPla WFar WHen WHoo
§ - 'Bertram Anderson' ♀H4 | More than 30 suppliers
- 'Foxley' (v) | CBod CBow CWan ECho EHoe ELau EOHP EPfP EUnu GBar LLWP LSou MHer MNHC NGHP NPro NTHB SHDw SIde SPlb WCHb WJek WRHF
- 'Golden Dwarf' | LLWP
§ - 'Goldentime' | GBar LLWP LRHS MWat NGHP WSel
- 'Sir John Lawes' | LLWP MHer SHDw
- 'Sundon Hills' | LLWP
- 'Tabor' | EUnu GBar GMaP MNHC NGHP NTHB SHDw WJek
* 'Rasta' (v) **new** | CStu LLWP
'Redstart' | CBod ECha ELau EOHP GBar LBee LLWP LRHS MHer SBch SHDw SIde WCHb
* **richardii** subsp. **nitidus** | STre WWye
- 'Compactus Albus' | see *T. vulgaris* 'Snow White'
'Rosa Ceeping' | SHDw
'Rosalicht' | LLWP
'Rosalind' | SHDw
'Rosedrift' | LLWP SHDw
§ 'Rosemary's Lemon Carpet' | LLWP
rotundifolius misapplied | see *T. vulgaris* 'Elsbeth'
§ 'Ruby Glow' | CHrt ELau EWes LLWP MHer MNHC SHDw
serpyllum ambig. | CArn ELau LLWP MBri NGHP SIde SPet SPlb SRms WJek WPer
§ **serpyllum** L. | EAro GKev WBVN XPep
- var. *albus* | ECha ECho ELau GPoy LAst LLWP MBow MNHC NGHP SBla SIde SPer SRms WHoo WRHF WWye XPep
- 'Albus Variegatus' | see *T.* 'Hartington Silver'
N - 'Annie Hall' | CMea CWan EAEE ECho EDAr ELau EPfP EPot GAbr GBar GGar LAst LLWP LRHS MBow MHer MNHC NFor NGHP SBch SIde WCFE WGwG WPer WWye
- 'Atropurpureus' | see *T.* (Coccineus Group)
'Atropurpureus' misapplied
- 'Barwinnock Snowdrift' (v) | GBar
- **coccineus** 'Minor' misapplied | see *T.* Coccineus Group
- **coccineus** 'Minor' Bloom | see *T.* 'Alan Bloom'
- 'Conwy Rose' | LLWP WAbe
N - 'East Lodge' | LLWP MNHC
- 'Elfin' | CArn CLyd ECho EDAr EWes LBee LRHS MBri NLAp SBla SHDw SIng SPlb WAbe XPep

	- 'Flossy'	LLWP
N	- 'Fulney Red'	EWes LLWP
	- 'Goldstream' (v)	CBrm CLyd CMea CPrp EAEE
		ECho ELau EPfP GBar IHMH LHop
		LLWP LRHS MBar MBri MHer
		NGHP NRya NSti SPlb SRms
		WCHb WGwG WPer
	- subsp. **lanuginosus**	see *T. pseudolanuginosus*
	- 'Lemon Curd'	CBod CBrm CWan ELau EOHP
		EUnu GBar LLWP MHer MNHC
		NGHP NHol NSti SHDw SIde SMer
		SPlb WCHb WFar WGHP WGwG
		WJek WRha WSel WWye XPep
§	- 'Minimalist'	CArn CBrm CLyd CMea ECha ELau
		GBar LLWP LRHS MBow MBri
		MHer MNHC MWat NGHP NLAp
		NRya NSti SIde SPet SPlb SRot
		WBVN WCHb WHoo WPat WPer
		WSel WTin WWye
	- 'Minimus'	see *T. serpyllum* 'Minimalist'
§	- 'Minor'	CArn CPrp ECho ECtt GBar
		GWCH LLWP NHol NMen NSla
		SBla SHDw WAbe WGwG WLin
		XPep
N	- 'Minor Albus'	ECho GAbr GBar
	- 'Minus'	see *T. serpyllum* 'Minor'
	- 'Petite'	EPot EWes LLWP
N	- 'Pink Chintz' ♀H4	CBrm CHar CLyd CMea ECha
		ECho ECtt EDAr ELau EPfP EPot
		GBar GBuc GPoy LLWP LRHS
		MBar MBri MHer MNHC MWgw
		NBlu NGHP NRya SBla SIng SPer
		SPlb WHoo WPer
	- 'Posh Pinky' **new**	EPot
	- subsp. **pulchellus**	LLWP
	- 'Purple Beauty'	see *T.* (Coccineus Group) 'Purple Beauty'
	- 'Purpurteppich'	see *T.* (Coccineus Group) 'Purpurteppich'
	- 'Pygmaeus'	LLWP
	- 'Rainbow Falls' (v)	CBod EOHP EPfP EWin GBar
		LLWP MHer MNHC NGHP NHol
		SHDw SIde WGHP WGwG
	- 'Red Elf'	see *T.* (Coccineus Group) 'Red Elf'
	- 'Red Glow' **new**	EPot
	- 'Roger's Snowdrift'	LLWP
N	- 'Roseus'	EOHP GBar SIde
N	- 'Russetings'	CBrm CLyd ECtt ELau EPfP EPot
		GBar LLWP MBar MHer MNHC
		NEgg NHol SIde SIng SRms WWye
N	- 'September'	LLWP MHer
	- 'Snowcarpet'	LLWP
N	- 'Snowdrift'	More than 30 suppliers
N	- 'Splendens'	LLWP
	- subsp. **tanaensis**	CArn
	- 'Variegatus'	see *T.* 'Hartington Silver'
	- 'Vey'	EAEE ECho EWes GBar GMaP
		LLWP MHer NTHB SHDw SIng
		WCHb
N	'Silver Posie'	see *T. vulgaris* 'Silver Posie'
	'Snowdonia Idris' **new**	LLWP
	'Snowdonia Ifor'	LLWP
	'Snowdonia Imperial Beauty'	LLWP
	'Snowdonia Iorwerth' **new**	LLWP
	'Snowdonia Isolde'	LLWP
	'Snowdonia Istyn' **new**	LLWP
	'Snowdonia Lass'	LLWP SHDw
	'Snowdonia Pearl'	LLWP
	'Snowdonia Pedr'	LLWP
	'Snowdonia Pink Gem'	LLWP
	'Snowdonia Pryderi' **new**	LLWP
	'Snowdonia Pwyll' **new**	LLWP
	'Snowdonia Rosie'	LLWP
	'Snowdonia Rowena'	LLWP
	'Snowman'	SHDw

	'Swaledale'	LLWP
*	**valesiacus**	LLWP SHDw
§	**villosus**	ECho
§	**vulgaris**	More than 30 suppliers
	– **albus**	ECho GBar LLWP WHen
	- 'Aureus'.	see *T. pulegioides* 'Goldentime'
	- 'Boule'	XPep
*	- 'Compactus'	GPoy LLWP MNHC
	- 'Diamantis'	LLWP
	- 'Dorcas White'	LLWP MHer WPer
§	- 'Elsbeth'	ECho ELau LLWP MHer SHDw XPep
	- 'English Winter'	GBar SIde
§	- 'Erectus'	CArn CLyd CStu ETow GBar LLWP
		MHer WPer WWye
	- French	ELau LLWP MHer SHDw SPlb
	- French, summer	SIde
	- 'Golden Pins'	GBar MNHC
	- 'Haute Vallée de l'Aude'	XPep
	- 'Lemon Queen'	ECho ELau
	- 'Lucy'	CPrp EOHP EUnu GBar LLWP MNHC
	- 'Pinewood'	LLWP MHer SIde
	- pink	LLWP
	- 'Saint Chinian Blanc'	XPep
	- 'Saint Chinian Rose'	XPep
	- 'Silver Pearl' (v)	ECho
§	- 'Silver Posie'	More than 30 suppliers
§	- 'Snow White'	ELau EWes LLWP SHDw SWal
	'Widecombe' (v)	LLWP MHer SHDw
	zygis	CArn XPep

Tiarella (Saxifragaceae)

	'Black Velvet'PBR	CBct GCai MLLN NCGa NLar SRot WCMO
	'Bronze Baby'	NEgg
	'Butterfly Wings'	EBee MBnl NRnb
	collina	see *T. wherryi*
	cordifolia ♀H4	More than 30 suppliers
	- 'Glossy'	CBct EBee GBuc WPGP
	- 'Oakleaf'	CLAP EChP EMan NBre NBro NEgg NSti WCAu
	- 'Rosalie'	see x *Heucherella alba* 'Rosalie'
	- 'Running Tapestry'	CFwr CLAP WMoo
	- 'Slick Rock'	EBee ECha EPPr MWgw
	'Cygnet'PBR	CBct CLAP EMan EPPr EShb GCai LAst MLLN NCGa NEgg SHar SPer SPoG SRot STes WFar
	'Dark Star'	ECtt NBre
	'Dunvegan'	EBee MLLN NRnb WFar WGHP WMoo WWeb
	'Elizabeth Oliver'	CLAP
	'Freckles'	MRav
	'Inkblot'	EBee EChP ELan MLLN NBro NRnb SHar WCAu WFar WMoo WPnP
	'Iron Butterfly'PBR	CBct CCol CLAP COfd CTbh CWCL EBee ECGP EMar ENot EPfP GAbr GBin LSRN MLLN MRav MSte NBro NCGa NEgg NPri SHar SPer SRot STes WFar WPGP WWhi
	'Jeepers Creepers'PBR	GCai NCob SHar
*	'Laciniate Runner'	CLAP
	'Martha Oliver'	CLAP EBee GBuc NBre SBch WPGP WTin
	'Mint Chocolate'PBR	More than 30 suppliers
	'Morning Star' **new**	SRot
	'Neon Lights'PBR	CBow CHar EKen EWes MAvo MBnl NBro NCGa NCob NGdn SHar SPoG SWvt
§	'Ninja'PBR	CWCL EBee EBrs EChP ECha EHrv ELan EMar GMaP GSki ITim LAst LRHS MDun MLLN MRav MSph NBir NEgg NGdn NLar SIng SMer SPer SRot SWvt WCot WFar WGHP WWhi

'Petite Pink Bouquet'	GSki NGdn
'Pink Bouquet'	CAbP CBow CLAP EAEE EBee EBrs EChP ECtt EHrv ENor GSki LRHS MBNS MLLN MSph MWgw NEgg SPla WBVN WCot WCra WFar WGor WMoo WPnP
'Pink Brushes'	NRnb
'Pink Skyrocket'^{PBR}	GCai NBre NCob SHar
'Pinwheel'	EBee EBrs ECha LRHS MRav NBre WTMC
'Pirate's Patch'	GCai LTwo
polyphylla	CBow ELan GAbr GBBs GBin MGol MLLN NBre NLRH NLar SMac SWal WCru WFar WMoo
- 'Filigran'	EBee MWrn NHol NLar
- 'Moorgrün'	EBrs GCal WFar
- pink	CLAP EHrv
- - BWJ 8088	WCru
'Running Tiger'	NRnb
'Skeleton Key'	LRHS
'Skid's Variegated' (v)	CBct CBow EBee EChP ECtt EMan LAst LSou MBNS MSph NPro NSti SWvt WBrk WCot
'Skyrocket'	EKen
'Spring Symphony'^{PBR}	CLAP CWCL EBee EShb GBin GCai GKev LSou MBri NBir NCGa NEgg NLar NPer SHar SIng SPoG WFar
'Starburst' **new**	MBnl
'Starfish'	EBee MLLN NBre NCob SHar WPrP
'Tiger Stripe'	COtt EBee ECha ELan EMan ENot EPfP LRHS MRav NBro NEgg NRnb SPer SPur WFar WMoo WPnP
trifoliata	ELan MRav NBre SBla WFar
unifoliata	CMCo EBee MSal
'Viking Ship'^{PBR}	see x *Heucherella* 'Viking Ship'
§ *wherryi* ♀^{H4}	More than 30 suppliers
- 'Bronze Beauty'	CBct CLAP COtt EBee EChP EPPr GBuc LAst MAvo MRav NDov NPro SAga SPla SWat WAbe WBrk WFar WGHP WMoo WPGP WWhi
- 'Green Velvet'	ECha
- 'Heronswood Mist' (v)	CAbP CBct CBow CFir EBee EChP GBri GEdr LSou MBNS MLLN NBro SPer SWvt WCot WWhi
- 'Montrose'	NBre WPGP

Tibouchina (Melastomataceae)

grandifolia	CRHN
graveolens	ERea
'Jules'	CBcs LSou SOWG
* *laxa* 'Skylab'	LSou
organensis	CBcs CHll GQui WPGP
paratropica	CPle CRHN
semidecandra misapplied	see *T. urvilleana*
§ *urvilleana* ♀^{H1}	CBcs CCCN CDoC CHEx CKno CRHN CSBt CSpe CTbh EBak ECre ELan ERea EShb ISea MTis NCGa SAPC SArc SBLw SDnm SOWG SPer SRkn SRms SYvo WCot WGwG WMul
- 'Edwardsii'	EMan LSou MLan SMrm SUsu
- 'Jazzie' **new**	LSou
- 'Rich Blue Sun'	CSpe
- variegated (v)	CCCN LSou WCMO WCot

Tigridia ✿ (Iridaceae)

lutea	ECho
pavonia	CAby CPLG ECho EDif ERea IGor MBri SPet
- 'Aurea'	CFwr
- 'Lilacea'	CFwr EBee ECho
- 'Speciosa'	CFwr

Tilia ✿ (Tiliaceae)

americana	CLnd CMCN EBee NWea
- 'Dentata'	CDul
- 'Nova'	CDoC SBLw
amurensis	CMCN GIBF
argentea	see *T. tomentosa*
begoniifolia	see *T. dasystyla*
chenmoui	MBlu WPGP
chinensis	CMCN
chingiana	CDul CMCN MBlu SBir SPoG
cordata ♀^{H4}	CAgr CBcs CCVT CDul CLnd CSBt EBee ECrN ELan EPfP IMGH LBuc MSwo NBee NWea SBLw SHBN SPer WDin WMou WOrn
§ - 'Böhlje'	CDul LPan SBLw WMoo
- 'Dainty Leaf'	CDul
- 'Erecta'	see *T. cordata* 'Böhlje'
- 'Greenspire' ♀^{H4}	CCVT CDoC CDul CLnd CTho CWib EBee ECrN LPan LRHS NBee SBLw WOrn
- 'Len Parvin'	WPGP
- 'Lico'	CMen WMou
- 'Monto' **new**	CMen
- 'Plymtree Gold'	CDul
- 'Swedish Upright'	CDul CLnd CTho
- 'Winter Orange'	CDul CEnd EBee LAst LRHS MBlu SBir SCoo
§ *dasystyla*	CMCN
x *euchlora* ♀^{H4}	CBcs CCVT CDul CLnd CMCN EBee ECrN EPfP LAst LPan NBee NWea SBLw SPer SSta WDin WFar WOrn
§ x *europaea*	CBcs CDul CLnd CRWN ELan NWea SBLw WMou
- 'Pallida'	CDul CLnd CTho SBLw WMou
- 'Wratislaviensis' ♀^{H4}	CDoC CDul CLnd EPfP LRHS MAsh MBlu MBri NWea SMad
x *flavescens* 'Glenleven'	CDul SBLw
§ 'Harold Hillier'	MBlu
henryana	CDoC CDul CEnd CMCN CTho CWib ECrN EPfP ERod IArd MBlu SBir SIFN WDin WPGP
- var. *subglabra*	WMou
§ *heterophylla*	CMCN CTho
- var. *michauxii*	CLnd
'Hillieri'	see *T.* 'Harold Hillier'
insularis	CMCN MBlu WMou
japonica	CDul CMCN WMou WPGP
kiusiana	CMCN WPGP
mandshurica	CMCN
maximowicziana	WPGP
mexicana	WPGP
miqueliana	CMCN
'Moltkei'	CLnd CMCN WPGP
mongolica	CDoC CDul CLnd CMCN CTho EBee EPfP SMHT WPGP
monticola	see *T. heterophylla*
oliveri	CDul CMCN MBlu NWea SBir WPGP
paucicostata	CMCN
'Petiolaris' ♀^{H4}	CCVT CDoC CDul CEnd CLnd CMCN EBee ECrN ELan EPfP LRHS MBlu MBri MSwo NBee NWea SBLw SHBN SPer SSta WDin
platyphyllos	CCVT CDul CLnd CMCN CSBt ECrN EPfP EWTr LBuc NBee NWea SBLw SCoo SPer WDin WMou
- 'Aurea'	CDul CLnd CTho ECrN MBlu
- 'Corallina'	see *T. platyphyllos* 'Rubra'
- 'Dakvorm'	SBLw
- 'Delft'	SBLw
- 'Erecta'	see *T. platyphyllos* 'Fastigiata'
§ - 'Fastigiata'	CDul CTho ECrN SBLw SLPl
- 'Laciniata'	CDul CEnd CMCN CTho EBee

- 'Örebro'   SLPl
* - 'Pendula'   CTho
§ - 'Rubra' ♀H4   CDoC CDul CLnd CTho ECrN
                                EPfP LBuc MGos NWea SBLw
                                WDin WFar
- 'Tortuosa'   CDoC
§ tomentosa   CDul CLnd CMCN CTho ECrN
                                ELan IMGH NWea SBLw SEND
                                WDin WMou
- 'Brabant' ♀H4   CDoC EPfP IMGH SBLw
tuan   CMCN
x *vulgaris*   see *T.* x *europaea*

Tillaea see *Crassula*

Tillandsia (Bromeliaceae)
aeranthos   EOas SChr
argentea ♀H1   MBri
cyanea ♀H1   LRHS MBri SMur
usneoides   CHal SHmp

Tinantia (Commelinaceae)
pringlei   CDes WPGP
- AIM 77   WCot

Titanopsis (Aizoaceae)
calcarea ♀H1   EPfP EShb

Tithonia (Asteraceae)
diversifolia **new**   LRav
rotundifolia 'Torch'   SMrm

Tofieldia (Melanthiaceae)
pusilla   ERos

Tolmiea (Saxifragaceae)
menziesii   ECha ECho EWTr MBNS MBri
                                MWgw NHol SPer SWal WBrE
                                WMoo
- 'Goldsplash'   see *T. menziesii* 'Taff's Gold'
- 'Maculata'   see *T. menziesii* 'Taff's Gold'
§ - 'Taff's Gold' (v) ♀H4   CBgR CWan EBee ECho EHoe
                                EMar EOHP GAbr GMaP GQue
                                IHMH MHer NBid NGdn NHol
                                NVic SPlb WEas WHoo WMoo
                                WTin WWye
- 'Variegata'   see *T. menziesii* 'Taff's Gold'

Tolpis (Asteraceae)
barbata   SUsu

Tonestus (Asteraceae)
§ lyallii   MHar WPer

Toona (Meliaceae)
§ sinensis   CDul CEnd CLnd CMCN CPle
                                CTho CWib EPfP SBrw WBVN
                                WFar WMul WPGP
- 'Flamingo' (v)   CBcs CWSG EPfP IDee LRHS NLar
                                SBig SPoG

Torenia (Scrophulariaceae)
concolor var.   MOak WCru
  formosana
  B&SWJ 124
Pink Moon = 'Dantopkmn'   LAst SPet
Purple Moon =   LAst SPet SVil
  'Dantopur'PBR
Summer Wave Series   SCoo
- 'Summer Wave   LSou
  Violet'PBR **new**
Violet Moon **new**   SVil
White Moon **new**   SVil

Torreya (Taxaceae)
grandis   CBcs EGFP

Townsendia (Asteraceae)
§ alpigena var. alpigena   CGra CPBP EHyt
  condensata   CPBP
  exscapa   EHyt WLin
  formosa   ECho NBir
  hookeri   CGra EHyt WLin
  incana   CPBP EHyt
  leptotes   CGra CPBP EHyt
  montana   see *T. alpigena* var. *alpigena*
  nuttallii   CGra
§ rothrockii   CGra CPBP EHyt NMen WLin
  spathulata   CGra CPBP EHyt WLin
  wilcoxiana misapplied   see *T. rothrockii*

Toxicodendron (Anacardiaceae)
vernicifluum   see *Rhus verniciflua*

Trachelium (Campanulaceae)
§ asperuloides   CPBP EHyt WAbe
  caeruleum ♀H1   SGar WBrE
- 'Purple Umbrella'   CPLG EMan NBre
- 'White Umbrella'   EMan
jacquinii subsp.   CPBP NWCA WPat
  rumelianum

Trachelospermum ❀ (Apocynaceae)
§ asiaticum ♀H2-3   More than 30 suppliers
- B&SWJ 4814   WCru
* - 'Aureum'   CDul ERea
- 'Golden Memories'   EMil EPfP LRHS MAsh MGos SBra
                                SBrw SMur SPoG SSpi SSta WCMO
- 'Goshiki' (v)   CBow ERea GQui MGos SBrw SSpi
- var. intermedium   WPGP
- - B&SWJ 8733   WCru
- 'Theta'   SSpi
'Christabel Bielenberg' **new** CPIN
jasminoides ♀H3-4   More than 30 suppliers
- B&SWJ 5117   WCru
§ - 'Japonicum'   CSPN GCal IArd LRHS SBra SBrw
                                SLPl SLon SPla
- 'Major'   CSPN CTrG EBee SBrw SPoG SSpi
* - 'Oblanceolatum'   GCal
- 'Tricolor' (v)   CBcs EBee IArd SBrw SSpi SWvt
- 'Variegatum' (v) ♀H3-4   More than 30 suppliers
- 'Waterwheel'   SBra SBrw SPoG SSpi WPGP WSHC
- 'Wilsonii'   CDul CSPN CSam EBee ELan EMil
                                EPfP EPla EShb GCal LRHS MCCP
                                SAPC SArc SBod SBrw SLim SPer
                                SPoG SSta SWvt WCot WCru WHar
                                WPGP WPat XPep
- - W 776   CMac LHop
majus misapplied   see *T. jasminoides* 'Japonicum'
majus Nakai   see *T. asiaticum*

Trachycarpus (Arecaceae)
from Manipur **new**   EZes MJnS
§ fortunei ♀H3-4   More than 30 suppliers
  latisectus   CBrP CKob EAmu EZes LPJP LPal
                                NPal SAin SBig WMul
  martianus   CKob CTrC EAmu LPJP LPal SBig
                                SChr WMul
- from Khasi Hills **new**   EZes
- from Nepal **new**   EZes
  nanus   CKob EZes LPal
  oreophilus   EZes LPal WMul
  princeps **new**   CKob EZes
I - 'Takaghii' **new**   SAin
  takil   CBrP CKob EAmu EZes LPJP LPal
                                MJnS NPal WMul
  wagnerianus   CBrP CPHo EAmu EPla EZes LPJP
                                LPal MJnS NPal SAin SChr WMul
                                WPGP

Trachymene (Apiaceae)
coerulea   CSpe

Trachystemon (Boraginaceae)

orientalis	CBre CHEx CPLG CSev ECha EGol ELan EPfP EWTr MHar MRav NBid SBig SDnm WBor WCAu WCru WDyG WFar WHer WMoo WPnP WWye

Tradescantia ✿ (Commelinaceae)

albiflora	see *T. fluminensis*
x *andersoniana*	see *T.* Andersoniana Group
W. Ludwig & Rohw.	
§ Andersoniana Group	CWib IHMM MSal NFor NJOw SPet WPer WWeb WWpP
- 'Baby Doll'	EGle
- 'Bilberry Ice'	More than 30 suppliers
- 'Blanca'	MWrn
- 'Blue and Gold'	CBcs CBct CFwr EAEE EBee ECtt EHoe EMFW EMon EPPr EPfP GBuc LAst LHop LRHS NEgg NPri NSti SPla SPoG SUsu WCAu WCMO WCot WHil
- 'Blue Stone'	CMdw CMea CSBt ECha ECho ECtt ERou LBBr MBNS NCGa NPri SRms WFar WHoo WTin
- 'Blushing Bride'	GSki
- 'Bridal Veil'	CHll
- 'Caerulea Plena'	see *T. virginiana* 'Caerulea Plena'
- Carmine Glow	see *T.* (Andersoniana Group) 'Karminglut'
- 'Charlotte'	CElw EBee EBrs ECGP EChP ECha EGle EMFW GSki LRHS MOne MWgw NBre NBro NEgg NGdn SBch SRGP WCAu WMnd WTMC
- 'Chedglow'	LHop
- 'Concord Grape'	More than 30 suppliers
- 'Danielle'	EBee EChP EGle EPfP GMac NGdn NMyG NRnb WTMC
- 'Domaine de Courson'	EBee
- 'In the Navy'	EBee ERou LDai MEHN NBre NLar WCot WDyG
- 'Innocence'	More than 30 suppliers
- 'Iris Prichard'	CPrp EBee EChP ELan EPfP ERou GMaP LHop LRHS NBre NCGa NFla NLar SRGP WFar
- 'Isis' ♀H4	CBcs CHar CPrp EBee EBrs EChP ECtt ELan EPfP LRHS MRav MWgw NBir NCGa NGdn NOrc SPer SPla WMnd WTin
- 'J.C. Weguelin' ♀H4	EGle EMil EPfP GQue LBMP NBir NBre NDlv SRms WCAu WMnd
§ - 'Karminglut'	EBee ECtt EGle ELan EPfP ERou GMaP IHMH LAst MNrw NBir NGdn NOrc NVic WCAu WHoo
- 'Leonora'	COlW EBrs ECho ENot EPfP ERou NLar
- 'Little Doll'	CWCL EBrs ECtt EGle ERou GBri GSki LAst MDKP MHar MLLN MNFA MSph NBro NCGa NPri NRnb WCot WFar WHil WTMC
- 'Little White Doll'	CPrp CWCL EBee ERou GMac GSki LAst MBNS MDKP MNFA MSph MSte NBre SHGN SPoG WCot WFar
- 'Mariella'	EBee EGle GMac
- 'Mrs Loewer'	EMon
- 'Navajo Princess' new	EBee
- 'Osprey' ♀H4	More than 30 suppliers
- 'Pauline'	CHar ECtt EPla ERou GSki LAst LRHS MNrw MRav NBir NLar SPoG WFar WHoo WTel WTin
- 'Perinne's Pink'	CWCL EBee EBrs EPfP MBri NBPC NLar NSti SHop SUsu
- 'Pink Chablis'	CWCL EBee ERou NBro NLar NMoo WHil
- 'Purewell Giant'	EBee ECot EMil ERou LHop NBro NDlv NEgg NLar SPer WGor WKif WMnd
- 'Purple Dome'	CHar EBee ECtt EMFW EPla GMaP LAst LRHS MHar MRav MWgw NBir NBro NCGa NGdn SPla SPoG STes WCAu WMnd WTin WWye
- 'Red Grape'	EBee EBrs ECho ECtt ERou GSki LRHS MBNS NCGa NPro NSti WBor WCAu
- 'Rosi' new	EBee
- 'Rubra'	CPrp CSBt EBee EChP ECho EPfP ERou GSki MWgw NDlv NOrc NPri SBod SRms WRHF
- 'Satin Doll'	COlW EBee EMan SPoG
- 'Sweet Kate'	CHar CWCL ERou MBNS MCCP MDKP NBro NMRc SAga SHop SMer SRGP
- 'Sylvana'	CMMP EBee EGle GMac WCAu WHil
- 'Valour'	CWat EBee LRHS WFar
- 'Zwanenburg Blue'	CMMP EBee EChP ECha ECtt ELan ERou GMac LBMP LRHS MLHP MWgw NCGa NRnb SPlb WMnd WTel
'Angel Eyes'	GSki MDKP
'Baerbel'	GSki
brevicaulis	EBee ECha EPla ERos GBuc NBre NBro
'Bridesmaid'	MOak
canaliculata	see *T. ohiensis*
cerinthoides	CHal
§ fluminensis	SChr
- 'Albovittata'	CHal
- 'Aurea' ♀H1	CHal MBri
- 'Laekenensis' (v)	CHal MBri
- 'Maiden's Blush' (v)	CHal CSpe EShb EWin MOak SGar SRms WFoF
- 'Quicksilver' (v) ♀H1	CHal MBri
- 'Tricolor Minima' ♀H1	CHal
multiflora	see *Tripogandra multiflora*
navicularis	see *Callisia navicularis*
§ ohiensis	CFee EBee LPBA
§ pallida ♀H2-3	CHal
§ - 'Purpurea' ♀H2-3	EShb MOak
pendula	see *T. zebrina*
'Purple Sabre'	CBcs ERou LAst
purpurea	see *T. pallida* 'Purpurea'
sillamontana ♀H1	CHal EOHP MBri
spathacea	EShb
- 'Vittata' ♀H1	CHal EShb
tricolor	see *T. zebrina*
virginiana	MWhi MWrn SGar
- 'Alba'	GCal WPer
§ - 'Caerulea Plena' (d)	CHar CMHG EBee EBrs EChP ELan EMan EPfP EPla ERou GSki LRHS MRav NCGa NLRH SPoG SRms WCra WFar WHil WTin
- 'Rubra'	ECGP MLHP NLRH SPlb WTin
§ zebrina ♀H1	CHal
- discolor	CHal
- pendula	see *T. zebrina*
- 'Purpusii' ♀H1	CHal SRms
- 'Quadricolor' (v) ♀H1	CHal

Tragopogon (Asteraceae)

crocifolius	CSpe LPhx WCMO WCot
porrifolius	ILis SECG WCMO WGwG
pratensis	CArn NMir

Trapa (Trapaceae)

natans	WFar

Trautvetteria (Ranunculaceae)

carolinensis var. japonica	CLAP GEdr WCru

- var. *occidentalis*   GEdr WCru

Trevesia (Araliaceae)
palmata   CKob WMul

Trichopetalum (Anthericaceae)
§ *plumosum*   CBro CMon ECho

Tricuspidaria see *Crinodendron*

Tricyrtis ✿ (Convallariaceae)
B&SWJ 6705   MSph
CC 3454   WCot
'Adbane'   CBct CLAP ELan EPPr EWes GBBs
                GBuc GKev LRHS MMHG NLar
                WCMO WCot WFar WRha WViv
affinis   CLAP GAbr GBBs GBin GBuc GGar
                GIBF NLar WFar
- B&SWJ 2804   WCru
- B&SWJ 5640   WCru
- B&SWJ 5847   WCru
- B&SWJ 6182   WCru
- 'Amanagowa'   CLAP
bakeri   see *T. latifolia*
'Blue Wonder' **new**   IBal NGdn
dilatata   see *T. macropoda*
'Empress'   CBct CPLG CWCL EBee EBla EMan
                EPfP ERou EWTr EWes GCai IBal
                LEdu LSou MAvo MBNS MBnl MBri
                MCCP NBPC NCob NEgg SPet
                SPoG WFar WSel
flava   WCru
formosana ♀[H4]   More than 30 suppliers
- B&SWJ 306   CLAP EBla MNrw WCot WCru
                WFar WRos
- B&SWJ 3073   WCru
- B&SWJ 355   WCru WFar
- B&SWJ 3616   WCru
- B&SWJ 3712   WCru WFar
- B&SWJ 6705   CLAP WCru WPrP
- B&SWJ 6741   WCru
- B&SWJ 6905   WCru
- B&SWJ 6970   WCru
- B&SWJ 7071   WFar
- dark   GAbr GBBs LBMP NCGa WFar
- 'Dark Beauty'   CDes CLAP CPom CWCL EBee
                EHrv EMan EMar ERou GBuc
                GSki MBnl MBri MCCP SPur
                SUsu WCMO WFar WPGP
                WPrP
- 'Gilt Edge' (v)   More than 30 suppliers
- f. *glandosa*   WCru
   B&SWJ 7084
- var. *grandiflora*   WFar
   B&SWJ 6905 **new**
- 'Lodge Farm'   EBla
- pale   CBct GBBs LRHS WFar
- 'Purple Beauty'   CBct EBee MDKP
- 'Samurai' (v)   CLAP CMil CWCL EBee EMan EPPr
                ERou EWes NCGa NMoo WCMO
                WCot WFar
- 'Shelley's'   CBct CLAP CPLG EBee GCal NBro
                WFar WPrP
- 'Small Wonder'   WCru
§ - Stolonifera Group   CBcs CBro CMHG CMMP EAEE
                EBee EBrs EHrv ELan EMar EPfP
                LEdu LHop LRHS MRav MWgw
                NEgg NGdn NHol NSti SDix SPoG
                WFar WMnd WWeb
- - B&SWJ 7046   WCru WFar
- 'Taroko Toad' **new**   WCru
- 'Tiny Toad' **new**   WCru
- 'Variegata' (v)   CBct CBro CLAP EPyc GBBs LEdu
                MMHG NBir WBor WCMO WCru
                WFar
'Harlequin'   LEdu NLar WFar

§ *hirta*   More than 30 suppliers
- B&SWJ 2827   WCru
§ - 'Alba'   CSam EBrs EHrv ELan WFar
* - 'Albomarginata' (v)   CPrp EBee EChP EMar EPPr EPfP
                LBMP MCCP MNFA NCGa NHol
                SBch SPoG SWvt WFar WMnd
                WPGP
- 'Golden Gleam'   WCMO WCot WFar
- hybrids   CMMP
- 'Makinoi Gold'   WFar
- var. *masamunei*   SAga WCru
- 'Matsukaze'   CLAP CPom WFar
- 'Miyazaki'   CBct CFir CLAP ECGP EGle ELan
                EMan GBuc LSou MHer MNrw
                NCGa NLar SAga SMac SMrm WFar
- 'Silver Blue'   WFar
- 'Taiwan Atrianne'   CSam EMar GAbr LRHS MAvo MBri
                MDKP NHol WFar
- 'Variegata' (v)   CBct CLAP EBrs EMan EPyc
                EWes GBuc GKev LHop SBla
                SMad SUsu WCot WCru WFar
                WPrP
N Hototogisu   CBro CLAP CMea CPom EBee EBla
                EBrs EGle ELan EMar GAbr GMac
                GSki LHop LRHS MCCP MTho
                NBir NCGa NEgg NHol SAga
                SDnm SPav SUsu WCMO WFar
                WMnd
ishiiana   CDes CLAP EBee EBla WCot WCru
                WFar WPGP
- var. *surugensis*   EBla LEdu WCru WFar
'Ivory Queen'   WFar
japonica   see *T. hirta*
'Kohaku'   CBct CLAP CPom EBee EBla ELan
                NPro SPav WCot WCru WFar
                WPGP
lasiocarpa   CBct CLAP GQue LEdu WFar
- B&SWJ 3635   CLAP CMil CPom EBla WCru WFar
- B&SWJ 6861   WCru
- B&SWJ 7013   WCru WPrP
- B&SWJ 7014   WCru
- B&SWJ 7104   WCru
§ *latifolia*   CBct EBee EChP ELan EPPr GAbr
                GBBs GGar GIBF GKev GMaP GSki
                MNrw NGdn NLar SPoG WBVN
                WBor WCot WCru WFar WViv
- from Japan **new**   WFar
'Lemon Lime' (v)   CBct CBro CLAP EBee EBla EMan
                LRHS LSou MDKP MSph NPro SBla
                SPav SUsu WCMO WFar
'Lightning Strike' (v)   EBee EWes GBuc GSki LSou MBnl
                MBri MDKP MDun NBPC NCob
                NMyG SPoG WCMO WCot WFar
                WOut
'Lilac Towers'   CBct ELan GBBs NLar WCru WFar
macrantha   GAbr GBBs GGar
§ - subsp. *macranthopsis*   CBct CLAP EBla EPot GBuc GEdr
                MDKP WCMO WCot WCru WDyG
                WFar
macranthopsis   see *T. macrantha* subsp.
                macranthopsis
* *macrocarpa*   EChP
N *macropoda*   CBct CFwr CSam EBee EBla ELan
                EMan EPfP GAbr GBuc GMaP IBal
                ITim LAst LEdu MAvo MCCP
                NCGa NGdn NWCA SMac SMad
                WFar WMnd WViv
- B&SWJ 1271   CBct EBla WCru
- B&SWJ 5013   WCru
- B&SWJ 5556   WCru
- B&SWJ 5847   WCru
- B&SWJ 6209   WCru
- B&SWJ 8700   WCru
- B&SWJ 8829   WCru
- from Yungi Temple, China   CLAP EBee EBla EPPr MDKP
                WCMO WCot WFar

- variegated (v)	CBow WCru
maculata	CPLG WFar WViv
- HWJCM 470	WCru
- HWJK 2010	WCru
- HWJK 2411	WCru
nana	CLAP LEdu WCru
- 'Raven's Back'	WCru
ohsumiensis	CBct CDes CLAP CPom EBee EBla
	ECha EMan GBuc GEdr LEdu
	MDKP MTho NGby SBch SUsu
	WCMO WCru WFar WPGP
perfoliata	CLAP LEdu WCru WFar
'Raspberry Mousse' **new**	EBee EHrv EMar MBNS NMoo
	NSti
setouchiensis	WCru
'Shimone'	CLAP CPLG CStu EBee ECha ELan
	GBuc SMac WFar WKif WPrP
stolonifera	see *T. formosana* Stolonifera
	Group
suzukii RWJ 10111 **new**	WCru
'Tojen'	More than 30 suppliers
'Tresahor White'	CBct WFar
§ - 'Variegata' (*affinis* hybrid)	WCru WFar
(v)	
'Washfields'	CBct WFar WPGP
'White Towers'	More than 30 suppliers
'White Towers' spotted	WBrE

Trifolium (*Papilionaceae*)

alpinum	WSan
angustifolium **new**	CArn
badium	GBri LPhx
dubium **new**	SECG
incarnatum	CSpe MHer SUsu
ochroleucon	CElw CFwr CHea EBee EBrs EChP
	EDAr EHrv EShb GBri GMaP LPhx
	MCCP MNFA MWgw MWrn NCGa
	NSti SBch SEND SSvw STes WCot
	WHil WMoo WSan
pannonicum	CBgR CFir CMea EBee EChP EHrv
	EMon GCal MLLN MSte NBre NCot
	SEND SUsu WFar WPGP WSHC
	WTin
pratense	MHer NSco SECG WSFF
- 'Dolly North'	see *T. pratense* 'Susan Smith'
- 'Ice Cool'	see *T. repens* 'Green Ice'
- 'Nina'	CBgR CNat EBee EMan EWin
	WWye
§ - 'Susan Smith' (v)	CBow EBee ECGP EChP EHoe
	EWes EWin LRHS MNrw NGHP
	SIng WFar
repens	COld EHrv NSco SIng WCAu WSFF
- 'Cherhill'	CNat
- 'Douglas Dawson'	LDai
- 'Dragon's Blood'	MBNS MSph NEgg NPro SVil
- 'Gold Net'	see *T. pratense* 'Susan Smith'
- 'Good Luck'	CRow MTho WWye
§ - 'Green Ice'	CBre EBee EChP EMan EWin
	GMac MRav MTho NBir NSti
	WCHb WDyG WFar WHal WPtf
	WWye
- 'Harlequin' (v)	CBre EBee EWin MAvo MFOX
	MHer MTho WCot WFar WPer
	WPtf WWye
- pale pink	CBgR
- 'Pentaphyllum'	see *T. repens* 'Quinquefolium'
- 'Purple Velvet'	MFOX
- 'Purpurascens'	CArn CBre CEnt EAEE GGar GMac
	ILis LRHS MBNS MBow MHer
	MWgw NSti SPoG WHen WKif
	WWhi
§ - 'Purpurascens	CMea CNic CStu CWCL CWan
Quadrifolium'	EBee EChP ECha ECho EGra EWes
	EWin NBid NEgg NGHP NMir
	NPer SIng SPer SPlb WCHb WFar
	WPtf WRHF WWye

- 'Quadrifolium'	EHoe
§ - 'Quinquefolium'	EBee IHMH
- 'Tetraphyllum	see *T. repens* 'Purpurascens
Purpureum'	Quadrifolium'
* - 'Velvet and Baize' (v)	CNat
- 'Wheatfen'	CBow CBre CRow EMan EWin
	GMac MRav NDov NGHP NPer
	WCot WDyG WPtf
- 'William'	CBow CBre EBee EMan EWin
	MRav SPur WCot
rubens	More than 30 suppliers
- 'Peach Pink'	CFwr CSpe EBee EChP EMan
	EMon EShb LHop LPhx LSou MHar
	MLLN MMHG NCob SUsu WCot
- 'Red Feathers'	EBrs EWin MWea WRHF
'White Bunnies'	NDov

Triglochin (*Juncaginaceae*)

maritimum	CRWN
palustre	CRWN

Trigonella (*Papilionaceae*)

foenum-graecum	CArn MSal SIde

Trillidium see *Trillium*

Trillium ✿ (*Trilliaceae*)

albidum	CLAP ECho EHyt EPot GBuc GCrs
	GMaP NMen SSpi WCru WHal
angustipetalum	CLAP GEdr
- hybrid	SSpi
apetalon	GEdr WCru
camschatcense	CLAP GBuc GCrs GEdr GIBF WCru
- from China	CFwr WWst
- from Japan	WWst
§ *catesbyi*	CBro CLAP EBee ECho EHrv EPot
	GEdr GKev IBal MNFA NMyG
	WCru WWst
cernuum	CLAP ECho IBal NMyG WCru WShi
chloropetalum	CBro ETow ITer ITim SBla SOkd
	SSpi SUsu WCMO WCru WKif
	WPGP
§ - var. *giganteum* ♀H4	CLAP GBuc GEdr GKev NDov
	NMen SSpi WAbe WCru
- var. *rubrum*	see *T. chloropetalum* var.
	giganteum
- white-flowered	CLAP ECha IBal
aff. *chloropetalum* **new**	GIBF
foetidum	More than 30 suppliers
foetidum x *luteum*	EMar
- red-flowered	GCrs
decipiens	SSpi
decumbens	WWst
erectum ♀H4	More than 30 suppliers
§ - f. *albiflorum*	CFir CLAP EBee EBrs ECho EPot
	GBuc GEdr GGar MNFA NMyG
	SSpi WCru
- 'Beige'	CLAP ETow GBBs GEdr GSki IBal
- f. *luteum*	CBct CLAP EPfP SSpi WCru
- purple-flowered	IBal
- red-flowered	IBal
erectum x *flexipes*	CAby CLAP ECho GBuc GEdr
	NMen SSpi
flexipes	CLAP EBee ECho EHrv EPot GCrs
	GEdr GIBF IBal WCru
govanianum	WCru
grandiflorum ♀H4	More than 30 suppliers
- dwarf	GEdr NHar
- 'Flore Pleno' (d) ♀H4	CLAP ECha ECho ETow GBuc
	MTho SBla SCnR SOkd WWst
- 'Jenny Rhodes'	IBlr
- f. *roseum*	CLAP
- 'Snowbunting' (d)	EBrs GCrs SOkd WCMO
kurabayashii	CFir CFwr CLAP EBee ECho
	GBuc GCrs ITim SSpi WAbe
	WPGP WWst

lancifolium **new**	WWst
ludovicianum	SSpi
§ *luteum* ♀H4	More than 30 suppliers
maculatum **new**	WWst
nivale	EBee GKev
ovatum	CLAP CMea GBuc GCrs GGar GKev NMen WHal
- from Oregon	CLAP
- f. *hibbersonii*	CBro CStu ETow GBuc GCrs NMen SBla WHal
- 'Roy Elliott'	EPot NBir
ovatum x *rivale*	ITim
parviflorum	CLAP ECho GEdr NMen SSpi
petiolatum **new**	GIBF
pusillum	CLAP EBee ECho ELan EPot GBBs GEdr GKev IBal ITim SSpi
- var. *pusillum*	GCrs SBla
- var. *virginianum*	CLAP WAbe WCru
recurvatum	CBcs CLAP CPen EBee ECho EHrv EMar EPot GAbr GEdr GKev GSki IBal MDun NMen NMyG SHBN WCru WFar WPnP
rivale ♀H3	CBro CElw CLAP CStu EBee ECho EHrv EPot GBuc GCrs GKev ITim NMen SBla SOkd SSpi SUsu WAbe WFar
- pink	GEdr NMen
- 'Purple Heart'	CLAP EPot GCrs GEdr
rugelii	CAby CBro CLAP ECho EPot GBuc GCrs GEdr GMaP NMen SSpi WCru WWst
- Askival hybrids	CLAP ECho GBuc NMen SSpi
rugelii x *vaseyi*	EWes SSpi WWst
sessile	CBct CFwr CLAP CMea EBee ECho EPot EWTr GBBs GBuc GEdr GKev GSki IBal MAvo NBir NCGa NMen NMyG SGar WCAu WCru WFar WKif WPnP WSHC WSan WShi
- var. *luteum*	see *T. luteum*
- 'Rubrum'	see *T. chloropetalum* var. *giganteum*
simile	CLAP ECho EPot GCrs SSpi
smallii	WCru WWst
stamineum	CLAP EBee ECho EMar EPot GEdr IBal MDun NMyG
stylosum	see *T. catesbyi*
sulcatum	CBro CLAP EBee ECho EHrv EPot GBBs GBuc GCrs GEdr GGar GIBF GMaP IBal NMen SSpi WCru WFar
tschonoskii	CLAP ECho GBuc GEdr WCot WCru
- var. *himalaicum*	WCru
underwoodii	SSpi
undulatum	CLAP EBee ECho EPot GEdr GGar IBal NMen NMyG WCru
vaseyi	CBro CLAP EBee ECho EHyt EMar GBBs GBuc GCrs GEdr GGar NMen SSpi WCru
viride	CLAP EPot GBBs IBal NGby WCru WFar WPnP
viridescens	CLAP EBee ECho GEdr NMyG WFar WWst

Trinia (Apiaceae)

glauca	EBee

Triosteum (Caprifoliaceae)

himalayanum	CLAP
- BWJ 7907	WCru
pinnatifidum	CDes CLAP GCal

Tripetaleia (Ericaceae)

§ *bracteata*	NLar

Tripleurospermum (Asteraceae)

§ *maritimum*	XPep

Tripogandra (Commelinaceae)

§ *multiflora*	CHal

Tripsacum (Poaceae)

dactyloides	EPPr

Tripterospermum (Gentianaceae)

* aff. *chevalieri* B&SWJ 8359	WCru
cordifolium B&SWJ 081	WCru
fasciculatum B&SWJ 7197	WCru
aff. *hirticalyx* B&SWJ 8264	WCru
japonicum	WBor
- B&SWJ 1168	WCru
lanceolatum B&SWJ 085	WCru
taiwanense B&SWJ 1205	WCru

Tripterygium (Celastraceae)

regelii	CBcs NLar WPGP
- B&SWJ 5453	WCru
wilfordii	WCru

Trisetum (Poaceae)

distichophyllum	EHoe
flavescens	CBig NBre

Tristagma (Alliaceae)

* *nivale* f. *nivale* F&W 9612	WCot

Tristellateia (Malpighiaceae)

australasiae	CPIN

Triteleia (Alliaceae)

bridgesii	CMon WCot
californica	see *Brodiaea californica*
§ 'Corrina'	CAvo CFFs EBee ECho EPot MNrw SMeo WHil
grandiflora	ECho WCot
hendersonii NNS 00-738	WCot
hyacinthina	EBee ECho ERos WCot
ixioides	ECho ERos
- var. *scabra*	ETow
- 'Splendens'	EBee ECho
- 'Starlight'	CAvo CFFs CMea CSpe EBee EBrs ECho EPPr EPot MWgw SBch SPer WCot WHil WLin
§ *laxa*	CAvo CMea ECho WBVN
- NNS 95-495	WCot
- 'Allure'	EBee ECho IPot WHil
§ - 'Koningin Fabiola'	CAvo CFFs CMea CTri EBee EBrs ECho EMan EPot IPot LHop MBri MWgw NBir SBch SMeo SPer WBrE WCot WLin
* - var. *nimia* NNS 00-743	WCot
- Queen Fabiola	see *T. laxa* 'Koningin Fabiola'
§ *peduncularis*	EBee ECho WCot
- NNS 95-499	WCot
x *tubergenii*	EBee ECho
uniflora	see *Ipheion uniflorum*

Trithrinax (Arecaceae)

acanthocoma	CBrP EAmu LPJP LPal SBig
campestris	CBrP EAmu LPal SBig WMul

Tritoma see *Kniphofia*

Tritonia (Iridaceae)

bakeri	LBow
- subsp. *lilacina* NNS 00-745	WCot
crocata ♀H2-3	CPou LBow WHil
- 'Baby Doll'	CDes WHil
- 'Bridal Veil'	EPot
- 'Pink Sensation'	CDes EBee ECho EPot WCot WHil WPGP
- 'Prince of Orange'	CDes CPou WPGP

- 'Princess Beatrix'	CDes WCot WPGP
- 'Serendipity'	CDes EBee
deusta subsp. *miniata*	LBow
§ *disticha* subsp.	More than 30 suppliers
rubrolucens	
flabellifolia **new**	LBow
laxifolia	CPne EBee ECho EPot LBow
lineata	CDes CPou EBee ECho LBow
	WPGP WPrP
pallida	SPlb
parvula	LBow
rosea	see *T. disticha* subsp. *rubrolucens*
squalida	LBow

Tritoniopsis (Iridaceae)
pulchra	CDes

Trochetiopsis (Sterculiaceae)
§ *ebenus*	EShb WPGP
melanoxylon misapplied	see *T. ebenus*

Trochiscanthes (Apiaceae)
§ *nodiflora*	EBee

Trochocarpa (Epacridaceae)
thymifolia white-flowered	WAbe

Trochodendron (Trochodendraceae)
aralioides	CBcs CDoC CHEx CTho CWib
	EBee EPfP IMGH LRHS MBri MGos
	SAPC SArc SBrw SHGC SLPl SLon
	SPer SReu SSpi SSta WCot WDin
	WPGP
- B&SWJ 6727 from	WCru
Taiwan	

Trollius (Ranunculaceae)
ACE 1187	GEdr
acaulis	EBee ECho EGle EWes GAbr LHop
	MTho NRya WFar
asiaticus	ECho GBuc
aff. *buddae* BWJ 7958	WCru
§ *chinensis*	EBee ECha GCal IHMH NChi SBla
	SRms SWat
- 'Golden Queen' ♀H4	More than 30 suppliers
x *cultorum* 'Alabaster'	CBgR CDes CFir CLAP CMea
	CRow CSam EBee EPfP ERou
	GBuc LAst MLHP MRav NDov
	NLar NRnb SBla SMad SPer WCFE
	WCot WFar WPGP WPnP WTin
- 'Baudirektor Linne'	MRav NGdn WFar
- Bressingham hybrids	WFar
- 'Byrne's Giant'	WFar WPnP
- 'Canary Bird'	ELan EMil EPfP GBri NGdn SMur
	SRms
- 'Cheddar'	COtt MBri MCCP MRav MTis NBro
	NGdn NLar NPro SMHy SUsu
	WCra WFar
- 'Commander-in-chief'	CDes EBee WFar WPGP WPnP
- 'Earliest of All'	CDWL CSam EGle LRHS MBri
	MSte NGby NGdn SPer SRms WFar
- 'Etna'	CDWL EBee EChP EGle ERou SPet
	WFar WPnP
§ - 'Feuertroll'	CDWL ECha EMar MBNS NCob
	NGby NPro SHar SMur SUsu WFar
- Fireglobe	see *T. x cultorum* 'Feuertroll'
- 'Glory of Leiden'	EBee
- 'Golden Cup'	ECot NBir NGdn
- 'Golden Monarch'	WFar
- 'Goldquelle' ♀H4	EHon SMur WWpP
- 'Goliath'	NCob SMad WFar
- 'Helios'	CSam ECha SBla
- 'Lemon Queen'	CDWL CWat EChP EPfP ERou
	GCal GMaP LPBA LRHS MBri
	MNFA MRav MTis NBlu NFor
	NRnb SPer SPoG SWat WCAu WFar

- 'Meteor'	WFar
- 'Orange Crest'	EBee EGle GCal WFar
- 'Orange Globe'	GAbr LBMP NBPC NCob NGby
	SMrm WFar WWeb
- 'Orange Glow' **new**	SMad
- 'Orange Princess' ♀H4	CDWL CWat EBee EPfP ERou
	GMaP LRHS MCCP MSte NBro
	NLar NPri SPer SRms
- 'Orange Queen'	SWvt
- 'Prichard's Giant'	CDWL CMHG CMMP CRez EChP
	EGle ELan EMar GBri LAst NBro
	NGby NRnb SPoG WCAu WFar
- 'Salamander'	SMur
§ - 'Superbus' ♀H4	CDes CPSs EBee EChP ECho EGle
	EHol ELan EPfP GMaP LAst MBNS
	MBri MTis NGdn NRnb SPer WBrE
	WFar WMoo
- 'T. Smith'	EGle GMac NBro NGby WCot
	WFar
* - 'Taleggio'	EMon NLar
- 'Yellow Beauty'	SMer WFar
dschungaricus **new**	EBee
europaeus	More than 30 suppliers
- 'Superbus'	see *T. x cultorum* 'Superbus'
hondoensis	CAby EPPr GBin NBur NLar NPro
ircuticus	EBee GKev
laxus	EWes NLar
- 'Albiflorus'	NWCA
ledebourii misapplied	see *T. chinensis*
* *orientalis*	GIBF
pumilus	EBee ECha ECho ELan GBri GCrs
	GKev GMaP ITim LRHS MHer
	NJOw NRya NWCA SPer WFar
	WPer WWeb
- ACE 1818	EPot GBuc WCot
- 'Wargrave'	EPot ITim
stenopetalus	CDes EChP ECha EWes GCal MBri
	MNrw MRav NRnb SBla SHar WFar
	WLin
yunnanensis	GBuc GIBF GKev LRHS NBid
	NGby WFar WPnP WWpP
- CD&R 2097	WCru
- f. *eupetalus* BWJ 7614	WCru

Tropaeolum ✿ (Tropaeolaceae)
azureum	LSou
beuthii F&W 8990	WCot
brachyceras	CSec LSou NLar WCot
ciliatum ♀H1	CBro CFir CMea CPLG CPIN CSam
	CStu ECho ELan EPot MPRe MTho
	NBid NSti SMad WBor WCot WCru
	WFar WHer WHil WNor WPGP
	WViv
hookerianum subsp.	EBee ERos GKev
austropurpureum	
- subsp. *hookerianum*	WPGP
F&W 9467	
incisum	EBee WCot
kingii F&W 8676 **new**	WCot
lepidum	LSou WCot
majus	MNHC WSel
- Alaska Series (v) ♀H3	CPrp SIde WJek WSel
- 'Banana Split' **new**	LAst
- 'Crimson Beauty'	CSpe
§ - 'Darjeeling Double' (d)	EShb EWin LRHS WCot WCru
♀H4	
- 'Darjeeling Gold' (d)	see *T. majus* 'Darjeeling Double'
- 'Empress of India'	CPrp LRHS WBor WEas WJek
- 'Forest Flame'	LRHS
- 'Hermine Grashoff' (d)	CSWP CSpe EREa EWin LRHS NPer
♀H2-3	
- 'Margaret Long' (d)	CSpe EWin GCal LRHS
	WCot
- 'Melba Yellow'	LSou
- 'Peach Melba'	LSou
* - 'Peaches and Cream'	CPrp WJek

- 'Red Wonder'	CSWP CSpe CTbh EPfP EWin LRHS LSou SMrm
- 'Ruffled Apricot'	CSpe
- 'Sunset Pink'	LSou
- Tom Thumb mixed	MNHC WJek
moritzianum	CPIN
pentaphyllum	CPIN CSpe EBee ECho ELan ETow GCal GCrs LTwo MTho WBor WCot
peregrinum	CSpe
polyphyllum	CDes CPIN EBee ECha EHyt GBuc GCrs SBla SCnR SMHy SMad WAbe WBGC WCot WPGP
rhomboideum F&W 8681 **new**	WCot
sessilifolium	CSec EBee
speciosum ♀H4	More than 30 suppliers
sylvestre	CPIN NVic WCru
tricolor ♀H1	CPIN ECho EHyt ELan EPot ETow LSou MTho WBor
tuberosum	CEnd ECho GPoy LRHS WBrE WPrP
- var. *lineamaculatum* 'Ken Aslet' ♀H3	CBro CPLG CPIN CPrp CRHN EBee EBrs ECha ECho ELan EPfP EPot ERea ERos EUnu EWin GGar LRHS MPRe MTho NGHP SPer SPoG WCru WFar WHil WPGP WPtf WViv
- var. *piliferum* 'Sidney'	IBlr WCru

Tsuga (Pinaceae)

canadensis	EHul GTSp LCon LPan MBar NBlu NWea SHBN WDin WMou
- 'Abbott's Dwarf'	CKen EOrn LCon MGos
§ - 'Abbott's Pygmy'	CKen
- 'Albospica' (v)	EOrn WFar WGor
- 'Arnold Gold Weeper'	CKen
- 'Aurea' (v)	LCon MBar NLar WEve
- 'Bacon Cristate'	CKen
- 'Baldwin Dwarf Pyramid'	MBar
- 'Beehive'	ECho WGor
- 'Bennett'	EHul LCon MBar
- 'Betty Rose' (v)	CKen
- 'Brandley'	CKen
§ - 'Branklyn'	CKen
- 'Cappy's Choice'	CKen
- 'Cinnamonea'	CKen
- 'Coffin'	CKen
- 'Cole's Prostrate'	CDoC CKen EOrn LCon LLin MAsh MBar NHol NLar SHBN
- 'Coryhill'	CDHC ECho MAsh
- 'Creamey' (v)	CKen
- 'Curley'	CKen
- 'Curtis Ideal'	CKen
- 'Essex'	NLar
* - 'Everitt's Dense Leaf'	CKen
- 'Everitt's Golden'	CKen
- 'Fantana'	CDoC CRob ECho EHul LBee LCon LLin LRHS MAsh MBar NHol NLar SCoo SLim
- 'Gentsch White' (v)	EBrs LCon LLin MGos
- 'Golden Splendor'	LLin
- 'Horsford'	CKen NLar
- 'Horstmann' No 1	CKen
- 'Hussii'	CKen LCon NLar
- 'Jacqueline Verkade'	CKen NLar
- 'Jeddeloh' ♀H4	CDoC CNic CRob ECho EHul EOrn IMGH LCon LLin LRHS MAsh MBar MBri MGos NHol SCoo SLim SPoG WDin WEve
- 'Jervis'	CDoC CKen LCon MAsh NLar
- 'Julianne'	CKen
- 'Kingsville Spreader'	CKen
- 'Little Joe'	CKen
- 'Little Snow'	CKen

I - 'Lutea'	CKen
- 'Many Cones'	CKen
- 'Minima'	CKen
- 'Minuta'	CDoC CKen ECho EHul EOrn LBee LCon LLin MBar MGos NLar SCoo SLon SPoG WGor
- 'Nana'	EHul WDin.
- 'Palomino'	CKen MAsh MBar
- 'Pendula' ♀H4	CBrm CDoC CKen ECho EHul EOrn EPfP LCon LRHS MAsh MBar NHol SLim SPoG WDin WEve WFar WMou
- 'Pincushion'	CKen
- 'Prostrata'	see *T. canadensis* 'Branklyn'
- 'Pygmaea'	see *T. canadensis* 'Abbott's Pygmy'
- 'Rugg's Washington Dwarf'	CKen SCoo
- 'Snowflake'	CKen LCon
- 'Stewart's Gem'	CKen
- 'Verkade Petite'	CKen
- 'Verkade Recurved'	CDoC CKen LCon MBar NLar
- 'Von Helms' Dwarf'	CKen
- 'Warnham'	CKen ECho EOrn LBee MAsh SCoo
caroliniana 'La Bar Weeping'	CKen NLar
diversifolia 'Gotelli'	CKen
heterophylla ♀H4	CDoC CDul CLnd EPfP EWTr LBue LCon LRHS MBar NWea SCoo SHBN SMad SPer SPoG STre WDin WEve WFar WWes
- 'Iron Springs'	CKen EOrn
- 'Laursen's Column'	CKen
- 'Thorsens Weeping'	CKen NLar
menziesii	see *Pseudotsuga menziesii*
mertensiana	LCon NWea
- 'Blue Star'	CKen
- 'Elizabeth'	CDoC CKen
- 'Glauca'	CKen
I - 'Glauca Nana'	CKen
- 'Quartz Mountain'	CKen
sieboldii 'Baldwin'	CKen
- 'Honeywell Estate'	CKen
- 'Nana'	CKen

Tsusiophyllum (Ericaceae)

tanakae	see *Rhododendron tsusiophyllum*

Tuberaria (Cistaceae)

lignosa	CMea CStu EMan MWrn WAbe

Tulbaghia ✿ (Alliaceae)

acutiloba	CAvo ERos WPrP
alliacea	CAvo CFee EBla ECho ERos EShb WCot WPrP
alliacea x *violacea*	EBee ECho
capensis	CFee MHom
cepacea	CStu ERos NBir WSPU
§ - var. *maritima*	CAvo CDes CMon EDif EMar ERea ERos EShb MHom WCMO WCot
cepacea x *natalensis*	ERos
cernua hybrid **new**	WPrP
coddii	CAvo CFee EBee EBla MHom WCMO WPrP
coddii x *violacea*	CPne EBee
cominsii	CPLG CStu EBee EDif ERea SBch SCnR
cominsii x *violacea*	CDes EBee ERos MHom WPrP
'Cosmic' **new**	WPrP
dregeana	ERos WCot
'Fairy Star'	CDes ERos WCMO WCot WPrP
fragrans	see *T. simmleri*
galpinii	CMon CPen ERos LBow NWCA WPrP
'Hazel' **new**	WPrP

'John May's Special' — CDes CKno EBee EGra EMan EMar MSph MSte WCMO WCot WPGP

leucantha — CAvo CStu EBee EBla ERos SBla WPrP

ludwigiana — ERea

maritima — see *T. cepacea* var. *maritima*

Marwood seedling — MTPN

montana — CDes EBee WPGP WPrP

natalensis — CPou EBee ECho LBow SUsu

 - B&V 421 — CDes

 - CD&R 84 — WPrP

 - pink — ECho ERos MHom WCot WPrP

§ *simmleri* — CMon CPou CSec EBla ECho EHrv EPyc ERos EShb EWes GSki LBow MSph WCMO WCot

 - pink-flowered — CDes CPen

 - white-flowered — CPen CPou LBow

verdoorniae — ERos EShb WCot WPrP

violacea — More than 30 suppliers

* - 'Alba' — CMon EBla ERos GSki NLAp WCMO WFar WHoo

 - deep mauve-flowered — EMar

I - 'Fine Form' — SMHy

* - *grandiflora* **new** — CAvo

 - 'John Rider' — LBow WPer

* - var. *maritima* **new** — WPrP

 - 'Pallida' — CAvo CBro CDes CMdw CPne CPou EBee ECho LBow NWCA WPGP WPrP

 - 'Pearl' — CPou WPrP

 - var. *robustior* — CPou EBee WPrP

§ - 'Silver Lace' (v) — More than 30 suppliers

 - 'Variegata' — see *T. violacea* 'Silver Lace'

Tulipa ✿ (*Liliaceae*)

'Abba' (2) — LBmB

'Abu Hassan' (3) — CAvo CFFs LPhx MBri SPer

acuminata (15) — CBro EBrs LPhx LRHS SMeo SUsu

'Ad Rem' (4) — MBri

aitchisonii — see *T. clusiana*

'Aladdin' (6) — LRHS

'Aladdin's Record' (6) — EBrs SPer
 new

albertii (15) — ECho NJOw

'Allegretto' (11) — MBri

altaica (15) ♀H4 — EPot

'Ancilla' (12) ♀H4 — CBro

'Angélique' (11) ♀H4 — CAvo CFFs CMea EBrs EPfP LBmB LRHS NBir SMeo SPer

'Apeldoorn' (4) — MBri SPer

'Apeldoorn's Elite' (4) ♀H4 — MBri

'Apricot Beauty' (1) ♀H4 — EBrs EPfP LBmB LRHS MBri NBir SPer

'Apricot Jewel' — see *T. linifolia* (Batalinii Group) 'Apricot Jewel'

'Apricot Parrot' (10) ♀H4 — CFFs EPfP LBmB MBri SPer

'Arabian Mystery' (3) — CAvo CFFs NBir NHol

armena var. *lycica* — WWst

'Artist' (8) ♀H4 — EChP MWgw NBir SPer

'Attila' (3) — EBrs

aucheriana (15) ♀H4 — CBro ECho EHyt EPot ERos LTwo

australis (15) — EBrs ECho

aximensis (15) — ECho

bakeri — see *T. saxatilis* Bakeri Group

'Ballade' (6) ♀H4 — MSte SPer

'Ballerina' (6) ♀H4 — CAvo CBro CFFs CMea EBrs LPhx MBri MWgw SMeo SPer

'Banja Luka' (4) — EBrs

batalinii — see *T. linifolia* Batalinii Group

'Beauty of Apeldoorn' (4) — MBri

§ *biflora* (15) — CBro CGrW EPot GKev LRHS LTwo

bifloriformis (15) — LRHS

'Bing Crosby' (3) — EBrs

'Bird of Paradise' (10) — EBrs

'Black Hero' — CAvo CFFs SPer

'Black Parrot' (10) ♀H4 — CAvo CFFs EBrs EPfP LBmB LPhx LRHS MBri MMHG MSte SMeo SPer

'Black Swan' (5) — LBmB

'Blenda' (3) — EBrs

'Bleu Aimable' (5) — CAvo CFFs EBrs

'Blue Diamond' (11) — CFFs
 new

'Blue Parrot' (10) — CAvo CFFs EBrs LRHS MSte

'Blue Ribbon' (3) — CAvo CFFs

'Blushing Apeldoorn' (4) — SPer
 new

'Blushing Beauty' (5) — LBmB

'Blushing Bride' (5) — LBmB

'Boutade' — NPer

'Burgundy' (6) — EBrs SMeo

'Calypso' (14) ♀H4 — EBrs

'Candy Club' (5) — LBmB SPer

'Cantata' (13) — CBro

'Cape Cod' (14) — EPfP

'Carnaval de Nice' (11/v) — CAvo CFFs MBri
 ♀H4

'Carrousel' (7) **new** — EBrs

'Cassini' (3) — SPer

§ *celsiana* (15) — ECho LRHS

'China Pink' (6) ♀H4 — CMea EBrs EPfP MBri SMeo

'China Town' (8) ♀H4 — EBrs MBri WSan

chrysantha Boiss. — see *T. montana*
 ex Baker

§ *clusiana* (15) — CBro CMea

- var. *chrysantha* (15) — CAvo CFFs CGrW CMea EBrs
 ♀H4 — ECho LPhx LRHS MEHN SBch WHoo

- - 'Tubergen's Gem' (15) — CBro LRHS MBri

- 'Cynthia' (15) ♀H4 — CSWP ECGP EPot LPhx LRHS MSte SMeo

'Colour Spectacle'PBR (5) — LBmB LSou SPer

'Concerto' (13) — CBro EBrs MBri NPer

'Corona' (12) — NBPC

'Couleur Cardinal' (3) — CBro EBrs

cretica (15) — ECho EHyt WWst

'Czaar Peter' ♀H4 — CFFs MBri NBPC NPer

'Dancing Show' (8) — CAvo CFFs EBrs

dasystemon (15) — EPot LTwo SBch

'Daydream' (4) ♀H4 — EPfP LBmB

'Doll's Minuet' (8) — SPer

'Don Quichotte' (3) — MBri
 ♀H4

'Donna Bella' (14) ♀H4 — EPfP

'Douglas Bader' (5) — CAvo CFFs

'Dreamboat' (14) **new** — MBri

'Dreamland' (5) ♀H4 — MBri

'Easter Surprise' (14) — MBri
 ♀H4

eichleri — see *T. undulatifolia*

'Electra' (5) — MBri

'Elegant Lady' (6) — CAvo CFFs EBrs SPer

'Erfurt' (11) — LBmB

'Esperanto' (8/v) ♀H4 — EChP

'Estella Rijnveld' (10) — EBrs MBri MSte NBir SPer

'Eye Catcher' (8) — EBrs

'Fancy Frills' (7) ♀H4 — LBmB

'Fantasy' (10) ♀H4 — LRHS

'Fashion' (12) — EPfP

ferganica (15) — ECho EPot

'Flaming Parrot' (10) — CAvo CFFs LBmB MBri

'Flaming Purissima' (13) — CFFs
 new

* 'Flowerdale' — CAvo CFFs CMea

'Für Elise' (14) **new** — CBgR

'Gavota' (3) — EBrs EPfP LBmB SPer

'Generaal de Wet' (1) — EBrs MBri

'Georgette' (5) — LSou MBri

'Giuseppe Verdi' (12) — MBri

'Golden Apeldoorn' (4) — MBri

'Golden Emperor' (13) — EPfP SPer

'Green Wave' (10)	EPfP LBmB
greigii (14)	CBro
grengiolensis (15)	ECho LRHS
'Groenland' (8)	CAvo CFFs EBrs MBri SPer
'H. D. Genscher'	EBrs
hageri (15)	MBri
- 'Splendens' (15)	EBrs EChP WBor
'Hamilton' (7) ♀H4	EPfP MBNS
'Happy Generation' (3)	LBmB MBri
'Heart's Delight' (12)	CBro EBrs MBri
'Hocus Pocus' (5)	LBmB SPer
§ *humilis* (15)	CBro CGrW LPhx MBri NBPC SBch
- 'Eastern Star' (15)	ECho GCrs GKev LRHS MBri
§ - 'Lilliput' (15)	CBro CMea ECho EPot GKev LRHS
- 'Odalisque' (15)	EPot LRHS
- 'Persian Pearl' (15)	ECho EPfP EPot GCrs LRHS MBri SBch SPer WBor
§ - var. *pulchella* Albocaerulea Oculata Group (15)	CMea CPou EBrs EPot GCrs LTwo MSte WWst
§ - Violacea Group (15)	CMea EChP ECho MBri SPer WBor
§ - - black base (15)	CBro EPot GCrs MBri NJOw
- - yellow base (15)	EPot
'Ice Follies' (3)	LBmB
'Ile de France' (5)	SPer
iliensis (15)	ECho EPot
ingens (15)	ECho
'Inzell' (3)	EBrs EPfP
'Ivory Floradale' (4) ♀H4	LBmB
'Jeantine' (12) ♀H4	EPfP
'Joffre' (1)	MBri
'Johann Strauss' (12)	CBro MBri
'Juan' (13) ♀H4	MBri
kaufmanniana (12)	CAvo CFFs ECho EPot
§ 'Kees Nelis' (3)	MBri
kolpakowskiana (15) ♀H4	EChP EPfP ITim LRHS MBri NJOw SBch
kurdica (15)	CPBP ECho LRHS WWst
- purple-flowered **new**	WWst
- red-flowered **new**	WWst
* 'Lady Diana' (14)	MBri
'Lady Jane' (15) **new**	SPer
'Leen van der Mark' (3)	MBri
'Lilac Perfection' (11)	LBmB MBri
'Lilac Wonder'	see *T. saxatilis* (Bakeri Group) 'Lilac Wonder'
'Lilliput'	see *T. humilis* 'Lilliput'
linifolia (15) ♀H4	CAvo CFFs CPBP EChP ECho EHyt EPfP EPot GKev ITim LRHS MBri NJOw NWCA SBch
§ - Batalinii Group (15) ♀H4	CBro ECho MBri
§ - - 'Apricot Jewel' (15)	CBro CGrW ECho EPot GKev MSte
- - 'Bright Gem' (15) ♀H4	CAvo CBro CFFs EBrs ECho EPot LPhx LRHS MBri SBch WCra WHoo
- - 'Bronze Charm' (15)	CAvo CBro CFFs CMea EPot EWTr LPhx MBri MSte
- - 'Red Gem' (15)	LPhx
- - 'Red Hunter' (15) ♀H4 **new**	SPer
- - 'Red Jewel' (15)	MSte SBch
- - 'Yellow Jewel' (15)	LPhx
§ - Maximowiczii Group	CBro ECho EPot LPhx NJOw NWCA SMeo
'Little Beauty' (15) ♀H4	CBgR CMea CSam EBrs ECho MBri SBch
'Little Princess'	CBgR CSam ECho EPfP SPer
'Lucky Strike' (3)	MBri
§ 'Madame Lefeber' (13)	CBro MBri
'Magier' (5)	MBri
'Maja' (7)	MBri
'March of Time' (14)	MBri
'Mariette' (6)	CBro LBmB MBri SPer
'Marilyn' (6)	CAvo CFFs CMea EBrs LBmB LRHS
marjolletii (15)	CAvo CBgR CBro CFFs EBrs ERos LPhx
'Mary Ann' (14)	WSan
'Maureen' (5) ♀H4	EBrs
maximowiczii	see *T. linifolia* Maximowiczii Group
'Maytime' (6)	CAvo CFFs MBri MWgw SPer
'Maywonder' (11) ♀H4	MBri
'Meissner Porzellan' (3)	LBmB
'Mickey Mouse' (1)	MBri
'Miss Holland' (3)	MBri
'Mona Lisa' (6)	LBmB
'Monsella' (2)	EBrs LBmB
§ *montana* (15)	ECho EPot LPhx NBid SMeo
'Monte Carlo' (2) ♀H4	LRHS MBri
'Mount Tacoma' (11)	CAvo CFFs EBrs EPfP MBri SPer
'Mr Van der Hoef' (2)	MBri
'Negrita' (3)	CBgR MBri SPer
neustruevae (15)	CBgR CBro ECho EPot LPhx NJOw
'New Design' (3/v)	CBgR EBrs MBri SPer
'Ollioules' (4) ♀H4	LBmB SPer
'Orange Bouquet' (3) ♀H4	MBri
'Orange Elite' (14)	MBri
'Orange Emperor' (13) ♀H4	CAvo CFFs LRHS MBri SPer
'Orange Favourite' (10)	CAvo CFFs LRHS
'Orange Princess' (11) ♀H4	EBrs LBmB
'Orange Triumph' (11)	MBri
'Oranje Nassau' (2) ♀H4	MBri
'Oratorio' (14) ♀H4	LRHS MBri
'Oriental Splendour' (14) ♀H4	EPfP
orphanidea (15)	CGrW EBrs ECho LRHS SCnR
- 'Flava' (15)	ECGP EPot LPhx
§ - Whittallii Group (15) ♀H4	CAvo CFFs CMea ECho LPhx SMeo WHal
'Oscar' (14)	LBmB
ostrowskiana (15)	ECho
'Page Polka' (3)	EBrs MBri
'Pandour' (14)	MBri
'Parade' (4) ♀H4	MBri
'Passionale' (3) **new**	EPfP
'Peach Blossom' (2)	CMea EBrs LRHS MBri SPer
'Peaches and Cream' **new**	SPer
'Perestroyka' (5)	LBmB MBri
persica	see *T. celsiana*
'Pieter de Leur'	EPfP MBri SPer
'Pink Impression' (4) ♀H4	MBri SPer
'Pinocchio' (14)	MBri
'Plaisir' (14) ♀H4	CAvo CFFs MBri
platystigma (15)	ECho
polychroma	see *T. biflora*
praestans (15)	CNic ECho EPfP
- 'Fusilier' (15) ♀H4	CBro CMea EBrs EPfP EPot LRHS MBri NBir NJOw SBch SGar
- 'Unicum' (15/v)	MBri
- 'Van Tubergen's Variety' (15)	EBrs NJOw
'Princeps' (13)	CBro MBri
'Princesse Charmante' (14) ♀H4	MBri
'Prinses Irene' (3) ♀H4	CMea EBrs EPfP MBri NBir SPer
pulchella humilis	see *T. humilis*
§ 'Purissima' (13) ♀H4	CAvo CBro CFFs EBrs LPhx LRHS MBri SPer
'Purple Prince' (5)	EPfP
'Queen of Night' (5)	CAvo CBro CFFs CMea EBrs EPfP LPhx LRHS MBri MWgw NHol SBch SPer
'Queen of Sheba' (6) ♀H4	CAvo CFFs
'Red Emperor'	see *T.* 'Madame Lefeber'
'Red Georgette' (5) ♀H4	LSou MBri NBir
'Red Riding Hood' (14) ♀H4	CAvo CBro CFFs CMea EBrs ENot EPfP LRHS MBri NBPC NBir NJOw SPer

'Red Shine' (6) ♀H4 — CBro MBri
'Red Wing' (7) ♀H4 — LBmB
Rembrandt mix — MBri
rhodopea — see *T. urumoffii*
'Ringo' — see *T.* 'Kees Nelis'
'Rococo' (10) — LBmB MBri
saxatilis (15) — CBro CNic ECho EPfP GKev MBri MWgw NJOw SMeo
§ - Bakeri Group (15) — CPou ECho
§ - - 'Lilac Wonder' (15) ♀H4 — CAvo CBro CFFs EBrs EChP ECho EPot GGar GKev MBri MWgw NBPC SBch SMeo SPer
'Scarlet Baby' (12) — EPfP LRHS MBri
'Schoonoord' (2) — MBri
schrenkii (15) — EPot
'Shakespeare' (12) — CBro
'Shirley' (3) — CAvo CFFs EBrs EPfP LRHS MBri
'Showwinner' (12) ♀H4 — CBro MBri
'Snow Parrot' (10) — CAvo LBmB
sosnowskyi (15) new — ECho
sprengeri (15) ♀H4 — CAvo CBro CFFs CLAP ECha SCnR WHal WIvy
- Trotter's form (15) — WCot
'Spring Green' (8) ♀H4 — CAvo CBro CFFs EBrs EPfP LBmB LPhx LRHS MBri MNFA MSte MWgw SBch SMeo SPer WSan
stapfii new — WWst
'Stresa' (12) ♀H4 — CBro ENot
subpraestans (15) — ECho EPot
'Swan Wings' (7) — SPer
'Sweet Harmony' (5) ♀H4 — MBri
'Sweetheart' (13) — CBro MBri SPer
sylvestris (15) — CBro EBrs LPhx LRHS MBow MBri WCot WHer WShi WTin
tarda (15) ♀H4 — CAvo CBro CFFs EBla ECho EPfP EPot GGar LPhx MBri MWgw NBPC NJOw SBch
'Texas Flame' (10) — LRHS MBri
'Texas Gold' (10) — CFFs
'The First' (12) — CBro
'Tinka' (15) — LBmB
'Toronto' (14) ♀H4 — ENot EPfP LRHS LSou MBri SBch MBri
'Toulon' (13) ♀H4 — MBri
'Toyota' (5) — LBmB SPer
turkestanica (15) ♀H4 — CAvo CBgR CBro CFFs CSWP EBrs EChP ECho EPfP EPot EWTr GKev LPhx MBri MWgw NJOw NSla SBch WHoo
'Turkish Delight' — NPer
'Twin Spark' new — SPer
'Uncle Tom' (11) — EPfP MBri
§ **undulatifolia** (15) — ECho
'United States' (14) — NPer
urumiensis (15) ♀H4 — CAvo CBro CFFs ECho EPot LPhx MBri NJOw SBch WHoo
§ **urumoffii** (15) — ECho
'Verona' (2) — EBrs
'Veronique Sanson' — EBrs
violacea — see *T. humilis* Violacea Group
'Viridiflora' (8) — EBrs
vvedenskyi (15) — EPot LPhx
- 'Tangerine Beauty' (15) ♀H4 — EBrs ECho LRHS MBri SBch
'Weber's Parrot' (10) — LBmB MBri
'Weisse Berliner' (3) — EPfP
'West Point' (6) ♀H4 — CAvo CBro CFFs EBrs MBri SPer
'White Dream' (3) — EBrs MBri SPer
'White Elegance' (6) — LBmB SPer
'White Emperor' — see *T.* 'Purissima'
'White Parrot' (10) — CAvo CFFs LPhx LRHS MSte
'White Triumphator' (6) ♀H4 — CAvo CBro CFFs CMea EBrs LPhx MWgw NBir SMeo
whittallii — see *T. orphanidea* Whittallii Group
'Willem van Oranje' (2) — EBrs
'Willemsoord' (2) — MBri

wilsoniana — see *T. montana*
'World Expression' (5) ♀H4 — LBmB
'World's Favourite' (4) new — SPer
'Yellow Dawn' (14) — LRHS
'Yellow Emperor' (5) — MBri
'Yellow Purissima' (13) ♀H4 — EPfP
'Yokohama' (3) — EBrs
'Zampa' (14) ♀H4 — MBri

tummelberry see *Rubus* 'Tummelberry'

Tunica see *Petrorhagia*

Tupistra (Convallariaceae)
aurantiaca — WCMO WCot
- B&SWJ 2267 — WCru WPrP
chinensis 'Eco China Ruffles' — WCMO WCot
nutans — CKob

Turbina (Convolvulaceae)
corymbosa — MGol

Turnera (Turneraceae)
ulmifolia — MSal

Turraea (Meliaceae)
obtusifolia — EShb

Tussilago (Asteraceae)
farfara — CArn CNat ELau GBar GPoy GWCH MHer MSal NMir NSco WHer

Tutcheria (Theaceae)
§ **spectabilis** — EPfP

Tweedia (Asclepiadaceae)
§ **caerulea** ♀H2 — CBcs CSpe EDsa EMan SAga SBch SHFr SPer SWal WCot

Tylecodon (Crassulaceae)
* **luteosquamata** — LToo
paniculatus — LToo
reticulatus — LToo
wallichii — LToo

Typha (Typhaceae)
angustifolia — CBen CKno CRow CWat EHon EMFW GAbr LNCo LPBA MMuc NPer NSco SPlb SWat WFar WPnP WWpP WWye
gracilis — CBen EMFW
latifolia — CBen CRow CWat EHon EMFW LPBA NPer NSco SWat WDyG WFar WHer WMAq WWpP WWye
- 'Variegata' (v) — CBen CBow CDWL CKno CRow CWat ELan EMFW LPBA NScw WCot WMAq
§ **laxmannii** — CBen CDWL CRow CStu EHon EMFW LPBA WPnP WWpP
minima — CBen CBgR CDWL CFwr CRow CStu CWat EHoe EHon EMFW EPfP GBin LEdu LNCo LPBA NPer SCoo SMad SWat WFar WMAq WPnP WRos WWpP
shuttleworthii — CRow
stenophylla — see *T. laxmannii*

Typhonium (Araceae)
giganteum — WCot

Typhonodorum (Araceae)
lindleyanum — XBlo

U

Ugni (Myrtaceae)

§ *molinae*	CBcs CDul CFir CPLG CSBt CTrC EBee IDee LEdu MCCP MDun SAdn SHFr SLPl SOWG SWvt WCHb WDin WFar WJek WMoo WPic WSHC WWye XPep
- 'Flambeau'	CAgr LEdu MGos NLar SWvt

Ulex (Papilionaceae)

europaeus	CArn CCVT CDoC CDul CRWN ECrN ELan ENot EPfP GPoy GWCH LBuc MCoo NWea SCoo SPoG WDin WHar WMou
§ - 'Flore Pleno' (d) ♀H4	CBcs CBgR CDoC CSBt EMon ENot EPfP EPla GAbr GGar IArd MBlu MGos NEgg NLar NWea SHBN SPer SPoG WFar
- 'Plenus'	see *U. europaeus* 'Flore Pleno'
- 'Prostratus'	MBar
gallii	WDin
- 'Mizen Head'	GCal GGGa GGar GSki MBlu MWhi SLon SPoG
§ *minor*	EPla
nanus	see *U. minor*

Ulmus ✿ (Ulmaceae)

americana 'Princeton'	CKno
'Dodoens'	IArd LBuc MGos SBLw
§ *glabra*	CDul CRWN ECrN NWea SBLw WDin
- 'Camperdownii'	CDoC CTho EBee ECrN ELan NBee NEgg SBLw SCoo SPer
- 'Exoniensis'	CTho SBLw
- 'Gittisham'	CTho
- 'Horizontalis'	see *U. glabra* 'Pendula'
- 'Lutescens'	CDoC CEnd CTho CTri LRHS MAsh NWea SBLw SCoo SLim
§ - 'Pendula'	CDul SBLw
x *hollandica* 'Commelin'	SBLw
- 'Dampieri'	SBLw
§ - 'Dampieri Aurea'	CDul CEnd CLnd CTho EBee ELan EPfP LBuc LRHS MAsh MBar MBlu MGos NBlu SBLw SHBN SPer WDin WOrn WPat
- 'Groeneveld'	SBLw
- 'Jacqueline Hillier'	CBgR CDul EBee ECho ELan EPfP EPla IMGH LAst MAsh MBar MGos NBlu NWea SBLw SLon SPer SPoG SSto STre WCFE WDin WFar WPat
- 'Lobel'	CDul MGos SBLw
- 'Wredei'	see *U. hollandica* 'Dampieri Aurea'
laevis	CDul CTho ECrN
minor	NEgg SBLw
- 'Dampieri Aurea'	see *U. x hollandica* 'Dampieri Aurea'
- subsp. *sarniensis*	SBLw
- 'Silvery Gem' (v) new	LRHS
- 'Variegata' (v)	EPot SCoo WPat
montana	see *U. glabra*
parvifolia	CMCN CMen CTho ECrN NWea SFam STre WNor WPGP
- 'Frosty' (v)	ECho
- 'Geisha' (v)	ECho ELan EMil MAsh MGos SPoG WPat
§ - 'Hokkaido'	CMen LTwo NLAp NLar SBla WAbe WPat
- 'Pygmaea'	see *U. parvifolia* 'Hokkaido'
- 'Yatsubusa'	CLyd ECho EPot EWes LTwo MAsh NLar SIng STre WPat
'Plantijn'	SBLw

procera	CDul CTho LBuc MDun WDin WSFF
- 'Argenteovariegata' (v)	CDul MGos SMad
pumila	CAgr CDul EPot NWea WNor
rubra	CArn MSal
'Sapporo Autumn Gold' PBR	WDin
x *vegeta*	SBLw

Umbellularia (Lauraceae)

californica	CArn CPne EPfP SAPC SArc SSpi WSHC

Umbilicus (Crassulaceae)

rupestris	CArn CHrt CRWN EChP EDsa GEdr NWCA SChr SECG WBri WHer WShi WWye

Uncinia (Cyperaceae)

* *cyparissias* from Chile	NBir
egmontiana	CMea EBee EBla EBrs EChP EHoe EKen EMan EPPr EShb GSki MNrw SHGN WFoF WHrl WLeb
from Chile	EWes GCal
lechleriana	GBin
N *rubra*	More than 30 suppliers
uncinata	CBcs CMMP ECha EMan GSki LHop MFOX NCob NHol SDix
* - *rubra*	CBrm CFir CHar CKno COIW CTri CWCL ECot EHol EHrv GSki IFro LAst LRHS MMHG MNrw MTis MWgw NCGa NCob NGdn SLim SMer SWvt WGwG WWeb

Uniola (Poaceae)

latifolia	see *Chasmanthium latifolium*

Urceolina (Amaryllidaceae)

miniata	see *Stenomesson miniatum*
peruviana	see *Stenomesson miniatum*

Urechites see Pentalinon

Urginea (Hyacinthaceae)

fugax	EBee
- SB&L 535 from Morocco new	CMon
maritima	CArn CMdw CPou EBee ECho ERea GCal MNrw MSal
ollivieri MS&CL 281 from Tunisia new	CMon
undulata MS&CL 251 from Morocco new	CMon

Urospermum (Asteraceae)

dalechampii	CSam CSec EBrs ECha LLWP

Ursinia (Asteraceae)

alpina	CPBP
montana	NWCA
nana new	EHyt WFar

Urtica (Urticaceae)

dioica 'Chedglow 2' (v) new	CNat
- 'Dog Trap Lane'	CNat
- 'Good as Gold'	CNat
- subsp. *gracilis* var. *procera*	CNat
galeopsifolia	CNat

Utricularia (Lentibulariaceae)

alpina	CSWC
australis	EFEx
bisquamata	CSWC SHmp
blancheti	CSWC
calycifida	CSWC SHmp

dichotoma	CSWC EFEx
exoleta R. Brown	see *U. gibba*
§ *gibba*	EFEx
heterosepala	CHew
intermedia	EFEx
lateriflora	CHew EFEx
livida	CSWC EFEx
longifolia	CSWC
macrorhiza	CSWC
menziesii	EFEx
monanthos	CHew CSWC EFEx
nephrophylla	SHmp
novae-zelandiae	CSWC
ochroleuca	EFEx
paulineae	CHew
praelonga	CSWC SHmp
pubescens	CHew CSWC SHmp
reniformis	CSWC EFEx SHmp
- *nana*	EFEx
sandersonii	CSWC SHmp
- blue	CSWC
subulata	EFEx
tricolor	CSWC SHmp
uniflora	CHew
vulgaris	CHew CDWL CSWC EFEx MCCP

Uvularia (Convallariaceae)

§ *caroliniana*	ECho IBlr
disporum	ECho
grandiflora ♀H4	More than 30 suppliers
- dwarf	ECho IBlr
- var. *pallida*	CAvo CBct CBos CLAP CPom CStu EBrs ECha ECho EGle EHrv EPot GBri GBuc GCal GEdr IBlr LEdu LPhx MRav NCGa SBla SMHy SUsu WAbe WCru WFar WPGP WPnP
- 'Susie Lewis'	WCru
grandiflora x *perfoliata*	ECho IBlr
perfoliata	CBct CLAP EBee ECha ECho EDAr EGle EHyt EPfP GBri GCrs GGar IBlr LEdu MRav SIng SOkd WAbe WBrE WCru WHil WPGP WPnP
pudica	see *U. caroliniana*
sessilifolia	CBct CLAP ECho EPPr GBBs IBlr LEdu NLar NMen WCru

V

Vaccaria (Caryophyllaceae)

§ *hispanica*	MSal
segetalis	see *V. hispanica*

Vaccinium ✿ (Ericaceae)

from Bolivia	EWes
arctostaphylos	NLar SReu SSta SWvt
'Berkeley' (F)	CTrh CWib GTwe LBuc LRHS MBlu SDea
'Blue Ray' (F)	CWib SCoo
'Bluejay' (F)	LRHS SCoo
caespitosum	SOkd
'Cinderella'	CDBb
corymbosum (F) ♀H4	CBcs EPfP MBar MGos MNHC SCoo SReu SSta WBVN WDin
- 'Blauweiss-goldtraube' (F)	CTri CWSG CWib ERea LSRN MBlu MGos SDea SKee SPoG WBVN
- 'Bluecrop' (F)	CAgr CDBb CTrh CWib EMui EPfP ERea GTwe LBuc LRHS LSRN MAsh MBlu MBri MGos NLar SCoo SDea SKee SPer SPoG SWvt WFar
- 'Bluegold' (F)	CDBb LRHS MAsh SCoo
- 'Bluetta' (F)	CAgr CDBb CWib EMui GTwe LRHS MBri SCoo WFar
- 'Brigitta' (F)	CDBb GTwe
- 'Chandler' (F) **new**	CDBb LRHS SPoG
- 'Concord' (F)	ENot SCoo
- 'Coville' (F)	EMui
- 'Darrow' (F)	CTrh GTwe LRHS SPoG
- 'Grover' (F) **new**	LRHS
- 'Hardyblue' (F) **new**	CDBb
- 'Herbert' (F)	CDBb CTrh EMui GTwe LBuc SCoo
- 'Ivanhoe' (F)	SCoo
- 'Jersey' (F)	LRHS MAsh SCoo SDea
- 'Legacy' (F) **new**	CDBb
- 'Nelson' (F)	SCoo
- 'Northblue' (F) **new**	CDBb
- 'Nui' (F) **new**	CDBb
- 'Pioneer' (F)	MBar
- 'Polaris' (F) **new**	LRHS SPoG
- 'Stanley'	ELan LRHS
- 'Toro' (F)	CDBb CTrh GTwe LRHS MAsh
- 'Weymouth' (F)	SDea
crassifolium subsp. *sempervirens* 'Well's Delight' (F)	LRHS MAsh
cylindraceum ♀H4	EPfP MAsh NLar SSta WAbe WFar WPat
- 'Tinkerbell'	ITim WAbe
delavayi	ECho LRHS MAsh MBar MDun SReu SSta WAbe WFar WThu
'Duke' (F) ♀H4	CDBb CTrh ELan EPfP LRHS MAsh
dunalianum var. *caudatifolium* B&SWJ 1716	WCru
'Earliblue' (F)	EMui LRHS MGos SDea
floribundum	CDoC CMHG ECho IDee LRHS MAsh MDun NLar SBrw SPoG SSpi WPGP WPic
glaucoalbum ♀H3-4	CAbP CDoC CPLG EPfP GGGa IDee LRHS MAsh MBar MRav SBrw SMad SPer SPoG SSpi WDin
* *grandiflorum*	ECho
griffithianum	CDBb SReu SSta
'Groover' **new**	LSRN
§ *macrocarpon* (F)	CDBb ECho ELan EMui GTwe LRHS MAsh MBar MBri NWCA SDea SPoG SRms
- 'Centennial' (F) **new**	CDBb
- 'Centerville' (F) **new**	CDBb
- 'CN' (F)	MGos SBrw
- 'Early Black' (F)	EWTr MGos
- 'Franklin' (F)	CDBb
- 'Hamilton'	CStu GCrs GEdr LTwo NHol NLAp WPat
- 'Howes' (F) **new**	CDBb
- 'McFarlin' (F)	EMui
- 'Pilgrim' (F)	CDBb ERea
'Misty' (F)	CAgr SPoG
mortinia	NMen
moupinense	CDoC ECho LRHS
- 'Variegatum' (v)	LTwo
myrsinites	ECho
myrtillus	CDBb CDul GPoy MBar WDin WSFF
'Nimo Pink'	MBar
'Northland' (F)	CWib GTwe SCoo SDea
nummularia	ECho GEdr NHar NLAp SBrw SSpi WAbe
ovatum	CDBb CMHG IDee LRHS MBar MDun SPer SSta
- 'Thundercloud'	CAbP LRHS
§ *oxycoccos* (F)	CArn GPoy
* - *rubrum*	NLar
'Ozarkblue' **new**	CDBb

padifolium	WCwm WPGP
pallidum	IBlr
palustre	see *V. oxycoccos*
'Patriot' (F)	CDBb CTrh CWib GTwe LRHS MGos SCoo
praestans	GIBF NHol
- Brown 0285	CStu
retusum	CTrw WDin WPic
sikkimense	GGGa
'Spartan' (F) ♥H4	CDBb GTwe LRHS SCoo
'Sunrise' (F)	GTwe LRHS
'Sunshine Blue' (F) **new**	CAgr CDBb
'Tophat' (F)	EMui LRHS
uliginosum	GIBF
vitis-idaea	CNic ECho EPfP EWes GGar GPoy MBar MGos MNHC SPoG SRot WFar
- Brown 0287	CStu
- 'Autumn Beauty'	NLar
- 'Compactum'	EWes LSou NLAp
- Koralle Group ♥H4	CAgr EPfP MAsh MBar MBri NHol SBrw SPer WPat
- subsp. *minus*	GCrs MAsh NLar NMen WAbe
- - 'Betsy Sinclair'	CStu
- 'Red Pearl'	CDBb CSBt EPfP LRHS MAsh MGos MSwo
* - 'Variegatum' (v)	EWes NLAp WPat
wrightii var. *formosanum*	ECho

Vagaria (Amaryllidaceae)

olivieri SF 266 from Morocco	CMon
parviflora from Israel	CMon

Valeriana (Valerianaceae)

'Alba'	see *Centranthus ruber* 'Albus'
alliariifolia	EBee EMon GCal NBro NSti WCot
arizonica	CStu MSte
'Coccinea'	see *Centranthus ruber*
coreana	CFee WMoo
dioica	SECG
hardwickii	EBee
jatamansii	CArn GPoy
montana	NBro NRya SRms SWat WMoo
officinalis	More than 30 suppliers
- subsp. *sambucifolia*	CFee CPom NDov SHar WCAu WHil WOut
* - 'Variegata' (v)	WCHb
phu 'Aurea'	More than 30 suppliers
pyrenaica	EBee ECha EHrv EPPr GCal LPhx MMHG WCot WMoo
saxatilis	NLar NRya
supina	NWCA
wallrothii	WCot

Valerianella (Valerianaceae)

§ *locusta*	CArn GPoy
olitoria	see *V. locusta*

Vallea (Elaeocarpaceae)

stipularis	CDoC
- var. *pyrifolia*	CPLG CPle

Vallota see *Cyrtanthus*

Vancouveria (Berberidaceae)

chrysantha	CDes CElw CLAP CPom EBee ECha EMan ERos GBuc IBlr MNrw MRav NLar NRya NWCA WCru WMoo
hexandra	CDes CLAP CPom CSpe EBee EBrs EHrv EPfP ERos GBuc GCal IBlr NRya NSti SMad WCru WPGP
planipetala	CLAP IBlr WCru
I - 'Bellevue Strain' **new**	WCot

Vania see *Thlaspi*

veitchberry see *Rubus* 'Veitchberry'

Vellozia (Velloziaceae)

elegans	see *Talbotia elegans*

Veltheimia (Hyacinthaceae)

§ *bracteata* ♥H1	CBgR CHal CHll CPrp EBak ECho IBlr LBow LToo NPal SYvo WCot WDav
§ *capensis* ♥H1	CSev
viridifolia misapplied	see *V. capensis*
viridifolia Jacq.	see *V. bracteata*

x *Venidioarctotis* see *Arctotis*

Venidium see *Arctotis*

Veratrum ✿ (Melanthiaceae)

album	EBee ECha GBuc GIBF GPoy LRHS MRav NEgg SBla WBrE WCot WCru WFar
- var. *flavum*	IPot LPhx WCru
- var. *oxysepalum*	WCru
californicum	EBee GCal IBlr LAst MDun WCMO WCot WGwG WSHC
dolichopetalum B&SWJ 4416	WCru
formosanum	CDes MNrw
- B&SWJ 1575	WCru
grandiflorum B&SWJ 4450 **new**	WCru
maackii var. *maackii*	GCal WSHC
- - B&SWJ 5831	WCru
mengtzeanum F&W 8990	WCot
nigrum ♥H4	CBos CBro CDes CFir CPom EBee EHrv GBuc GCal IPot LPhx MDun MNrw NBhm NBir NChi NCob NEgg NGdn SBla SMad SPer SPlb SPoG WCot WCru WFar WPnP
schindleri B&SWJ 4068 **new**	WCru
stamineum	WCru
viride	EWes IBlr SBla

Verbascum ✿ (Scrophulariaceae)

adzharicum	IFro NBur WHoo
Allestree hybrids	EHrv
'Annie May'	CBos CDes EBee EBla EMag EMan EPfP EShb LPhx LRHS LSRN MAvo NCob NDov NGdn NOrc SPur SUsu SVil WCra
'Apricot Sunset'	CDes EAEE EBee EMag EMan LPhx LRHS MAvo NCob NDov NGdn SMeo SUsu SVil WCra WPGP WWlt
'Arctic Summer'	see *V. bombyciferum* 'Polarsommer'
arcturus	EBee LPhx WPer
'Aurora'	LPhx MAvo SJoh SMeo
'Aztec Gold'	CDes LPhx MAvo SJoh
* *bakerianum*	EBla ECtt
'Banana Custard'	EBee ECtt EKen ENot EWin LSou MBNS SPet SPoG WCMO
'Bill Bishop'	ECho NHar SIng
blattaria	EBee EHrv LIck NBir NRnb SPav SWat WFar WHer WPer WWhi
- f. *albiflorum*	CNic CSpe EBee EChP EMar ERou IFro LHop LLWP LPhx MNFA NDov NSti SBch SGar SPlb WHer WMoo WPer WTin
- 'Pink White Blush' **new**	LSou
- pink-flowered	EGoo SPav
- yellow-flowered	NRnb SPav SWat
'Blushing Bride' **new**	MBnl NBhm WCot

***boerhavii* new**	EBee
* – bicolor	WRos
§ ***bombyciferum***	CBre CSev EChP ECha GMaP MFOX NGdn NSti SRms WCot WRHF XPep
– BSSS 232	WCru
* – 'Arctic Snow'	SPav
§ – 'Polarsommer'	CHrt CSpe EBee ENot EPfP ERou LRHS MBri MDun NBir NBlu NScw NVic SPav SPer SPet SPoG SRms SWal SWat WViv WWeb
– 'Silver Lining'	NBur NLRH NLar NPer SDnm SPav
'Brookside'	EMag LPhx MSte
'Broussa'	see *V. bombyciferum*
'Buttercup'	SPoG
'Butterscotch'	MSph SUsu
'Caribbean Crush'	CPen EBee ECtt ELan EMan EPfP EShb LAst LPhx LSou MBNS MBri NCGa NEgg NLar NMoo NPri SPav SPoG WCMO WGor WSan WWlt
(Caribbean Crush Group) 'Mango'	ENot EPfP
chaixii	CHea CSam EBee EBrs ECha ECtt EHrv EUnu GAbr GBuc MMHG MWat MWgw NBir NEgg SBla WFar WMoo WPer
– 'Album' ♀H4	More than 30 suppliers
– 'Helene Bowles'	CHar
– 'Sixteen Candles' **new**	NBHF NChi WHil
***chaixii* x 'Wendy's Choice'**	MAvo MDKP
'Charles Harper'	EMag LPhx MSph MSte SMeo
'Charlotte' **new**	MAvo
'Cherokee'	LPhx MAvo
'Cherry Helen'	CPen EBee EMar EPfP GMac LAst LHop LRHS MBNS MWgw NLar NMoo NRnb SMrm SPoG SRGP WCMO WHlf WOVN WSan WWeb
'Claire'	LPhx SJoh
'Clementine'	LPhx MAvo SJoh
(Cotswold Group)	CHad COtt CPar CSam EBee EBla EChP ECtt EMar EPfP ERou GMac LAst LPhx LRHS MAvo MRav MTis MWat MWgw NGdn NLar SBla SPer SPla SUsu WCAu WMnd WPGP
'Cotswold Beauty' ♀H4	
– 'Cotswold Queen'	CBcs CMMP COIW CWCL EBee EBla EChP ECtt ELan EPfP ERou GBBs LPhx LRHS MAvo MRav MWat MWgw NGdn NPri SBla SPer SPet SWvt WCAu WCMO WMnd WWeb
– 'Gainsborough' ♀H4	More than 30 suppliers
– 'Mont Blanc'	EBla EChP ECot EHrv GMaP LAst LPhx LRHS SPer SWat
– 'Pink Domino' ♀H4	More than 30 suppliers
– 'Royal Highland'	COIW CPrp CWCL EBee EChP ECot ECtt EHrv ELan EMar EPfP ERou GAbr LPhx LRHS MTis NGdn NLar SDnm SPav SWvt WCMO WFar WMnd WWeb
– 'White Domino'	EBee EMar ERou LBmB LRHS MBNS NGby SMrm SPer SPla WCAu WHlf WViv
'Cotswold King'	see *V. creticum*
§ ***creticum***	CSpe EBee ERou LHop MBri MSph NEgg NLRH SBch SDnm SPav SPla SUsu WCMO WCot WPer WPGP WSan
'Daisy Alice'	EMag LPhx MAvo MSte SBla
§ ***densiflorum***	CArn EBee EMag ERou LPhx SMar SPer WFar WPer
'Dijon'	EBee ECtt EWes WCMO
dumulosum ♀H2-3	EHyt NWCA WAbe
'Dusky Maiden' **new**	NWCA
'Ebenezer Howard'	LPhx
'Ellenbank Jewel' **new**	GMac
epixanthinum	CEnt EBrs EMag ITer LPhx LSou MCCP MDKP NCGa NLar NRnb WCMO
'Golden Wings' ♀H2-3	ECtt ITim NMen
Harptree smokey hybrids **new**	CHar
'Helen Johnson'	More than 30 suppliers
'Hiawatha'	LPhx SJoh SMeo
'High Noon'	LPhx MAvo SJoh
x ***hybridum*** 'Copper Rose'	CWan ENot EPfP MBri MHer NRnb SPet WHil WPer
– 'Snow Maiden'	CWan EBee ECtt ENot MHer NRnb SDnm WHil
– 'Wega'	EBee NLar WHil
'Hyde Hall Sunrise'	ENot LBuc LRHS
'Innocence'	CDes MAvo MDKP
'Jackie'	More than 30 suppliers
'Jackie in Pink'	ERou EWes MBNS MCCP NMoo
'Jolly Eyes'	EChP NCGa NRnb WHil
'June Johnson'	EAEE EBee SHar SRGP
'Kalypso'	LPhx MAvo SJoh
'Klondike'	LPhx SJoh
'Kynaston'	EAEE EBee EBla EMar IPot NCGa SHar
'Lavender Lass' **new**	MBnl
'Letitia' ♀H3	CBcs CMea EAEE EBee ECho ECtt EHyt ELan EPot EWes GCal LAst LRHS MTho NJOw NMen NPri NWCA SBla SIng SPav SPoG SRot SWvt WAbe WKif
longifolium	LRHS WFar
– var. ***pannosum***	see *V. olympicum*
* ***luridifolium***	EBee LPhx WPGP
lychnitis	CArn LPhx SMeo WHer
'Megan's Mauve'	EBee EBla ECot EWll MSph NEgg SPer SWvt
'Monster'	EMag LPhx MSph MSte
'Moonshadow'	LPhx MAvo SJoh
'Mystery Blonde'	LPhx SBla SJoh
nigrum	CArn EBee ECtt EPfP GAbr MBNS MBow NChi NGHP SECG SEND WBrE WFar WMoo WPer
– var. ***album***	GMac NChi NGHP NLar WMoo
'Nimrod'	LPhx SJoh
'Norfolk Dawn'	CDes EAEE EBee EBla EMag EMan EMar EPfP EShb LAst LPhx MAvo MSte MWgw NCob NDov NGdn SMeo SUsu SVil WCra WPGP
§ ***olympicum***	CHrt CSam EBee ECtt EGoo ELan ENot EPfP GGar MBNS MWat NLRH NOak SDix SEND SPoG WBrE WCAu WCot WFar WPer XPep
oreophilum	EBee
'Patricia'	EAEE EBla EKen EMag LPhx MAvo MSph MSte NCGa NCob NDov WPGP
'Petra'	CDes LPhx
phlomoides	LPhx
phoeniceum	CArn CEnt ELan EPfP ITim LRHS MNHC MWgw NBlu NBro NEgg NOak SBri SGar SPet SPlb SWal WBrE WEas WHen WMoo WPer
* – 'Album'	CSpe LIck NJOw WBrE
– 'Flush of Pink'	ECtt
– 'Flush of White'	CMea CWCL ECtt EGoo EPPr ERou GMac LAst LPhx LRHS MNFA MWat NChi SDnm SPav STes WGor WHen WHil WMoo WRHF
– hybrids	CBgR CSpe ECtt EGoo GMaP NChi NEgg NGdn NJOw NVic SRms SWat WFar WGor WPer
– 'Rosetta'	EMar EPPr EShb GBri
– 'Violetta'	More than 30 suppliers
'Phoenix'	CDes LPhx SJoh

'Pink Glow' — LRHS
'Pink Ice' — EPPr MAvo MDKP MHar
'Pink Kisses' — LRHS
'Pink Petticoats' — CPen ENot NLar SPoG
'Plum Smokey' **new** — WCot
'Primrose Cottage' — CPen EMag LPhx
'Primrose Path' **new** — LRHS SRot
'Purple Prince' — ECtt
pyramidatum — LPhx
'Raspberry Ripple' — EAEE EBee ELan EMan EMar EPfP IHMH LAst NCGa NMoo SMac SPav SPer SPet SPoG
rorippifolium — LPhx NCGa NRnb
'Southern Charm' — EBee EChP ECtt ERou EWll GMaP GMac LRHS MBri MCCP NChi NGHP NVic SPav SPoG STes WFar WHil WPtf WSan
* 'Spica' — LPhx NLar
spicatum — WFar
spinosum — SBla
'Sugar Plum' **new** — WCot
'Summer Sorbet' — CPen ELan EMan EPfP SMac SPer SPoG
* Sunset shades — MSph
thapsiforme — see *V. densiflorum*
thapsus — CBgR COld CSev GPoy GWCH MHer MNHC NMir NRnb NSco WSel WWye
'Tilney Moonbeam' — ECtt EMar
'Tilney Sundown' **new** — EMar
'Twilight' **new** — EBrs
undulatum — CArn
'Valerie Grace' — EMag LPhx MSte
'Virginia' — LPhx MAvo SJoh
wiedemannianum — EBee
'Yellow Johnson' — WCMO

Verbena (Verbenaceae)

'Adonis Light Blue' (G) — LRHS
'Aphrodite' — LAst
'Apple Blossom' (G) — LRHS
'Aveyron' (G) — GBri
(Aztec Series) Aztec Magic Silver = 'Balazsilma' (G) — SCoo
- Aztec Pearl (G) — SCoo
- Aztec Red = 'Balazred'PBR (G) — SCoo
(Babylon Series) Babylon Dark Blue with Eye = 'Darkeyena' **new** — WGor
- Babylon Red = 'Oxena'PBR **new** — NBlu
'Betty Lee' — ECtt
'Blue Cascade' (G) — LAst
'Blue Prince' (G) — CSpe
§ *bonariensis* ♀H3-4 — More than 30 suppliers
'Boon' (G) — ECtt LSou
'Booty' (G) — ECtt LSou
'Boughton House' (G) — MSte
brasiliensis Vell. — MDKP
canadensis 'Perfecta' (G) — WWhi
'Candy Carousel' (G) — SPet
'Carousel' (G) — CWCL LAst SPoG
chamaedrifolia — see *V. peruviana*
§ 'Claret' (G) — CAby CElw CSam ECtt EMan EPfP EShb EWin GBri LPhx LSou MWea SAga SCoo SMHy SMeo SMrm SUsu WViva
'Corsage Peach' — LAst LSou
'Corsage Red' — LAst
corymbosa — CBrm CEnt CHea CHll CMMP CPLG CWCL EBee EChP ECha EGra EPPr GSki LHop MDKP NLar SAga SBla SBod WLin WPer WPtf WWpP

- 'Gravetye' — CHrt GBuc NCob WFar
'Diamond Butterfly' (G) — EWin SAga
'Diamond Carouselle' (G) — EWin
'Diamond Merci' (G) — EShb SAga WHoo
'Edith Eddleman' (G) — EBee EChP ECtt EWin MNrw
Flamenco Dark Red = 'Wesverdark'PBR **new** — LSou
* 'Foxhunter' (G) — ECtt
'Hammerstein Pink' **new** — EBee EPfP
hastata — More than 30 suppliers
- 'Alba' — CHar EBee EChP EMan EMon EPyc GBar GBuc GSki LDai MDKP MLLN NBPC NDov NRnb MLLN NBPC NDov NRnb SPoG STes WMoo WPer WWhi WWpP
- 'Rosea' — More than 30 suppliers
'Hidcote Purple' (G) — MSte
'Homestead Purple' (G) — CSev EBee ECGP EChP ECtt EMan ENor EPfP EShb GSki LAst LDai LIck LSRN NRnb SAga SGar SMrm SPoG SUsu SWvt
'Huntsman' (G) — GBuc
'Imagination' (G) — LRHS
'Jenny's Wine' (G) — see *V.* 'Claret'
'La France' (G) — CAby CHea CSam EBee ECha ECtt EMan EPfP EShb EWTr EWin LPhx LSou SAga SDix SMHy SMeo SMrm SUsu WHoo
(Lanai Series) Lanai Burgundy = 'Lan Burg' (G) — ECtt LAst
- Lanai Lavender Star = 'Lan Lav Star' (G) — ECtt
- Lanai Peach (G) — ECtt LAst
lasiostachys **new** — EBee
litoralis — EBee
'Lois' Ruby' — see *V.* 'Claret'
macdougalii — CBos EChP EDsa EGoo EMan LPhx LRav MDKP MWgw NEgg NRnb
officinalis — CArn CRWN CWan EDAr GBar GPoy MBow MGol MHer MNHC MSal SECG SIde SMar WGHP WHer WJek WPer WSel WWye XPep
patagonica — see *V. bonariensis*
'Peaches and Cream' (G) ♀H3 — LRHS LSou NPri
§ *peruviana* (G) — EAEE EBee EPfP EShb EWin SAga SBla SDix SIng SRms
'Pink Bouquet' — see *V.* 'Silver Anne'
'Pink Cascade' — EShb
'Pink Parfait' (G) — CHal CHrt EMan EPfP EWin LAst LHop SAga SPet SPoG
'Pink Pearl' (G) — ECtt
'Pink Stars' **new** — NPri
platensis (G) — EBee GCal
- RCB/Arg P-2 — WCot
'Raspberry Crush' (G) — LRHS
'Red Cascade' — SPet
§ *rigida* ♀H3 — More than 30 suppliers
- 'Lilacina' — WCot XPep
- 'Polaris' — CHar EBee ECGP EMan EShb LHop LPhx LRHS LSou NDov SMHy SMar SMrm SUsu WRos WWpP
§ 'Silver Anne' (G) ♀H3 — CHrt CSam EBee ECtt EMan EWin LDai LSou SDix SMer SUsu WHen
§ 'Sissinghurst' (G) ♀H2-3 — CSam ECtt EMan EWin NPri SAga SIng SMrm SPoG SRms WHen
'Sissinghurst Pink' — LAst
* 'Snow Flurry' — CFir
(Splash Series) 'Splash Rose' — LAst
- 'Splash Violet' — LAst
stricta — EBee MDKP
(Superbena Series) Superbena Burgundy = 'Usbenal5' — LSou

- Superbena Bushy   NPri
  Merlot = 'Usbena5117'
  new
- Superbena Ruby   LSou NPri
  Red = 'Usbena5122'
- Superbena Violet   NPri
  Blue = 'UsbenaS10'
(Tapien Series) Tapien   LAst NBlu
  Pink = 'Sunver'PBR (G)
- Tapien Salmon =   LAst LSou WGor
  'Sunmaref TP-SAP' (G)
- Tapien Sky Blue (G) **new** LSou
- Tapien Violet =   LAst LSou NBlu
  'Sunvop'PBR (G)
- Tapien White =   LAst
  'Suntapipurew' (G)
(Temari Series) Temari   LAst NBlu
  Blue = 'Sunmariribu'PBR
  (G)
- Temari Burgundy (G)   LAst WGor
  new
- Temari Coral Pink =   LAst
  'Sunmariripi'PBR (G)
- Temari Neon Red (G)   LAst
  new
- Temari Scarlet =   LAst NBlu
  'Sunmarisu'PBR (G)
- Temari Violet =   WGor
  'Sunmariba'PBR (G)
- Temari White =   LAst
  'Sunmaririho'PBR (G)
'Tenerife'   see *V.* 'Sissinghurst'
tenuisecta (G)   LRav SMar WPer XPep
Tukana Scarlet =   WGor
  'Scarlena'PBR (Tukana
  Series) **new**
venosa   see *V. rigida*
'White Sissinghurst' (G)   LAst

Verbesina (Asteraceae)

alternifolia   CArn EMan MGol
- 'Goldstrahl'   EPPr NDov WPer
encelioides   CPLG CSec
helianthoides   CPLG CSec EWll LSou MGol
                            WGwG WHil

Vernonia (Asteraceae)

crinita   CAby ECha EWes NLar SMad SMer
                            WBor
- 'Mammuth'   CFwr EBee LHop LPhx NCob SPoG
fasciculata   EBee EBrs EChP EMan EShb EWes
                            LRHS MNFA NLar SSvw WCot
gigantea   EBee NLar
missurica **new**   EBee
noveboracensis   EBee MGol MWea NLar WPer
- 'Albiflora'   WPer

Veronica (Scrophulariaceae)

amethystina   see *V. spuria* L.
anagallis-aquatica   NSco
  new
'Anna'PBR   NDov
armena   ECho EWes MDKP MHer MSte
                            MWat NJOw NMen NWCA SBla
                            SPoG SRot WFar
§ *austriaca*   GSki MLLN NBre NChi WFar WMoo
- var. *dubia*   see *V. prostrata*
- 'Ionian Skies'   CLyd CMea CPBP CTri EBee ECtt
                            EGoo EPPr EWes GBuc LBee LRHS
                            MNrw NCGa NDov SBla SEND
                            SGar SPer WCMO WFar WKif WPat
                            WPer WSHC
- 'Jacqueline' **new**   NBre
§ - subsp. *teucrium*   CArn CSam EBee ECho GBin GSki
                            MFOX MWgw NDlv NEgg SRms
                            WBrk WFar WPer

- - 'Crater Lake Blue' ♀H4   EBee ECtt ENot ERou EShb LAst
                              LHop LPhx LRHS MAvo MRav NBid
                              NBre NCGa NFor NVic SMrm SPla
                              SPlb SRms WCMO WCot WEas
                              WFar WMnd WPat WPer
- - 'Kapitän'   ECha GBuc MNrw NPro WFar
                              WPer
- - 'Knallblau'   EBee EMil MBri NCGa NGby SSvw
- - 'Royal Blue' ♀H4   CMea EAEE EBee ECot EPfP EWin
                              GBuc GMaP GSki LAst LRHS MArl
                              MNFA NOak NSti SPer SRms WFar
                              WMnd WWeb
- subsp. *vahlii* MESE 124   EBee
  new
'Baby Doll' **new**   EBee ERou IBal MAvo MBNS MBnl
                              NBhm
bachofenii   WTin
beccabunga   CArn CBen CWat EHon ELan
                              EMFW EPfP GPoy LNCo LPBA
                              MBow NMir NPer NSco SWat WFar
                              WHer WMAq WPnP WSFF WWpP
- var. *limosa*   WWye
'Bergen's Blue'   EBee EChP EPfP GMac NLar SHGN
                              SHar
Blue Bouquet   see *V. longifolia* 'Blaubündel'
'Blue Indigo'   CBgR CHar EBee ELan IBal NBre
                              NCGa
'Blue Spire'   SWat WPer
bombycina   ECho EHyt NWCA
- subsp. *bolkardaghensis*   NMen SBla
bonarota   see *Paederota bonarota*
caespitosa   CPBP
- subsp. *caespitosa*   CLyd NMen
candida   see *V. spicata* subsp. *incana*
x *cantiana* 'Kentish Pink'   GBuc MHer SPla WDyG WMoo
                              WPer
caucasica   WCru
chamaedrys   ECho NMir XPep
§ - 'Miffy Brute' (v)   EBee NBir NHol NPro
- 'Pam' (v)   CBow ECtt EMan EPPr LSou
                              WCHb
- 'Variegata'   see *V. chamaedrys* 'Miffy Brute'
cinerea ♀H4   CLyd MLHP SBch WEas WHoo
                              WSHC
dabneyi   CDes EBee WPGP WSPU
'Dark Martje' **new**   WCot
'Darwin's Blue'PBR   CMHG EChP GAbr MBNS MBri
                              MSph NLar NMoo NOrc SPoG
                              SPur WCot WHrl
'Ellen Mae'   ECtt WCAu
'Eveline'PBR   EBee ECtt EPfP ERou LSou MAvo
                              MBNS MBnl MSph NLar SUsu
                              WCot
exaltata   EBee EChP GBuc MSte NBur NChi
                              NDov WCot WPer
'Fantasy'   NDov
filiformis   GWCH
- 'Fairyland' (v)   EMan EWes WCHb
formosa   see *Parahebe formosa*
§ *fruticans*   ECho NMen
fruticulosa   NEgg NWCA
- HZ 2000-036   EHyt
gentianoides ♀H4   More than 30 suppliers
- 'Alba'   CMea GCal LAst NBid NBre NChi
                              NGby NSti
- 'Barbara Sherwood'   EBee EBrs GMac MLLN NBre
                              WCot
- 'Blue Streak'   GSki NDlv WRHF
- 'Lilacina'   EBee
- 'Nana'   CAby CEnt EBee EPfP
- 'Pallida'   EBee EMan EPfP GAbr IHMH LRHS
                              MBrN MRav MSph NMoo NPri
                              SPlb WBor WFar
- 'Robusta'   CHrt EBee ECGP EHrv GMac GSki
                              LRHS MSph NCGa NCob SPet
                              WMnd

- 'Tissington White'	CHar EBee EBla EGle EMar EWTr GMaP GMac LAst LHop LPhx LRHS MLLN MTis NBir NCob NPri SBla SHar SPoG SWat WAbb WCAu WFar WGHP WLin WWeb
- 'Variegata' (v)	More than 30 suppliers
gigantea	EDAr MGol
'Goodness Grows'	EBee
grandis	CDMG CEnt EBee EChP EPPr EWsh GAbr MAvo MDKP MGol MTis MWhi NBur NChi NLar SHGN SWal WBrk WHoo WHrl WMoo WWye
x *guthrieana*	CAbP CNic ELan MBNS NMen SRms SRot WFar WPer
'Heraud'	WCAu
incana	see *V. spicata* subsp. *incana*
* - 'Candidissima'	GCal
'Inspiration'	EBee MLLN NBre NDov
kellereri	see *V. spicata*
kiusiana	CMHG EBee EKen MTis NBPC NLar WHrl
* - var. *maxima*	CSec MGol SGar
liwanensis	ECho NMen XPep
- Mac&W 5936	EPot MDKP
longifolia	CHar CMea CSBt EBrs ECha ELan EPfP EShb EWTr GSki GWCH MLHP MWgw NEgg NSti NVic SHGN WBVN WEas WFar WGHP WMoo WWye
- 'Alba'	CHea EChP ELan EPfP NLar STes WCAu WMoo
§ - 'Blaubündel'	CMdw EBee ERou NDlv NGdn
- 'Blauer Sommer'	EAEE EBee EChP MWgw NFla NGdn SPer SPur
§ - 'Blauriesin'	CMMP COlW CTri ECGP EMil ERou GMaP MBnl MBri NBre NSti SMHy SPer SSvw WFar
- Blue Giantess	see *V. longifolia* 'Blauriesin'
- 'Blue John'	EBee NBre WCAu
- 'Fascination'	NGdn NPro SMrm WSan
- 'Foerster's Blue'	see *V. longifolia* 'Blauriesin'
- 'Joseph's Coat' (v)	CBow EBee EGle NBre
- 'Lila Karina'	WPer
- 'Lilac Fantasy'	CMMP EBee NSti WCAu
- 'Oxford Blue'	EBee WHoo WRHF
- 'Rose Tone'	ECha ERou GSki MFOX MGol NEgg NLar WHal WHrl WMoo
- 'Rosea'	EChP ERou MGol WBrE WPer
- 'Schneeriesin'	CHar CPrp EAEE EBee ECha EHrv GMaP LRHS MBnl MBri NBir NLar SPer SPur
lyallii	see *Parahebe lyallii*
montana 'Corinne Tremaine' (v)	CBow EBee EMan EMar EWin IFro IHMH LSou MHar NBir NCGa NLar SRms WCot WHer WWye
- golden variegated	EWin
nipponica	WPer
nummularia	NBur WPer
oenei	CPBP WLin
officinalis	CArn WHbs
oltensis	CLyd CPBP ECho EHyt EPot EWes LTwo MHer NHol NMen WLin WPat
orchidea	EBee SRms
orientalis subsp. *orientalis*	EPot NMen
ornata	EBee EMan MGol WCot WPer
'Pacific Ocean'	CBgR EBee
pectinata	ECtt
- 'Rosea'	ECho ECtt EWes NJOw WPer XPep
peduncularis	LRHS WEas
- 'Alba'	WPer
§ - 'Georgia Blue'	More than 30 suppliers
- 'Oxford Blue'	see *V. peduncularis* 'Georgia Blue'

perfoliata	see *Parahebe perfoliata*
petraea 'Madame Mercier'	EWin SRot
'Pink Damask'	CFwr CHar CSpe CWCL EAEE EBee EChP ECtt ELan ERou GMaP LRHS MBri MWat NCob NDov NLar NSti SMrm SUsu WEas WFar WHoo WMnd WTin WWlt
pinnata 'Blue Eyes'	LBee LHop
- 'Blue Feathers' **new**	CBrm SSvw
ponae **new**	WLin
porphyriana **new**	EPPr
prenja	see *V. austriaca*
'Prince of Wales Feathers'	NCGa
§ *prostrata* ♀H4	CEnt CLyd CMea CSam CTri ECho ECtt EPfP GKev IHMH LAst LBee LRHS MLHP NHol NJOw SHFr SIng SMHy SRms WAbe WEas WFar WHoo WLin WMoo
- 'Alba'	MLHP MWat WHoo WLin
- 'Aztec Gold' PBR	EBee NBro NLar NPro WCot
§ - 'Blauspiegel'	CPBP SBla
- Blue Mirror	see *V. prostrata* 'Blauspiegel'
- 'Blue Sheen'	CBrm ECho ECtt EHyt GEdr MBNS NBir SIng WAbe WMoo WPer
- 'Lilac Time'	EAEE NBir NLar SIng SRms
- 'Loddon Blue'	ECho LRHS NVic SBla SRms WCot WPer
- 'Miss Willmott'	see *V. prostrata* 'Warley Blue'
- 'Mrs Holt'	CLyd CPBP CSam EAEE ECho ECtt EHyt GEdr LRHS NBir NFor NHol NMen SBla SIng SRGP SRms WBrk WCru WFar
- 'Nana'	ECho ECtt EPot EWes MWat NMen WAbe
- 'Nestor'	NDlv WMoo WOut
- 'Rosea'	ECho MWat WLin WPer
- 'Spode Blue' ♀H4	CHar CMea COfd COlW ECho ECtt GAbr GKev LAst LHop LRHS NWCA SBla SIng SPoG SRms SSvw WBVN WFar WLin WMoo
- 'Trehane'	CEnt COlW EBee ECho ECtt EDAr LAst LBee LHop LRHS MHer MWat NOak NRya SIng SPlb SPoG SRms SRot SWat WBVN WFar WMoo
§ - 'Warley Blue'	ECho
* *pseudolysimachion*	WCot WMoo
'Purpleicious' **new**	EBee MBnl SPoG
repens	ECho IHMH NBlu NHol NJOw NNor SPlb SSvw WGwG WPer
'Rosalinde'	GBuc WPer
'Royal Pink'	CMMP EChP LAst NCGa NLar WWye
rupestris	see *V. prostrata*
saturejoides	CPBP SRms WPer
saxatilis	see *V. fruticans*
schmidtiana	GSki WPer
- 'Nana'	CPBP EWTr GKev
selleri	see *V. wormskjoldii*
§ 'Shirley Blue' ♀H4	CPrp CWib EBee EGra ELan EPfP IHMH MBNS MHer MWat NCGa SMer SPoG SRGP SRms WCFE WGHP WHen WPer WTel WWhi
§ *spicata*	CEnt ELan EPfP LEdu LRHS MBNS MDun MWgw NBid NBlu NFor SECG SPet SRms WBrk WCAu WFar WMoo WPer WWye
- 'Alba'	EBee EMil MBNS MRav MWat NLar SMar WPer WTin
- 'Barcarolle'	ELan EPfP MLLN NBro NGby
§ - 'Blaufuchs'	CSam ECtt WTel
- 'Blue Bouquet'	IBal NBre NLar WWeb
- 'Blue Candles' **new**	CFwr
- Blue Fox	see *V. spicata* 'Blaufuchs'
§ - 'Erika'	ECha ECtt EPfP GBuc IHMH IPot MAvo MLLN NBir NBre NOak SAga SMar

§ - 'Glory'^PBR — CFwr EBee ELan ENot EPfP GAbr GBri GMac LSou MWgw NBPC NBre NCGa NMoo SPer SPoG WBrE WCFE WCot WGwG

- 'Heidekind' — More than 30 suppliers
- 'High Five' **new** — EBee IBal MBnl NBhm SPoG
- subsp. *hybrida* — WCot WHer
§ - 'Icicle' — CMMP EBee MBrN MSte NBre NBro SUsu
§ - subsp. *incana* — CMea EBee ECho EHoe EHyt ELan EPfP ERou EShb GEdr GSki IFro NFor SBla SPlb SRms SWat WCFE WFar WMoo WPer WTin WWeb XPep
- - 'Nana' — ECha MLHP NBir SRms
- - 'Saraband' — WPer
- - 'Silbersee' — CBrm CMdw MLHP WLin
- - 'Silver Carpet' — EBee EMan LAst LBBr LBMP LRHS LSou MNFA MRav MWgw NBre NFla NSti SPer SPla WMnd
- - 'Wendy' — GCal
- 'Nana Blauteppich' — MWhi NBre NLar NVic WWeb
- 'Noah Williams' (v) — EBee EChP EGle EMan GBuc MBNS MFOX NPro
- 'Pink Goblin' — NBre WPer
- 'Pink Panther' **new** — ERou MBnl NBhm
- Red Fox — see *V. spicata* 'Rotfuchs'
- 'Romiley Purple' — EBee ERou MLLN MSte NBre SPer WCMO WFar
- 'Rosalind' — NLar
- *rosea* — see *V. spicata* 'Erika'
- 'Rosenrot' — ECho MHar
§ - 'Rotfuchs' — CFwr CPrp EBee ECtt EHoe ELan ENot ERou EWsh IHMH MRav MWgw NBPC NBir NBro NEgg NMoo NOrc NPri NSti SRms WBVN WCMO WCot WFar WPer WSHC WTel
- 'Royal Candles'^PBR — see *V. spicata* 'Glory'
- 'Sightseeing' — CWib ERou MGol MMHG NBir NBre SPet SRms SWal
- 'Twilight' **new** — MBnl
- *variegata* (v) — MLLN NBir
§ *spuria* L. — NBur WPer
stelleri — see *V. wormskjoldii*
subsessilis — WPer
- 'Blaue Pyramide' — EBee NBre NMyG WPtf
* - *hendersonii* — NBre NGby
'Sunny Border Blue' — EBee EMan EMar EPfP GBuc GMac MBNS MSph NBre NDov NLar SUsu WCot WFar
telephiifolia — ECho ECtt EMan EWes MDKP NJOw NMen NWCA WAbe
teucrium — see *V. austriaca* subsp. *teucrium*
thessalica — ECho
thymoides subsp. *pseudocinerea* — NWCA
virginica — see *Veronicastrum virginicum*
'Waterperry Blue' — LRHS WFar WPer
wherryi — WPer
'White Icicle' — see *V. spicata* 'Icicle'
'White Jolanda' — CBgR EBee EChP EPfP ERou MBnl MSph NLar NPro NSti WWye
whitleyi — CNic MMuc
§ *wormskjoldii* — EBee ECho EDAr IHMH LAst MBrN NCGa NEgg NJOw NLar NMen NWCA SBla SRms WLin WPer
- 'Alba' — MDKP MLHP WPer

Veronicastrum (Scrophulariaceae)

brunonianum — GCal
japonicum — CSec MWgw SGar
latifolium — WSHC
- BWJ 8158 — WCru
sibiricum — EBee ECha EMar EShb GCal LEdu NBid NBre SBla SMar WCot WMoo

---

- BWJ 6352 — WCru
- var. *yezoense* — EBee GIBF WBVN
- - AER 0290 — MGol
- - RBS 0290 — NPro
villosulum — CMdw CPlN CSpe EBee NBid NBro NLar WCot WCru WSHC
§ *virginicum* — CArn CHea CKno EBee EChP ECha ECtt EHrv EPyc LBMP MGol MLHP NBir SRms WGwG WMoo WPer WWhi WWlt
- 'Alboroseum' — WTin
- 'Album' — More than 30 suppliers
- 'Apollo' — CBre EBee EChP ECtt EGle EMan EPfP ERou GAbr GMac LAst LHop LPhx MBri MLLN MWgw NBro NCGa NLar NOrc NSti WAul WCAu WHoo WHrl WTMC
- 'Diane' — CElw EBee EGle NBre NDov
- 'Erica' **new** — EBee GQue MBNS MBnl NChi NDov NMoo NSti
- 'Fascination' — More than 30 suppliers
- 'Lavendelturm' — CAby EBee EBrs ECha EGle EMil ERou IPot LHop LPhx MLLN NCGa NDov NMRc NSti SPer WAul WCot WTMC
- 'Pointed Finger' — LEdu NBre SMrm SUsu WWlt
- f. *roseum* — CKno CMea EBee ECha ELan GMaP LPhx MRav MWgw NBro NDov SMHy SPoG STes WFar WHoo WKif WMoo WSHC
- - 'Pink Glow' — CHar COlW EBee EBrs ECtt EHoe ELan EMan EMil EPfP GAbr LHop LPhx MBnl MTis MWat NBPC NCGa NGdn NSti SAga SMrm SPer SPla STes WCAu WFar WMnd
- 'Spring Dew' — CBre EBee EChP EGle EMan ERou LPhx MLLN MWgw NBid NBro NDov NLar WMnd
- 'Temptation' — EBee EChP EGle EMan ERou LPhx MLLN NBre NBro NLar SMHy SUsu WCAu
'White Jolan' — CFir

Verschaffeltia (Arecaceae)
splendida — XBlo

Verticordia (Myrtaceae)
chrysantha — SOWG
longistylis — SOWG
minutiflora — SOWG
plumosa purple — SOWG

Vestia (Solanaceae)
§ *foetida* ♀^H1 — CBcs CPom CSec CSpe CWib EChP ELan EMan EPfP EShb MNrw NLar SBig SBrw SDnm SGar SHFr SOWG WHil WKif WPGP WPer WPic WSHC WWye
lycioides — see *V. foetida*

Vetiveria (Poaceae)
zizanioides — MSal

Viburnum ✿ (Caprifoliaceae)
acerifolium — CPle GIBF MAsh WFar WHCG WPat
alnifolium — see *V. lantanoides*
atrocyaneum — CPle EBee MAsh NLar WFar WHCG WPGP WPat
- B&SWJ 7272 — WCru
awabuki — CHEx EPfP MBlu NLar WPGP
- B&SWJ 6913 — WCru
- B&SWJ 8404 — WCru
§ - 'Emerald Lustre' — CDoC CHEx

betulifolium	CAbP CBcs CMCN CPLG CPMA CTrw EPfP EPla GIBF NLar SBrw SLon SMad WHCG WPat
- B&SWJ 1619	WCru
- B&SWJ 3200	WCru
bitchiuense	CPMA CPle ELan
x ***bodnantense***	CMac CTri CTrw CWSG MDun MRav NFor NPen SAga WHar WTel
- 'Charles Lamont' ♀H4	More than 30 suppliers
- 'Dawn' ♀H4	More than 30 suppliers
- 'Deben' ♀H4	CDoC CMac ENot EPfP LRHS MRav MWya NLar SPer WCru WDin WFar
bracteatum	EPfP NLar
buddlejifolium	CMac EPfP EWes SPoG WCru WFar WHCG WPGP
burejaeticum	GIBF
x ***burkwoodii***	More than 30 suppliers
- 'Anika' **new**	NLar
- 'Anne Russell' ♀H4	CAbP CBcs CMac CPMA CTri EBee ECrN ELan ENot EPfP EWes IArd LRHS MAsh MGos MRav MSwo NHol NSti SHBN SLon SPer SPla SPlb SSta SWvt WBrE WDin WFar
- 'Chenaultii'	EPfP WCru WDin
- 'Compact Beauty'	CPMA EPfP WPat
- 'Conoy'	CPMA
- 'Fulbrook' ♀H4	CAbP CMHG EPfP LRHS MAsh MGos WDin WFar
- 'Mohawk'	CAbP CDoC CEnd CPMA ELan EPfP LRHS MAsh MBri NLar SCoo SMur SPla SPoG SWvt WFar WPGP WPat
- 'Park Farm Hybrid' ♀H4	CAbP CDoC CMac CPLG CPMA CPSs CSam CTri CWSG EBee ECrN ELan ENot EPfP LAst LRHS MAsh MRav MSwo NBea NSti SLPl SPer SRms WPat
x ***carlcephalum*** ♀H4	More than 30 suppliers
- 'Cayuga'	MAsh NLar WPat
* - 'Variegatum' (v)	CPMA
carlesii	CBcs CMac CWib ENot EPfP GIBF LAst LRHS MBlu MGan MRav MSwo NPri SBLw SCoo SLim SMer SPer SReu WTel
- B&SWJ 8838	WCru
- 'Aurora' ♀H4	More than 30 suppliers
- 'Charis'	CMac CPLG CPMA CSBt LRHS NLar
- 'Compactum'	CPMA
- 'Diana'	CEnd CMHG CMac CPMA EPfP LRHS MAsh MWya NLar SPer WCFE WPGP WPat
- 'Marlou'	CPMA NLar WPat
cassinoides	EPfP GBin WFar WPat
'Chesapeake'	CDoC CPMA EWes LRHS NLar SEND WDin
chingii	CPMA GGGa SLon WCru WPGP
'Chippewa'	NLar
cinnamomifolium ♀H3	CAbP CBcs CHEx CMac CPLG EBee ECre EPfP LRHS MAsh SAPC SArc SLon SPer SPoG SSpi WFar WHCG WPGP WSHC
cotinifolium CC 4541	MGol
cylindricum	CMCN CPle EPfP GIBF SSpi WCru WPGP
- B&SWJ 6479 from Thailand	WCru
- B&SWJ 7239	WCru
- B&SWJ 9719	WCru
- BWJ 7778 from China **new**	WCru
- HWJCM 434 from Nepal	WCru
dasyanthum	EPfP GIBF IArd NLar
davidii ♀H4	More than 30 suppliers
- (f)	CBcs CDoC CSBt ELan EPfP MAsh MDun MGos SHBN SPer SPla SPoG SReu SRms SSta WPat

- (m)	CBcs CDoC CSBt CWSG ELan EPfP MDun MGos MRav SPer SPla SPoG SReu SRms SSta
dentatum	CPLG EPfP
- var. ***deamii***	GIBF
- 'Moon Glo'	NLar
dilatatum	CPne GIBF SPoG
- B&SWJ 4456	WCru
- 'Erie'	EBee EPfP NLar
- 'Iroquois'	EPfP
- 'Michael Dodge' **new**	NLar
erosum B&SWJ 3585	WCru
erubescens	CAbP CPMA WFar
- B&SWJ 8281	WCru
- var. ***gracilipes***	CPMA EPfP
'Eskimo'	CAbP CBcs CMac CWSG ECrN EPfP LAst LRHS LSRN MAsh MBNS MBlu MGos MRav NBlu NMoo SLim SMur SPoG SReu SWvt WDin WFar WHCG WWes
§ ***farreri*** ♀H4	More than 30 suppliers
- 'Album'	see *V. farreri* 'Candidissimum'
§ - 'Candidissimum'	CDul CMac EBee ELan EPfP IArd LHop LRHS MAsh MMHG NLar SPer SPoG SSpi WPat
- 'December Dwarf'	NLar
- 'Farrer's Pink'	CAbP CPMA NHol NLar
- 'Fioretta'	NLar
- 'Nanum'	CMac CPMA EPfP LRHS MAsh MBar MBrN MRav MWat NHol NLar WFar WHCG WPat
foetens	see *V. grandiflorum* f. *foetens*
foetidum var. ***rectangulatum*** B&SWJ 3637	WCru
fragrans Bunge	see *V. farreri*
'Fragrant Cloud'	ECrN ENot
furcatum ♀H4	CPLG EPfP IArd IDee NLar SBrw SSpi WHCG
- B&SWJ 5939	WCru
x ***globosum*** 'Jermyns Globe'	CAbP CDoC CEnd CMHG EBee MBar MGos MSte MTis SLon SMur SPoG WCru WDin WFar WHCG WPGP
grandiflorum	CPMA CSBt EPfP NLar WDin
- HWJK 2163	WCru
§ - f. ***foetens***	EPfP
harryanum	CMHG CPle EBee EPfP LRHS MBNS SOWG WCru WFar
henryi	CAbP CPMA ECrN EPfP NLar WDin WHCG WPat
x ***hillieri***	GBin MWhi WFar WHCG WKif
- 'Winton' ♀H4	CAbP CDoC CEnd CPMA EBee EPfP EPla LHop LRHS LSRN MBri MGos MTis NPal SBrw SHBN SLim SLon SOWG SPoG SSpi WCru WDin WFar WPGP
'Huron'	NEgg
ichangense	NLar
japonicum	CHEx CMac CPLG CPle EPfP NLar SBrw SHBN SLon
- B&SWJ 5968	WCru
x ***juddii*** ♀H4	More than 30 suppliers
koreanum B&SWJ 4231	WCru
lantana	CBgR CCVT CDul CLnd CRWN CTri ECrN GWCH LBuc MBow NWea SPer SPoG WDin WFar WMou
- 'Aureum'	EBee ECtt EHoe MAsh MBlu NLar
- 'Mohican'	NLar
- 'Variefolium' (v)	CPMA
§ ***lantanoides***	EPfP NLar SSpi
lentago	CAbP CPle NLar
lobophyllum	EPfP NLar
luzonicum B&SWJ 3930	WCru

*	- var. *floribundum*	WCru
	B&SWJ 8281	
	- var. *oblongum*	WCru
	B&SWJ 3549	
	macrocephalum	CPMA SLon WDin
	- f. *keteleeri*	CEnd CPMA
	mariesii	see *V.plicatum* f. *tomentosum* 'Mariesii'
	mongolicum	NLar
	nervosum B&SWJ 2251a	WCru
	nudum	EBee EPfP GIBF NLar
	- var. *angustifolium*	GIBF
	- 'Pink Beauty'	CPMA CWSG LRHS NLar WFar WPGP
	- 'Winterthur'	NLar
	odoratissimum	CBcs CHEx CPLG CSam EMil
	misapplied	EPfP EWTr IArd MWea SBrw SHBN SMad SMur SSpi WSHC XPep
	- B&SWJ 6913	WCru
	- RWJ 10046	WCru
	- 'Emerald Lustre'	see *V.awabuki* 'Emerald Lustre'
	'Oneida'	NLar WDin
	opulus	More than 30 suppliers
§	- var. *americanum*	GIBF NLar
	- 'Apricot'	NLar
	- 'Aureum'	CDul CHar CMHG CMac CSam CTri CWib EBee ECtt EHoe ELan EPfP LRHS MAsh MBar MGos MRav NEgg NHol NMyG SHBN SPer SPoG SSta WDin WFar WHCG WMoo WPat
	- 'Compactum' ♀H4	More than 30 suppliers
*	- 'Harvest Gold'	SCoo SLim
	- 'Nanum'	CAbP CBcs CPle EBee ELan EPfP EPla EShb MBar MRav NHol NLar NMen NPro WDin WHCG WPat
	- 'Notcutt's Variety' ♀H4	EBee ENot EPfP MBlu MGos NLar SHBN SMur SRms WPat
	- 'Park Harvest'	LRHS MAsh NLar NSti SLPl WPat
§	- 'Roseum' ♀H4	More than 30 suppliers
	- 'Sterile'	see *V.opulus* 'Roseum'
*	- 'Sterile Compactum'	IMGH SWvt
N	- 'Xanthocarpum' ♀H4	More than 30 suppliers
	parvifolium	NLar
N	*plicatum*	CTri CWib IArd MBar WDin
	- 'Janny'	MBlu
	- 'Mary Milton'	NLar
	- 'Nanum'	see *V.plicatum* f. *tomentosum* 'Nanum Semperflorens'
	- 'Pink Sensation' **new**	CPMA
	- 'Popcorn'	CAbP LRHS MAsh SLon SPoG SReu SSta WHCG WPat
	- 'Rosace'	MBlu MBri
	- 'Roseum'	CPle
	- f. *tomentosum*	EWTr WDin
	- - 'Cascade'	NEgg NLar SHBN
	- - 'Dart's Red Robin'	ECtt MAsh NHol NLar WPat
	- - 'Grandiflorum'	CAbP CDoC CPle EPfP LRHS MBar MBri SPer WHCG WMoo
	- - 'Lanarth'	CBcs CDoC CDul CMac CSBt CSam CWSG CWib EBee ECrN ECtt EMil EPfP LHop LRHS MBlu MGos MRav MWhi NHol NSti SPer SPla SPoG SWal SWvt WDin WFar WHCG
§	- - 'Mariesii' ♀H4	More than 30 suppliers
	- - 'Molly Schroeder'	MBri NLar
§	- - 'Nanum Semperflorens'	CBcs CDoC CMac CWSG ECtt EGra IArd MBlu MDun MGos NBlu NHol SHBN SPer SPoG WFar WHCG WPat
	- - 'Pink Beauty' ♀H4	More than 30 suppliers
	- - 'Rotundifolium'	NHol NLar SHBN WPat
	- - 'Rowallane'	EPfP WPat
	- - 'Saint Keverne'	SHBN
	- - 'Shasta'	CMCN EPfP MBri NHol NLar WDin
	- - 'Summer Snowflake'	CDoC CEnd CWSG EBee ECrN ENot EPfP LRHS MRav NEgg NHol SHBN SPer SPoG WDin WFar WHCG
	- 'Watanabe'	see *V.plicatum* f. *tomentosum* 'Nanum Semperflorens'
	'Pragense' ♀H4	CAbP CBcs CDul CMCN EBee EPfP MBar MGos MRav NBlu NHol NRib SEND SLon SPer WDin WFar WHCG WPat
	propinquum	CAbP NLar WFar
	- B&SWJ 4009	WCru
	prunifolium	NLar
	punctatum B&SWJ 9532	WCru
	x *rhytidophylloides*	WFar
	- 'Alleghany'	EBee NLar
	- Dart's Duke = 'Interduke'	LRHS SLPl
	- 'Willowwood'	EBee LRHS MAsh NLar SMad SPoG WPat
	rhytidophyllum	CBcs CDul CHEx CMac CSBt EBee ECrN ENot EPfP ISea LPan MBar MDun MGos MRav NBlu NEgg SBLw SCoo SHBN SMer SPer SReu SRms WCFE WDin WFar WMoo WTel
	- 'Roseum'	CPLG MRav SLPl SWvt
	- 'Variegatum' (v)	CPMA NLar
	rufidulum	NLar
	sargentii	EPfP GBin GIBF
	- f. *flavum*	NLar
	- 'Onondaga' ♀H4	More than 30 suppliers
	- 'Susquehanna'	EPfP
	semperflorens	see *V.plicatum* f. *tomentosum* 'Nanum Semperflorens'
§	*setigerum*	EPfP IArd IDee NLar SBrw SLPl
	- 'Aurantiacum'	EPfP
	sieboldii	GIBF
	- B&SWJ 2837	WCru
	- 'Seneca'	CPLG EPfP NLar
	subalpinum	NLar
	taiwanianum	WCru
	B&SWJ 3009	
	theiferum	see *V.setigerum*
	tinus	More than 30 suppliers
	- 'Bewley's Variegated' (v)	CBcs CDoC ECrN ENot MGos MRav SPer
I	- 'Compactum'	NLar SWvt
	- 'Eve Price' ♀H4	More than 30 suppliers
	- 'French White' ♀H4	CDoC CDul CMac CWSG ECrN EPfP EPla LRHS MAsh MGos MRav MSwo SCoo SLim SPoG STop SWvt WFar
	- 'Gwenllian' ♀H4	More than 30 suppliers
	- 'Israel'	SPer SPla WFar
	- 'Little Bognor'	NLar
	- 'Lucidum'	CBcs CPMA CSam SHBN SHGC WDin WFar
	- 'Lucidum Variegatum' (v)	CMac CPMA EHol SLim
*	- 'Macrophyllum'	EWTr SPoG SWvt WFar WWeb XPep
	- 'Pink Prelude'	EBee MWya
	- 'Purpureum'	CDul CSBt EBee ECrN EHoe EPfP EPla LRHS MAsh MGos MRav MSwo NBlu NEgg SCoo SHBN SLPl SLim SPer SPoG WDin WFar WGwG WMoo WPat WWeb
	- Spirit = 'Anvi'PBR	MBri MGos NLar SPoG WRHF
	- 'Spring Bouquet'	MGos MWya NLar
	- 'Variegatum' (v)	More than 30 suppliers
	- 'Villa Noailles'	XPep
	tomentosum	see *V.plicatum*
	trilobum	see *V.opulus* var. *americanum*
	- 'Bailey's Compact'	MAsh WPat
	- 'Phillips'	CAgr

- 'Wentworth' — CAgr
urceolatum B&SWJ 6988 — WCru
utile — EPfP WFar WHCG WWes
wrightii — EPfP NLar WHCG WPat
- B&SWJ 8780 — WCru
- 'Hessei' — EPfP
- var. *stipellatum* — WCru
  B&SWJ 5844

Vicia (Papilionaceae)
cracca — GWCH MBow NLan NMir NSco WOut WSFF
sepium — NSco
sylvatica — CBgR CPom EDsa EWes
unijuga **new** — CPom

Vigna (Papilionaceae)
adenantha — CPlN
§ *caracalla* — CPlN MJnS

Viguiera (Asteraceae)
multiflora — WCot

Villarsia (Menyanthaceae)
bennettii — see *Nymphoides peltata* 'Bennettii'

Vinca (Apocynaceae)
difformis ♀H3-4 — CBgR CHad CHar COIW CTri CWan EBee ECha EMan LLWP LRHS MGos NCGa SBri SDix WHer WPic WWye
* - 'Alba' — CPom SBch
- subsp. *difformis* — EMon
- Greystone form — EPPr EPfP EPla LHop MBNS NLar SEND WCAu WGwG WPnP WRHF
- 'Jenny Pym' — CBgR CFwr CPom EBee EPPr EWes LRHS MSte SBch SMad SPoG WFar WWeb
- 'Oxford' — SLPl WBrE
- 'Ruby Baker' — NChi WHrl WSPU
- 'Snowmound' — CBgR CWan EBee LRHS MRav SPoG
'Hidcote Purple' — see *V.major* var. *oxyloba*
major — CAgr CBcs CDul CSBt CWib EBee ELan ENot EPfP GPoy LBuc LRHS MGan MGos MHer MSwo NCGa NPri NWea SHBN SPer SPoG SRms WDin WFar WGwG WMoo XPep
- 'Alba' — CPLG GBuc WEas
- 'Caucasian Blue' — WPGP
- 'Elegantissima' — see *V.major* 'Variegata'
§ - subsp. *hirsuta* (Boiss.) Stearn — EMon MWgw WWye
- var. *hirsuta* misapplied — see *V.major* var. *oxyloba*
- 'Honeydew' (v) — EMon
- 'Jason Hill' — EMon
§ - 'Maculata' (v) — CBgR CDoC COIW CSBt EBee EMon LRHS MBar MLHP MSwo MWat NBPC NEgg NHol SLim SPer SPoG WDin WMoo WWeb
§ - var. *oxyloba* — CBgR CFis CNic COld CPLG CTri EBee ECtt ELan EMon EPla GSki LHop MRav MWgw SLPl SLim SMac SRms WFar WHen WHer WPic WSel
- var. *pubescens* — see *V.major* subsp. *hirsuta* (Boiss.) Stearn
- 'Reticulata' (v) — ELan EMon
- 'Surrey Marble' — see *V.major* 'Maculata'
§ - 'Variegata' (v) ♀H4 — More than 30 suppliers
- Westwood form **new** — CFee
- 'Wojo's Jem' (v) **new** — ENot EWes LBuc LRHS MGos SPoG
minor — CAgr CBgR CDoC CDul COfd ELan ENot EPfP GAbr GPoy MAsh MBar MHer MNHC NBlu NPri NWea

SHFr SPoG WBrE WDin WFar WWye XPep
- f. *alba* ♀H4 — CBcs CDoC EBee ECha EGoo ENot EPfP GBar LRHS MAsh MBar MGos MHer MWgw NBlu NPri SHBN SMac SPer STre WCot WFar WWye
- 'Alba Aureovariegata' — see *V.minor* 'Alba Variegata'
- f. *alba* 'Gertrude Jekyll' ♀H4 — More than 30 suppliers
§ - 'Alba Variegata' (v) — CBgR CPLG EHoe EPla GAbr GGar MBar MGos MHer NChi NGHP NHol NPri NPro SPer SRms STre WEas WFar WTel
§ - 'Argenteovariegata' (v) ♀H4 — More than 30 suppliers
§ - 'Atropurpurea' ♀H4 — More than 30 suppliers
- 'Aurea' — LBBr SPla WFar
§ - 'Aureovariegata' (v) — CBcs CPLG EBee GAbr IHMM LRHS MBar MGos MRav NBlu NCGa NFor NHol NPri SPlb WFar WHen WTel WWye
§ - 'Azurea Flore Pleno' (d) ♀H4 — More than 30 suppliers
* - 'Blue and Gold' — EGoo EMon
- 'Blue Cloud' — NHol
- 'Blue Drift' — EWes MBNS MSwo NHol
- 'Blue Moon' — ECtt NHol SPer SPla
- 'Bowles' Blue' — see *V.minor* 'La Grave'
- 'Bowles' Variety' — see *V.minor* 'La Grave'
- 'Burgundy' — CFee SRms WWye
- 'Caerulea Plena' — see *V.minor* 'Azurea Flore Pleno'
- 'Dartington Star' — see *V.major* var. *oxyloba*
- 'Double Burgundy' — see *V.minor* 'Multiplex'
- Green Carpet — see *V.minor* 'Grüner Teppich'
§ - 'Grüner Teppich' — EMon WFar
- 'Illumination' (v) — More than 30 suppliers
§ - 'La Grave' ♀H4 — More than 30 suppliers
- 'Maculata' (v) — ELan
- 'Marie' — LBuc MGos
- 'Marion Cran' — GSki
§ - 'Multiplex' (d) — CBgR EBee ECtt EMan EPPr EPla GBar LBuc MAsh MBar NChi NHol NPri SRms WCFE WHrl WSel
- 'Persian Carpet' (v) — EMon
- 'Purpurea' — see *V.minor* 'Atropurpurea'
- 'Ralph Shugert' — EPPr EWes NLar SPoG
- 'Rubra' — see *V.minor* 'Atropurpurea'
- 'Sabinka' — EGoo EMon EPla
- 'Silver Service' (d/v) — CFee CWan EMan EMon GBuc MRav NHol WCot WHoo
- 'Variegata' — see *V.minor* 'Argenteovariegata'
- 'Variegata Aurea' — see *V.minor* 'Aureovariegata'
- 'White Gold' — EBee NHol NPri NPro
sardoa — EMon EPPr

Vincetoxicum (Asclepiadaceae)
§ *hirundinaria* — EBee EPPr GPoy LEdu WWye
nigrum — MGol NChi WCot WTin
officinale — see *V.hirundinaria*

Viola ✿ (Violaceae)
B&SWJ 8301 from Vietnam — WCru
'Ada Jackson' (ExVa) — WOFF
'Admiral' (Va) — WWhi
'Admiration' (Va) — GMac WBou WOFF
adunca — NWCA
- var. *minor* — see *V.labradorica* ambig.
aetolica — CSec WOut
'Agnes Cochrane' (ExVa) — WOFF
'Alanta' (Va) — WWhi
§ *alba* — EWes NMen WBrE
'Alethia' (Va) — GMac WOFF
'Alex Blackwood' (SP) — WOFF
'Alexander Rayfield' (Va) — WOFF
'Alice' (Vt) — CDev CGro
'Alice Kate' **new** — WBou

'Alice Witter' (Vt)	CBre CDev EBee ECha NChi
'Alice Wood' (ExVa)	WOFF
* 'Alison' (Va)	GMac WBou WOFF WWhi
'Alma' (Va)	WOFF
'Amelia' (Va)	WBou
§ 'Amiral Avellan' (Vt)	CDev CGro
'Ann' (SP)	WOFF
'Annette Hays Wallace' (FP) **new**	WOFF
'Annette Ross' (Va)	WOFF
I 'Annie' (Vt)	CGro
'Annie Roberts' (FP)	WOFF
'Arabella' (Va)	WBou
'Ardross Gem' (Va)	CAby CCge CSam EBee EChP ECho ECtt GAbr GMaP GMac NChi SMeo WBou WEas WFar WPer WWhi
arenaria	see *V. rupestris*
'Arkwright's Ruby' (Va)	SRms
'Ashvale Blue' (PVt)	CGro
'Aspasia' (Va) ♀H4	GMac NCob WBou WOFF WWhi
'Avril' (Va)	NCob
'Avril Lawson' (Va)	SHar WBou WOFF
'Baby Franjo'	NVic
'Baby Lucia' (Va)	NVic SBch SRms
'Barbara' (Va)	WBou WOFF
'Barnsdale Gem'	MBNS
'Baroness de Rothschild' misapplied	see *V.* 'Baronne Alice de Rothschild'
'Baroness de Rothschild' ambig. (Vt)	CGro WHer
§ 'Baronne Alice de Rothschild' (Vt)	CCge CDev
'Beatrice' (Vtta)	WBou
'Becky Groves' (Vt)	CGro
* *bella*	WEas
'Bella' (C)	EBee
§ 'Belmont Blue' (C)	CCge CEnt CSpe EBee ECho ECtt EWes GMaP GMac LHop MHer MRav MWat MWgw NBir NCGa NChi NDov SAga SBla SPer SRkn SRms WBou WFar WSHC WWhi
'Bernard Cox' (FP)	WOFF
§ *bertolonii*	WBou
'Beshlie' (Va) ♀H4	CAby ECtt GMac MBNS WBou WEas WTin
* *betonicifolia albescens*	EBee GKev
- var. *oblongosagittata*	EBee
'Betty' (Va)	WOFF
'Betty Dale' (ExVa)	WOFF
biflora	CMHG MTho NChi
'Bishop's Belle' (FP)	WOFF
'Black Bun' **new**	CElw CKno WPGP
* 'Black Velvet' **new**	MWat
'Blackfaulds Gem' (SP)	WOFF
'Blue Bird' (Va)	GMac
'Blue Butterfly' (C)	GMac WSHC
'Blue Carpet' (Va)	GMac
'Blue Horns' (C)	SUsu
'Blue Moon' (C)	WBou WTin
'Blue Moonlight' (C)	CAby CElw EBee GBuc GMac LRHS NChi
'Boughton Blue'	see *V.* 'Belmont Blue'
'Bournemouth Gem' (Vt)	CBre CDev CGro
§ 'Bowles' Black' (T)	CArn CSWP CSpe EBee ECho EPfP EWTr LEdu LRHS MHer MWat NBro NGHP NVic SBla SPla SRGP SRms WBou WEas WGwG WHlf
'Boy Blue' (Vtta)	ECho ECtt WOFF
* 'Bryony' (Vtta)	WBou
'Bullion' (Va)	EBee WCot
'Burncoose Yellow'	WBou
'Buttercup' (Vtta)	COfd COlW EBee EWin GMac NCob NEgg SPoG WBou WWhi
'Butterpat' (C)	GMac

'Buxton Blue' (Va)	GBuc WOFF
* 'California' (Vt)	CDev
canadensis	NWCA
'Candy'	CDev
canina	NBro NMir
* - *alba*	CBre
* 'Catforth Gold'	NCob
'Catforth Suzanne'	NCob
'Catherine Williams' (ExVa)	WOFF
'Cat's Whiskers'	CElw EBee
cazorlensis	CGra SBla
chaerophylloides var. *chaerophylloides* **new**	CGro
§ - var. *sieboldiana*	CPMA
'Chandler's Glory' (Va)	WOFF
'Chantal' (Vtta)	WOFF
'Chantreyland' (Va)	NBir
'Charles William Groves' (Vt)	CGro
'Charlotte'	WBou
'Cinders' (Vtta)	GMac
'Citron' (Va)	NCob
'Cleeway Crimson' (FP)	WOFF
'Clementina' (Va) ♀H4	MRav WBou
'Cleo' (Va)	EBee GMac WBou WOFF
'Clive Groves' (Vt)	CBre CGro
'Coeur d'Alsace' (Vt)	CBre CDev CNic EBee NLar WCot WEas WHal WOFF WWhi
'Collette' **new**	WOFF
'Colombine' (Vt)	NSti
'Columbine' (Va)	CDev CElw EBee EChP EPfP GMaP GMac LAst LRHS MBow MHer NBir NEgg NPri SIng SMrm SPer SPoG SSto WBou WCot WEas WFar WKif WWhi
'Comte de Chambord' (dVt)	SHar WFar WRha
'Connigar'	CSam
'Connor Glendinning' (ExVa)	WOFF
§ 'Conte di Brazza'	CDev CGro EShb GMac SHar WHer WOFF WRha
'Cordelia' (Va)	EBee SBla WFar
I 'Cordelia' (Vt) **new**	CGro
'Cornetto'	MBow MHer
cornuta ♀H4	CElw CMea ECho EPot GGar MWat NBir NBro NChi NCob SBch SRms WBou WFar WGHP WHen WHoo WRos WWye
- Alba Group ♀H4	More than 30 suppliers
§ - 'Alba Minor'	ECho EPfP EWes GBuc GMac IGor MBNS MWat NBro NChi SHGN WAbe WFar
- blue	ECho MHer MLHP NCob SHGN WMoo WWhi
- 'Cleopatra' (C)	GMac
- 'Clouded Yellow'	GMac SMeo
- 'Gypsy Moth' (C)	GMac
- 'Icy But Spicy'	EBee EHrv SSvw WBou WCot
- Lilacina Group (C)	ECha MRav MSte NChi SWat WFar WMnd
- 'Maiden's Blush'	EMan GMac NChi
- 'Minor' ♀H4	CAby GMac NBro SBla WBou
- 'Minor Alba'	see *V. cornuta* 'Alba Minor'
- 'Pale Apollo' (C)	GMac
* - 'Paris White'	EBee EPfP
- 'Purple Gem'	GAbr GMac
- Purpurea Group	CBos CMea ECha GBuc NCob WMnd
- 'Spider'	CAby CRez GMac WGwG WWhi
- 'Victoria's Blush' (C)	CAby CBos CCge CSpe EBee ECtt GBuc GMaP GMac MHer MSte NBir NChi NDov SPoG SSvw WBou WWhi

- 'Violacea'	GMac
- 'Yellow King'	EHrv WCot
corsica	CEnt CSpe GIBF NChi SHGN
	WGwG WHil WOFF WOut
	XPep
- subsp. *limbarae* new	WOFF
'Cox's Moseley' (ExVa)	WOFF
'Crepuscle' (Vt)	CGro
§ *cucullata* ♀H4	ECho SRms WFar WPrP
§ - 'Alba' (Vt)	CBro CGro ECho LLWP NBir NChi
	NSti SRms WEas
- *rosea*	EWes
* - 'Striata Alba'	MWgw NBre NBro
I 'Czar'	see V. 'The Czar'
§ 'Czar Bleu' (Vt)	CDev
'Daisy Smith' (Va)	GMac NChi WBou WOFF
'Dancing Geisha' (Vt)	EBee EHrv ENot EPfP GCai MBNS
	WAul WCot
'David Rhodes' (FP)	WOFF
'David Wheldon' (Va)	WOFF
'Davina' (Va)	WOFF
'Dawn' (Vtta)	EBee EWin GMaP LSou NPri SRGP
	WBou WOFF
declinata	EBee
'Delicia' (Vtta)	NChi WBou
'Delmonden' (Va)	SBla
delphinantha	WAbe
'Delphine' (Va)	MSte NChi
'Des Charentes' (Vt) new	CGro
'Desdemona' (Va)	GMac WBou
'Desmonda' (Va)	WOFF
'Devon Cream' (Va)	CAby GMac WBou
'Diana Groves' (Vt)	CGro
diffusa new	EBee
§ *dissecta*	WCot WPer
- var. *chaerophylloides*	see V. *eizanensis*
f. *eizanensis*	
- var. *sieboldiana*	see V. *chaerophylloides* var.
	sieboldiana
'Donau' (Vt)	CBre CDev CGro
'Doreen' (Vt) new	CGro
'Double White' (dVt)	CGro NWCA
douglasii new	CGro
dubyana	GBuc NChi
'Duchesse de Parme'	CDev CGro EShb GBar GMac IFro
(dPVt)	NWCA SHar SRms WOFF
'D'Udine' (dPVt)	CDev CGro WOFF WSPU
'Dusk'	WBou
'E.A. Bowles'	see V. 'Bowles' Black'
'Eastgrove Blue Scented'	GMac NCob WBou WCot WEas
(C)	WPtf WWFP
'Eastgrove Elizabeth Booth'	WEas WSHC
'Eastgrove Ice Blue' (C)	WBou WEas
'Eastgrove Twinkle' (C)	NCob WEas
§ *eizanensis*	CGro MTho
'Elaine Quin'	CEIw NDov NPri SPoG SRGP
	WBou
§ *elatior*	CEnt CNic CSWP EBee EBla EMon
	EPPr EShb GBri GBuc LRHS MNrw
	NChi WCot WLin WPer WPtf
	WSHC WWye
'Elizabeth' (Va)	ECtt NCGa WBou WOFF
'Elizabeth Bailes' (Vt) new	CGro
'Elizabeth Lee'	CGro
'Elizabeth McCallum' (FP)	WOFF
'Elliot Adam' (Va)	WBou
'Elsie Coombs' (Vt)	CDev CGro WPer
'Emma' (Va)	CAby
'Emperor Blue Vein'	LSou
'Emperor Magenta Red'	LSou
'Emperor White'	LSou
erecta	see V. *elatior*
'Eris' (Va)	NChi WBou
'Etain' (Va)	CCge CKno COfd COlW EBee
	ECho ECtt ELan EWes GBuc GMaP
	GMac LAst LPhx MSte NCGa

	NCob NDov NEgg NPri SPoG
	WBou WEas WGwG WOFF WWhi
'Evelyn Jackson' (Va)	WOFF
'Fabiola' (Vtta)	GMac NBir
'Famecheck Apricot'	EFam LSou NChi
* 'Fantasy'	WBou
'Farewell' (ExVa)	WOFF
'Fiona' (Va)	CAby EBee GMaP GMac MSte
	NChi NCob WBou WOFF
'Fiona Lawrenson' (Va)	WOFF
flettii	CSec NChi
'Florence' (Va)	WBou
'Foxbrook Cream' (C)	EMan GBuc GMac WBou WWhi
'Frances Perry'	WWhi
'Francesca' (Va)	WOFF
'Freckles'	see V. *sororia* 'Freckles'
'Frederica' (Vt)	CDev
'Gazania' (Va)	WBou
'George Carter' (FP)	WOFF
'George Hughes' (FP)	WOFF
'Giuletto Fanin' (Vt) new	CGro
glabella	WOFF
'Gladys Findlay' (Va)	GMac WBou WOFF
'Gladys Hughes' (FP)	WOFF
* 'Glenda'	WBou
'Glenholme'	CAby GMac SMeo WGwG
'Gloire de Verdun' (PVt)	CGro NWCA
'Governor Herrick' (Vt)	CCge CDev CGro WPer
§ *gracilis*	NBir WFar
- 'Lutea'	CSam
- 'Major'	WBou
- 'Granddad's Violet' (Vt)	CGro
new	
'Graziella'	CBos
'Green Goddess'PBR	CSpe EBee EWin GKev LAst MBNS
	MWea NCGa NEgg NPri
'Green Jade' (v)	MBNS NBir
'Grey Owl' (Va)	LRHS WBou WCot WEas WKif
	WOFF WPGP
'Grovemount Blue' (C)	CMea
§ *grypoceras* var. *exilis*	CDev CNic EHoe EMan GBri GIBF
	MWgw NGdn
- - 'Sylettas'	CBow CStu GBin LSou MCCP
	MHer MMuc NBPC NJOw NSti
	SAga WPtf
- f. *variegata* (v)	CGro NBir
'Gustav Wermig' (C)	NDov WBou
'H.H. Hodge' (ExVa)	WOFF
'Hansa' (C)	NChi
'Haslemere'	see V. 'Nellie Britton'
* 'Heaselands'	SMHy SUsu
§ *hederacea*	CDev CMHG CStu EBee ECho
	ECou GQui NBro SAga SRms
	WOFF WWye
- blue	CFee SIng WPer
- 'Putty Road' (Vt) new	CGro
'Helen' (Va)	EChP ECtt
§ 'Helen Mount'	ECho MNHC
'Helen W. Cochrane' (ExVa)	WOFF
'Helena' (Va)	WBou
'Hespera' (Va)	WOFF
heterophylla subsp.	see V. *bertolonii*
epirota	
* 'Hetty Gatenby'	WOFF
hirsutula	EBla EHrv EMon
I - 'Alba'	EBla
I - 'Purpurea'	EBla
'Hudsons Blue'	CEIw WEas
'Hugh Campbell' (ExVa)	WOFF
'Huntercombe Purple' (Va)	CBos LHop MWat NBir SBch SBla
♀H4	SRms SUsu WBou WHal WKif
	WOFF
'I.G. Sherwood' (FP)	WOFF
'Iden Gem' (Va)	WBou WOFF
'Inverurie Beauty' (Va)	GMaP GMac NChi NDov WBou
♀H4	WOFF

'Irene Hastings' (ExVa)	WOFF
'Irish Elegance' (Vt)	see V. 'Sulfurea'
'Irish Molly' (Va)	More than 30 suppliers
'Ivory Queen' (Va)	CAby CBos EBee GMac MWgw WBou WOFF
'Jack Frost' (FP)	WOFF
'Jack Sampson' (Vt)	CDev
'Jackanapes' (Va) ♀H4	EBee ECho ECtt ELan EPfP LAst LRHS NEgg NPri SIng SPer SPoG SRms WBou WFar WOFF WWhi
'Jacqueline Snocken' (ExVa)	WOFF
'James Pilling' (Va)	WOFF
'Janet' (Va)	EBee EWin NCGa NPri SPer SRGP WOFF
japonica	GGar
'Jeannie Bellew' (Va)	EBee ECtt IHMH NCob NSti SPer SPoG SRms WBou WFar WKif
'Jennifer Andrews' (Va)	WOFF
'Jersey Gem' (Va)	GMac WOFF
'Jessie' (SP)	WOFF
'Jessie East'	WEas
'Jessie Taylor' (FP)	WOFF
'Jimmy's Dark' (ExVa)	WOFF
'Joanna' (Va)	WBou
'John Powell' (FP)	WOFF
* 'John Raddenbury' (Vt)	CDev SHar
'John Rodger' (SP)	WOFF
'Johnny Jump Up' (T)	see V. 'Helen Mount'
jooi	CPBP EBee ECho EShb GKev MWea NBir NChi NMen SBla SRms WOFF WPat WRha
'Jordieland Gem' (c)	GMac
'Josie' (Va)	WOFF
'Joyce Gray' (Va)	WBou
'Judy Goring' (Va)	GMac
'Julia' (Va)	WBou
'Julian' (Va)	CAby EBee GMac SBla SRms WBou WOFF
'Juno' (Va)	GMac WOFF
'Jupiter' (Va)	EBee WOFF
'Kathleen' (Vt) **new**	CGro
'Kathleen Hoyle' (ExVa)	WOFF
keiskei	NEgg WGwG
- pale pink-flowered	GKev
- white-flowered	EBee GKev
'Kim'	CDev
'Kitten'	GMac MSte NChi NDov WBou
I 'Kitty'	CCge
§ 'Königin Charlotte' (Vt)	CCge CDev CGro GMac MHer MWgw NChi NJOw NVic NWCA SSto WCMO WCot WHil WMoo WOFF
koreana	see V. grypoceras var. exilis
kunawurensis	CSec
'La France' (Vt)	CGro SBla
N *labradorica* misapplied	see V. riviniana Purpurea Group
§ *labradorica* ambig.	CHar ECho EMil EWTr LRHS MRav SHFr SMer WCra WFar
N - *purpurea* misapplied	see V. riviniana Purpurea Group
lactiflora	EBee
'Lady Hume Campbell' (PVt)	CBre CGro EShb NWCA WHer
'Lady Saville'	see V. 'Sissinghurst'
'Lady Tennyson' (Va)	WOFF
'Laura' (C)	GBuc IHMH NCob
'Laura Cawthorne'	EBee NDov
'Lavender Lady' (Vt)	CBre CGro
'Lavinia' (Va)	LRHS WBou
'Lees Peachy Pink' (Vt) **new**	CGro
'Lemon Sorbet'	GBuc
'Lesley Keay' (ExVa)	WOFF
'Letitia' (Va)	EBee NEgg SRms WBou WCot WFar
'Lianne' (Vt)	CDes CDev CGro WPer
'Lilac Rose' (Va)	NDov WBou
'Lindsay'	WBou
'Lise Lazare' (Vt) **new**	CGro
'Little David' (Vtta) ♀H4	CAby CSam CTri GMac SRms WBou WPGP WWhi
'Lord Plunket' (Va)	WBou WOFF
'Lorna' (Va) ♀H4	WOFF
'Lorna Cawthorne' (C)	CAby MSte WBou
'Lorna Moakes' (Va)	SAga
'Louisa' (Va)	GMac
'Louise'	WBou
'Love Duet'	NBir
§ *lutea*	GKev NChi WBou
- subsp. *elegans*	see V. lutea
'Luxonne' (Vt)	CBre CGro
'Lydia Groves' (Vt)	CGro
'Lydia's Legacy' (Vt)	CGro
'Madame Armandine Pagès' (Vt)	CBre
'Maggie Mott' (Va) ♀H4	CElw EBee ECha ECho ECtt GAbr GBuc GMaP LHop LRHS MBri NChi NDov NPri NSti SBch SBla SPer SRGP WBou WFar WOFF WWFP WWhi
'Magic'	CAby EBee GBuc GMaP GMac WBou
'Magnifico'	LRHS
mandshurica	NWCA
- f. *albiflora*	EBee
- 'Fuji Dawn' (v)	CBow EBee EHoe EMan GKev ITer MFOX WCot WPtf
- f. *hasegawae*	EPPr
- 'Ikedaeana' **new**	EBee
'Margaret' (Va)	WBou
'Marie Rose' (Vt) **new**	CGro
'Marie-Louise' (dPVt)	CDes CDev CGro CTri EBee EShb SHar WCMO
'Maroon Picotee'	ECho
I 'Mars'	ENot GBin LHop LSRN LSou MWgw NCGa WCot
'Mars' (Va)	EBee ECtt MCCP NEgg SBch SHGN SPoG
'Martin' (Va) ♀H4	CAby COIW EBee ECha EWin GAbr GMac MHer MRav NDov SPer SRGP SSto WBou WFar WOFF
'Mary Mouse' **new**	WBou
'Mauve Haze' (Va)	GMac MSte WBou WEas
'Mauve Radiance' (Va)	GMac NBre NVic WBou WOFF
'May Mott' (Va)	GMac WBou
'Mayfly' (Va)	MSte WBou
'Melinda' (Vtta)	WBou
'Melting Moments' (Va) **new**	CHVG SIng
'Mercury' (Va)	WBou
'Merry Cheer' (C)	SUsu
'Milkmaid' (Va)	NBir WWhi
'Mina Walker' (ExVa)	WOFF
minor pale purple-flowered	EBee GKev
'Miss Brookes' (Va)	WBou WOFF
'Misty Guy' (Vtta)	NChi NDov WBou
'Molly Sanderson' (Va) ♀H4	More than 30 suppliers
'Moonbeam'	WPtf
'Moonlight' (Va) ♀H4	CAby ECha ECho ELan GMac LHop MHer SBla WBou WWhi
'Moonraker'	NBir
'Morwenna' (Va)	WBou
'Moseley Ideal' (ExVa)	WOFF
'Mother's Day'	CGro
'Mrs C.M. Snocken' (FP)	WOFF
'Mrs Chichester' (Va)	WBou WOFF
'Mrs Cotterell'	EBee GBuc
'Mrs David Lloyd George' (dVt)	CDev CGro
'Mrs G. Robb' (ExVa)	WOFF

'Mrs Lancaster' (Va)	EBee EWin GMaP GMac MBNS NBir NChi NPri SPoG SRGP SRms WBou
'Mrs M.B. Wallace' (ExVa)	WOFF
'Mrs R. Barton' (Vt)	CDev CGro SHar
'Myfawnny' (Va)	CAby CElw EBee ECho ECtt ELan EWes GMac LRHS MWat NChi SPer SPoG SRms WBou WFar
'Neapolitan'	see *V.* 'Pallida Plena'
§ 'Nellie Britton' (Va) ♀[H4]	CAby ECho ECtt GMac SRms WWhi
'Netta Statham'	see *V.* 'Belmont Blue'
'Noni' (Vt)	CGro
'Nora'	WBou
'Norah Church' (Vt)	CDev CGro NBre SBla SHar SSvw
'Norah Leigh' (Va)	EOHP WBou
obliqua	see *V. cucullata*
odorata (Vt)	More than 30 suppliers
- 'Alba' (Vt)	CBre CDev CGro CPom CSWP EBee ECho ELan EWTr GBar GEdr ILis LAst MBow MHer MWgw NCob NPri SRms WCMO WMoo WWhi WWye
- 'Alba Plena' (d Vt)	NChi SBla WHer
- blue double (d) **new**	LHop WCMO
- var. *dumetorum*	see *V. alba*
- 'Katy' **new**	CPom
- 'King of Violets' (dVt)	SHar WCMO WCot
- pink	see *V. odorata* Rosea Group
- 'Red Devil'	WFar
- *rosea*	see *V. odorata* Rosea Group
§ - Rosea Group (Vt)	CAby CDes CEnt CGro CPom EBee GBar GMac MRav SIde WCMO WCot WOFF
'Opéra' (Vt)	CGro
'Orange' (Vt) **new**	CGro
'Orchid Pink' (Vt)	CGro SHar
§ 'Pallida Plena' (dPVt)	CBre CDev CGro
palmata	NPro
'Palmer's White' (Va)	WBou WOFF
palustris	CRWN MBow WHer WSFF WShi
'Pamela Zambra' (Vt)	CDev SHar WPrP
'Pam's Fancy' (ExVa)	WOFF
papilionacea	see *V. sororia*
* 'Paradise Blue' (Vt)	CGro
'Parme de Toulouse' (dPVt)	CBre CDev CGro NLar WOFF
'Pasha' (Va)	GMac
'Pat Creasy' (Va)	GMac WBou WOFF
'Pat Kavanagh' (C)	GMac NChi NDov WBou
'Patience' **new**	WBou
pedata	CBro EBee EPot MWrn SOkd WAbe WHil WPer
- 'Bicolor'	WAbe
pedatifida	CElw EBee MBNS MTho NJOw
'Peggy Brookes' (FP)	WOFF
'Penelope' (SP)	WOFF
pensylvanica	see *V. pubescens* var. *eriocarpa*
'Peppered-palms'	EHrv
'Perle Rose' (Vt)	CDev CGro EShb SBla
'Petra' (Vtta)	GMac
phalacrocarpa **new**	GKev
'Phyl Dove' (Vt)	CGro
'Pickering Blue' (Va)	WBou WOFF
pilosa B&SWJ 7204	WCru
'Primrose Dame' (Va)	WBou
'Primrose Pixie' (Va)	WBou
'Prince Henry' (T)	MNHC
'Prince John' (T)	MNHC
'Princess Mab' (Vtta)	WBou
'Princess of Prussia' (Vt)	CBre CDev CGro WHer
'Princess of Wales'	see *V.* 'Princesse de Galles'
§ 'Princesse de Galles' (Vt)	CDev CGro CTri NSti SHar
§ *pubescens* var. *eriocarpa*	SRms
pumila	MHer
'Purity' (Vtta)	GMac WOFF

'Purple Wings' (Va)	WBou
'Putty'	ECou WCru
Queen Charlotte (Vt)	see *V.* 'Königin Charlotte'
'Queen Victoria'	see *V.* 'Victoria Regina'
'R.N. Denby' (ExVa)	WOFF
'Raven'	GMac LPhx NChi WBou
'Rawson's White' (Vt)	CDev CGro SHar
'Rebecca' (Vtta)	More than 30 suppliers
'Red Charm' (Vt)	EAEE EBee MWgw
'Red Giant' (Vt)	CGro CPrp EBla
'Red Lion' (Vt)	CDev CGro
'Red Queen' (Vt)	CGro NSti
reichei	CRWN
reniforme	see *V. hederacea*
'Richard's Yellow' (Va)	NCob
riviniana	CArn CRWN GWCH MBow MHer NSco SEND WHer WJek WSFF WShi
- 'Ed's Variegated' (v)	CBow EBee EMan EPPr LSou WCot
§ - Purpurea Group	More than 30 suppliers
- white	EWes
'Rodney Davey' (Vt/v)	CBow EBee EMan LSou NBir
'Rodney Fuller' (FP)	WOFF
'Rodney Marsh'	NBir
'Rosanna' (Vt)	CDev NCob
'Roscastle Black'	CElw CMea EBee GMac LRHS MBNS SBch SMrm WBou WCot WPGP WWhi
'Rose Madder' (Vt) **new**	CGro
'Rosine' (Vt)	CGro WOFF
'Royal Elk' (Vt)	CDev CGro
'Royal Robe' (Vt)	CGro
'Rubra' (Vt)	CGro EBrs EGoo WPer WPtf
§ *rupestris*	ECho
* - *rosea*	CNic CPom EBee EDAr EShb GAbr IFro LLWP MHer MWgw NWCA SBch STre WEas
'Russian Superb' (Vt)	CDev
* 'Ruth Elkins' (Va)	GMac WOFF
'Saint Helena' (Vt)	CBre CDev CGro
'Sarah Binnie' (ExVa)	WOFF
schariensis	EWes
selkirkii	CNic EHyt GKev ITer NBro NWCA
- 'Variegata' (v)	GBri GBuc NBir
septentrionalis	see *V. sororia*
- *alba*	see *V. sororia* 'Albiflora'
'Serena' (Va)	WBou
'Sheila' (Va)	WBou
'Sherbet Dip'	WBou
'Shirobana'	NBir WCru
'Sidborough Poppet'	CStu EGoo EWes
§ 'Sissinghurst' (Va)	MHer NBir
'Sisters' (Vt)	CGro
'Smugglers' Moon'	MSte WBou
'Snow Queen' (Va)	WWhi
'Sophie' (Vtta)	WBou
§ *sororia*	EAEE EBee ECha ECho EMan EPPr GSki LRHS MFOX MNrw MRav NBir NBro WBrE WEas WPtf
* - 'Albiflora' ♀[H4]	CBre CGro CMMP CSWP EAEE EBee EChP ECho EDAr EMil EPfP GEdr GGar GSki IHMH LRHS MBNS MRav MSph NJOw NWCA WCAu WCFE WFar WPer
§ - 'Freckles'	More than 30 suppliers
- 'Freckles' dark	EBee ECho LHop NWCA SMar
- 'Priceana'	CBre CCge CDes CDev CElw CMMP EAEE EBee ECGP ECha EPyc NBir NCGa NChi WPGP
- 'Speckles' (v)	CBow CDev EBla EMon
* 'Spencer's Cottage'	WBou
stojanowii	CEnt ECho SBla WEas WOFF
striata	WRos
'Sue's Choice' (FP) **new**	WOFF
§ 'Sulfurea' (Vt)	CBos CDev CPBP CPMA CSWP ECho EShb MHar MHer MMHG

	NCGa NRya NWCA WCMO WCot
	WEas WFar WOFF WPer WWhi
'Susie' (Va)	WBou
'Sybil' (SP)	WBou
'Sylvia Hart'	MTho WPnP
'Talitha' (Va)	GAbr WOFF
'Tanith' (Vt)	CBre EBee
§ 'The Czar' (Vt)	CBre CCge CGro ILis NChi
'Tiger Eyes' (Va)	CCge CSpe EBee EBla ITer MBNS
	MWat MWea NCGa NEgg
'Tinpenny Purple'	WCot WTin
'Titania' (Va)	CGro
'Tom' (SP)	WOFF
'Tom Tit' (Va)	WBou
'Tony Venison' (C/v)	EBee EHoe EMan EPPr EWin LAst
	LSou MBNS MTho NEgg SPoG
	WBou WFar WHer
tricolor	CPrp ECho GBar GPoy GWCH
	MHer MNHC MWat NGHP NPri
	NSco SBch SIde WGHP WHer WJek
	WSel
- 'Sawyer's Blue'	WPer
'Valentine' **new**	LRHS
'Vanessa' (Va)	GMac
velutina	see *V. gracilis*
verecunda	CLAP
- B&SWJ 604a	WCru
§ - var. *yakusimana*	CStu
'Victoria'	see *V.* 'Czar Bleu'
'Victoria Cawthorne' (C)	CAby CElw EBee EMan GBuc
	GMaP GMac MHer MSte MWat
	NDov SBla WBou WEas WWhi
§ 'Victoria Regina' (Vt)	CBre CDev
'Virginia' (Va)	WBou
'Vita' (Va)	CAby GBuc GMac MBNS NDov
	SBla SRms WBou WGwG WWhi
'Wasp' (Va)	CAby GMac
'Wendy' (SP)	WOFF
'White Ladies'	see *V. cucullata* 'Alba'
'White Pearl' (Va)	CBos LPhx WBou
'White Perfection' (C)	CBcs CWib LRHS MBNS
'White Swan' (Va)	GMac NChi WOFF
'William' (Va)	NDov
'William Fife' (ExVa)	WOFF
'William Snocken' (FP)	WOFF
'Winifred Jones' (Va)	WBou WOFF
'Winifred Warden' (Va)	MBNS
'Winona Cawthorne' (C)	CAby EBee GMac NChi NDov
	WWhi
'Wisley White'	EBee EWes LBmB WFar
'Woodlands Cream' (Va)	GMac MHer NCob WBou WOFF
'Woodlands Lilac' (Va)	WBou WOFF
'Woodlands White' (Va)	WBou WOFF
yakusimana	see *V. verecunda* var. *yakusimana*
'Zoe' (Vtta)	CAby EBee EWin GMac NCGa
	NPri SPer SRGP WBou WFar

Viscaria (Caryophyllaceae)

vulgaris	see *Lychnis viscaria*

Vitaliana (Primulaceae)

§ *primuliflora*	ECho GCrs NLAp NMen NRya NSla
- subsp. *cinerea* **new**	GKev
- subsp. *praetutiana*	EHyt EPot NHol NMen NWCA SBla
	WAbe WFar WLin WPat
- subsp. *tridentata*	NMen

Vitex (Verbenaceae)

agnus-castus	CAgr CArn CBcs CDul COld EBee
	EDÁr ELau EShb EUnu GPoy LEdu
	LRHS MCCP MHer SLon SMad SPer
	WDin WFar WHer WSHC WWye
	XPep
- 'Alba'	CWib EBee WWye XPep
- var. *latifolia*	CWib EBee ELan EPfP LRHS LSRN
	NLar SBrw SPoG WPGP XPep

I	- 'Rosea'	NLar XPep
	- 'Silver Spire'	ELan LRHS SBrw SPoG WPGP
	incisa	see *V. negundo* var. *heterophylla*
	lucens	CHEx
	negundo	CArn
§	- var. *heterophylla*	EWes

Vitis ✿ (Vitaceae)

	'Abundante' (F)	WSuV
	'Alden' (O/B)	WSuV
	'Amandin' (G/W)	WSuV
	amurensis	CPIN EBee EPfP GIBF LRHS NLar
	- B&SWJ 4138	WCru
	'Aurore' Seibel 5279 (W)	WSuV
	'Baco Noir' (O/B)	GTwe SDea WSuV
	'Bianca' (O/W)	WSuV
	Black Hamburgh	see *V. vinifera* 'Schiava Grossa'
*	'Black Strawberry' (B)	WSuV
§	'Boskoop Glory' (O/B) ♀H4	CMac EMil LAst LBuc MAsh MCoo
		NBlu NPal SCoo SDea WSuV
	'Brant' (O/B) ♀H4	More than 30 suppliers
	'Brilliant' (B)	WSuV
	'Buffalo' (B)	WSuV
	'Canadice' (O/R/S)	SDea WSuV
	'Cascade' (O/B)	see *V.* Seibel 13053
	Castel 19637 (B)	WSuV
	'Chambourcin' (B)	WSuV
	coignetiae ♀H4	More than 30 suppliers
	- B&SWJ 4550 from Korea	WCru
	- B&SWJ 4744	WCru
	- Claret Cloak = 'Frovit' PBR	CBcs CPIN CWCL EBee ELan EPfP
		LRHS LSRN MAsh MRav NLar SBra
		SMur SPer SPoG SSpi WPGP WPat
	- 'Purple Cloak'	CHEx
	'Dalkauer' (W)	WSuV
I	'Diamond' (B)	WSuV
	'Dutch Black' (O/B)	WSuV
	'Edwards No 1' (O/W)	WSuV
	'Eger Csillaga' (O/W)	WSuV
	'Einset' (B/S)	WSuV
	ficifolia	see *V. thunbergii*
	'Flame Red' **new**	CCCN
	flexuosa B&SWJ 5568	WCru
	- var. *choii* B&SWJ 4101	WCru
§	'Fragola' (O/R)	CAgr CMac CPIN ENot EPfP EPla
		ERea GTwe LRHS MAsh MRav
		SDea SPoG SRms WSuV
	'Gagarin Blue' (O/B)	CAgr EMui ERea GTwe NPer SDea
		WSuV
	'Glenora' (F/B/S)	ERea WSuV
	'Hecker' (O/W)	WSuV
	henryana	see *Parthenocissus henryana*
	'Himrod' (O/W/S)	ERea GTwe SDea WSuV
	inconstans	see *Parthenocissus tricuspidata*
	'Interlaken' (O/W/S)	ERea WSuV
	'Kempsey Black' (O/B)	WSuV
	'Kozmapalme Muscatoly' (O/W)	WSuV
	'Kuibishevski' (O/R)	WSuV
	labrusca 'Concord' (O/B)	ERea
	Landot 244 (O/B)	WSuV
	'Léon Millot' (O/G/B)	CAgr CSBt EMui ERea LRHS LSRN
		SDea WSuV
	'Maréchal Foch' (O/B)	WSuV
	'Maréchal Joffre' (O/B)	GTwe WSuV
	'Muscat Bleu' (O/B)	CCCN WSuV
	'New York Muscat' (O/B) ♀H4	ERea WSuV
	Oberlin 595 (O/B)	WSuV
	'Orion' (O/W)	EMui WSuV
	'Paletina' (O/W)	WSuV
	parsley-leaved	see *V. vinifera* 'Ciotat'
	parvifolia	CPIN WPat
	'Perdin' (O/W)	WSuV
	'Phönix' (O/W)	CAgr EMui GTwe MBri MGos SKee
		SLim WSuV

piasezkii   WCru
- B&SWJ 5236   WCru
* 'Pink Strawberry' (O)   WSuV
'Pirovano 14' (O/B)   GTwe SDea WSuV
§ 'Plantet' (O/B)   WSuV
* 'Poloske Muscat' (W)   GTwe WSuV
pseudoreticulata   WPGP
'Pulchra'   CPIN
purpurea 'Spetchley Park' (O/B)   WSuV
quinquefolia   see *Parthenocissus quinquefolia*
Ravat 51 (O/W)   WSuV
'Rayon d'Or' (O/W)   WSuV
'Regent'PBR   CAgr CWSG EMui GTwe MBri MCoo MGos NLar SKee SLim SPoG WOrn WSuV
'Reliance' (O/R/S)   ERea WSuV
'Rembrant' (R)   NPal WSuV
riparia   NLar WCru
'Rondo' (O/B)   EMui
- EM 6494-5   WSuV
'Schuyler' (O/B)   WSuV
Seibel (F)   GTwe SDea SPoG
§ Seibel 13053 (O/B)   LRHS MAsh SDea WSuV
Seibel 138315 (R)   WSuV
Seibel 5409 (W)   WSuV
Seibel 5455   see *V.* 'Plantet'
Seibel 7053   WSuV
Seibel 9549   WSuV
'Seneca' (W)   WSuV
'Serena' (O/W)   WSuV
§ 'Seyval Blanc' (O/W)   CAgr GTwe SDea WSuV
Seyve Villard 12.375   see *V.* 'Villard Blanc'
Seyve Villard 20.473 (F)   LRHS MAsh WSuV
Seyve Villard 5276   see *V.* 'Seyval Blanc'
'Suffolk Seedless' (B/S)   WSuV
'Tereshkova' (O/B)   CAgr ERea SDea WSuV
'Thornton' (O/S)   WSuV
§ *thunbergii* B&SWJ 4702   WCru
'Triomphe d'Alsace' (O/B)   CAgr CSBt EMui LRHS NPer SDea WSuV
'Trollinger'   see *V.vinifera* 'Schiava Grossa'
'Vanessa' (O/R/S)   ERea SDea WSuV
§ 'Villard Blanc' (O/W)   WSuV
vinifera EM 323158B   WSuV
- 'Abouriou' (O/B)   WSuV
- 'Adelheidtraube' (O/W)   WSuV
- 'Albalonga' (W)   WSuV
§ - 'Alicante' (G/B)   ERea GTwe NPal SDea WSuV
- 'Apiifolia'   see *V.vinifera* 'Ciotat'
- 'Appley Towers' (G/B)   ERea
- 'Augusta Louise' (O/W)   WSuV
- 'Auxerrois' (O/W)   WSuV
- 'Bacchus' (O/W)   SDea WSuV
- 'Baresana' (G/W)   NPal WSuV
- 'Black Alicante'   see *V.vinifera* 'Alicante'
- 'Black Corinth' (G/B/S)   ERea
- 'Black Frontignan' (G/O/B)   ERea WSuV
- Black Hamburgh   see *V.vinifera* 'Schiava Grossa'
- 'Black Monukka' (G/B/S)   ERea WSuV
- 'Black Prince' (G/B)   WSuV
- 'Blauburger' (O/B)   WCru
- 'Blue Portuguese'   see *V.vinifera* 'Portugieser'
§ - 'Bouvier' (W)   WSuV
- 'Bouviertraube'   see *V.vinifera* 'Bouvier'
- 'Buckland Sweetwater' (G/W)   ERea GTwe MGos SDea WSuV
- 'Cabernet Sauvignon' (O/B)   LRHS MAsh MGos SDea WSuV
- 'Canners' (F/S)   ERea
- 'Canon Hall Muscat' (G/W)   ERea
- 'Cardinal' (O/R)   ERea WSuV
- 'Chaouch' (G/W)   ERea

- 'Chardonnay' (O/W)   CCCN LRHS MAsh NPer SDea WSuV
§ - 'Chasselas' (G/O/W)   ERea LRHS MAsh SDea WSuV
- 'Chasselas de Fontainebleau' (F)   CCCN EMil
- 'Chasselas de Tramontaner' (F)   EMil
- 'Chasselas d'Or'   see *V. vinifera* 'Chasselas'
- 'Chasselas Rosé' (G/R)   ERea WSuV
- 'Chasselas Rose Royal' (O/R) **new**   CCCN
- 'Chasselas Vibert' (G/W)   ERea WSuV
- 'Chenin Blanc' (O/W)   WSuV
§ - 'Ciotat' (F)   CPIN EPla ERea SDea WSuV
- 'Crimson Seedless' (R/S)   ERea
- 'Csabyongye' (O/W)   WSuV
- 'Dattier de Beyrouth' (G/W)   WSuV
- 'Dattier Saint Vallier' (O/W)   WSuV
- 'Dolcetto' (O/B)   WSuV
- 'Dornfelder' (O/R)   CCCN SPoG WSuV
- 'Dunkelfelder' (O/R)   WSuV
- 'Early Van der Laan' (F)   EMil NBlu
- 'Ehrenfelser' (O/W)   WSuV
- 'Elbling' (O/W)   WSuV
- 'Excelsior' (W)   WSuV
- 'Faber' (O/W)   WSuV
- 'Fiesta' (W/S)   WSuV
- 'Findling' (W)   WSuV
- 'Flame'   EMui
- 'Flame Seedless' (G/O/R/S)   SPoG WSuV
- 'Forta' (O/W)   WSuV
- 'Foster's Seedling' (G/W)   ERea GTwe SDea SPoG WSuV
- 'Frühburgunder' (O/B)   WSuV
- 'Gamay Hâtif' (O/B)   ERea
- 'Gamay Hâtif des Vosges'   WSuV
- 'Gamay Noir' (O/B)   WSuV
- Gamay Teinturier Group (O/B)   WSuV
- 'Gewürztraminer' (O/R)   LRHS MAsh SDea WSuV
- 'Glory of Boskoop'   see *V.* 'Boskoop Glory'
- 'Golden Chasselas'   see *V. vinifera* 'Chasselas'
- 'Goldriesling' (O/W)   WSuV
- 'Gros Colmar' (G/B)   ERea
- 'Grüner Veltliner' (O/W)   WSuV
- 'Gutenborner' (O/W)   WSuV
- 'Helfensteiner' (O/R)   WSuV
- 'Huxelrebe' (O/W)   WSuV
- 'Incana' (O/B)   CPIN EPfP EPla MRav WCFE WCot WSHC
- 'Juliaumsrebe' (O/W)   WSuV
- 'Kanzler' (O/W)   WSuV
- 'Kerner' (O/W)   WSuV
- 'Kernling' (F)   WSuV
- 'King's Ruby' (F/S)   ERea
- 'Lady Downe's Seedling' (G/B)   ERea
- 'Lady Hastings' (G/B)   ERea
- 'Lady Hutt' (G/W)   ERea
- 'Lakemont' (O/W/S)   ERea GTwe LRHS MLan SKee SPoG WSuV
- 'Lival' (O/B)   WSuV
- 'Madeleine Angevine' (O/W)   CAgr CDul EMui ERea GTwe LRHS LSRN MAsh MGos SDea WSuV
- 'Madeleine Celine' (B)   WSuV
- 'Madeleine Royale' (G/W)   ERea WSuV
- 'Madeleine Silvaner' (O/W)   CSBt EMui ERea GTwe LRHS MAsh MGos NPer SDea WBVN WSuV
- 'Madresfield Court' (G/B)   ERea GTwe WSuV
- 'Merlot' (G/B)   SDea WSuV
§ - 'Meunier' (B)   WSuV
- 'Mireille' (F)   GTwe SDea WSuV
- 'Morio Muscat' (O/W)   WSuV

- 'Mrs Pince's Black Muscat' (G/B)   ERea
- 'Muscat Blanc à Petits Grains' (O/W)   SWvt WSuV
- 'Muscat Champion' (G/R)   ERea
- 'Muscat de Lierval' (O/B)   WSuV
- 'Muscat de Saumur' (O/W)   WSuV
- 'Muscat Hamburg' (G/B)   EMil EMui ERea LRHS LSRN MAsh MGos SDea SWvt WSuV
- 'Muscat of Alexandria' (G/W)   CBcs CCCN CMac EHol EMui ERea NPal SDea SPoG
- 'Muscat of Hungary' (G/W)   ERea
- 'Muscat Ottonel' (O/W)   WSuV
- 'Muscat Saint Laurent' (W)   WSuV
§ - 'Müller-Thurgau' (O/W)   EMui ERea GTwe LRHS LSRN MAsh MGos SDea WSuV
- 'No 69' (W)   WSuV
- 'Noir Hâtif de Marseille' (O/B)   WSuV
- 'Oliver Irsay' (O/W)   ERea WSuV
- 'Optima' (O/W)   WSuV
- 'Ora' (O/W/S)   WSuV
- 'Ortega' (O/W)   CCCN WSuV
- 'Perle' (O/W)   WSuV
- 'Perle de Czaba' (G/O/W)   EMil ERea WSuV
- 'Perlette' (O/W/S)   CCCN EMui ERea WSuV
- 'Petit Rouge' (R)   WSuV
- 'Pinot Blanc' (O/W)   CCCN LRHS MAsh WSuV
- 'Pinot Gris' (O/B)   SDea WSuV
- 'Pinot Noir' (O/B)   CCCN LRHS NPal WSuV
§ - 'Portugieser' (O/B)   WSuV
- 'Précoce de Bousquet' (O/W)   WSuV
- 'Précoce de Malingre' (O/W)   ERea SDea
- 'Prima' (O/B)   WSuV
- 'Primavis Frontignan' (G/W)   WSuV
- 'Prince of Wales' (G/B)   ERea
- 'Purpurea' (O/B) ♀H4   More than 30 suppliers
- 'Queen of Esther' (B)   GTwe MBri SKee SLim SPoG WSuV
- 'Reichensteiner' (O/G/W)   SDea WSuV
- 'Reine Olga' (O/W)   ERea
- 'Riesling' (O/W)   CCCN LRHS MAsh WSuV
- 'Riesling-Silvaner'   see *V. vinifera* 'Müller-Thurgau'
- 'Rish Baba'   ERea
- 'Royal Muscadine' (G/O/W)   WSuV
- 'Saint Laurent' (G/O/W)   ERea WSuV
- 'Sauvignon Blanc' (O/W)   CCCN WSuV
- 'Scheurebe' (O/W)   WSuV
§ - 'Schiava Grossa' (G/B/D)   More than 30 suppliers
- 'Schönburger' (O/W)   SDea WSuV
- 'Schwarzriesling'   see *V. vinifera* 'Meunier'
- 'Sémillon'   LRHS MAsh
- 'Septimer' (O/W)   WSuV
- 'Shiraz' (B)   WSuV
- 'Siegerrebe' (O/W/D)   CAgr EMui ERea GTwe LRHS SDea WSuV
- 'Silvaner' (O/W)   EMui WSuV
- 'Spetchley Red'   CPlN MAsh WCru WPGP WPat WSPU
- strawberry grape   see *V.* 'Fragola'
- 'Suffolk Red' (G/R/S)   ERea
§ - 'Sultana' (W/S)   CAgr CCCN EMui ERea GTwe SDea WSuV
- 'Syrian' (G/W)   ERea
- 'Teinturier Group' (F)   ERea
- 'Theresa'   MBri SPoG WOrn WSuV
- 'Thompson Seedless'   see *V. vinifera* 'Sultana'
- 'Trebbiano' (G/W)   ERea

* - 'Triomphe' (O/B)   EMui
- 'Triomphrebe' (W)   WSuV
- 'Vroegeivan der Laan' **new**   NPal
- 'Wrotham Pinot' (O/B)   SDea WSuV
- 'Würzer' (O/W)   WSuV
- 'Zweigeltrebe' (O/B)   WSuV
* 'White Strawberry' (O/W)   WSuV
'Zalagyöngye' (W)   WSuV

Vriesea (Bromeliaceae)
carinata   MBri
hieroglyphica   MBri
philippo-coburgii   EOas
x **poelmanii**   MBri
x **polonia**   MBri
saundersii ♀H1   MBri
splendens ♀H1   MBri XBlo
'Vulkana'   MBri

W

Wachendorfia (Haemodoraceae)
brachyandra   EMan GCal WCot
thyrsiflora   CAbb CAby CDes CFir CHEx CMCo CPLG CPne EBee IGor LEdu WCot WDyG WFar WPGP WPic WPrP

Wahlenbergia (Campanulaceae)
sp.   ECou
albomarginata   ECho ECou GKev LRHS NJOw NLAp NLar NWCA
- 'Blue Mist'   ECho ECou
ceracea   GKev NJOw NLAp
congesta   CNic ECho EHyt LRHS NSfd
gloriosa   ECho GCrs LRHS NJOw NLAp WAbe WFar
hederacea new   WWye
pumilio   see *Edraianthus pumilio*
pygmaea   NLAp
rivularis   CSec
§ **saxicola**   CRow ECho EHyt EMan NDlv NLAp NSfd NWCA
serpyllifolia   see *Edraianthus serpyllifolius*
tasmanica   see *W. saxicola*
undulata   CSec CSpe

Waldsteinia (Rosaceae)
fragarioides   WPer WPtf
geoides   EBee EBrs EMan EPPr EPfP IHMH LAst NBre NLar NPro SPer More than 30 suppliers
§ - 'Mozaick' (v)   EBee NBid NBir NBre NPro
- 'Variegata'   see *W. ternata* 'Mozaick'

Wallichia (Arecaceae)
densiflora   CBrP LPal
disticha   LPal

walnut, black   see *Juglans nigra*

walnut, common   see *Juglans regia*

Wasabia (Brassicaceae)
japonica   CArn GPoy LEdu

Washingtonia (Arecaceae)
filifera ♀H1   CAbb CBrP CCCN CDoC CPHo CRoM EAmu EShb LPal MBri SAPC SAin SArc SBig SEND SPlb WMul
robusta   CRoM CTrC EAmu LPal NPal SAin SChr SPlb WMul

Watsonia (Iridaceae)

aletroides	CCtw CDes EBee ECho NCGa WCot WPGP
amatolae	CPLG
angusta	CDes CPne CPrp EBee IBlr WPGP
– JCA 3.950.409	WCot
ardernei	see *W. borbonica* subsp. *ardernei* 'Arderne's White'
beatricis	see *W. pillansii*
I 'Best Red'	WCot
§ *borbonica*	CAbb CCtw CPne CPou EShb GGar IBlr WCot
– subsp. *ardernei* misapplied	see *W. borbonica* subsp. *ardernei* 'Arderne's White'
– subsp. *ardernei* (Sander) Goldblatt	EShb
§ – – 'Arderne's White'	CBre CDes CPne CPrp EBee ECho ERos EShb GCal GGar IBlr MSte SBla WPGP
– subsp. *borbonica*	CDes EBee WPGP
brevifolia	see *W. laccata*
coccinea	CDes CMon CPBP EBee WCot WPGP
densiflora	CPou EBee EShb IBlr IDee MSte WCot
distans	EBee
'Flame'	NCGa
fourcadei	CAby CPne CPrp EBee EShb WPGP
– S&SH 89	CDes
fulgens	CPne LEdu MSte
galpinii	CFir IBlr WPGP
– pink-flowered **new**	CPrp
gladioloides	CPLG WPGP
§ *humilis*	CDes CMon CPBP CPou EBee WPGP
'Ida Edwards'	EBee
knysnana	CPou EBee EShb IBlr WPGP
§ *laccata*	CFir CPBP CPou EBee EShb WCot WPGP
lepida	CPou EBee
x *longifolia*	CAbb WCot
marginata	CDes CHen CPou WCot WPGP
– 'Star Spike'	WCot
meriana	CPen CPou GGar GSki IBlr NCGa WCot WHil
– var. *bulbillifera*	CAby EBee ECho GAbr GGar GMac IBlr WPGP
§ *pillansii*	CCtw CHEx CPen CPne CPou CPrp CTrC EBee EBrs EDsa ERos EShb GMac GSki IBlr LRHS WCot WFar WMnd
– pink-flowered	CDes CPen CPrp EBee
– salmon-flowered	CPen
pyramidata	see *W. borbonica*
roseoalba	see *W. humilis*
schlechteri	WPGP
§ *spectabilis*	CPne WFar WPGP
'Stanford Scarlet'	CDes CHen CPne CPou EBee IBlr SBla SHom WPGP WSHC
stenosiphon	IBlr
strubeniae	IBlr
tabularis	CAbb CCtw CHen GGar IBlr
transvaalensis **new**	EBee
'Tresco Dwarf Pink'	CAby CDes CPrp CSam EBee EMan IBlr LEdu WCot WPGP
Tresco hybrids	CAbb CPen CPne CTbh WCFE
vanderspuyae	CCtw CPou GGar IBlr WCot WPGP
versfeldii	CPrp
watsonioides	WCot
wilmaniae	CPou CPrp EBee IBlr WPGP

Wattakaka see *Dregea*

Weigela ✿ (Caprifoliaceae)

CC 1231	CPLG
'Abel Carrière'	CMac CTri ECtt EPfP MGos NWea SEND WCFE WFar WTel
'Anne Marie' **new**	MGos
'Avalanche' Lemoine	see *W. praecox* 'Avalanche'
'Avalanche' misapplied	see *W.* 'Candida'
'Boskoop Glory'	GQui SPer
Briant Rubidor = 'Olympiade' (v)	CDoC CDul CSBt CWSG EBee ECtt EGra EHoe ENot EPfP LRHS MAsh MBNS MBar MGos MRav MWhi NEgg NFor NHol NVic SEND SLim SPer SPlb SPoG WFar WWeb
'Bristol Ruby'	More than 30 suppliers
§ 'Candida'	CTri ELan EWes GSki LRHS MBar MRav NBlu NHol SMer SPer WTel
'Cappuccino' **new**	SPoG
Carnaval = 'Courtalor' PBR	CBcs COtt CWib EBee LRHS NHol SPoG
'Conquête'	SLon
coraeensis	CHll IArd MBlu MMHG MWgw
– 'Alba'	SPer
decora	GQui
'Eva Rathke'	CTri NWea SCoo WFar WTel
'Evita'	MBar MGos NLar WFar
Feline = 'Courtamon'	MBri
florida	CDul CTrw EPfP MBar MGos SMer WGwG
– B&SWJ 8439	WCru
– f. *alba*	CBcs WFar
* – 'Albovariegata' (v)	CPLG LAst WBVN
– 'Bicolor'	CMac ELan
– 'Bristol Snowflake'	CDul EPfP LSou MBar MHer MSwo NEgg NHol NLar SLon SPoG
– 'Foliis Purpureis' ♀H4	More than 30 suppliers
– Monet = 'Verwaig' **new**	MGos
– Moulin Rouge = 'Brigela' PBR	CBcs CDoC ENot EPfP LBuc MAsh MBri MGos SPoG
– 'Pink Princess'	LRHS MSwo WWeb
– 'Samabor'	WFar
– 'Sunny Princess'	NHol
– 'Suzanne' (v)	LRHS MGos NPro
– 'Tango'	CPMA ECtt LRHS MAsh MWya NPro WWeb
'Florida Variegata' (v) ♀H4	More than 30 suppliers
florida 'Versicolor'	CMHG CMac CPLG CWib GQui SLon SMrm WFar WGor
– Wine and Roses = 'Alexandra'	CAbP CBcs CBgR CDoC EGra ELan EMil ENot EPfP LAst LBuc LRHS LSRN MAsh MBri MGos MWat NPri SMac SPoG SWvt WLeb WOVN WWeb
'Gold Rush'	NHol NLar
'Golden Candy'	NPro
'Gustave Malet'	CMCN GQui
hortensis	CPLG GIBF
– 'Nivea'	MBri
japonica	CPle
– 'Dart's Colourdream'	ECtt EWes LAst LSou MRav NHol SCoo SLPl SLim SMer WBVN
'Jean's Gold'	EBee ELan MGos MRav NCGa WCot
'Kosteriana Variegata' (v)	EWTr LRHS MAsh SLon WFar
'Looymansii Aurea'	CMHG CPLG CTri EBee ELan EPfP LAst MRav NHol SBch SLon SPer WDin WFar WHar
Lucifer = 'Courtared' PBR	CDoC NHol NLar
maximowiczii	CPLG CPle GQui GSki
§ *middendorffiana*	More than 30 suppliers
'Minuet'	EPfP GSki LRHS MBar MGos MRav MSwo NPro WWeb
'Mont Blanc'	MMHG
Nain Rouge = 'Courtanin' PBR	CBcs LRHS MBri NHol

'Nana Variegata' (v)	CPLG EPfP LRHS MBar MBri NBlu NHol WGwG
Naomi Campbell = 'Bokrashine'^{PBR}	CBow MWea SCoo WMoo
'Newport Red'	ENot MBNS MRav NWea SMer WFar
'Pink Poppet'	CSBt EKen GTSp LAst LBuc LRHS LSRN LSou MAsh SCoo SPoG SWvt WOVN
praecox	GIBF
§ - 'Avalanche'	ECtt MRav SGar
'Praecox Variegata' (v) ♀^{H4}	CTri ELan EPfP LAst LRHS MAsh MRav SMac SPer SPla SPoG SReu SRms WCFE WFar WHCG
'Red Prince' ♀^{H4}	ELan GWCH LAst LRHS MGos MSwo NBlu NCGa NEgg NHol SPoG
'Red Trumpet'	SLon
'Ruby Queen'^{PBR}	EPfP
'Rumba'	MMHG MRav NPro
sessilifolia	see *Diervilla sessilifolia*
'Snowflake'	ECtt NPri NPro SRms WDin WFar
subsessilis	GIBF
- B&SWJ 1056	WCru
'Victoria'	CDoC CDul CMHG CWib ECtt ELan EPfP LAst LRHS MAsh MGos MSwo NEgg SCoo SPer SPla SPoG WBrE WGor WHar WMoo
'Wessex Gold' (v)	WHCG

Weinmannia (*Cunoniaceae*)

racemosa 'Kamahi'	CTrC
trichosperma	ISea SAPC SArc

Weldenia (*Commelinaceae*)

candida	EBla ECho EHyt LTwo NMen SIng WAbe

Westringia (*Lamiaceae*)

angustifolia	ECou
brevifolia	ECou EDsa
- var. *raleighii*	ECou
§ *fruticosa* ♀^{H1}	CArn CBcs CPLG ECou EShb WJek XPep
- 'Morning Light' (v)	WCot
- 'Smokie' **new**	ECou
- 'Variegata' (v)	GQui LHop MNHC WJek
- 'Wynyabbie Gem'	EMan LHop
longifolia	ECou
rosmariniformis	see *W. fruticosa*
'Smokie'	SOWG

Wettinia (*Arecaceae*)

maynensis	LPal

whitecurrant see *Ribes rubrum* (W)

Whitfieldia (*Acanthaceae*)

elongata	EShb

Widdringtonia (*Cupressaceae*)

cedarbergensis	CPne GGar
cupressoides	see *W. nodiflora*
§ *nodiflora*	CPne GGar
schwarzii	CBcs GGar

Wigandia (*Hydrophyllaceae*)

caracasana	CHll CKob

Wikstroemia (*Thymelaeaceae*)

gemmata	SCoo SSta
kudoi	WCru

Willdenowia (*Restionaceae*)

incurvata	CBig

wineberry see *Rubus phoenicolasius*

Wisteria ✿ (*Papilionaceae*)

§ *brachybotrys*	CMCN SLim
§ - Murasaki-kapitan	CEnd SIFN
- 'Okayama'	SIFN
- 'Pink Chiffon'	LRHS
- 'Shiro-beni' **new**	LRHS
§ - 'Shiro-kapitan'	CBcs CEnd CHad CSPN CTri EBee ENot EPfP LPan LRHS MAsh MBri MDun MGos NHol SBra SHBN SIFN SLim SLon SPer WPGP
* - 'White Silk'	CBcs CEnd LRHS MAsh MGos NCGa
§ 'Burford'	CEnd CSPN EMui LRHS MAsh MBri MDun MGan NHol NRib SCoo SLim SPoG WHar WPGP
'Caroline'	CBcs CDoC CEnd CMen CPIN CSBt CSPN EBee EPfP ERea EWTr LRHS MAsh MBlu MGos NBea SBLw SPer SPur SSpi WPGP
floribunda	CBcs CRHN CWib ELan LRHS SBLw SBra SHBN WDin WFar WNor
§ - 'Alba' ♀^{H4}	More than 30 suppliers
- 'Black Dragon'	see *W. floribunda* 'Yae-kokuryû'
- 'Burford'	see *W.* 'Burford'
- 'Cannington'	EBee ERea SLim
* - 'Cascade'	CBcs CPMA MGos NCGa
§ - 'Domino'	CEnd CTri EBee EPfP ERea LPan LRHS MAsh MBar MGan MGos NHol SBLw SBra SLim SPer SSta WFar WSHC
- 'Fragrantissima'	see *W. sinensis* 'Jako'
- 'Geisha'	CBcs CEnd SBLw SIFN
- 'Golden Dragon' **new**	SPoG
- 'Hagoromo Nishiki' (V) **new**	MGos
* - 'Harlequin'	CBcs CDul CSPN EBee LRHS MGos NLar SPoG
- 'Hon-beni'	see *W. floribunda* 'Rosea'
- 'Honey Bee Pink'	see *W. floribunda* 'Rosea'
- 'Honko'	see *W. floribunda* 'Rosea'
- 'Issai' **new**	LRHS
- 'Issai Perfect'	LPan LRHS LSRN NLar SPoG
- 'Jakohn-fuji'	see *W. sinensis* 'Jako'
§ - 'Kuchi-beni'	CBcs CEnd CSBt CSPN EBee ELan ENot LRHS MAsh MGos NCGa NLar SLim SPer SPoG
- 'Lawrence'	CBcs CEnd CSPN EBee LRHS MBri SIFN
- 'Lipstick'	see *W. floribunda* 'Kuchi-beni'
- 'Longissima'	see *W. floribunda* 'Multijuga'
- 'Longissima Alba'	see *W. floribunda* 'Alba'
- 'Macrobotrys'	see *W. floribunda* 'Multijuga'
- 'Magenta'	CBcs LRHS
§ - 'Multijuga' ♀^{H4}	More than 30 suppliers
- Murasaki-naga	see *W. floribunda* 'Purple Patches'
- 'Nana Richin's Purple'	CEnd LRHS
- 'Peaches and Cream'	see *W. floribunda* 'Kuchi-beni'
- 'Pink Ice'	see *W. floribunda* 'Rosea'
§ - 'Purple Patches'	LRHS MGos NPri SLim
- Reindeer	see *W. sinensis* 'Jako'
§ - 'Rosea' ♀^{H4}	More than 30 suppliers
- 'Royal Purple'	LRHS MBri SMad SPoG WGor
- 'Russelliana'	CBcs SLim
- 'Shiro-naga'	see *W. floribunda* 'Alba'
- 'Shiro-noda'	see *W. floribunda* 'Alba'
- 'Snow Showers'	see *W. floribunda* 'Alba'
N - 'Violacea Plena' (d)	CBcs CDoC EBee EPfP LPan LRHS MGos MRav NBlu NPri SHBN SPer SPur SSto SWvt WDin WFar
N - 'Yae-kokuryû' (d)	CEnd CMen CSBt CSPN ECrN ELan ENot EPfP LRHS MBri MGos NHol

	SBra SHBN SIFN SLim SPer SReu SSpi SSta SWvt WDin WFar WGor
x *formosa*	MGan SLim
- 'Black Dragon' (d)	see *W. floribunda* 'Yae-kokuryū'
- 'Domino'	see *W. floribunda* 'Domino'
- 'Issai' Wada pro parte	see *W. floribunda* 'Domino'
- 'Kokuryū' (d)	see *W. floribunda* 'Yae-kokuryū'
§ - 'Yae-kokuryū' (d)	see *W. floribunda* 'Yae-kokuryū'
frutescens	GIBF SBLw WNor
- 'Alba'	see *W. frutescens* 'Nivea'
- 'Amethyst Falls'PBR	CEnd SIFN
- 'Magnifica'	see *W. macrostachya* 'Magnifica'
§ - 'Nivea'	SIFN
Kapitan-fuji	see *W. brachybotrys*
§ 'Lavender Lace'	CBcs CDul CEnd EBee EPfP LRHS MAsh NCGa NLar SPoG WFar
macrostachya 'Bayou Two o'Clock'	SIFN
- 'Clara Mack'	SIFN
§ - 'Magnifica'	LRHS
- 'Pondside Blue'	SIFN
multijuga 'Alba'	see *W. floribunda* 'Alba'
'Showa-beni'	CEnd LRHS MAsh MGos SCoo SIFN SLim SPoG WPGP
sinensis ♀H4	More than 30 suppliers
- 'Alba' ♀H4	CBcs CDoC CDul CHad CMen CWib EBee ECrN ELan EPfP ERea ISea LAst LBuc LRHS LSRN MBar MGan MGos MNHC NBlu SBra SEND SLim SPla SPoG SSto WDin WFar WOrn
- 'Amethyst'	CBcs CEnd CSBt CSPN EBee EPfP LRHS MBri MDun MGos MRav NSti SBLw SBra SIFN SPla SPoG SReu
- 'Blue Sapphire'	CBcs CMen CSPN EBee LRHS SBra SPur
- 'Consequa'	see *W. sinensis* 'Prolific'
- 'Cooke's Special'	SIFN
§ - 'Jako'	CEnd EWTr MAsh MGos NHol SBra SIFN
- 'Oosthoek's Variety'	see *W. sinensis* 'Prolific'
I - 'Pink Ice'	ISea
- 'Prematura'	see *W. floribunda* 'Domino'
- 'Prematura Alba'	see *W. brachybotrys* 'Shiro-kapitan'
§ - 'Prolific'	CDul CPlN CSBt CSam CTri CWib EBee ELan EPfP EWTr LBuc LRHS MBri MDun MGos NBlu NHol SBLw SBra SPer SPla SSpi SSto SWvt WFar WOrn WPGP
- 'Rosea'	CMen LSRN MGos MNHC SPur SWvt
'Tiverton' new	CBcs
venusta	see *W. brachybotrys* 'Shiro-kapitan'
- var. *violacea* misapplied	see *W. brachybotrys* Murasaki-kapitan
- var. *violacea* Rehder	see *W. brachybotrys* Murasaki-kapitan
villosa	WNor

Withania (Solanaceae)

somnifera	CArn EOHP EUnu GPoy MGol MSal

Wittsteinia (Alseuosmiaceae)

vacciniacea	EBee WCru

Wodyetia (Arecaceae)

bifurcata	EAmu LPal

Woodsia (Woodsiaceae)

obtusa	CLAP EBee EFer GCal GMaP LAst LRHS NLar NMyG SRot
polystichoides ♀H4	GQui SRms WAbe

Woodwardia (Blechnaceae)

from Emei Shan, China	CLAP
fimbriata	CCCN CFwr CLAP CWCL EBee EDsa ERod GBin GCal MAsh MAvo MWgw NMyG NWCA SBig SPer WBor WFib WMoo WPGP WPnP WPtf
orientalis	WCot WFib WPic
- var. *formosana*	CLAP
- - B&SWJ 6865	WCru
radicans ♀H3	CAbb CHEx CLAP CPLG EWes GQui ISea SAPC SArc WFib WPic
unigemmata	CHEx CLAP EFer SAPC SArc SSpi WAbe WFib WHal WPnP
virginica	CLAP

Worcesterberry see *Ribes divaricatum*

Wulfenia (Scrophulariaceae)

amherstiana	GCrs
blechicii subsp. *rohlenae*	GIBF
carinthiaca	EBee ECho GAbr GEdr GIBF GKev NBir NHol NLar
x *schwarzii*	CDes EBee WCMO

Wurmbea (Colchicaceae)

recurva new	CStu

Wyethia (Asteraceae)

arizonica	LRav
scabra	LRav

X

Xanthium (Asteraceae)

sibiricum	CArn

Xanthoceras (Sapindaceae)

sorbifolium ♀H3-4	CAgr CArn CBcs CLnd CMCN CWib EBee ECrN ELan EPfP GIBF IArd IDee LEdu MBlu MBri NHol SBrw SCoo SPoG SSpi WDin WFar WNor WPat XPep

Xanthocyparis see *Chamaecyparis*

Xanthorhiza (Ranunculaceae)

simplicissima	CBcs CPLG CRow EBee EPfP GCal LEdu NLar SBrw SDys SPer SSpi WPGP

Xanthorrhoea (Xanthorrhoeaceae)

australis	EShb SPlb
johnsonii	WMul
preisii	WMul

Xanthosoma (Araceae)

sagittifolium	CKob EAmu MOak WMul
violaceum	CDWL CKob EAmu MOak WMul

Xerochrysum (Asteraceae)

§ *bracteatum* 'Coco'	CMHG CSpe EMan GMac MAJR WCot WWlt
§ - 'Dargan Hill Monarch'	CHll CMHG CSev CSpe MAJR SRms WWlt
§ - 'Skynet'	CSev EBee GCal GMac
- Sundaze White = 'Redbrawhi'PBR new	SPoG
- 'Wollerton'	WWlt

Xeronema (Phormiaceae)

callistemon	CTrC

Xerophyllum (Melanthiaceae)
   tenax   CFir EWes GBin NMen

Xylorhiza see *Machaeranthera*

Xyris (Xyridaceae)
   juncea   ECou
   torta   WPGP

Y

Ypsilandra (Melanthiaceae)
   cavaleriei   GEdr
   thibetica   CDes EBla GEdr WCot WCru
                 WSHC

Youngberry see *Rubus* 'Youngberry'

Yucca ✿ (Agavaceae)
   aloifolia   CCCN CHEx ISea LRHS MGos
                 MPRe SAPC SArc SBig SChr SEND
                 SNew SPlb WMul
   - f. *marginata* (v) LPal MPRe SAPC SArc SBig
   - 'Purpurea'   MAga SPlb
   - 'Tricolor' (v)   MPRe
   - 'Variegata' (v) see *Y. aloifolia* f. *marginata*
   angustifolia   see *Y. glauca*
   angustissima   GCal
   - NNS 99-509   WCot
   arizonica   CBrP GCal
   baccata   CTrC GCal LEdu WMul XPep
   - NNS 99-510   WCot
   brevifolia   CHEx WMul
   carnerosana   CTrC EAmu WMul
§ *elata*   CTrC SChr WMul
§ *elephantipes* ♀H1 EAmu LRHS MBri SEND SMur
                 WMul
   - 'Jewel' (v)   EAmu SEND WMul
   - 'Puck' (v)   MPRe
   faxoniana   MAga
   faxoniana x *glauca* MAga
   filamentosa ♀H4 More than 30 suppliers
   - 'Bright Edge' (v) ♀H3 More than 30 suppliers
   - 'Color Guard' (v) CDul CTrC LAst MBri NLar WBrk
                 WCot WFar
   - 'Garland's Gold' (v) CBcs CBrm CCCN CDoC GQui
                 LRHS MAsh MDun MGos MSph
                 SBig WCot WFar
   - 'Variegata' (v) ♀H3 CBcs EBee EPfP LRHS MGos SRms
                 WDin WFar WGer
   flaccida   CBcs NEgg SDix SEND SPoG
   - 'Golden Sword' (v) ♀H3 More than 30 suppliers
   - 'Ivory' ♀H3-4   More than 30 suppliers
   x *floribunda*   SAPC SArc
§ *glauca*   CAbb CBcs CBrP EPfP GCal LEdu
                 LRHS MBri MPRe NPal SAPC SPoG
                 WMul XPep
* - var. *radiosa*   CTrC
   gloriosa ♀H4   CBcs CDoC CDul CHEx CTri
                 EBee EPfP EPla LRHS LRav
                 MPRe NPal NScw SAPC SArc
                 SEND SHBN SPer SPoG SWvt
                 WBrE WBrk WMul
   - 'Aureovariegata' see *Y. gloriosa* 'Variegata'
   - 'Moon Frost'   LHop WFar
§ - 'Variegata' (v) ♀H4 More than 30 suppliers
   guatemalensis   see *Y. elephantipes*
   harrimaniae   GCal
   kanabensis   GCal
   linearis <u>new</u>   EAmu
   navajoa   GCal
   'Nobilis'   CHEx SDix

   radiosa   see *Y. elata*
   recurvifolia ♀H4 CHEx EPfP MGos NPal SAPC SArc
                 WPic
   - 'Variegata' (v)   WCot
   rigida   CBrP WMul
   rostrata   CAbb CBrP CCCN CTrC EAmu
                 EShb LPal MPRe SAPC SArc SChr
                 WMul XPep
   schidigera   GCal WCot WMul
   - NNS 03-597   WCot
   schottii   CAbb CBrP CTrC GCal MAga
   thompsoniana   CTrC EAmu GCal
   torreyi   CTrC GCal SChr XPep
   treculeana <u>new</u> EAmu MAga
   'Vittorio Emanuele II' SMad
   whipplei   CAbb CBrP CCCN CCtw CDoC
                 CRoM LEdu LRHS MAga MPRe
                 NPal SAPC SBig SSpi WBrE WPGP
                 XPep
   - subsp. *caespitosa* WCot
   - subsp. *intermedia* WCot
   - subsp. *parishii*   WCot
   - subsp. *percursa* WCot

Yushania (Poaceae)
   from Yunnan <u>new</u> WPGP
   - B&V 421 CLONE 2 WPGP
§ *anceps*   CBcs CDoC CHEx CHad EFul
                 ENBC EPfP EPla GBin MBar MGos
                 MMoz MWht NVic SAPC SArc SBig
                 WBrE WDin WFar WMoo WMul
                 WPGP
§ - 'Pitt White'   EPla WJun WPGP
   - 'Pitt White Rejuvenated' EPla ERod WPGP
   brevipaniculata <u>new</u> EPla
   chungii   EPla WPGP
   maculata   EPla ERod MMoz MWht SBig WJun
§ *maling*   EPfP EPla ERod MMoz WJun

Z

Zaluzianskya (Scrophulariaceae)
   JCA 15665   WAbe
   capensis   WGwG
   'Katherine'   EMan SIng SRot
   'Orange Eye'   CPBP CStu EBee EHyt LHop SBla
                 WAbe
   ovata   CBcs CPBP EBee EHyt EPot GBri
                 LHop MAvo MTho NBir NBur
                 NJOw NSla NWCA SAga SBla SIng
                 SPoG
   pulvinata   CPBP SPlb WAbe
   'Semonkong'   CMdw EMan GCal LSou MNrw
                 MSte SUsu

Zamia (Zamiaceae)
   fischeri   WMul
   floridana   CRoM LPal
   furfuracea   CBrP CKob EAmu LPal WMul
   muricata   LPal
   neurophyllidia   CBrP
   pumila   CBrP WMul
   roezlii   CBrP
   skinneri   LPal
   standleyi   CBrP
   vazquezii   CBrP

Zamioculcas (Araceae)
   zamiifolia   CCCN

Zantedeschia (Araceae)
§ *aethiopica* ♀H3   More than 30 suppliers
   - B&SWJ 3959   WCru

- 'Apple Court Babe' — CElw CRow CStu EZes MNrw WDyG
- 'Caerwent' — CPen EZes
- 'Childsiana' — EBee EZes
- 'Crowborough' ♀H3 — More than 30 suppliers
- 'Gigantea' — CHEx EZes
- 'Glow' — CBct EBee EZes ITer LAst LSou MNrw NCGa NGdn WCMO WCot WGwG
- 'Green Goddess' ♀H3 — More than 30 suppliers
- 'Little Gem' — SAga SMad WFar
* - 'Marshmallow' — EBla ELan EShb EZes LRHS NCGa
- 'Mr Martin' — CBct CCCN CDes EBee EWll EZes MNrw NCGa SBig SPoG SWvt WCMO WCot WPGP
- 'Pershore Fantasia' (v) — EBee EBla EZes ITer MAvo MNrw WCMO WCot WFar WSPU
- pink — CHEx
- 'Tiny Tim' — SChr
- 'Whipped Cream' — EZes MNrw
- 'White Gnome' — CDes EZes WCot WFar WPGP
- 'White Mischief' — EBee EZes
- 'White Sail' — EBee EBla EMar ETow EZes GCal LRHS MNrw MRav NGdn SPoG WFib
albomaculata — CPLG CWib EPfP MNrw SGar SPlb
'Anneke' — CStu CWib ECho EPfP EPot SPer WBrE WFar WViv
'Apricot Glow' — CHll WViv
'Best Gold' — see Z. 'Florex Gold'
black — CSut
'Black Eyed Beauty' — CBgR CWib EBrs IHMH WPnP WViv
'Black Magic' — ECho EPfP SPer WFar WViv
'Cameo' — CBgR ECho EPfP MNrw WFar WViv
'Carmine Red' — MNrw WBrE
'Celeste' — WViv
'Chianti' — MNrw WViv
'Crystal Blush' — CWib EPot
'Crystal Glow' — WViv
'Dominique' — MNrw
elliottiana ♀H1 — CBcs CFir CHEx CHal CPou CStu EPfP GQui MNrw WViv
§ 'Florex Gold' — WViv
'Galaxy' — WViv
'Golden Sun' — WViv
'Hot Shot' — WViv
'Kiwi Blush' — More than 30 suppliers
'Lilac Mist' — WViv
'Lime Lady' — ECha
'Little Suzie' — WViv
'Majestic Red' — EPfP EPot WViv
'Mango' — CBgR CWib EPfP EWll IHMH MNrw WCot WPnP WViv
'Moonglow' — WViv
'Mozart' — WViv
'Pacific Pink' — WViv
'Pink Mist' — EBee EMar EShb EZes WHil WPnP
'Pink Persuasion' — CWib MNrw WFar WPnP WViv
'Pot of Gold' — WViv
'Purple Haze'PBR — WViv
'Red Sox'PBR — WViv
rehmannii ♀H1 — CBgR CPou CStu EPfP EPot GQui IHMH MNrw NLar SRms WSPU WViv
- 'Little Dream' — WViv
'Schwarzwalder'PBR — WViv
'Sensation' — WViv
'Silver Lining' — MNrw
'Solfatare' — ECho MNrw WPnP
'Sunshine' **new** — EWll
'Treasure' — EPot WViv
'White Pixie' — COtt EBee EMan ENot EPfP EZes LSou NPal SAga SPoG WViv
'Yellow Queen' — WViv

Zanthorhiza see *Xanthorhiza*

Zanthoxylum (Rutaceae)

acanthopodium — WCru
  B&SWJ 7237
ailanthoides — EPfP
- B&SWJ 8535 — WCru
americanum — CAgr CBcs ELan LEdu
armatum — CAgr
bungeanum — CAgr
- HWJK 2131 — WCru
piasezkii — CBcs
piperitum — SMad WPGP
- B&SWJ 8593 — WCru
schinifolium — CAgr LEdu
- B&SWJ 1245 — WCru
simulans — CAgr CArn CBcs CLnd CPLG EBee GIBF LEdu MBlu WPGP
stenophyllum — CBcs

Zauschneria (Onagraceae)

arizonica — see Z. *californica* subsp. *latifolia*
§ **californica** — CBrm CHll CSam ECho EPfP MBrN NMen SGar SLon SWat WHrl
- 'Albiflora' — EPot WAbe
§ - subsp. **cana** — ECha MHar SWat XPep
- - 'Sir Cedric Morris' — EPfP LRHS MAsh SMur
- 'Catalina' — XPep
- 'Clover Dale' — EWes
§ - 'Dublin' ♀H3 — CBcs CTri EBee EChP ECha ECho ECtt EPfP ERea ETow LAst LHop LRHS MAsh MHer MWat NMen NWCA SBla SHFr SIng SPer SPoG SRot SUsu WAbe WHoo WKif WPat WSHC
- 'Ed Carman' — EBee ECtt EMan LSou MAvo
§ - subsp. **garrettii** — ECho NWCA SDys SWat XPep
- 'Glasnevin' — see Z. *californica* 'Dublin'
§ - subsp. **latifolia** — EPot XPep
- - 'Sally Walker' — EWes
§ - subsp. **mexicana** — CWib EPot MHer SRms
- 'Olbrich Silver' — EBee ECha EMan EShb EWes LHop NMen NWCA SUsu WAbe WHoo WPat
- 'Schieffelin's Choice' — XPep
- 'Sierra Salmon' — WPat XPep
- 'Solidarity Pink' — MTho NMen NWCA WKif WPat XPep
- 'Western Hills' ♀H4 — CFir CLyd CSpe EBee ECha ECho ECtt LHop LPhx LSou MRav NWCA SAga SBch SBla SIng WAbe WHoo WPat XPep
cana villosa — see Z. *californica* subsp. *mexicana*
I 'Pumilio' — NMen
§ **septentrionalis** — ETow SBla

Zebrina see *Tradescantia*

Zelkova ✿ (Ulmaceae)

carpinifolia — CDoC CDul CMCN CMen CTho LRHS SBLw STre WDin WNor
'Kiwi Sunset' — ENot
schneideriana — CMen EGFP
serrata ♀H4 — CBcs CDul CLnd CMCN CMen CTho EBee ECrN ELan EPfP EWTr IArd MBar NBea NHol NWea SBLw SBir SEND SPer STre WDin WFar WHCr WMou WNor WOrn
- B&SWJ 8491from Korea — WCru
- 'Goblin' — CLnd WPat
- 'Green Vase' — CLnd LPan LRHS SCoo
- 'Variegata' (v) — CPMA MBlu MGos
- 'Yatsubusa' — STre

- 'Yrban Ruby'   MGos
sinica   CBcs CLnd CMCN CMen WNor

Zenobia (Ericaceae)
pulverulenta   More than 30 suppliers
- 'Blue Sky'   CDul CMCN EPfP MBlu MBri NLar
                        SSpi WPGP
- 'Raspberry Ripple'   MBlu NLar
- 'Viridis' new   NLar

Zephyranthes ✿ (Amaryllidaceae)
atamasca   CStu ERos
candida   CAvo CBro CFFs CStu EBee ECho
                        EMan EMon EPot ERea ERos EShb
                        ITim LRHS SDix WCMO
citrina   CGrW EBee ECho EPot ERos WCot
drummondii   CMon CStu EBee ECho WCot
flavissima   CBro CMon ECho WPGP WPrP
grandiflora ♀H2-3   ECho
'Grandjax'   WCMO WCot
'La Buffa Rose'   CStu WCMO WCot
x *lancasterae*   CMon
lindleyana   WCot
macrosiphon   CMon
'Mary'   CMon
mexicana   ERos
minima   CMon CStu ECho
'Norma Pearl' new   WCMO
robusta   see *Habranthus robustus*
rosea   CGrW EBee EPot
smallii   CMon
verecunda   CStu SIng

Zieria (Rutaceae)
cytisoides   ECou

Zigadenus (Melanthiaceae)
elegans   EBee ECha EHyt ERos GAbr GIBF
                        LRHS SMad SUsu WTin
exaltatus new   GIBF
fremontii   EBee EBla GIBF MDKP WCot WLin

micranthus new   GIBF
nuttallii   EBee ECho EMan ERos LHop LPhx
                        MDKP WCot
venenosus   EBee
aff. *venenosus* new   GIBF

Zingiber (Zingiberaceae)
chrysanthum   CKob
clarkei   CKob MOak WMul
malaysianum   CKob MAsh MOak WCMO
mioga   CKob GPoy LEdu MSal WDyG
                        WPGP
- 'Dancing Crane' (v)   CKob EBee EShb IFro
officinale   CKob MOak MSal
purpureum   CKob MOak
rubens   CKob MOak
'Yellow Delight'   CKob
zerumbet   CKob MJnS MOak WMul
- 'Darceyi' (v)   CKob MOak

Zinnia (Asteraceae)
'Red Spider'   CSpe

Zizia (Apiaceae)
aptera   CDes EBee EDAr EMar ITer LPhx
                        WPGP
aurea   EBee EDsa WSHC WTin

Ziziphora (Lamiaceae)
subnivalis   CFwr

Ziziphus (Rhamnaceae)
§ *jujuba* (F)   CAgr CBcs LEdu
- 'Lang' (F)   ERea
- 'Li' (F)   LPan
- var. *spinosa*   CArn
sativa   see *Z. jujuba*

Zoysia (Poaceae)
matrella   XPep
tenuifolia   XPep

BIBLIOGRAPHY

This is by no means exhaustive but lists some of the more useful works used in the preparation of the *RHS Plant Finder*. The websites of raisers of new plants (not listed here) are also an invaluable source of information.

GENERAL

Allan, H.H., et al. 2000. *Flora of New Zealand.* Wellington. (5 vols).

Bailey, L.H. & Bailey, E.Z. et al. 1976. *Hortus Third.* New York: Macmillan.

Bean, W.J. 1988. *Trees and Shrubs Hardy in the British Isles.* (8th ed. edited by Sir George Taylor & D.L. Clarke & Supp. ed. D.L. Clarke). London: John Murray.

Beckett, K. (ed.). 1994. *Alpine Garden Society Encyclopaedia of Alpines.* Pershore, Worcs: Alpine Garden Society (2 vols).

Boufford, D.E., et al. (eds.) 2003. *Flora of Taiwan Checklist.* A checklist of the vascular plants of Taiwan. Taipei, Taiwan: NTU. http://tai2.ntu.edu.tw/fot/v6/v6checklist.pdf

Brickell, C. (ed.). 2003. *The Royal Horticultural Society A-Z Encyclopedia of Garden Plants.* London: Dorling Kindersley.

Brickell, C. (ed.). 2003. *The RHS New Encyclopedia of Plants and Flowers.* London: Dorling Kindersley.

Brickell, C.D. et al (eds.) 2004. *International Code of Nomenclature for Cultivated Plants* (7th ed.). ISHS

Brummitt, R.K. & Powell, C.E. (eds.) 1992. *Authors of Plant Names.* Kew: Royal Botanic Gardens.

Brummitt, R.K. (comp.). 1992. *Vascular Plant Families and Genera.* Kew: Royal Botanic Gardens.

African Botany Supplementary Vol. No. 13. Kirstenbosch, South Africa: National Botanic Gardens.

Bramwell, D. & Bramwell, Z.I. 2001. *Wild Flowers of the Canary Islands.* (2nd ed.). Madrid: Editorial Rueda, S.L.

Castroviejo, S., Laínz, M., López González, G., Montserrat, P., Munoz Garmendia, F., Paiva, J. & Villar, L. (eds) *Flora Iberica.* 1987-2001. (Vols 1-8, 14). Madrid: Real Jardín Botánico, C.S.I.C.

Cave, Y. & Paddison, V. 1999. *The Gardener's Encyclopaedia of New Zealand Native Plants.* Auckland: Godwit.

Clement, E.J. & Foster, M.C. 1994. *Alien Plants of the British Isles.* London: Botanical Society of the British Isles.

Cooke, I. 1998. *The Plantfinder's Guide to Tender Perennials.* Newton Abbot, Devon: David & Charles.

Cronquist, A., Holmgren, A.H., Holmgren, N.H.,

Reveal, J.L. & Holmgren, P.H. et al. (eds). *Intermountain Flora: Vascular Plants of the Intermountain West, USA.* (1986-97). (Vols 1, 3-6). New York: New York Botanical Garden.

Cullen, J. (ed.). 2001. *Handbook of North European Garden Plants.* Cambridge University Press.

Davis, P.H., Mill, R.R. & Tan, K. (eds). 1965. *Flora of Turkey and the East Aegean Islands* (1965-1988) (Vols 1-10). Edinburgh University Press.

Dufresne, R.E. 1995. *Sage Advice.* American Nurseryman 15.8.1995:57

Forrest, M. (comp.) & Nelson, E.C. (ed.). 1985. *Trees and Shrubs Cultivated in Ireland.* Dublin: Boethius Press for An Taisce.

Goldblatt, P. & Manning, J. 2000. *Cape Plants. A Conspectus of the Cape Flora of South Africa.* South Africa / USA: National Botanical Institute of South Africa / Missouri Botanical Garden.

Graf, A.B. 1963. *Exotica 3. Pictorial Cyclopedia of Exotic Plants.* (3rd ed.). New Jersey, USA: Roehrs

Graf, A.B. 1986. *Tropica.* Color Cyclopedia of Exotic Plants and Trees. (3rd ed.). New Jersey, USA: Roehrs

Greuter, W., et al. (eds) 2000. *International Code of Botanical Nomenclature (Saint Louis Code).* Königstein, Germany: Koeltz Scientific Books.

Greuter, W., Brummitt, R.K., Farr, E., Kilian, N., Kirk, P.M. & Silva, P.C. (comps). 1993. *NCU-3. Names in Current Use for Extant Plant Genera.* Konigstein, Germany: Koeltz Scientific Books.

Grierson, A.J.C., Long, D.G. & Noltie, H.J. et al. (eds). 2001. *Flora of Bhutan.* Edinburgh: Royal Botanic Garden.

Güner, A., Özhatay, N., Ekîm, T., Baser, K.H.C. & Hedge, I.C. 2000. *Flora of Turkey and the East Aegean Islands.* Supplement 2. Vol. 11. Edinburgh: Edinburgh University Press.

Harkness, M.G. 1993. *The Bernard E. Harkness Seedlist Handbook.* (2nd ed.). London: Batsford.

Hickman, J.C. (ed.). 1993. *The Jepson Manual. Higher Plants of California.* Berkeley & Los Angeles: University of California Press.

Hillier, J. & Coombes, A. (eds). 2002. *The Hillier Manual of Trees & Shrubs.* (7th ed.). Newton Abbot, Devon: David & Charles.

Hirose, Y. & Yokoi, M. 1998. *Variegated Plants in Colour.* Iwakuni, Japan: Varie Nine

Hirose, Y. & Yokoi, M. 2001. *Variegated Plants in Colour.* Vol. 2. Iwakuni, Japan: Varie Nine

Hoffman, M.H.A., van de Laar, H.J., de Jong, P.C. & Geers, F. (eds). 2000. *Naamlijst van Houtige Gewassen.* (List of Names of Woody Plants). Boskoop, Netherlands: Boomteelt Praktijkonderzoek.

Hoffman, M.H.A., van de Laar, H.J., de Jong, P.C. & Geers, F. (eds). .2000. *Naamlijst van Vaste Planten. (List of Names of Perennials).* Boskoop, Netherlands: Boomteelt Praktijkonderzoek.

Huxley, A., Griffiths, M. & Levy, M. (eds). 1992. *The New RHS Dictionary of Gardening.* London: Macmillan.

Jellitto, L. & Schacht, W. 1990. *Hardy Herbaceous Perennials.* Portland, Oregon: Timber Press. (2 vols).

Krüssmann, G. & Epp, M.E. (trans.). 1986. *Manual of Cultivated Broad-leaved Trees and Shrubs.* London: Batsford (3 vols).

Leslie, A.C. (trans.). *New Cultivars of Herbaceous Perennial Plants 1985-1990.* Hardy Plant Society.

Mabberley, D.J. 1997. *The Plant-Book. A Portable Dictionary of the Vascular Plants.* (2nd ed.). Cambridge: Cambridge University Press.

McGregor, R.L., Barkley, T.M., Brooks, R.E. & Schofield, E.K. et al. (eds). 1987. *Flora of the Great Plains.* Lawrence, Kansas: University Press of Kansas.

Metcalf, L.J. 1987. *The Cultivation of New Zealand Trees and Shrubs.* Auckland: Reed Methuen.

Munz, P. 1973. *A Californian Flora and Supplement.* London: University of California Press.

Nelson, E.C. 2000. *A Heritage of Beauty: The Garden Plants of Ireland: An Illustrated Encyclopaedia.* Dublin: Irish Garden Plant Society.

Ohwi, J. 1965. *Flora of Japan.* Washington DC: Smithsonian Institution.

Phillips, R. & Rix, M. 1989. *Shrubs.* London: Pan

Phillips, R. & Rix, M. 1993. *Perennials.* London: Pan (2 vols).

Phillips, R. & Rix, M. 1997. *Conservatory and Indoor Plants.* London: Macmillan. (2 vols).

Platt, K. (comp.). 2002. *The Seed Search.* (5th ed.). Sheffield: Karen Platt

Polunin, O. & Stainton, A. 1984. *Flowers of the Himalaya.* Oxford: Oxford University Press.

Press, J.R. & Short, M.J. (eds). 1994. *Flora of Madeira.* London: Natural History Museum/HMSO.

Rehder, A. 1940. *Manual of Cultivated Trees and Shrubs Hardy in North America.* (2nd ed.). New York: Macmillan.

Stace, C. 1997. *New Flora of the British Isles.* (2nd ed.). Cambridge: Cambridge University Press.

Stainton, A. 1988. *Flowers of the Himalaya. A Supplement.* Oxford University Press.

Stearn, W.T. 1992. *Botanical Latin.* (4th ed.). Newton Abbot, Devon: David & Charles.

Stearn, W.T. 1996. *Stearn's Dictionary of Plant Names for Gardeners.* London: Cassell

Thomas, G.S. 1990. *Perennial Garden Plants. A Modern Florilegium.* (3rd ed.). London: Dent.

Thomas, G.S. 1992. *Ornamental Shrubs, Climbers & Bamboos.* London: John Murray

Trehane, P. (comp.). 1989. *Index Hortensis. Volume 1: Perennials.* Wimborne: Quarterjack

Tutin, T.G., et al. (ed.). 1993. *Flora Europaea. Volume 1. Psilotaceae to Platanaceae.* (2nd ed.). Cambridge University Press.

Tutin, T.G., et al. 1964. *Flora Europaea.* Cambridge University Press. Vols 1-5.

Walter, K.S. & Gillett, H.J. (eds). 1998. *1997 IUCN Red List of Threatened Plants.* Gland, Switzerland and Cambridge, UK: IUCN.

Walters, S.M. & Cullen, J. et al. (eds). 2000. *The European Garden Flora.* Cambridge: Cambridge University Press. (6 vols).

Willis, J.C. & Airy-Shaw, H.K. (eds). 1973. *A Dictionary of the Flowering Plants and Ferns.* (8th ed.). Cambridge University Press.

GENERAL PERIODICALS

New, Rare and Unusual Plants.
The Hardy Plant Society. *The Hardy Plant.*
The Hardy Plant Society. *The Sport.*
Internationale Stauden-Union. *ISU Yearbook.*
Royal Horticultural Society. *The Garden.*
Royal Horticultural Society. *The Plantsman.*
Royal Horticultural Society. *The New Plantsman.*

GENERAL WEBSITES

Australian Cultivar Registration Authority. Jan 2005. www.anbg.gov.au/acra

Australian Plant Breeders Rights – Database Search. Jan 2005. http://cber.bio.waikato.ac.nz

Australian Plant Names Index. Australian National Botanic Gardens (comp.). Apr 2004. www.anbg.gov.au/anbg/names.html

Canadian Plant Breeders' Rights Office: Canadian Food Inspection Agency. Jan 2005. www.inspection.gc.ca/english/plaveg/pbrpov/pbrpove.shtml

Catálogo de las Plantas Vasculares de las República Argentina. www.darwin.edu.ar

Checklist of UK Recorded Species. www.mapmate.co.uk/checklist/index.htm Flora Mesoamericana Internet Version (W3FM). Apr 2003 Missouri Botanical Garden. www.mobot.org

Flora of Korea. http://user.Ksucc.ac.kr/~ecolab/flora.html

Flora of North America Website. 2002. Morin, N.R., et al. http://hua.huh.harvard.edu/fna/index.html

GRIN (Germplasm Resources Information Network) Taxonomy. Aug 2000. www.ars-grin.gov/npgs/tax/index.html

Index Synonymique de la Flore de France. www.inra.fr/flore-france/consult.htm~Recherche

International Perennial Plant Register. 2003. Internationale Stauden-Union. www.isu-perennials.org/e/indexe.htm

International Plant Names Index. (2004). www.ipni.org

IOPI Provisional Global Plant Checklist. Sept 2003. www.bgbm.fu-berlin.de/iopi/gpc/query.asp

List of Plant Species of the Waikato. University of Waikato. Dec 2003. http://cber.bio.waikato.ac.nz

Manual de plantas de Costa Rica. www.mobot.org/manual.plantas/lista.html

New Ornamentals Database. Oct 2003. Hatch, L.C. (comp.). http://members.tripod.com.~Hatch_L/nos.html

Plants Database. Version 3.5. Jan 2004. USDA, NRCS. http://plants.usda.gov/

Suntory Collection: Dec 2004. www.suntory collection.info

Synonymized Checklist of the Vascular Flora of the United States, Puerto Rico and the Virgin Isles. July 1998. BIOTA of North America Program. www.csdl.tamu.edu/FLORA/b98/check98.htm

US Patent Full-Text Database. US Patent and Trademark Office, (comp.). Jan 2004. www.uspto.gov/patft/index.html

VAST TROPICOS. Jan 2004. Missouri Botanical Garden. http://mobot.mobot.org/W3T/Search/vast.html

GENERA

Acacia
Beckett, K.A. 1993. Some Australian Wattles in Cultivation. *The Plantsman* 15(3):131-47.
Simmons, M.H. 1987. *Acacias of Australia.* (2nd ed.). Melbourne: Nelson.

Acer
Harris, J.G.S. 2000. *The Gardener's Guide to Growing Maples.* Newton Abbot, Devon: David & Charles.
Van Gelderen, C.J. & Van Gelderen, D.M. 1999. *Maples for Gardens.* A Color Encyclopedia. Portland, Oregon: Timber Press.
Vertrees, J.D. 2001. *Japanese Maples.* Momiji and Kaede. (3rd ed.). Portland, Oregon: Timber Press.

Actaea
Compton, J. 1992. *Cimicifuga* L. Ranunculaceae. *The Plantsman* 14(2):99-115.
Compton, J. 1992. *Cimicifuga.* A Bane of a Name for a Fine Plant. *The Garden* (RHS) 117(11):504-506.
Compton, J.A. & Culham, A. 2000. The Name is the Game. *The Garden* (RHS) 125(1):48-52.
Compton, J.A., Culham, A. & Jury, S.L. 1998. Reclassification of *Actaea* to Include *Cimicifuga* and *Souliea* (*Ranunculaceae*). *Taxon* 47:593-634.

Adiantum
Goudey, C.J. 1985. *Maidenhair Ferns in Cultivation.* Melbourne: Lothian.

Agapanthus
Snoeijer, Wim 2004. *Agapanthus. A Revision of the Genus.* Timber Press.

Agavaceae
Irish, M. & Irish, G. 2000. *Agaves, Yuccas and Related Plants.* A Gardener's Guide. Portland, Oregon: Timber Press.

Aizoaceae
Burgoyne, P., Hartmann, H., Hammer, S., Chesselet, P., van Jaarsveld, E., Klak, C., Smith, G., van Wyk & H. Kurzweil, B. 1998. *Mesembs of the World. Illustrated Guide to a Remarkable Succulent Group.* South Africa: Briza Publications.

Allium
Dadd, R. 1997. RHS Trials: Grand Alliums. *The Garden* (RHS) 122(9) p658-661.
Davies, D. 1992. *Alliums. The Ornamental Onions.* London: Batsford .
Gregory, M., et al. 1998. *Nomenclator Alliorum.* London: RBG, Kew.
Mathew, B. 1996. *A Review of Allium Section Allium.* Kew: Royal Botanic Gardens.

Androsace
Smith, G. & Lowe, D. 1997. *The Genus Androsace.* Pershore, Worcs: Alpine Garden Society Publications Limited.

Anemone, Japanese
McKendrick, M. 1990. Autumn Flowering Anemones. *The Plantsman* 12(3):140-151.
McKendrick, M. 1998. Japanese Anemones. *The Garden* (RHS) 123(9):628-633.

Anthemis
Leslie, A. 1997. Focus on Plants: *Anthemis tinctoria. The Garden* (RHS) 122(8):552-555.

Apiaceae
Ingram, T. 1993. *Umbellifers.* Pershore, Worcs: Hardy Plant Society.
Pimenov, M.G. & Leonov, M.V. 1993. *The Genera of the Umbelliferae.* Kew: Royal Botanic Gardens.

Aquilegia
Munz, P.A. 1946. *Aquilegia:* the Cultivated and Wild Columbines. *Gentes Herb.* 7(1):1-150.

Araceae
Govaerts, R. & Frodin, D.G. 2002. *World Checklist and Bibliography of Araceae (and Acoraceae).* RBG Kew.

Arecaceae (Palmae, palms)
Jones, D.L. 1995. *Palms Throughout the World.* Chatswood, NSW: Reed Books.
Uhl, N.W. & Dransfield, J. 1987. *Genera Palmarum.* A Classification of Palms Based on the Work of Harold E. Moore Jr. Lawrence, Kansas: Allen Press.

Argyranthemum
Cheek, R. 1993. La Belle Marguerite. *The Garden* (RHS) 118(8):350-355.
Humphries, C.J. 1976. A Revision of the Macaronesian Genus *Argyranthemum. Bull. Brit. Mus. (Nat. Hist.) Bot.* 5(4):145-240.

Arisaema
Gusman, G. & Gusman, L. 2002. *The Genus Arisaema: A Monograph for Botanists and Nature Lovers.* Ruggell, Leichtenstein: A.R. Gantner Verlag Kommanditgesellschaft.

Pradhan, U.C. 1997. *Himalayan Cobra Lilies* (Arisaema). Their Botany and Culture. (2nd ed.). Kalimpong, West Bengal, India: Primulaceae Books.

Arum

Bown, D. 2000. *Plants of the Arum Family.* (2nd ed.). Portland, Oregon: Timber Press.

Boyce, P. 1993. *The Genus Arum.* London: HMSO.

Asclepiadaceae

Eggli, U. (ed.). 2002. *Illustrated Handbook of Succulent Plants: Asclepiadaceae.* Heidelberg, Germany: Springer-Verlag.

Aster

Picton, P. 1999. *The Gardener's Guide to Growing Asters.* Newton Abbot: David & Charles.

Ranson, E.R. 1946. *Michaelmas Daisies and Other Garden Asters.* London: John Gifford Ltd.

Astilbe

Noblett, H. 2001. *Astilbe.* A Guide to the Identification of Cultivars and Common Species. Cumbria: Henry Noblett.

Aubrieta

1975. *International Registration Authority Checklist.* Weihenstephan, Germany: (Unpublished).

Bamboos

Ohrnberger, D. 1999. *The Bamboos of the World.* Amsterdam: Elsevier.

Begonia

American Begonia Society Astro Branch Begonia Data Base. Jan 2000. http://absastro.tripod.com/data.htm.

Ingles, J. 1990. *American Begonia Society Listing of Begonia Cultivars.* Revised Edition Buxton Checklist. American Begonia Society.

Thompson, M.L. & Thompson, E.J. 1981. *Begonias.* The Complete Reference Guide. New York: Times Books.

Berberidaceae

Stearn, W.T. & Shaw, J.M.H. 2002. *The Genus Epimedium and Other Herbaceous Berberidaceae including the Genus Podophyllum.* Kew: Royal Botanic Gardens.

Betula

Ashburner, K. & Schilling. T. 1985. *Betula utilis* and its Varieties. *The Plantsman* 7(2):116-125.

Ashburner, K.B. 1980. *Betula* – a Survey. *The Plantsman* 2(1):31-53.

Hunt, D. (ed.). 1993. *Betula: Proceedings of the IDS Betula Symposium 1992.* Richmond, Surrey: International Dendrology Society.

Boraginaceae

Bennett, M. 2003. *Pulmonarias and the Borage Family.* London: Batsford.

Bougainvillea

Bor, N.L. & Raizada, M.B. 1982. *Some Beautiful Indian Climbers and Shrubs.* (2nd ed.). Bombay Nat. Hist. Soc.

Gillis, W.T. 1976. Bougainvilleas of Cultivation (*Nyctaginaceae*). *Baileya* 20(1):34-41.

Iredell, J. 1990. *The Bougainvillea Grower's Handbook.* Brookvale, Australia: Simon & Schuster.

Iredell, J. 1994. *Growing Bougainvilleas.* London: Cassell.

MacDaniels, L.H. 1981. A Study of Cultivars in *Bougainvillea* (*Nyctaginaceae*). *Baileya* 21(2):77-100.

Singh, B., Panwar, R.S., Voleti, S.R., Sharma, V.K. & Thakur, S. 1999. *The New International Bougainvillea Check List.* (2nd ed.). New Delhi: Indian Agricultural Research Institute.

Bromeliaceae

Beadle, D.A. 1991. *A Preliminary Listing of all the Known Cultivar and Grex Names for the Bromeliaceae.* Corpus Christi, Texas: Bromeliad Society.

Bromeliad Cultivar Registry Online Databases. Jan 2004. Bromeliad Society International http://fcbs.org

Luther, H.E. 2002. *An Alphabetical List of Bromeliad Binomials.* (8th ed.) Orlando, Florida: Bromeliad Society International.

Rauh, W. 1979. *Bromeliads for Home, Garden and Greenhouse.* Blandford, Dorset: Blandford Press.

Brugmansia

Haik, M. (comp.). Dec 2003. Brugmansia Database. American Brugmansia and Datura Society. http://abads-database.org.

Bulbs

Bryan, J.E. 1989. *Bulbs.* Vols 1 & 2. Bromley, Kent: Christopher Helm.

Du Plessis, N. & Duncan, G. 1989. *Bulbous Plants of Southern Africa.* Cape Town: Tafelberg.

Grey-Wilson, C. & Mathew, B. 1981. *Bulbs.* London: Collins.

Leeds, R. 2000. *The Plantfinder's Guide to Early Bulbs.* Newton Abbot, Devon: David & Charles.

Phillips, R., Rix, M. & Mathew. B. (ed.). 1981. *The Bulb Book. A Photographic Guide to Over 800 Hardy Bulbs.* London: Ward Lock Ltd.

Van Scheepen, J. (ed.). 1991. *International Checklist for Hyacinths and Miscellaneous Bulbs.* Hillegom, Netherlands: Royal General Bulbgrowers' Association (KAVB).

Buxus

Batdorf, L.R. 1995. *Boxwood Handbook. A Practical Guide to Knowing and Growing Boxwood.* Boyce, VA, USA: The American Boxwood Society.

Camellia

Trujillo, D. J. (ed.). 2002. *Camellia Nomenclature.* (24th revd ed.). Southern California Camellia Society.

Savige, T.J. (comp.). 1993. *The International Camellia Register.* The International Camellia Society. (2 vols)

Savige, T.J. (comp.). 1997. *The International Camellia Register.* Suppl. to vols 1 and 2. The International Camellia Society.

Campanula

Lewis, P. & Lynch, M. 1998. *Campanulas*. A Gardeners Guide. (2nd ed.). London: Batsford.

Lewis, P 2002. *Campanulas in the Garden*. Pershore, Worcs.: Hardy Plant Society.

Canna

Cooke, I. 2001. *The Gardener's Guide to Growing Cannas*. Newton Abbot, Devon: David & Charles.

Hayward, K. 2000. *Canna Handbook*. (Edition 1.01). Farnborough, Hants: Hart Canna.

Carnivorous Plants

D'Amato, P. 1998. *The Savage Garden*. Berkeley, USA: Ten Speed Press.

Pietropaulo, J. & Pietropaulo, P. 1986. *Carnivorous Plants of the World*. Oregon, USA: Timber Press.

Schlauer, J. (comp.). Jan 2005. Carnivorous Plant Database. www.omnisterra.com/bot/cp_home.cgi

Slack, A. 1988. *Carnivorous Plants*. (Revd ed.). Sherborne, Dorset: Alphabooks.

Cercidiphyllum

Dosmann, M.S. 1999. Katsura: a Review of *Cercidiphyllum* in Cultivation and in the Wild. *The New Plantsman* 6(1):52-62.

Dosmann, M., Andrews, S., Del Tredici, P. & Li, J. 2003. Classification and Nomenclature of Weeping Katsuras. *The Plantsman* 2(1): 21-27.

Chaenomeles

Weber, C. 1963. Cultivars in the Genus *Chaenomeles*. *Arnoldia (Jamaica Plain)* 23(3):17-75.

Chrysanthemum (Dendranthema)

Brummitt, D. 1997. *Chrysanthemum* Once Again. *The Garden* (RHS) 122(9):662-663.

Gosling, S.G. (ed.). 1964. *British National Register of Chrysanthemums*. Whetstone, London: National Chrysanthemum Society.

National Chrysanthemum Society. 2000. *British National Register of Names of Chrysanthemums Amalgamated Edition 1964-1999*. Tamworth, Staffordshire: The National Chrysanthemum Society.

Cistus

Bygrave, P. & Page, R.G. 2002. *Cistus – a Guide to the Collection at Chelsea Physic Garden*. Wisley: NCCPG.

Page, R.G. July 2003. National Collection of Cistus and Halimium Website. www.cistuspage.org.uk

Citrus

Davies, F.S. & Albrigo, L.G. 1994. *Citrus*. Wallingford, Oxon: Cab International.

Saunt, J. 1990. *Citrus Varieties of the World*. An Illustrated Guide. Norwich: Sinclair

Clematis

Grey-Wilson, C. 2000. *Clematis: the Genus*. London: Batsford

HelpMeFind Clematis. Nov 2003. www.helpmefind.com/clematis

Johnson, M. 2001. *The Genus Clematis*. Södertälje, Sweden: Magnus Johnsons Plantskola AB & Bengt Sundström.

Matthews, V. (comp.). 2002. *The International Clematis Register and Checklist 2002*. London: Royal Horticultural Society.

Toomey, M. & Leeds, E. 2001. *An Illustrated Encyclopedia of Clematis*. Portland, Oregon: Timber Press.

Conifers

den Ouden, P. & Boom, B.K. 1965. *Manual of Cultivated Conifers*. The Hague: Martinus Nijhof.

Farjon, A. 1998. *World Checklist and Bibliography of Conifers*. Kew: Royal Botanic Gardens.

Krüssmann, G. & Epp, M.E. (trans.). 1985. *Manual of Cultivated Conifers*. London: Batsford.

Lewis, J. & Leslie, A.C. 1987. *The International Conifer Register. Part 1. Abies to Austrotaxus*. London: Royal Horticultural Society.

Lewis, J. & Leslie, A.C. 1989. *The International Conifer Register. Part 2. Belis to Pherosphaera*, excluding the Cypresses. London: Royal Horticultural Society.

Lewis, J. & Leslie, A.C. 1992. *The International Conifer Register. Part 3. The Cypresses*. London: Royal Horticultural Society.

Lewis, J. & Leslie, A.C. 1998. *The International Conifer Register. Part 4. Juniperus*. London: Royal Horticultural Society.

Trehane, P. Mar 2000. Complete List of Conifer Taxa Accepted for Registration. Royal Horticultural Society. www.rhs.org.uk/research/registration_conifers_accepted.asp

Welch, H.J. 1979. *Manual of Dwarf Conifers*. New York: Theophrastus.

Welch, H.J. 1991. *The Conifer Manual*. Vol. 1. Dordrecht, Netherlands: Kluwer Academic Publishers.

Welch, H.J. 1993. *The World Checklist of Conifers*. Bromyard, Herefordshire: Landsman's Bookshops Ltd.

Cornus

Howard, R.A. 1961. Registration Lists of Cultivar Names in *Cornus L. Arnoldia (Jamaica Plain)* 21(2):9-18.

Corydalis

Lidén, M. & Zetterlund, H. 1997. *Corydalis. A Gardener's Guide and a Monograph of the Tuberous Species*. Pershore, Worcs.: Alpine Garden Society Publications Limited.

Mathew, B. 2001. Earning their Spurs (*Corydalis*). *The Garden* (RHS) 126(3):184-187.

Corylus

Crawford, M. 1995. *Hazelnuts: Production and Culture*. Dartington, Devon: Agroforestry Research Trust.

Game, M. 1995. Champion of the Cobnut. *The Garden* (RHS) 120(11):674-677.

Cotoneaster

Fryer, J. & Hylmö, B. 1998. Seven New Species of *Cotoneaster* in Cultivation. *The New Plantsman* 5(3):132-144.

Fryer, J. & Hylmö, B. 2001. Captivating Cotoneasters. *The New Plantsman* 8(4):227-238.

Fryer, J. 1996. Undervalued Versatility. *Cotoneaster. The Garden* (RHS) 121(11):709-715.

Crassulaceae

Rowley, G. 2003. *Crassula: A Grower's Guide.* Venegono superiore, Italy: Cactus & Co.

Eggli, U. (ed.) 2003. *Illustrated Handbook of Succulent Plants.* Springer.

Crocosmia

Goldblatt, P., Manning, J.C. & Dunlop, G. 2004. *Crocosmia and Chasmanthe.* Portland, Oregon: Timber Press.

Crocus

Jacobsen, N., van Scheepen, J. & Ørgaard, M. 1997. The *Crocus chrysanthus – biflorus* Cultivars. *The New Plantsman* 4(1):6-38.

Mathew, B. 1982. *The Crocus. A Review of the Genus Crocus (Iridaceae).* London: Batsford.

Mathew, B. 2002. *Crocus* Up-date. *The Plantsman* 1(1): 44-56

Cyclamen

Clennett, C. Jan. 2003. Register of Cultivar Names. www.cyclamen.org/registrar_set.html

Grey-Wilson, C. 2003. *Cyclamen. A Guide for Gardeners, Horticulturists & Botanists.* London: Batsford.

Grey-Wilson, C. 2002 Sprenger's Alpine Cyclamen. *The Plantsman* 1(3): 173-177

Cypripedium

Cribb, P. 1997. *The Genus Cypripedium.* Portland, Oregon: Timber Press.

Dahlia

American Dahlia Society website. Oct 2003. www.dahlia.org

National Dahlia Society. 2003. *Classified Directory and Judging Rules.* (27th ed.) Aldershot, Hants: National Dahlia Society.

RHS & Hedge, R. (comps). 1969. *Tentative Classified List and International Register of Dahlia Names 1969.* (& Supplements 1-13). London: Royal Horticultural Society.

Daphne

Brickell, C. & White, R. 2000. A Quartet of New Daphnes. *The New Plantsman* 7(1):6-18.

Brickell, C. 2000. *Daphne.* Part 2: Henderson's Daphne. *The New Plantsman* 7(2):114-122.

Brickell, C.D. & Mathew, B. 1976. *Daphne. The Genus in the Wild and in Cultivation.* Woking, Surrey: Alpine Garden Society.

Grey-Wilson, C. (ed.). 2001. *The Smaller Daphnes. The Proceedings of 'Daphne 2000', a Conference held at the Royal Horticultural Society.* Pershore, Worcs: Alpine Garden Society Publications Ltd.

Delphinium

1949. *A Tentative Check-list of Delphinium Names.* London: Royal Horticultural Society.

1970. *A Tentative Check-list of Delphinium Names.* Addendum to the 1949 tentative check-list of *Delphinium* names. London: Royal Horticultural Society.

Leslie, A.C. 1995. The International Delphinium Register Supplement 1993-94. *The Delphinium Society Year Book 1995.*

Leslie, A.C. 1996. *The International Delphinium Register Cumulative Supplement 1970-1995.* London: Royal Horticultural Society.

Leslie, A.C. 1996-2000. The International Delphinium Register Supplement 1994-99. *The Delphinium Society Year Book 1996-98.* London: Royal Horticultural Society.

Dianthus

Bird, R. 1994. *Border Pinks.* London: Batsford.

Galbally, J. & Galbally, E. 1997. *Carnations and Pinks for Garden and Greenhouse.* Portland, Oregon: Timber Press.

Leslie, A.C. *The International Dianthus Register.* 1983-2002. (2nd ed & Supps 1-19). London: Royal Horticultural Society.

Diascia

Benham, S. 1987. *Diascia:* A Survey of the Species in Cultivation. *The Plantsman* 9(1):1-17.

Harrison, H. 1996. *Diascia (Scrophulariaceae). Hardy Plant* 18(1):41-47.

Lord, T. 1996. *Diascia* on Trial. *The Garden* (RHS) 121(4):192-194.

Dierama

Hilliard, O.M. & Burtt, B.L. 1991. *Dierama. The Harebells of Africa.* Johannesburg; London: Acorn Books.

Dionysia

Grey-Wilson, C. 1989. *The Genus Dionysia.* Woking, Surrey: Alpine Garden Society.

Douglasia

Mitchell, B. 1999. Celebrating the Bicentenary of David Douglas: a Review of *Douglasia* in Cultivation. *The New Plantsman* 6(2):101-108.

Dracaena

Bos, J.J., Graven, P., Hetterscheid, W.L.A. & van de Wege, J.J. 1992. Wild and cultivated *Dracaena fragrans. Edinburgh J. Bot.* 49(3):311-331.

Echinacea

Vernon, J. 1999. Power Flowers. *The Garden* (RHS) 124(8):588-593.

Epimedium

Barker, D.G. 1996. *Epimediums and other herbaceous Berberidaceae.* Pershore, Worcs.: The Hardy Plant Society.

Episcia

Dates, J.D. 1993. *The Gesneriad Register 1993.* Check List of Names with Descriptions of Cultivated Plants in the Genera *Episcia* & *Alsobia.* Galesburg, Illinois: American Gloxinia & Gesneriad Society, Inc.

Erica

Baker, H.A. & Oliver, E.G.H. 1967. *Heathers in Southern Africa.* Cape Town: Purnell.

Schumann, D., Kirsten, G. & Oliver, E.G.H. 1992. *Ericas of South Africa.* Vlaeberg, South Africa: Fernwood Press.

Erodium

Clifton, R. 1994. *Geranium Family Species Checklist. Part 1 Erodium.* (4th ed.). The Geraniaceae Group.

Leslie, A.C. 1980. The Hybrid of *Erodium corsicum* With *Erodium reichardii. The Plantsman* 2:117-126.

Toomey, N., Cubey, J. & Culham, A. 2002. *Erodium × variabile. The Plantsman* 1(3): 166-172

Victor, D.X. (comp.). 2000. *Erodium: Register of Cultivar Names.* The Geraniaceae Group.

Erythronium

Mathew, B. 1992. A Taxonomic and Horticultural Review of *Erythronium* L. (*Liliaceae*). *J. Linn. Soc., Bot.* 109:453-471.

Mathew, B. 1998. The Genus *Erythronium. Bull. Alpine Gard. Soc. Gr. Brit.* 66(3):308-321.

Euonymus

Brown, N. 1996. Notes on Cultivated Species of *Euonymus. The New Plantsman* 3(4):238-243.

Lancaster, C.R. 1982. *Euonymus* in Cultivation – Addendum. *The Plantsman* 4:61-64, 253-254.

Lancaster, R.C. 1981. An Account of *Euonymus* in Cultivation and its Availability in Commerce. *The Plantsman* 3(3):133-166.

Euphorbia

Turner, R. 1995. *Euphorbias. A Gardeners Guide.* London: Batsford.

Witton, D. 2000. *Euphorbias.* Pershore, Worcs: Hardy Plant Society.

Fagales:

Govaerts, R. & Frodin, D.G. 1998. *World Checklist and Bibliography of Fagales.* Royal Botanic Gardens, Kew.

Fagus

Dönig, G. 1994. *Die Park-und Gartenformen der Rotbuche Fagus sylvatica L.* Erlangen, Germany: Verlag Gartenbild Heinz Hansmann.

Wyman, D. 1964. Registration List of Cultivar Names of *Fagus* L. *J. Arnold Arbor.* 24(1):1-8.

Fascicularia

Nelson, E.C. & Zizka, G. 1997. *Fascicularia* (*Bromeliaceae*): Which Species are Cultivated and Naturalized in Northwestern Europe. *The New Plantsman* 4(4):232-239.

Nelson, E.C., Zizka, G., Horres, R. & Weising, K. 1999. Revision of the Genus *Fascicularia* Mez (*Bromeliaceae*). *Botanical Journal of the Linnean Society* 129(4):315-332.

Ferns

Checklist of World Ferns. Oct 2001. http://home pages.caverock.net.nz/~bj/fern/

Johns, R.J. 1996. *Index Filicum.* Supplementum Sextum pro annis 1976-1990. RBG, Kew.

Johns, R.J. 1997. *Index Filicum.* Supplementum Septimum pro annis 1991-1995. RBG, Kew.

Jones, D.L. 1987. *Encyclopaedia of Ferns.* Melbourne, Australia: Lothian.

Kaye, R. 1968. *Hardy Ferns.* London: Faber & Faber

Rickard, M.H. 2000. *The Plantfinder's Guide to Garden Ferns.* Newton Abbot, Devon: David & Charles.

Rush, R. 1984. *A Guide to Hardy Ferns.* London: British Pteridological Society.

Forsythia

INRA Forsythia website. Dec 2000. www.angers.inra.fr/forsy/indexeng.html

Fragaria

Day, D. (ed.). 1993. *Grower Digest 3: Strawberries.* (Revd ed.). London: Nexus Business Communications.

Fritillaria

Clark, T. & Grey-Wilson, C. 2003. Crown Imperials. *The Plantsman* 2(1):33-47.

Mathew, B., et al. 2000. *Fritillaria* Issue. *Bot. Mag.* 17(3):145-185.

Pratt, K. & Jefferson-Brown, M. 1997. *The Gardener's Guide to Growing Fritillaries.* Newton Abbot: David & Charles.

Turrill, W.B. & Sealy, J.R. 1980. *Studies in the Genus Fritillaria (Liliaceae).* Hooker's Icones Plantarum Vol. 39 (1 & 2). Royal Botanic Gardens, Kew.

Fruit

Anon. 1997. *Catalogue of Cultivars in the United Kingdom National Fruit Collection.* Kent, UK: Brogdale Horticultural Trust.

Bowling, B.L. 2000. *The Berry Grower's Companion.* Portland, Oregon: Timber Press.

Hogg, R. 1884. *The Fruit Manual.* (5th Ed.). London: Journal of Horticulture Office.

Index of the Bush Fruit Collection at the National Fruit Trials 1987. 1987. Faversham, Kent: MAFF.

Fuchsia

Bartlett, G. 1996. *Fuchsias – A Colour Guide.* Marlborough, Wilts: Crowood Press.

Boullemier, Leo.B. (comp.). 1991. *The Checklist of Species, Hybrids and Cultivars of the Genus Fuchsia.* London, New York, Sydney: Blandford Press.

Boullemier, Leo.B. (comp.). 1995. *Addendum No. 1 to the 1991 Checklist of Species, Hybrids and Cultivars of the Genus Fuchsia.* Dyfed, Wales: The British Fuchsia Society.

Goulding, E. 1995. *Fuchsias: The Complete Guide.* London: Batsford.

Johns, E.A. 1997. *Fuchsias of the 19th and Early 20th Century.* An Historical Checklist of Fuchsia Species & Cultivars, pre-1939. Kidderminster, Worcs: The British Fuchsia Society

Nijhuis, M. 1994. *1000 Fuchsias.* London: Batsford.

Nijhuis, M. 1996. *500 More Fuchsias.* London: Batsford.

Stevens, R. Jan 2004. Find That Fuchsia. www.findthatfuchsia.info

Van Veen, G. Dec 2003. Gelderse Fuchsia Info-site. http://home.tiscali.nl/veenvang

Galanthus

Bishop, M., Davis, A. & Grimshaw, J. 2001. *Snowdrops. A monograph of cultivated Galanthus.* Maidenhead: Griffin Press.

Davis, A.P., Mathew, B. (ed.) & King, C. (ill.). 1999. *The Genus Galanthus. A Botanical Magazine Monograph.* Oregon: Timber Press.

Gentiana

Bartlett, M. 1975. *Gentians.* Dorset: Blandford Press.

Halda, J.J. 1996. *The Genus Gentiana.* Dobré, Czech Republic: Sen.

Wilkie, D. 1950. *Gentians.* (2nd ed. revised). London: Country Life.

Geranium

Bath, T. & Jones, J. 1994. *The Gardener's Guide to Growing Hardy Geraniums.* Newton Abbot, Devon: David & Charles.

Clifton, R.T.F. 1995. *Geranium Family Species Check List Part 2.* Geranium. (4th ed. issue 2). Dover: The Geraniaceae Group.

Jones, J., et al. 2001. *Hardy Geraniums for the Garden.* (3rd ed.), revised and enlarged). Pershore, Worcs: Hardy Plant Society.

Victor, D.X. 2001. *Geranium.* Register of Cultivar Names. The Geraniaceae Group. www.hardy geraniums.com/register_of_cultivar_names.htm

Yeo, P.F. 2002. *Hardy Geraniums.* (3rd ed.). Kent: Croom Helm.

Gesneriaceae

American Gloxinia and Gesneriad Society. Listing of registered gesneriads. Sept 2003. www.aggs.org/ir_ges

Dates, J.D. 1986-1990. *The Gesneriad Register 1986-1987 & 1990.* Galesburg, Illinois: American Gloxinia & Gesneriad Society, Inc.

Gladiolus

British Gladiolus Society List of Cultivars Classified for Show Purposes 1994. Mayfield, Derbyshire: British Gladiolus Society.

1997-1998. British Gladiolus Society List of European Cultivars Classified for Exhibition Purposes 1997 & 1998. Mayfield, Derbyshire: British Gladiolus Society.

1997-1998. British Gladiolus Society List of New Zealand Cultivars Classified for Exhibition Purposes 1997 & 1998. Mayfield, Derbyshire: British Gladiolus Society.

1997-1998. British Gladiolus Society List of North American Cultivars Classified for Exhibition Purposes 1997 & 1998. Mayfield, Derbyshire: British Gladiolus Society.

Goldblatt, P. & Manning, J. 1998. *Gladiolus in Southern Africa.* Vlaeberg, South Africa: Fernwood Press.

Goldblatt, P. 1996. *Gladiolus in Tropical Africa.* Systematics Biology and Evolution. Oregon: Timber Press.

Lewis, G.J., Obermeyer, A.A. & Barnard, T.T. 1972. A Revision of the South African Species of *Gladiolus. J. S. African Bot.* (Supp. Vol.)

Gleditsia

Santamour, F.S. & McArdle, A.J. 1983. Checklist of Cultivars of Honeylocust (*Gleditsia triacanthos* L.). *J. Arboric.* 9:271-276.

Grevillea

Olde, P. & Marriott, N. 1995. *The Grevillea Book.* (3). Kenthurst, NSW: Kangaroo Press.

Haemanthus

Snijman, D. 1984. A Revision of the Genus *Haemanthus. J. S. African Bot.* (Supp.) 12.

Hamamelis

Coombes, A.J. 1996. Winter Magic. Introduction to Witch Hazels. *The Garden* (RHS) 121(1):28-33.

Lane, C. 1998. *Hamamelis* in Small Spaces. *The Garden* (RHS) 123(1):38-41.

Strand, C. 1998. Asian Witch Hazels and their Hybrids: a History of *Hamamelis* in cultivation. *The New Plantsman* 5(4):231-245.

Heathers

Nelson, E.C. Sept 2004. International Cultivar Registration Authority for Heathers. www.heathersociety.org.uk/registration.html

Nelson, E.C. & Small, D.J. (eds). 2000. *International Register of Heather Names.* Volume 1: Hardy Cultivars & European Species. Part 1-4. The Heather Society.

Small, D. & Small, A. (comps). 2001. *Handy Guide to Heathers.* (3rd ed.) Creeting St Mary, Suffolk: The Heather Society.

Hebe

Chalk, D. 1988. *Hebes and Parahebes.* Bromley, Kent: Christopher Helm (Publishers) Ltd.

Hutchins, G. 1997. *Hebes: Here and There.* A Monograph on the Genus *Hebe.* Caversham, Berks: Hutchins & Davies.

Metcalf, L.J. 2001. *International Register of Hebe Cultivars.* Canterbury, New Zealand: Royal New Zealand Institute of Horticulture (Inc.).

Hedera

McAllister, H. 1988. Canary and Algerian Ivies. *The Plantsman* 10(1):27-29.

McAllister, H.A. & Rutherford, A. 1990. *Hedera helix* and *H. hibernica* in the British Isles. *Watsonia* 18:7-15.

Rose, P.Q. 1996. *The Gardener's Guide to Growing Ivies.* David & Charles.

Rutherford, A., McAllister, H. & Mill, R.R. 1993. New Ivies from the Mediterranean Area and Macaronesia. *The Plantsman* 15(2):115-128.

Hedychium

Schilling, T. 1982. A Survey of Cultivated Himalayan and Sino-Himalayan *Hedychium* Species. *The Plantsman* 4:129-149.

Spencer-Mills, L. 1996. Glorious *Hedychium. The Garden* (RHS) 121(12):754-759.

Heliconia
Berry, F. & Kress, W.J. 1991. *Heliconia*. An Identification Guide. Washington: Smithsonian Institution Press.
Helleborus
Mathew, B. 1989. *Hellebores*. Woking: Alpine Garden Society.
Rice, G. & Strangman, E. 1993. *The Gardener's Guide to Growing Hellebores*. Newton Abbot, Devon: David & Charles.
Hemerocallis
AHS – Registered Daylily Database. May 2003. http://database.tinkersgardens.com
Baxter, G.J. (comp.) 2003. *Hemerocallis Cultivar Registrations 1890-2002*. (CD-ROM Version 2003a.) Jackson, Tennessee: American Hemerocallis Society.
Kitchingman, R.M. 1985. Some Species and Cultivars of *Hemerocallis*. *The Plantsman* 7(2):68-89.
Herbs
Page, M. & Stearn, W. *Culinary Herbs: A Wisley Handbook*. London: Royal Horticultural Society.
Phillips, R. & Foy, N. 1990. *Herbs*. London: Pan Books Ltd.
Hibiscus
Beers, L. & Howie, J. 1990. *Growing Hibiscus*. (2nd ed.). Kenthurst, Australia: Kangaroo Press.
Noble, C. July 2003. Official International Hibiscus Cross Check List and Register Database. Australian Hibiscus Society. *Hibiscus Register*. www.geocities.com/auhibsoc/ira/register.htm
Walker, J. 1999. *Hibiscus*. London: Casell.
Hippeastrum
Alfabetische Lijst van de in Nederland in Cultuur Zijnde Amaryllis (Hippeastrum) Cultivars. 1980. Hillegom, Netherlands: Koninklijke Algemeene Vereeniging Voor Bloembollencultur (KAVB).
Read, V.M. 2004. *Hippeastrum*. Portland, Oregon: RHS/Timber Press
Hosta
Hammelman, T. Mar 2001. Giboshi.com Hosta Database. www.giboshi.com
Hosta Library. Jan. 2003. www.hostalibrary.org
Schmid, W.G. 1991. *The Genus Hosta*. London: Batsford.
Hyacinthus
Clark, T. 2000. Focus on Plants: Treasures of the East (Hyacinths). *The Garden* (RHS) 125(9):672-675.
Stebbings, G. 1996. Heaven Scent. *The Garden* (RHS) 121(2):68-72.
Hydrangea
Church, G. 1999. *Hydrangeas*. London: Cassell.
Haworth-Booth, M. 1975. *The Hydrangeas*. London: Garden Book Club.
Lawson-Hall, T. & Brian, R. 1995. *Hydrangeas. A Gardener's Guide*. London: B.T. Batsford.
Van Gelderen, C.J. & D.M. 2004. *Encyclopedia of Hydrangeas*. Portland, Oregon: Timber Press.

Hypericum
Lancaster, R. & Robson, N. 1997. Focus on Plants: Bowls of Beauty. *The Garden* (RHS) 122(8):566-571.
Ilex
Andrews, S. 1983. Notes on Some *Ilex* × *altaclerensis* Clones. *The Plantsman* 5(2):65-81.
Andrews, S. 1984. More Notes on Clones of *Ilex* × *altaclerensis*. *The Plantsman* 6(3):157-166. Erratum vol.6 p.256.
Andrews, S. 1985. Holly Berries of a Varied Hue. *The Garden* (RHS) 110(11):518-522.
Andrews, S. 1994. Hollies with a Difference. *The Garden* (RHS) 119(12):580-583.
Dudley, T.R. & Eisenbeiss, G.K. 1992. *International Checklist of Cultivated Ilex*. Part 1 *Ilex opaca*. Washington USA: United States Department of Agriculture.
Dudley, T.R. & Eisenbeiss, G.K. 1992. *International Checklist of Cultivated Ilex*. Part 2 *Ilex crenata*. United States National Arboretum: United States Department of Agriculture.
Galle, F.C. 1997. *Hollies: the Genus Ilex*. Portland, Oregon: Timber Press.
Iridaceae
Innes, C. 1985. *The World of Iridaceae. A Comprehensive Record*. Ashington, Sussex: Holly Gate International Ltd.
Iris
American Iris Society Database. 2000. www.irisregister.com/
Hoog, M.H. 1980. Bulbous Irises . *The Plantsman* 2(3):141-64.
Mathew, B. 1981. *The Iris*. London: Batsford.
Mathew, B. 1993. The Spuria Irises. *The Plantsman* 15(1):14-25.
Service, N. 1990. *Iris unguicularis*. *The Plantsman* 12(1):1-9.
Stebbings, G. 1997. *The Gardener's Guide to Growing Iris*. Newton Abbot: David & Charles.
The Species Group of the British Iris Society, (ed.). 1997. *A Guide to Species Irises*. Their Identification and Cultivation. Cambridge, UK: Cambridge University Press.
Jovibarba* see under *Sempervivum
Kalmia
Jaynes, R.A. 1997. *Kalmia. Mountain Laurel and Related Species*. Oregon: Timber Press.
Pullen, A. 1997. *Kalmia latifolia*. *The Garden* (RHS) 122(6):400-403.
Kniphofia
Grant-Downton, R. 1997. Notes on *Kniphofia thomsonii* in Cultivation and in the Wild. *The New Plantsman* 4(3):148-156.
Taylor, J. 1985. *Kniphofia* – a Survey. *The Plantsman* 7(3):129-160.
Kohleria
Dates, J.D. (ed.) & Batcheller, F.N. (comp.). 1985. *The Gesneriad Register 1985. Check List of Names with*

Descriptions of Cultivated Plants in the Genus Kohleria. Lincoln Acres, California: American Gloxinia and Gesneriad Society, Inc.

Lachenalia
Duncan, G.D. 1988. *The Lachenalia Hand Book.*

Lantana
Howard, R.A. 1969. A Check List of Names Used in the Genus *Lantana. J. Arnold Arbor.* 29(11): 73-109.

Lathyrus
Norton, S. 1996. *Lathyrus. Cousins of Sweet Pea.* Surrey: NCCPG

Lavandula
McNaughton, V. 2000. *Lavender. The Grower's Guide.* Woodbridge, Suffolk: Garden Art Press
Upson, T. & Andrews, S. 2004. *The Genus Lavandula.* Richmond, Surrey: RBG Kew.

Legumes
ILDIS. International Legume Database and Information Service. Aug 2003. V6.06. www.biodiversity.soton.ac.uk/LegumeWeb
Lewis, G.P. 1987. *Legumes of Bahia.* London: Royal Botanic Gardens, Kew.
Lock, J.M. & Heald, J. 1994. *Legumes of Indo-China.* Kew: Royal Botanic Gardens.
Lock, J.M. & Simpson, K. 1991. *Legumes of West Asia.* Kew: Royal Botanic Gardens.
Lock, J.M. 1989. *Legumes of Africa: A Checklist.* Kew: Royal Botanic Gardens.
Roskov, Yu, R., Sytin, A.K. & Yakovlev, G.P. 1996. *Legumes of Northern Eurasia.* Kew: Royal Botanic Gardens.

Leptospermum
Check List of *Leptospermum* Cultivars. 1963. *J. Roy. New Zealand Inst. Hort.* 5(5):224-30.
Dawson, M. 1997. A History of *Leptospermum scoparium* in Cultivation – Discoveries from the Wild. *The New Plantsman* 4(1):51-59.
Dawson, M. 1997. A History of *Leptospermum scoparium* in Cultivation – Garden Selections. *The New Plantsman* 4(2):67-78.

Lewisia
Davidson, B.L.R. 2000. *Lewisias.* Portland, Oregon: Timber Press.
Elliott, R. 1978. *Lewisias.* Woking: Alpine Garden Society.
Mathew, B. 1989. *The Genus Lewisia.* Bromley, Kent: Christopher Helm.

Liliaceae sensu lato
Mathew, B. 1989. Splitting the *Liliaceae.* *The Plantsman* 11(2):89-105.

Lilium
Leslie, A.C. *The International Lily Register 1982-2002.* (3rd ed. & suppls 1-20). London: Royal Horticultural Society.

Lonicera
Bradshaw, D. 1996. *Climbing Honeysuckles.* Surrey: NCCPG

Magnolia
Callaway, D.J. Nov 2004. Magnolia Cultivar Checklist. www.magnoliasociety.org/index.html
Frodin, D.G. & Govaerts, R. 1996. *World Checklist and Bibliography of Magnoliaceae.* Kew: Royal Botanic Garden.

Malus
Crawford, M. 1994. *Directory of Apple Cultivars.* Devon: Agroforestry Research Trust.
Fiala, J.L. 1994. *Flowering Crabapples.* The genus *Malus.* Portland, Oregon: Timber Press.
Rouèche, A. Dec 2004. Les Crets Fruits et Pomologie. http://lescrets.free.fr
Smith, M.W.G. 1971. *National Apple Register of the United Kingdom.* London: MAFF
Spiers, V. 1996. *Burcombes, Queenies and Colloggetts.* St Dominic, Cornwall: West Brendon.

Meconopsis
Brickell, C. & Stevens, E. 2002. *Meconopsis* 'Lingholm'. *The New Plantsman* 1(2): 88-92
Grey-Wilson, C. 1992. A Survey of the Genus *Meconopsis* in Cultivation. The Plantsman 14(1): 1-33
Stevens, E. & Brickell, C. 2001. Problems with the Big Perennial Poppies. *The New Plantsman* 8(1):48-61.
Stevens, E. 2001. Further Observations on the Big Perennial Blue Poppies. *The New Plantsman* 8(2):105-111.

Moraea
Goldblatt, P. 1986. *The Moraeas of Southern Africa.* Kirstenbosch: National Botanic Gardens

Musa
Germplasm available from INIBAP (list of accessions with genome groups). Jan 2003. International Network for the Improvement of Banana and Plantain. www.inibap.org/research/itctable2_eng.htm
Rimmington, G. July 2002. Sorting Musa Names. http://gmr.landfood.unimelb.edu.au/Plantnames/Sorting/Musa.html

Narcissus
Blanchard, J.W. 1990. *Narcissus – a guide to wild daffodils.* Woking, Surrey: Alpine Garden Society.
Kington, S. (comp.). 1998. *The International Daffodil Register and Classified List 1998* (3rd ed. & Supps 1-5, 1998-2002). London: Royal Horticultural Society. www.rhs.org.uk/research/registerpages/intro.asp

Nematanthus
Arnold, P. 1978. *The Gesneriad Register 1978.* Check List of *Nematanthus.* American Gloxinia and Gesneriad Society, Inc.

Nerium
Pagen, F.J.J. 1987. Oleanders. *Nerium* L. and the Oleander Cultivars. Agricultural University Wageningen Papers.
Toogood, A. 1997. *Nerium oleander. The Garden* (RHS) 122(7):488-491.

Nymphaea
International Water Lily Society. 1993. *Identification of Hardy Nymphaea.* Stapeley Water Gardens Ltd.
Knotts, K. & Sacher, R. (comps). 2000. *Provisional Check List of Names/Epithets of Nymphaea L.* International Waterlily & Water Gardening Society. Cocoa Beach, Florida.
Swindells, P. 1983. *Waterlilies.* London: Croom Helm.

Orchidaceae
Shaw, J.M.H. 2003. The International Orchid Register. www.rhs.org.uk/research/registration_orchids.asp

Origanum
Paton, A. 1994. Three Membranous-bracted Species of *Origanum. Kew Mag.* 11(3):109-117.
White, S. 1998. *Origanum. The Herb Marjoram and its Relatives.* Surrey: NCCPG.

Paeonia
Kessenich, G.M. 1976. *Peonies.* (Variety Check List Pts 1-3). American Peony Society.
Osti, G.L. 1999. *The Book of Tree Peonies.* Turin: Umberto Allemandi
Page, M. 1997. *The Gardener's Guide to Growing Peonies.* Newton Abbott: David & Charles
Rogers, A. 1995. *Peonies.* Portland, Oregon: Timber Press
Wang, L., et al. 1998. *Chinese Tree Peony.* Beijing: China Forestry Publishing House.

Papaver
Grey-Wilson, C. 1998. Oriental Glories. *The Garden* (RHS) 123(5):320-325.
Grey-Wilson, C. 2000. *Poppies. The Poppy Family in the Wild and in Cultivation.* London: Batsford.

Passiflora
Vanderplank, J. 2002. *Passion Flowers.* (3rd ed.). London, England: Cassell.

Pelargonium
Abbott, P.G. 1994. *A Guide to Scented Geraniaceae.* Angmering, West Sussex: Hill Publicity Services.
Anon. 1985. *A Checklist and Register of Pelargonium Cultivar Names.* Pt 2: C-F. Australian Pelargonium Society.
Anon. 1978. *A Checklist and Register of Pelargonium Cultivar Names.* Pt 1 A-B. Australian Pelargonium Society.
Bagust, H. 1988. *Miniature and Dwarf Geraniums.* London: Christopher Helm.
Clifford, D. 1958. *Pelargoniums.* London: Blandford Press.
Clifton, R. 1999. *Geranium Family Species Checklist, Part 4: Pelargonium.* The Geraniaceae Group.
Complete Copy of the Spalding Pelargonium Checklist. (Unpublished). USA.
Key, H. 2000. *1001 Pelargoniums.* London: Batsford.
Miller, D. 1996. *Pelargonium.* A Gardener's Guide to the Species and Cultivars and Hybrids. London: B. T. Batsford.

Pelargonium Palette: The Geranium and Pelargonium Society of Sydney Incorporated. Varieties – Alphabetical List. July 2000. www.elj.com/geranium/var/alphaind.htm
Van der Walt, J.J.A., et al. 1977. *Pelargoniums of South Africa.* (1-3). Kirstenbosch, South Africa: National Botanic Gardens.

Penstemon
Lindgren, D.T. & Davenport, B. 1992. List and description of named cultivars in the genus *Penstemon* (1992). University of Nebraska.
Lord, T. 1994. Peerless Penstemons. *The Garden* (RHS) 119(7):304-309.
Nold, R. 1999. *Penstemons.* Portland, Oregon: Timber Press.
Way, D. & James, P. 1998. *The Gardener's Guide to Growing Penstemons.* Newton Abbott: David & Charles.

Phlomis
Mann Taylor, J. 1998. *Phlomis: The Neglected Genus.* Wisley: NCCPG.

Phlox
Harmer, J. & Elliott, J. 2001. *Phlox.* Pershore, Worcs: Hardy Plant Society
Stebbings, G. 1999. Simply Charming. *The Garden* (RHS) 124(7):518-521.
Wherry, E.T. 1955. The Genus *Phlox.* Morris Arboretum Monographs III.

Phormium
Heenan, P.B. 1991. *Checklist of Phormium Cultivars.* Royal New Zealand Institute of Horticulture.
McBride-Whitehead, V. 1998. Phormiums of the Future. *The Garden* (RHS) 123(1):42-45.

Pieris
Bond, J. 1982. *Pieris* – a Survey. *The Plantsman* 4(2):65-75.
Wagenknecht, B.L. 1961. Registration Lists of Cultivar Names in the Genus *Pieris* D. Don. *Arnoldia (Jamaica Plain)* 21(8):47-50.

Plectranthus
Miller, D. & Morgan, N. 2000. Focus on Plants: A New Leaf. *The Garden* (RHS) 125(11):842-845.
Shaw, J.M.H. 1999. Notes on the Identity of Swedish Ivy and Other Cultivated *Plectranthus. The New Plantsman* 6(2):71-74.

Pleione
Cribb, P. & Butterfield, I. 1999. *The Genus Pleione.* (2nd ed.). Kew: Royal Botanic Gardens.
Shaw, J.M.H. (comp.). Oct 2002. Provisional List of *Pleione* Cultivars. Royal Horticultural Society. www.rhs.org.co.uk/research/registerpages/Pleione_cv.PDF

Poaceae (Gramineae, grasses*)*
Clayton, W.D. & Renvoize, S.A. 1986. *Genera Graminum.* Grasses of the World. London: HMSO.
Darke, R. 1999. *The Colour Encyclopedia of Ornamental Grasses.* Sedges, Rushes, Restios, Cat-tails and Selected Bamboos. London: Weidenfeld & Nicolson.

Grounds, R. 1998. *The Plantfinder's Guide to Ornamental Grasses*. Newton Abott, Devon: David & Charles.

Ryves, T.B., Clement, E.J. & Foster, M.C. 1996. *Alien Grasses of the British Isles*. London: Botanical Society of the British Isles.

Wood, T. 2002. *Garden Grasses, Rushes and Sedges*. (3rd ed.). Abingdon: John Wood.

Polemonium

Nichol-Brown, D. 1997. *Polemonium*. Teeside: Trimdon.

Potentilla

Davidson, C.G., Enns, R.J. & Gobin, S. 1994. *A Checklist of Potentilla fruticosa: the Shrubby Potentillas*. Morden, Manitoba: Agriculture & Agri-Food Canada Research Centre. Data also on Plant Finder Reference Library professional version CD-ROM 1999/2000.

Miller, D.M. 2002. *RHS Plant and Trials Awards. Shrubby Potentilla*. London: Royal Horticultural Society.

Primula

Richards, J. 2002 (2nd ed.). *Primula*. London: Batsford.

Primula allionii

Archdale, B. & Richards, D. 1997. *Primula allionii Forms and Hybrids*. National Auricula & Primula Society, Midland & West Section.

Primula auricula hort.

Baker, G. *Double Auriculas*. National Auricula & Primula Society, Midland & West Section.

Baker, G. & Ward, P. 1995. *Auriculas*. London: Batsford.

Hawkes, A. 1995. Striped Auriculas. National Auricula & Primula Society, Midland & West Section.

Nicholle, G. 1996. *Border Auriculas*. National Auricula & Primula Society, Midland & West Section.

Robinson, M.A. 2000. *Auriculas for Everyone*. How to Grow and Show Perfect Plants. Lewes: Guild of Master Craftsmen Publications.

Telford, D. 1993. *Alpine Auriculas*. National Auricula & Primula Society, Midland & West Section.

Ward, P. 1991. *Show Auriculas*. National Auricula & Primula Society, Midland & West Section.

Proteaceae

Rebelo, T. 1995. *Proteas*. A Field Guide to the Proteas of Southern Africa. Vlaeberg: Fernwood Press / National Botanical Institute.

Sadie, J. (Comp.) 2000. *The International Protea Register*. Directorate Genetic Resources, NDA.

Prunus

1986. *Index of the Cherry Collection at the National Fruit Trials 1986*. Faversham, Kent: MAFF.

Crawford, M. 1996. *Plums*. Dartington, Devon: Agroforestry Research Trust.

Crawford, M. 1997. *Cherries: Production and Culture*. Dartington, Devon: Agroforestry Research Trust.

Grubb, N.H. 1949. *Cherries*. London: Crosby Lockwood.

Jacobsen, A.L. 1992. *Purpleleaf Plums*. Portland, Oregon: Timber Press.

Jefferson, R.M. & Wain, K.K. 1984. *The Nomenclature of Cultivated Flowering Cherries (Prunus)*. The Satu-Zakura Group. Washington: USDA.

Kuitert, W. 1999. *Japanese Flowering Cherries*. Oregon: Timber Press.

Taylor, H.V. 1949. *The Plums of England*. London: Crosby Lockwood.

Pulmonaria

Hewitt, J. 1994. *Pulmonarias*. Pershore, Worcs.: The Hardy Plant Society.

Hewitt, J. 1999. Well Spotted. *The Garden* (RHS) 124(2):98 – 103.

Pyracantha

Egolf, D.R. & Andrick, A.O. 1995. *A Checklist of Pyracantha Cultivars*. Agricultural Research Service.

Pyrus

Crawford, M. 1996. *Directory of Pear Cultivars*. Totnes, Devon: Agroforestry Research Institute.

Parfitt, B. 1981. *Index of the Pear Collection at the National Fruit Trials*. Faversham, Kent: MAFF.

Smith, M.W.G. 1976. *Catalogue of the British Pear*. Faversham, Kent: MAFF.

Quercus

Avalos, S.V. 1995. *Contribución al Concimiento del Género Quercus (Fagaceae) en el Estado de Guerrero, Mexico*. Mexico City: Facultad de Ciencias, UNAM.

Miller, H.A. & Lamb, S.H. 1985. *Oaks of North America*. Happy Camp, California: Naturegraph Publishers.

Mitchell, A. 1994. The Lucombe Oaks. *The Plantsman* 15(4):216-224.

Rhododendron

Argent, G., Fairweather, C. & Walter, K. 1996. *Accepted Names in Rhododendron section Vireya*. Royal Botanic Garden, Edinburgh.

Argent, G., Bond, J., Chamberlain, D., Cox, P. & Hardy, A. 1997. *The Rhododendron Handbook 1998*. Rhododendron Species in Cultivation. London: The Royal Horticultural Society.

Chamberlain, D.F. & Rae, S.J. 1990. A Revision of *Rhododendron* IV. Subgenus *Tsutsusi*. Edinburgh *J. Bot.* 47(2).

Chamberlain, D.F. 1982. A Revision of *Rhododendron* II. Subgenus *Hymenanthes*. Notes Roy. Bot. Gard. *Edinburgh* 39(2).

Chamberlain, D., Hyam, R., Argent, G., Fairweather, G. & Walter, K.S. 1996. *The Genus Rhododendron*. RBG Edinburgh.

Cox, P. & Cox, K. 1988. *Encyclopedia of Rhododendron Hybrids*. London: Batsford.

Cullen, J. 1980. A Revision of *Rhododendron* I. Subgenus *Rhododendron* sections *Rhododendron* and *Pogonanthum*. Notes Roy. Bot. Gard. Edinburgh 39(1).

Davidian, H.H. 1982-1992 *The Rhododendron Species Volume I-IV.* Batsford.

Galle, F.C. 1985. *Azaleas.* Portland, Oregon: Timber Press.

Leslie, A. C. (comp.). 1980. *The Rhododendron Handbook 1980.* London: The Royal Horticultural Society.

Leslie, A.C. (Comp.) 2004. *The International Rhododendron Register and Checklist* (2nd ed.). London: RHS

Tamura, T. (ed.). 1989. *Azaleas in Kurume.* Kurume, Japan: International Azalea Festival '89.

Ribes

Crawford, M. 1997. *Currants and Gooseberries: Production and Culture.* Dartington, Devon: Agroforestry Research Trust.

Rosa

Beales, P., Cairns, T., Duncan, W., Fagan, G., Grant, W., Grapes, K., Harkness, P., Hughes, K., Mattock, J. & Ruston, D. 1998. *Botanica's Roses.* The Encyclopedia of Roses. UK: Grange Books PLC.

Cairns, T. (ed.). 2000. *Modern Roses XI.* The World Encyclopedia of Roses. London: Academic Press.

Dickerson, B.C. 1999. *The Old Rose Advisor.* Portland, Oregon: Timber Press.

Dobson, B.R. & Schneider, P. (comps). 1996. *Combined Rose List.*

Haw, S.G. 1996. Notes on Some Chinese and Himalayan Rose Species of Section *Pimpinellifoliae. The New Plantsman* 3(3):143-146.

Help Me Find Roses. Jan 2004. www.helpmefind. com/sites/rose/index.html

McCann, S. 1985. *Miniature Roses.* Newton Abbot: David & Charles.

Phillips, R. & Rix, M. 1988. *Roses.* London: Macmillan.

Phillips, R. & Rix, M. 1993. *The Quest for the Rose.* London: BBC Books.

Quest-Ritson, C. 2003. *Climbing Roses of the World.* Portland, Oregon: Timber Press.

Quest-Ritson, C. & Quest-Ritson, B. 2003. *The Royal Horticultural Society Encyclopedia of Roses: The Definitive A-Z Guide.* London: Dorling Kindersley.

Thomas, G.S. 1995. *The Graham Stuart Thomas Rose Book.* London: John Murray.

Verrier, S. 1996. *Rosa Gallica.* Balmain, Australia: Florilegium.

Rosularia

Eggli, U. 1988. A Monographic Study of the Genus *Rosularia. Bradleya* (Suppl.) 6:1-118.

Saintpaulia

Goodship, G. 1987. *Saintpaulia Variety List.* Supplement. Slough, Bucks: Saintpaulia & Houseplant Society

Moore, H.E. 1957. *African Violets, Gloxinias and Their Relatives.* A Guide to the Cultivated Gesneriads. New York: Macmillan

Salix

Newsholme, C. 1992. *Willows.* The Genus *Salix.* London: Batsford

Stott, K.G. 1971 *Willows for Amenity, Windbreaks and Other Uses.* Checklist of the Long Ashton Collection of Willows, with Notes on their Suitability for Various Purposes. Long Ashton Research Station: University of Bristol

Salvia

Clebsch, B. 2003. *A Book of Salvias.* (2nd ed.). Oregon: Timber Press.

Compton, J. 1994. Mexican Salvias in Cultivation. *The Plantsman* 15(4):193-215.

Saxifraga

Bland, B. 2000. *Silver Saxifrages.* Pershore, Worcs: Alpine Garden Society Publications.

Kohlein, F. 1984. *Saxifrages and Related Genera.* London: Batsford.

McGregor, M. Feb 2003. Saxbase. The Saxifrage Society. www.saxifraga.org/plants/saxbase/ default.asp

McGregor, M. (ed.). 2000. *Saxifrage 2000.* Driffield, E. Yorks: Saxifrage Society.

McGregor, M. 1995. *Saxifrages: The Complete Cultivars & Hybrids.* International Register of Saxifrages. (2nd ed.).

Stocks, A. 1995. *Saxifragaceae.* Hardy Plant Society.

Webb, D.A. & Gornall, R.J. 1989. *Saxifrages of Europe.* Bromley, Kent: Christopher Helm.

Sedum

Evans, R.L. 1983. *Handbook of Cultivated Sedums.* Motcombe, Dorset: Ivory Head Press.

Stephenson, R. 1994. *Sedum.* The Cultivated Stonecrops. Portland, Oregon: Timber Press.

Sempervivum

Miklánek, M. 2000. *List of Cultivars: Sempervivum and Jovibarba* v. 15.1. http://miklanek.tripod.com-miklanek/MCS/cv.html

Sinningia

Dates, J.D. 1988. *The Gesneriad Register 1988.* Check List of Names with Descriptions of Cultivated Plants in the Genus Sinningia. Galesburg, Illinois: American Gloxinia and Gesneriad Society, Inc.

Solenostemon

Pedley, W.K. & Pedley, R. 1974. *Coleus – A Guide to Cultivation and Identification.* Edinburgh: Bartholemew.

Sorbus

McAllister, H. 1984. The Aucuparia Section of *Sorbus. The Plantsman* 6(4):248-255.

McAllister, H. 1996. *Sorbus:* Mountain Ash and its Relatives. *The Garden* (RHS) 121(9):561-567.

Snyers d'Attenhoven, C. 1999. *Sorbus* Lombarts hybrids *Belgische Dendrologie*: 76-81. Belgium.

Wright, D. 1981. Sorbus – a Gardener's Evaluation. *The Plantsman* 3(2):65-98.

Spiraea

Miller, D.M. 2003. *Spiraea japonica with coloured leaves*. RHS Bulletin No. 4. www.rhs.org.uk/plants/spiraea03.pdf

Streptocarpus

Arnold, P. 1979. *The Gesneriad Register 1979: Check List of Streptocarpus*. Binghamton, New York: American Gloxinia & Gesneriad.

Dibleys Nurseries Online Catalogue. 19 Jan 2004. www.dibleys.com.

Succulents

Eggli, U. (ed.) 2002. *Illustrated Handbook of Succulent Plants*. Heidelberg, Germany: Springer-Verlag.

Eggli, U. & Taylor, N. 1994. *List of Names of Succulent Plants other than Cacti Published 1950-92*. Kew: Royal Botanic Gardens.

Grantham, K. & Klaassen, P. 1999. *The Plantfinder's Guide to Cacti and Other Succulents*. Newton Abbot, Devon: David & Charles.

Jacobsen, H. 1973. *Lexicon of Succulent Plants*. London: Blandford.

Syringa

Fiala, J.L. 1988. *Lilacs. The Genus Syringa*. London: Christopher Helm.

Rogers, O.M. 1976. *Tentative International Register of Cultivar Names in the Genus Syringa*. Research Report no. 49.

Vrugtman, F. 2000. *International Register of Cultivar Names in the Genus Syringa L. (Oleaceae)*. (Contribution No. 91). Hamilton, Canada: Royal Botanic Gardens.

Tiliaceae

Wild, H. 1984. *Flora of Southern Africa 21 (1: Tiliaceae)*. Pretoria: Botanical Research Institute, Dept. of Agriculture.

Tillandsia

Kiff, L.F. 1991. *A Distributional Checklist of the Genus Tillandsia*. Encino, California: Botanical Diversions.

Trillium

Case, F.W.J. & Case, R.B. 1997. *Trilliums*. Portland, Oregon: Timber Press.

Jacobs, D.L. & Jacobs, R.L. 1997. *American Treasures. Trilliums in Woodland Garden*. Decatur, Georgia: Eco-Gardens.

Tulipa

van Scheepen, J. (ed.). 1996. *Classified List and International Register of Tulip Names*. Hillegom, The Netherlands: Koninklijke Algemeene Vereeniging Voor Bloembollencultuur.

Ulmus

Green, P.S. 1964. Registratration of Cultivar Names in *Ulmus. Arnoldia (Jamaica Plain)* 24:41-80.

Vegetables

Official Journal of the European Communities. Common catalogue of varieties of vegetable species (22nd ed.). Luxembourg: Office for Official Publications of the European Communities. http://europa.eu.int/eur_lex/en/archive/1999/ca16719990615en.html

Viola

Coombes, R.E. 2003. *Violets*. (2nd ed.). London: Batsford

Farrar, R. 1989. *Pansies, Violas & Sweet Violets*. Reading: Hurst Village Publishing.

Fuller, R. 1990. *Pansies, Violas & Violettas*. The Complete Guide. Marlborough: The Crowood Press.

Perfect, E.J. 1996. *Armand Millet and his Violets*. High Wycombe: Park Farm Press.

Silvers, T.E. 2003. Checklist of the Cultivated Forms of the Genus *Viola* including the Register of Cultivars. American Violet Society. www.americanvioletsociety.org/Registry

Zambra, G.L. 1950. *Violets for Garden and Market*. (2nd ed.). London: Collingridge.

Vitis

Pearkes, G. 1989. *Vine Growing in Britain*. London: Dent.

Robinson, J. 1989. *Vines, Grapes and Wines*. London: Mitchell Beazley.

Watsonia

Goldblatt, P. 1989. *The Genus Watsonia*. A Systematic Monograph. South Africa: National Botanic Gardens.

Weigela

Howard, R.A. 1965. A Checklist of Cultivar Names in *Weigela. Arnoldia (Jamaica Plain)* 25:49-69.

Wisteria

Valder, P. 1995. *Wisterias*. A Comprehensive Guide. Australia: Florilegium.

Yucca

Smith, C. 2004. *Yuccas: Giants among the Lilies*. NCCPG

Zauschneria

Raven, P.H. 1977. Generic and Sectional Delimitation in *Onagraceae*, Tribe *Epilobieae*. *Ann. Missouri Bot. Gard.* 63(2):326-340.

Robinson, A. 2000. Focus on Plaßnts: Piping Hot (*Zauschneria* Cultivars). *The Garden* (RHS) 125(9): 698-699.

INTERNATIONAL PLANT FINDERS

NETHERLANDS

Terra/Lannoo (5th edition) *Plantenvinder voor de lage landen.* ISBN 90-5897-056-6. Approx. 50,000 plants and 150 nurseries. Orders: Terra/Lannoo Publishing, PO box 1080, 7230 AB Warnsveld, Netherlands. T +31 (575) 581310, F +31 (575) 525242. E-mail: info@terralannoo.nl; website: www.terralannoo.com Price €14.95.

UNITED KINGDOM

Pawsey, Angela (ed.). (23rd ed.) 2005-2006. *Find that Rose!* Published May 2004. Lists approximately 3,400 varieties available in the U.K. with basic type, colour and fragrance. New varieties are highlighted and cross-referenced where applicable to alternative selling names. Includes standard roses. Details of around 60 growers/outlets, many offering mail order. How to find a rose with a particular Christian name or to celebrate a special event and where to see roses in bloom. For further information send S.A.E. to: 303 Mile End Road, Colchester, Essex CO4 5EA. To order send a cheque for £3.25 made out to *Find That Rose!* to the above address.

USA

Hill, Susan & Narizny, Susan (comp.) (2004), *The Plant Locator®: Western Region.* ISBN 0-88192-633-7. Directory of sources for plants (not seeds) available at retail and mail-order nurseries in 13 western states of the USA (California, Oregon, Washington, Idaho, Montana, Colorado, Wyoming, Utah, New Mexico, Arizona, Neveda, Alaska, and Hawaii) and British Columbia, Canada. Information on how to contact nurseries and purchase plants. Includes a common name/botanical name index. Co-published by Black-Eyed Susans Press. E-mail: susans@blackeyedsusanspress.com; website: www.blackeyedsusanspress.com and Timber Press. Price: UK £14.99, Europe €22.95, elsewhere US$19.95, plus postage. Order Online only from: www.timberpress.com

NURSERIES

THE FOLLOWING NURSERIES BETWEEN THEM STOCK
AN UNRIVALLED CHOICE OF PLANTS. BEFORE MAKING
A VISIT, PLEASE REMEMBER TO CHECK WITH THE NURSERY
THAT THE PLANT YOU SEEK IS CURRENTLY AVAILABLE.

Nursery Codes and Symbols

The first letter of each nursery code represents the area of the country in which the nursery is situated.

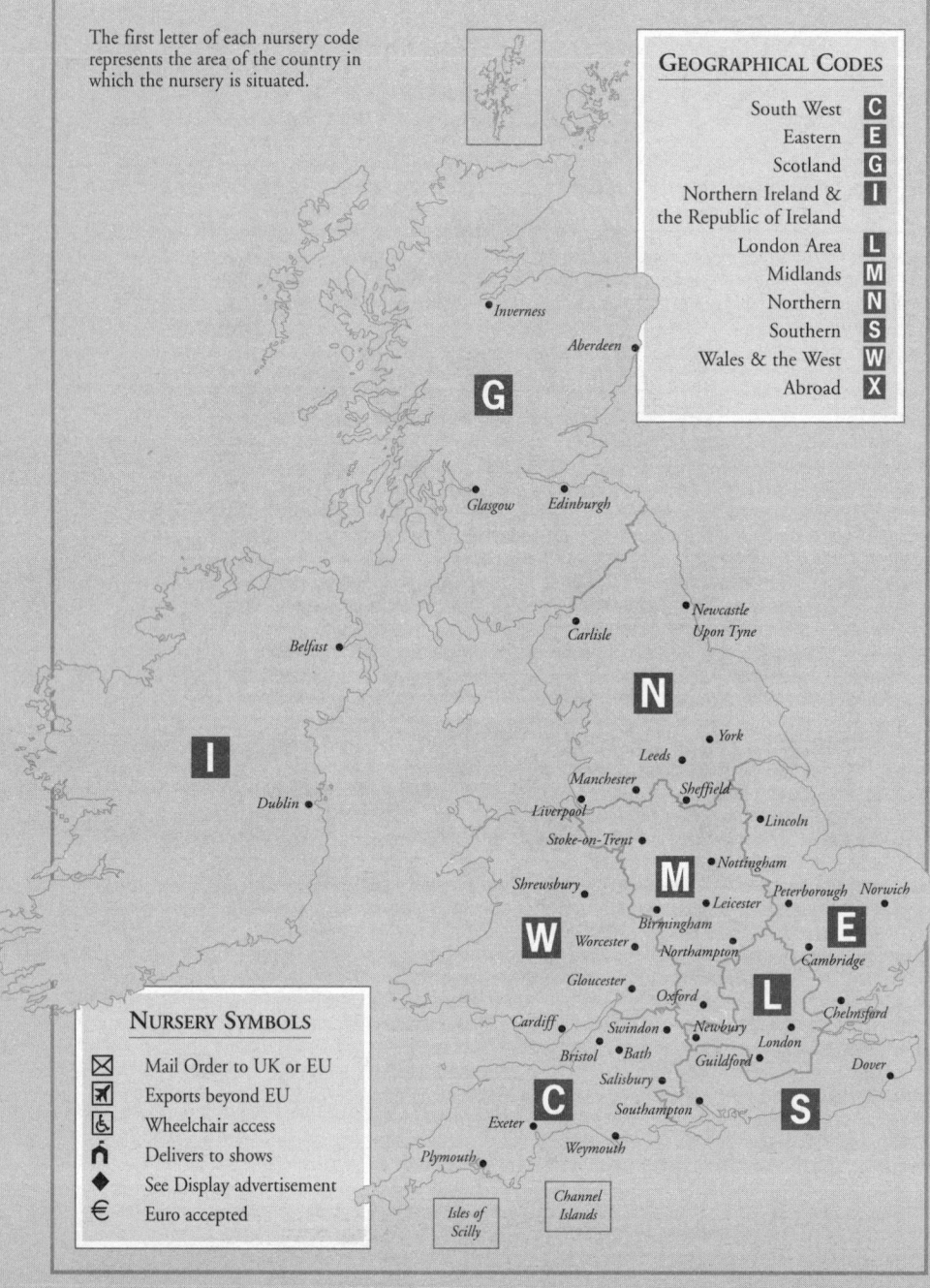

Geographical Codes

South West	**C**
Eastern	**E**
Scotland	**G**
Northern Ireland & the Republic of Ireland	**I**
London Area	**L**
Midlands	**M**
Northern	**N**
Southern	**S**
Wales & the West	**W**
Abroad	**X**

Nursery Symbols

⊠ Mail Order to UK or EU
✈ Exports beyond EU
♿ Wheelchair access
♁ Delivers to shows
♦ See Display advertisement
€ Euro accepted

USING THE THREE NURSERY LISTINGS

Your main reference from the Plant Directory is the Nursery Details by Code listing, which includes all relevant information for each nursery in order of nursery code. The Nursery Index by Name is an alphabetical list for those who know a nursery's name but not its code and wish to check its details in the main list. The Specialist Nurseries index is to aid those searching for a particular plant group.

1 NURSERY DETAILS BY CODE

Once you have found your plant in the Plant Directory, turn to this list to find out the name, address, opening times and other details of the nurseries whose codes accompany the plant.

KEY	⊠ Mail order to UK or EU	♠ Delivers to shows
	⊠ Exports beyond EU	€ Euro accepted
	⬔ Wheelchair access	◆ See Display advertisement

A geographical code is followed by three letters reflecting the nursery's name

WHil   **HILLVIEW HARDY PLANTS** ⊠ ⊠ ♠ € ⬔ ◆
(off B4176), Worfield,
Nr Bridgnorth, Shropshire,
WV15 5NT
Ⓣ (01746) 716454
Ⓕ (01746) 716454
Ⓔ hillview@onetel.net
Ⓦ www.hillviewhardyplants.com
Contact: Ingrid Millington, John Millington
Opening Times: 0900-1700 Mon-Sat Mar-mid Oct. At other times, please phone first.
Min Mail Order UK: £15.00 + p&p
Min Mail Order EU: £15.00 + p&p
Cat. Cost: 5 x 2nd class
Credit Cards: All major credit/debit cards
Specialities: Choice herbaceous perennials incl. *Aquilegia, Astrantia, Auricula, Primula, Crocosmia, Eucomis, Phlox, Schizostylis, Verbascum, Acanthus.* Nat. Coll. of *Acanthus.*
Notes: Also sells wholesale.
Map Ref: W, B4 **OS Grid Ref:** SO772969

Refer to the box at the base of each right-hand page for a key to the symbols

Other information about the nursery

The map letter is followed by the map square in which the nursery is located

A brief summary of the plants available

The Ordnance Survey national grid reference for use with OS maps

2 NURSERY INDEX BY NAME

If you seek a particular nursery, look it up in this alphabetical index. Note its code and turn to the Nursery Details by Code list for full information.

Highfield Hollies	SHHo
Hill Garth Nursery	SHGN
Hill House Nursery & Gardens	CHll
Hillview Hardy Plants	WHil
Hoecroft Plants	EHoe
Holden Clough Nursery	**NHol**
Holkham Gardens	EHol
Holly Gate Cactus Nursery	**SHol**

3 SPECIALIST NURSERIES

A list of 32 categories under which nurseries have classified themselves if they exclusively, or predominantly, supply this range of plants.

DROUGHT TOLERANT

CMdw, CPne, ECha, EFam, EGln, EGoo, EHoe, EOas, IPPs, LLWP, LPen, LPhx, LSss, MAga, MHrb, SAft, SAll, SEND, SHzl, SJoh, SLdr, SUsu, WHil, WKin, WWye, XPep

HOW TO USE THE NURSERY LISTINGS

The details given for each nursery have been compiled from information supplied to us in answer to a questionnaire. In some cases, because of constraints of space, the entries have been slightly abbreviated.

Nurseries are not charged for their entries and inclusion in no way implies a value judgement.

NURSERY DETAILS BY CODE (*page 788*)

Each nursery is allocated a code, for example GPoy. The first letter of each code indicates the main area of the country in which the nursery is situated. In this example, G=Scotland. The remaining three letters reflect the nursery's name, in this case Poyntzfield Herb Nursery.

In this main listing the nurseries are given in alphabetical order of codes for quick reference from the Plant Directory. All of the nurseries' details, such as address, opening times, mail order service etc., will be found here.

OPENING TIMES

Although opening times have been published as submitted and where applicable, it is always advisable, especially if travelling a long distance, to check with the nursery first. The initials NGS indicate that the nursery is open under the National Gardens Scheme.

MAIL ORDER - ✉

Many nurseries provide a mail order service. **This is, however, often restricted to certain times of the year or to particular genera**. Please check the **Notes** section of each nursery's entry for any restrictions or special conditions.

In some cases, the mail order service extends to all members of the European Union. Where this is offered, the minimum charge to the EU will be noted in the Nursery entry.

Where '**No minimum charge**' (Nmc) is shown, please note that to send even one plant may involve the nursery in substantial postage and packing costs. Some nurseries may not be prepared to send tender or bulky plants.

Where a nursery offers a **mail order only** service, this will be noted under **Opening Times** in the nursery entry.

EXPORT ✉

Export refers to mail order beyond the European Union. Nurseries that are prepared to consider exporting are indicated. However, there is usually a substantial minimum charge and, in addition, all the costs of Phytosanitary Certificates and Customs have to be met by the purchaser.

CATALOGUE COST

Some nurseries offer their catalogue free, or for a few stamps, but a large (at least A5) stamped addressed envelope is always appreciated as well. Overseas customers should use an equivalent number of International Reply Coupons (IRCs) in place of stamps.

Increasingly, nurseries are finding it more cost effective to produce catalogues on the Internet rather than printing them. Many nurseries also offer an online mail order facility.

WHEELCHAIR ACCESS ♿

Nurseries are asked to indicate if their premises are suitable for wheelchair users. Where only partial access is indicated, this is noted in the Specialities field and the nursery is not marked with the symbol.

The assessment of ease-of-access is entirely the responsibility of the individual nursery.

SPECIALITIES

Nurseries list here the plants or genera that they supply and any National Collections of plants they may hold. Please note that some nurseries may charge an entry fee to visit a National Collection. Always enquire before visiting.

Nurseries will also note here if they only have small quantities of individual plants available for sale or if they will propagate to order.

NOTES

In this section, you will find notes on any restrictions to mail order or export; on limited wheelchair access; or the nursery site address, if this differs from the office address; together with any other non-horticultural information.

DELIVERY TO SHOWS ⌂

Many nurseries will deliver pre-ordered plants to flower shows for collection by customers. These are indicated by a marquee symbol. Contact the nursery for details of shows they attend.

PAYMENT IN EUROS €

A number of UK nurseries have indicated that they will accept payment in Euros. You should, however, check with the nursery concerned before making such a payment, as some will only accept cash and some only cheques, whilst others will expect the purchaser to pay bank charges.

MAPS

If you wish to visit any of the nurseries you can find its approximate location on the relevant map (following p.917), unless the nursery has requested this is not shown. Nurseries are also encouraged to provide their Ordnance Survey national grid reference for use with OS publications such as the Land Ranger series.

NURSERY INDEX BY NAME (*page 907*)

For convenience, an alphabetical index of nurseries is included on p.907. This gives the names of all nurseries listed in the book in alphabetical order of nursery name together with their code.

SPECIALIST NURSERIES (*page 914*)

This list of nurseries is intended to help those with an interest in finding specialist categories of plant. Nurseries have been asked to classify themselves under one or more headings where this represents the type of plant they *predominantly* or *exclusively* have in stock. For example, if you wish to find a nursery specialising in ornamental grasses, look up 'Grasses' in the listing where you will find a list of nursery codes. Then turn to the Nursery Details by Code, for details of the nurseries.

Please note that not all nurseries shown here will have plants listed in the Plant Directory. This may be their choice or because the *RHS Plant Finder* does not list seeds or annuals and only terrestrial orchids and hardy cacti. For space reasons, it is rare to find a nursery's full catalogue listed in the Plant Directory.

In all cases, please ensure you ring to confirm the range available before embarking on a journey to the nursery.
The specialist plant groups listed in this edition are:

Acid-loving	Grasses
Alpines/rock	Hedging
Aquatics/marginals	Herbs
Bamboos	Marginal/bog plants
British wild flowers	Orchids
Bulbous plants	Organic
Cacti & succulents	Ornamental trees
Carnivorous	Peat-free
Chalk-loving	Period plants
Climbers	Propagate to order
Coastal	Roses
Conifers	Seeds
Conservatory	Specimen-sized plants
Drought-tolerant	Topiary
Ferns	Tropical plants
Fruit	

Perennials and shrubs have been omitted as these are considered to be too general and serviced by a great proportion of the nurseries.

DELETED NURSERIES

Every year some nurseries ask to be removed from the book. This may be a temporary measure because they are moving, or it may be permanent due to closure, sale, retirement, or a change in the way in they trade. Occasionally, nurseries are unable to meet the closing date and will re-enter the book in the following edition. Some nurseries simply do not reply and, as we have no current information on them, they are deleted.

Please, never use an old edition

NURSERY DETAILS BY CODE

Please note that all these nurseries are listed in alphabetical order by their code. All nurseries are listed in alphabetical order by their name in the **Nursery Index by Name** on page 907.

SOUTH WEST

CAbb **ABBOTSBURY SUB-TROPICAL GARDENS** ⊠ &
Abbotsbury, Nr Weymouth, Dorset, DT3 4LA
ⓣ (01305) 871344
ⓕ (01305) 871344
ⓔ info@abbotsburygardens.co.uk
ⓦ www.abbotsburyplantsales.co.uk
Contact: David Sutton
Opening Times: 1000-1800 daily mid Mar-1st Nov. 1000-1500 Nov-mid Mar.
Min Mail Order UK: £10.00 + p&p
Cat. Cost: £2.00 + A4 Sae + 42p stamp
Credit Cards: Visa Access MasterCard Switch
Specialities: Less common & tender shrubs incl. palms, tree ferns, bamboos & plants from Australia, New Zealand & S. Africa.
Map Ref: C, C5

CAbP **ABBEY PLANTS** ⊠
Chaffeymoor, Bourton, Gillingham, Dorset, SP8 5BY
ⓣ (01747) 840841
Contact: K Potts
Opening Times: 1000-1300 & 1400-1700 Tue-Sat Mar-Nov. Dec-Feb by appt.
Min Mail Order UK: Nmc.
Cat. Cost: 2 x 2nd class
Credit Cards: None
Specialities: Flowering trees & shrubs. Shrub roses incl. many unusual varieties. Limited stock.
Map Ref: C, B4 OS Grid Ref: ST762304

CAby **THE ABBEY NURSERY** &
Forde Abbey, Chard, Somerset, TA20 4LU
ⓣ (01460) 220088
ⓕ (01460) 220088
ⓔ TheAbbeyNursery@btconnect.com
Contact: Paul Bygrave and Peter Sims
Opening Times: 1000-1700 7 days, 1st Mar-31st Oct. Please phone first to check opening times in Mar.
Cat. Cost: None issued.
Credit Cards: All major credit/debit cards
Specialities: Hardy herbaceous perennials & grasses.
Map Ref: C, C4 OS Grid Ref: ST359052

CAgr **AGROFORESTRY RESEARCH TRUST** ⊠
46 Hunters Moon, Dartington, Totnes, Devon, TQ9 6JT
ⓣ (01803) 840776
ⓕ (01803) 840776
ⓔ mail@agroforestry.co.uk
ⓦ www.agroforestry.co.uk
Contact: Martin Crawford
Opening Times: Not open. Mail order only.
Min Mail Order UK: Nmc
Min Mail Order EU: Nmc
Cat. Cost: 4 x 1st class
Credit Cards: Visa MasterCard
Specialities: Top & soft fruit & nut trees. Mostly trees, shrubs & perennials. *Alnus, Berberis, Amelanchier, Carya, Elaeagnus, Juglans, Pinus, Quercus* & *Salix*. Also seeds. Some plants in small quantities only.

CAni **ANITA ALLEN** ⊠ &
Shapcott Barton Estate, East Knowstone, South Molton, Devon, EX36 4EE
ⓣ (01398) 341664
ⓕ (01389) 341664
Contact: Anita Allen
Opening Times: By appt. only. Garden open under NGS.
Min Mail Order UK: Nmc.
Cat. Cost: 5 x 1st class
Credit Cards: None
Specialities: Nat. Coll. of *Leucanthemum superbum*. 70+ accurately named Shasta daisies, a few in very short supply. Also some hardy perennials & *Anthemis tinctoria* cultivars.
Map Ref: C, B3 OS Grid Ref: SS846235

C

CArn ARNE HERBS ⊠ ☑ € 🖫
Limeburn Nurseries, Limeburn Hill,
Chew Magna, Bristol, BS40 8QW
Ⓣ (01275) 333399
Ⓕ (01275) 333399
Ⓔ lyman@lyman-dixon.freeserve.co.uk
Ⓦ www.arneherbs.co.uk
Contact: A Lyman-Dixon & Jenny Thomas
Opening Times: Most times, please check
first.
Min Mail Order UK: Nmc
Min Mail Order EU: Nmc
Cat. Cost: £3.75 UK, 10 x IRC refundable on
first order. Or online.
Credit Cards: None
Specialities: Herbs, wild flowers & cottage
flowers. Some in small quantities only, please
see catalogue for details.
Notes: Will deliver to Farmers' Markets. Also
sells wholesale
Map Ref: C, A5 OS Grid Ref: ST563638

CAvo AVON BULBS ⊠
Burnt House Farm, Mid-Lambrook, South
Petherton, Somerset, TA13 5HE
Ⓣ (01460) 242177
Ⓕ (01460) 242177
Ⓔ info@avonbulbs.co.uk
Ⓦ www.avonbulbs.co.uk
Contact: C Ireland-Jones
Opening Times: Mail order only. Open Thu,
Fri, Sat mid Sep-end Oct & mid Feb-end Mar
for collection of pre-booked orders.
Min Mail Order UK: £10.00 + p&p
Min Mail Order EU: £20.00 + p&p
Cat. Cost: 4 x 2nd class
Credit Cards: Visa Access Switch MasterCard
Specialities: Mail order supply of a very wide
range of smaller, often unusual bulbs.
Map Ref: C, B5

CBcs BURNCOOSE NURSERIES ⊠ ☑ 🐾 🖫
Gwennap, Redruth, Cornwall, TR16 6BJ
Ⓣ (01209) 860316
Ⓕ (01209) 860011
Ⓔ burncoose@eclipse.co.uk
Ⓦ www.burncoose.co.uk
Contact: C H Williams
Opening Times: 0830-1700 Mon-Sat &
1100-1700 Sun.
Min Mail Order UK: Nmc
Min Mail Order EU: Individual quotations
for EU sales.
Cat. Cost: £1.50 incl. p&p
Credit Cards: Visa Access Switch
Specialities: Extensive range of over 3500
ornamental trees & shrubs and herbaceous.
Rare & unusual *Magnolia*, *Rhododendron*.

Conservatory plants. 30 acre garden.
Notes: Also sells wholesale
Map Ref: C, D1 OS Grid Ref: SW742395

CBct BARRACOTT PLANTS ⊠ 🐾 € ◆
Old Orchard, Calstock Road, Gunnislake,
Cornwall, PL18 9AA
Ⓣ (01822) 832234
Ⓔ GEOFF@geoff63.freeserve.co.uk
Contact: Geoff Turner, Thelma Watson
Opening Times: 0900-1700 Thu-Sat, Mar-
end Sep. Other times by appt.
Min Mail Order UK: £10.00
Cat. Cost: 2 x 1st class
Credit Cards: None
Specialities: Herbaceous plants: shade-loving,
foliage & form. *Acanthus*, *Astrantia*, *Bergenia*,
Convallaria, *Ligularia*, *Liriope*, *Roscoea*,
Smilacina, *Symphytum* & *Tricyrtis*.
Notes: Also sells wholesale
Map Ref: C, C3 OS Grid Ref: SX436702

CBdw BODWEN NURSERY ⊠
Pothole, St Austell, Cornwall, PL26 7DW
Ⓣ (01726) 883855
Ⓦ www.bodwen-nursery.co.uk
Contact: John Geraghty
Opening Times: Not open. Mail order only.
Min Mail Order UK: Nmc
Cat. Cost: 2 x 2nd class
Credit Cards: None
Specialities: Japanese maples. Some rarer
cultivars available in limited quantities only.
Notes: Also sells wholesale.

CBel BELMONT HOUSE NURSERY ⊠ €
Little Horton, Devizes, Wiltshire, SN10 3LJ
Ⓣ (01380) 860510
Ⓔ rcottis@supanet.com
Contact: Gordon Cottis
Opening Times: By appt. Please phone.
Min Mail Order UK: £2.50
Cat. Cost: 2 x 2nd class
Credit Cards: None
Specialities: *Helleborus* hybrids & true species,
Galanthus & *Cyclamen*, some in small
quantities only.
Notes: Mail order *Cyclamen* & *Galanthus* only,
Nov-Feb.
Map Ref: C, A6 OS Grid Ref: SU042623

CBen BENNETT'S WATER LILY FARM ⊠ 🖫
Putton Lane, Chickerell, Weymouth, Dorset,
DT3 4AF
Ⓣ (01305) 785150
Ⓕ (01305) 781619
Ⓔ JB@waterlily.co.uk
Ⓦ www.waterlily.co.uk

C

Contact: J Bennett
Opening Times: Tue-Sun Apr-Aug, Tue-Sat Sept & Mar.
Min Mail Order UK: £25.00 + p&p
Min Mail Order EU: £25.00 + p&p
Cat. Cost: Sae for price list
Credit Cards: Visa Access MasterCard Switch
Specialities: Aquatic plants. Nat. Coll. of Water Lilies.
Notes: Mail order Apr-Sep only.
Map Ref: C, C5 **OS Grid Ref:** SY651797

CBgR **BEGGAR'S ROOST PLANTS** 🔊
Lilstock, Bridgwater, Somerset, TA5 1SU
ⓣ (01278) 741519
ⓕ (01278) 741519
ⓔ nunnington@aol.com
Contact: Rosemary FitzGerald, Kate Harris
Opening Times: By appt. only.
Credit Cards: None
Specialities: British native plants & their garden-worthy varieties. Hardy ferns. Classic perennials, incl. *Salvia, Hemerocallis* & winter interest plants. Available in small quantities only.
Map Ref: C, B4 **OS Grid Ref:** ST168450

CBig **THE BIG GRASS CO.** ✉ 📧 📱 €
Hookhill Plantation, Woolfardisworthy East, Black Dog, Nr. Crediton, Devon, EX17 4RX
ⓣ (01363) 866146
ⓕ (01363) 866146
ⓔ alison@big-grass.com
ⓦ www.big-grass.com
Contact: Alison & Scott Evans
Opening Times: Mail order only. Open by appt. only.
Min Mail Order UK: Nmc
Min Mail Order EU: Nmc
Cat. Cost: £2.50 cheque or stamps
Credit Cards: None
Specialities: Grasses & restios.
Notes: Also sells wholesale.
Map Ref: C, B3

CBod **BODMIN PLANT AND HERB NURSERY** 🔊
Laveddon Mill, Laninval Hill, Bodmin, Cornwall, PL30 5JU
ⓣ (01208) 72837
ⓕ (01208) 76491
ⓔ bodminnursery@aol.com
Contact: Mark Lawlor
Opening Times: 0900-1700 Mon-Sat Nov-Mar, 0900-1800 Mon-Sat Apr-Oct. 1000-1600 Sun.
Credit Cards: All major credit/debit cards
Specialities: Herbs, herbaceous & grasses, hardy geraniums & coastal plants. Interesting shrubs, fruit & ornamental trees.
Map Ref: C, C2 **OS Grid Ref:** SX053659

CBos **BOSVIGO PLANTS**
Bosvigo House, Bosvigo Lane, Truro, Cornwall, TR1 3NH
ⓣ (01872) 275774
ⓕ (01872) 275774
ⓔ bosvigo.plants@virgin.net
ⓦ www.bosvigo.com
Contact: Wendy Perry
Opening Times: 1100-1800 Thu & Fri Mar-end Sep.
Cat. Cost: 4 x 1st class
Credit Cards: None
Specialities: Rare & unusual herbaceous.
Map Ref: C, D2 **OS Grid Ref:** SW815452

CBow **BOWLEY PLANTS** 🔊 ◆
Church Farm, North End, Ashton Keynes, Nr. Swindon, Wiltshire, SN6 6QR
ⓣ (01285) 640352
Ⓜ 07855 524929
Contact: G P Bowley
Opening Times: 1000-1600 Tue & Sat, 1300-1600 Sun, Mar-Oct incl.
Cat. Cost: 2 x 1st class
Credit Cards: None
Specialities: Variegated plants & coloured foliage. Alpines, perennials, shrubs, ferns, grasses & herbs. Some varieties in small numbers.
Notes: Also sells wholesale.
Map Ref: C, A6 **OS Grid Ref:** SU043945

CBrd **BROADLEAS GARDENS LTD**
Broadleas, Devizes, Wiltshire, SN10 5JQ
ⓣ (01380) 722035
ⓕ (01380) 722035
ⓔ broadleasgardens@btinternet.com
Contact: Lady Anne Cowdray
Opening Times: 1400-1800 Wed, Thu & Sun Apr-Oct.
Cat. Cost: 1 x 1st class
Credit Cards: None
Specialities: General range.
Map Ref: C, A6

CBre **BREGOVER PLANTS** ✉ 📱
Hillbrooke, Middlewood, North Hill, Nr Launceston, Cornwall, PL15 7NN
ⓣ (01566) 782661
Contact: Jennifer Bousfield
Opening Times: 1100-1700 Wed, Mar-mid Oct and by appt.
Min Mail Order UK: Nmc
Min Mail Order EU: Nmc
Cat. Cost: 3 x 1st class

C

Credit Cards: None
Specialities: Unusual hardy perennials grown in small garden nursery. Available in small quantities only.
Notes: Mail order Oct-Mar only.
Map Ref: C, C2 OS Grid Ref: SX273752

CBrm   **BRAMLEY LODGE GARDEN NURSERY** € &
Beech Tree Lane, Ipplepen, Newton Abbot, Devon, TQ12 5TW
Ⓣ (01803) 813265
Ⓔ blnursery@btopenworld.com
Ⓦ www.bramleylodge-nursery.co.uk
Contact: Susan Young
Opening Times: 1000-1600 Fri-Mon Mar-Jul, 1000-1600 Sun-Mon Aug-Oct. Phone for appt. at all other times.
Cat. Cost: 3 x 1st class
Credit Cards: All major credit/debit cards
Specialities: Grasses. Also trees, shrubs, perennials & rock plants. Several small model themed gardens.
Map Ref: C, C3 OS Grid Ref: SX828673

CBro   **BROADLEIGH GARDENS** ⊠ n &
Bishops Hull, Taunton, Somerset, TA4 1AE
Ⓣ (01823) 286231
Ⓕ (01823) 323646
Ⓔ info@broadleighbulbs.co.uk
Ⓦ www.broadleighbulbs.co.uk
Contact: Lady Skelmersdale
Opening Times: 0900-1600 Mon-Fri for viewing only. Orders collected if notice given.
Min Mail Order UK: Nmc
Min Mail Order EU: Nmc
Cat. Cost: 2 x 1st class
Credit Cards: Visa MasterCard
Specialities: Jan catalogue: bulbs in growth (*Galanthus*, *Cyclamen* etc.) & herbaceous woodland plants (trilliums, hellebores etc). Extensive list of *Agapanthus*. June catalogue: dwarf & unusual bulbs, *Iris* (DB & PC). Nat. Coll. of Alec Grey hybrid daffodils.
Map Ref: C, B4 OS Grid Ref: ST195251

CBrP   **BROOKLANDS PLANTS** ⊠
25 Treves Road, Dorchester, Dorset, DT1 2HE
Ⓣ (01305) 265846
Ⓔ IanWatt@quicklink.freeserve.co.uk
Contact: Ian Watt
Opening Times: By appt. for collection of plants only.
Min Mail Order UK: £25.00 + p&p
Min Mail Order EU: £25.00 + p&p
Cat. Cost: 2 x 2nd class
Credit Cards: None
Specialities: Cycad nursery specialising in the more cold tolerant species of *Encephalartos*,

Dioon, *Macrozamia* & *Cycas*. Also hardy palms, *Agave*, *Yucca*, *Dasylirion*, *Restio* & bamboos. Some species available in small quantities only.
Map Ref: C, C5

CBur   **BURNHAM NURSERIES** ⊠ ⊠ n &
Forches Cross, Newton Abbot, Devon, TQ12 6PZ
Ⓣ (01626) 352233
Ⓕ (01626) 362167
Ⓔ mail@orchids.uk.com
Ⓦ www.orchids.uk.com
Contact: Any member of staff
Opening Times: 1000-1600 Mon-Sun.
Min Mail Order UK: Nmc
Min Mail Order EU: £100.00 + p&p
Cat. Cost: A4 Sae + 44p stamp
Credit Cards: Visa Switch American Express MasterCard
Specialities: All types of orchid except British native types.
Notes: Please ask for details on export beyond EU.
Map Ref: C, C4

CCAT   **CIDER APPLE TREES** ⊠ €
Kerian, Corkscrew Lane, Woolston, Nr. North Cadbury, Somerset, BA22 7BP
Ⓣ (01963) 441101
Contact: Mr J Dennis
Opening Times: By appt. only.
Min Mail Order UK: £9.50
Min Mail Order EU: £9.50
Cat. Cost: Free
Credit Cards: None
Specialities: *Malus* (speciality standard trees).
Notes: Also sells wholesale.
Map Ref: C, B5

CCCN   **CROSS COMMON NURSERY** ⊠
c/o Higher Treal Farm, Ruan Minor, Helston, Cornwall, TR12 7LS
Ⓣ (01326) 290722/290668
Ⓔ info@crosscommonnursery.co.uk
Ⓦ www.crosscommonnursery.co.uk
Contact: Suzy Bosustow
Opening Times: 1000-1700 7 days, Apr-Oct. Reduced hours in winter, please phone or check website.
Min Mail Order UK: Nmc
Cat. Cost: Check website for details.

C

Specialities: Tropical/sub-tropical, coastal plants & conservatory plants. Wide range of grapevines and citrus trees.
Notes: Credit cards only accepted for mail order & online sales.
Map Ref: C, D1 OS Grid Ref: SW704116

CCge   COTTAGE GARDEN PLANTS AND HERBS 🏠 🔾
North Lodge, Canonteign, Christow, Exeter, Devon, EX6 7NS
Ⓣ (01647) 252950
Contact: Shirley Bennett
Opening Times: 1000-1700 w/ends & B/hols Mar-Sep. Ring for private visit at other times.
Credit Cards: None
Specialities: Cottage garden plants, herbs and esp. hardy geraniums (over 200 kinds available).
Map Ref: C, C3 OS Grid Ref: SX836829

CCha   CHAPEL FARM HOUSE NURSERY € 🔾
Halwill Junction, Beaworthy, Devon, EX21 5UF
Ⓣ (01409) 221594
Ⓕ (01409) 221594
Contact: Robin or Toshie Hull
Opening Times: 0900-1700 Tue-Sat, 1000-1600 Sun & B/hol Mons.
Cat. Cost: None issued.
Credit Cards: None
Specialities: Plants from Japan. Also herbaceous.
Map Ref: C, C3

CCol   COLD HARBOUR NURSERY ✉ 🏠
(Office) 28 Moor Road, Swanage, Dorset, BH19 1RG
Ⓣ (01929) 423520 evenings
Ⓔ coldharbournursery@hotmail.com
Ⓦ www.dorset-perennials.co.uk
Contact: Steve Saunders
Opening Times: 1000-1700 Tue-Fri & most w/ends 1st Mar-end Oct. Other times by appt.
Min Mail Order UK: £6.00 + p&p
Cat. Cost: 3 x 1st class
Credit Cards: None
Specialities: Unusual herbaceous perennials incl. hardy *Geranium*, daylilies & grasses.
Notes: Nursery is at Bere Road (opp. Silent Woman Inn), Wareham.
Map Ref: C, C5

CCtw   CHURCHTOWN NURSERIES ✉ 🏠
Gulval, Penzance, Cornwall, TR18 3BE
Ⓣ (01736) 362626
Ⓕ (01736) 362626
Ⓔ Chris@churchtownnurseries.com
Ⓦ www.churchtownnurseries.co.uk
Contact: Chris or Fay Osborne

Opening Times: 1000-1700 Apr-Sep, 1000-1600 Oct-Mar or by appt.
Min Mail Order UK: £25.00 + p&p
Cat. Cost: 1 x 1st class Sae for list.
Credit Cards: None
Specialities: Good, ever-increasing, range of shrubs, herbaceous & tender perennials & ornamental grasses incl. some more unusual.
Map Ref: C, D1 OS Grid Ref: SW486317

CCVN   CULM VIEW NURSERY 🏠
Waterloo Farm, Clayhidon, Devon, EX15 3TN
Ⓣ (01823) 680698
Ⓔ plants@culmviewnursery.co.uk
Ⓦ www.culmviewnursery.co.uk
Contact: Brian & Alison Jacobs
Opening Times: By appt. only for collection.
Credit Cards: None
Specialities: Hebaceous perennials grown in peat-free compost.

CCVT   CHEW VALLEY TREES ✉
Winford Road, Chew Magna, Bristol, BS40 8QE
Ⓣ (01275) 333752
Ⓕ (01275) 333746
Ⓔ info@chewvalleytrees.co.uk
Ⓦ www.chewvalleytrees.co.uk
Contact: J Scarth
Opening Times: 0800-1700 Mon-Fri all year. 0900-1600 Sat beginning Sep-mid May. Closed Sun & B/hols.
Min Mail Order UK: Nmc
Cat. Cost: Free
Credit Cards: All major credit/debit cards
Specialities: Native British & ornamental trees, shrubs, apple trees & hedging.
Notes: Partial wheelchair access. Max. plant height for mail order 2m incl. roots. Also sells wholesale.
Map Ref: C, A5 OS Grid Ref: ST558635

CDBb   DORSET BLUEBERRY COMPANY ✉ 🏠
(office) 352 Church Cottages, Hampreston, Wimborne, Dorset, BH21 7LX
Ⓣ (01202) 579342 (office) or 579368
Ⓕ (01202) 579014
Ⓔ info@dorset-blueberry.co.uk
Ⓦ www.dorset-blueberry.co.uk
Contact: Jennifer Trehane or David Trehane
Opening Times: Not open. Mail order only.
Min Mail Order UK: £7.50 + p&p mainland Britain. Please enquire for islands, N Ireland & Rep. of Ireland.
Cat. Cost: 4 x 1st class
Credit Cards: All major credit/debit cards
Specialities: Blueberries, cranberries & other *Vaccinium*.

CDes DESIRABLE PLANTS ⊠ ⋔
(Office) Pentamar, Crosspark, Totnes, Devon,
TQ9 5BQ
Ⓣ (01803) 864489 evenings
Ⓔ sutton.totnes@lineone.net
Ⓦ www.desirableplants.com
Contact: Dr J J & Mrs S A Sutton
Opening Times: Not open. Mail order only.
Min Mail Order UK: £15.00
Cat. Cost: 5 x 1st class.
Credit Cards: None
Specialities: Eclectic range of choice &
interesting herbaceous plants by mail order.
Notes: Monthly retail event in Totnes, phone
or see web for details. Nursery not at this
address.

CDev DEVON VIOLET NURSERY ⊠ € 🖑 ◆
10 Totnes Road, Newton Abbot, Devon,
TQ12 1LX
Ⓣ (01626) 336336
Ⓕ (01803) 310381
Ⓔ violetnursery@aol.com
Ⓦ www.sweetviolets.co.uk
Contact: John & Melanie Bray
Opening Times: Primarily mail order. 0900-
1500, Mon-Sat, all year round. Please ring first.
Min Mail Order UK: £4.50
Min Mail Order EU: £6.50
Cat. Cost: 2 x 1st class
Credit Cards: None
Specialities: Violets & Parma violets.
Notes: Also sells wholesale.
Map Ref: C, C3 OS Grid Ref: SX852706

CDHC DON HATCH CONIFERS ⊠ 🖑
Combe Raleigh, Honiton, Devon, EX14 4TQ
Ⓣ (01404) 42981
Ⓕ (01404) 42167
Ⓔ sales@conifers.co.uk
Ⓦ www.conifers.co.uk
Contact: Chris Padget
Opening Times: Mail order only. Open by
prior appt.
Min Mail Order UK: £40.00
Min Mail Order EU: £40.00
Cat. Cost: Conifer list £5.00 + p&p. Full
catalogue online only.
Credit Cards: None
Specialities: Conifers & a limited range of
Japanese maples. Peat free cuttings.
Notes: Also sells wholesale.
Map Ref: C, C4 OS Grid Ref: ST160022

CDMG DOCTON MILL GARDENS 🖑
Lyme Bridge, Hartland, Devon, EX39 6EA
Ⓣ (01237) 441369
Ⓕ (01237) 441369

Ⓔ john@doctonmill.freeserve.co.uk
Ⓦ www.doctonmill.co.uk
Contact: John Borrett
Opening Times: 1000-1800 7 days, 1st Mar-
31st Oct.
Credit Cards: All major credit/debit cards
Specialities: Most plants available in small
quantities only.
Map Ref: C, B2

CDob SAMUEL DOBIE & SON ⊠
Long Road, Paignton, Devon, TQ4 7SX
Ⓣ 0870 112 3623
Ⓕ 0870 112 3624
Ⓦ www.dobies.co.uk
Contact: Customer Services
Opening Times: 0830-1700 Mon-Fri
(office). Also answerphone.
Min Mail Order UK: Nmc
Cat. Cost: Free
Credit Cards: Visa MasterCard Switch Delta
Specialities: Wide selection of popular flower
& vegetable seeds. Also includes young
plants, summer flowering bulbs & garden
sundries.
Notes: Mail order to UK & Rep. of Ireland
only.

CDoC DUCHY OF CORNWALL ⊠ ◆
Cott Road, Lostwithiel, Cornwall, PL22 0HW
Ⓣ (01208) 872668
Ⓕ (01208) 872835
Ⓔ sales@duchynursery.co.uk
Ⓦ www.duchyofcornwallnursery.co.uk
Contact: Tracy Wilson
Opening Times: 0900-1700 Mon-Sat, 1000-
1700 Sun & B/hols.
Min Mail Order UK: £12.50
Cat. Cost: 8 x 1st class, CD catalogue 12 x
1st class.
Credit Cards: Visa American Express,Access
Switch Delta
Specialities: Very wide range of garden plants
incl. trees, shrubs, conifers, roses, perennials,
fruit & half-hardy exotics.
Notes: Nursery partially accessible for
wheelchair users.
Map Ref: C, C2 OS Grid Ref: SX112614

CDul DULFORD NURSERIES ⊠ ⋔ 🖑
Cullompton, Devon, EX15 2DG
Ⓣ (01884) 266361
Ⓕ (01884) 266663

KEY		
⊠ Mail order to UK or EU	⋔ Delivers to shows	
✖ Exports beyond EU	€ Euro accepted	
🖑 Accessible by wheelchair	◆ See Display advertisement	

C

Ⓔ dulford.nurseries@virgin.net
Ⓦ www.dulford-nurseries.co.uk
Contact: Paul & Mary Ann Rawlings
Opening Times: 0730-1630 Mon-Fri.
Min Mail Order UK: Nmc
Min Mail Order EU: Nmc
Cat. Cost: Free
Credit Cards: All major credit/debit cards
Specialities: Native, ornamental & unusual
trees & shrubs incl. oaks, maples, beech,
birch, chestnut, ash, lime, *Sorbus* & pines.
Notes: Also sells wholesale.
Map Ref: C, C4 OS Grid Ref: SY062062

CDWL DORSET WATER LILIES ⋔ &
Yeovil Road, Halstock, Yeovil, Somerset,
BA22 9RR
Ⓣ (01935) 891668
Ⓕ (01935) 891946
Ⓔ dorsetwaterlily@tiscali.co.uk
Ⓦ www.dorsetwaterlily.co.uk
Contact: Richard Gallehawk
Opening Times: 0900-1600 Mon & Fri only,
plus Sat in summer.
Cat. Cost: Free
Credit Cards: None
Specialities: Hardy & tropical water lilies,
lotus, marginal & bogside plants.
Notes: Also sells wholesale.
Map Ref: C, C5 OS Grid Ref: ST543083

CElm ELM TREE NURSERY ⊠
Sidbury, Sidmouth, Devon, EX10 0QG
Ⓣ (01395) 597790
Ⓔ elmtreecyclamen@btopenworld.com
Contact: M Saunders
Opening Times: Not open. Mail order only.
Min Mail Order UK: Nmc
Cat. Cost: 1 x 1st class
Credit Cards: None
Specialities: Hardy *Cyclamen*. Rarest cultivars
only available in small quantities.

CElw ELWORTHY COTTAGE PLANTS ⋔ &
Elworthy Cottage, Elworthy, Nr. Lydeard
St Lawrence, Taunton, Somerset, TA4 3PX
Ⓣ (01984) 656427
Ⓔ mike@elworthy-cottage.co.uk
Ⓦ www.elworthy-cottage.co.uk
Contact: Mrs J M Spiller
Opening Times: 1000-1600 Thu, Fri & Sat mid
Mar-end May, Thu only Jun-Oct. Also by appt.
Cat. Cost: 3 x 2nd class
Credit Cards: None
Specialities: *Clematis* & unusual herbaceous
plants esp. hardy *Geranium*, *Geum*, grasses,
Campanula, *Crocosmia*, *Pulmonaria*, *Astrantia*
& *Viola*.

Notes: Nursery on B3188, 5 miles north
of Wiveliscombe, in centre of Elworthy
village.
Map Ref: C, B4 OS Grid Ref: ST084349

CEnd ENDSLEIGH GARDENS ⊠ & ◆
Milton Abbot, Tavistock, Devon,
PL19 0PG
Ⓣ (01822) 870235
Ⓕ (01822) 870513
Ⓔ Treemail@endsleigh-gardens.com
Ⓦ www.endsleigh-gardens.com
Contact: Michael Taylor
Opening Times: 0800-1700 Mon-Sat. 1000-
1700 Sun.
Min Mail Order UK: £12.00 + p&p
Cat. Cost: 2 x 1st class
Credit Cards: Visa Access Switch MasterCard
Specialities: Choice & unusual trees & shrubs
incl. *Acer* & *Cornus* cvs. Old apples &
cherries. *Wisteria*. Grafting service.
Map Ref: C, C3

CEnt ENTWOOD FARM PLANTS
Harcombe, Lyme Regis, Dorset,
DT7 3RN
Ⓣ (01297) 444034
Contact: Jenny & Ivan Harding
Opening Times: 1000-1600 most days, but
please phone first.
Cat. Cost: 3 x 1st class.
Credit Cards: None
Specialities: Perennials & grasses. Some
shrubs/bamboos. Interest in *Digitalis* & plants
suited to moisture-retentive soil. Some stock
in small quantities only.
Map Ref: C,C4 OS Grid Ref: SY335953

CFee FEEBERS HARDY PLANTS ⊠ & ◆
1 Feeber Cottage, Westwood,
Broadclyst, Nr Exeter, Devon,
EX5 3DQ
Ⓣ (01404) 822118
Ⓔ Feebers@onetel.com
Contact: Mrs E Squires
Opening Times: 1000-1700 Wed Mar-Jul &
Sep-Oct. Sat & Sun by prior appt.
Min Mail Order UK: Nmc
Min Mail Order EU: Nmc
Cat. Cost: Sae + 36p stamp
Credit Cards: None
Specialities: Plants for wet clay soils, alpines
& hardy perennials incl. those raised by Amos
Perry. Small quantities of plants held unless
grown from seed.
Notes: Mail order limited. Nursery accessible
for wheelchairs in dry weather only.
Map Ref: C, C4

C

CFen FENTONGOLLON FARM ⊠ ⬜
Tresillian, Truro, Cornwall, TR2 4AQ
Ⓣ (01872) 520209
Ⓕ (01872) 520606
Ⓔ james@flowerfarm.co.uk
Ⓦ www.flowerfarm.co.uk
Contact: James Hosking
Opening Times: 0900-1800 7 days, Aug-end Oct.
Min Mail Order UK: Nmc
Min Mail Order EU: Nmc
Cat. Cost: 2 x 1st class
Credit Cards: MasterCard Switch
Specialities: *Narcissus*.
Notes: Also sells wholesale.
Map Ref: C, D2

CFFs FLORAL FIREWORKS ⊠
Burnt House Farm, Mid Lambrook, South Petherton, Somerset, TA13 5HE
Ⓣ (01460) 249060
Ⓕ (01490) 249025
Ⓔ info@floralfireworks.co.uk
Ⓦ www.floralfireworks.co.uk
Contact: Charlie Pattisson
Opening Times: Not open. Mail order only. Orders can be collected by prior arrangement.
Min Mail Order UK: £10.00 + p&p
Min Mail Order EU: £20.00 + p&p
Cat. Cost: 4 x 2nd class.
Credit Cards: All major credit/debit cards
Specialities: Bulbs.

CFir FIR TREE FARM NURSERY ⊠ € ⬜
Tresahor, Constantine, Falmouth, Cornwall, TR11 5PL
Ⓣ (01326) 340593
Ⓔ plants@cornwallgardens.com
Ⓦ www.cornwallgardens.com
Contact: Glynn Wrapson & Sorcha Hitchcox
Opening Times: 1000-1700 Mon-Sat & 1100-1600 Sun, Feb-Sep. By appt. Oct-Jan.
Min Mail Order UK: £25.00 + p&p
Min Mail Order EU: £40.00 + p&p
Cat. Cost: 6 x 1st class
Credit Cards: Visa Access Delta Switch
Specialities: Over 4000 varieties of cottage garden & rare perennials with many specialities. Also 80 varieties of *Clematis*.
Map Ref: C, D1

CFis MARGERY FISH GARDENS €
East Lambrook Manor, East Lambrook, South Petherton, Somerset, TA13 5HL
Ⓣ (01460) 240328
Ⓕ (01460) 242344
Ⓔ enquiries@eastlambrook.com
Ⓦ www.eastlambrook.com

Contact: Mark Stainer
Opening Times: 1000-1700 1st Feb-31st Oct 7 days.
Credit Cards: Visa Switch MasterCard
Specialities: Hardy *Geranium*, *Euphorbia*, *Helleborus* & herbaceous. Small quantities only. Major collection of hardy *Geranium*.
Map Ref: C, B5

CFol FOLLY GATE PLANTS ⬜
The Old Post Office, Folly Gate,
Nr Okehampton, Devon, EX20 3AF
Ⓣ (01837) 659164
Ⓔ perrylamb@hotmail.com
Contact: Sara Lamb
Opening Times: 1000-1700, Wed-Sun, Mar-Oct.
Cat. Cost: 2 x 1st class.
Specialities: Hardy herbaceous perennials, shrubs and grasses.
Map Ref: C, C3 OS Grid Ref: SX573978

CFRD FORD NURSERY ♠ ⬜
The Willows, Broom Lane, Oake, Taunton, Somerset, TA4 1BE
Ⓣ (01823) 461961
Ⓕ (01823) 461961
Ⓔ clematis@fordnursery.freeserve.co.uk
Contact: Mr P F Dunn
Opening Times: 0900-1300 & 1400-1700 Mon-Fri. Sat & Sun by appt. only.
Cat. Cost: 4 x 2nd class
Specialities: Approx. 230 varieties of *Clematis* and other climbers. Available in small quantities.
Notes: Also sells wholesale.
Map Ref: C, B4 OS Grid Ref: ST160244

CFul THE RODNEY FULLER HELIANTHEMUM COLLECTION
Coachman's Cottage, Higher Bratton Seymour, Wincanton, Somerset, BA9 8DA
Ⓣ (01963) 34480
Ⓔ coachmans@tinyworld.co.uk
Contact: Rodney Fuller
Opening Times: Open by appt. only.
Cat. Cost: 2 x 1st class
Credit Cards: None
Specialities: *Helianthemum*. Nat. Coll. holder. Stock available in small quantities only.
Map Ref: C, B5

CFwr THE FLOWER BOWER ⊠
Woodlands, Shurton, Stogursey,
Nr Bridgwater, Somerset, TA5 1QE
Ⓣ (01278) 732134
Ⓕ (01278) 732134
Ⓔ flower.bower@virgin.net

C

ⓦ www.theflowerbower.co.uk
Contact: Sheila Tucker
Opening Times: 1000-1700, open most days mid-Mar-30th Sep. Please phone first.
Min Mail Order UK: £15.00 + p&p
Min Mail Order EU: £20.00 + p&p
Cat. Cost: 4 x 1st class
Credit Cards: None
Specialities: Unusual perennials. *Anemone*, *Epimedium*, lilies, hardy geraniums, *Phlox*, grasses & ferns.
Notes: Mail order Mar onwards.
Map Ref: C, B4 OS Grid Ref: ST203442

CGra   GRAHAM'S HARDY PLANTS ⊠ ♋ €
"Southcroft", North Road, Timsbury, Bath, BA2 0JN
ⓣ (01761) 472187
ⓔ graplant@aol.com
ⓦ www.members.aol.com/graplant
Contact: Graham Nicholls
Opening Times: Not open to the public. Mail order and show sales only.
Min Mail Order UK: £2.00 + p&p
Min Mail Order EU: £2.00 + p&p
Cat. Cost: 2 x 1st class or 2 x IRC
Credit Cards: None
Specialities: North American alpines esp. *Lewisia, Eriogonum, Penstemon, Campanula, Kelseya, Phlox.*
Map Ref: C, B5

CGro   C W GROVES & SON ⊠ ▣
West Bay Road, Bridport, Dorset, DT6 4BA
ⓣ (01308) 422654
ⓕ (01308) 420888
ⓔ violets@grovesnurseries.co.uk: garden@grovesnurseries.co.uk
ⓦ www.grovesnursery.co.uk
Contact: Clive Groves
Opening Times: 0830-1700 Mon-Sat, 1030-1630 Sun.
Min Mail Order UK: Nmc
Min Mail Order EU: £15.00 + p&p
Cat. Cost: 2 x 1st class
Credit Cards: All major credit/debit cards
Specialities: Nursery & garden centre specialising in Parma & hardy *Viola*. Nat. Coll. of *Viola odorata* cvs & Parma Violets.
Notes: Mainly violets by mail order. Main display at nursery in Feb & Mar.
Map Ref: C, C5 OS Grid Ref: SY466918

CGrW   THE GREAT WESTERN GLADIOLUS NURSERY ⊠ €
17 Valley View, Clutton, Bristol, BS39 5SN
ⓣ (01761) 452036
ⓕ (01761) 452036

ⓔ clutton.glads@btinternet.com
ⓦ www.greatwesterngladiolus.co.uk
Contact: G F & J C Hazell
Opening Times: Mail order only. Open by appt. only.
Min Mail Order UK: Nmc
Min Mail Order EU: Nmc
Cat. Cost: 4 x 1st class (2 catalogues)
Credit Cards: None
Specialities: *Gladiolus* species & hybrids, corms & seeds. Other South African bulbous plants.
Notes: Also sells wholesale.

CHad   HADSPEN GARDEN & NURSERY € ▣
Hadspen House, Castle Cary, Somerset, BA7 7NG
ⓣ (01749) 813707
ⓕ (01749) 813707
ⓔ pope@hadspengarden.co.uk
ⓦ www.hadspengarden.co.uk
Contact: N & S Pope
Opening Times: 1000-1700 Thu-Sun & B/hols. 1st Mar-30th Sep inc. Garden open at the same time.
Cat. Cost: 4 x 1st class
Credit Cards: All major credit/debit cards
Specialities: Large-leaved herbaceous. Old fashioned and shrub roses.
Map Ref: C, B5

CHal   HALSWAY NURSERY ⊠
Halsway, Nr Crowcombe, Taunton, Somerset, TA4 4BB
ⓣ (01984) 618243
Contact: T A & D J Bushen
Opening Times: Most days, please phone first.
Min Mail Order UK: £2.00 + p&p
Cat. Cost: 2 x 1st class (list for *Coleus* & *Begonia* only, no nursery list).
Credit Cards: None
Specialities: *Coleus* & *Begonia* (excl. tuberous & winter flowering). Good range of greenhouse & garden plants.
Map Ref: C, B4 OS Grid Ref: ST125383

CHar   WEST HARPTREE NURSERY ⊠ ♋ €
Bristol Road, West Harptree, Bath, Somerset, BS40 6HG
ⓣ (01761) 221370
ⓕ (01761) 221989
ⓔ bryn@harptreenursery.co.uk
ⓦ www.harptreenursery.co.uk
Contact: Bryn & Helene Bowles
Opening Times: From 1000 Tue-Sun 7 days, 1st Mar-31st Oct.
Min Mail Order UK: Nmc

C

Min Mail Order EU: Nmc
Cat. Cost: Large sae for free names list.
Credit Cards: Visa MasterCard Maestro
Specialities: Unusual herbaceous perennials &
shrubs. Bulbs & grasses. Many AGM plants.
Notes: Mail order Oct-Mar only. Also sells
wholesale.
Map Ref: C, B5

CHby   THE HERBARY ⊠ ⊠ €
161 Chapel Street, Horningsham, Warminster,
Wiltshire, BA12 7LU
Ⓣ (01985) 844442
Ⓔ info@beansandherbs.co.uk
Ⓦ www.beansandherbs.co.uk
Contact: Pippa Rosen
Opening Times: Apr-Oct by appt. only.
Min Mail Order UK: Nmc
Min Mail Order EU: Nmc
Cat. Cost: 4 x 1st class
Credit Cards: None
Specialities: Culinary, medicinal & aromatic
herbs organically grown.
Notes: Mail order all year for organic
vegetable seed & large variety of organic bean
& herb seed.
Map Ref: C, B5 OS Grid Ref: ST812414

CHdy   HARDY ORCHIDS ⊠ ⊠
New Gate Farm, Scotchey Lane, Stour
Provost, Gillingham, Dorset, SP8 5LT
Ⓣ (01747) 838368
Ⓕ (01747) 838368
Ⓔ hardyorchids@supanet.com
Ⓦ www.hardyorchids.supanet.com
Contact: N J Heywood
Opening Times: Mail order only. Open by
appt. only.
Min Mail Order UK: £10.00 + p&p
Min Mail Order EU: £10.00 + p&p
Cat. Cost: 2 x 1st class
Credit Cards: None
Specialities: Hardy orchids. *Dactylorhiza,
Pleione, Anacamptis, Orchis, Ophrys* & *Epipactis*.
Map Ref: C, B5 OS Grid Ref: ST778217

CHea   HEATHER BANK NURSERY ⊠ ň
Woodlands, 1 High Street, Littleton Panell,
Devizes, Wiltshire, SN10 4EL
Ⓣ (01380) 812739
Ⓔ mullanhbn.fsnet.co.uk
Ⓦ www.heatherbanknursery.co.uk
Contact: Mrs B Mullan
Opening Times: 0900-1800 Mon, Tue, Thu
& Fri & w/ends. Please check by phone first if
coming a long distance.
Min Mail Order UK: £10.00 + p&p
Cat. Cost: 3 x 1st class

Credit Cards: Visa
Specialities: *Campanula* & cottage garden
plants.
Map Ref: C, B6 OS Grid Ref: ST995547

CHen   HENLADE GARDEN NURSERY ň ⬨
Lower Henlade, Taunton, Somerset,
TA3 5NB
Ⓣ (01823) 443701
Ⓕ (01823) 443701
Ⓔ plants@deserttojungle.com
Ⓦ www.deserttojungle.com
Contact: Robert Gudge
Opening Times: 1000-1700 Wed-Sat 1st
Apr-31st Oct. Nov-Mar & all other times,
please phone first.
Cat. Cost: 1 x 1st class sae.
Credit Cards: Visa MasterCard Switch
Specialities: Exotic-looking plants giving a
desert or jungle effect in the garden. Incl.
Hedychium, Canna, aroids, succulents.
Map Ref: C,B4 OS Grid Ref: ST273232

CHew   HEWITT-COOPER CARNIVOROUS
PLANTS ⊠ ň
The Homestead, Glastonbury Road, West
Pennard, Somerset, BA6 8NN
Ⓣ 01458 835660
Ⓕ 01458 832712
Ⓔ nigel@nigelandpolly.fsnet.co.uk
Ⓦ www.hccarnivorousplants.co.uk
Contact: Nigel Hewitt-Cooper
Opening Times: By appt.
Min Mail Order UK: £10.00 + p&p
Min Mail Order EU: £50.00
Cat. Cost: 1 x 1st class/1 x IRC
Credit Cards: Visa MasterCard
Specialities: Carnivorous plants.
Notes: Mail order May-Nov. Credit cards not
accepted for mail order.
Map Ref: C, B4

CHEx   HARDY EXOTICS ⊠ ⬨
Gilly Lane, Whitecross, Penzance, Cornwall,
TR20 8BZ
Ⓣ (01736) 740660
Ⓕ (01736) 741101
Ⓔ contact@hardyexotics.co.uk
Ⓦ www.hardyexotics.co.uk
Contact: C Shilton/J Smith
Opening Times: 1000-1700 7 days Mar-Oct,
1000-1700 Mon-Sat Nov-Feb. Please phone
first in winter months if travelling a long way.

KEY		
⊠ Mail order to UK or EU	ň Delivers to shows	
⊠ Exports beyond EU	€ Euro accepted	
⬨ Accessible by wheelchair	◆ See Display advertisement	

C

Min Mail Order UK: £40 + carriage
Cat. Cost: £1.00 postal order or 4 x 1st class
(no cheques)
Credit Cards: All major credit/debit cards
Specialities: Largest selection in the UK of
trees, shrubs & herbaceous plants for tropical
& desert effects. Hardy & half-hardy plants
for gardens, patios & conservatories.
Map Ref: C, D1 OS Grid Ref: SW524345

CHll   HILL HOUSE NURSERY & GARDENS
€ 🖳
Landscove, Nr Ashburton, Devon, TQ13 7LY
Ⓣ (01803) 762273
Ⓕ (01803) 762716
Ⓔ sacha@garden.506.fsnet.co.uk
Ⓦ www.hillhousenursery.co.uk
Contact: Raymond, Sacha & Matthew
Hubbard
Opening Times: 1100-1700 7 days, all year.
Open all B/hols incl. Easter Sun. Tearoom
open 1st Mar-30th Sep.
Cat. Cost: None issued.
Credit Cards: Delta MasterCard Switch Visa
Specialities: 3000+ varieties of plants, most
propagated on premises, many rare or
unusual. Garden open.
Map Ref: C, C3 OS Grid Ref: SX774664

CHrt   HORTUS NURSERY ✉ 🖳
Shrubbery Bungalow, School Lane, Rousdon,
Lyme Regis, Dorset, DT7 3XW
Ⓣ (01297) 444019
Ⓜ 07747 043997
Ⓕ (01297) 444019
Ⓔ plants@hortusnursery.com
Ⓦ www.hortusnursery.com
Contact: Marie-Elaine Houghton
Opening Times: 1000-1700 Wed-Sat, Mar-
Oct. Other times by appt.
Min Mail Order UK: £15.00 + p&p
Cat. Cost: 2 x 1st class
Credit Cards: None
Specialities: Ornamental grasses & perennials,
particularly *Carex, Aster, Digitalis, Euphorbia,
Geranium* & *Penstemon.*
Notes: Garden open as nursery.
Map Ref: C, C4 OS Grid Ref: SY296914

CHVG   HIDDEN VALLEY GARDENS 🖳
Treesmill, Nr. Par, Cornwall, PL24 2TU
Ⓣ (01208) 873225
Ⓦ www.hiddenvalleygardens.co.uk
Contact: Mrs P Howard
Opening Times: 1000-1800 beginning Mar-
end Oct 7 days. Please phone for directions.
Cat. Cost: None issued
Credit Cards: None

Specialities: Cottage garden plants, *Crocosmia,
Iris sibirica* & many unusual perennials which
can be seen growing in the garden. Some stock
available in small quantities. Display garden.
Map Ref: C, D2 OS Grid Ref: SX094567

CIri   THE IRIS GARDEN ✉ € ◆
Yard House, Pilsdon, Bridport, Dorset, DT6 5PA
Ⓣ (01308) 868797
Ⓕ (01308) 868797
Ⓔ theirisgarden@aol.com
Ⓦ www.theirisgarden.co.uk
Contact: Clive Russell
Opening Times: Show garden open by appt.
Please email or phone for details.
Min Mail Order UK: £15.00 + p&p
Min Mail Order EU: £25.00 + p&p
Cat. Cost: 8 x 1st class.
Credit Cards: All major credit/debit cards
Specialities: Modern bearded & beardless *Iris*
from breeders in UK, USA, France, Italy &
Australia.
Notes: Orders for bearded iris & sibiricas
must be received by end Jun & by end Aug
for ensatas & spurias.
Map Ref: C, C5

CJas   JASMINE COTTAGE GARDENS ✉ 🖳
26 Channel Road, Walton St Mary, Clevedon,
Somerset, BS21 7BY
Ⓣ (01275) 871850
Ⓔ margaret@bologrew.demon.co.uk
Ⓦ www.bologrew.pwp.blueyonder.co.uk
Contact: Mr & Mrs M Redgrave
Opening Times: May to Sep, daily by appt.
Garden open at the same times.
Min Mail Order UK: Nmc
Cat. Cost: None issued
Credit Cards: None
Specialities: *Rhodochiton, Asarina, Maurandya,
Dicentra macrocapnos, Salvia, Solenopsis,
Isotoma,* half-hardy geraniums.
Notes: Mail order seed only.
Map Ref: C, A4 OS Grid Ref: ST405725

CKel   KELWAYS LTD ✉ ✉ 🏠 € 🖳
Langport, Somerset, TA10 9EZ
Ⓣ (01458) 250521
Ⓕ (01458) 253351
Ⓔ sales@kelways.co.uk
Ⓦ www.kelways.co.uk
Contact: Mr David Root
Opening Times: 0900-1700 Mon-Fri, 1000-
1700 Sat, 1000-1600 Sun.
Min Mail Order UK: £4.00 + p&p
Min Mail Order EU: £8.00 + p&p
Cat. Cost: Free
Credit Cards: Visa Access

Specialities: *Paeonia, Iris, Hemerocallis* & herbaceous perennials. Nat. Coll. *Paeonia lactiflora.*
Notes: Mail order for *Paeonia* & *Iris* only. Also sells wholesale
Map Ref: C, B5 **OS Grid Ref:** ST434273

CKen   KENWITH NURSERY (GORDON HADDOW) ⊠ ✉ € ♿ ◆
Blinsham, Nr Torrington, Beaford, Winkleigh, Devon, EX19 8NT
Ⓣ (01805) 603274
Ⓕ (01805) 603663
Ⓔ conifers@kenwith63.freeserve.co.uk
Ⓦ www.kenwithnursery.co.uk
Contact: Gordon Haddow
Opening Times: 1000-1630 Wed-Sat Nov-Feb & by appt. 1000-1630 Tue-Sat, Mar-Oct.
Min Mail Order UK: £10.00 + p&p
Min Mail Order EU: £50.00 + p&p
Cat. Cost: 3 x 1st class
Credit Cards: Visa MasterCard
Specialities: All conifer genera. Grafting a speciality. Many new introductions to UK. Nat. Coll. of Dwarf Conifers.
Map Ref: C, B3 **OS Grid Ref:** SS518160

CKno   KNOLL GARDENS ⊠ ♟ ♿
Hampreston, Stapehill, Nr Wimborne, Dorset, BH21 7ND
Ⓣ (01202) 873931
Ⓕ (01202) 870842
Ⓔ enquiries@knollgardens.co.uk
Ⓦ www.knollgardens.co.uk
Contact: N R Lucas
Opening Times: 1000-1700 (or dusk if earlier) Wed-Sun. Closed Xmas period.
Min Mail Order UK: Nmc
Cat. Cost: 9 x 2nd class or order online
Credit Cards: Visa MasterCard
Specialities: Grasses (main specialism). Select perennials. Nat. Collections of *Pennisetum, Phygelius* & deciduous *Ceanothus.*
Notes: Also sells wholesale.
Map Ref: C, C6

CKob   KOBAKOBA ⊠ ✉ ♟
2 High Street, Ashcott, Bridgwater, Somerset, TA7 9PL
Ⓣ (01458) 210700
Ⓜ 07870 624969
Ⓕ (01458) 210650
Ⓔ plants@kobakoba.co.uk
Ⓦ www.kobakoba.co.uk
Contact: Christine Smithee & David Constantine
Opening Times: Please phone for opening times.
Min Mail Order UK: Nmc

Min Mail Order EU: Nmc
Cat. Cost: Plantlist 1 x 1st class or catalogue £3.50.
Credit Cards: Visa MasterCard Delta
Specialities: Plants for tropical effect incl. *Ensete, Musa, Hedychium, Curcuma* & other *Zingiberaceae.* Conservatory & greenhouse plants.
Map Ref: C, B5 **OS Grid Ref:** ST4237

CLAP   LONG ACRE PLANTS ⊠ ♟ ♿
South Marsh, Charlton Musgrove, Nr Wincanton, Somerset, BA9 8EX
Ⓣ (01963) 32802
Ⓕ (01963) 32802
Ⓔ info@longacreplants.co.uk
Ⓦ www.longacreplants.co.uk
Contact: Nigel & Michelle Rowland
Opening Times: 1000-1700 Thu-Sat Feb-Jun, Sep & Oct.
Min Mail Order UK: £15.00 + p&p
Min Mail Order EU: £30.00 + p&p
Cat. Cost: 3 x 1st class
Credit Cards: Switch Visa MasterCard
Specialities: Ferns, lilies, woodland bulbs & perennials. Nat. Coll. of *Asarum.*
Notes: Lilies only outside EU.
Map Ref: C, B5

CLCN   LITTLE CREEK NURSERY ⊠ ♿
39 Moor Road, Banwell, Weston-super-Mare, Somerset, BS29 6EF
Ⓣ (01934) 823739
Ⓕ (01934) 823739
Ⓦ www.littlecreeknursery.co.uk
Contact: Julie Adams
Opening Times: Mail order only. Open by appt only.
Min Mail Order UK: Nmc
Min Mail Order EU: Nmc
Cat. Cost: 3 x 1st class
Credit Cards: Visa MasterCard Switch
Specialities: Species *Cyclamen* (from seed), *Helleborus, Agapanthus* & *Schizostylis.*
Map Ref: C, B4

CLnd   LANDFORD TREES ⊠ €
Landford Lodge, Landford, Salisbury, Wiltshire, SP5 2EH
Ⓣ (01794) 390808
Ⓕ (01794) 390037
Ⓔ sales@landfordtrees.co.uk
Ⓦ www.landfordtrees.co.uk

C

Contact: C D Pilkington
Opening Times: 0800-1700 Mon-Fri.
Min Mail Order UK: Please enquire
Min Mail Order EU: Please enquire
Cat. Cost: Free
Credit Cards: None
Specialities: Deciduous ornamental trees.
Notes: Mail order maximum size 120cms.
Also sells wholesale.
Map Ref: C, B6 OS Grid Ref: SU247201

CLoc   C S Lockyer ⊠ ⊠ ♠ € ◆
Lansbury, 70 Henfield Road, Coalpit Heath,
Bristol, BS36 2UZ
Ⓣ (01454) 772219
Ⓕ (01454) 772219
Ⓔ sales@lockyerfuchsias.co.uk
Ⓦ www.lockyerfuchsias.co.uk
Contact: C S Lockyer
Opening Times: 1000-1300, 1430-1700 most
days, please ring.
Min Mail Order UK: 6 plants + p&p
Min Mail Order EU: £12.00 + p&p
Cat. Cost: 4 x 1st class
Credit Cards: None
Specialities: *Fuchsia*.
Notes: Open days. Limited wheelchair access.
Also sells wholesale.
Map Ref: C, A5

CLyd   Lydford Alpine Nursery ⊠ ♠
2 Southern Cottages, Lydford, Okehampton,
Devon, EX20 4BL
Ⓣ (01822) 820398
Contact: Julie & David Hatchett
Opening Times: By appt. only. Please ring for
directions.
Min Mail Order UK: £10.00 + p&p
Cat. Cost: Sae for saxifrage list.
Credit Cards: None
Specialities: *Saxifraga*. Very wide range of
choice & unusual alpines in small quantities.
Notes: Mail order *Saxifraga* only.
Map Ref: C, C3 OS Grid Ref: SX504830

CMac   Macpennys Nurseries ⊠
154 Burley Road, Bransgore, Christchurch,
Dorset, BH23 8DB
Ⓣ (01425) 672348
Ⓕ (01425) 673917
Ⓔ office@macpennys.co.uk
Ⓦ www.macpennys.co.uk
Contact: T & V Lowndes
Opening Times: 0900-1700 Mon-Sat, 1100-
1700 Sun. Closed Xmas & New Year.
Min Mail Order UK: Nmc
Cat. Cost: A4 Sae with 4 x 1st class
Credit Cards: All major credit/debit cards

Specialities: General. Plants available in small
quantities only.
Notes: Mail order not available Jun-Aug incl.
Nursery partially accessible for wheelchairs.
Map Ref: C, C6

CMCN   Mallet Court Nursery ⊠ ⊠ ♠ € ⬛
Curry Mallet, Taunton, Somerset, TA3 6SY
Ⓣ (01823) 481493
Ⓕ (01823) 481493
Ⓔ harris@malletcourt.freeserve.co.uk
Ⓦ www.malletcourt.co.uk
Contact: J G S & P M E Harris F.L.S.
Opening Times: 0930-1700 Mon-Fri summer,
0930-1600 winter. Sat & Sun by appt.
Min Mail Order UK: Nmc
Min Mail Order EU: Nmc
Cat. Cost: £1.50
Credit Cards: All major credit/debit cards
Specialities: Maples, oaks, *Magnolia*, hollies &
other rare and unusual plants including those
from China & South Korea.
Notes: Mail order Oct-Mar only. Also sells
wholesale.
Map Ref: C, B4

CMCo   Meadow Cottage Plants ♠ € ⬛
Pitt Hill, Ivybridge, Devon, PL21 0JJ
Ⓣ (01752) 894532
Contact: Mrs L P Hunt
Opening Times: By appt. only.
Cat. Cost: 2 x 2nd class
Credit Cards: None
Specialities: Hardy geranium, other hardy
perennials, ornamental grasses and bamboos.
Some varieties available in small numbers
only. All plants grown in peat-free compost.
Notes: Also sells wholesale.
Map Ref: C, D3

CMdw   Meadows Nursery ⊠ ♠
5 Rectory Cottages, Mells, Frome, Somerset,
BA11 3PN
Ⓣ (01373) 812268
Ⓔ plants@meadowsnurserymells.co.uk
Contact: Sue Lees & Eddie Wheatley
Opening Times: 1000-1800 Wed-Sun 1st
Feb-31st Oct & B/hols.
Min Mail Order UK: Nmc
Cat. Cost: 4 x 1st class
Credit Cards: None
Specialities: Hardy perennials, shrubs & some
conservatory plants. *Kniphofia*.
Map Ref: C, B5 OS Grid Ref: ST729492

CMea   The Mead Nursery ⬛
Brokerswood, Nr Westbury, Wiltshire,
BA13 4EG

Ⓣ (01373) 859990
Contact: Steve & Emma Lewis-Dale
Opening Times: 0900-1700 Wed-Sat &
B/hols, 1200-1700 Sun, 1st Feb-10th Oct.
Closed Easter Sun.
Cat. Cost: 5 x 1st class
Credit Cards: All major credit/debit cards
Specialities: Perennials, alpines, pot grown
bulbs and grasses.
Map Ref: C, B5 **OS Grid Ref:** ST833517

CMen   MENDIP BONSAI STUDIO ⋔ ⬚
Byways, Back Lane, Downside,
Shepton Mallet, Somerset,
BA4 4JR
Ⓣ (01749) 344274
Ⓕ (01749) 344274
Ⓔ jr.trott@ukonline.co.uk
Ⓦ www.mendipbonsai.co.uk
Contact: John Trott
Opening Times: By appt. only.
Cat. Cost: Large sae for plant & workshop lists
Credit Cards: Visa MasterCard
Specialities: Bonsai & garden stock. Acers,
conifers, *Stewartia*. Many plants available in
small numbers only.
Map Ref: C, B5

CMHG   MARWOOD HILL GARDENS ⬚
Barnstaple, Devon,
EX31 4EB
Ⓣ (01271) 342528
Ⓔ malcolmpharoah@supanet.com
Ⓦ www.marwoodhillgarden.co.uk
Contact: Malcolm Pharoah
Opening Times: 1100-1630, 7 days.
Cat. Cost: 3 x 1st class
Credit Cards: Visa Delta MasterCard Switch
Solo
Specialities: Large range of unusual trees &
shrubs. *Eucalyptus*, alpines, *Camellia*, *Astilbe*,
bog plants & perennials. Nat. Colls. of *Astilbe*,
Tulbaghia & *Iris ensata*.
Map Ref: C, B3

CMil   MILL COTTAGE PLANTS ⊠ ⋔ ⬚
The Mill, Henley Lane, Wookey, Somerset,
BA5 1AP
Ⓣ (01749) 676966
Ⓔ mcp@tinyworld.co.uk
Ⓦ www.millcottageplants.co.uk
Contact: Sally Gregson
Opening Times: 1000-1800 Wed Mar-Sep or
by appt. Phone for directions.
Min Mail Order UK: £5.00 + p&p
Min Mail Order EU: £10.00 + p&p
Cat. Cost: 4 x 1st class
Credit Cards: None

Specialities: Rare *Hydrangea serrata*,
H. aspera. Also *Papaver orientale*, *Dierama*,
hardy *Geranium*, ferns, & grasses.
Map Ref: C, B5

CMMP   M & M PLANTS ⬚
Lloret, Chittlehamholt, Umberleigh, Devon,
EX37 9PD
Ⓣ (01769) 540448
Ⓕ (01769) 540448
Ⓔ MMPlants@Chittlehamholt.freeserve.co.uk
Contact: Mr M Thorne
Opening Times: 0930-1730 Tue-Sat, Apr-
Oct & 1000-1600 Tue-Fri, Nov-Mar. Sat by
appt. Aug.
Cat. Cost: 3 x 1st class
Credit Cards: None
Specialities: Perennials. We also carry a good
range of alpines, shrubs, trees & roses.
Map Ref: C, B3

CMon   MONOCOT NURSERY ⊠ ⊠
St Michaels, Littleton, Somerton, Somerset,
TA11 6NT
Ⓣ (01458) 272356
Ⓕ (01458) 272065
Contact: M R Salmon
Opening Times: 1000-1800 Wed-Sun, Feb-
Nov, or by appt.
Min Mail Order UK: Nmc
Min Mail Order EU: Nmc
Cat. Cost: Free to UK & EU. Overseas $2.00
or equivalent.
Credit Cards: None
Specialities: Bulbs, corms, tubers, rhizomes.
Hardy to tropical.

CNat   NATURAL SELECTION ⊠ €
1 Station Cottages, Hullavington,
Chippenham, Wiltshire, SN14 6ET
Ⓣ (01666) 837369
Ⓔ martin@worldmutation.demon.co.uk
Ⓦ www.worldmutation.demon.co.uk
Contact: Martin Cragg-Barber
Opening Times: Please phone first.
Min Mail Order UK: £9.00 + p&p
Cat. Cost: £1.00 or 5 x 2nd class
Credit Cards: None
Specialities: Unusual British natives & others.
Also seed. Only available in small quantities.
Map Ref: C, A5 **OS Grid Ref:** ST898828

CNCN   NAKED CROSS NURSERIES ⊠ ⬚
Waterloo Road, Corfe Mullen, Wimborne,
Dorset, BH21 3SR
Ⓣ (01202) 693256
Ⓕ (01202) 693259
Contact: Peter French

C

Opening Times: 0900-1700 7 days.
Min Mail Order UK: 10 heathers
Cat. Cost: 2 x 1st class
Credit Cards: Visa American Express Switch
MasterCard
Specialities: Heathers.
Notes: Also sells wholesale.
Map Ref: C, C6

CNic   NICKY'S ROCK GARDEN NURSERY ⋔
Broadhayes, Stockland, Honiton, Devon,
EX14 9EH
Ⓣ (01404) 881213
Ⓔ Dianabob.Dark@nickys.sagehost.co.uk
Contact: Diana & Bob Dark
Opening Times: 0900-dusk 7 days. Please
phone first to check & for directions.
Cat. Cost: 3 x 1st class
Credit Cards: None
Specialities: Plants for rock gardens, scree,
troughs, banks, walls & front of border &
dwarf shrubs. Many unusual. Plants
propagated in small numbers. Ring to check
availability before travelling.
Notes: Partial wheelchair access.
Map Ref: C, C4 OS Grid Ref: ST236027

CNMi   NEWPORT MILLS NURSERY ⊠
Wrantage, Taunton, Somerset, TA3 6DJ
Ⓣ (01823) 490231
Ⓜ 07950 035668
Ⓕ (01823) 490231
Contact: John Barrington, Rachel Pettitt
Opening Times: By appt. only.
Min Mail Order UK: Nmc
Min Mail Order EU: Nmc
Cat. Cost: Free
Credit Cards: None
Specialities: *Delphinium.* English scented
varieties of perpetual flowering carnations.
Some varieties only available in small
quantities & propagated to order.
Notes: Mail order Apr-Sep for young
delphiniums in 7cm pots. Dormant plants can
be sent out in autumn/winter if requested.
Map Ref: C, B4

COfd   OLDFIELD NURSERY ⓖ
Beaminster Bottom Farm, Beaminster,
Dorset, DT8 3SG
Ⓣ (01308) 861113
Ⓕ (01308) 861737
Ⓔ nursery@chamalrugs.com
Ⓦ www.chamalrugs.com
Contact: Tracy Oldfield
Opening Times: 0900-1600 Mon, Wed &
Fri, please phone first. Other times by appt.
Credit Cards: All major credit/debit cards

Specialities: Low allergenic plants & herbs
suitable for growing by eczema, asthma &
hayfever sufferers in child-friendly gardens.
Map Ref: C, B5 OS Grid Ref: ST507036

COld   THE OLD MILL HERBARY
Helland Bridge, Bodmin, Cornwall, PL30 4QR
Ⓣ (01208) 841206
Ⓔ oldmillHERBARY@aol.com
Ⓦ www.oldmillherbary.co.uk
Contact: Mrs B Whurr
Opening Times: 1000-1700 Thu-Tue 25th
Mar-30th Sep. Closed Wed.
Cat. Cost: 6 x 1st class
Credit Cards: None
Specialities: Culinary, medicinal & aromatic
herbs.
Notes: Limited sales of medicinal herbs.
Map Ref: C, C2 OS Grid Ref: SX065717

COlW   THE OLD WITHY GARDEN NURSERY ⊠
Grange Fruit Farm, Gweek, Helston,
Cornwall, TR12 6BE
Ⓣ (01326) 221171
Ⓔ WithyNursery@fsbdial.co.uk
Contact: Sheila Chandler or Nick Chandler
Opening Times: 1000-1700 Wed-Mon, mid
Feb-end Oct. 1000-1730 7 days, Apr-Sep.
Min Mail Order UK: £15.00
Cat. Cost: 4 x 1st class
Credit Cards: Maestro Visa MasterCard Delta
Specialities: Cottage garden plants, perennials,
some biennials & grasses. Good selection of
Achillea, Eryngium, hardy geraniums,
Penstemon & *Sedum.* Some in small quantities.
Notes: Also sells wholesale.
Map Ref: C, D1 OS Grid Ref: SW688255

COtt   OTTER NURSERIES LTD ⓖ
Gosford Road, Ottery St. Mary, Devon,
EX11 1LZ
Ⓣ (01404) 815815
Ⓕ (01404) 815816
Ⓔ otter@otternurseries.co.uk
Contact: Mrs Pam Poole
Opening Times: 0800-1730 Mon-Sat, 1030-
1630 Sun. Closed 25-26 Dec & Easter Sun.
Cat. Cost: None issued
Credit Cards: All major credit/debit cards
Specialities: Large garden centre & nursery
with extensive range of trees, shrubs, conifers,
climbers, roses, fruit & hardy perennials.
Map Ref: C, C4

CPar   PARKS PERENNIALS
242 Wallisdown Road, Wallisdown,
Bournemouth, Dorset, BH10 4HZ
Ⓣ (01202) 524464

C

Contact: S Parks
Opening Times: Apr-Oct most days, please phone first.
Cat. Cost: None issued.
Credit Cards: None
Specialities: Hardy herbaceous perennials.
Map Ref: C, C6

CPas   PASSIFLORA (NATIONAL COLLECTION) ⊠ ⊠ €
Lampley Road, Kingston Seymour, Clevedon, Somerset, BS21 6XS
⊤ (01934) 838895
Ⓕ (01934) 877255
Ⓔ johnvanderplank@yahoo.co.uk
Contact: John Vanderplank
Opening Times: 0900-1700 7 days, 1st Aug-31st Aug.
Min Mail Order UK: £10.00 + p&p
Min Mail Order EU: £10.00 + p&p
Cat. Cost: 3 x 1st class
Credit Cards: Visa Access EuroCard MasterCard
Specialities: *Passiflora*. Nat. Coll. of over 200 species & cultivars. Scientific status, Brickell Award 2004.
Notes: Mail order seed only. Plants must be collected from nursery. Pre-ordered plants may be picked up from the nursery at any time. Also sells wholesale.
Map Ref: C, A4

CPbn   PENBORN GOAT FARM ⊠ 🔄
Penborn, Bounds Cross, Holsworthy, Devon, EX22 6LH
⊤ (01288) 381569
Ⓕ penborn@classicfm.net
Contact: P R Oldfield
Opening Times: Not open. Mail order only.
Min Mail Order UK: £18.00
Cat. Cost: 2 x 1st class.
Credit Cards: None
Specialities: *Mentha*. Small quantities only.
Map Ref: C, C2

CPBP   PARHAM BUNGALOW PLANTS ⊠ 🔄 €
Parham Lane, Market Lavington, Devizes, Wiltshire, SN10 4QA
⊤ (01380) 812605
Ⓔ jjs@pbplants.freeserve.co.uk
Contact: Mrs D E Sample
Opening Times: Please ring first.
Min Mail Order UK: Nmc
Min Mail Order EU: Nmc
Cat. Cost: Sae
Credit Cards: None
Specialities: Alpines & dwarf shrubs.
Map Ref: C, B6

CPen   PENNARD PLANTS ⊠ ⊠ 🔄 €
3 The Gardens, East Pennard, Shepton Mallet, Somerset, BA4 6TU
⊤ (01749) 860039
Ⓕ (01749) 860232
Ⓔ sales@pennardplants.com
Ⓦ www.pennardplants.com
Contact: Chris Smith
Opening Times: By appt. only.
Min Mail Order UK: Nmc
Min Mail Order EU: Nmc
Cat. Cost: 3 x 1st class
Credit Cards: All major credit/debit cards
Specialities: Ornamental grasses, *Agapanthus*, *Crocosmia*, *Dierama*, *Kniphofia*, phormiums & South African bulbous plants.
Notes: Nursery at The Walled Garden at East Pennard.
Map Ref: C, B5

CPhi   ALAN PHIPPS CACTI ⊠ €
62 Samuel White Road, Hanham, Bristol, BS15 3LX
⊤ (0117) 9607591
Ⓦ www.cactus-mall.com/alan-phipps/index.html
Contact: A Phipps
Opening Times: 10.00-1700 but prior phone call essential to ensure a greeting.
Min Mail Order UK: £5.00 + p&p
Min Mail Order EU: £20.00 + p&p
Cat. Cost: Sae or 2 x IRC (EC only)
Credit Cards: None
Specialities: *Mammillaria*, *Astrophytum* & *Ariocarpus*. Species & varieties will change with times. Ample quantities exist in spring. Limited range of *Agave*.
Notes: Euro accepted as cash only.
Map Ref: C, A5 **OS Grid Ref:** ST644717

CPHo   THE PALM HOUSE ⊠
8 North Street, Ottery St Mary, Devon, EX11 1DR
⊤ (01404) 815450
Ⓔ george@thepalmhouse.co.uk
Ⓦ www.thepalmhouse.co.uk
Contact: George Gregory
Opening Times: Mail order only. Open by appt. only.
Min Mail Order UK: £15.00
Cat. Cost: 2 x 1st class
Credit Cards: All major credit/debit cards
Specialities: Palms.
Notes: Also sells wholesale.
Map Ref: C, C4 **OS Grid Ref:** SY098955

C

CPin   PINSLA GARDEN AND NURSERY 🔥
Pinsla Lodge, Glynn, Bodmin, Cornwall,
PL30 4AY
Ⓣ (01208) 821339
Ⓕ (01208) 821339
Ⓔ info@pinslagarden.co.uk
Ⓦ www.pinslagarden.co.uk
Contact: Mark and Claire Woodbine
Opening Times: 1000-1800, 7 days, 1st Mar-
31st Oct. Winter, w/ends only.
Cat. Cost: None issued.
Credit Cards: All major credit/debit cards
Specialities: Plant-lovers paradise, overflowing
with perennials, ferns, acers, bamboos, grasses,
succulents, alpines, climbers & shrubs.
Map Ref: C, C2 **OS Grid Ref:** SX665117

CPle   PLEASANT VIEW NURSERY ✉ 🔥
Two Mile Oak, Nr Denbury, Newton Abbot,
Devon, TQ12 6DG
Ⓣ (01803) 813388 answerphone
Contact: Mrs B D Yeo
Opening Times: Nursery open 1000-1700
Wed-Fri mid Mar-end Sep (closed for lunch
1245-1330).
Min Mail Order UK: £20.00 + p&p
Min Mail Order EU: £20.00 + p&p (salvias
only)
Cat. Cost: 3 x 2nd class or 2 x IRC
Credit Cards: None
Specialities: *Salvia* & unusual shrubs for
garden & conservatory. Nat. Colls. of *Salvia*
& *Abelia*.
Notes: Nursery off A381 at T.M. Oak Cross
towards Denbury.
Map Ref: C, C3 **OS Grid Ref:** SX8368

CPLG   PINE LODGE GARDENS & NURSERY 🔥
Cuddra, Holmbush, St Austell, Cornwall,
PL25 3RQ
Ⓣ (01726) 73500
Ⓕ (01726) 77370
Ⓔ garden@pine-lodge.co.uk
Ⓦ www.pine-lodge.co.uk
Contact: Ray & Shirley Clemo
Opening Times: 1000-1700 7 days 1st Mar-
31st Oct.
Cat. Cost: 5 x 2nd class
Credit Cards: None
Specialities: Rare & unusual shrubs &
herbaceous, some from seed collected on plant
expeditions each year. Nat. Coll. of *Grevillea*.
All plants available in small quantities only.
Map Ref: C, D2 **OS Grid Ref:** SX045527

CPIN   THE PLANTSMAN NURSERY ✉ 🗹 ◆
North Wonson Farm, Throwleigh,
Okehampton, Devon, EX20 2JA

Ⓣ (01647) 231699 office/(01647) 231618
nursery
Ⓕ (01647) 231157
Ⓔ pnursery@aol.com
Ⓦ www.plantsman.com
Contact: Guy & Emma Sisson
Opening Times: Not open. Mail order
only.
Min Mail Order UK: £40.00 + p&p
Min Mail Order EU: £50.00 + p&p
Cat. Cost: £2.50 for full colour catalogue.
Credit Cards: All major credit/debit cards
Specialities: Unusual hardy & tender climbers
and wall shrubs.

CPMA   P M A PLANT SPECIALITIES ✉ 🗹
Junker's Nursery Ltd., Lower Mead,
West Hatch, Taunton, Somerset,
TA3 5RN
Ⓣ (01823) 480774
Ⓕ (01823) 481046
Ⓔ karan@junker.co.uk
Ⓦ www.junker.co.uk
Contact: Karan or Nick Junker
Opening Times: Strictly by appt. only.
Min Mail Order UK: Nmc
Min Mail Order EU: Nmc
Cat. Cost: 6 x 2nd class
Credit Cards: None
Specialities: Choice & unusual shrubs incl.
grafted *Acer palmatum*, *Cornus*, *Magnolia* & a
wide range of *Daphne*. Small quantities of
some hard to propagate plants, esp. daphnes.
Reserve orders accepted.
Notes: Also sells wholesale.
Map Ref: C, B4

CPne   PINE COTTAGE PLANTS ✉ 🗹 €
Pine Cottage, Fourways, Eggesford,
Chulmleigh, Devon,
EX18 7QZ
Ⓣ (01769) 580076
Ⓕ (01769) 581427
Ⓔ pcplants@supanet.com
Ⓦ www.pcplants.co.uk
Contact: Dick Fulcher
Opening Times: By appt. only. Special open
weeks for *Agapanthus*, 1000-1800 daily, excl.
Sun am, Jul & Aug 2005.
Min Mail Order UK: £15.00 + p&p
Min Mail Order EU: £20.00 + p&p
Cat. Cost: 4 x 1st class
Credit Cards: Maestro Visa MasterCard
Specialities: Nat. Coll. of *Agapanthus*. Some
cvs available in small quantities only.
Notes: Mail order *Agapanthus* from Oct-Jun.
Also sells wholesale.
Map Ref: C, B3 **OS Grid Ref:** SS6171

CPom   POMEROY PLANTS
Tower House, Pomeroy Lane, Wingfield,
Trowbridge, Wiltshire, BA14 9LJ
(T) (01225) 769551
Contact: Simon Young
Opening Times: Mar-Nov. Please phone first.
Cat. Cost: 2 x 1st class
Credit Cards: None
Specialities: Hardy, mainly species, herbaceous
perennials. Many unusual and often small
numbers. Specialities *Allium*, *Salvia* & shade-
lovers, esp. *Epimedium*.
Map Ref: C, B5 OS Grid Ref: ST817569

CPou   POUNSLEY PLANTS ⊠ ń € 🅖
Pounsley Combe, Spriddlestone, Brixton,
Plymouth, Devon, PL9 0DW
(T) (01752) 402873
(F) (01752) 402873
(E) pou599@aol.com
(W) www.pounsleyplants.com
Contact: Mrs Jane Hollow
Opening Times: Normally 1000-1700 Mon-
Sat but please phone first.
Min Mail Order UK: £10.00 + p&p
Min Mail Order EU: £20.00 + p&p
Cat. Cost: 2 x 1st class
Credit Cards: None
Specialities: Unusual herbaceous perennials &
cottage plants. Selection of *Clematis* & old roses.
Large selection of South African monocots.
Notes: Mail order Nov-Feb only. Also sells
wholesale.
Map Ref: C, D3 OS Grid Ref: SX521538

CPrp   PROPERPLANTS.COM ⊠ ń
Penknight, Edgcumbe Road, Lostwithiel,
Cornwall, PL22 0JD
(T) (01208) 872291
(F) (01208) 872291
(E) info@Properplants.com
(W) www.ProperPlants.com
Contact: Sarah Wilks
Opening Times: 1000-1800 or dusk if earlier,
Tue & B/hols mid-Mar to end-Sep & by appt.
Min Mail Order UK: Nmc
Min Mail Order EU: Nmc
Cat. Cost: 4 x 1st class
Credit Cards: All major credit/debit cards
Specialities: Wide range of unusual & easy
herbaceous perennials, ferns & grasses. Less
common herbs.
Notes: Partially accessible for wheelchair users.
Map Ref: C, C2 OS Grid Ref: SX093596

CPSs   PLANTS FOR THE SENSES ⊠
Corner Cottage, North Street, Dolton,
Winkleigh, Devon, EX19 8QQ

(T) (01805) 804467
(E) michaelross@freenetname.co.uk
Contact: Michael Ross
Opening Times: Not open. Mail order only.
Min Mail Order UK: Nmc
Cat. Cost: 1 x 1st class
Credit Cards: None
Specialities: Some emphasis on scented
plants. Some stock in small quantities only.
Notes: Nursery is 5 miles away from above
address.

CQua   QUALITY DAFFODILS ⊠ 🅜 € ◆
14 Roscarrack Close, Falmouth, Cornwall,
TR11 4PJ
(T) (01326) 317959
(F) (01326) 317959
(E) rascamp@daffodils.uk.com
(W) www.qualitydaffodils.co.uk
Contact: R A Scamp
Opening Times: Not open. Mail order only.
Min Mail Order UK: Nmc
Min Mail Order EU: Nmc
Cat. Cost: 3 x 1st class
Credit Cards: All major credit/debit cards
Specialities: *Narcissus* hybrids & species.
Some stocks are less than 100 bulbs.
Notes: Also sells wholesale.
Map Ref: C, D1

CRde   ROWDE MILL NURSERY € 🅖
Rowde, Devizes, Wiltshire, SN10 1SZ
(T) (01380) 723016
(F) (01380) 723016
(E) cholmeley@supanet.com
Contact: Mrs J Cholmeley
Opening Times: 1000-1700 Thu-Sun &
B/hol Mon Apr-Sep.
Cat. Cost: None issued
Credit Cards: None
Specialities: Wide range of hardy perennials,
all grown on the nursery. Plants offered in
pots or lifted from stockbeds.
Map Ref: C, A6 OS Grid Ref: ST973628

CRea   REALLY WILD FLOWERS ⊠ €
H V Horticulture Ltd, Spring Mead,
Bedchester, Shaftesbury, Dorset,
SP7 0JU
(T) (01747) 811778
(F) (01747) 811499
(E) rwflowers@aol.com
(W) www.reallywildflowers.co.uk
Contact: Grahame Dixie
Opening Times: Not open. Mail order only.
Min Mail Order UK: £40.00 + p&p
Min Mail Order EU: £100.00 + p&p
Cat. Cost: 3 x 1st class

C

Credit Cards: None
Specialities: Wild flowers for grasslands, woodlands, wetlands & heaths. Seeds, orchids.
Notes: Advisory & soil analysis services. Also sells wholesale.

CRez   REZARE NURSERIES ✉
Rezare, Nr Treburley, Launceston, Cornwall, PL15 9NX
Ⓣ (01579) 370969
Ⓔ REZARENURSERIES@aol.com
Contact: Mel & Jim Gearing
Opening Times: 1000-1700, 7 days 1st Feb-end Oct. Other times by appt.
Min Mail Order UK: £10.00
Cat. Cost: 4 x 1st class
Credit Cards: Visa MasterCard
Specialities: Growers of a full & varied range of choice & unusual plants of the highest quality, incl. a good selection of herbaceous perennials, shrubs & trees.
Notes: Mainly perennials, grasses & ferns by mail order. Credit cards not accepted for mail order.
Map Ref: C, C2

CRHN   ROSELAND HOUSE NURSERY ✉ ♠
Chacewater, Truro, Cornwall, TR4 8QB
Ⓣ (01872) 560451
Ⓔ clematis@roselandhouse.co.uk
Ⓦ www.roselandhouse.co.uk
Contact: C R Pridham
Opening Times: 1300-1800 Tue & Wed, Apr-Sep.
Min Mail Order UK: Nmc
Cat. Cost: 2 x 1st class
Credit Cards: None
Specialities: Climbing & conservatory plants. Nat. Coll. of *Clematis viticella* cvs.
Notes: Garden open to the public.
Map Ref: C, D1 OS Grid Ref: SW752445

CRob   ROBERTS NURSERIES ✉
East Allington, Totnes, Devon, TQ9 7QE
Ⓣ (01548) 521412 Ⓜ 07940 858778
Ⓕ (01548) 521533
Ⓔ info@conifersdirect.com
Ⓦ www.conifersdirect.com
Contact: W R Bartoszyn
Opening Times: By appt. only.
Min Mail Order UK: Nmc
Cat. Cost: 3 x 1st class stamps
Credit Cards: None
Specialities: Extensive range of hardy dwarf, ornamental conifers incl. old favourites, choice varieties & new introductions. A selected range of specimen shrubs & conifers in patio planters.
Notes: Also sells wholesale
Map Ref: C, D3 OS Grid Ref: SX763495

CRoM   ROSEDOWN MILL PALMS AND EXOTICS ✉
Hartland, Bideford, Devon, EX39 6AH
Ⓣ (01237) 441527
Ⓔ sales@rosedownmill.co.uk
Ⓦ www.rosedownmill.co.uk
Contact: Huw Collingbourne
Opening Times: By appt. only.
Min Mail Order UK: £25.00
Min Mail Order EU: £25.00
Cat. Cost: Sae for list
Credit Cards: None
Specialities: Palms, cycads, pachypodiums.
Map Ref: C, B2 OS Grid Ref: SS276248

CRow   ROWDEN GARDENS ✉ ✉ ♿
Brentor, Nr Tavistock, Devon, PL19 0NG
Ⓣ (01822) 810275
Ⓕ (01822) 810275
Ⓔ rowdengardens@btopenworld.com
Contact: John R L Carter
Opening Times: By appt only.
Min Mail Order UK: Nmc
Min Mail Order EU: Nmc
Cat. Cost: 6 x 1st class
Credit Cards: None
Specialities: Aquatics, damp loving & associated plants incl. rare & unusual varieties. Nat. Coll. of *Polygonum, Ranunculus ficaria, Caltha* & Water *Iris*. Some stock available in small quantities only.
Notes: Also sells wholesale.
Map Ref: C, C3

CRWN   THE REALLY WILD NURSERY ✉ ✉ ♠ €
19 Hoopers Way, Torrington, Devon, EX38 7NS
Ⓣ (01805) 624739
Ⓕ (01805) 624739
Ⓔ thereallywildnursery@yahoo.co.uk
Ⓦ www.thereallywildnursery.co.uk
Contact: Kathryn Moore
Opening Times: Not open. Mail order only.
Min Mail Order UK: £10.00 + p&p
Min Mail Order EU: £20.00 + p&p
Cat. Cost: 3 x 1st class
Specialities: Wildflowers, bulbs & seeds.
Notes: Mail order all year round, grown to order (plants in pots or plugs). Credit card payment accepted in person only. Also sells wholesale.

CSam   SAMPFORD SHRUBS € ♿
Sampford Peverell, Tiverton, Devon, EX16 7EN
Ⓣ (01884) 821164
Ⓔ martin@samshrub.co.uk
Ⓦ www.samshrub.co.uk
Contact: M Hughes-Jones & S Proud

C

Opening Times: 0900-1700 Mon-Sat, 1000-1600 Sun, Feb-Jun. 0900-1700 (or dusk) Wed-Sat, Jul-Nov.
Cat. Cost: A5 35p stamps sae
Credit Cards: All major credit/debit cards
Specialities: Large displays of *Pulmonaria* & *Crocosmia*. Nat. Coll. of *Helenium*.
Notes: Mail order available for heleniums only, min. order £15.00 + p&p. Despatched Mar.
Map Ref: C, B4 **OS Grid Ref:** ST043153

CSBt ST BRIDGET NURSERIES LTD ✉ ♿
Old Rydon Lane, Exeter, Devon, EX2 7JY
Ⓣ (01392) 873672
Ⓕ (01392) 876710
Ⓔ info@stbridgetnurseries.co.uk
Ⓦ www.stbridgetnurseries.co.uk
Contact: Garden Centre Plant Advice
Opening Times: 0800-1700 Mon-Sat, 1030-1630 Sun, 0900-1700 Bank Hols. Closed Xmas Day, Boxing Day, New Year's Day & Easter Sunday.
Min Mail Order UK: Nmc
Cat. Cost: Free
Credit Cards: Visa MasterCard Switch Solo
Specialities: Large general nursery, with two garden centres.
Notes: Mail order available between Nov & Mar.
Map Ref: C, C4 **OS Grid Ref:** SX955905

CSdC SHERWOOD COTTAGE €
Newton St Cyres, Exeter, Devon, EX5 5BT
Ⓣ (01392) 851589
Ⓔ vaughan.gallavan@connectfree.co.uk
Contact: Vaughan Gallavan
Opening Times: By appt. only.
Cat. Cost: 2 x 1st class
Credit Cards: None
Specialities: Magnolias, trees & shrubs. Nat. Coll. of Knap Hill Azaleas. Ghent & species deciduous azaleas. Sherwood Garden new Nat. Coll. of *Magnolia*. Stock available in small quantities only.
Map Ref: C, C3

CSec SECRET SEEDS ✉ 🗷 ♈ € ♿
Cove, Tiverton, Devon, EX16 7RU
Ⓣ (01398) 331946
Ⓜ 07870 389889
Ⓕ (01398) 331946
Ⓔ mike@secretseeds.com
Ⓦ www.secretseeds.com
Contact: Mike Burgess
Opening Times: 1000-1730 7 days. Closed Xmas.

Min Mail Order UK: Nmc
Min Mail Order EU: Nmc
Cat. Cost: 2 x 1st class
Credit Cards: All major credit/debit cards
Specialities: *Echium*.
Notes: Garden open. Also sells wholesale.
Map Ref: C, B4 **OS Grid Ref:** SS959197

CSev LOWER SEVERALLS NURSERY ✉ ♿
Crewkerne, Somerset, TA18 7NX
Ⓣ (01460) 73234
Ⓕ (01460) 76105
Ⓔ mary@lowerseveralls.co.uk
Ⓦ www.lowerseveralls.co.uk
Contact: Mary R Pring
Opening Times: 1000-1700 Tue, Wed, Fri, Sat, mid-Mar-end Sep. 1400-1700 Sun in May only.
Min Mail Order UK: £20.00
Cat. Cost: 4 x 1st class
Credit Cards: None
Specialities: Herbs, herbaceous.
Notes: Mail order perennials only.
Map Ref: C, B5 **OS Grid Ref:** ST457111

CSil SILVER DALE NURSERIES €
Shute Lane, Combe Martin, Devon, EX34 0HT
Ⓣ (01271) 882539
Ⓔ silverdale.nurseries@virgin.net
Contact: Roger Gilbert
Opening Times: 1000-1800 7 days.
Cat. Cost: 4 x 1st class
Credit Cards: Visa MasterCard EuroCard
Specialities: Nat. Coll. of *Fuchsia*. Hardy fuchsias (cultivars and species).
Map Ref: C, B3

CSim SIMPSON'S SEEDS LTD ✉ ♿
The Walled Garden Nursery, Horningsham, Warminster, Wiltshire, BA12 7NT
Ⓣ (01985) 845004
Ⓕ (01985) 845052
Ⓔ sales@simpsonsseeds.co.uk
Contact: Jane Simpson
Opening Times: 1100-1700 Wed-Sun, Apr-May. 1100-1700 Tue-Fri & 1000-1300 Sat, rest of the year.
Min Mail Order UK: Nmc
Min Mail Order EU: Nmc
Credit Cards: Visa MasterCard Switch
Specialities: Large range of hardy perennials, limited quantities of each. Large range of seeds

C

& vegetable plants. Specialities tomato & pepper.
Notes: Mail order catalogue currently only for seed & veg plants.
Map Ref: C, B5

CSli   **SLIPPS GARDEN CENTRE** 🅰
Butts Hill, Frome, Somerset, BA11 1HR
Ⓣ (01373) 467013
Ⓕ (01373) 467013
Contact: James Hall
Opening Times: 0900-1730 Mon-Sat, 1000-1630 Sun.
Cat. Cost: None issued
Credit Cards: Visa Access MasterCard Delta Switch
Specialities: *Achillea*.
Notes: Also sells wholesale.
Map Ref: C, B5

CSna   **SNAPE COTTAGE**
Chaffeymoor, Borton, Dorset, SP8 5BY
Ⓣ (01747) 840330 (evenings only).
Ⓕ (01747) 840330
Ⓔ ianandangela@snapecottagegarden.co.uk
Ⓦ www.snapestakes.com
Contact: Mrs Angela Whinfield
Opening Times: 1030-1700, last 2 Suns in each month Feb-Sep incl. & every Thu May-Aug.
Cat. Cost: None issued
Credit Cards: None
Specialities: *Galanthus* & *Helleborus*. 'Old' forms of many popular garden plants. Stock available in small quantities.
Notes: Plantsman's garden open same time as nursery.
Map Ref: C, B5 **OS Grid Ref:** ST762303

CSpe   **SPECIAL PLANTS** ✉ 🔊 €
Hill Farm Barn, Greenways Lane, Cold Ashton, Chippenham, Wiltshire, SN14 8LA
Ⓣ (01225) 891686
Ⓔ derry@specialplants.net
Ⓦ www.specialplants.net
Contact: Derry Watkins
Opening Times: 1000-1700 7 days Mar-Oct. Other times please ring first to check.
Min Mail Order UK: £10.00 + p&p
Min Mail Order EU: £20.00 + p&p
Cat. Cost: 5 x 2nd class (sae only for seed list)
Credit Cards: All major credit/debit cards
Specialities: Tender perennials, *Mimulus*, *Pelargonium*, *Salvia*, *Streptocarpus*. Hardy geraniums, *Anemone*, *Erysimum*, *Papaver*, *Viola* & grasses. Many varieties prop. in small numbers only. New introductions of S. African plants.
Notes: Mail order Sep-Mar only.
Map Ref: C, A5 **OS Grid Ref:** ST749726

CSPN   **SHERSTON PARVA NURSERY** ✉ 🔊 €
Malmesbury Road, Sherston, Wiltshire, SN16 0NX
Ⓣ (01666) 840348 Ⓜ 07887 814843
Ⓕ (01666) 840059
Ⓔ martin@sherstonparva.com
Ⓦ www.sherstonparva.com
Contact: Martin Rea
Opening Times: 1000-1700 7 days 1st Feb-31th Dec. Closed Jan.
Min Mail Order UK: Nmc
Min Mail Order EU: Nmc
Cat. Cost: Free
Credit Cards: MasterCard Delta Visa Switch
Specialities: *Clematis*, wall shrubs & climbers.
Map Ref: C, A5

CSto   **STONE LANE GARDENS** ✉ 🅰
Stone Farm, Chagford, Devon, TQ13 8JU
Ⓣ (01647) 231311
Ⓕ (01647) 231311
Ⓔ kenneth_ashburner@talk21.com
Ⓦ www.mythicgarden.com
Contact: Kenneth Ashburner
Opening Times: Garden open May-Sep. Charges apply. Other times by appt.
Min Mail Order UK: Nmc
Cat. Cost: £2.00 or 6 x 1st class for descriptive catalogue
Credit Cards: None
Specialities: Wide range of wild provenance *Betula* & *Alnus*. Interesting varieties of *Rubus*, *Sorbus* etc. Nat. Coll. of Birch & Alder.
Notes: Also sells wholesale.
Map Ref: C, C3 **OS Grid Ref:** SX708908

CStr   **SUE STRICKLAND PLANTS** 🔊
The Poplars, Isle Brewers, Taunton, Somerset, TA3 6QN
Ⓣ (01460) 281454
Ⓕ (01460) 281454
Ⓔ sues@stricklandc.freeserve.co.uk
Contact: Sue Strickland
Opening Times: By appt. only.
Cat. Cost: 2 x 1st class
Credit Cards: None
Specialities: *Salvia*.
Map Ref: C, B4

CStu   **STUCKEY'S ALPINES** 🔊
38 Phillipps Avenue, Exmouth, Devon, EX8 3HZ
Ⓣ (01395) 273636
Ⓔ stuckeysalpines@aol.com
Contact: Roger & Brenda Stuckey
Opening Times: As NGS dates or by appt.
Cat. Cost: None issued
Credit Cards: None

C

Specialities: Alpines in general. Hardy & half-hardy bulbs. NZ *Clematis* hybrids. Extensive choice of plants, many available only in small quantities.
Map Ref: C, C4

CSut   SUTTONS SEEDS ⊠
Woodview Road, Paignton, Devon, TQ4 7NG
Ⓣ 0870 220 2899
Ⓕ 0870 220 2265
Ⓦ www.suttons-seeds.co.uk
Contact: Customer Services
Opening Times: (Office) 0830-1700 Mon-Fri. Also answerphone.
Min Mail Order UK: Nmc
Cat. Cost: Free
Credit Cards: Visa MasterCard Switch Delta
Specialities: Over 1,000 varieties of flower & vegetable seed, bulbs, plants & sundries.

CSWC   SOUTH WEST CARNIVOROUS PLANTS ⊠ ☒ ♠
2 Rose Cottages, Culmstock, Cullompton, Devon, EX15 3JJ
Ⓣ (01884) 841549
Ⓕ (01884) 841549
Ⓔ flytraps@littleshopofhorrors.co.uk
Ⓦ www.littleshopofhorrors.co.uk
Contact: Jenny Pearce & Alistair Pearce
Opening Times: By appt.
Min Mail Order UK: Nmc
Min Mail Order EU: Nmc
Cat. Cost: 2 x 2nd class
Credit Cards: All major credit/debit cards
Specialities: *Cephalotus, Nepenthes, Dionea, Drosera, Darlingtonia, Saracenia, Pinguicula* & *Utricularia*. Specialists in hardy carnivorous plants & *Dionea muscipula* cvs.
Map Ref: C, B4

CSWP   SONIA WRIGHT PLANTS ⊠ ⓓ
Buckerfields Nursery, Ogbourne St George, Marlborough, Wiltshire, SN8 1SG
Ⓣ (01672) 841065
Ⓕ (01672) 541047
Contact: Sonia Wright & Alison Duxbury
Opening Times: 1000-1800 Tue-Sat.
Min Mail Order UK: £15.00 primulas only
Min Mail Order EU: £15.00 primulas only
Cat. Cost: 4 x 1st class
Credit Cards: All major credit/debit cards
Specialities: Barnhaven polyanthus & primroses. Grasses, grey-leaved plants, *Iris, Euphorbia, Penstemon*, old roses.
Notes: Mail order primroses only despatched autumn. Credit cards not accepted over the phone.
Map Ref: C, A6

CTbh   TREBAH ENTERPRISES LTD ⊠
Trebah, Mawnan Smith, Falmouth, Cornwall, TR11 5JZ
Ⓣ (01326) 250448
Ⓕ (01326) 250781
Ⓔ mail@trebah-garden.co.uk
Ⓦ www.trebah-garden.co.uk
Contact: Plant Sales Staff
Opening Times: 1030-1700 all year.
Min Mail Order UK: Nmc
Min Mail Order EU: Nmc
Cat. Cost: None issued
Credit Cards: All major credit/debit cards
Specialities: Tree ferns, *Camellia, Gunnera* & conservatory climbers.
Map Ref: C, D1 OS Grid Ref: SW770276

CTho   THORNHAYES NURSERY ⊠
St Andrews Wood, Dulford, Cullompton, Devon, EX15 2DF
Ⓣ (01884) 266746
Ⓕ (01884) 266739
Ⓔ trees@thornhayes-nursery.co.uk
Ⓦ www.thornhayes-nursery.co.uk
Contact: K D Croucher
Opening Times: 0800-1600 Mon-Fri.
Min Mail Order UK: Nmc
Min Mail Order EU: Nmc
Credit Cards: None
Specialities: A broad range of forms of ornamental, amenity & fruit trees incl. West Country apple varieties.
Notes: Also sells wholesale.
Map Ref: C, C4

CThr   THREE COUNTIES NURSERIES ⊠
Marshwood, Bridport, Dorset, DT6 5QJ
Ⓣ (01297) 678257
Ⓕ (01297) 678257
Contact: A & D Hitchcock
Opening Times: Not open.
Min Mail Order UK: Nmc
Cat. Cost: 2 x 2nd class
Credit Cards: Visa MasterCard
Specialities: Aquilegias.

CTrC   TREVENA CROSS NURSERIES ⊠ € ⓓ
Breage, Helston, Cornwall, TR13 9PS
Ⓣ (01736) 763880
Ⓕ (01736) 762828
Ⓔ sales@trevenacross.co.uk
Ⓦ www.trevenacross.co.uk
Contact: Graham Jeffery, John Eddy

⅄	⊠ Mail order to UK or EU	♠ Delivers to shows
⅄	☒ Exports beyond EU	€ Euro accepted
⅄	ⓓ Accessible by wheelchair	◆ See Display advertisement

C

Opening Times: 0900-1700 Mon-Sat, 1030-
1630 Sun.
Min Mail Order UK: Nmc
Cat. Cost: Online only.
Credit Cards: Visa Access Switch
Specialities: South African, Australian & New
Zealand plants, incl. *Aloe, Protea*, tree ferns,
palms, *Restio*, hardy succulents & wide range
of other exotics.
Map Ref: C, D1 OS Grid Ref: SW614284

CTrG   TREGOTHNAN NURSERY ⊠ ✉ ♠ € ▣
Estate Office, Tregothnan, Truro, Cornwall,
TR2 4AN
Ⓣ (01872) 520325
Ⓕ (01872) 520291
Ⓔ bigplants@tregothnan.co.uk
Ⓦ www.tregothnan.com
Contact: Jonathon Jones
Opening Times: By appt. for collection only.
Min Mail Order UK: £250.00
Min Mail Order EU: £500.00
Cat. Cost: Online only.
Credit Cards: Visa MasterCard Delta
EuroCard
Specialities: Unusual & rare plants from own
stock. Extra large specimens available for
instant effect. Known wild origin plants.
Notes: Also sells wholesale.

CTrh   TREHANE CAMELLIA NURSERY ⊠ ♠ € ▣
J Trehane & Sons Ltd, Stapehill Road,
Hampreston, Wimborne, Dorset,
BH21 7ND
Ⓣ (01202) 873490
Ⓕ (01202) 873490
Ⓦ www.trehane.com
Contact: Lorraine or Jeanette
Opening Times: 0900-1630 Mon-Fri all year
(excl. Xmas & New Year). 1000-1600 Sat-Sun
in spring & by special appt.
Min Mail Order UK: Nmc
Min Mail Order EU: Nmc
Cat. Cost: £1.70 cat./book
Credit Cards: All major credit/debit cards
Specialities: Extensive range of *Camellia*
species, cultivars & hybrids. Many new
introductions. Evergreen azaleas, *Pieris,
Magnolia* & blueberries.
Notes: Also sells wholesale.
Map Ref: C, C6

CTri   TRISCOMBE NURSERIES ⊠ ▣ ♦
West Bagborough, Nr Taunton, Somerset,
TA4 3HG
Ⓣ (01984) 618267
Ⓔ triscombe.nurseries2000@virgin.net
Ⓦ www.triscombenurseries.co.uk

Contact: S Parkman
Opening Times: 0900-1300 & 1400-1730
Mon-Sat. 1400-1730 Sun & B/hols.
Min Mail Order UK: Nmc
Cat. Cost: 2 x 1st class
Credit Cards: None
Specialities: Trees, shrubs, roses, fruit,
Clematis, herbaceous & rock plants.
Map Ref: C, B4

CTrw   TREWITHEN NURSERIES €
Grampound Road, Truro, Cornwall,
TR2 4DD
Ⓣ (01726) 882764
Ⓕ (01726) 882301
Ⓔ gardens@trewithen-estate.demon.co.uk
Ⓦ www.trewithengardens.co.uk
Contact: L Hazelton
Opening Times: 0800-1630 Mon-Fri.
Cat. Cost: £1.25
Credit Cards: All major credit/debit cards
Specialities: Shrubs, especially *Camellia &
Rhododendron*.
Notes: Also sells wholesale.
Map Ref: C, D2

CTuc   EDWIN TUCKER & SONS ⊠ ▣
Brewery Meadow, Stonepark, Ashburton,
Newton Abbot, Devon,
TQ13 7DG
Ⓣ (01364) 652233
Ⓕ (01364) 654211
Ⓔ seeds@edwintucker.com
Ⓦ www.edwintucker.com
Contact: Geoff Penton
Opening Times: 0800-1700 Mon-Fri, 0800-
1600 Sat.
Min Mail Order UK: Nmc
Min Mail Order EU: Nmc
Cat. Cost: Free
Credit Cards: Visa MasterCard Switch
Specialities: Nearly 120 varieties of seed
potatoes, incl. 50 organic varieties. Wide
range of vegetables, flowers, green manures &
sprouting seeds in packets. All not treated.
Nearly 200 varieties of organically produced
seeds.

CWan   WANBOROUGH HERB NURSERY
Callas Hill, Wanborough, Swindon, Wiltshire,
SN4 0AG
Ⓣ (01793) 790327 (answering machine)
Ⓔ Biggs@wanbherbnursery.fsnet.co.uk
Contact: Peter Biggs
Opening Times: 1000-1700 Tue-Fri (closed
1300-1400), w/ends 1000-1600, Mar-Oct.
1000-1600 (closed 1300-1400) Thu-Sun, Nov
& Dec. Other times by appt.

C

Cat. Cost: 2 x 1st or A4 Sae
Credit Cards: None
Specialities: Herbs, Herbaceous, esp. culinary. Available in small quantities only.
Map Ref: C, A6 OS Grid Ref: SU217828

CWat   THE WATER GARDEN ⊠ ⑤
Hinton Parva, Swindon, Wiltshire, SN4 0DH
Ⓣ (01793) 790558
Ⓕ (01793) 791298
Ⓔ watergarden@supanet.com
Contact: Mike & Anne Newman
Opening Times: 1000-1700 Wed-Sun.
Min Mail Order UK: £10.00 + p&p
Cat. Cost: 4 x 1st class
Credit Cards: Visa Access Switch
Specialities: Water lilies, marginal & moisture plants, oxygenators & alpines.
Map Ref: C, A6

CWCL   WESTCOUNTRY NURSERIES (INC. WESTCOUNTRY LUPINS) ⊠ ♠ ⑤ ◆
Donkey Meadow, Woolsery, Devon, EX39 5QH
Ⓣ (01237) 431111
Ⓕ (01237) 431111
Ⓔ info@westcountry-nurseries.co.uk
Ⓦ www.westcountry-nurseries.co.uk
Contact: Sarah Conibear
Opening Times: 1000-1600 7 days.
Min Mail Order UK: £15.00
Min Mail Order EU: £50.00
Cat. Cost: 2 x 1st class + A5 Sae for full colour cat.
Credit Cards: None
Specialities: *Lupinus, Lewisia, Hellebore,* cyclamen, lavender, select perennials, grasses, ferns & climbers. Nat. Coll. of Lupins.
Notes: Also sells wholesale.
Map Ref: C, B2 OS Grid Ref: SS3521

CWdb   WOODBOROUGH GARDEN CENTRE LTD € ⑤
Nursery Farm, Woodborough, Nr Pewsey, Wiltshire, SN9 5PF
Ⓣ (01672) 851249
Ⓕ (01672) 851465
Ⓔ clanparker@aol.com
Ⓦ www.woodboroughgardencentre.co.uk
Contact: Alison Parker
Opening Times: 0900-1700 Mon-Sat, 1100-1700 Sun.
Cat. Cost: None issued
Credit Cards: All major credit/debit cards
Specialities: Wide range of shrubs, trees, herbaceous, alpines & herbs. Large selection of climbers esp. *Clematis,* & spring bulbs.
Map Ref: C, A6 OS Grid Ref: SU119597

CWGr   WINCHESTER GROWERS LTD. ⊠ ⊠ ⑤
Varfell Farm, Long Rock, Penzance, Cornwall, TR20 8AQ
Ⓣ (01736) 335851
Ⓕ (01736) 851033
Ⓔ dahlias@wgltd.co.uk
Ⓦ www.wgltd.co.uk
Contact: Sarah Thomas
Opening Times: 1300-1630 Thu, Fri & Sat, 14th Jul 2005-27th Aug 2005. Open day 1000-1600 Sun 21st Aug 2005.
Min Mail Order UK: Nmc
Min Mail Order EU: Nmc
Cat. Cost: Free
Credit Cards: Visa Delta MasterCard Switch
Specialities: Nat. Coll. of *Dahlia.* Due to large number of varieties, some stock available in small quantities only.
Notes: Also sells wholesale.
Map Ref: C, D1

CWib   WIBBLE FARM NURSERIES ⊠ ⊠ ♠ ⑤
Wibble Farm, West Quantoxhead, Nr Taunton, Somerset, TA4 4DD
Ⓣ (01984) 632303
Ⓕ (01984) 633168
Ⓔ sales@wibblefarmnurseries.co.uk
Ⓦ www.wibblefarmnurseries.co.uk
Contact: Mrs M L Francis
Opening Times: 0800-1700 Mon-Fri, 1000-1600 Sat. All year excl. B/hols.
Min Mail Order UK: Nmc
Min Mail Order EU: Nmc
Cat. Cost: 2 x 1st class
Credit Cards: All major credit/debit cards
Specialities: Growers of a wide range of hardy plants, many rare & unusual.
Notes: Also sells wholesale.
Map Ref: C, B4

CWil   FERNWOOD NURSERY ⊠ ⊠ € ⑤
Peters Marland, Torrington, Devon, EX38 8QG
Ⓣ (01805) 601446
Ⓔ hw@fernwood-nursery.co.uk
Ⓦ www.fernwood-nursery.co.uk
Contact: Howard Wills & Sally Wills
Opening Times: Any time by appt. Please phone first.
Min Mail Order UK: Nmc
Min Mail Order EU: Nmc
Cat. Cost: Sae for list.
Credit Cards: None
Specialities: Nat. Coll. of *Sempervivum, Jovibarba, Rosularia & Phormium.*
Map Ref: C, C3 OS Grid Ref: SS479133

C

CWiW   WINDRUSH WILLOW ✉ ✇ €
Higher Barn, Sidmouth Road, Aylesbeare,
Exeter, Devon, EX5 2JJ
Ⓣ (01395) 233669
Ⓕ (01395) 233669
Ⓔ windrushw@aol.com
Ⓦ www.windrushwillow.com
Contact: Richard Kerwood
Opening Times: Mail order only. Open by appt.
Min Mail Order UK: Nmc
Min Mail Order EU: Nmc
Cat. Cost: 2 x 1st class
Credit Cards: None
Specialities: *Salix*. Unrooted cuttings available
Dec-Mar.
Notes: Also sells wholesale.

CWon   THE WONDER TREE ✉
35 Beaconsfield Road, Knowle, Bristol, BS4 2JE
Ⓣ 0117 908 9057
Ⓜ 07989 333507
Ⓔ Kevin@wondertree.org.uk
Contact: Kevin Lindegaard
Opening Times: Not open. Mail order only.
Min Mail Order UK: £8.00
Cat. Cost: 2 x 1st class.
Credit Cards: None
Specialities: *Salix*.
Notes: Also sells wholesale.

CWoo   IAN AND ROSEMARY WOOD ✉
Newlands, 28 Furland Road, Crewkerne,
Somerset, TA18 8DD
Ⓣ (01460) 74630
Ⓔ ianwood@ukgateway.net
Contact: Ian and Rosemary Wood
Opening Times: By appt. only. Primarily mail
order service.
Min Mail Order UK: Nmc
Cat. Cost: 2 x 1st or 2nd class
Credit Cards: None
Specialities: *Erythronium, Cyclamen* species &
dwarf *Narcissus* species. Some species available
in small quantities only, see catalogue.
Notes: Enquirers welcome to collect growing
plants in season.
Map Ref: C, B5

CWoW   WILL OF THE WISP PLANTS ✉ ⋔
(office) 5 Standards Road, Westonzoyland,
Bridgwater, Somerset, TA7 0EL
Ⓣ (01278) 691649
Ⓜ 07779 003998
Ⓕ (01278) 691649
Ⓔ mail@willofthewispplants.com
Contact: Jane East or Paul Coles
Opening Times: By appt. only.
Min Mail Order UK: Nmc.

Cat. Cost: 3 x 1st class.
Credit Cards: None
Specialities: Honeysuckle, *Clematis* & shrubs.
Notes: Nursery at Haygrass Nursery,
Shoreditch Road, Taunton, TA3 7BS. Also
sells wholesale.
Map Ref: C, B4

CWrd   WARD ALPINES ✉ ✇ ⋔ €
Newton Farm Nursery, Hemyock,
Cullompton, Devon, EX15 3QS
Ⓣ (01823) 680410
Ⓕ (01823) 680410
Ⓔ wardalpines@btopenworld.com
Ⓦ www.wardalpines@btopenworld.com
Contact: J.F. & S.M. Ward
Opening Times: By appt only & when garden
open under NGS.
Min Mail Order UK: Nmc
Min Mail Order EU: Nmc
Cat. Cost: 3 x 1st class
Specialities: Wide range of *Gentiana sino-
ornata, Rhodohypoxis/Rhodoxis, Iris sibirica &
I. ensata*. Nat. Coll. of *Gentiana sino-ornata*
associated species & hybrids.
Notes: Also sells wholesale.
Map Ref: C, B4 **OS Grid Ref:** ST140123

CWri   NIGEL WRIGHT RHODODENDRONS ⓖ
The Old Glebe, Eggesford, Chulmleigh,
Devon, EX18 7QU
Ⓣ (01769) 580632
Contact: Nigel Wright
Opening Times: By appt. only.
Cat. Cost: 2 x 1st class
Credit Cards: None
Specialities: *Rhododendron* & deciduous
azaleas. 200 varieties field grown, root-balled,
some potted. For collection only. Specialist
grower. Free advice & planting plans.
Notes: Also sells wholesale.
Map Ref: C, B3 **OS Grid Ref:** SS6171

CWSG   WEST SOMERSET GARDEN CENTRE ✉ ⓖ
Mart Road, Minehead, Somerset,
TA24 5BJ
Ⓣ (01643) 703812
Ⓕ (01643) 706476
Ⓔ wsgc@btconnect.com
Ⓦ www.westsomersetgardencentre.co.uk
Contact: Mrs J K Shoulders
Opening Times: 0800-1700 Mon-Sat, 1000-
1600 Sun.
Min Mail Order UK: Nmc
Cat. Cost: Not available
Credit Cards: Visa Access Switch Solo
Specialities: Wide general range. *Ceanothus.*
Map Ref: C, B4

E

CWVF   WHITE VEIL FUCHSIAS ⊠ &
Verwood Road, Three Legged Cross,
Wimborne, Dorset,
BH21 6RP
Ⓣ (01202) 813998
Contact: A. C. Holloway
Opening Times: 0900-1300 & 1400-1700
Mon-Fri Jan-Dec, & Sat Jan-Aug. 0900-1300
Sun Jan-Jul, closed Sun Aug, closed Sat & Sun
Sep-Dec.
Min Mail Order UK: 8 plants
Cat. Cost: 4 x 1st class
Credit Cards: None
Specialities: Fuchsias. Small plants grown from
Jan-Apr. Available in small quantities only.
Map Ref: C,C6

EASTERN

EAEE   AEE ⊠
38 Church Close,
Roydon, Diss, Norfolk,
IP22 5RQ
Ⓣ (01379) 643574
Ⓕ (01379) 651230
Ⓔ etheridge@myinternetpass.com
Ⓦ www.aeesupplyingplantlovers.com
Contact: Anne Etheridge
Opening Times: Not open. Mail order only.
Min Mail Order UK: Nmc.
Cat. Cost: 3 x 1st class.
Specialities: Perennials & grasses plus a few
enticing alpines & shrubs. Alpines & shrubs
available in small quantities only.
Notes: Border plans. Credit card payment
accepted through Paypal online only.

EAmu   AMULREE EXOTICS ⊠ &
The Turnpike, Norwich Road (B1113),
Fundenhall, Norwich, Norfolk,
NR16 1EL
Ⓣ (01508) 488101
Ⓕ (01508) 488101
Ⓔ SDG@exotica.fsbusiness.co.uk
Ⓦ www.turn-it-tropical.co.uk
Contact: S Gridley
Opening Times: 0930-1730 7 days spring-
autumn, 1000-1630 7 days autumn-spring.
Min Mail Order UK: Nmc
Cat. Cost: 2 x 1st class
Credit Cards: Visa MasterCard Electron Solo
Switch
Specialities: Hardy & half-hardy plants for
home, garden & conservatory. Palms,
bamboos, bananas, tree ferns, cannas, gingers
& much more.
Notes: Also sells wholesale.
Map Ref: E, B3 OS Grid Ref: DX123740

EApt   APPLETREE COTTAGE PLANTS ⊠
18 Shaftesbury Avenue, Forest Park, Lincoln,
Lincolnshire, LN6 0QN
Ⓣ (01522) 682770
Ⓔ JANY@time-designs.co.uk
Ⓦ www.time-designs.co.uk
Contact: Jany Sefyllian
Opening Times: 1000-1700 Mon-Fri, please
ring first. W/ends by appt.
Min Mail Order UK: £10.00
Min Mail Order EU: £15.00
Cat. Cost: 2 x 1st class
Credit Cards: None
Specialities: *Hosta*. Grasses. Some herbs.
Notes: Also sells wholesale.
Map Ref: E, A1

EAro   AROMAFOLIA ⊠ ⋔
Barbers Farm, Leys Lane, Old Buckenham,
Norfolk, NR17 1NT
Ⓣ (01953) 887713
Ⓔ enquiries@aromafolia.co.uk
Ⓦ www.aromafolia.co.uk
Contact: John Holden
Opening Times: 0930-1630 Thu-Sun &
B/hols, Apr-Oct. Other times by appt.
Min Mail Order UK: £15.00
Cat. Cost: 3 x 1st class.
Credit Cards: None
Specialities: Wide range of plants with
aromatic foliage, incl. *Salvia, Monarda,
Agastache, Nepeta*. All plants grown in peat-
free compost. Some varieties available in small
quantities only.
Map Ref: E,C3 OS Grid Ref: TM042913

EAVC   AFRICAN VIOLET CENTRE ⊠ &
Terrington St Clement, King's Lynn, Norfolk,
PE34 4PL
Ⓣ (01553) 828374
Ⓕ (01553) 828376
Ⓔ info@africanvioletcentre.ltd.uk
Ⓦ www.africanvioletcentre.ltd.uk
Contact: Mark Leach
Opening Times: 0900-1700 Mon-Sat, 1000-
1600 Sun. Closed Xmas Day, Boxing Day,
New Year's Day.
Min Mail Order UK: £11.70
Cat. Cost: Free
Credit Cards: All major credit/debit cards
Specialities: African violets (*Saintpaulia
ionantha*).
Map Ref: E,B2

KEY	
⊠ Mail order to UK or EU	⋔ Delivers to shows
⊠ Exports beyond EU	€ Euro accepted
& Accessible by wheelchair	◆ See Display advertisement

E

EBak **B & H M BAKER**
Bourne Brook Nurseries, Greenstead Green,
Halstead, Essex, CO9 1RJ
Ⓣ (01787) 476369/472900
Contact: B, HM and C Baker
Opening Times: 0800-1630 Mon-Fri, 0900-
1200 & 1400-1630 Sat & Sun, Mar-30th Jun.
Cat. Cost: 2 x 1st class + 33p
Credit Cards: MasterCard Delta Visa Switch
Specialities: *Fuchsia* & conservatory plants.
Notes: Also sells wholesale.
Map Ref: E, C2

EBee **BEECHES NURSERY** ✉ ♿
Village Centre, Ashdon, Saffron Walden,
Essex, CB10 2HB
Ⓣ (01799) 584362
Ⓕ (01799) 584421
Ⓦ www.beechesnursery.co.uk
Contact: Alan Bidwell/Kevin Marsh
Opening Times: 0830-1700 Mon-Sat, 1000-
1700 Sun & B/hols.
Min Mail Order UK: £10.00
Min Mail Order EU: £20.00
Cat. Cost: 6 x 2nd class herbaceous list
Credit Cards: All major credit/debit cards
Specialities: Herbaceous specialists &
extensive range of other garden plants.
Notes: Mail order generally from Oct-Feb,
Mar-Sep where conditions permit. Trees NOT
available by mail order.
Map Ref: E, C2 OS Grid Ref: TL5842

EBla **BLACKSMITHS COTTAGE NURSERY** ✉ ♠
€ ♿
Langmere Road, Langmere, Nr Dickleburgh,
Diss, Norfolk, IP21 4QA
Ⓣ (01379) 740982
Ⓕ (01379) 741917
Ⓔ Blackcottnursery@aol.com
Contact: Ben or Jill Potterton
Opening Times: 1000-1700 Thu-Sun Mar-
Oct & B/hols, or by appt.
Min Mail Order UK: Nmc
Min Mail Order EU: Nmc
Cat. Cost: 3 x 1st class
Credit Cards: All major credit/debit cards
Specialities: Over 2000 species grown. Large
selection of shade plants. Large new display
gardens.
Notes: Also sells wholesale.
Map Ref: E, C3

EBrs **BRESSINGHAM GARDENS (INCORP. VAN**
TUBERGEN UK) ✉ ♿
Bressingham, Diss, Norfolk, IP22 2AG
Ⓣ (01379) 688282
Ⓕ (01379) 687227

Ⓔ info@bressinghamgardens.com
Ⓦ www.bressinghamgardens.com
Contact: Fiona-Louise Tilden
Opening Times: Mail order 0900-1700 Mon-
Fri. Gardens only open daily 1030-1730 1st
Apr-31st Oct 2004.
Min Mail Order UK: Nmc
Min Mail Order EU: Nmc
Cat. Cost: Free on request.
Credit Cards: Maestro Visa Access
MasterCard
Specialities: Bulbs, grafted conifers, grasses &
perennials. Nat. Coll. of *Miscanthus*.
Notes: Also sells wholesale.
Map Ref: E, C3 OS Grid Ref: TM071807

EBur **JENNY BURGESS** ✉ ♨ € ♿
Alpine Nursery, Sisland, Norwich, Norfolk,
NR14 6EF
Ⓣ (01508) 520724
Contact: Jenny Burgess
Opening Times: Any time by appt.
Min Mail Order UK: £5.00 + p&p
Min Mail Order EU: £10.00 + p&p
Cat. Cost: 3 x 1st class
Credit Cards: None
Specialities: Alpines, *Sisyrinchium* &
Campanula. Nat. Coll. of *Sisyrinchium*.
Notes: Mail order for *Sisyrinchium* only.
Map Ref: E, B3

ECGP **CAMBRIDGE GARDEN PLANTS** ♿
The Lodge, Clayhithe Road, Horningsea,
Cambridgeshire, CB5 9JD
Ⓣ (01223) 861370
Contact: Mrs Nancy Buchdahl
Opening Times: 1100-1730 Thu-Sun mid
Mar-31st Oct. Other times by appt.
Cat. Cost: 4 x 1st class
Credit Cards: None
Specialities: Hardy perennials incl. wide range
of *Geranium, Allium, Euphorbia, Penstemon,
Digitalis*. Some shrubs, roses & *Clematis*.
Map Ref: E, C2 OS Grid Ref: TL497637

ECha **THE BETH CHATTO GARDENS LTD** ✉ ♿
Elmstead Market, Colchester, Essex, CO7 7DB
Ⓣ (01206) 822007
Ⓕ (01206) 825933
Ⓔ info@bethchatto.fsnet.co.uk
Ⓦ www.bethchatto.co.uk
Contact: Beth Chatto
Opening Times: 0900-1700 Mon-Sat 1st
Mar-31st Oct. 0900-1600 Mon-Fri 1st Nov-
1st Mar. Closed Sun.
Min Mail Order UK: £20.00
Min Mail Order EU: Ask for details
Cat. Cost: £3.00 incl. p&p

E

Credit Cards: Visa Switch MasterCard
Specialities: Predominantly herbaceous. Many unusual for special situations.
Map Ref: E, D3 OS Grid Ref: TM069238

ECho   CHOICE LANDSCAPES ⊠ ⊠ ñ € ⌑
Priory Farm, 101 Salts Road, West Walton, Wisbech, Cambridgeshire, PE14 7EF
Ⓣ (01945) 585051
Ⓕ (01945) 580053
Ⓔ info@choicelandscapes.org
Ⓦ www.choicelandscapes.org
Contact: Michael Agg & Jillian Agg
Opening Times: 1000-1700 Tue-Sat 22nd Feb-29th Oct 2005. Not open on show dates, please phone. Other times by appt.
Min Mail Order UK: £10.00
Min Mail Order EU: £10.00 + p&p
Cat. Cost: 6 x 1st class or 6 IRC
Credit Cards: Maestro Visa MasterCard Solo
Specialities: Dwarf conifers, alpines, acers, rhododendrons, hostas, bulbs, pines & lilies.
Map Ref: E, B1

EChP   CHOICE PLANTS ⊠ ñ ◆
83 Halton Road, Spilsby, Lincolnshire, PE23 5LD
Ⓜ 07887 913704
Ⓕ (01790) 752524
Ⓔ jgunson@spilsby94.fsnet.co.uk
Ⓦ www.choiceplants.net
Contact: Joan Gunson
Opening Times: 1000-1700 Wed-Sun & B/hol Mon Mar-Sep.
Min Mail Order UK: £10.00 + p&p
Cat. Cost: 2 x 1st class
Credit Cards: None
Specialities: Hardy *Geranium, Crocosmia, Hemerocallis, Iris* & a good selection of unusual hardy perennials.
Map Ref: E, B1

ECnt   CANTS OF COLCHESTER ⊠ ⊠
Nayland Road, Mile End, Colchester, Essex, CO4 5EB
Ⓣ (01206) 844008
Ⓕ (01206) 855371
Ⓔ finder@cantsroses.co.uk
Ⓦ www.cantsroses.co.uk
Contact: Angela Pawsey
Opening Times: 0900-1300, 1400-1630 Mon-Fri. Sat varied, please phone first. Sun closed.
Min Mail Order UK: Nmc
Min Mail Order EU: Nmc
Cat. Cost: Free
Credit Cards: Visa MasterCard Delta Solo Switch

Specialities: Roses. Unstaffed rose field can be viewed dawn-dusk every day from end Jun-end Sep.
Notes: Mail order end Oct-end Mar only. Partial wheelchair access.
Map Ref: E, C3

ECot   THE COTTAGE GARDEN ⌑
Langham Road, Boxted, Colchester, Essex, CO4 5HU
Ⓣ (01206) 272269
Ⓔ enquiries@thecottage-garden.co.uk
Ⓦ www.thecottage-garden.co.uk
Contact: Alison Smith
Opening Times: 0800-1700 7 days spring & summer. 0800-1700 Thu-Mon Sep-Feb.
Cat. Cost: Free leaflet
Credit Cards: Visa Access Connect Switch Delta
Specialities: 400 varieties of shrubs, 500 varieties of herbaceous. Huge range of trees, grasses, alpines, herbs, hedging, all home grown.
Map Ref: E, C3 OS Grid Ref: TM003299

ECou   COUNTY PARK NURSERY
Essex Gardens, Hornchurch, Essex, RM11 3BU
Ⓣ (01708) 445205
Ⓦ www.countyparknursery.co.uk
Contact: G Hutchins
Opening Times: 0900-dusk Mon-Sat excl. Wed, 1000-1700 Sun Mar-Oct. Nov-Feb by appt. only.
Cat. Cost: 3 x 1st class
Credit Cards: None
Specialities: Alpines & rare and unusual plants from New Zealand, Tasmania & Falklands. Nat. Coll. of *Coprosma*. Many plants in small quantities only.
Map Ref: E, D2

ECre   CREAKE PLANT CENTRE ⌑
Nursery View, Leicester Road, South Creake, Fakenham, Norfolk, NR21 9PW
Ⓣ (01328) 823018
Contact: Mr T Harrison
Opening Times: 1000-1300 & 1400-1730 7 days excl. Xmas.
Cat. Cost: None issued
Credit Cards: None
Specialities: Unusual shrubs, herbaceous, conservatory plants.
Map Ref: E, B1

KEY   ⊠ Mail order to UK or EU   ñ Delivers to shows
⊠ Exports beyond EU   € Euro accepted
⌑ Accessible by wheelchair   ◆ See Display advertisement

E

ECri   CRIN GARDENS ✉
79 Partons Road, Kings Heath, Birmingham,
B14 6TD
ⓣ 0121 443 3815
ⓕ 0121 443 3815
ⓔ cringardens@tiscali.co.uk
Contact: M Milinkovic
Opening Times: Not open. Mail order only.
Min Mail Order UK: Nmc
Cat. Cost: 2 x 1st class
Credit Cards: None
Specialities: Lilies. Limited stock available on
first come, first served, basis.

ECrN   CROWN NURSERY ✉ ♿
High Street, Ufford, Woodbridge, Suffolk,
IP13 6EL
ⓣ (01394) 460755
ⓕ (01394) 460142
ⓔ enquiries@crown-nursery.co.uk
ⓦ www.crown-nursery.co.uk
Contact: Jill Proctor
Opening Times: 0900-1700 (or dusk if
sooner) Mon-Sat.
Min Mail Order UK: Nmc
Cat. Cost: 2 x 1st class
Credit Cards: All major credit/debit cards
Specialities: Mature & semi-mature native,
ornamental & fruit trees.
Notes: Mail order for small/young stock only.
Also sells wholesale.
Map Ref: E, C3 OS Grid Ref: TM292528

ECtt   COTTAGE NURSERIES ✉ ♿
Thoresthorpe, Alford, Lincolnshire,
LN13 0HX
ⓣ (01507) 466968
ⓕ (01507) 463409
ⓔ bill@cottagenurseries.net
ⓦ www.cottagenurseries.net
Contact: W H Denbigh
Opening Times: 0900-1700 7 days 1st Mar-
31st Oct, 1000-1600 Mon-Sun Nov-Feb.
Min Mail Order UK: Nmc
Cat. Cost: 3 x 1st class
Credit Cards: None
Specialities: Hardy perennials. Wide general
range.
Notes: Also sells wholesale.
Map Ref: E, A2 OS Grid Ref: TF423716

EDAr   D'ARCY & EVEREST ✉ ♿ € ♿
(Office) PO Box 78, St Ives, Huntingdon,
Cambridgeshire, PE27 4UQ
ⓣ (01480) 497672
Ⓜ 07715 374440/1
ⓕ (01480) 466042
ⓔ angela@darcyeverest.co.uk

ⓦ www.darcyeverest.co.uk
Contact: Angela Whiting, Richard Oliver
Opening Times: By appt. only. Coach parties
welcome by appt.
Min Mail Order UK: £10.00 + p&p
Min Mail Order EU: £10.00 + p&p
Cat. Cost: 6 x 1st class
Credit Cards: None
Specialities: Alpines, herbs & selected perennials.
Notes: Nursery is at Pidley Sheep Lane
(B1040), Somersham, Huntingdon.
Map Ref: E, C2 OS Grid Ref: TL533276

EDif   DIFFERENT PLANTS ♿ ♿
The Mellis Stud, Gate Farm, Cranley Green,
Eye, Suffolk, IP23 7NX
ⓣ (01379) 870291
Contact: Fleur Waters
Opening Times: Sat-Thu by appt. only,
closed Fri. Plant stall Eye market 0900-1200
Fri.
Cat. Cost: 4 x 1st class
Credit Cards: None
Specialities: Mimulus aurantiacus & hybrids,
half-hardy bulbous/cormous perennials incl.
Dietes, Aristea, Cypella, Tigridia & *Anomatheca
laxa.* Bulbs may be available in small
quantities only.
Map Ref: E, C3

EDsa   DARASINA NURSERY ♿
Ingatestone Hall, Hall Lane, Ingatestone,
Essex, CM4 9NR
ⓣ (01277) 353235
Contact: Stephen Nelson
Opening Times: 1130-1730 Sat, Sun &
B/Hol, Easter Sat-end Sep. Other times by
appt.
Cat. Cost: Free list
Credit Cards: None
Specialities: Courtyard style & container
planting. Hardy & half-hardy shrubs incl. figs,
Pittosporum, Melianthus. Many uncommon
perennials, ferns, herbs & veg. plants.
Notes: Also sells wholesale.
Map Ref: E, D2 OS Grid Ref: TQ653987

EEls   ELSWORTH HERBS ✉ ♿
Avenue Farm Cottage, 31 Smith Street,
Elsworth, Cambridgeshire, CB3 8HY
ⓣ (01954) 267414
ⓕ (01954) 267414
ⓔ john.twibell@btintenet.com
Contact: Drs J D & J M Twibell
Opening Times: By appt. only.
Min Mail Order UK: £10.00
Cat. Cost: 3 x 1st class
Credit Cards: None

Specialities: Nat. Colls. of *Artemisia* (incl. *Seriphidium*) & *Nerium oleander*. Wide range of *Artemisia* & *Seriphidium*, *Nerium oleander*. Stock available in small quantities only. Orders may require propagation from collection material, for which we are the primary reference source.
Map Ref: E, C2

EExo   THE EXOTIC GARDEN COMPANY ⊠ ⓖ
Saxmundham Road, Aldeburgh, Nr Ipswich, Suffolk, IP15 5JD
ⓣ (01728) 454456
ⓕ (01473) 780651
ⓦ www.theexoticgardenco.co.uk
Contact: Matthew Couchy
Opening Times: 1000-1700 Mon-Sat, 1000-1600 Sun.
Min Mail Order UK: Nmc
Cat. Cost: A4 Sae
Credit Cards: All major credit/debit cards
Specialities: Palms (hardy & half-hardy), bamboos, tree ferns & other exotics.
Map Ref: E, C3

EFam   FAMECHECK REBLOOMING IRIS ⊠ ⓜ € ⓖ
Hilltrees, Wandlebury Hill (A1307), Cambridge, Cambridgeshire, CB2 4AD
ⓣ (01223) 243734 repeat ring after dark or leave phone number (not mobile).
ⓔ famecheck@hotmail.com
Contact: Miss F Cook N.D.H.
Opening Times: 1500-1700 except Wed & Sat, all year unless frost. Other times by appt. Please phone first, previous evening.
Min Mail Order UK: £5.00
Min Mail Order EU: £5.00
Cat. Cost: 4 x 1st class for list.
Credit Cards: None
Specialities: Daffodils, long-lasting & weatherproof cut-flower varieties. Bearded *Iris* & orange violets. Space Age & Reblooming Bearded *Iris*. Some only available in small quantities. About 1000 modern varieties, mostly imported. NCH status applied for daffodils & *Iris*.
Notes: Nursery between Cambridge Botanic Garden & Wandlebury Wildlife Park, next to Gogmagog Golf Course on A1307.
Map Ref: E, C2

EFer   THE FERN NURSERY ⊠ ⓖ
Grimsby Road, Binbrook, Lincolnshire, LN8 6DH
ⓣ (01472) 398092
ⓔ richard@timm.984fsnet.co.uk
ⓦ www.fernnursery.co.uk
Contact: R N Timm

Opening Times: 0900-1700 Sat & Sun Apr-Oct or by appt.
Min Mail Order UK: Nmc
Min Mail Order EU: Nmc
Cat. Cost: 2 x 1st class
Credit Cards: None
Specialities: Ferns.
Notes: Only plants listed in the mail order part of the catalogue will be sent mail order. Also sells wholesale.
Map Ref: E, A1 OS Grid Ref: TF212942

EFEx   FLORA EXOTICA ⊠ ⓜ €
Pasadena, South-Green, Fingringhoe, Colchester, Essex, CO5 7DR
ⓣ (01206) 729414
Contact: J Beddoes
Opening Times: Not open. Mail order only.
Min Mail Order UK: Nmc
Min Mail Order EU: Nmc
Cat. Cost: 4 x 1st class
Credit Cards: None
Specialities: Exotica flora incl. orchids.

EFly   THE FLY TRAP PLANTS ⊠ ⓝ
160 Kimberley Road, Lowestoft, Suffolk, NR33 0UA
ⓣ (01502) 584689
ⓜ 07765 061629
ⓕ (01502) 584689
ⓔ sales@tftplants.co.uk
ⓦ http://tftplants.co.uk
Contact: Pauline Steward
Opening Times: By appt. only.
Min Mail Order UK: Nmc
Cat. Cost: 1 x 1st class sae
Credit Cards: None
Specialities: All kinds of carnivorous plants, such as *Sarracenia, Drosera, Pinquicula*, to the *Utricularia* aquatic plants.
Map Ref: E, C3

EFtx   FERNATIX ⊠ ⓝ ◆
Ivy Cottage, Ixworth Road, Honington, Suffolk, IP31 1QY
ⓣ (01359) 269373
ⓔ fernatix@supanet.com
ⓦ www.fernatix.co.uk
Contact: Steven Fletcher & Kerry Robinson
Opening Times: By appt. only.
Min Mail Order UK: £15.00
Cat. Cost: 5 x 1st class for cat., or sae for plant list.
Credit Cards: None
Specialities: Ferns, hardy & greenhouse species & cultivars. Some available in small quantities only.
Map Ref: E, C2

E

EFul   FULBROOKE NURSERY ✉
Home Farm, Westley Waterless, Newmarket,
Suffolk, CB8 0RG
Ⓣ (01638) 507124
Ⓕ (01638) 507124
Ⓔ bamboo@fulbrooke.co.uk
Ⓦ www.fulbrooke.co.uk
Contact: Paul Lazard
Opening Times: By appt. most times incl.
w/ends.
Min Mail Order UK: £5.50 + p&p
Min Mail Order EU: £6.00 + p&p
Cat. Cost: 3 x 1st class
Credit Cards: None
Specialities: Bamboos & grasses.
Map Ref: E, C2

EGFP   GRANGE FARM PLANTS ✉ ♿
Grange Farm, 38 Fishergate Road, Sutton
St James, Spalding, Lincolnshire, PE12 0EZ
Ⓣ (01945) 440240
Ⓜ 07742 138760
Ⓕ (01945) 440355
Ⓔ ellis.family@tinyonline.co.uk
Contact: M C Ellis
Opening Times: Mail order only. Open by
appt. only.
Min Mail Order UK: Nmc
Cat. Cost: 1 x 1st class
Credit Cards: None
Specialities: Rare trees & shrubs, esp. *Juglans,
Fraxinus.* Some species available in small
quantities only.
Map Ref: E, B2 **OS Grid Ref:** TF3818

EGle   GLEN CHANTRY €
Ishams Chase, Wickham Bishops, Essex,
CM8 3LG
Ⓣ (01621) 891342
Ⓕ (01621) 891342
Contact: Sue Staines & Wol Staines
Opening Times: 1000-1600 Fri & Sat from
1st Apr-24th Sep. Sae for details.
Cat. Cost: 5 x 1st class
Credit Cards: None
Specialities: A wide & increasing range of
perennials, many unusual.
Notes: Partial wheelchair access.
Map Ref: E, D2 **OS Grid Ref:** TM834133

EGln   GLENHIRST CACTUS NURSERY ✉ ✉
Station Road, Swineshead, Nr Boston,
Lincolnshire, PE20 3NX
Ⓣ (01205) 820314
Ⓕ (01205) 820614
Ⓔ info@cacti4u.co.uk
Ⓦ www.cacti4u.co.uk
Contact: N C & S A Bell

Opening Times: Visitors welcome, but by
telephone appt. only.
Min Mail Order UK: Nmc
Min Mail Order EU: Nmc
Cat. Cost: 2 x 1st class
Credit Cards: Visa MasterCard Switch Solo
Electron
Specialities: Extensive range of cacti &
succulent plants & seeds, incl. Christmas cacti
& orchid cacti. Hardy & half-hardy desert
plants. Display gardens. Palms, *Cordyline,
Phormium* & other hardy architectural plants.
Notes: Exports plants & seeds to EU, seeds
only outside the EU.
Map Ref: E, B1 **OS Grid Ref:** TF245408

EGlv   GLENVILLE NURSERIES ✉ ◆
King John Bank, Walpole St Andrew,
Wisbech, Cambridgeshire, PE14 7LD
Ⓣ (01945) 780020
Ⓕ (01945) 780078
Ⓔ brtowler@btopenworld.com
Ⓦ www.glenvillenurseries.co.uk
Contact: B R Towler
Opening Times: 1000-1600 Mon-Fri, Sat by
arrangement, closed Sun.
Min Mail Order UK: £6.00 + p&p
Min Mail Order EU: £30.00 + p&p
Cat. Cost: 2 x 2nd class
Credit Cards: MasterCard Switch Delta Visa
Specialities: Young flowering, ornamental &
climbing shrubs. Also conifers.
Notes: Also sells wholesale.
Map Ref: E, B1 **OS Grid Ref:** TF487188

EGol   GOLDBROOK PLANTS ✉ ✉
Hoxne, Eye, Suffolk, IP21 5AN
Ⓣ (01379) 668770
Ⓕ (01379) 668770
Contact: Sandra Bond
Opening Times: 1000-1700 or dusk if earlier,
Thu-Sun Apr-Sep, Sat & Sun Oct-Mar or by
appt. Closed during Jan, Chelsea & Hampton
Court Shows.
Min Mail Order UK: £15.00 + p&p
Min Mail Order EU: £100.00 + p&p
Cat. Cost: 4 x 1st class
Credit Cards: None
Specialities: Very large range of *Hosta*
(1100+), *Hemerocallis.*
Map Ref: E, C3

EGoo   ELISABETH GOODWIN NURSERIES ✉ ⌂ ♿
Elm Tree Farm, 1 Beeches Road, West Row,
Bury St Edmunds, Suffolk, IP28 8NP
Ⓣ (01638) 713050
Ⓔ mail@e-g-n.co.uk
Ⓦ www.e-g-n.co.uk

E

Contact: Elisabeth Goodwin
Opening Times: Please see website or phone for details.
Min Mail Order UK: £15.00
Cat. Cost: Online only.
Credit Cards: None
Specialities: Drought tolerant plants for both sun & shade esp. *Helianthemum, Sedum, Teucrium, Vinca, grasses, Aquilegia, Digitalis, Achillea, Agastache* & *Onosma*. Some plants grown in small quantities.
Notes: Also sells wholesale.
Map Ref: E, C2

EGra   GRASMERE PLANTS ⊠ ⓑ
Grasmere, School Road, Terrington St John, Wisbech, Cambridgeshire, PE14 7SE
Ⓣ (01945) 880514
Contact: Roger Fleming
Opening Times: 1000-1700 Fri-Wed, closed Thu, Mar-late Oct, other times by appt. Please phone first. Garden open.
Min Mail Order UK: £15.00 + p&p
Cat. Cost: 2 x 2nd class
Credit Cards: None
Specialities: Hardy perennials incl. *Geranium* & crocosmias, shrubs. Some stock available in small quantities only.
Notes: Mail order perennials only.
Map Ref: E, B1 OS Grid Ref: TF537143

EHea   THE HEATHER SOCIETY ⊠ €
Denbeigh, All Saints Road, Creeting St. Mary, Ipswich, Suffolk, IP6 8PJ
Ⓣ (01449) 711220
Ⓕ (01449) 711220
Ⓔ heathers@zetnet.co.uk
Ⓦ www.heathersociety.org.uk
Contact: David & Anne Small
Opening Times: Not open.
Min Mail Order UK: Nmc for members.
Min Mail Order EU: Nmc for members.
Cat. Cost: 1 x 1st class
Credit Cards: Visa MasterCard
Specialities: Heathers.
Notes: Mail order for Heather Society members within the EU, Apr only. UK Membership £11.50 (for 1 yr), EC £12.50 (for 1 yr).

EHoe   HOECROFT PLANTS ⊠ € ⓑ ◆
Severals Grange, Holt Road, Wood Norton, Dereham, Norfolk, NR20 5BL
Ⓣ (01362) 684206
Ⓕ (01362) 684206
Ⓔ hoecroft@acedial.co.uk
Ⓦ www.hoecroft.co.uk
Contact: Jane Lister

Opening Times: 1000-1600 Thu-Sun 1st Apr-16th Oct or by appt.
Min Mail Order UK: Nmc
Min Mail Order EU: Nmc
Cat. Cost: 5 x 2nd class/£1coin
Credit Cards: None
Specialities: 270 varieties of variegated and 350 varieties of coloured-leaved plants in all species. 250 grasses.
Notes: Nursery 2 miles north of Guist on B1110.
Map Ref: E, B3 OS Grid Ref: TG008289

EHol   HOLKHAM GARDENS ⊠ ⓑ
Holkham Park, Wells-next-the-Sea, Norfolk, NR23 1AB
Ⓣ (01328) 711636
Ⓔ info@holkhamgardens.com
Contact: Peter Gill, Trevor Gill
Opening Times: 1000-1700 7 days Mar-Oct. 1100-dusk 7 days Jan-Feb. Closed Nov-Dec.
Min Mail Order UK: £10.00
Cat. Cost: 3 x 1st class
Credit Cards: Visa Access Switch MasterCard
Specialities: Wide range of shrubs, herbaceous perennials, alpines, wall plants, climbers, roses, conservatory plants and herbs, both common & unusual. Some plants available in small quantities only.
Map Ref: E, B1

EHon   HONEYSOME AQUATIC NURSERY ⊠
The Row, Sutton, Nr Ely, Cambridgeshire, CB6 2PB
Ⓣ (01353) 778889
Ⓕ (01353) 777291
Contact: Mrs L S Bond
Opening Times: At all times by appt. only.
Min Mail Order UK: Nmc
Cat. Cost: 2 x 1st class
Credit Cards: None
Specialities: Hardy aquatic, bog & marginal.
Notes: Also sells wholesale.
Map Ref: E, C2

EHrv   HARVEYS GARDEN PLANTS ⊠ ⋔ € ⓑ
(office) Bradfield St George, Bury St Edmunds, Suffolk, IP30 0AY
Ⓣ (01284) 386777
Ⓕ (01284) 386777 & answerphone
Ⓔ roger@harveysgardenplants.co.uk
Ⓦ www.harveysgardenplants.co.uk
Contact: Roger Harvey

E

Opening Times: 0930-1630 Tue-Sat, 11th Jan-23rd Dec.
Min Mail Order UK: 6 plants + p&p
Min Mail Order EU: Please enquire.
Cat. Cost: 7 x 2nd class
Credit Cards: All major credit/debit cards
Specialities: *Helleborus, Anemone, Epimedium, Euphorbia, Eryngium, Astrantia, Pulmonaria* & other herbaceous perennials. Woodland plants, heleniums. Nat. Coll. of *Helenium* applied for.
Notes: Nursery at Great Green, Thurston, Bury St Edmunds, IP31 3SJ.
Map Ref: E, C2

EHul **HULL FARM** ⊠
Spring Valley Lane, Ardleigh, Colchester, Essex, CO7 7SA
Ⓣ (01206) 230045
Ⓕ (01206) 230820
Contact: J Fryer & Sons
Opening Times: 1000-1600 6 days excl. Xmas.
Min Mail Order UK: £40.00 + p&p
Cat. Cost: 5 x 2nd class
Credit Cards: Visa MasterCard
Specialities: Conifers, grasses.
Notes: Also sells wholesale.
Map Ref: E, C3 OS Grid Ref: GR043274

EHyt **HYTHE ALPINES** ⊠ 🛖 € 🖾
Methwold Hythe, Thetford, Norfolk, IP26 4QH
Ⓣ (01366) 728543
Ⓕ (01366) 728543
Ⓔ mike.hythealpines@tinyworld.co.uk
Ⓦ www.hythe-alpines.co.uk
Contact: Mike Smith
Opening Times: 1000-1700 Tue & Wed Mar-Oct. Also every w/end Apr-Jun.
Min Mail Order UK: Nmc
Min Mail Order EU: Nmc
Cat. Cost: 6 x 1st class, 4 x IRCs
Credit Cards: None
Specialities: Rare & unusual alpines, rock garden plants & bulbs for enthusiasts & exhibitors.
Map Ref: E, C2

EJRN **JOHN RAY NURSERY** 🛖 🖾
36 Station Road, Braintree, Essex, CM7 3QJ
Ⓣ (m.) 07866 296531
Ⓕ (01376) 322484
Contact: Brian James
Opening Times: 0900-1730 Sat, 1030-1630 Sun & B/Hol.
Cat. Cost: None issued.
Credit Cards: None
Specialities: *Pittosporum.*
Notes: Also sells wholesale.
Map Ref: E, D2

EJWh **JILL WHITE** ⊠ 🛖
St Davids', Recreation Way, Brightlingsea, Essex, CO7 ONJ
Ⓣ (01206) 303547
Contact: Jill White
Opening Times: By appt. only.
Min Mail Order UK: Nmc
Cat. Cost: Sae
Credit Cards: None
Specialities: *Cyclamen* species esp. *Cyclamen parviflorum. Cyclamen elegans.* Also seed.
Notes: Also sells wholesale.
Map Ref: E, D3

EKen **KENWICK FARMHOUSE NURSERIES** ⊠ ◆
Kenwick Road, Louth, Lincolnshire, LN11 8NW
Ⓣ (01507) 606469
Ⓕ (01507) 606469
Ⓔ info@kenwicknursery.co.uk
Ⓦ www.kenwicknursery.co.uk
Contact: Janet Elmhirst
Opening Times: 0930-1700 (dusk in winter)Tue-Sat, closed Mon except B/hol. 1000-1600 Sun. Closed Jan.
Min Mail Order UK: £12.00
Cat. Cost: 2 x 1st class
Credit Cards: None
Specialities: Hardy plants.
Notes: Mail order only if stock is available, as grown in small quantities.
Map Ref: E, A2 OS Grid Ref: TF342853

EKMF **KATHLEEN MUNCASTER FUCHSIAS** 🖾
18 Field Lane, Morton, Gainsborough, Lincolnshire, DN21 3BY
Ⓣ (01427) 612329
Ⓔ jim@smuncaster.freeserve.co.uk
Ⓦ www.kathleenmuncasterfuchsias.co.uk
Contact: Kathleen Muncaster
Opening Times: 1000-dusk Thu-Tue. After mid-Jun please phone to check.
Cat. Cost: 2 x 1st class
Credit Cards: None
Specialities: *Fuchsia.* Nat. Coll. of Hardy *Fuchsia* (full status).
Map Ref: E, A1

ELan **LANGTHORNS PLANTERY** ⊠ 🖾
High Cross Lane West, Little Canfield, Dunmow, Essex, CM6 1TD
Ⓣ (01371) 872611
Ⓕ (01371) 872611
Ⓔ info@langthorns.com
Ⓦ www.langthorns.com
Contact: E Cannon
Opening Times: 1000-1700 or dusk (if earlier) 7 days excl. Xmas fortnight.

Min Mail Order UK: Nmc
Cat. Cost: £1.50
Credit Cards: Visa Access Switch MasterCard Delta
Specialities: Wide general range with many unusual plants.
Notes: Mail order 9cm perennials, 2 & 3 litre shrubs.
Map Ref: E, D2 **OS Grid Ref:** TL592204

ELau   LAUREL FARM HERBS ⊠ &
Main Road, Kelsale, Saxmundham, Suffolk, IP13 2RG
Ⓣ (01728) 668223
Ⓔ laurelfarmherbs@aol.com
Ⓦ www.theherbfarm.co.uk
Contact: Chris Seagon
Opening Times: 1000-1700 Wed-Mon 1st Mar-30 Jun (closed Tues). 1000-1700 Mon-Fri 1st Jul-31st Oct (closed w/ends). 1000-1500 Wed-Fri 1st Nov-28th Feb. Other times by appt. only.
Min Mail Order UK: 6 plants + p&p
Min Mail Order EU: 12 plants
Cat. Cost: Online only.
Credit Cards: Visa MasterCard Switch Delta
Specialities: Herbs esp. rosemary, thyme, lavender, mint, comfrey & sage.
Notes: Mail orders accepted by email, phone or post.
Map Ref: E, C3

EMag   MAGPIES NURSERY &
Green Lane, Mundford, Norfolk, IP26 5HS
Ⓣ (01842) 878496
Ⓔ magpies@eidosnet.co.uk
Contact: Patricia Cooper
Opening Times: 0900-1700 Tue-Fri, 1000-1700 Sat & Sun. Closed Mon.
Cat. Cost: Free
Credit Cards: None
Specialities: Unusual hardy perennials, grasses & foliage plants.
Map Ref: E, C2

EMal   MARSHALL'S MALMAISON ⊠ ⊠ € &
Hullwood Barn, Shelley,
Ipswich, Suffolk,
IP7 5RE
Ⓣ (01473) 822400
Ⓔ marshalls.malmaisons@btinternet.com
Contact: J M Marshall
Opening Times: By appt. only.
Min Mail Order UK: £24.00 incl. p&p
Min Mail Order EU: £35.00 incl. p&p
Cat. Cost: 1st class sae
Credit Cards: None

Specialities: Nat. Coll. of Malmaison Carnations.
Notes: Also sells wholesale.
Map Ref: E,C3 **OS Grid Ref:** TM006394

EMan   MANOR NURSERY &
Thaxted Road, Wimbish, Saffron Walden, Essex, CB10 2UT
Ⓣ (01799) 513481
Ⓕ (01799) 513481
Ⓔ flora@gardenplants.co.uk
Ⓦ www.gardenplants.co.uk
Contact: William Lyall
Opening Times: 0900-1700 summer. 0900-1600 winter. Closed Xmas.
Cat. Cost: 4 x 2nd class
Credit Cards: Visa Access Switch EuroCard MasterCard
Specialities: Uncommon perennials, grasses, hardy *Geranium, Sedum* & cottage garden plants. Variegated & coloured foliage plants. Many newly introduced cultivars.
Map Ref: E, C2

EMar   LESLEY MARSHALL ⊠ &
Uncommon Garden Plants, Islington Lodge Cottage, Tilney All Saints, King's Lynn, Norfolk, PE34 4SF
Ⓣ (01553) 765103
Ⓔ daylilies@tiscali.co.uk
Contact: Lesley & Peter Marshall
Opening Times: 0930-1800 Mon, Wed, Fri-Sun Mar-Oct.
Min Mail Order UK: 6 plants
Cat. Cost: £1 refundable. £1 coin/4 x 1st class
Credit Cards: None
Specialities: Uncommon garden plants, hardy perennials & plants for foliage effect. *Hemerocallis & Crocosmia.* Choice seed list. Some plants available in small quantities only.
Notes: Mail order daylilies only.
Map Ref: E, B1

EMcA   S M McARD (SEEDS) ⊠
39 West Road, Pointon, Sleaford, Lincolnshire, NG34 0NA
Ⓣ (01529) 240765
Ⓕ (01529) 240765
Ⓔ seeds@smmcard.com
Ⓦ www.smmcard.com
Contact: Susan McArd
Opening Times: Not open. Mail order only.

K E Y		
⊠ Mail order to UK or EU	🏠 Delivers to shows	
⊠ Exports beyond EU	€ Euro accepted	
& Accessible by wheelchair	◆ See Display advertisement	

E

Min Mail Order UK: Nmc
Min Mail Order EU: Nmc
Cat. Cost: 2 x 2nd class
Credit Cards: None
Specialities: Unusual & giant vegetables esp.
tree (Egyptian) onion. Seeds & plants.
Notes: Also sells wholesale.

EMFP   MILLS' FARM PLANTS & GARDENS ⊠ ⓖ
Norwich Road, Mendlesham, Suffolk,
IP14 5NQ
ⓣ (01449) 766425
ⓕ (01449) 766425
ⓔ sue@millsfarmplants.co.uk
ⓦ www.millsfarmplants.co.uk
Contact: Peter & Susan Russell
Opening Times: Mail order only. Open by
appt. only for the collection of orders.
Min Mail Order UK: Nmc
Min Mail Order EU: Nmc
Cat. Cost: 5 x 2nd class
Credit Cards: All major credit/debit cards
Specialities: Pinks and rambling roses.
Map Ref: E, C3 OS Grid Ref: TM119650

**EMFW   MICKFIELD WATERGARDEN CENTRE
LTD ⊠ ⓜ € ⓖ**
Debenham Road, Mickfield, Stowmarket,
Suffolk, IP14 5LP
ⓣ (01449) 711336
ⓕ (01449) 711018
ⓔ mike@mickfield.co.uk
ⓦ www.watergardenshop.co.uk
Contact: Mike & Yvonne Burch
Opening Times: 0930-1700 7 days.
Min Mail Order UK: Nmc
Min Mail Order EU: £25.00 + p&p
Cat. Cost: £1.00
Credit Cards: Visa Access MasterCard Switch
Specialities: Hardy aquatics, *Nymphaea* &
moisture lovers.
Notes: Also sells wholesale.
Map Ref: E, C3 OS Grid Ref: TM141616

EMic   MICKFIELD HOSTAS ⊠ ⓝ € ⓖ
The Poplars, Mickfield,
Stowmarket, Suffolk,
IP14 5LH
ⓣ (01449) 711576
ⓜ 07720 380361
ⓕ (01449) 711576
ⓔ mickfieldhostas@btconnect.com
ⓦ www.mickfieldhostas.co.uk
Contact: Mr & Mrs R L C Milton
Opening Times: For specified dates see
catalogue or website.
Min Mail Order UK: Nmc
Min Mail Order EU: Nmc

Cat. Cost: 4 x 1st class
Credit Cards: Visa MasterCard
Specialities: *Hosta*, over 1000 varieties (some
subject to availability) mostly from USA. New
varieties become available during the season.
Map Ref: E, C3

EMil   MILL RACE GARDEN CENTRE € ⓖ
New Road, Aldham, Colchester, Essex,
CO6 3QT
ⓣ (01206) 242521
ⓕ (01206) 241616
ⓔ admin@millracenursery.co.uk
ⓦ www.millracegardencentre.co.uk
Contact: Steve Canham
Opening Times: 0900-1730 7 days.
Credit Cards: Visa Access Diners Switch
Specialities: Around 4000 varieties of plants
always in stock.
Map Ref: E, C2 OS Grid Ref: TL918268

EMon   MONKSILVER NURSERY ⊠ €
Oakington Road, Cottenham,
Cambridgeshire, CB4 8TW
ⓣ (01954) 251555
ⓕ (01223) 502887
ⓔ plants@monksilver.com
ⓦ www.monksilver.com
Contact: Joe Sharman & Alan Leslie
Opening Times: 1000-1600 Fri & Sat 1st
Mar-30th Jun, 17th Sep & Fri & Sat Oct.
Min Mail Order UK: £15.00 + p&p
Min Mail Order EU: £30.00 + p&p
Cat. Cost: 8 x 1st class
Credit Cards: None
Specialities: Herbaceous plants, grasses,
*Anthemis, Arum, Helianthus, Lamium, Nepeta,
Monarda, Salvia, Vinca*, sedges & variegated
plants. Many NCCPG 'Pink Sheet' plants.
Ferns.
Map Ref: E, C2 OS Grid Ref: TQ437665

EMui   KEN MUIR LTD ⊠
Honeypot Farm, Rectory Road,
Weeley Heath, Essex,
CO16 9BJ
ⓣ 0870 7479111
ⓕ (01255) 831534
ⓔ info@kenmuir.co.uk
ⓦ www.kenmuir.co.uk
Contact: Ming Yang, Claire Higgins
Opening Times: 1000-1600.
Min Mail Order UK: Nmc
Cat. Cost: Free
Credit Cards: Visa Access Switch
Specialities: Fruit.
Notes: Also sells wholesale.
Map Ref: E, D3

E

ENBC   NORFOLK BAMBOO COMPANY ⊠
Vine Cottage, The Drift, Ingoldisthorpe,
Kings Lynn, Norfolk, PE31 6NW
Ⓣ (01485) 543935
Ⓕ (01485) 543314
Ⓔ Lewdyer@hotmail.com
Contact: Lewis Dyer
Opening Times: 1000-1800 Fri, Apr-Sep, or
by appt.
Min Mail Order UK: £12.00 + p&p
Cat. Cost: 1 x 1st class sae for price list
Credit Cards: None
Specialities: Bamboos.
Map Ref: E, B2 OS Grid Ref: TF683331

ENor   NORFOLK LAVENDER ⊠ ⊠ 🖑
Caley Mill, Heacham, King's Lynn, Norfolk,
PE31 7JE
Ⓣ (01485) 570384
Ⓕ (01485) 571176
Ⓔ admin@norfolk-lavender.co.uk
Ⓦ www.norfolk-lavender.co.uk
Contact: Henry Head
Opening Times: 0930-1700 7 days.
Min Mail Order UK: £15.00 + p&p
Min Mail Order EU: £15.00 + p&p
Cat. Cost: 2 x 1st class
Credit Cards: Visa Access Switch
Specialities: Nat. Coll. of *Lavandula*.
Map Ref: E, B2

ENot   NOTCUTTS NURSERIES ⊠ ⊠ € 🖑
Woodbridge, Suffolk, IP12 4AF
Ⓣ (01394) 445400
Ⓕ (01394) 445440
Ⓔ sales@notcutts.co.uk
Ⓦ www.notcutts.co.uk
Contact: Plant Adviser
Opening Times: Garden centres 0900-1800
Mon-Sat & 1030-1630 Sun. Check for local
variations and late night openings.
Min Mail Order UK: £250.00 + p&p (£30.00
if collected from a Notcutts Garden Centre)
Min Mail Order EU: £1000.00 + p&p
Cat. Cost: £6.00 + £1.25
Credit Cards: Maestro Visa Access Connect
Specialities: Wide general range. Specialist list
of *Syringa*. Nat. Coll. of *Hibiscus*.
Notes: Also sells wholesale.
Map Ref: E, C3 OS Grid Ref: TM268487

EOas   OASIS ⊠
42 Greenwood Avenue, South Benfleet, Essex,
SS7 1LD
Ⓣ (01268) 757666
Ⓔ paul@oasisdesigns.co.uk
Ⓦ www.oasisdesigns.co.uk
Contact: Paul Spracklin

Opening Times: Strictly by appt. only.
Min Mail Order UK: Nmc
Cat. Cost: None issued, see website.
Credit Cards: None
Specialities: Small nursery offering exciting
new range of cold-hardy bromeliads. Most
items available in small quantities only.
Notes: Mail order sent by overnight courier.
Map Ref: E, D2 OS Grid Ref: TQ781863

EOHP   OLD HALL PLANTS ⊠ €
1 The Old Hall, Barsham, Beccles, Suffolk,
NR34 8HB
Ⓣ (01502) 717475
Ⓔ info@oldhallplants.co.uk
Ⓦ www.oldhallplants.co.uk
Contact: Janet Elliott
Opening Times: By appt. most days, please
phone first.
Min Mail Order UK: Nmc
Min Mail Order EU: Nmc
Cat. Cost: 4 x 1st class
Credit Cards: None
Specialities: Herbs, over 500 varieties grown.
Mentha, Plectranthus, Streptocarpus.
Notes: Partial wheelchair access.
Map Ref: E, C3 OS Grid Ref: TM395904

EOrn   ORNAMENTAL CONIFERS ◆
22 Chapel Road, Terrington St Clement,
Kings Lynn, Norfolk, PE34 4ND
Ⓣ (01553) 828874
Ⓕ (01553) 828874
Contact: Peter Rotchell
Opening Times: 0930-1700 Thu-Tue, closed
Wed. Closed 20th Dec-2nd Feb.
Credit Cards: None
Specialities: Conifers.
Map Ref: E, B1

EPem   PEMBROKE FARM NURSERY ⊠ 🛉 € 🖑
Pembroke Farm, Barway, Ely,
Cambridgeshire, CB7 5UB
Ⓣ (01353) 722903
Ⓕ (01353) 722903
Ⓔ Pemcacti@aol.com/enquiries@cactiand
succulents.co.uk
Ⓦ www.cactiandsucculents.co.uk
Contact: Richard & Sheena Drane
Opening Times: Please phone or check
website for opening times.
Min Mail Order UK: Nmc
Cat. Cost: 1 x 1st class

KEY		
⊠ Mail order to UK or EU	🛉 Delivers to shows	
⊠ Exports beyond EU	€ Euro accepted	
🖑 Accessible by wheelchair	◆ See Display advertisement	

E

Credit Cards: None
Specialities: Cacti & succulents incl. *Agave,
Aloe* & *Sempervivum*. Many plants are
available in small quantities only.
Notes: Mail order sempervivums only. Also
sells wholesale.
Map Ref: E, C2

EPfP THE PLACE FOR PLANTS € ⌨
East Bergholt Place, East Bergholt, Suffolk,
CO7 6UP
Ⓣ (01206) 299224
Ⓕ (01206) 299224
Ⓔ sales@placeforplants.co.uk
Contact: Rupert & Sara Eley
Opening Times: 1000-1700 (or dusk if
earlier) 7 days. Closed Easter Sun. Garden
open Mar-Oct.
Cat. Cost: 2 x 1st class
Credit Cards: All major credit/debit cards
Specialities: Wide range of specialist &
popular plants. 15 acre mature garden.
Map Ref: E, C3

EPGN PARK GREEN NURSERIES ⊠ ⌨ ⋔
Wetheringsett, Stowmarket, Suffolk,
IP14 5QH
Ⓣ (01728) 860139
Ⓕ (01728) 861277
Ⓔ nurseries@parkgreen.fsnet.co.uk
Ⓦ www.parkgreen.co.uk
Contact: Richard & Mary Ford
Opening Times: 1000-1600 Mon-Fri &
1000-1300 Sat, 1 Mar-30 Sep.
Min Mail Order UK: Nmc
Min Mail Order EU: Nmc
Cat. Cost: 4 x 1st class
Credit Cards: Visa MasterCard Delta Switch
Specialities: *Hosta*, ornamental grasses &
herbaceous.
Notes: Mail order *Hosta* only.
Map Ref: E, C3 OS Grid Ref: TM136644

EPla P W PLANTS ⊠ ⋔ ⌨
Sunnyside, Heath Road,
Kenninghall, Norfolk,
NR16 2DS
Ⓣ (01953) 888212
Ⓕ (01953) 888212
Ⓔ pw.plants@paston.co.uk
Ⓦ www.hardybamboo.com
Contact: Paul Whittaker
Opening Times: Every Fri & last Sat in every
month, plus all Sats Apr-Sep.
Min Mail Order UK: Nmc
Min Mail Order EU: Nmc
Cat. Cost: 5 x 1st class
Credit Cards: All major credit/debit cards

Specialities: Bamboos, grasses, choice shrubs
& perennials.
Notes: Does not deliver to Chelsea Show.
Map Ref: E, C3

EPot POTTERTONS NURSERY ⊠ ⌨ ⋔ € ⌨
Moortown Road, Nettleton, Caistor,
Lincolnshire, LN7 6HX
Ⓣ (01472) 851714
Ⓕ (01472) 852580
Ⓔ sales@pottertons.co.uk
Ⓦ www.pottertons.co.uk
Contact: Robert Potterton
Opening Times: 0900-1630 7 days.
Min Mail Order UK: Nmc
Min Mail Order EU: Nmc
Cat. Cost: £2.00 in stamps
Credit Cards: Maestro Visa MasterCard
Specialities: Alpines, dwarf bulbs & woodland
plants. Hardy orchids & *Pleione*.
Notes: Seed list sent out in Nov.
Map Ref: E, A1 OS Grid Ref: TA091001

EPPr THE PLANTSMAN'S PREFERENCE ⊠ ⋔ ⌨
(Office) Lynwood, Hopton Road,
Garboldisham, Diss, Norfolk, IP22 2QN
Ⓣ (01953) 681439 (office) (07799) 855559
(nursery)
Ⓔ info@plantpref.co.uk
Ⓦ www.plantpref.co.uk
Contact: Jenny & Tim Fuller
Opening Times: 0930-1700 Fri, Sat & Sun
Mar-Oct. Other times by appt.
Min Mail Order UK: £15.00
Min Mail Order EU: £30.00
Cat. Cost: 4 x 1st class/IRCs. Also online.
Credit Cards: All major credit/debit cards
Specialities: Hardy *Geranium* (450), grasses &
sedges (600+). Unusual & interesting
perennials. Nat. Coll. of *Molinia*.
Notes: Nursery is at Hall Farm, Church Road,
South Lopham, Diss.
Map Ref: E, C3 OS Grid Ref: TM041819

EPts POTASH NURSERY ⊠ ⋔ ⌨
Cow Green, Bacton, Stowmarket, Suffolk,
IP14 4HJ
Ⓣ (01449) 781671
Ⓔ enquiries@potashnursery.co.uk
Ⓦ www.potashnursery.co.uk
Contact: M W Clare
Opening Times: 1000-1700 Fri-Sun & B/hol
Mons mid Feb-early Jun.
Min Mail Order UK: £10.00
Cat. Cost: 4 x 1st class
Credit Cards: Visa Delta MasterCard
Specialities: *Fuchsia*.
Map Ref: E, C3 OS Grid Ref: TM0565NE

E

EPyc PENNYCROSS PLANTS
Earith Road, Colne, Huntingdon,
Cambridgeshire, PE28 3NL
Ⓣ (01487) 841520
Ⓔ plants@pennycross99.freeserve.co.uk
Contact: Janet M Buist
Opening Times: 1000-1600 Mon-Fri, 1st
Mar-31st Oct by appt.
Credit Cards: None
Specialities: Hardy perennials. Salvias. Some
plants available in small quantities only.
Map Ref: E, C2 OS Grid Ref: TL378759

ERea READS NURSERY ⊠ ⊠ ⓐ
Hales Hall, Loddon, Norfolk, NR14 6QW
Ⓣ (01508) 548395
Ⓕ (01508) 548040
Ⓔ plants@readsnursery.co.uk
Ⓦ www.readsnursery.co.uk
Contact: Stephen Read
Opening Times: 1000-1630 (dusk if earlier)
Mon-Sat, 1100-1600 Sun & B/hols Easter-
end Sep & by appt.
Min Mail Order UK: Nmc
Min Mail Order EU: £10.00 + p&p
Cat. Cost: 4 x 1st class
Credit Cards: All major credit/debit cards
Specialities: Conservatory plants, vines, *Citrus*,
figs & unusual fruits & nuts. Wall shrubs &
climbers. Scented & aromatic hardy plants.
UK grown. Nat. Colls. of *Citrus*, figs, vines.
Notes: Mostly accessible by wheelchair (some
gravel paths).
Map Ref: E, B3 OS Grid Ref: TM369960

ERhR RHODES & ROCKLIFFE ⊠ ⊠ €
2 Nursery Road, Nazeing, Essex, EN9 2JE
Ⓣ (01992) 463693 (office hours)
Ⓕ (01992) 440673
Ⓔ RRBegonias@aol.com
Contact: David Rhodes or John Rockliffe
Opening Times: By appt.
Min Mail Order UK: £2.50 + p&p
Min Mail Order EU: £5.00 + p&p
Cat. Cost: 2 x 1st class
Credit Cards: None
Specialities: *Begonia* species & hybrids. Nat.
Coll. of *Begonia*. Plants propagated to order.
Notes: Mail order Apr-Sep only.
Map Ref: E, D2

ERob ROBIN SAVILL CLEMATIS SPECIALIST ⊠ ⊠
(office) The Old Nursery, Butts Green Road,
Sandon, Chelmsford, Essex, CM2 7RN
Ⓣ (01245) 224576
Ⓔ robinsavill@blueyonder.co.uk
Contact: Robin Savill
Opening Times: Visitors by appt. only.

Min Mail Order UK: 1 plant + p&p
Min Mail Order EU: 1 plant + p&p
Cat. Cost: £3.50
Credit Cards: None
Specialities: Over 800 varieties of *Clematis*
incl. many unusual species & cvs from around
the world. Nat. Coll. of *Clematis viticella*.
Notes: Nursery at The Garden Company,
Mayes Lane, Sandon CM2 7RW. Also sells
wholesale.
Map Ref: E, D2

ERod THE RODINGS PLANTERY ⊠ ⊠ ⋔ €
Anchor Lane, Abbess Roding, Essex,
CM5 0JW
Ⓣ (01279) 876421
Ⓔ janeandandy@therodingsplantery.co.uk
Contact: Jane & Andy Mogridge
Opening Times: By appt. only. Occasional
open days, please phone for details.
Min Mail Order UK: £15.00 + p&p
Min Mail Order EU: £500.00 + p&p
Cat. Cost: 3 x 1st class
Credit Cards: None
Specialities: *Bamboo*. Rare & unusual trees.
Map Ref: E, D2

ERom THE ROMANTIC GARDEN ⊠ ⊠ € ⓐ ◆
Swannington, Norwich, Norfolk, NR9 5NW
Ⓣ (01603) 261488
Ⓕ (01603) 864231
Ⓔ enquiries@romantic-garden-nursery.co.uk
Ⓦ www.romantic-garden-nursery.co.uk
Contact: John Powles/John Carrick
Opening Times: 1000-1700 Wed Fri & Sat
all year.
Min Mail Order UK: £5.00 + p&p
Min Mail Order EU: £30.00 + p&p
Cat. Cost: 4 x 1st class
Credit Cards: Visa Access American Express
Specialities: Half-hardy & conservatory.
Buxus topiary, ornamental standards, large
specimens.
Notes: Also sells wholesale.
Map Ref: E, B3

ERos ROSEHOLME NURSERY ⊠ ⊠ ⓐ
Roseholme Farm, Howsham, Market Rasen,
Lincolnshire, LN7 6JZ
Ⓣ (01652) 678661
Ⓕ (01472) 852450
Ⓔ Pbcenterpr@aol.com
Contact: P B Clayton

KEY: ⊠ Mail order to UK or EU ⋔ Delivers to shows | ⊠ Exports beyond EU € Euro accepted | ⓐ Accessible by wheelchair ◆ See Display advertisement

E

Opening Times: Mail order only. By appt. for collection of orders.
Min Mail Order UK: Nmc
Min Mail Order EU: Nmc
Cat. Cost: 2 x 2nd class
Credit Cards: None
Specialities: Underground lines – bulbs, corms, rhizomes & tubers (esp. *Crocus, Iris*).
Notes: Also sells wholesale.
Map Ref: E, A1

ERou   ROUGHAM HALL NURSERIES ⊠ ☒ ⋔ € ◆
Ipswich Road, Rougham, Bury St Edmunds, Suffolk, IP30 9LZ
Ⓣ 0800 970 7516
Ⓕ (01359) 271149
Ⓔ hardyperennials@aol.com
Ⓦ www.roughamhallnurseries.co.uk
Contact: A A & K G Harbutt
Opening Times: 1000-1600 7 days. Closed from Xmas Day to New Year's Day.
Min Mail Order UK: Nmc
Min Mail Order EU: Nmc
Cat. Cost: Free
Credit Cards: All major credit/debit cards
Specialities: Hardy perennials esp. *Aster* (*n-a*, *n-b* & species), *Delphinium, Hemerocallis, Iris, Kniphofia, Papaver* & *Phlox.* Nat. Colls. of *Delphinium* & gooseberry.
Notes: *Delphinium* list available Apr-Jun. Despatch Jun-Aug. Also sells wholesale.
Map Ref: E, C2

ESCh   SHEILA CHAPMAN CLEMATIS ⊠ ⋔ ⬜
Crowther Nurseries, Ongar Road, Abridge, Romford, Essex, RM4 1AA
Ⓣ (01708) 688090
Ⓕ (01708) 688090
Ⓦ www.sheilachapman.co.uk
Contact: Sheila Chapman
Opening Times: 0930-1700 (or dusk in winter) all year excl. Xmas week.
Min Mail Order UK: Nmc
Cat. Cost: 5 x 2nd class
Credit Cards: All major credit/debit cards
Specialities: Over 600 varieties of *Clematis*.
Map Ref: E, D2 OS Grid Ref: TQ483969

ESgl   SEAGATE IRISES ⊠ ☒ € ⬜
A17 Long Sutton By-Pass, Long Sutton, Lincolnshire, PE12 9RX
Ⓣ (01406) 365138
Ⓕ (01406) 365447
Ⓔ Sales@irises.co.uk
Ⓦ www.irises.co.uk
Contact: Julian Browse or Wendy Browse
Opening Times: 1000-1700 daily May-Sep. Please phone for appt. Oct-Apr.

Min Mail Order UK: £30.00
Min Mail Order EU: Nmc. Carriage at cost.
Cat. Cost: £3.00 or 6 euros, no stamps pls.
Credit Cards: Maestro Visa MasterCard
Specialities: Bearded *Iris*, over 800 varieties, modern & historic tall bearded, medians & dwarfs. Many container grown available.
Map Ref: E, B1 OS Grid Ref: TF437218

EShb   SHRUBLAND PARK NURSERIES ⊠ ⋔ € ◆
Coddenham, Ipswich, Suffolk, IP6 9QJ
Ⓣ (01473) 833187
Ⓜ 07890 527744
Ⓕ (01473) 832838
Ⓔ gill@shrublandparknurseries.co.uk
Ⓦ www.shrublandparknurseries.co.uk
Contact: Gill Stitt
Opening Times: 1000-1700 Wed-Sun, Mar-Sep. Oct-Feb, please ring first.
Min Mail Order UK: £10.00
Min Mail Order EU: £25.00
Cat. Cost: 3 x 1st class, free by email
Credit Cards: All major credit/debit cards
Specialities: A wide range of conservatory plants, houseplants, tender perennials & succulents. Over 700 hardy perennials. Display beds.
Notes: Groups welcome. Partial wheelchair access. Enter Shrubland Park via gate opposite Sorrel Horse pub, 1 mile north of Claydon. Also sells wholesale.
Map Ref: E, C3 OS Grid Ref: TM128524

ESou   SOUTHFIELD NURSERIES ⊠ ⋔ ⬜ ◆
Bourne Road, Morton, Nr Bourne, Lincolnshire, PE10 0RH
Ⓣ (01778) 570168
Contact: Mr & Mrs B Goodey
Opening Times: 1000-1215 & 1315-1600 7 days. Nov-Jan by appt. only.
Min Mail Order UK: Nmc
Min Mail Order EU: Nmc
Cat. Cost: 3 x 1st class
Credit Cards: None
Specialities: A wide range of cacti & succulents incl. some of the rarer varieties, all grown on our own nursery.
Notes: Also sells wholesale.
Map Ref: E, B1 OS Grid Ref: TF094234

ESty   STYLE ROSES ⊠ ⋔ ⬜
10 Meridian Walk, Holbeach, Spalding, Lincolnshire, PE12 7NR
Ⓣ (01406) 424089
Ⓜ 07932 044093/07780 860415
Ⓕ (01406) 424089
Ⓔ styleroses@aol.com
Ⓦ www.styleroses.co.uk

E

Contact: Chris Styles, Margaret Styles
Opening Times: Vary, please phone.
Min Mail Order UK: Nmc
Min Mail Order EU: Nmc
Cat. Cost: Free
Credit Cards: None
Specialities: Roses: standard & bush roses.
Notes: Export subject to countries' plant
health requirements, carriage & export
certificates where required charged at cost.
Also sells wholesale.
Map Ref: E, B1

ESul   BRIAN & PEARL SULMAN ⊠ 🏠 ♿
54 Kingsway, Mildenhall, Bury St Edmunds,
Suffolk, IP28 7HR
Ⓣ (01638) 712297
Ⓕ (01638) 712297
Ⓔ pearl@sulmanspelargoniums.co.uk
Ⓦ www.sulmanspelargoniums.co.uk
Contact: Pearl Sulman
Opening Times: Mail order only. Not open
except for Open W/ends (see **Notes**).
Min Mail Order UK: £20.00
Cat. Cost: 4 x 1st class
Credit Cards: Visa MasterCard
Specialities: *Pelargonium*. Some varieties only
available in small quantities.
Notes: Open w/ends 7/8 May & 4/5Jun 2005
Phone for information on 2006 dates.
Map Ref: E, C2 OS Grid Ref: TL715747

ETho   THORNCROFT CLEMATIS NURSERY ⊠ ⊠ 🏠 ♿
The Lings, Reymerston, Norwich, Norfolk,
NR9 4QG
Ⓣ (01953) 850407
Ⓕ (01953) 851788
Ⓔ sales@thorncroft.co.uk
Ⓦ www.thorncroft.co.uk
Contact: Ruth P Gooch
Opening Times: 1000-1600 Tue-Sat all year,
closed Sun & Mon. Open B/hol Mon.
Min Mail Order UK: Nmc
Min Mail Order EU: Nmc
Cat. Cost: 6 x 2nd class
Credit Cards: Maestro MasterCard Solo Visa
Delta
Specialities: *Clematis*.
Notes: Does not export to USA, Canada or
Australia.
Map Ref: E, B3 OS Grid Ref: TG039062

ETow   TOWN FARM NURSERY ⊠ ♿
Street House, The Street, Metfield, Harleston,
Norfolk, IP20 0LA
Ⓣ (01379) 586189
Ⓔ david.baker@themail.co.uk

Contact: F D Baker
Opening Times: Feb-Oct by appt. only.
Min Mail Order UK: £5.00 + p&p
Min Mail Order EU: £20.00 + p&p
Cat. Cost: Sae
Credit Cards: None
Specialities: Unusual alpines, border
perennials. Also seed. Limited stocks
available.
Map Ref: E, C3 OS Grid Ref: TM2942805

EUnu   UNUSUAL HERBS AND EDIBLES ⊠
39 Oxford Road, Lowestoft, Suffolk,
NR32 1TN
Ⓣ (01502) 502001
Ⓔ laurenrayner@aol.com
Ⓦ www.unusualherbsandedibles.co.uk
Contact: Lauren Rayner
Opening Times: By appt. only. Please email
or phone first.
Min Mail Order UK: Nmc
Cat. Cost: Free
Specialities: Much stock available in small
quantities only.
Notes: Credit card payment available Online
through PAYPAL and NOCHEX.

EWes   WEST ACRE GARDENS ⊠ 🏠 ♿
West Acre, Kings Lynn, Norfolk, PE32 1UJ
Ⓣ (01760) 755562
Contact: J J Tuite
Opening Times: 1000-1700 7 days 1st Feb-
30th Nov. Other times by appt.
Min Mail Order UK: Nmc
Cat. Cost: 4 x 1st class
Credit Cards: Visa MasterCard Delta Switch
Specialities: Unusual shrubs, herbaceous &
alpines. Large selection of *Rhodohypoxis* &
grasses.
Map Ref: E, B1 OS Grid Ref: TF792182

EWin   WINTER FLORA PLANT CENTRE ♿
Hall Farm, Weston, Beccles, Suffolk,
NR34 8TT
Ⓣ (01502) 716810
Ⓜ 07771 882613
Ⓕ (01502) 716666
Ⓔ retail@goosegreennurseries.co.uk
Ⓦ www.goosegreennurseries.co.uk
Contact: Stephen Malster
Opening Times: 1000-1700 Mon-Sun all
year, except 25th Dec-1st Jan.
Cat. Cost: Online only.
Credit Cards: All major credit/debit cards
Specialities: All plants grown in large
quantities.
Notes: Also sells wholesale.
Map Ref: E, C3 OS Grid Ref: TM423878

E

EWll   THE WALLED GARDEN 🔲 ◆
Park Road, Benhall, Saxmundham, Suffolk,
IP17 1JB
Ⓣ (01728) 602510
Ⓕ (01728) 602510
Ⓔ jim@thewalledgarden.co.uk
Ⓦ www.thewalledgarden.co.uk
Contact: Jim Mountain
Opening Times: 0930-1700 Tue-Sun Mar-
Oct, Tue-Sat Nov-Feb.
Cat. Cost: 2 x 1st class
Credit Cards: All major credit/debit cards
Specialities: Tender & hardy perennials, over
1000 varieties, & wall shrubs.
Map Ref: E, C3 **OS Grid Ref:** TM371613

EWoo   WOOTTEN'S PLANTS 🔲 🔲
Wenhaston, Blackheath, Halesworth, Suffolk,
IP19 9HD
Ⓣ (01502) 478258
Ⓕ (01502) 478888
Ⓔ sales@woottensplants.co.uk
Ⓦ www.woottensplants.co.uk
Contact: M Loftus
Opening Times: 0930-1700 7 days.
Min Mail Order UK: Nmc
Min Mail Order EU: Nmc
Cat. Cost: Free, illustrated *Hemerocallis, Iris* &
P. auricula catalogues.
Credit Cards: Visa Access American Express
Switch
Specialities: *Pelargonium, Hemerocallis, P.
auricula* & *Iris*. Grasses.
Notes: Also sells wholesale.
Map Ref: E, C3 **OS Grid Ref:** TM42714375

EWsh   WESTSHORES NURSERIES 🔲
82 West Street, Winterton, Lincolnshire,
DN15 9QF
Ⓣ (01724) 733940
Ⓔ westshnur@aol.com
Ⓦ www.westshores.co.uk
Contact: Gail & John Summerfield
Opening Times: 0930-1800 (or dusk) Wed-
Sun & B/hols 1st Mar-mid Nov.
Min Mail Order UK: £15.00
Cat. Cost: 2 x 1st class
Credit Cards: All major credit/debit cards
Specialities: Ornamental grasses & herbaceous
perennials.
Notes: Mail order grasses only.
Map Ref: E, A1

EWTr   WALNUT TREE GARDEN NURSERY 🔲 €
Flymoor Lane, Rocklands, Attleborough,
Norfolk, NR17 1BP
Ⓣ (01953) 488163
Ⓕ (01953) 483187

Ⓔ info@wtgn.co.uk
Ⓦ www.wtgn.co.uk
Contact: Jim Paine & Clare Billington
Opening Times: 0900-1800 Tue-Sun Feb-
Nov & B/hols.
Min Mail Order UK: £30.00
Cat. Cost: 4 x 1st class
Credit Cards: Visa MasterCard Switch Solo
Map Ref: E, B1 **OS Grid Ref:** TL978973

EZes   ZEST EXOTICS 🔲
262 Aylsham Road, Norwich, Norfolk,
NR3 2RG
Ⓣ (01603) 452740
Ⓕ (01603) 452740
Ⓔ plants@zestexotics.co.uk
Ⓦ www.zestexotics.co.uk
Contact: Ben Blake
Opening Times: Not open. Mail order only.
Min Mail Order UK: Nmc
Cat. Cost: 2 x 1st class
Credit Cards: All major credit/debit cards
Specialities: Hardy & unusual *Citrus, poncirus
trifoliata* varieties, unusual plants and exotics.
We are a new & small nursery, so plants are
only available in small quantities. Growing to
order may be possible on request.
Notes: Check website for stock levels.

SCOTLAND

GAbr   ABRIACHAN NURSERIES 🔲 🔲
Loch Ness Side, Inverness, Inverness-shire,
IV3 8LA
Ⓣ (01463) 861232
Ⓕ (01463) 861232
Ⓔ info@lochnessgarden.com
Ⓦ www.lochnessgarden.com
Contact: Mr & Mrs D Davidson
Opening Times: 0900-1900 daily (dusk if
earlier) Feb-Nov.
Min Mail Order UK: Nmc
Min Mail Order EU: Nmc
Cat. Cost: 4 x 1st class
Credit Cards: None
Specialities: Herbaceous, *Primula,
Helianthemum*, hardy *Geranium, Sempervivum*
& *Primula auricula*.
Map Ref: G, B2 **OS Grid Ref:** NH571347

GBar   BARWINNOCK HERBS 🔲 €
Barrhill, by Girvan, Ayrshire, KA26 0RB
Ⓣ (01465) 821338
Ⓔ herbs@barwinnock.com
Ⓦ www.barwinnock.com
Contact: Dave & Mon Holtom
Opening Times: 1000-1700 Easter to end
Sep. Closed Wed.

G

Min Mail Order UK: Nmc
Min Mail Order EU: Nmc
Cat. Cost: UK free, EU 2 x IRC.
Credit Cards: All major credit/debit cards
Specialities: Culinary, medicinal, fragrant-leaved plants & wildflowers organically grown.
Map Ref: G, D2 OS Grid Ref: NX309772

GBBs BORDER BELLES ⊠ 🕯 🌣
Old Branxton Cottages, Innerwick,
Nr. Dunbar, East Lothian, EH42 1QT
Ⓣ (01368) 840325
Ⓕ (01368) 840325
Ⓔ borderbelles@whsmithnet.co.uk
Ⓦ www.borderbelles.com
Contact: Gillian Moynihan & Kirstie Wenham
Opening Times: Please phone before visiting.
Min Mail Order UK: Nmc
Min Mail Order EU: On request
Cat. Cost: 3 x 1st class
Credit Cards: None
Specialities: *Anemone, Allium, Campanula, Diplarrhena*, hardy geraniums, *Hosta, Trillium, Tricyrtis*, woodland plants incl. *Actaea, Mertensia* & *Mitchella*.
Notes: Mail order Oct-Mar only. Also sells wholesale.
Map Ref: G, C3

GBin BINNY PLANTS ⊠ €
West Lodge, Binny Estate, Ecclesmachen Road,
Nr Broxbourn, West Lothian, EH52 6NL
Ⓣ (01506) 858931
Ⓕ (01506) 858155
Ⓔ binnyplants@aol.com
Ⓦ www.binnyplants.co.uk
Contact: Billy Carruthers
Opening Times: 1000-1700 7 days. Closed mid-Dec to mid-Jan.
Min Mail Order UK: Nmc
Min Mail Order EU: £25.00
Cat. Cost: £2.00 refundable on ordering.
Credit Cards: Visa MasterCard Switch EuroCard
Specialities: Perennials incl. *Euphorbia, Geranium, Hosta, Paeonia* & *Iris*. Plus large selection of grasses & ferns.
Notes: Mail order Oct-Mar only. Also sells wholesale.
Map Ref: G, C3

GBri BRIDGE END NURSERIES 🕯 🌣
Gretna Green, Dumfriesshire, DG16 5HN
Ⓣ (01461) 800612
Ⓕ (01461) 800612
Ⓔ enquiries@bridgendnurseries.co.uk
Ⓦ www.bridgendnurseries.co.uk
Contact: R Bird

Opening Times: 0930-1700 all year.
Evenings by appt.
Cat. Cost: None issued
Credit Cards: All major credit/debit cards
Specialities: Hardy cottage garden perennials. Many unusual & interesting varieties.
Map Ref: G, D3

GBuc BUCKLAND PLANTS ⊠ € 🌣
Whinnieliggate, Kirkcudbright,
Kirkcudbrightshire, DG6 4XP
Ⓣ (01557) 331323
Ⓕ (01557) 331323
Ⓦ www.bucklandplants.co.uk
Contact: Rob or Dina Asbridge
Opening Times: 1000-1700 Thu-Sun 1st Mar-1st Nov.
Min Mail Order UK: £15.00 + p&p
Min Mail Order EU: £50.00 + p&p
Cat. Cost: 3 x 1st class
Credit Cards: All major credit/debit cards
Specialities: A very wide range of scarce herbaceous & woodland plants incl. *Anemone, Cardamine, Crocosmia, Erythronium, Helleborus, Lilium, Meconopsis, Primula, Tricyrtis* & *Trillium*.
Map Ref: G, D2 OS Grid Ref: NX719524

GBut BUTTERWORTHS' ORGANIC NURSERY ⊠
Garden Cottage, Auchinleck Estate,
Cumnock, Ayrshire, KA18 2LR
Ⓣ (01290) 551088
Ⓜ 07732 254300
Ⓔ butties@webage.co.uk
Ⓦ www.butterworthsorganicnursery.co.uk
Contact: John Butterworth
Opening Times: By appt. only.
Min Mail Order UK: £6.50
Cat. Cost: 2 x 1st class
Credit Cards: None
Specialities: Fruit trees. Scottish apple varieties. Much of stock is available in small quantities only. All stock is certified organic.
Notes: Nursery partially accessible for wheelchairs.
Map Ref: G, D2 OS Grid Ref: NS502231

GCai CAIRNSMORE NURSERY ⊠ 🕯 🌣
Chapmanton Road, Castle Douglas,
Kirkcudbrightshire, DG7 2NU
Ⓣ (01556) 504819
Ⓜ 07980 176458
Ⓔ cairnsmorenursery@hotmail.com

G

Ⓦ www.cairnsmorenursery.co.uk
Contact: Valerie Smith
Opening Times: 1000-1700, Tue-Sat, Mar-Oct.
Min Mail Order UK: Nmc
Min Mail Order EU: Nmc
Cat. Cost: 4 x 1st class
Credit Cards: Visa MasterCard
Specialities: Primulas for the garden and cold greenhouse, incl. auriculas. Heucheras and tiarellas.
Map Ref: G, D2 OS Grid Ref: NX756637

GCal CALLY GARDENS ⊠ ⓛ
Gatehouse of Fleet, Castle Douglas, Kirkcudbrightshire, DG7 2DJ
Ⓕ (01557) 815029. Also information line.
Ⓦ www.callygardens.co.uk
Contact: Michael Wickenden
Opening Times: 1000-1730 Sat-Sun, 1400-1730 Tue-Fri. Easter Sat-last Sun in Sept.
Min Mail Order UK: £15.00 + p&p
Cat. Cost: 3 x 1st class
Credit Cards: None
Specialities: Unusual perennials. *Agapanthus, Crocosmia, Eryngium, Euphorbia*, hardy *Geranium* & grasses. Some rare shrubs, climbers & conservatory plants.
Notes: Also sells wholesale.
Map Ref: G, D2

GCoc JAMES COCKER & SONS ⊠ ⓛ
Whitemyres, Lang Stracht, Aberdeen, Aberdeenshire, AB15 6XH
Ⓣ (01224) 313261
Ⓕ (01224) 312531
Ⓔ sales@roses.uk.com
Ⓦ www.roses.uk.com
Contact: Alec Cocker
Opening Times: 0900-1730 7 days.
Min Mail Order UK: Nmc
Min Mail Order EU: £5.15 + p&p
Cat. Cost: Free
Credit Cards: Visa MasterCard Delta Switch
Specialities: Roses.
Notes: Also sells wholesale.
Map Ref: G, B3

GCrs CHRISTIE'S NURSERY ⊠ ⊠ ⓝ € ⓛ ◆
Downfield, Westmuir, Kirriemuir, Angus, DD8 5LP
Ⓣ (01575) 572977
Ⓕ (01575) 572977
Ⓔ ianchristie@btconnect.com
Ⓦ www.christiealpines.co.uk
Contact: Ian & Ann Christie
Opening Times: 1000-1700 Mon, Wed-Sat 15th Mar-31st Oct. Closed Tue & Sun. By appt. only at other times.

Min Mail Order UK: 5 plants + p&p
Min Mail Order EU: On request
Cat. Cost: 3 x 1st class
Credit Cards: All major credit/debit cards
Specialities: Alpines, esp. gentians, *Cassiope, Primula, Lewisia*, orchids, *Trillium* & ericaceous.
Map Ref: G, B3

GEdr EDROM NURSERIES ⊠ ⓝ ⓛ
Coldingham, Eyemouth, Berwickshire, TD14 5TZ
Ⓣ (01890) 771386
Ⓕ (01890) 71387
Ⓔ info@edromnurseries.co.uk
Ⓦ www.edromnurseries.co.uk
Contact: Mr Terry Hunt
Opening Times: 0900-1700 Mon-Sun, 1 Mar-30 Sep. Other times by appt.
Min Mail Order UK: Nmc
Min Mail Order EU: £20.00
Cat. Cost: 3 x 2nd class. More plants listed online than in printed catalogue.
Credit Cards: Visa MasterCard
Specialities: *Trillium, Arisaema, Primula, Gentiana, Meconopsis, Anemone* & other alpines. *Fritillaria*, hardy orchids.
Map Ref: G, C3 OS Grid Ref: NT8866

GEve EVELIX DAFFODILS ⊠ €
Aird Asaig, Evelix, Dornoch, Sutherland, IV25 3NG
Ⓣ (01862) 810715
Ⓔ dugaldmacarthur@lineone.net
Contact: D C MacArthur
Opening Times: By appt. only.
Min Mail Order UK: Nmc
Min Mail Order EU: Nmc
Cat. Cost: 3 x 1st class, available end May
Credit Cards: None
Specialities: New *Narcissus* cultivars for garden display & exhibition. Many in limited supply.
Map Ref: G, A2

GFai FAIRHOLM PLANTS ⊠
Fairholm, Larkhall, Lanarkshire, ML9 2UQ
Ⓣ (01698) 881671
Ⓕ (01698) 888135
Ⓔ james_sh@btconnect.com
Contact: Mrs J M Hamilton
Opening Times: Apr-Oct by appt.
Min Mail Order UK: Nmc
Cat. Cost: 1 x 2nd class for descriptive list.
Credit Cards: None
Specialities: *Abutilon* & unusual half hardy perennials esp. South African. Nat. Coll. of *Abutilon* cvs.

Notes: Mail order for young/small plants.
Map Ref: G, C2 **OS Grid Ref:** NS754515

GFle   FLEURS PLANTS ✉
2 Castlehill Lane, Abington Road, Symington,
Biggar, Lanarkshire, ML12 6SJ
ⓣ (01899) 308528
ⓔ jell.flrs@tiscali.co.uk
Contact: Jim Elliott
Opening Times: Please phone to arrange a visit.
Min Mail Order UK: £8.00 + p&p
Min Mail Order EU: £20.00 + p&p
Cat. Cost: Sae
Credit Cards: None
Specialities: *Primula, Meconopsis.*
Map Ref: G, C3 **OS Grid Ref:** NS996349

GGar   GARDEN COTTAGE NURSERY ✉
Tournaig, Poolewe, Achnasheen, Ross-shire,
IV22 2LH
ⓣ (01445) 781777
ⓔ sales@gcnursery.co.uk
ⓦ www.gcnursery.co.uk
Contact: Ben Rushbrooke
Opening Times: 1030-1800 Mon-Sat mid
Mar-mid Oct or by appt.
Min Mail Order UK: 5 plants + p&p
Cat. Cost: 4 x 2nd class
Credit Cards: None
Specialities: A wide range of plants esp. those
from the southern hemisphere, Asiatic
primulas & plants for coastal gardens.
Map Ref: G, A2 **OS Grid Ref:** NG878835

GGGa   GLENDOICK GARDENS LTD ✉ ✈
Glencarse, Perth, Perthshire, PH2 7NS
ⓣ (01738) 860205
ⓕ (01738) 860630
ⓔ sales@glendoick.com
ⓦ www.glendoick.com
Contact: P A, E P & K N E Cox
Opening Times: 2005:1000-1600 Mon-Fri
only, mid- Apr-mid-Jun, otherwise by appt.
1400-1700 1st & 3rd Sun in May. Garden
centre open 7 days.
Min Mail Order UK: £40.00 + p&p
Min Mail Order EU: £100.00 + p&p
Cat. Cost: £2.00 or £1.50 stamps
Credit Cards: Visa MasterCard Delta Switch
JCB
Specialities: Rhododendrons, azaleas and
ericaceous, *Primula* & *Meconopsis*. Plants from
wild seed. Many catalogue plants available at
garden centre. 3 National Collections awaiting
ratification.
Notes: Wheelchair access to garden centre.
Also sells wholesale.
Map Ref: G, C3

GGre   GREENHEAD ROSES ✉ ♿
Greenhead Nursery, Old Greenock Road,
Inchinnan, Renfrew, Renfrewshire, PA4 9PH
ⓣ (0141) 812 0121
ⓕ (0141) 812 0121
ⓔ greenheadnursery@aol.com
Contact: C N Urquhart
Opening Times: 1000-1700 7 days.
Min Mail Order UK: Nmc
Min Mail Order EU: Nmc
Cat. Cost: Sae
Credit Cards: Visa Switch
Specialities: Roses. Wide general range, dwarf
conifers, trees, heathers, rhododendrons &
azaleas, shrubs, alpines, fruit, hardy
herbaceous. Spring & summer bedding.
Notes: Mail order for bush roses throughout
year. Also sells wholesale.
Map Ref: G, C2

GIBF   IAIN BRODIE OF FALSYDE ✉
(Office) Cuilalunn, Kinchurdy Road, Boat of
Garten, Inverness-shire, PH24 3BP
ⓣ (01479) 831464
ⓕ (01479) 831672
ⓔ plants&seeds@falsyde.sol.co.uk
Contact: Iain Brodie of Falsyde
Opening Times: Please phone first.
Min Mail Order UK: £35.00 + p&p min.
£15.00, thereafter at cost.
Min Mail Order EU: £40.00 + p&p min.
£15.00, thereafter at cost.
Cat. Cost: Online only (not available until Nov.)
Credit Cards: None
Specialities: *Betulaceae, Rosaceae* & *Ericaceae*.
Notes: Nursery is at Auchgourish Gardens,
Boat of Garten. Anchgourish Gardens are
open Apr-Sep.
Map Ref: G, B2

GKev   KEVOCK GARDEN PLANTS & FLOWERS
✉ ✈ ♙ €
16 Kevock Road, Lasswade, Midlothian,
EH18 1HT
ⓣ 0131 454 0660
ⓜ 07811 321585
ⓕ 0131 454 0660
ⓔ info@kevockgarden.co.uk
ⓦ www.kevockgarden.co.uk
Contact: Stella Rankin
Opening Times: Not open. Mail order only.
Min Mail Order UK: Nmc
Min Mail Order EU: Nmc

KEY
✉ Mail order to UK or EU   ♙ Delivers to shows
✈ Exports beyond EU   € Euro accepted
♿ Accessible by wheelchair   ◆ See Display advertisement

G GLld

Cat. Cost: 4 x 1st class
Credit Cards: Visa MasterCard Switch
Specialities: Chinese & Himalayan plants.
Primula, Meconopsis, Iris.
Notes: Also sells wholesale.

LOCHLANDS (HRB LTD.) ⊠ &
Dundee Road, Forfar, Angus, DD8 1XF
Ⓣ (01307) 463621
Ⓕ (01307) 469665
Ⓔ vandelft@btinternet.com
Ⓦ www.lochlands.co.uk
Contact: John van Delft
Opening Times: 0830-1730 Mon-Sat, 1030-1630 Sun.
Min Mail Order UK: £25.00
Cat. Cost: Free.
Credit Cards: All major credit/debit cards
Specialities: Camellias.
Notes: Also sells wholesale.
Map Ref: G, C3 **OS Grid Ref:** DD4548

GMac **ELIZABETH MACGREGOR** ⊠ ⊠
Ellenbank, Tongland Road, Kirkcudbright,
Dumfries & Galloway, DG6 4UU
Ⓣ (01557) 330620
Ⓕ (01557) 330620
Ⓔ elizabeth@violas.abel.co.uk
Contact: Elizabeth MacGregor
Opening Times: 1000-1700 Mon, Fri & Sat
May-Sep, or please phone.
Min Mail Order UK: 6 plants £15.20 + p&p
Min Mail Order EU: £50.00 + p&p
Cat. Cost: 4 x 1st class or 5 x 2nd class
Credit Cards: Visa MasterCard
Specialities: Violets, violas & violettas, old
and new varieties. *Campanula, Geranium,
Eryngium, Penstemon, Aster, Primula, Iris* &
other unusual herbaceous.
Map Ref: G, D2

GMaP **MACPLANTS** ⋔
Berrybank Nursery, 5 Boggs Holdings,
Pencaitland, East Lothian, EH34 5BA
Ⓣ (01875) 341179
Ⓕ (01875) 340842
Ⓔ sales@macplants.co.uk
Ⓦ www.macplants.co.uk
Contact: Claire McNaughton
Opening Times: 1030-1700, 7 days, Mar-end
Jul.
Cat. Cost: 4 x 2nd class
Credit Cards: MasterCard Switch Visa
Specialities: Herbaceous perennials, alpines,
hardy ferns, violas & grasses.
Notes: Nursery partially accessible to
wheelchairs. Also sells wholesale.
Map Ref: G, C3 **OS Grid Ref:** NT447703

GNor **SHEILA NORTHWAY AURICULAS** ⊠ &
Balmaclellan, Castle Douglas,
Kirkcudbrightshire, DG7 3QR
Ⓣ (01644) 420661
Contact: Sheila Northway & M Northway
Opening Times: Mail order (Feb-Nov) & by
appt. only.
Min Mail Order UK: £10.00 + p&p
Min Mail Order EU: £20.00+p&p, payment
with order (normally 48hr priority rate).
Cat. Cost: A4 Sae + 2 x 2nd class or 2 x IRCs.
Credit Cards: None
Specialities: *Primula allionii, P. auricula* plus a
few other *Primula.*
Map Ref: G, D2

GPoy **POYNTZFIELD HERB NURSERY** ⊠ ⊠ € &
Nr Balblair, Black Isle, Dingwall, Ross-shire,
IV7 8LX
Ⓣ (01381) 610352
Ⓕ (01381) 610352
Ⓔ info@poyntzfieldherbs.co.uk
Ⓦ www.poyntzfieldherbs.co.uk
Contact: Duncan Ross
Opening Times: 1300-1700 Mon-Sat 1st
Mar-30th Sep, 1300-1700 Sun Apr-Aug.
Min Mail Order UK: £10.00 + p&p
Min Mail Order EU: £20.00 + p&p
Cat. Cost: 4 x 1st class
Credit Cards: All major credit/debit cards
Specialities: Over 400 popular, unusual &
rare herbs esp. medicinal. Also seeds.
Notes: Phone between 1200-1300 & 1800-1900 only.
Map Ref: G, B2 **OS Grid Ref:** NH711642

GQue **QUERCUS GARDEN PLANTS** &
Rankeilour Gardens, Rankeilour Estate,
Springfield, Fife, KY15 5RE
Ⓣ (01337) 810444
Ⓕ (01337) 810444
Ⓔ colin@quercus.uk.net
Contact: Colin McBeath
Opening Times: 1000-1700 Sat-Wed 19th
Mar-19th Oct. 1000-1600 Tues, Wed &
0900-1300 Sat Nov-Mar.
Cat. Cost: 4 x 1st class.
Credit Cards: None
Specialities: Easy & unusual perennials &
grasses for contemporary gardens, incl.
Agapanthus, Achillea, Kniphofia, Crocosmia,
Siberian *Iris* & *Sedum.*
Notes: Delivery service available. Also sells
wholesale.
Map Ref: G, C3 **OS Grid Ref:** NO330118

GQui **QUINISH GARDEN NURSERY** ⊠
Dervaig, Isle of Mull, Argyll, PA75 6QL

Ⓣ (01688) 400344
Ⓕ (01688) 400344
Ⓔ quinishplants@aol.com
Ⓦ www.Q-gardens.org
Contact: Nicholas Reed
Opening Times: By appt. only.
Min Mail Order UK: Nmc
Min Mail Order EU: Nmc
Cat. Cost: 2 x 1st class
Credit Cards: None
Specialities: Choice garden shrubs &
conservatory plants.
Map Ref: G, C1

GSki   SKIPNESS PLANTS ✉ 👤 ♿
The Gardens, Skipness, Nr Tarbert, Argyll,
PA29 6XU
Ⓣ (01880) 760201
Ⓕ (01880) 760201
Ⓔ info@plants-scotland.co.uk
Ⓦ www.plants-scotland.co.uk
Contact: Bill & Joan McHugh
Opening Times: 0900-1800 Mon-Fri, 0900-
1600 Sat-Sun end Mar-Oct.
Min Mail Order UK: Nmc
Min Mail Order EU: Nmc
Cat. Cost: £1.00
Credit Cards: Visa MasterCard
Specialities: Unusual herbaceous perennials,
shrubs, climbers & grasses.
Notes: Also sells wholesale.
Map Ref: G, C2

GTSp   THE TREE SHOP ✉ ♿ ◆
Ardkinglas Estate Nurseries Ltd., Cairndow,
Argyll, PA26 8BH
Ⓣ (01499) 600263
Ⓕ (01499) 600348
Ⓔ tree.shop@virgin.net
Ⓦ www.scottishtrees.co.uk
Contact: Glyn Toplis or Sally Hall
Opening Times: 0930-1730 Apr-Sep, 0930-
1630 Oct-Mar.
Min Mail Order UK: Nmc
Min Mail Order EU: Nmc
Cat. Cost: 2 x 1st class
Credit Cards: All major credit/debit cards
Specialities: Scottish native species grown
from local seed. Rare & unusual conifers.
Rhododendrons and an interesting range of
trees, shrubs & perennials. Many plants
available in small numbers only.
Map Ref: G, C2 OS Grid Ref: NN189127

GTwe   J TWEEDIE FRUIT TREES ✉
Maryfield Road Nursery, Nr Terregles,
Dumfriesshire, DG2 9TH
Ⓣ (01387) 720880

Contact: John Tweedie
Opening Times: Please ring for times.
Collections by appt.
Min Mail Order UK: Nmc
Cat. Cost: Sae
Credit Cards: None
Specialities: Fruit trees & bushes. A wide
range of old & new varieties.
Map Ref: G, D2

GUzu   UZUMARA ORCHIDS ✉ ✉ €
9 Port Henderson, Gairloch,
Ross-shire,
IV21 2AS
Ⓣ (01445) 741228
Ⓕ (01445) 741228
Ⓔ i.la_croix@virgin.net
Ⓦ www.uzumaraorchids.com
Contact: Mrs I F La Croix
Opening Times: Mail order only. Open by
appt only.
Min Mail Order UK: Nmc
Min Mail Order EU: Nmc
Cat. Cost: Sae
Credit Cards: None
Specialities: African & Madagascan orchids.

GWCH   WOODSIDE COTTAGE HERBS ✉
Woodside Cottage, Longriggend,
Airdrie, Lanarkshire,
ML6 7RU
Ⓣ (01236) 843826
Ⓕ (01236) 842545
Ⓔ mail@herbscents.co.uk
Ⓦ www.herbscents.co.uk
Contact: Brenda Brown
Opening Times: Mail order only. Open by
appt.only.
Min Mail Order UK: Minimum 10 plants.
Cat. Cost: 4 x 1st class
Credit Cards: Visa MasterCard Switch Solo
Specialities: Herbs, wild flowers & hardy
plants incl. shrubs, grasses & cottage garden
flowers.
Map Ref: G, C2 OS Grid Ref: NS824708

**GWWP   THE WEIRD AND WONDERFUL PLANT
CO.** ✉ 👤 € ♿
Fenton Barns, Drem, North Berwick,
East Lothian,
EH39 5BW
Ⓣ (01620) 850755
Ⓔ admin@weirdandwonderfulplant.co.uk
Ⓦ www.weirdandwonderfulplant.co.uk
Contact: Douglas Kerr
Opening Times: Beginning Mar-end Sep,
1100-1700 hours, 7 days. Year-round mail
order available via website.

G

Min Mail Order UK: Nmc.
Min Mail Order EU: Nmc.
Cat. Cost: 2 x 2nd class stamps
Credit Cards: All major credit/debit cards
Specialities: Rare and unusual hardy
perennials, especially 'black' flowered cultivars
and old-fashioned varieties.
Notes: Also sells wholesale.
Map Ref: G, C3 OS Grid Ref: NT512817

N. IRELAND & REPUBLIC

IArd   ARDCARNE GARDEN CENTRE € ⑤
Ardcarne, Boyle, Co. Roscommon, Ireland
Ⓣ 00 353 (0)7196 67091
Ⓕ 00 353 (0)7196 67341
Ⓔ ardcarne@indigo.ie
Ⓦ www.ardcarnegc.com
Contact: James Wickham, Mary Frances
Dwyer, Kirsty Ainge
Opening Times: 0900-1800 Mon-Sat, 1400-
1800 Sun & B/hols.
Credit Cards: Visa Access American Express
Specialities: Coastal plants, native & unusual
trees, specimen plants & semi-mature trees.
Wide general range.
Map Ref: I, B1

**IBal   BALI-HAI MAIL ORDER NURSERY ⊠ ⊠
€ ⑤**
42 Largy Road, Carnlough,
Ballymena, Co. Antrim, N. Ireland,
BT44 0EZ
Ⓣ 028 2888 5289
Ⓕ 028 2888 5976
Ⓔ ianwscroggy@btopenworld.com
Ⓦ www.balihainursery.com
Also sells wholesale
Contact: Mrs M E Scroggy
Opening Times: Mon-Sat by appt. only.
Min Mail Order UK: Nmc
Min Mail Order EU: Nmc
Cat. Cost: £3.00 cheque, made payable to
Mrs M.E. Scroggy.
Credit Cards: None
Specialities: *Hosta, Phormium, Rhodohypoxis* &
other perennials. Tree ferns.
Notes: Exports beyond EU restricted to bare
root perennials, no grasses.
Map Ref: I, A3

IBlr   BALLYROGAN NURSERIES ⊠ ⊠ € ⑤
The Grange, Ballyrogan, Newtownards, Co.
Down, N. Ireland, BT23 4SD
Ⓣ (028) 9181 0451 (evenings)
Ⓔ gary.dunlop@btinternet.com
Contact: Gary Dunlop
Opening Times: Only open by appt.

Min Mail Order UK: £10.00 + p&p
Min Mail Order EU: £20.00 + p&p
Cat. Cost: 2 x 1st class
Credit Cards: None
Specialities: Choice herbaceous. *Agapanthus,
Celmisia, Crocosmia, Euphorbia, Meconopsis,
Rodgersia, Iris, Dierama, Erythronium, Roscoea
& Phormium.*
Notes: Limited exports beyond EU. Also sells
wholesale.
Map Ref: I, B3

ICro   CROCKNAFEOLA NURSERY €
Killybegs, Co. Donegal, Ireland
Ⓣ 00 353 (0)74 97 51018
Ⓕ 00 353 (0)74 97 51095
Ⓔ crocknafeola@hotmail.com
Contact: Fionn McKenna
Opening Times: 0900-1800 Mon, Tue, Thu-
Sat, closed Wed. 1200-1800 Sun.
Cat. Cost: None issued
Credit Cards: None
Specialities: Bedding plants, herbaceous
perennials, rhododendrons, plants for
containers, roses, plus shrubs & hedging for
coastal areas.
Map Ref: I, D2

IDee   DEELISH GARDEN CENTRE ⊠ €
Skibbereen, Co. Cork, Ireland
Ⓣ 00 353 (0)28 21374
Ⓕ 00 353 (0)28 21374
Ⓔ deel@eircom.net
Ⓦ www.deelish.ie
Contact: Bill & Rain Chase
Opening Times: 1000-1300 & 1400-1800
Mon-Sat, 1400-1800 Sun.
Min Mail Order UK: 100 Euros + p&p
Min Mail Order EU: 100 Euros + p&p
Cat. Cost: Sae
Credit Cards: Visa Access
Specialities: Unusual plants for the mild
coastal climate of Ireland. Conservatory
plants. Sole Irish agents for Chase Organic
Seeds.
Map Ref: I, D1

IDic   DICKSON NURSERIES LTD ⊠ ⊠
Milecross Road, Newtownards, Co. Down,
N. Ireland, BT23 4SS
Ⓣ (028) 9181 2206
Ⓕ (028) 9181 3366
Ⓔ mail@dickson-roses.co.uk
Ⓦ www.dickson-roses.co.uk
Contact: Linda Stewart
Opening Times: 0800-1230 & 1300-1700
Mon-Thu. 0800-1230 Fri. Closes at 1600
Mon-Thu Dec-Jan.

Min Mail Order UK: One plant
Min Mail Order EU: £25.00 + p&p
Cat. Cost: Free
Credit Cards: None
Specialities: Roses esp. modern Dickson
varieties. Most in small quantities.
Notes: Also sells wholesale.
Map Ref: I, B3

IFoB   FIELD OF BLOOMS ⊠ €
Ballymackey, Lisnamoe,
Nenagh, Co. Tipperary,
Ireland
Ⓣ 00 353 (0)67 29974 (m.) 08764 06044
Ⓔ guy2002@eircom.ie
Ⓦ www.nenagh.net/main/fieldofblooms.htm
Contact: Guy de Schrijver
Opening Times: Strictly by appt.
Min Mail Order UK: Nmc
Min Mail Order EU: Nmc
Cat. Cost: Free
Credit Cards: None
Specialities: *Hellebores*, herbaceous, hardy
perennials, ornamental grasses.
Map Ref: 1, C2

IFro   FROGSWELL NURSERY €
Cloonconlon, Straide, Foxford, Co. Mayo,
Ireland
Ⓣ 00 353 (0)94 903 1420
Ⓕ 00 353 (0)94 903 1420
Ⓔ frogswell@utvinternet.com
Ⓦ www.frogswell.com
Contact: Jane Stanley
Opening Times: Please phone first. Garden
open by appt., group bookings welcome.
Cat. Cost: None issued.
Credit Cards: None
Specialities: A small nursery growing unusual
perennials & shrubs, many from seed,
specialising in woodland plants, often in small
quantities & propagated to order.
Map Ref: I, B1

IGor   GORTKELLY CASTLE NURSERY ⊠ €
Upperchurch, Thurles, Co. Tipperary,
Ireland
Ⓣ 00 353 (0)504 54441
Contact: Clare Beumer
Opening Times: Mail order only. Not open to
the public.
Min Mail Order UK: Nmc
Min Mail Order EU: Nmc
Cat. Cost: 5 x 1st class (UK), 5 x 48c (Rep. of
Ireland)
Credit Cards: None
Specialities: Choice perennials.
Map Ref: I, C2

IHMH   HUBERT MCHALE ⊠ €
Foghill, Carrowmore-Lacken, Ballina,
Co. Mayo, Ireland
Ⓣ 00 353 (0)96 34996
Ⓔ hubertmchale@eircom.net
Contact: Hubert McHale
Opening Times: Mail order only. Open by
appt. only.
Min Mail Order UK: Nmc
Min Mail Order EU: Nmc
Cat. Cost: 2 x IRCs
Credit Cards: None
Specialities: Perennial herbs, aquatics, foliage
& rockery plants.
Notes: Also sells wholesale.
Map Ref: I, B1

ILis   LISDOONAN HERBS ⊠ € 🖥
98 Belfast Road, Saintfield, Co. Down,
N. Ireland, BT24 7HF
Ⓣ (028) 9081 3624
Ⓔ b.pilcher@dial.pipex.com
Contact: Barbara Pilcher
Opening Times: Wed & Sat am. For other
times, please phone to check.
Min Mail Order UK: Nmc
Min Mail Order EU: Nmc
Cat. Cost: 2 x 1st class
Credit Cards: None
Specialities: Aromatics, herbs, kitchen garden
plants, period plants, some native species.
Freshly cut herbs & salads. Some stock
available in limited quanities only. All peat-free.
Map Ref: I, B3 OS Grid Ref: J390624

IMGH   M G H NURSERIES € 🖥
50 Tullyhenan Road, Banbridge, Co. Down,
N. Ireland, BT32 4EY
Ⓣ (028) 4062 2795
Contact: Miss M G Heslip
Opening Times: 1000-1800 Thu, Fri & Sat
& B/Hol Mons.
Cat. Cost: 3 x 1st class
Credit Cards: None
Specialities: Grafted conifers, holly, maples,
box, ornamental trees & flowering shrubs.
Map Ref: I, B3

IOrc   ORCHARDSTOWN NURSERIES ⊠ ⊠ € 🖥
4 Miles Out, Cork Road, Waterford, Ireland
Ⓣ 00 353 (0)513 84273
Ⓕ 00 353 (0)513 84422
Ⓔ info@orchardstown.com

I

Ⓦ www.orchardstown.com
Contact: Ron Dool
Opening Times: 0900-1800 Mon-Sat, 1400-1800 Sun.
Min Mail Order UK: Nmc
Min Mail Order EU: Nmc
Cat. Cost: None issued
Credit Cards: Visa MasterCard
Specialities: Unusual hardy plants incl. shrubs, shrub roses, trees, climbers, *Rhododendron* species & water plants.
Notes: Only some plants mail order.
Map Ref: I, D2

IPot   THE POTTING SHED ✉ ⋔ €
Bolinaspick, Camolin, Enniscorthy, Co. Wexford, Ireland
Ⓣ 00 353 (0)548 3629
Ⓕ 00 353 (0)548 3629
Ⓔ sricher@iol.ie
Ⓦ www.camolinpottingshed.com
Contact: Susan Carrick
Opening Times: 1100-1800 Wed-Sat, 1400-1800 Sun, 23rd Mar-25th Sep 2005. Other times by appt.
Min Mail Order UK: Nmc
Min Mail Order EU: Nmc
Cat. Cost: 3 x 1st class
Credit Cards: Visa MasterCard
Specialities: Herbaceous & ornamental grasses.
Map Ref: I, C3

IPPN   PERENNIAL PLANTS NURSERY ✉ ⋔ €
Nr Ballymaloe , Barnabrow, Midleton, Co. Cork, Ireland
Ⓣ 00 353 21 465 2122
Ⓕ 00 353 21 465 2122
Ⓔ perennialplants@eircom.net
Contact: Sandy McCarthy
Opening Times: Please ring for times.
Min Mail Order UK: Nmc
Min Mail Order EU: Nmc
Cat. Cost: None issued.
Credit Cards: None
Specialities: Many unusual herbaceous, ornamental grasses, tender perennials.
Map Ref: I, D2 OS Grid Ref: W9568

IPPs   PEONY PASSIONS ✉ €
The Old School House, Bracknagh, Rathangan, Co. Kildare, Ireland
Ⓣ 00 353 (0)502 29109
Ⓜ 00 353 (0)8724 48636
Ⓕ 00 353 (0)502 29109
Ⓔ Ciaran.flood@gmail.com
Ⓦ www.peonypassions.com
Contact: Ciaran Flood
Opening Times: Not open. Mail order only.

Min Mail Order UK: £20.00
Min Mail Order EU: £20.00
Cat. Cost: 2 x IRC
Credit Cards: None
Specialities: Chinese tree peonies. *Paeonia suffruticosa* hybrids. *Paeonia rockii* varieties.
Map Ref: I, C2

IRhd   RINGHADDY DAFFODILS ✉ ✉ €
Ringhaddy Road, Killinchy, Newtownards, Co. Down, N. Ireland, BT23 6TU
Ⓣ (028) 9754 1007
Ⓕ (028) 9754 2276
Ⓔ ringdaff@nireland.com
Contact: Nial Watson
Opening Times: Mail order only. Not open.
Min Mail Order UK: £20.00 + p&p
Min Mail Order EU: £50.00 + p&p
Cat. Cost: £2.50 redeemable on order.
Credit Cards: None
Specialities: New daffodil varieties for exhibitors and hybridisers. Small stock of some varieties.

ISea   SEAFORDE GARDENS ✉ ✉ € ⅃
Seaforde, Co. Down, N. Ireland, BT30 8PG
Ⓣ (028) 4481 1225
Ⓕ (028) 4481 1370
Ⓔ plants@seafordegardens.com
Ⓦ www.seafordegardens.com
Contact: P Forde
Opening Times: 1000-1700 Mon-Fri all year. 1000-1700 Sat & 1300-1800 Sun mid Feb-end Oct.
Min Mail Order UK: Nmc
Min Mail Order EU: Nmc
Cat. Cost: Free
Credit Cards: None
Specialities: Over 600 varieties of self-propagated trees & shrubs. Nat. Coll. of *Eucryphia*.
Notes: Also sells wholesale.
Map Ref: I, B3

ISsi   SEASIDE NURSERY ✉ € ⅃
Claddaghduff, Co. Galway, Ireland
Ⓣ 00 353 (0)95 44687
Ⓕ 00 353 (0)95 44761
Ⓔ seaside@anu.ie
Ⓦ www.anu.ie/seaside/
Contact: Tom Dyck
Opening Times: 1000-1300 & 1400-1800 Mon-Sat, 1400-1800 Sun. Closed Sun 1 Nov-31 Mar.
Min Mail Order UK: Nmc
Min Mail Order EU: Nmc
Cat. Cost: 3.50 euros
Credit Cards: Visa MasterCard

Specialities: Plants & hedging suitable for seaside locations. Rare plants originating from Australia & New Zealand esp. *Phormium, Astelia.*
Notes: Also sells wholesale
Map Ref: I, B1

ITer TERRA NOVA PLANTS ⊠ 🖷 €
Dromin, Kilmallock, Co. Limerick, Ireland
Ⓣ 00 353 (0)63 90744
Ⓔ terranovaplants@eircom.net
Ⓦ http://homepage.eircom.net/~terranovaplants
Contact: Deborah Begley
Opening Times: Garden & nursery open by appt.
Min Mail Order UK: Nmc
Min Mail Order EU: Nmc
Cat. Cost: 2 x IRC
Credit Cards: None
Specialities: Bulbous aroids, variegated plants, unusual plants grown from seed. Large seedlist in autumn. Most plants available in small quantities only.
Map Ref: I, C2

ITim TIMPANY NURSERIES & GARDENS ⊠ 🖷 🛊 🖳
77 Magheratimpany Road, Ballynahinch, Co. Down, N. Ireland, BT24 8PA
Ⓣ (028) 9756 2812
Ⓕ (028) 9756 2812
Ⓔ timpany@alpines.freeserve.co.uk
Ⓦ www.alpines.freeserve.co.uk
Contact: Susan Tindall
Opening Times: 1000-1730 Tue-Sat, Sun by appt. Closed Mon excl. B/hols.
Min Mail Order UK: Nmc
Min Mail Order EU: £30.00 + p&p
Cat. Cost: £1.50
Credit Cards: Visa MasterCard
Specialities: *Celmisia, Androsace, Primula, Saxifraga, Helichrysum, Dianthus, Meconopsis, Primula auricula* & *Cassiope.*
Notes: Also sells wholesale.
Map Ref: I, B3

LONDON AREA

LAst ASTERBY & CHALKCROFT NURSERIES 🖳
The Ridgeway, Blunham, Bedfordshire, MK44 3PH
Ⓣ (01767) 640148
Ⓕ (01767) 640667
Ⓔ sales@asterbyplants.co.uk
Ⓦ www.asterbyplants.co.uk
Contact: Simon & Eva Aldridge
Opening Times: 1000-1700 7 days. Closed Xmas & Jan.

Cat. Cost: 2 x 1st class
Credit Cards: Visa MasterCard Switch
Specialities: Hardy shrubs & herbaceous. *Clematis* & trees.
Map Ref: L, A3 **OS Grid Ref:** TL151497

LAyl AYLETT NURSERIES LTD 🖳
North Orbital Road,
London Colney, St Albans,
Hertfordshire, AL2 1DH
Ⓣ (01727) 822255
Ⓕ (01727) 823024
Ⓔ info@aylettnurseries.co.uk
Ⓦ www.aylettnurseries.co.uk
Contact: Roger S Aylett
Opening Times: 0830-1730 Mon-Fri, 0830-1700 Sat, 1030-1630 Sun.
Cat. Cost: Free
Credit Cards: All major credit/debit cards
Specialities: *Dahlia.*
Notes: Trial grounds at Bowmans Farm nr Jct. 22 M25. At MacDonalds roundabout take B556 to Colney Heath on left hand side 500m. Also sells wholesale.
Map Ref: L, B3 **OS Grid Ref:** TL169049

LBBr BELL BAR NURSERY 🛊 🖳
Bulls Lane, Bell Bar, Nr Hatfield,
Hertfordshire, AL9 7BB
Ⓣ (01707) 650007
Ⓕ (01707) 650008
Ⓔ swener@globalnet.co.uk
Ⓦ www.bellbarnursery.co.uk
Contact: S Wener
Opening Times: 0900-1630 Fri & Sat Mar-Nov. 1000-1600 Sun, Mar-Oct. Other times by appt.
Cat. Cost: None issued.
Credit Cards: None
Specialities: Hardy perennials, grasses, bulbs, ferns & bamboos. *Euphorbia, Geranium, Carex, Miscanthus,* & *Penstemon.*
Notes: Also sells wholesale.
Map Ref: L, B4 **OS Grid Ref:** TL243053

LBee BEECHCROFT NURSERY 🖳
127 Reigate Road, Ewell, Surrey, KT17 3DE
Ⓣ (020) 8393 4265
Ⓕ (020) 8393 4265
Contact: C Kimber
Opening Times: 1000-1600 Mon-Sat, 1000-1400 Sun and B/hols. Closed Xmas-New Year week.
Cat. Cost: None issued
Credit Cards: All major credit/debit cards
Specialities: Conifers & alpines.
Map Ref: L, C3

L

LBmB   BLOMS BULBS ⊠ ⊠ €
Primrose Nurseries, Melchbourne, Bedford,
MK44 1ZZ
Ⓣ (01234) 709099
Ⓕ (01234) 709799
Ⓔ chrisblom@blomsbulbs.com
Ⓦ www.blomsbulbs.com
Contact: R J M Blom
Opening Times: Mail order only. Nursery not
open to the public. 0900-1700 for phone
enquiries or to collect orders.
Min Mail Order UK: Nmc
Min Mail Order EU: Nmc
Cat. Cost: Free
Credit Cards: Visa MasterCard Switch
Specialities: Spring & summer flowering
bulbs, hardy border plants.
Notes: Exports bulbs only worldwide.

LBMP   BLOOMING MARVELLOUS PLANTS ⑤
Korketts Farm, Aylesbury Road, Shipton,
Winslow, Buckinghamshire, MK18 3JL
Ⓜ 07963 747305
Ⓔ alexballance@yahoo.co.uk
Ⓦ www.bmplants.co.uk
Contact: Alex Ballance
Opening Times: 1000-1900 Thu, 1000-1700
Fri-Mon (closed Tue & Wed).
Credit Cards: All major credit/debit cards
Specialities: A mixture of unusual and familiar
perennials. Some shrubs & grasses.
Notes: Located on the A413 just outside
Winslow on the Aylesbury side.
Map Ref: L, A2 OS Grid Ref: SP777271

LBow   RUPERT BOWLBY, THE BULB NURSERY ⊠
Gatton Park, Reigate, Surrey, RH2 0TA
Ⓣ (01737) 642221
Ⓔ Rupert.Bowlby@care4free.net
Ⓦ www.rupert.bowlby.care4free.net
Contact: Rupert Bowlby
Opening Times: By appt. only.
Min Mail Order UK: Nmc
Min Mail Order EU: Nmc
Cat. Cost: 2 x 2nd class
Credit Cards: None
Specialities: South African bulbs & corms.
Some in small quantities.
Map Ref: L, C4

LBuc   BUCKINGHAM NURSERIES ⊠ ⊠ € ⑤ ◆
14 Tingewick Road, Buckingham,
MK18 4AE
Ⓣ (01280) 822133
Ⓕ (01280) 815491
Ⓔ enquiries@buckingham-nurseries.co.uk
Ⓦ www.buckingham-nurseries.co.uk
Contact: R J & P L Brown

Opening Times: 0830-1730 (1800 in
summer) Mon-Fri, 1000-1600 Sun. 0900-
1800 Sat (0900-1900 in summer).
Min Mail Order UK: Nmc
Min Mail Order EU: Nmc
Cat. Cost: Free
Credit Cards: Visa MasterCard Switch
Specialities: Bare rooted and container grown
hedging. Trees, shrubs, herbaceous perennials,
alpines, grasses & ferns.
Map Ref: L, A2 OS Grid Ref: SP675333

**LBut   YAFFLES (FOMERLY BUTTERFIELDS
NURSERY)** ⊠ ⑤
Harvest Hill, Bourne End,
Buckinghamshire,
SL8 5JJ
Ⓣ (01628) 525455
Contact: I Butterfield
Opening Times: 0900-1300 & 1400-1700.
Please phone beforehand in case we are
attending shows.
Min Mail Order UK: Nmc
Min Mail Order EU: £30.00 + p&p
Cat. Cost: 2 x 2nd class
Credit Cards: None
Specialities: Nat. Coll. of *Pleione. Dahlia* for
collection. Scientific Award 1999.
Notes: Only *Pleione* by mail order. Also sells
wholesale.
Map Ref: L, B3

LChw   CHADWELL SEEDS ⊠ ⊠ €
81 Parlaunt Road, Slough, Buckinghamshire,
SL3 8BE
Ⓣ (01753) 542823
Ⓕ (01753) 542823
Contact: Chris Chadwell
Opening Times: Not open. Mail order only.
Min Mail Order UK: Nmc
Min Mail Order EU: Nmc
Cat. Cost: 3 x 2nd class
Credit Cards: None
Specialities: Seed collecting expedition to the
Himalayas. Separate general seed list of
Japanese, N. American & Himalayan plants.

LCla   CLAY LANE NURSERY ⊠ ⋔
3 Clay Lane, South Nutfield, Nr Redhill,
Surrey, RH1 4EG
Ⓣ (01737) 823307
Ⓔ claylane.nursery@btinternet.com
Contact: K W Belton
Opening Times: 1000-1700 Tue-Sun 1st Feb-
30th Jun. Other times by appt. Please phone
before travelling.
Min Mail Order UK: £9.00
Cat. Cost: 4 x 2nd class

Credit Cards: None
Specialities: *Fuchsia*. Many in small quantities.
Notes: Mail order by telephone pre-arangement only.
Map Ref: L, C4

LCon   THE CONIFER GARDEN ⊠ ♉
Herons Mead, Little Missenden, Amersham,
Buckinghamshire, HP7 0RA
ⓣ (01494) 862086 (0900-1800 hrs)
ⓕ (01494) 862086
ⓔ sales@conifergarden.co.uk
ⓦ www.conifergarden.co.uk
Contact: Mr & Mrs M P S Powell
Opening Times: Open by appt. only.
Min Mail Order UK: Nmc
Cat. Cost: 2 x 1st class for list only
Credit Cards: None
Specialities: Conifers only, over 400 varieties
always available.
Notes: Mail order to UK only, by overnight
carrier.
Map Ref: L, B3

LCtg   COTTAGE GARDEN NURSERY ◆
Barnet Road, Arkley, Barnet, Hertfordshire,
EN5 3JX
ⓣ (020) 8441 8829
ⓕ (020) 8531 3178
ⓔ nurseryinfo@cottagegardennursery-
barnet.co.uk
ⓦ www.cottagegardennursery-barnet.co.uk
Contact: David and Wendy Spicer
Opening Times: 0930-1700 Tue-Sat Mar-
Oct, 0930-1600 Tue-Sat Nov-Feb, 1000-1600
Sun & B/hol Mon all year.
Cat. Cost: None issued.
Credit Cards: All major credit/debit cards
Specialities: General range of hardy shrubs,
trees & perennials. Architectural & exotics,
Fuchsia, seasonal bedding, patio plants.
Map Ref: L, B3 OS Grid Ref: TQ226958

LDai   DAISY ROOTS ⊠ ♉
(office) 8 Gosselin Road, Bengeo, Hertford,
Hertfordshire, SG14 3LG
ⓣ (01992) 582401
ⓕ (01992) 582401
ⓔ anne@daisyroots.com
ⓦ www.daisyroots.com
Contact: Anne Godfrey
Opening Times: 0900-1700 Fri only Mar-
Oct, or by appt.
Min Mail Order UK: Nmc
Cat. Cost: 4 x 1st class
Credit Cards: None
Specialities: Ever-increasing range of choice
& unusual perennials, particularly *Agastache*,

*Anthemis, Centaurea, Digitalis, Erysimum,
Salvia* & *Sedum*.
Notes: Nursery is at Jenningsbury, London
Road, Hertford Heath.
Map Ref: L, B4

LDea   DEREK LLOYD DEAN ⊠ ⊠ ♉
8 Lynwood Close,
South Harrow, Middlesex,
HA2 9PR
ⓣ (020) 8864 0899
ⓔ lloyddeancbtinternet.com
ⓦ www.dereklloyddean.com
Contact: Derek Lloyd Dean
Opening Times: Not open. Mail order only.
Min Mail Order UK: £2.50 + p&p
Min Mail Order EU: £2.50 + p&p
Cat. Cost: 2 x 1st class
Credit Cards: None
Specialities: Regal, angel, ivy & scented leaf
Pelargonium. Nat. Coll. of Angel *Pelargonium*.

LEar   EARLSTONE NURSERY ⊠
Earlstone Manor Farm, Burghclere, Newbury,
Berkshire, RG20 9NG
ⓣ (01635) 278648
ⓕ (01635) 278672
ⓔ earlstonenursery@wistbray.com
ⓦ www.earlstoneboxandtopiary.co.uk
Contact: B C Ginsberg or G MacPherson
Opening Times: By appt.
Min Mail Order UK: £30.00 + p&p
Cat. Cost: Free
Credit Cards: None
Specialities: Some varieties of *Buxus*. *Buxus
sempervirens* topiary. Large orders of *Taxus* &
Ilex can be sourced.
Notes: Also sells wholesale.

LEdu   EDULIS ⊠ ♉ € ⓖ
(office) 1 Flowers Piece, Ashampstead,
Berkshire, RG8 8SG
ⓣ (01635) 578113
ⓕ (01635) 578113
ⓔ edulis.nursery@virgin.net
ⓦ www.edulis.co.uk
Contact: Paul Barney
Opening Times: By appt. only.
Min Mail Order UK: £10.00 + p&p
Min Mail Order EU: £50.00 + p&p
Cat. Cost: 6 x 1st class
Credit Cards: None
Specialities: Unusual edibles, architectural
plants, permaculture plants.
Notes: Nursery is at Bere Court Farm,
Tidmarsh Lane, Pangbourne, RG8 8HT. Also
sells wholesale
Map Ref: L, B2

L

L

LFol FOLIAGE SCENTED & HERB PLANTS
🔨🖐️
Walton Poor, Crocknorth Road, Ranmore
Common, Dorking, Surrey, RH5 6SX
Ⓣ (01483) 282273
Ⓕ (01483) 282273
Contact: Mrs Prudence Calvert
Opening Times: Open during Apr-Sep, please
phone for appt. if possible.
Cat. Cost: 3 x 2nd class
Credit Cards: None
Specialities: Herbs, aromatic & scented plants.
Map Ref: L, C3

LFox FOXGROVE PLANTS ✉ 🔨🖐️
Foxgrove, Enborne, Nr Newbury, Berkshire,
RG14 6RE
Ⓣ (01635) 40554
Ⓕ (01635) 30555
Contact: Mrs Louise Peters
Opening Times: 1000-1300 & 1400-1600
Thu, Fri, Sat, mid-Jan to end-Oct. Other
times by appt. only.
Min Mail Order UK: Nmc
Min Mail Order EU: Nmc
Cat. Cost: £1.00
Credit Cards: None
Specialities: Hardy & unusual plants, incl.
Galanthus, hellebores, grasses, *Penstemon*,
alpines.
Notes: Mail order for *Galanthus* only.
Map Ref: L, C2

LGod GODLY'S ROSES ✉ 🖐️
Redbourn, St Albans, Hertfordshire,
AL3 7PS
Ⓣ (01582) 792255
Ⓕ (01582) 794267
Contact: Colin Godly
Opening Times: 0900-1700 summer, 7 days.
0900-dusk winter, 7 days. Closed Xmas &
New Year's Day.
Min Mail Order UK: Nmc
Cat. Cost: Free
Credit Cards: Visa American Express Switch
MasterCard
Specialities: Roses.
Notes: Standard roses not sent mail order.
Also sells wholesale.
Map Ref: L, B3 **OS Grid Ref:** TL096137

LHop HOPLEYS PLANTS LTD ✉ 🔨🖐️ ◆
High Street, Much Hadham, Hertfordshire,
SG10 6BU
Ⓣ (01279) 842509
Ⓕ (01279) 843784
Ⓔ sales@hopleys.co.uk
Ⓦ www.hopleys.co.uk

Contact: Aubrey Barker
Opening Times: 0900-1700 Mon & Wed-Sat,
1400-1700 Sun. Closed Nov-Feb except by
appt.
Min Mail Order UK: Nmc
Cat. Cost: 5 x 1st class
Credit Cards: Visa Access Switch
Specialities: Wide range of hardy & half-
hardy shrubs & perennials.
Notes: £2.00 charge for delivery to shows.
Also sells wholesale.
Map Ref: L, A4 **OS Grid Ref:** TL428196

LHyd HYDON NURSERIES ✉ € ◆
Clock Barn Lane, Hydon Heath, Godalming,
Surrey, GU8 4AZ
Ⓣ (01483) 860252
Ⓕ (01483) 419937
Contact: A F George, Rodney Longhurst &
Mrs A M George
Opening Times: 0930-1700 Mon-Sat (closed
for lunch 12.45-1400), Feb-mid Jun & Oct-
mid Nov. Other months 0930-1600 Mon-Fri,
0930-1300 Sat. Sun by appt.
Min Mail Order UK: Nmc
Min Mail Order EU: £25.00 + p&p
Cat. Cost: £2.00 or 7 x 1st class or 10 x 2nd
class
Credit Cards: None
Specialities: Large and dwarf *Rhododendron*,
yakushimanum hybrids, azaleas (deciduous &
evergreen), *Camellia* & other trees & shrubs.
Specimen rhododendrons. Conservatory:
scented tender rhododendrons & winter-
flowering camellias.
Notes: Also sells wholesale.
Map Ref: L, C3

LIck LOWER ICKNIELD FARM NURSERIES 🖐️
Lower Icknield Way, Great Kimble, Aylesbury,
Buckinghamshire, HP17 9TX
Ⓣ (01844) 343436 (m.) 0780 3979993
Ⓕ (01844) 343436
Contact: S Baldwin, D Baldwin
Opening Times: 0900-1700 7 days excl.
Xmas-New Year.
Credit Cards: None
Specialities: Patio & basket plants. Tender &
hardy perennials. Salvias. Grasses.
Argyranthemum.
Map Ref: L, B3 **OS Grid Ref:** SP814058

LKna KNAP HILL & SLOCOCK NURSERIES
✉ ☑ 🖐️
Barrs Lane, Knaphill, Woking, Surrey, GU21
2JW
Ⓣ (01483) 481214/5
Ⓕ (01483) 797261

Ⓦ www.knaphillrhododendrons.co.uk
Contact: Mrs Joy West
Opening Times: 0900-1700 Mon-Fri by appt. only.
Min Mail Order UK: Nmc
Min Mail Order EU: Nmc
Cat. Cost: 3 x 1st class
Credit Cards: Visa Access MasterCard
Specialities: Wide variety of rhododendrons & azaleas.
Notes: Also sells wholesale.
Map Ref: L, C3

LLin LINCLUDEN NURSERY ⊠ ⊠ ⋔ € ♿
Shaftesbury Road, Bisley Green, Bisley, Woking, Surrey, GU24 9EN
Ⓣ (01483) 797005
Ⓕ (01483) 474015
Ⓔ sales@lincludennursery.co.uk
Ⓦ www.lincludennursery.co.uk
Contact: Mr & Mrs K Hayward
Opening Times: 0930-1630 Tue-Sat all year excl. B/hols. Closed Chelsea week & Xmas.
Min Mail Order UK: Nmc
Min Mail Order EU: Nmc
Cat. Cost: 3 x 1st class
Credit Cards: Visa MasterCard Solo Switch
Specialities: Dwarf, slow-growing & unusual conifers.
Notes: Also sells wholesale.
Map Ref: L, C3 OS Grid Ref: SU947596

LLWP L W PLANTS ⊠ ⋔
23 Wroxham Way, Harpenden, Hertfordshire, AL5 4PP
Ⓣ (01582) 768467
Ⓔ lwplants@waitrose.com
Ⓦ www.thymus.co.uk
Contact: Mrs M Easter
Opening Times: 1000-1700 most days, but please phone first.
Min Mail Order UK: £15.00 + p&p
Cat. Cost: A5 Sae + 5 x 2nd class (loose)
Credit Cards: None
Specialities: Plants from a plantsman's garden, esp. *Geranium*, grasses, *Penstemon* & *Thymus*. Nat. Colls. of *Thymus* (Scientific), *Hyssopus* & *Satureja*.
Notes: Mail order late Sep-Apr, *Thymus* all year round & no minimum charge.
Map Ref: L, B3 OS Grid Ref: TL141153

LMil MILLAIS NURSERIES ⊠ ♿
Crosswater Lane, Churt, Farnham, Surrey, GU10 2JN
Ⓣ (01252) 792698
Ⓕ (01252) 792526
Ⓔ sales@rhododendrons.co.uk

Ⓦ www.rhododendrons.co.uk
Contact: David Millais
Opening Times: 1000-1300 & 1400-1700 Mon-Fri. Sat spring & autumn. Daily in May and early Jun.
Min Mail Order UK: £30.00 + p&p
Min Mail Order EU: £60.00 + p&p
Cat. Cost: 4 x 1st class
Credit Cards: Visa Switch Delta MasterCard
Specialities: Rhododendrons, azaleas, magnolias & acers.
Notes: Mail order Oct-Mar only. Also sells wholesale.
Map Ref: L, C3 OS Grid Ref: SU856397

LMor MOREHAVENS ⊠ ♿
Sandpit Hill, Buckland Common, Tring, Hertfordshire, HP23 6NG
Ⓣ (01494) 758642
Ⓦ www.camomilelawns.co.uk
Contact: B Farmer
Opening Times: Mail order only. Open only for collection.
Min Mail Order UK: £14.95
Min Mail Order EU: £64.95
Cat. Cost: Free
Credit Cards: None
Specialities: *Camomile* 'Treneague'.
Notes: Also sells wholesale.
Map Ref: L, B3

LNCo NATURE'S CORNERS ⊠
11 Bunyan Close, Pirton, Nr. Hitchin, Hertfordshire, SG5 3RE
Ⓣ (01462) 712519
Ⓔ DouglasCrawley@Naturescorners.co.uk
Ⓦ www.Naturescorners.co.uk
Contact: Douglas Crawley
Opening Times: Not open. Mail order only.
Min Mail Order UK: Nmc
Cat. Cost: 1 x 1st class
Credit Cards: None
Specialities: *Nymphaea*.

LPal THE PALM CENTRE ⊠ ⊠ € ♿
Ham Central Nursery, opposite Riverside Drive, Ham Street, Ham, Richmond, Surrey, TW10 7HA
Ⓣ (020) 8255 6191
Ⓕ (020) 8255 6192
Ⓔ mail@thepalmcentre.co.uk
Ⓦ www.thepalmcentre.co.uk

L

Contact: Martin Gibbons
Opening Times: 0900-1700 (dusk in winter)
7 days. Admin & Order Dept. 0900-1700
Mon-Fri.
Min Mail Order UK: £10.00 + p&p
Min Mail Order EU: £10.00 + p&p
Cat. Cost: Free
Credit Cards: Visa MasterCard Switch
Specialities: Palms & cycads, exotic & sub-tropical, hardy, half-hardy & tropical.
Seedlings to mature trees. Also bamboo, tree
ferns & other exotics.
Notes: Also sells wholesale
Map Ref: L, B3

LPan   PANTILES PLANT & GARDEN CENTRE
⊠ ⊠ ⋔ ⊠ ◆
Almners Road, Lyne,
Chertsey, Surrey,
KT16 0BJ
Ⓣ (01932) 872195
Ⓕ (01932) 874030
Ⓔ sales@pantiles-nurseries.co.uk
Ⓦ www.pantiles-nurseries.co.uk
Contact: Brendan Gallagher
Opening Times: 0900-1800 Mon-Sat, 1100-1700 Sun summer. 0900-1700 Mon-Sat,
1000-1600 Sun winter.
Min Mail Order UK: £100.00 + p&p
Min Mail Order EU: £100.00 + p&p
Cat. Cost: Free
Credit Cards: Visa Switch MasterCard
Specialities: Large trees, shrubs, conifers &
climbers in containers. Australasian & other
unusual plants. Selection of tree ferns from
New Zealand & Australia.
Notes: Also sells wholesale.
Map Ref: L, C3 **OS Grid Ref:** TQ0166

LPBA   PAUL BROMFIELD – AQUATICS ⊠ ⊠ € ⊠
Maydencroft Lane, Gosmore,
Hitchin, Hertfordshire,
SG4 7QD
Ⓣ (01462) 457399 (m.) 07801 656848
Ⓔ info@bromfieldaquatics.co.uk
Ⓦ www.bromfieldaquatics.co.uk
Contact: P. Bromfield
Opening Times: Mail order only. Order
online at website. 1000-1700 Mon-Sat Feb-Oct, please ring first.
Min Mail Order UK: £15.00 incl.
Min Mail Order EU: £100.00 incl.
Cat. Cost: Available Online only.
Credit Cards: Visa MasterCard Delta JCB
Switch
Specialities: Water lilies, marginals & bog.
Notes: Also sells wholesale.
Map Ref: L, A3

LPen   PENSTEMONS BY COLOUR
Peterley Manor, Peterley, Prestwood,
Great Missenden, Buckinghamshire,
HP16 0HH
Ⓣ (01494) 866420
Ⓕ (01494) 866420
Ⓔ debra.hughes1@virgin.net
Contact: Debra Hughes
Opening Times: Any time by appt.
Cat. Cost: Free
Credit Cards: None
Specialities: *Penstemon*.
Map Ref: L, B3

LPhx   PHOENIX PERENNIAL PLANTS ⋔ € ⊠
Paice Lane, Medstead, Alton, Hampshire,
GU34 5PR
Ⓣ (01420) 560695
Ⓕ (01420) 563640
Ⓔ GreenFarmPlants.Marina.Christopher@
Care4free.net
Contact: Marina Christopher
Opening Times: 1000-1800 Thu-Sat, 24th
Mar-22nd Oct 2005. Also 1000-1600, 10th &
11th Feb 2006, 24th & 25th Feb 2006.
Cat. Cost: 4 x 1st class
Credit Cards: All major credit/debit cards
Specialities: Perennials, many uncommon.
*Sanguisorba, Thalictrum, Achillea, Eryngium,
Monarda, Phlox, Verbascum,* centaureas, bulbs
& grasses.
Map Ref: L, C2 **OS Grid Ref:** SU657362

LPJP   PJ'S PALMS AND EXOTICS ⊠ €
41 Salcombe Road, Ashford, Middlesex,
TW15 3BS
Ⓣ (01784) 250181
Contact: Peter Jenkins
Opening Times: Mail order only 1st Mar-30th Nov. Visits by arrangement.
Min Mail Order UK: Nmc
Min Mail Order EU: Nmc
Cat. Cost: 2 x 1st class
Credit Cards: None
Specialities: Palms, bananas & other exotic
foliage plants, hardy & half-hardy.
Trachycarpus wagnerianus seeds available.
Plants available in small quantities.
Notes: Also sells wholesale.
Map Ref: L, B3

LRav   RAVEN VALLEY PLANT NURSERY
Mayfields, Whitmore Lane, Woking, Surrey,
GU4 7QB
Ⓣ (01483) 234605 (m.) 07887 925945
Ⓔ ravenvalley@aol.com
Ⓦ www.plantexperience.co.uk
Contact: Maria & Terry Milton

Opening Times: 1100-1500 Mon, Thu & Fri. 1000-1600 (1700 in summer) Sat, Sun & B/hols. Closed Jan & Feb.
Cat. Cost: On floppy disc only. Sae.
Credit Cards: None
Specialities: *Eucalyptus*, grasses, chillis, exotic hedging.
Notes: Also sells wholesale.
Map Ref: L, C3 OS Grid Ref: SU997544

LRHS   WISLEY PLANT CENTRE (RHS) ⬛ ◆
RHS Garden, Wisley, Woking, Surrey, GU23 6QB
Ⓣ (01483) 211113
Ⓕ (01483) 212372
Ⓔ wisleyplantcentre@rhs.org.uk
Ⓦ www.rhs.org.uk/rhsplantfinder
Opening Times: 1000-1800 Mon-Sat 1100-1700 Sun summer, 1000-1730 Mon-Sat 1000-1600 Sun winter. Closed 25-26 Dec & Easter Sun.
Cat. Cost: None issued
Credit Cards: All major credit/debit cards
Specialities: Very wide range, many rare & unusual.
Map Ref: L, C3

LSee   SEEDS BY SIZE ⊠ ☒ €
45 Crouchfield, Boxmoor, Hemel Hempstead, Hertfordshire, HP1 1PA
Ⓣ (01442) 251458
Ⓔ john-robert-size@seeds-by-size.co.uk
Ⓦ www.seeds-by-size.co.uk
Contact: John Robert Size
Opening Times: Not open, mail order only.
Min Mail Order UK: Nmc
Min Mail Order EU: Nmc
Cat. Cost: Online only.
Credit Cards: None
Specialities: Flowers & vegetables. 1,400 varieties of vegetable, (175 cabbage, 99 cauliflower, 70 onion, 100 tomatoes) & 6,000 flowers such as 400 varieties of sweet pea, 100 herbs.
Notes: Cash only euro payments. Also sells wholesale.

LSiH   SINO-HIMALAYAN PLANT ASSOCIATION ⊠
81 Parlaunt Road, Slough, Buckinghamshire, SL3 8BE
Ⓣ (01753) 542823
Ⓕ (01753) 542823
Contact: Chris Chadwell
Opening Times: Mail order seed exchange only.
Min Mail Order UK: Nmc
Cat. Cost: None issued
Notes: Seed available for exchange to members. Please apply for membership.

LSou   SOUTHON PLANTS ⊠ ⬛ ◆
Mutton Hill, Dormansland, Lingfield, Surrey, RH7 6NP
Ⓣ (01342) 870150
Ⓔ info@southonplants.com
Contact: Mr Southon
Opening Times: 0900-1700 Mar-Oct, closed Wed in Nov. Dec & Jan please phone first.
Min Mail Order UK: Nmc
Cat. Cost: £2.00 or free on website.
Credit Cards: All major credit/debit cards
Specialities: New & unusual hardy & tender perennials. Also hardy ferns, alpines, grasses, shrubs & climbers incl. many variegated plants.
Notes: Mail order. Please phone/email for details.
Map Ref: L, C4

LSRN   SPRING REACH NURSERY ⊠ ♁ ◆
Long Reach, Ockham, Guildford, Surrey, GU23 6PG
Ⓣ (01483) 284769
Ⓜ 07884 432666
Ⓕ (01483) 284769
Ⓔ n.hourhan@btopenworld.com
Contact: Nick Hourhan
Opening Times: 7 days. Mon-Sat 1000-1700, Sun 1030-1630. Closed Wed 1st Jul-1st Feb.
Min Mail Order UK: £25.00
Cat. Cost: 2 x 1st class
Credit Cards: All major credit/debit cards
Specialities: Shrubs, grasses, bamboos, climbers, perennials, trees & *Clematis*.
Notes: Not a mail order specialist but will do occasional orders by post. Nursery partially accessible for wheelchair users. Also sells wholesale.
Map Ref: L, C3

LSss   SELECT SEEDS ⊠ ♁ € ⬛
Paice Lane, Medstead, Nr. Alton, Hampshire, GU34 5PR
Ⓣ (01420) 560695
Ⓕ (01420) 563640
Ⓔ GreenFarmPlants.Marina.Christopher@Care4free.net
Contact: Marina Christopher
Opening Times: Not open. Mail order only.
Min Mail Order UK: £10.00

Cat. Cost: 3 x 1st class
Credit Cards: All major credit/debit cards
Specialities: Seeds. *Aconitum, Eryngium, Thalictrum, Sanguisorba* & *Angelica*.
Map Ref: L, C2 OS Grid Ref: SU657362

LStr   HENRY STREET NURSERY ☒ ⓖ
Swallowfield Road, Arborfield, Reading, Berkshire, RG2 9JY
ⓣ (0118) 9761223
ⓕ (0118) 9761417
ⓔ info@henrystreet.co.uk
ⓦ www.henrystreet.co.uk
Contact: Mr M C Goold
Opening Times: 0900-1730 Mon-Sat, 1030-1630 Sun.
Min Mail Order UK: Nmc
Min Mail Order EU: Nmc
Cat. Cost: Free
Credit Cards: Visa Access Switch
Specialities: Roses.
Notes: Also sells wholesale.
Map Ref: L, C3

LToo   TOOBEES EXOTICS ☒ ☒ €
(Office) 20 Inglewood, St Johns, Woking, Surrey, GU21 3HX
ⓣ (01483) 722600
ⓕ (01483) 751995
ⓔ bbpotter@woking.plus.com
ⓦ www.toobees-exotics.com
Contact: Bob Potter
Opening Times: Not open. Mail order only.
Min Mail Order UK: Nmc
Min Mail Order EU: Nmc
Cat. Cost: Sae
Specialities: South African & Madagascan succulents, many rare & unusual species, plus air plants, *Euphorbia* & *Pachypodium*.
Map Ref: L, C3

LTwo   TWO JAYS ALPINES
(Office) 35 Greenways, Luton, Bedfordshire, LU2 8BL
ⓣ (01442) 864951
ⓕ (01442) 864951
ⓔ john.spokes@talk21.com
Contact: John Spokes
Opening Times: 1000-1700 or dusk if earlier, 7 days.
Cat. Cost: 3 x 2nd class
Credit Cards: Visa MasterCard
Specialities: Large range of alpines, herbaceous, shrubs, many available in small quantities only.
Notes: Nursery is at Little Heath Farm, Little Heath Lane, Potten End, Berkhamstead.
Map Ref: L, A3

LVER   THE VERNON GERANIUM NURSERY ☒ ⓖ
Cuddington Way, Cheam, Sutton, Surrey, SM2 7JB
ⓣ (020) 8393 7616
ⓕ (020) 8786 7437
ⓔ mrgeranium@aol.com
ⓦ www.geraniumsuk.com
Contact: Philip James & Liz Sims
Opening Times: 0930-1730 Mon-Sat, 1000-1600 Sun, 1st Mar-30th Jun.
Min Mail Order UK: Nmc
Min Mail Order EU: Nmc
Cat. Cost: £2.00 UK, £2.50 EU.
Credit Cards: All major credit/debit cards
Specialities: *Pelargonium* & *Fuchsia*.
Map Ref: L, C4

MIDLANDS

MACG   ASHDALE COTTAGE GARDEN PLANTS ⓖ
204 Lambley Lane, Gedling, Nottinghamshire, NG4 4PB
ⓣ (0115) 966 6060
ⓕ (0115) 966 6060
Contact: Stephen Mills
Opening Times: 0900-1700 Wed-Sun, Mar-Oct. Closed Nov-Feb.
Cat. Cost: None issued.
Credit Cards: All major credit/debit cards
Specialities: Wide range of rare and unusual herbaceous perennials.
Map Ref: M, B3

MAga   AGAVE NURSERY ☒ ☒ €
15 Sleetmoor Lane, Somercotes, Derbyshire, DE55 1RB
ⓜ 01773 605843
ⓔ jon@jdudek.freeserve.co.uk
ⓦ www.agavenursery
Contact: Jon & Sue Dudek
Opening Times: Mail order only. Open by appt. only.
Min Mail Order UK: Nmc
Min Mail Order EU: Nmc
Cat. Cost: Free
Credit Cards: None
Specialities: *Agave, Furcraea, Manfreda* & *Yucca*.

MAJR   A J ROBINSON ☒
Sycamore Farm, Foston, Derbyshire, DE65 5PW
ⓣ (01283) 815635:(01283) 815635
ⓕ (01283) 815635
Contact: A J Robinson
Opening Times: By appt. for collection of plants only.

M

Min Mail Order UK: £12.50
Cat. Cost: 2 x 1st class for list.
Credit Cards: None
Specialities: Extensive collection of tender perennials. Salvias. Nat. Coll. of *Argyranthemum.*
Notes: Mail order argyranthemums & heliotrope only.
Map Ref: M, B2

MAln   L A ALLEN ⊠
178 Hill Village Road, Four Oaks, Sutton Coldfield, W Midlands, B75 5JG
Ⓣ (0121) 308 0697
Ⓦ www.fidalgo.freeserve.co.uk
Contact: L A Allen
Opening Times: By prior appt.
Min Mail Order UK: Nmc
Min Mail Order EU: Nmc
Cat. Cost: 4 x 1st class
Credit Cards: None
Specialities: Nat. Coll. of *Primula auricula.* Alpine auricula, show edged, show self, doubles, stripes. Surplus plants from the Collection so available in small quantities.
Notes: Also sells wholesale.

MArl   ARLEY HALL NURSERY ⑤
Arley Hall Nursery, Northwich, Cheshire, CW9 6NA
Ⓣ (01565) 777479/777231
Ⓕ (01565) 777465
Contact: Jane Foster
Opening Times: 1100-1730 Tue-Sun Easter-end Sep. Also B/hol Mons.
Cat. Cost: 4 x 1st class
Credit Cards: All major credit/debit cards
Specialities: Wide range of herbaceous incl. many unusual varieties. Wide range of pelargoniums.
Map Ref: M, A1

MAsh   ASHWOOD NURSERIES LTD ⊠ ⑤
Greensforge, Kingswinford, W Midlands, DY6 0AE
Ⓣ (01384) 401996
Ⓕ (01384) 401108
Ⓔ ashwoodnurs@btconnect.com
Ⓦ www.ashwood-nurseries.co.uk
Contact: Mark Warburton & Philip Baulk
Opening Times: 0900-1800 Mon-Sat & 0930-1800 Sun excl. Xmas & Boxing Day.
Min Mail Order UK: Nmc
Cat. Cost: 6 x 1st class
Credit Cards: Visa Access MasterCard
Specialities: Large range of hardy plants & dwarf conifers. Nat. Colls. of *Lewisia* &

Cyclamen species. Hellebores, *Hepatica, Hydrangea* & *Salvia.*
Notes: Mail order seeds & special offers only.
Map Ref: M, C2 OS Grid Ref: SO865879

MAus   DAVID AUSTIN ROSES LTD ⊠ ⊠ € ⑤
Bowling Green Lane, Albrighton, Wolverhampton, WV7 3HB
Ⓣ (01902) 376300
Ⓕ (01902) 372142
Ⓔ retail@davidaustinroses.co.uk
Ⓦ www.davidaustinroses.com
Contact: Retail Dept
Opening Times: 0900-1700, 7 days.
Min Mail Order UK: Nmc
Min Mail Order EU: Nmc
Cat. Cost: Free
Credit Cards: Switch Visa MasterCard
Specialities: Roses. Nat. Coll. of English Roses.
Notes: Also sells wholesale.
Map Ref: M, B1

MAvo   AVONDALE NURSERY ♪ ⑤
(Office) 3 Avondale Road, Earlsdon, Coventry, Warwickshire, CV5 6DZ
Ⓣ (024) 766 73662
Ⓜ 07979 093096
Ⓕ (024) 766 73662
Ⓔ enquiries@avondalenursery.co.uk
Ⓦ www.avondalenursery.co.uk
Contact: Brian Ellis
Opening Times: 1000-1230, 1400-1700 Tue-Sun, Mar-Sep. Other times by appt.
Cat. Cost: 4 x 1st class
Credit Cards: None
Specialities: Rare & unusual perennials esp. *Campanula, Eryngium, Leucanthemum, Geum, Crocosmia, Pulmonaria* & grasses.
Notes: Nursery is at Russell's Nursery, Mill Hill, Baginton, Nr Coventry.
Map Ref: M, C2 OS Grid Ref: SP339751

MBar   BARNCROFT NURSERIES ⊠ ⑤
Dunwood Lane, Longsdon, Nr Leek, Stoke-on-Trent, Staffordshire, ST9 9QW
Ⓣ (01538) 384310
Ⓕ (01538) 384310
Contact: S Warner
Opening Times: 0930-1730 or dusk if earlier Fri-Sun all year, plus Mon-Thu 0930-1730 Mar-Dec. Closed Xmas to New Year.
Min Mail Order UK: £20.00 + p&p

KEY: ⊠ Mail order to UK or EU   ♪ Delivers to shows
⊠ Exports beyond EU   € Euro accepted
⑤ Accessible by wheelchair   ◆ See Display advertisement

Cat. Cost: £2.50 incl. p&p
Credit Cards: None
Specialities: Extensive range of over 2000 heathers, conifers, shrubs, trees, climbers, dwarf grasses & rhododendrons. Display garden containing 400 heather cvs.
Notes: Also sells wholesale.
Map Ref: M, B1 **OS Grid Ref:** SJ948552

MBlu BLUEBELL ARBORETUM & NURSERY ⊠ € ♿
Annwell Lane, Smisby, Nr Ashby de la Zouch, Derbyshire, LE65 2TA
Ⓣ (01530) 413700
Ⓕ (01530) 417600
Ⓔ sales@bluebellnursery.com
Ⓦ www.bluebellnursery.com
Contact: Robert & Suzette Vernon
Opening Times: 0900-1700 Mon-Sat & 1030-1630 Sun Mar-Oct, 0900-1600 Mon-Sat (not Sun) Nov-Feb. Closed 24th Dec-4th Jan. Closed Easter Sun.
Min Mail Order UK: Nmc
Min Mail Order EU: Nmc
Cat. Cost: £1.30 + 3 x 1st class
Credit Cards: Visa Access Switch
Specialities: Uncommon trees & shrubs. Display garden & arboretum.
Map Ref: M, B1

MBnl BENSLEY NURSERIES ⊠ ♿
(office) 7 Bramble Way, Kilburn, Derbyshire, DE56 0LH
Ⓣ (01332) 781961
Ⓜ 07968 951019
Ⓕ (01332) 690546
Ⓔ info@bensleynurseries.co.uk
Ⓦ www.bensleynurseries.co.uk
Contact: Mairi Longdon
Opening Times: 1000-1630 Mon-Thu, 1st Mar-31st Oct. Other times by appt. Closed B/hols.
Min Mail Order UK: Nmc
Cat. Cost: 4 x 1st class
Credit Cards: None
Specialities: Choice & unusual perennials esp. *Achillea, Geranium, Geum, Helenium, Heuchera, Pulmonaria* , grasses & ferns.
Notes: Nursery is at White Gables, Dale Road, Stanley, Derbyshire.
Map Ref: M, B2 **OS Grid Ref:** SK417398

MBNS BARNSDALE GARDENS ⊠ ♿
Exton Avenue, Exton, Oakham, Rutland, LE15 8AH
Ⓣ (01572) 813200
Ⓕ (01572) 813346
Ⓔ office@barnsdalegardens.co.uk
Ⓦ www.barnsdalegardens.co.uk
Contact: Nick or Sue Hamilton
Opening Times: 0900-1700 Mar-May & Sep-Oct, 0900-1900 Jun-Aug, 1000-1600 Nov-Feb, 7 days. Closed 23th & 25th Dec.
Min Mail Order UK: Nmc
Min Mail Order EU: Nmc
Cat. Cost: A5 + 5 x 1st class
Credit Cards: All major credit/debit cards
Specialities: Wide range of choice & unusual garden plants. Over 140 varieties of *Penstemon*, over 200 varieties of *Hemerocallis*.
Map Ref: M, B3

MBow BOWDEN HALL NURSERY ⊠
(Office) Malcoff Farmhouse, Malcoff, Chapel-en-le-Frith, High Peak, Derbyshire, SK23 0QR
Ⓣ (01663) 751969
Ⓜ 07867 502775
Ⓔ info@bowdenhallnursery.co.uk
Ⓦ www.bowdenhallnursery.co.uk
Contact: Julie Norfolk
Opening Times: 1000-1700 B/hols from 1st Mar-30th Jun & Sep. Other times by appt.
Min Mail Order UK: £12.00 + p&p
Cat. Cost: £2.50.
Credit Cards: All major credit/debit cards
Specialities: Herbs, wild flowers & hardy cottage garden plants & some old roses. Plants grown in peat-free compost using organic fertilisers.
Notes: Mail order excl. roses. Nursery at Bowden Hall, Bowden, Chapel-en-le-Frith, High Peak.
Map Ref: M, A2 **OS Grid Ref:** SK065817

MBPg BARNFIELD PELARGONIUMS ⊠
Barnfield, Off Wilnecote Lane, Belgrave, Tamworth, Staffordshire, B77 2LF
Ⓣ (01827) 250123
Ⓕ (01827) 250123
Ⓔ brianandjenniewhite@hotmail.com
Contact: Jennie & Brian White
Opening Times: Not open to the public.
Min Mail Order UK: £4.00
Min Mail Order EU: £6.50
Cat. Cost: 4 x 2nd class
Credit Cards: None
Specialities: Over 200 varieties of scented leaf pelargoniums.

MBri BRIDGEMERE NURSERIES € ♿ ◆
Bridgemere, Nr Nantwich, Cheshire, CW5 7QB
Ⓣ (01270) 521100
Ⓕ (01270) 520215
Ⓔ info@bridgemere.co.uk
Ⓦ www.bridgemere.co.uk

Contact: Keith Atkey, Roger Pierce
Opening Times: 0900-1800 7 days, except Xmas Day & Boxing Day.
Cat. Cost: None issued
Credit Cards: Visa Access MasterCard Switch
Specialities: Perennials, shrubs, trees, roses, climbers, fruit, rhododendrons & deciduous azaleas, alpines, heathers, bamboos, ferns, grasses, aquatics, houseplants.
Map Ref: M, B1 OS Grid Ref: SJ727435

MBrN   BRIDGE NURSERY € ⌖
Tomlow Road, Napton-on-the-Hill,
Nr Rugby, Warwickshire,
CV47 8HX
ⓣ (01926) 812737
ⓔ pmartino@beeb.net
ⓦ www.Bridge-Nursery.co.uk
Contact: Christine Dakin & Philip Martino
Opening Times: 1000-1600 Fri-Sun 1st Feb-22nd Dec. Other times by appt.
Cat. Cost: 4 x 1st class
Credit Cards: None
Specialities: Ornamental grasses, sedges & bamboos. Also range of shrubs & perennials.
Notes: Also sells wholesale.
Map Ref: M, C2 OS Grid Ref: SP463625

MBSH   BRITISH SEED HOUSES LTD ⊠ ⊠ €
Camp Road, Witham St Hughs,
Lincoln,LN6 9QJ
ⓣ (01522) 868714
ⓕ (01522) 868095
ⓔ seeds@bshlincoln.co.uk
ⓦ www.britishseedhouses.com
Contact: Simon Taylor
Opening Times: 0830-1700 Mon-Fri excl. B/hols.
Min Mail Order UK: £50.00 + p&p
Min Mail Order EU: £50.00 + p&p
Cat. Cost: 3 x 1st class
Credit Cards: All major credit/debit cards
Specialities: Seed.
Notes: Also sells wholesale.

MCCP   COLLECTORS CORNER PLANTS ⊠
33 Rugby Road, Clifton-upon-Dunsmore,
Rugby, Warwickshire, CV23 0DE
ⓣ (01788) 571881
Contact: Pat Neesam
Opening Times: By appt. only.
Min Mail Order UK: £20.00
Cat. Cost: 6 x 1st class
Credit Cards: None
Specialities: General range of choice herbaceous perennials, grasses, shrubs, palms, ferns & bamboos.
Map Ref: M, C3

MCls   COLES PLANT CENTRE ⌖
624 Uppingham Road, Thurnby,
Leicestershire, LE7 9QB
ⓣ (0116) 241 8394
ⓕ (0116) 243 2311
ⓔ info@colesplantcentre.co.uk
ⓦ www.colesplantcentre.co.uk
Contact: Mark Goddard
Opening Times: 0800-1700 Mon-Fri, 0900-1700 Sat & Sun.
Credit Cards: MasterCard Switch
Specialities: Fruit, ornamental trees & shrubs.
Notes: Also sells wholesale.
Map Ref: M, B3

MCoo   COOL TEMPERATE ⊠ ⊠ ⌖
c/o Trinity Farm, Awsworth Lane, Cossall,
Nottinghamshire, NG16 2RZ
ⓣ (0115) 917 0416
ⓕ (0115) 917 0416
ⓔ philcorbett53@hotmail.com
ⓦ www.cooltemperate.co.uk
Contact: Phil Corbett
Opening Times: 0900-1700, 7 days.
Min Mail Order UK: Nmc
Min Mail Order EU: Nmc
Cat. Cost: 3 x 1st class
Credit Cards: None
Specialities: Tree fruit, soft fruit, nitrogen-fixers, hedging, own-root fruit trees.
Notes: Also sells wholesale.
Map Ref: M, B2 OS Grid Ref: SK482435

MDKP   D K PLANTS ⋔
(Office) 19 Harbourne Road, Cheadle, Stoke on Trent, Staffordshire, ST10 1JU
ⓣ (01538) 754460 (office)
ⓜ 07779 545015 (nursery)
ⓔ davidknoxc@aol.com
ⓦ www.dkplants.co.uk
Contact: Dave Knox
Opening Times: 0900-2000 (or dusk if earlier) Mon-Tue & Thu-Fri. Other times by appt.
Cat. Cost: 4 x 1st class A4 Sae plus 42p 1st or 34p 2nd class stamps.
Credit Cards: None
Specialities: Unusual hardy alpines & perennials. All grown on the nursery.
Notes: Nursery is at new roundabout across from Queen's Arms pub, Freehay Crossroads, Cheadle, ST10 1TR.
Map Ref: M, B1

KEY   ⊠ Mail order to UK or EU   ⋔ Delivers to shows
      ⊠ Exports beyond EU   € Euro accepted
      ⌖ Accessible by wheelchair   ◆ See Display advertisement

M

MDun DUNGE VALLEY GARDENS € ⑤
Windgather Rocks, Kettleshulme, High Peak,
Cheshire, SK23 7RF
Ⓣ (01663) 733787
Ⓕ (01663) 733787
Ⓔ plants@dungevalley.co.uk
Ⓦ www.dungevalley.co.uk
Contact: David Ketley
Opening Times: 1030-1700 Thu-Sun Mar &
Apr, Tue-Sun May, Thu-Sun Jun, Jul & Aug.
Open B/Hols. Otherwise by appt.
Cat. Cost: 2 x 1st class
Credit Cards: All major credit/debit cards
Specialities: *Rhododendron* species & hybrids.
Magnolias, acers, *Meconopsis*, trilliums, trees,
shrubs & perennials, some rare & wild
collected.
Notes: Also sells wholesale.
Map Ref: M, A2 OS Grid Ref: SJ989777

MEHN ELIZABETH HOUSE NURSERY ⋔ ⑤
Weedon Lois, Towcester, Northamptonshire,
NN12 8PN
Ⓣ (01327) 860056
Ⓕ (01327) 860779
Ⓔ elizabeth.house@andertontiger.com
Contact: Lindsey Cartwright
Opening Times: 1000-1700 Thu-Sat, Mar-
Oct.
Cat. Cost: 2 x 1st class
Credit Cards: None
Specialities: Wide range of hardy perennials.
Notes: Also sells wholesale.
Map Ref: M, C3 OS Grid Ref: SP604472

MFie FIELD HOUSE NURSERIES ⊠
Leake Road, Gotham, Nottinghamshire,
NG11 0JN
Ⓣ (0115) 9830278
Ⓕ (0115) 9831486
Ⓔ dlvwjw@field-house-alpines.fsbusiness.co.uk
Contact: Doug Lochhead & Valerie A Woolley
Opening Times: 0900-1600 Fri-Wed or by appt.
Min Mail Order UK: Min. order 4 plants
Min Mail Order EU: £30.00
Cat. Cost: 4 x 1st or 4 x IRCs
Credit Cards: Visa Access
Specialities: *Primula*, auriculas, alpines & rock
plants. 3 Nat. Colls. of *Primula, P. auricula*.
Notes: Mail order for *Primula*, auriculas &
seeds only.
Map Ref: M, B3

MFOX FOX COTTAGE PLANTS ⋔ ⑤
Yew Tree Farm, Thatchers Lane, Tansley,
Matlock, Derbyshire, DE4 5FD
Ⓣ (01629) 57493 Ⓜ 07787 963966
Ⓕ (01629) 57493

Ⓔ avril@yewtreefarm1.fslife.co.uk
Contact: Mrs Avril Buckley
Opening Times: 1200-1700 Wed-Sat, Feb-
Sep, Nov-Oct by appt. Please ring to confirm.
Cat. Cost: 2 x 1st class
Credit Cards: None
Specialities: Unusual hardy & tender perennials.
Stock available in small quantities only.
Map Ref: M, C2 OS Grid Ref: SK324594

MFry FRYER'S NURSERIES LTD ⊠ ⊠ € ⑤
Manchester Road, Knutsford, Cheshire,
WA16 0SX
Ⓣ (01565) 755455
Ⓕ (01565) 653755
Ⓔ garethfryer@fryers-roses.co.uk
Ⓦ www.fryers.co.uk
Contact: Gareth Fryer
Opening Times: 0900-1730 Mon-Sat &
1030-1630 Sun & 1000-1730 B/hols.
Min Mail Order UK: Nmc
Min Mail Order EU: Nmc
Cat. Cost: Free
Credit Cards: All major credit/debit cards
Specialities: Extensive rose nursery & garden
centre producing over half a million bushes
annually. Rose fields in bloom Jun-Sep.
Notes: Also sells wholesale.
Map Ref: M, A1 OS Grid Ref: SJ738803

MGag GAGGINI'S PLANT CENTRE ⊠ ⊠ ⑤
Glebe House, Glebe Road, Mears Ashby,
Northamptonshire, NN6 0DL
Ⓣ (01604) 812371/811811
Ⓕ (01604) 812353
Ⓦ www.gagginis.co.uk
Contact: John B & Mrs J E Gaggini
Opening Times: 0800-1730 Mon-Fri. 0900-
1730 Sat & Sun.
Min Mail Order UK: £8.00 + p&p
Cat. Cost: £1.00 (please state retail)
Credit Cards: Visa Access Switch MasterCard
Specialities: Specialist growers of container
trees, shrubs, conifers & fruit, esp. *Wisteria*.
Notes: Mail order for *Wisteria* only. Also sells
wholesale.
Map Ref: M, C3

MGan GANDY'S (ROSES) LTD ⊠
North Kilworth, Nr Lutterworth,
Leicestershire, LE17 6HZ
Ⓣ (01858) 880398
Ⓕ (01858) 880433
Ⓔ sales@gandys-roses.co.uk
Ⓦ www.gandys-roses.co.uk
Contact: Miss R D Gandy
Opening Times: 0900-1700 Mon-Sat &
1400-1700 Sun.

Min Mail Order UK: Nmc
Min Mail Order EU: £25.00 + p&p
Cat. Cost: Free
Credit Cards: All major credit/debit cards
Specialities: Wide range of rose varieties,
hardy nursery stock & fruit.
Notes: Also sells wholesale.
Map Ref: M, C3 OS Grid Ref: SP621836

MGol   GOLDEN COTTAGE PLANTS ⊠
Golden Cottage, Scarcliffe Lanes, Upper
Langwith, Mansfield, Nottinghamshire,
NG20 9RQ
Ⓜ 07952 804077
Contact: C Coleman
Opening Times: By appt. only.
Min Mail Order UK: Nmc
Min Mail Order EU: Nmc
Cat. Cost: 1 x 1st class
Credit Cards: None
Specialities: Ethnobotanical plants. Hardy,
tropical & sub-tropical. All plants available in
small quantities.

MGos   GOSCOTE NURSERIES LTD 🅰 ◆
Syston Road, Cossington, Leicestershire,
LE7 4UZ
Ⓣ (01509) 812121
Ⓕ (01509) 814231
Ⓔ sales@goscote.co.uk
Ⓦ www.goscote.co.uk
Also sells wholesale
Contact: James Toone, Brian Phipps
Opening Times: 7 days, closed between Xmas
& New Year.
Cat. Cost: Free Online.
Credit Cards: Visa Access MasterCard Delta
Switch
Specialities: Japanese maples, rhododendrons &
azaleas, *Magnolia, Camellia, Pieris* & other
Ericaceae. Ornamental trees & shrubs, conifers,
fruit, heathers, alpines, *Clematis* & unusual
climbers. Show garden to visit.
Notes: Also sells wholesale.
Map Ref: M, B3

MHar   HARTS GREEN NURSERY
89 Harts Green Road, Harborne,
Birmingham, B17 9TZ
Ⓣ (0121) 427 5200
Contact: B Richardson
Opening Times: 1400-1730 Wed Apr-Jul &
Sep. Other times, excl. Aug, by appt.
Cat. Cost: None issued.
Credit Cards: None
Specialities: Hardy perennials. Some in small
quantities only.
Map Ref: M, C2 OS Grid Ref: SP030845

MHer   THE HERB NURSERY 🅰
Thistleton, Oakham, Rutland, LE15 7RE
Ⓣ (01572) 767658
Ⓕ (01572) 768021
Contact: Peter Bench
Opening Times: 0900-1800 (or dusk) 7 days
excl. Xmas-New Year.
Cat. Cost: A5 Sae.
Credit Cards: None
Specialities: Herbs, wild flowers, cottage
garden plants, scented-leaf pelargoniums.
Especially *Thymus, Mentha, Lavandula*.
Map Ref: M, B3

MHom   HOMESTEAD PLANTS ⊠
The Homestead, Normanton, Bottesford,
Nottingham, NG13 0EP
Ⓣ (01949) 842745
Ⓕ (01949) 842745
Contact: Mrs S Palmer
Opening Times: By appt.
Min Mail Order UK: Nmc
Cat. Cost: 4 x 2nd class
Credit Cards: None
Specialities: Unusual hardy & half-hardy
perennials, especially *Paeonia* species. *Hosta,
Jovibarba, Sempervivum* & heliotrope.
Drought-tolerant asters. Most in small
quantities. Nat. Coll. of *Heliotropium* cvs.
Map Ref: M, B3 OS Grid Ref: SK812407

MHrb   THE HERB GARDEN 🅰
Kingston House Estate, Race Farm Lane,
Kingston Bagpuize, Oxfordshire,
OX13 5AU
Ⓣ (01865) 823101
Ⓕ (01865) 820159
Ⓔ vcjw37@yahoo.com
Ⓦ www.KingstonHerbGarden.co.uk
Contact: Val Williams
Opening Times: Phone for appt. or check
website for details.
Cat. Cost: 2 x 1st class
Credit Cards: None
Specialities: Small nursery specialising in the
more unusual lavenders, herbs, dye plants,
olive & citrus fruit trees according to season,
displayed in a walled garden setting.
Map Ref: M, D2

MIDC   IAN AND DEBORAH COPPACK ⊠ 🅰 ◆
Woodside, Langley Road, Langley,
Macclesfield, Cheshire, SK11 0DG
Ⓣ (01260) 253308
Ⓕ (01260) 253308
Ⓔ coppack@worldonline.co.uk
Contact: Ian & Deborah Coppack
Opening Times: 0900-1700 Mar-Sep.

M

Min Mail Order UK: Nmc
Cat. Cost: 2 x 1st class
Credit Cards: None
Specialities: *Hosta*.
Notes: Also sells wholesale.
Map Ref: M, A2 **OS Grid Ref:** SJ938715

MJac JACKSON'S NURSERIES
Clifton Campville, Nr Tamworth,
Staffordshire, B79 0AP
Ⓣ (01827) 373307
Contact: N Jackson
Opening Times: 0900-1800 Mon Wed-Sat,
1000-1700 Sun.
Cat. Cost: 2 x 1st class
Credit Cards: None
Specialities: *Fuchsia*.
Notes: Also sells wholesale.
Map Ref: M, B1

MJnS JUNGLE SEEDS AND GARDENS ✉
PO Box 45, Watlington SPDO,
Oxfordshire,
OX49 5YR
Ⓣ (01491) 614765
Ⓕ (01491) 612034
Ⓔ enquiry@junglegardens.co.uk
Ⓦ www.junglegardens.co.uk
Contact: Penny White
Opening Times: Mail order only. Open by
appt. only to collect plants.
Min Mail Order UK: £11.95 plants.
Cat. Cost: 2 x 1st class
Credit Cards: Visa MasterCard Switch
Specialities: Hardy, semi-hardy &
conservatory exotics. Some items ltd.
availability.

MJon C & K JONES ✉ ☒ ♠ € ♿
Golden Fields Nurseries,
Barrow Lane, Tarvin,
Cheshire, CH3 8JF
Ⓣ (01829) 740663
Ⓕ (01829) 741877
Ⓔ keith@ckjones.freeserve.co.uk
Ⓦ www.jonestherose.co.uk
Contact: Keith Jones/P Woolley
Opening Times: Office hours 0930-1600 Fri-
Mon. 1st w/end in each month only & the Fri
& Mon either side. Closed Jan & Feb.
Min Mail Order UK: 1 plant + p&p
Min Mail Order EU: Nmc.
Cat. Cost: £1.00
Credit Cards: Visa MasterCard Maestro
Electron Solo
Specialities: Roses.
Notes: Also sells wholesale.
Map Ref: M, B1

MKay KAYES GARDEN NURSERY ♿
1700 Melton Road, Rearsby, Leicestershire,
LE7 4YR
Ⓣ (01664) 424578
Ⓔ hazelkaye.kgn@nascr.net
Contact: Hazel Kaye
Opening Times: 1000-1700 Tue-Sat & B/hols
1000-1200 Sun Mar-Oct. By appt. Nov, Dec
& Feb. Closed Jan.
Cat. Cost: 2 x 1st class
Credit Cards: None
Specialities: Herbaceous, climbers & aquatic
plants. Grasses. Nat. Coll. of *Tradescantia
Andersoniana* Group.
Map Ref: M, B3 **OS Grid Ref:** SK648140

MLan LANE END NURSERY
Old Cherry Lane, Lymm, Cheshire, WA13 0TA
Ⓣ (01925) 752618
Ⓔ rsawyer@onetel.net
Ⓦ www.laneendnursery.co.uk
Contact: I Sawyer
Opening Times: 0930-1730 Thu-Tue Feb-
Dec.
Cat. Cost: None issued
Credit Cards: None
Specialities: AGM plants with a wide range of
choice & unusual shrubs, trees, perennials &
ferns.
Notes: Nursery mostly accessible to wheelchair
users.
Map Ref: M, A1 **OS Grid Ref:** SJ664850

MLea LEA RHODODENDRON GARDENS LTD
✉ ☒ ♿
Lea, Matlock, Derbyshire, DE4 5GH
Ⓣ (01629) 534380/534260
Ⓕ (01629) 534260
Contact: Peter Tye
Opening Times: 1000-1730 7 days 20 Mar-
30 Jun. Out of season by appt.
Min Mail Order UK: £15.00 + p&p
Min Mail Order EU: £15.00 + p&p
Cat. Cost: 30p + Sae
Credit Cards: All major credit/debit cards
Specialities: Rhododendrons & azaleas.
Map Ref: M, B1 **OS Grid Ref:** SK324571

MLHP LONGSTONE HARDY PLANTS NURSERY
✉ ♿
Stancil House, Barn Furlong, Great
Longstone, Nr Bakewell, Derbyshire,
DE45 1TR
Ⓣ (01629) 640136
Ⓜ 07762 083674
Ⓔ lucyinlongstone@hotmail.com
Ⓦ www.longstonehardyplants.co.uk
Contact: Lucy Wright

M

Opening Times: 1300-1700 Tue-Fri, 1st Apr-
30th Sep. Other times by appt.
Min Mail Order UK: Nmc
Cat. Cost: 2 x 1st class
Credit Cards: None
Specialities: Specialist peat free nursery
displaying and producing all own hardy
perennials & shrubs, incl. many unusual
varieties. Some stock in small quantities. Can
propagate to order.
Notes: Nursery 150yds on right after turning
into Station Road at the village green.
Map Ref: M, A2 OS Grid Ref: SK198717

MLLN   LODGE LANE NURSERY & GARDENS ⋔
Lodge Lane, Dutton,
Nr Warrington, Cheshire,
WA4 4HP
Ⓣ (01928) 713718
Ⓕ (01928) 713718
Ⓔ rod@lodgelanenursery.co.uk
Ⓦ www.lodgelanenursery.co.uk
Contact: Rod or Diane Casey
Opening Times: 1000-1700 Wed-Sun &
B/hols, mid Mar-mid Sep. By appt. outside
these dates.
Cat. Cost: 3 x 1st class
Credit Cards: None
Specialities: Unusual perennials & shrubs incl.
*Achillea, Allium, Astrantia, Campanula,
Digitalis, Penstemon, Euphorbia, Geranium,
Heuchera, Inula, Kniphofia, Nepeta, Papaver,
Penstemon, Salvia* & ornamental grasses. Nat.
Coll. of *Inula*.
Map Ref: M, A1 OS Grid Ref: SJ586779

**MLod   LODGE FARM HERBS, PLANTS &
WILDFLOWERS** ✉ ⋔ € ♿
Case Lane, Fiveways, Hatton,
Warwickshire,
CV35 7JD
Ⓣ (01926) 484649
Ⓜ 07977 631368
Ⓔ richard.a.cook@btinternet.com
Contact: Janet Cook & Nick Cook
Opening Times: 1000-1700 Tue-Sun (closed
Mon), Mar-end Oct. Please phone to check
availability & directions. Nov-Feb by appt.
only.
Min Mail Order UK: Nmc
Cat. Cost: 2 x 1st class
Credit Cards: None
Specialities: Wildflowers, herbs and sensual
plants. Vegetable plants, fruit, topiary. Native
trees & hedging. Old fashioned cottage garden
plants.
Notes: Also sells wholesale.
Map Ref: M, C2 OS Grid Ref: SP223700

MLul   LULWORTH PLANTS ⋔ ♿
28 Gladstone Street, Wigston Magna,
Leicestershire, LE18 1AE
Ⓜ 07814 042889
Contact: Chris Huscroft
Opening Times: By appt. only.
Cat. Cost: Sae
Credit Cards: None
Specialities: *Arisaema*, plus small selection of
shade-loving plants, small quantities only.
Map Ref: M, B3

MMat   MATTOCK'S ROSES ✉ ♿
Notcutts Ltd, Ipswich Road, Woodbridge,
Suffolk, IP12 4AF
Ⓣ (01865) 343454
Ⓕ (01865) 343166
Ⓔ roses@mattocks.co.uk
Ⓦ www.mattocks.co.uk
Contact: Plant Adviser
Opening Times: 0900-1800 Mon-Sat, 1030-
1630 Sun.
Min Mail Order UK: £30.00 if collected
from a Notcutts garden centre.
Credit Cards: Visa MasterCard Maestro
Specialities: Roses. All Mattocks roses are
part of the Notcutts range of plants.
Notes: Mail order only available at Notcutts
Garden Centres.
Map Ref: M, D3

MMHG   MORTON HALL GARDENS ✉ ⋔ ♿
Morton Hall, Ranby,
Retford, Nottinghamshire,
DN22 8HW
Ⓣ (01777) 702530
Ⓔ gill@mortonhall.fsbusiness.co.uk
Contact: Gill McMaster
Opening Times: By appt.only
Min Mail Order UK: £5.00 + p&p
Cat. Cost: 3 x 1st class
Credit Cards: None
Specialities: Shrubs & perennials.
Map Ref: M, A3

MMoz   MOZART HOUSE NURSERY GARDEN ⋔
84 Central Avenue, Wigston, Leicestershire,
LE18 2AA
Ⓣ (0116) 288 9548
Contact: Des Martin
Opening Times: By appt. only.
Cat. Cost: 5 x 1st class
Credit Cards: None

KEY   ✉ Mail order to UK or EU ⋔ Delivers to shows
🅧 Exports beyond EU   € Euro accepted
♿ Accessible by wheelchair ◆ See Display advertisement

M

Specialities: *Bamboo*, ornamental grasses, rushes & sedges, ferns. Some stock available in small quantities.
Map Ref: M, C3

MMuc   MUCKLESTONE NURSERIES ⊠ € ⌂ ◆
Church Farm, Mucklestone,
Nr Market Drayton, Shropshire,
TF9 4DN
Ⓜ 07714 241668
Ⓔ enquiries@botanyplants.com
Ⓦ www.botanyplants.com
Contact: William Friend
Opening Times: Mail order only. Open by appt. only.
Min Mail Order UK: Nmc
Cat. Cost: Online only.
Credit Cards: Visa Switch MasterCard
Specialities: Plants for acid & damp soils of the north & western UK.
Notes: Also sells wholesale.
Map Ref: M, B2 OS Grid Ref: SJ728373

MNew   NEWINGTON NURSERIES € ⌂
Newington, Wallingford,
Oxfordshire,
OX10 7AW
Ⓣ (01865) 400533
Ⓔ plants@newington-nurseries.co.uk
Ⓦ www.newington-nurseries.co.uk
Contact: Mrs A T Hendry
Opening Times: 1000-1700 Tues-Sun Mar-Oct, 1000-1600 Tues-Sun Nov-Feb.
Cat. Cost: 2 x 1st class & A4 sae
Credit Cards: Access Visa MasterCard Switch
Specialities: Unusual cottage garden plants, alpines, hardy exotics, conservatory plants & herbs. Nat. Coll. of *Alocasia* (*Araceae*).
Map Ref: M, D3

MNFA   THE NURSERY FURTHER AFIELD ⊠ ⌂
Evenley Road, Mixbury,
Nr Brackley, Northamptonshire,
NN13 5YR
Ⓣ (01280) 848808
Ⓕ (01280) 848539
Contact: Gerald & Mary Sinclair
Opening Times: 1000-1700 Wed-Sat, mid-Mar-early Oct.
Min Mail Order UK: Nmc
Cat. Cost: 2 x 1st class
Credit Cards: None
Specialities: Hardy perennials, many unusual, incl. *Anemone, Aster, Campanula, Geranium, Hemerocallis* & *Iris sibirica*. Nat. Coll. of *Hemerocallis*.
Notes: Mail order for *Hemerocallis* only.
Map Ref: M, C3 OS Grid Ref: SP608344

MNHC   THE NATIONAL HERB CENTRE ⌂
Banbury Road, Warmington, Nr. Banbury,
Oxfordshire, OX17 1DF
Ⓣ (01295) 690999
Ⓕ (01295) 690034
Ⓦ www.herbcentre.co.uk
Contact: Nick Turner
Opening Times: 0900-1730 Mon-Sat, 1030-1700 Sun.
Credit Cards: All major credit/debit cards
Specialities: Herbs, culinary & medicinal. Extensive selection of rosemary, thyme & lavender in particular.

MNrw   NORWELL NURSERIES ⊠ ♠ ⌂ ◆
Woodhouse Road, Norwell,
Newark, Nottinghamshire,
NG23 6JX
Ⓣ (01636) 636337
Ⓔ wardha@aol.com
Contact: Dr Andrew Ward
Opening Times: 1000-1700 Mon, Wed-Fri & Sun (Wed-Mon May & Jun). By appt. Aug & 20th Oct-1st Mar.
Min Mail Order UK: £12.00 + p&p
Cat. Cost: 3 x 1st class
Credit Cards: None
Specialities: A large collection of unusual & choice herbaceous perennials & alpines esp. *Penstemon*, hardy *Geranium, Geum*, summer bulbs, *Hemerocallis*, grasses & woodland plants. Gardens open.
Notes: Also sells wholesale.
Map Ref: M, B3 OS Grid Ref: SK767616

MOak   OAKLAND NURSERIES ⊠ ▣ ♠ ⌂
147 Melton Road,
Burton-on-the-Wolds,
Loughborough, Leicestershire,
LE12 5TQ
Ⓣ (01509) 880646
Ⓕ (01509) 889294
Ⓔ info@oaklandnurseries.co.uk
Ⓦ www.oaklandnurseries.co.uk
Contact: Tim & John Oakland
Opening Times: Strictly by appt. Apr-Sep.
Min Mail Order UK: £15.00 + p&p
Min Mail Order EU: £15.00 + p&p
Cat. Cost: 4 x 1st class
Credit Cards: Visa MasterCard
Specialities: Tender perennials, *Canna, Coleus, Caladium, Abutilon, Streptocarpus*, conservatory & exotic plants. Some *Canna* in small quantities, *Coleus* propagate to order. *Iris, Plumeria*.
Notes: Export *Canna/Caladium* only as dormant plants. Also sells wholesale.
Map Ref: M, B3 OS Grid Ref: SK615214

MOne   **ONE HOUSE NURSERY** ☒ ⋔ ♿
Buxton New Road,
Macclesfield, Cheshire,
SK11 0AD
Ⓣ (01625) 427087
Contact: Miss J L Baylis
Opening Times: 1000-1700 Tue-Sun & B/hol
Mons Mar-Oct, Nov-Feb ring for opening times.
Min Mail Order UK: Nmc
Cat. Cost: 3 x 1st class
Credit Cards: None
Specialities: Alpines & perennials. Good range
of *Primula auricula, Sempervivum* & bulbs.
Notes: Mail order for *Sempervivum* &
auriculas only.
Map Ref: M, A2 **OS Grid Ref:** SJ943741

MPet   **PETER GRAYSON (SWEET PEA
SEEDSMAN)** ☒ ⊠
34 Glenthorne Close,
Brampton, Chesterfield,
Derbyshire, S40 3AR
Ⓣ (01246) 278503
Ⓕ (01246) 278503
Contact: Peter Grayson
Opening Times: Not open. Mail order only.
Min Mail Order UK: Nmc
Min Mail Order EU: Nmc
Cat. Cost: C5 Sae, 1 x 2nd class
Credit Cards: None
Specialities: *Lathyrus* species & cvs. Large
collection of old-fashioned sweet peas, 100+
Spencer sweet peas incl. own cultivars and
collection of old-fashioned cottage garden
annuals & perennials.
Notes: Also sells wholesale.

MPhe   **PHEDAR NURSERY** ☒ ⊠ €
Bunkers Hill, Romiley, Stockport, Cheshire,
SK6 3DS
Ⓣ (0161) 430 3772
Ⓕ (0161) 430 3772
Ⓔ mclewin@phedar.com
Ⓦ www.phedar.com
Contact: Will McLewin
Opening Times: Frequent esp. in spring but
very irregular. Please phone to arrange appt.
Min Mail Order UK: Nmc
Min Mail Order EU: Nmc
Cat. Cost: 2 x A5 AE or address labels + 4 x
1st class
Credit Cards: None
Specialities: *Helleborus, Paeonia.* Limited stock
of some rare items.
Notes: Non-EU exports subject to destination
& on an ad hoc basic only. Please contact
nursery for details. Also sells wholesale.
Map Ref: M, A2 **OS Grid Ref:** SJ936897

MPkF   **PACKHORSE FARM NURSERY** ⋔ ♿
Sandyford House, Lant Lane, Tansley,
Matlock, Derbyshire, DE4 5FW
Ⓣ (01629) 57206
Ⓜ 07974 095752
Ⓕ (01629) 57206
Contact: Hilton W. Haynes
Opening Times: 1000-1700 Tues & Wed, 1st
Mar-31st Oct. Any other time by appt. only.
Cat. Cost: 3 x 1st class.
Credit Cards: None
Specialities: *Acer,* rare stock is limited in
supply. Other more unusual hardy shrubs,
trees & conifers.
Map Ref: M, B2 **OS Grid Ref:** SK322617

MPRe   **PLANTS FOR ALL REASONS** ☒ ♿
Woodshoot Nurseries, King's Bromley,
Burton-upon-Trent,
Staffordshire,
DE13 7HN
Ⓣ (01543) 472233
Ⓕ (01543) 472115
Ⓔ sales@plants-for-all-reasons.com
Ⓦ www.plants-for-all-reasons.com
Contact: Richard Flint
Opening Times: 0900-1700, 7 days.
Min Mail Order UK: £20.00 + p&p
Cat. Cost: 2 x 1st class
Credit Cards: All major credit/debit cards
Specialities: *Phormium, Pittosporum,
Tropaeolum, Daphne,* palms, *Agave* & *Acacia.*
Notes: Also sells wholesale.
Map Ref: M, B2 **OS Grid Ref:** SK127164

MRav   **RAVENSTHORPE NURSERY** ☒ ♿
6 East Haddon Road, Ravensthorpe,
Northamptonshire, NN6 8ES
Ⓣ (01604) 770548
Ⓕ (01604) 770548
Ⓔ ravensthorpenursery@hotmail.com
Contact: Jean & Richard Wiseman
Opening Times: 1000-1800 (dusk if earlier)
Tue-Sun. Also B/hol Mons.
Min Mail Order UK: Nmc
Min Mail Order EU: Nmc
Cat. Cost: None issued.
Credit Cards: Visa MasterCard
Specialities: Over 2,600 different trees,
shrubs & perennials with many unusual
varieties. Search & delivery service for large
orders, winter months only.
Map Ref: M, C3 **OS Grid Ref:** SP665699

M

M

MRea   REARSBY ROSES ⊠ ⬚
Melton Road, Rearsby, Leicestershire, LE7 4YP
Ⓣ 0116 2601211
Ⓕ 0116 2640013
Contact: Mark Halford
Opening Times: 1000-1600 Mon, Fri & Sat.
1200-1600 Sun. Closed Tue, Wed, Thu.
Please phone for confirmation as times may
change.
Min Mail Order UK: Nmc
Cat. Cost: Free
Credit Cards: All major credit/debit cards
Specialities: Roses. Baskets & planters.
Notes: Also sells wholesale.
Map Ref: M, B3

MRMR   ROBERT MATTOCK ROSES ⬚ € ⬚
The Rose Nurseries, Lodge Hill, Abingdon,
Oxfordshire, OX14 2JD
Ⓣ (01865) 735382
Ⓜ 07710 170660
Ⓕ (01865) 736382
Ⓔ robert@robertmattockroses.com
Ⓦ www.robertmattockroses.com
Contact: Robert E. Mattock
Opening Times: 08.00-1600 Mon-Fri by appt.
Cat. Cost: Free
Credit Cards: None
Specialities: Roses. Specialists in growing large
specimen plants in 10ltr. containers. Some
available in small quantities.
Notes: Also sells wholesale.
Map Ref: M, D3 **OS Grid Ref:** SU504998

MSGs   SHOWGLADS ⊠
105 Derby Road, Bramcote, Nottingham,
NG9 3GZ
Ⓣ (0115) 925 5498
Ⓔ rogerbb@lineone.net
Contact: Roger Braithwaite
Opening Times: Not open. Mail order only.
Min Mail Order UK: £4.00
Cat. Cost: 3 x 1st class
Credit Cards: None
Specialities: *Gladiolus.*

MSal   SALLEY GARDENS ⊠ ⬚ € ⬚
32 Lansdowne Drive, West Bridgford,
Nottinghamshire, NG2 7FJ
Ⓣ (0115) 9233878 evenings
Ⓜ 07811 703982
Ⓔ richienothavens@hotmail.com
Ⓦ www.thesalleygardens.co.uk
Contact: Richard Lewin
Opening Times: 0900-1700 Sun only, 1st
Apr-30th Sep and by appt.
Min Mail Order UK: Nmc
Min Mail Order EU: Nmc

Cat. Cost: Sae
Credit Cards: None
Specialities: Medicinal plants esp. from North
America & China. Dye plants, herbs, spices,
seeds. Some sp. in small quanitities only.
Notes: Nursery is at Simkins Farm, Adbolton
Lane, West Bridgford, Notts.
Map Ref: M, B3

MSph   SPRINGHILL PLANTS ⬚
(Office) 18 Westfields, Abingdon,
Oxfordshire, OX14 1BA
Ⓣ (01235) 530889 after 1800
Ⓜ 07790 863378
Contact: Caroline Cox
Opening Times: Open for collection of orders
only.
Cat. Cost: None
Credit Cards: None
Specialities: Small nursery offering a wide
range of unusual & garden-worthy perennials
& shrubs. Many AGM & rare plants. Some
stock in small quantities only.
Notes: Nursery is at Buildings Farm,
Gozzard's Ford, Nr. Marcham, Abingdon.
Map Ref: M, D2

MSSP   S & S PERENNIALS ⊠
24 Main Street, Normanton Le Heath,
Leicestershire, LE67 2TB
Ⓣ (01530) 262250
Contact: Shirley Pierce
Opening Times: Afternoons only, otherwise
please phone.
Min Mail Order UK: Nmc
Cat. Cost: 2 x 1st class
Credit Cards: None
Specialities: *Erythronium, Fritillaria*, hardy
Cyclamen, dwarf *Narcissus* & *Anemone*. Stock
available in small quantities only.
Map Ref: M, B1

MSte   STEVENTON ROAD NURSERIES € ⬚
Steventon Road, East Hanney, Wantage,
Oxfordshire, OX12 0HS
Ⓣ (01235) 868828
Ⓕ (01235) 763670
Ⓔ johngraham.steventonroadnursery@
virgin.net
Ⓦ www.steventonroadnurseries.co.uk
Contact: John Graham
Opening Times: 0900-1700 Mon-Fri, 1000-
1700 Sat Mar-Nov. Winter by appt. Closed
Sun.
Cat. Cost: 4 x 1st class
Credit Cards: None
Specialities: Tender & hardy perennials.
Map Ref: M, D2

MSwo   SWALLOWS NURSERY ⊠ 🖉
Mixbury, Brackley, Northamptonshire,
NN13 5RR
Ⓣ (01280) 847721
Ⓕ (01280) 848611
Ⓔ enq@swallowsnursery.co.uk
Ⓦ www.swallowsnursery.co.uk
Contact: Chris Swallow
Opening Times: 0900-1300 & 1400-1700
(earlier in winter) Mon-Fri, 0900-1300 Sat.
Min Mail Order UK: £15.00
Cat. Cost: 3 x 1st class (plus phone number)
Credit Cards: Visa MasterCard Switch
Specialities: A wide range of shrubs, trees,
roses and heathers.
Notes: Trees not for mail order unless part of
larger order. Nursery transport used where
possible, esp. for trees. Also sells wholesale.
Map Ref: M, C3 OS Grid Ref: SP607336

MTho   A & A THORP
Bungalow No 5, Main Street, Theddingworth,
Leicestershire, LE17 6QZ
Ⓣ (01858) 880496
Contact: Anita & Andrew Thorp
Opening Times: 1000-1700.
Cat. Cost: 4 x 1st class
Credit Cards: None
Specialities: Unusual plants or those in short
supply.
Map Ref: M, C3

MTis   TISSINGTON NURSERY 🔔 🖉
Tissington, Nr Ashbourne, Derbyshire,
DE6 1RA
Ⓣ (01335) 390650
Ⓕ (01335) 390693
Ⓔ info@tissingtonnursery.co.uk
Ⓦ www.tissingtonnursery.co.uk
Contact: Mrs Sue Watkins
Opening Times: 1000-1800 daily 1st Mar-
30th Sep incl. Easter Sun & B/hols.
Cat. Cost: 3 x 1st class
Credit Cards: Visa MasterCard
Specialities: Perennials, shrubs & climbers
incl. unusual varieties. In small quantities.
Map Ref: M, B1 OS Grid Ref: SK176521

MTPN   SMART PLANTS ⊠ 🔔 🖉
Sandy Hill Lane, Off Overstone Road,
Moulton, Northampton, NN3 7JB
Ⓣ (01604) 454106
Contact: Stuart Smart
Opening Times: 1000-1500 Thu & Fri,
1000-1700 Sat. Other times by appt.
Min Mail Order UK: Nmc
Cat. Cost: 3 x 1st class
Credit Cards: None

Specialities: Wide range of herbaceous,
alpines, shrubs, grasses, hardy *Geranium*,
Sempervivum & succulents.
Map Ref: M, C3

MWar   WARD FUCHSIAS ⊠
5 Pollen Close, Sale, Cheshire, M33 3LS
Ⓣ (0161) 282 7434
Contact: K Ward
Opening Times: 0930-1700 Tue-Sun Feb-Jun
incl. B/hols.
Min Mail Order UK: Nmc
Cat. Cost: Free
Credit Cards: None
Specialities: *Fuchsia*. Available in small
quantities.
Map Ref: M, A2

MWat   WATERPERRY GARDENS LTD ⊠ 🖉
Waterperry, Nr Wheatley,
Oxfordshire,
OX33 1JZ
Ⓣ (01844) 339226/254
Ⓕ (01844) 339883
Ⓔ office@waterperrygardens.co.uk
Ⓦ www.waterperrygardens.co.uk
Contact: Mr R Jacobs
Opening Times: 0900-1730 summer. 0900-
1700 winter.
Min Mail Order UK: Nmc
Cat. Cost: None issued.
Credit Cards: All major credit/debit cards
Specialities: General, plus Nat. Coll. of
Saxifraga (*Porophyllum*).
Notes: Limited mail order, please phone.
Map Ref: M, D3 OS Grid Ref: SP630064

MWea   WEAR'S NURSERY 🖉
(office) 84 Wantage Road,
Wallingford, Oxfordshire,
OX10 0LY
Ⓣ 07790 425284
Ⓕ (01491) 837803
Contact: David Wear
Opening Times: 1000-1700 Mon-Sat, Feb-
Oct. 1000-1600 Sun (closed Sun in Aug).
1000-1600 Mon-Sat, Nov-Jan, please
telephone first as may be closed on some
days.
Cat. Cost: 3 x 1st class.
Credit Cards: None
Specialities: Unusual herbaceous varieties &
shrubs. Large selection of *Geranium*. Some
plants in small numbers.
Notes: Nursery at High Road, Brightwell
cum Sotwell, Wallingford. Also sells
wholesale.
Map Ref: M, D3 OS Grid Ref: SU590910

M

M

MWgw   WINGWELL NURSERY ⊠
Top Street, Wing, Oakham, Rutland,
LE15 8SE
Ⓣ (01572) 737727
Ⓕ (01572) 737788
Ⓔ rosedejardin@btopenworld.com
Ⓦ www.wingwellnursery.com
Contact: Rose Dejardin
Opening Times: 1000-1700 daily Feb-Oct, or
by appt.
Min Mail Order UK: Nmc
Cat. Cost: £1.00 for descriptive cat.
Credit Cards: All major credit/debit cards
Specialities: Herbaceous perennials.
Notes: Mail order Oct-Mar for herbaceous
plants, grasses & ferns only.
Map Ref: M, B3 OS Grid Ref: SP892029

MWhe   A D & N WHEELER ↬
Pye Court, Willoughby, Rugby, Warwickshire,
CV23 8BZ
Ⓣ (01788) 890341
Ⓕ (01788) 890341
Contact: Mrs N Wheeler
Opening Times: 1000-1630 7 days mid Feb-
late Jun. Other times please phone for appt.
Cat. Cost: 3 x 1st class
Credit Cards: None
Specialities: *Fuchsia, Pelargonium* & hardy
Geranium.
Map Ref: M, C3

MWhi   WHITEHILL FARM NURSERY ⊠ € ⬚
Whitehill Farm, Burford, Oxfordshire,
OX18 4DT
Ⓣ (01993) 823218
Ⓕ (01993) 822894
Ⓔ whitehill.farm@virgin.net
Contact: P J M Youngson
Opening Times: 0900-1800 (or dusk if
earlier) 7 days.
Min Mail Order UK: £5.00 + p&p
Min Mail Order EU: £5.00 + p&p
Cat. Cost: 4 x 1st class
Credit Cards: All major credit/debit cards
Specialities: Grasses & bamboos, less common
shrubs & perennials.
Notes: £1.00 of catalogue cost refunded on
1st order.
Map Ref: M, D2 OS Grid Ref: SP268113

MWht   WHITELEA NURSERY ⊠ ⬚
Whitelea Lane, Tansley, Matlock, Derbyshire,
DE4 5FL
Ⓣ (01629) 55010
Ⓔ whitelea@nursery-stock.freeserve.co.uk
Ⓦ www.nursery-stock.freeserve.co.uk
Contact: David Wilson

Opening Times: By appt.
Min Mail Order UK: No minimum charge
Cat. Cost: 2 x 1st class
Credit Cards: None
Specialities: *Bamboo*, ivies. Substantial
quantities of 45 cvs & species of bamboo,
remainder stocked in small numbers only.
Notes: Palletised deliveries only.
Map Ref: M, B1 OS Grid Ref: SK325603

MWrn   WARREN HILLS NURSERY ⊠ ↬ ⬚
Warren Hills Cottage, Warren Hills Road,
Coalville, Leicestershire, LE67 4UY
Ⓣ (01530) 812350
Ⓔ warrenhills@tinyworld.co.uk
Ⓦ www.warrenhills.co.uk
Contact: Bob Taylor
Opening Times: By appt. only, please phone.
See NGS for open days.
Min Mail Order UK: £10.00 + p&p
Cat. Cost: 4 x 1st class
Credit Cards: None
Specialities: *Astrantia*. Genuine hardy &
unusual perennials. Nat. Coll. *Astrantia*.
Map Ref: M, B1 OS Grid Ref: SK459146

MWtn   WALTON NURSERIES ⊠ ↬ € ⬚
Cherry Lane, Lymm, Warrington, Cheshire,
WA13 0SY
Ⓣ (01925) 759026
Ⓕ (01925) 759026
Ⓔ info@waltonnurseries.co.uk
Ⓦ www.waltonnurseries.co.uk
Contact: Roy Walton & Lesley Smyth
Opening Times: 1000-1600 7 days summer.
1000-1600 Tue-Sun winter.
Min Mail Order UK: Nmc
Min Mail Order EU: Nmc
Cat. Cost: Free.
Credit Cards: None
Specialities: Fuchsias.
Notes: Also sells wholesale.
Map Ref: M, A1

MWya   WYATTS ↬ € ⬚
Hill Barn Farm, Great Rollright, Chipping
Norton, Oxfordshire, OX7 5SH
Ⓣ (01608) 684835:(01608) 684990
Ⓔ wyatts@callnetuk.com
Ⓦ www.wyattscountry.com
Contact: John Wyatt or Christine
Chittenden
Opening Times: 0900-1700 7 days 21st Oct-
1st Mar, 0900-1800 2nd Mar-20th Oct.
Cat. Cost: 2 x 1st class
Credit Cards: MasterCard Switch Delta Visa
Specialities: Many unusual, rare & exotic
plants, shrubs & trees incl. *Daphne,*

*Euonymus, Viburnum, Magnolia, Clematis,
Cornus* & *Acer*. Alpines, fruit trees & cane
fruit. Please check availability list.
Map Ref: M, C2 OS Grid Ref: SP317313

MYeo   YEOMANS' EXOTICS ⊠ ⋔ ⬙
2 Carrington Lane, Calverton, Nottingham,
NG14 6HQ
ⓣ 0115 965 4350
ⓦ www.yeomansexotics.co.uk
Contact: Chris Yeomans
Opening Times: By appt. only Feb-Dec.
Min Mail Order UK: Nmc
Min Mail Order EU: Nmc
Cat. Cost: 1 x 1st class
Credit Cards: None
Specialities: Carnivorous plants.
Notes: Mail order seeds only. Also sells
wholesale.

NORTHERN

NAsh   ASHTONS NURSERY GARDENS ⬙
Mythop Road, Lytham, Lytham St Annes,
Lancashire, FY8 4JP
ⓣ (01253) 736627/794808
ⓕ (01253) 735311
ⓔ sales@ashtons-lytham.co.uk
ⓦ www.ashtons-lytham.co.uk
Contact: T M Ashton
Opening Times: 0900-1700 daily.
Cat. Cost: None issued
Credit Cards: Visa MasterCard Switch Delta
American Express
Specialities: Herbaceous plants. Hardy shrubs.
Notes: Also sells wholesale.
Map Ref: N, D1

NBea   BEAMISH CLEMATIS NURSERY € ⬙
Burntwood Cottage, Stoney Lane, Beamish,
Co. Durham, DH9 0SJ
ⓣ (0191) 370 0202
ⓕ (0191) 370 0202
ⓦ www.beamishclematisnursery.co.uk
Contact: Colin Brown or Jan Wilson
Opening Times: 0900-1700 Wed-Mon,
closed Tue. Closed Easter Sun & Xmas week.
Cat. Cost: Available Online only.
Credit Cards: None
Specialities: *Clematis*, climbers, shrubs &
ornamental trees.
Map Ref: N, B2

NBee   BEECHCROFT JUST TREES ⊠ ⬙
Bongate, Appleby-in-Westmorland, Cumbria,
CA16 6UE
ⓣ (01768) 351201
ⓕ (01768) 351201

Contact: Roger Brown
Opening Times: 0900-1700 Tue-Sun, closed
Mon.
Min Mail Order UK: Nmc
Cat. Cost: Sae for tree list.
Credit Cards: None
Specialities: Hardy field-grown trees.
Notes: Mail order trees Nov-Mar only.
Formerly Beechcroft Nurseries.
Map Ref: N, C1

NBHF   BOUNDARY HOUSE FARM ⊠ ⬙
Holmeswood, Rufford, West Lancashire,
L40 1UA
ⓣ (01704) 821333
ⓕ (01704) 821333
Contact: Linda Birchall
Opening Times: Fri & Sun, Apr-Sep. Phone
first.
Min Mail Order UK: Nmc
Cat. Cost: 2 x 1st class.
Credit Cards: None
Specialities: *Achillea*. Grasses.
Notes: Mail order available from Oct 2005.
Map Ref: N, D1 OS Grid Ref: SD4217SE

NBhm   BEETHAM NURSERIES ⬙
Pool Darkin Lane, Beetham, Nr Milnthorpe,
Cumbria, LA7 7AP
ⓣ (01539) 563630
ⓕ (01539) 564487
Contact: S & L Abbit
Opening Times: 0900-1730 Summer, 0900-
dusk Winter.
Cat. Cost: None issued.
Credit Cards: Visa American Express Switch
Specialities: Comprehensive range of trees,
shrubs & herbaceous plants. Many unusual
varieties.
Map Ref: N, C1

NBid   BIDE-A-WEE COTTAGE GARDENS ⊠ ⬙
Stanton, Netherwitton, Morpeth,
Northumberland, NE65 8PR
ⓣ (01670) 772262
ⓕ (01670) 772238
ⓔ bideaweecg@aol.com
ⓦ www.bideawee.co.uk
Contact: Mark Robson
Opening Times: 1330-1700 Sat & Wed 23rd
Apr-27th Aug 2005.
Min Mail Order UK: Nmc
Cat. Cost: 3 x 1st class

N

Credit Cards: None
Specialities: Unusual herbaceous perennials, *Primula*, ferns, grasses. Nat. Coll. of *Centaurea*.
Map Ref: N, B2 OS Grid Ref: NZ132900

NBir BIRKHEADS COTTAGE GARDEN NURSERY ✉ ♿
Nr Causey Arch, Sunniside, Newcastle upon Tyne, NE16 5EL
Ⓣ (01207) 232262 Ⓜ 07778 447920
Ⓕ (01207) 232262
Ⓔ birkheads.nursery@virgin.net
Ⓦ www.birkheadsnursery.co.uk
Contact: Mrs Christine Liddle
Opening Times: 1000-1700 daily (except Mon) Mar-end Oct. Groups by appt.
Min Mail Order UK: £30.00
Cat. Cost: None issued
Credit Cards: All major credit/debit cards
Specialities: Hardy herbaceous perennials, grasses, bulbs & herbs. *Allium, Campanula, Digitalis, Euphorbia, Geranium, Primula*. Max. 30 of any plant propagated each year.
Notes: Mail order Nov-Feb only. Orders taken all year for winter deliveries.
Map Ref: N, B2 OS Grid Ref: NZ220569

NBlu BLUNDELL'S NURSERIES ♿
68 Southport New Road, Tarleton, Preston, Lancashire, PR4 6HY
Ⓣ (01772) 815442
Ⓔ jerplusjeff@aol.com
Contact: Any member of staff
Opening Times: 0900-1700 daily. Closed Dec-Feb.
Cat. Cost: None issued
Credit Cards: None
Specialities: Trees, shrubs, incl. topiary & large specimens, conifers. Perennials, alpines, ferns, heathers, herbs, bedding, conservatory plants, aquatics, hedging, roses.
Notes: Also sells wholesale.
Map Ref: N, D1

NBPC THE BARN PLANT CENTRE & GIFT SHOP ♿
The Square, Scorton, Preston, Lancashire, PR3 1AU
Ⓣ (01524) 793533
Ⓕ (01524) 793533
Ⓔ neil.anderton@virgin.net
Ⓦ www.plantsandgifts.co.uk
Contact: Neil Anderton, Karen Macleod
Opening Times: 0900-1700 Mon-Sat, 1000-1800 Sun.
Cat. Cost: 2 1st class
Credit Cards: All major credit/debit cards

Specialities: 600 varieties of perennials. Old roses.
Map Ref: N, C1 OS Grid Ref: GR501487

NBre BREEZY KNEES NURSERIES ✉ ♿
Common Lane, Warthill, York, YO19 5XS
Ⓣ (01904) 488800
Ⓦ www.breezyknees.co.uk
Contact: Any member of staff
Opening Times: 0930-1700 7 days, mid-March-end Sep.
Min Mail Order UK: Nmc
Cat. Cost: Free.
Credit Cards: All major credit/debit cards
Specialities: Wide range of perennials from popular favourites to something decidedly different.
Map Ref: N, C3 OS Grid Ref: SE675565

NBro BROWNTHWAITE HARDY PLANTS ✉ ♿
Fell Yeat, Casterton, Kirkby Lonsdale, Lancashire, LA6 2JW
Ⓣ (015242) 71340 (after 1800).
Contact: Chris Benson
Opening Times: Tue-Sun 1st Apr-30th Sep.
Min Mail Order UK: Nmc
Cat. Cost: 3 x 1st class sae for catalogue, sae for auricula list.
Credit Cards: None
Specialities: Herbaceous perennials & grasses incl. *Geranium, Hosta, Iris*, especially *I. ensata* & *I. sibirica, Heucherella, Tiarella, Primula auricula* & *P. sieboldii*.
Map Ref: N, C1

NBtw BRAITHWELL NURSERIES € ♿
2 Holywell Cottages, Braithwell, Rotherham, South Yorkshire, S66 7AB
Ⓣ (01709) 812093
Contact: Philip Yardley
Opening Times: 1000-1800 Mar-Nov, times vary Dec-Feb, please phone first. Closed Xmas & New Year.
Cat. Cost: None issued
Credit Cards: None
Specialities: Wide range incl. shrubs, perennials, grasses, climbers, alpines, bamboos, palms, *Agave*. Many seasonal plants. Some in small quantities.
Notes: Nursery on B6427 between Braithwell & Maltby.
Map Ref: N, D2 OS Grid Ref: SK535938

NBur BURTON AGNES HALL NURSERY ✉ ♿
Burton Agnes Hall Preservation Trust Ltd, Estate Office, Burton Agnes, Driffield, East Yorkshire, YO25 0ND
Ⓣ (01262) 490324

Ⓕ (01262) 490513
Ⓔ burton.agnes@farmline.com
Ⓦ www.burton-agnes.com
Contact: Mrs S Cunliffe-Lister
Opening Times: 1100-1700 Apr-Oct.
Min Mail Order UK: £15.00 + p&p
Min Mail Order EU: £15.00 + p&p
Cat. Cost: 4 x 1st class
Credit Cards: None
Specialities: Large range perennials & alpines.
Many unusual varieties esp. *Penstemon,
Osteospermum, Digitalis, Anemone, Geranium.*
Nat. Coll. of *Campanula.*
Notes: Mail order Nov-Mar only.
Map Ref: N, C3

NCGa CATH'S GARDEN PLANTS ⊠ ♠ ⓖ
The Walled Garden, Heaves Hotel, Levens,
Nr Kendal, Cumbria, LA8 8EF
Ⓣ (01539) 561126
Ⓕ (01539) 561126
Ⓔ cath@cathsgardenplants.fsbusiness.co.uk
Ⓦ www.cathsgardenplants.co.uk
Contact: Bob Sanderson
Opening Times: 1030-1700 Mon-Fri all year,
except Xmas & New Year weeks. 1030-1700
Sat & Sun, Mar-Oct.
Min Mail Order UK: Nmc
Min Mail Order EU: £25.00
Cat. Cost: 4 x 1st class
Credit Cards: All major credit/debit cards
Specialities: Wide variety of perennials, incl.
uncommon varieties & selections of grasses,
ferns, shrubs & climbing plants.
Notes: Also sells wholesale.
Map Ref: N, C1 **OS Grid Ref:** SD497867

NChi CHIPCHASE CASTLE NURSERY ♠ ⓖ
Chipchase Castle, Wark, Hexham,
Northumberland, NE48 3NT
Ⓣ (01434) 230083
Ⓦ www.northernperennials.co.uk
Contact: Suzanne Newell & Janet Beakes
Opening Times: 1000-1700 Thu-Sun &
B/hol Mons Easter (or 1st Apr)-mid Oct.
Cat. Cost: A5 sae for list
Credit Cards: None
Specialities: Unusual herbaceous esp. *Erodium,
Eryngium, Geranium* & *Viola.* Some plants
only available in small quantities.
Notes: Suitable for accompanied wheelchair
users.
Map Ref: N, B2 **OS Grid Ref:** NY880758

NChl CHILTERN SEEDS ⊠ ⊠ € ◆
Bortree Stile, Ulverston, Cumbria, LA12 7PB
Ⓣ (01229) 581137 (24 hrs)
Ⓕ (01229) 584549

Ⓔ info@chilternseeds.co.uk
Ⓦ www.chilternseeds.co.uk
Opening Times: Mail order only. Normal
office hours, Mon-Fri.
Min Mail Order UK: Nmc
Min Mail Order EU: Nmc
Cat. Cost: 3 x 2nd class
Credit Cards: All major credit/debit cards
Specialities: Over 4,600 items of all kinds –
wild flowers, trees, shrubs, cacti, annuals,
houseplants, vegetables & herbs.

NCiC CICELY'S COTTAGE GARDEN PLANTS
43 Elmers Green, Skelmersdale, Lancashire,
WN8 6SG
Ⓣ (01695) 720790
Ⓔ maureen.duncan@ic24.net
Contact: Maureen Duncan
Opening Times: Please phone to avoid
disappointment as opening times vary.
Cat. Cost: Free plant list
Credit Cards: None
Specialities: Hardy, half-hardy & tender
perennials incl. *Penstemon.* Traditional &
unusual cottage garden plants & pelargoniums.
Stock available in small quantities.
Map Ref: N, D1

NCob COBBLE HEY GARDENS ⓖ
Off Hobbs Lane, Claughton-on-Brock,
Garstang, Nr. Preston, Lancashire,
PR3 0QN
Ⓣ (01995) 602643
Ⓕ (01995) 602643
Ⓔ cobblehey@aol.com
Ⓦ www.cobblehey.co.uk
Contact: Edwina Miller
Opening Times: 1030-1630 every Sat & Sun
from Easter (27th Mar) to end Sep, or by
appt.
Credit Cards: All major credit/debit cards
Specialities: Wide range of unusual plants
grown on hill farm at over 600ft, especially
Phlox paniculata.
Map Ref: N, C1

NCot COTTAGE GARDEN PLANTS ⊠ €
1 Sycamore Close, Whitehaven, Cumbria,
CA28 6LE
Ⓣ (01946) 695831
Ⓔ jnprkss@aol.com
Ⓦ www.cottagegardenplants.com
Contact: Mrs J Purkiss

KEY		
⊠ Mail order to UK or EU	♠ Delivers to shows
⊠ Exports beyond EU	€ Euro accepted
ⓖ Accessible by wheelchair	◆ See Display advertisement

Opening Times: Mail order only. Open by appt. only. For garden, consult local press & radio for charity openings.
Min Mail Order UK: Nmc
Cat. Cost: 3 x 1st class sae
Credit Cards: None
Specialities: Hardy perennials incl. *Geranium, Polemonium, Primula* & bog plants. Small quantities only.
Map Ref: N, C1

NCro CROSTON CACTUS ⊠ ♠ ⑤
43 Southport Road, Eccleston, Chorley, Lancashire, PR7 6ET
ⓣ (01257) 452555
ⓔ sales@croston-cactus.co.uk
ⓦ www.CROSTON-CACTUS.CO.UK
Contact: John Henshaw
Opening Times: 0930-1700 Wed-Sat & by appt.
Min Mail Order UK: £5.00 + p&p
Min Mail Order EU: £10.00 + p&p
Cat. Cost: 2 x 1st or 2 x IRCs
Credit Cards: None
Specialities: Mexican cacti, *Echeveria* hybrids & some bromeliads & *Tillandsia*. Some items held in small quantities only.
Map Ref: N, D1

NDlv DALESVIEW NURSERY ⊠ ⑤
24 Braithwaite Edge Road, Keighley, West Yorkshire, BD22 6RA
ⓣ (01535) 606531
ⓔ nursery@dalesviewnursery.yourideal.co.uk
ⓦ www.dalesviewnursery.co.uk
Contact: David Ellis & Eileen Morgan
Opening Times: 1000-1700 Wed-Sun & B/hols, Feb-Oct. Nov-Jan by appt. please telephone.
Min Mail Order UK: Nmc
Min Mail Order EU: Nmc
Cat. Cost: 4 x 1st class
Credit Cards: None
Specialities: Dwarf *Hebe, Saxifraga, Primula, Rhododendron, Fuchsia* & conifers.
Notes: Also sells wholesale.
Map Ref: N, C2

NDov DOVE COTTAGE NURSERY & GARDEN ⑤
23 Shibden Hall Road, Halifax, West Yorkshire, HX3 9XA
ⓣ (01422) 203553
ⓔ dovecottage.nursery@virgin.net
ⓦ www.dovecottagenursery.co.uk
Contact: Stephen & Kim Rogers
Opening Times: 1000-1800 Wed-Sun & B/hols Feb-Sep. Closed Sun Aug & Sep.

Cat. Cost: Free
Credit Cards: All major credit/debit cards
Specialities: *Helleborus* & selected perennials & grasses for naturalistic planting.
Notes: Also sells wholesale.
Map Ref: N, D2 OS Grid Ref: SE115256

NDvn DEVINE NURSERIES ⊠ ⊠ ♠ €
Withernsea Road, Hollym, East Yorkshire, HU19 2QJ
ⓣ (01964) 613840
ⓕ (01964) 613840
ⓔ T1onys@hotmail.com
ⓦ www.devinenurseries.co.uk
Contact: Tony Devine
Opening Times: Not open.
Min Mail Order UK: Nmc
Min Mail Order EU: Nmc
Cat. Cost: 4 x 1st class
Credit Cards: Visa MasterCard
Specialities: *Gladiolus*, alliums, *Eremurus*, bulbous.
Notes: Also sells wholesale.

NEgg EGGLESTON HALL GARDENS ⊠ €
Eggleston, Barnard Castle, Co. Durham, DL12 0AG
ⓣ (01833) 650115
ⓕ (01833) 650971
ⓔ mbhock@btinternet.com
ⓦ www.egglestonhallgardens.co.uk
Contact: Malcolm Hockham, Gordon Long
Opening Times: 1000-1700 7 days.
Min Mail Order UK: £12.95
Cat. Cost: Online only.
Credit Cards: All major credit/debit cards
Specialities: Rare & unusual plants with particular emphasis on flower arranging.
Notes: Mail order for *Celmisia spectabilis* Oct-Mar only. Also sells wholesale.
Map Ref: N, C2 OS Grid Ref: NY997233

NEqu EQUATORIAL PLANT CO. ⊠ ⊠ ♠ €
7 Gray Lane, Barnard Castle, Co. Durham, DL12 8PD
ⓣ (01833) 690519
ⓕ (01833) 690519
ⓔ equatorialplants@teesdaleonline.co.uk
ⓦ www.equatorialplants.com
Contact: Dr Richard Warren
Opening Times: By appt. only.
Min Mail Order UK: Nmc
Min Mail Order EU: Nmc
Cat. Cost: Free
Credit Cards: Visa Access
Specialities: Laboratory raised orchids only.
Notes: Also sells wholesale.

NFir FIR TREES PELARGONIUM NURSERY
⊠ ♁ ⅃
Stokesley, Middlesbrough, Cleveland,
TS9 5LD
Ⓣ (01642) 713066
Ⓕ (01642) 713066
Ⓦ www.firtreespelargoniums.co.uk
Contact: Helen Bainbridge
Opening Times: 1000-1600 7 days 1st Apr-31st
Aug, 1000-1600 Mon-Fri 1st Sep-31st Mar.
Min Mail Order UK: £3.00 + p&p
Cat. Cost: 4 x 1st class or £1.00 coin
Credit Cards: Visa MasterCard Switch
Specialities: All types of *Pelargonium*: fancy
leaf, regal, decorative regal, oriental regal,
angel, miniature, zonal, ivy leaf, stellar,
scented, dwarf, unique, golden stellar & sp.
Map Ref: N, C2

NFla FLAXTON HOUSE NURSERY
Flaxton, York, North Yorkshire, Y060 7RJ
Ⓣ (01904) 468753
Ⓕ (01904) 468753
Contact: Mrs H Williams
Opening Times: 1000-1700 Tue-Sun 1st
Mar-mid-Oct.
Cat. Cost: 2 x 1st class
Credit Cards: None
Specialities: Wide general range of herbaceous
& alpines with many unusual plants. Selection
of climbers & shrubs. Plants available in small
quantities, so phone before travelling.
Notes: Accessible for wheelchair users with
assistance.
Map Ref: N, C2 **OS Grid Ref:** SE678625

NFor FORD NURSERY ⊠ ⅃
Castle Gardens, Ford, Berwick-upon-Tweed,
TD15 2PZ
Ⓣ (01890) 820379
Ⓕ (01890) 820594
Ⓔ sales@fordnursery.co.uk
Ⓦ www.FordNursery.co.uk
Contact: Roy Harmeston
Opening Times: 0930-1700 7 days Mar-Sep,
0930-1630 Mon-Fri Nov-Feb.
Min Mail Order UK: £10.00
Cat. Cost: None issued
Credit Cards: All major credit/debit cards
Specialities: Over 1200 different species of
container grown hardy ornamental shrubs,
perennials, trees & herbs, climbers & grasses.
Map Ref: N, A2

NGby GILBEY'S PLANTS ⊠ ♁ € ⅃
(office) 42 Park Street, Masham, Ripon,
North Yorkshire, HG4 4HN
Ⓣ (01765) 689927:(01845) 525285
Ⓕ (01765) 689927
Ⓔ gilbeyplants@aol.com
Contact: Giles N Gilbey
Opening Times: 1000-1700 Mon-Sat, 1400-
1700 Sun, 1st Mar-1st Oct. Winter by appt.
only.
Min Mail Order UK: Nmc
Min Mail Order EU: Nmc
Cat. Cost: 4 x 1st class
Credit Cards: All major credit/debit cards
Specialities: Unusual hardy perennials &
ferns.
Notes: Mail order Oct-Mar only. Nursery at
The Walled Garden, Cemetery Road, Thirsk
YO7 4DL. Also sells wholesale.
Map Ref: N, C2

NGdn GARDEN HOUSE NURSERIES ⅃
The Square, Dalston, Carlisle,
Cumbria,
CA5 7LL
Ⓣ (01228) 710297
Ⓔ david@gardenhousenursery.co.uk
Ⓦ www.gardenhousenursery.co.uk
Contact: David Hickson
Opening Times: 0900-1700 7 days Mar-Oct.
Cat. Cost: None issued, plant list online
Credit Cards: None
Specialities: *Geranium, Hosta, Hemerocallis,
Iris*, grasses & bamboos.
Notes: Also sells wholesale.
Map Ref: N, B1 **OS Grid Ref:** NY369503

NGHP GREEN GARDEN HERBS ⊠ ♁ ⅃
13 West Bank, Carlton,
North Yorkshire,
DN14 9PZ
Ⓣ (01405) 860708
Ⓔ greengardenherbs@onetel.uk
Ⓦ www.greengardenherbs.co.uk
Contact: Sarah Clark, Stefan Vida
Opening Times: 1000-1700 Wed-Mon, Mar-
Sep. Other times by appt.
Min Mail Order UK: £10.00
Min Mail Order EU: £10.00
Cat. Cost: Free with sae or Online.
Credit Cards: All major credit/debit cards
Specialities: Herbs, aromatic, culinary,
medicinal & ornamental, incl. *Salvia,
Monarda, Thymus* & wide selection of
Lavandula. Plants & seed available.
Notes: Also sells wholesale.
Map Ref: N, D3 **OS Grid Ref:** SE626242

N

N

NHal HALLS OF HEDDON ⊠ ☒ 🅐
(Office) West Heddon Nurseries, Heddon-on-
the-Wall, Northumberland, NE15 0JS
Ⓣ (01661) 852445
Ⓕ (01661) 852398
Ⓔ orders@hallsofheddon.co.uk
Ⓦ www.hallsofheddon.co.uk
Contact: David Hall
Opening Times: 0900-1700 Mon-Sat 1000-
1700 Sun.
Min Mail Order UK: Nmc
Min Mail Order EU: £25.00 + p&p
Cat. Cost: 3 x 2nd class
Credit Cards: Visa MasterCard Switch Delta
Specialities: *Chrysanthemum* & *Dahlia*. Wide
range of herbaceous.
Notes: Mail order *Dahlia* & *Chrysanthemum*
only. EU & export *Dahlia* tubers only. Also
sells wholesale.
Map Ref: N, B2

NHar HARTSIDE NURSERY GARDEN ⊠ ☒ ♠
Nr Alston, Cumbria, CA9 3BL
Ⓣ (01434) 381372
Ⓕ (01434) 381372
Ⓔ Hartside@macunlimited.net
Ⓦ www.hartsidenursery.co.uk
Contact: S L & N Huntley
Opening Times: 0930-1630 Mon-Fri, 1230-
1600 Sat, Sun & B/hols, mid Mar-31st Oct.
By appt. 1st Nov-mid Mar.
Min Mail Order UK: Nmc
Min Mail Order EU: £50.00 + p&p
Cat. Cost: 4 x 1st class or 3 x IRC
Credit Cards: All major credit/debit cards
Specialities: Alpines grown at altitude of 1100
feet in Pennines. *Primula*, ferns, *Gentian* &
Meconopsis.
Map Ref: N, B1

NHaw THE HAWTHORNES NURSERY ⊠ 🅐
Marsh Road, Hesketh Bank,
Nr Preston, Lancashire,
PR4 6XT
Ⓣ (01772) 812379
Ⓦ www.hawthornes-nursery.co.uk
Contact: Irene & Richard Hodson
Opening Times: 0900-1800 7 days 1st Mar-
30th Jun, Thu-Sun July-Oct. Gardens open
for NGS.
Min Mail Order UK: £10.00
Cat. Cost: 5 x 1st class
Credit Cards: None
Specialities: *Clematis*, honeysuckle, choice
selection of shrub & climbing roses, extensive
range of perennials, mostly on display in the
garden.
Map Ref: N, D1

NHer HERTERTON HOUSE GARDEN NURSERY
Hartington, Cambo,
Morpeth, Northumberland,
NE61 4BN
Ⓣ (01670) 774278
Contact: Mrs M Lawley & Mr Frank Lawley
Opening Times: 1330-1730 Mon Wed Fri-
Sun 1st Apr-end Sep. (Earlier or later in the
year weather permitting.)
Cat. Cost: None issued
Credit Cards: None
Specialities: Country garden flowers.
Map Ref: N, B2

NHHG HARDSTOFT HERB GARDEN 🅐
Hall View Cottage, Hardstoft,
Pilsley, Nr Chesterfield, Derbyshire,
S45 8AH
Ⓣ (01246) 854268
Contact: Lynne & Steve Raynor
Opening Times: 1000-1700 daily 15th Mar-
15th Sep. Closed Tue excl. Easter & B/hol
weeks.
Cat. Cost: Free
Credit Cards: MasterCard Switch Delta
Visa
Specialities: Wide range of herbs. Over 40
lavenders & 12 rosemary. Scented
pelargoniums. Nat. Coll. of *Echinacea*.
Notes: Wheelchair access to gardens, tearoom
& shop. Plant nursery aisles are narrow.
Map Ref: N, D2

NHol HOLDEN CLOUGH NURSERY ⊠ ☒ ♠ 🅐 ◆
Holden, Bolton-by-Bowland,
Clitheroe, Lancashire,
BB7 4PF
Ⓣ (01200) 447615
Ⓕ (01200) 447197
Ⓔ enquiries@holdencloughnursery.co.uk
Ⓦ www.holdencloughnursery.co.uk
Contact: P J Foley
Opening Times: 0900-1630 Mon-Fri Mar-
Oct & B/hol Mons, 0900-1630 Sat all year,
1300-1630 Easter Sun & Sun May B/hol
w/ends. Closed 25th Dec-2nd Jan 2006 &
Good Fri. Other times by appt. only.
Min Mail Order UK: Nmc
Min Mail Order EU: Nmc
Cat. Cost: £1.50
Credit Cards: Visa MasterCard Delta
Specialities: Large general list incl. *Crocosmia*,
Primula, *Saxifraga*, *Sempervivum*, *Jovibarba*,
Astilbe, grasses, *Hosta*, heathers &
Rhododendron.
Notes: Seasonal mail order on some items.
Also sells wholesale.
Map Ref: N, C2 OS Grid Ref: SD773496

NHor   HORN'S GARDEN CENTRE 🔲
Dixon Estate, Shotton Colliery, Co. Durham,
DH6 2PX
Ⓣ (0191) 526 2987
Ⓕ (0191) 526 2889
Contact: G Horn & Theresa Horn
Opening Times: 0900-1730 Mon-Sat 1000-
1600 Sun, all year excl. Easter Mon.
Cat. Cost: 3 x 1st class
Credit Cards: All major credit/debit cards
Specialities: *Fuchsia, Solenostemon*. Wide range
of trees, shrubs & perennials.
Map Ref: N, B2

NJOw   JOHN OWEN NURSERIES ✉
20 West Bank, Carlton, Nr Goole,
East Yorkshire, DN14 9PZ
Ⓣ (01405) 861415 (m.) 07762 650131
Ⓕ (01405) 861415
Ⓔ johnowen-nurseries@njow.fsnet.co.uk
Contact: John D W Owen
Opening Times: By appt. only.
Min Mail Order UK: Nmc
Cat. Cost: 3 x 2nd class
Credit Cards: None
Specialities: Alpines & perennials, especially
*Allium, Campanula, Dianthus, Oxalis, Primula
& Saxifraga*. A few varieties available in small
quantities only.
Map Ref: N, D3 OS Grid Ref: SE629243

NLan   LANDLIFE WILDFLOWERS LTD ✉ 🔲
National Wildflower Centre, Court Hey Park,
Liverpool, L16 3NA
Ⓣ (0151) 737 1819
Ⓕ (0151) 737 1820
Ⓔ gill@landlife.org.uk
Ⓦ www.wildflower.org.uk
Contact: Gillian Watson
Opening Times: 1000-1700, 7 days, 1 Apr-
30 Sep only.
Min Mail Order UK: £30.00 (plants), no
min. for seeds.
Cat. Cost: Sae + 2 x 2nd class
Credit Cards: Visa Delta Access Switch Solo
Specialities: Wild herbaceous plants & seeds.
Notes: Cafe & shop. Admission charge for
visitor centre. Also sells wholesale.
Map Ref: N, D1

NLAp   LANESIDE ALPINES ✉ 🐾 🔲
74 Croston Road, Garstang, Preston,
Lancashire, PR3 1HR
Ⓣ (01995) 605537
Ⓜ 0794 6659661
Ⓔ jcrhutch@aol.com
Ⓦ www.lanesidealpines.com
Contact: Jeff Hutchings

Opening Times: 0930-1630 Thu-Sat, 1st
Mar-30th Sep. 1000-1600 Sun.
Min Mail Order UK: Nmc
Cat. Cost: Sae
Specialities: Alpines, incl. gentians, *Penstemon*
species, primulas, *Saxifraga*, dwarf evergreen
shrubs, hardy orchids, New Zealand plants,
planted bowls & planted tufa. Many sp. in
small quantities.
Notes: Mail order orchids, auriculas, primulas,
saxifrage & trough plants. Nursery at Bells
Bridge Lane, off Cockerham Rd, Garstang.
Map Ref: N, D1

NLar   LARCH COTTAGE NURSERIES ✉ € 🔲 ◆
Melkinthorpe, Penrith, Cumbria, CA10 2DR
Ⓣ (01931) 712404
Ⓕ (01931) 712727
Ⓔ plants@larchcottage.freeserve.co.uk
Ⓦ www.larchcottagenurseries.com
Contact: Joanne McCullock/Peter Stott
Opening Times: Daily from 1000-1730.
Min Mail Order UK: Nmc
Min Mail Order EU: Nmc
Cat. Cost: £3.50
Credit Cards: Visa Access Switch Delta Solo
Specialities: Unusual & old fashioned
perennials. Rare & dwarf conifers. Unusual
shrubs & trees.
Map Ref: N, C1 OS Grid Ref: NY315602

NLLv   LEEDS LAVENDER ✉
at Greenscapes Nursery, Brandon Crescent,
Shadwell, Leeds, LS17 9JH
Ⓣ (0113) 2892922
Ⓦ www.leedslavender.co.uk
Contact: Ruth Dorrington
Opening Times: 1000-1630, Mon-Fri, 1000-
1700 Sat & Sun all year round, or by appt.
Min Mail Order UK: Nmc
Cat. Cost: 2 x 1st class
Credit Cards: None
Specialities: *Lavandula*. Limited numbers of
particular varieties available at certain times,
especially at end of summer.
Notes: Wheelchair access difficult in some
areas. Also sells wholesale.
Map Ref: N, D2

NLRH   LITTLE RED HEN NURSERIES ✉
91 Denholme Road, Oxenhope, Keighley,
West Yorkshire, BD22 9SJ
Ⓣ (01535) 643786

Ⓔ louise@redhens.co.uk
Ⓦ www.redhens.co.uk
Contact: Louise Harris
Opening Times: Please phone first.
Min Mail Order UK: Nmc
Cat. Cost: Free
Credit Cards: None
Specialities: Small nursery with limited stock.
Details in catalogue or on website.
Map Ref: N, D2 OS Grid Ref: SE045343

NMen MENDLE NURSERY ⊠ ♠ ♿
Holme, Scunthorpe, Lincolnshire,
DN16 3RF
Ⓣ (01724) 850864
Ⓔ annearnshaw@lineone.net
Ⓦ www.mendlenursery.com
Contact: Mrs A Earnshaw
Opening Times: 1000-1600 Tue-Sun.
Min Mail Order UK: Nmc
Min Mail Order EU: Nmc
Cat. Cost: 3 x 1st class
Credit Cards: All major credit/debit cards
Specialities: Many unusual alpines esp.
Saxifraga & *Sempervivum*.
Map Ref: N, D3 OS Grid Ref: SE925070

NMir MIRES BECK NURSERY ⊠ ♿
Low Mill Lane, North Cave, Brough, East
Riding, Yorkshire, HU15 2NR
Ⓣ (01430) 421543
Ⓔ admin@miresbeck.co.uk
Ⓦ www.miresbeck.co.uk
Contact: Irene Tinklin & Martin Rowland
Opening Times: 1000-1600 Wed-Sat 1st
Mar-30th Sep. 1000-1500 Wed-Fri 1st Oct-
30th Nov & by appt.
Min Mail Order UK: Nmc
Min Mail Order EU: Nmc
Cat. Cost: 3 x 1st class
Credit Cards: None
Specialities: Wild flower plants of Yorkshire
provenance.
Notes: Mail order for wild flower plants, plugs
& seeds only. Also sells wholesale.
Map Ref: N, D3 OS Grid Ref: SE889316

NMoo MOOR MONKTON NURSERIES ⊠ ♿
Moor Monkton, York Road, Nr York,
Yorkshire, YO26 8JJ
Ⓣ (01904) 738770
Ⓕ (01904) 738770
Ⓔ sales@bamboo-uk.co.uk
Ⓦ www.bamboo-uk.co.uk
Contact: Peter Owen
Opening Times: 0900-1700.
Min Mail Order UK: Nmc
Min Mail Order EU: £20.00

Cat. Cost: 5 x 2nd class or email for details.
Credit Cards: None
Specialities: Bamboos, palms, ferns, unusual
trees, shrubs & perennials.
Notes: Mail order for bamboo only.
Map Ref: N, C2

NMRc MILLRACE NURSERY ⊠ ♿
84 Selby Road, Garforth, Leeds, LS25 1LP
Ⓣ (0113) 286 9233
Ⓕ (0113) 286 9908
Contact: C Carthy
Opening Times: 1000-1700 Tue, Thu-Sun,
Mar-May & Tue, Thu-Sat Jun-Sep.
Min Mail Order UK: Nmc
Cat. Cost: 4 x 1st class
Credit Cards: None
Specialities: Unusual perennials, especially
drought-resistant, incl. hardy geraniums,
alliums, campanulas, penstemnons, potentillas
& veronicas. Some plants in small quantities.
Map Ref: N, D2

NMyG MARY GREEN ⊠ ♠
The Walled Garden, Hornby, Lancaster,
Lancashire, LA2 8LD
Ⓣ (01257) 270821, (m.) 07778 910348
Ⓕ (01257) 270821
Ⓔ Marygreenplants@aol.com
Contact: Mary Green
Opening Times: By appt. only.
Min Mail Order UK: £10.00
Cat. Cost: 4 x 1st class
Credit Cards: None
Specialities: Hostas, astilbes, ferns & other
shade-loving perennials.
Map Ref: N, C1 OS Grid Ref: SD588688

NNew NEWTON HILL ALPINES € ♿
335 Leeds Road, Wakefield, West Yorkshire,
WF1 2JH
Ⓣ (01924) 377056
Ⓔ newtalp@aol.com
Contact: Sheena Vigors
Opening Times: 0900-1700 Fri-Wed all year.
Closed Thu. Please phone first.
Cat. Cost: 2 x 1st class
Credit Cards: None
Specialities: Alpines esp. *Saxifraga*, also *Erica*,
conifers & dwarf shrubs.
Notes: Also sells wholesale.
Map Ref: N, D2 OS Grid Ref: SE328229

NNor NORCROFT NURSERIES ♿
Roadends, Intack, Southwaite, Carlisle,
Cumbria, CA4 0LH
Ⓣ (016974) 73933
Ⓜ 07789 050633

F (016974) 73969
E stellaandkeithbell@sbell44.fsnet.co.uk
Contact: Keith Bell
Opening Times: Every afternoon excl. Mon
but open B/hols.
Cat. Cost: 2 x 2nd class
Credit Cards: None
Specialities: Hardy herbaceous, ornamental
grasses, hostas, *Lilium, Hemerocallis,
Penstemon.*
Notes: Also sells wholesale.
Map Ref: N, B1 OS Grid Ref: NY474433

NOaD OAK DENE NURSERIES ⊠
10 Back Lane West, Royston, Barnsley, South
Yorkshire, S71 4SB
T (01226) 722253
F (01226) 722253
Contact: J Foster or G Foster
Opening Times: 0900-1800 1st Apr-30th
Sep, 1000-1600 1st Oct-31st Mar. (Closed
1230-1330.)
Min Mail Order UK: Please phone for further
info.
Cat. Cost: None issued.
Credit Cards: None
Specialities: Cacti, succulents & South
African *Lachenalia* bulbs.
Notes: Also sells wholesale.
Map Ref: N, D2

NOak OAK TREE NURSERY ⊠ ⋔ 🕭
Mill Lane, Barlow, Selby, North Yorkshire,
YO8 8EY
T (01757) 618409
Contact: Gill Plowes
Opening Times: By appt. only.
Min Mail Order UK: £10.00 + p&p
Cat. Cost: 2 x 1st class
Credit Cards: None
Specialities: Cottage garden plants, grasses &
ferns.
Map Ref: N, D3

NOGN THE ORNAMENTAL GRASS NURSERY ⊠ 🕭
Church Farm, Westgate, Rillington, Malton,
North Yorkshire, YO17 8LN
T (01944) 758247
M 07813 327886
F (01944) 758247
E sales@ornamentalgrass.co.uk
W www.ornamentalgrass.co.uk
Contact: Angela Kilby
Opening Times: 0930-1630 Sat & Sun, May
& Jun. Other times by appt.
Min Mail Order UK: Nmc
Cat. Cost: 4 x 1st class
Credit Cards: Visa MasterCard

Specialities: Ornamental grasses, bamboos,
ferns, hostas & herbaceous perennials,
alliums, *Eremurus.*
Notes: Mail order bulbs only. Also sells
wholesale.
Map Ref: N, C3

NOrc ORCHARD HOUSE NURSERY
Orchard House, Wormald Green, Nr
Harrogate, North Yorkshire, HG3 3NQ
T (01765) 677541
F (01765) 677541
Contact: Mr B M Corner
Opening Times: 0800-1630 Mon-Fri.
Cat. Cost: Retail catalogue available at nursery.
Credit Cards: None
Specialities: Herbaceous perennials, ferns,
grasses, water plants & unusual cottage
garden plants.
Notes: Also sells wholesale.
Map Ref: N, C2

NPal THE PALM FARM ⊠ € 🕭
Thornton Hall Gardens, Station Road,
Thornton Curtis, Nr Ulceby, Humberside,
DN39 6XF
T (01469) 531232
F (01469) 531232
E bill@thepalmfarm.com
W www.thepalmfarm.com
Contact: W W Spink
Opening Times: 1400-1700 7 days.
Min Mail Order UK: £11.00 + p&p
Min Mail Order EU: £25.00 + p&p
Cat. Cost: 1 x 2nd class
Credit Cards: None
Specialities: Hardy & half-hardy palms,
unusual trees, shrubs & conservatory plants.
Some plants available only in small quantities.
Notes: Euro payment if purchaser pays bank
commission. Mail order if small enough to
post (min. £12.50 p&p) or large enough to
go by Palletline (min. charge £35.00 p&p).
Also sells wholesale.
Map Ref: N, D3 OS Grid Ref: TA100183

**NPen PENTON MILL RHODODENDRONS ⊠ ▣
⋔ €**
Penton, Carlisle, Cumbria, CA6 5QU
T (01228) 577336
F (01228) 577336
E info@pentonmill.com
W www.pentonmill.com

N

N

Contact: Amanda Cullen
Opening Times: Vary, due to off-site working. Please phone first.
Min Mail Order UK: Nmc
Min Mail Order EU: Nmc
Cat. Cost: 6 x 1st class
Credit Cards: None
Specialities: Rhododendrons & azaleas. Some stock available in small quantities only.
Map Ref: N, B1 **OS Grid Ref:** NY434764

NPer   PERRY'S PLANTS ▣
The River Garden, Sleights, Whitby, North Yorkshire, YO21 1RR
T (01947) 810329
E perry@rivergardens.fsnet.co.uk
Contact: Pat & Richard Perry
Opening Times: 1000-1700 mid-March to Oct.
Cat. Cost: Large (A4) Sae
Credit Cards: None
Specialities: *Lavatera, Malva, Erysimum, Euphorbia, Anthemis, Osteospermum & Hebe.* Uncommon hardy & container plants & aquatic plants.
Map Ref: N, C3 **OS Grid Ref:** NZ869082

NPol   POLEMONIUM PLANTERY ✉ ☂ ▣
28 Sunnyside Terrace, Trimdon Grange, Trimdon Station, Co. Durham, TS29 6HF
T (01429) 881529
E DANDD@Polemonium.co.uk
W www.polemonium.co.uk
Contact: David or Dianne Nichol-Brown
Opening Times: Open for NGS 30 May 2004. Other times by appt. only. Donation to NGS please.
Min Mail Order UK: £10.00
Cat. Cost: Sae for list
Credit Cards: None
Specialities: Nat. Coll. of *Polemonium* & related genera, plus some rare North American plants. The collection holds scientific status.
Notes: Also sells wholesale.
Map Ref: N, B2 **OS Grid Ref:** NZ369353

NPri   PRIMROSE COTTAGE NURSERY ▣ ◆
Ringway Road, Moss Nook, Wythenshawe, Manchester, M22 5WF
T (0161) 437 1557
F (0161) 499 9932
E info@primrosecottagenursery.co.uk
W www.primrosecottagenursery.co.uk
Contact: Caroline Dumville
Opening Times: 0830-1730 Mon-Sat, 0930-1730 Sun (summer). 0830-1700 Mon-Sat, 0930-1700 Sun (winter).
Cat. Cost: 1 x 1st class
Credit Cards: All major credit/debit cards

Specialities: Hardy herbaceous perennials, alpines, herbs, roses, patio plants. Shrubs.
Map Ref: N, D2

NPro   PROUDPLANTS ☂ ▣
East of Eden Nurseries, Ainstable, Carlisle, Cumbria, CA4 9QN
T (01768) 896604
F (01768) 896604
Contact: Roger Proud
Opening Times: 0900-1800 7 days Mar-Nov. Other times by appt.
Cat. Cost: None issued
Credit Cards: None
Specialities: Interesting & unusual shrubs, perennials & alpines, esp. dwarf & ground cover plants.
Map Ref: N, B1 **OS Grid Ref:** HA1336186

NRar   RARER PLANTS ▣
Ashfield House, Austfield Lane, Monk Fryston, Leeds, LS25 5EH
T (01977) 682263
Contact: Anne Watson
Opening Times: 1000-1600 Sat & Sun 20th Feb-1st Apr.
Cat. Cost: Sae
Credit Cards: None
Specialities: *Helleborus* & *Galanthus.*
Map Ref: N, D2

NRib   RIBBLESDALE NURSERIES ▣
Newsham Hall Lane, Woodplumpton, Preston, Lancashire, PR4 0AS
T (01772) 863081
F (01772) 861884
Contact: Mr & Mrs Dunnett
Opening Times: 0900-1800 Mon-Sat Apr-Sep, 0900-1700 Mon-Sat Oct-Mar. 1030-1630 Sun.
Credit Cards: Visa MasterCard Delta Switch
Specialities: Trees, shrubs & perennials. Conifers, hedging, alpines, fruit, climbers, herbs, aquatics, ferns & wildflowers.
Map Ref: N, D1 **OS Grid Ref:** SD515351

NRnb   RAINBOW PLANTS
Springvale Nursery, Springvale, Penistone, Sheffield, Yorkshire, S36 6HJ
T (m.) 07798 691853
E gilly@cockerline.force9.co.uk
Contact: Brian Cockerline

NRob   W ROBINSON & SONS LTD ✉ ⚑ € ▣
Sunny Bank, Forton, Nr Preston, Lancashire, PR3 0BN
T (01524) 791210
F (01524) 791933

(E) info@mammothonion.co.uk
(W) www.mammothonion.co.uk
Contact: Miss Robinson
Opening Times: 0900-1700 7 days Mar-Jun,
0800-1700 Mon-Fri Jul-Feb.
Min Mail Order UK: Nmc
Min Mail Order EU: Nmc
Cat. Cost: Free
Credit Cards: Visa Access American Express
Switch
Specialities: Mammoth vegetable seed.
Onions, leeks, tomatoes & beans. Range of
vegetable plants in the spring.
Notes: Also sells wholesale.

NRya   RYAL NURSERY ⊠ ⬓
East Farm Cottage, Ryal, Northumberland,
NE20 0SA
(T) (01661) 886562
(F) (01661) 886918
(E) alpines@ryal.freeserve.co.uk
Contact: R F Hadden
Opening Times: Mar-Jul 1300-1600 Mon-
Tue but please phone first, 1000-1600 Sun &
other times by appt.
Min Mail Order UK: £10.00 + p&p
Min Mail Order EU: £10.00 + p&p
Cat. Cost: Sae
Credit Cards: None
Specialities: Alpine & woodland plants.
Mainly available in small quantities only.
Notes: Also sells wholesale.
Map Ref: N, B2 **OS Grid Ref:** NZ015744

NSco   SCOTT'S WILDFLOWERS ⊠ ⬓
Swallow Hill Barn, 31 Common Side,
Distington, Workington, Cumbria, CA14 4PU
(T) (01946) 830486
(E) wildflowers@btinternet.com
(W) www.scottswildflowers.co.uk
Contact: Ted Scott
Opening Times: 1000-1600 Mar-Oct, 1130-
1500 Nov-Feb, 7 days.
Min Mail Order UK: £6.00 + p&p
Cat. Cost: 3 x 1st class
Specialities: Native British wildflowers,
including aquatics.
Notes: Also sells wholesale.
Map Ref: N, C1

NScw   SCAWSBY HALL NURSERIES ⊠ ⬓
Barnsley Road, Scawsby, Doncaster, South
Yorkshire, DN5 7UB
(T) (01302) 782585
(F) (01302) 783434
(E) mail@the-plant-directory.com
(W) www.the-plant-directory.com
Contact: David Lawson

Opening Times: 0930-1730 Mon-Sat, 1100-
1700 Sun, Mar-Sep, 0930-1700 Mon-Sat
1100-1700 Sun, Oct-Feb.
Min Mail Order UK: Nmc
Min Mail Order EU: Nmc
Cat. Cost: None issued
Credit Cards: Maestro Visa MasterCard Solo
Specialities: A wide range of herbaceous
perennials, hardy trees, shrubs & indoor plants.
Map Ref: N, D3 **OS Grid Ref:** SE542049

NSfd   SPRINGFIELD NURSERIES ⊠ ⬓
Back Gisburn Road, Blacko, Nr Nelson,
Lancashire, BB9 6LT
(T) (01282) 690518
(F) (01282) 690518
(E) yvonneholden@tiscali.co.uk
Contact: Peter & Yvonne Holden
Opening Times: Not open. Mail order only.
Min Mail Order UK: Nmc
Cat. Cost: 2 x 1st class.
Credit Cards: None
Specialities: *Campanulaceae* family.
Notes: Mail order seeds & plants. Also sells
wholesale.

NShi   SHIRLEY'S PLANTS ⊠ ⬓
6 Sandheys Drive, Churchtown,
Southport, Merseyside,
PR9 9PQ
(T) (01704) 213048
(M) 07951 834066
(W) www.stbegonias.com
Contact: Shirley & Terry Tasker
Opening Times: By appt. only.
Min Mail Order UK: Nmc
Cat. Cost: 2 x 1st class
Credit Cards: None
Specialities: Nat. Coll. of *Begonia* species &
hybrids.
Map Ref: N, D1 **OS Grid Ref:** SD355183

NSla   SLACK TOP NURSERIES ⊠ ⬓ € ⬓
Hebden Bridge, West Yorkshire,
HX7 7HA
(T) (01422) 845348
Contact: M R or R Mitchell
Opening Times: 1000-1700 Wed-Sun 1st
Mar-30th Sep & B/hol Mons 1st Mar-30th
Sep.
Min Mail Order UK: £20.00
Cat. Cost: Sae
Credit Cards: None

N

Specialities: Alpine & rockery plants. *Celmisia semi-cordata, Gentiana, Saxifraga, Primula, Hepatica, Paeonia & Pulsatilla.*
Notes: Also sells wholesale.
Map Ref: N, D2 OS Grid Ref: SD977286

NSpr SPRINGWOOD PLEIONES ⊠ ☑ ♠ € ⑤
8 Tredgold Avenue, Leeds, LS16 9BU
Ⓣ (0113) 230 1158
Ⓔ simon@pleiones.com
Ⓦ www.pleiones.com
Contact: Simon Redshaw
Opening Times: By appt. only.
Min Mail Order UK: £3.00 + p&p
Min Mail Order EU: £3.00 + p&p
Cat. Cost: 1 x 1st class
Credit Cards: None
Specialities: *Pleione.*
Map Ref: N, D2 OS Grid Ref: SE256429

NSRo SCENTED ROSES ⑤
Stewart Hill Cottage, Near Hesket
Newmarket, Cumbria, CA7 8HX
Ⓣ (01768) 484172
Ⓕ (01768) 484172
Contact: Iain Billot
Opening Times: 1300-1700 Thu-Sun May-mid-July. Nov-May by arrangement
Cat. Cost: Free.
Credit Cards: None
Specialities: Roses. Carefully selected to survive in a wet, cold climate, such as Cumbria. Ramblers & climbers a speciality.
Notes: Also sells wholesale.
Map Ref: N, B1 OS Grid Ref: NY365354

NSti STILLINGFLEET LODGE NURSERIES ⊠ ⑤
Stillingfleet, North Yorkshire, YO19 6HP
Ⓣ (01904) 728506
Ⓕ (01904) 728506
Ⓔ vanessa.cook@still-lodge.freeserve.co.uk
Ⓦ www.stillingfleetlodgenurseries.co.uk
Contact: Vanessa Cook
Opening Times: 1000-1600 Tue Wed Fri & Sat 1st Apr-18th Oct. Closed Sat in Aug.
Min Mail Order UK: Nmc
Cat. Cost: 10 x 2nd class
Credit Cards: None
Specialities: Foliage & unusual perennials. Hardy *Geranium, Pulmonaria,* variegated plants & grasses. Nat. Coll. of *Pulmonaria.*
Notes: Mail order Nov-mid Mar only.
Map Ref: N, C2

NTar TARLETON SPECIMEN PLANTS ♠ € ⑤
Gorse Lane, Tarleton, Preston, Lancashire,
PR4 6LH
Ⓣ (01772) 816879

Ⓕ (01772) 816226
Contact: Mr Aughton
Opening Times: 0900-1700, 7 days.
Min Mail Order UK: Nmc
Cat. Cost: None issued.
Credit Cards: All major credit/debit cards
Specialities: Large specimen plants, shrubs, palms, topiary. Large pot herbaceous, acers, screening plants.
Notes: Also sells wholesale.
Map Ref: N, D1

NTay TAYLORS CLEMATIS NURSERY ⊠ ♠ ⑤ ♦
Sutton Road, Sutton, Nr. Askern,
Doncaster, South Yorkshire, DN6 9JZ
Ⓣ (01302) 700716
Ⓕ (01302) 708415
Ⓔ info@taylorsclematis.co.uk
Ⓦ www.taylorsclematis.co.uk
Contact: John Taylor
Opening Times: 1000-1600, 15th Feb-15th Nov. Phone for opening times 16th Nov-14th Feb.
Min Mail Order UK: 1 plant + p&p
Cat. Cost: free
Credit Cards: All major credit/debit cards
Specialities: *Clematis* (over 300 varieties).
Notes: Also sells wholesale.
Map Ref: N, D2 OS Grid Ref: SE552121

NTHB TAVISTOCK HERB NURSERY ⊠ ♠
Tavistock, Preston Old Road, Clifton,
Lancashire, PR4 0ZA
Ⓣ (01772) 683505
Ⓕ (01772) 683505
Ⓔ tavistockherbs@themail.co.uk
Contact: Mrs C Jones
Opening Times: By appt. only.
Min Mail Order UK: Nmc
Cat. Cost: 2 x 1st class stamps
Credit Cards: None
Specialities: Herbs. *Mentha* & *Thymus* species.
Notes: Main nursery at Garstang Road, Barton, near Preston, Lancs. Also sells wholesale.
Map Ref: N, D1

NVic THE VICARAGE GARDEN ⊠ ⑤
Carrington, Manchester, M31 4AG
Ⓣ (0161) 775 2750
Ⓔ info@vicaragebotanicalgardens.co.uk
Ⓦ www.vicaragebotanicalgardens.co.uk
Contact: Paul Haine
Opening Times: 0900-1700 Mon-Sat, closed Thu. 1000-1630 Sun all year.
Min Mail Order UK: Nmc
Cat. Cost: 2 x 2nd class for list
Credit Cards: All major credit/debit cards

Specialities: Herbaceous, alpines, grasses, ferns.
Notes: Free admission to 7 acre gardens.
Map Ref: N, D2 OS Grid Ref: SJ729926

NWCA   WHITE COTTAGE ALPINES ⊠ ♪ 🅐 ◆
Sunnyside Nurseries, Hornsea Road,
Sigglesthorne, East Yorkshire,
HU11 5QL
Ⓣ (01964) 542692
Ⓕ (01964) 542692
Ⓔ plants@whitecottagealpines.co.uk
Ⓦ www.whitecottagealpines.co.uk
Contact: Sally E Cummins
Opening Times: 1000-1700 (or dusk) Thu-
Sun & B/hol Mon 1 Mar-30 Sep. If travelling
far, please phone first. In winter by appt. only.
Min Mail Order UK: Nmc.
Min Mail Order EU: £15.00 + p&p by card
only.
Cat. Cost: 4 x 1st class
Credit Cards: Visa MasterCard Switch
Specialities: Alpines & rock plants. 500+
species incl. American, dwarf *Salix* &
Helichrysum, also increasing range of *Penstemon*.
Notes: Euro payments by card only.
Map Ref: N, C3

NWea   WEASDALE NURSERIES LTD. ⊠ €
Newbiggin-on-Lune, Kirkby Stephen,
Cumbria, CA17 4LX
Ⓣ (01539) 623246
Ⓕ (01539) 623277
Ⓔ sales@weasdale.com
Ⓦ www.weasdale.com
Contact: Andrew Forsyth
Opening Times: 0830-1730 Mon-Fri. Closed
w/ends, B/hols, Xmas through to the New Year.
Min Mail Order UK: Nmc
Min Mail Order EU: Nmc
Cat. Cost: £2.00 or 7 x 1st class. £2.50 by
credit/debit card
Credit Cards: All major credit/debit cards
Specialities: Hardy forest trees, hedging,
broadleaved & conifers. Specimen trees &
shrubs grown at 850 feet (260 metre) elevation.
Notes: Mail order Nov-Apr only.
Map Ref: N, C1

NWit   D S WITTON ⊠
26 Casson Drive, Harthill, Sheffield,
Yorkshire, S26 7WA
Ⓣ (01909) 771366
Ⓕ (01909) 771366
Ⓔ donshardyeuphorbias@btopenworld.com
Contact: Don Witton
Opening Times: By appt. only.
Min Mail Order UK: Nmc
Cat. Cost: 1 x 1st class + sae

Specialities: Nat. Coll. of Hardy *Euphorbia*.
Over 130 varieties.
Notes: Mail order *Euphorbia* seed only.
Map Ref: N, D2 OS Grid Ref: SK494812

NZep   ZEPHYRWUDE IRISES ⊠
48 Blacker Lane, Crigglestone, Wakefield,
West Yorkshire, WF4 3EW
Ⓣ (01924) 252101
Ⓜ 07813 978165
Ⓔ zephyrwude@aol.com
Ⓦ http://hometown.aol.co.uk/zephyrwude
Contact: Richard L Brook
Opening Times: Mail order only. Viewing by
appt. 0900-dusk most days May-early June,
peak late May. Phone 0900-2300.
Min Mail Order UK: £15.00 + p&p
Min Mail Order EU: £15.00 + p&p
Cat. Cost: Contact nursery for details.
Credit Cards: None
Specialities: Bearded *Iris*, 1970s-80s hybrids
only. Mainly 12" dwarf & intermediate, a few
tall. Delivery Aug-Oct only.
Map Ref: N, D2 OS Grid Ref: SE302161

SOUTHERN

**SAdn   ASHDOWN FOREST GARDEN CENTRE
& NURSERY** 🅐
Duddleswell, Ashdown Forest, Nr Uckfield,
East Sussex, TN22 3JP
Ⓣ (01825) 712300
Ⓦ www.ashdownforestgardencentre.co.uk
Contact: Victoria Tolton
Opening Times: 0900-1730 winter, 0900-
1900 summer.
Credit Cards: All major credit/debit cards
Specialities: Ornamental grasses, *Lavandula*,
fuchsias.
Notes: Also sells wholesale.
Map Ref: S, C4

SAft   AFTON PARK NURSERY ♪ 🅐
Newport Road, Afton, Freshwater, Isle of
Wight, PO40 9XR
Ⓣ (01983) 755774,
Ⓜ 09665 43031
Ⓔ chris@aftonpark.co.uk
Ⓦ www.aftonpark.co.uk
Contact: Chris Barnes
Opening Times: 0930-1700 7 days1st Mar-
end Nov. Winter, please phone first.
Cat. Cost: 4 x 1st class

KEY: ⊠ Mail order to UK or EU ♪ Delivers to shows
🅧 Exports beyond EU € Euro accepted
🅐 Accessible by wheelchair ◆ See Display advertisement

Credit Cards: Visa MasterCard
Specialities: Wide general range, emphasis on unusual perennials, grasses, coastal shrubs & plants for Mediterranean gardens.
Map Ref: S, D2 OS Grid Ref: SZ349864

SAga AGAR'S NURSERY €
Agars Lane, Hordle, Lymington, Hampshire, SO41 0FL
℗ (01590) 683703
Contact: Diana Tombs, Debbie Ursell
Opening Times: 1000-1700 Fri-Wed (closed Thu) Mar-Sep, 1000-1600 Fri-Mon (closed Tue-Thu) Feb & Oct-Dec, or by appt.
Credit Cards: None
Specialities: *Penstemon* & *Salvia*. Also wide range of hardy plants incl. hardy & tender shrubs, climbers & herbaceous.
Map Ref: S, D2

S

SAin AINSWORTH DISPLAYS ⊠ ṅ
5 Kentidge Road, Waterlooville, Hampshire, PO7 5NH
℗ (023) 92 255057
Ⓔ Britishpalms@aol.com
Contact: Mark Ainsworth
Opening Times: Not open. Mail order only.
Min Mail Order UK: £10.00 + p&p
Cat. Cost: 2 x 1st class for price list.
Credit Cards: Visa MasterCard
Specialities: Palm trees.
Notes: Also sells wholesale.

SAll ALLWOOD BROS ⊠ ṅ
London Road, Hassocks, West Sussex, BN6 9NB
℗ (01273) 844229
Ⓕ (01273) 846022
Ⓔ info@allwoodbros.co.uk
Ⓦ www.allwoodbros.co.uk
Contact: David James or Emma
Opening Times: 0900-1630 Mon-Fri. Answer machine all other times.
Min Mail Order UK: Nmc
Min Mail Order EU: Nmc
Cat. Cost: 2 x 1st class
Credit Cards: Visa Access MasterCard Switch
Specialities: *Dianthus* incl. hardy border carnations, pinks, perpetual & *Allwoodii*, some available as seed.
Notes: Exports seed only.
Map Ref: S, D4

SAPC ARCHITECTURAL PLANTS (CHICHESTER) LTD ⊠ ṅ € ◆
Lidsey Road Nursery, Westgate, Nr Chichester, West Sussex, PO20 6SU
℗ (01243) 545008

Ⓕ (01243) 545009
Ⓔ chichester@architecturalplants.com
Ⓦ www.architecturalplants.com
Contact: Christine Shaw
Opening Times: 1000-1600 Sun-Fri all year. Closed Sat & B/hol Mons. Open Good Fri.
Min Mail Order UK: Nmc
Min Mail Order EU: £150.00 + p&p
Cat. Cost: Free
Credit Cards: All major credit/debit cards
Specialities: Architectural plants & hardy exotics esp. rare evergreen broadleaved trees & seaside exotics, spiky plants, yuccas/agaves.
Notes: Also sells wholesale.
Map Ref: S, D3

SArc ARCHITECTURAL PLANTS ⊠ ṅ € ◆
Cooks Farm, Nuthurst, Horsham, West Sussex, RH13 6LH
℗ (01403) 891772
Ⓕ (01403) 891056
Ⓔ enquiries@architecturalplants.com
Ⓦ www.architecturalplants.com
Contact: Christine Shaw
Opening Times: 0900-1700 Mon-Sat, closed Sun.
Min Mail Order UK: Nmc
Min Mail Order EU: £150.00 + p&p
Cat. Cost: Free
Credit Cards: All major credit/debit cards
Specialities: Architectural plants & hardy exotics & rare broadleaved trees, bamboos & spiky plants.
Notes: Second nursery near Chichester, code SAPC. Also sells wholesale.
Map Ref: S, C3

SBai STEVEN BAILEY LTD ⊠
Silver Street, Sway, Lymington, Hampshire, SO41 6ZA
℗ (01590) 682227
Ⓕ (01590) 683765
Ⓦ www.steven-bailey.co.uk
Contact: Stef Bailey
Opening Times: 1000-1600 all year.
Credit Cards: Visa MasterCard Switch
Specialities: Carnations, pinks, *Alstroemeria* & penstemons.
Notes: Mail order *Alstroemeria* only. Also sells wholesale.
Map Ref: S, D2

SBch BIRCHWOOD PLANTS
(office) 10 Westering, Romsey, Hampshire, SO51 7LY
℗ (01794) 502192
Ⓔ lesleybaker@lycos.co.uk
Ⓦ www.birchwoodplants.co.uk

S

Contact: Lesley Baker
Opening Times: By appt. only at nursery for collection of plants. Plants available at Mottisfont Abbey (NT) but ring first to check availability.
Cat. Cost: Free by email or 5 x 1st class.
Credit Cards: None
Specialities: Wide range of plants, mainly herbaceous, many unusual. Salvias, geraniums, grasses & herbs. Good range for bees & butterflies. Some stock in small quantities.
Notes: Nursery at Gardener's Lane, Nr. Romsey, SO51 6AD. Mottisfont accessible for wheelchairs.
Map Ref: S, D2 OS Grid Ref: SU333190

SBig   BIG PLANT NURSERY ⊠
Hole Street, Ashington, West Sussex, RH20 3DE
Ⓣ (01903) 891466
Ⓕ (01903) 892829
Ⓔ info@bigplantnursery.co.uk
Ⓦ www.bigplantnursery.co.uk
Contact: Bruce Jordan
Opening Times: 0900-1700 Mon-Sat, 1000-1600 Sun & B/hols.
Min Mail Order UK: Please phone for info.
Cat. Cost: A5 sae with 2 x 1st class
Credit Cards: All major credit/debit cards
Specialities: Bamboos, hardy exotics & palms.
Notes: Also sells wholesale.

SBir   BIRCHFLEET NURSERY
Nyewood, Petersfield, Hampshire, GU31 5JQ
Ⓣ (01730) 821636
Ⓕ (01730) 821636
Ⓔ gammoak@aol.com
Ⓦ www.birchfleetnurseries.co.uk
Contact: John & Daphne Gammon
Opening Times: By appt. only. Please phone.
Cat. Cost: 2 x 1st class
Credit Cards: None
Specialities: Oaks. Beech. *Carpinus*. Nat. Coll. of *Liquidambar*.
Notes: Nursery accessible for wheelchairs in dry weather.
Map Ref: S, C3

SBla   BLACKTHORN NURSERY € ♿
Kilmeston, Alresford, Hampshire, SO24 0NL
Ⓣ (01962) 771796
Ⓕ (01962) 771071
Contact: A R & S B White
Opening Times: 0900-1700 Fri & Sat only, 4th Mar-25th Jun & 2nd-24th Sep 2005. 1000-1600 every 2nd & 4th Fri & Sat, Jan, Feb, Mar & Sep 2006.

Cat. Cost: Plant list for 3 x 1st class
Credit Cards: None
Specialities: Choice perennials & alpines, esp. *Daphne, Epimedium, Helleborus* & *Hepatica*.
Map Ref: S, C2 OS Grid Ref: SU590264

SBLw   BRIAN LEWINGTON ⊠ ♿
(office) 9 Meadow Rise, Horam, Heathfield, East Sussex, TN21 0LZ
Ⓣ (01435) 810124
Ⓕ (01435) 810124
Ⓔ BHLewington@aol.com
Ⓦ www.treesandhedges.co.uk
Contact: Brian Lewington
Opening Times: 0800-1700 Sat. Other times by appt. only.
Min Mail Order UK: Nmc
Specialities: Larger size trees and hedging.
Notes: Nursery is at Leverett Farm, Dallington, nr Heathfield, Sussex. Also sells wholesale.
Map Ref: S, D4 OS Grid Ref: TQ578172

SBod   BODIAM NURSERY ⊠ ♿
Cowfield Cottage, Bodiam, Robertsbridge, East Sussex, TN32 5RA
Ⓣ (01580) 830811
Ⓕ (01580) 831989
Ⓔ daniseymour@hotmail.com
Ⓦ www.bodiamnursery.co.uk
Contact: Danielle Seymour
Opening Times: 1000-1700 7 days. Closed Mon, Nov-Feb.
Min Mail Order UK: £5.00
Cat. Cost: 4 x 1st class
Credit Cards: Visa MasterCard Solo JCB
Specialities: Herbaceous perennials, grasses, conifers, *Camellia* & climbers. Acers. Shrubs, trees.
Map Ref: S, C5

SBra   J BRADSHAW & SON ⊠ ♪ ♿ ◆
Busheyfield Nursery, Herne, Herne Bay, Kent, CT6 7LJ
Ⓣ (01227) 375415
Ⓕ (01227) 375415
Contact: D J Bradshaw & Martin Bradshaw
Opening Times: 1000-1700 Tue-Sat 1st Mar-31st Oct & B/hol Mons. Other times by appt. only.
Min Mail Order UK: 2 plants + p&p
Cat. Cost: 2 x 1st class
Credit Cards: Visa MasterCard Switch

Specialities: *Clematis, Lonicera*, other climbers & wall shrubs.
Notes: Also sells wholesale.
Map Ref: S, C5 OS Grid Ref: TR174646

SBri   BRICKWALL COTTAGE NURSERY ⬛
1 Brickwall Cottages, Frittenden, Cranbrook, Kent, TN17 2DH
Ⓣ (01580) 852425
Ⓔ suemartin@brickcot.fsnet.co.uk
Contact: Sue Martin
Opening Times: By appt. only.
Credit Cards: None
Specialities: Hardy perennials. Stock in small quantities. *Geum, Potentilla* (herbaceous).
Map Ref: S, C5 OS Grid Ref: TQ815410

SBrm   BRAMBLY HEDGE ✉
Mill Lane, Sway, Hampshire, SO41 8LN
Ⓣ (01590) 683570
Ⓔ RWKW@waitrose.com
Contact: Kim Williams
Opening Times: 1000-1400 certain Sats, Jul-Oct, phone or write for dates.
Min Mail Order UK: Nmc
Cat. Cost: 9"x 7" sae
Credit Cards: None
Specialities: Nat. Coll. of *Streptocarpus*. Available in small quantities.
Notes: Mail order Mar-Oct.
Map Ref: S, D2 OS Grid Ref: SZ294973

SBrw   BROADWATER PLANTS ✉ ◆
Fairview Lane, Tunbridge Wells, Kent, TN3 9LU
Ⓣ (01892) 534760
Ⓕ (01892) 513149
Ⓔ Broadwaterplants@aol.com
Contact: John Moaby
Opening Times: 0900-1600 Mon-Sat.
Min Mail Order UK: Nmc
Cat. Cost: 3 x 1st class
Credit Cards: Visa MasterCard
Specialities: Rare & exciting plants, in addition to a range of rhododendrons & ericaceous plants. Limited stocks of some varieties.
Notes: Limited wheelchair access. Also sells wholesale.
Map Ref: S, C4 OS Grid Ref: TQ558377

SCac   CACTI & SUCCULENTS ✉
Hammerfield, Crockham Hill, Edenbridge, Kent, TN8 6RR
Ⓣ (01732) 866295
Contact: Geoff Southon
Opening Times: Flexible. Please phone first.

Min Mail Order UK: Nmc.
Cat. Cost: None issued.
Credit Cards: None
Specialities: *Echeveria* & related genera & hybrids. *Agave*, haworthias, aloes, gasterias, crassulas. (Large range of plants available in small quantities.)

SCam   CAMELLIA GROVE NURSERY ✉ ⬛ ♜ € ⬛
Market Garden, Lower Beeding, West Sussex, RH13 6PP
Ⓣ (01403) 891143
Ⓕ (01403) 891336
Ⓔ rhs20@camellia-grove.com
Ⓦ www.camellia-grove.com
Contact: Chris Loder
Opening Times: 1000-1600 Mon-Sat, please phone first so we can give you our undivided attention.
Min Mail Order UK: Nmc
Min Mail Order EU: £100.00 +p&p
Cat. Cost: 2 x 1st class
Credit Cards: Switch Visa MasterCard
Specialities: Camellias & azaleas.
Notes: Also sells wholesale.
Map Ref: S, C3

SChr   JOHN CHURCHER ✉ ⬛
47 Grove Avenue, Portchester, Fareham, Hampshire, PO16 9EZ
Ⓣ (023) 9232 6740
Ⓕ (023) 9232 6740
Ⓔ John@plants-palms.freeserve.co.uk
Contact: John Churcher
Opening Times: By appt. only. Please phone.
Min Mail Order UK: Nmc
Min Mail Order EU: Nmc
Cat. Cost: 4 x 1st class
Credit Cards: None
Specialities: Hardy *Opuntia, Aeonium, Agave, Aloe, Hedychium*, plus hardy bananas, palms, treeferns & echiums for the exotic Mediterranean garden.
Map Ref: S, D2 OS Grid Ref: SU614047

SCnR   COLIN ROBERTS ✉
Tragumna, Morgay Wood Lane, Three Oaks, Guestling, East Sussex, TN35 4NF
Ⓣ (m.) 07718 029909
Contact: Colin Roberts
Opening Times: Not open. Mail order only.
Min Mail Order UK: £20.00
Cat. Cost: 2 x 1st class
Credit Cards: None
Specialities: Dwarf bulbs & woodland plants incl. many rare & unusual, in small numbers.

SCog COGHURST CAMELLIAS ✉ ♕ € &
Ivy House Lane, Near Three Oaks, Hastings,
East Sussex, TN35 4NP
Ⓣ (01424) 756228
Ⓕ (01424) 428944
Ⓔ rotherview@btinternet.com
Ⓦ www.rotherview.com
Contact: R Bates & W Bates
Opening Times: 0930-1600 7 days.
Min Mail Order UK: Nmc
Min Mail Order EU: Nmc
Cat. Cost: 4 x 1st class
Credit Cards: All major credit/debit cards
Specialities: *Camellia*.
Notes: Also sells wholesale.
Map Ref: S, D5

SCoo COOLING'S NURSERIES LTD &
Rushmore Hill, Knockholt, Sevenoaks, Kent,
TN14 7NN
Ⓣ (01959) 532269
Ⓕ (01959) 534092
Ⓔ Plantfinder@coolings.co.uk
Ⓦ www.coolings.co.uk
Contact: Mark Reeve & Gary Carvosso
Opening Times: 0900-1700 Mon-Sat &
1000-1630 Sun.
Cat. Cost: None issued
Credit Cards: All major credit/debit cards
Specialities: Large range of perennials, conifers
& bedding plants. Some unusual shrubs & trees.
Notes: Third generation family business.
Map Ref: S, C4

SCrf CROFTERS NURSERIES € &
Church Hill, Charing Heath, Near Ashford,
Kent, TN27 0BU
Ⓣ (01233) 712798
Ⓕ (01233) 712798
Ⓔ crofters.nursery1@virgin.net
Contact: John & Sue Webb
Opening Times: 1000-1700. Closed Sun-Tue.
Please check first.
Cat. Cost: 3 x 1st class
Credit Cards: None
Specialities: Fruit, ornamental trees &
conifers. Old apple varieties. Small number of
Prunus serrula with grafted ornamental heads.
Map Ref: S, C5 OS Grid Ref: TQ923493

SDay A LA CARTE DAYLILIES ✉ € ♦
Little Hermitage, St Catherine's Down,
Nr Ventnor, Isle of Wight, PO38 2PD
Ⓣ (01983) 730512
Contact: Jan & Andy Wyers
Opening Times: Mail order only. Open by
appt. Difficult to find, on an unmade private
road.

Min Mail Order UK: Nmc
Min Mail Order EU: Nmc
Cat. Cost: 3 x 1st class
Credit Cards: None
Specialities: *Hemerocallis*. Nat. Colls. of
Miniature & Small Flowered *Hemerocallis* &
Large Flowered *Hemerocallis* (post-1960
award-winning cultivars).
Notes: Also sells wholesale.
Map Ref: S, D2 OS Grid Ref: SZ499787

SDea DEACON'S NURSERY ✉ ✉ € ♦
Moor View, Godshill, Isle of Wight,
PO38 3HW
Ⓣ (01983) 840750 (24 hrs):(01983) 522243
Ⓕ (01983) 523575
Ⓔ deacons.nursery@btopenworld.com
Ⓦ www.deaconsnurseryfruits.co.uk
Contact: G D & B H W Deacon
Opening Times: 0800-1600 Mon-Fri May-
Sep, 0800-1700 Mon-Fri 0800-1200 Sat
Oct-Apr.
Min Mail Order UK: Nmc
Min Mail Order EU: Nmc
Cat. Cost: Free
Credit Cards: All major credit/debit cards
Specialities: Over 300 varieties of apple, old
& new, pears, plums, gages, damsons,
cherries. Modern soft fruit, grapes, hops, nuts
& family trees.
Notes: Also sells wholesale.
Map Ref: S, D2

SDEP DAVID'S EXOTIC PLANTS UK ✉ ✉
37 Shalloak Road, Broad Oak, Canterbury,
Kent, CT2 0QH
Ⓣ (01227) 711897
Ⓔ Bushtress@aol.com
Ⓦ www.Davids-Exoticplants.co.uk
Contact: David Hamer
Opening Times: Mail order only. Not open.
Min Mail Order UK: £12.50
Min Mail Order EU: £90.00
Cat. Cost: Online only.
Credit Cards: All major credit/debit cards
Specialities: *Bougainvillea,* citrus trees,
brunfelsias, plumerias. Cinnamon plants.
Mango, litchi, guava, avocado & star fruit
trees. Other exotics.

SDix GREAT DIXTER NURSERIES ✉ &
Northiam, Rye, East Sussex,
TN31 6PH
Ⓣ (01797) 253107
Ⓕ (01797) 252879
Ⓔ nursery@greatdixter.co.uk
Ⓦ www.greatdixter.co.uk
Contact: K Leighton

S

S

Opening Times: 0900-1230 & 1330-1700
Mon-Fri, 0900-1200 Sat all year. Also 1400-
1700 Sat, Sun & B/hols Apr-Oct.
Min Mail Order UK: Nmc
Min Mail Order EU: Nmc
Cat. Cost: 4 x 1st class
Credit Cards: All major credit/debit cards
Specialities: *Clematis*, shrubs and plants.
Gardens open.
Notes: Plants dispatched Sep-Mar only.
Map Ref: S, C5

**SDnm   DENMANS GARDEN, (JOHN BROOKES
LTD)** [符]
Clock House, Denmans, Fontwell,
Nr Arundel, West Sussex, BN18 0SU
Ⓣ (01243) 542808
Ⓕ (01243) 544064
Ⓔ denmans@denmans-garden.co.uk
Ⓦ www.denmans-garden.co.uk
Contact: Andrew Muggeridge
Opening Times: 0900-1700 7 days 1st Feb-
24th Dec.
Cat. Cost: None issued
Credit Cards: Visa MasterCard
Specialities: Rare and unusual plants.
Map Ref: S, D3

SDow   DOWNDERRY NURSERY ⊠ ⊠ € [符]
Pillar Box Lane, Hadlow,
Nr Tonbridge, Kent,
TN11 9SW
Ⓣ (01732) 810081
Ⓕ (01732) 811398
Ⓔ info@downderry-nursery.co.uk
Ⓦ www.downderry-nursery.co.uk
Contact: Dr S J Charlesworth
Opening Times: 1000-1700 Tue-Sun 1st
May-31st Oct & by appt.
Min Mail Order UK: Nmc
Min Mail Order EU: Nmc
Cat. Cost: 3 x 1st class
Credit Cards: Delta MasterCard Switch Visa
Specialities: Nat. Colls. of *Lavandula* &
Rosmarinus.
Map Ref: S, C4 **OS Grid Ref:** TQ625521

SDys   DYSONS NURSERIES ⊠ [符]
Great Comp Garden, Platt, Sevenoaks, Kent,
TN15 8QS
Ⓣ (01732) 886154
Ⓔ dysonsnurseries@aol.com
Ⓦ www.greatcomp.co.uk
Contact: William T Dyson
Opening Times: 1100-1730 7 days 1st Apr-
31st Oct. Other times by appt.
Min Mail Order UK: £9.00 + p&p
Cat. Cost: 2 x 1st class

Credit Cards: None
Specialities: Salvias, especially New World
species and cultivars.
Notes: Also sells wholesale.
Map Ref: S, C4

**SECG   THE ENGLISH COTTAGE GARDEN
NURSERY** ⊠
Herons, Giggers Green Road, Aldington,
Kent, TN25 7BU
Ⓣ (01233) 720907
Ⓕ (01233) 720907
Ⓔ enquiries@englishplants.co.uk
Ⓦ www.englishplants.co.uk
Contact: Teresa Sinclair
Opening Times: 7 days, please phone first.
Min Mail Order UK: £10.00
Cat. Cost: Free
Credit Cards: Visa MasterCard Solo Electron
Switch
Specialities: Small nursery offering variety of
traditional cottage garden plants, wildflowers
& herbs. Some wildflowers in small quantities.
Native hedging, meadow & wildflower seed.
Notes: Plants can be ordered & paid for
online. Also sells wholesale.
Map Ref: S, C5

SEND   EAST NORTHDOWN FARM ⊠ € [符] ◆
Margate, Kent, CT9 3TS
Ⓣ (01843) 862060
Ⓕ (01843) 860206
Ⓔ friend.northdown@ukonline.co.uk
Ⓦ www.botanyplants.com
Contact: Louise & William Friend
Opening Times: 0900-1700 Mon-Sat, 1000-
1700 Sun all year. Closed Xmas week &
Easter Sun.
Min Mail Order UK: Nmc
Cat. Cost: Available Online only.
Credit Cards: Visa Switch MasterCard
Specialities: Chalk & coast-loving plants.
Map Ref: S, B6

SFai   FAIRWEATHER'S GARDEN CENTRE ⊠ ⊠
€ [符]
High Street, Beaulieu, Hampshire,
SO42 7YB
Ⓣ (01590) 612113
Ⓕ (01590) 612615
Ⓔ chrisfairweather@waitrose.com
Ⓦ www.vireya.co.uk
Contact: Christopher Fairweather
Opening Times: 0930-1700 7 days.
Min Mail Order UK: Nmc
Min Mail Order EU: Nmc
Cat. Cost: 2 x 1st class
Credit Cards: Visa MasterCard

Specialities: Nat. Coll. of Vireya
Rhododendrons. Our main collection, at local
nursery, can be viewed by appt.
Notes: Also sells wholesale.
Map Ref: S, D2

SFam   FAMILY TREES ⊠ &
Sandy Lane, Shedfield, Hampshire,
SO32 2HQ
Ⓣ (01329) 834812
Contact: Philip House
Opening Times: 0930-1230 Wed & Sat mid
Oct-end May.
Min Mail Order UK: Nmc
Min Mail Order EU: Nmc
Cat. Cost: Free
Credit Cards: None
Specialities: Fruit & ornamental trees. Trained
fruit tree specialists: standards, espaliers,
cordons. Other trees, old-fashioned &
climbing roses, evergreens. Trees, except
evergreens, sold bare rooted. Large specimens
in pots.
Map Ref: S, D2

SGar   GARDEN PLANTS ⊠ ♠
Windy Ridge, Victory Road, St Margarets-at-
Cliffe, Dover, Kent, CT15 6HF
Ⓣ (01304) 853225
Ⓔ GardenPlants@GardenPlants-nursery.co.uk
Ⓦ www.GardenPlants-nursery.co.uk
Contact: Teresa Ryder & David Ryder
Opening Times: 1000-1700 (closed Wed).
Min Mail Order UK: Nmc
Cat. Cost: 2 x 1st class + A5 sae
Credit Cards: None
Specialities: Unusual perennials, *Penstemon* &
Salvia.
Notes: Plantsman's garden open to view. Map
essential for first visit. Also sells wholesale.
Map Ref: S, C6 OS Grid Ref: TR358464

SHaC   HART CANNA ⊠ € &
27 Guildford Road West, Farnborough,
Hampshire, GU14 6PS
Ⓣ (01252) 514421
Ⓕ (01252) 514421
Ⓔ plants@hartcanna.com
Ⓦ www.hartcanna.com
Contact: Keith Hayward
Opening Times: Visitors by arrangement.
Min Mail Order UK: Nmc
Min Mail Order EU: Nmc
Cat. Cost: Free.
Credit Cards: All major credit/debit cards
Specialities: *Canna*. Nat. Coll. of *Canna*.
Notes: Also sells wholesale.
Map Ref: S, C3

SHar   HARDY'S COTTAGE GARDEN PLANTS
⊠ ♠ &
Freefolk Priors, Freefolk, Whitchurch,
Hampshire, RG28 7NJ
Ⓣ (01256) 896533
Ⓕ (01256) 896572
Ⓔ hardy@cottagegardenplants.fsnet.co.uk
Ⓦ www.hardys-plants.co.uk
Contact: Rosy Hardy
Opening Times: 1000-1700 7 days 1st Mar-
31st Oct.
Min Mail Order UK: Nmc
Cat. Cost: 8 x 1st class.
Credit Cards: Visa Access Electron Switch
Solo
Specialities: Hardy *Geranium* & other
herbaceous both old & new. Collection of
Viola odorata & Parma violets now available.
Notes: A charge of £2.00 is made for delivery
of pre-ordered plants to shows.
Map Ref: S, C2

SHay   HAYWARD'S CARNATIONS ⊠
The Chace Gardens, Stakes Road,
Purbrook, Waterlooville, Hampshire,
PO7 5PL
Ⓣ (023) 9226 3047
Ⓕ (023) 9226 3047
Contact: A N Hayward
Opening Times: Mail order only. Office
hours 0930-1600 Mon-Fri.
Min Mail Order UK: £10.00 + p&p
Min Mail Order EU: £50.00 + p&p
Cat. Cost: 1 x 1st class
Credit Cards: None
Specialities: Hardy pinks & border carnations
(*Dianthus*). Greenhouse perpetual carnations.
Notes: Also sells wholesale.
Map Ref: S, D2

SHBN   HIGH BANKS NURSERIES &
Slip Mill Road,
Hawkhurst, Kent,
TN18 5AD
Ⓣ (01580) 754492
Ⓕ (01580) 754450
Contact: Jeremy Homewood
Opening Times: 0800-1700 (1630 in winter)
daily.
Cat. Cost: £1.50 (stamps) + A4 Sae
Credit Cards: All major credit/debit cards
Specialities: Wide general range with many
unusual plants. Minimum of 250,000 plants

KEY		
⊠ Mail order to UK or EU	♠ Delivers to shows	
⊠ Exports beyond EU	€ Euro accepted	
& Accessible by wheelchair	◆ See Display advertisement	

on site at any one time. Many unusual plants. Open ground stock limited between Nov and Feb.
Notes: Also sells wholesale.
Map Ref: S, C5

SHDw HIGHDOWN NURSERY ⊠ ☒ ♿ €
New Hall Lane, Small Dole,
Nr Henfield, West Sussex,
BN5 9YH
Ⓣ (01273) 492976
Ⓕ (01273) 492976
Ⓔ highdown.herbs@btopenworld.com
Contact: A G & J H Shearing
Opening Times: 0900-1700 7 days.
Min Mail Order UK: £10.00 + p&p
Min Mail Order EU: £10.00 + p&p
Cat. Cost: 3 x 1st class
Credit Cards: Visa MasterCard Delta JCB EuroCard
Specialities: Herbs.
Notes: Partial wheelchair access. Also sells wholesale.
Map Ref: S, D3

SHFr SUE HARTFREE
25 Crouch Hill Court,
Lower Halstow, Nr Sittingbourne,
Kent, ME9 7EJ
Ⓣ (01795) 842426
Contact: Sue Hartfree
Opening Times: Any time by appt. Please phone first.
Cat. Cost: A5 Sae + 4 x 1st class
Credit Cards: None
Specialities: Rare & unusual plants for the garden & conservatory incl. many varieties of *Salvia*. Some in small quantities but can be propagated to order.
Map Ref: S, C5 **OS Grid Ref:** TQ860672

SHGC HAMBROOKS GROWING CONCERN ♿
Wangfield Lane, Curdridge,
Southampton, Hampshire,
SO32 2DA
Ⓣ (01489) 780505/779993
Ⓕ (01489) 785396/779389
Ⓔ timedwards@hambrooks.co.uk
Ⓦ www.hambrooks.co.uk
Contact: Tim Edwards
Opening Times: 0730-1730 Mon-Fri.
Cat. Cost: 2 x 1st class
Credit Cards: All major credit/debit cards
Specialities: Specimen stock, herbaceous, conifers, shrubs, grasses, climbers & hedging.
Notes: Delivery limited to Hampshire & just beyond at cost. Also sells wholesale.
Map Ref: S, D2 **OS Grid Ref:** SU523141

SHGN HILL GARTH NURSERY ♿
Woodgreen Road, Godshill, Fordingbridge, Hampshire, SP6 2LP
Ⓣ (01425) 657619
Ⓕ (01425) 657619
Contact: Mrs S J Giddins
Opening Times: 0930-1700 Thu & Sun, Mar-end Oct.
Cat. Cost: None issued
Credit Cards: None
Specialities: Small nursery offering a range of rare, unusual & traditional hardy perennials, shrubs & trees. Some stock may be limited.
Map Ref: S, D1

SHHo HIGHFIELD HOLLIES ⊠ ◆
Highfield Farm, Hatch Lane, Liss, Hampshire, GU33 7NH
Ⓣ (01730) 892372
Ⓕ (01730) 894853
Ⓔ louise@highfieldhollies.com
Ⓦ www.highfieldhollies.com
Contact: Mrs Louise Bendall Duck
Opening Times: By appt.
Min Mail Order UK: £30.00
Cat. Cost: £3.50 for illustrated cat.
Credit Cards: None
Specialities: 150+ species & cultivars *Ilex* incl. specimen trees, hedging & topiary. Some in short supply.
Map Ref: S, C3 **OS Grid Ref:** SU787276

SHmp HAMPSHIRE CARNIVOROUS PLANTS ⊠ ☒ ♿ €
Ya-Mayla, Allington Lane, West End,
Southampton, Hampshire, SO30 3HQ
Ⓣ (023) 8047 3314
Ⓜ 07703 258296
Ⓕ (023) 8047 3314
Ⓔ matthew@msoper.freesave.co.uk
Ⓦ www.hampshire-carnivorous-plants.co.uk
Contact: Matthew Soper
Opening Times: Mail order only. Open by appt. only.
Min Mail Order UK: Nmc
Min Mail Order EU: £50.00 + p&p
Cat. Cost: 2 x 2nd class
Credit Cards: Visa MasterCard
Specialities: Carnivorous plants esp. *Nepenthes, Heliamphora, Sarracenia Pinguicula* & *Utricularia*.
Notes: Also sells wholesale.

SHol HOLLY GATE CACTUS NURSERY ⊠ € ♿
Billingshurst Road, Ashington, West Sussex, RH20 3BB
Ⓣ (01903) 892 930
Ⓔ info@hollygatecactus.co.uk

@ www.hollygatecactus.co.uk
Contact: Mr T M Hewitt
Opening Times: 0900-1700 7 days Feb-Oct,
0900-1600 Nov-Jan.
Min Mail Order UK: £10.00 + p&p
Min Mail Order EU: £10.00 + p&p
Cat. Cost: 2 x 1st class
Credit Cards: All major credit/debit cards
Specialities: Cacti & succulents, plants &
seeds. World famous cactus garden.
Notes: Also sells wholesale.
Map Ref: S, D3 **OS Grid Ref:** TQ133175

SHom   HOME PLANTS
52 Dorman Ave North, Aylesham,
Canterbury, Kent, CT3 3BW
T (01304) 841746
Contact: Stuart & Sue Roycroft
Opening Times: By appt. only, please phone
first.
Cat. Cost: SAE for list
Credit Cards: None
Specialities: *Phygelius* & unusual South
African hardy plants. Limited stock, please
phone first.

SHop   HOPALONG NURSERY ♿
Crabtree Close, Fairseat,
Sevenoaks, Kent,
TN15 7JR
T (01732) 822422
F (01732) 822422
E jon@hopalong.fsworld.co.uk
W www.hopalongnursery.co.uk
Contact: Jon Clark
Opening Times: 1000-1700 Wed-Sat, 1100-
1600 Sun, 1st Mar-31st Oct. Open B/hols.
Cat. Cost: £2.00 or free Online
Credit Cards: None
Specialities: Unusual hardy herbaceous
perennials, grasses, ferns, *Cistus*. Some in small
quantities.
Map Ref: S, C4 **OS Grid Ref:** TQ632613

SHyH   HYDRANGEA HAVEN ⊠ ✉ ♈ € ♿
Market Garden, Lower Beeding, West Sussex,
RH13 6PP
T (01403) 892580
F (01403) 891336
E rhspf@hydrangea-haven.com
W www.hydrangea-haven.com
Contact: Chris Loder
Opening Times: 1000-1600 Mon-Sat, please
phone first, so we can give you our undivided
attention.
Min Mail Order UK: Nmc
Min Mail Order EU: £100.00 + p&p
Cat. Cost: 2 x 1st class

Credit Cards: Switch Visa MasterCard
Specialities: *Hydrangea*.
Notes: Also sells wholesale.
Map Ref: S, C3

SIde   IDEN CROFT HERBS ⊠ ♿ ◆
Frittenden Road, Staplehurst, Kent,
TN12 0DH
T (01580) 891432
F (01580) 892416
E idencroftherbs@yahoo.co.uk
W www.herbs-uk.com
Contact: Tracey Pearman
Opening Times: 0900-1700 Mon-Sat &
1100-1700 Sun & B/hols during summer.
Open all winter with reduced hours – please
phone to confirm prior to visit.
Min Mail Order UK: £10.00
Min Mail Order EU: £25.00
Cat. Cost: 2 x 1st class for descriptive list.
Credit Cards: All major credit/debit cards
Specialities: Herbs, aromatic & wild flower
plants & plants for bees & butterflies. Nat.
Colls. of *Mentha, Nepeta* & *Origanum*.
Notes: Wheelchairs available at nursery.
Exports seed only.
Map Ref: S, C5

SIFN   IAN FITZROY NURSERYMAN ⊠ ♈
(Office) 2 Moor Cottages, Moor Lane, Marsh
Green, Edenbridge, Kent, TN8 5RA
T (01342) 851179
F (01342) 851179
E sales@ianfitzroy.com
W www.ianfitzroy.com
Contact: Ian FitzRoy
Opening Times: Mail order only. Open by
appt. only.
Min Mail Order UK: Nmc
Min Mail Order EU: Nmc
Cat. Cost: 4 x 1st class
Credit Cards: Switch Visa MasterCard
Specialities: Japanese maple. Rare and
unusual grafted trees and shrubs.
Notes: Nursery is at Scarlets, Smithers Lane,
Cowden, Kent. Also sells wholesale.
Map Ref: S, C4

SIng   W E TH. INGWERSEN LTD ♈
Birch Farm Nursery, Gravetye, East
Grinstead, West Sussex, RH19 4LE
T (01342) 810236
E info@ingwersen.co.uk

KEY: ⊠ Mail order to UK or EU ♈ Delivers to shows
✉ Exports beyond EU € Euro accepted
♿ Accessible by wheelchair ◆ See Display advertisement

S

Ⓦ www.ingwersen.co.uk
Contact: M P & M R Ingwersen
Opening Times: 0900-1600 daily excl. Sun &
B/hols, Mar-Sep. 0900-1600 Mon-Fri
Oct-Feb.
Cat. Cost: 2 x 1st class
Credit Cards: None
Specialities: Very wide range of hardy plants
mostly alpines. Also seed.
Notes: Wheelchair-accessible with assistance.
Map Ref: S, C4

SIri IRIS OF SISSINGHURST ⊠ € 🅰 ◆
Plummers Farmhouse, Biddenden Road,
Sissinghurst, Kent, TN17 2JP
Ⓣ (01580) 715137
Ⓔ irisofs@aol.com
Ⓦ www.irisofsissinghurst.com
Contact: Margaret Roberts
Opening Times: 1000-1700 following
w/ends: 30th-1st May, 4th-5th & 11th-12th
Jun 2005. Contact nursery or see website for
additional opening times.
Min Mail Order UK: Nmc
Min Mail Order EU: Nmc
Cat. Cost: 2 x 1st class
Credit Cards: None
Specialities: *Iris*, short, intermediate & tall
bearded, ensata, sibirica & many species.
Map Ref: S, C5 OS Grid Ref: TQ796375

SJoh VIC JOHNSTONE AND
CLAIRE WILSON
43 Winchester Street, Whitchurch,
Hampshire, RG28 7AJ
Ⓣ (01256) 893144
Contact: Vic Johnstone, Claire Wilson
Opening Times: By appt. Please telephone
first.
Cat. Cost: 2 x 1st class
Credit Cards: None
Specialities: Nat. Coll. of *Verbascum*.
Verbascum only.
Map Ref: S, C2 OS Grid Ref: SU463478

SKee KEEPERS NURSERY ⊠
Gallants Court, Gallants Lane, East Farleigh,
Maidstone, Kent, ME15 0LE
Ⓣ (01622) 726465
Ⓕ 0870 705 2145
Ⓔ info@keepers-nursery.co.uk
Ⓦ www.keepers-nursery.co.uk
Contact: Hamid Habibi
Opening Times: All reasonable hours by appt.
Min Mail Order UK: Nmc
Cat. Cost: 2 x 1st class. Free by email.
Credit Cards: Visa MasterCard American
Express Switch Solo

Specialities: Old & unusual top fruit varieties.
Top fruit propagated to order.
Map Ref: S, C4

SKen KENT STREET NURSERIES ⊠ €
Sedlescombe, Battle, East Sussex, TN33 0SF
Ⓣ (01424) 751134
Ⓔ peter@1066-countryplants.co.uk
Ⓦ www.1066-countryplants.co.uk
Contact: P Stapley
Opening Times: 0900-1800 7 days.
Min Mail Order UK: £6.50
Min Mail Order EU: £6.50
Cat. Cost: 2 x 1st class, email, or online.
Credit Cards: All major credit/debit cards
Specialities: *Pelargonium*, bedding &
perennials.
Notes: Mail order *Pelargonium* list only.
Credit cards not accepted for mail order.
Nursery partially accessible for wheelchair
users. Also sells wholesale.
Map Ref: S, D5 OS Grid Ref: TQ790155

SLan LANGLEY BOXWOOD NURSERY ⊠ 🖾 €
🅰 ◆
Langley Lane, Rake, Nr Liss, Hampshire,
GU33 7JN
Ⓣ (01730) 894467
Ⓕ (01730) 894703
Ⓔ sales@boxwood.co.uk
Ⓦ www.boxwood.co.uk
Contact: Russell Coates
Opening Times: 0900-1630 Mon-Fri, 1000-
1600 Sat. Please phone for directions.
Min Mail Order UK: Nmc
Min Mail Order EU: Nmc
Cat. Cost: 4 x 1st class
Credit Cards: Visa MasterCard
Specialities: *Buxus* species, cultivars &
hedging. Good range of topiary, *Taxus*, and
'character-pruned' specimens. Nat. Coll. of
Buxus. Evergreen topiary & hedging.
Notes: Also sells wholesale.
Map Ref: S, C3 OS Grid Ref: SU812290

SLau THE LAURELS NURSERY ⊠ 🏠 €
Benenden, Cranbrook, Kent, TN17 4JU
Ⓣ (01580) 240463
Ⓕ (01580) 240463
Ⓦ www.thelaurelsnursery.co.uk
Contact: Peter or Sylvia Kellett
Opening Times: 0800-1700 Mon-Thu, 0800-
1600 Fri, 0900-1200 Sat, Sun by appt. only.
Min Mail Order UK: £20.00
Cat. Cost: Free
Credit Cards: None
Specialities: Open ground & container
ornamental trees, shrubs & climbers incl.

flowering cherries, birch, beech & *Wisteria*.
Notes: Mail order of small *Wisteria* only. Also sells wholesale.
Map Ref: S, C5 **OS Grid Ref:** TQ815313

SLay   LAYHAM GARDEN CENTRE & NURSERY ⊠ ⬙
Lower Road, Staple, Nr Canterbury, Kent, CT3 1LH
ⓣ (01304) 813267
ⓕ (01304) 814007
ⓔ layham@gcstaple.fsnet.co.uk
Contact: Ellen Wessel
Opening Times: 0900-1700 7 days.
Min Mail Order UK: Nmc
Min Mail Order EU: £25.00 + p&p
Cat. Cost: Free
Credit Cards: Visa Switch MasterCard
Specialities: Roses, herbaceous, shrubs, trees & hedging plants.
Notes: Also sells wholesale.
Map Ref: S, C6 **OS Grid Ref:** TR276567

SLBF   LITTLE BROOK FUCHSIAS ⬙
Ash Green Lane West, Ash Green, Nr Aldershot, Hampshire, GU12 6HL
ⓣ (01252) 329731
ⓔ carol.gubler@business.ntl.com
ⓦ www.littlebrookfuchsias.co.uk
Contact: Carol Gubler
Opening Times: 0900-1700 Wed-Sun 1st Jan-4th Jul.
Cat. Cost: 50p + Sae
Credit Cards: None
Specialities: Fuchsias, old & new.
Notes: Also sells wholesale.
Map Ref: S, C3

SLdr   LODER PLANTS ⊠ ⬙ ⋔ € ⬙
Market Garden, Lower Beeding, West Sussex, RH13 6PP
ⓣ (01403) 891412
ⓕ (01403) 891336
ⓔ rhspf@rhododendrons.com
ⓦ www.rhododendrons.com
Contact: Chris Loder
Opening Times: 1000-1600 Mon-Sat, please ring first so we can give you our undivided attention.
Min Mail Order UK: Nmc
Min Mail Order EU: £100.00 + p&p
Cat. Cost: 2 x 1st class
Credit Cards: Switch Visa MasterCard
Specialities: Rhododendrons & azaleas in all sizes. *Camellia, Acer, Hydrangea* & ferns.
Notes: Also sells wholesale.
Map Ref: S, C3

SLim   LIME CROSS NURSERY ⬙ ◆
Herstmonceux, Hailsham, East Sussex, BN27 4RS
ⓣ (01323) 833229
ⓕ (01323) 833944
ⓔ LimeCross@aol.com
ⓦ www.Limecross.co.uk
Contact: J A Tate, Mrs A Green
Opening Times: 0830-1700 Mon-Sat & 1000-1600 Sun.
Cat. Cost: 3 x 1st class
Credit Cards: Visa MasterCard Delta Switch
Specialities: Conifers, trees & shrubs, climbers.
Notes: Also sells wholesale.
Map Ref: S, D4 **OS Grid Ref:** TQ642125

SLon   LONGSTOCK PARK NURSERY ⬙
Longstock, Stockbridge, Hampshire, SO20 6EH
ⓣ (01264) 810894
ⓕ (01264) 810924
ⓔ longstocknursery@leckfordestate.co.uk
ⓦ www.longstocknursery.co.uk
Contact: David Roberts
Opening Times: 0830-1630 Mon-Sat all year excl. Xmas & New Year, & 1100-1700 Sun Mar-Oct, 1000-1600 Sun, Nov-Feb.
Cat. Cost: £2.00 cheque incl. p&p
Credit Cards: Visa Access Switch MasterCard
Specialities: A wide range, over 2000 varieties, of trees, shrubs, perennials, climbers, aquatics & ferns. Nat. Colls. of *Buddleja* & *Clematis viticella*.
Map Ref: S, C2

SLPl   LANDSCAPE PLANTS ⊠ ⬙ ⬙
Cattamount, Grafty Green, Maidstone, Kent, ME17 2AP
ⓣ (01622) 850245
ⓕ (01622) 858063
ⓔ landscapeplants@aol.com
Contact: Tom La Dell
Opening Times: 0800-1600 Mon-Fri, by appt. only.
Min Mail Order UK: £100.00 + p&p
Min Mail Order EU: £200.00 + p&p
Cat. Cost: 2 x 1st class
Credit Cards: None
Specialities: Garden & landscape shrubs & perennials.
Notes: Also sells wholesale.
Map Ref: S, C5 **OS Grid Ref:** TQ772468

S

KEY: ⊠ Mail order to UK or EU ⋔ Delivers to shows ⬙ Exports beyond EU € Euro accepted ⬙ Accessible by wheelchair ◆ See Display advertisement

S

SMac **MACGREGORS PLANTS FOR SHADE** ⊠ ♠
Carters Clay Road, Lockerley, Romsey,
Hampshire, SO51 0GL
Ⓣ (01794) 340256
Ⓔ plants@macgregors-shadeplants.co.uk
Ⓦ www.macgregors-shadeplants.co.uk
Contact: Irene & Stuart Bowron
Opening Times: By appt. only. Please phone
before travelling to make arrangements.
Min Mail Order UK: Nmc
Cat. Cost: Online only.
Credit Cards: Visa MasterCard
Specialities: All types of shade plants & other
less usual shrubs & perennials. Limited stock
of rarer plants.
Notes: Mail order usually restricted to small
numbers sent by 24hr carrier. Other
arrangements by negotiation. Also sells
wholesale.
Map Ref: S, C2 **OS Grid Ref:** SU308239

SMad **MADRONA NURSERY** ⊠ ♠ € ♿
Pluckley Road, Bethersden, Kent, TN26 3DD
Ⓣ (01233) 820100
Ⓕ (01233) 820091
Ⓔ madrona@fsmail.net
Ⓦ www.madrona.co.uk
Contact: Liam MacKenzie
Opening Times: 1000-1700 Sat-Tue 12th
Mar-30th Oct. Closed 6th-19th Aug.
Min Mail Order UK: Nmc
Cat. Cost: Free
Credit Cards: Visa MasterCard American
Express JCB Switch
Specialities: Unusual shrubs, conifers &
perennials. *Eryngiums, Pseudopanax*.
Map Ref: S, C5 **OS Grid Ref:** TQ918419

SMar **THE MARKET GARDEN** ♠ ♿
Ganders Gate Pig Farm, Glasshouse Lane,
Kirdford, West Sussex, RH14 0LW
Ⓣ (01403) 820634 Ⓜ 0771 404 4024
Ⓔ foxglovegardendesign@hotmail.com
Contact: Sally Welch, Terri Lefevre
Opening Times: 1000-1600 Fri & Sun Mar-
end Sep, or by appt.
Cat. Cost: 2 x 1st class
Credit Cards: None
Specialities: Herbaceous perennials & grasses.
A small nursery propagating all our plants,
some grown in small quantities.
Map Ref: S, C3 **OS Grid Ref:** TQ014253

SMDP **MARCUS DANCER PLANTS** ♠ ♿
Kilcreggan, Alderholt Road, Sandleheath,
Fordingbridge, Hampshire, SP6 1PT
Ⓣ (01425) 652747
Ⓔ marcus.dancer@btopenworld.com
Contact: Marcus Dancer
Opening Times: By appointment only.
Cat. Cost: 2 x 1st class.
Credit Cards: None
Specialities: Wide range of *Clematis*, smaller
range of *Daphne*. Some in small quantities.
Map Ref: S, D1

SMeo **MEON VALLEY PLANTS** ⊠ ♠ ♿
(office) PO Box 155, Petersfield,
Hampshire,
GU32 1XQ
Ⓜ 07818 088019
Ⓔ info@meonvalleyplants.co.uk
Ⓦ www.meonvalleyplants.co.uk
Contact: Camilla Moreton
Opening Times: 1000-1700 Fri & Sat, 11th
Mar-15th Oct 2005 and by appt.
Min Mail Order UK: £20.00
Cat. Cost: 4 x 1st class.
Credit Cards: None
Specialities: Unusual bulbs, perennials & grasses.
Many plants produced in small quantities.
Notes: Nursery at Broadhanger Farm,
Froxfield, Nr. Petersfield GU32 1DW.
Map Ref: S, C2 **OS Grid Ref:** SU713259

SMer **MERRYFIELD NURSERIES**
(CANTERBURY) LTD ⊠ ♿ ◆
Stodmarsh Road, Canterbury,
Kent,
CT3 4AP
Ⓣ (01227) 462602
Ⓔ merry1field@tiscali.co.uk
Contact: Mrs A Downs
Opening Times: 0930-1730 Tue-Sat, 1000-
1700 Sun B/hol Mons.
Min Mail Order UK: £10.00 + p&p
Cat. Cost: 2 x 1st class.
Credit Cards: All major credit/debit cards
Specialities: Wide range of shrubs, conifers,
herbaceous, many unusual.
Map Ref: S, C5

SMHT **MOUNT HARRY TREES** € ♿ ◆
Offham, Lewes, East Sussex,
BN7 3QW
Ⓣ (01273) 474456
Ⓕ (01273) 474266
Ⓔ mountharry@btopenworld.com
Contact: A Renton
Opening Times: By appt.
Cat. Cost: 2 x 1st class
Credit Cards: None
Specialities: Deciduous trees, specialising in
heavy-standard to semi-mature sizes, incl.
Sorbus varieties.
Map Ref: S, D4 **OS Grid Ref:** TQ313913

SMHy   MARCHANTS HARDY PLANTS �
2 Marchants Cottages, Ripe Road, Laughton,
East Sussex, BN8 6AJ
ⓣ (01323) 811737
ⓕ (01323) 811737
Contact: Graham Gough
Opening Times: 0930-1730 Wed-Sat, 9th
Mar-22rd Oct 2005.
Cat. Cost: 4 x 1st class
Specialities: Uncommon herbaceous
perennials. *Agapanthus, Kniphofia, Sedum*,
choice grasses, *Miscanthus, Molinia*.
Map Ref: S, D4 OS Grid Ref: TQ506119

SMrm   MERRIMENTS GARDENS 🛆
Hawkhurst Road, Hurst Green, East Sussex,
TN19 7RA
ⓣ (01580) 860666
ⓕ (01580) 860324
ⓔ alanasharp@beeb.net
ⓦ www.merriments.co.uk
Contact: Alana Sharp
Opening Times: 0930-1730 Mon-Sat, 1030-
1730 Sun (or dusk in winter).
Cat. Cost: Online only
Credit Cards: Visa Access American Express
Specialities: Unusual shrubs. Tender & hardy
perennials.
Map Ref: S, C4

SMur   MURRELLS PLANT & GARDEN CENTRE
🛆
Broomers Hill Lane, Pulborough, West Sussex,
RH20 2DU
ⓣ (01798) 875508
ⓕ (01798) 872695
Contact: Clive Mellor
Opening Times: 0900-1730 summer, 0900-
1700 winter, 1000-1600 Sun.
Cat. Cost: 3 x 1st class
Credit Cards: Switch Visa MasterCard Solo
Specialities: Shrubs, trees & herbaceous plants
incl. many rare & unusual varieties.
Map Ref: S, D3

SNew   NEW FOREST PALMS & EXOTICS ✉ 🛆
Pauls Lane, Sway, Lymington, Hampshire,
SO41 6BR
ⓣ (01590) 683864
ⓜ 07870 483972
ⓕ (01590) 681244
ⓔ Paulsnursery@farmersweekly.net
ⓦ www.newforestpalms.co.uk
Contact: F R Toyne
Opening Times: 1000-1700 Tue-Sun Mar-
Oct. 1000-1500 Tue-Sun Nov-Feb. Closed
Mon. Closed Jan.
Min Mail Order UK: Nmc

Cat. Cost: 2 x 1st class
Credit Cards: All major credit/debit cards
Specialities: Ornamental grasses & plants for
the Mediterranean look, incl. bamboos, tree
ferns.
Notes: Free delivery within 30 miles for
orders over £100. Also sells wholesale.
Map Ref: S, D2 OS Grid Ref: SZ292978

SNut   NUTLIN NURSERY 🜚 🛆
Crowborough Road, Nutley,
Nr Uckfield, East Sussex,
TN22 3HU
ⓣ (01825) 712670
ⓕ (01825) 712670
Contact: Mrs Morven Cox
Opening Times: Phone in evening (before
2100) before visiting.
Cat. Cost: 1 x 1st class
Credit Cards: None
Specialities: *Hydrangea, Wisteria*, hardy ferns.
Largely grown peat free.
Map Ref: S, C4 OS Grid Ref: TQ4428

SOkd   OAKDENE NURSERY ✉ ✉ 🜚
Street End Lane, Broad Oak,
Heathfield, East Sussex,
TN21 8TU
ⓣ (01435) 864382
ⓔ sampson500@aol.com
Contact: David Sampson
Opening Times: By appt. only and for
collection.
Min Mail Order UK: £10.00
Min Mail Order EU: £25.00
Cat. Cost: 3 x 1st class
Credit Cards: None
Specialities: Rare & unusual woodland
plants. Bulbs.
Map Ref: S, C4

SOWG   THE OLD WALLED GARDEN ✉ 🜚 € 🛆
Oxonhoath, Hadlow, Kent, TN11 9SS
ⓣ (01732) 810012
ⓕ (01732) 810856
ⓔ amyrtle@aol.com
ⓦ www.theoldwalledgarden.co.uk
Contact: John & Heather Angrave
Opening Times: 0900-1700 Mon-Sat. Sun
by appt.
Min Mail Order UK: Nmc
Cat. Cost: 4 x 1st class
Credit Cards: All major credit/debit cards
Specialities: Many rare & unusual shrubs.
Wide range of conservatory plants esp.
Australian. Nat. Coll. of *Callistemon*.
Notes: Also sells wholesale.
Map Ref: S, C4

S

S

SPav   PAVILION PLANTS ⊠ ⋔
18 Pavilion Road, Worthing, West Sussex,
BN14 7EF
Ⓣ (01903)· 821338 Ⓜ 07881 876037
Ⓔ rewrew18@hotmail.com
Contact: Andrew Muggeridge
Opening Times: Please phone for details.
Min Mail Order UK: Nmc
Cat. Cost: 4 x 1st class
Credit Cards: None
Specialities: Perennials and bulbs.
Notes: Also sells wholesale.
Map Ref: S, D3

SPer   PERRYHILL NURSERIES LTD ⊠ ⋔ ⬛
Hartfield, East Sussex, TN7 4JP
Ⓣ (01892) 770377
Ⓕ (01892) 770929
Ⓔ sales@perryhillnurseries.co.uk
Ⓦ www.perryhillnurseries.co.uk
Contact: P J Chapman
Opening Times: 0900-1700 7 days 1st Mar-
31st Oct. 0900-1630 1st Nov-28th Feb.
Min Mail Order UK: Nmc
Cat. Cost: £2.00 or on web
Credit Cards: Visa Access MasterCard Switch
Specialities: Wide range of trees, shrubs,
conifers, *Rhododendron* etc. Over 1300
herbaceous varieties, over 500 rose varieties.
Notes: Will deliver to some non-RHS shows.
Mail order despatch depends on size & weight
of plants.
Map Ref: S, C4 OS Grid Ref: TQ480375

SPet   PETTET'S NURSERY ⊠ ⋔ € ⬛
Poison Cross, Eastry, Sandwich, Kent,
CT13 0EA
Ⓣ (01304) 613869
Ⓕ (01304) 613869
Ⓔ terry@pettetsnursery.fsnet.co.uk
Ⓦ www.pettetsnursery.co.uk
Contact: T & EHP Pettet
Opening Times: 0900-1700 daily Mar-Jul.
1000-1600 Aug-Oct weekdays only.
Min Mail Order UK: £10.00
Min Mail Order EU: £20.00
Credit Cards: None
Specialities: Climbers, shrubs, herbaceous
perennials, alpines, pelargoniums, fuchsias.
Notes: Mail order Oct-Mar only. Also sells
wholesale.
Map Ref: S, C6

SPin   JOHN AND LYNSEY'S PLANTS
2 Hillside Cottages, Trampers Lane,
North Boarhunt, Fareham, Hampshire,
PO17 6DA
Ⓣ (01329) 832786

Contact: Mrs Lynsey Pink
Opening Times: By appt. only.
Cat. Cost: None issued
Credit Cards: None
Specialities: Mainly *Salvia* with a wide range
of other unusual perennials. Stock in small
quantities. Will propagate to order. Nat. Coll.
of *Salvia* species.
Map Ref: S, D2 OS Grid Ref: SU603109

SPla   PLAXTOL NURSERIES ⊠ ⬛
The Spoute, Plaxtol, S
evenoaks, Kent,
TN15 0QR
Ⓣ (01732) 810550
Ⓕ (01732) 810149
Ⓔ info@plaxtol-nurseries.co.uk
Ⓦ www.plaxtol-nurseries.co.uk
Contact: Alan Harvey
Opening Times: 1000-1700 7 days. Closed
2 weeks from Xmas Eve.
Min Mail Order UK: Nmc
Min Mail Order EU: £30.00 + p&p
Cat. Cost: 2 x 1st class
Credit Cards: All major credit/debit cards
Specialities: Hardy shrubs & herbaceous esp.
for flower arrangers. Old-fashioned roses, ferns
& climbers.
Map Ref: S, C4 OS Grid Ref: TQ611535

SPlb   PLANTBASE € ⬛
Lamberhurst Vineyard,
Lamberhurst Down, Lamberhurst,
Kent, TN3 8ER
Ⓣ (01892) 891453
Ⓔ graham@plantbase.freeserve.co.uk
Contact: Graham Blunt
Opening Times: 1000-1700 7 days Mar-Oct.
Cat. Cost: 2 x 1st class
Credit Cards: Visa Switch Access MasterCard
Delta
Specialities: Wide range of alpines, perennials,
shrubs, climbers, waterside plants, herbs,
Australasian shrubs & South African plants.
Map Ref: S, C5

SPoc   POCOCK'S ROSES ⊠ ⋔ ⬛
Jermyn's Lane, Romsey, Hampshire,
SO51 0QA
Ⓣ (01794) 367500
Ⓕ (01794) 367503
Ⓔ sales@pococksroses.co.uk
Ⓦ www.pococksroses.co.uk
Contact: Stewart Pocock
Opening Times: 1000-1600 Tue-Sun Mar-
Sep, 1000-1600 Thu-Sun Oct-Feb.
Min Mail Order UK: Nmc
Min Mail Order EU: Nmc

Cat. Cost: 2 x 1st class
Credit Cards: All major credit/debit cards
Specialities: Roses.
Notes: Also sells wholesale.

SPoG   THE POTTED GARDEN NURSERY
Ashford Road, Bearsted, Maidstone, Kent,
ME14 4NH
Ⓣ (01622) 737801
Ⓕ (01622) 632459
Ⓔ pottedgarden@btconnect.com
Ⓦ www.thepottedgarden.co.uk
Contact: Any staff member
Opening Times: 0900-1730 (dusk in winter)
7 days. Closed Xmas, Boxing Day & New
Year's Day.
Credit Cards: All major credit/debit cards
Notes: Mail order not available. Nursery
partially accessible for wheelchair users.
Map Ref: S, C5

**SPol   POLLIE'S PERENNIALS AND DAYLILY
NURSERY ⊠**
Lodore, Mount Pleasant Lane,
Sway, Lymington, Hampshire,
SO41 8LS
Ⓣ (01590) 682577
Ⓕ (01590) 682577
Ⓔ terry@maasz.fsnet.co.uk
Ⓦ www.polliesdaylilies.co.uk
Contact: Pollie Maasz
Opening Times: 0930-1730 w/ends only
during the daylily season mid-May to mid-
Aug. Other times by appt. only.
Min Mail Order UK: £10.00
Cat. Cost: 2 x 1st class
Credit Cards: None
Specialities: *Hemerocallis*, also less commonly
available hardy perennials. Stock in small
quantities. Nat. Coll. of spider & unusual
form *Hemerocallis*. 1000+ cvs can be viewed,
late Jun-mid Sep.
Notes: Mail order, daylilies only. Nursery
partially accessible for wheelchair users.
Map Ref: S, D2

SPop   POPS PLANTS ⊠ ⊠ ⋔ €
Pops Cottage, Barford Lane, Downton,
Salisbury, Wiltshire, SP5 3PZ
Ⓣ (01725) 511421
Ⓔ mail@popsplants
Ⓦ www.popsplants.com
Contact: G Dawson or L Roberts
Opening Times: By appt. only.
Min Mail Order UK: Nmc
Min Mail Order EU: Nmc
Cat. Cost: £2.00 for colour brochure.
Credit Cards: None

Specialities: *Primula auricula*. Some in ltd.
numbers. Nat. Coll. of Show, Alpine &
Double Auriculas.
Notes: Credit cards accepted online only.

SPur   PURE PLANTS
Blackboys Nursery, Blackboys, Uckfield, East
Sussex, TN22 5LS
Ⓣ (01825) 890858
Ⓕ (01825) 890878
Contact: Brian Fidler
Opening Times: 0900-1700 Tue-Sat. Closed
Sun & Mon except B/hol Sun 1000-1600 &
B/hol Mon 0900-1700.
Cat. Cost: 2 x 1st class
Credit Cards: All major credit/debit cards
Specialities: Trees, shrubs, herbaceous, grasses
& ferns. Many unusual varieties offered.
Map Ref: S, C4 OS Grid Ref: TQ515206

SRat   UNUSUAL PLANTS AT RATSBURY € ⑤
Smallhythe Road, Tenterden, Kent,
TN30 7LU
Ⓣ (01580) 762066
Ⓔ Ratsbury@aol.com
Ⓦ www.ratsbury.com
Contact: Jane Kirk
Opening Times: 1000-1700 daily, 26th Mar-
5th June.
Credit Cards: None
Specialities: Unusual and traditional cottage
garden plants.
Map Ref: S, C5 OS Grid Ref: TQ887322

SReu   G REUTHE LTD ⊠
Crown Point Nursery, Sevenoaks Road,
Ightham, Nr Sevenoaks,
Kent, TN15 0HB
Ⓣ (01732) 810694
Ⓕ (01732) 862166
Contact: C & P Tomlin
Opening Times: 0900-1600 Mon-Sat (closed
Wed). 1000-1600 Sun & B/hols Apr & May
only, occasionally in Jun, please check. Closed
Jan, Jul & Aug.
Min Mail Order UK: £30.00 + p&p
Min Mail Order EU: £500.00
Cat. Cost: £2.00
Credit Cards: Visa Access
Specialities: Rhododendrons & azaleas, trees,
shrubs & climbers.
Notes: Mail order certain plants only to EU.
Map Ref: S, C4

S

S

SRGP ROSIE'S GARDEN PLANTS ⊠ ☑ ♠
Rochester Road, Aylesford, Kent,
ME20 7EB
Ⓣ (01622) 715777 (m.) 07740 696277
Ⓕ (01622) 715777
Ⓔ JC Aviolet@aol.com
Ⓦ www.rosiesgardenplants.biz
Contact: J C Aviolét
Opening Times: Mail order & shows only.
Closed for 4-acre redevelopment. Ring or
check website for details.
Min Mail Order UK: Nmc
Min Mail Order EU: Nmc
Cat. Cost: 2 x 1st class
Credit Cards: Visa MasterCard Switch
Specialities: Hardy *Geranium, Buddleja* &
Aster. 'Named' herbaceous & shrubs.
Map Ref: S, C4 OS Grid Ref: TQ7460

SRiv RIVER GARDEN NURSERIES ⊠ ♠ € 🅱
Troutbeck, Otford, Sevenoaks, Kent,
TN14 5PH
Ⓣ (01959) 525588
Ⓕ (01959) 525810
Ⓔ box@river-garden.co.uk
Ⓦ www.river-garden.co.uk
Contact: Jenny Alban Davies
Opening Times: By appt. only.
Min Mail Order UK: £10.00 + p&p
Min Mail Order EU: £50.00 + p&p
Cat. Cost: 2 x 1st class
Credit Cards: All major credit/debit cards
Specialities: *Buxus* species, cultivars &
hedging. *Buxus* topiary.
Notes: Also sells wholesale.
Map Ref: S, C4 OS Grid Ref: TQ523593

SRkn RAPKYNS NURSERY ♠ 🅱
(Office) Brinkwells, School Lane, Hadlow
Down, East Sussex, TN22 4HY
Ⓣ (01825) 830065
Ⓜ 07771 916933
Ⓕ (01825) 830065
Contact: Fiona Moore, Steven Moore
Opening Times: 1000-1700 Tue , Thu & Fri,
Mar-Oct incl.
Cat. Cost: 2 x 1st class
Credit Cards: None
Specialities: Unusual shrubs, perennials &
climbers. *Azaleas, Campanulas, Ceanothus*,
geraniums, lavenders, lobelias, *Clematis*,
penstemons & grasses. New collections of
*Phormium, Phygelius, Agastache, Anemone,
Heuchera, Heucherella* & salvias.
Notes: Nursery at Scotsford Farm, Street End
Lane, Broad Oak. Heathfield, TN21 8UB.
Also sells wholesale.
Map Ref: S, C4 OS Grid Ref: TQ604248

SRms RUMSEY GARDENS ⊠ 🅱 ♦
117 Drift Road, Clanfield, Waterlooville,
Hampshire, PO8 0PD
Ⓣ (023) 9259 3367
Ⓔ info@rumsey-gardens.co.uk
Ⓦ www.rumsey-gardens.co.uk
Contact: Mr N R Giles
Opening Times: 0900-1700 Mon-Sat &
1000-1700 Sun & B/hols. Closed Sun Nov-
Feb.
Min Mail Order UK: Nmc
Cat. Cost: Online only.
Credit Cards: Visa MasterCard Switch
Specialities: Wide general range. Herbaceous,
alpines, heathers & ferns. Nat. &
International Collection of *Cotoneaster*.
Map Ref: S, D2

SRos ROSEWOOD DAYLILIES ⊠
70 Deansway Avenue, Sturry, Nr Canterbury,
Kent, CT2 0NN
Ⓣ (01227) 711071
Ⓕ (01227) 711071
Ⓔ Rosewoodgdns@aol.com
Contact: Chris Searle
Opening Times: By appt. only. Please phone.
Min Mail Order UK: Nmc
Cat. Cost: 2 x 1st class
Credit Cards: None
Specialities: *Hemerocallis*, mainly newer
American varieties. *Agapanthus*.
Map Ref: S, C5

SRot ROTHERVIEW NURSERY ⊠ ♠ € 🅱
Ivy House Lane, Three Oaks, Hastings,
East Sussex, TN35 4NP
Ⓣ (01424) 756228
Ⓕ (01424) 428944
Ⓔ rotherview@btinternet.com
Ⓦ www.rotherview.com
Contact: Ray Bates
Opening Times: 1000-1700 Mar-Oct, 1000-
1530 Nov-Feb, 7 days.
Min Mail Order UK: £10.00 + p&p
Min Mail Order EU: £20.00 + p&p
Cat. Cost: 4 x 1st class
Credit Cards: All major credit/debit cards
Specialities: Alpines.
Notes: Also sells wholesale.
Map Ref: S, D5

SSea SEALE NURSERIES 🅱 ♦
Seale Lane, Seale, Farnham, Surrey, GU10 1LD
Ⓣ (01252) 782410
Ⓔ plants@sealesuperroses.com
Contact: David & Catherine May
Opening Times: Tue-Sun & B/hol Mons.
Closed 25th Dec-10th Jan 2005.

Credit Cards: Visa Switch Access Delta
Specialities: Roses & *Pelargonium*. Some varieties in short supply, please phone first.
Map Ref: S, C3 OS Grid Ref: SU887477

SSpi   SPINNERS GARDEN € 🖔
School Lane, Boldre, Lymington, Hampshire, SO41 5QE
Ⓣ (01590) 673347
Contact: Peter Chappell
Opening Times: 1000-1700 Tue-Sat. By appt. Dec & Jan.
Cat. Cost: Sae for plant list.
Credit Cards: None
Specialities: Less common trees & shrubs esp. *Acer, Magnolia*, species & lace-cap *Hydrangea*. Bog & woodland plants, especially trilliums.
Map Ref: S, D2 OS Grid Ref: SZ323981

SSta   STARBOROUGH NURSERY ✉ 🖔
Starborough Road, Marsh Green, Edenbridge, Kent, TN8 5RB
Ⓣ (01732) 865614
Ⓕ (01732) 862166
Contact: C & P Tomlin
Opening Times: 0900-1600 Mon-Sat (closed Wed & Sun). Closed Jan, Jul & Aug.
Min Mail Order UK: £30.00 + p&p
Min Mail Order EU: £500.00
Cat. Cost: £2.00
Credit Cards: Visa Access
Specialities: Rare and unusual shrubs especially *Daphne, Acer*, rhododendrons & azaleas, *Magnolia* & *Hamamelis*.
Notes: Certain plants only to EU.
Map Ref: S, C4

SSth   SOUTHEASE PLANTS 🖔
Corner Cottage, Southease, Nr Lewes, East Sussex, BN7 3HX
Ⓣ (01273) 513681 m. 07791 856206
Ⓕ (01273) 513681
Contact: Adrian Orchard
Opening Times: 1100-1700 Wed-Sat, 1400-1700 Sun & by appt.
Cat. Cost: 2 x 1st class
Credit Cards: None
Specialities: A small nursery concentrating on hellebores, species & hybrids, grown on the nursery from seed collected from selected plans or obtained from specialist growers. Limited quantities.
Map Ref: S, D4 OS Grid Ref: TQ422052

SSto   STONE CROSS GARDEN CENTRE 🖔 ◆
Rattle Road, Pevensey, Sussex, BN24 5EB
Ⓣ (01323) 763250
Ⓕ (01323) 763195

Ⓔ gardencentre@stone-cross-nurseries.co.uk
Ⓦ www.stone-cross-nurseries.co.uk
Contact: Mrs J Birch
Opening Times: 0830-1730 Mon-Sat & 1000-1600 Sun & B/hols.
Cat. Cost: None issued
Credit Cards: Visa Access Switch
Specialities: *Hebe* & *Clematis*, evergreen shrubs. Lime tolerant & coastal shrubs & plants.
Notes: Also sells wholesale.
Map Ref: S, D4 OS Grid Ref: 6104

SSvw   SOUTHVIEW NURSERIES ✉ 🔼
Chequers Lane, Eversley Cross, Hook, Hampshire, RG27 0NT
Ⓣ (0118) 9732206
Ⓕ (0118) 9736160
Ⓔ Mark@Trenear.freeserve.co.uk
Ⓦ www.southviewnurseries.co.uk
Contact: Mark & Elaine Trenear
Opening Times: Mail order only. Orders for collection by prior arrangement.
Min Mail Order UK: Nmc
Cat. Cost: Free
Credit Cards: None
Specialities: Unusual hardy plants, specialising in old fashioned pinks & period plants. Nat. Coll. of Old Pinks. Pinks Collection open in June. Please ring for details.
Notes: Orders by prior arrangement only.
Map Ref: S, C3

STes   TEST VALLEY NURSERY ✉ 🔼 €
Stockbridge Road, Timsbury, Romsey, Hampshire, SO51 0NG
Ⓣ (01794) 368881
Ⓕ (01794) 368493
Ⓔ jbenn@tvn.demon.co.uk
Ⓦ www.testvalleynursery.co.uk
Contact: Julia Benn
Opening Times: 1000-1700 Tue-Sun Mar-Oct, or by appt.
Min Mail Order UK: Nmc.
Cat. Cost: 3 x 1st class
Credit Cards: All major credit/debit cards
Specialities: Large range of herbaceous perennials, incl. unusual & new varieties. Some in small quantities. Phone first to avoid disappointment.
Map Ref: S, C2

K E Y		
✉ Mail order to UK or EU	🔼 Delivers to shows	
🗶 Exports beyond EU	€ Euro accepted	
🖔 Accessible by wheelchair	◆ See Display advertisement	

STil   TILE BARN NURSERY ⊠ ✉ €
Standen Street, Iden Green,
Benenden, Kent,
TN17 4LB
Ⓣ (01580) 240221
Ⓕ (01580) 240221
Ⓔ tilebarn.nursery@virgin.net
Ⓦ www.tilebarn-cyclamen.co.uk
Contact: Peter Moore
Opening Times: 0900-1700 Wed-Sat.
Min Mail Order UK: £10.00 + p&p
Min Mail Order EU: £25.00 + p&p
Cat. Cost: Sae
Credit Cards: None
Specialities: *Cyclamen* species.
Notes: Also sells wholesale.
Map Ref: S, C5 OS Grid Ref: TQ805301

S

STop   SUSSEX TOPIARY ⊠ 🅱 ◆
Naldretts Lane, Bucks Green, Horsham,
West Sussex, RH12 3BU
Ⓣ (01403) 823131
Ⓜ 07811 467743
Ⓔ sussextopiary.freeserve.co.uk
Ⓦ www. sussextopiary.freeserve.co.uk
Contact: Denis De Ambrosi
Opening Times: Please ring before visiting.
Min Mail Order UK: £5.00
Min Mail Order EU: Nmc
Cat. Cost: 2 x 1st class
Credit Cards: None
Specialities: Specimen plants, trainers,
hedging, box species.
Notes: Also sells wholesale.
Map Ref: S, C3 OS Grid Ref: TQ082329

STre   PETER TRENEAR ⊠ 🅱
Chantreyland, Chequers Lane,
Eversley Cross, Hampshire,
RG27 0NX
Ⓣ (0118) 9732300
Ⓔ peter@babytrees.co.uk
Ⓦ www.babytrees.co.uk
Contact: Peter Trenear
Opening Times: 0900-1630 Mon-Sat.
Min Mail Order UK: £5.00 + p&p
Cat. Cost: 1 x 1st class
Credit Cards: None
Specialities: Trees, shrubs, conifers & *Pinus*.
Map Ref: S, C3 OS Grid Ref: SU795612

SUsu   USUAL & UNUSUAL PLANTS 🄽 €
Onslow House, Magham Down, Hailsham,
East Sussex, BN27 1PL
Ⓣ (01323) 840967
Ⓕ (01323) 844725
Ⓔ jennie@uuplants.co.uk
Ⓦ www.uuplants.co.uk

Contact: Jennie Maillard
Opening Times: 0930-1730 Wed-Sat &
B/Hol Mons 17 Mar-16 Oct. Other times
strictly by appt. only.
Cat. Cost: Sae + £1.00
Credit Cards: None
Specialities: Small quantities of a wide variety
of unusual perennials esp. *Erysimum,
Euphorbia*, hardy *Geranium, Salvia* & grasses.
Map Ref: S, D4 OS Grid Ref: TQ607113

SVil   THE VILLAGE NURSERIES 🄽 € 🅱 ◆
Sinnocks, West Chiltington, Pulborough,
West Sussex, RH20 2JX
Ⓣ (01798) 813040
Ⓕ (01798) 817240
Ⓔ petermanfield@aol.com
Ⓦ www.village-nurseries.co.uk
Contact: Peter Manfield
Opening Times: 0900-1800 or dusk, 7 days.
Cat. Cost: None issued
Credit Cards: All major credit/debit cards
Specialities: Wide range of hardy perennials &
grasses, incl. many new varieties. Selected
shrubs, climbers & Japanese maples.
Map Ref: S, D3 OS Grid Ref: TQ095182

SWal   WALLACE PLANTS 🄽
Lewes Road Nursery, Lewes Road,
Laughton, East Sussex,
BN8 6BN
Ⓣ (01323) 811729
Ⓔ sjk@wallaceplants.fsnet.co.uk
Contact: Simon Wallace
Opening Times: 0930-1800 7 days, incl.
b/hols, Mar-Sep, 0930-1600 Oct-Feb.
Cat. Cost: 3 x 1st class
Credit Cards: None
Specialities: Ornamental grasses, hebes, hardy
fuchsias, salvias, penstemons, unusual plants.
Map Ref: S, D4 OS Grid Ref: TQ513126

SWat   WATER MEADOW NURSERY ⊠ ✉ 🄽 €
Cheriton, Nr Alresford, Hampshire,
SO24 0QB
Ⓣ (01962) 771895
Ⓕ (01962) 771895
Ⓔ plantaholic@onetel.com
Ⓦ www.plantaholic.co.uk
Contact: Mrs Sandy Worth
Opening Times: 1000-1700 Wed-Sat Mar-Jul
or by appt.
Min Mail Order UK: £10.00 + p&p
Min Mail Order EU: £50.00 + p&p
Cat. Cost: £2.00 cheque or stamps.
Credit Cards: Visa MasterCard
Specialities: Water lilies, extensive water
garden plants, unusual herbaceous perennials,

W

aromatic herbs & wildflowers. New Super Poppy range. Nat. Coll. of *Papaver orientale* group.
Notes: Also sells wholesale.
Map Ref: S, C2

SWCr   WYCH CROSS NURSERIES 🅐
Wych Cross, Forest Row, East Sussex, RH18 5JW
Ⓣ (01342) 822705
Ⓕ (01342) 825329
Ⓔ roses@wychcross.co.uk
Ⓦ www.wychcross.co.uk
Contact: J Paisley
Opening Times: 0900-1730 Mon-Sat.
Cat. Cost: Free
Credit Cards: All major credit/debit cards
Specialities: Roses.
Map Ref: S, C4 **OS Grid Ref:** TQ42133190

SWvt   WOLVERTON PLANTS LTD € 🅐 ◆
Wolverton Common, Tadley, Hampshire, RG26 5RU
Ⓣ (01635) 298453
Ⓕ (01635) 299075
Ⓔ Julian@wolvertonplants.co.uk
Ⓦ www.wolvertonplants.co.uk
Contact: Julian Jones
Opening Times: 0900-1800 (or dusk Nov-Feb), 7 days. Closed Xmas/New Year.
Cat. Cost: Online
Credit Cards: All major credit/debit cards
Notes: Also sells wholesale.
Map Ref: S, C2 **OS Grid Ref:** SU555589

SYvo   YVONNE'S PLANTS
66 The Ridgway, Woodingdean, Brighton, Sussex, BN2 6PD
Ⓣ (01273) 300883
Ⓔ yvonne@yvonnesplants.co.uk
Ⓦ www.yvonnesplants.co.uk
Contact: Mrs Yvonne Law
Opening Times: Mar-Oct, by appt. only.
Cat. Cost: None issued, plant list Online
Credit Cards: None
Specialities: Conservatory, tender & herbaceous perennials, incl. *Cestrum, Agapanthus, Canna, Fuchsia, Hedychium* & grasses.
Map Ref: S, D4 **OS Grid Ref:** TQ360056

WALES AND THE WEST

WAba   ABACUS NURSERIES ✉
Drummau Road, Skewen, Neath, West Glamorgan, SA10 6NW
Ⓣ (01792) 817994
Ⓔ plants@abacus-nurseries.co.uk

Ⓦ www.abacus-nurseries.co.uk
Contact: David Hill
Opening Times: Not open to the public. Collection by arrangement.
Min Mail Order UK: Nmc
Min Mail Order EU: Nmc
Cat. Cost: 2 x 2nd class
Credit Cards: None
Specialities: *Dahlia.*
Notes: Euros only accepted as cash. Also sells wholesale.
Map Ref: W, D3

WAbb   ABBEY DORE COURT GARDEN € 🅐
Abbey Dore Court, Abbey Dore, Herefordshire, HR2 0AD
Ⓣ (01981) 240419
Ⓕ (01981) 240419
Ⓔ www.abbeydorecourt.co.uk
Contact: Mrs C Ward
Opening Times: 1100-1730 26th Mar-2nd Oct. Closed Mon, Wed & Fri. Open B/hol Mons.
Cat. Cost: None issued
Credit Cards: None
Specialities: Mainly hardy perennials, many unusual, which may be seen growing in the garden. *Astrantia, Crocosmia, Helleborus, Paeonia, Pulmonaria* & *Sedum.*
Map Ref: W, C4 **OS Grid Ref:** SO388308

WAbe   ABERCONWY NURSERY 🏃 🅐
Graig, Glan Conwy, Colwyn Bay, Conwy, LL28 5TL
Ⓣ (01492) 580875
Contact: Dr & Mrs K G Lever
Opening Times: 1000-1700 Tue-Sun mid-Feb-mid-Oct.
Cat. Cost: 2 x 2nd class
Credit Cards: Visa MasterCard
Specialities: Alpines, including specialist varieties, esp. autumn gentians, *Saxifraga* & dwarf ericaceous. Shrubs & woodland plants incl. *Helleborus* & smaller ferns.
Map Ref: W, A3 **OS Grid Ref:** SH799744

WAct   ACTON BEAUCHAMP ROSES ✉ 🗶
Acton Beauchamp, Worcestershire, WR6 5AE
Ⓣ (01531) 640433
Ⓕ (01531) 640802
Ⓔ enquiries@actonbeaurose.co.uk
Ⓦ www.actonbeaurose.co.uk
Contact: Lindsay Bousfield

KEY		
✉ Mail order to UK or EU	🏃 Delivers to shows	
🗶 Exports beyond EU	€ Euro accepted	
🅐 Accessible by wheelchair	◆ See Display advertisement	

Opening Times: 1400-1700 Wed-Sun Mar-Oct, 1000-1700 B/hol Mon. Note: Nov-Feb mail order, visitors by appt.
Min Mail Order UK: Nmc
Min Mail Order EU: Nmc
Cat. Cost: 3 x 1st class
Credit Cards: Switch Solo Visa MasterCard
Specialities: Species roses, old roses, modern shrub, English, climbers, ramblers & ground-cover roses.
Map Ref: W, C4 **OS Grid Ref:** SO683492

WAul   AULDEN FARM ✉ ⋔ ⑤
Aulden, Leominster, Herefordshire, HR6 0JT
Ⓣ (01568) 720129
Ⓔ pf@auldenfarm.co.uk
Ⓦ www.auldenfarm.co.uk
Contact: Alun & Jill Whitehead
Opening Times: 1000-1700 Tue & Thu Apr-Aug. Other times by appt. Please phone.
Min Mail Order UK: Nmc
Min Mail Order EU: £20.00
Cat. Cost: 2 x 1st class
Credit Cards: None
Specialities: Hardy herbaceous perennials, with a special interest in Hemerocallis & Iris.
Notes: Limited mail order for *Hemerocallis* & *Iris* only. Credit card payments can be made by Paypal.
Map Ref: W, C4 **OS Grid Ref:** SO462548

WBar   BARNCROFT NURSERIES ⑤
Olden Lane, Ruyton-xi-Towns, Shrewsbury, Shropshire, SY4 1JD
Ⓣ (01939) 261619
Contact: Mrs R E Eccleston
Opening Times: 1000-1730 Tue-Sat 1000-1600 Sun. Closed throughout Jan. Open B/hols.
Cat. Cost: None available
Credit Cards: None
Specialities: Wide range of unusual herbaceous plants, shrubs, water plants, water lily ponds & ferns, as well as cottage garden favourites.
Notes: Also sells wholesale.
Map Ref: W, B4

WBGC   BURFORD GARDEN COMPANY ✉ € ⑤
Burford House Gardens, Tenbury Wells, Worcestershire, WR15 8HQ
Ⓣ (01584) 810777
Ⓕ (01584) 810673
Ⓔ info@burford.co.uk
Ⓦ www.burford.co.uk
Opening Times: 0900-1800 7 days. Gardens close at dusk if earlier.
Min Mail Order UK: Nmc

Cat. Cost: 4 x 1st class stamps
Credit Cards: Visa Access Switch
Specialities: *Clematis* and herbaceous, trees & shrubs. Nat. Coll. of *Clematis*.
Notes: Mail order *Clematis* only.
Map Ref: W, C4

WBor   BORDERVALE PLANTS ⋔ ⑤
Nantyderi, Sandy Lane, Ystradowen, Cowbridge, Vale of Glamorgan, CF71 7SX
Ⓣ (01446) 774036
Ⓦ www.bordervale.co.uk
Contact: Claire E Jenkins
Opening Times: 1000-1700 Fri-Sun & B/hols mid Mar-mid Oct. Other times by appt.
Cat. Cost: 2 x 1st class large sae or on website.
Credit Cards: None
Specialities: Unusual herbaceous perennials trees & shrubs, as well as cottage garden plants, many displayed in the 2 acre garden.
Map Ref: W, D3 **OS Grid Ref:** ST022776

WBou   BOUTS COTTAGE NURSERIES ✉
Bouts Lane, Inkberrow, Worcestershire, WR7 4HP
Ⓣ (01386) 792923
Ⓦ www.boutsviolas.co.uk
Contact: M & S Roberts
Opening Times: Not open to the public.
Min Mail Order UK: Nmc
Min Mail Order EU: Nmc
Cat. Cost: 1st class sae.
Credit Cards: None
Specialities: *Viola.*

WBrE   BRON EIFION NURSERY ✉
Bron Eifion, Criccieth, Caernarfonshire, LL52 0SA
Ⓣ (01766) 522890
Ⓔ gardencottage@onetel.com
Contact: Suzanne Evans
Opening Times: 1000-dusk 7 days 1st Mar-31st Oct. 1st Nov-29th Feb by appt. only.
Min Mail Order UK: £30.00 + p&p
Min Mail Order EU: £50.00 + p&p
Cat. Cost: 4 x 2nd class
Credit Cards: None
Specialities: *Kalmia, Daphne, Embothrium,* plants for coastal regions & wide and interesting range of hardy plants.
Map Ref: W, B2

WBri   BRINGSTY NURSERY ✉ ⑤
Bringsty Common, Nr Bromyard, Herefordshire, WR6 5UW
Ⓣ (01886) 821482
Ⓔ jennifer@bringstyherbs.fsnet.co.uk
Contact: Ms JM Powles

W

W

Opening Times: 1000-1700 Wed-Sun 1 Apr-30 Sep.
Min Mail Order UK: £10.00
Cat. Cost: 3 x 1st class
Credit Cards: None
Specialities: Over 350 varieties of container grown medicinal, decorative & culinary herbs. Rockery & cottage garden plants. Wild flowers. Some stock is limited where hard to raise.
Map Ref: W, C4

WBrk   BROCKAMIN PLANTS 🏠 ♿
Brockamin, Old Hills, Callow End,
Worcestershire, WR2 4TQ
Ⓣ (01905) 830370
Ⓔ dickstonebrockamin@tinyworld.co.uk
Contact: Margaret Stone
Opening Times: 1100-1600 Sun only. Other times by appt.
Cat. Cost: Free.
Credit Cards: None
Specialities: Hardy perennials, especially hardy geraniums and some asters. Stock available in small quantities only.
Notes: Sells at Gardeners' Markets.
Map Ref: W, C5 OS Grid Ref: SO830488

WBuc   BUCKNELL NURSERIES ✉
Bucknell, Shropshire, SY7 0EL
Ⓣ (01547) 530606
Ⓕ (01547) 530699
Contact: A N Coull
Opening Times: 0800-1700 Mon-Fri & 1000-1300 Sat.
Min Mail Order UK: Nmc
Cat. Cost: Free
Credit Cards: None
Specialities: Bare rooted hedging conifers & forest trees.
Notes: Also sells wholesale.
Map Ref: W, C4 OS Grid Ref: SO356736

WBVN   BANWY VALLEY NURSERY ♿
Foel, Llangadfan, Nr. Welshpool, Powys,
SY21 0PT
Ⓣ (01938) 820281
Ⓕ (01938) 820281
Ⓔ banwy.valley@virgin.net
Contact: Syd Luck
Opening Times: 1000-1700 Tue-Sun. Open B/hols.
Cat. Cost: 2 x 1st class
Credit Cards: None
Specialities: Perennials, shrubs, incl. climbers, ornamental & fruit trees. Ever expanding range of magnolias & rhododendrons. All grown on the nursery.
Map Ref: W, B3 OS Grid Ref: SH993107

WCAu   CLAIRE AUSTIN HARDY PLANTS ✉ ✉ €
♿ ◆
The Stone House, Cramp Pool,
Shifnal, Shropshire,
TF11 8PE
Ⓣ (01952) 463700
Ⓕ (01952) 463111
Ⓔ enquiries@claireaustin-hardyplants.co.uk
Ⓦ www.claireaustin-hardyplants.co.uk
Contact: Claire Austin
Opening Times: 1000-1600 7 days, 1st Mar-30th Sep. Oct-Feb w/days by appt.
Min Mail Order UK: Nmc
Min Mail Order EU: £50.00 + p&p
Cat. Cost: UK Free, £5.00 Europe.
Credit Cards: Visa MasterCard Switch
Specialities: *Paeonia, Iris, Hemerocallis* & hardy plants. Nat. Colls. of Bearded *Iris* & Hybrid Herbaceous *Paeonia*.
Notes: Exports tree peonys only beyond EU.
Map Ref: W, B4

WCel   CELYN VALE EUCALYPTUS NURSERIES
✉ ✉
Carrog, Corwen, Merioneth,
LL21 9LD
Ⓣ (01490) 430671
Ⓕ (01490) 430671
Ⓔ info@eucalyptus.co.uk
Ⓦ www.eucalyptus.co.uk
Contact: Andrew McConnell & Paul Yoxall
Opening Times: 0900-1600 Mon-Fri Jan-Nov. Please phone first outside these days.
Min Mail Order UK: 3 plants + p&p
Min Mail Order EU: 3 plants + p&p
Cat. Cost: 2 x 1st class
Credit Cards: All major credit/debit cards
Specialities: Hardy *Eucalyptus* & *Acacia*.
Notes: Also sells wholesale.
Map Ref: W, A3 OS Grid Ref: SJ116452

WCFE   CHARLES F ELLIS & SON €
(Office) Barn House, Wormington,
Nr Broadway, Worcestershire,
WR12 7NL
Ⓣ (01386) 584077 (nursery)
Ⓕ (01386) 584491
Contact: Charles Ellis
Opening Times: 1000-1600 7 days 1st Apr-30th Sep.
Cat. Cost: None issued.
Credit Cards: None
Specialities: Wide range of more unusual shrubs, conifers & climbers.
Notes: Nursery is at Oak Piece Farm Nursery, Stanton, near Broadway.
Map Ref: W, C5

WCHb   THE COTTAGE HERBERY ⋔
Mill House, Boraston, Nr Tenbury Wells,
Worcestershire, WR15 8LZ
Ⓣ (01584) 781575
Ⓕ (01584) 781483
Ⓦ www.thecottageherbery.co.uk
Contact: K & R Hurst
Opening Times: By appt. only. Order
collection service available.
Cat. Cost: 6 x 1st class
Credit Cards: None
Specialities: Over 600 varieties of herbs.
Aromatic & scented foliage plants, esp.
*Monarda, Ajuga, Lobelia, Rosmarinus,
Campanula*, alliums & seeds. Soil Assoc.
licence no. G6475.
Map Ref: W, C4

W

**WChG   CHENNELS GATE GARDENS &
NURSERY** ⬚
Eardisley, Herefordshire, HR3 6LT
Ⓣ (01544) 327288
Contact: Mark Dawson
Opening Times: 1000-1700 7 days Mar-Oct.
Cat. Cost: None issued.
Credit Cards: None
Specialities: Interesting & unusual cottage
garden plants, grasses, hedging & shrubs.
Map Ref: W, C4

WCLn   COUNTRY LANE NURSERIES ⬚
Plwmp, Llandysul, Ceredigion, SA44 6HU
Ⓣ (01239) 851015
Ⓜ 07976 411884
Ⓕ (01239) 858921
Ⓔ Theresa.Glover@btinternet.com
Contact: Theresa Glover
Opening Times: 1000-1700 Wed-Sun, Easter-
end of Sep. Other times please phone first.
Cat. Cost: None issued.
Specialities: Good range of unusual hardy
perennials and shrubs, incl. large range of
moisture-loving & bog plants.
Notes: Also sells wholesale.
Map Ref: OS Grid Ref: SN3658

WCMO   COTSWOLD GARDEN MAIL ORDER ⊠ ⊠
⋔ € ⬚ ◆
Siding Nursery, Offenham Road, Evesham,
Worcestershire, WR11 8DX
Ⓣ (01386) 49671(m.) 07966 589473
Ⓕ (01386) 761603
Ⓔ enquiries@cotswoldgarden.co.uk
Ⓦ www.cotswoldgarden.co.uk
Contact: Andrew Houghton
Opening Times: Opens Feb 2005, please
contact nursery for details.
Min Mail Order UK: Nmc

Min Mail Order EU: £25.00
Cat. Cost: 3 x 1st class
Credit Cards: All major credit/debit cards
Specialities: Rare and unusual plants. Wide
range of *Hippeastrum* sp. & cultivars. Some
stock available in small quantities only.
Map Ref: W, C5 OS Grid Ref: SP052444

WCot   COTSWOLD GARDEN FLOWERS ⊠ ⋔ €
Sands Lane, Badsey, Evesham, Worcestershire,
WR11 5EZ
Ⓣ nursery (01386) 833849, mail order
(01386) 422829
Ⓕ nursery (01386) 49844
Ⓔ info@cgf.net
Ⓦ www.cgf.net
Contact: Bob Brown/Vicky Parkhouse
Opening Times: 0900-1730 Mon-Fri all year.
1000-1730 Sat & Sun Mar-Sep, Sat & Sun
Oct-Feb by appt.
Min Mail Order UK: £15.00 + p&p
Min Mail Order EU: £15.00 + p&p
Cat. Cost: £1.50 or 6 x 1st class.
Credit Cards: Visa MasterCard Access Switch
Specialities: A very wide range of easy &
unusual perennials. Nat. Coll. of *Lysimachia*.
Notes: Mail order Oct to mid-Feb only. Also
sells wholesale.
Map Ref: W, C5 OS Grid Ref: SP077426

WCra   CRANESBILL NURSERY ⊠ € ⬚
White Cottage, Stock Green, Nr Redditch,
Worcestershire, B96 6SZ
Ⓣ (01386) 792414
Ⓕ (01386) 792280
Ⓔ smandjbates@aol.com
Ⓦ www.cranesbillnursery.com
Contact: Mrs S M Bates
Opening Times: 1000-1700 19th Mar-30th
Sep. Closed Wed & Thu. Aug by appt. only.
Please contact for w/end opening.
Min Mail Order UK: Nmc
Min Mail Order EU: Nmc
Cat. Cost: 4 x 1st class
Credit Cards: All major credit/debit cards
Specialities: Hardy geraniums & other
herbaceous plants.
Map Ref: W, C5

WCre   CRESCENT PLANTS ⊠ ⋔ ⬚
Stoney Cross, Marden, Hereford, HR1 3EW
Ⓣ (01432) 880262
Ⓕ (01432) 880262
Ⓔ june@auriculas.co.uk
Ⓦ www.auriculas.co.uk
Contact: June Poole
Opening Times: Open by appt. Please phone.
Min Mail Order UK: Nmc

Min Mail Order EU: Nmc
Cat. Cost: Free
Credit Cards: None
Specialities: Named varieties of *Primula auricula* incl. show, alpine, double, striped & border types.
Notes: Payment by Paypal via website. Orders dispatched post free.
Map Ref: W, C4 OS Grid Ref: SO525477

WCru CRÛG FARM PLANTS 🔣
Griffith's Crossing, Nr Caernarfon, Caernarfonshire, LL55 1TU
ⓣ (01248) 670232
ⓔ bleddyn&sue@crug-farm.co.uk
ⓦ www.crug-farm.co.uk
Contact: B and S Wynn-Jones
Opening Times: 1000-1800 Thu-Sun last Sat Feb-last Sun Sep, plus B/hols.
Cat. Cost: 3 x 2nd class
Credit Cards: Visa Access Delta MasterCard
Specialities: Shade plants, climbers, hardy *Geranium*, *Pulmonaria*, rare shrubs, *Tropaeolum*, herbaceous & bulbous incl. self-collected new introductions from the Far East.
Nat. Colls. of *Coriaria, Paris* & *Polygonatum*.
Map Ref: W, A2 OS Grid Ref: SH509652

WCwm CWMRHAIADR NURSERY ✉
Glaspwll, Machynlleth, Montgomeryshire, SY20 8UB
ⓣ (01654) 702223
ⓕ (01654) 702223
ⓔ glynne.jones@btinternet.com
Contact: Glynne Jones
Opening Times: By appt. only. Please phone.
Min Mail Order UK: Nmc
Cat. Cost: Sae for list
Credit Cards: None
Specialities: *Acer* species. Rhododendrons.
Notes: Mail order Nov & Mar only. Garden open under NGS & to nursery visitors.
Map Ref: W, B3

WDav MARTIN DAVIS PLANTS ✉ ✖ ♞ €
Osric, 115 Calton Road, Gloucester, GL1 5ES
ⓣ (01452) 539749
ⓔ martin@osrics.freeserve.co.uk
Contact: Martin Davis
Opening Times: By appt. only.
Min Mail Order UK: Nmc
Min Mail Order EU: Nmc
Cat. Cost: 4 x 1st class
Credit Cards: None
Specialities: *Allium, Lilium, Canna*, dwarf bearded Iris & other bulbous/rhizomatous subjects.

Notes: Mail order for bulbs Oct-Jan, for plants Mar-May, limited stock.
Map Ref: W, D5

WDib DIBLEY'S NURSERIES ✉ ♞ € 🔣 ◆
Llanelidan, Ruthin, Denbighshire, LL15 2LG
ⓣ (01978) 790677
ⓕ (01978) 790668
ⓔ sales@dibleys.com
ⓦ www.dibleys.com
Contact: R Dibley
Opening Times: 1000-1700 7 days Mar-Oct.
Min Mail Order UK: Nmc
Min Mail Order EU: Nmc
Cat. Cost: Free
Credit Cards: Visa Access Switch Electron Solo
Specialities: *Streptocarpus, Columnea, Solenostemon* & other gesneriads & *Begonia*.
Nat. Coll. of *Streptocarpus*.
Notes: Also sells wholesale.
Map Ref: W, A3

WDin DINGLE NURSERIES € 🔣
Welshpool, Powys, SY21 9JD
ⓣ (01938) 555145
ⓕ (01938) 555778
ⓔ kerry@dinglenurseries.co.uk
ⓦ www.dinglenurseries.co.uk
Contact: Kerry Hamer
Opening Times: 0900-1700 Wed-Mon, 1400-1700 Tue.
Cat. Cost: Free plant list
Credit Cards: MasterCard Switch EuroCard Delta Visa
Specialities: Largest range of trees & shrubs in Wales. Wide seasonal selection of garden plants incl. roses, herbaceous perennials, conifers & barerooted forestry, hedging & fruit. All sizes incl. many mature specimens.
Notes: Also sells wholesale.
Map Ref: W, B4 OS Grid Ref: SJ196082

WDyf DYFFRYN NURSERIES ✉ ♞ € 🔣
Home Farm, Dyffryn, Cardiff, CF5 6JU
ⓣ (02920) 592085
ⓕ (02920) 593462
ⓔ sales@dyffryn-nurseries.co.uk
ⓦ www.dyffryn-nurseries.co.uk
Contact: Victoria Hardaker
Opening Times: 0800-1600 Mon-Fri, 1100-1600 Sat & Sun.

KEY		
✉ Mail order to UK or EU	♞ Delivers to shows	
✖ Exports beyond EU	€ Euro accepted	
🔣 Accessible by wheelchair	◆ See Display advertisement	

W

Min Mail Order UK: £25.00
Min Mail Order EU: £25.00
Cat. Cost: Information on request
Credit Cards: MasterCard Access Switch
Delta Visa
Specialities: Native & exotic mature, hardy
specimen & architectural plants.
Notes: Also sells wholesale.
Map Ref: W, D3

WDyG DYFFRYN GWYDDNO NURSERY ♠
Dyffryn Farm, Lampeter Velfrey, Narberth,
Pembrokeshire, SA67 8UN
Ⓣ (01834) 861684
Ⓔ sally.polson@virgin.net
Ⓦ www.pembrokeshireplants.co.uk
Contact: Mrs S L Polson
Opening Times: 1300-1700 Mon-Sun, 1st
Mar-1st Oct. Other times by prior telephone
appt. only.
Credit Cards: None
Specialities: Eclectic, yet wide-ranging, from
tender salvias & grasses to bog. Peat free &
principled. Plants in small quantities.
Notes: Also sells wholesale.
Map Ref: W, D2 OS Grid Ref: SR138148

WEas EASTGROVE COTTAGE GARDEN
NURSERY Ⓖ
Sankyns Green, Nr Shrawley, Little Witley,
Worcestershire, WR6 6LQ
Ⓣ (01299) 896389
Ⓦ www.eastgrove.co.uk
Contact: Malcolm & Carol Skinner
Opening Times: 1400-1700 Thu, Fri, Sat
14th Apr-30th Jul & B/hol Sun & Mon.
Closed throughout Aug. 1400-1700 Thu, Fri,
Sat 8th Sep-15th Oct.
Cat. Cost: Online
Credit Cards: None
Specialities: Unique cottage garden &
arboretum. Many varieties of *Viola, Iris,
Dianthus & Aquilegia*, plus a wide range of old
favourites & many unusual plants.
Notes: RHS Partnership garden. Extra 2 acres
of arboretum 2005.
Map Ref: W, C5 OS Grid Ref: SO795644

WEve EVERGREEN CONIFER CENTRE ⊠ Ⓖ ◆
Tenbury Road, Rock, Nr Kidderminster,
Worcestershire, DY14 9RB
Ⓣ (01299) 266581
Ⓕ (01299) 266755
Ⓔ brian@evergreen-conifers.co.uk
Ⓦ www.evergreen-conifers.co.uk
Contact: Mr B Warrington
Opening Times: 0900-1700 (dusk in winter)
Mon-Sat.

Min Mail Order UK: Nmc
Cat. Cost: 4 x 1st class for list
Credit Cards: All major credit/debit cards
Specialities: Conifers mainly but also acers,
heathers, trees, evergreen shrubs.
Notes: Mail order for conifers only.
Map Ref: W, C4 OS Grid Ref: SO731737

WFar FARMYARD NURSERIES ⊠ ⊠ Ⓖ ◆
Llandysul, Ceridigion, SA44 4RL
Ⓣ (01559) 363389:(01267) 220259
Ⓕ (01559) 362200
Ⓔ richard@farmyardnurseries.co.uk
Ⓦ www.farmyardnurseries.co.uk
Contact: Richard Bramley
Opening Times: 1000-1700 7 days excl.
Xmas, Boxing & New Year's Day.
Min Mail Order UK: Nmc
Min Mail Order EU: Nmc
Cat. Cost: 4 x 1st class
Credit Cards: Visa Switch MasterCard
Specialities: Excellent general range esp.
Helleborus, Hosta, Tricyrtis & Schizostylis, plus
shrubs, trees, climbers, alpines & esp.
herbaceous. Nat. Coll. of *Tricyrtis*.
Notes: Also sells wholesale.
Map Ref: W, C2 OS Grid Ref: SN421406

WFib FIBREX NURSERIES LTD ⊠ ⊠ ♠ Ⓖ
Honeybourne Road, Pebworth, Stratford-on-
Avon, Warwickshire, CV37 8XP
Ⓣ (01789) 720788
Ⓕ (01789) 721162
Ⓔ sales@fibrex.co.uk
Ⓦ www.fibrex.co.uk
Contact: U Key-Davis & R L Godard-Key
Opening Times: 0900-1700 Mon-Fri, 1200-
1700 Sat & Sun Mar-Jul. 0900-1600 Mon-Fri
Aug-Feb. Office hours 0930-1700 Mon-Fri all
year excl. last 2 wks Dec/1st wk Jan.
Min Mail Order UK: £10.00 + p&p
Min Mail Order EU: £20.00 + p&p
Cat. Cost: 2 x 2nd class
Credit Cards: Switch Visa MasterCard
Specialities: *Hedera*, ferns, *Pelargonium* &
Helleborus. National Collections of
Pelargonium & *Hedera*.
Notes: Plant collections subject to time of
year, please check by phone. Restricted
wheelchair access. Also sells wholesale.
Map Ref: W, C5 OS Grid Ref: SP1246

WFoF FLOWERS OF THE FIELD
Field Farm, Weobley, Herefordshire,
HR4 8QJ
Ⓣ (01544) 318262
Ⓕ (01544) 318262
Ⓔ flowerofthefield@tesco.net

Contact: Kathy Davies
Opening Times: 0900-1900 7 days.
Cat. Cost: 2 x 1st class
Credit Cards: None
Specialities: Traditional & unusual perennials, grasses, shrubs, trees & herbs. Oriental lilies & freesias for cutting.
Notes: Nursery partially accessible for wheelchairs. Also sells wholesale.
Map Ref: W, C4

WGei   W G GEISSLER ⊠ ♿
Winsford, Kingston Road,
Slimbridge, Gloucestershire,
GL2 7BW
Ⓣ (01453) 890340
Ⓕ (01453) 890340
Ⓔ geissler.w@virgin.net
Ⓦ www.t.mann.taylor.clara.net/ptero.html
Contact: W G Geissler
Opening Times: 0900-1700 Mar-Nov or by arrangement.
Cat. Cost: None issued.
Credit Cards: None
Specialities: Hardy cacti & succulents & related books. Also agaves & other succulents. Nat. Colls. of *Opuntia* (sect. *Tephrocactus*) & *Pterocactus*.
Map Ref: W, D4

WGer   FRON GOCH GARDEN CENTRE ♿
Pant Road, Llanfaglan,
Caernarfon, Carnarfonshire,
LL54 5RL
Ⓣ (01286) 672212
Ⓕ (01286) 678912
Ⓔ info@frongoch-gardencentre.co.uk
Ⓦ www.frongoch-gardencentre.co.uk
Contact: RA & Mrs V Williams
Opening Times: 0900-1800 Mon-Sat, 1030-1630 Sun all year.
Cat. Cost: None issued
Credit Cards: All major credit/debit cards
Specialities: Wide range of trees, shrubs, conifers & herbaceous perennials, ferns & grasses; emphasis on plants for coastal & damp sites.
Map Ref: W, A2

WGHP   GREEN HILL PLANTS ♿
Goodrich Court Stables, Goodrich,
Ross-on-Wye, Herefordshire, HR9 6HT
Ⓣ 0845 458 1164
Ⓜ 07977 555089
Ⓔ greenhillplants@phonecoop.coop
Contact: Darren or Elizabeth Garman
Opening Times: Easter-Sep, variable hours, please phone for details.

Cat. Cost: 2 x 1st class
Credit Cards: None
Specialities: Herbs, grasses, herbaceous perennials & willows. Some in small quantities.
Map Ref: W, C4 OS Grid Ref: SO569200

WGob   THE GOBBETT NURSERY ⊠
Farlow, Kidderminster, Worcestershire,
DY14 8TD
Ⓣ (01746) 718647
Ⓕ (01746) 718647
Ⓔ christine.link@lineone.net
Contact: C H Link
Opening Times: 1030-1700, Mon-Sat.
Min Mail Order UK: £10.00
Cat. Cost: 3 x 1st class.
Credit Cards: None
Specialities: *Syringa, Magnolia*. Some varieties available in small quantities only.
Map Ref: W, B4 OS Grid Ref: SO648811

WGor   GORDON'S NURSERY ⊠ ♿
1 Cefnpennar Cottages, Cefnpennar,
Mountain Ash, Mid-Glamorgan,
CF45 4EE
Ⓣ (01443) 474593
Ⓕ (01443) 475835
Ⓔ ddgordonsnursery@aol.com
Ⓦ www.gordonsnursery.co.uk
Contact: D A Gordon
Opening Times: 1000-1800 7 days 1st Mar-31st Oct. 1100-1600 Sat & Sun 1st Nov-28th Feb.
Min Mail Order UK: Nmc
Cat. Cost: 3 x 1st class
Credit Cards: All major credit/debit cards
Specialities: Shrubs, perennials, alpines & dwarf conifers.
Notes: Mail order only available in some cases, please check for conditions in catalogue.
Map Ref: W, D3 OS Grid Ref: SO037012

WGwG   GWYNFOR GROWERS ⊠ ♘ € ♿
Gwynfor, Pontgarreg, Llangranog, Llandysul,
Ceredigion, SA44 6AU
Ⓣ (01239) 654151
Ⓔ info@gwynfor.co.uk
Ⓦ www.gwynfor.co.uk
Contact: Steve & Angie Hipkin
Opening Times: 1000-1700 Wed, Thu & Sun, all year round.

W

Min Mail Order UK: Nmc
Min Mail Order EU: Nmc
Cat. Cost: 4 x 1st class, free by email.
Credit Cards: None
Specialities: Plants for wildlife, herbs &
intriguing perennials for everyone from novice
gardeners to specialist plantsmen. We use
organic, peat-free compost.
Notes: Also sells wholesale.
Map Ref: W, C2 OS Grid Ref: SN331536

WGWT GRAFTED WALNUT TREES ✉ € ♿
The Manse, Capel Isaac,
Llandeilo, Carmarthenshire,
SA19 7TN
Ⓣ (01558) 669043
Ⓔ sales@graftedwalnuts.co.uk
Ⓦ www.graftedwalnuts.co.uk
Contact: Pete Wignall
Opening Times: 0900-1800 Mon-Fri.
Nursery visits by appt. only.
Min Mail Order UK: Nmc
Min Mail Order EU: Nmc
Cat. Cost: 3 x 1st class
Credit Cards: None
Specialities: Grafted walnut trees incl. nut
bearing varieties of English walnut,
ornamental forms of English & black walnut,
minor species & hybrids. Limited supply of
ornamental varieties.
Notes: Also sells wholesale.
Map Ref: W, C3 OS Grid Ref: SN580266

WHal HALL FARM NURSERY ♘ €
Vicarage Lane, Kinnerley, Nr Oswestry,
Shropshire, SY10 8DH
Ⓣ (01691) 682135
Ⓕ (01691) 682135
Ⓔ hallfarmnursery@ukonline.co.uk
Ⓦ www.hallfarmnursery.co.uk
Contact: Christine & Nick Ffoulkes-Jones
Opening Times: 1000-1700 Tue-Sat 1st Mar-
8th Oct 2005. Winter by appt.
Cat. Cost: 4 x 1st class
Credit Cards: None
Specialities: Unusual herbaceous plants incl.
hardy *Geranium*, grasses, bog plants & pool
marginals, late-flowering perennials, foliage
plants.
Notes: Nursery partially accessible for
wheelchairs.
Map Ref: W, B4 OS Grid Ref: SJ333209

WHar HARLEY NURSERY ♿
Harley, Shropshire, SY5 6LP
Ⓣ (01952) 510241
Ⓕ (01952) 510570
Ⓔ Harleynurseries@farmersweekly.net

Contact: Duncan Murphy, Moira Murphy &
Nicholas Murphy
Opening Times: 0900-1730 Mon-Sat, 1000-
1600 Sun & B/hols. Winter hours 1000-1600
Sun & B/hols.
Cat. Cost: 2 x 1st class
Credit Cards: All major credit/debit cards
Specialities: Wide range of ornamental & fruit
trees. Own grown shrubs, climbers, wide
range of hedging plants year round.
Conservation, wildlife plants & native trees a
speciality.
Map Ref: W, B4

WHCG HUNTS COURT GARDEN & NURSERY ♿
North Nibley, Dursley, Gloucestershire,
GL11 6DZ
Ⓣ (01453) 547440
Ⓕ (01453) 549944
Ⓔ keith@huntscourt.fsnet.co.uk
Contact: T K & M M Marshall
Opening Times: 0900-1230 & 1345-1700
Tue-Sat excl. Aug, nursery & garden. Also by
appt. See NGS for Sun openings.
Cat. Cost: 5 x 2nd class
Credit Cards: None
Specialities: Old roses species & climbers.
Hardy *Geranium, Penstemon* & unusual
shrubs.
Map Ref: W, D4

WHCr HERGEST CROFT GARDENS
Kington, Herefordshire, HR5 3EG
Ⓣ (01544) 230160
Ⓕ (01544) 232031
Ⓔ gardens@hergest.co.uk
Ⓦ www.hergest.co.uk
Contact: Stephen Lloyd
Opening Times: 1230-1730 7 days Apr-Oct,
1200-1800 7 days May-Jun.
Cat. Cost: None issued
Credit Cards: All major credit/debit cards
Specialities: *Acer, Betula* & unusual woody
plants.
Notes: Limited wheelchair access.
Map Ref: W, C4

WHbs HERBS AT MYDDFAI ♿
Beiliglas, Myddfai, Nr Llandovery,
Carmarthenshire, SA20 0QB
Ⓣ (01550) 720494/ 720628
Ⓕ (01550) 720628
Ⓔ gill@myddfai.com
Ⓦ www.myddfai.com
Contact: Gill Swan
Opening Times: 1400-1800 Tue-Sat Apr-Oct,
or by appt.
Cat. Cost: 2 x 1st class

Credit Cards: None
Specialities: Herbs & wild flowers. Organic.
Map Ref: W, C3 OS Grid Ref: SN781310

WHen   HENLLYS LODGE PLANTS 🛆
Henllys Lodge, Beaumaris, Anglesey,
Gwynedd, LL58 8HU
Ⓣ (01248) 810106
Ⓔ cranesbill@hugheslane.freeserve.co.uk
Contact: Mrs E Lane
Opening Times: 1100-1700 Mon Wed Sat
Sun & by appt. Apr-Oct.
Cat. Cost: None issued.
Credit Cards: None
Specialities: Hardy *Geranium*, ground cover &
cottage style perennials.
Map Ref: W, A3 OS Grid Ref: SH601773

**WHer   THE HERB GARDEN & HISTORICAL
PLANT NURSERY ⊠**
Ty Capel Pensarn, Pentre Berw, Anglesey,
Gwynedd, LL60 6LG
Ⓣ (01248) 422208 (m.) 07751 583958
Ⓕ (01248) 422208
Ⓦ www.HistoricalPlants.co.uk
Contact: Corinne & David Tremaine-
Stevenson
Opening Times: By appt. only.
Min Mail Order UK: £15.00 + p&p
Min Mail Order EU: £50.00 + p&p
Cat. Cost: List £2.50
Credit Cards: None
Specialities: Wide range of herbs, rare natives
& wild flowers; rare, unusual & historical
perennials. Old roses.
Map Ref: W, A2

WHil   HILLVIEW HARDY PLANTS ⊠ ☒ ♙ € 🛆 ◆
(off B4176), Worfield,
Nr Bridgnorth, Shropshire,
WV15 5NT
Ⓣ (01746) 716454
Ⓕ (01746) 716454
Ⓔ hillview@onetel.net
Ⓦ www.hillviewhardyplants.com
Contact: Ingrid Millington, John Millington
Opening Times: 0900-1700 Mon-Sat Mar-
mid Oct. At other times, please phone first.
Min Mail Order UK: £15.00 + p&p
Min Mail Order EU: £15.00 + p&p
Cat. Cost: 5 x 2nd class
Credit Cards: All major credit/debit cards
Specialities: Choice herbaceous perennials
incl. *Aquilegia, Astrantia, Auricula, Primula,
Crocosmia, Eucomis, Phlox, Schizostylis,
Verbascum, Acanthus*. Nat. Coll. of *Acanthus*.
Notes: Also sells wholesale.
Map Ref: W, B4 OS Grid Ref: SO772969

WHlf   HAYLOFT PLANTS ⊠
Manor Farm, Pensham, Pershore,
Worcestershire, WR10 3HB
Ⓣ (01386) 554440
Ⓕ (01386) 553833
Ⓔ info@hayloftplants.co.uk
Ⓦ www.hayloftplants.co.uk
Contact: Yvonne Walker
Opening Times: Not open. Mail order only.
Min Mail Order UK: Nmc
Min Mail Order EU: Nmc
Cat. Cost: Free
Credit Cards: All major credit/debit cards

WHoo   HOO HOUSE NURSERY € 🛆 ◆
Hoo House, Gloucester Road, Tewkesbury,
Gloucestershire, GL20 7DA
Ⓣ (01684) 293389
Ⓕ (01684) 293389
Ⓔ nursery@hoohouse.co.uk
Ⓦ www.hoohouse.plus.com
Contact: Robin & Julie Ritchie
Opening Times: 1000-1700 Mon-Sat, 1100-
1700 Sun.
Cat. Cost: 3 x 1st class
Credit Cards: None
Specialities: Wide range of herbaceous &
alpines – many unusual, incl. *Campanula,
Geranium* & *Penstemon*. Nat. Colls. of
Platycodon & *Gentiana asclepiadea* cvs.
Notes: Also sells wholesale.
Map Ref: W, C5 OS Grid Ref: SO893293

WHPP   HP PLANTS ⊠
Yew Tree House, High Street, Hillesley,
Wooton-under-Edge, Gloucestershire,
GL12 7RD
Ⓣ (01453) 845355
Ⓕ (01453) 844147
Ⓔ chrism@hawkesbury@virgin.net
Ⓦ www.hpplants.com
Contact: Pauline Mapp
Opening Times: Mail order or by appt. only.
Min Mail Order UK: Nmc
Cat. Cost: Free
Credit Cards: None
Specialities: Pelargoniums

WHrl   HARRELLS HARDY PLANTS ⊠
(Office) 15 Coxlea Close, Evesham,
Worcestershire, WR11 4JS
Ⓣ (01386) 443077
Ⓕ (01386) 443852

W

Ⓔ enicklin@evesham11.fsnet.co.uk
Ⓦ www.harrellshardyplants.co.uk
Contact: Liz Nicklin & Kate Phillips
Opening Times: 1000-1200 Sun Mar-Nov.
Other times by appt. Please phone.
Min Mail Order UK: Nmc
Cat. Cost: 3 x 1st class
Credit Cards: None
Specialities: We are now developing display
gardens to showcase our wide range of hardy
plants, many unusual.
Notes: Nursery located off Rudge Rd,
Evesham. Please phone for directions or see
catalogue. Partial wheelchair access. Mail order
Nov-Mar only.
Map Ref: W, C5 **OS Grid Ref:** SP033443

WIvy   IVYCROFT PLANTS ⊠ 🅖
Upper Ivington, Leominster, Herefordshire,
HR6 0JN
Ⓣ (01568) 720344
Ⓔ rogerandsue@ivycroft.freeserve.co.uk
Ⓦ www.ivycroft.freeserve.co.uk
Contact: Roger Norman
Opening Times: 0900-1600 Thu Feb, Wed &
Thu Mar-Sep. Other times by appt., please
phone.
Min Mail Order UK: Nmc
Min Mail Order EU: Nmc
Cat. Cost: 2 x 1st class
Credit Cards: None
Specialities: *Cyclamen, Galanthus, Salix,*
alpines, herbaceous & ferns.
Notes: Mail order Feb/Mar *Galanthus* & *Salix*
only.
Map Ref: W, C4 **OS Grid Ref:** SO464562

WJas   PAUL JASPER TREES ⊠
The Lighthouse, Bridge Street, Leominster,
Herefordshire, HR6 8DX
Ⓕ (01568) 616499 for orders.
Ⓔ enquiries@jaspertrees.co.uk
Ⓦ www.jaspertrees.co.uk
Contact: Paul Jasper
Opening Times: Not open. Mail order only.
Min Mail Order UK: £40.00 + p&p
Cat. Cost: 2 x 1st class
Credit Cards: None
Specialities: Full range of fruit & ornamental
trees. Over 100 modern and traditional apple
varieties + 220 others all direct from the grower.
Many unusual varieties of *Malus domestica*.
Notes: Also sells wholesale.

WJek   JEKKA'S HERB FARM ⊠ 🄝 € 🅖
Rose Cottage, Shellards Lane, Alveston,
Bristol, BS35 3SY
Ⓣ (01454) 418878

Ⓕ (01454) 411988
Ⓔ farm@jekkasherbfarm.com
Ⓦ www.jekkasherbfarm.com
Contact: Jekka McVicar
Opening Times: 4 times a year. Please check
website for dates.
Min Mail Order UK: £10 plants
Min Mail Order EU: Nmc
Cat. Cost: 4 x 1st class
Credit Cards: Visa MasterCard Delta Switch
Specialities: Culinary, medicinal, aromatic,
decorative herbs. Soil Association licensed
herb farm.
Notes: Individual quotations for EU Sales.
Map Ref: W, D4

WJun   JUNGLE GIANTS ⊠ 🄝 €
Ferney, Onibury, Craven Arms, Shropshire,
SY7 9BJ
Ⓣ (01584) 856200
Ⓕ (01584) 856663
Ⓔ bamboo@junglegiants.co.uk
Ⓦ www.junglegiants.co.uk
Contact: Michael Brisbane
Opening Times: 7 days. By appt. only please.
Min Mail Order UK: £25.00 + p&p
Min Mail Order EU: £100.00 + p&p
Cat. Cost: 2 x 1st class
Credit Cards: Access Visa MasterCard
Specialities: *Bamboo.*
Notes: Also sells wholesale.
Map Ref: W, C4 **OS Grid Ref:** SO430779

WKif   KIFTSGATE COURT GARDENS 🅖
Kiftsgate Court, Chipping Camden,
Gloucestershire, GL55 6LW
Ⓣ (01386) 438777
Ⓕ (01386) 438777
Ⓔ kiftsgte@aol.com
Ⓦ www.kiftsgate.co.uk
Contact: Mrs J Chambers
Opening Times: 1400-1800 Wed, Thu & Sun
1st Apr -30th Sep & B/hol Mons. Also Mon
& Sat in Jun & Jul.
Cat. Cost: None issued
Credit Cards: None
Specialities: Small range of unusual plants.
Map Ref: W, C5

WKin   KINGSTONE COTTAGE PLANTS ⊠ 🅖
Weston-under-Penyard, Ross-on-Wye,
Herefordshire, HR9 7PH
Ⓣ (01989) 565267
Contact: Mr M Hughes
Opening Times: By appt. and as under NGS.
Min Mail Order UK: Nmc
Min Mail Order EU: Nmc
Cat. Cost: 2 x 1st class

Credit Cards: None
Specialities: Nat. Coll. of *Dianthus*.
Map Ref: W, C4

WLav THE LAVENDER GARDEN ✉ ♠ €
Ashcroft Nurseries, Nr Ozleworth, Kingscote,
Tetbury, Gloucestershire, GL8 8YF
ⓣ (01453) 860356 or 549286
Ⓜ 07837 582943
Ⓔ Andrew007Bullock@aol.com
Ⓦ www.TheLavenderG.co.uk
Contact: Andrew Bullock
Opening Times: 1100-1700 Sat & Sun.
Weekdays variable, please phone.
Min Mail Order UK: £50.00 + p&p
Min Mail Order EU: £50.00 + p&p
Cat. Cost: 2 x 1st class
Credit Cards: None
Specialities: *Lavandula, Buddleja*, plants to
attract butterflies. Herbs, wild flowers. Nat.
Coll. of *Buddleja*.
Notes: Also sells wholesale.
Map Ref: W, D5 OS Grid Ref: ST798948

WLeb LEBA ORCHARD – GREEN'S LEAVES ✉ ♠
Lea Bailey, Nr Ross-on-Wye, Herefordshire,
HR9 5TY
ⓣ (01989) 750303
Contact: Paul Green
Opening Times: By appt. only, w/ends
preferred.
Min Mail Order UK: £10.00 + p&p
Cat. Cost: 4 x 2nd class
Credit Cards: None
Specialities: Ornamental grasses, sedges &
phormiums. Increasing range of rare & choice
shrubs, also some perennials.
Notes: Also sells wholesale.
Map Ref: W, C4

WLin LINGEN NURSERY AND GARDEN ✉ ♠
Lingen, Nr Bucknell, Shropshire, SY7 0DY
ⓣ (01544) 267720
Ⓕ (01544) 267720
Ⓔ kim&maggie@lingen.freeserve.co.uk
Ⓦ www.lingennursery.co.uk
Contact: Kim W Davis
Opening Times: 1000-1700 Thu-Mon Feb-
Oct. Closed Tue-Wed all year.
Min Mail Order UK: £15.00
Min Mail Order EU: £20.00 + p&p
Cat. Cost: 3 x 1st class
Credit Cards: All major credit/debit cards
Specialities: Alpines, rock plants, herbaceous
esp. *Androsace, Aquilegia, Campanula, Iris,
Primula, auriculas* & *Penstemon*. Nat. Coll. of
Herbaceous Campanula & housing *Iris sibirica*.
Many in small quantities.

Notes: Partially accessible to wheelchair users
with help. Also sells wholesale.
Map Ref: W, C4 OS Grid Ref: SO366669

WMAq MEREBROOK WATER PLANTS ✉ ♿
Merebrook Farm, Hanley Swan,
Worcestershire, WR8 0DX
ⓣ (01684) 310950
Ⓔ enquiries@pondplants.co.uk
Ⓦ www.pondplants.co.uk
Contact: Roger Kings & Biddi Kings
Opening Times: 1000-1600 1st Apr-30th
Sep, closed Wed & Sun.
Min Mail Order UK: Nmc
Min Mail Order EU: £25.00
Cat. Cost: Free
Credit Cards: Visa Access Switch Delta
Specialities: *Nymphaea* & other aquatic
plants. Int. Waterlily & Water Gardening
Soc. accredited collection.
Notes: Display gardens open to the public
(no charge).
Map Ref: W, C5 OS Grid Ref: SO802425

WMnd MYND HARDY PLANTS ✉
Delbury Hall Estate, Diddlebury, Craven
Arms, Shropshire, SY7 9DH
Ⓜ 07812 689155
Ⓕ (01547) 530459
Ⓔ sales@myndplants.co.uk
Ⓦ www.myndplants.co.uk
Contact: Steve Adams
Opening Times: 1000-1700 Mon, Wed-Sat,
closed Tues, 1100-1700 Sun, Mar-end Sep.
Other times phone for appt.
Min Mail Order UK: £10.00 + p&p
Min Mail Order EU: £10.00 + p&p
Cat. Cost: 4 x 2nd class
Credit Cards: Visa MasterCard
Specialities: Herbaceous plants.
Notes: Also sells wholesale.
Map Ref: W, B4 OS Grid Ref: SO510852

WMoo MOORLAND COTTAGE PLANTS ✉ ♿
Rhyd-y-Groes, Brynberian, Crymych,
Pembrokeshire, SA41 3TT
ⓣ (01239) 891363
Ⓔ jenny@moorlandcottageplants.co.uk
Ⓦ www.moorlandcottageplants.co.uk
Contact: Jennifer Matthews
Opening Times: 1000-1800 daily excl. Wed
end Feb-end Sep.
Min Mail Order UK: See cat. for details.

W

Cat. Cost: 4 x 1st class
Credit Cards: None
Specialities: Traditional & unusual hardy
perennials. Many garden-worthy rarities.
Cottage garden plants; ferns & many shade
plants; moisture lovers; ornamental grasses &
bamboos; colourful ground cover.
Notes: Display garden open for NGS from
mid-May.
Map Ref: W, C2 OS Grid Ref: SN091343

WMou MOUNT PLEASANT TREES €
Rockhampton, Berkeley, Gloucestershire,
GL13 9DU
Ⓣ (01454) 260348
Contact: P & G Locke
Opening Times: By appt. only.
Cat. Cost: 3 x 2nd class
Credit Cards: None
Specialities: Wide range of trees for forestry,
hedging, woodlands & gardens esp. *Tilia,
Populus* & *Platanus*.
Notes: Also sells wholesale.
Map Ref: W, D4

W

WMow COTTAGE GARDEN PLANTS ⊠
Barley Mow House, Aston Rogers,
Nr Westbury, Shropshire, SY5 9HQ
Ⓣ (01743) 891565
Ⓜ 07779 936006
Contact: Tony Faulkner
Opening Times: 1200-1700 Wed, Thu, Fri &
Sat Mar-Oct. Other times by appt.
Min Mail Order UK: Nmc
Cat. Cost: None issued.
Credit Cards: None
Specialities: *Sidalcea* & other hardy
herbaceous perennial plants.
Map Ref: W, B4 OS Grid Ref: SJ3406

WMul MULU NURSERIES ⊠ ⛴ ⋔ € ⬡
Longdon Hill, Wickhamford, Evesham,
Worcestershire, WR11 7RP
Ⓣ (01386) 833171
Ⓕ (01386) 833136
Ⓔ plants@mulu.co.uk
Ⓦ www.mulu.co.uk
Contact: Andy Bateman
Opening Times: 1000-1800 or dusk 7 days,
Mar-Oct. 1000-1700 Mon, Tue, Fri & Sat ,
Nov-Feb. Wed-Thu by appt. only Nov-Feb.
Min Mail Order UK: Nmc
Cat. Cost: free
Credit Cards: Visa MasterCard Delta Switch
Specialities: Exotic plants, hardy & tender
incl. bananas, gingers, palms, tree ferns,
aroids.
Map Ref: W, C5 OS Grid Ref: SP060417

WNor NORFIELDS ⊠ ⋔ €
Llangwm Arboretum, Usk, Monmouthshire,
NP15 1NQ
Ⓣ (01291) 650306
Ⓕ (01291) 650577
Ⓔ andrew@norfields.co.uk
Ⓦ www.Norfields.co.uk
Contact: Andrew Norfield
Opening Times: Not open.
Min Mail Order UK: £3.00 + p&p
Min Mail Order EU: £3.00 + p&p
Cat. Cost: 2 x 1st class
Credit Cards: None
Specialities: Wide range of tree seedlings for
growing on. *Acer, Betula, Stewartia* & pre-
treated seed.
Notes: Also sells wholesale.

WOFF OLD FASHIONED FLOWERS ⊠ ⛴
Cleeway, Eardington, Bridgnorth, Shropshire,
WV16 5JT
Ⓣ (01746) 766909
Ⓔ jand.cm@virgin.net
Contact: John Snocken
Opening Times: By appt. only.
Min Mail Order UK: Nmc
Min Mail Order EU: Nmc
Cat. Cost: 2 x 2nd class
Credit Cards: None
Specialities: Show pansies, fancy pansies &
exhibition violas. Bedding violas, pinks,
auriculas, chrysanthemums, violets & species
Viola. Nat. Coll. of Florists' Violas & Pansies.
Map Ref: W, B4 OS Grid Ref: 723907

WOld OLD COURT NURSERIES ⊠ ⛴ € ⬡
Colwall, Nr Malvern, Worcestershire,
WR13 6QE
Ⓣ (01684) 540416
Ⓔ picton@dircon.co.uk
Ⓦ www.autumnasters.co.uk
Contact: Paul & Meriel Picton
Opening Times: 1100-1700 Fri-Sun May-
Oct, 7 days 1st week Sep-2nd week Oct.
Min Mail Order UK: Nmc
Min Mail Order EU: Nmc
Cat. Cost: 1 x 1st class
Credit Cards: None
Specialities: Nat. Coll. of Michaelmas Daisies.
Herbaceous perennials.
Notes: Mail order for *Aster* only.
Map Ref: W, C4 OS Grid Ref: SO759430

WOrn ORNAMENTAL TREE NURSERIES ⊠ ⬡
Broomy Hill Gardens, Cobnash, Kingsland,
Herefordshire, HR6 9QZ
Ⓣ (01568) 708016
Ⓕ (01568) 709022

Ⓔ enquiries@ornamental-trees.co.uk
Ⓦ www.ornamental-trees.co.uk
Contact: Russell Mills
Opening Times: 0900-1800 Mon-Sat. 1000-1600 Sun.
Min Mail Order UK: £9.95
Cat. Cost: 3 x 1st class
Credit Cards: All major credit/debit cards
Specialities: Ornamental trees. Fruit trees.
Notes: Also sells wholesale.
Map Ref: W, C4

WOut   OUT OF THE COMMON WAY ⊠ ň
(Office) Penhyddgan, Boduan,
Pwllheli, Gwynedd,
LL53 8YH
Ⓣ (01758) 721577 (Office):(01407) 720431
(Nursery)
Ⓔ penhyddgan@tiscali.co.uk
Contact: Joanna Davidson (nursery) Margaret Mason (office & mail order)
Opening Times: By arrangement.
Min Mail Order UK: Nmc
Min Mail Order EU: Nmc
Cat. Cost: A5 sae 35p.
Credit Cards: None
Specialities: *Aster, Nepeta, Geranium, Salvia, Digitalis* & *Stachys.* Some plants propagated in small quantities only.
Notes: Nursery is at Pandy Treban, Bryngwran, Anglesey. Partially accessible for wheelchairs.
Map Ref: W, A2 **OS Grid Ref:** SH370778

WOVN   THE OLD VICARAGE NURSERY ⊠
Lucton, Leominster, Herefordshire,
HR6 9PN
Ⓣ (01568) 780538
Ⓕ (01568) 780818
Contact: Mrs R M Flake
Opening Times: Most days. Please phone first if making a special journey.
Min Mail Order UK: Nmc
Cat. Cost: 2 x 1st class
Credit Cards: None
Specialities: Roses: old roses; climbers & ramblers; species & ground cover. *Euphorbia* & half-hardy *Salvia.*
Map Ref: W, C4

WPat   CHRIS PATTISON ⊠ ň € ⑤
Brookend, Pendock, Gloucestershire,
GL19 3PL
Ⓣ (01531) 650480
Ⓕ (01531) 650480
Ⓔ cpplants@redmarley.freeserve.co.uk
Ⓦ www.chrispattison.fsnet.co.uk
Contact: Chris Pattison

Opening Times: 0900-1700 Mon-Fri. W/ends by appt. only.
Min Mail Order UK: £10.00 +p&p
Cat. Cost: 3 x 1st class
Credit Cards: None
Specialities: Choice, rare shrubs & alpines. Grafted stock esp. Japanese maples & *Liquidambar.* Wide range of *Viburnum, Phormium,* dwarf willows & dwarf ericaceous shrubs.
Notes: Mail order Nov-Feb only. Also sells wholesale.
Map Ref: W, C5 **OS Grid Ref:** SO781327

WPBF   P & B FUCHSIAS ⊠ ň € ⑤
Maes y Gwaelod, Penclawdd Road,
Penclawdd, Swansea, West Glamorgan,
SA4 3RB
Ⓣ (01792) 851669
Ⓔ sales@gower-fuchsias.co.uk
Ⓦ www.gower-fuchsias.co.uk
Contact: Paul Fisher
Opening Times: 0900-1800 7 days 1 Mar-30 Sep.
Min Mail Order UK: £9.00 (6 plants @ £1.50 incl. P&P)
Cat. Cost: 3 x 1st class
Credit Cards: None
Specialities: Fuchsias. Hybrid & species.
Notes: Cuttings only available Mar-May. Very small quantities.
Map Ref: W, D3

WPer   PERHILL NURSERIES ⊠ € ⑤
Worcester Road, Great Witley,
Worcestershire, WR6 6JT
Ⓣ (01299) 896329
Ⓕ (01299) 896990
Ⓔ PerhillP@aol.com
Ⓦ www.perhillplants.co.uk
Contact: Duncan Straw
Opening Times: 0900-1700 Mon-Sat, 1000-1600 Sun, 1st Feb-15th Oct & by appt.
Min Mail Order UK: Nmc
Min Mail Order EU: £10.00
Cat. Cost: 6 x 2nd class
Credit Cards: All major credit/debit cards
Specialities: 2500+ varieties of rare, unusual alpines & herbaceous perennials incl. *Penstemon, Campanula, Salvia, Thymus,* herbs, *Veronica.*
Notes: Also sells wholesale.
Map Ref: W, C4 **OS Grid Ref:** SO763656

W

KEY   ⊠ Mail order to UK or EU   ň Delivers to shows
      ⊠ Exports beyond EU   € Euro accepted
      ⑤ Accessible by wheelchair   ◆ See Display advertisement

W

WPGP   PAN-GLOBAL PLANTS 🅶
The Walled Garden, Frampton Court,
Frampton-on-Severn,
Gloucestershire,
GL2 7EX
Ⓣ (01452) 741641 (m.) 07801 275138
Ⓕ (01453) 768858
Ⓔ info@panglobalplants.com
Ⓦ www.panglobalplants.com
Contact: Nick Macer
Opening Times: 1100-1700 Wed-Sun 1st Feb-
31st Oct. Also B/hols. Closed 2nd Sun in Sep.
Winter months by appt., please phone first.
Cat. Cost: 4 x 1st class
Credit Cards: Maestro Visa MasterCard Solo
Delta
Specialities: A plantsman's nursery offering a
wide selection of rare & desirable trees,
shrubs, herbaceous, bamboos, exotics,
climbers, ferns etc. Specialities incl. *Magnolia,
Hydrangea* & *Bamboo.*
Map Ref: W, D5

WPic   THE PICTON CASTLE TRUST NURSERY 🅶
Picton Castle, Haverfordwest, Pembrokeshire,
SA62 4AS
Ⓣ (01437) 751326
Ⓕ (01437) 751326
Ⓔ pct@pictoncastle.freeserve.co.uk
Ⓦ www.pictoncastle.co.uk
Contact: D L Pryse Lloyd
Opening Times: 1030-1700 7 days except
Mon Apr-Sep. Other times by arrangement.
Cat. Cost: 1 x 1st class
Credit Cards: None
Specialities: *Rhododendron. Myrtle* and
relatives. Woodland & unusual shrubs.
Map Ref: W, D2 **OS Grid Ref:** SN011135

WPnn   THE PERENNIAL NURSERY
Rhosygilwen, Llanrhian Road, St Davids,
Pembrokeshire, SA62 6DB
Ⓣ (01437) 721954
Ⓕ (01437) 721954
Ⓔ pdsymons@tiscali.co.uk
Contact: Mrs Philipa Symons
Opening Times: 1030-1730 Mar-Oct. Nov-
Feb by appt.
Credit Cards: None
Specialities: Herbaceous perennials & alpines.
Tender perennials. Coastal plants.
Map Ref: W, C1 **OS Grid Ref:** SM775292

WPnP   PENLAN PERENNIALS ✉ 🗹 ♠ € 🅶
Penlan Farm, Penrhiwpal, Llandysul,
Ceredigion, SA44 5QH
Ⓣ (01239) 851244
Ⓕ (01239) 851244

Ⓔ rcain@penlanperennials.co.uk
Ⓦ www.penlanperennials.co.uk
Contact: Richard & Jane Cain
Opening Times: 0930-1730 Wed-Sun Mar-
Sep & B/hols. Oct-Feb by appt.
Min Mail Order UK: Nmc
Min Mail Order EU: Nmc
Cat. Cost: 4 x 2nd class or free online
Credit Cards: All major credit/debit cards
Specialities: Aquatic, marginal & bog plants.
Shade-loving & woodland perennials, ferns &
grasses, all grown peat free.
Notes: Mail order all year, next day delivery.
Secure online ordering.
Map Ref: W, C2 **OS Grid Ref:** SN344457

WPrP   PRIME PERENNIALS ✉ ♠
Llety Moel, Rhos-y-Garth, Llanilar,
Nr Aberystwyth, Ceredigion,
SY23 4SG
Ⓣ (01974) 241505
Ⓜ 07891 333656
Ⓔ liz@prime-perennials.co.uk
Ⓦ www.prime-perennials.co.uk
Contact: Elizabeth Powney
Opening Times: Open by appt. only.
Min Mail Order UK: Nmc
Min Mail Order EU: Nmc
Cat. Cost: 4 x 1st class
Credit Cards: None
Specialities: Unusual & interesting perennials,
bulbs & grasses. *Tulbaghia, Kniphofia, Tricyrtis*
& many others grown in peat free compost.
Nursery 650ft above sea level.
Notes: Mail order all year.
Map Ref: W, C3

WPtf   PANTYFOD GARDEN NURSERY ✉ 🅶
Llandewi Brefi, Tregaron,
Ceredigion,
SY25 6PE
Ⓣ (01570) 493564
Ⓕ (01570) 493585
Ⓔ pantyfodgarden@btopenworld.com
Ⓦ www.pantyfodgarden.co.uk
Contact: Susan Rowe
Opening Times: 1000-1600 16th Apr-18th
Sep 2005, weekends and B/hols only.
Min Mail Order UK: Nmc
Min Mail Order EU: Nmc
Cat. Cost: A5 sae, 47p stamp.
Credit Cards: None
Specialities: Hardy geraniums, unusual hardy
perennials, woodland plants, plants for moist
soil, all grown largely peat-free. Some plants
are in small quantities. Nursery at 950ft with
spectacular views.
Map Ref: W, C3 **OS Grid Ref:** SN654540

WRHF   **RED HOUSE FARM** 🦽
Flying Horse Lane, Bradley Green, Nr
Redditch, Worcestershire, B96 6QT
Ⓣ (01527) 821269
Ⓕ (01527) 821674
Ⓔ contact@redhousefarmgardenandnursery.co.uk
Ⓦ www.redhousefarmgardenandnursery.co.uk
Contact: Mrs Maureen Weaver
Opening Times: 0900-1700 Mon-Sat all year.
1000-1700 Sun & B/Hols.
Cat. Cost: 2 x 1st class
Credit Cards: None
Specialities: Cottage garden perennials.
Map Ref: W, C5 **OS Grid Ref:** SO986623

WRai   **RAILS END NURSERY** 🦽
Back Lane, Ashton under Hill, Evesham,
Worcestershire, WR11 7RG
Ⓣ (01386) 881884
Ⓕ (01386) 881884
Ⓔ salski@quinweb.net
Ⓦ www.ashtonunderhill.org.uk/business
Contact: Sally Skinner
Opening Times: 1000-1700 7 days, mid-Feb-
end Oct. Nov-Jan by appt. only.
Cat. Cost: 2 x 1st class sae. Also on website.
Credit Cards: All major credit/debit cards
Specialities: Family-run nursery, specialising
in hardy herbaceous perennials, with an
extending range of the unusual. All stock in
small quantities.
Notes: Partially accessible for wheelchair users.
Map Ref: W, C5 **OS Grid Ref:** SO999375

WRha   **RHANDIRMWYN PLANTS**
2 Tremcecynog, Rhandirmwyn,
Nr Llandovery, Carmarthenshire,
SA20 0NU
Ⓣ (01550) 760220
Contact: Sara Fox/Thomas Sheppard
Opening Times: Open most days, but please
ring first to avoid disappointment.
Credit Cards: None
Specialities: 1000+ varieties & species incl.
aquilegias, campanulas, chrysanthemums,
digitalis, geraniums, geums, *Lychnis, Mentha,
Monarda, Origanum,* primulas, *Rosmarinus,*
salvias & violas. Stock limited in quantity but
not variety!
Map Ref: W, C3 **OS Grid Ref:** SN796428

WRos   **ROSEMARY'S FARMHOUSE NURSERY** 🦽
Llwyn-y-moel-gau, Llanfihangel, Llanfyllin,
Montgomeryshire, SY22 5JE
Ⓣ (01691) 648196
Ⓕ (01691) 648196
Ⓔ rosemary@farmhouse-nursery.fsnet.co.uk
Contact: Rosemary Pryce

Opening Times: 1000-1700 most days all
year, but advisable to phone to confirm.
Cat. Cost: None issued.
Credit Cards: None
Specialities: Unusual perennials &
ornamental grasses. Hardy geraniums.
Map Ref: W, B3 **OS Grid Ref:** SJ083149

WRou   **ROUALEYN NURSERIES** 🛒 🦽
Trefriw, Conwy, LL27 0SX
Ⓣ (01492) 640548
Ⓕ (01492) 640548
Ⓔ roualeyn@beeb.net
Contact: Doug Jones
Opening Times: 1000-1700 weekdays 1st
Mar-31st Aug, 1000-1600 Sat, Sun & B/hols.
Cat. Cost: 2 x 1st class.
Credit Cards: None
Specialities: Fuchsias, incl. species.
Map Ref: W, A3 **OS Grid Ref:** SH632778

WSAf   **SAFLORA PLANT NURSERY** ✉ €
Pen-y-Lan, North Road, Lampeter,
Ceredigion, SA48 7JA
Ⓣ (01570) 422924
Ⓕ (01570) 422924
Ⓔ nursery@safloraplants.co.uk
Ⓦ www.safloraplants.co.uk
Contact: Tricia Carter
Opening Times: Not open. Mail order only.
Min Mail Order UK: Nmc
Min Mail Order EU: Nmc
Cat. Cost: Free of charge
Credit Cards: All major credit/debit cards
Specialities: South African and Australian
plants, in particular *Proteaceae,* also *Clivia
miniata* 'Citrina'.
Notes: Plants sent within EU only, seeds sent
worldwide.

WSan   **SANDSTONES COTTAGE GARDEN
PLANTS** ✉ 🛒 €
58 Bolas Heath, Great Bolas, Shropshire,
TF6 6PS
Ⓣ (01952) 541657
Ⓜ 07801 338133
Ⓕ (01952) 541657
Ⓔ brelsforths@supernet.com
Ⓦ www.sandstoneplants.co.uk
Contact: Joanne Brelsforth/Paul Brelsforth
Opening Times: By appt. only.
Min Mail Order UK: £10.00 + p&p
Min Mail Order EU: £25.00 + p&p

Cat. Cost: 4 x 1st class
Credit Cards: All major credit/debit cards
Specialities: Unusual & interesting hardy perennials. Specialing in plants for shade & moist areas.
Map Ref: W, B4

WSel   THE SELSLEY HERB NURSERY 🏠 ⬛
Hayhedge Lane, Bisley, Stroud, Gloucestershire, GL6 7AN
Ⓣ (01452) 770073
Ⓕ (01452) 770073
Ⓔ selsleyherbs@btconnect.com
Contact: Rob Wimperis
Opening Times: 1000-1700 Tue-Sat, 1400-1700 Sun & B/hols Mar-Oct. Nov-Feb variable, please phone to check. only.
Cat. Cost: 4 x 1st class
Credit Cards: Visa MasterCard
Specialities: Culinary, aromatic & medicinal herbs & selected garden plants.
Map Ref: W, D5 OS Grid Ref: SO058906

WSFF   SAITH FFYNNON FARM ✉ 🏠 ⬛
Whitford, Holywell, Flintshire, CH8 9EQ
Ⓣ (01352) 711198
Ⓕ (01352) 716777
Ⓔ jan@7wells.org
Ⓦ www.northwalesbutterflies.org.uk
Contact: Jan Miller
Opening Times: By appt. only.
Min Mail Order UK: Nmc.
Cat. Cost: 2 x 1st class.
Credit Cards: None
Specialities: Plants and seeds to attract butterflies and moths. Nat. Coll. of *Eupatorium* applied for. Stock available in small quantities unless ordered well in advance.
Notes: Profits go to Butterfly Conservation. Also sells wholesale.
Map Ref: W, A3 OS Grid Ref: SJ154775

WSHC   STONE HOUSE COTTAGE NURSERIES ⬛
Stone, Nr Kidderminster, Worcestershire, DY10 4BG
Ⓣ (01562) 69902
Ⓔ louisa@shcn.co.uk
Ⓦ www.shcn.co.uk
Contact: L N Arbuthnott
Opening Times: 1000-1730 Wed-Sat. By appt. only mid Sep-Mar.
Cat. Cost: Sae
Credit Cards: None
Specialities: Small general range esp. wall shrubs, climbers & unusual plants.
Map Ref: W, C5 OS Grid Ref: SO863750

WShi   SHIPTON BULBS ✉ €
Y Felin, Henllan Amgoed, Whitland, Pembrokeshire, SA34 0SL
Ⓣ (01994) 240125
Ⓕ (01994) 241180
Ⓔ bluebell@zoo.co.uk
Ⓦ www.bluebellbulbs.co.uk
Contact: John Shipton & Alison Foot
Opening Times: By appt. only.
Min Mail Order UK: Nmc
Min Mail Order EU: Nmc
Cat. Cost: Sae
Credit Cards: None
Specialities: Native British bulbs. Bulbs & plants for naturalising.
Map Ref: W, D2 OS Grid Ref: SN188207

WSPU   PERSHORE COLLEGE OF HORTICULTURE ⬛
Specialist Plant Unit & Plant Centre, Avonbank, Pershore, Worcestershire, WR10 3JP
Ⓣ (01386) 561385
Ⓕ (01386) 551108
Contact: Jo Yates (Plant Centre)
Opening Times: (Plant centre) 0900-1700 Mon-Sat, 1030-1630 Sun.
Cat. Cost: £1.00
Credit Cards: Visa Access
Specialities: Nat. Coll. of *Penstemon*. Open for viewing 0830-1630 Mon-Fri.
Notes: Also sells wholesale.
Map Ref: W, C5

WSSs   SHROPSHIRE SARRACENIAS ✉ ✉ 🏠 ⬛
5 Field Close, Malinslee, Telford, Shropshire, TF4 2EH
Ⓣ (01952) 501598
Ⓔ mike@carnivorousplants.uk.com
Ⓦ www.carnivorousplants.uk.com
Contact: Mike King
Opening Times: By appt. only.
Min Mail Order UK: Nmc
Min Mail Order EU: Nmc
Cat. Cost: 2 x 1st class
Credit Cards: None
Specialities: *Sarracenia. Dionaea muscipula* & forms. Some stock available in small quantities only. Nat. Coll. of *Sarracenia*.
Map Ref: W, B4 OS Grid Ref: SJ689085

WSuV   SUNNYBANK VINE NURSERY ✉ ✉
King Street, Ewyas Harold, Herefordshire, HR2 OEE
Ⓣ (01981) 240256
Ⓔ vinenursery@hotmail.com
Ⓦ http://vinenursery.netfirms.com
Contact: B R Edwards

W

Opening Times: Not open. Mail order only.
Min Mail Order UK: £8.00 incl. p&p
Min Mail Order EU: £10.00 incl. p&p
Cat. Cost: Sae
Credit Cards: None
Specialities: Vines. Nat. Coll. of *Vitis vinifera*
(hardy, incl. dessert & wine).
Notes: EU sales by arrangement. Also sells
wholesale.
Map Ref: W, C4

WTan   TAN-Y-LLYN NURSERIES
Meifod, Powys, SY22 6YB
Ⓣ (01938) 500370
Ⓕ (01938) 500303
Ⓔ callumjohnston@tanyllyn.the-nursery.co.uk
Ⓦ www.tanyllyn.the-nursery.co.uk
Contact: Callum Johnston
Opening Times: 1000-1700 Tue-Fri Mar-Jun
and at other times by appt.
Cat. Cost: 2 x 1st class
Credit Cards: None
Specialities: Herbs, alpines, perennials.
Map Ref: W, B3 **OS Grid Ref:** SJ167125

WTel   TELLING AND COATES ✉
64A Church Street, Charlton Kings,
Cheltenham, Gloucestershire, GL53 8AS
Ⓣ (01242) 514472
Ⓔ tellingandcoates@freenet.co.uk
Ⓦ www.tellingandcoates.freeola.net
Contact: John Coates
Opening Times: 0830-1300 & 1400-1730
Mon, Fri & Sat, or by appt. on other days.
Min Mail Order UK: Nmc
Cat. Cost: 3 x 1st class or 4 x 2nd class
Credit Cards: None
Specialities: A traditional hardy plant nursery
offering a wide range of shrubs, climbers,
heathers, alpines & herbaceous plants at
reasonable prices.
Map Ref: W, C5 **OS Grid Ref:** SO966205

WThu   THUYA ALPINE NURSERY ✉
Glebelands, Hartpury, Gloucestershire,
GL19 3BW
Ⓣ (01452) 700548
Contact: S W Bond
Opening Times: 1000-dusk Sat & Bank hol.
1100-dusk Sun, Weekdays appt. advised.
Min Mail Order UK: £4.00 + p&p
Min Mail Order EU: £10.00 + p&p
Cat. Cost: 4 x 2nd class
Credit Cards: None
Specialities: Wide and changing range including
rarities, available in smallish numbers.
Notes: Partially accessible for wheelchair users.
Map Ref: W, C5

WTin   TINPENNY PLANTS ♿
Tinpenny Farm, Fiddington,
Tewkesbury, Gloucestershire,
GL20 7BJ
Ⓣ (01684) 292668
Ⓔ plants@tinpenny.plus.com
Contact: Elaine Horton
Opening Times: 1200-1700 Tue-Thu or by
appt.
Cat. Cost: 2 x 1st class
Credit Cards: None
Specialities: Wide range of hardy garden-
worthy plants esp. *Helleborus, Iris* &
Sempervivum. Small nursery will propagate to
order rare plants from own stock. Small
quantities only of some plants.
Map Ref: W, C5 **OS Grid Ref:** SO919318

WTMC   TIR MAB CYNAN NURSERY ✉ ♿
Brithdir, Dolgellau,
Caernarfonshire,
LL40 2RW
Ⓣ (01341) 450339
Ⓕ (01341) 450339
Ⓦ www.tirmabcynan.nursery@btopenworld.
com
Contact: Jim Haunch
Opening Times: 1000-1700, 7 days, Easter-
1 Sep. Other times by appt.
Min Mail Order UK: £10.00
Cat. Cost: None issued
Specialities: Hardy *Geranium, Hemerocallis,*
hostas, ferns, *Iris,* a wide range of hardy
perennials & sought after plants. Provisional
Nat. Coll. holder status for *Geranium phaeum*
cvs.
Notes: Also sells wholesale.
Map Ref: W, B3

WVaB   VALDUCCI BRUGMANSIAS ✉ ♙ € ♿
61 Green Lane, Bayston Hill, Shrewsbury,
Shropshire, SY3 0NR
Ⓣ (01743) 354764 day: (01743) 872030
evening
Ⓕ (01743) 246716
Ⓔ brugmansias@hotmail.com
Contact: Luigi Valducci
Opening Times: 1000-1600 by appt. only.
Min Mail Order UK: Nmc
Credit Cards: None
Specialities: Brugmansias.
Notes: Main nursery site at Meole Brace
Garden Club, Vicarage Road, Shrewsbury.

WViv VIV MARSH POSTAL PLANTS ✉ 📧 € ♿
Walford Heath, Shrewsbury, Shropshire,
SY4 2HT
ⓣ (01939) 291475
ⓕ (01939) 290743
ⓔ mail@PostalPlants.co.uk
ⓦ www.PostalPlants.co.uk
Contact: Mr Viv Marsh
Opening Times: Selected w/ends in Sep &
Oct. Please phone for details.
Min Mail Order UK: £30.00 plant value
Min Mail Order EU: £30.00 plant value
Cat. Cost: 5 x 1st class or 2 x IRCs (£1 refund
on first order). Also Online.
Credit Cards: Visa MasterCard Switch
Specialities: Specialists in *Alstroemeria*,
Zantedeschia, phormiums, *Lathyrus*, plus other
new worldwide introductions.
Notes: Also sells wholesale.
Map Ref: W, B4 OS Grid Ref: SJ446198

WWeb WEBBS OF WYCHBOLD € ♦
Wychbold, Droitwich, Worcestershire,
WR9 0DG
ⓣ (01527) 860000
ⓕ (01527) 861284
ⓔ gardenplants@webbsofwychbold.co.uk
ⓦ www.webbsofwychbold.co.uk
Contact: Garden Plants Dept.
Opening Times: 0900-1800 Mon-Fri winter.
0900-2000 Mon-Fri summer. 0900-1800 Sat
& 1030-1630 Sun all year. Closed Xmas Day,
Boxing Day & Easter Sun.
Cat. Cost: None issued
Credit Cards: Visa Access American Express
Specialities: Hardy trees & shrubs, climbers,
conifers, alpines, heathers, herbaceous, herbs,
roses, fruit & aquatics. Nat. Coll. of Shrubby
Potentilla.
Notes: Also sells wholesale.
Map Ref: W, C5

WWes WESTONBIRT ARBORETUM
(Forest Enterprise), The National Arboretum,
Tetbury, Gloucestershire, GL8 8QS
ⓣ (01666) 880544
ⓕ (01666) 880386
ⓔ plant.centre@forestry.gsi.gov.uk
ⓦ www.westonbirtarboretum.com
Contact: Rose Birks, Sarah Landers, Luke
Harding
Opening Times: 1000-1700 7 days all year.
Cat. Cost: None issued.
Credit Cards: Visa Access Switch Solo Delta
Specialities: Japanese maples, conifers, general
range of trees & shrubs, many rare. Specimen
trees. Most available in small quantities.
Map Ref: W, D5

WWFP WHITEHALL FARMHOUSE PLANTS ✉
Sevenhampton, Cheltenham, Gloucestershire,
GL54 5TL
ⓣ (01242) 820772
ⓜ 07711 021034
ⓕ (01242) 821226
ⓔ wfplants@btopenworld.com
Contact: Victoria Logue
Opening Times: By appt. only.
Min Mail Order UK: Nmc
Cat. Cost: 2 x 1st class
Credit Cards: None
Specialities: A small nursery producing a
range of interesting & easy hardy perennials
for the garden. Some in small quantities.
Map Ref: W, C5 OS Grid Ref: SP018229

WWhi WHIMBLE NURSERY ♿
Kinnerton, Presteigne, Powys,
LD8 2PD
ⓣ (01547) 560413
Contact: Liz Taylor
Opening Times: 1030-1730 Thu-Mon, closed
Tue & Wed, Apr-mid Oct.
Cat. Cost: 5 x 1st class sae for plant list (no
descriptions).
Credit Cards: None
Specialities: Mainly herbaceous, some
unusual. Small collections of *Achillea*,
Crocosmia, Geranium, Viola.
Map Ref: W, C4

WWHy WELSH HOLLY ✉ ♿
Llyn-y-gors, Tenby Road, St Clears,
Carmarthenshire, SA33 4JP
ⓣ (01994) 231789
ⓕ (01994) 231789
ⓔ info@welsh-holly.co.uk
ⓦ www.welsh-holly.co.uk
Contact: Philip Lanc
Opening Times: By appt. only.
Min Mail Order UK: Nmc
Cat. Cost: 2 x 1st class
Credit Cards: None
Specialities: Hollies. Limited stock of less
common plants.
Notes: Also sells wholesale.

WWll WEST WALES WILLOWS ✉ 📧 ♿
Martinique Farm, Wolfs Castle,
Haverfordwest, Pembrokeshire, SA62 5DY
ⓣ (01437) 741714
ⓕ (01437) 741714
ⓔ info@westwaleswillows.co.uk
ⓦ www.westwaleswillows.co.uk
Contact: Billa Schleicher & David Clark
Opening Times: Mail order only. Not open
except on Open Day in Oct or by appt.

Min Mail Order UK: £5.00
Min Mail Order EU: £5.00
Cat. Cost: Online only.
Credit Cards: Visa MasterCard
Specialities: Willows.

WWlt   WOLLERTON OLD HALL GARDEN 🅶
Wollerton, Market Drayton,
Shropshire,
TF9 3NA
ⓣ (01630) 685760
ⓕ (01630) 685583
ⓔ info@wollertonoldhallgarden.com
ⓦ www.wollertonoldhallgarden.com
Contact: Mr John Jenkins
Opening Times: 1200-1700 Fri, Sun &
B/hols Easter-end Aug. Sun only in Sep.
Cat. Cost: None issued
Credit Cards: All major credit/debit cards
Specialities: Perennials.
Map Ref: W, B4 OS Grid Ref: SJ624296

WWpP   WATERPUMP PLANTS ✉
Waterpump Farm, Ryeford,
Ross-on-Wye, Herefordshire,
HR9 7PU
ⓣ (01989) 750177
ⓔ liz@sugden2.btinternet.com
Contact: Mrs E Sugden
Opening Times: Open under the NGS
scheme & by private appt. Order collection
service available.
Min Mail Order UK: £15.00
Cat. Cost: 4 x 1st class
Credit Cards: None
Specialities: Hardy geraniums, aquatics,
moisture loving and unusual herbaceous
plants. Small nursery with limited stock, will
propagate to order.
Map Ref: W, C4 OS Grid Ref: SO642226

WWst   WESTONBIRT PLANTS ✉ 🗷 €
9 Westonbirt Close, Worcester,
WR5 3RX
ⓣ (01905) 350429 (answerphone)
ⓕ (01905) 350429
Contact: Garry Dickerson
Opening Times: Not open. Mail order only.
Min Mail Order UK: Nmc
Min Mail Order EU: Nmc
Cat. Cost: 3 x 1st class
Credit Cards: None
Specialities: *Iris, Fritillaria, Erythronium*,
particular interest in Juno *Iris* species. *Crocus,
Corydalis, Lilium, Arisaema, Trillium, Arum* &
tulip species. Woodland plants & hardy
orchids, esp. *Calanthe* & *Cypripedium* Many
rare plants in limited numbers.

WWye   THE NURTONS GARDEN & NURSERY
🅶 ◆
Tintern, Chepstow, Monmouthshire,
NP16 7NX
ⓣ (01291) 689253
ⓕ (01291) 689253
ⓔ info@thenurtons.co.uk
ⓦ www.thenurtons.co.uk
Contact: Adrian & Elsa Wood
Opening Times: 1030-1700 Wed-Mon, mid
Feb-mid Oct. Other times by appt. (closed Tue).
Cat. Cost: 3 x 1st class
Credit Cards: None
Specialities: Wide range of garden-worthy
perennials to suit many garden situations;
herbs, *Salvia*, grasses, hostas. Soil Association
symbol. Cert UK 5.
Map Ref: W, D4 OS Grid Ref: SO536011

ABROAD

XBlo   TABLE BAY VIEW NURSERY ✉ 🗷
(Office) 60 Molteno Road,
Oranjezicht, Cape Town 8001,
South Africa
ⓣ 00 27 21 683 5108/424 4854
ⓕ 00 27 21 683 5108
ⓔ info@tablebayviewnursery.co.za
Contact: Terence Bloch
Opening Times: Mail order only. No
personal callers.
Min Mail Order UK: £15.00 + p&p
Min Mail Order EU: £15.00
Cat. Cost: £3.40 (cheque/postal order)
Credit Cards: None
Specialities: Tropical & sub-tropical
ornamental & fruiting plants.

XBTW   B & T WORLD SEEDS ✉ 🗷 €
Paguignan, 34210 Aigues-Vives,
France
ⓣ 00 33 (0) 4689 12963
ⓕ 00 33 (0) 4689 13039
ⓔ le@b-and-t-world-seeds.com
ⓦ www.b-and-t-world-seeds.com
Contact: Lesley Sleigh
Opening Times: Not open. Mail order only.
Min Mail Order UK: £14.00 inc. carriage
Min Mail Order EU: £14.00 inc. carriage
Cat. Cost: £10 Europe, £14 elsewhere.
Credit Cards: Visa MasterCard
Specialities: Master list contains over 30,000
items. 700 sub-lists available.

X

Notes: Exports seed only. Catalogue/botanical reference system available on CD Rom. SeedyRom (TM) catalogue £20 worldwide. Also sells wholesale.

XDoo   IGNACE VAN DOORSLAER ✉ ⋔ € ⬚
Kapellendries 52, 9090,
Melle Gontrode,
Belgium
Ⓣ 0032 (09) 252 11 23
Ⓕ 0032 (09) 252 44 55
Contact: Ignace van Doorslaer
Opening Times: Mail order only. 6 days per week, by appt.
Min Mail Order UK: Depends on weight
Min Mail Order EU: Depends on weight
Cat. Cost: Free
Credit Cards: None
Specialities: *Agapanthus*.
Notes: Invoice sent when transport charges known. £ stirling accepted. Located 12km south of Gent. Will deliver to shows in Belgium, France & Holland. Also sells wholesale. Nursery closing end 2005.

X

XFro   FROSCH EXCLUSIVE PERENNIALS ✉ ✉ €
Lindener Str. 5, D-83623
Dietramszell-Lochen,
Germany
Ⓣ 00 49 172 842 2050
Ⓕ 00 49 8027 9049975
Ⓔ info@cypripedium.de
Ⓦ www.cypripedium.de
Contact: Michael Weinert
Opening Times: Not open. Mail order only. Orders taken between 0700-2200 hours.
Min Mail Order UK: £120.00 + p&p
Min Mail Order EU: £120.00 + p&p
Cat. Cost: None issued.
Credit Cards: None
Specialities: *Cypripedium* hybrids. Hardy orchids.
Notes: Also sells wholesale.

XJel   JELITTO PERENNIAL SEED ✉ ✉ € ◆
(UK Agent) Meadows (Fenton) Ltd, PO Box 78, St Ives, Cambridgeshire, PE27 6ZA
Ⓣ (01480) 463570
Ⓕ (01480) 466042
Ⓔ richard@jelitto.com
Ⓦ www.jelitto.com
Contact: Richard Oliver
Opening Times: Not open. Mail order & Online shop.
Min Mail Order UK: 40 euros + p&p
Min Mail Order EU: 40 euros + p&p
Cat. Cost: 5 euros
Credit Cards: Visa MasterCard JCB

Specialities: Alpines, perennials, herbs, wild flowers, ornamental grass seed, 2700+ varieties.
Notes: Head Office: Postfach 1264, D-29685 Schwarmstedt, Germany. Tel: 00 49 50 71-98 29-0, fax 00 49 50 71-98 29-27, email info@jelitto.com. Also sells wholesale.

XPde   PÉPINIÈRE DE l'ÎLE ✉ €
Keranroux, 22870, Ile de Brehat, France
Ⓣ 00 33 (0)296 200384
Ⓜ 0686 128609
Ⓕ 00 33 (0)296 200305
Ⓔ contact@pepiniere-brehat.com
Ⓦ www.pepiniere-brehat.com
Contact: Laurence Blasco & Charles Blasco
Opening Times: 1400-1800 spring & summer. Other times by appt. incl. Aug.
Min Mail Order UK: Nmc
Min Mail Order EU: Nmc
Cat. Cost: 4 Euros.
Credit Cards: None
Specialities: *Agapanthus* & *Echium*. Plants from South Africa.

XPep   PÉPINIÈRE FILIPPI ✉ €
RN 113, 34140 Meze, France
Ⓣ 04 67 43 88 69
Ⓕ 04 67 43 84 59
Ⓔ olivier.filippi@wanadoo.fr
Ⓦ www.jardin-sec.com
Contact: Olivier Filippi
Opening Times: 0900-1200 & 1330-1730 Mon-Fri, 0900-1200 Sat, Sep-Jun. Closed Sun & B/hols. 0830-1200 Mon-Sat, Jul-Aug.
Min Mail Order UK: 30 Euros
Min Mail Order EU: 30 Euros
Cat. Cost: 10 Euros or Online
Credit Cards: Visa MasterCard
Specialities: *Cistus* and botanical range of mediterranean plants. CCVS French National Collections of *Cistus* & *Nerium*.
Notes: Also sells wholesale.

NURSERY INDEX
BY NAME

Nurseries that are included in the *RHS Plant Finder* for the first time this year (or have been reintroduced) are marked in **bold type**. Full details of the nurseries will be found in **Nursery Details by Code** on page 788. For a key to the geographical codes, see the start of **Nurseries**.

Dorset Blueberry Company	**CDBb**
Dorset Water Lilies	CDWL
Dove Cottage Nursery & Garden	NDov
Downderry Nursery	SDow
Duchy of Cornwall	CDoC
Dulford Nurseries	CDul
Dunge Valley Gardens	MDun
Dyffryn Gwyddno Nursery	WDyG
Dyffryn Nurseries	WDyf
Dysons Nurseries	SDys
Earlstone Nursery	LEar
East Northdown Farm	SEND
Eastgrove Cottage Garden Nursery	WEas
Edrom Nurseries	GEdr
Edulis	LEdu
Eggleston Hall Gardens	NEgg
Elizabeth House Nursery	MEHN
Charles F Ellis & Son	WCFE
Elm Tree Nursery	CElm
Elsworth Herbs	EEls
Elworthy Cottage Plants	CElw
Endsleigh Gardens	CEnd
The English Cottage Garden Nursery	SECG
Entwood Farm Plants	**CEnt**
Equatorial Plant Co.	NEqu
Evelix Daffodils	GEve
Evergreen Conifer Centre	WEve
The Exotic Garden Company	EExo
Fairholm Plants	GFai
Fairweather's Garden Centre	**SFai**
Famecheck Reblooming Iris	**EFam**
Family Trees	SFam
Farmyard Nurseries	WFar
Feebers Hardy Plants	CFee
Fentongollon Farm	CFen
The Fern Nursery	EFer
Fernatix	EFtx
Fernwood Nursery	CWil
Fibrex Nurseries Ltd	WFib
Field House Nurseries	MFie
Field of Blooms	**IFoB**
Fir Tree Farm Nursery	CFir
Fir Trees Pelargonium Nursery	NFir
Margery Fish Gardens	CFis
Ian FitzRoy Nurseryman	SIFN
Flaxton House Nursery	NFla
Fleurs Plants	GFle
Flora Exotica	EFEx
Floral Fireworks	**CFFs**
The Flower Bower	CFwr
Flowers of the Field	WFoF
The Fly Trap Plants	EFly
Foliage Scented & Herb Plants	LFol
Folly Gate Plants	**CFol**
Ford Nursery	NFor
Ford Nursery	**CFRD**
Fox Cottage Plants	MFOX
Foxgrove Plants	LFox
Frogswell Nursery	IFro
Fron Goch Garden Centre	WGer
Frosch Exclusive Perennials	XFro
Fryer's Nurseries Ltd	MFry
Fulbrooke Nursery	EFul
The Rodney Fuller Helianthemum Collection	CFul
Gaggini's Plant Centre	MGag
Gandy's (Roses) Ltd	MGan
Garden Cottage Nursery	GGar
Garden House Nurseries	NGdn
Garden Plants	SGar
W G Geissler	WGei
Gilbey's Plants	NGby
Glen Chantry	**EGle**
Glendoick Gardens Ltd	GGGa
Glenhirst Cactus Nursery	EGln
Glenville Nurseries	EGlv
The Gobbett Nursery	**WGob**
Godly's Roses	LGod
Goldbrook Plants	EGol
Golden Cottage Plants	MGol
Elisabeth Goodwin Nurseries	EGoo
Gordon's Nursery	WGor
Gortkelly Castle Nursery	IGor
Goscote Nurseries Ltd	MGos
Grafted Walnut Trees	WGWT
Graham's Hardy Plants	CGra
Grange Farm Plants	EGFP
Grasmere Plants	EGra
Peter Grayson (Sweet Pea Seedsman)	MPet
Great Dixter Nurseries	SDix
The Great Western Gladiolus Nursery	**CGrW**
Green Garden Herbs	NGHP
Green Hill Plants	WGHP
Mary Green	NMyG
Greenhead Roses	GGre
C W Groves & Son	CGro
Gwynfor Growers	WGwG
Hadspen Garden & Nursery	CHad
Hall Farm Nursery	WHal
Halls of Heddon	NHal
Halsway Nursery	CHal
Hambrooks Growing Concern	SHGC
Hampshire Carnivorous Plants	SHmp
Hardstoft Herb Garden	NHHG
Hardy Exotics	CHEx
Hardy Orchids	CHdy
Hardy's Cottage Garden Plants	SHar
Harley Nursery	WHar
Harrells Hardy Plants	WHrl
Hart Canna	SHaC
Sue Hartfree	SHFr
Harts Green Nursery	MHar
Hartside Nursery Garden	NHar
Harveys Garden Plants	EHrv
The Hawthornes Nursery	NHaw
Hayloft Plants	WHlf

Marcus Dancer Plants	**SMDP**
The Market Garden	SMar
Lesley Marshall	EMar
Marshall's Malmaison	**EMal**
Marwood Hill Gardens	CMHG
Mattock's Roses	MMat
S M McArd (Seeds)	EMcA
Hubert McHale	IHMH
The Mead Nursery	CMea
Meadow Cottage Plants	CMCo
Meadows Nursery	CMdw
Mendip Bonsai Studio	CMen
Mendle Nursery	NMen
Meon Valley Plants	SMeo
Merebrook Water Plants	**WMAq**
Merriments Gardens	SMrm
Merryfield Nurseries (Canterbury) Ltd	SMer
Mickfield Hostas	EMic
Mickfield Watergarden Centre Ltd	EMFW
Mill Cottage Plants	CMil
Mill Race Garden Centre	EMil
Millais Nurseries	LMil
Millrace Nursery	NMRc
Mills' Farm Plants & Gardens	EMFP
Mires Beck Nursery	NMir
Monksilver Nursery	EMon
Monocot Nursery	CMon
Moor Monkton Nurseries	NMoo
Moorland Cottage Plants	WMoo
Morehavens	LMor
Morton Hall Gardens	MMHG
Mount Harry Trees	SMHT
Mount Pleasant Trees	WMou
Mozart House Nursery Garden	MMoz
Mucklestone Nurseries	**MMuc**
Ken Muir Ltd	**EMui**
Mulu Nurseries	WMul
Kathleen Muncaster Fuchsias	EKMF
Murrells Plant & Garden Centre	SMur
Mynd Hardy Plants	WMnd
Naked Cross Nurseries	CNCN
The National Herb Centre	MNHC
Natural Selection	CNat
Nature's Corners	LNCo
New Forest Palms & Exotics	SNew
Newington Nurseries	**MNew**
Newport Mills Nursery	CNMi
Newton Hill Alpines	NNew
Nicky's Rock Garden Nursery	CNic
Norcroft Nurseries	NNor
Norfields	WNor
Norfolk Lavender	**ENor**
Norfolk Bamboo Company	ENBC
Sheila Northway Auriculas	**GNor**
Norwell Nurseries	MNrw
Notcutts Nurseries	ENot
The Nursery Further Afield	MNFA
The Nurtons Garden & Nursery	WWye
Nutlin Nursery	SNut
Oak Dene Nurseries	NOaD
Oak Tree Nursery	NOak
Oakdene Nursery	SOkd
Oakland Nurseries	MOak
Oasis	EOas
Old Court Nurseries	WOld
Old Fashioned Flowers	WOFF
Old Hall Plants	EOHP
The Old Mill Herbary	COld
The Old Vicarage Nursery	WOVN
The Old Walled Garden	**SOWG**
The Old Withy Garden Nursery	COlW
Oldfield Nursery	**COfd**
One House Nursery	MOne
Orchard House Nursery	NOrc
Orchardstown Nurseries	IOrc
Ornamental Conifers	EOrn
The Ornamental Grass Nursery	NOGN
Ornamental Tree Nurseries	WOrn
Otter Nurseries Ltd	COtt
Out of the Common Way	WOut
John Owen Nurseries	NJOw
P & B Fuchsias	WPBF
P M A Plant Specialities	CPMA
P W Plants	EPla
Packhorse Farm Nursery	MPkF
The Palm Centre	**LPal**
The Palm Farm	NPal
The Palm House	CPHo
PJ's Palms and Exotics	LPJP
Pan-Global Plants	WPGP
Pantiles Plant & Garden Centre	**LPan**
Pantyfod Garden Nursery	WPtf
Parham Bungalow Plants	CPBP
Park Green Nurseries	EPGN
Parks Perennials	CPar
Passiflora (National Collection)	**CPas**
Chris Pattison	WPat
Pavilion Plants	SPav
Pembroke Farm Nursery	EPem
Penborn Goat Farm	**CPbn**
Penlan Perennials	WPnP
Pennard Plants	CPen
Pennycross Plants	EPyc
Penstemons by Colour	LPen
Penton Mill Rhododendrons	NPen
Peony Passions	**IPPs**
Pépinière de l'île	**XPde**
Pépinière Filippi	XPep
The Perennial Nursery	WPnn
Perennial Plants Nursery	**IPPN**
Perhill Nurseries	WPer
Perry's Plants	NPer
Perryhill Nurseries Ltd	SPer
Pershore College of Horticulture	WSPU
Pettet's Nursery	SPet
Phedar Nursery	MPhe

Starborough Nursery	SSta
Steventon Road Nurseries	MSte
Stillingfleet Lodge Nurseries	NSti
Stone Cross Garden Centre	SSto
Stone House Cottage Nurseries	WSHC
Stone Lane Gardens	CSto
Sue Strickland Plants	CStr
Stuckey's Alpines	CStu
Style Roses	ESty
Brian & Pearl Sulman	ESul
Sunnybank Vine Nursery	WSuV
Sussex Topiary	**STop**
Suttons Seeds	CSut
Swallows Nursery	MSwo
Table Bay View Nursery	XBlo
Tan-y-Llyn Nurseries	**WTan**
Tarleton Specimen Plants	**NTar**
Tavistock Herb Nursery	NTHB
Taylors Clematis Nursery	NTay
Telling and Coates	WTel
Terra Nova Plants	ITer
Test Valley Nursery	STes
Thorncroft Clematis Nursery	ETho
Thornhayes Nursery	CTho
A & A Thorp	MTho
Three Counties Nurseries	**CThr**
Thuya Alpine Nursery	WThu
Tile Barn Nursery	STil
Timpany Nurseries & Gardens	ITim
Tinpenny Plants	WTin
Tir Mab Cynan Nursery	WTMC
Tissington Nursery	MTis
Toobees Exotics	LToo
Town Farm Nursery	ETow
Trebah Enterprises Ltd	CTbh
The Tree Shop	GTSp
Tregothnan Nursery	**CTrG**
Trehane Camellia Nursery	CTrh
Peter Trenear	STre
Trevena Cross Nurseries	CTrC
Trewithen Nurseries	CTrw
Triscombe Nurseries	CTri
Edwin Tucker & Sons	CTuc
J Tweedie Fruit Trees	GTwe
Two Jays Alpines	LTwo
Unusual Herbs and Edibles	EUnu
Unusual Plants at Ratsbury	**SRat**
Usual & Unusual Plants	SUsu
Uzumara Orchids	GUzu
Valducci Brugmansias	WVaB
The Vernon Geranium Nursery	LVER
The Vicarage Garden	NVic
The Village Nurseries	SVil
Viv Marsh Postal Plants	**WViv**
Wallace Plants	SWal
The Walled Garden	EWll
Walnut Tree Garden Nursery	EWTr
Walton Nurseries	**MWtn**
Wanborough Herb Nursery	CWan
Ward Alpines	CWrd
Ward Fuchsias	MWar
Warren Hills Nursery	MWrn
The Water Garden	CWat
Water Meadow Nursery	**SWat**
Waterperry Gardens Ltd	MWat
Waterpump Plants	WWpP
Wear's Nursery	**MWea**
Weasdale Nurseries Ltd.	NWea
Webbs of Wychbold	WWeb
The Weird and Wonderful Plant Co.	**GWWP**
Welsh Holly	WWHy
West Acre Gardens	EWes
West Harptree Nursery	CHar
West Somerset Garden Centre	CWSG
West Wales Willows	**WWll**
Westcountry Nurseries	
(inc. Westcountry Lupins)	CWCL
Westonbirt Arboretum	WWes
Westonbirt Plants	WWst
Westshores Nurseries	EWsh
A D & N Wheeler	MWhe
Whimble Nursery	WWhi
White Cottage Alpines	NWCA
Jill White	EJWh
White Veil Fuchsias	CWVF
Whitehall Farmhouse Plants	WWFP
Whitehill Farm Nursery	MWhi
Whitelea Nursery	MWht
Wibble Farm Nurseries	CWib
Will of the Wisp Plants	**CWoW**
Winchester Growers Ltd.	CWGr
Windrush Willow	CWiW
Wingwell Nursery	MWgw
Winter Flora Plant Centre	EWin
Wisley Plant Centre (RHS)	LRHS
D S Witton	NWit
Wollerton Old Hall Garden	WWlt
Wolverton Plants Ltd	SWvt
The Wonder Tree	**CWon**
Ian and Rosemary Wood	CWoo
Woodborough Garden Centre Ltd	CWdb
Woodside Cottage Herbs	GWCH
Wootten's Plants	EWoo
Nigel Wright Rhododendrons	CWri
Sonia Wright Plants	CSWP
Wyatts	MWya
Wych Cross Nurseries	SWCr
Yaffles (fomerly Butterfields Nursery)	LBut
Yeomans' Exotics	**MYeo**
Yvonne's Plants	SYvo
Zephyrwude Irises	**NZep**
Zest Exotics	EZes

SPECIALIST NURSERIES

Nurseries have classified themselves under the following headings where they *exclusively* or *predominantly* supply this range of plants. Plant groups are set out in alphabetical order. Refer to

Nursery Details by Code on page 788 for details of the nurseries whose codes are listed under the plant group which interests you. See page 785 for a fuller explanation.

ACID LOVING PLANTS

CBcs, CDBb, CMen, CPLG, CTrh, CWCL, CWrd, CWri, ECri, EFly, EHea, GCrs, GGGa, GWCH, ISea, LHyd, LMil, MBar, MGos, MLea, MMuc, MWtn, NDlv, NHar, NLAp, NPen, SBrw, SCam, SFai, SHmp, SHyH, SLdr, SOkd, WAbe, WCru, WThu

ALPINE/ROCK PLANTS

CBrm, CFul, CGra, CLyd, CMea, CMMP, CNic, CPBP, CPMA, CStu, CWil, CWon, CWrd, ECho, ECri, EEls, EHyt, EPot, ETow, GCrs, GFle, GKev, IBal, ITim, LBmB, MDHE, MOne, NBro, NDlv, NHar, NHol, NJOw, NLAp, NMen, NNew, NPol, NRya, NSla, NWCA, NWoo, SIng, SPop, WAbe, WBri, WGor, WHoo, WLin, WPrP, WThu, WWst, XFro

AQUATIC PLANTS

CRow, CWat, EMFW, IHMH, LNCo, LPBA, NPer, NSco, SWat, WMAq, WPnP, WWpP

BAMBOOS

CBig, CHen, EAmu, EExo, EFul, ENBC, EPla, ERod, EZes, GBin, LEdu, LPal, MBrN, MMoz, MMuc, MWhi, MWht, NGdn, NMoo, NOGN, NPal, SAPC, SArc, SBig, SLan, SNew, WJun, WMul, WPGP, Xblo

BRITISH WILD FLOWERS

CArn, CHby, COld, CRea, CRWN, CTuc, GBar, GWCH, MBow, MBSH, MHer, MLod, MSal, NHHG, NLan, NMir, NPol, NSco, NTHB, SECG, SWat, WBri, WCHb, WHbs, WHer, WJek, WSFF, WShi, XHHs

BULBOUS PLANTS

CAvo, CBro, CElm, CFFs, CGrW, CLAP, CMea, CMon, CPne, CQua, CStu, CWoo, ECho, ECri, EDif, EFam, EHyt, EMon, EMui, EPot, ERos, GEve, IBal, LBmB, LBow, LPhx, MSSP, NDvn, NOaD, WDav, WHil, WPrP, WShi, WWst, XBlo

CACTI & SUCCULENTS

CHen, CPhi, CSec, CWil, EGln, EShb, ESou, LSou, LToo, MAga, NCro, NMen, NOaD, SChr, SHol, SHvs, WGei

CARNIVOROUS PLANTS

CHew, CSWC, EFly, MYeo, SHmp, WSSs

CHALK-LOVING PLANTS

CMdw, CSev, CSpe, EFam, EGoo, LBmB, LGro, LSss, SAll, SEND, SJoh, SLon, SMHT, SSvw, SYvo

CLIMBERS

CFRD, CPlN, CPou, CRHN, CSPN, CTri, CWoW, ELan, ERob, ESCh, ETho, LFol,

MGos, NBea, NSRo, NSti, SBra, SLau, SLay, SLim, SMDP, SRkn, WBGC, WCru, WSHC

COASTAL PLANTS

CBod, CCCN, CMHG, CTrC, GGar, SAft, SChr, SEND, SLdr, WPnn

CONIFERS

CDHC, CKen, CLnd, CMen, CRob, CTho, ECho, EOrn, LCon, LLin, MBar, MPkF, NHol, SCrf, SLim, WEve, WGor, WMou

CONSERVATORY PLANTS

CBcs, CBrP, CCCN, CKob, CPlN, CPne, CRHN, CRoM, CSec, CSpe, EBak, EEls, EOas, EOHP, ERea, EShb, ESou, ESul, GFai, LHyd, LPal, LToo, MAga, MNew, MOak, MYeo, NCro, NFir, SCam, SDEP, SHaC, SHol, SOWG, SYvo, WDib, WSAf, XBlo

DROUGHT TOLERANT

CMdw, CPne, ECha, EFam, EGln, EGoo, EHoe, EOas, IPPs, LLWP, LPen, LPhx, LSss, MAga, MHrb, SAft, SAll, SEND, SHzl, SJoh, SLdr, SUsu, WHil, WKin, WWye, XPep

FERNS

CFwr, CLAP, CRow, CRWN, CTrC, ECha, EExo, EFer, EFtx, EMon, GBin, IBal, LPBA, MMoz, NMoo,

NMyG, NOrc, NWoo, SArc, SHmp, SNut, WAbe, WFib, WMoo

FRUIT

CAgr, CCAT, CCVT, CTho, CTri, ECrN, EMui, ERea, EUnu, EZes, GBut, GTwe, LEdu, MCls, MCoo, MLod, SCrf, SDea, SDEP, SFam, SKee, WHar, WJas, WSuV, XBlo

GRASSES

CBig, CBod, CBrm, CFwr, CKno, CMea, CMMP, CPen, CPLG, CRWN, EApt, ECha, EFul, EGle, EHoe, ELan, EPla, EPPr, EPyc, EWsh, GBin, GCal, GIBF, GQue, IFoB, IHMH, LEdu, LFox, LLWP, LPhx, MBar, MBrN, MMoz, MNrw, MWhi, NBHF, NBro, NGdn, NOak, NOrc, NSti, SAft, SHel, SHzl, SMar, SMHy, SNew, SRkn, SUsu, SWal, SYvo, WDin, WHal, WLeb, WMoo, WOVN, WPGP, WPrP, WWye

HEDGING

CCVT, CDul, CLnd, CTrG, CTri, ECrN, ERom, LBuc, LEar, MCoo, MHrb, MWtn, NBee, SAft, SBLw, SHHo, SLan, SRiv, WCel, WDin, WEve, WHar, WLav, WMou, WOrn, WWeb

HERBS

CArn, CBod, CHby, COfd, COld, CPbn, CSev, CWan, EApt, ELau, EOHP, EUnu, GBar, GPoy, GWCH, IHMH, ILis, LFol, LLWP, LMor, MHer, MHrb, MLod, MSal, MWhi, NGHP, NHHG, NLan, NLLv, NTHB, NWoo, SECG, SHDw, SWat, WBri, WCHb, WHbs, WJek, WLav, WRha, WSel, WWye, XHHs

MARGINAL/BOG PLANTS

CBig, CDWL, CLAP, CMHG, COld, CRow, CWat, CWon, CWrd, EFly, GBar, GGar,

GKev, LPBA, MMuc, MYeo, NCot, NHol, NOrc, NPer, NSco, SHaC, SHzl, WHal, WMAq, WMoo, WPnP, WSFF, WShi, WWpP

ORCHIDS

CBur, CHdy, CRea, EFEx, EPot, GCrs, GUzu, LBut, MNew, NEqu, NLAp, NSpr, WHer, WWst, XFro

ORGANIC

CBgR, CBig, CHby, CRow, CSec, CTuc, CWan, EApt, GBar, GBut, GPoy, ILis, LEdu, LLWP, MSal, NPol, NSRo, NTHB, SECG, WCHb, WGWT, WJek, WSFF, WShi, Wwye

ORNAMENTAL TREES

CAgr, CBcs, CBdw, CCAT, CCVT, CDul, CEnd, CLnd, CMen, CMMP, CPMA, CSto, CTho, CTri, CWon, ECrN, EGFP, ELan, EMui, ERod, ERom, GIBF, IMGH, IPPs, LPan, MCls, MGos, MPkF, NBea, NBee, NPal, SBir, SBLw, SCrf, SHHo, SLau, SLay, SLim, SMHT, WCel, WDin, WEve, WHar, WJas, WMou, WNor, WOrn, WPGP

PALMS

CPHo, CRoM, EAmu, EExo, EGln, EZes, LPal, NPal, SAin, SAPC, SArc, SBig, SChr, SNew, WMul

PEAT FREE

CBgR, CCVN, CElw, CFRD, CHby, CKno, CKob, CMdw, CMea, CNic, CPen, CPom, CRHN, CRWN, CSam, CSec, CSev, CWan, CWon, EAro, EBla, ECri, EDsa, EGoo, ELau, EMag, EMal, EPts, ERea, ERob, GBut, GCai, GPoy, ILis, LEdu, LLWP, MBNS, MBow, MEHN, MLHP, MLod, MMoz, MPhe, MRod, MSal, MWgw, NBid, NGby, NLan, NLRH, NOGN, NPol, NSRo, SAft,

SBch, SECG, SMDP, SYvo, WCHb, WDyG, WGWT, WHbs, WHoo, WJek, WPnP, WPrP, WRha, WSel, WSFF, WShi, WWpP, WWye

PERIOD PLANTS

CArn, CKel, CSna, CWGr, EKMF, EMFP, ERob, GBut, ILis, LPen, NFir, SAll, SDea, SRGP, WHer, WKin, WOFF, WRha

PROPAGATE TO ORDER

CArn, CBig, CBre, CCAT, CDHC, CKel, CMdw, CMen, CPas, CPMA, CPne, CRow, CRWN, CStr, CTho, CWan, CWCL, CWGr, CWon, EBla, ECho, ECrN, ECtt, EEls, EGFP, EMal, EOHP, EPyc, ERea, EShb, EZes, GBut, GFai, GKev, GQue, ILis, IPPN, ITer, LHyd, LLWP, LMil, LPBA, MDHE, MEHN, MLHP, MLod, MMoz, MOak, MRMR, MRod, MWtn, NCot, NCro, NLLv, NPol, NRya, NShi, NTHB, NWCA, NWoo, SAft, SAga, SBch, SCam, SChr, SDea, SECG, SHDw, SHel, SHyH, SLau, SLdr, SLon, SMDP, SOWG, SPol, SPop, SRiv, SSea, SWat, WCHb, WHer, WHil, WJek, WJun, WLav, WOrn, WOut, WPBF, WPrP, WSFF, WSSs, WTin, WVaB, WWHy, WWpP, WWye, XBlo

ROSES

CPou, ECnt, ESty, GCoc, IDic, LFol, LGod, MAus, MFry, MGan, MMat, MRMR, NSRo, SLay, SPoc, SSea, SWCr, WAct, WOVN

SEED

CAgr, CDob, CElm, CHby, CMon, CPas, CRea, CRWN, CSec, CSpe, CSut, CTuc, EMcA, GIBF, GPoy, ITer, LSee, LSss, MBSH, MPet, NChl, NGHP, NLan, NOGN, NRob, SAft, SECG, SHel, SPop, WCHb, WHen, WJek, WNor, WRha, WSFF, XJel

SPECIMEN SIZED PLANTS

CBig, CDHC, CDul, CHen,
CKel, CMen, CPMA, CPne,
CTho, CTrC, CTrG, CTrh,
CWon, EAmu, EBla, ECho,
ECrN, EExo, EKMF, ELan,
ELau, ENBC, EShb, ESou,
GIBF, GLld, LHyd, LMil,
LPan, LRav, MAga, MBar,
MBrN, MGos, MLea,
MLod, MMoz, MMuc,
MNew, MOak, MPhe,
MRea, MWtn, MYeo, NCro,
NOrc, NPol, SAft, SBig,
SBLw, SBrw, SCam, SChr,
SDEP, SEND, SFai, SFam,
SHGC, SHHo, SHmp,
SHyH, SLan, SLdr, SNew,
SOWG, WCel, WDin,
WEve, WJek, WJun, WOrn,
WPat, WSFF, WWeb,
WWye

TOPIARY

ERom, LEar, LPan, SHHo,
SLan, SRiv, STop, WWeb

TROPICAL PLANTS

CCCN, CHen, CKob, CMon,
CPas, CPLG, CPIN, CRoM,
CTrC, EAmu, EOas, ERea,
EUnu, LToo, MNew, MOak,
NDvn, SAPC, SBig, SDEP,
SHaC, SHmp, SOWG, WCru,
WDib, WMul, XBlo

INDEX MAP

The maps on the following pages show the approximate location of the nurseries whose details are listed in this directory.

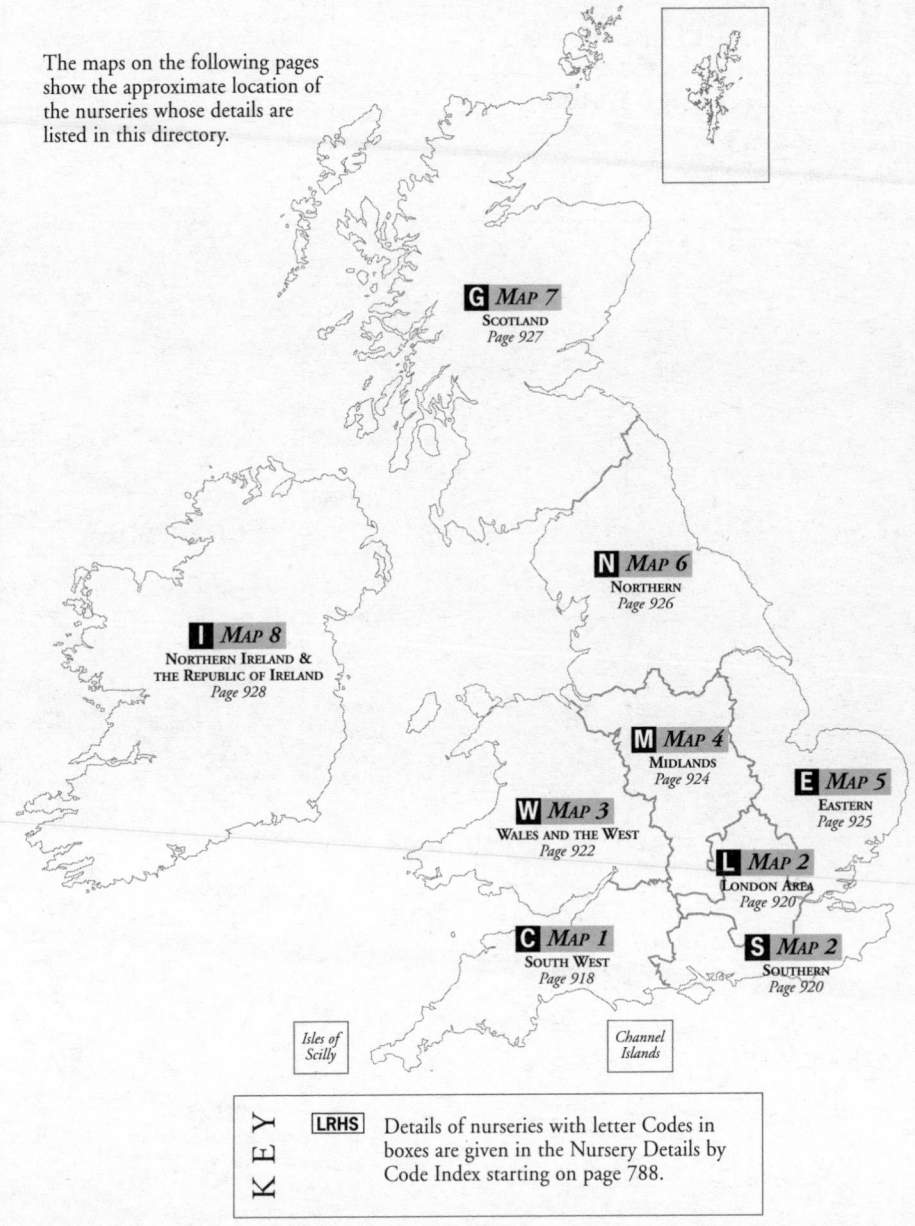

G *MAP 7*
SCOTLAND
Page 927

N *MAP 6*
NORTHERN
Page 926

I *MAP 8*
NORTHERN IRELAND &
THE REPUBLIC OF IRELAND
Page 928

M *MAP 4*
MIDLANDS
Page 924

E *MAP 5*
EASTERN
Page 925

W *MAP 3*
WALES AND THE WEST
Page 922

L *MAP 2*
LONDON AREA
Page 920

C *MAP 1*
SOUTH WEST
Page 918

S *MAP 2*
SOUTHERN
Page 920

Isles of Scilly

Channel Islands

KEY   **LRHS**   Details of nurseries with letter Codes in boxes are given in the Nursery Details by Code Index starting on page 788.

MAP ONE
C SOUTH WEST

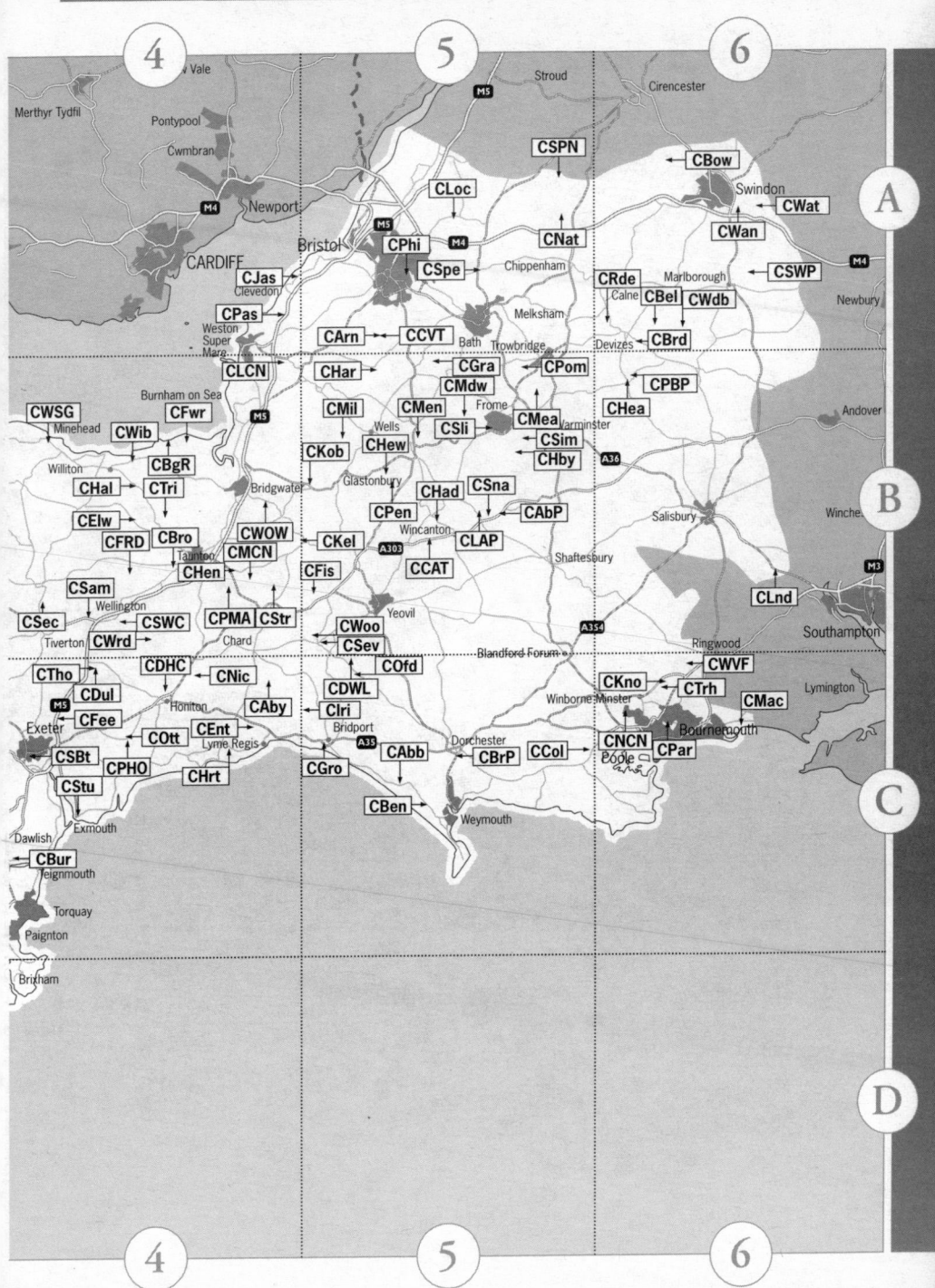

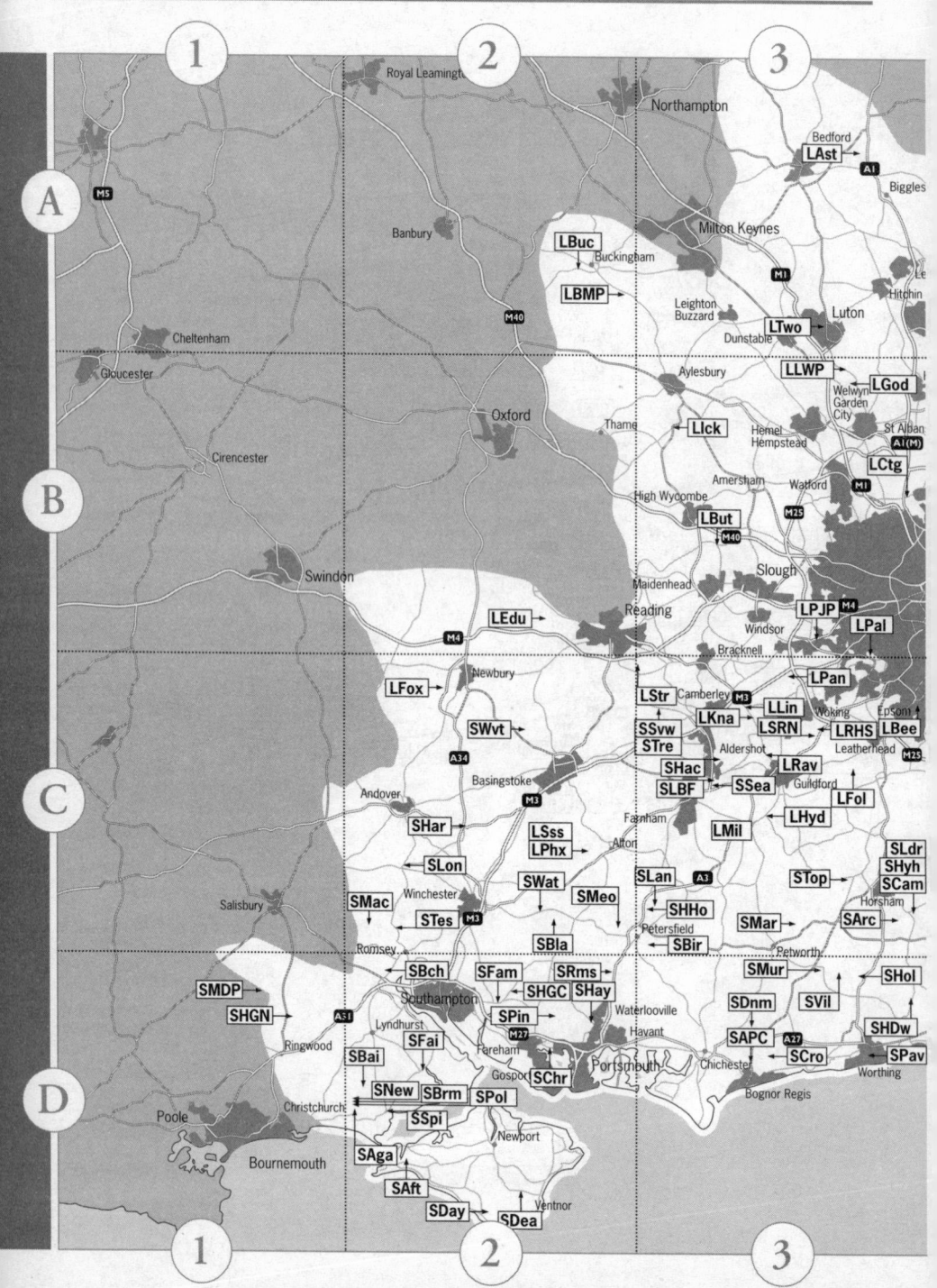

MAP TWO
LONDON AREA
& SOUTHERN

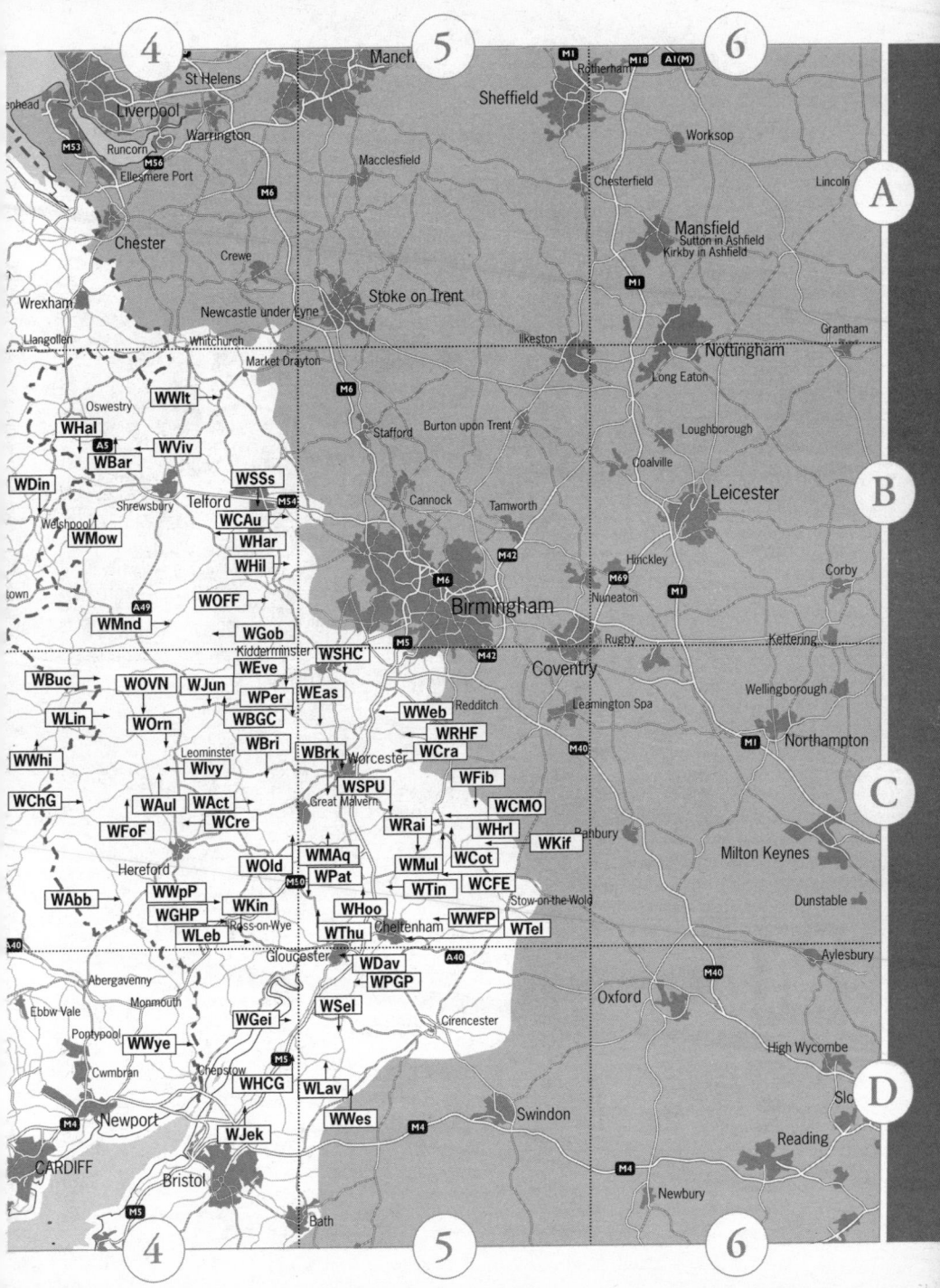

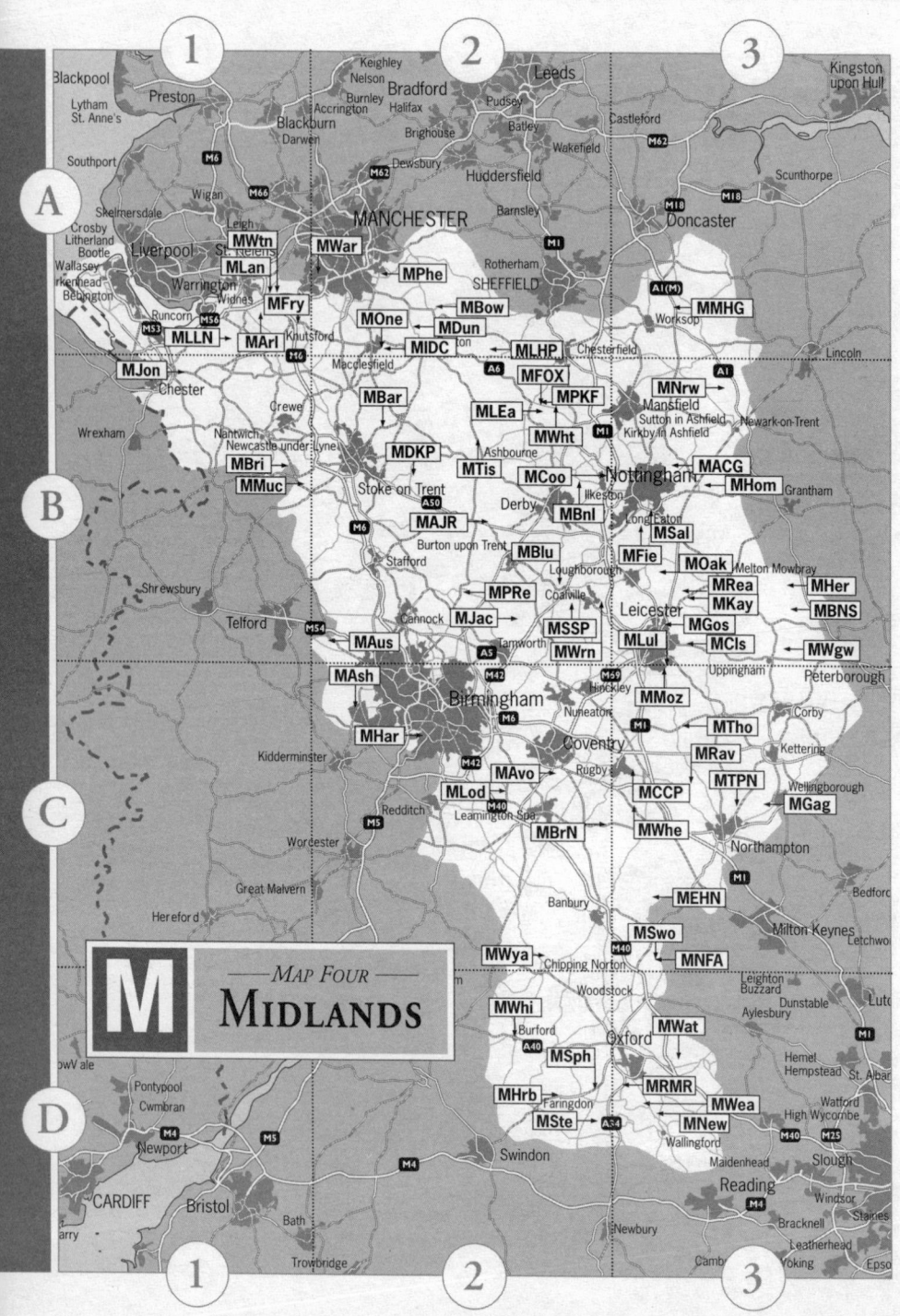

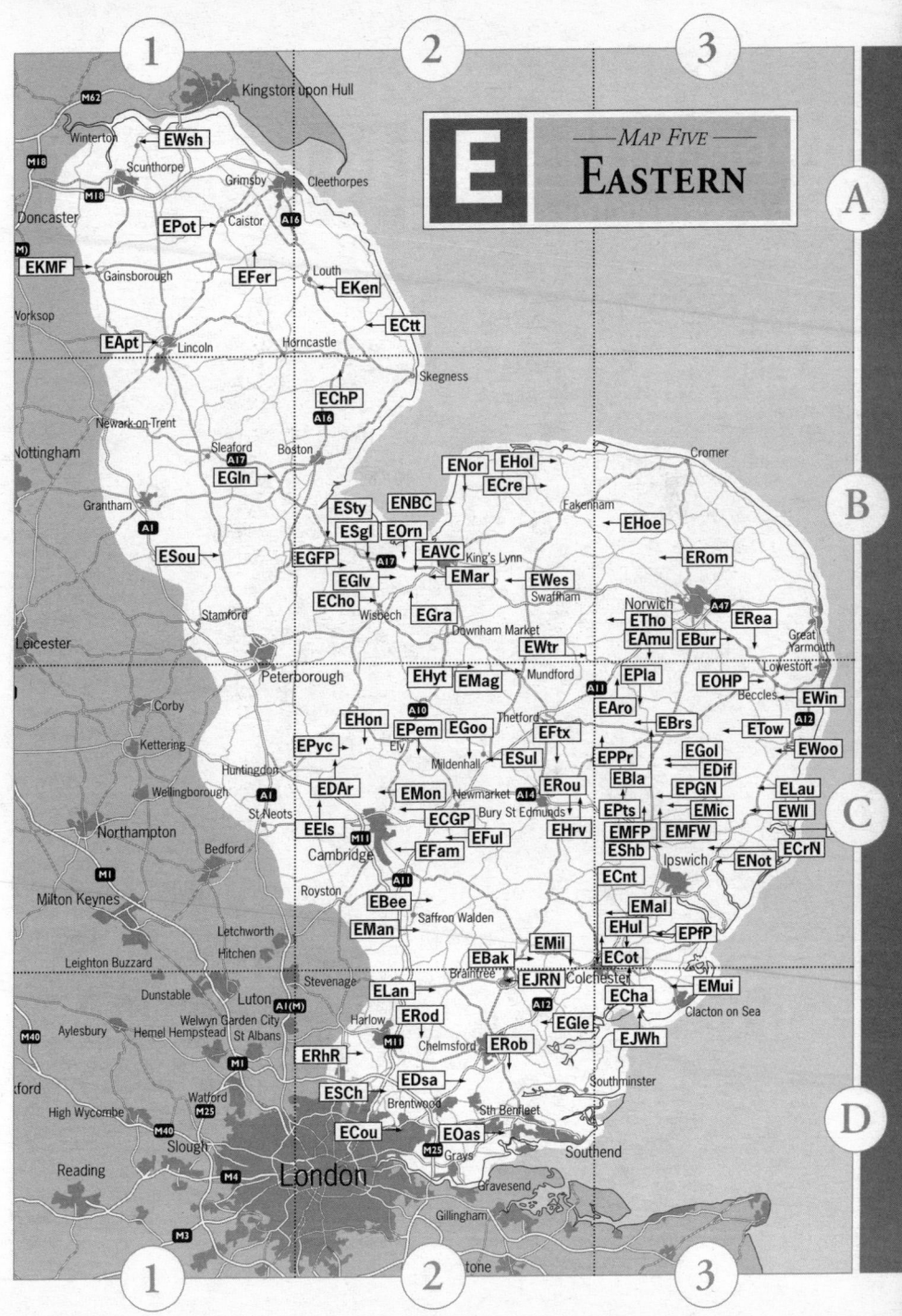

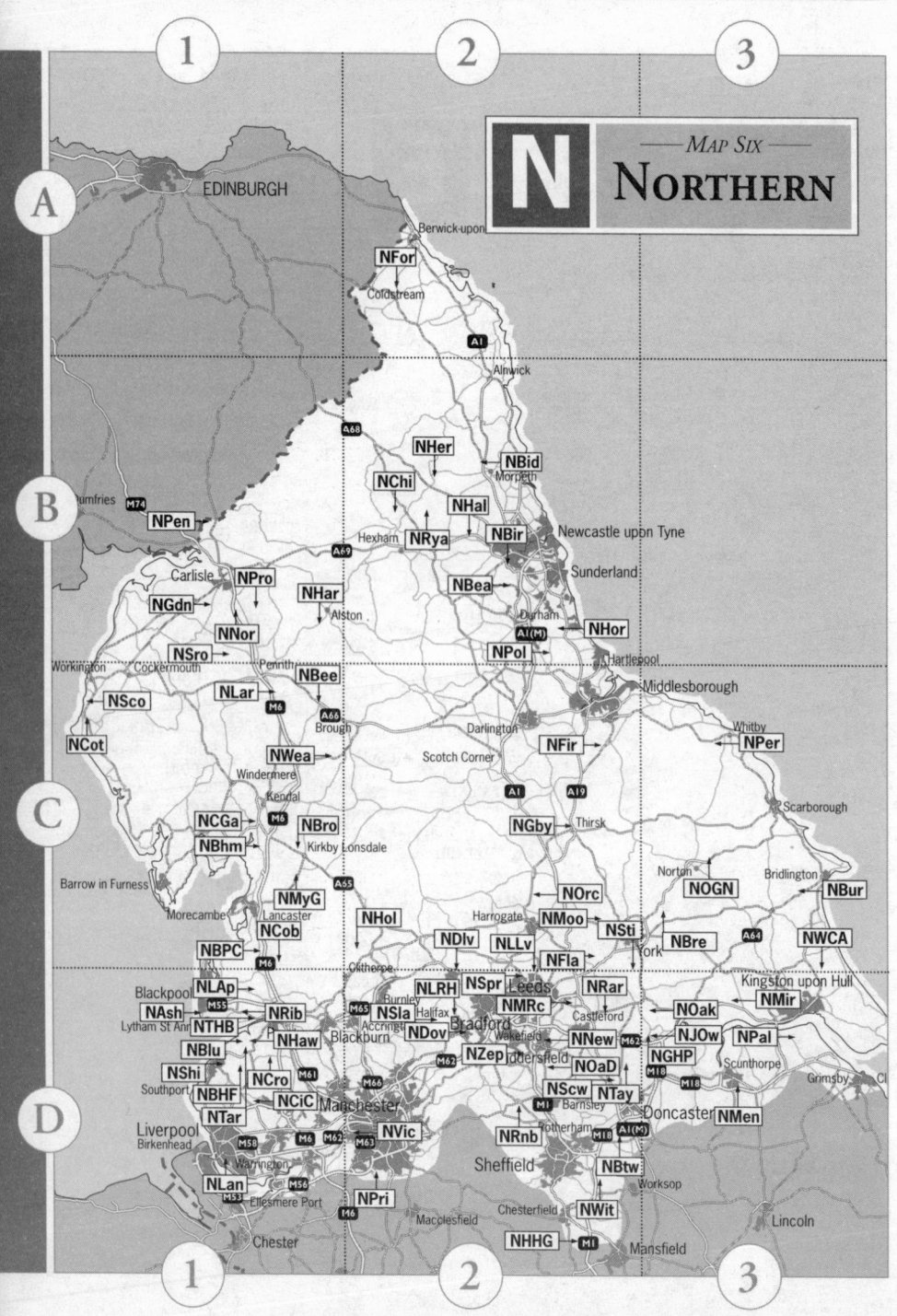

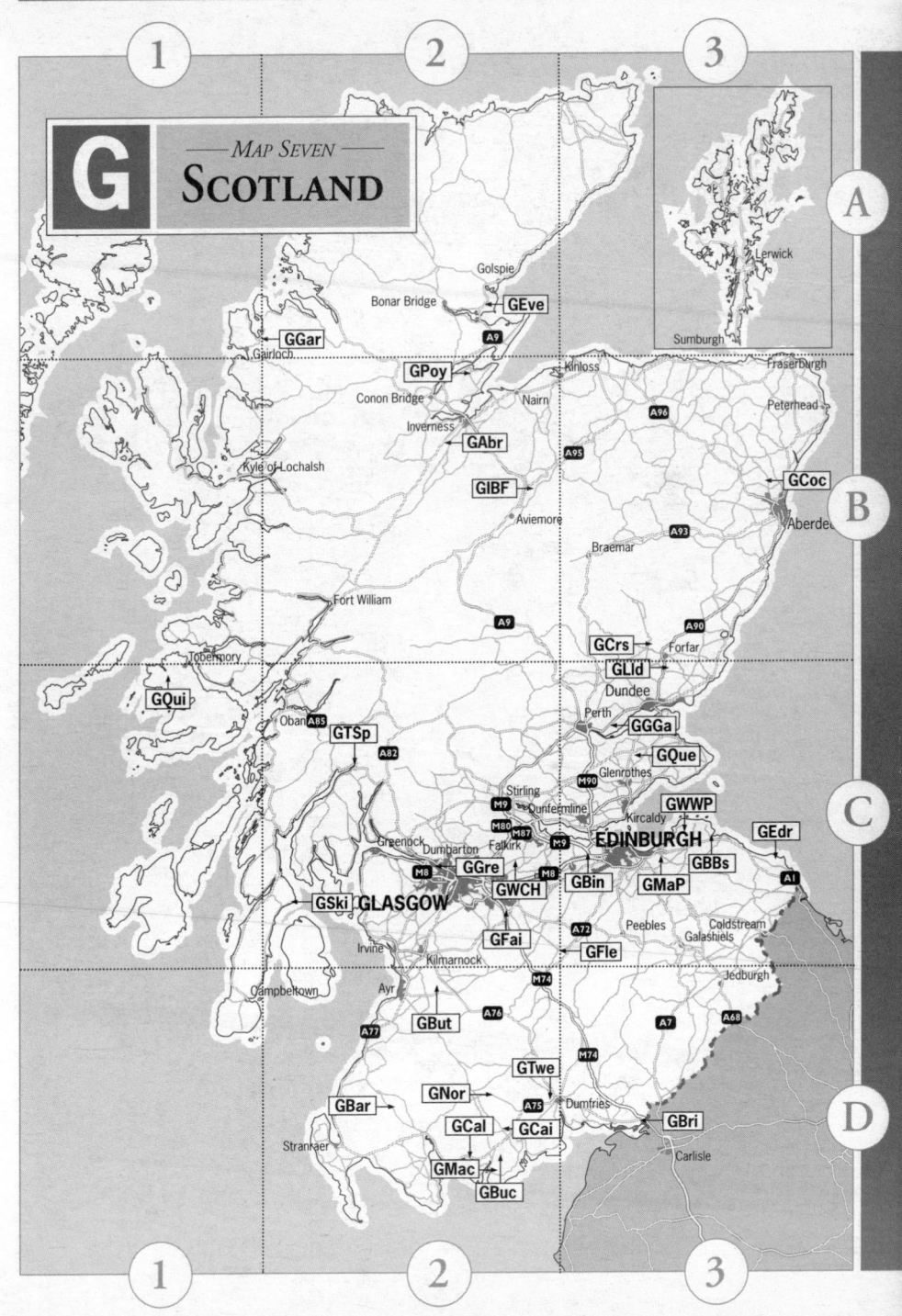

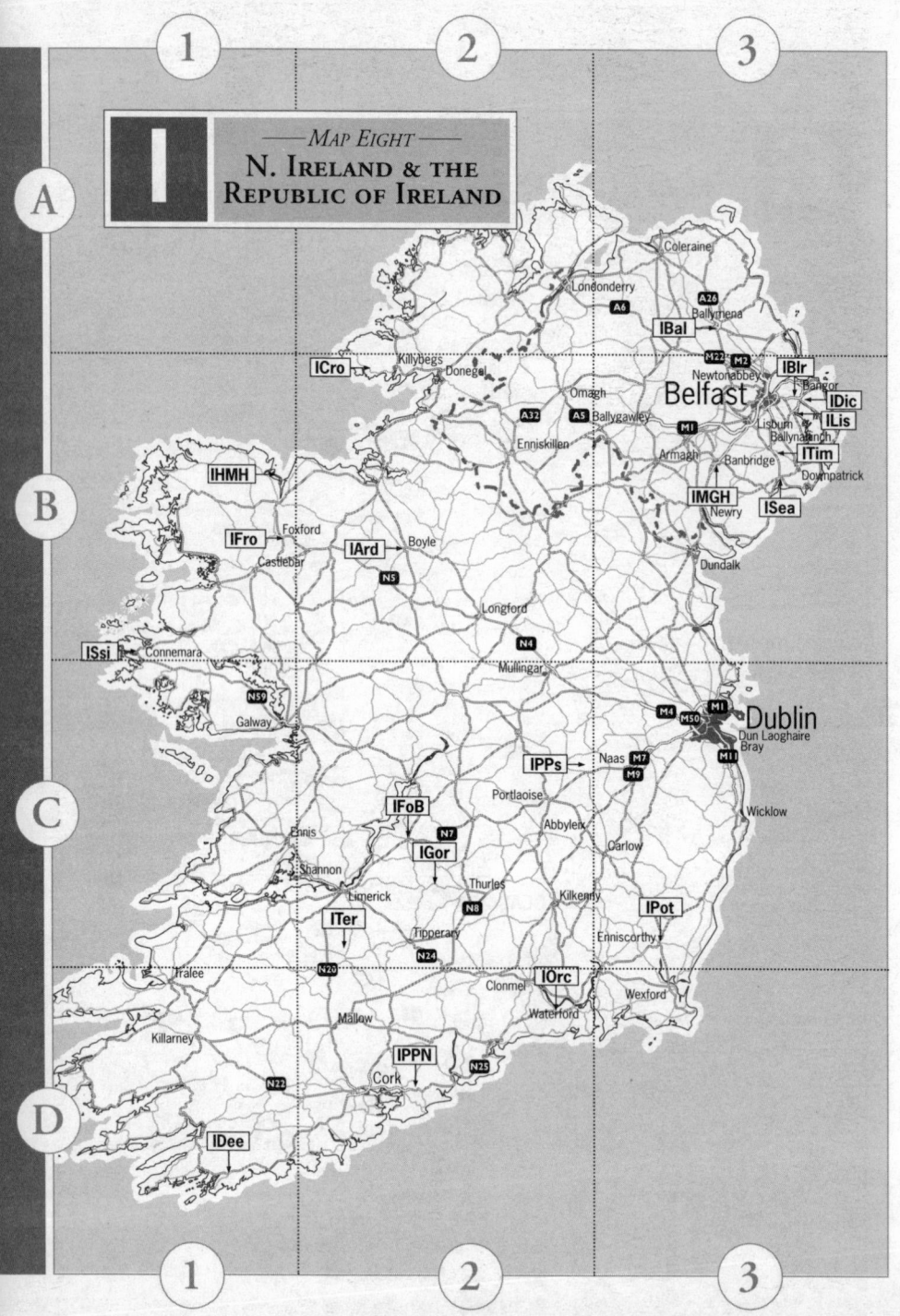

I

— MAP EIGHT —
N. IRELAND & THE REPUBLIC OF IRELAND

Have you found or bred a new plant?

Trust us to realise the full worldwide potential of your new plant discovery.

The new plant that you've found or bred may well have the potential to be developed and marketed to achieve world-wide commercial success.

Blooms of Bressingham® has built an enviable reputation for more than fifty years as a leader in plant development.

Our know-how and expertise, the depth of our resources and the breadth of our international network of contacts, makes us the natural choice of partner to realize the full potential of your new plant discovery.

It's so easy... Just call
United Kingdom Agent:
Paul Gooderham at 01379 688500 or
pgooderham@bloomsofbressingham.com
Blooms of Bressingham® • *R A Meredith (Blooms) Ltd.*
Bressingham, Diss, Norfolk IP22 2AB, England

Worldwide Agent:
Gary Doerr at 001-916-716-1889 or
grdoerr@bloomsofbressingham.com
Blooms of Bressingham®, P.O. Box 660872
Sacramento, California, USA 95866-0872

www.bloomsofbressingham.com

934

WHAT THERE IS TO SEE & DO AT

LONGFRAMLINGTON GARDENS

NURSERY & PLANT CENTRE

Thousands of different types of trees, shrubs, perennial, herbs, climbers, and rock garden plants to choose from - produced here in the nursery, under our Commitment to the Environment growing policy. All container grown, for planting all year round

GARDEN & ARBORETUM WALKS

around the 12 acre gardens and arboretum. Take in the seasonal change of the planting schemes, the range of plants (now all with labels), wonderful countryside views, garden features, overall original design of the gardens & Climate Change Display.
SEE WEBSITE FOR FURTHER INFORMATION.

GARDEN DESIGN MANAGEMENT & ADVISORY SERVICE

ENROUTE COFFEE STOP

OPEN EVERY DAY ALL YEAR 8.30-5.00pm (or dusk when sooner) (Closed Xmas - New Year)

SWARLAND ROAD, LONGFRAMLINGTON, MORPETH, NORTHUMBERLAND
TEL/FAX 01665 570382
Email: info@longframlingtongardens.co.uk   Website: www.longframlingtongardens.co.uk

Easy to find, follow road signs to **LONGFRAMLINGTON VILLAGE** on A697 approx 30 miles north of Newcastle-Upon-Tyne, then take B6345 Felton/Swarland Road for 3/4 mile.

NATIONAL FRUIT TREE SPECIALIST
SEND NOW FOR FREE CATALOGUE

EARLY ORDERS WILL ENJOY A SPECIAL DISCOUNT

Special offers on Apples, Family Trees, Self Fertile Cox Apples, Pears, Peach, Plum, Soft Fruits, Grapes, Nuts, Hops; also Upright Cordons etc.

DEACONS NURSERY
Established 1966

(RHS) GODSHILL
ISLE OF WIGHT PO38 3HW
Tel: 01983 840750 / 522243 or Fax: 01983 523575 (24 hrs)
Email: deacons.nursery@btopenworld.com
www.deaconsnurseryfruits.co.uk

938

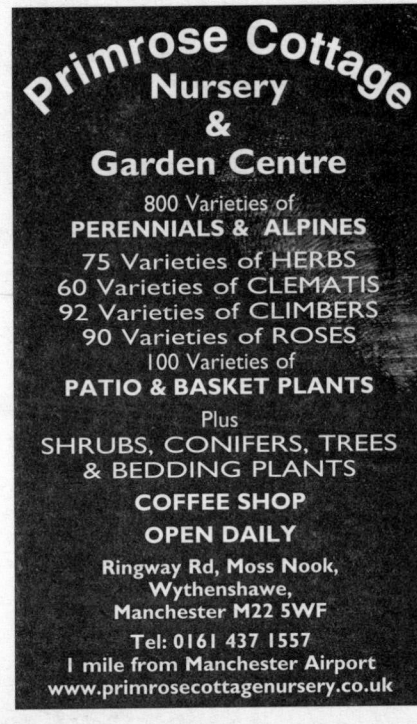

948

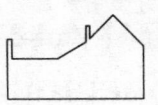

INDEX OF ADVERTISERS

RHS Show Awards 2004

RHS Plant Finder nurseries who were awarded RHS medals at the three major RHS Shows in 2004

Chelsea Gold

Allwoods
David Austin Roses
Avon Bulbs
Steven Bailey
Bloms Bulbs
Downderry Nursery
Edrom Nursery
Fernatix
Fir Trees Pelargonium Nursery
Goldbrook Plants
Hampshire Carnivorous Plants
Hardy's Cottage Garden Plants
Jekka's Herb Farm
Kelways
Knoll Gardens
Mattock's Roses
Norfields
Notcutts Nurseries
P W Plants
Park Green Nurseries
Pops Plants
Romantic Garden Nursery
Roualeyn Nurseries
South West Carnivorous Plants
Southfield Nurseries
Toobees Exotics
Trevena Cross Nurseries

Chelsea Silver Gilt

Ainsworth Displays
Burncoose Nurseries
Burnham Nurseries
Sheila Chapman Clematis
The Cottage Herbery
Dibleys Nurseries
Dysons Nurseries
Lincluden Nursery
Oakland Nurseries
Rhodes & Rockliffe
Rotherview Nursery
Rougham Hall Nurseries
Brian & Pearl Sulman

Thorncroft Clematis Nursery
Three Counties Nurseries
Westcountry Nurseries
White Veil Fuchsias

Chelsea Silver Gilt Hogg

Ken Muir

Chelsea Silver

African Violet Centre
Broadleigh Gardens
Devine Nurseries
Fibrex Nurseries
C S Lockyer
Pococks Roses
Potash Nursery

Chelsea Silver Knightian

W Robinson & Son

Chelsea Bronze

The Big Grass Company
Mallet Court Nursery

Hampton Court Gold

Allwood Bros
Steven Bailey
Devine Nurseries
Dibley's Nurseries
Fernatix
Foxgrove Plants
Goldbrook Plants
Hampshire Carnivorous Plants
Hardy's Cottage Garden Plants
Hewitt-Cooper Carnivorous Plants
Jekka's Herb Farm
Lincluden Nursery
Norfields
Park Green Nurseries
Roualeyn Nurseries
Southfields Nurseries
Trevena Cross Nurseries

Hampton Court Silver-Gilt

Ainsworth Displays
Burncoose Nurseries
Sheila Chapman Clematis

Derek Lloyd Dean
Fir Trees Pelargonium Nursery
C S Lockyer
Oakland Nurseries
P W Plants
Pine Cottage Plants
Potash Nursery
Toobees Exotics
White Veil Fuchsias
Winchester Growers

HAMPTON COURT SILVER

Avon Bulbs
The Big Plant Nursery
Burnham Nurseries
Churchtown Nurseries
County Park Nursery
Duchy of Cornwall
Dysons Nurseries
Edrom Nurseries
Hopleys Plants
Long Acre Plants
Mallet Court Nursery
Rotherview Nursery
Rougham Hall Nurseries
Brian & Pearl Sulman
Three Counties Nurseries

HAMPTON COURT SILVER HOGG

Ken Muir

HAMPTON COURT BRONZE

Clay Lane Nursery
Fibrex Nurseries
Hartside Nursery
Highdown Nursery
Tregothnan Nursery

TATTON GOLD

Croston Cactus
Dibley's Nurseries
Fir Trees Pelargonium Nursery
Hall Farm Nursery
Hampshire Carnivorous Plants
Hardy's Cottage Garden Plants
Jekka's Herb Farm
Elizabeth MacGregor
Mendip Bonsai Studio
Norfields

P W Plants
Roualeyn Nurseries
South West Carnivorous Plants
Southfields Nurseries

TATTON SILVER-GILT

Steven Bailey
Bluebell Arboretum & Nursery
Broadleigh Gardens
Burncoose Nurseries
Cairnsmore Nursery
Devine Nurseries
Downderry Nursery
Edrom Nurseries
Foxgrove Plants
Fryer's Nurseries
Holden Clough Nusery
Lincluden Nursery
Long Acre Plants
Oak Tree Nursery
Oakland Nurseries
Park Green Nurseries
Shirley's Plants
Brian & Pearl Sulman
Toobees Exotics

TATTON SILVER-GILT KNIGHTIAN

W Robinson & Sons

TATTON SILVER

Border Belles
Cath's Garden Plants
Chipchase Castle Nursery
Fibrex Nurseries
Gilbey's Plants
Mary Green
Hartside Nursery
Kobakoba
ProudPlants
Rougham Hall Nurseries
Springfield Nurseries
Taylors Clematis Nursery
Three Counties Nurseries
Walton Nurseries

TATTON BRONZE

Bridge End Nurseries
Mickfield Hostas
Rearsby Roses

The HARDY PLANT SOCIETY

Explores, encourages and conserves all that is best in gardens

The Hardy Plant Society encourages interest in growing hardy perennial plants and provides members with information about familiar and less well known perennial plants that flourish in our gardens, how to grow them and where they may obtained. This friendly society offers a range of activities locally and nationally, giving members plenty of opportunity to meet other keen gardeners to share ideas and information in a convivial atmosphere. The activities and work of the Society inform and encourage the novice gardener, stimulate and enlighten the more knowledgeable, and entertain and enthuse all gardeners bonded by a love for, and an interest in, hardy perennial plants.

LOCAL GROUPS

There are over 40 local groups across the UK and national members are invited to join the group nearest to them. Each group offers a wide range of gardening activities including informative lectures, garden visits and plant plus educational and social events throughout the year. Most groups produce their own newsletters. Full details of how to join a local group are sent out to new members.

SPECIALIST GROUPS AND GARDENING BY POST

Specialist Groups produce their own newsletters and organise meetings and events for fellow enthusiasts. The Correspondents Group ensures that members who are unable to attend meetings can exchange gardening ideas and information.

SEED DISTRIBUTION

Every member can join in the annual Seed Distribution Scheme by obtaining or donating hardy perennial seed. The Seed List offers over 2,500 tempting varieties of rare, unusual and familiar seeds and is sent to every member in December.

Please see overleaf for an application form

SHOWS AND EVENTS

Exhibits at major shows throughout the country let visitors see hardy plants in bloom and leaf in their natural season and more information about the work of the Society is available. Events hosted by local group members are also organised, from plant study days to residential weekends to garden visits. The Society also organises overseas garden tours.

CONSERVATION

The Hardy Plant Society is concerned about the conservation of garden plants and is working towards ensuring that older, rarer and lesser-known perennial plants are conserved and made available to gardeners generally.

PUBLICATIONS AND THE SLIDE LIBRARY

The Society's journal, *The Hardy Plant*, is published twice a year and regular newsletters provide information on all the Society's events, activities, interests and group contacts. The Society also publishes a series of booklets on special plant families which include Hardy Geraniums, Pulmonarias, Hostas, Grasses, Iris, Epemendiums, Success with Seeds, Euphorbias, Phlox, Campanulas for the garden and Umbellifers. Other publications for members include a B&B list and a gardens to visit list. The Slide Library has a wide range of hardy plant slides available on loan.

INFORMATION ABOUT THE SOCIETY IS AVAILABLE FROM:

The Administrator
Mrs Pam Adams
The Hardy Plant Society
Little Orchard
Great Comberton
Pershore
Worcestershire WR10 3DP

Tel: 01386 710317
Fax: 01386 710117
E-mail: admin@hardy-plant.org.uk
Website: www.hardy-plant.org.uk

The HARDY PLANT SOCIETY

MEMBERSHIP APPLICATION FOR 2005

The Annual Subscriptions are:
Single £13.00 per year (one member)
Joint £15.00 per year (two members at the same address)

• Subscriptions are renewable annually on **1 January**.
• Subscriptions of members joining after 1 October are valid until the end of the following year.
• Overseas members are requested to pay in pounds sterling by International Money Order
or by credit card. An optional charge of £10.00 is made for airmail postage outside Western Europe of
all literature, if preferred.

Please fill in the details in BLOCK CAPITALS, tear off this form and send it with your payment to the
Administrator or telephone the Administrator with details of your credit card.

Please tick the type of membership required

☐   Single £13.00 per year (one member)

☐   Joint £15.00 per year (two members at one address)

☐   Airmail postage £10.00 per year (optional for members outside Western Europe)

NAME/S ....

ADDRESS ....

....

.... POST CODE ....

TELEPHONE NUMBER ....

E-mail ....

I enclose a cheque/postal order* payable to **THE HARDY PLANT SOCIETY** (in pounds sterling ONLY) for £..........

OR
Please debit my Visa/Master Card* by the sum of £ ....
(* delete as required)

CARD NUMBER ☐☐☐☐ ☐☐☐☐ ☐☐☐☐ ☐☐☐☐

EXPIRY DATE ☐☐☐☐

Name as embossed on card ....

Signature ....

*Please print your name and address clearly, tear out the page and send it to
The Administrator at the address overleaf*

The Hardy Plant Society is a Registered Charity, number 208080

NCCPG

THE NATIONAL PLANT COLLECTIONS®

National Council for the Conservation of Plants & Gardens

Patron: HRH The Prince of Wales

THE LOST GARDEN OF BRITAIN

We have a long history of gardening, plant collecting and breeding in the British Isles so our gardens contain an amazing diversity of plants. Due to the imperatives of marketing and fashion, the desire for 'new' varieties and the practicalities of bulk cultivation, many plants unique to British gardens have been lost. This diversity is important as a genetic resource for the future and as a cultural link to the past.

WHAT IS THE NATIONAL COUNCIL FOR THE CONSERVATION OF PLANTS & GARDENS?

The NCCPG's mission is to conserve, document and make available this resource for the benefit of horticulture, education and science. The main conservation vehicle is the National Plant Collection® scheme where individuals or organisations undertake to preserve a group of related plants in trust for the future. Our 39 local groups across Britain support the administration of the scheme, the collection holders and propagate rare plants; working to promote the conservation of cultivated plants.

WHO ARE THE NATIONAL PLANT COLLECTION® HOLDERS?

Collection holders come from every sector of horticulture, amateur and professional. Almost half of the existing 656 National Collections are in private ownership and include allotments, back gardens and large estates. 21% of collections are found in nurseries, which range from large commercial concerns to the small specialist grower. 20 local authorities are involved in the scheme, including Sir Harold Hillier Gardens & Arboretum (Hampshire County Council) and Leeds City Council each caring for 11 collections. Universities, agricultural colleges, schools, arboreta and botanic gardens all add to the diversity, and there are also a number of collections on properties belonging to English Heritage, The National Trust and The National Trust for Scotland.

WHAT DO COLLECTION HOLDERS DO?

Collection holders subscribe to the scheme's ideals and stringent regulations. As well as protecting the living plants in their chosen group, they also work on areas including education, scientific research and nomenclature, with the common aim of conserving cultivated plants.

HOW CAN YOU HELP?

You can play your part in supporting plant conservation by becoming a national member of NCCPG. Regular journals will keep you informed of how your support is helping to save our plant biodiversity. Join your local group for the opportunity to play a more active role in plant conservation through co-operation with collection holders, a varied programme of talks, plant sales, involvement in local horticultural shows and nursery visits.

HOW TO JOIN:

Please contact
Membership
NCCPG National Office
RHS Garden, Wisley
Woking, Surrey
GU23 6QP

Tel: 01483 211465
Fax: 01483 212404
E-mail: membership@nccpg.org.uk
Website: www.nccpg.com

*Please see overleaf for Membership
Application Form*

*'The NCCPG seeks to conserve, document, promote and make available Britain and Ireland's rich
biodiversity of garden plants for the benefit of everyone through horticulture, education and science'*

Membership Application Form

Simply complete and detach this form enclosing your payment and send to:
Membership, NCCPG, The Stable Courtyard, Wisley Garden, Woking, Surrey GU23 6QP

How to Join

By post: complete form and send to the above address
On line: www.nccpg.com

FREE

A copy of The National Plant Collections® Directory when you join by Direct Debit

Annual Subscription Rates

(please tick relevant boxes)

☐ Individual UK £15*

☐ Joint UK £25* (two people at same address)

☐ Individual Europe £17.50

☐ Individual Rest of World £20

☐ Student (up to age 25 in full time education) £4
Name of College _____

☐ Gardening clubs and non-commercial groups £25

☐ Corporate £50

☐ Friend _____ **(min £100)**

Friends make annual donations in support of our work
(in addition to the membership fee)

* there is a small additional fee to join local Group

☐ Please send me information on legacies

☐ Please send me information on becoming a
Collection Holder

☐ Payment enclosed
Subscription   £ _____
Book order   £ _____
Donation   £ _____
Total amount enclosed   £ _____

Please complete in CAPITALS

Title _____ Forename _____

Last Name _____

Address _____

_____

_____ Postcode _____

Daytime Telephone _____

Email _____

giftaid it

Gift Aid Declaration: Are you a UK taxpayer? If you are, we can claim 28% from the government on your subscription at no extra cost to you.

☐ I would like the National Council for the Conservation of Plants & Gardens to reclaim the tax on any membership subscription or donation that I make/have made since 6th April 2000 and all subscriptions and donations I make in the future, until I notify you otherwise. I have paid an amount of UK income tax or capital gains tax equal to any tax reclaimed. (Remember that if you receive a company pension, income tax may well be paid at source.)

Instruction to your Bank or Building Society to pay by Direct Debit

DIRECT Debit

Please fill in the form and send to:
**Membership, NCCPG,
The Stable Courtyard, Wisley Garden,
Woking, Surrey GU23 6QP.**

Originators Identification Number

9 7 4 2 1 2

Name and full postal address of your Bank or Building Society

To: The Manager

_____ Bank/Building Society

Address _____

_____

Postcode

Name(s) of Account Holder(s)

Branch Sort Code   NCCPG use only

Bank/Building Society account number

Instruction to your Bank or Building Society. Please pay The National Council for the Conservation of Plants & Gardens Direct Debits from the account detailed in the instruction subject to the safeguards assured by the Direct Debit Guarantee. I understand that this instruction may remain with the NCCPG and if so, details will be passed electronically to my Bank/Building Society.

Signature(s)

Date   /   /

Banks and Building Societies may not accept Direct Debit Instructions for
some types of account.

Payment by Credit or Debit card (Excluding American Express/Diners)

Card No:

Issue No *(Switch only)*   Security code

Start Date   /   Expiry Date   /

Issuing Bank Name _____

Name on Card _____

Signature _____ Date _____

Payment by cheque: Please make sterling cheques payable to **NCCPG**

Data Protection Act: Records for each member are kept on computer at NCCPG national office. Under no circumstances are membership records used fo purposes other than those connected to the working of "The National Council for the Conservation of Plants & Gardens"

SUBSCRIBE TO THE PLANTSMAN

The premier publication for informed gardeners